Contents

ASM Specialty Handbook®

Stainless Steels

Edited by
J.R. Davis
Davis & Associates

Prepared under the direction of the
ASM International Handbook Committee

Scott D. Henry, Manager of Reference Book Development
Faith Reidenbach, Chief Copy Editor
Grace M. Davidson, Manager of Handbook Production
Rebecca C. McCullam, Production Coordinator
Ann-Marie O'Loughlin, Production Coordinator

William W. Scott, Jr., Director of Technical Publications

ASM INTERNATIONAL®

**The Materials
Information Society**

First printing, December 1994

This book is a collective effort involving hundreds of technical specialists. It brings together a wealth of information from worldwide sources to help scientists, engineers, and technicians solve current and longrange problems.

Great care is taken in the compilation and production of this Volume, but it should be made clear that NO WARRANTIES, EXPRESS OR IMPLIED, INCLUDING, WITHOUT LIMITATION, WARRANTIES OF MERCHANTABILITY OR FITNESS FOR A PARTICULAR PURPOSE, ARE GIVEN IN CONNECTION WITH THIS PUBLICATION. Although this information is believed to be accurate by ASM, ASM cannot guarantee that favorable results will be obtained from the use of this publication alone. This publication is intended for use by persons having technical skill, at their sole discretion and risk. Since the conditions of product or material use are outside of ASM's control, ASM assumes no liability or obligation in connection with any use of this information. No claim of any kind, whether as to products or information in this publication, and whether or not based on negligence, shall be greater in amount than the purchase price of this product or publication in respect of which damages are claimed. THE REMEDY HEREBY PROVIDED SHALL BE THE EXCLUSIVE AND SOLE REMEDY OF BUYER, AND IN NO EVENT SHALL EITHER PARTY BE LIABLE FOR SPECIAL, INDIRECT OR CONSEQUENTIAL DAMAGES WHETHER OR NOT CAUSED BY OR RESULTING FROM THE NEGLIGENCE OF SUCH PARTY. As with any material, evaluation of the material under enduse conditions prior to specification is essential. Therefore, specific testing under actual conditions is recommended.

Nothing contained in this book shall be construed as a grant of any right of manufacture, sale, use, or reproduction, in connection with any method, process, apparatus, product, composition, or system, whether or not covered by letters patent, copyright, or trademark, and nothing contained in this book shall be construed as a defense against any alleged infringement of letters patent, copyright, or trademark, or as a defense against liability for such infringement.

Comments, criticisms, and suggestions are invited, and should be forwarded to ASM International.

Library of Congress Cataloging-in-Publication Data

Stainless Steels / edited by J.R. Davis;

Prepared under the direction of the ASM International Handbook Committee
p. cm.—(ASM Specialty Handbook)

1. Steel, Stainless
I. Davis, J.R. (Joeseph R.)
II. ASM International. Handbook Committee.
III. Series
TA479.S7S677 1994   620.1'7—dc20
SAN: 204-7586

ISBN: 0-87170-503-6

ASM International®
Materials Park, OH 440730002

Preface

The past decade has witnessed a dramatic increase in the use of stainless steels. The attractive combination of excellent corrosion resistance, a wide range of strength levels including strength retention at cryogenic and elevated temperatures, good formability, and an aesthetically pleasing appearance have made stainless steels the material of choice for a diverse range of applications, from critical piping components in boiling water nuclear reactors to the ubiquitous kitchen sink.

Historical Development. The discovery of stainless steels dates back to a period just after the turn of this century when French, German, English, and later U.S. metallurgists began publishing the results of their studies on low-carbon, chromium-containing ferrous alloys. Between 1904 and 1909, French metallurgists Léon B. Guillet and Albert M. Portevin published a series of studies on the structure and properties of 13% Cr martensitic and 17% Cr ferritic steels containing from 0.12 to 1.0% C. In 1909 Guillet and the German metallurgist W. Giesen published studies on iron-chromium-nickel austenitic alloys. These early studies thus covered all stainless steels as classified by structure (martensitic, ferritic, and austenitic).

Beginning in 1908 in Germany, Philipp Monnartz studied the role of carbon content on the corrosion resistance of iron-chromium steels. His research disclosed that the "stainless" *(inoxydable* in French or *rostfrei* in German) quality of these materials was a function of the passivity phenomenon.

The industrial usefulness of stainless steels became evident between 1910 and 1915 and was spurred by the work of Harry Brearley in England (martensitic stainless steels), Frederick Becket and Christian Dantsizen in the United States (ferritic stainless steels), and Eduard Maurer and Benno Strauss in Germany (austenitic stainless steels).

Subsequent research on the compositions, properties and structures, and heat treatment of stainless steels, and the role of alloying elements, led to the development of precipitation-hardenable stainless steels in the 1940s by the United States Steel Corporation. Nickel shortages during World War II resulted in the development of high-manganese austenitic stainless steels, in which some or all of the nickel was replaced with manganese. Although duplex stainless steels containing both austenite and ferrite were discovered in the 1930s, commercial development did not occur until the 1960s when studies on the superplasticity of fine-grain austenitic-ferritic alloys renewed interest in these materials.

The next significant development in stainless steel technology, which was the precursor to the stainless steel industry as we know it today, was the development of the argon-oxygen decarburization (AOD) process. In April 1968, the first commercial AOD vessel for refining stainless steels was placed in operation at the Fort Wayne, IN plant of Joslyn Manufacturing and Supply Company. This 17-ton-capacity installation was the culmination of an eight-year cooperative development program conducted by the Linde Division of Union Carbide Corporation and the Stainless Division of Joslyn. Use of AOD refining enhanced carbon-removal efficiency without excessive oxidation, improved desulfurization and chemistry control, and made possible gaseous (nitrogen) alloying. Argon-oxygen decarburization and subsequent developments in alternative or supplemental melting and refining methods such as vacuum oxygen decarburization, vacuum induction melting, vacuum arc remelting, electroslag remelting, and electron beam melting/remelting made possible the production of an unprecedented variety of new alloys. These include nitrogen-alloyed austenitic and duplex grades and "superaustenitic" and "superferritic" alloys with vastly improved corrosion resistance.

Volume Contents. As a result of the aforementioned developments, stainless steels represent one of the fastest growing segments of the metals industry. Recognizing the need to provide a convenient single-source guide to the properties, selection, and application of these materials, ASM International responded by publishing the *ASM Specialty Handbook: Stainless Steels*. To optimize the usefulness of this volume and to appeal to as wide an audience as possible, the Handbook is divided into five major sections.

Following a general overview of stainless steels, the first section presents articles that describe the basic metallurgy and room-temperature properties of wrought, cast, and powder metallurgy stainless steels as well as stainless steel cladding and weld overlay materials. Two articles on melting/refining and recycling conclude the section.

Section 2 is a comprehensive review of the selection of stainless steels for use in corrosive environments. The first three articles describe corrosion in aqueous solutions and atmospheric corrosion, the causes and solutions associated with stress-corrosion cracking and hydrogen embrittlement, and the response of stainless steels to high-temperature corrosive environments. Emphasis in these articles is on wrought alloys; articles on corrosion of castings and weldments follow.

The articles in the section on fabrication and finishing describe the practical aspects of forming, heat treating, machining, joining, and surface engineering. The article on welding is one of the most detailed accounts of the metallurgical aspects of welded stainless steels available in the technical literature.

Metallography, microstructures, and phase diagrams are covered in section 4. Included are some 210 micrographs depicting typical and atypical structures and 42 phase diagrams illustrating eight binary and ternary systems.

The final section reviews physical properties, the effects of cryogenic and elevated temperatures on mechanical properties, and the friction and wear characteristics of stainless steels. Although not exhaustive, the data should serve as a roadmap for the properties that may be encountered over widely varying conditions.

Acknowledgments. In order to produce a volume of such wide coverage, the editor had to call upon a number of colleagues for help. I would like to thank Kathleen M. Mills for her assistance in editing the book, Barbara E. Helmrich for handling all aspects of word processing, and ASM staff associates Scott Henry and Faith Reidenbach for their support and cooperation. My thanks are also extended to the following individuals who contributed to the book: John H. Reinshagen, Ametek Specialty Metal Products Division; J.R. Merhar, Parmatech Corporation; Erhard Klar, SCM Metal Products, Inc.; Raynold Simoneau, Institut de Recherche d'Hydro-Québec: Howard Ocken, Electric Power Research Institute; Jon Feinstein, Praxair, Inc.; William D. Riley, U.S. Department of the Interior Bureau of Mines; Michelle M. Gauthier, Raytheon Company; Malcolm Blair, Steel Founders' Society of America; and George F. Vander Voort, Carpenter Technology Corporation. Without the collective efforts of all these individuals, successful completion of this Handbook would not have been possible.

Joseph R. Davis
Davis & Associates
Chagrin Falls, Ohio

Contents

Contents

General Introduction

STAINLESS STEELS are iron-base alloys that contain a minimum of approximately 11% Cr, the amount needed to prevent the formation of rust in unpolluted atmospheres (hence the designation *stainless*). Few stainless steels contain more than 30% Cr or less than 50% Fe. They achieve their stainless characteristics through the formation of an invisible and adherent chromium-rich oxide surface film. This oxide forms and heals itself in the presence of oxygen. Other elements added to improve particular characteristics include nickel, molybdenum, copper, titanium, aluminum, silicon, niobium, nitrogen, sulfur, and selenium. Carbon is normally present in amounts ranging from less than 0.03% to over 1.0% in certain martensitic grades. Figure 1 provides a useful summary of some of the compositional and property linkages in the stainless steel family.

With specific restrictions in certain types, the stainless steels can be shaped and fabricated in conventional ways. They can be produced and used in the as-cast condition; shapes can be produced by powder-metallurgy (P/M) techniques; cast ingots can be rolled or forged; and flat products (sheet, strip, and plate) can be produced from continuously cast slabs. The rolled product can be drawn, bent, extruded, or spun. Stainless steels can be further shaped by machining, and they can be joined by welding, brazing, soldering, and adhesive bonding. Stainless steels can also be used as an integral cladding on plain carbon or low-alloy steels as well as some nonferrous metals and alloys.

Original discoveries and developments in stainless steel technology began in England and Germany about 1910 (the historical development of stainless steels is described in the Preface to this Volume). The commercial production and use of stainless steels in the United States began in the 1920s, with Allegheny, Armco, Carpenter, Crucible, Firth-Sterling, Jessop, Ludlum, Republic, Rustless, and U.S. Steel being among the early producers.

The development of precipitation-hardenable stainless steels was spearheaded by the successful production of Stainless W by U.S. Steel in 1945. Since then, Armco, Allegheny-Ludlum, and Carpenter Technology have developed a series of precipitation-hardenable alloys.

The problem of obtaining raw materials has been a significant one, particularly in regard to nickel during the 1950s when civil wars raged in Africa and Asia, prime sources of nickel (and chromium), and Cold War politics played a role because Eastern-bloc nations were also prime sources of the element. This led to the development of a series of alloys (AISI 200 type) in which manganese and nitrogen are partially substituted for nickel. These stainless steels are being used in increasing amounts today.

New refining techniques were adopted in the early 1970s that revolutionized stainless steel melting. Most important was the argon-oxygen-decarburization (AOD) process (see the article "Melting and Refining Methods" in this Volume). The AOD and related processes, with different gas injections or partial pressure systems, permitted the ready removal of carbon without substantial loss of chromium to the slag. Furthermore, low carbon contents were readily achieved in 18% Cr alloys when using high-carbon ferrochromium in furnace charges in place of the much more expensive low-carbon ferrochromium. Major alloying elements could also be controlled more precisely: nitrogen became an easily controlled, intentional alloying element, and sulfur could be reduced to exceptionally low levels when desired. Oxygen could also be reduced to low levels and, when coupled with low sulfur, resulted in marked improvements in steel cleanliness.

During the same period, continuous casting grew in popularity throughout the steel industry, particularly in the stainless steel segment. The incentive for continuous casting was primarily economic. Piping can be confined to the last segment to be cast such that yield improvements of approximately 10% are commonly achieved. Improvements in homogeneity are also attained.

Over the years, stainless steels have become firmly established as materials for cooking utensils, fasteners, cutlery, flatware, decorative architectural hardware, and equipment for use in chemical plants, dairy and food-processing plants, health and sanitation applications, petro-

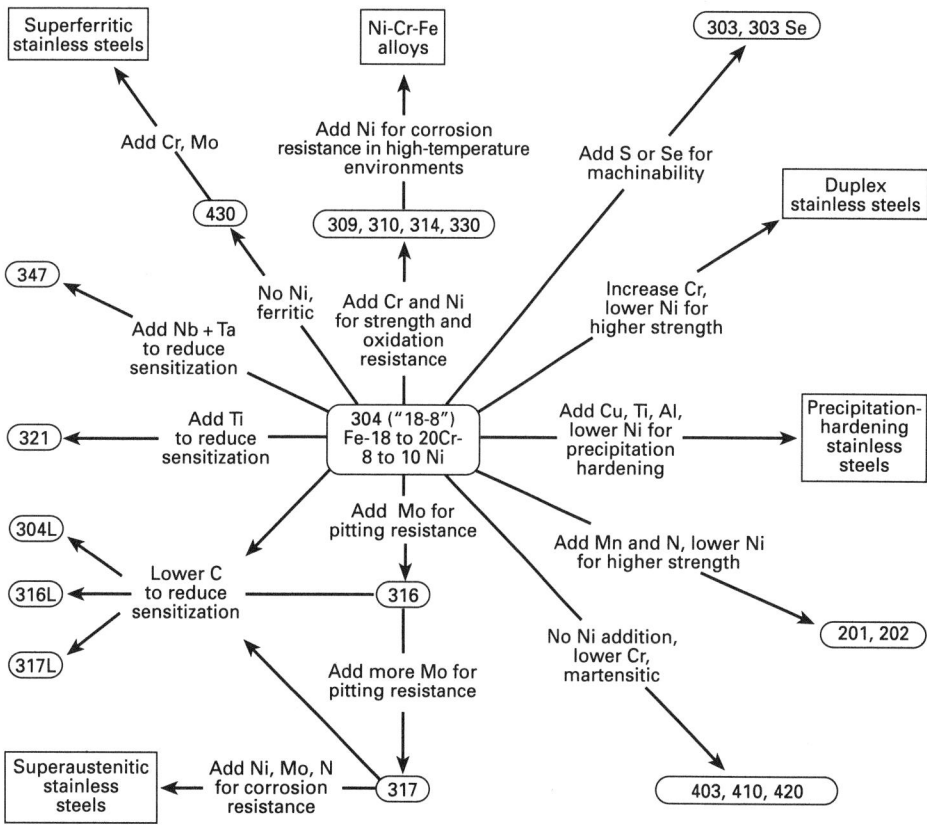

Fig. 1 Compositional and property linkages in the stainless steel family of alloys. Source: Ref 1

Table 1 Composition of selected standard and special stainless steels

UNS designation	AISI type	C	Mn	Si	P	S	Cr	Ni	Mo	N	Others
							Composition, wt% max				
Ferritic alloys											
S40500	405	0.08	1.00	1.00	0.040	0.030	11.50-14.50	...	...	...	0.10-0.30 Al
S40900	409	0.08	1.00	1.00	0.045	0.045	10.50-11.75	0.50	...	...	6 × C-0.75 Ti
S43000	430	0.12	1.00	1.00	0.040	0.030	16.00-18.00	...	...	...	...
S43020	430F	0.12	1.25	1.00	0.060	0.15(a)	16.00-18.00	...	0.60	...	...
S43023	430FSe	0.12	1.25	1.00	0.060	0.060	16.00-18.00	...	...	...	0.15 min Se
S43400	434	0.12	1.00	1.00	0.040	0.030	16.00-18.00	...	0.75-1.25	...	...
S44200	442	0.20	1.00	1.00	0.040	0.030	18.00-23.00	...	...	...	...
S44300	443(b)	0.20	1.00	1.00	0.040	0.030	18.00-23.00	0.50	...	...	0.90-1.25 Cu
S44400	444(b)	0.025	1.00	1.00	0.040	0.030	17.50-19.50	1.00	1.75-2.50	0.025	[0.20 + 4 (C + N)]-0.80 Ti + Nb
S44600	446(b)	0.20	1.50	1.00	0.040	0.030	23.00-27.00	...	...	0.25	...
S18200	18-2FM(c)	0.08	1.25-2.50	1.00	0.040	0.15(a)	17.50-19.50	...	1.50-2.50	...	...
Martensitic alloys											
S40300	403	0.15	1.00	0.50	0.040	0.030	11.50-13.00	...	...	...	...
S41000	410	0.15	1.00	1.00	0.040	0.030	11.50-13.00	...	...	...	...
S41400	414	0.15	1.00	1.00	0.040	0.030	11.50-13.50	1.25-2.50	...	...	...
S41600	416	0.15	1.25	1.00	0.060	0.15(a)	12.00-14.00	...	0.60	...	...
S41610	416 Plus X(d)	0.15	1.50-2.50	1.00	0.060	0.15(a)	12.00-14.00	...	0.60	...	...
S41623	416Se	0.15	1.25	1.00	0.060	0.060	12.00-14.00	...	...	...	0.15 min Se
S42000	420	0.15(a)	1.00	1.00	0.040	0.030	12.00-14.00	...	...	...	...
S42010	Trim Rite(e)	0.15-0.30	1.00	1.00	0.040	0.030	13.50-15.00	0.25-1.00	0.40-1.00	...	...
S42020	420F	0.15(a)	1.25	1.00	0.060	0.15(a)	12.00-14.00	...	0.60	...	...
S42023	420FSe(b)	0.30-0.40	1.25	1.00	0.060	0.060	12.00-14.00	...	0.60	...	0.15 min Se; 0.60 Zr or Cu
S43100	431	0.20	1.00	1.00	0.040	0.030	15.00-17.00	1.25-2.50	...	...	...
S44002	440A	0.60-0.75	1.00	1.00	0.040	0.030	16.00-18.00	...	0.75	...	...
S44003	440B	0.75-0.95	1.00	1.00	0.040	0.030	16.00-18.00	...	0.75	...	...
S44004	440C	0.95-1.20	1.00	1.00	0.040	0.030	16.00-18.00	...	0.75	...	...
S44020	440F(b)	0.95-1.20	1.25	1.00	0.040	0.10-0.35	16.00-18.00	0.75	0.40-0.60	0.08	...
S44023	440FSe(b)	0.95-1.20	1.25	1.00	0.040	0.030	16.00-18.00	0.75	0.60	0.08	0.15 min Se
Austenitic alloys											
S20100	201	0.15	5.50-7.50	1.00	0.060	0.030	16.00-18.00	3.50-5.50	...	0.25	...
S20161	Gall-Tough(e)	0.15	4.00-6.00	3.00-4.00	0.040	0.040	15.00-18.00	4.00-6.00	...	0.08-0.20	...
S20300	203EZ(f)	0.08	5.00-6.50	1.00	0.040	0.18-0.35	16.00-18.00	5.00-6.50	0.50	...	1.75-2.25 Cu
S20910	22-13-5(c)	0.06	4.00-6.00	1.00	0.040	0.030	20.50-23.50	11.50-13.50	1.50-3.00	0.20-0.40	0.10-0.30 Nb; 0.10-0.30 V
S21000	SCF19(e)	0.10	4.00-7.00	0.60	0.030	0.030	18.00-23.00	16.00-20.00	4.00-6.00	0.15	2.00 Cu
S21300	15-15LC(e)	0.25	15.00-18.00	1.00	0.050	0.050	16.00-21.00	3.00	0.50-3.00	0.20-0.80	0.50-2.00 Cu
S21800	Nitronic 60(g)	0.10	7.00-9.00	3.50-4.50	0.040	0.030	16.00-18.00	7.00-9.00	...	0.08-0.20	...
S21904	21-6-9LC(c)	0.04	8.00-10.00	1.00	0.060	0.030	19.00-21.50	5.50-7.50	...	0.15-0.40	...
S24100	18-2Mn(c)	0.15	11.00-14.00	1.00	0.060	0.030	16.50-19.50	0.50-2.50	...	0.20-0.45	...
S28200	18-18 Plus(e)	0.15	17.00-19.00	1.00	0.045	0.030	17.00-19.00	...	0.50-1.50	0.40-0.60	0.50-1.50 Cu
...	Nitronic 30(g)	0.10	7.00-9.00	1.00	...	...	15.00-17.00	1.50-3.00	...	0.15-0.30	1.00 Cu
S30100	301	0.15	2.00	1.00	0.045	0.030	16.00-18.00	6.00-8.00	...	...	...
S30200	302	0.15	2.00	1.00	0.045	0.030	17.00-19.00	8.00-10.00	...	...	...
S30300	303	0.15	2.00	1.00	0.20	0.15(a)	17.00-19.00	8.00-10.00	0.60	...	...
S30310	303 Plus X(d)	0.15	2.50-4.50	1.00	0.20	0.25(a)	17.00-19.00	7.00-10.00	0.75	...	...
S30323	303Se	0.15	2.00	1.00	0.20	0.060	17.00-19.00	8.00-10.00	...	...	0.15 min Se
S30330	303 Cu(b)	0.15	2.00	1.00	0.15	0.10(a)	17.00-19.00	6.00-10.00	...	...	2.50-4.00 Cu; 0.10 Se
S30400	304	0.08	2.00	1.00	0.045	0.030	18.00-20.00	8.00-10.50	...	...	...
S30403	304L	0.03	2.00	1.00	0.045	0.030	18.00-20.00	8.00-12.00	...	...	...
S30430	302 HQ(b)	0.10	2.00	1.00	0.045	0.030	17.00-19.00	8.00-10.00	...	...	3.00-4.00 Cu
S30431	302 HQ-FM(e)	0.06	2.00	1.00	0.040	0.14	16.00-19.00	9.00-11.00	...	...	1.30-2.40 Cu
S30452	304 HN(b)	0.08	2.00	1.00	0.045	0.030	18.00-20.00	8.00-10.50	...	0.16-0.30	...
S30500	305	0.12	2.00	1.00	0.045	0.030	17.00-19.00	10.00-13.00	...	...	...
S30900	309	0.20	2.00	1.00	0.045	0.030	22.00-24.00	12.00-15.00	...	...	...
S30908	309S	0.08	2.00	1.00	0.045	0.030	22.00-24.00	12.00-15.00	...	...	...
S31000	310	0.25	2.00	1.50	0.045	0.030	24.00-26.00	19.00-22.00	...	...	...
S31008	310S	0.08	2.00	1.50	0.045	0.030	24.00-26.00	19.00-22.00	...	...	...
S31600	316	0.08	2.00	1.00	0.045	0.030	16.00-18.00	10.00-14.00	2.00-3.00	...	...
S31603	316L	0.030	2.00	1.00	0.045	0.030	16.00-18.00	10.00-14.00	2.00-3.00	...	...
S31620	316F	0.08	2.00	1.00	0.20	0.10(a)	17.00-19.00	12.00-14.00	1.75-2.50	...	...
S31700	317	0.08	2.00	1.00	0.045	0.30	18.00-20.00	11.00-15.00	3.00-4.00	...	...
S31703	317L	0.030	2.00	1.00	0.045	0.030	18.00-20.00	11.00-15.00	3.00-4.00	...	...
S32100	321	0.08	2.00	1.00	0.045	0.030	17.00-19.00	9.00-12.00	...	...	5 × C min Ti
S34700	347	0.08	2.00	1.00	0.045	0.030	17.00-19.00	9.00-13.00	...	...	10 × C min Nb
S34720	347F(b)	0.08	2.00	1.00	0.045	0.18-0.35	17.00-19.00	9.00-12.00	...	...	10 × C-1.10 Nb
S34723	347FSe(b)	0.08	2.00	1.00	0.11-0.17	0.030	17.00-19.00	9.00-12.00	...	...	10 × C-1.10 Nb; 0.15-0.35 Se
S38400	384	0.08	2.00	1.00	0.045	0.030	15.00-17.00	17.00-19.00	...	...	...
N08020	20Cb-3(e)	0.07	2.00	1.00	0.045	0.035	19.00-21.00	32.00-38.00	2.00-3.00	...	8 × C-1.00 Nb; 3.00-4.00 Cu

(continued)

Note: All compositions include Fe as balance. (a) Minimum, rather than maximum wt%. (b) Designation resembles AISI type, but is not used in that system. (c) Common trade name, rather than AISI type. (d) Trade name of Crucible Inc. (e) Trade name of Carpenter Technology Corporation. (f) Trade name of Al-Tech Corp. (g) Trade name of Armco Inc.

Table 1 (continued)

| UNS designation | AISI type | Composition, wt% max | | | | | | | | | |
		C	Mn	Si	P	S	Cr	Ni	Mo	N	Others
Duplex alloys											
S31803	2205(c)	0.030	2.00	1.00	0.030	0.020	21.0-23.0	4.50-6.50	2.50-3.50	0.08-0.20	...
S32550	Alloy 255(c)	0.04	1.50	1.00	0.04	0.03	24.0-27.0	4.50-6.50	2.00-4.00	0.10-0.25	1.50-2.50 Cu
S32900	329	0.20	1.00	0.75	0.040	0.030	23.00-28.00	2.50-5.00	1.00-2.00	...	...
S32950	7-Mo Plus(e)	0.03	2.00	0.60	0.035	0.010	26.0-29.0	3.50-5.20	1.00-2.50	0.15-0.35	...
Precipitation-hardenable alloys											
S13800	PH13-8 Mo(g)	0.05	0.20	0.10	0.010	0.008	12.25-13.25	7.50-8.50	2.00-2.50	0.01	0.90-1.35 Al
S15500	15-5PH(g)	0.07	1.00	1.00	0.040	0.030	14.00-15.50	3.50-5.50	...	...	0.15-0.45 Nb; 2.50-4.50 Cu
S15700	15-7PH(g)	0.09	1.00	1.00	0.040	0.030	14.00-16.00	6.50-7.25	2.00-3.00	...	0.75-1.50 Al
S17400	17-4PH(g)	0.07	1.00	1.00	0.040	0.030	15.50-17.50	3.00-5.00	...	...	0.15-0.45 Nb; 3.00-5.00 Cu
S17700	PH 17-7(g)	0.09	1.00	1.00	0.040	0.040	16.00-18.00	6.50-7.75	...	...	0.75-1.50 Al
S35000	633(b)	0.07-0.11	0.50-1.25	0.50	0.040	0.030	16.00-17.00	4.00-5.00	2.50-3.25	0.07-0.13	...
S35500	634(b)	0.10-0.15	0.50-1.25	0.50	0.040	0.030	15.00-16.00	4.00-5.00	2.50-3.25	0.07-0.13	...
S44000	Custom 450(e)	0.05	1.00	1.00	0.030	0.030	14.00-16.00	5.00-7.00	0.50-1.00	...	8 × C min; 1.25-1.75 Cu
S45500	Custom 455(e)	0.05	0.50	0.50	0.040	0.030	11.00-12.50	7.50-9.50	0.50	...	0.10-0.50 Nb; 1.50-2.50 Cu 0.80-1.40 Ti
S66286	A286(c)	0.08	2.00	1.00	0.040	0.030	13.50-16.00	24.0-27.0	1.00-1.50	...	0.35 Al; 0.0010-0.010 B 1.90-2.35 Ti; 0.10-0.50 V

Note: All compositions include Fe as balance. (a) Minimum, rather than maximum wt%. (b) Designation resembles AISI type, but is not used in that system. (c) Common trade name, rather than AISI type. (d) Trade name of Crucible Inc. (e) Trade name of Carpenter Technology Corporation. (f) Trade name of Al-Tech Corp. (g) Trade name of Armco Inc.

leum and petrochemical plants, textile plants, and the pharmaceutical and transportation industries. Some of these applications involve exposure to either elevated or cryogenic temperatures; austenitic stainless steels are well suited to either type of service. Properties of stainless steels at elevated temperatures are discussed in the article "Elevated-Temperature Properties" in this Volume. Properties at cryogenic temperatures are discussed in the article "Low-Temperature Properties."

Modifications in composition are sometimes made to facilitate production. For instance, basic compositions are altered to make it easier to produce stainless steel tubing and castings. Similar modifications are made for the manufacture of stainless steel welding electrodes; here, combinations of electrode coating and wire composition are used to produce desired compositions in deposited weld metal.

Designations for Stainless Steels

In the United States, wrought grades of stainless steels are generally designated by the American Iron and Steel Institute (AISI) numbering system, the Unified Numbering System (UNS), or the proprietary name of the alloy. In addition, designation systems have been established by most of the major industrial nations (Ref 2). Of the two institutional numbering systems used in the U.S., AISI is the older and more widely used. Most of the grades have a three-digit designation; the 200 and 300 series are generally austenitic stainless steels, whereas the 400 series are either ferritic or martensitic. Some of the grades have a one- or two-letter suffix that indicates a particular modification of the composition.

The UNS system is a broader-based system that comprises a list of all metallic materials, including stainless steel. This system includes a considerably greater number of stainless steels than AISI, because it incorporates all of the more recently developed stainless steels. The UNS designation for a stainless steel consists of the letter S, followed by a five-digit number. For those alloys that have an AISI designation, the first three digits of the UNS designation usually correspond to an AISI number. When the last two digits are 00, the number designates a basic AISI grade. Modifications of the basic grades use two digits other than zeroes. For stainless steels that contain high nickel contents (~ 25 to 35% Ni), the UNS designation consists of the letter N followed by a five-digit number. Examples include N08020 (20 Cb-3), N08024 (20Mo-4), N08026 (20Mo-6), N08366 (AL-6X), and N08367 (AL-6XN). Although classified as nickel-base alloys by the UNS system, the aforementioned materials constitute the "superaustenitic" category of stainless steels as described below in the section on "Classification of Stainless Steels."

Table 1 provides the compositional limits for selected stainless steels, listed by UNS and AISI type designations and separated into the basic families described below. Where AISI type designations are not available, common trade names are listed. These names, the third commonly used identification of stainless steels, have often become the popular means of identifying a particular alloy. More thorough listings of chemical compositions for wrought, cast, and P/M stainless steels can be found in the articles "Metallurgy and Properties of Wrought Stainless Steels," "Metallurgy and Properties of Cast Stainless Steels," and "Powder Metallurgy Stainless Steels" in this Volume.

Classification of Stainless Steels

Stainless steels can be divided into five families. Four are based on the characteristic crystallographic structure/microstructure of the alloys in the family: ferritic, martensitic, austenitic, or duplex (austenitic plus ferritic). The fifth family, the precipitation-hardenable alloys, is based on the type of heat treatment used, rather than microstructure.

Ferritic stainless steels are so named because their body-centered-cubic (bcc) crystal structure is the same as that of iron at room temperature. These alloys are magnetic and cannot be hardened by heat treatment. In general, ferritic stainless steels do not have particularly high strength. Their annealed yield strengths range from 275 to 350 MPa (40 to 50 ksi), and their poor toughness and susceptibility to sensitization limit their fabricability and the usable section size. Their chief advantages are their resistance to chloride stress-corrosion cracking, atmospheric corrosion, and oxidation at a relatively low cost.

Ferritic stainless steels contain between 11 and 30% Cr, with only small amounts of austenite-forming elements, such as carbon, nitrogen, and nickel. Their general use depends on their chromium content.

The low-chromium (11%) alloys (S40500 and S40900, the latter being the most widely used ferritic stainless steel) have fair corrosion and oxidation resistance and good fabricability at low cost. They have gained wide acceptance for use in automotive exhaust systems.

The intermediate-chromium (16 to 18%) alloys (S43000 and S43400) are used for automotive trim and cooking utensils. These alloys are not as readily fabricated as the lower chromium alloys because of their poor toughness and weldability.

The high-chromium (19 to 30%) alloys (S44200 and S44600), which are often referred to as superferritics (Fig. 1), are used for applications that require a high level of corrosion and oxidation resistance. These alloys often contain either aluminum or molybdenum and have a very low carbon content. Their fabrication is possible because of special melting techniques that can achieve very low carbon con-

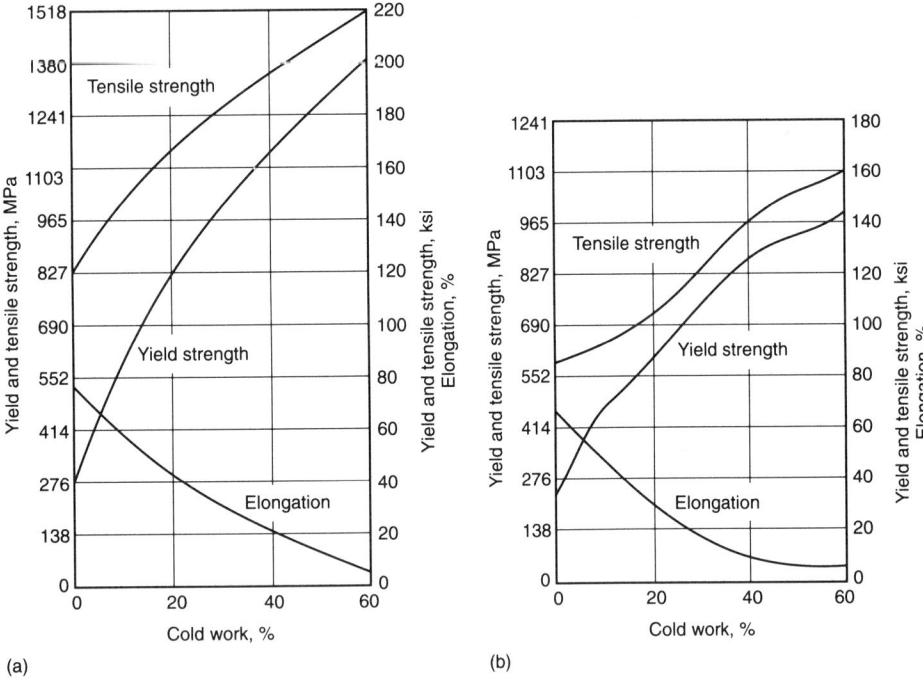

(a)

(b)

Fig. 2 Effect of cold working on mechanical properties of stainless steels. (a) Type 301. (b) Type 305

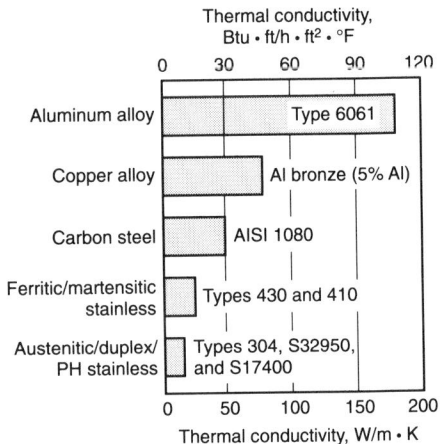

Fig. 3 Comparison of thermal conductivity for carbon steel, copper alloy, aluminum, and stainless steels

tents as well as very low nitrogen contents. Stabilizing elements such as titanium and niobium can be added to prevent sensitization and to improve as-welded properties.

Austenitic stainless steels constitute the largest stainless family in terms of number of alloys and usage. Like the ferritic alloys, they cannot be hardened by heat treatment. However, their similarity ends there. The austenitic alloys are nonmagnetic, and their structure is face-centered-cubic (fcc), like that of high-temperature (900 to 1400 °C, or 1650 to 2550 °F) iron. They possess excellent ductility, formability, and toughness, even at cryogenic temperatures. In addition, they can be substantially hardened by cold work.

Although nickel is the chief element used to stabilize austenite, carbon and nitrogen are also used because they are readily soluble in the fcc structure. A wide range of corrosion resistance can be achieved by balancing the ferrite-forming elements, such as chromium and molybdenum, with austenite-forming elements.

Austenitic stainless steels can be subdivided into two categories: chromium-nickel alloys, such as S30400 and S31600, and chromium-manganese-nitrogen alloys, such as S20100 and S24100. The latter group generally contains less nickel and maintains the austenitic structure with high levels of nitrogen. Manganese (5 to 20%) is necessary in these low-nickel alloys to increase nitrogen solubility in austenite and to prevent martensite transformation. The addition of nitrogen also increases the strength of austenitic alloys. Typical chromium-nickel alloys have tensile yield strengths from 200 to 275 MPa (30 to 40 ksi) in the annealed condition, whereas the high-nitrogen alloys have yield strengths up to 500 MPa (70 ksi).

As previously mentioned, austenitic alloys can be substantially hardened by cold working.

The degree of work hardening depends on the alloy content, with increasing alloy content decreasing the work-hardening rate. Figure 2 depicts the higher work-hardening rate of type 301 (7% Ni) versus that of type 305 (11.5% Ni), which is primarily due to its lower nickel content. Austenitic stainless steels that have a low alloy content, such as S20100, S20161, S30100, and S30400, often become magnetic because of the transformation to martensite when sufficiently cold worked or heavily deformed in machining or forming operations. The rapid work hardening of S20161 is a major advantage in sliding wear. In S30430, copper is intentionally added to lower the work-hardening rate for enhanced headability in the production of fasteners.

Another property that depends on alloy content is corrosion resistance. Molybdenum is added to S31700 and S31600 to enhance corrosion resistance in chloride environments. High-chromium grades (S30900 and S31000) are used in oxidizing environments and high-temperature applications, whereas a high-nickel grade (N08020) is used in severe reducing acid environments. To prevent intergranular corrosion after elevated-temperature exposure, titanium or niobium is added to stabilized carbon in S32100 or S34700. Also, lower-carbon grades (AISI L or S designations), such as S30403 (type 304L), have been established to prevent intergranular corrosion. Some of the more corrosion-resistant alloys, such as N08020 (20Cb-3), have nickel levels high enough (32 to 38% Ni) to rate classification as nickel-base alloys. Alloys containing nickel, molybdenum (~ 6%) and nitrogen (~ 0.20%) are sometimes referred to as superaustenitics (Fig. 1).

Martensitic stainless steels are similar to iron-carbon alloys that are austenitized, hardened by quenching, and then tempered for increased

ductility and toughness. These alloys are magnetic, and their heat-treated structure is body-centered tetragonal (bct). In the annealed condition, they have a tensile yield strength of about 275 MPa (40 ksi) and are generally machined, cold formed, and cold worked in this condition.

The strength obtained by heat treatment depends on the carbon content of the alloy. Increasing carbon content increases strength but decreases ductility and toughness. The most commonly used alloy in this family is S41000, which contains about 12% Cr and 0.1% C. This alloy is tempered to a variety of hardness levels, from 20 to 40 HRC. Both chromium and carbon contents are increased in alloys S42000, S44002, S44003, and S44004. The first of these contains 14% Cr and 0.3% C and has a hardness capability of 50 HRC. The other three alloys contain 16% Cr and from 0.6 to 1.1% C. These alloys are capable of 60 HRC and a tensile yield strength of 1900 MPa (280 ksi). The amount of primary carbides increases with increased carbon content in these three alloys.

Wear resistance for martensitic stainless steels is very dependent on carbon content. S44004 (1.1% C) has excellent adhesive and abrasive wear, similar to tool steels, whereas S41000 (0.1% C) has relatively poor wear resistance. The key to adhesive wear resistance is a high hardness. Abrasive wear resistance requires both high hardness and primary carbides.

Molybdenum and nickel can be added to martensitic stainless steel to improve corrosion and toughness properties. Nickel also serves to maintain the desired microstructure, preventing excessive free ferrite when higher chromium levels are used to improve corrosion resistance. However, the addition of these elements is somewhat restricted because higher amounts result in a microstructure that is not fully martensitic.

Precipitation-hardenable (PH) stainless steels are chromium-nickel grades that can be hardened by an aging treatment. These grades are classified as austenitic (such as S66286), semi-austenitic (such as S17700), or martensitic (such as S17400). The classification is determined by their solution-annealed microstructure. The semi-austenitic alloys are subsequently heat treated so that the austenite transforms to martensite. Cold work is sometimes used to facilitate the aging reaction. Various alloying elements, such as aluminum, titanium, niobium, or copper, are used to achieve aging. They generally form intermetallic compounds, but in S17400, fine copper precipitates are formed.

Like the martensitic stainless steels, PH alloys can attain high tensile yield strengths, up to 1700 MPa (250 ksi). Cold working prior to aging can result in even higher strengths. The PH grades generally have good ductility and toughness with moderate-to-good corrosion resistance. A better combination of strength and corrosion resistance is achieved than with the martensitic alloys. These improved properties are related to their higher chromium, nickel, and molybde-

num contents, as well as their restricted carbon (0.040 max) levels. The low carbon content of the martensitic PH stainless steels is especially critical for toughness and good ductility. However, this low carbon content reduces the wear resistance of these alloys.

The most well-known precipitation-hardenable stainless steel is S17400. It contains chromium and nickel, as do all precipitation-hardenable stainless steels, with copper for age hardening and niobium for stabilizing the carbon. The age-hardening agents used in other alloys include titanium (S45500), aluminum (S13800), and niobium (S45000). Molybdenum can be added to improve mechanical properties or corrosion resistance. Both molybdenum and copper are added for corrosion resistance in S45000. Carbon is normally restricted, except in semiaustenitic alloys such as S35500, which require it to provide the desired phase transformations.

Duplex stainless steels are chromium-nickel-molybdenum alloys that are balanced to contain a mixture of austenite and ferrite and are magnetic, as well. Their duplex structure results in improved stress-corrosion cracking resistance, compared with the austenitic stainless steels, and improved toughness and ductility, compared with the ferritic stainless steels. They are capable of tensile yield strengths ranging from 550 to 690 MPa (80 to 100 ksi) in the annealed condition, which is approximately twice the strength level of either phase alone.

The original alloy in this family was the predominantly ferritic S32900. The addition of nitrogen to duplex alloys, such as S32950 and S31803, increases the amount of austenite to nearly 50%. In addition, nitrogen improves as-welded corrosion properties, chloride corrosion resistance, and toughness. The improvement in toughness is probably related to the higher amount of austenite

Table 2 Properties of selected stainless steels relative to various ferrous and nonferrous alloys

UNS or AISI type	Condition	Rockwell hardness	Yield strength, 0.2% offset MPa	ksi	Ultimate tensile strength MPa	ksi	Elongation in 50.8 mm (2.0 in.), %	Reduction of area, %	Charpy V-notch impact strength J	ft · lbf
Austenitic stainless										
Type 304	Annealed	81 HRB	241	35	586	85	60.0	70.0	≥325	≥240
N08020	Annealed	84 HRB	276	40	621	90	50.0	65.0	271	200
S20161	Annealed	93 HRB	365	53	970	140	59.0	64.0	≥325	≥240
S21800	Annealed	95 HRB	414	60	710	103	64.0	74.0	≥325	≥240
Ferritic										
Type 405	Annealed	81 HRB	276	40	483	70	30.0	60.0	...	...
Type 430	Annealed	82 HRB	310	45	517	75	30.0	65.0	217	161
Duplex										
S32950	Annealed	100 HRB	570	82	760	110	38.0	78.0	157	116
Martensitic										
Type 410	Annealed	82 HRB	276	40	517	75	35.0	70.0	...	...
	Oil quenched from 1010 °C (1850 °F) and tempered:									
	at 250 °C (500 °F)	43 HRC	1089	158	1337	193	17.0	62.0	76	56
	at 593 °C (1100 °F)	26 HRC	724	105	827	120	20.0	63.0	52	38
Type 420	Annealed	92 HRB	345	50	655	95	25.0	55.0	...	...
	Oil quenched from 1038 °C (1900 °F) and tempered at 316 °C (600 °F)	52 HRC	1482	215	1724	250	8.0	25.0	20	15
Type 440C	Annealed	97 HRB	448	65	758	110	14.0	30.0	...	...
	Oil quenched from 1038 °C (1900 °F) and tempered at 316 °C (600 °F)	57 HRC	1896	275	1975	285	2.0	10.0	2	3
Precipitation hardened										
S45500	Annealed	31 HRC	793	115	1000	145	14.0	70.0	...	...
	Water quenched from 1038 °C (1900 °F) and aged:									
	at 482 °C (900 °F)	49 HRC	1620	235	1689	245	10.0	45.0	12	9
	at 566 °C (1050 °F)	40 HRC	1207	175	1310	190	15.0	55.0	47	35
S17400	Annealed	31 HRC	793	115	965	140	12.0	50.0	...	...
	Water quenched from 1038 °C (1900 °F) and aged:									
	at 482 °C (900 °F)	44 HRC	1262	183	1365	198	15.0	52.0	21	16
	at 621 °C (1150 °F)	33 HRC	869	126	1131	164	17.0	59.0	75	55
Carbon steel										
AISI 1080	Annealed	97 HRB	455	66	821	119	15.0	22.0	...	...
	Oil quenched from 816 °C (1500 °F) and tempered at 204 °C (400 °F)	42 HRC	980	142	1304	189	12.0	35.0	...	...
Aluminum alloy										
Type 6061	Annealed	...	55	8	124	18	25.0	...	...	...
	Aged	56 HRB	276	40	311	45	12.0	...	...	...
Copper alloy										
Al bronze (95 Cu-5 Al)	Annealed	45 HRB	173	25	380	55	65.0	...	...	...

present, which makes it possible to produce heavier product forms such as plates and bars.

Physical and Mechanical Properties of Stainless Steels

The physical and mechanical properties of stainless steels are quite different from those of commonly used nonferrous alloys such as aluminum and copper alloys. However, when comparing the various stainless families with carbon steels, many similarities in properties exist, although there are some key differences. Like carbon steels, the density of stainless steels is ~8.0 g/cm^3, which is approximately three times greater than that of aluminum alloys (2.7 g/cm^3). Like carbon steels, stainless steels have a high modulus of elasticity (200 MPa, or 30 ksi) that is nearly twice that of copper alloys (115 MPa, or 17 ksi) and nearly three times that of aluminum alloys (70 MPa, or 10 ksi).

Differences among these materials are evident in thermal conductivity, thermal expansion, and electrical resistivity, as well. Figure 3 shows the large variation in thermal conductivity between various types of materials; 6061 aluminum alloy (Al-1Mg-0.6Si-0.3Cu-0.2Cr) has a very high thermal conductivity, followed by aluminum bronze (Cu-5Al), 1080 carbon steel, and then stainless steels. For stainless steels, alloying additions, especially nickel, copper, and chromium, greatly decrease thermal conductivity.

Thermal expansion (Fig. 4) is greatest for type 6061 aluminum alloy, followed by aluminum bronze and austenitic stainless alloys, and then ferritic and martensitic alloys. For austenitic stainless alloys, additions of nickel and copper can decrease thermal expansion. Stainless steels have high electrical resistivity (Fig. 5). Alloying additions tend to increase electrical resistivity. Therefore, the ferritic and martensitic stainless steels have lower electrical resistivity than the austenitic, duplex, and PH alloys, but higher electrical resistivity than 1080 carbon steel. Electrical resistivity of stainless steels is ~7.5 times greater than aluminum bronze and nearly 20 times greater than type 6061 aluminum alloy.

Table 2 lists tensile properties and toughness for selected stainless alloys representing the five families. The four grades listed under austenitic alloys have relatively low yield strength, compared with the heat-treatable alloys, but have the highest tensile ductility and toughness. Two austenitic alloys, S20161 and S21800, were specifically developed to have superior resistance to galling and metal-to-metal wear for stainless steels. Alloy N08020 is a high-nickel (33%) superaustenitic stainless alloy for use in harsh corrosive environments.

The ferritic stainless steels (type 405 and 409) listed have tensile yield strengths similar to those of the austenitic grades but lower values for ultimate tensile strength, ductility, and toughness. However, strength, ductility, and toughness are still excellent compared with other materials, such as 6061 aluminum alloy and aluminum bronze. The duplex stainless alloy (S32950) listed

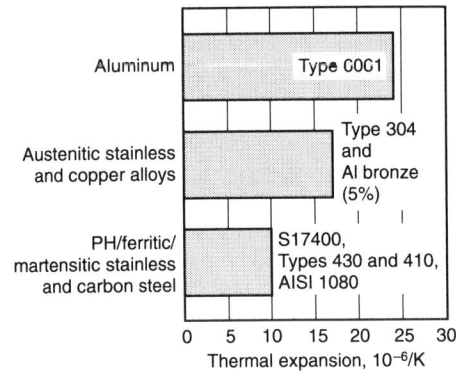

Fig. 4 Comparison of thermal expansion for carbon steel, copper alloy, aluminum, and stainless steels

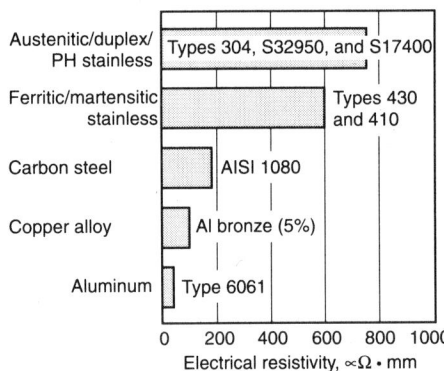

Fig. 5 Comparison of electrical resistivity for carbon steel, copper alloy, aluminum, and stainless steels

has twice the tensile yield strength of the austenitic and ferritic grades and approximately half the toughness. Again, its toughness is far superior to that of alloys that are heat treated and hardened.

The martensitic alloys listed in Table 2 have a large variation in strength, ductility, and toughness. In the annealed condition, their properties are similar to those of the ferritic alloys, with strength increasing and ductility decreasing with increasing carbon content. The higher-carbon-containing alloys, type 420 and type 440C, are generally tempered at a low temperature (330 °C, or 625 °F max) to maximize their strength. On the other hand, type 410 is tempered over a wide temperature range, from 260 to 650 °C (500 to 1200 °F). The tensile properties of type 410 are similar to those of carbon steel (AISI 1080).

The martensitic PH alloys, such as S45500 and S17400, have higher annealed strength and lower ductility than the martensitic alloys and are aged at temperatures ranging from 480 to 620 °C (895 to 1150 °F). Their strength is dependent on the hardener (titanium, niobium, copper), the amount of hardener, and the aging temperatures used. Toughness is either similar or superior to the martensitic alloys at a given strength level.

Selection of Stainless Steels

Factors in Selection. The selection of stainless steels may be based on corrosion resistance, fabrication characteristics, availability, mechanical properties in specific temperature ranges, and product cost. However, corrosion resistance and mechanical properties are usually the most important factors in selecting a grade for a given application.

Characteristics to be considered in selecting the proper type of stainless steel for a specific application include:

- Corrosion resistance
- Resistance to oxidation and sulfidation (see the article "High-Temperature Corrosion" in this Volume)
- Strength and ductility at ambient and service temperatures
- Suitability for intended fabrication techniques

- Suitability for intended cleaning procedures (see the article "Surface Engineering" in this Volume)
- Stability of properties in service
- Toughness
- Resistance to abrasion, erosion, galling, and seizing (see the article "Tribological Properties" in this Volume)
- Surface finish and/or reflectivity
- Physical property characteristics, such as magnetic properties, thermal conductivity, and electrical resistivity (see the article "Physical Properties" in this Volume)
- Sharpness, or retention of cutting edge (see the article "Machining" in this Volume)
- Rigidity

Corrosion resistance is frequently the most important characteristic of a stainless steel but often is also the most difficult to assess for a specific application. General corrosion resistance to pure chemical solutions is comparatively easy to determine, but actual environments are usually much more complex. Table 3 shows resistance of standard types of stainless steels to various common media.

General corrosion is often much less serious than localized forms such as stress-corrosion cracking, crevice corrosion in tight spaces or under deposits, pitting attack, and intergranular attack in sensitized material such as weld heat-affected zones. Such localized corrosion can cause unexpected and sometimes catastrophic failure while most of the structure remains unaffected, and therefore it must be considered carefully in the design and selection of the proper grade of stainless steel. Corrosive attack can also be increased dramatically by seemingly minor impurities in the medium that may be difficult to anticipate but that can have major effects, even when present in only parts-per-million concentrations: heat transfer through the steel to or from the corrosive medium; contact with dissimilar metallic materials; by stray electrical currents; and many other subtle factors. At elevated temperatures, attack can be accelerated significantly by seemingly minor changes in atmosphere that affect scaling, sulfidation, or carburization.

Despite these complications, a suitable steel can be selected for most applications on the basis of experience, perhaps with assistance from the steel producer. Laboratory corrosion data can be misleading in predicting service performance. Even actual service data have limitations, because similar corrosive media may differ substantially because of slight variations in some of the corrosion factors listed above. For difficult applications, extensive study of comparative data may be necessary, sometimes followed by pilot plant or in-service testing.

As a general rule-of-thumb, it is best to initiate the selection process with the basic type 304 (S30400), the most commonly used stainless alloy. Type 304 is in the middle range of corrosion resistance provided by stainless steels (Ref 3). It resists most oxidizing acids, many sterilizing solutions, most organic chemicals and dyestuffs, and a wide range of inorganic chemicals (see Table 3).

For applications in industrial processes requiring a higher level of corrosion resistance, type 316 (S31600) should be considered. This grade has added molybdenum (see Fig. 1) to increase its resistance to pitting caused by chlorides. Generally, type 316 is specified to resist corrosive process chemicals used to produce inks, rayons, photographic chemicals, paper, textiles, bleaches, and rubber (Ref 3). It is also used for surgical implants within the hostile environment of the human body.

For severe environments in which chloride stress-corrosion cracking is the primary concern, superaustenitics, duplex stainless steels, or superferritics should be considered. These materials are discussed and compared in the article "Stress-Corrosion Cracking and Hydrogen Embrittlement" in this Volume.

For less severe corrosive environments, ferritic stainless steels such as type 430 (S43000) may be adequate. Although type 430 is less resistant to corrosion than austenitic or duplex grades because it contains no nickel and slightly less chromium, it is less costly than 304, 316, superaustenitics, or duplex grades because of its lower alloy content. Type 430 effectively resists foods, fresh water, and nonmarine atmospheric corrosion (Ref 3).

Experience in the use of stainless steels indicates that many factors can affect their corrosion resistance. Some of the more prominent factors are:

- Chemical composition of the corrosive medium, including impurities
- Physical state of the medium: liquid, gaseous, solid, or combinations thereof
- Temperature
- Temperature variations
- Aeration of the medium
- Oxygen content of the medium
- Bacteria content of the medium
- Ionization of the medium
- Repeated formation and collapse of bubbles in the medium
- Relative motion of the medium with respect to the steel
- Chemical composition of the metal

Table 3   Relative corrosion resistance of standard stainless steel grades for different environments

Environment	Grades(a)
Acids	
Hydrochloric acid	Stainless is not generally recommended except when solutions are very dilute and at room temperature (pitting may occur).
Mixed acids	There is usually no appreciable attack on type 304 or 316 as long as sufficient nitric acid is present.
Nitric acid	Type 304L and 430 and some higher-alloy stainless grades have been used.
Phosphoric acid	Type 304 is satisfactory for storing cold phosphoric acid up to 85% and for handling concentrations up to 5% in some unit processes of manufacture. Type 316 is more resistant and is generally used for storing and manufacture if the fluorine content is not too high. Type 317 is somewhat more resistant than type 316. At concentrations ≤85%, the metal temperature should not exceed 100 °C (212 °F) with type 316 and slightly higher with type 317. Oxidizing ions inhibit attack.
Sulfuric acid	Type 304 can be used at room temperature for concentrations >80 to 90%. Type 316 can be used in contact with sulfuric acid ≤10% at temperatures ≤50 °C (120 °F) if the solutions are aerated; the attack is greater in air-free solutions. Type 317 may be used at temperatures as high as 65 °C (150 °F) with ≤5% concentration. The presence of other materials may markedly change the corrosion rate. As little as 500 to 2000 ppm of cupric ions make it possible to use type 304 in hot solutions of moderate concentration. Other additives may have the opposite effect.
Sulfurous acid	Type 304 may be subject to pitting, particularly if some sulfuric acid is present. Type 316 is usable at moderate concentrations and temperatures.
Bases	
Ammonium hydroxide, sodium hydroxide, caustic solutions	Steels in the 300 series generally have good corrosion resistance at virtually all concentrations and temperatures in weak bases, such as ammonium hydroxide. In stronger bases, such as sodium hydroxide, there may be some attack, cracking, and etching in more concentrated solutions and/or at higher temperatures. Commercial-purity caustic solutions may contain chlorides, which will accentuate any attack and may cause pitting of type 316, as well as type 304.
Organics	
Acetic acid	Acetic acid is seldom pure in chemical plants but generally includes numerous and varied minor constituents. Type 304 is used for a wide variety of equipment including stills, base heaters, holding tanks, heat exchangers, pipelines, valves, and pumps for concentrations ≤99% at temperatures ≤ ~50 °C (120 °F). Type 304 is also satisfactory—if small amounts of turbidity or color pickup can be tolerated—for room-temperature storage of glacial acetic acid. Types 316 and 317 have the broadest range of usefulness, especially if formic acid is also present or if solutions are unaerated. Type 316 is used for fractionating equipment, for 30-99% concentrations where type 304 cannot be used, for storage vessels, pumps, and process equipment handling glacial acetic acid, which would be discolored by type 304. Type 316 is likewise applicable for parts having temperatures >50 °C (120 °F), for dilute vapors, and for high pressures. Type 317 has somewhat greater corrosion resistance than type 316 under severely corrosive conditions. None of the stainless steels has adequate corrosion resistance to glacial acetic acid at the boiling temperature or at superheated vapor temperatures.
Aldehydes	Type 304 is generally satisfactory.
Amines	Type 316 is usually preferred to type 304.
Cellulose acetate	Type 304 is satisfactory for low temperatures, but type 316 or type 317 is needed for high temperatures.
Formic acids	Type 304 is generally acceptable at moderate temperatures, but type 316 is resistant to all concentrations at temperatures up to boiling.
Esters	With regard to corrosion, esters are comparable to organic acids.
Fatty acids	Type 304 is resistant to fats and fatty acids ≤ ~150 °C (300 °F), but type 316 is needed at 150-260 °C (300-500 °F), and type 317, at higher temperatures.
Paint vehicles	Type 316 may be needed if exact color and lack of contamination are important.
Phthalic anhydride	Type 316 is usually used for reactors, fractionating columns, traps, baffles, caps, and piping.
Soaps	Type 304 is used for parts such as spray towers, but type 316 may be preferred for spray nozzles and flake-drying belts to minimize off-color product.
Synthetic detergents	Type 316 is used for preheat, piping, pumps, and reactors in catalytic hydrogenation of fatty acids to give salts of sulfonated high-molecular alcohols.
Tall oil (pulp and paper industry)	Type 304 has only limited use in tall-oil distillation service. High rosin acid streams can be handled by type 316L with a minimum molybdenum content of 2.75%. Type 316 can also be used in the more corrosive high fatty acid streams at temperatures ≤245 °C (475 °F), but type 317 will probably be required at higher temperatures.
Tar	Tar distillation equipment is almost all type 316 because coal tar has a high chloride content; type 304 does not have adequate resistance to pitting.
Urea	Type 316L is generally required.
Pharmaceuticals	
	Type 316 is usually selected for all parts in contact with the product because of its inherent corrosion resistance and greater assurance of product purity.

(a) The stainless steels mentioned may be considered for use in the indicated environments. Additional information or corrosion expertise may be necessary prior to use in some environments; for example, some impurities may cause localized corrosion (such as chlorides causing pitting or stress-corrosion cracking of some grades).

Table 4 Typical physical properties of wrought stainless steels in the annealed condition

Type	UNS number	Density g/cm³ (lb/in.³)	Elastic modulus GPa (10⁶ psi)	Mean CTE from 0 °C (32 °F) to: 100 °C (212 °F) μm/m · °C (μin./in. · °F)	315 °C (600 °F) μm/m · °C (μin./in. · °F)	538 °C (1000 °F) μm/m · °C (μin./in. · °F)	Thermal conductivity at 100 °C (212 °F) W/m · K (Btu/ft · h · °F)	at 500 °C (932 °F) W/m · K (Btu/ft · h · °F)	Specific heat(a) J/kg · K (Btu/lb · °F)	Electrical resistivity, n Ω · m	Magnetic permeability (b)	Melting range °C (°F)
201	S20100	7.8 (0.28)	197 (28.6)	15.7 (8.7)	17.5 (9.7)	18.4 (10.2)	16.2 (9.4)	21.5 (12.4)	500 (0.12)	690	1.02	1400-1450 (2550-2650)
202	S20200	7.8 (0.28)	...	17.5 (9.7)	18.4 (10.2)	19.2 (10.7)	16.2 (9.4)	21.6 (12.5)	500 (0.12)	690	1.02	1400-1450 (2550-2650)
205	S20500	7.8 (0.28)	197 (28.6)	...	17.9 (9.9)	19.1 (10.6)	...	...	500 (0.12)	...	...	...
301	S30100	8.0 (0.29)	193 (28.0)	17.0 (9.4)	17.2 (9.6)	18.2 (10.1)	16.2 (9.4)	21.5 (12.4)	500 (0.12)	720	1.02	1400-1420 (2550-2590)
302	S30200	8.0 (0.29)	193 (28.0)	17.2 (9.6)	17.8 (9.9)	18.4 (10.2)	16.2 (9.4)	21.5 (12.4)	500 (0.12)	720	1.02	1400-1420 (2550-2590)
302B	S30215	8.0 (0.29)	193 (28.0)	16.2 (9.0)	18.0 (10.0)	19.4 (10.8)	15.9 (9.2)	21.6 (12.5)	500 (0.12)	720	1.02	1375-1400 (2550-2550)
303	S30300	8.0 (0.29)	193 (28.0)	17.2 (9.6)	17.8 (9.9)	18.4 (10.2)	16.2 (9.4)	21.5 (12.4)	500 (0.12)	720	1.02	1400-1420 (2550-2590)
304	S30400	8.0 (0.29)	193 (28.0)	17.2 (9.6)	17.8 (9.9)	18.4 (10.2)	16.2 (9.4)	21.5 (12.4)	500 (0.12)	720	1.02	1400-1450 (2550-2650)
304L	S30403	8.0 (0.29)	...	...	...	...	...	...	...	...	1.02	1400-1450 (2550-2650)
302Cu	S30430	8.0 (0.29)	913 (28.0)	17.2 (9.6)	17.8 (9.9)	...	11.2 (6.5)	21.5 (12.4)	500 (0.12)	720	1.02	1400-1450 (2550-2650)
304N	S30451	8.0 (0.29)	196 (28.5)	...	...	...	...	...	500 (0.12)	720	1.02	1400-1450 (2550-2650)
305	S30500	8.0 (0.29)	193 (28.0)	17.2 (9.6)	17.8 (9.9)	18.4 (10.2)	16.2 (9.4)	21.5 (12.4)	500 (0.12)	720	1.02	1400-1450 (2550-2650)
308	S30800	8.0 (0.29)	193 (28.0)	17.2 (9.6)	17.8 (9.9)	18.4 (10.2)	15.2 (8.8)	21.6 (12.5)	500 (0.12)	720	...	1400-1420 (2550-2590)
309	S30900	8.0 (0.29)	200 (29.0)	15.0 (8.3)	16.6 (9.2)	17.2 (9.6)	15.6 (9.0)	18.7 (10.8)	500 (0.12)	780	1.02	1400-1450 (2550-2650)
310	S31000	8.0 (0.29)	200 (29.0)	15.9 (8.8)	16.2 (9.0)	17.0 (9.4)	14.2 (8.2)	18.7 (10.8)	500 (0.12)	780	1.02	1400-1450 (2550-2650)
314	S31400	7.8 (0.28)	200 (29.0)	...	15.1 (8.4)	...	17.5 (10.1)	20.9 (12.1)	500 (0.12)	770	1.02	...
316	S31600	8.0 (0.29)	193 (28.0)	15.9 (8.8)	16.2 (9.0)	17.5 (9.7)	16.2 (9.4)	21.5 (12.4)	500 (0.12)	740	1.02	1375-1400 (2500-2550)
316L	S31603	8.0 (0.29)	...	...	...	...	...	...	...	...	1.02	1375-1400 (2500-2550)
316N	S31651	8.0 (0.29)	196 (28.5)	...	...	...	...	...	500 (0.12)	740	1.02	1375-1400 (2500-2550)
317	S31700	8.0 (0.29)	193 (28.0)	15.9 (8.8)	16.2 (9.0)	17.5 (9.7)	16.2 (9.4)	21.5 (12.4)	500 (0.12)	740	1.02	1375-1400 (2500-2550)
317L	S31703	8.0 (0.29)	200 (29.0)	16.5 (9.2)	...	18.1 (10.1)	14.4 (8.3)	...	500 (0.12)	790	...	1375-1400 (2500-2550)
321	S32100	8.0 (0.29)	19.3 (28.0)	16.6 (9.2)	17.2 (9.6)	18.6 (10.3)	16.1 (9.3)	22.2 (12.8)	500 (0.12)	720	1.02	1400-1425 (2550-2600)
329	S32900	7.8 (0.28)	...	...	...	...	...	...	460 (0.11)	750	...	...
330	N08330	8.0 (0.29)	196 (28.5)	14.4 (8.0)	16.0 (8.9)	16.7 (9.3)	...	...	460 (0.11)	1020	1.02	1400-1425 (2550-2600)
347	S34700	8.0 (0.29)	193 (28.0)	16.6 (9.2)	17.2 (9.6)	18.6 (10.3)	16.1 (9.3)	22.2 (12.8)	500 (0.12)	730	1.02	1400-1425 (2550-2600)
384	S38400	8.0 (0.29)	193 (28.0)	17.2 (9.6)	17.8 (9.9)	18.4 (10.2)	16.2 (9.4)	21.5 (12.4)	500 (0.12)	790	1.02	1400-1450 (2550-2650)
405	S40500	7.8 (0.28)	200 (29.0)	10.8 (6.0)	11.6 (6.4)	12.1 (6.7)	27.0 (15.6)	...	460 (0.11)	600	...	1480-1530 (2700-2790)
409	S40900	7.8 (0.28)	...	11.7 (6.5)	...	...	...	...	...	...	...	1480-1530 (2700-2790)
410	S41000	7.8 (0.28)	200 (29.0)	9.9 (5.5)	11.4 (6.3)	11.6 (6.4)	24.9 (14.4)	28.7 (16.6)	460 (0.11)	570	700-1000	1480-1530 (2700-2790)
414	S41400	7.8 (0.28	200 (29.0)	10.4 (5.8)	11.0 (6.1)	12.1 (6.7)	24.9 (14.4)	28.7 (16.6)	460 (0.11)	700	...	1425-1480 (2600-2700)
416	S41600	7.8 (0.28)	200 (29.0)	9.9 (5.5)	11.0 (6.1)	11.6 (6.4)	24.9 (14.4)	28.7 (16.6)	460 (0.11)	570	700-1000	1480-1530 (2700-2790)
420	S42000	7.8 (0.28)	200 (29.0)	10.3 (5.7)	10.8 (6.0)	11.7 (6.5)	24.9 (14.4)	...	460 (0.11)	550	...	1450-1510 (2650-2750)
422	S42200	7.8 (0.28)	...	11.2 (6.2)	11.4 (6.3)	11.9 (6.6)	23.9 (13.8)	27.3 (15.8)	460 (0.11)	...	...	1470-1480 (2675-2700)
429	S42900	7.8 (0.28)	200 (29.0)	10.3 (5.7)	...	...	25.6 (14.8)	...	460 (0.11)	590	...	1450-1510 (2650-2750)
430	S43000	7.8 (0.28)	200 (29.0)	10.4 (5.8)	11.0 (6.1)	11.4 (6.3)	26.1 (15.1)	26.3 (15.2)	460 (0.11)	600	600-1100	1425-1510 (2600-2750)
430F	S43020	7.8 (0.28)	200 (29.0)	10.4 (5.8)	11.0 (6.1)	11.4 (6.3)	26.1 (15.1)	26.3 (15.2)	460 (0.11)	600	...	1425-1510 (2600-2750)
431	S43100	7.8 (0.28)	200 (29.0)	10.2 (5.7)	12.1 (6.7)	...	20.2 (11.7)	...	460 (0.11)	720	...	...
434	S43400	7.8 (0.28)	200 (29.0)	10.4 (5.8)	11.0 (6.1)	11.4 (6.3)	...	26.3 (15.2)	460 (0.11)	600	600-1100	1425-1510 (2600-2750)
436	S43600	7.8 (0.28)	200 (29.0)	9.3 (5.2)	...	...	23.9 (13.8)	26.0 (15.0)	460 (0.11)	600	600-1100	1425-1510 (2600-2750)
439	S43035	7.7 (0.28)	200 (29.0)	10.4 (5.8)	11.0 (6.1)	11.4 (6.3)	24.2 (14.0)	...	460 (0.11)	630	...	...
440A	S44002	7.8 (0.28)	200 (29.0)	10.2 (5.7)	...	...	24.2 (14.0)	...	460 (0.11)	600	...	1370-1480 (2500-2700)
440C	S44004	7.8 (0.28)	200 (29.0)	10.2 (5.7)	...	...	24.2 (14.0)	...	460 (0.11)	600	...	1370-1480 (2500-2700)
444	S44400	7.8 (0.28)	200 (29.0)	10.0 (5.6)	10.6 (5.9)	11.4 (6.3)	26.8 (15.5)	...	420 (0.10)	620	...	...
446	S44600	7.5 (0.27)	200 (29.0)	10.4 (5.8)	10.8 (6.0)	11.2 (6.2)	20.9 (12.1)	24.4 (14.1)	500 (0.12)	670	400-700	1425-1510 (2600-2750)
PH 13-8 Mo	S13800	7.8 (0.28)	203 (29.4)	10.6 (5.9)	11.2 (6.2)	11.9 (6.6)	14.0 (8.1)	22.0 (12.7)	460 (0.11)	1020	...	1400-1440 (2560-2625)
15-5 PH	S15500	7.8 (0.28)	196 (28.5)	10.8 (6.0)	11.4 (6.3)	...	17.8 (10.3)	23.0 (13.1)	420 (0.10)	770	95	1400-1440 (2560-2625)
17-4 PH	S17400	7.8 (0.28)	196 (28.5)	10.8 (6.0)	11.6 (6.4)	...	18.3 (10.6)	23.0 (13.1)	460 (0.11)	800	95	1400-1440 (2560-2625)
17-7 PH	S17700	7.8 (0.28)	204 (29.5)	11.0 (6.1)	11.6 (6.4)	...	16.4 (9.5)	21.8 (12.6)	460 (0.11)	830	...	1400-1440 (2560-2625)

CTE, coefficient of thermal expansion. (a) At 0 to 100 °C (32 to 212 °F). (b) Approximate values

- Nature and distribution of microstructural constituents
- Continuity of exposure of the metal to the medium
- Surface condition of the metal
- Stresses in the metal during exposure to the medium
- Contact of the metal with one or more dissimilar metallic materials
- Stray electrical currents
- Differences in electric potential
- Marine growth such as barnacles
- Sludge deposits on the metal
- Carbon deposits from heated organic compounds
- Dust on exposed surfaces
- Effects of welding, brazing, and soldering

More detailed information on selection of stainless steels for use in various corrosive environments can be found in the Section "Corrosion Behavior" in this Volume.

Mechanical properties at service temperature are obviously important, but satisfactory performance at other temperatures must be considered also. Thus, a product for arctic service must have suitable properties at subzero temperatures even though steady-state operating temperature may be much higher; room-temperature properties after extended service at elevated temperature can be important for applications such as boilers and jet engines, which are intermittently shut down.

Table 2 compares tensile and impact values for selected stainless steel grades. More detailed information on properties of stainless steels can be found in the articles that immediately follow in this Section of the Handbook as well as the Section "Properties of Stainless Steels."

Physical Properties. Although there are few applications for stainless steels in which physical properties are the determining factors in selection, the magnetic and electrical properties of stainless steels are critical in selected applications. These include the use of stainless steels for soft magnetic applications (for example, ferritic solenoid-quality types 430F or 430FR) and iron-chromium-aluminum alloys containing 15 to 22% Cr and 4 to 5.5% Al for resistance heating elements. These materials are described in the article "Physical Properties" in this Volume.

There are also many applications in which physical properties are important in product design. For instance, stainless steels are used for many elevated-temperature applications, often in conjunction with steels of lesser alloy content. Because austenitic stainless steels have higher coefficients of thermal expansion and lower thermal

Table 5 Total U.S. shipments of stainless steel, 1982-1992

| Year | Shipments | |
	kt(a)	1000 tons
1982	811	894
1983	1032	1137
1984	1132	1248
1985	1135	1251
1986	1077	1187
1987	1287	1418
1988	1439	1586
1989	1336	1472
1990	1376	1516
1991	1315	1449
1992	1374	1514

(a) kt = kilotonnes (metric tonnes $\dot{o}10^3$). Source: American Iron and Steel Institute

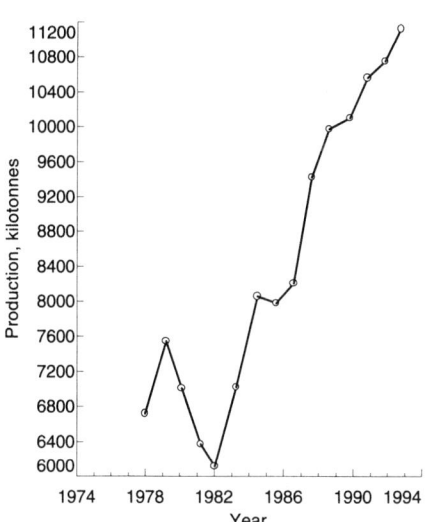

Fig. 6 Trends in worldwide stainless steel production. Source: Ref 4

Table 6 U.S. mill shipments of stainless steel, 1992

Steel product	Net tonnes	Net tons	%
Semifinished(a)	87,423	96,340	6.4
Shapes and plates	158,078	174,202	11.5
Bars	122,770	135,293	8.9
Pipe and tubing	28,906	31,854	2.1
Wire	22,194	24,458	1.6
Hot-rolled sheets	62,437	68,806	4.5
Cold-rolled sheets	638,446	703,568	46.5
Hot-rolled strip	7,343	8,092	0.5
Cold-rolled strip	246,525	271,671	17.9
Total net shipments	**1,374,123**	**1,514,284**	

(a) Includes ingots and steel for castings, blooms, slabs, billets, and wire rods. Source: American Iron and Steel Institute

conductivities than carbon and alloy steels (Fig. 3 and 4), these characteristics must be taken into account in the design of stainless steel-to-carbon steel or stainless steel-to-alloy steel products such as heat exchangers. In such products, different thermal expansion imposes stresses on the unit that would not be present were the unit made entirely of carbon or alloy steel; also, if the heat-transfer surface is made of stainless steel, it must be larger than if it were made of carbon or alloy steel.

Typical physical properties of selected grades of annealed wrought stainless steels are given in Table 4. Physical properties may vary slightly with product form and size, but such variations are usually not of critical importance to the application.

Fabrication and Cleaning. Frequently a particular stainless steel is chosen for a fabrication characteristic such as machinability, formability, or weldability. Even a required or preferred cleaning procedure may dictate the selection of a specific type. For instance, a weldment that is to be cleaned in a medium such as nitric-hydrofluoric acid, which attacks sensitized stainless steel, should be produced from stabilized or low-carbon stainless steel even though sensitization may not affect performance under service conditions. Examples of alloys designed to improve cold headability or provide enhanced machinability are described in the articles "Forging and Extrusion" and "Machining," respectively, in this Volume.

Surface Finish. Other characteristics in the stainless steel selection checklist are vital for some specialized applications but of little concern for others. Among these characteristics, surface finish is important more often than any other except corrosion resistance. Stainless steels are sometimes selected because they are available in a variety of attractive finishes. Surface finish selection may be made on the basis of appearance, frictional characteristics, or sanitation. The effect of finish on sanitation sometimes is thought to be simpler than it actually is, and tests of several candidate finishes may be advisable. The selection of finish may in turn influence the selection of the alloy because of differences in availability or durability of the various finishes for different types. For example, a more corrosion-resistant stainless steel will maintain a bright finish in a corrosive environment that would dull a lower-alloy type. Selection among finishes is described in the article "Surface Engineering" in this Volume.

Stainless Steel Production

Production and Consumption Statistics. Only modest tonnages of stainless steel were produced in the United States in the mid-1920s, but annual production has risen steadily since that time. Even so, tonnage has never exceeded about 2% of total production for the U.S. steel industry. Table 5 shows shipments of stainless steel over a recent ten-year period.

Figure 6 shows that world stainless steel production has a mean annual growth rate of 4% from 1978 to 1992 with a significant acceleration from 1987 to 1992. In 1988, world production (excluding what was then the Soviet-bloc East Europe,

Table 7 U.S. production of nickel-bearing stainless steels for 1993

Type No.	UNS No.	Net tonnes	Net tons
Austenitic stainless steels			
201, 202, 205	S20100, S20200, S20500	50,493	55,659
301	S30100	129,744	143,019
302, 302B	S30200, S30215	10,217	11,262
303, 303Se	S30300, S30323	31,263	34,462
304	S30400	548,740	604,885
304H, 304N	S30409, S30451	6,783	7,477
304L, 304LN	S30403, S30453	137,748	151,842
305, 308	S30500, S30800	11,217	12,365
309, 309S	S30900, S30908	8,660	9,546
310S	S31008	2,893	3,189
316	S31600	26,652	29,379
316F, 316H, 316N	S31620, S31609, S31651	2,165	2,386
316L, 316LN	S31603, S31653	121,941	134,418
316, 317L	S31700, S31703	4,407	4,858
321, 321H	S32100, S32109	11,270	12,423
347, 347H	S34700, S34709	2,512	2,769
348, 348H	S34800, S34809	...	...
Precipitation-hardening stainless steels			
...	S13800, S15500	4,550	5,015
...	S17400	10,685	11,778
...	S17700 plus all other precipitation-hardening grades	3,181	3,507
Duplex stainless steels			
329 plus all other duplex grades	S32900	2,265	2,497
Other chromium-nickel stainless steels with:			
Nickel under 8%		28,349	31,250
Nickel 8-16%		10,751	11,851
Nickel over 16-24%		5,569	6,139
Nickel over 24%		6,758	7,450
Total		**1,178,813**	**1,299,426**

Source: American Iron and Steel Institute

the U.S.S.R, and other Communist nations) exceeded ten million metric tonnes of primary products (ingots, slabs, blooms, and billets) for the first time in history.

Per capita stainless steel consumption varies greatly in different regions of the world. It is less than 1 kg/person per year in the developing countries, whereas the U.S. and Europe average 4 to 6 kg/person and Japan and Southeast Asia average 6 to 8 kg/person (Ref 4).

Product Forms. Stainless steels are available in the form of plate, sheet, strip, foil, bar, wire, semifinished products, pipes, tubes, and tubing. Table 6 lists U.S. shipments of stainless steel products in 1992. As indicated, cold-rolled sheets are the most common product form. Worldwide, cold-rolled flat products (sheet, strip, and plate) account for 61% of stainless steel product forms (Ref 4). More detailed information on product forms can be found in the article " Metallurgy and Properties of Wrought Stainless Steels" in this Volume.

Common Grades. As indicated earlier in this article, S30400 (type 304) is the most widely used stainless steel. As shown in Table 7, this alloy and its variations constitute about 63% of all austenitic grades produced and about 58% of all nickel-bearing stainless steels, including duplex and PH grades.

Of the nickel-free stainless steels, S40900 (type 409) is the most widely used ferritic grade (~64% of all nickel-free stainless steels produced) and S41000 (type 410) is the most widely used martensitic grade (<5% of all nickel-free stainless steel produced). U.S. production statistics for nickel-free stainless steels are given in Table 8.

Markets and Applications (Ref 4)

Since they were first used in the cutlery industry, the number of applications for stainless has increased dramatically. The relative importance of the major fields of application for flat and long stainless steel products are as follows:

Application	Percentage
Industrial equipment	
Chemical and power engineering	34
Food and beverage industry	18
Transportation	9
Architecture	5
Consumer goods	
Domestic appliances, household utensils	28
Small electrical and electronic appliances	6

More detailed information on the industrial applications for stainless steels, including selection criteria in various environments/industries, can be found in the article "Atmospheric and Aqueous Corrosion" in this Volume.

Chemical and power engineering is the largest market for both long and flat products. It began in about 1920 with the nitric acid industry.

Table 8 U.S. production of nickel-free stainless steels for 1993

Type No.	UNS No.	Net tonnes	Net tons
403	S40300	2,341	2,581
405	S40500	364	401
409	S40900	370,540	408,453
410, 410S	S41000, S41008	27,335	30,132
414, 416	S41400, S41600	18,998	20,942
420	S42000	7,484	8,250
420F	S42020	804	886
422	S42200	1,618	1,784
430	S43000	56,471	68,249
430F	S43020	3,488	3,845
431	S43100	1,106	1,219
434	S43400	10,050	11,078
436	S43600	4,061	4,477
439	S43035	18,998	20,942
440A	S44002	1,645	1,813
440B, 440C	S44003, S44004	5,407	5,960
444	S44400	387	427
446	S44600	1,419	1,564
All other nickel-free with:			
15% Cr or less		11,187	12,332
Over 15% Cr		21,539	23,743
Total		**570,687**	**629,078**

Source: American Iron and Steel Institute

Today, it includes an extremely diversified range of service conditions, including nuclear reactor vessels, heat exchangers, oil industry tubulars, components for the chemical processing and pulp and paper industries, furnace parts, and boilers used in fossil fuel electric power plants.

Food and Beverage Industry. Many varieties of stainless steels are used in food and beverage production (milk and cheese production, beer brewing, fruit juice production), storage (wine and beer vats), and food preparation (large kitchens for restaurants).

Transportation Industry. A wide range of functional and decorative components for transportation vehicles are fabricated from stainless steels:

- Automobile parts such as trim, fasteners, wheel covers, mirror mounts, windshield wiper arms, and exhaust manifolds
- Railroad cars and large vehicles such as buses and tanker trucks

- Seagoing chemical tankers
- Aerospace components such as structural parts, fasteners, and engine cooling sections

Architecture. Stainless steel has been employed in a number of well-known architectural landmarks. One of the oldest cases is the use of type 304 sheet to decorate the summit of the Chrysler building in New York in 1929. Another example is the "Gateway to the West" arch on the bank of the Mississippi River in St. Louis, Missouri. Other outstanding examples of stainless steel architecture are frequently shown in *Nickel*, a quarterly publication of the Nickel Development Institute (Toronto, Canada).

Consumer goods include domestic kitchenware and tableware, kitchen sinks, laundry equipment, and electrical and electronic appliances. A common feature of these applications is that they all involve less severe corrosive conditions than those encountered in industrial equipment.

ACKNOWLEDGMENT

The information in this article is largely taken from:

- S.D. Washko and G. Aggen, Wrought Stainless Steels, *Properties and Selection: Irons, Steels, and High-Performance Alloys*, Vol 1, *ASM Handbook* (formerly 10th ed., *Metals Handbook*), ASM International, 1990, p 841-907
- J.H. Magee, Wear of Stainless Steels, *Friction, Lubrication, and Wear Technology*, Vol 18, *ASM Handbook*, ASM International, 1992, p 710-724

REFERENCES

1. A.J. Sedricks, *Corrosion of Stainless Steels*, John Wiley and Sons, 1979
2. D.L. Potts and J.G. Gensure, *International Metallic Materials Cross-Reference*, Genium Publishing, 1989
3. R.S. Brown, How to Select the Right Stainless Steel, *Advanced Materials & Processes*, Vol 145 (No. 4), April 1994, p 20-24
4. J. Lefévre, Stainless Steel Selection Criteria for Different Applications, *Stainless Steels*, Les Editions de Physique, 1993, p 919-937

SELECTED REFERENCE

- R.A. Lula, *Stainless Steel*, American Society for Metals, 1986

Metallurgy and Properties of Wrought Stainless Steels

WROUGHT STAINLESS STEELS are an important class of engineering alloys used for a wide range of applications and in many environments. Stainless steels are used extensively in the power generation, pulp and paper, and chemical processing industries, but they are also chosen for use in many everyday household and commercial products.

Fundamentally, stainless steels are based on the iron-chromium, iron-chromium-carbon, and iron-chromium-nickel systems, but they may contain a number of other alloying additions that alter their microstructures and/or properties. The "stainless" nature of these steels arises primarily from the addition of chromium in quantities greater than approximately 11 wt%. This level of chromium ensures that a continuous layer of protective chromium-rich oxide forms on the surface. In practice, however, stainless steels may contain as little as 9 wt% Cr and be subject to general corrosion ("rusting") at ambient temperatures. Few stainless steels contain more than 30 wt% Cr or less than 50 wt% Fe.

Historically, stainless steels have been classified by microstructure and are described as martensitic, ferritic, austenitic, or duplex (austenitic and ferritic). In addition, a number of precipitation-hardening (PH) martensitic, semi-austenitic, and austenitic stainless steels exist and are normally classified separately as PH stainless steels.

In order to control microstructure and properties, a number of alloying elements are added to the basic iron-chromium, iron-chromium-carbon, and iron-chromium-nickel systems; these alloying elements include manganese, silicon, molybdenum, niobium, titanium, and nitrogen. In order to broadly describe the effect of composition on microstructure in a wide range of stainless steels, the concept of chromium and nickel equivalents was developed to normalize the effect of these alloying additions on microstructural evolution, relative to the effects of chromium and nickel. Plotting the chromium and nickel equivalents on opposing axes provides a graphic depiction of the relationship between composition and microstructure for stainless steels. The Schaeffler diagram (Fig. 1) has become known as the "roadmap" of stainless steels. The compositional

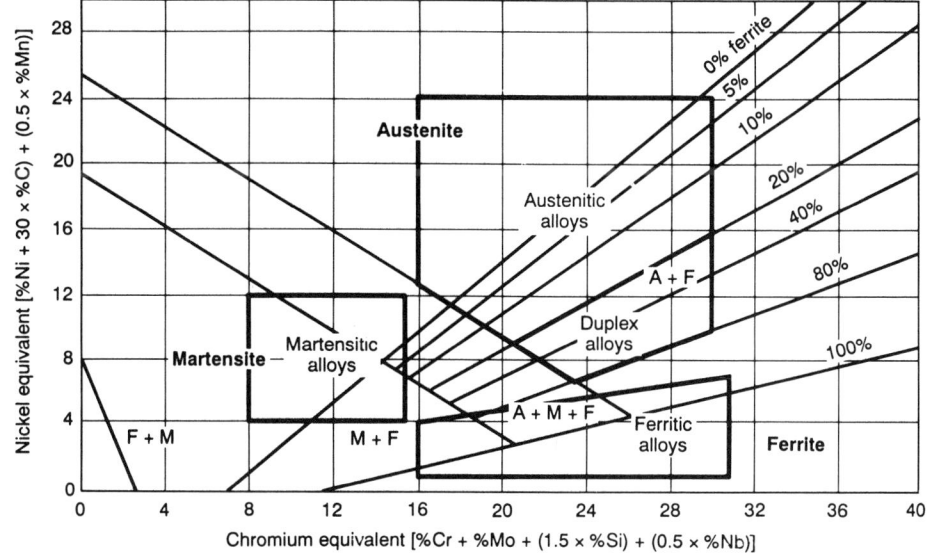

Fig. 1 Schaeffler constitution diagram for stainless steels

Table 1 Chemical compositions of standard wrought martensitic stainless steels

Type	UNS No.	C	Mn	Si	Cr	Ni	P	S	Other
403	S40300	0.15	1.00	0.50	11.5-13.0	...	0.04	0.03	...
410	S41000	0.15	1.00	1.00	11.5-13.5	...	0.04	0.03	...
414	S41400	0.15	1.00	1.00	11.5-13.5	1.25-2.50	0.04	0.03	...
416	S41600	0.15	1.25	1.00	12.0-14.0	...	0.06	0.15 min	0.6 Mo(b)
416Se	S41623	0.15	1.25	1.00	12.0-14.0	...	0.06	0.06	0.15 min Se
420	S42000	0.15 min	1.00	1.00	12.0-14.0	...	0.04	0.03	...
420F	S42020	0.15 min	1.25	1.00	12.0-14.0	...	0.06	0.15 min	0.6 Mo(b)
422	S42200	0.20-0.25	1.00	0.75	11.5-13.5	0.5-1.0	0.04	0.03	0.75-1.25 Mo; 0.75-1.25 W; 0.15-0.3 V
431	S43100	0.20	1.00	1.00	15.0-17.0	1.25-2.50	0.04	0.03	...
440A	S44002	0.60-0.75	1.00	1.00	16.0-18.0	...	0.04	0.03	0.75 Mo
440B	S44003	0.75-0.95	1.00	1.00	16.0-18.0	...	0.04	0.03	0.75 Mo
440C	S44004	0.95-1.20	1.00	1.00	16.0-18.0	...	0.04	0.03	0.75 Mo

(a) Single values are maximum values unless otherwise indicated. (b) Optional

Table 2 Chemical compositions of nonstandard wrought martensitic stainless steels

Designation(a)	UNS No.	Composition, %(b)							
		C	Mn	Si	Cr	Ni	P	S	Other
Type 410S	S41008	0.08	1.00	1.00	11.5-13.5	0.60	0.040	0.030	...
Type 410 Cb (XM-30)	S41040	0.15	1.00	1.00	11.5-13.5	...	0.040	0.030	0.05-0.20 Nb
HT9	DIN 1.4935(c)	0.17-0.23	0.30-0.80	0.10-0.50	11.0-12.5	0.30-0.80	0.035	0.035	0.80-1.20 Mo; 0.25-0.35 V; 0.4-0.6 W
416 Plus X (XM-6)	S41610	0.15	1.5-2.5	1.00	12.0-14.0	...	0.060	0.15 min	0.6 Mo
Type 418 (Greek Ascolloy)	S41800	0.15-0.20	0.50	0.50	12.0-14.0	1.8-2.2	0.040	0.030	2.5-3.5 W
TrimRite	S42010	0.15-0.30	1.00	1.00	13.5-15.0	0.25-1.00	0.040	0.030	0.40-1.00 Mo
Type 429 F Se	S42023	0.3-0.4	1.25	1.00	12.0-14.0	...	0.060	0.060	0.15 min Se; 0.6 Zr; 0.6 Cu
Lapelloy	S42300	0.27-0.32	0.95-1.35	0.50	11.0-12.0	0.50	0.025	0.025	2.5-3.0 Mo; 0.2-0.3 V
Type 440 F	S44020	0.95-1.20	1.25	1.00	16.0-18.0	0.75	0.040	0.10-0.35	0.08 N
Type 440 F Se	S44023	0.95-1.20	1.25	1.00	16.0-18.0	0.75	0.040	0.030	0.15 min Se; 0.60 Mo

(a) XM designations in this column are ASTM designations for the listed alloy. (b) Single values are maximum values unless otherwise indicated. (c) German (DIN) specification

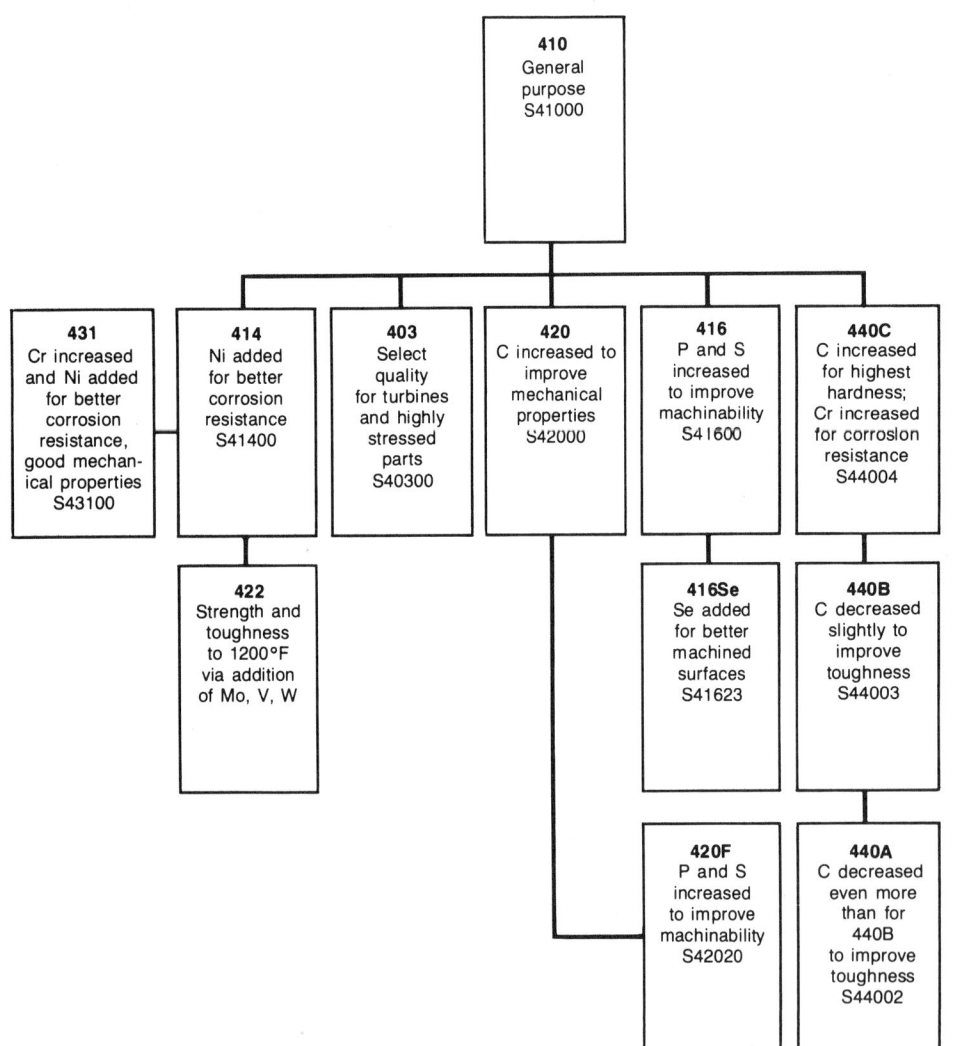

Fig. 2 Family relationships for standard martensitic stainless steels

Properties" in this Volume. Although some information on corrosion characteristics for the various grades is presented, the reader is referred to the articles in the Section of this Handbook on "Corrosion Behavior" for more detailed discussions. Additional information on applications and properties of specific grades can be found in Ref 1 and 2.

Martensitic Stainless Steels

Martensitic stainless steels are essentially alloys of chromium and carbon that possess body-centered teragonal (bct) crystal structure (martensitic) in the hardened condition. They are ferromagnetic, hardenable by heat treatments, and generally resistant to corrosion only in relatively mild environments. Chromium content is generally in the range of 10.5 to 18%, and carbon content may exceed 1.2%. The chromium and carbon contents are balanced to ensure a martensitic structure after hardening. Excess carbides may be present to increase wear resistance or to maintain cutting edges, as in the case of knife blades. Elements such as niobium, silicon, tungsten, and vanadium may be added to modify the tempering response after hardening. Small amounts of nickel may be added to improve corrosion resistance in some media and to improve toughness. Sulfur or selenium is added to some grades to improve machinability.

Tables 1 and 2 provide chemical compositions for standard (American Iron and Steel Institute, AISI) and nonstandard grades. Figure 2 shows the relationships between the various standard grades.

Basic Metallurgy

At high temperatures, the equilibrium microstructure of martensitic stainless steels is either entirely or almost entirely austenite. At room temperature, the equilibrium microstructure of these steels is a mixture of ferrite and carbides. The reformation of austenite upon heating occurs very rapidly, but the transformation back to ferrite upon cooling is extremely slow. As a result, these steels have a very high tendency to transform to martensite upon cooling from temperatures at

ranges of the ferritic, martensitic, austenitic, and duplex alloys have been superimposed on this diagram.

This article will review the basic metallurgy of the five families of stainless steels as well as their properties and applications. Emphasis is placed on minimum room-temperature tensile property values, impact properties, embrittlement mechanisms, and fracture properties. High- and low-temperature mechanical properties of stainless steels are described in the articles "Low-Temperature Properties" and "Elevated-Temperature

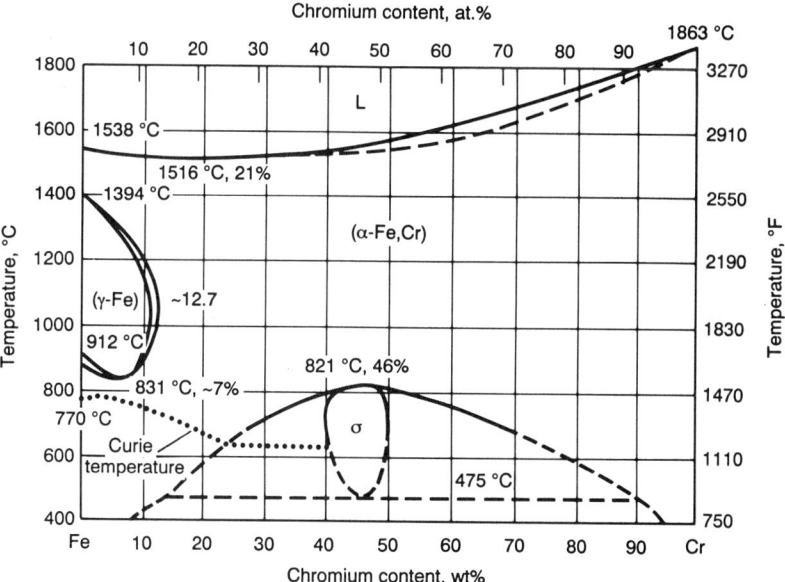

Fig. 3 Binary iron-chromium equilibrium phase diagram

which austenite is the stable phase. In fact, it is very difficult to avoid martensite in these steels. They are air hardening, which means that even upon slow cooling in heavy sections, they form martensite.

The binary iron-chromium phase diagram shown in Fig. 3 indicates that above a level of approximately 12% Cr, binary alloys will not form austenite at any temperature, so they cannot be hardened by heating and cooling. However, the addition of carbon to iron-chromium alloys increases the range of chromium contents over which austenite can be formed at elevated temperatures (Fig. 4). It should be noted that nitrogen, nickel, copper, and, possibly, manganese also expand this range. Even with 17% Cr, a fully

austenitic microstructure can be achieved with about 0.4% C at 1250 °C (2280 °F). It can then be fully hardened. When the corrosion-resisting properties of iron-chromium alloys were first discovered early in the 20th century, it was extremely difficult to remove carbon from melts of iron-chromium alloys. Thus, the first stainless steels, which were discovered more or less simultaneously in Germany and England, were martensitic.

Carbon content almost entirely determines the hardness of martensite. Figure 5 shows several relationships that have been found experimentally between carbon and hardness. In particular, it shows that as little as 0.10% C in martensite will result in a hardness value of approximately 35 HRC. The hardness of martensite increases to

over 60 HRC at approximately 0.5% C, and it does not change significantly at higher levels of carbon, at least on a macroscale.

Figure 5 presents the situation if essentially all martensite is obtained in a steel. In carbon and low-alloy steels, rapid cooling is usually necessary to avoid the formation of ferrite. However, as more alloying elements are added, the avoidance of ferrite becomes easier. At a 12% Cr level, nearly any cooling rate will result in virtually 100% martensite. The prototype of all martensitic stainless steels is type 410 (approximately 12% Cr and 0.10% C). The isothermal transformation diagram for type 410 stainless steel (Fig. 6) indicates that, after cooling from high temperatures and being held at approximately 700 °C (1290 °F), it will take approximately 2 min before any ferrite forms, and several hours will be required before the transformation to ferrite with carbides is complete. Cooling to a holding temperature of 400 °C (750 °F) will require more than 1 week before any ferrite forms.

Figure 6 further shows that martensite begins to form at about 350 °C (660 °F) upon cooling of type 410 stainless steel and is finished when cooling reaches about 250 °C (480 °F). Alloying at levels that are either above or in addition to 12% Cr serves to further delay ferrite formation and further reduces the martensite-start (M_s) temperature. In the extreme case, some austenite will exist indefinitely, even at room temperature, and refrigeration or complex heat treatments (such as double tempering) may be necessary to induce complete martensite transformation in highly alloyed martensitic stainless steels.

Properties and Applications

The most commonly used alloy within the martensitic stainless steel family is type 410, which contains about 12 wt% Cr and 0.1 wt% C to provide strength. The carbon level and, conse-

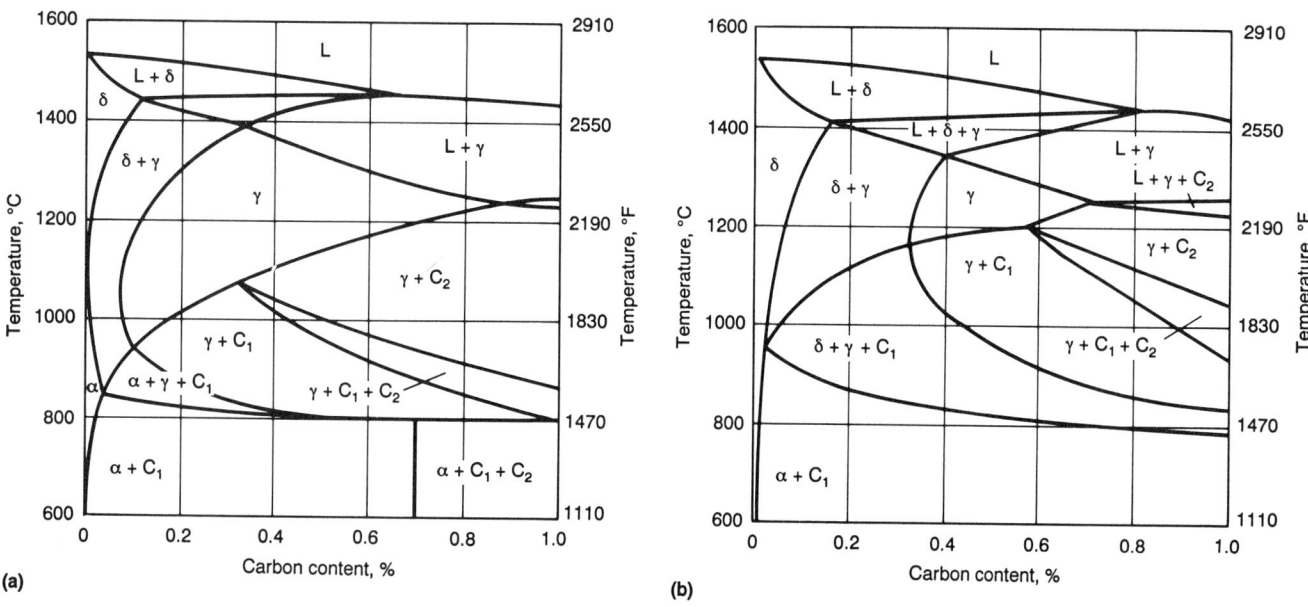

Fig. 4 Concentration profile in ternary iron-chromium-carbon constitution diagram. (a) 13% Cr. (b) 17% Cr

Table 3 Minimum mechanical properties of martensitic stainless steels

Product form(a)	Condition	Tensile strength MPa	Tensile strength ksi	0.2% yield strength MPa	0.2% yield strength ksi	Elongation, %	Reduction in area, %	Rockwell hardness	ASTM specification
Type 403 (UNS S40300)									
B, F	Annealed, hot finished	485	70	275	40	20	45	...	A 276, A 473, A 479
B	Annealed, cold finished	485	70	275	40	16	45	...	A 276
B	Intermediate temper, hot finished	690	100	550	80	15	45	...	A 276
B	Intermediate temper, cold finished	690	100	550	80	12	40	...	A 276
B	Hard temper, hot or cold finished	825	120	620	90	12	40	...	A 276
W	Annealed	485	70	275	40	20	45	...	A 580
W	Annealed, cold finished	485	70	275	40	16	45	...	A 580
W	Intermediate temper, cold finished	690	100	550	80	12	40	...	A 580
W	Hard temper, cold finished	825	120	620	90	12	40	...	A 580
P, Sh, St	Annealed	485	70	205	30	25(b)	...	88 HRB max	A 176
Type 410 (UNS S41000)									
B, F	Annealed, hot finished	485	70	275	40	20	45	...	A 276, A 473, A 479
B	Annealed, cold finished	485	70	275	40	16	45	...	A 276
B	Intermediate temper, hot finished	690	100	550	80	15	45	...	A 276
B	Intermediate temper, cold finished	690	100	550	80	12	40	...	A 276
B	Hard temper, hot or cold finished	825	120	620	90	12	40	...	A 276
W	Annealed	485	70	275	40	20	45	...	A 580
W	Annealed, cold finished	485	70	275	40	16	45	...	A 580
W	Intermediate temper, cold finished	690	100	550	80	12	40	...	A 580
W	Hard temper, cold finished	825	120	620	90	12	40	...	A 580
P, Sh, St	Annealed	450	65	205	30	22(b)	...	95 HRB max	A 176
P, Sh, St	Annealed	450	65	205	30	20	...	95 HRB max	A 240
Type 410S (UNS S41008)									
F	Annealed	450	65	240	35	22	45	...	A 473
P, Sh, St	Annealed	415	60	205	30	22(b)	...	88 HRB max	A 176, A 240
Type 410Cb (UNS S41040)									
B	Annealed, hot finished	485	70	275	40	13	45	...	A 276, A 479
B	Annealed, cold finished	485	70	275	40	12	35	...	A 276, A 479
B	Intermediate temper, hot finished	860	125	690	100	13	45	...	A 276, A 479
B	Intermediate temper, cold finished	860	125	690	100	12	35	...	A 276, A 479
E-4 (UNS S41050)									
P, Sh, St	Annealed	415	60	205	30	22	...	88 HRB max	A 276, A 240
Type 414 (UNS S41400)									
B	Intermediate temper, cold or hot finished	795	115	620	90	15	45	...	A 276, A 479
W	Annealed, cold finished	1030 max	150 max	...	...	...	...	...	A 580
CA6NM (UNS S41500)									
P, Sh, St	Tempered	795	115	620	90	15	...	32 HRC max	A 176, A 240
B, F	Tempered	795	115	620	90	15	45	...	A 276, A 473, A 479
Types 416 (UNS S41600) and 416Se (UNS S41623)									
F	Annealed	485	70	275	40	20	45	...	A 473
W	Annealed	585-860	85-125	...	...	...	...	...	A 581
W	Intermediate temper	795-1000	115-145	...	...	...	...	...	A 581
W	Hard temper	965-1210	140-175	...	...	...	...	...	A 581
Type 416 plus X (UNS S41610)									
W	Annealed	585-860	85-125	...	...	...	...	...	A 581
W	Intermediate temper	795-1000	115-145	...	...	...	...	...	A 581
W	Hard temper	965-1210	140-175	...	...	...	...	...	A 581
Type 418 (UNS S41800)									
B, F	Tempered at 620 °C (1150 °F)	965	140	760	110	15	45	...	A 565
Type 420 (UNS S42000)									
B	Tempered at 204 °C (400 °F)	1720	250	1480(c)	215(c)	8(c)	25(c)	52 HRC(c)	...
W	Annealed, cold finished	860 max	125 max	...	...	...	...	...	A 580
P, Sh, St	Annealed	690	100	...	...	15	...	96 HRB max	A 176
TrimRite (UNS S42010)									
W	Annealed	690 max	100 max	...	...	...	...	...	A 493
W	Lightly drafted	725 max	105 max	...	...	...	...	...	A 493
Type 422 (UNS S42200)									
B, F	Tempered at 675 °C (1250 °F)	825	120	585	85	17(d)	35	...	A 565
B, F	Tempered at 620 °C (1150 °F)	965	140	760	110	13	30	...	A 565
Lapelloy (UNS S42300)									
B, F	Tempered at 620 °C (1150 °F)	965	140	760	110	8	20	...	A 565

(continued)

(a) B, bar; F, forgings; P, plate; Sh, sheet; St, strip; W, wire. (b) 20% elongation for 1.3 mm (0.050 in.) and under in thickness. (c) Typical values. (d) Minimum elongation of 15% for forgings

Table 3 (continued)

Product form(a)	Condition	Tensile strength MPa	Tensile strength ksi	0.2% yield strength MPa	0.2% yield strength ksi	Elongation, %	Reduction in area, %	Rockwell hardness	ASTM specification
Type 431 (UNS S43100)									
F	Intermediate temper	795	115	620	90	15	...	...	A 473
F	Hard temper	1210	175	930	135	13	...	...	A 473
W	Annealed, cold finished	965 max	140 max	...	...	...	...	...	A 580
W	Annealed	760	110	...	...	...	...	...	A 493
W	Lightly drafted	795	115	...	...	...	...	...	A 493
Type 440A (UNS S44002)									
B	Annealed	725(c)	105(c)	415(c)	60(c)	20(c)	...	95 HRB(c)	...
B	Tempered at 315 °C (600 °F)	1790(c)	260(c)	1650(c)	240(c)	5(c)	20(c)	51 HRC(c)	...
W	Annealed, cold finished	965 max	140 max	...	...	...	...	...	A 580
Type 440B (UNS S44003)									
B	Annealed	740(c)	107(c)	425(c)	62(c)	18(c)	...	96 HRB(c)	...
B	Tempered at 315 °C (600 °F)	1930(c)	280(c)	1860(c)	270(c)	3(c)	15(c)	55 HRC(c)	...
W	Annealed, cold finished	965 max	140 max	...	...	...	...	...	A 580
Type 440C (UNS S44004)									
B	Annealed	760(c)	110(c)	450(c)	65(c)	14(c)	...	97 HRB(c)	...
B	Tempered at 315 °C (600 °F)	1970(c)	285(c)	1900(c)	275(c)	2(c)	10(c)	57 HRC(c)	...
W	Annealed, cold finished	965 max	140 max	...	...	...	...	...	A 580

(a) B, bar; F, forgings; P, plate; Sh, sheet; St, strip; W, wire. (b) 20% elongation for 1.3 mm (0.050 in.) and under in thickness. (c) Typical values. (d) Minimum elongation of 15% for forgings

quently, strength increase in the 420, 440A, 440B, and 440C alloy series. The latter three alloys, in particular, have an increased chromium level in order to maintain corrosion resistance.

Molybdenum can be added to improve mechanical properties or corrosion resistance, as it is in type 422 stainless steel. Nickel can be added for the same reasons in types 414 and 431. When higher chromium levels are used to improve corrosion resistance, nickel also serves to maintain the desired microstructure and to prevent excessive free ferrite. The limitations on the alloy content required to maintain the desired fully martensitic structure restrict the obtainable corrosion resistance to moderate levels.

In the annealed condition, martensitic stainless steels have a tensile yield strength of approximately 275 MPa (40 ksi) and can be moderately hardened by cold working. However, martensitic alloys are typically heat treated by both hardening and tempering in order to yield strength levels up to 1900 MPa (275 ksi), depending on carbon level, primarily. These alloys have good ductility and toughness properties, which decrease as strength increases. Depending on the heat treatment, hardness values range from approximately 150 HB (80 HRB) for materials in the annealed condition to levels greater than 600 HB (58 HRC) for fully hardened materials. Minimum room-temperature properties of the martensitic types are given in Table 3.

Martensitic stainless steels are specified when the application requires good tensile strength, creep, and fatigue strength properties, in combination with moderate corrosion resistance and heat resistance up to approximately 650 °C (1200 °F). In the United States, low- and medium-carbon martensitic steels (for example, type 410 and modified versions of this alloy) have been used primarily in steam turbines, jet engines, and gas turbines.

Type 420 and similar alloys are used in cutlery, valve parts, gears, shafts, and rollers. One extensive application is a weld overlay on rolls for steel mill continuous casters. This type of alloy is quite brittle in the freshly hardened condition and usually must be tempered to obtain useful toughness properties.

Martensitic stainless steels are also used in petroleum and petrochemical equipment. Other applications for higher-carbon-level grades (type 440 grades) include cutlery, surgical and dental

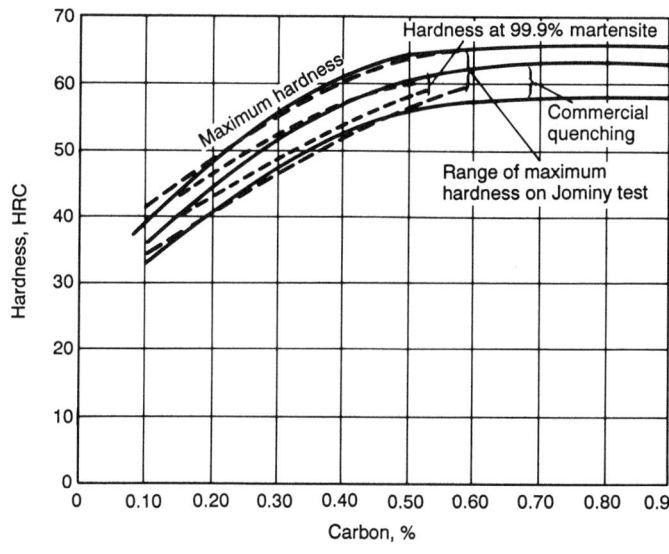

Fig. 5   Hardness values of fully hardened steels with a range of carbon contents

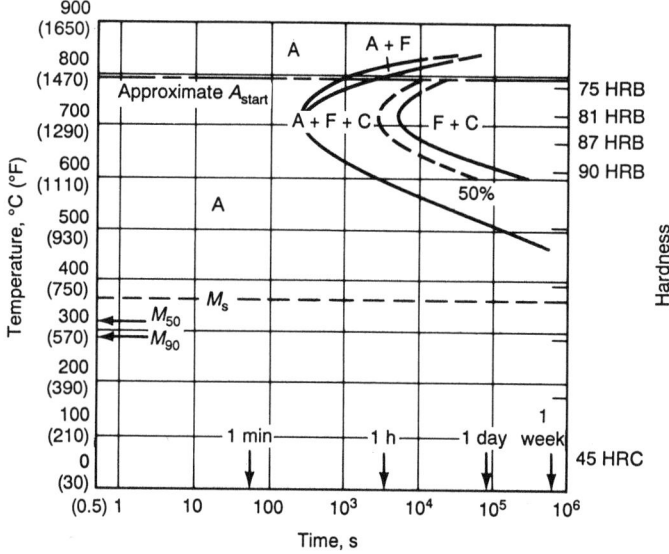

Fig. 6   Isothermal transformation diagram for type 410 stainless steel (12Cr-0.1C) austenitized at 980 °C (1800 °F), with grain size of 6 to 7. A, austenite; F, ferrite; C, carbide; M, martensite; B, bainite; P, pearlite

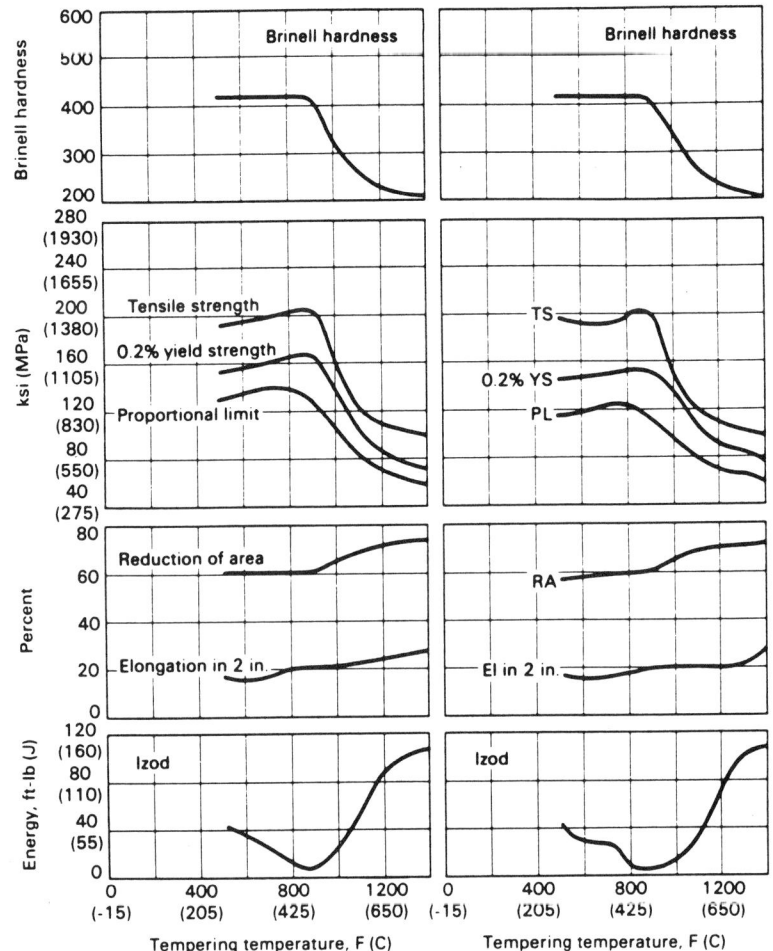

Fig. 7 Effect of austenitizing and tempering temperatures on room-temperature mechanical properties of type 410 martensitic stainless steel. Austenitized (left) at 925 °C (1700 °F) and (right) at 1010 °C (1850 °F) for 30 min; oil quenched to 65 to 95 °C (150 to 200 °F); double stress relieved at 175 °C (350 °F) for 15 min; water quenched; tempered 2 h. Source: Ref 3

Table 4 Nominal chemical composition of first-generation standard-grade 400-series ferritic stainless steels

UNS No.	Type	Composition(a), wt%			
		C	Cr	Mo	Other
S42900	429	0.12	14.0-16.0	...	...
S43000	430	0.12	16.0-18.0	...	...
S43020	430F	0.12	16.0-18.0	0.6	0.06 P; 0.15 min S
S43023	430FSe	0.12	16.0-18.0	...	0.15 min Se
S43400	434	0.12	16.0-18.0	0.75-1.25	...
S43600	436	0.12	16.0-18.0	0.75-1.25	Nb + Ta = 5 × %C min
S44200	442	0.20	18.0-23 0	...	...
S44600	446	0.20	23.0-27.0	...	...

(a) Single values are maximum unless otherwise indicated.

instruments, scissors, springs, valves, gears, shafts, cams, and ball bearings.

In Europe, these alloys have been used in similar applications. In addition, certain alloys, particularly 12Cr-1Mo-0.3V (HT9), have been widely used in elevated-temperature pressure-containment applications, including steam piping and steam generator reheater and superheater tubing used in fossil fuel power plants. The 12Cr-1Mo-0.3V alloy also has been investigated as a candidate material for the first wall of fusion reactors in both Europe and the UnitedStates.

Temper Embrittlement. The mechanical property changes produced by tempering an oil-quenched type 410 martensitic stainless steel are shown in Fig. 7. As-quenched hardness and strength are maintained well after tempering up to 450 °C (840 °F) and then drop rapidly. Higher austenitizing temperatures dissolve more chromium, and therefore the secondary hardening peak is sharpened in the specimens austenitized at 1010 °C (1850 °F). Temper embrittlement develops during tempering between 425 and 565 °C (800 and 1050 °F) (Ref 3), as shown by the minimum in Izod impact toughness, and tempering in this temperature range should be avoided for impact-sensitive applications. Additional information on the effect of tempering temperature on the properties of martensitic stainless steels can be found in the article "Heat Treating" in this Volume.

Ferritic Stainless Steels

Ferritic stainless steels are essentially chromium-containing alloys with body-centered cubic (bcc) crystal structures. Chromium content is usually in the range of 10.5 to 30%. Some grades may contain molybdenum, silicon, aluminum, titanium, and niobium to confer particular characteristics. Sulfur or selenium may be added, as in the case of the austenitic grades, to improve machinability. The ferritic alloys are ferromagnetic. They can have good ductility and formability, but high-temperature strengths are relatively poor compared to those of the austenitic grades. Toughness may be somewhat limited at low temperatures and in heavy sections.

Tables 4 to 6 provide chemical compositions for first-, second-, and third-generation ferritic grades, respectively. Figure 8 shows the relationships between the various standard (AISI) grades.

Basic Metallurgy

In the iron-chromium phase diagram shown in Fig. 3, the ferritic steel compositions are on the right of the gamma loop. Because the carbon content found in commercial steels shifts the austenite phase boundary to higher chromium contents, the addition of strong ferritizing elements becomes necessary in order to prevent formation of austenite.

There are essentially three generations of ferritic stainless steels. The first—in which carbon is not very low, so that chromium needs to be high—dates from the early decades of the 20th century, when the decarburization of iron-chromium alloys was quite inefficient. The prototype alloy is type 430 stainless, typically 0.12maxC-17Cr. Figure 4(b) indicates that this alloy would be fully ferritic at temperatures above approximately 1250 °C (2280 °F). At lower temperatures, ferrite and austenite would coexist to about 1030 °C (1890 °F). Further cooling would cause carbides to appear as well. Then, at about 920 °C (1690 °F), the austenite would disappear and only ferrite and some carbides would remain at room temperature, under equilibrium conditions. Type 446 stainless (typically, 0.20maxC-25Cr) is also of this first generation, and it behaves similarly.

It is something of a misnomer to call these first-generation ferritic stainless steels "ferritic," because some austenite appears at certain high temperatures. This austenite has a beneficial ef-

Table 5 Chemical compositions of second-generation ferritic stainless steels

| UNS No. | Alloy designation | Composition(a), wt% | | | | |
		C	Cr	Mo	Ni	Other
S40500	405	0.08	11.5-14.5	...	...	0.10-0.30 Al
S40900	409	0.08	10.5-11.75	...	0.5	Ti = 6 × C min to 0.75 max
...	409Cb	0.02(b)	12.5(b)	...	0.2(b)	0.4 Nb(b)
S44100	441	0.02(b)	18.0(b)	...	0.3(b)	0.7 Nb(b), 0.3 Ti(b)
...	AL433	0.02(b)	19.0(b)	...	0.3(b)	0.4 Nb(b), 0.5 Si(b), 0.4 Cu(b)
...	AL446	0.01(b)	11.5(b)	...	0.2(b)	0.2 Nb(b), 0.1 Ti(b)
...	AL468	0.01(b)	18.2(b)	...	0.2(b)	0.2 Nb(b), 0.1 Ti(b)
...	YUS436S	0.01(b)	17.4(b)	1.2(b)	...	0.2 Ti(b)
S43035	439	0.07	17.00-19.00	...	0.5	Ti = 0.20 + 4 (C + N) min to 1.0 max
...	12SR	0.2	12.0	...	...	1.2 Al; 0.3 Ti
...	18SR	0.04	18.0	...	...	2.0 Al; 0.4 Ti
K41970	406	0.06	12.0-14.0	...	0.5	2.75-4.25 Al; 0.6 Ti

(a) Single values are maximum unless otherwise indicated. (b) Typical value

Table 6 Nominal chemical compositions of third-generation superferritic stainless steels

| Alloy | C(max) | Composition, % | | | | | | UNS No. |
		Cr	Fe	Mo	N	Ni	Other	
Intermediate-purity grades								
26-1Ti	0.02	26	bal	1	0.025	0.25	0.5Ti	S44626
AISI type 444	0.02	18	bal	2	0.02	0.4	0.5Ti	S44400
SEA-CURE	0.02	27.5	bal	3.4	0.025	1.7	0.5Ti	S44660
Nu Monit	0.025	25	bal	4	0.025	4	0.4Ti	S44635
AL 29-4C	0.030	29	bal	4	0.045	1.0	(Nb + Ti)	
Ultrahigh-purity grades								
E-Brite 26-1	0.002	26	bal	1	0.01	0.1	0.1Nb	S44726
AL 29-4-2	0.005	29	bal	4	0.01	2	...	S44800
SHOMAC 26-4	0.003	26	bal	4	0.005	...	...	...
SHOMAC 30-2	0.003	30	bal	2	0.007	0.18	...	...
YUS 190L	0.004	19	bal	2	0.0085	...	0.15Nb	...

fect in that it retards grain growth, which has an important embrittling effect when it occurs. However, because it also tends to transform to martensite under welding conditions, first-generation ferritic stainless steels generally have hard spots after welding and must therefore be postweld heat treated (see the article "Welding" in this Volume).

The second generation of ferritic stainless steels have lower carbon and low nitrogen contents, to which a stabilizer is added to tie up whatever carbon and/or nitrogen is present. The prototype of this second generation is type 409, typically 0.04C-11Cr-0.5Ti. The titanium ties up both carbon and nitrogen, leaving all of the chromium free. Surplus titanium is also a ferritizer. Therefore, the alloy is ferritic at all temperatures. Type 405 is a similar alloy, but it is stabilized with aluminum, which ties up nitrogen but not carbon. Aluminum is also a powerful ferritizer. The various carbides and/or nitrides produced by the addition of stabilizers help to resist embrittling grain growth in second-generation ferritic stainless steels during welding.

The third generation of ferritic stainless steels arose around 1970, with the advent of more efficient decarburization techniques in steelmaking (see the article "Melting and Refining Methods" in this Volume). Carbon and nitrogen levels are typically 0.02% or less, and stabilizers, such as titanium and/or niobium, are often added to tie up any free interstitials. The prototype alloy is type 444 (18Cr-2Mo). There are also a number of proprietary alloys that are not yet covered by an ASTM designation. These alloys are frequently referred to as *superferritics*.

The third-generation ferritic stainless steel alloys are austenite-free at all temperatures. However, they can be embrittled by the formation of intermetallic phases at elevated temperatures. They are sensitive to 475 °C (885 °F) embrittlement, because of precipitation of the chromium-rich α'-phase, and to embrittlement by σ, χ, and other phases at higher temperatures. Figure 3 indicates that the σ-phase is approximately FeCr, whereas α' is a chromium-rich ferrite that precipitates from the iron-rich ferrite. The χ-phase is a complex iron-chromium-molybdenum intermetallic that can only appear in molybdenum-bearing steels. Except in the case of α' embrittlement, which disappears rapidly upon exposure to temperatures above approximately 575 °C (1070 °F), temperatures that are high enough to dissolve all of these phases are also high enough to cause severe grain growth in the ferrite. Because this grain growth also has an embrittling effect, heat treatment alone is not usually desirable. In general, hot working to reduce grain size is necessary to restore full ductility and toughness once the alloy is embrittled by σ, χ, or other high-temperature intermetallic compounds. More detailed informa-

tion on 475 °C (885 °F) embrittlement can be found in the section "Embrittlement Mechanisms" in this article.

Properties and Applications

Unlike the martensitic stainless steels, the ferritic stainless steels cannot be strengthened by heat treatment. Also, because the strain-hardening rates of ferrite are relatively low and cold work significantly lowers ductility, the ferritic stainless steels are not often strengthened by cold work. Figure 9 compares the work-hardening characteristics of ferritic and austenitic stainless steels. Typical annealed yield and tensile strengths for ferritic stainless steels are 35 to 55 ksi (240 to 380 MPa) and 60 to 85 ksi (415 to 585 MPa), respectively. Ductilities tend to range between 20 and 35%. Higher strengths, up to 75 ksi (515 MPa) for yield strength and 95 ksi (655 MPa) for tensile strength, are obtained in the more highly alloyed superferritic steels. Minimum room-temperature tensile properties for selected ferritic grades are given in Table 7.

Whereas the martensitic stainless steels offer only moderate corrosion resistance, that of the ferritic stainless steels can range from moderate, for types 430 or 409, to outstanding, for the third-generation superferritics such as type 444 and UNS Nos. S44627, S44635, S44660, S44700, and S44800. Types 405 and 409 have resistance to atmospheric corrosion. Type 430 also resists mild oxidizing acids and organic acids and is therefore used in food-handling equipment, sinks, and such. The superferritics offer exceptional resistance to localized corrosion induced by exposure to aqueous chlorides. Localized corrosion, such as pitting, crevice corrosion, and stress-corrosion cracking (SCC) are problems that plague many austenitic stainless steels. Therefore, the superferritics are often used in heat exchangers and piping systems for chloride-bearing aqueous solutions and seawater.

Because of 475 °C (885 °F) embrittlement and σ-phase formation, long-term service temperatures for most ferritic stainless steels are usually limited to 250 °C (480 °F), maximum. However, 475 °C (885 °F) embrittlement does not seem to be a serious problem in the low-chromium types 409 and 405, which have been extensively used in automobile exhaust systems (where temperatures can exceed 575 °C, or 1070 °F, at times, which can dissolve α'). Another exception to the maximum service temperature limit is type 446, which offers outstanding resistance to scaling in air at high temperatures because of its high chromium content. It is used in compressive loading, as the supports in heat-treat furnaces and the like, where brittleness at room temperature is not an important issue. Because ferritic stainless steels lose toughness and ductility at low temperatures, their use below ambient temperatures is very limited.

The ferritic stainless steels generally require rapid cooling from hot-working temperatures to avoid grain growth and embrittlement from the α-phase. As a result, most ferritic stainless steel is used in relatively thin gages, especially in alloys

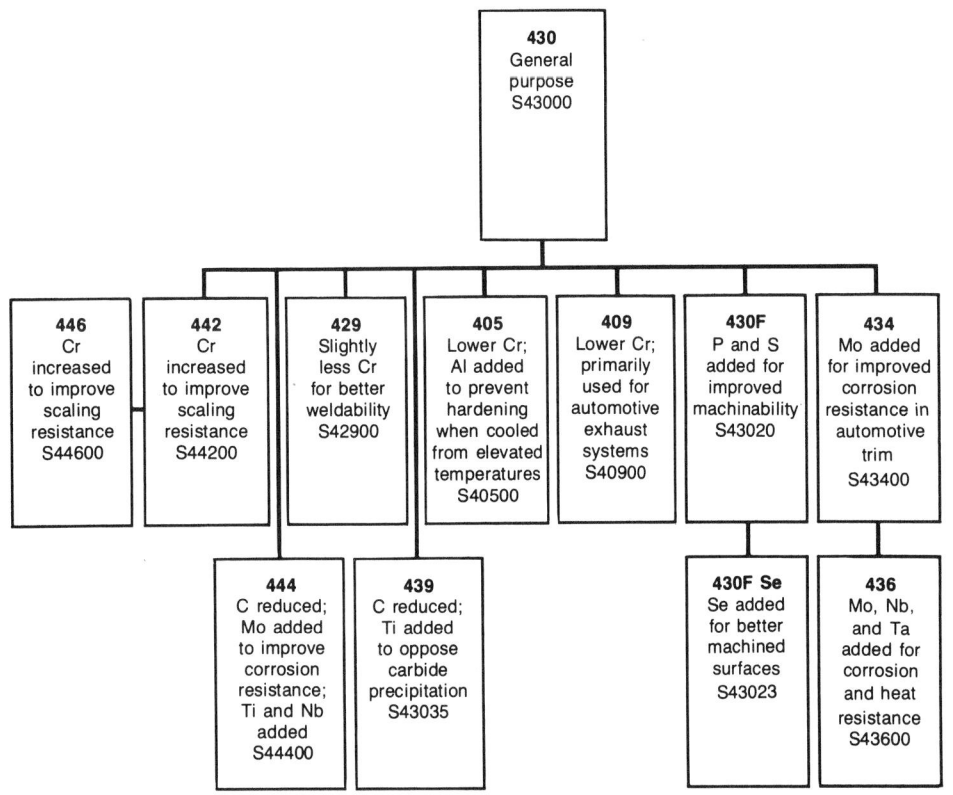

Fig. 8 Family relationships for standard ferritic stainless steels

transition, and they maintain good ductility and toughness to temperatures well below room temperature. In ferritic stainless steels the DBTT may be well above room temperature. Figure 10 shows the DBTT as a function of section thickness for several ferritic stainless steels. The thicker sections offer more constraint to plastic flow, and consequently brittle fracture occurs without exception above room temperature as section size increases. In contrast, thin sheets in which yielding can take place through the thickness remain ductile and highly formable well below room temperature.

Other factors that influence the DBTT of ferritic stainless steels are grain size, interstitial carbon and nitrogen content, and the presence of various types of second phases. Thus, fine grain size, low-interstitial element contents, and the elimination of second phases by proper heat treatment all enhance ductility and toughness (Ref 3, 4). Improved melting practices, including argon-oxygen decarburization (AOD) and vacuum melting, and stabilization by additions of titanium or niobium have been extremely important approaches to lower carbon and nitrogen contents and associated carbide and nitride precipitates detrimental to toughness of ferritic stainless steels (Ref 8).

Austenitic Stainless Steels

Austenitic stainless steels have a face-centered cubic (fcc) structure. This structure is attained through the liberal use of austenitizing elements such as nickel, manganese, and nitrogen. These steels are essentially nonmagnetic in the annealed condition and can be hardened only by cold working. They usually possess excellent cryogenic properties and good high-temperature strength. Chromium content generally varies from 16 to 26%; nickel content, up to about 35%; and manganese content, up to 15%. The 200-series steels contain nitrogen, 4 to 15.5% Mn, and

that are high in chromium. The superferritics are limited to thin plate, sheet, and tube forms.

The ductility and toughness of ferritic stainless steels are affected by many factors (Ref 4). Fundamentally, the strength and ability of the bcc ferrite structure to sustain plastic deformation are very temperature dependent, especially below room temperature. Strength increases rapidly and ductility drops sharply with decreasing temperature, apparently because screw dislocations lose their ability to cross slip in the bcc structure (Ref

5). As a result, ferritic steels undergo a transition from ductile fracture, characterized by microvoid coalescence, to brittle fracture, characterized by cleavage. The temperature at which this fracture transition occurs is referred to as the ductile-to-brittle transition temperature (DBTT), and the cleavage fracture may be initiated by intergranular cracking or strain-induced cracking of second-phase particles (Ref 6, 7). In contrast, austenitic stainless steels do not undergo a ductile-to-brittle

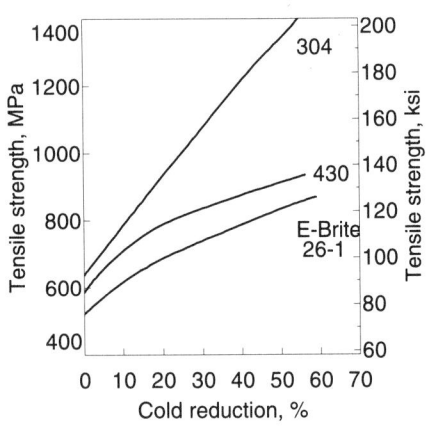

Fig. 9 Work-hardening characteristics of 17% Cr (430) and 26Cr-1Mn (26-1) ferritic stainless steels compared with those of type 304 austenitic stainless steel

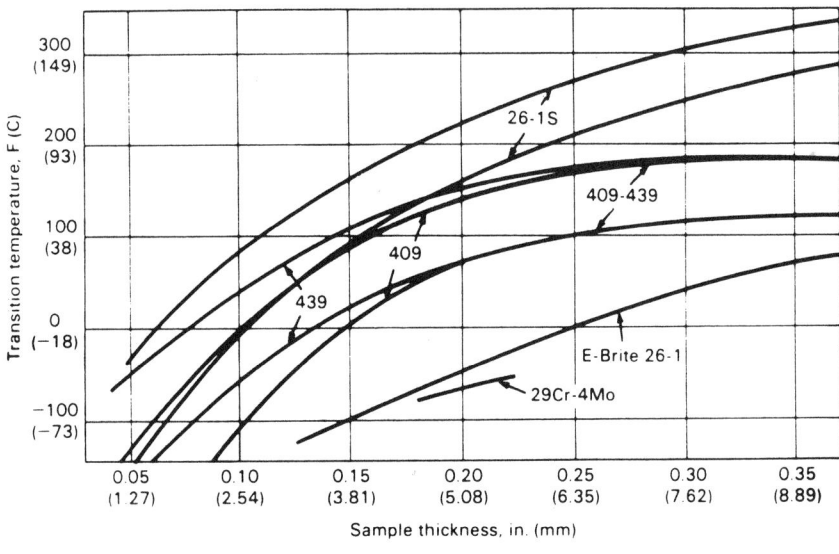

Fig. 10 Ductile-to-brittle transition temperatures as a function of section thickness for various ferritic stainless steels. Source: Ref 3

Table 7 Minimum mechanical properties of ferritic stainless steels

Product form(a)	Condition	Tensile strength		0.2% yield strength		Elongation, %	Reduction in area, %	Hardness, HRB	ASTM specification
		MPa	ksi	MPa	ksi				
Type 405 (UNS S40500)									
B	Annealed	415	60	170	25	20	45	...	A 479
F	Annealed	415	60	205	30	20	45	...	A 473
W	Annealed	480	70	280	40	20	45	...	A 580
P, Sh, St	Annealed	415	60	170	25	20	...	88 max	A 176, A 240
Type 409 (UNS S40900)									
P, Sh, St	Annealed	380	55	205	30	20	...	80 max	A 240
P, Sh, St	Annealed	380	55	205	30	22(c)	...	80 max	A 176
Type 429 (UNS S42900)									
B	Annealed	480	70	275	40	20	45	...	A 276
P, Sh, St	Annealed	450	65	205	30	22(c)	...	88 max	A 176, A 240
Type 430 (UNS S43000)									
B	Annealed	415	60	205	30	20	45	...	A 276
W	Annealed	480	70	275	40	20	45	...	A 580
P, Sh, St	Annealed	450	65	205	30	22(c)	...	88 max	A 176, A 240
Type 430F (UNS S43020)									
F	Annealed	485	70	275	40	20	45	...	A 473
W	Annealed	585-860	85-125	...	...	...	...	...	A 581
Type 439 (UNS S43035)									
B	Annealed	485	70	275	40	20	45	...	A 479
P, Sh, St	Annealed	450	65	205	30	22	...	88 max	A 240
Type 430Ti (UNS S43036)									
B	Annealed	515(b)	75(b)	310(b)	45(b)	30(b)	65(b)	...	...
Type 434 (UNS S43400)									
W	Annealed	545(b)	79(b)	415(b)	60(b)	33(b)	78(b)	90 max(b)	...
Sh	Annealed	530(b)	77(b)	365(b)	53(b)	23(b)	...	83 max(b)	...
Type 436 (UNS S43600)									
Sh, St	Annealed	530(b)	77(b)	365(b)	53(b)	23(b)	...	83 max(b)	...
Type 442 (UNS S44200)									
B	Annealed	550(b)	80(b)	310(b)	45(b)	20(b)	40(b)	90 max(b)	...
P, Sh, St	Annealed	515	75	275	40	20	...	95 max	A 176
Type 444 (UNS S44400)									
P, Sh, St	Annealed	415	60	275	40	20	...	95 max	A 176
Type 446 (UNS S44600)									
B	Annealed, hot finished	480	70	275	40	20	45	...	A 276
B	Annealed, cold finished	480	70	275	40	16	45	...	A 276
W	Annealed	480	70	275	40	20	45	...	A 580
W	Annealed, cold finished	480	70	275	40	16	45	...	A 580
P, Sh, St	Annealed	515	75	275	40	20	...	95 max	A 176
18 SR									
Sh, St	Annealed	620(b)	90(b)	450(b)	65(b)	25(b)	...	90 min(b)	...
E-Brite 26-1 (UNS S44627)									
B	Annealed, hot finished	450	65	275	40	20	45	...	A 276
B	Annealed, cold finished	450	65	275	40	16	45	...	A 276
P, Sh, St	Annealed	450	65	275	40	22(c)	...	90 max	A 176, A 240
MONIT (UNS S44635)									
P, Sh, St	Annealed	620	90	515	75	20	...	...	A 176, A 240
Sea-Cure/SC-1 (UNS S44660)									
P, Sh, St	Annealed	585	85	450	65	18	...	100 max	A 176, A 240
29-4C (UNS S44735)									
P, Sh, St	Annealed	550	80	415	60	18	...	...	A 276, A 240
29-4-2 (UNS S44800)									
P, Sh, St	Annealed	550	80	415	60	20	...	98 max	A 176, A 240
B	Hot finished	480	70	380	55	20	40	...	A 276
B	Cold finished	520	75	415	60	15	30	...	A 276
B	Annealed	480	70	380	55	20	40	...	A 479

(a) B, bar; F, forgings; W, wire; P, plate; Sh, sheet; St, strip. (b) Typical values. (c) 20% reduction for 1.3 mm (0.050 in.) and under in thickness

Table 8 Compositions of standard austenitic stainless steels

Type	UNS No.	Composition, %(a)							
		C	Mn	Si	Cr	Ni	P	S	Other
201	S20100	0.15	5.5-7.5	1.00	16.0-18.0	3.5-5.5	0.06	0.03	0.25 N
202	S20200	0.15	7.5-10.0	1.00	17.0-19.0	4.0-6.0	0.06	0.03	0.25 N
205	S20500	0.12-0.25	14.0-15.5	1.00	16.5-18.0	1.0-1.75	0.06	0.03	0.32-0.40 N
301	S30100	0.15	2.0	1.00	16.0-18.0	6.0-8.0	0.045	0.03	...
302	S30200	0.15	2.0	1.00	17.0-19.0	8.0-10.0	0.045	0.03	...
302B	S30215	0.15	2.0	2.0-3.0	17.0-19.0	8.0-10.0	0.045	0.03	...
303	S30300	0.15	2.0	1.00	17.0-19.0	8.0-10.0	0.20	0.15 min	0.6 Mo(b)
303Se	S30323	0.15	2.0	1.00	17.0-19.0	8.0-10.0	0.20	0.06	0.15 min Se
304	S30400	0.08	2.0	1.00	18.0-10.0	8.0-10.5	0.045	0.03	...
304H	S30409	0.04-0.10	2.0	1.00	18.0-20.0	8.0-10.5	0.045	0.03	...
304L	S30403	0.03	2.0	1.00	18.0-20.0	8.0-12.0	0.045	0.03	...
304LN	S30453	0.03	2.0	1.00	18.0-20.0	8.0-12.0	0.045	0.03	0.10-0.16 N
302Cu	S30430	0.08	2.0	1.00	17.0-19.0	8.0-10.0	0.045	0.03	3.0-4.0 Cu
304N	S30451	0.08	2.0	1.00	18.0-20.0	8.0-10.5	0.045	0.03	0.10-0.16 N
305	S30500	0.12	2.0	1.00	17.0-19.0	10.5-13.0	0.045	0.03	...
308	S30800	0.08	2.0	1.00	19.0-21.0	10.0-12.0	0.045	0.03	...
309	S30900	0.20	2.0	1.00	22.0-24.0	12.0-15.0	0.045	0.03	...
309S	S30908	0.08	2.0	1.00	22.0-24.0	12.0-15.0	0.045	0.03	...
310	S31000	0.25	2.0	1.50	24.0-26.0	19.0-22.0	0.045	0.03	...
310S	S31008	0.08	2.0	1.50	24.0-26.0	19.0-22.0	0.045	0.03	...
314	S31400	0.25	2.0	1.5-3.0	23.0-26.0	19.0-22.0	0.045	0.03	...
316	S31600	0.08	2.0	1.00	16.0-18.0	10.0-14.0	0.045	0.03	2.0-3.0 Mo
316F	S31620	0.08	2.0	1.00	16.0-18.0	10.0-14.0	0.20	0.10 min	1.75-2.5 Mo
316H	S31609	0.04-0.10	2.0	1.00	16.0-18.0	10.0-14.0	0.045	0.03	2.0-3.0 Mo
316L	S31603	0.03	2.0	1.00	16.0-18.0	10.0-14.0	0.045	0.03	2.0-3.0 Mo
316LN	S31653	0.03	2.0	1.00	16.0-18.0	10.0-14.0	0.045	0.03	2.0-3.0 Mo; 0.10-0.16 N
316N	S31651	0.08	2.0	1.00	16.0-18.0	10.0-14.0	0.045	0.03	2.0-3.0 Mo; 0.10-0.16 N
317	S31700	0.08	2.0	1.00	18.0-20.0	11.0-15.0	0.045	0.03	3.0-4.0 Mo
317L	S31703	0.03	2.0	1.00	18.0-20.0	11.0-15.0	0.045	0.03	3.0-4.0 Mo
321	S32100	0.08	2.0	1.00	17.0-19.0	9.0-12.0	0.045	0.03	5 × %C min Ti
321H	S32109	0.04-0.10	2.0	1.00	17.0-19.0	9.0-12.0	0.045	0.03	5 × %C min Ti
330	N08330	0.08	2.0	0.75-1.5	17.0-20.0	34.0-37.0	0.04	0.03	...
347	S34700	0.08	2.0	1.00	17.0-19.0	9.0-13.0	0.045	0.03	10 × %C min Nb
347H	S34709	0.04-0.10	2.0	1.00	17.0-19.0	9.0-13.0	0.045	0.03	8 × %C min – 1.0 max Nb
348	S34800	0.08	2.0	1.00	17.0-19.0	9.0-13.0	0.045	0.03	0.2 Co; 10 × %C min Nb; 0.10 Ta
348H	S34809	0.04-0.10	2.0	1.00	17.0-19.0	9.0-13.0	0.045	0.03	0.2 Co; 10 × %C min – 1.0 max Nb; 0.10 Ta
384	S38400	0.08	2.0	1.00	15.0-17.0	17.0-19.0	0.045	0.03	...

(a) Single values are maximum values unless otherwise indicated. (b) Optional

up to 7% Ni. The 300-series steels contain larger amounts of nickel and up to 2% Mn. Molybdenum, copper, silicon, aluminum, titanium, and niobium may be added to confer certain characteristics such as halide pitting resistance or oxidation resistance. Sulfur or selenium may be added to certain grades to improve machinability.

Tables 8 and 9 provide chemical compositions for standard (AISI) and nonstandard steels. Figure 11 shows the relationships between the various standard grades.

Basic Metallurgy

Austenitic stainless steel compositions are based on a balance between alloy elements that promote ferrite formation and those that promote austenite formation. The prototype ferritizing element is chromium, but molybdenum, niobium, titanium, aluminum, tungsten, and vanadium also promote ferrite. The prototype austenitizing element is nickel, but carbon, nitrogen, and copper all promote transformation of ferrite to austenite at high temperatures. In addition, although manganese does not seem to promote transformation of ferrite to austenite at high temperatures, it clearly does tend to stabilize austenite with respect to transformation to marten-site at low temperatures. Further, manganese promotes the solubility of nitrogen in steel (as does chromium), making possible a low-nickel family of austenitic stainless steels that are high in manganese and nitrogen.

Austenitic stainless steels can be best described in terms of the iron-chromium-nickel ternary alloy system. The commercial alloys also contain a certain amount of carbon, silicon, manganese, sulfur, and so on. These elements might alter somewhat the phase balance, but by and large, the structure is determined by the three primary constituents iron, chromium, and nickel. Figure 12 shows the equilibrium iron-chromium-nickel phase diagram at 1100 °C (2010 °F). This is the temperature of maximum austenite stability and is used as the optimum annealing temperature for the 18-8 chromium-nickel steels.

When comparing the ternary diagram with the binary iron-chromium diagram, it can be seen that the nickel addition extends the austenite phase field. The 18-8 steels fall in the gamma range, close to the iron-rich corner, beside the duplex phase field. Actually, above 1150 °C (2100 °F) some δ-ferrite will form. The phase diagram also indicates that as the chromium content increases above 18.0%, it also becomes necessary to raise the nickel content; otherwise, increasing amounts of ferrite will be formed.

Besides extending the austenite phase field, nickel also lowers the M_s after cooling from the solution annealing temperature. In fact, all the alloying elements found commonly in these steels lower the M_s, including chromium and molybdenum, which at high temperatures promote the formation of ferrite.

The combined effect of all the alloying elements on the ratio of austenite to δ-ferrite can be determined by referring to the Schaeffler diagram (Fig. 1). Although this diagram applies primarily to weld metal, it is very useful in illustrating the relative potency of the austenitizing and ferritizing elements and in determining the structure of a certain composition.

Carbide Precipitation and Intergranular Corrosion. Sensitization, or carbide precipitation at grain boundaries, can occur when austenitic stainless steels are heated for a period of time in the range of about 425 to 870 °C (800 to 1600 °F). Time at temperature will determine the amount of carbide precipitation. When the chromium carbides precipitate in grain boundaries, the area immediately adjacent is depleted of chromium. The carbide formed in conventional austenitic steels is $(Cr,Fe)_{23}C_6$, or $M_{23}C_6$

Table 9 Compositions of nonstandard austenitic stainless steels

Designation(a)	UNS No.	C	Mn	Si	Cr	Ni	P	S	Other
						Composition, %(b)			
Gall-Tough	S20161	0.15	4.00-6.00	3.00-4.00	15.0-18.0	4.00-6.00	0.040	0.040	0.08-0.20 N
203 EZ (XM-1)	S20300	0.08	5.0-6.5	1.00	16.0-18.0	5.0-6.5	0.040	0.18-0.35	0.5 Mo; 1.75-2.25 Cu
Nitronic 50 (XM-19)	S20910	0.06	4.0-6.0	1.00	20.5-23.5	11.5-13.5	0.040	0.030	1.5-3.0 Mo; 0.2-0.4 N; 0.1-0.3 Nb; 0.1-0.3 V
Tenelon (XM-31)	S21400	0.12	14.5-16.0	0.3-1.0	17.0-18.5	0.75	0.045	0.030	0.35 N
Cryogenic Tenelon (XM-14)	S21460	0.12	14.0-16.0	1.00	17.0-19.0	5.0-6.0	0.060	0.030	0.35-0.50 N
Esshete 1250	S21500	0.15	5.5-7.0	1.20	14.0-16.0	9.0-11.0	0.040	0.030	0.003-0.009 B; 0.75-1.25 Nb; 0.15-0.40 V
Type 216 (XM-17)	S21600	0.08	7.5-9.0	1.00	17.5-22.0	5.0-7.0	0.045	0.030	2.0-3.0 Mo; 0.25-0.50 N
Type 216 L (XM-18)	S21603	0.03	7.5-9.0	1.00	17.5-22.0	7.5-9.0	0.045	0.030	2.0-3.0 Mo; 0.25-0.50 N
Nitronic 60	S21800	0.10	7.0-9.0	3.5-4.5	16.0-18.0	8.0-9.0	0.040	0.030	0.08-0.18 N
Nitronic 40 (XM-10)	S21900	0.08	8.0-10.0	1.00	19.0-21.5	5.5-7.5	0.060	0.030	0.15-0.40 N
21-6-9 LC	S21904	0.04	8.00-10.00	1.00	19.00-21.50	5.50-7.50	0.060	0.030	0.15-0.40 N
Nitronic 33 (18-3 Mn)	S24000	0.08	11.50-14.50	1.00	17.0-19.00	2.50-3.75	0.060	0.030	0.20-0.40 N
Nitronic 32 (18-2 Mn)	S24100	0.15	11.00-14.00	1.00	16.50-19.50	0.50-2.50	0.060	0.030	0.20-0.40 N
18-18 Plus	S28200	0.15	17.0-19.0	1.00	17.5-19.5	...	0.045	0.030	0.5-1.5 Mo; 0.5-1.5 Cu; 0.4-0.6 N
303 Plus X (XM-5)	S30310	0.15	2.5-4.5	1.00	17.0-19.0	7.0-10.0	0.020	0.25 min	0.6 Mo
MVMA(c)	S30415	0.05	0.60	1.30	18.5	9.50	...	...	0.15 N; 0.04 Ce
304BI(d)	S30424	0.08	2.00	0.75	18.0-20.00	12.00-15.00	0.045	0.030	0.10 N; 1.00-1.25 B
304 HN (XM-21)	S30452	0.04-0.10	2.00	1.00	18.0-20.0	8.0-10.5	0.045	0.030	0.16-0.30 N
Cronifer 1815 LCSi	S30600	0.018	2.00	3.73-4.3	17.0-18.5	14.0-15.5	0.020	0.020	0.2 Mo
RA 85 H(c)	S30615	0.20	0.80	3.50	18.5	14.50	...	...	1.0 Al
253 MA	S30815	0.05-0.10	0.80	1.4-2.0	20.0-22.0	10.0-12.0	0.040	0.030	0.14-0.20 N; 0.03-0.08 Ce; 1.0 Al
Type 309 S Cb	S30940	0.08	2.00	1.00	22.0-24.0	12.0-15.0	0.045	0.030	10 × %C min to 1.10 max Nb
Type 310 Cb	S31040	0.08	2.00	1.50	24.0-26.0	19.0-22.0	0.045	0.030	10 × %C min to 1.10 max Nb + Ta
254 SMO	S31254	0.20	1.00	0.80	19.50-20.50	17.50-18.50	0.030	0.010	6.00-6.50 Mo; 0.50-1.00 Cu; 0.180-0.220 N
Type 316 Ti	S31635	0.08	2.00	1.00	16.0-18.0	10.0-14.0	0.045	0.030	5 × %(C + N) min to 0.70 max Ti; 2.0-3.0 Mo; 0.10 N
Type 316 Cb	S31640	0.08	2.00	1.00	16.0-18.0	10.0-14.0	0.045	0.030	10 × %C min to 1.10 max Nb + Ta; 2.0-3.0 Mo; 0.10 N
Type 316 HQ	...	0.030	2.00	1.00	16.00-18.25	10.00-14.00	0.030	0.015	3.00-4.00 Cu; 2.00-3.00 Mo
Type 317 LM	S31725	0.03	2.00	1.00	18.0-20.0	13.5-17.5	0.045	0.030	4.0-5.0 Mo; 0.10 N
17-14-4 LN	S31726	0.03	2.00	0.75	17.0-20.0	13.5-17.5	0.045	0.030	4.0-5.0 Mo; 0.10-0.20 N
Type 317 LN	S31753	0.03	2.00	1.00	18.0-21.0	11.0-15.0	0.030	0.030	0.10-0.22 N
Type 370	S37000	0.03-0.05	1.65-2.35	0.5-1.0	12.5-14.5	14.5-16.5	0.040	0.010	1.5-2.5 Mo; 0.1-0.4 Ti; 0.005 N; 0.05 Co
18-18-2 (XM-15)	S38100	0.08	2.00	1.5-2.5	17.0-19.0	17.5-18.5	0.030	0.030	...
19-9 DL	S63198	0.28-0.35	0.75-1.50	0.03-0.8	18.0-21.0	8.0-11.0	0.040	0.030	1.0-1.75 Mo; 0.1-0.35 Ti; 1.0-1.75 W; 0.25-0.60 Nb
20Cb-3	N08020	0.07	2.00	1.00	19.0-21.0	32.0-38.0	0.045	0.035	2.0-3.0 Mo; 3.0-4.0 Cu; 8 × %C min to 1.00 max Nb
20Mo-4	N08024	0.03	1.00	0.50	22.5-25.0	35.0-40.0	0.035	0.035	3.50-5.00 Mo; 0.50-1.50 Cu; 0.15-0.35 Nb
20Mo-6	N08026	0.03	1.00	0.50	22.0-26.00	33.0-37.20	0.03	0.03	5.00-6.70 Mo; 2.00-4.00 Cu
Sanicro 28	N08028	0.02	2.00	1.00	26.0-28.0	29.5-32.5	0.020	0.015	3.0-4.0 Mo; 0.6-1.4 Cu
AL-6X	N08366	0.035	2.00	1.00	20.0-22.0	23.5-25.5	0.030	0.030	6.0-7.0 Mo
AL-6XN	N08367	0.030	2.00	1.00	20.0-22.0	23.50-25.50	0.040	0.030	6.0-7.0 Mo; 0.18-0.25 N
JS-700	N08700	0.04	2.00	1.00	19.0-23.0	24.0-26.0	0.040	0.030	4.3-5.0 Mo; 8 × %C min to 0.5 max Nb; 0.5 Cu; 0.005 Pb; 0.035 S
Type 332	N08800	0.01	1.50	1.00	19.0-23.0	30.0-35.0	0.045	0.015	0.15-0.60 Ti; 0.15-0.60 Al
904L	N08904	0.02	2.00	1.00	19.0-23.0	23.0-28.0	0.045	0.035	4.0-5.0 Mo; 1.0-2.0 Cu
Cronifer 1925 hMo	N08925	0.02	1.00	0.50	24.0-26.0	19.0-21.0	0.045	0.030	6.0-7.0 Mo; 0.8-1.5 Cu; 0.10-0.20 N
Cronifer 2328	...	0.04	0.75	0.75	22.0-24.0	26.0-28.0	0.030	0.015	2.5-3.5 Cu; 0.4-0.7 Ti; 2.5-3.0 Mo

(a) XM designations in this column are ASTM designations for the listed alloy. (b) Single values are maximum values unless otherwise indicated. (c) Nominal compositions. (d) UNS designation has not been specified; this designation appears in ASTM A 887 and merely indicates the form to be used.

carbide. When the precipitation is relatively continuous, the depletion renders the stainless steel susceptible to intergranular corrosion, which is the dissolution of the low-chromium layer or envelope surrounding each grain. Sensitization also lowers resistance to other forms of corrosion, such as pitting, crevice corrosion, and SCC.

Time-temperature-sensitization curves are available that provide guidance for avoiding sensitization and illustrate the effect of carbon content on this phenomenon (Fig. 13). The curves shown in Fig. 13 indicate that a type 304 stainless steel with 0.062% C would have to cool below 595 °C (1100 °F) within about 5 min to avoid sensitization, but a type 304L with 0.030% C could take about 20 h to cool below 480 °C (900 °F) without becoming sensitized. These curves are general guidelines and should be verified before they are applied to various types of stainless steels.

Another method of avoiding sensitization is to use stabilized steels. Such stainless steels contain titanium and/or niobium. These elements have an affinity for carbon and form car-

bides readily; this allows the chromium to remain in solution even for extremely long exposures to temperatures in the sensitizing range. Type 304L can avoid sensitization during the relatively brief exposure of welding, but it will be sensitized by long exposures.

Annealing is the only way to correct a sensitized stainless steel. Because different stainless steels require different temperatures, times, and quenching procedures, the user should contact the material supplier for such information.

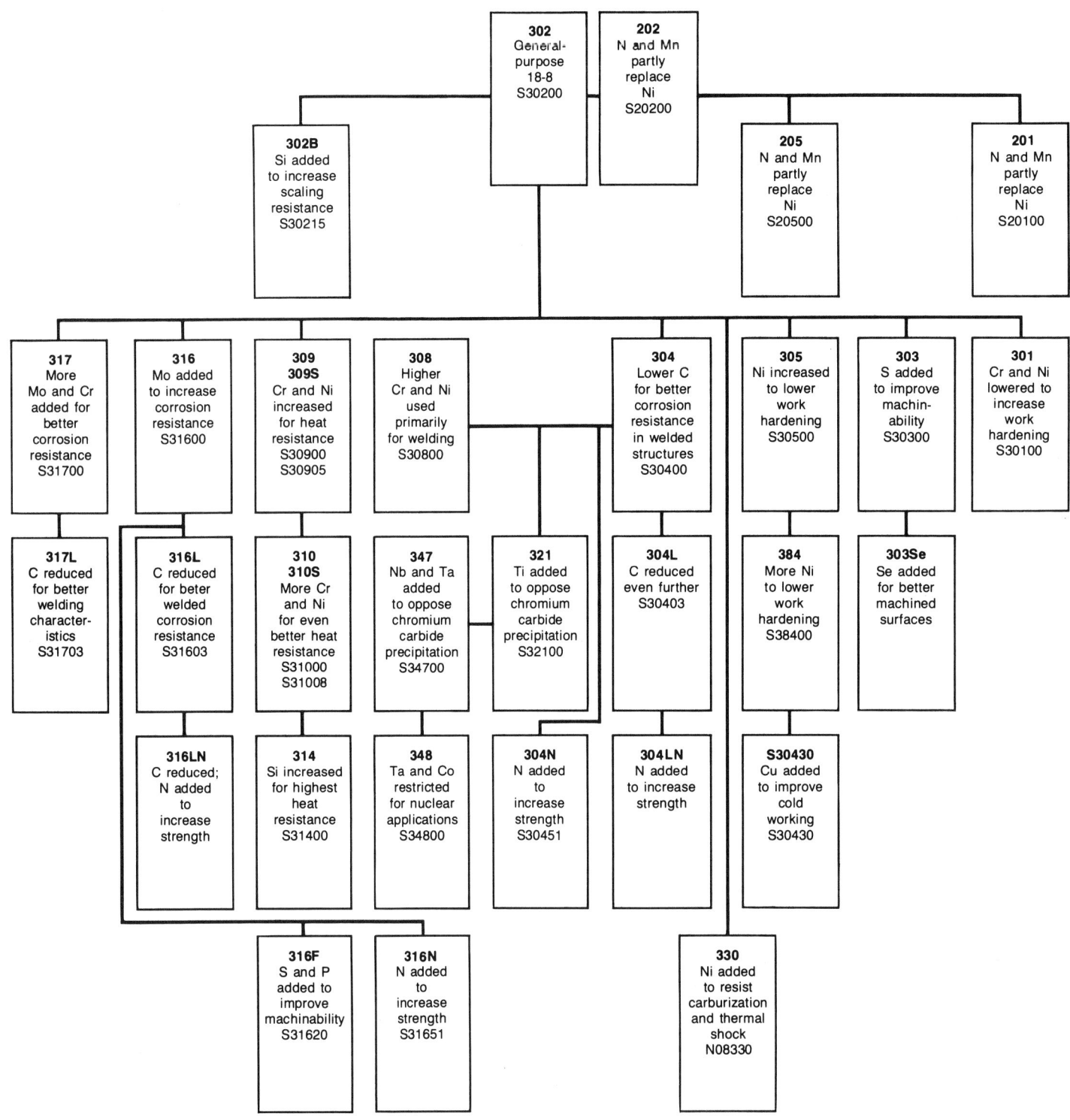

Fig. 11 Family relationships for standard austenitic stainless steels

More detailed information on intergranular corrosion of stainless steels due to carbide precipitation can be found in the article "Atmospheric and Aqueous Corrosion" in this Volume (see also the section "Embrittlement Mechanisms" in this article).

Precipitation of Intermetallic Phases. Sigma-phase precipitation and precipitation of other intermetallic phases also increase susceptibility to corrosion and embrittlement. Sigma phase is a chromium-molybdenum-rich phase that can render stainless steels susceptible to intergranular corrosion, pitting, and crevice corrosion. It generally occurs in higher-alloyed stainless steels (high-chromium, high-molybdenum stainless steels). Sigma phase can occur at a temperature range between 540 and 900 °C (1000 and 1650 °F). Like sensitization, it can be corrected by solution annealing. Sigma-phase embrittlement is discussed in the section "Embrittlement Mechanisms" in this article. The effects of precipitated intermetallic phases on corrosion resistance of stainless steels are described in the article "Atmospheric and Aqueous Corrosion" in this Vol-

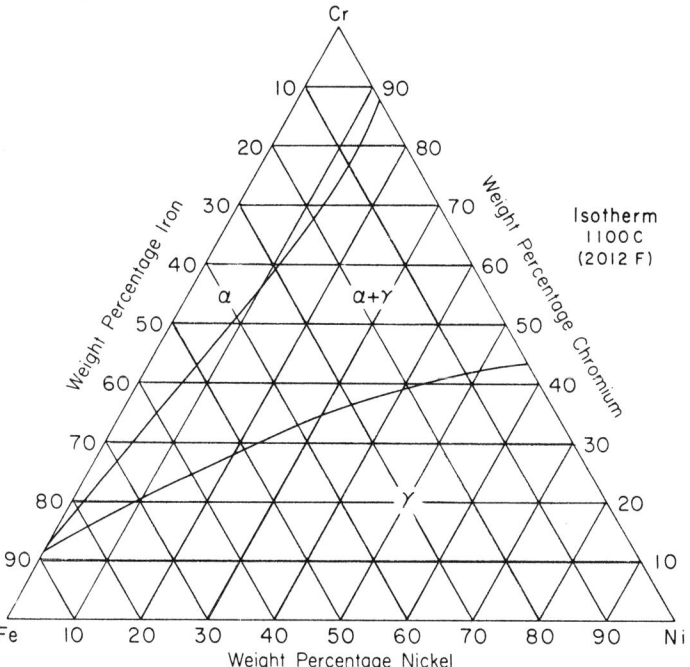

Fig. 12   The iron-nickel-chromium system at 1100 °C (2012 °F)

ume. A summary of all intermetallic phases in stainless steels can be found in Table 1 in the article "Microstructures of Wrought Stainless Steels" in this Volume.

Martensite Formation. Martensite may form in austenitic stainless steels during cooling below room temperature (i.e., thermally) or in response to cold work (i.e., mechanically). Eichelman and Hull (Ref 9) have developed the following equation for the M_s of austenitic stainless steels:

$$M_s \, (°F) = 75(14.6 - Cr) + 110(8.9 - Ni)$$
$$+ 60(1.33 - Mn) + 50(0.47 - Si)$$
$$+ 3000[0.068 - (C + N)] \qquad (Eq \, 1)$$

This equation shows that the substitutional alloying elements chromium and nickel have a moderate effect on the M_s compared to the very strong effect of carbon and nitrogen. Residual nitrogen contents of austenitic stainless steel are usually in the range of 300 to 700 ppm (0.03 to 0.07 wt.%) (Ref 10), and thus when combined with carbon they may have a strong effect on stabilizing austenite with respect to martensite formation. When $M_{23}C_6$ carbides form at austenite grain boundaries, both carbon and chromium are removed from the adjacent austenite, M_s is locally raised, and martensite may form at grain boundaries (Ref 11, 12). This phenomenon is in fact used as one approach to develop martensitic struc-

tures in semiaustenitic PH stainless steels, as discussed below.

Two types of martensite form spontaneously on cooling austenitic stainless steels below room temperature: hexagonal close-packed (hcp) ε-martensite and bcc α′-martensite. The ε-martensite forms on close-packed (111) planes in the austenite and, except for size, is morphologically very similar to deformation twins or stacking fault clusters, which also form on (111) planes (Ref 13, 14). The α′-martensite forms as plates with (225) habit planes in groups bounded by faulted sheets of austenite on (111) planes (Ref 13). The nucleation of α′-martensite and its relationship to ε-martensite has been difficult to resolve; evidence for α′ formation directly from austenite and with ε as an intermediate phase is reviewed in Ref 10.

Deformation-induced or strain-induced martensite formation is another unique feature of austenitic stainless steels. Strain-induced martensite forms at higher temperatures than does martensite, which forms on cooling, and the parameter M_D, the highest temperature at which a designated amount of martensite forms under defined deformation conditions, is used to characterize austenite stability relative to deformation. Angel (Ref 15) has published the following correlations of M_D to the composition of austenitic stainless steels:

$$M_{D30} \, (°C) = 413 - 462(C + N) - 9.2(Si)$$
$$- 8.1 (Mn) - 13.7(Cr) - 9.5(Ni) - 18.5(Mo)$$
$$(Eq \, 2)$$

where M_{D30} is the temperature at which martensite is formed by 30% true strain in tension. Again, carbon and nitrogen have a very strong effect on austenite stability, and the extra-low carbon grades such as 304L are quite sensitive to strain-induced martensite formation, a characteristic that may render them susceptible to reduced performance in high-pressure hydrogen (Ref 16). Deformation-induced martensite, however, significantly enhances strength generated by cold work, and types 301 and 302 stainless steels are designed to have lower chromium and nickel contents in order to exploit this

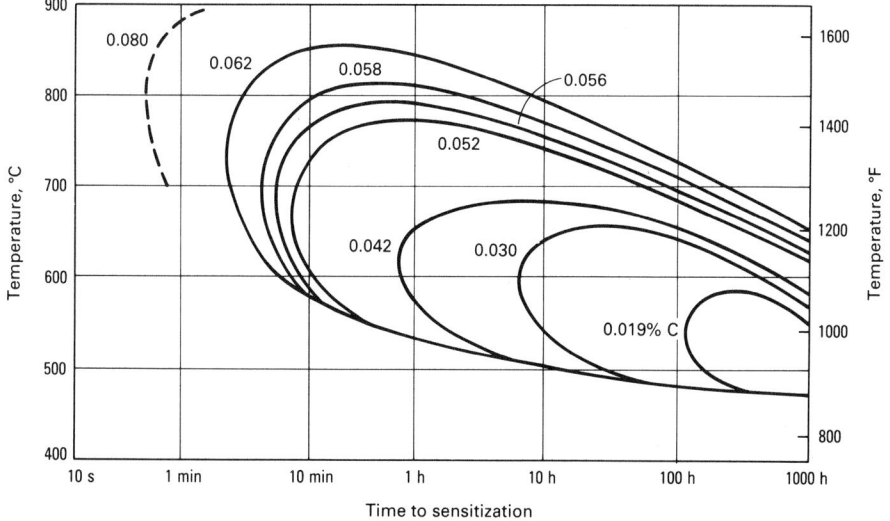

Fig. 13   Time-temperature curves showing effect of carbon content on carbide precipitation, which forms in the areas to the right of the various carbon-content curves

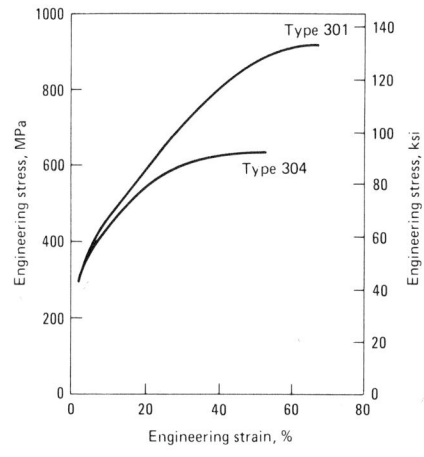

Fig. 14   Typical stress-strain curves for types 301 and 304 stainless steel. Source: Ref 17

Table 10　Minimum room-temperature mechanical properties of austenitic stainless steels

Product form(a)	Condition	Tensile strength MPa	Tensile strength ksi	0.2% yield strength MPa	0.2% yield strength ksi	Elonga-tion, %	Reduction in area, %	Hardness, HRB	ASTM specification
Type 301 (UNS S30100)									
B	Annealed	620	90	205	30	40	...	95 max	A 666
B, P, Sh, St	Annealed	515	75	205	30	40	...	92 max	A 167
B, P, Sh, St	¼ hard	860	125	515	75	25	...	...	A 666
B, P, Sh, St	½ hard	1030	150	760	110	18	...	...	A 666
B, P, Sh, St	¾ hard	1210	175	930	135	12	...	...	A 666
B, P, Sh, St	Full hard	1280	185	965	140	9	...	...	A 666
Type 302 (UNS S30200)									
B, F	Hot finished and annealed	515	75	205	30	40	50	...	A 276, A 473
B	Cold finished(b) and annealed	620	90	310	45	30	40	...	A 276
B	Cold finished(c) and annealed	515	75	205	30	30	40	...	A 276
W	Annealed	515	75	205	30	35(d)	50(d)	...	A 580
W	Cold finished	620	90	310	45	30(d)	40	...	A 580
P, Sh, St	Annealed	515	75	205	30	40	...	92 max	A 167, A 240, A 666
B, P, Sh, St	High tensile, ¼ hard	860	125	515	75	10	...	...	A 666
B, P, Sh, St	High tensile, ½ hard	1030	150	760	110	10	...	...	A 666
B, P, Sh, St	High tensile, ¾ hard	1205	175	930	135	6	...	...	A 666
B, P, Sh, St	Full hard	1275	185	965	140	4	...	...	A 666
Type 302B (UNS S30215)									
B, F	Hot finished and annealed	515	75	205	30	40	50	...	A 276, A 473
B	Cold finished(b) and annealed	620	90	310	45	30	40	...	A 276
B	Cold finished(c) and annealed	515	75	205	30	30	40	...	A 276
W	Annealed	515	75	205	30	35(d)	50(d)	...	A 580
W	Cold finished	620	90	310	45	30(d)	40	...	A 580
P, Sh, St	Annealed	515	75	205	30	40	...	95 max	A 167
Type 302Cu (UNS S30430)									
W(e)	Annealed	550	80	...	...	...	...	...	A 493
W(e)	Lightly drafted	585	85	...	...	...	...	...	A 493
Types 303 (UNS S30300) and 303Se (UNS S30323)									
F	Annealed	515	75	205	30	40	50	...	A 473
W	Annealed	585-860	85-125	...	...	...	...	...	A 581
W	Cold worked	790-1000	115-145	...	...	...	...	...	A 581
Type 304 (UNS S30400)									
B, F(f)	Hot finished and annealed	515	75	205	30	40	50	...	A 276, A 473
B	Cold finished(b) and annealed	620	90	310	45	30	40	...	A 276
B	Cold finished(c) and annealed	515	75	205	30	30	40	...	A 276
W	Annealed	515	75	205	30	35(d)	50(d)	...	A 580
W	Cold finished	620	90	310	45	30(d)	40	...	A 580
P, Sh, St	Annealed	515	75	205	30	40	...	92 max	A 167
B, P, Sh, St	⅛ hard	690	100	380	55	35	...	...	A 666
B, P, Sh, St	¼ hard	860	125	515	75	10	...	...	A 666
B, P, Sh, St	½ hard	1035	150	760	110	7	...	...	A 666
Type 304L (UNS S30403)									
F	Annealed	450	65	170	25	40	50	...	A 473
B	Hot finished and annealed	480	70	170	25	40	50	...	A 276
B	Cold finished(b) and annealed	620	90	310	45	30	40	...	A 276
B	Cold finished (c) and annealed	480	70	170	25	30	40	...	A 276
W	Annealed	480	70	170	25	35(d)	50(d)	...	A 580
W	Cold finished	620	90	310	45	30(d)	40	...	A 580
P, Sh, St	Annealed	480	70	170	25	40	...	88 max	A 167, A 240
Type 304B4 (UNS S30424)									
P, Sh, St grade A	Annealed	515	75	205	30	27	...	95 max	A 887
P, Sh, St grade B	Annealed	515	75	205	30	16	...	95 max	A 887
Type 305 (UNS S30500)									
B, F	Hot finished and annealed	515	75	205	30	40	50	...	A 276, A 473
B	Cold finished(b) and annealed	260	90	310	45	30	40	...	A 276
B	Cold finished(c) and annealed	515	75	205	30	30	40	...	A 276
W	Annealed	515	75	205	30	35(d)	50(d)	...	A 580
W	Cold finished	620	90	310	45	30(d)	40	...	A 580
P, Sh, St	Annealed	480	70	170	25	40	...	88 max	A 167
B, W	High tensile(d)	1690	245	...	...	...	...	...	...
Cronifer 18-15 LCSi (UNS S30600)									
P, Sh, St	Annealed	540	78	240	35	40	...	...	A 167, A 240

(continued)

(a) B, bar; F, forgings; P, plate; Pi, pipe; Sh, sheet; St, strip; T, tube; W, wire. (b) Up to 13 mm (0.5 in.) thick. (c) Over 13 mm (0.5 in.) thick. (d) For wire 3.96 mm (5⁄32 in.) and under, elongation and reduction in area shall be 25 and 40%, respectively. (e) 4 mm (0.156 in.) in diameter and over. (f) For forged sections 127 mm (5 in.) and over, the tensile strength shall be 485 MPa (70 ksi). (g) For information only, not a basis for acceptance or rejection

Table 10 (continued)

Product form(a)	Condition	Tensile strength MPa	Tensile strength ksi	0.2% yield strength MPa	0.2% yield strength ksi	Elonga-tion, %	Reduction in area, %	Hardness, HRB	ASTM specification
Type 308 (UNS S30800)									
B, F	Hot finished and annealed	515	75	205	30	40	50	...	A 276, A 473
B	Cold finished(b) and annealed	620	90	310	45	30	40	...	A 276
B	Cold finished(c) and annealed	515	75	205	30	30	40	...	A 276
W	Annealed	515	75	205	30	35(d)	50(d)	...	A 580
W	Cold finished	620	90	310	45	30(d)	40	...	A 580
P, Sh, St	Annealed	515	75	205	30	40	...	88 max	A 167
Types 309 (UNS S30900), 309S (UNS S30908), 310 (UNS S31000) and 310S (UNS S31008)									
B, F	Hot finished and annealed	515	75	205	30	40	50	...	A 276, A 473
B	Cold finished(b) and annealed	620	90	310	45	30	40	...	A 276
B	Cold finished(c) and annealed	515	75	205	30	30	40	...	A 276
W	Annealed	515	75	205	30	35(d)	50(d)	...	A 580
W	Cold finished	620	90	310	45	30(d)	40	...	A 580
P, Sh, St	Annealed	515	75	205	30	40	...	95 max	A 167
310Cb (UNS S31040)									
P, Sh, St	Annealed	515	75	205	30	40	...	95	A 167, A 240
B, Shapes	Hot finished and annealed	515	75	205	30	40	50	...	A 276
B, Shapes	Cold finished(b) and annealed	620	90	310	45	30	40	...	A 276
B, Shapes	Cold finished(c) and annealed	515	75	205	30	30	40	...	A 276
W	Annealed	515	75	205	30	35(d)	50(d)	...	A 580
W	Cold finished	620	90	310	45	30(d)	40	...	A 580
Type 314 (UNS S31400)									
B, F	Hot finished and annealed	515	75	205	30	40	50	...	A 276, A 473
B	Cold finished(b) and annealed	620	90	310	45	30	40	...	A 276
B	Cold finished(c) and annealed	515	75	205	30	30	40	...	A 276
W	Annealed	515	75	205	30	35(d)	50(d)	...	A 580
W	Cold finished	620	90	310	45	30(d)	40	...	A 580
Type 316 (UNS S31600)									
B, F(f)	Hot finished and annealed	515	75	205	30	40	50	...	A 276, A 473
B	Cold finished(b) and annealed	620	90	310	45	30	40	...	A 276
B	Cold finished(c) and annealed	515	75	205	30	30	40	...	A 276
W	Annealed	515	75	205	30	35(d)	50(d)	...	...
W	Cold finished	620	90	310	45	40(d)	40	...	A 580
P, Sh, St	Annealed	515	75	205	30	40	...	95 max	A 167, A 240
Type 316L (UNS S31603)									
F	Annealed	450	65	170	25	40	50	...	A 473
B	Hot finished and annealed	480	70	170	25	40	50	...	A 276
B	Cold finished(b) and annealed	620	90	310	45	30	40	...	A 276
B	Cold finished(c) and annealed	480	70	170	25	30	40	...	A 276
W	Annealed	480	70	170	25	35(d)	50(d)	...	A 580
W	Cold finished	620	90	310	45	30(d)	40	...	A 580
P, Sh, St	Annealed	485	70	170	25	40	...	95 max	A 167, A 240
Type 316Cb (UNS S31640)									
P, Sh, St	Annealed	515	75	205	30	30	...	95	A 167, A 240
B, Shapes	Hot finished and annealed	515	75	205	30	40	50	...	A 276
B, Shapes	Cold finished(b) and annealed	620	90	310	45	30	40	...	A 276
B, Shapes	Cold finished(c) and annealed	515	75	205	30	30	40	...	A 276
W	Annealed	515	75	205	30	35(d)	50(d)	...	A 580
W	Cold finished	620	90	310	45	30(d)	40	...	A 580
Type 317 (UNS S31700)									
B, F	Hot finished and annealed	515	75	205	30	40	50	...	A 276, A 473
B	Cold finished(b) and annealed	620	90	310	45	30	40	...	A 276
B	Cold finished(c) and annealed	515	75	205	30	30	40	...	A 276
W	Annealed	515	75	205	30	35(d)	50(d)	...	A 580
W	Cold finished	620	90	310	45	30(d)	40	...	A 580
P, Sh, St	Annealed	515	75	205	30	35	...	95 max	A 167, A 240
Type 317L (UNS S31703)									
B	Annealed	585(g)	85(g)	240(g)	35(g)	55(g)	65(g)	85 max(g)	...
P, Sh, St	Annealed	515	75	205	30	40	...	95 max	A 167
Type 317LM (UNS S31725)									
B, P	Annealed	515	75	205	30	40	...	...	A 276
P, Sh, St	Annealed	515	75	205	30	40	...	96 max	A 167

(continued)

(a) B, bar; F, forgings; P, plate; Pi, pipe; Sh, sheet; St, strip; T, tube; W, wire. (b) Up to 13 mm (0.5 in.) thick. (c) Over 13 mm (0.5 in.) thick. (d) For wire 3.96 mm (5/32 in.) and under, elongation and reduction in area shall be 25 and 40%, respectively. (e) 4 mm (0.156 in.) in diameter and over. (f) For forged sections 127 mm (5 in.) and over, the tensile strength shall be 485 MPa (70 ksi). (g) For information only, not a basis for acceptance or rejection

Table 10 (continued)

Product form(a)	Condition	Tensile strength MPa	ksi	0.2% yield strength MPa	ksi	Elonga- tion, %	Reduction in area, %	Hardness, HRB	ASTM specification
Types 321 (UNS S32100) and 321H (UNS 32109)									
B, F	Hot finished and annealed	515	75	205	30	40	50	...	A 276, A 473
B	Cold finished(b) and annealed	620	90	310	45	30	40	...	A 276
B	Cold finished(c) and annealed	515	75	205	30	30	40	...	A 276
W	Annealed	515	75	205	30	35(d)	50(d)	...	A 580
W	Cold finished	620	90	310	45	30(d)	40	...	A 580
P, Sh, St	Annealed	515	75	205	30	40	...	95 max	A 167, A 240
Types 347 (UNS S34700) and 348 (UNS S34800)									
B, F	Hot finished and annealed	515	75	205	30	40	50	...	A 276, A 473
B	Cold finished(b) and annealed	620	90	310	45	30	40	...	A 276
B	Cold finished(c) and annealed	515	75	205	30	30	40	...	A 276
W	Annealed	515	75	205	30	35(d)	50(d)	...	A 580
W	Cold finished	620	90	310	45	30(d)	40	...	A 580
P, Sh, St	Annealed	515	75	205	30	40	...	92 max	A 167, A 240
18-18-2 (UNS S38100)									
P, Sh, St	Annealed	515	75	205	30	40	...	95 max	A 167, A 240
Type 384 (UNS S38400)									
W(e)	Annealed	550	80	...	...	...	...	...	A 493
W(e)	Lightly drafted	585	85	...	...	...	...	...	A 493
20Cb-3 (UNS N08020), 20Mo-4 (UNS N08024), and 20Mo-6 (UNS N08026)									
B, W	Annealed	550	80	240	35	30	50	...	B 473
Shapes	Annealed	550	80	240	35	15	50	...	B 473
B, W	Annealed and strain hardened	620	90	415	60	15	40	...	B 473
W	Annealed and cold finished	620-830	90-120	...	...	...	...	...	B 473
P, Sh, St	Annealed	550	80	240	35	30	...	95 max	B 463
Pi, T	Annealed	550	80	240	35	30	...	...	B 464, B 468, B 474, B 729
Sanicro 28 (UNS N08028)									
P, Sh, St	Annealed	500	73	215	31	40	...	70-90(g)	B 709
Seamless Tube	Annealed	500	73	215	31	40	...	...	B 668
Type 330 (UNS N08330)									
B	Annealed	485	70	210	30	30	...	...	B 511
P, Sh, St	Annealed	485	70	210	30	30	...	70-90(g)	B 536
Pi	Annealed	485	70	210	30	30	...	70-90(g)	B 535, B 546
AL-6X (UNS N08366)									
B, W	Annealed	515	75	210	30	30	...	...	B 691
P, Sh, St	Annealed	515	75	240	35	30	...	95 max	B 688
Pi, T	Annealed	515	75	210	30	30	...	...	B 675, B 676, B 690
Welded T	Cold worked	515	75	210	30	10	...	...	B 676
JS-700 (UNS N08700)									
B, W	Annealed	550	80	240	35	30	50	...	B 672
P, Sh, St	Annealed	550	80	240	35	30	...	75-90(g)	B 599
Type 332 (UNS N08800)									
Pi, T	Annealed	515	75	210	30	30	...	...	B 163, B 407, B 514, B 515
Seamless Pi, T	Hot finished	450	65	170	25	30	...	...	B 407
B	Hot worked	550	80	240	35	25	...	...	B 408
B	Annealed	515	75	210	30	30	...	...	B 408
P	Hot rolled	550	80	240	35	25	...	...	B 409
P, Sh, St	Annealed	515	75	210	30	30	...	...	B 409
Type 904L (UNS N08904)									
B	Annealed	490	71	220	31	35	...	...	B 649
W	Cold finished	620-830	90-120	...	...	...	...	...	B 649
Pi, T	Annealed	490	71	220	31	35	...	...	B 673, B 674, B 677
P, Sh, St	Annealed	490	71	220	31	35	...	70-90(g)	B 625

(a) B, bar; F, forgings; P, plate; Pi, pipe; Sh, sheet; St, strip; T, tube; W, wire. (b) Up to 13 mm (0.5 in.) thick. (c) Over 13 mm (0.5 in.) thick. (d) For wire 3.96 mm ($5/32$ in.) and under, elongation and reduction in area shall be 25 and 40%, respectively. (e) 4 mm (0.156 in.) in diameter and over. (f) For forged sections 127 mm (5 in.) and over, the tensile strength shall be 485 MPa (70 ksi). (g) For information only, not a basis for acceptance or rejection

strengthening mechanism. The effectiveness of this approach is demonstrated in the comparison of the stress-strain curves of types 301 and 304 stainless steels shown in Fig. 14. The much more stable type 304 does not strain harden nearly as much as the type 301 stainless steel.

The extent of strain-induced transformation of austenite to martensite is dependent on temperature strain rate, and strain, in addition to composition (Ref 18). Figure 15 shows the effect of temperature and strain on strain-induced marten- site formation in type 304 stainless steels. Large

Table 11 Minimum mechanical properties of high-nitrogen austenitic stainless steels

Product form(a)	Condition	Tensile strength		0.2% yield strength		Elongation, %	Reduction in area, %	Hardness, HRB	ASTM specification
		MPa	ksi	MPa	ksi				
Type 201 (UNS S20100)									
B	Annealed	515	75	275	40	40	45	...	A 276
P, Sh, St	Annealed	655	95	310	45	40	...	100 max	A 276, A 666
Sh, St	¼ hard	860	125	515	75	25	...	...	A 666
Sh, St	½ hard	1030	150	760	110	18	...	...	A 666
Sh, St	¾ hard	1210	175	930	135	12	...	...	A 666
Sh, St	Full hard	1280	185	965	140	9	...	...	A 666
Type 202 (UNS S20200)									
B	Annealed	515	75	275	40	40	45	...	A 276
P, Sh, St	Annealed	620	90	260	38	40	...	...	A 666
Sh, St	¼ hard	860	125	515	75	12	...	...	A 660
Type 205 (UNS S20500)									
B, P, Sh, St	Annealed	790	115	450	65	40	...	100 max	A 666
Nitronic 50 (UNS S20910)									
B	Annealed	690	100	380	55	35	55	...	A 276
W	Annealed	690	100	380	55	35	55	...	A 580
Sh, St	Annealed	725	105	415	60	30	...	100 max	A 240
P	Annealed	690	100	380	55	35	...	100 max	A 240
Cryogenic Tenelon (UNS S21460)									
B, P, Sh, St	Annealed	725	105	380	55	40		...	A 666
Types 216 (UNS S21600) and 216L (UNS S21603)									
Sh, St	Annealed	690	100	415	60	40	...	100 max	A 240
P	Annealed	620	90	345	50	40	...	100 max	A 240
Nitronic 40 (UNS S21900)									
B, W	Annealed	620	90	345	50	45	60	...	A 276, A 580
21-6-9 LC (XM-11) (UNS S21904)									
B, W, shapes	Annealed	620	90	345	50	45	60	...	A 276, A 580
Sh, St	Annealed	690	100	415	60	40	...	...	A 666
P	Annealed	620	90	345	50	45	...	...	A 666
Nitronic 33 (UNS S24000)									
B, W	Annealed	690	100	380	55	30	50	...	A 276, A 580
Sh, St	Annealed	690	100	415	60	40	...	100 max	A 240
P	Annealed	690	100	380	55	40	...	100 max	A 240
Nitronic 32 (UNS S24100)									
B, W	Annealed	690	100	380	55	30	50	...	A 276, A 580
Type 304N (UNS S30451)									
B	Annealed	550	80	240	35	30	...	...	A 276
P, Sh, St	Annealed	550	80	240	35	30	...	92 max	A 240
Type 340HN (UNS S30452)									
B	Annealed	620	90	345	50	30	50	...	A 276
Sh, St	Annealed	620	90	345	50	30	...	100 max	A 240
P	Annealed	585	85	275	40	30	...	100 max	A 240
Type 304LN (UNS 30453)									
B	Annealed	515	75	205	30	...	...	...	A 276
P, Sh, St	Annealed	515	75	205	30	40	...	92 max	A 167, A 240
253 MA (UNS S30815)									
P, Sh, St	Annealed	600	87	310	45	40	...	95 max	A 167, A 240
B, shapes	Annealed	600	87	310	45	40	50	...	A 276
254 SMO (UNS S31254)									
P, Sh, St	Annealed	650	94	300	44	35	...	96	A 167, A 240
B, shapes	Annealed	650	95	300	44	35	50	...	A 276
Type 316N (UNS S31651)									
B	Annealed	550	80	240	35	30	...	...	A 276
P, Sh, St	Annealed	550	80	240	35	35	...	95 max	A 240
17-14-4 LN (UNS S31726)									
P, Sh, St	Annealed	550	80	240	35	40	...	96	A 167, A 240
B, Shapes	Annealed	550	80	240	35	40	...	...	A 276
Type 317LN (UNS S31753)									
P, Sh, St	Annealed	550	80	240	35	40	...	95	A 167, A 240

(continued)

(a) B, bar; P, plate; Pi, pipe; Sh, sheet; St, strip; T, tube; W, wire

Table 11 (continued)

Product form(a)	Condition	Tensile strength		0.2% yield strength		Elongation, %	Reduction in area, %	Hardness, HRB	ASTM specification
		MPa	ksi	MPa	ksi				
AL 6XN (UNS N08367)									
B, W	Annealed	715	104	315	46	30	...	...	B691
P, Sh, St	Annealed	715	104	315	46	30	...	100	B688
Flanges, fittings, valves, and so on	Annealed	715	104	315	46	30	50	...	B462
Seamless Pi, T	Annealed	715	104	315	46	30	...	...	B690
Welded Pi	Annealed	715	104	315	46	30	...	...	B676
Welded T	Solution treated and annealed	715	104	315	46	30	...	...	B676
Welded T	Cold worked	...	...	...	...	10	...	...	B676
Cronifer 1925 hMO (UNS N08925)									
B, W	Annealed	600	87	300	43	40	...	...	B649
Seamless Pi, T	Annealed	600	87	300	43	40	...	...	B677
Welded Pi	Annealed	600	87	300	43	40	...	...	B673
Welded T	Annealed	600	87	300	43	40	...	...	B674

(a) B, bar; P, plate; Pi, pipe; Sh, sheet; St, strip; T, tube; W, wire

amounts of martensite form at low strains during low-temperature deformation, and the amount of strain-induced transformation becomes negligible above room temperature.

Properties and Applications

300-Series Steels. The yield strengths of austenitic stainless steels are rather modest and are comparable to those of mild steels. Typical minimum mechanical properties of annealed 300-series steels are yield strengths of 205 to 275 MPa (30 to 40 ksi), ultimate tensile strengths of 520 to 760 MPa (75 to 110 ksi), and elongations of 40 to 60%. Austenitic stainless steels cannot be hardened by heat treatment, but they do work harden rapidly. Therefore, high strength is possible in cold-worked forms, especially in drawn wire, in which a tensile strength of 1200 MPa (175 ksi) or higher is achievable. The heat of welding will soften a heat-affected zone in heavily cold-worked austenitic stainless steel. Minimum room-temperature properties of annealed and cold-worked austenitic stainless steels are given in Table 10.

Even the leanest austenitic stainless steels (such as types 302 and 304, which can be considered the base alloys of the austenitic stainless steels) offer general corrosion resistance in the atmosphere, in many aqueous media, in the presence of foods, and in oxidizing acids such as nitric acid. Types 321 and 347 are essentially type 304 with additions of either titanium or niobium, respectively, which stabilize carbides against sensitization.

The addition of molybdenum in type 316L provides pitting resistance in phosphoric and acetic acids and dilute chloride solutions, as well as corrosion resistance in sulfurous acid (H_2SO_3). An even higher molybdenum content, as in type 317L (3%), and even richer alloys further enhance pitting resistance.

Nitrogen is added to enhance strength at room temperature and, especially, at cryogenic temperatures (as in type 304LN, for example). Nitrogen is also added to reduce the rate of chromium carbide precipitation and, therefore, the susceptibility to sensitization. Nitrogen is also added to molybdenum-containing alloys to increase resis-

tance to chloride-induced pitting and crevice corrosion. Minimum room-temperature properties of nitrogen-bearing alloys are given in Table 11.

Higher amounts of chromium and/or nickel are used to enhance high-temperature oxidation resistance (as in types 309, 310, and 330, for example). Copper and nickel can be added to enhance resistance to reducing acids, such as sulfuric acid (type 320). Nickel and molybdenum, when present in sufficient amounts, promote resistance to chloride-induced stress-corrosion cracking.

Other Austenitic Stainless Steels. In addition to the wrought austenitic stainless steel containing roughly 18% Cr and 8% Ni, several other groups of austenitic stainless steels are available for specific applications or processing requirements. Each of the wrought austenitic stainless steels has a counterpart cast alloy with a specific cast alloy designation. For example, CF-3, CF-8, CF-3M, and CF-8M correspond to the wrought types 304L, 304, 316L, and 316, respectively. The cast austenitic stainless steels are designed for good castability, and therefore the composition ranges may vary from those of their counterpart wrought steels. In particular, the chromium and silicon contents are higher and the nickel contents are lower in cast alloys compared to wrought alloys.

Many cast heat-resisting grades of stainless steel also have austenitic structures. The cast heat-resisting grades have much higher chromium and nickel contents for scaling resistance and greater high-temperature strength compared to the 18Cr-8Ni types of stainless steel. Again there are counterpart wrought and cast grades of heat-resisting stainless steels (for example, types 309 and 310, and HH and HK, respectively). There are, however, many other cast grades of heat-resistant alloys, and these alloys have much higher carbon contents (0.20 to 0.75%) than do the wrought grades. Thus alloy carbides, which contribute substantially to creep resistance, are an important component of the microstructure of the cast austenitic high-temperature alloys. The heat-resistant austenitic stainless steels are used at tem-

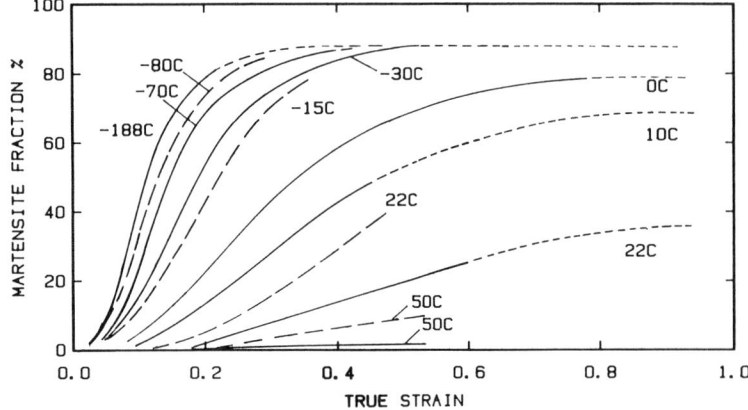

Fig. 15 Strain-induced martensite formation in austenitic stainless steels as a function of strain at various temperatures (Ref 19). Solid lines are original data of Angel (Ref 15), dashed lines are data of Hecker et al. (Ref 20), and dotted extrapolations are from Olson's analysis (Ref 21).

Table 12 Design stress (ksi), ASME Boiler and Pressure Vessel Code, Section VIII, Division 1 for plate(a)

UNS No.	Grade	100	200	300	400	500	600	650	700	750	800
S31254	254 SMO	23.5	23.5	21.4	19.9	18.5	17.9	17.7	17.5	17.3	...
	254 SMO(b)	23.5	23.5	22.4	21.3	20.5	20.1	19.9	19.9	19.8	...
N08366	AL-6X	18.8	18.8	15.6	...	...	...	...	...	...	...
N08367	Al-6XN(b)	...	26.0	24.3	22.7	20.9	19.9	19.3	19.3	18.7	18.4
N08925	1925 hMo	...	21.7	20.9	19.6	18.3	17.3	16.9	16.9	16.9	16.9
N08026	20Mo-6	20.0	20.0	18.9	17.5	16.3	15.3	14.9	14.6	14.2	13.9
	20Mo-6(b)	20.0	20.0	19.6	19.2	18.5	18.1	17.8	17.5	17.3	17.0
S30451	Type 304N	20.0	19.1	16.7	15.0	13.9	13.2	13.0	12.7	12.5	12.3
	Type 304N(b)	20.0	20.0	19.0	18.3	17.8	17.4	17.3	17.1	16.9	16.6
S31603	Type 316L	16.7	14.1	12.7	11.7	10.9	10.4	10.2	10.0	9.8	9.6
	Type 316L(b)	16.7	16.7	16.0	15.6	14.8	14.0	13.8	13.5	13.2	13.0
N08904	Alloy 904L	17.8	16.7	15.1	13.8	12.7	12.0	11.7	11.4	...	...

(a) ASME Code Tables are published in English units only. (b) The higher stress values (included in entire lines of data) were established at temperatures where the short-time tensile properties govern to permit the use of these alloys where slightly greater deformation is acceptable due to the relatively low yield strengths of these materials. These higher stress values exceed 67% but do not exceed 90% of the yield strength at temperature. Source: Ref 22

Table 13 Composition and pitting resistance equivalent values of selected wrought duplex stainless steels

UNS number	C	Mn	S	P	Si	Cr	Ni	Mo	N₂	Other	PRE range(b)
S31200	0.03	2.00	0.03	0.045	1.00	24.0-26.0	5.5-6.5	1.2-2.0	0.14-0.20	...	30.2-35.8
S31260	0.03	1.00	0.030	0.030	0.75	24.0-26.0	5.5-7.5	2.5-3.5	0.10-0.30	0.10-0.50 W, 0.20-0.80 Cu	33.9-42.4
S31500	0.03	1.2-2.0	0.03	0.03	1.4-2.0	18.0-19.0	4.25-5.25	2.5-3.0	0.05-0.10	...	27.1-30.5
S31803	0.03	2.00	0.02	0.03	1.00	21.0-23.0	4.5-6.5	2.5-3.5	0.08-0.20	...	30.5-37.8
S32304	0.03	2.5	0.04	0.04	1.0	21.5-24.5	3.0-5.5	0.05-0.60	0.05-0.20	0.05-0.60 Cu	22.5-29.7
S32550	0.03	1.5	0.03	0.04	1.0	24.0-27.0	4.5-6.5	2.9-3.9	0.10-0.25	1.5-2.5 Cu	35.2-43.9
S32750	0.03	1.2	0.02	0.035	1.0	24.0-26.0	6.0-8.0	3.0-5.0	0.24-0.32	0.5 Cu	37.7-47.6
S32760	0.03	1.0	0.01	0.03	1.0	24.0-26.0	6.0-8.0	3.0-4.0	0.30	0.5-1.0 Cu, 0.5-1.0 W	40(c)
S32900	0.06	1.00	0.03	0.04	0.75	23.0-28.0	2.5-5.0	1.0-2.0	(d)	...	26.3-34.6
S32950	0.03	2.00	0.01	0.035	0.60	26.0-29.0	3.5-5.2	1.0-2.5	0.15-0.35	...	...

(a) Single values are maximum. (b) PRE = %Cr + 3.3(%Mo) + 16(%N). (c) Minimum value. (d) Not specified

Table 14 Composition and pitting resistance equivalent values for selected commercial duplex stainless steels

Steel producer	Grade	Cr	Ni	Mo	N	Cu	Other	Typical PRE value	Applicable UNS No.
Fe-23Cr-4Ni-0.1N									
Avesta	2304	23	4	...	0.10	...	...	25	S32304
CLI	UR 35 N	23	4	...	0.12	...	...	25	S32304
Sandvik	SAF 2304	23	4	...	0.10	...	...	25	S32304
Fe-22Cr-5.5Ni-3Mo-0.15N									
Allegheny Ludlum	AL 2205	22	5.5	3.0	0.16	...	...	33-35	S31803
Avesta	2205	22	5.5	3.0	0.16	...	...	33-35	S31803
Bohler	A 903	22	5.5	3.0	0.16	...	...	33-35	S31803
CLI	UR 45 N	22	5.5	3.0	0.16	...	...	33-35	S31803
Knupp	Falc 223	22	5.5	3.0	0.16	...	...	33-35	S31803
Mannesmann	AF22	22	5.5	3.0	0.16	...	...	33-35	S31803
Nippon Kokan	NKCr22	22	5.5	3.0	0.16	...	...	33-35	S31803
Sandvik	SAF 2205	22	5.5	3.0	0.16	...	...	33-35	S31803
Sumitomo	SM22Cr	22	5.5	3.0	0.16	...	...	33-35	S31803
Thyssen	Remanit 4462	22	5.5	3.0	0.16	...	...	33-35	S31803
Valourec	VS22	22	5.5	3.0	0.16	...	...	33-35	S31803
British Steel	Hyresist 22/5	22	5.5	3.0	0.16	...	...	33-35	S31803
Fe-25Cr-5Ni-2.5Mo-0.17N-Cu									
Bohler	A905	25.5	3.7	2.3	0.37	...	5.8 Mn	39	...
Carpenter	7-Mo PLUS	27.5	4.5	1.5	0.25	...	...	37	...
CLI	UR 47N	25	7	3.0	0.16	0.2	...	38	S31260
CLI	UR 52N	25	7	3.0	0.16	1.5	...	38	S32550
Langley Alloys	Ferralium 255	26	5.5	3.3	0.17	2.0	...	39	S32550
Mather and Platt	Zeron 25	25	4	2.5	0.15	...	...	36	...
Sumitomo	DP-3	25	6.5	3.0	0.2	0.5	0.3 W	38	...
Fe-25Cr-7Ni-3.5Mo-0.25N-Cu-W									
Krupp-VDM	Falc 100	25	7	3.5	0.25	0.7	0.7 W	41	S32760
Avesta	2507	25	7	4	0.28	...	...	43	S32750
Sandvik	SAF 2507	25	7	4	0.28	...	...	43	S32750
Weir Materials Ltd.	Zeron 100	25	6.5	3.7	0.25	0.7	0.7 W	41	S32760
CLI	UR 52N +	25	6.5	3.7	0.24	1.6	...	41	S32550

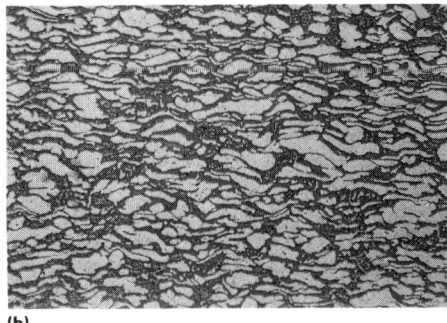
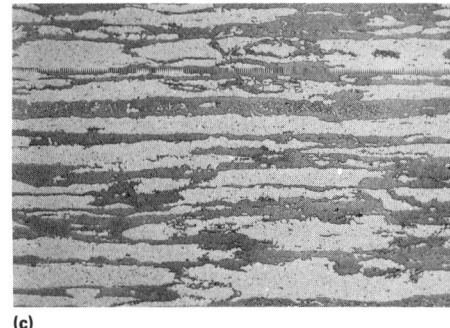

(a) **(b)** **(c)**

Fig. 16 Effect of orientation plane on the microstructure of Fe-22Cr-5.5Ni-3Mo-0.15N wrought duplex stainless steel base material electrolytically etched in 40% NaOH. (a) Parallel to rolling direction. (b) Transverse to rolling direction. (c) Plan view. 100×

peratures as high as 1100 °C (2012 °F), sometimes in very aggressive gaseous environments, and are expected to provide many years of service. Temperature-induced microstructural changes, creep-rupture mechanisms, scaling and oxidation, carburization, decarburization, and sulfidation are critical phenomena that affect the selection and performance of heat-resistant austenitic stainless steels. Properties of cast corrosion- and heat-resistant stainless steels are discussed in the articles "Metallurgy and Properties of Cast Stainless Steels" and "Corrosion of Cast Stainless Steels" in this Volume.

Powder metallurgy (P/M) materials manufactured from prealloyed austenitic or martensitic stainless steel powders are also produced. These P/M steels are primarily produced by pressing and sintering in a protective atmosphere. Higher-strength P/M stainless steels are produced by metal injection molding. Processing and properties of these materials are described in the articles "Powder Metallurgy Processing" and "Powder Metallurgy Stainless Steels" in this Volume.

Other groups of austenitic stainless steels include those in which substitutions for nickel are made. Type 200 austenitic stainless steels (Table 8) are alloyed with manganese and nitrogen, both austenite-stabilizing elements, to replace nickel. The 200-series austenitic stainless steels have properties and work-hardening characteristics similar to those of types 301 and 302 steels. Higher-strength austenitic stainless steels with high manganese and nitrogen contents and reduced nickel contents have also been developed. Several of these steels have the trademark Nitronic (Table 9) and are sometimes referred to in terms of their composition in nominal amounts of chromium, nickel, and manganese (for example, 21-6-9 in Table 9). The yield strengths of these steels range from 345 to 480 MPa (50 to 70 ksi), significantly above those attainable in annealed 300-series stainless steels.

Highly alloyed stainless steels have also been developed for specific corrosion applications. For example, iron-base nickel-chromium-molybdenum alloys have been developed for use in sulfuric acid environments. Examples include 20Cb-3 (Fe-35Ni-20Cr-3.0Mo) and JS-700 (Fe-25Cr-20Ni-2.0Mn-4.0Mo). In addition, "superausteni-tics" containing 6% Mo and nitrogen additions have been developed for improved resistance to chloride corrosion. Equipment fabricated of 6% Mo austenitics has included crystallizers, mixing vessels, pressure vessels, tanks, columns, evaporators, heat exchangers, piping, pumps, and valves. Seawater-cooled condensers, service water piping for nuclear power plants, and flue gas desulfurization for scrubbers' components (including ducting, absorbers, and internals) have also been fabricated from 6% Mo austenitics.

In addition to improved corrosion properties, the 6% Mo austenitics have higher strength levels than 300-series grades such as 316L. As shown in Table 12, these higher strength levels are reflected in the ASME Boiler and Pressure Vessel Code tables (Ref 22).

Duplex Stainless Steels

Duplex stainless steels have a mixed structure of bcc ferrite and fcc austenite. The exact amount of each phase is a function of composition and heat treatment. Most alloys are designed to contain about equal amounts of each phase in the annealed condition. The principal alloying elements are chromium and nickel, but nitrogen, molybdenum, copper, silicon, and tungsten may be added to control structural balance and to impart certain corrosion-resistance characteristics.

The corrosion resistance of duplex stainless steels is like that of austenitic stainless steels with similar alloying contents. However, duplex stainless steels possess higher tensile and yield strengths and improved resistance to SCC than their austenitic counterparts. The toughness of duplex stainless steels is between that of austenitic and ferritic stainless steels.

Tables 13 and 14 provide chemical compositions and pitting resistance equivalent (PRE) values for selected wrought duplex grades. The PRE value concept is described in the article "Atmospheric and Aqueous Corrosion" in this Volume.

Basic Metallurgy

Duplex ferritic-austenitic stainless steels solidify as essentially 100% ferrite. At high temperatures (of the order of 1300 °C, or 2370 °F), austenite nucleates and grows first at ferrite grain boundaries and later along preferred crystallographic directions within the ferrite grains. Diffusion of alloying elements must occur as the transformation of ferrite to austenite proceeds, with austenite-stabilizing elements (carbon, nickel, nitrogen, and copper) concentrating in the austenite and ferrite-stabilizing elements (chromium, molybdenum, and tungsten) concentrating in the ferrite. The extent of the transformation depends not only on the balance between austenite-stabilizing elements and ferrite-stabilizing elements in the alloy, but also on the time available for diffusion and on the actual diffusion of specific elements. It is possible to quench a duplex stainless steel from near the solidification temperature and to obtain nearly 100% ferrite at room temperature. Slow cooling, annealing, and hot working promote transformation of ferrite to austenite by promoting diffusion.

In a duplex ferritic-austenitic stainless steel, the optimum phase balance is usually approximately equal amounts of ferrite and austenite. Alloy compositions are usually adjusted to obtain this phase balance as the equilibrium structure at approximately 1040 °C (1900 °F) after hot working and/or annealing. Of the alloying elements that affect the phase balance, carbon is generally undesirable for reasons of corrosion resistance. All of the other elements are slow to diffuse substitutional alloy elements, except for nitrogen. The other alloy elements contribute to determining the equilibrium phase balance, but nitrogen is most important in determining the relative ease of achieving a near-equilibrium phase balance.

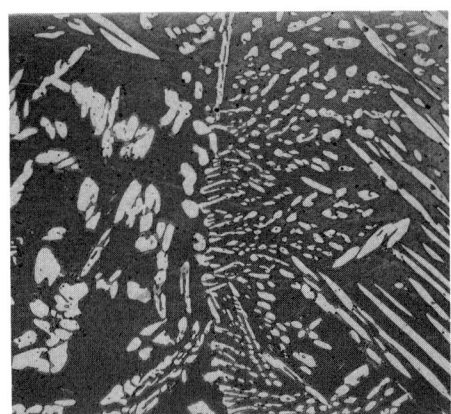

Fig. 17 Microstructure of cast Fe-22Cr-5.5Ni-3Mo-0.15N duplex stainless steel etched electrolytically in 40% NaOH. 25×

Table 15 Room-temperature mechanical properties of selected duplex stainless steels per ASTM A 790

UNS No.	Minimum yield strength MPa	Minimum yield strength ksi	Minimum tensile strength MPa	Minimum tensile strength ksi	Elongation (minimum), %	Hardness HB	Hardness HRC
S31200	450	65	690	100	25	280	...
S31500	440	64	630	92	30	290	30.5
S31803	450	65	620	90	25	290	30.5
S32304	400	58	600	87	25	290	30.5
S32550	550	80	760	110	15	297	31.5
S32750	550	80	800	116	15	310	32
S32760(a)	550	80	750	109	25	200-270	...
S32900	485	70	620	90	20	271	28
S32950	480	70	690	100	20	290	30.5

(a) Not listed in ASTM A 790

Table 16 ASTM standards incorporating wrought duplex stainless steels or their equivalents

ASTM standard	Product application	UNS numbers included
A 790/A 790M-91	Seamless and welded ferritic/austenitic stainless steel pipe	S31803, S31500, S32550, S31200, S31260, S32304, S32750, S32900, S32950
A 240-91a	Heat-resisting chromium and chromium-nickel stainless steel plate, sheet, and strip for pressure vessels	S31200, S31260, S31803, S32304, S32550, S32750, S32900, S32950
A 182/A 182M-90b	Forged or rolled alloy-steel pipe flanges, forged fittings, and valves and parts for high-temperature service	S31200, S31803
A 789/A 789M-90	Seamless and welded ferritic/austenitic stainless steel tubing for general service	S31803, S31500, S32550, S31200, S31260, S32304, S32750, S32900, S32950
A 276-91	Stainless and heat-resisting steel bars and shapes	S31803

When the earliest duplex stainless steels were developed (such as types 329 and CD-4MCu), nitrogen was not a deliberate alloying element. As a result, these first-generation alloys have lower mechanical properties and poorer corrosion resistance when compared with the more recently developed nitrogen-bearing grades.

Microstructure. Duplex stainless steels have approximately equal proportions of austenite and ferrite, with ferrite comprising the matrix. Representative wrought and cast microstructures are shown in Fig. 16 and 17. Both exhibit a ferritic matrix with austenite islands of various morphologies, but the cast microstructure (Fig. 17) is coarser and displays a different morphology of austenite than that observed in the wrought plate.

Properties and Applications

The specific advantages offered by duplex stainless steels over conventional 300-series stainless steels are strength (about twice that of austenitic stainless steels), chloride SCC resistance, and pitting corrosion resistance (Ref 23). These materials are used in the intermediate temperature range (about –60 to 300 °C, or –75 to 570 °F) where resistance to acids and aqueous chlorides is required.

Wrought duplex stainless steel development in the 1970s and 1980s was particularly rapid, although the steels had been available in a number of compositions for several decades, particularly in the form of castings (Ref 24). Early grades were alloyed with approximately 18% Cr, about 4 to 6% Ni, and sometimes with molybdenum. Current commercial grades contain between 22 and 26% Cr, 4 to 7% Ni, up to 4.5% Mo, and 0.7% Cu and W, and they are alloyed with 0.08 to 0.35% N (Ref 25). Continual modifications to the alloy compositions have been made to improve corrosion resistance, workability, and weldability. In particular, nitrogen additions have been effective in improving pitting corrosion resistance and weldability.

The current commercial duplex grades can be loosely divided into four generic types. Listed in order of increasing corrosion resistance, these alloy groups are:

- Fe-23Cr-4Ni-0.1N
- Fe-22Cr-5.5Ni-3Mo-0.15N
- Fe-25Cr-5Ni-2.5Mo-0.17N-Cu
- Fe-25Cr-7Ni-3.5Mo-0.25N-W-Cu

As with 18-8 austenitic stainless steels, duplex stainless steels are also frequently referred to by their chromium and nickel contents to describe the alloy class. The alloys listed above are described as 2304, 2205, 2505, and 2507, respectively. The last alloy class is also frequently termed "super" duplex stainless steel. A minimum pitting resistance equivalent value of 40 is often used to define the "super" duplex grades (see Tables 13 and 14).

Mechanical Properties. The high yield strength of duplex stainless steels offers designers the use of thin-wall material with adequate pressure-containing and load-bearing capacity. This can lead to major reductions in weight and weld-

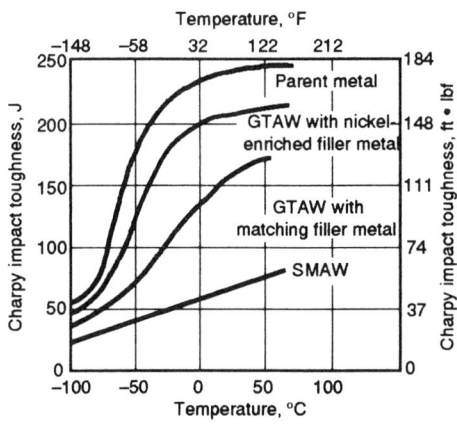

Fig. 18 Plot of Charpy impact toughness vs. temperature for Fe-22Cr-5.5Ni-3Mo-0.15N duplex stainless steel base metal and welds produced with gas-tungsten arc welding and shielded metal arc welding. Source: Ref 23

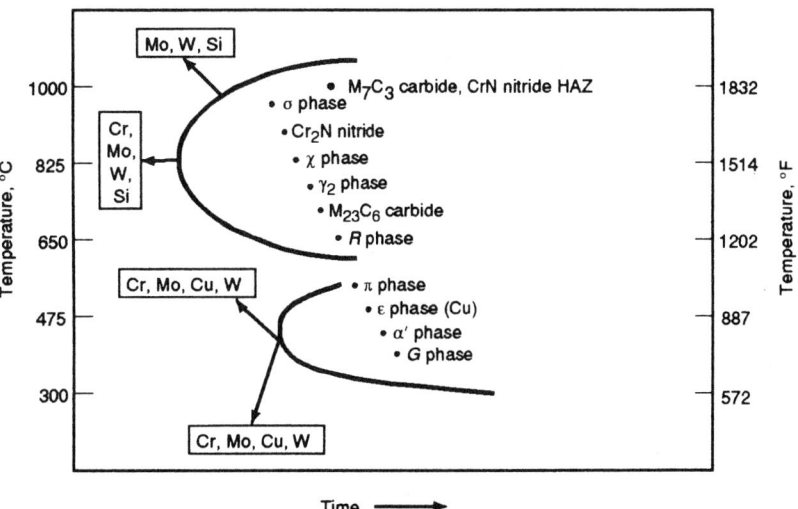

Fig. 19 Time-temperature transformation diagram showing effect of alloying elements on precipitation reactions in duplex stainless steels. Source: Ref 26

Table 17 Typical applications of duplex stainless steels

Grade(s)	Application
S31803, S32760, S32750, S32550	Tubing for heat exchangers in refineries, chemical industries, process industries, and other industries using water as a coolant; kraft paper digesters
All	Heat exchangers, chemical tankers, chemical reactor vessels, flue gas filters, acetic and phosphoric acid handling systems, oil and gas industry equipment (multiphase flow lines, downhole production tubulars, commonly cold worked)
S32304	Domestic water heaters and where pitting resistance is not of overriding importance
S32750, S32760, S32550	Pipe for seawater handling and firefighting systems, oil and gas separators, salt evaporation equipment, desalination plants, geothermal well heat exchangers, human body implants (S32550 may suffer slight pitting and crevice corrosion in seawater service)

ing time. The yield strength of the Fe-22Cr-5.5Ni-3Mo-0.15N grade is 450 MPa (65 ksi) minimum, which is double that of austenitic stainless steels and significantly higher than that of ferritic stainless steels. Hardness varies, depending on processing route and extent of cold working, but it generally averages about 260 HV 10 (25 HRC) for the Fe-22Cr-5.5Ni-3Mo-0.15N grade (Ref 23). Details of room-temperature tensile properties and hardnesses for each grade are given in Table 15. ASTM standards incorporating wrought duplex stainless steels are listed in Table 16.

The nonwelded base metal toughness down to approximately –100 °C (–150 °F) is good, but the weld metal and heat-affected zone are commonly much less tough and are frequently the limiting factor in duplex stainless steel application. The base metal will undergo a slight ductile-to-brittle transition (Fig. 18), but the change is not as marked as in other steels with bcc matrices. These alloys are not suitable for cryogenic applications.

Because of their high yield strengths, duplex stainless steels are more difficult to cold form than are the austenitic stainless steels. Further, because of the various high-temperature embrittlements that can occur in these alloys, forging and other hot-working processes require more care than do the same processes with austenitic stainless steels.

The high alloy content and the presence of a ferritic matrix render duplex stainless steels susceptible to embrittlement and loss of mechanical properties, particularly toughness, through prolonged exposure to elevated temperatures. This is caused by the precipitation of intermetallic phases, principally σ-phase, χ-phase, and η-phase (Laves phase) (Ref 26). For this reason, the upper temperature of application is typically approximately 280 °C (535 °F) for nonwelded material and 250 °C (480 °F) for welded structures (Ref 25). The more highly alloyed steels (for example, the Fe-25Cr-5Ni-2.5Mo-0.17N-Cu and Fe-25Cr-7Ni-3.5Mo-0.25N-Cu-W grades) are the most susceptible to the formation of these detrimental phases. Figure 19 shows the phases that can be formed in duplex stainless steels, the approximate temperature range over which they will develop, and the effects of alloying elements on the transformation kinetics. Additional information on the embrittling effect of intermetallic phases on duplex stainless steels can be found in the section "Embrittlement Mechanisms" in this article.

Applications. Duplex stainless steels have found widespread use in a range of industries, particularly the oil and gas, petrochemical, pulp and paper, and pollution control industries. They are commonly used in aqueous, chloride-containing environments and as replacements for austenitic stainless steels that have suffered from either chloride SCC or pitting during service (Ref 27). The more highly alloyed grades (that is, the "super" duplex stainless steels) are resistant to oxygenated or chlorinated seawater (Ref 28). The leaner alloy materials are not resistant to live seawater and will suffer from pitting. Several grades have been used for transportation of wet, CO_2-containing gas

where carbon would have suffered general corrosion (Ref 29). Table 17 gives a list of duplex grades and typical applications.

Precipitation-Hardening Stainless Steels

Precipitation-hardening stainless steels are chromium-nickel alloys containing PH elements such as copper, aluminum, or titanium. Precipitation-hardening stainless steels may be either austenitic or martensitic in the annealed condition. Those that are austenitic in the annealed condition are frequently transformable to martensite through conditioning heat treatments, sometimes with a subzero treatment. In most cases, these stainless steels attain high strength by precipitation hardening of the martensitic structure. Table 18 lists chemical compositions of PH stainless steels.

Basic Metallurgy

Precipitation-hardening stainless steels are iron-chromium-nickel alloys characterized by their high strengths obtained by precipitation hardening a martensitic or austenitic matrix with one or more of the following elements: copper, aluminum, titanium, niobium (columbium), and molybdenum. Precipitation-hardening steels can be grouped into three types—martensitic, semi-austenitic, and austenitic—based on their martensite start and finish temperatures (M_s and M_f) and resultant behavior upon cooling from a suitable solution-treatment temperature.

The martensitic PH steels, such as 17-4PH, have M_f just above room temperature, so they transform completely to martensite upon air cooling from the solution-treatment temperature and thus are martensitic in the annealed condition. Hardening is accomplished by a single aging treatment of 1 to 4 h at 480 to 620 °C (900 to 1150 °F).

The semiaustenitic PH steels, such as 17-7PH, have compositions that are balanced so that their

Table 18 Compositions of precipitation-hardening stainless steels

Alloy	UNS No.	C	Mn	Si	Cr	Ni	Mo	P	S	Other
Martensitic types										
PH13-8 Mo	S13800	0.05	0.10	0.10	12.25-13.25	7.5-8.5	2.0-2.5	0.01	0.008	0.90-1.35 Al; 0.01 N
15-5PH	S15500	0.07	1.00	1.00	14.0-15.5	3.5-5.5	...	0.04	0.03	2.5-4.5 Cu; 0.15-0.45 Nb
17-4PH	S17400	0.07	1.00	1.00	15.0-17.5	3.0-5.0	...	0.04	0.03	3.0-5.0 Cu; 0.15-0.45 Nb
Custom 450	S45000	0.05	1.00	1.00	14.0-16.0	5.0-7.0	0.5-1.0	0.03	0.03	1.25-1.75 Cu; 8 × %C min Nb
Custom 455	S45500	0.05	0.50	0.50	11.0-12.5	7.5-9.5	0.50	0.04	0.03	1.5-2.5 Cu; 0.8-1.4 Ti; 0.1-0.5 Nb
Semiaustenitic types										
PH15-7 Mo	S15700	0.09	1.00	1.00	14.0-16.0	6.50-7.75	2.0-3.0	0.04	0.04	0.75-1.50 Al
17-7PH	S17700	0.09	1.00	1.00	16.0-18.0	6.50-7.75	...	0.04	0.04	0.75-1.50 Al
AM-350	S35000	0.07-0.11	0.50-1.25	0.50	16.0-17.0	4.0-5.0	2.50-3.25	0.04	0.03	0.07-0.13 N
AM-355	S35500	0.10-0.15	0.50-1.25	0.50	15.0-16.0	4.0-5.0	2.50-3.25	0.04	0.03	0.07-0.13 N
Austenitic types										
A-286	S66286	0.08	2.00	1.00	13.5-16.0	24.0-27.0	1.0-1.5	0.025	0.025	1.90-2.35 Ti; 0.35 max Al; 0.10-0.50 V; 0.0030-0.0100 B
JBK-75(b)	...	0.015	0.05	0.02	14.5	29.5	1.25	0.006	0.002	2.15 Ti; 0.25 Al; 0.27 V; 0.0015 B

(a) Single values are maximum values unless otherwise indicated. (b) Typical values

Table 19 Precipitation-hardening phases in precipitation-hardening steels

Alloy	Precipitation-hardening phase	Ref
Martensitic types		
PH13-8 Mo	Coherent NiAl + fine γ particles	30
15-5PH	Face-centered cubic Cu-rich phase(a)	
17-4PH	Face-centered cubic Cu-rich phase	31, 32
Custom 450	Laves-type phase containing Fe, Nb, Mo	33, 34
Custom 455	Hexagonal close-packed ordered coherent Ni₃Ti	35
Semiaustenitic types		
17-7PH	Ordered body-centered cubic	36-38
PH15-7 Mo	β-NiAl + Ni₃Al	39, 40
AM-350	Cr₂N	41
AM-355	Cr₂N	41
Austenitic types		
A-286	Ni₃ (Al, Ti)	42, 43
JBK-75	Ni₃ (Al, Ti)	44

(a) Assumed to be the same precipitate as formed in 17-4PH

M_s are well below room temperature. Therefore, they are predominantly austenitic upon cooling from the solution-treatment temperature and are highly ductile and readily formed in that condition. After forming, transformation to martensite is accomplished by a conditioning treatment, which raises their M_s and M_f by precipitating carbon and alloying elements from solution. If a low conditioning temperature is used (730 to 760 °C,

or 1350 to 1400 °F), the M_f is raised to the vicinity of room temperature and transformation to martensite is complete upon cooling. If a high conditioning temperature (930 to 955 °C, or 1710 to 1750 °F) is used, less carbon is precipitated, the M_f remains below zero, and refrigeration is required to accomplish transformation to martensite. However, since the martensite produced in this manner contains more carbon, it is of higher strength than that produced by transformation at lower temperatures. Transformation may also be accomplished by cold working. In all cases, the martensite structure is then hardened by aging at a temperature in the range of 455 to 565 °C (850 to 1050 °F) for 1 to 3 h.

The austenitic PH steels, such as A-286, have M_s so low that they cannot be transformed to martensite. Strengthening is obtained by the precipitation of intermetallic compounds in an austenitic matrix. A detailed treatment of aging in PH stainless steels is beyond the scope of this article because many different PH phases are involved. Table 19, which was compiled from Ref 30 to 44, lists the phases produced in martensitic, semiaustenitic, and austenitic PH grades. However, certain aging characteristics are common to most PH stainless steels. For martensitic and semiaustenitic types, maximum strengthening is obtained by aging at 455 to 510 °C (850 to 950 °F). Higher temperatures increase ductility and toughness but reduce both the maximum strength level and the time required to attain it. Typical aging curves for selected martensitic and semiaustenitic PH steels aged at 480 °C (900 °F) and

510 °C (950 °F) are shown in Fig. 20(a) and (b), respectively (Ref 45-49)

For any alloy, a wide range of properties can be obtained by varying the heat-treatment practice. However, certain standard heat treatments for which mechanical property data are available are generally used. These are summarized in Table 20.

The standard aging times used for aging temperatures of 480 and 510 °C (900 and 950 °F) are such that most steels so heat treated are in the fully aged or slightly overaged condition, whichever gives the best combination of strength and ductility. PH 15-7 Mo stainless steel is unusual in that it has the best combination of strength and ductility when slightly underaged. Material aged at temperatures above 510 °C (950 °F) and, therefore, in a significantly overaged condition, is used when greater ductility or toughness is required. Precipitation in austenitic PH steels is markedly slower than in martensitic or semiaustenitic PH steels. For example, 16 h at 720 °C (1325 °F) is required to produce near-maximum hardening in A-286.

Properties and Applications

The PH stainless steels have yield strengths ranging from 515 to 1415 MPa (75 to 205 ksi), tensile strengths from 860 to 1520 MPa (125 to 220 ksi), and elongations from 1 to 25%. Minimum room-temperature properties for PH stainless steels are listed in Table 21. Because of their high strengths, most of the applications for PH stainless steels are in the aerospace and other high-technology industries.

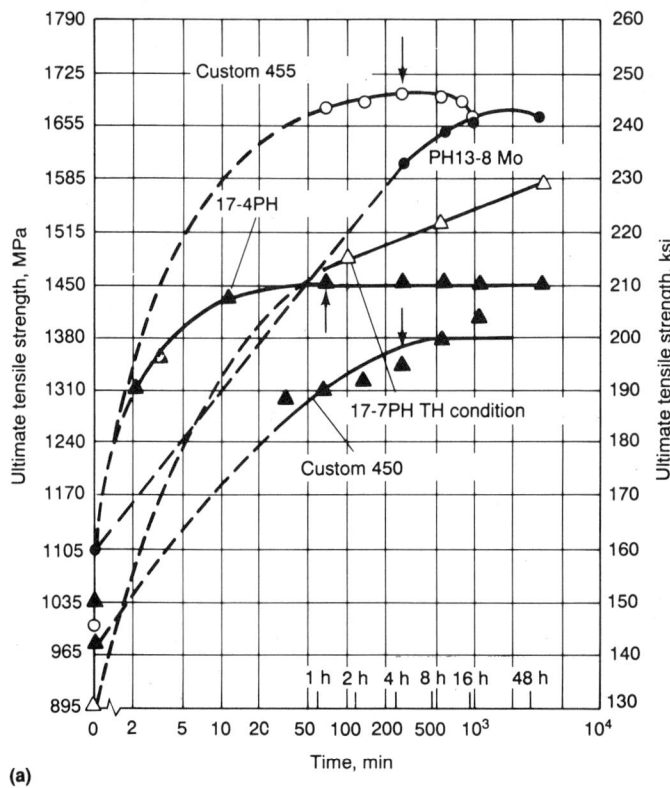

(a)

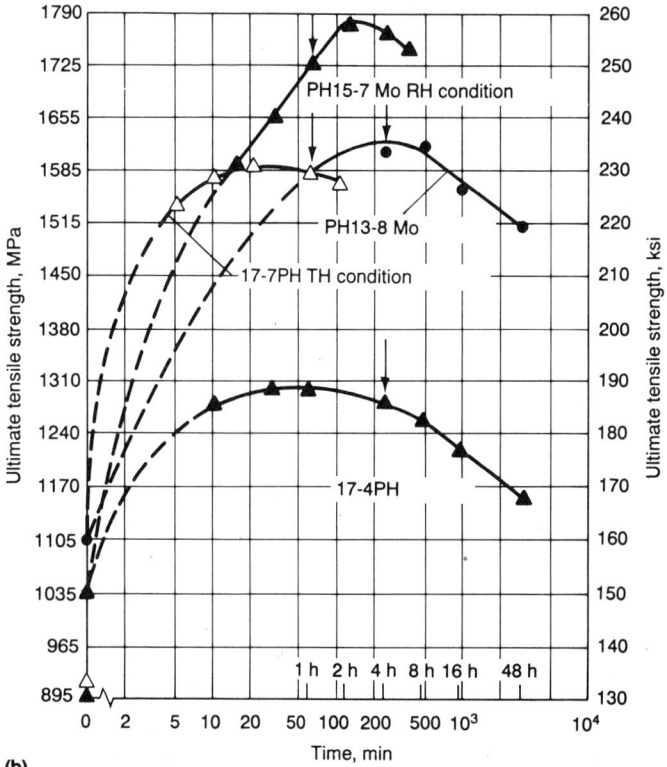

(b)

Fig. 20 Aging curves for selected precipitation-hardening stainless steels. (a) Aged at 480 °C (900 °F). (b) Aged at 510 °C (950 °F). Arrows indicate standard aging time for each steel. Source: Ref 45-49

Table 20 Heat treatment of precipitation-hardening stainless steels

Alloy	Condition code	Solution anneal	Conditioning and hardening treatment	Aging and/or tempering treatment
Martensitic types				
PH13-8 Mo	A	925 °C (1700 °F) for 15-30 min; oil or air cool (AC) below 15 °C (60 °F)	...	...
	RH950	925 °C (1700 °F) for 15-30 min; oil or AC below 15 °C (60 °F)	Refrigerate at –75 °C (–100 °F) for 8 h	Age 510 °C (950 °F) for 4 h; AC
	H950	925 °C (1700 °F) for 15-30 min; oil or AC below 15 °C (60 °F)	...	Age 510 °C (950 °F) for 4 h; AC
	H1000	925 °C (1700 °F) for 15-30 min; oil or AC below 15 °C (60 °F)	...	Age 535 °C (1000 °F) for 4 h; AC
	H1050	925 °C (1700 °F) for 15-30 min; oil or AC below 15 °C (60 °F)	...	Age 565 °C (1050 °F) for 4 h; AC
	H1100	925 °C (1700 °F) for 15-30 min; oil or AC below 15 °C (60 °F)	...	Age 595 °C (1100 °F) for 4 h; AC
	H1150	925 °C (1700 °F) for 15-30 min; oil or AC below 15 °C (60 °F)	...	Age 620 °C (1150 °F) for 4 h; AC
15-5PH	A	1035 °C (1900 °F) for 30 min; oil or AC below 30 °C (90 °F)	...	...
	H900	1035 °C (1900 °F) for 30 min; oil or AC below 30 °C (90 °F)	...	Age 480 °C (900 °F) for 1 h; AC
	H925	1035 °C (1900 °F) for 30 min; oil or AC below 30 °C (90 °F)	...	Age 495 °C (925 °F) for 4 h; AC
	H1025	1035 °C (1900 °F) for 30 min; oil or AC below 30 °C (90 °F)	...	Age 550 °C (1025 °F) for 4 h; AC
	H1075	1035 °C (1900 °F) for 30 min; oil or AC below 30 °C (90 °F)	...	Age 580 °C (1075 °F) for 4 h; AC
	H1150	1035 °C (1900 °F) for 30 min; oil or AC below 30 °C (90 °F)	...	Age 620 °C (1150 °F) for 4 h; AC
17-4PH	A	1035 °C (1900 °F) for 30 min; oil or AC below 30 °C (90 °F)	...	...
	H900	1035 °C (1900 °F) for 30 min; oil or AC below 30 °C (90 °F)	...	Age 480 °C (900 °F) for 1 h; AC
	H925	1035 °C (1900 °F) for 30 min; oil or AC below 30 °C (90 °F)	...	Age 495 °C (925 °F) for 4 h; AC
	H1025	1035 °C (1900 °F) for 30 min; oil or AC below 30 °C (90 °F)	...	Age 550 °C (1025 °F) for 4 h; AC
	H1075	1035 °C (1900 °F) for 30 min; oil or AC below 30 °C (90 °F)	...	Age 580 °C (1075 °F) for 4 h; AC
	H1100	1035 °C (1900 °F) for 30 min; oil or AC below 30 °C (90 °F)	...	Age 595 °C (1100 °F) for 4 h; AC
	H1150	1035 °C (1900 °F) for 30 min; oil or AC below 30 °C (90 °F)	...	Age 620 °C (1150 °F) for 4 h; AC
Custom 450	A	1035 °C (1900 °F) for 1 h; water quench	...	...
	H900	1035 °C (1900 °F) for 1 h; water quench	...	Age 480 °C (900 °F) for 4 h; AC
	H1000	1035 °C (1900 °F) for 1 h; water quench	...	Age 535 °C (1000 °F) for 4 h; AC
	H1150	1035 °C (1900 °F) for 1 h; water quench	...	Age 620 °C (1150 °F) for 4 h; AC
Custom 455	A	830 °C (1525 °F) for 1 h; water quench	...	...
	H900	830 °C (1525 °F) for 1 h; water quench	...	Age 480 °C (900 °F) for 4 h; AC
	H950	830 °C (1525 °F) for 1 h; water quench	...	Age 510 °C (950 °F) for 4 h; AC
	H1000	830 °C (1525 °F) for 1 h; water quench	...	Age 535 °C (1000 °F) for 4 h; AC
Semiaustenitic types				
17-7PH and PH15-7 Mo	A	1065 °C (1950 °F) for 30 min/25 mm (1 in.) of thickness; AC	...	...
	T	1065 °C (1950 °F) for 30 min/25 mm (1 in.) of thickness; AC	760 °C (1400 °F) 1½ h; AC to 15 °C (60 °F) for 30 min	...
	TH1050	1065 °C (1950 °F) for 30 min/25 mm (1 in.) of thickness; AC	760 °C (1400 °F) 1½ h; AC to 15 °C (60 °F) for 30 min	Age 565 °C (1050 °F) for 1½ h; AC
	A1750	1065 °C (1950 °F) for 30 min/25 mm (1 in.) of thickness; AC	955 °C (1750 °F) for 10 min; AC	...
	R100	1065 °C (1950 °F) for 30 min/25 mm (1 in.) of thickness; AC	955 °C (1750 °F) for 10 min; AC; Refrigerate at –75 °C (–100 °F) for 8 h	...
	RH950	1065 °C (1950 °F) for 30 min/25 mm (1 in.) of thickness; AC	955 °C (1750 °F) for 10 min; AC; Refrigerate at –75 °C (–100 °F) for 8 h	Age 510 °C (950 °F) for 1 h; AC
	C	1065 °C (1950 °F) for 30 min/25 mm (1 in.) of thickness; AC	Cold reduce	...
	CH900	1065 °C (1950 °F) for 30 min/25 mm (1 in.) of thickness; AC	Cold reduce	Age 480 °C (900 °F) for 1 h; AC
AM-350	H	1065 °C (1950 °F) for 90 min/25 mm (1 in.) of thickness; rapid cool	...	...
	L	1065 °C (1950 °F) for 90 min/25 mm (1 in.) of thickness; rapid cool	930 °C (1710 °F) for 90 min/25 mm (1 in.) of thickness; AC	...
	SCT850	1065 °C (1950 °F) for 90 min/25 mm (1 in.) of thickness; rapid cool	930 °C (1710 °F) for 90 min/25 mm (1 in.) of thickness; AC; refrigerate at –75 °C (–100 °F) for 3 h	Temper 455 °C (850 °F) for 3 h; AC
	SCT1000	1065 °C (1950 °F) for 90 min/25 mm (1 in.) of thickness; rapid cool	930 °C (1710 °F) for 90 min/25 mm (1 in.) of thickness; AC; refrigerate at –75 °C (–100 °F) for 3 h	Temper 535 °C (1000 °F) for 3 h; AC
AM-355	H	1025 °C (1875 °F) for 90 min/25 mm (1 in.) of thickness; rapid cool	...	...
	L	1025 °C (1875 °F) for 90 min/25 mm (1 in.) of thickness; rapid cool	930 °C (1710 °F) for 90 min/25 mm (1 in.) of thickness; AC(a)	...
	SCT850	1025 °C (1875 °F) for 90 min/25 mm (1 in.) of thickness; rapid cool	Refrigerate at –75 °C (–100 °F); 930 °C (1710 °F) for 90 min/25 mm (1 in.) of thickness; AC; refrigerate at –75 °C (–100 °F) for 3 h	Temper 455 °C (850 °F) for 3 h; AC
	SCT1000	1025 °C (1875 °F) for 90 min/25 mm (1 in.) of thickness; rapid cool	Refrigerate at –75 °C (–100 °F); 930 °C (1710 °F) for 90 min/25 mm (1 in.) of thickness; AC; refrigerate at –75 °C (–100 °F) for 3 h	Temper 535 °C (1000 °F) for 3 h; AC
Austenitic type				
A-286	ST1650	900 °C (1650 °F) for 2 h; oil or water quench	...	...
	ST1650A	900 °C (1650 °F) for 2 h; oil or water quench	...	Age 730 °C (1350 °F) for 16 h; AC
	ST1800	980 °C (1800 °F) for 1 h; oil or water quench	...	...
	ST1800A	980 °C (1800 °F) for 1 h; oil or water quench	...	Age 730 °C (1350 °F) for 16 h; AC

(a) For bars and forging billets, employ an equalizing treatment of 3 h at 745-800 °C (1375-1475 °F) + 3 h at 535-620 °C (1000-1150 °F) (condition E + OT) before the re-solution treatment at 930 °C (1710 °F).

Table 21 Minimum mechanical properties of precipitation-hardening stainless steels per specification noted

Alloy and product form(a)		Condition	Tensile strength MPa	ksi	Yield strength MPa	ksi	Elongation, %	Reduction in area, %	Hardness, HRC min	max	ASTM specification
Martensitic types											
PH13-8 Mo (UNS S13800)											
B, F		H950	1520	220	1410	205	10	45; 35(b)	45	...	A 564, A 705
B, F		H1000	1410	205	1310	190	10	50; 40(b)	43	...	A 564, A 705
B, F		H1025	1275	185	1210	175	11	50; 45(b)	41	...	A 564, A 705
B, F		H1050	1210	175	1140	165	12	50; 45(b)	40	...	A 564, A 705
B, F		H1100	1030	150	930	135	14	50	34	...	A 564, A 705
B, F		H1150	930	135	620	90	14	50	30	...	A 564, A 705
B, F		H1150M	860	125	585	85	16	55	26	...	A 564, A 705
P, Sh, St		H950	1520	220	1410	205	6-10(c)	...	45	...	A 693
P, Sh, St		H1000	1380	200	1310	190	6-10(c)	...	43	...	A 693
15-5PH (UNS S15500)											
B, F		H900	1310	190	1170	170	10; 6(b)	35; 15(b)	40	...	A 564, A 705
B, F		H925	1170	170	1070	155	10; 7(b)	38; 20(b)	38	...	A 564, A 705
B, F		H1025	1070	155	1000	145	12; 8(b)	45; 27(b)	35	...	A 564, A 705
B, F		H1075	1000	145	860	125	13; 9(b)	45; 28(b)	32	...	A 564, A 705
B, F		H1100	965	140	795	115	14; 10(b)	45; 29(b)	31	...	A 564, A 705
B, F		H1150	930	135	725	105	16; 11(b)	50; 30(b)	28	...	A 564, A 705
B, F		H1150M	795	115	515	75	18; 14(b)	55; 35(b)	24	...	A 564, A 705
P, Sh, St		H900	1310	190	1170	170	5-10(c)	...	40	48	A 693
P, Sh, St		H1100	965	140	790	115	5-14(c)	...	29	40	A 693
17-4PH (UNS S17400)											
B, F		H900(d)	1310	190	1170	170	10	40; 35(e)	40	...	A 564, A 705
B, F		H925(d)	1170	170	1070	155	10	44; 38(e)	38	...	A 564, A 705
B, F		H1025(d)	1070	155	1000	145	12	45	35	...	A 564, A 705
B, F		H1075(d)	1000	145	860	125	13	45	32	...	A 564, A 705
B, F		H1100(d)	965	140	795	115	14	45	31	...	A 564, A 705
B, F		H1150(d)	930	135	725	105	16	50	28	...	A 564, A 705
B, F		H1150M(d)	795	115	515	75	18	55	24	...	A 564, A 705
P, Sh, St		H900	1310	190	1170	170	5-10(c)	...	40	48	A 693
P, Sh, St		H1100	965	140	790	115	5-14(c)	...	29	40	A 693
Custom 450 (UNS S45000)											
B, shapes		Annealed	895(f)	130(f)	655	95	10	40	...	32	A 564(f)
F, shapes		Annealed	860(f)	125(f)	655	95	10	40	...	33	A 705(f)
B, F, shapes		H900	1240(g)	180(g)	1170	170	6; 10(b)	20; 40(b)	39	...	A 564(g), A 705(g)
B, F, shapes		H950	1170(g)	170(g)	1100	160	7; 10(b)	22; 40(b)	37	...	A 564(g), A 705(g)
B, F, shapes		H1000	1100	160(g)	1030	150	8; 12(b)	27; 45(b)	36	...	A 564(g), A 705
B, F, shapes		H1025	1030(g)	150(g)	965	140	12	45	34	...	A 564(g), A 705
B, F, shapes		H1050	1000(g)	145(g)	930	135	9; 12(b)	30; 45(b)	34	...	A 564(g), A 705
B, F, shapes		H1100	895(g)	130(g)	725	105	11; 16(b)	30; 50(b)	30	...	A 564(g), A 705
B, F, shapes		H1150	860(g)	125(g)	515	75	12-18(h)	35-55(h)	26	...	A 564(g), A 705
P, Sh, St		Annealed	895-1205	130-165	620-1035	90-150	4 min	...	25	33	A 693
P, Sh, St		H900	1240	180	1170	170	3-5(c)	...	40	...	A 693
P, Sh, St		H1000	1105	160	1035	150	5-7(c)	...	36	...	A 693
P, Sh, St		H1150	860	125	515	75	8-10(c)	...	26	...	A 693
Martensitic types											
Custom 455 (UNS S45500)											
B, F, shapes		H900(i)	1620	235	1520	220	8	30	47	...	A 564(g), A 705(g)
B, F, shapes		H950(i)	1520	220	1410	205	10	40	44	...	A 564(g), A 705(g)
B, F, shapes		H1000(i)	1410	205	1280	185	10	40	40	...	A 564(g), A 705(g)
P, Sh, St		H950	1530	222	1410	205	≤4	...	44	...	A 693
Semiaustenitic types											
PH15-7 Mo (UNS S15700)											
B, F		RH950	1380	200	1210	175	7	25	...	...	A 564, A 705
B, F		TH1050	1240	180	1100	160	8	25	...	...	A 564, A 705
P, Sh, St		Annealed	1035 max	150 max	450 max	65 max	25 min	...	...	...	A 693
P, Sh, St		RH950(d)	1550	225	1380	200	1-4(c)	...	45-46	...	A 693
P, Sh, St		TH1050(d)	1310	190	1170	170	2-5(c)	...	40	...	A 693
P, Sh, St		Cold rolled condition C	1380	200	1210	175	1	...	41	...	A 693
P, Sh, St		CH900	1650	240	1590	230	1	...	46	...	A 693
17-7PH (UNS S17700)											
B, F		RH950(d)	1275	185	1030	150	6	10	41	...	A 564, A 705
B, F		TH1050(d)	1170	170	965	140	6	25	38	...	A 564, A 705
P, Sh, St		RH950	1450(c)	210(c)	1310(c)	190(c)	1-6(c)	...	43(c)	44(c)	A 693
P, Sh, St		TH1050	1240(c)	180(c)	1030(c)	150(c)	3-7(c)	...	38	...	A 693
P, Sh, St		Cold rolled condition C	1380	200	1210	175	1	...	41	...	A 693
P, Sh, St		CH900	1650	240	1590	230	1	...	46	...	A 693
W		Cold drawn condition C	1400-2035(c)	203-295(c)	...	...	...	...	...	...	A 313
W		CH900	1585-2515(c)	230-365(c)	...	...	...	...	...	...	A 313

(continued)

(a) B, bar; F, forgings; P, plate; Sh, sheet; St, strip; W, wire. (b) Higher value is longitudinal; lower value is transverse. (c) Values vary with thickness or diameter. (d) Longitudinal properties only. (e) Higher values are for sizes up to and including 75 mm (3 in.); lower values are for sizes over 75 mm (3 in.) up to and including 200 mm (8 in.). (f) Tensile strengths of 860 to 140 MPa (125 to 165 ksi) for sizes up to 13 mm (½ in.). (g) Tensile strength only applicable up to sizes of 13 mm (½ in.). (h) Varies with section size and test direction. (i) Up to and including 150 mm (6 in.)

Table 21 (continued)

Alloy and product form(a)	Condition	Tensile strength		Yield strength		Elongation, %	Reduction in area, %	Hardness, HRC		ASTM specification
		MPa	ksi	MPa	ksi			min	max	
AM-350 (UNS S35000)										
P, Sh, St	Annealed	1380 max	200 max	585-620 max(c)	85-90 max(c)	8-12(c)	...	...	30	A 693
P, Sh, St	SCT850	1275	185	1030	150	2-8(c)	...	42	...	A 693
P, Sh, St	SCT1000	1140	165	1000	145	2-8(c)	...	36	...	A 693
AM-355 (UNS 35500)										
F	SCT1000	1170	170	1070	155	12	25	37	...	A 705
P, Sh, St	SCT850	1310	190	1140	165	10	...	...	...	A 693
P, Sh, St	SCT1000	1170	170	1030	150	12	...	37	...	A 693
Austenitic type										
A-286 (UNS S66286)										
B, F	ST 1650	724 max	105 max	...	...	...	...	...	201 HB	AMS No. 5734, 5737
B, F	ST 1650A	965	140	655	95	12	15	277 HB	363 HB	AMS No. 5734, 5737
B, F	ST 1800	724 max	105 max	...	...	...	...	...	201 HB	AMS No. 5731, 5732
B, F	ST 1800A	895	130	585	85	15	20	248 HB	341 HB	AMS No. 5731, 5732
P, Sh, St	ST 1800	724 max	105 max	...	...	10-25	...	...	90 HRB	AMS No. 5525, 5858
P, Sh, St	ST 1800A	896-965	125-140	655	95	4-15	...	24	35	AMS No. 5525, 5858

(a) B, bar; F, forgings; P, plate; Sh, sheet; St, strip; W, wire. (b) Higher value is longitudinal; lower value is transverse. (c) Values vary with thickness or diameter. (d) Longitudinal properties only. (e) Higher values are for sizes up to and including 75 mm (3 in.); lower values are for sizes over 75 mm (3 in.) up to and including 200 mm (8 in.). (f) Tensile strengths of 860 to 140 MPa (125 to 165 ksi) for sizes up to 13 mm (½ in.). (g) Tensile strength only applicable up to sizes of 13 mm (½ in.). (h) Varies with section size and test direction. (i) Up to and including 150 mm (6 in.).

Type 17-4PH (17Cr-4Ni-3Cu) is the prototype martensitic PH stainless steel. In the solution-annealed (martensitic) condition, its yield strength is already above 750 MPa (110 ksi). The PH phase is copper, which, after aging at 480 °C (900 °F), is so fine that it can only be detected with a high-powered electron microscope. A yield strength of more than 1200 MPa (170 ksi) is obtained after this aging treatment. Higher aging temperatures coarsen the precipitate and reduce the strength.

Type PH15-7Mo (15Cr-7Ni-2Mo-1Al) is an example of a semiaustenitic PH stainless steel. In the solution-annealed (austenitic) condition, its yield strength is only of the order of 380 MPa (55 ksi), which is not very different from that of an ordinary austenitic stainless steel. Heat treatment at 955 °C (1750 °F) precipitates carbides and destabilizes the austenite, which transforms to martensite upon subsequent cooling. Then, aging at 510 °C (950 °F) precipitates nickel-aluminum intermetallic compounds. The aged martensite can exhibit a strength of approximately 1500 MPa (220 ksi). Again, aging at a higher temperature coarsens the precipitates and softens the steel.

Type A-286 is the prototype austenitic PH stainless steel. Its high alloy content (15Cr-25Ni-1Mo-2Ti) provides higher corrosion resistance than that of the martensitic or semiaustenitic types. Furthermore, it contains no magnetic phases, which makes it suitable for use in high magnetic fields, such as those associated with superconducting magnets used for fusion energy research. Aging at about 730 °C (1350 °F) causes nickel-titanium intermetallic compound particles to precipitate, hardening the alloy. Its fully hardened yield strength (approximately 590 MPa, or 86 ksi), however, is considerably lower than that

available from the martensitic or semiaustenitic grades.

Product Forms

Stainless steels are available in the form of plate, sheet, strip, foil, bar, wire, semifinished products, and tubular products. Additional information on stainless steel product forms can be found in the *ASTM Book of Standards* and in Ref 2.

Plate

Plate is a flat-rolled or forged product more than 250 mm (10 in.) in width and at least 4.76 mm (0.1875 in.) in thickness. Stainless steel plate is produced in most of the standard grades. Exceptions include highly alloyed ferritic stainless steels, some of the martensitic stainless steels, and a few of the free-machining grades. Plate is usually produced by hot rolling from slabs that have been directly cast or rolled from ingots and that usually have been conditioned to improve plate surface. Some plate may be produced by direct rolling from ingot. This plate is referred to as *sheared plate* or *sheared mill plate* when rolled between horizontal rolls and trimmed on all edges, and as *universal plate* or *universal mill plate* when rolled between horizontal and vertical rolls and trimmed only on the ends. Universal plate is sometimes rolled between grooved rolls.

Stainless steel plate is generally produced in the annealed condition and is either blast cleaned or pickled. Blast cleaning is generally followed by further cleaning in appropriate acids to remove surface contaminants such as particles of steel

picked up from the mill rolls. Plate can be produced with mill edge and uncropped ends.

Sheet

Sheet is a flat-rolled product in coils or cut lengths at least 610 mm (24 in.) wide and less than 4.76 mm (0.1875 in.) thick. Stainless steel sheet is produced in nearly all types except the free-machining and certain martensitic grades. Sheet from the conventional grades is almost exclusively produced on continuous mills. Hand mill production is usually confined to alloys that cannot be produced economically on continuous mills, such as certain high-temperature alloys.

The steel is cast in ingots, and the ingots are rolled on a slabbing mill or a blooming mill into slabs or sheet bars. The slabs or sheet bars are then conditioned prior to being hot rolled on a finishing mill. Alternatively, the steel may be continuous cast directly into slabs that are ready for hot rolling on a finishing mill. The current trend worldwide is toward greater production from continuous cast slabs.

Sheet produced from slabs on continuous rolling mills is coiled directly off the mill. After they are descaled, these hot bands are cold rolled to the required thickness, and coils off the cold mill are either annealed and descaled or bright annealed. Belt grinding to remove surface defects is frequently required at hot bands or at an intermediate stage of processing. Full coils or lengths cut from coils may then be lightly cold rolled on either dull or bright rolls to produce the required finish. Sheet may be shipped in coils, or cut sheets may be produced by shearing lengths from a coil and flattening them by roller leveling or stretcher leveling.

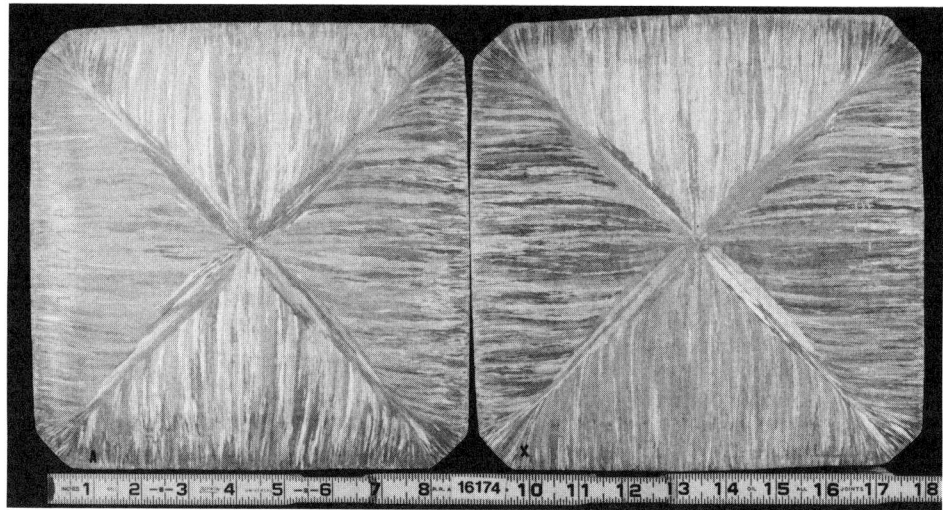

Fig. 21 As-cast macrostructure of a type 316 continuously cast billet. Courtesy of G.F. Vander Voort, Carpenter Technology Corp.

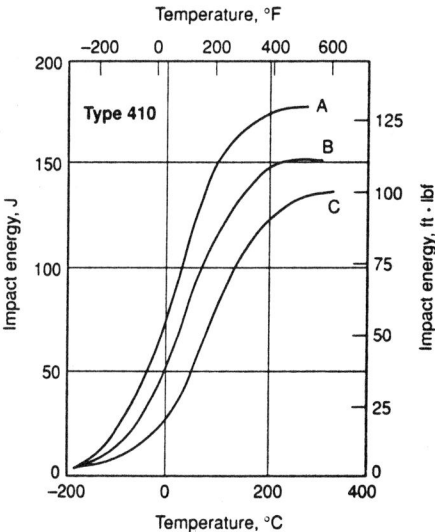

Fig. 23 Typical transition behavior of type 410 martensitic stainless steel. All data from Charpy V-notch tests. A represents material tempered at 790 °C (1450 °F); final hardness, 95 HRB. B represents material tempered at 665 °C (1225 °F); final hardness, 24 HRC. C represents material tempered at 595 °C (1100 °F); final hardness, 30 HRC.

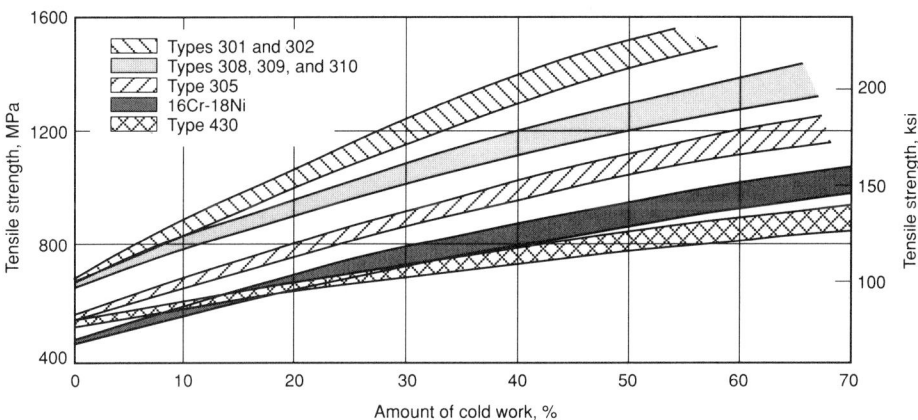

Fig. 22 Typical effect of cold rolling on the tensile strength of selected stainless steels

Sheet produced on hand mills from sheet bars is rolled in lengths and then annealed and descaled. It may be subjected to additional operations, including cold reduction, annealing, descaling, light cold rolling for finish, or flattening.

A specified minimum tensile strength, minimum yield strength, or hardness level higher than that normally obtained on sheet in the annealed condition, or a combination thereof, can be attained by controlled cold rolling.

Sheet made of chromium-nickel stainless steel (often type 301) or of chromium-nickel-manganese stainless steel (often type 201) is produced in the following cold-rolled tempers:

Temper	Minimum tensile strength		Minimum yield strength	
	MPa	ksi	MPa	ksi
¼ hard	860	125	515	75
½ hard	1035	150	760	110
¾ hard	1205	175	930	135
Full hard	1275	185	965	140

Strip

Strip is a flat-rolled product, in coils or cut lengths, less than 610 mm (24 in.) wide and 0.13 to 4.76 mm (0.005 to 0.1875 in.) thick. Cold-finished material 0.13 mm (0.005 in.) thick and less than 610 mm (24 in.) wide fits the definitions of both strip and foil and may be referred to by either term.

Cold-rolled stainless steel strip is manufactured from hot-rolled, annealed, and pickled strip (or from slit sheet) by rolling between polished rolls. Depending on the desired thickness, various numbers of cold-rolling passes through the mill are required for effecting the necessary reduction and securing the desired surface characteristics and mechanical properties.

Hot-rolled stainless steel strip is a semifinished product obtained by hot-rolling slabs or billets and is produced for conversion to finished strip by cold rolling.

Heat Treatment. Strip of all types of stainless steel is usually either annealed or annealed and skin passed, depending on requirements. When severe forming, bending, and drawing operations

are involved, it is recommended that such requirements be indicated so that the producer will have all the information necessary to supply the proper type and condition. When stretcher strains are objectionable in ferritic stainless steels such as type 430, they can be minimized by specifying a No. 2 finish. Cold-rolled strip in types 410, 414, 416, 420, 431, 440A, 440B, and 440C can be produced in the hardened-and-tempered condition.

Strip made of 300-series chromium-nickel stainless steel or of 200-series chromium-nickel-manganese stainless steel is produced in the same cold-rolled tempers in which sheet is produced.

For strip, edge condition is often important— more important than it usually is for sheet. Strip can be furnished with various edge specifications:

- Mill edge (as-produced, condition unspecified)
- No. 1 edge (edge rolled, rounded, or square)
- No. 3 edge (as-slit)
- No. 5 edge (square edge produced by rolling or filing after slitting)

Mill edge is the least expensive edge condition and is adequate for many purposes. No. 1 edge provides improved width tolerance over mill edge plus a cold-rolled edge condition; rounded edges are preferred for applications requiring the lowest degree of stress concentration at corners. No. 3 and No. 5 edges give progressively better width tolerance and squareness over No. 1 edge.

Foil

Foil is a flat-rolled product, in coil form, up to 0.13 mm (0.005 in.) thick and less than 610 mm (24 in.) wide. Foil is produced in slit widths with edge conditions corresponding to No. 3 and No. 5 edge conditions for strip.

Table 22   Room-temperature tensile strength of stainless steel spring wire

Diameter		Tensile strength	
mm	in.	MPa	ksi
Types 302 and 304			
≤0.23	≤0.009	2241-2448	325-355
>0.23-0.25	>0.009-0.010	2206-2413	320-350
>0.25-0.28	>0.010-0.011	2192-2399	318-348
>0.28-0.30	>0.011-0.012	2179-2385	316-346
>0.30-0.33	>0.012-0.013	2165-2372	314-344
>0.33-0.36	>0.013-0.014	2151-2358	312-342
>0.36-0.38	>0.014-0.015	2137-2344	310-340
>0.38-0.41	>0.015-0.016	2124-2330	308-338
>0.41-0.43	>0.016-0.017	2110-2317	306-336
>0.43-0.46	>0.017-0.018	2096-2303	304-334
>0.46-0.51	>0.018-0.020	2068-2275	300-330
>0.51-0.56	>0.020-0.022	2041-2248	296-326
>0.56-0.61	>0.022-0.024	2013-2220	292-322
>0.61-0.66	>0.024-0.026	2006-2206	291-320
>0.66-0.71	>0.026-0.028	1993-2192	289-318
>0.71-0.79	>0.028-0.031	1965-2172	285-315
>0.79-0.86	>0.031-0.034	1944-2137	282-310
>0.86-0.94	>0.034-0.037	1930-2124	280-308
>0.94-1.04	>0.037-0.041	1896-2096	275-304
>1.04-1.14	>0.041-0.045	1875-2068	272-300
>1.14-1.27	>0.045-0.050	1841-2034	267-295
>1.27-1.37	>0.050-0.054	1827-2020	265-293
>1.37-1.47	>0.054-0.058	1800-1993	261-289
>1.47-1.60	>0.058-0.063	1779-1965	258-285
>1.60-1.78	>0.063-0.070	1737-1937	252-281
>1.78-1.90	>0.070-0.075	1724-1917	250-278
>1.90-2.03	>0.075-0.080	1696-1896	246-275
>2.03-2.21	>0.080-0.087	1668-1868	242-271
>2.21-2.41	>0.087-0.095	1641-1848	238-268
>2.41-2.67	>0.095-0.105	1600-1806	232-262
>2.67-2.92	>0.105-0.115	1565-1772	227-257
>2.92-3.18	>0.115-0.125	1531-1744	222-253
>3.18-3.43	>0.125-0.135	1496-1710	217-248
>3.43-3.76	>0.135-0.148	1448-1662	210-241
>3.76-4.12	>0.148-0.162	1413-1620	205-235
>4.12-4.50	>0.162-0.177	1365-1572	198-228
>4.50-4.88	>0.177-0.192	1338-1551	194-225
>4.88-5.26	>0.192-0.207	1296-1517	188-220
>5.26-5.72	>0.207-0.225	1255-1475	182-214
>5.72-6.35	>0.225-0.250	1207-1413	175-205
>6.35-7.06	>0.250-0.278	1158-1365	168-198
>7.06-7.77	>0.278-0.306	1110-1324	161-192
>7.77-8.41	>0.306-0.331	1069-1282	155-186
>8.41-9.20	>0.331-0.362	1020-1241	148-180
>9.20-10.01	>0.362-0.394	979-1193	142-173
>10.01-11.12	>0.394-0.438	931-1138	135-165
>11.12-12.70	>0.438-0.500	862-1069	125-155
Types 305 and 316			
≤0.25	≤0.010	1689-1896	245-275
>0.25-0.38	>0.010-0.015	1655-1862	240-270
>0.38-1.04	>0.015-0.041	1620-1827	235-265
>1.04-1.19	>0.041-0.047	1586-1723	230-260
>1.19-1.37	>0.047-0.054	1551-1758	225-255
>1.37-1.58	>0.054-0.062	1517-1724	220-250
>1.58-1.85	>0.062-0.072	1482-1689	215-245
>1.85-2.03	>0.072-0.080	1448-1655	210-240
>2.03-2.34	>0.080-0.092	1413-1620	205-235
>2.34-2.67	>0.092-0.105	1379-1586	200-230
>2.67-3.05	>0.105-0.120	1344-1551	195-225
>3.05-3.76	>0.120-0.148	1276-1482	185-215
>3.76-4.22	>0.148-0.166	1241-1448	180-210
>4.22-4.50	>0.166-0.177	1172-1379	170-200
>4.50-5.26	>0.177-0.207	1103-1310	160-190
>5.26-5.72	>0.207-0.225	1069-1276	155-185
>5.72-6.35	>0.225-0.250	1034-1241	150-180
>6.35-7.92	>0.250-0.312	931-1138	135-165
>7.92-12.68	>0.312-0.499	793-1000	115-145
>12.68	>0.499	Consult producer	

Foil is made from types 201, 202, 301, 302, 304, 304L, 305, 316, 316L, 321, 347, 430, and 442, as well as from certain proprietary alloys.

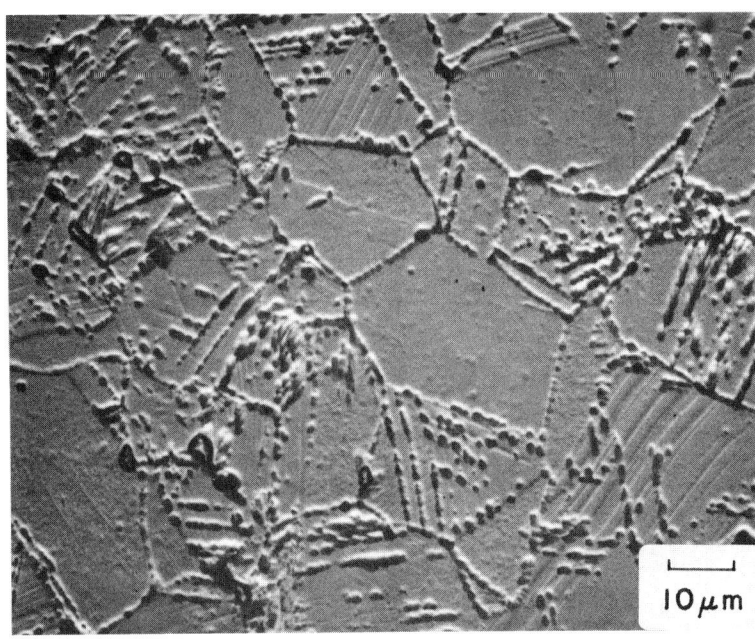

Fig. 24   Microstructure of type 304 stainless steel with chromium carbide precipitation at grain boundaries. ASTM A 262 Practice A oxalic acid etch. Scanning electron micrograph

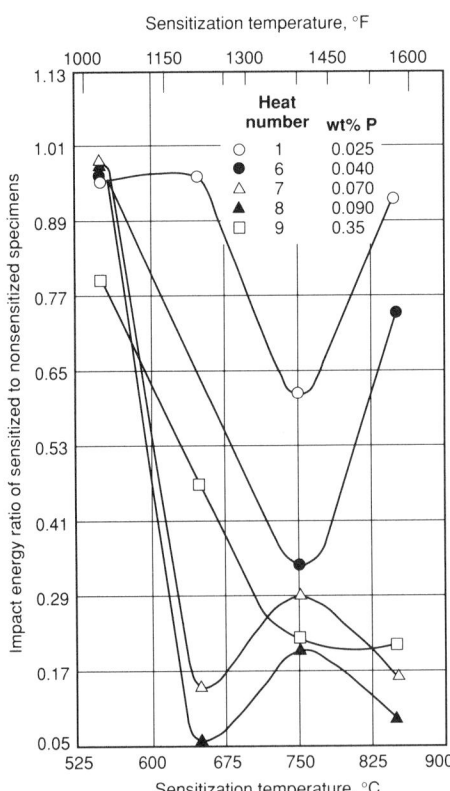

Fig. 25   Influence of phosphorus content and aging temperature on the relative loss in Charpy impact energy (tested using half-size specimens broken after cooling in liquid nitrogen) for sensitized type 304 stainless steel. Sensitization time, 5100 s. Source: Ref 88

The finishes, tolerances, and mechanical properties of foil differ from those of strip because of limitations associated with the way in which foil is manufactured. Nomenclature for finishes, and for width and thickness tolerances, vary among producers.

Finishes for foil are described by the finishing operations employed in their manufacture. However, each finish in itself is a category of finishes, with variations in appearance and smoothness that depend on composition, thickness, and method of manufacture. Chromium-nickel and chromium-nickel-manganese stainless steels have a characteristic appearance different from that of straight chromium types for corresponding finish designations.

Mechanical Properties. In general, mechanical properties of foil vary with thickness. Tensile strength is increased somewhat, and ductility is lowered, by a decrease in thickness.

Bar

Bar is a product supplied in straight lengths; it is either hot or cold finished and is available in various shapes, sizes, and surface finishes. This category includes small shapes whose dimensions do not exceed 127 mm (5 in.) and hot-rolled flat stock from 6.35 to 254 mm (0.25 to 10 in.), inclusive, in width and 3.18 mm (0.125 in.) and over in thickness.

Hot-finished bar is commonly produced by hot rolling, forging, or pressing ingots to blooms or billets of intermediate size, which are subsequently hot rolled, forged, or extruded to final dimensions. Whether rolling, forging, or extrusion is selected as the finishing method depends on several factors, including composition and final size.

Following hot rolling or forging, hot-finished bar may be subjected to various operations, including:

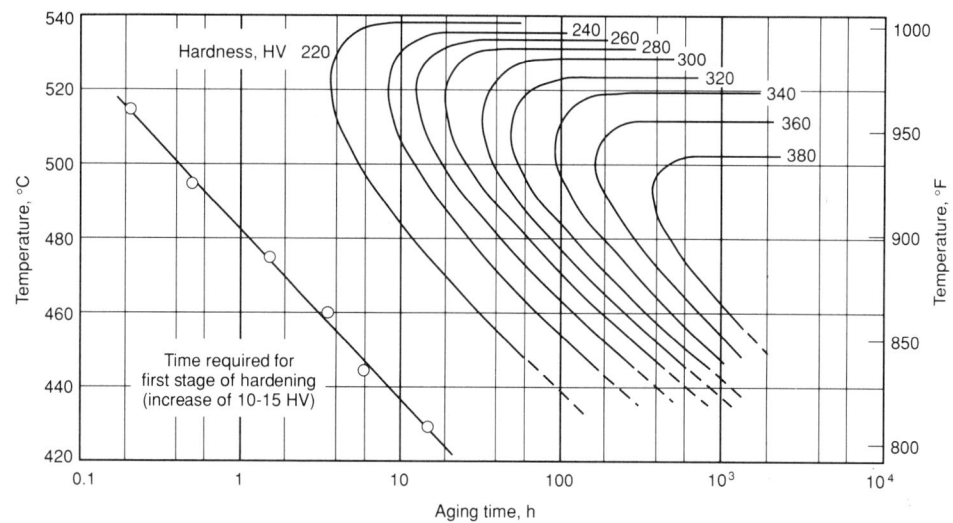

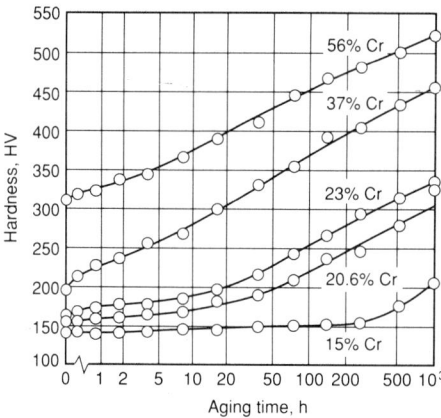

Fig. 27 Influence of aging time at 475 °C (885 °F) on the hardness of iron-chromium alloys with 15, 20.6, 23, 37, and 56% Cr. Source: Ref 109

Fig. 26 Time-temperature-constant hardness curves for Fe-30Cr after aging done between approximately 430 and 540 °C (805 and 1005 °F), around the region of 475 °C embrittlement. Specimens rolled at 900 °C (1650 °F); starting hardness, 195 to 205 HV. Source: Ref 109

- Annealing or other heat treatment
- Descaling by pickling, blast cleaning, or other methods
- Surface conditioning by grinding or rough turning
- Machine straightening

Cold-finished bar is produced from hot-finished bar or rod by additional operations such as cold rolling or cold drawing, which result in the close control of dimensions, a smooth surface finish, and higher tensile and yield strengths. Sizes and shapes of cold-reduced stock classified as bar are essentially the same as for hot-finished bar, except that all cold-reduced flat stock less than 4.76 mm (0.1875 in.) thick and over 9.5 mm (0.375 in.) wide is classified as strip.

Cold-finished round bar is commonly machine straightened; afterward, it can be centerless ground or centerless ground and polished. Centerless grinding and polishing do not alter the mechanical properties of cold-finished bar and are used only to improve surface finish or provide closer tolerances. Some increase in hardness, more marked at the surface and particularly in 200- and 300-series stainless steels, results from machine straightening. The amount of increase varies chiefly with composition, size, and amount of cold work necessary to straighten the bar.

Cold-finished bars that are square, flat, hexagonal, octagonal, or of certain special shapes are produced from hot-finished bars by cold drawing or cold rolling.

When cold-finished bar is required to have high strength and hardness, it is cold drawn or heat treated, depending on composition, section size, and required properties. Round sections can be subsequently centerless ground or centerless ground and polished.

Free machining wire is a bar commodity used for making parts in automatic screw machines or other types of machining equipment. The principal types used are 303, 303Se, 416, 416Se, 420F, 430F,

and 430FSe. Free-machining wire is commonly produced with a cold-drawn or centerless ground finish and with selected hardnesses, depending on the machining operation involved.

Structural Shapes. Hot-rolled, bar-size structural shapes are produced in angles, channels, tees, and zees. They can be purchased in various conditions:

- Hot rolled
- Hot rolled and annealed

- Hot rolled, annealed, and blast cleaned
- Hot rolled, annealed, and chemically cleaned
- Hot rolled, annealed, blast cleaned, and chemically cleaned

Wire

Wire is a coiled product derived by cold finishing hot-rolled and annealed coiled rod. Cold finishing imparts excellent dimensional accuracy, good surface smoothness, a fine finish, and specific mechanical properties. Wire is produced in several tempers and finishes.

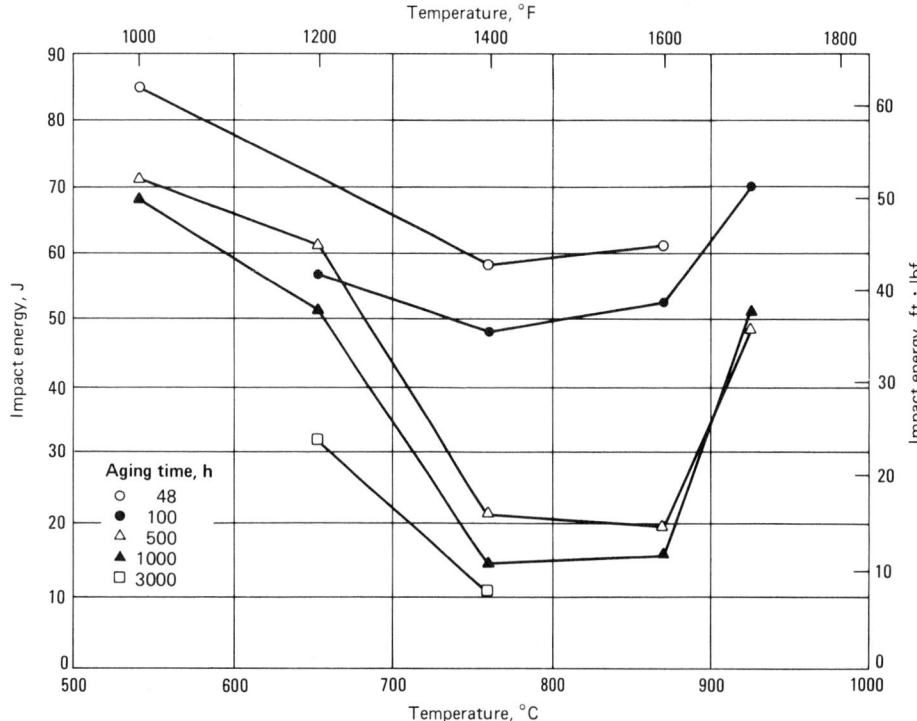

Fig. 28 Influence of aging time and temperature on the room-temperature impact energy of an Fe-25Cr-20Ni alloy. Annealed value, 89 J (66 ft · lbf). Source: Ref 142

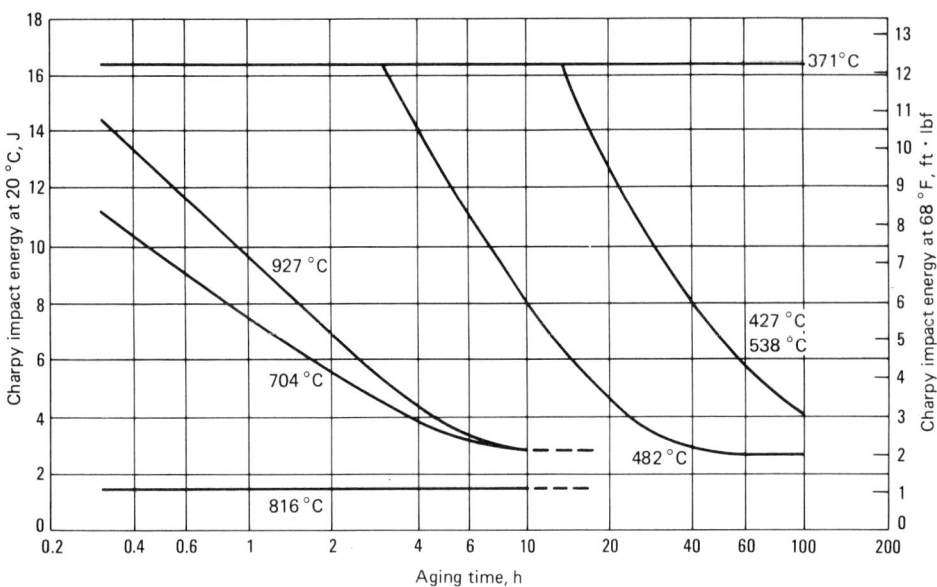

Fig. 29 Influence of aging time and temperature on the room-temperature Charpy impact energy of a low interstitial content 29Cr-4Mo ferritic stainless steel. Source: Ref 143

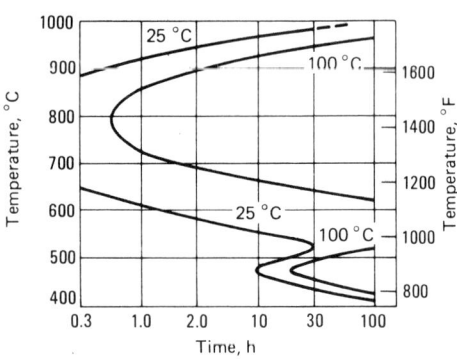

Fig. 30 Time-temperature relationships to produce 25 and 100 °C (75 and 212 °F) ductile-to-brittle transition temperatures for a 29Cr-4Mo ferritic stainless steel as a function of aging times that cover both the 475 °C (885 °F) embrittlement range and the σ-phase embrittlement range. Source: Ref 143

Wire is customarily referred to as *round wire* when the contour is completely cylindrical and as *shape wire* when the contour is other than cylindrical. For example, wires that are half round, half oval, oval, square, rectangular, hexagonal, octagonal, or triangular in cross section are all referred to as shape wire. Shape wire is cold finished either by drawing or by a combination of drawing and rolling.

In the production of wire, rod (which is a coiled hot-rolled product approximately round in cross section) is drawn through the tapered hole of a die or a series of dies. The smallest size of hot-rolled rod commonly made is 5.5 mm (0.218 in.). Rod smaller than this is produced by cold work, the number of dies employed depending on the finished diameter required.

Round stainless steel wire is commonly produced within the approximate size range 0.08 to 15.9 mm (0.003 to 0.625 in.). Shape wire, except cold-finished flat wire, is commonly produced within the approximate size range of 1.12 to 12.7 mm (0.044 to 0.500 in.), although the particular shape governs the specific sizes that can be produced.

Tempers of Wire. There are four classifications of wire temper: annealed temper, soft temper, intermediate temper, and spring temper.

Annealed-temper wire is soft wire that has undergone no further cold drawing after the last annealing treatment. Wire in this temper is made by annealing in open-fired furnaces or molten salt, and annealing ordinarily is followed by pickling that produces a clean, gray, matte finish. It is also made with a bright finish by annealing in a protec-

tive atmosphere and sometimes is described as *bright annealed wire*.

Soft-temper wire is given a single light draft following the final annealing operation and generally is produced to a defined upper limit of tensile strength or hardness. Wire in this temper is produced with various dry-drawn finishes, including lime soap, lead, copper, and oxide. It may

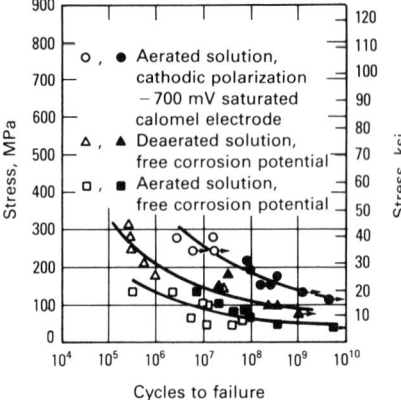

Fig. 32 Effect of cathodic polarization on ultrasonic and conventional-frequency high-cycle corrosion fatigue performance of type 403 stainless steel in aqueous chloride solution. 22% NaCl; pH, 7; load ratio, –1. Open data points, 40 Hz; closed data points, 20 kHz. Source: Ref 151

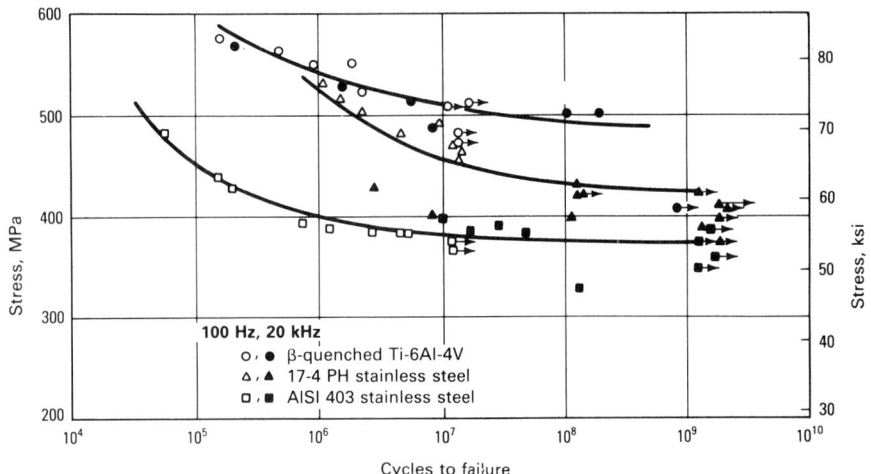

Fig. 31 Ranking of high-cycle fatigue strength of three engineering alloys tested at ultrasonic and conventional frequencies. Environment, high-purity water; temperature, 80 °C (175 °F); <20 ppb O₂; load ratio, –1. Source: Ref 151

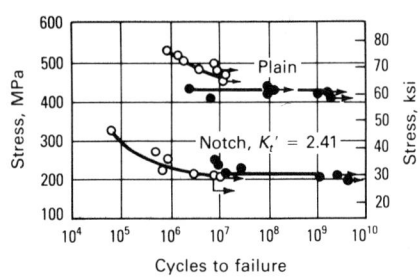

Fig. 33 Notched and plain bar high-cycle fatigue properties of 17-4PH stainless steel. Tested at 100 Hz (open circles) and 20 kHz (closed circles) frequencies. Source: Ref 151

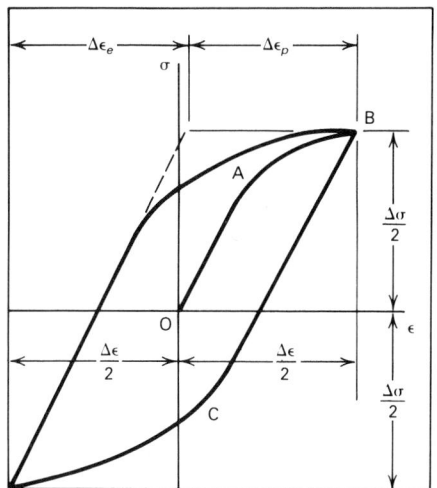

Fig. 34 Stress-strain loop for constant-strain cycling

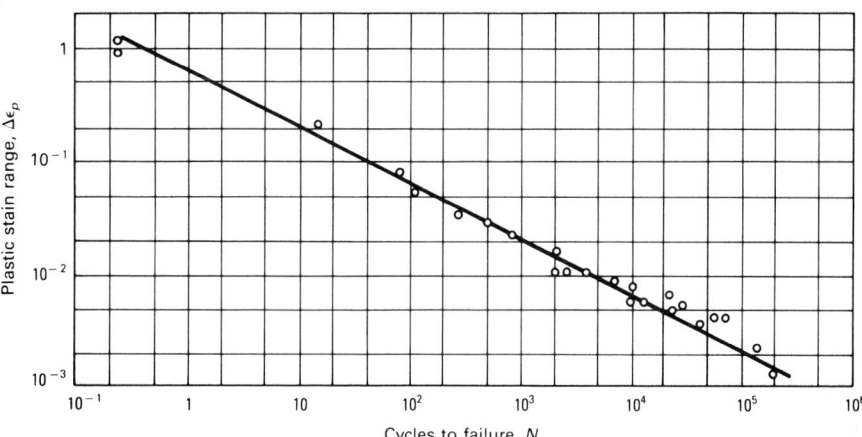

Fig. 35 Low-cycle fatigue curve (plastic strain vs. cycles-to-failure) for type 347 stainless steel. Source: Ref 152

also be given a bright finish produced by oil or grease drawing.

Intermediate-temper wire is drawn one or more drafts after annealing as required to produce a specific minimum strength or hardness. The properties of this wire can vary between the properties of soft-temper wire and properties approaching those of spring-temper wire. Intermediate-temper wire is usually produced with one of the dry-drawn finishes.

Spring-temper wire is drawn several drafts after annealing as required to produce high tensile strengths.

Special Wire Commodities. There are many classes of stainless steel wire that have been developed for specific components or for particular applications. The unique properties of each of these individual wire commodities are developed by employing a particular combination of composition, steel quality, process heat treatment, and cold-drawing practice. The details of manufacture may vary slightly from one wire manufacturer to another, but the finished wire will fulfill the specified requirements.

Cold-heading wire is produced in any of the various types of stainless steel. In all instances, cold-heading wire is subjected to special testing and inspection to ensure satisfactory performance in cold-heading and cold-forging operations.

Of the chromium-nickel group, types 305 and 302Cu are used for cold-heading wire and generally are necessary for severe upsetting. Other

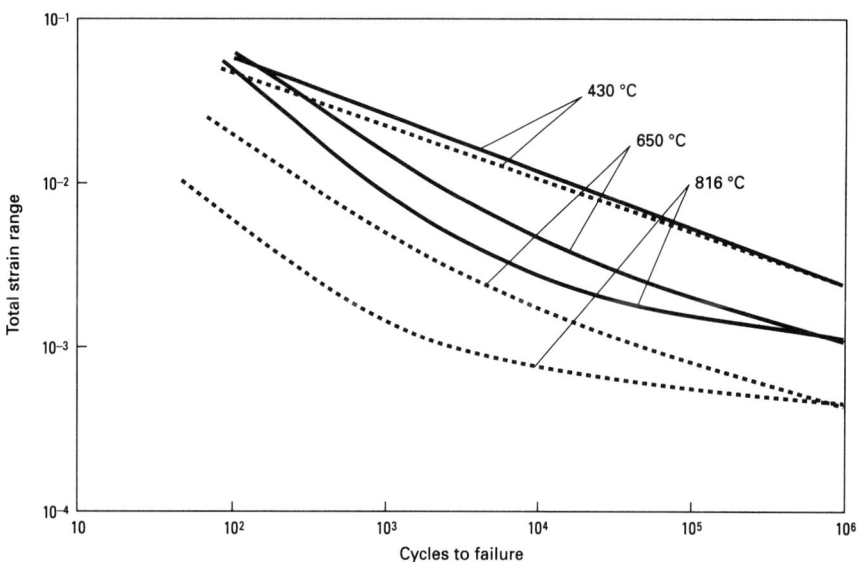

Fig. 36 The effect of temperature and frequency on low-cycle fatigue of type 304 stainless steel. Solid lines represent 10 cycles/min; dashed lines, 10^{-3} cycles/min. Source: Ref 158

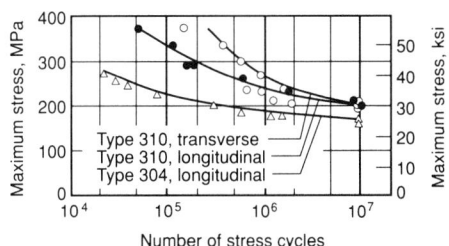

Fig. 37 Typical rotating-beam fatigue behavior of types 304 and 310 stainless steel

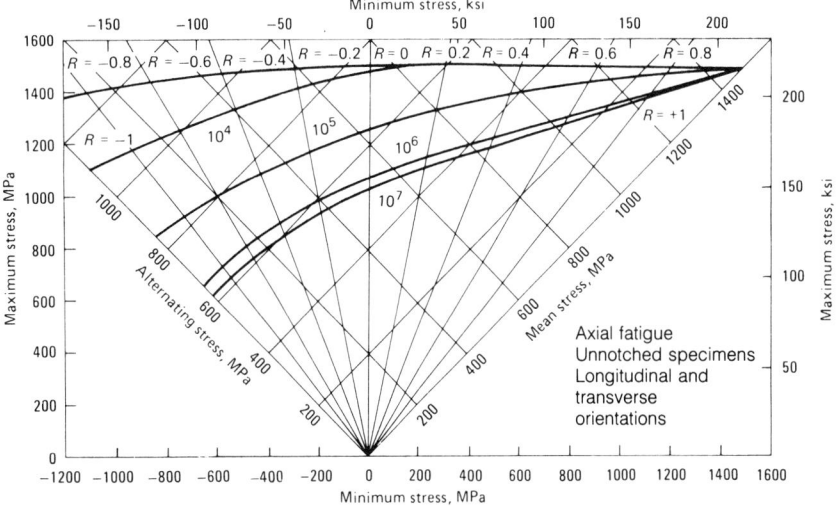

Fig. 38 Constant-life fatigue diagram for PH13-8 Mo stainless steel, condition H1000

grades commonly cold formed include 304, 316, 321, 347, and 384.

Of the 400 series, types 410, 420, 430, and 431 are used for a variety of cold-headed products. Types 430 and 410 are commonly used for severe upsetting and for recessed-head screws and bolts. Types 416, 416Se, 430F, and 430FSe are intended primarily for free cutting and are not recommended for cold heading.

Cold-heading wire is manufactured using a closely controlled annealing treatment that produces optimum softness and still permits a very light finishing draft after pickling. The purposes of the finishing draft are to provide a lubricating coating that will aid the cold-heading operation and to produce a kink-free wire coil having more uniform dimensions.

Cold-heading wire is produced with a variety of finishes, all of which have the function of providing proper lubrication in the header dies. The finish or coating should be suitably adherent to prevent galling and excessively rapid die wear. A copper coating is available that is applied after the annealing treatment and just prior to the finishing draft; the copper-coated wire is then lime coated and drawn, using soap as the drawing lubricant. Coatings of lime and soap or of oxide and soap are also employed.

Spring wire is drawn from annealed rod and is subjected to mill tests and inspection that ensure the quality required for extension and compression springs. The types of stainless steel of which spring wire is commonly produced include 302, 304, and, for additional corrosion resistance, 316 and 20Cb-3 (UNS N08020).

Spring wire in large sizes can be furnished in a variety of finishes, such as dry-drawn lead, copper, lime and soap, and oxide and soap. Fine sizes are usually wet drawn, although they can be dry drawn.

Tensile strength ranges or minimums for types 302, 304, 305, and 316 spring wire in various sizes are given in Table 22.

The torsional modulus for stainless steel spring wire may range from 59 to 76 GPa (8.5 to 11×10^6 psi), depending on alloy and wire size. Magnetic permeability is extremely low compared to that of carbon steel wire. Springs made from stainless steel wire retain their physical and mechanical properties at temperatures up to about 315 °C (600 °F).

Rope wire is used to make rope, cable, and cord for a variety of uses, such as aircraft control cable, marine rope, elevator cable, slings, and anchor cable. Because of special requirements for fatigue strength, rope wire is produced from specially selected and processed material.

Rope wire is made of type 302 or type 304 unless a higher level of corrosion resistance is required, in which case type 316 is generally selected. Special nonmagnetic characteristics may be required, which necessitate the selection of grades that have little or no ferrite or martensite in the microstructure and the use of special drawing practices to limit or avoid deformation-induced transformation to martensite.

Tensile properties of regular rope wire are slightly lower than those of stainless steel spring wire. Finishes for rope wire vary from a gray matte finish to a bright finish and include a series of bright to dark soap finishes. Soap finishes afford some lubrication that facilitates laying up of rope and also to some extent aids in-service use.

Weaving wire is used in the weaving of screens for many different applications in coal mines, sand-and-gravel pits, paper mills, chemical plants, dairy plants, oil refineries, and food-processing plants. Annealing and final drawing must be carefully controlled to maintain uniform temper and finish throughout each coil or spool. Because weaving wire must be ductile, it is usually furnished in the annealed temper with a bright annealed finish, or in the soft temper with either a lime-soap finish or an oil- or grease-drawn finish.

Most types of stainless steel are available in weaving wire; the most widely used types are 302, 304, 309, 310, 316, 410, and 430. Annealed wire in the 300 series commonly has a tensile strength of 655 to 860 MPa (95 to 125 ksi) and an elongation (in 50 mm, or 2 in.) of 35 to 60%. Soft-temper wire, which is commonly specified for sizes over 0.75 mm (0.030 in.), averages 860 to 1035 MPa (1125 to 150 ksi) in tensile strength and exhibits 15 to 40% elongation. For annealed wire in types 410 and 430, tensile strength averages 495 to 585 MPa (72 to 85 ksi), and elongation averages 17 to 23%.

Armature binding wire is produced in types 302 or 304 stainless steel of a composition that is balanced to produce high tensile and yield strengths and low magnetic permeability. Minimum tensile strength of 1515 MPa (220 ksi), minimum yield strength (0.2% offset) of 1170 MPa (170 ksi), and maximum permeability of 4.0 at 16 kA · m⁻¹ (200 Oe) are usually specified. The wire must be strong enough to withstand the centrifugal forces encountered in use, yet ductile enough to withstand being bent sharply back on itself without cracking when a hook is formed to hold the armature wire during the binding operation. Armature binding wire is furnished on spools and has a smooth, tightly adherent tinned coating that facilitates soldering.

Slide forming wire is produced in all standard types, particularly in types 302, 304, 316, 410, and 430. It can be produced in any temper suitable for forming any of the numerous shapes made on slide-type wire-forming machines.

Wool wire is designed for the production of wool by shredding. It is commonly furnished in an intermediate temper and produced to rigid standards so that it will perform satisfactorily in the wool-cutting operation. Wool wire usually is made from type 430 and has a lime-soap finish.

Reed wire is high-quality wire produced for the manufacture of dents for reeds that, once assembled, are used in weaving textiles and other products. Dents are made by rolling the round reed wire into a flat section, then machining and polishing the edges to a very smooth and accurate contour before cutting the wire into individual dents. Accuracy in size and

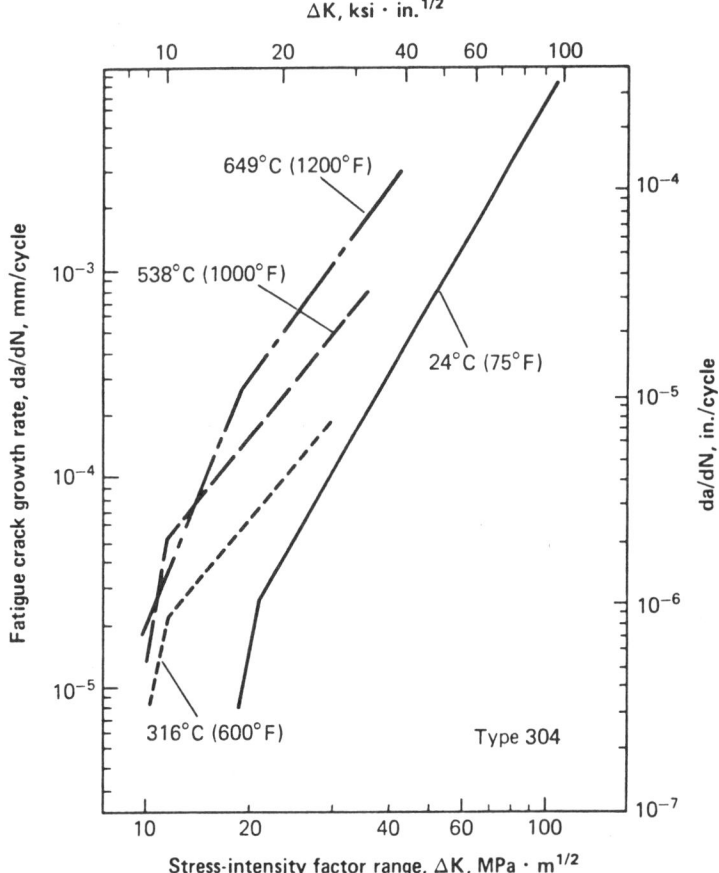

Fig. 39 Effect of testing temperature on fatigue crack growth rates for annealed type 304 stainless steel tested in air at 0.066 Hz and a load ratio of 0 to 0.05. Source: Ref 162

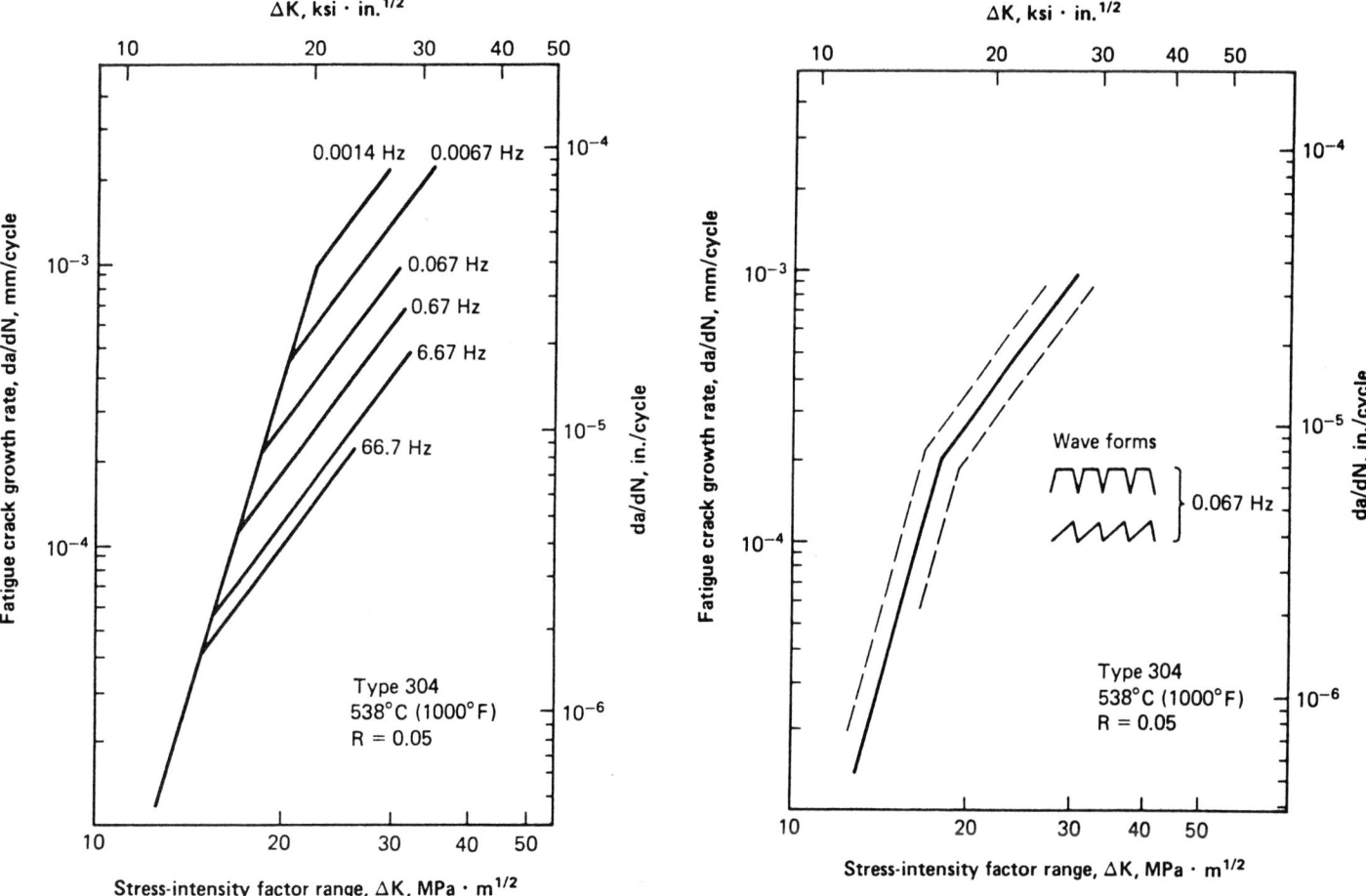

Fig. 40 Effect of variation in cyclic frequency on fatigue crack growth rates for annealed type 304 stainless steel at 538 °C (1000 °F) for a load ratio of 0.05 in air with a sawtooth waveform. Source: Ref 166, 167

Fig. 41 Scatter band of fatigue crack growth rates for annealed type 304 stainless steel at 538 °C (1000 °F) in air at a load ratio of 0.05 with two different waveforms at 0.067 Hz. Source: Ref 168

shape are necessary because of the various processes that the wire must undergo.

Reed wire is usually made from type 430 in an intermediate temper that must be uniform in properties throughout each coil and each shipment. The finish also must be uniform and bright.

Lashing wire is designed for lashing electric power transmission lines to support cables. Lashing wire is usually made from type 430. It is furnished in the annealed temper with a bright finish and has a maximum tensile strength of 655 MPa (95 ksi) and minimum elongation of 17% in 255 mm (10 in.). It is normally furnished on coreless spools.

Cotter pin wire is approximately half-round wire designed for fabricating cotter pins. It is generally produced by rolling round wire between power-driven rolls, by drawing it between power-driven rolls, or by drawing it through a die or Turk's-head roll. To facilitate the spreading of the cotter pin ends, it is desirable that the flat side of the wire have a small radius rather than sharp corners at the edges.

Cotter pin wire is commonly furnished in vibrated or hank-wound coils with the flat side of the wire facing inward. Ordinarily it is produced in the soft temper to prevent undesirable spring-back in the legs of formed cotter pins. Usually it is furnished with a bright finish, but it is also available with a metallic coating.

Stainless welding wire is available for many grades to provide good weldability with optimized mechanical properties and corrosion resistance of the weldment. For example, the weldability of austenitic stainless steels is enhanced by controlling unwanted residual elements or balancing the wire composition to provide a small amount of ferrite in the as-deposited weld metal. Also, the composition of duplex stainless weld wire is generally controlled to produce levels of austenite and ferrite in the weld metal that will optimize mechanical properties and corrosion resistance.

Stainless steel weld wire is produced in layer-level wound spools, straight lengths (both included in the American Welding Society AWS A5.9) and coated electrodes (AWS A5.4).

Semifinished Products

Blooms, billets, and slabs are hot rolled, hot forged, or hot pressed to approximate cross-sectional dimensions and generally have rounded corners (Fig. 21). Round billets are also produced, typically for extrusion or closed-die forging. These semifinished products, as well as tube rounds, are produced in random lengths or are cut to specified lengths or to specified weights. There are no invariable criteria for distinguishing between the terms *bloom* and *billet*, and often they are used interchangeably.

Dimensions. The nominal cross-sectional dimensions of blooms, billets, and slabs are designated in inches and fractions of an inch. The size ranges commonly listed as hot-rolled stainless steel blooms, billets, and slabs include square sections 100 × 100 mm (4 × 4 in.) and larger, as shown in Fig. 21, and rectangular sections at least 10,300 mm^2 (16 in.^{2}) in cross-sectional area.

Annealing. Blooms, billets, and slabs made of 400-series stainless steels that are highly hardenable (types 414, 420, 420F, 422, 431, 440A, 440B, and 440C) are annealed before shipment to prevent cracking. Other hardenable types, such as 403, 410, 416, and 416Se, also may be furnished in the annealed condition, depending on composition and size.

Processing. In general practice, blooms, billets, and slabs are cut to length by hot shearing. Hot sawing and flame cutting are also used. When the end distortion or burrs normally encountered in regular mill cutting are not acceptable, ends can be prepared for subsequent operations by any method that does not leave distortion or burrs. Usually, this is grinding. Blooms, billets, tube rounds, and slabs are surface conditioned by grinding or turning prior to being processed by hot rolling, hot forging, hot extruding, or hot piercing. Material can be tested by ultrasonic and macroetching techniques in the as-worked condition; however, a more critical evaluation is possible after the material has been conditioned. At the time an order is placed, producer and customer should come to an agreement regarding the manner in which testing or inspection is to be conducted and results interpreted.

Tubular Products

Pipe, tubes, and tubing are hollow products made either by piercing rounds or by rolling and welding strip. They are used for conveying gases, liquids, and solids and for various mechanical and structural purposes. (Cylindrical forms intended for use as containers for storage and shipping purposes and products cast to tubular shape are not included in this category.) The number of terms used in describing sizes and other characteristics of stainless steel tubular products has grown with the industry, and in some cases terms may be difficult to define or to distinguish from one another. For example, the terms *pipe*, *tubes*, and *tubing* are distinguished from one another only by general use, not by clear-cut rules. Pipe is distinguished from tubes chiefly by the fact that it is commonly produced in relatively few standard sizes. Tubing is generally made to more exacting specifications than either pipe or tubes regarding dimensions, finish, chemical composition, and mechanical properties.

Stainless steel tubular products are classified according to intended service, as described in the following paragraphs and tabular matter.

Stainless Steel Tubing for General Corrosion-Resisting Service. Straight chromium (ferritic or martensitic) types are produced in the annealed or heat-treated condition, and chromium-nickel (austenitic) types are produced in the annealed or cold-worked condition. Austenitic types are inherently tougher and more ductile than ferritic types for similar material conditions or tempers.

ASTM specifications A 268 and A 269 apply to stainless steel tubing for general service: A 268 applies to ferritic grades, and A 269 applies to austenitic grades. Most ferritic grades are also covered by ASME SA268, which sets forth the same material requirements as does ASTM A 268.

Stainless steel pressure pipe is made from straight chromium and chromium-nickel types and is governed by the follwing specifications:

Specifications		
ASTM	ASME	Description
A 312	SA312	Seamless and welded pipe
A 358	SA358	Electric fusion welded pipe for high-temperature service
A 376	SA376	Seamless pipe for high-temperature central-station service
A 409	...	Large-diameter welded pipe for corrosion or high-temperature service
A 790	SA790	Seamless and welded ferritic/austenitic stainless steel pipe

Stainless steel pressure tubes include boiler, superheater, condenser, and heat-exchanger tubes, which commonly are manufactured from chromium-nickel types; requirements are set forth in the following specifications:

Specifications		
ASTM	ASME	Description
A 213	SA213	Ferritic and austenitic alloy seamless tubes for boilers, superheaters, and heat exchangers
A 249	SA249	Austenitic alloy welded tubes for boilers, superheaters, heat exchangers, and condensers
A 271	SA271	Austenitic alloy seamless still tubes for refinery service
A 498	...	Ferritic and austenitic alloy seamless and welded tubes with integral fins
A 688	SA688	Welded austenitic stainless steel feedwater heater tubes
A 789	SA789	Seamless and welded ferritic/austenitic stainless steel tubing

Stainless steel sanitary tubing is used extensively in the dairy and food industries, where cleanliness and exceptional corrosion resistance are important surface characteristics. In many instances, even the slight amounts of corrosion that result in tarnishing or in release of a few parts per million of metallic ions into the process stream are objectionable. Sanitary tubing may be polished on the outside or the inside, or both, to provide smooth, easily cleanable surfaces. Special finishes and close dimensional tolerances for special fittings are sometimes required. ASTM A 270 is in common use for this tubing.

Stainless steel mechanical tubing is produced in round, square, rectangular, and special-shape cross sections. It is used for many different applications, most of which do not require the tubing to be pressurized. Mechanical tubing is used for bushings, small cylinders, bearing parts, fittings, various types of hollow, cylindrical or ringlike formed parts, and structural members such as furniture frames, machinery frames, and architectural members. ASTM A 511 and A 554 apply to seamless and welded mechanical tubing, respectively.

Stainless steel aircraft tubing, produced from various chromium-nickel types, has many structural and hydraulic applications in aircraft construction because of its high resistance to both heat and corrosion. Work-hardened tubing can be used in high-strength applications, but it is not recommended for parts that may be exposed to certain corrosive substances or to certain combinations of corrosive static or fluctuating stress. Low-carbon types or compositions stabilized by titanium or by niobium with or without tantalum are commonly used when welding is to be done without subsequent heat treatment.

Aircraft tubing is made to close tolerances and with special surface finishes, special mechanical properties, and stringent requirements for testing and inspection. It is used for structural components of aircraft fuselages, engine mounts, engine oil lines, landing gear components, and engine parts and is finding increasing application in parts

for hydraulic, fuel-injection, exhaust, and heating systems.

Aircraft structural tubing is both seamless and welded stainless steel tubing in sizes larger than those referred to as *aircraft tubing*. It is commonly used in exhaust systems (including stacks), cross headers, collector rings, engine parts, heaters, and pressurizers. Sometimes, stainless steel aircraft structural tubing is produced especially for parts that are to be machined. Stabilized types are used for welded and brazed structures.

Seamless and welded stainless steel aircraft structural tubing is made in sizes ranging from 1.6 to 125 mm ($\frac{1}{16}$ to 5 in.) in outside diameter and from 0.25 to 6.35 mm (0.010 to 0.250 in.) in wall thickness. It is ordinarily produced to the federal and Aerospace Material Specification (AMS) specifications listed below. However, because the U.S. government has embarked on a program of replacing military (MIL) specifications with AMS and ASTM specifications, the MIL specifications listed may no longer apply.

Specification	UNS number, composition, and condition
Seamless tubing	
AMS 5560	S30400; 19Cr-9Ni; annealed
AMS 5561	S21900; 21Cr-6Ni-9Mn; annealed
AMS 5570	S32100; 18Cr-11Ni (Ti stabilized); annealed
AMS 5571	S34700; 18Cr-11Ni (Nb + Ta stabilized); annealed
AMS 5572	S31008; 25Cr-20Ni; annealed
AMS 5573	S31600; 17Cr-12.5Ni-2.5Mo; annealed
AMS 5574	S30908; 23Cr-13.5Ni; annealed
AMS 5578	S45500; 12.5Cr-8.5Ni-0.03 (Nb + Ta)-1.1Ti-2.0Cu; annealed
Welded tubing	
MIL-T-6737	18-8 (stabilized); annealed
AMS 5565	S30400; 19Cr-9Ni; annealed
AMS 5575	S34700; 18Cr-11Ni (Nb + Ta stabilized); annealed
AMS 5576	S32100; 18Cr-10Ni (Ti stabilized); annealed
AMS 5577	S31008; 25Cr-20Ni; annealed
Seamless and welded tubing	
MIL-T-5695	18-8; hardened (cold worked)
MIL-T-8506	S30400; 18-8; annealed
MIL-T-8686	18-8 (stabilized); annealed

Aircraft Hydraulic-Line Tubing. Stainless steel tubing is used widely in aircraft and aerospace vehicles for fuel-injection lines and hydraulic systems. Most of the tubing used for such applications is relatively small; types 304, 304L, 321, 347, and 21-6-9 are most often specified. Aircraft hydraulic-line tubing must have high strength, high ductility, high fatigue resistance, high corrosion resistance, and good cold-working qualities. The ability to be flared for use with standard flare fittings, the ability to be bent without excessive distortion or fracture, and cleanliness of the inside surface are important requirements.

Stainless steel aircraft hydraulic-line tubing is produced in either the annealed or the cold-worked ($\frac{1}{8}$-hard) condition. The $\frac{1}{8}$-hard temper

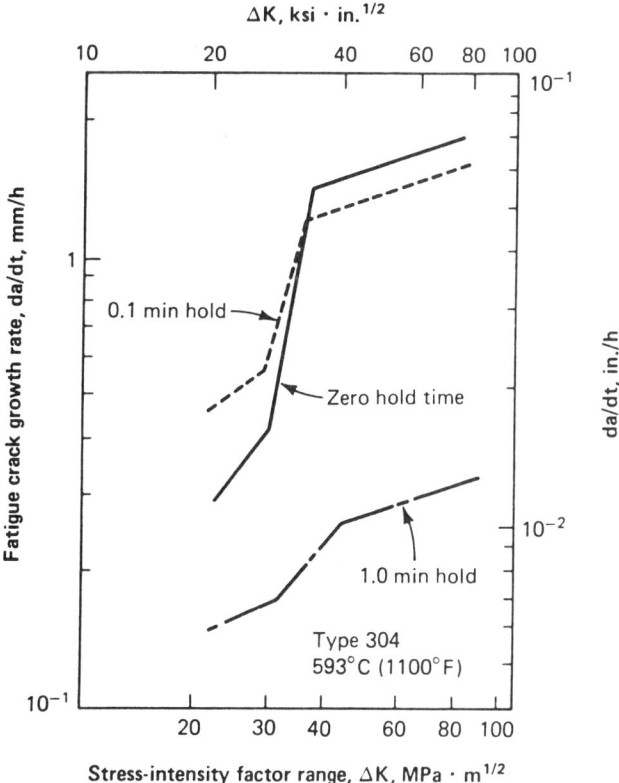

Fig. 42 Fatigue crack growth rates per unit of time (*da/dt*) for annealed type 304 stainless steel for continuous cycling (0.17 Hz), for 0.1 and 1.0 min hold times at maximum load for each cycle at 593 °C (1100 °F), and for a load ratio of 0. Source: Ref 169

is used wherever possible to save weight. Specifications for stainless steel aircraft hydraulic-line tubing, either seamless or welded, are:

Specification	UNS number, or type, and condition
MIL-T-6845	S30400; ⅛ hard
MIL-T-8504	S30400; annealed
MIL-T-8808	321 or 347; annealed
AMS 5556	S34700; annealed
AMS 5557	S32100; annealed
AMS 5560	S30400; annealed
AMS 5566	S30400; ⅛ hard

Influence of Product Form on Properties

The mechanical properties of cast or wrought stainless steels vary widely from group to group, vary less widely from type to type within groups, and may vary with product form for a given type. Because of the wide variation from group to group, one must first decide whether a martensitic, ferritic, austenitic, duplex, or PH stainless steel is most suitable for a given application. Once the appropriate group is selected, the method of fabrication or service conditions may then dictate which specific type is required.

Before typical properties of the various product forms are discussed, it is important that two key points about stainless steels be recognized. First, many stainless steels are manufactured and/or used

in a heat-treated condition, that is, in some thermally treated condition other than process annealed or, typically, mill processed. When this is the case, a tabulation of typical properties may not give all the required information. Second, in many products strain hardening during fabrication is a very important consideration. All stainless steels strain harden to some degree, depending on structure, alloy content, and amount of cold working. Consequently, for applications in which the service performance of the finished product depends on the enhancement of properties during fabrication, it is essential that the manufacturer determine this effect independently for each individual product. Here, techniques such as statistical-reliability testing are invaluable.

Cast Structures. Whether produced as ingot, slab, or billet in a mill or as shape castings in a foundry, cast structures can exhibit wide variations in properties. Because of the possible existence of large dendritic grains, intergranular phases, and alloy segregation, typical mechanical properties cannot be stated precisely and generally are inferior to those of any wrought structure. Detailed information on the composition and properties of cast stainless steels is given in the article "Metallurgy and Properties of Cast Stainless Steels" in this Volume.

Hot Processing. The initial purpose of hot rolling or forging an ingot, slab, or billet is to refine the cast structure and improve mechanical properties. Hot-reduced products and hot-re-

duced-and-annealed products exhibit coarser grain structures and lower strengths than cold-processed products. Grain size and shape depend chiefly on start and finish temperatures and on the method of hot reduction. For instance, cross-rolled hand mill plate will exhibit a more equiaxed grain structure than continuous hot-rolled strip.

Hot reduction may be a final sizing operation, as in the case of hot-rolled bar, billet, plate, or bar flats, or it may be an intermediate processing step for products such as cold-finished bar, rod, and wire and cold-rolled sheet and strip.

Typical properties of hot-processed products and of hot-processed-and-annealed products are different from those of either cast or cold-reduced products. Hot-processed products tend to have coarser grain sizes than cold-reduced products.

Cold-Reduced Products. When strained at ambient temperatures, stainless steels (particularly the austenitic grades) tend to work harden, as shown in Fig. 22. Because recrystallization does not occur during cold working, the final properties of thermally treated products depend on the:

- Amount of cold reduction (which helps determine the number of potential recrystallization sites)
- Type of mill thermal treatment (subcritical annealing, normalizing, or solution treatment)
- Time at any given temperature

Wrought products that have been cold reduced and annealed generally have finer grain sizes, which produce higher strengths than hot-processed products. Cold-reduced products sometimes exhibit greater differences between transverse and longitudinal properties than hot-processed products.

Cold finishing is generally done to improve dimensional tolerances or surface finish or to raise mechanical strength. Cold-finished products—whether they have been previously hot worked and annealed or have been hot worked, cold worked, and annealed—have higher mechanical strengths and slightly lower ductilities than their process-annealed counterparts.

Notch Toughness and Transition Temperature

Notched-bar impact testing of stainless steels is likely to show a wide scatter in test results, regardless of type or test conditions. Because of this wide scatter, only general behavior of the different classes can be described.

Austenitic types have good notched-bar impact resistance. Charpy impact energies of 135 J (100 ft · lb) or greater are typical of all types at room temperature. Cryogenic temperatures have little or no effect on notch toughness; ordinarily, austenitic stainless steels maintain values exceeding 135 J even at very low temperatures. On the other hand, cold work lowers the resistance to impact at all temperatures.

Martensitic and ferritic stainless steels exhibit a decreasing resistance to impact with decreasing

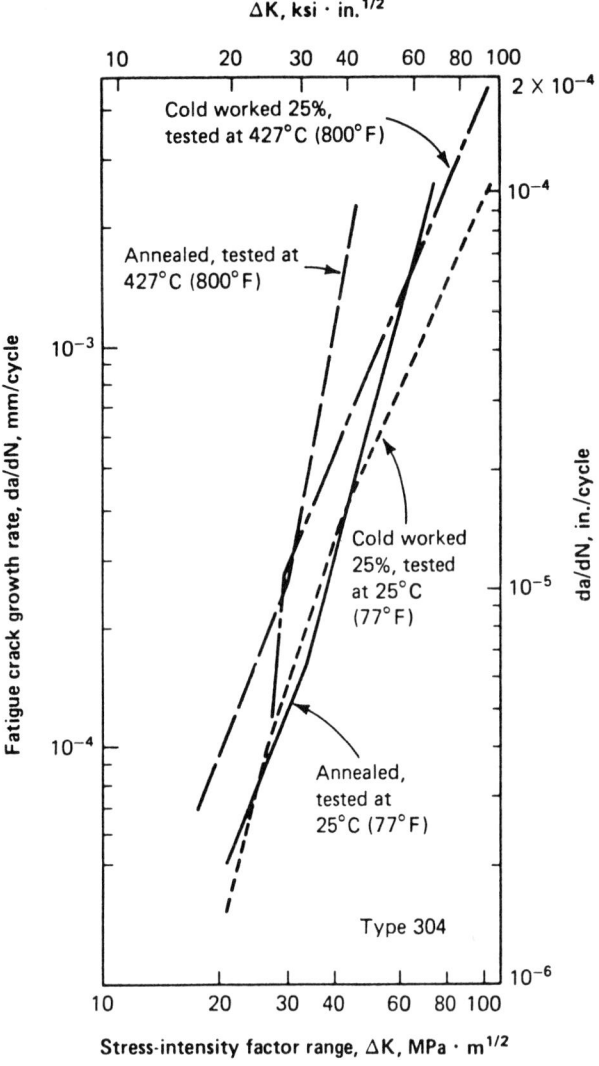

ΔK, ksi · in.$^{1/2}$

Cold worked 25%, tested at 427°C (800°F)

Annealed, tested at 427°C (800°F)

Cold worked 25%, tested at 25°C (77°F)

Annealed, tested at 25°C (77°F)

Type 304

Fatigue crack growth rate, da/dN, mm/cycle

da/dN, in./cycle

Stress-intensity factor range, ΔK, MPa · m$^{1/2}$

Fig. 43 Fatigue crack growth rates for annealed and cold-worked type 304 stainless steel at 25 and 427 °C (77 and 800 °F), 0.17 Hz, and a load ratio of 0. Source: Ref 170

temperature, and the fracture appearance changes from a ductile mode at mildly elevated temperatures to a brittle mode at low temperatures. This fracture transition is characteristic of martensitic and ferritic materials. Both the upper-shelf energy and the lower-shelf energy are not greatly influenced by heat treatment in these stainless steels. However, the temperature range over which transition occurs is affected by heat treatment, minor variations in composition, and cold work. Heat treatments that result in high hardness move the transition range to higher temperatures, and those that result in low hardness move the transition range to lower temperatures. As indicated in Fig. 23, transition generally occurs in the range of –75 to 95 °C (–100 to 200 °F), which is the temperature range in which martensitic stainless steels are ordinarily used. Consequently, it may be necessary to investigate fracture behavior thoroughly before specifying a martensitic or ferritic stainless steel for a particular application. Additional information on the ductility and toughness of stainless steels can be found in the section "Ferritic Stain-

less Steels" in this article. The effect of prolonged elevated-temperature exposure on Charpy V-notch properties of stainless steels is described in the next section.

Embrittlement Mechanisms

As mentioned previously in this article, stainless steels are susceptible to embrittlement (the severe loss of ductility or toughness, or both) during thermal treatment or elevated-temperature service (thermally induced embrittlement). The forms of embrittlement that most affect stainless steels include sensitization, 475 °C (885 °F) embrittlement, and σ-phase embrittlement. The mechanisms for each of these forms of embrittlement are described below. Additional information on sensitization can be found in the articles "Atmospheric and Aqueous Corrosion" and "Corrosion of Weldments" in this Volume. Information on how these forms of embrittlement influence the fracture morphology of stainless steels can be

found in the article "Visual Examination and Light Microscopy" in Volume 12 of the *ASM Handbook.*

Sensitization

Austenitic stainless steels become susceptible to intergranular corrosion when subjected to temperatures in the range of 480 to 815 °C (900 to 1500 °F), generally from welding or service conditions. This susceptibility has been termed *sensitization* and has been attributed to the precipitation of $M_{23}C_6$ carbides on the austenite grain boundaries. The mechanism for sensitization was initially proposed as being due to the depletion of chromium at the grain boundaries when the carbides form (Ref 50, 51). The chromium content adjacent to the grain-boundary carbides was thought to drop below some critical limit, which rendered the alloy susceptible to severe localized attack by the corrosive environment.

This theory for the sensitization mechanism was widely accepted, and considerable indirect evidence for its validity was subsequently developed. However, when the electron microprobe was developed in the 1950s and researchers tried to detect the impoverished chromium zone, they were unable to do so (Ref 52, 53), or they could show chromium depletion only when the steel was carburized (Ref 54), or they detected only small regions of possible chromium depletion (Ref 55). Therefore, it was concluded that if such a zone exists, it must be less than 1 μm (40 μin.) wide and the concentration gradient must be rather steep. This prompted a number of other theories to be developed to explain sensitization, for example, electrochemical consideration of the nobility of the carbides (Ref 56, 57), strains at the carbide-austenite interface (Ref 56), and grain-boundary strain energy acting as the driving force for intergranular attack (Ref 58).

The picture was further complicated by a number of observations of intergranular corrosion in austenitic stainless steels under conditions unfavorable for sensitization, and in nonsensitized stainless steels with no detectable grain-boundary precipitation (Ref 59-66). The latter occurred in highly oxidizing solutions, such as the nitric dichromate solution. Because of these difficulties, attention was focused on the influence of impurity elements, such as phosphorus, that are segregated to the austenite grain boundaries. It was subsequently proposed that intergranular corrosion of austenitic stainless steels was due to the presence of a continuous grain-boundary path of either carbides or solute segregated regions (Ref 59). Direct evidence for impurity segregation, chiefly of phosphorus, has been obtained from intergranular fracture surfaces of both sensitized and nonsensitized austenitic stainless steels (Ref 65-69).

The development of scanning transmission electron microscopes with electron beam sizes of about 10 nm (100 Å) in diameter, coupled with energy-dispersive x-ray analysis, has provided direct proof of chromium depletion due to carbide precipitation at the grain boundaries (Ref 70-76). These studies have demonstrated that significant

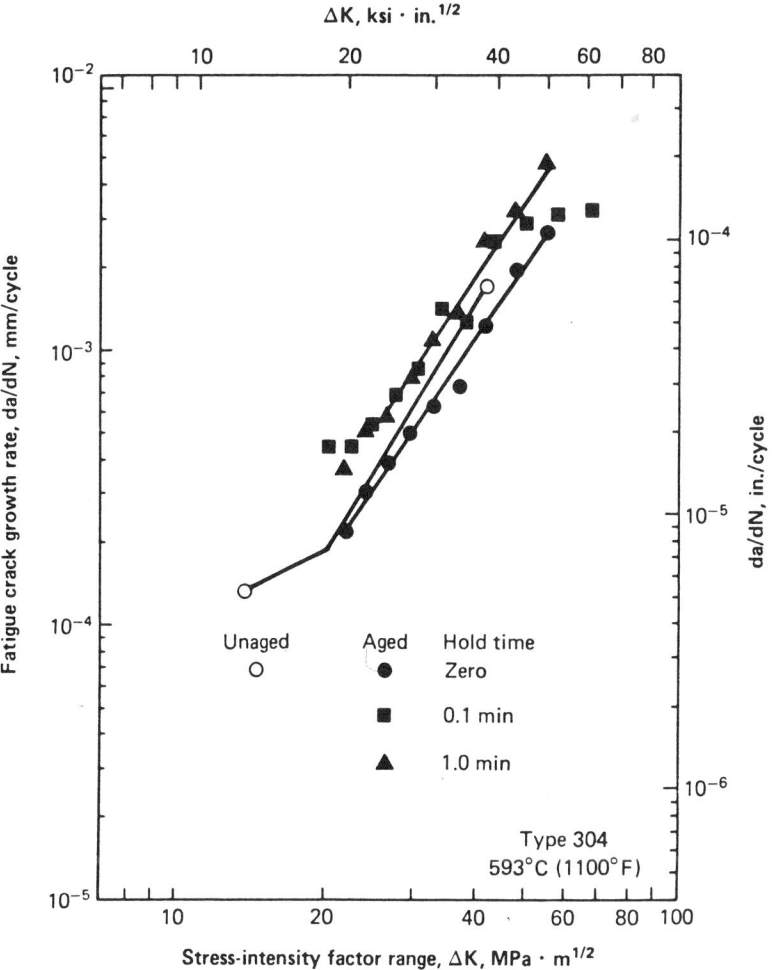

Fig. 44   Effect of aging at 593 °C (1100 °F) for 5000 h, and hold times of 0.1 and 1.0 min for each cycle, on fatigue crack growth rates of longitudinal-transverse oriented specimens of type 304 stainless steel tested in air at 0.17 Hz and a load ratio of 0. Source: Ref 171

chromium depletion occurs after sensitization at grain boundaries adjacent to precipitated carbides. For equal times, the degree of chromium depletion for type 316LN was greater with aging at 650 °C (1200 °F) than at 700 °C (1290 °F). Increasing the holding time caused the width of the depleted zone to increase. The width of chromium depletion along the grain boundaries around individual carbides was much greater than the width of the depletion zone into the grain interior (~3 μm, or 120 μin., vs. ~0.15 μm, or 6 μin., for samples aged 100 h at 700 °C, or 1290 °F) (Ref 73). Evidence of molybdenum depletion has also been obtained. These direct measurements are in relative agreement with theoretical calculations of chromium levels in equilibrium with growing carbides during sensitization (Ref 77-80) and with empirical modifications of such theories (Ref 81).

Transmission electron microscopy studies of the precipitated carbides have demonstrated that the susceptibility to intergranular corrosion with sensitization temperature and time correlates well with the morphology of the grain-boundary carbide precipitates (Ref 82-86). These studies have demonstrated that the grain-boundary precipitate

due to sensitization is always $(Cr_3Fe)_{23}C_6$, that is, $M_{23}C_6$ carbide. The preferred sites for the nucleation of $M_{23}C_6$ are, in decreasing order of occurrence (Ref 83):

• Delta ferrite-austenite phase boundaries
• Austenite grain boundaries
• Incoherent twin boundaries
• Coherent twin boundaries

The carbides grow in the plane of the grain or twin boundaries. The morphology of the precipitated $M_{23}C_6$ depends on the type of boundary where precipitation occurs and the temperature (Ref 83). Precipitates that form at δ-ferrite-austenite phase boundaries or at austenite grain boundaries are dendritic or geometric in shape; the shape depends on the boundary orientation and misfit between the grains, the temperature, and the time at temperature.

Figure 24 shows the microstructure of type 304 austenitic stainless steel in which chromium carbides have precipitated at grain boundaries. Those that form at incoherent twin boundaries look like ribbons of connected trapezoids, whereas those that form at coherent twin boundaries have an equilateral thin triangular shape.

Grain-boundary precipitates are classified into three categories:

• Dendritic shapes
• Separate geometric shapes
• Sheets of interconnected geometric particles

The sheets form at the lower temperatures, dendrites form at higher temperatures within the sensitization range, and the small, isolated geometric particles can form over the entire sensitization range and above, up to about 980 °C (1800 °F) (Ref 83). Sensitization is most severe for specimens sensitized at temperatures in the lower portion of the range where sheets of interconnected geometrically shaped carbides are formed. It is well known that healing occurs with very long times in the sensitization range; that is, long holding times result in reduced chromium depletion and reduced intergranular attack. When this occurs, the sheets of interconnected particles gradually separate into arrays of thick geometric particles (Ref 83).

Minimizing Sensitization. Several approaches have been taken to minimize or prevent the sensitization of austenitic stainless steels. If sensitization results from welding heat and the component is small enough, solution annealing will dissolve the precipitates and restore immunity. However, in many cases this cannot be done because of distortion problems or the size of the component. In these cases, a low-carbon version of the grade or a stabilized composition should be used. Complete immunity requires a carbon content below about 0.015 to 0.02% (Ref 87). Additions of niobium or titanium to tie up the carbon are also effective in preventing sensitization as long as the ratio of these elements to the carbon content is high enough. Stabilizing heat treatments aimed at producing intergranular carbides are not very effective.

Effect on Properties. Few studies have been conducted on the influence of sensitization on mechanical properties. In general, carbide precipitation produces a slight increase in tensile strength (Ref 51). Heats of type 304 containing various levels of phosphorus and sulfur after sensitization were tested using half-size Charpy V-notch specimens fractured at liquid nitrogen temperature. Longitudinally oriented specimens were sensitized at 550 to 850 °C (1020 to 1560 °F) for 15 to 105 min. The decrease in impact energy, relative to the results before sensitization, were much greater in phosphorus-doped steels than in sulfur-doped steels. Fractures were intergranular for phosphorus-doped steels and transgranular for sulfur-doped steels. Figure 25 shows the reduction in half-size Charpy V-notch impact energy for phosphorus-doped steels aged at different temperatures for 5100 s (85 min); the specimens were tested after cooling in liquid nitrogen. For heats 1 and 6, embrittlement was greatest at 750 °C (1380 °F); somewhat higher or lower temperatures produced near-normal toughness. Embrittlement was greater for high-phosphorus heats, but these levels are greater than those encountered in commercial heats. The loss in toughness for phosphorus-doped heats increased with holding times at temperatures between 650 and 825 °C (1200 and 1515 °F); somewhat higher or lower temperatures again

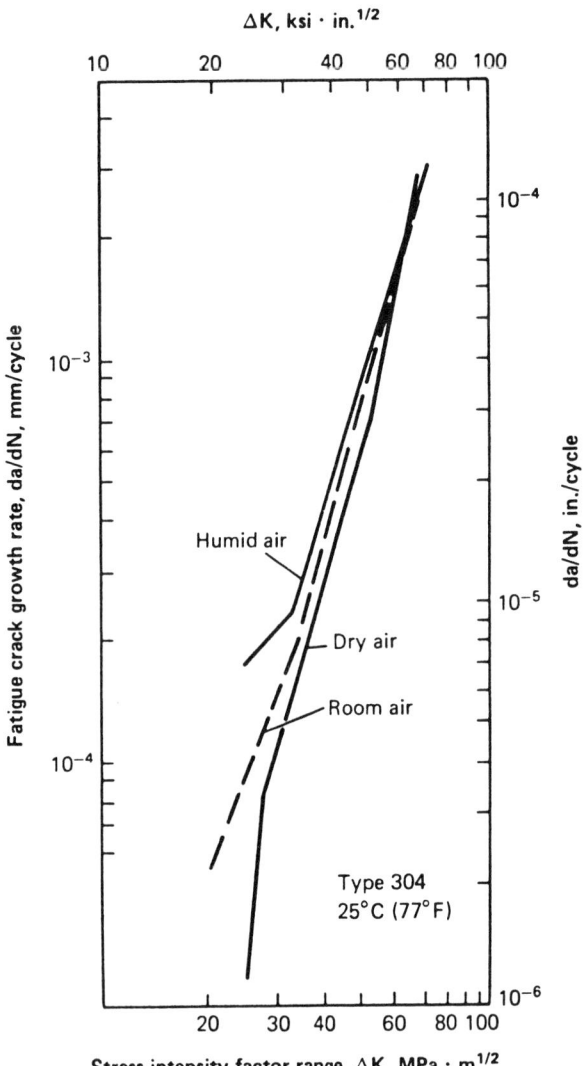

ΔK, ksi · in.$^{1/2}$

Fig. 45 Effect of humidity on fatigue crack growth rates for type 304 stainless steel tested at room temperature, 0.17 Hz, and a load ratio of 0. Source: Ref 170

produced near-normal toughness. The modified Strauss test produced higher corrosion rates for heats sensitized at 650 °C (1200 °F), and the corrosion rate increased linearly with increasing time and increasing impurity content.

Ferritic Stainless Steels. Sensitization and intergranular corrosion also occur in ferritic stainless steels (Ref 89-95). A wider range of corrosive environments can produce intergranular attack in ferritic grades than is the case for austenitic grades. In the case of welds, the attacked region is usually larger for ferritic grades than for austenitic grades because temperatures above 925 °C (1700 °F) are involved in causing sensitization. Ferritic grades with less than 15% Cr are not susceptible, however. One study demonstrated that ferritic grades with 16 to 28% Cr were susceptible to intergranular corrosion when rapidly cooled from above 925 °C (1700 °F). This susceptibility was due to solution of carbides and nitrides followed by their reprecipitation in the grain boundaries. Subsequent annealing at 650 to 815 °C (1200 to 1500 °F) restored corrosion resis-

tance (Ref 89). Therefore, the thermal processes causing intergranular corrosion in ferritic stainless steels are different from those for austenitic stainless steels. Reducing the carbon and nitrogen interstitial levels improves the intergranular corrosion resistance of ferritic stainless steels.

Sensitization can occur in titanium-stabilized ferritic stainless steels (Ref 94, 95). The thermal treatment that causes sensitization, however, is altered by the addition of titanium. First, high-temperature exposure requires a temperature in excess of 1050 °C (1920 °F) to dissolve the Ti(C,N) that reprecipitates upon cooling, even with water, forming grain-boundary precipitates of (Ti,Cr)(C,N) (Ref 94). The chromium-to-titanium (Cr/Ti) ratio in these precipitates is approximately 1/3. Aging at 480 to 550 °C (895 to 1020 °F) causes these precipitates to grow, and the Cr/Ti ratio increases to approximately 1/2. This depletes the grain-boundary zone around the precipitates of chromium, thereby increasing the susceptibility to intergranular corrosion. Again, long times at 480 to 550 °C (895 to 1020 °F) reduce the chromium

gradient around the particles and restore corrosion resistance. Aging above 600 °C (1110 °F) also produces resistance to intergranular corrosion because the chromium in the (Ti,Cr)(C,N) precipitates is replaced by titanium, that is, the Cr/Ti ratio decreases. A titanium-stabilized 12% Cr ferritic grade was also found to sensitize under similar heat treatment conditions (Ref 95).

Duplex stainless steels are resistant to intergranular corrosion when aged in the region of 480 to 700 °C (895 to 1290 °F). It has been recognized for some time that duplex grades with 20 to 40 vol% ferrite exhibit excellent resistance to intergranular corrosion (Ref 96). A study of intergranular corrosion in AISI 308 stainless steel that was heat treated to produce 15% ferrite found that aging at 600 °C (1100 °F) caused the precipitation of $M_{23}C_6$ at austenite-ferrite boundaries (Ref 97). When this occurs, most of the chromium in the $M_{23}C_6$ comes from the ferrite grains; only a very small amount comes from the austenite grains. A chromium-depleted zone is formed at the austenite-carbide interface, which is very narrow compared to those in fully austenitic sensitized stainless steels. Aging for 7 h at 600 °C (1110 °F) replenished the chromium-depleted zone and stopped the localized intergranular attack (ASTM A 262E test). Therefore, the heating of depleted zones is much more rapid in duplex grades.

The aging of duplex stainless steels produces a variety of phases in the ferrite (Ref 97). Aging at 480 °C (895 °F) does not produce $M_{23}C_6$, but it will produce an extremely small, finely distributed, chromium-rich α'-phase in the ferrite. Aging at 600 to 700 °C (1110 to 1290 °F) produces a complex series of transformations of the ferrite phase.

Another study of AISI 308 showed that for a given carbon content there is a critical amount and distribution of the ferrite-austenite interfacial boundary area (Ref 98). Above this critical level, the alloy is immune to intergranular corrosion with aging between 480 and 700 °C (895 and 1290 °F) for up to 1000 h. If the amount and distribution of these boundaries is below the critical level, two types of sensitization behavior can occur. The amount and distribution of the ferrite-austenite interfaces may be adequate to produce the rapid heating of chromium-depleted regions that form at the austenite-carbide interface during aging. If not, the alloy will behave as a fully austenitic grade.

475 °C Embrittlement

Iron-chromium alloys containing 13 to 90% Cr are susceptible to embrittlement when held within or cooled slowly through the temperature range of 550 to 400 °C (1020 to 750 °F). This phenomenon, called *475 °C (885 °F) embrittlement*, increases tensile strength and hardness and decreases tensile ductility, impact strength, electrical resistivity, and corrosion resistance (Ref 99-120). Microstructure effects are minor: Grain boundaries etch more widely, and the grain interiors darken.

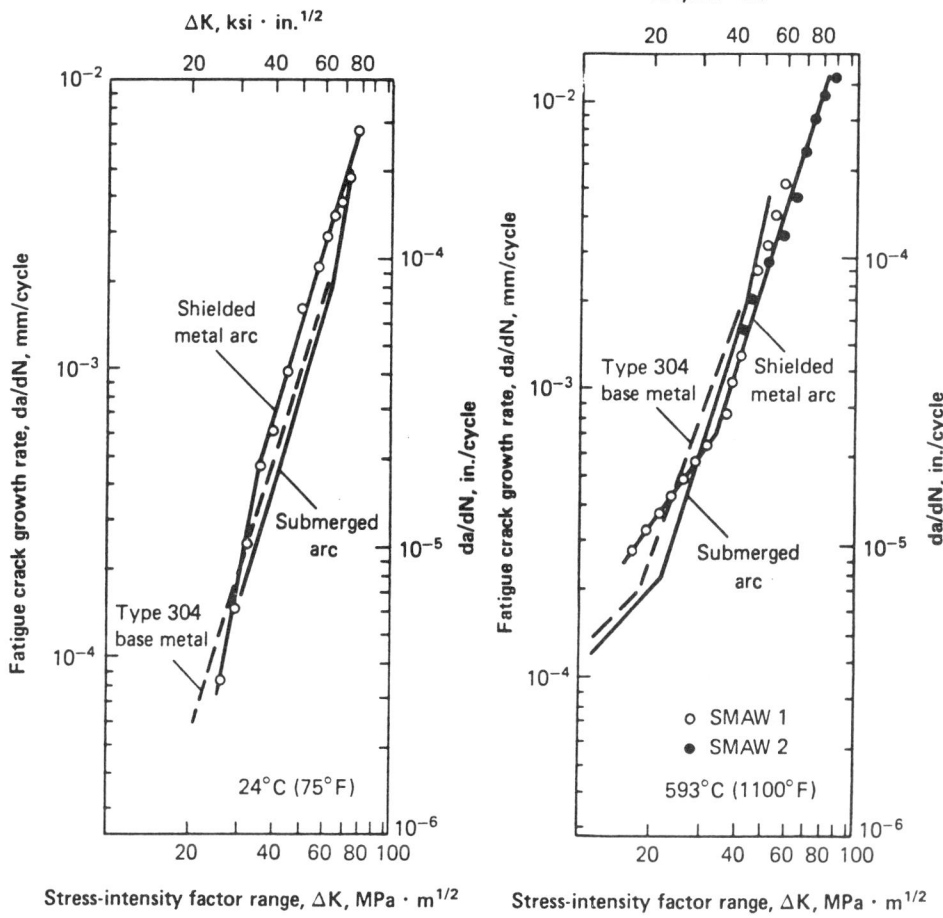

Fig. 46   Fatigue crack growth rates for annealed type 304 base metal and type 308 weld metal at 24 and 593 °C (75 and 1100 °F), 0.17 Hz, and a load ratio of 0. Source: Ref 173

Numerous theories have been proposed to account for 475 °C embrittlement. The problem occurs with iron-chromium ferritic and duplex ferritic-austenitic stainless steels, but not with austenitic grades. The earliest theories suggested that embrittlement was due to precipitation of second phases such as phosphides (Ref 100), carbides or nitrides (Ref 101), or oxides (Ref 105). Others suggested that embrittlement was due to σ-phase, which does form in iron-chromium alloys, or some transitional phase that precedes a formation (Ref 102-104). However, σ forms at higher temperatures and has never been detected in 475 °C embrittled specimens. Japanese researchers (Ref 106, 107) suggested that 475 °C embrittlement was due to ordering, that is, from the formation of Fe_3Cr, FeCr, and $FeCr_3$ superlattices. However, subsequent experiments using neutron diffraction failed to detect evidence of ordering.

A 1953 study using transmission electron microscopy observed that 475 °C embrittlement caused the precipitation of a coherent chromium-rich bcc phase with a lattice parameter only slightly greater than the iron-rich bcc ferritic matrix phase. These precipitates were extremely small, for example, about 15 to 30 nm (150 to 300 Å) in diameter for an Fe-27Cr alloy aged from 10,000 to 34,000 h at 480 °C (900 °F). The precipitates were nonmagnetic and contained about

80% Cr. The rate of growth of the precipitates was very slow, and they did not appear to overage (Ref 108). Other studies have confirmed these findings (Ref 109, 116). The 1953 study was unable to explain its observations based on the existing iron-chromium phase diagram. Later work (Ref 109) concluded that 475 °C embrittlement was a precipitation-hardening phenomenon resulting from the presence of a miscibility gap in the iron-chromium system below 600 °C (1110 °F). The location of the miscibility gap was later refined (Ref 117).

Aging at 475 °C (885 °F) has been shown to cause a rapid rate of hardening with aging between about 20 and 120 h because of homogeneous precipitation. The rate of hardening is much slower with continued aging from 120 to 1000 h. During this aging period, the precipitates grow. Aging beyond 1000 h produces little increase in hardness because of the stability of the precipitates, which do not grow larger than about 30 nm (300 Å).

Precipitation of the chromium-rich α′-phase in iron-chromium alloys can occur either by spinodal decomposition or by nucleation and growth, depending on the aging temperature and alloy composition. For example, an Fe-30Cr alloy will decompose to chromium-rich precipitates in

an iron-rich matrix (chromium-depleted) inside the spinodal at 475 °C (885 °F), forming spherical α′, or outside the spinodal at 550 °C (1020 °F), forming disk-shape α′ (Ref 113). An Fe-20Cr alloy will decompose by nucleation and growth at 470 °C (880 °F), while Fe-30Cr, Fe-40Cr, and Fe-50Cr alloys will decompose spinodally at 470 °C (880 °F).

Even for a severely embrittled alloy, 475 °C embrittlement is reversible. Properties can be restored within minutes by reheating the alloy to 675 °C (1250 °F) or above (Ref 105, 111). The degree of embrittlement increases with chromium content; however, embrittlement is negligible below 13% Cr. Carbide-forming alloying additions, such as molybdenum, vanadium, titanium, and niobium, appear to increase embrittlement, particularly with higher chromium levels. Increased levels of carbon and nitrogen also enhance embrittlement and, of course, are detrimental to nonembrittled properties as well. Cold work prior to 475 °C (885 °F) exposure accelerates embrittlement, particularly for higher-chromium alloys.

Figure 26 demonstrates the C-curve nature of the increase in hardness due to aging for an Fe-30Cr ferritic stainless steel (Ref 109). The nose of the curve decreases with time. Figure 27 shows the results for aging at 475 °C (885 °F) for up to 1000 h for iron-chromium alloys with 15, 20.6, 23, 37, and 56% Cr. As the chromium content increased, the time to the initial increase in hardness decreased. Over 200 h were required for the 15% Cr alloy, only about 4 h for the 20.6% Cr alloy, and less than 1 h for the 23% Cr alloy. The initial increase in hardness was nearly instantaneous for the 37 and 56% Cr alloys. Accompanying the increase in hardness with aging at 475 °C (885 °F) are an increase in tensile and yield strength and a decrease in tensile ductility and impact energy. Examples of such data can be found in Ref 102, 103, 116, and 118 to 120.

Sigma-Phase Embrittlement

The existence of σ-phase in iron-chromium alloys was first detected in 1907 by the observation of a thermal arrest in cooling curves (Ref 121). It was suggested that the thermal arrest could be due to the formation of an FeCr intermetallic compound. The first actual observation of σ in iron-chromium alloys was reported in 1927 (Ref 122). The phase was referred to as the brittle constituent (B-constituent) and was reported to be corundum hard. In a discussion of this paper, it was suggested that the B-constituent was the FeCr intermetallic phase detected in 1907. The σ-phase was identified by x-ray diffraction in 1927 (Ref 123) and in 1931 (Ref 124). Numerous earlier investigators, however, had failed to detect the presence of σ; this failure caused considerable confusion.

After the existence of σ was firmly established, numerous studies were conducted to define the compositions and temperatures over which σ could be formed. This produced a series of refinements to the iron-chromium equilibrium diagram, as in the case of 475 °C embrittlement. Successive studies demonstrated that σ could form in alloys with lower and lower chromium

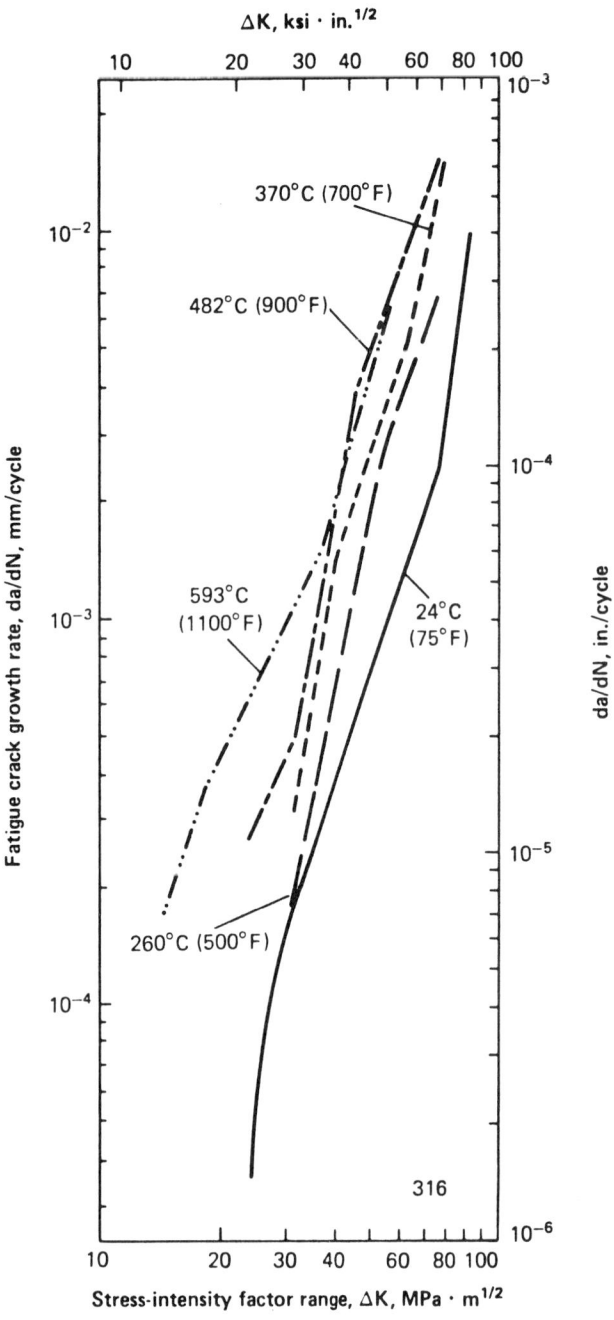

Fig. 47 Effect of testing temperature on fatigue crack growth rates for annealed type 316 stainless steel tested in air at 0.17 Hz and a load ratio of 0. Source: Ref 164, 175

amounts, markedly accelerates the formation of σ. In general, all of the elements that stabilize ferrite promote σ formation. Molybdenum has an effect similar to that of silicon; aluminum has a lesser influence. Increasing the chromium content, of course, also favors σ formation. Small amounts of nickel and manganese increase the rate of σ formation, but large amounts, which stabilize austenite, retard σ formation. Carbon additions decrease σ formation by forming chromium carbides, thereby reducing the amount of chromium in solid solution. Additions of tungsten, vanadium, titanium, and niobium also promote σ formation. As might be expected, σ forms more readily in ferritic than in austenitic stainless steels. Coarse grain sizes from high solution-annealing temperatures retard σ formation, and prior cold working enhances it. The influence of cold work on σ formation depends on the amount of cold work and its effect on recrystallization. If the amount of cold work is sufficient to produce recrystallization at the service temperature, σ formation is enhanced. If recrystallization does not occur, the rate of σ formation may not be affected. Small amounts of cold work that do not promote recrystallization may actually retard σ formation (Ref 135).

The composition of σ in austenitic stainless steels is more complex than it is for simple iron-chromium ferritic grades. Several studies, particularly for type 316, have analyzed the composition of σ. These studies have used a traditional wet chemical analysis of bulk-extracted σ, wavelength-dispersive spectroscopy (WDS) with an electron microprobe, or energy-dispersive spectroscopy (EDS) with either a scanning transmission electron microscope (STEM) for thin foils or a scanning electron microscope (SEM) for bulk specimens (Ref 136).

An analysis of σ in type 316 by the SEM-EDS approach obtained a composition of 11Mo-29Cr-55Fe-5Ni in a specimen aged 3000 h at 815 °C (1500 °F) (Ref 137). A WDS analysis using the electron microprobe of type 316 heated 60 h at 870 °C (1600 °F) obtained a σ composition of 26.4Cr-3.3Ni-53.7Fe-8.5Mo (Ref 138). An analysis of σ in a failed type 316 superheater tube using STEM-EDS of thin foils obtained a composition of 52.7Fe-37Cr-3.7Mo-4.8Ni-0.7Si-0.4Mn (Ref 139).

Reference 140 presents an analysis of σ in three versions of type 310 (a standard version, a low-carbon version, and a high-silicon version) and titanium-stabilized type 316. The analysis was done using the electron microprobe. For the low-carbon type 310S, the chromium-to-iron (Cr/Fe) ratio in σ was constant and equal to 1 for all temperatures and times; the composition was 46Cr-46Fe-8Ni. For the type 310 and type 310Si, the composition of σ varied with temperature and time, and the Cr/Fe ratio of 1 was obtained after a certain time at any temperature used. The higher the temperature, the shorter the time required to obtain a Cr/Fe ratio of 1. When the Cr/Fe ratio stabilized at 1 for 310 and 310Si, σ had the same composition as in the low-carbon version. The work with 316Ti showed that the molybdenum content in σ increased with temperature. As the molybdenum content in σ increased, the iron con-

contents under the proper conditions; one study demonstrated the formation of σ at 480 °C (900 °F) in an alloy with less than 12% Cr. In general, σ forms with long-time exposure in the range of 565 to 980 °C (1050 to 1800 °F), although this range varies somewhat with composition and processing. Sigma formation exhibits C-curve behavior with the shortest time for formation (nose of the curve) generally occurring between about 700 and 810 °C (1290 and 1490 °F); the temperature that produces the greatest amount of σ with time is usually somewhat lower.

The general characteristics of σ-phase have been reviewed extensively (Ref 125-133). The name

sigma stems from work done in 1936 (Ref 134). Sigma-type phases have since been identified in over fifty binary systems and in other commercial alloys (for example, nickel-base superalloys). Sigma phase has a tetragonal crystal structure with 30 atoms per unit cell and a c/a ratio of approximately 0.52 (Ref 133). Sigma in iron-chromium alloys has a hardness equivalent to approximately 68 HRC (940 HV). Because of its brittleness, σ often fractures during indentation. At room temperature, σ is nonmagnetic. Embrittlement effects due to σ are greatest at room temperature.

Austenitic and Ferritic Stainless Steels. In commercial alloys, silicon, even in small

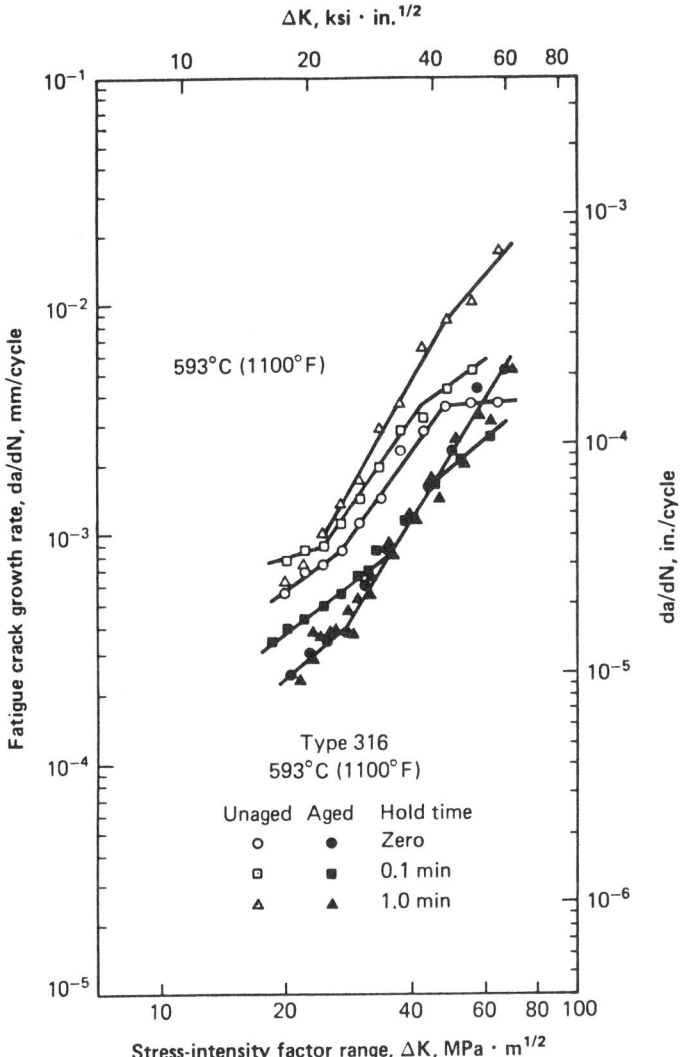

Fig. 48 Effect of exposure in air at 593 °C (1100 °F) for 5000 h, and hold times, on fatigue crack growth rates for annealed type 316 stainless steel at 593 °C in air. Source: Ref 171

tent increased, and the chromium and nickel contents decreased. The (Cr+Mo)/(Fe+Ni) ratio was constant, and the formula for σ was expressed as $(Cr,Mo)_{35}(Fe,Ni)_{65}$. Although the chemical composition of σ varied with temperature and time, the c/a ratio of the tetragonal unit cell was constant at 0.519.

The influence of molybdenum, which is known to promote σ formation, was examined using wrought 25Cr-20Ni alloys with additions of up to 8.2% Mo (Ref 141). Sigma was analyzed with the electron microprobe using specimens aged at 850 °C (1560 °F) for 525 h (the 8.2% Mo specimen was aged for 350 h). As the molybdenum content in the 25Cr-20Ni alloys increased to 8.2%, the chromium content in σ decreased from 42.6 to 31.0%, the iron content decreased from 43.3 to 38.8%, the nickel content remained constant at about 10%, and the molybdenum content increased to 14.3%. In addition, as the molybdenum content of the steels increased, the volume fraction of σ increased from 3 to 60% for these aging treatments.

Sigma formation in pure iron-chromium alloys is rather sluggish, which accounts for much of the confusion in early studies concerning its existence. Subsequent work showed that the formation of σ was dramatically accelerated by prior cold work and by silicon additions (Ref 134). In ferritic stainless steels, the addition of even minor amounts of other alloying elements expands the compositional range over which σ may form and increases the rate of formation. All of the ferritic stabilizing elements promote σ formation.

Sigma will also form in austenitic alloys. In fully austenitic alloys, σ forms from the austenite along grain boundaries. If δ-ferrite is present in the austenitic alloy, σ formation is more rapid and occurs in the δ-ferrite. Sigma will form more readily in austenitic alloys containing additions of ferrite-stabilizing elements such as molybdenum and titanium; the rate of formation can be quite rapid in these alloys.

The most sensitive room-temperature property for assessing the influence of σ is the impact strength. A study of the influence of σ on the

toughness of type 310 shows the dramatic loss in toughness due to σ (Fig. 28). With increasing time at temperature, particularly in the range of 760 to 870 °C (1400 to 1600 °F), the toughness decreased by about 85%.

The influence of high-temperature exposure on the toughness of a low-interstitial 29Cr-4Mo ferritic stainless steel has been examined (Ref 143). Figure 29 shows the room-temperature impact strength trends for this alloy as a function of aging temperature and time. Aging at 371 °C (700 °F) produced no loss in toughness. However, aging at 427, 482, and 538 °C (800, 900, and 1000 °F), in the range of 475 °C embrittlement, produced a loss of toughness that was most pronounced at 482 °C (900 °F). Aging at higher temperatures, where σ was formed, produced more pronounced embrittlement, which was greatest at 816 °C (1500 °F). Figure 30, which is a summary of this data, shows the time at aging temperatures between 371 and 978 °C (700 and 1790 °F) required to produce a DBTT of 25 and 100 °C (77 and 212 °F). This produces a C-curve presentation of the time for embrittlement as a function of aging temperature. For σ formation, embrittlement was most rapid at about 775 °C (1425 °F); 475 °C embrittlement was slower with a maximum rate at about 480 °C (900° F). Chi phase was also observed, along with σ, after aging in the high-temperature range. Sigma formed over the range of 595 to 925 °C (1100 to 1700 °F). Embrittlement was most pronounced when intergranular σ films formed, producing intergranular tensile and impact fractures.

While some studies have demonstrated only a minor increase in hardness and strength because of σ formation, studies of some steels have demonstrated more substantial changes. Tensile ductility, like toughness, is generally substantially reduced. One study has demonstrated that high-chromium σ-hardenable alloys are useful in applications involving high-temperature erosion or wear, for example, exhaust valves (Ref 144). Such steels generally contain from 20 to 30% Cr, about 0.25 to 0.45% C, and additions of manganese and nickel to produce a duplex structure; they also generally contain additions of elements that promote σ formation, such as silicon and molybdenum. Such steels can be hardened to about 40 HRC by σ and retain their strength at high temperatures. Although the toughness of such steels is reduced about 35% by the presence of σ, they do perform well as long as the extent of σ-phase embrittlement is not severe. The toughness and ductility of σ-containing steels at high temperatures is considerably better than at room temperature; however, such steels are not useful at high temperatures if shock resistance is required.

An examination of the high-temperature properties of a 25Cr-20Ni-2Si (type 314) austenitic stainless steel aged between 650 and 980 °C (1200 and 1800 °F) showed that with the proper amount and distribution of σ, substantial increases in yield and tensile strengths result for test temperatures up to 760 °C (1400 °F) (Ref 145). For conditions involving slow strain rates, σ-phase reduces creep resistance. Variations in austenite grain size, however, can exert an even

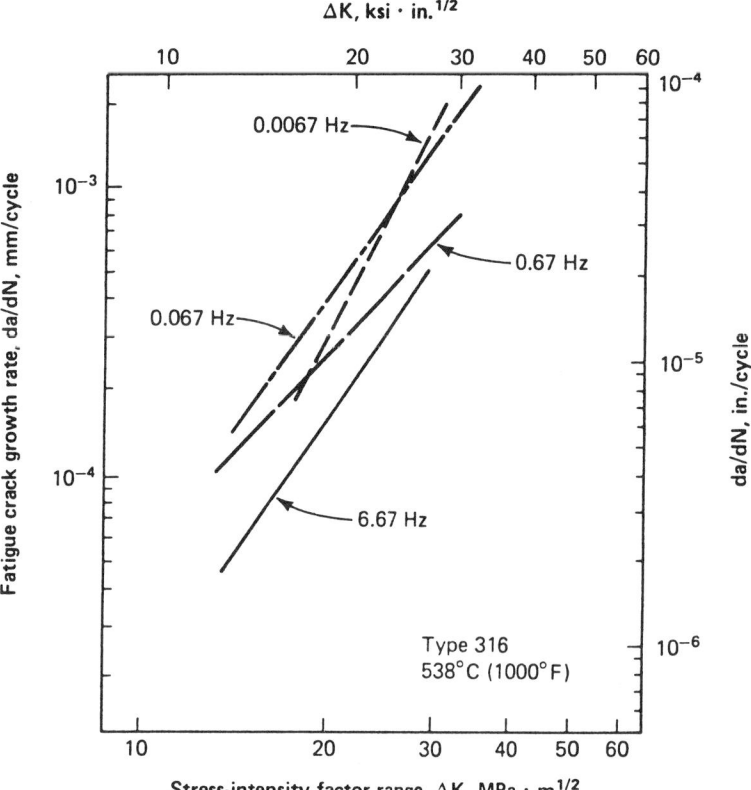

Fig. 49 Effect of variation in cyclic frequency on fatigue crack growth rate of annealed type 316 stainless steel in air at 538 °C (1000 °F) and a load ratio of 0.05. Source: Ref 166

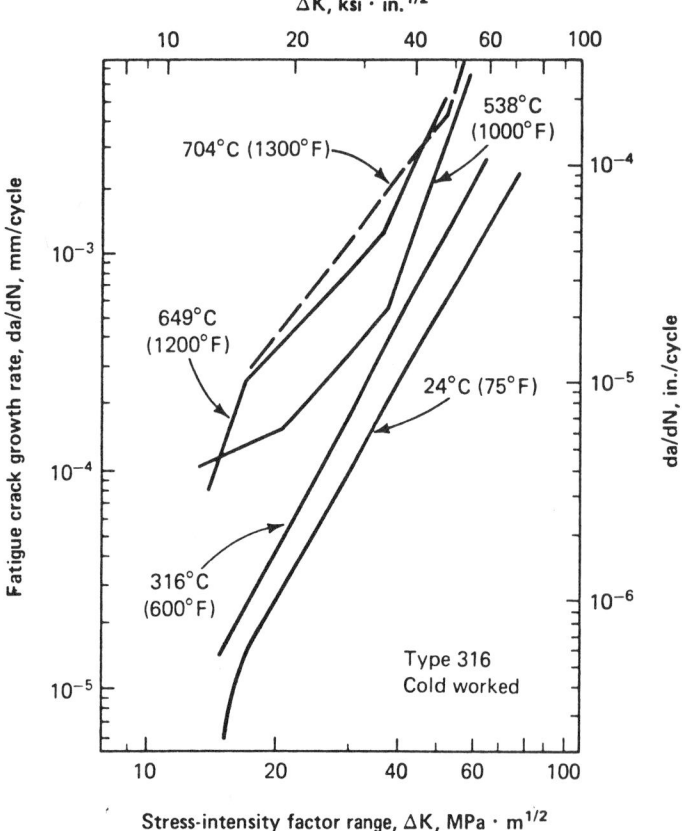

Fig. 50 Fatigue crack growth rates of 20% cold-worked type 316 stainless steel for various temperatures. Curves are averages for longitudinal-transverse specimens at each temperature in air; 3 Hz at 24 °C, 0.67 Hz at elevated temperatures; and a load ratio of 0.05. Source: Ref 176

greater effect on high-temperature tensile and creep properties. Fine grain sizes increase short-time high-temperature tensile strength but reduce long-time creep strength. The room-temperature ductility of these alloys is poor but is restored at temperatures above 540 to 650 °C (1000 to 1200 °F). A fine distribution of σ is detrimental to creep strength but minimizes loss of ductility at room temperature. Sigma has also been found to be detrimental in thermal fatigue situations (Ref 146). High-temperature exposure can produce a variety of phases, and embrittlement is not always due solely to σ formation (Ref 147). Therefore, each situation must be carefully evaluated to determine the true cause of the degradation of properties.

Duplex Stainless Steels. Sigma phase is known to form quite rapidly in duplex stainless steels. One study, for example, observed σ after 15 min at 750 °C (1380 °F) and 2 min at 850 °C (1560 °F) in a 20Cr-10Ni-3Mo duplex alloy (Ref 148). Another study found that σ formed after 2 min at 900 °C (1650 °F) in a 21Cr-7Ni-2.4Mo-1.3Cu (UNS S32404) duplex stainless steel containing 33% ferrite (Ref 149). Sigma formed in a C-curve manner along with a number of other phases, but σ was the worst embrittler and led to massive pit initiation in corrosion tests. Sigma formed in the ferrite, and pitting occurred in the chromium-molybdenum-depleted ferrite-σ regions.

An evaluation of the effects of alloying elements on σ formation in duplex stainless steels found that increasing chromium and molybdenum contents caused an increase in the rate of σ formation and in the maximum amount produced (Ref 150). Increasing the nickel content decreased the maximum amount of σ that could form but increased the rate of σ formation. Sigma formation occurred primarily by the decomposition of ferrite into σ and austenite.

The influence of σ on corrosion characteristics is rather complex. In many instances, little influence is observed in environments normally used with a particular alloy. Large σ particles appear to be rather harmless: a fine distribution of particles, particularly if present at the grain boundaries and in highly oxidizing solutions, is more harmful.

Fatigue Crack Initiation

Fatigue crack initiation tests are procedures in which a specimen or part is subjected to cyclic loading to failure. A large portion of the total number of cycles in these tests is spent initiating the crack. Although crack initiation tests conducted on small specimens do not precisely establish the fatigue life of a large part, such tests do provide data on the intrinsic fatigue crack initiation behavior of a stainless steel. As a result, such data can be used to develop criteria to prevent fatigue failures in engineering design. Examples of the use of small-specimen fatigue test data can be found in the basis of the fatigue design codes for boilers and pressure vessels, complex welded, riveted, or bolted structures, and automotive and aerospace components.

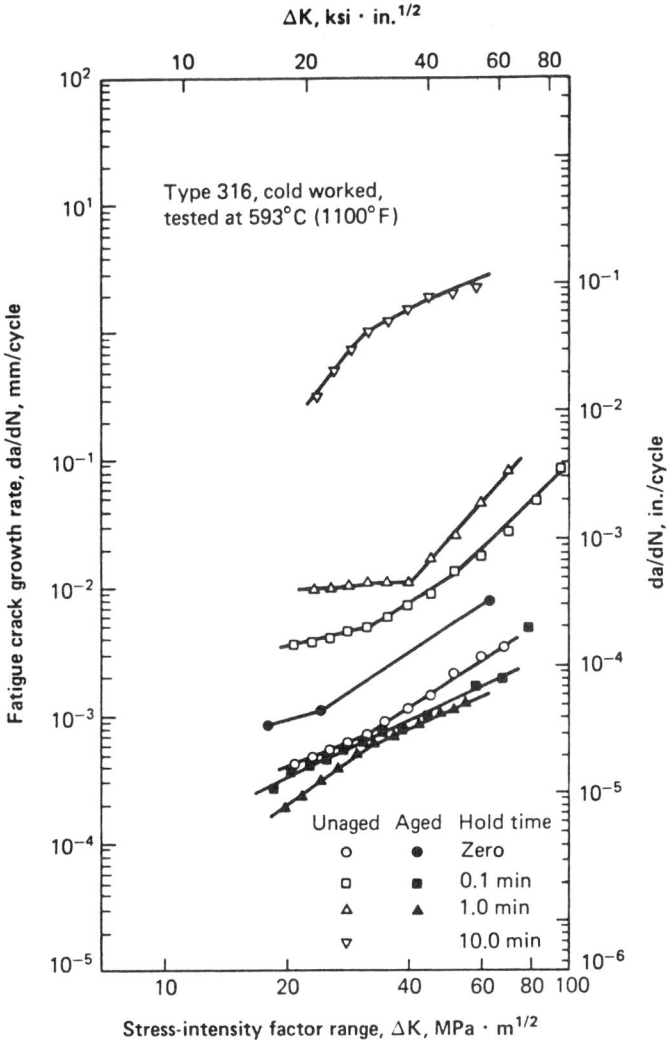

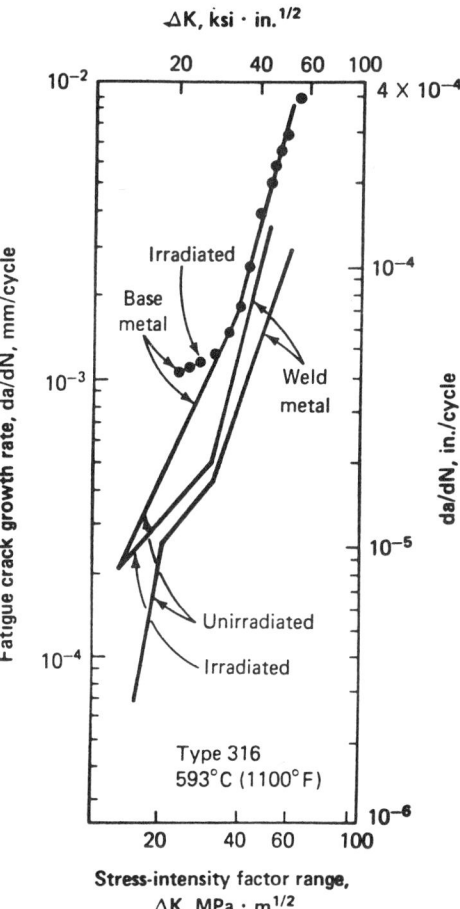

Fig. 52 Fatigue crack growth rates in type 316 base metal and weld metal in the unirradiated and irradiated conditions at 593 °C (1100 °F) in air [fluence 1.2 × 10^{22} n/cm², >0.1 MeV at 410 °C (770 °F)]. Source: Ref 177

Fig. 51 Effect of exposure at 593 °C (1100 °F) for 5000 h, and hold times during cycling, on fatigue crack growth rate of 20% cold-worked type 316 stainless steel at 593 °C in air. Source: Ref 171

Fatigue Testing Regimes. The magnitude of the nominal stress on a cyclically loaded component frequently is measured by the amount of overstress—that is, the amount by which the nominal stress exceeds the fatigue limit or the long-life fatigue strength of the material used in the component. The number of load cycles that a component under low overstress can endure is high; thus, the term *high-cycle fatigue* is often applied.

As the magnitude of the nominal stress increases, initiation of multiple cracks is more likely. Also, spacing between fatigue striations, which indicate the progressive growth of the crack front, is increased, and the region of final fast fracture is increased in size.

Low-cycle fatigue is the regime characterized by high overstress. The arbitrary, but commonly accepted, dividing line between high-cycle and low-cycle fatigue is considered to be about 10^4 to 10^5 cycles. In practice, this distinction is made by determining whether the dominant component of the strain imposed during cyclic loading is elastic (high cycle) or plastic (low cycle), which in turn depends on the properties of the metal as well as the magnitude of the nominal stress.

Special test techniques are required for control and monitoring of low-cycle fatigue tests. Typically, strain-controlled tests (constant strain amplitude) are used. Because high-cycle fatigue tests require uninterrupted operation for long periods of time, simple reliable test machines are used. Constant load amplitude or constant-deflection tests commonly are conducted. Test methods for both low-cycle and high-cycle fatigue are described in the articles "Fatigue Crack Initiation" and "Ultrasonic Fatigue Testing" in Volume 8 of the *ASM Handbook*.

In routine low- and high-cycle fatigue crack initiation testing, complete fracture of a small specimen is the failure criteria. Approximately 30 to 40% of the low-cycle fatigue life and about 80 to 90% of the high-cycle fatigue life measured by cycles-to-failure involves nucleation of the fatigue microcrack.

Presentation of Fatigue Data. High-cycle fatigue data are presented graphically as stress (*S*) versus cycles-to-failure (*N*) in *S-N* diagrams or *S-N* curves. Because the stress in high-cycle fatigue tests is usually within the elastic range, the calculation of stress amplitude, stress range, or maxi-

mum stress on the *S*-axis is made using simple equations from mechanics of materials (i.e., stress calculated using the specimen dimensions and the controlled load or deflection applied axially, in flexure, or in torsion). Examples of high-cycle fatigue results on stainless steels are shown in Fig. 31 to 33.

Until World War II, little attention was paid to the low-cycle range, and most of the existing fatigue results were for high cycles only. It was then realized that only a short fatigue life is required for some pressure vessels, pressurized fuselages, mechanisms for extending landing gears and controlling wing flaps, missiles, spaceship launching equipment, and so forth. Consequently, interest in low-cycle fatigue testing developed.

Figure 34 illustrates a stress-strain loop under controlled constant-strain cycling in a low-cycle fatigue test. During initial loading, the stress-strain curve is O-A-B. Upon unloading, yielding begins in compression at a lower stress, C, due to the Bauschinger effect. In reloading in tension, a hysteresis loop develops. The dimensions of this loop are described by its width $\Delta\varepsilon$ (the total strain range) and its height $\Delta\sigma$ (the stress range). The total strain range $\Delta\varepsilon$ consists of an elastic strain

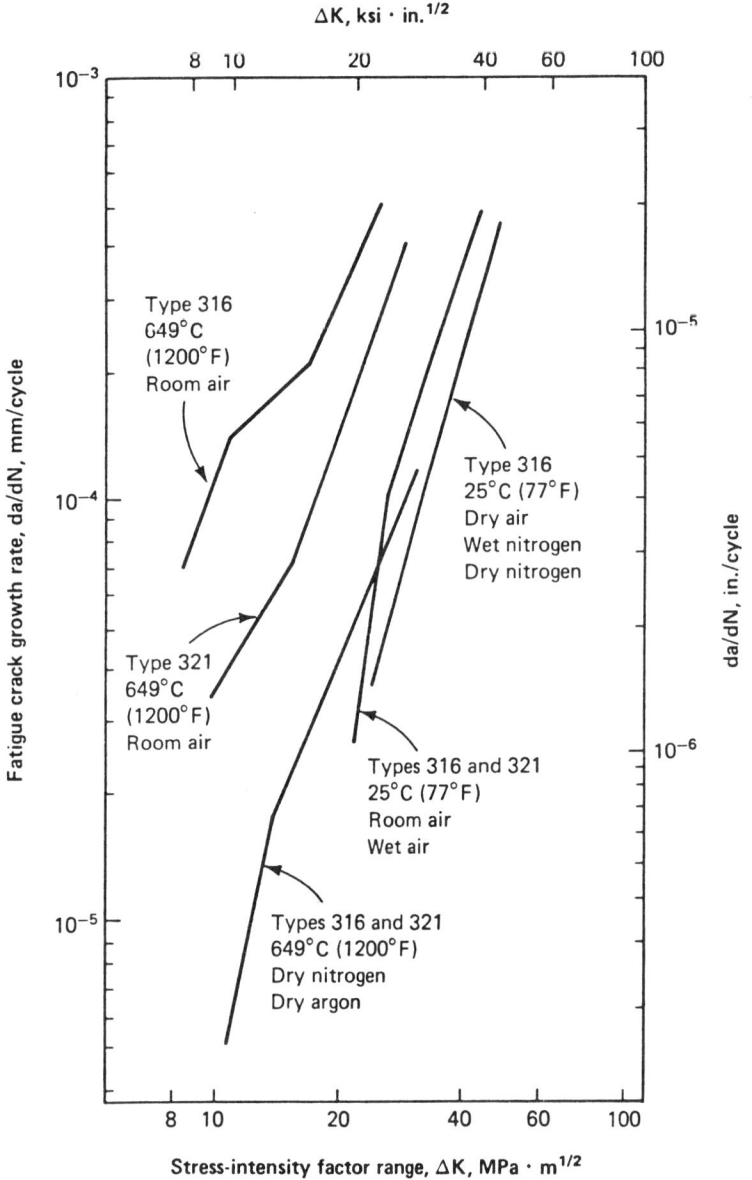

Fig. 53 Effect of gas environments on fatigue crack growth rates for types 316 and 321 stainless steels at 25 and 649 °C (77 and 1200 °F). Source: Ref 178

component $\Delta\varepsilon_e = \Delta\sigma/E$ and a plastic strain component $\Delta\varepsilon_p$.

The width of the hysteresis loop depends on the level of cyclic strain. When the level of cyclic strain is small, the hysteresis loop becomes very narrow. For tests conducted under constant $\Delta\varepsilon$, the stress range $\Delta\sigma$ usually changes with an increasing number of cycles. Annealed materials undergo cyclic strain hardening so that $\Delta\sigma$ increases with an increasing number of strain cycles and then levels off after about 100 strain cycles. The larger the value of $\Delta\varepsilon$, the greater the increase in stress range. Materials that are initially cold worked undergo cyclic strain softening so that $\Delta\sigma$ decreases with increasing number of strain cycles.

The common method of presenting low-cycle fatigue data is to plot either the plastic strain range, $\Delta\varepsilon_p$, or the total strain range, $\Delta\varepsilon$, versus N. When plotted using log-log coordinates, a straight line can be fit to the $\Delta\varepsilon_p$-N plot. The slope of this line in the region where plastic strain dominates has shown little variation for the large number of metals and alloys tested in low-cycle fatigue, the average value being $\frac{1}{2}$. This power-law relationship between $\Delta\varepsilon_p$ and N is known as the Coffin-Manson relationship (Ref 152-157). Figure 35 is an example of the typical presentation of low-cycle fatigue test results. Figure 36 shows the effect of temperature and strain rate on low-cycle fatigue of type 304 stainless steel.

When lines of curves are presented with fatigue data, the equation and the method of the fit should be indicated. Any presentation of fatigue data should include the following pertinent information, when applicable, regarding the material and the test:

- Material identification (product form)
- Tensile strength
- Orientation of the specimen (Fig. 37)
- Surface condition
- Notch description, stress-concentration factor (Fig. 33)
- Type of fatigue test (mode of loading)
- Controlled test parameters
- Stress ratio
- Test frequency (Fig. 31 to 33, 35)
- Test temperature and environment (Fig. 31 to 33, 35)

Consolidation of Fatigue Data. In some situations, the available quantity of fatigue data at a given condition is so limited that it is difficult to define even a mean S/N or ε/N curve with confidence. In other situations, it is of interest to project the fatigue response of a material at conditions intermediate to those for which data are available. In these situations, appropriate analytical models can be used to consolidate available fatigue data.

Fatigue loading on actual components generally involves variable-amplitude conditions, which produce local stress and strain cycles covering a range of amplitudes and mean levels. Both the stress or strain amplitude and the mean stress or strain have a major impact on the fatigue resistance of a material.

This interrelationship between stress amplitude, mean stress, and fatigue life has been represented in constant-life diagrams, known as Goodman diagrams (Ref 159, 160). Each line represents the combinations of mean stress and stress amplitude that will produce an average fatigue life for a specified number of cycles. An example of a constant-life diagram for a PH stainless steel is shown in Fig. 38.

Fatigue Crack Propagation and Fracture Toughness (Ref 161)

There are certain limitations in obtaining usable fracture mechanics data for structural alloys, depending on their strength, toughness, and intended service environments. For example, all of the austenitic stainless steels are too tough for obtaining valid plane strain fracture toughness (K_{Ic}) data on specimens of reasonable size, even at cryogenic temperatures. However, some of the austenitic grades, particularly types 304 and 316, are of interest for certain nuclear reactor components that are subjected to cyclic loading at elevated temperatures. In order to evaluate the fatigue crack growth rate properties of these steels under conditions that would show effects of cyclic loading, elevated-temperature exposure, and various environments, fatigue crack growth rate tests have been conducted on precracked specimens of types 304, 316, and others. Results of these tests have been analyzed on the basis of fracture mechanics concepts, leading to a well-documented collection of fatigue crack growth rate data for the austenitic stainless steels—particularly type 304.

Fatigue crack growth rate data also have been obtained on precracked specimens of type 403 martensitic stainless steel because it has been used for steam turbine buckets and for rotors in some turbines. Results of these tests show the effects of a number of variables on fatigue crack

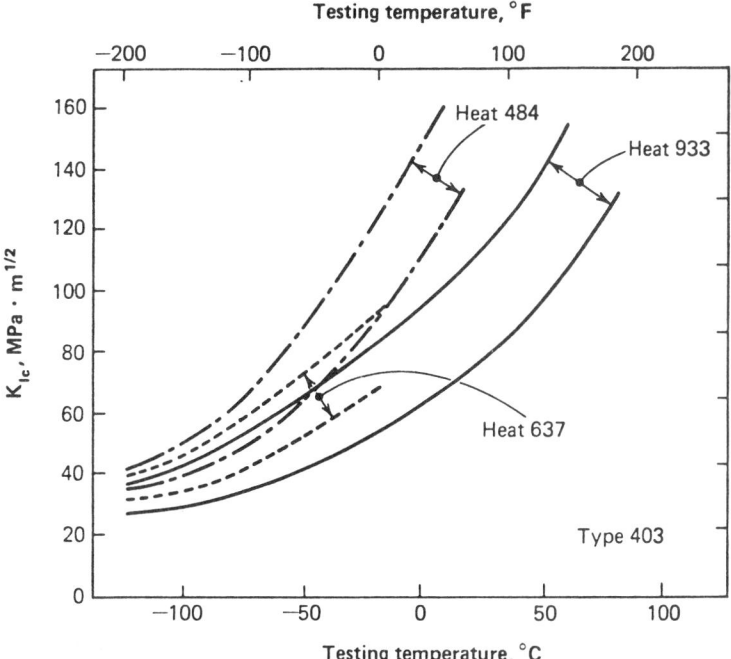

Fig. 54 Scatter bands of fracture toughness data for three heats of type 403 stainless steel in the heat-treated condition. Source: Ref 179

growth rates. A limited amount of K_{Ic} data also has been obtained on large specimens of type 403 stainless steel over a range of temperatures. Results of J-integral tests also show the estimated fracture toughness, $K_{Ic}(J)$, for type 403 at room temperature and at elevated temperatures.

Of the PH stainless steels, the largest amount of fracture mechanics data has been obtained on PH13-8 Mo because this steel was considered for certain components of the B-1 bomber during prototype production at Rockwell International. Because all major structural alloys supplied for this aircraft were subjected to fracture mechanics evaluations, a well-documented backlog of fracture mechanics data is available for the PH13-8 Mo alloy.

The data presented in the following sections will show the effects on fracture of many variables in alloy processing, loading conditions, and environments for the most widely used austenitic, martensitic, and PH stainless steels. Additional information can be found in Ref 161, from which the following material was adapted.

Austenitic Stainless Steels

Available fracture mechanics data for austenitic stainless steels are primarily limited to fatigue crack growth rate data in air and in several other environments, and at elevated and cryogenic temperatures. Emphasis in this section is placed on types 304 and 316 and their variations. Effects of material variables and stressing variables are reviewed, along with effects of various environments and temperature variations. Additional fracture mechanics data on other austenitic grades, including types 301, 308, 309, 321, and 348 and high-manganese, high-nitrogen alloys

21-6-9, 22-13-15, and Kromarc 58, can be found in Ref 161.

Types 304 and 304L. Fatigue crack growth rate data have been obtained for specimens of type 304 and type 304L stainless steels to show the effects of many of the variables associated with applications of these alloys. Types 304 and 304L are generally used in the annealed condition, but for improved strength they may be applied in the warm-worked or cold-worked condition (cold-drawn or cold-rolled). They are used extensively in construction of nuclear power station structures, and in this application they are exposed to elevated temperatures and static stressing combined with cyclic stressing over a wide range of frequencies and load ratios while being exposed to potentially corrosive environments. Exposure to fast neutron fluences must also be considered. The effects of all of these factors have been evaluated on a number of fatigue testing programs.

Results of fatigue crack growth rate tests on types 304 and 304L stainless steels at room temperature and at elevated temperatures have been reported by James and Schwenk (Ref 162), by James (Ref 163), and by others (Ref 164, 165). As shown in Fig. 39, increasing the exposure temperature from room temperature to 650 °C (1200 °F) increases the fatigue crack growth rates at any stress-intensity factor, ΔK, within the range of the tests in an air environment. These data, reported by James and Schwenk, are for specimens of both the longitudinal-transverse (L-T) and T-L orientations, for several different maximum alternating loads, for load ratios (R) of 0 to 0.05, and for cyclic frequencies from 0.033 to 6.66 Hz for the room-temperature tests and 0.067 Hz for the elevated-temperature tests. Data points were omitted from the curves in Fig. 39 and from many of the fatigue crack growth rate (da/dN) curves in other

figures to show the trends more clearly, but the scatter in data points was relatively narrow.

For fatigue crack growth rate tests on specimens of annealed type 304 stainless steel at elevated temperatures, increasing the cyclic frequency will decrease the crack growth rate over part of the ΔK range, as shown in Fig. 40, for tests at 538 °C (1000 °F) and at $R = 0.05$ (Ref 166, 167). The data in Fig. 40 were obtained in tests with a sawtooth waveform. Changing from a sawtooth waveform to a waveform with a short holding period at maximum load did not influence the overall fatigue crack growth rates, according to additional data reported by James and shown in Fig. 41 (Ref 168).

Effects of holding times of 0.1 and 1.0 min on fatigue crack growth rates for specimens of annealed type 304 based on crack extension per unit of time, da/dt, for tests at 417 and 593 °C (800 and 1100 °F) have been reported by Shahinian (Ref 169).

At 427 °C (800 °F), the fatigue crack growth rates were substantially greater for specimens tested with no holding time (continuous cycling) than for specimens held at maximum load for 0.1 or 1.0 minute per cycle. The lowest fatigue crack growth rates occurred for specimens with the longest holding time, based on da/dt. The same trend was observed for tests at 593 °C (1100 °F), as shown in Fig. 42. Therefore, cyclic loading has a more damaging effect than static loading on crack growth per unit of time.

In some applications, type 304 stainless steel components are fabricated in the cold-worked condition to improved strength properties. A comparison of fatigue crack growth rate data by Shahinian, Watson, and Smith (Ref 170), illustrated in Fig. 43, shows that the high-ΔK crack growth rates were lower for the cold-worked specimens than for the annealed specimens. Crack growth rates were higher for the specimens tested at 427 °C (800 °F) than for corresponding specimens tested at room temperature.

Because the expected service lives of most components of austenitic stainless steels are many years, an evaluation of the effect of long-time aging at service temperatures is important. Results of fatigue crack growth rate tests on specimens that were tested in the unaged and aged conditions (5000 h at 593 °C, or 1100 °F) are shown in Fig. 44 as reported by Michel and Smith (Ref 171). After aging for 5000 h at this temperature, precipitation of $M_{23}C_6$ carbides is essentially complete. These results indicate that at 593 °C (1100 °F) there are no deleterious effects of aging on the crack growth rates of specimens that are continuously cycled. When a holding time of 0.1 or 1.0 min is included in each loading cycle, there tends to be a slight increase in the fatigue crack growth rate at a given ΔK level.

The effects of humid air environments on the room-temperature fatigue crack growth rates of specimens of annealed type 304 stainless steel are shown in Fig. 45 for specimens cycled at 0.17 Hz with an R = zero (Ref 170). At the lower end of the ΔK range, fatigue crack growth rates in humid air are substantially greater than crack growth rates in dry air. However, fatigue crack growth rates of specimens of type 304 stainless steel tested in a

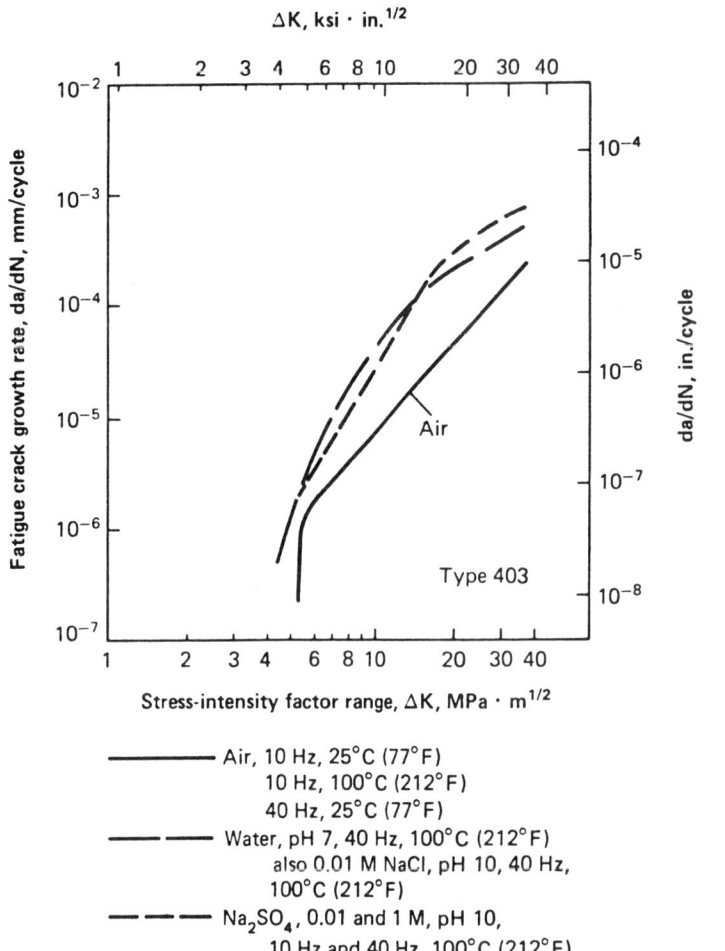

ΔK, ksi $\cdot$ in.$^{1/2}$

Fig. 55   Fatigue crack growth rates in type 403 stainless steel in air, water, 0.01 M NaCl solution, and 0.01 and 1.0 M Na$_2$SO$_4$ solutions. Source: Ref 180

Key:
— Air, 10 Hz, 25°C (77°F)
   10 Hz, 100°C (212°F)
   40 Hz, 25°C (77°F)
— Water, pH 7, 40 Hz, 100°C (212°F)
   also 0.01 M NaCl, pH 10, 40 Hz,
   100°C (212°F)
– – – Na$_2$SO$_4$, 0.01 and 1 M, pH 10,
   10 Hz and 40 Hz, 100°C (212°F)

pressurized water reactor environment at 260 to 315 °C (500 to 600 °F) with $R = 0.2$ and 0.7 were no greater than the fatigue crack growth rates in air at the same temperature with $R < 0.1$ (Ref 172). However, variations in R influenced the fatigue crack growth rates in the pressurized water reactor environment.

Type 304 Welds in Type 304 Stainless Steel. Type 308 stainless steel is the alloy that is usually used for welding rod for weldments in type 304 stainless steel when those weldments are to be exposed to room temperature or to elevated temperatures in service. Because service experience has shown that failures are more likely to originate in weld metal or in heat-affected zones than in the base metal, it is important to have frac-

ture information on weldments. In general, fatigue studies at elevated temperatures on specimens from type 304 weldments have shown that the fatigue crack growth rates in the type 308 weld metal and heat-affected zones are not greater than in comparable specimens of the base metal. Fatigue crack growth rate data obtained by Shahinian (Ref 173) for specimens of type 304 welded with type 308 rod by the submerged arc and shielded metal arc processes are shown in Fig. 46 for tests at room temperature and at 593 °C (1100 °F). At eleven temperatures, the fatigue crack growth rates in the weld metal are higher than at room temperature, particularly at the lower ΔK levels, but the trend is the same as that for the base metal. Aging the welded specimens at 593

°C (1100 °F) for 1000 h and testing at 593 °C (1100 °F) reduced the fatigue crack growth rates in the weld metal, the same as for the base metal (Ref 174).

Types 316 and 316N. Type 316 stainless steel contains 2.0 to 3.0% Mo in addition to chromium and nickel. The major effect of the molybdenum is to increase the tensile yield strength. Addition of 0.10 to 0.16% N to type 316N increases both yield and ultimate tensile strengths without reducing ductility.

Most of the fatigue crack growth rate testing on type 316 stainless steel has been oriented toward its use in components for nuclear reactors, but the data also are applicable to design of equipment for fossil fuel power stations, petrochemical refineries, and chemical plants. Its improved yield strength compared with that of type 304 stainless steel is an advantage for these applications. The austenite stability in type 316 is greater than that in type 304, so it is advantageous to use type 316 instead of type 304 for critical applications at cryogenic temperatures.

Effects of elevated temperatures on fatigue crack growth rates for type 316 have been reported by Shahinian, Smith, and Watson and are summarized in Fig. 47 (Ref 175). The data were obtained on single-edge-notch specimens with side grooves during cantilever loading. They were obtained, at the L-T orientation, from annealed type 316 plate. The tests were conducted in air at a frequency of 0.17 Hz according to a sawtooth waveform at $R = 0$. As shown by the curves in Fig. 47, the fatigue crack growth rates tend to increase as the testing temperature is increased, much the same as for specimens of type 304 stainless steel.

The effects of long-time exposure (5000 h of aging) at 593 °C (1100 °F) in air on the fatigue crack growth rates of specimens of type 316 are shown in Fig. 48, according to data reported by Michel and Smith (Ref 171). Aging substantially reduced the fatigue crack growth rates at ΔK levels from 18 to 55 MPa$\sqrt{m}$ (16 to 50 ksi$\sqrt{in}$.) for the continuous cycling tests and over the whole testing range for specimens cycled with 0.1 and 1.0 min holding times for each cycle. Fatigue crack growth rates for specimens tested without prior exposure with holding times of 0.1 and 1.0 min for each cycle were higher than those for specimens cycled continuously under the same conditions. However, the effect of holding time was less significant for specimens that had been aged at 593 °C (1100 °F) before testing at the same temperature.

James has shown that the effects of variations in cyclic frequency on fatigue crack growth for specimens of type 316 stainless steel do not show the same pattern as for specimens of type 304 (Ref 166). For tests at frequencies in the range from 0.0067 to 6.67 Hz at 538 °C (1000 °F), the trend is for the crack growth rate to increase as the frequency is decreased, but there is more scatter than for type 304. This trend is shown in Fig. 49.

Fatigue crack growth rates obtained by James for specimens of cold-worked type 316 stainless steel were lower than those for comparable annealed specimens of type 316 at room temperature and at elevated temperatures. Results of tests on compact

Table 23   Compositions of type 403 modified stainless steels

Heat No.	Composition, %								
	C	Mn	P	S	Si	Ni	Cr	Mo	Cu
637	0.13	0.46	0.013	0.009	0.20	0.32	12.18	0.43	0.12
933	0.15	0.54	0.010	0.008	0.32	0.38	12.37	0.08	0.10
484	0.13	0.57	0.009	0.006	0.33	1.60	12.32	0.55	...

Note: See also Fig. 54. Source: Ref 179

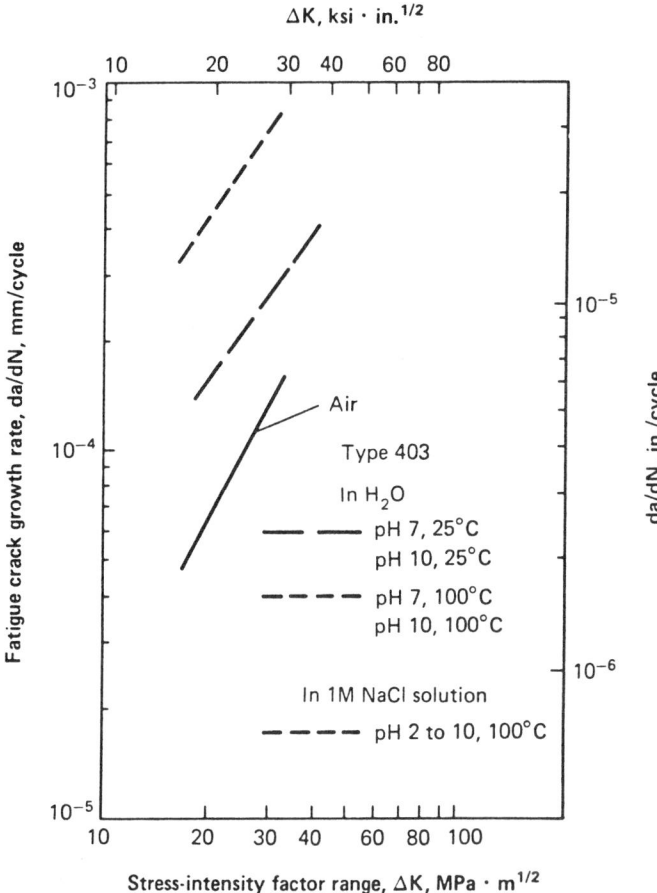

Fig. 56 Fatigue crack growth rates in type 403 stainless steel in air, water, and a 1 M NaCl solution at 10 Hz and a load ratio of 0.5. Source: Ref 180

increased the fatigue crack growth rates as shown. For the aged specimens, holding at maximum load for 0.1 or 1.0 min for each loading cycle reduced the fatigue crack growth rates over those obtained with no holding time. These data indicate that cold working and aging at 593 °C (1100 °F) before or during service exposure can lead to improved fatigue crack growth resistance and that short holding times at maximum load reduce fatigue crack growth rates.

Results of fatigue crack growth rate tests on weldments of type 316 stainless steel have shown that the crack growth rates in the weld metal are generally no higher than in the base metal and may be somewhat lower at elevated temperatures. The curve shown in Fig. 52 for unirradiated weld metal tested at 593 °C (1100 °F) represents fatigue crack growth rates substantially lower than those for the unirradiated base metal at any given ΔK level (Ref 177). The weld was produced by the submerged arc method using type 316 welding rod. Weldments were stress-relief annealed at 480 °C (900 °F). Specimens were single-edge-notch specimens for cantilever loading and were tested at 0.17 Hz and at $R = 0$. Irradiation slightly reduced the fatigue crack growth resistance of the weld metal, but its fatigue crack growth resistance was better than that of the unirradiated base metal.

Results of an investigation of the effects of several gaseous environments on the fatigue crack growth rates in types 316 and 321 stainless steel have been reported by Mahoney and Paton (Ref 178). Compact specimens were tested in fatigue loading according to a sine wave loading pattern at 5 Hz with $R = 0.05$ in room air, dry air, humid air, dry nitrogen, wet nitrogen, and dry argon, at room temperature and at 649 °C (1200 °F). The results are summarized in Fig. 53. Fatigue crack growth rate data at 25 °C (77 °F) show that crack growth rates increased slightly with increased humidity when oxygen was present but that high humidity in an inert gas had no significant effect. Fatigue crack growth rates in room air at room temperature were the same for types 316 and 321

specimens of 20% cold-worked type 316 stainless steel at frequencies of 0.67 and 3.0 Hz and at $R = 0.05$ are summarized in Fig. 50 (Ref 176).

Effects of holding times on cyclic loading of unaged and aged specimens of 20% cold-worked type 316 as determined by Michel and Smith (Ref 171) are shown in Fig. 51 for tests at 593 °C (1100 °F). The frequency for specimens cycled with zero holding time was 0.17 Hz, and R was zero. Aging was done for 5000 h at 593 °C (1100 °F), and testing was done in air. For the unaged specimens, increasing the holding time significantly

Table 24   Fracture toughness (K_{Ic}) data for 15-5PH, 17-4PH, PH13-8 Mo, and Custom 455 martensitic precipitation-hardening stainless steels

Type(a)	Condition(b)	Testing temperature °C	°F	Yield strength MPa	ksi	Tensile strength MPa	ksi	Orientation	Fracture toughness K_{Ic} MPa√m	ksi√in.
15-5 PH (VAR)	H900	RT	RT	1280	185	1380	200	L-T	96	87
	H900	RT	RT	1210	175	1320	192	...	81	74
	H900	RT	RT	1180	171	1330	193	T-L	81	74
	H1080	22	72	1030	149	1040	151	Random	115-122	104-111
	H1080	0	32	1044	151	1052	152	Random	96-114	87-104
	H1080	−20	−4	1041	151	1054	153	Random	89-101	81-92
17-4 PH	H900	RT	RT	1210	176	1380	200	T-L	48	44
	H975	RT	RT	1160	168	1230	178	L-T	93	85
	H1100	RT	RT	883	128	972	141	T-L	153(c)	139(c)
17-4 PH (AM)	H900	RT	RT	1170	170	1310	190	L-T	53	48
	H900	RT	RT	1210	176	1340	195	...	57	52
PH 13-8 Mo	H950	RT	RT	1360	197	1550	225	T-L	70	64
	H1050	RT	RT	1230	178	1320	192	T-L	112	102
Custom 455 (VAR)	H900	RT	RT	1760	255	...	...	L-T	51	46
	H950	RT	RT	1700	246	...	...	L-T	79	72
	H1000	RT	RT	1365(d)	198(d)	...	...	L-T	110	100

(a) Heat treatments: 15-5PH and 17-4PH were austenitized at 1040 °C (1900 °F), air cooled; PH13-8 Mo was austenitized at 1000 °C (1825 °F), air cooled; Custom 455 was annealed at 980 °C (1800 °F), water quenched, reheated to 815 °C (1500 °F), oil quenched. (b) Aging treatments: H900 at 480 °C (900 °F), air cooled; H950 at 510 °C (950 °F), air cooled; H975 at 525 °C (975 °F), air cooled; H1000 at 540 °C (1000 °F), air cooled; H1050 at 565 °C (1050 °F), air cooled; H1080 at 580 °C (1080 °F), air cooled; H1100 at 595 °C (1100 °F), air cooled. (c) $K_{Ic}(J)$ data. (d) Typical. Source: Ref 161

Table 25   Summary of fracture toughness (K_{Ic}) data for compact specimens of PH13-8 Mo stainless steel from the B-1 Program

Product form	Condition(a)	Yield strength (L)		Tensile strength (L)		Average fracture toughness, K_{Ic}			
						L-T orientation		T-L orientation	
		MPa	ksi	MPa	ksi	MPa√m	ksi√in.	MPa √m	ksi√in.
Forged bar	H950	1410	204	1490	216	66	60	63	57
Rolled bar	RH950	1500	217	1630	236	68	62	...	...
		1510	219	1630	237	64	58	...	...
Rolled bar	RH975	1490	216	1610	233	79	72	...	...
		1510	219	1590	231	72	66	...	...
Forged bar	H1000	1390	201	1460	212	104	95	99	90
		1320	191	1430	208	87	79	89	81
		1460	212	1510	219	113	103	99	90
Rolled bar	H1000	1430	208	1490	216	96	87	82	75
	Welded joint(b)	...	...	...	...	91	83	...	...
	Welded joint(c)	...	...	...	...	97	88	...	...
Rolled bar	RH1000	1480	215	1530	222	122	111	...	...
		1500	218	1560	226	104	95	...	...
Extruded bar	H1000	1480	214	1520	221	74	67	72	66

(a) Heat treatments: H950 and H1000—austenitized at 925 °C (1700 °F), air cooled; RH950, RH975 and RH1000—austenitized at 925 °C (1700 °F), air cooled, cooled to –73 °C (–100 °F) for 5 h; H950 and RH950—aged at 510 °C (950 °F) for 4 h; RH975—aged at 525 °C (975 °F) for 4 h; H1000 and RH1000—aged at 540 °C (1000 °F) for 4 h. (b) Weld metal. (c) Heat-affected zone. Source: Ref 182

stainless steel. Furthermore, in tests at 649 °C (1200 °F) in dry nitrogen, fatigue crack growth rates for types 316 and 321 also were the same. In air, however, fatigue crack growth rates in type 316 specimens increased by a factor of about 22 over rates in an inert environment at the same temperature. The corresponding increase in fatigue crack growth rates for specimens of type 321 was about five times that for the inert environment at 649 °C (1200 °F). If components of these stainless steels are exposed to inert environments instead of to air or oxygen-containing environments, fatigue crack growth rates will be substantially lower than those expected on the basis of tests in air.

Martensitic Stainless Steels

Because martensitic stainless steels harden on air cooling from the hot-working processes, the hot-worked and air-cooled material may be tempered and used in this condition or given a process annealing treatment prior to rehardening. Fracture toughness data on martensitic grades 403, 403 modified, and 422 are presented in this section. Additional data may be found in Ref 161.

Type 403 Standard and Modified Versions. Type 403 martensitic stainless steel has been used for steam turbine rotor blades and rotors that operate at temperatures up to 480 °C (900 °F). For this type of application, the components are tempered at 590 °C (1100 °F) or higher, after which embrittlement at service temperatures is negligible.

Fracture toughness test data have been obtained by Logsdon (Ref 179) on three heats of type 403 modified stainless steel using compact specimens from 50 to 200 mm (2 to 8 in.) thick for tests in the temperature range from –196 to +80 °C (–310 to +175 °F). These specimens were obtained from rotor forgings and were oriented so that crack growth would be in a radial direction. The compositions of these heats constituted a modified type 403 because they contained nickel and molybdenum, as shown in Table 23. Heat treatment of these forgings consisted of preheating to 260 °C (500 °F), holding at 260 °C for 2 or 3 h, heating slowly to 955 °C (1750 °F), holding at 955 °C for 16 to 20 h, and oil quenching to 95/150 °C (200/300 °F). They were tempered by preheating to 260 °C (500 °F), heating slowly to 595 to 620 °C (1100 to 1150 °F), holding at temperature for 27 to 32 h, and cooling in air.

Scatter bands for the K_{Ic} data for each heat are shown in Fig. 54. The thicker specimens were tested at the higher temperatures in order to obtain valid fracture data. These results show that there is some heat-to-heat scatter in the fracture data with small variations in composition and in other heat-to-heat variables. The results also illustrate the requirements for obtaining valid data near room temperature for unusually thick specimens of relatively tough materials.

Fatigue crack growth rates for type 403 stainless steel obtained in air at frequencies of 10 and 40 Hz and at 25 °C (77 °F) and 100 °C (212 °F) are shown as the solid line in Fig. 55 (Ref 180). The curve for tests in water at a pH of 7 at 100 °C (212 °F) in Fig. 55 shows that the water environment caused increased fatigue crack growth rates over the entire ΔK range.

Tests on type 403 stainless steel in the 0.01 M and 1.0 M sodium chloride solutions were made with the solutions at pH levels of 2, 7, and 10 and with an open circuit. Fatigue crack growth rates in 0.01 M sodium chloride at pH 10 and 100 °C (212

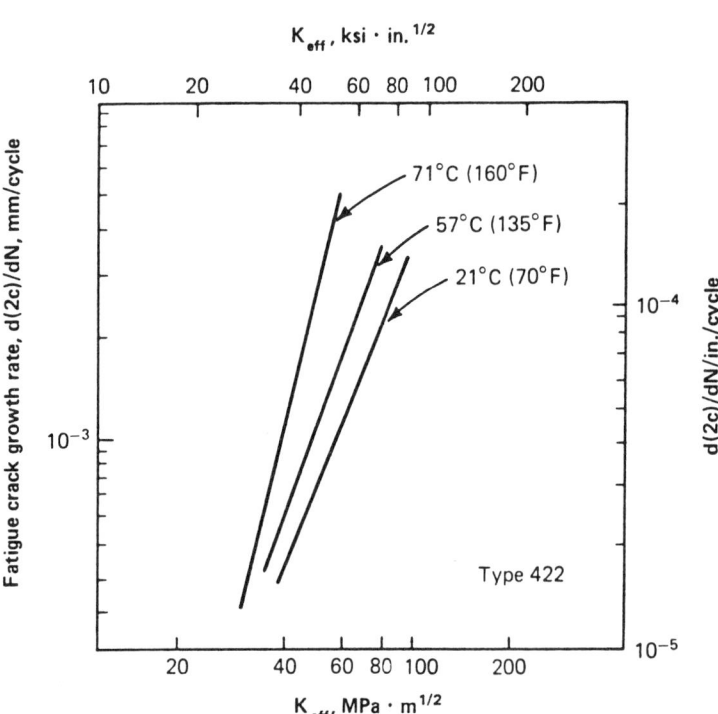

Fig. 57   Fatigue crack growth rates in precracked round rotating beam specimens of type 422 stainless steel in 4.5% NaCl solution at room and elevated temperatures, 10 Hz, and a load ratio of 1. Source: Ref 181

Table 26 Fracture toughness (K_{Ic}) and threshold stress corrosion (K_{ISCC}) data for 17-7PH, PH15-7 Mo, and AM355 semiaustenitic precipitation-hardening stainless steels at room temperature

Type	Condition(a)	Yield strength MPa	Yield strength ksi	Orientation	Fracture toughness K_{Ic} MPa√m	Fracture toughness K_{Ic} ksi√in.	Fracture toughness K_{ISCC} MPa √m	Fracture toughness K_{ISCC} ksi√in.
17-7PH	RH950	1180	171	L-T	35	32	<21(b)	<19(b)
	TH1050	...	...	L-T	43	39	17.5(b)	16(b)
	RH1050	1310	190	T-L	52	47	<20(c)	<18(c)
PH15-7 Mo	RH950	1405	204	T-L	34	31	<16(c)	<15(c)
	RH950	1350	196	L-T	35	32	15(b)	14(b)
	RH1050	1345	195	T-L	44	40	<22(c)	<20(c)
	TH1050	1160	168	L-T	37	34	20(b)	18(b)
	TH1080	...	...	L-T	55	50	...	...
AM355	SCT850	1240	180	L-T	65	59	35(b)	32(b)
	SCT850	1240	180	T-L	53	48	9(c)	8(c)
	SCT1000	1170	170	T-L	115	105	41(c)	37(c)

(a) **RH heat treatments for 17-7PH and PH15-7 Mo:** solution annealed at 1065 °C (1950 °F) and air cooled; conditioned by heating at 955 °C (1750 °F) for 10 min, air cooling, subzero cooling to –75 °C (–100 °F) for 8 h, and warming in air; then aged at 510 °C (950 °F) for 1 h (RH950) or aged at 565 °C (1050 °F) for 1 h (RH1050). **TH heat treatments for 17-7PH and PH15-7 Mo:** solution annealed at 1065 °C (1950 °F) and air cooled; conditioned by heating at 760 °C (1400 °F) for 1½ h, cooling to 16 °C (60 °F) within 1 h of removal from furnace, and holding for 30 min; then aged at 565 °C (1050 °F) for 1½ h and air cooled (TH1050) or aged at 580 °C (1080 °F) for 1½ h and air cooled (TH1080). **SCT heat treatments for AM355:** solution annealed at 1040 °C (1900 °F), water quenched, subzero cooled to –75 °C (–100 °F), held for 3 h, reheated to 955 °C (1750 °F), air cooled or water quenched, subzero cooled to – 75 °C (–100 °F), and held for 3 h; then aged at 455 °C (850 °F) for 3 h (SCT850) or aged at 540 °C (1000 °F) for 3 h (SCT1000). (b) In 3.5% NaCl solution. (c) In 20% NaCl solution. Source: Ref 161

Table 27 Fracture toughness of A-286 austenitic precipitation-hardening stainless steel based on the *J*-integral method

Heat treatment	Room-temperature yield strength MPa	Room-temperature yield strength ksi	Specimen orientation	Specimen thickness mm	Specimen thickness in.	Testing temperature °C	Testing temperature °F	J_{Ic} kJ/m²	J_{Ic} in. · lb/in.²	$K_{Ic(J)}$ MPa√m	$K_{Ic(J)}$ ksi√in.
980 °C (1800 °F) ½ h, WQ, 720 °C (1325 °F) 16 h	769	112	T-L	12.6	0.5	25	77	133	758	167	152
						430	800	92	524	139	126
						540	1000	81	463	130	119
980 °C (1800 °F) ½ h, WQ, 720 °C (1325 °F) 16 h	722	105	...	3.05	0.12	25	77	120	686	159	144
						540	1000	99	563	144	131
STA (solution treated and aged)	...	...	L-T	...	...	25	77	121	692	159	145
900 °C (1650 °F) 2 h, OQ, 730 °C (1350 °F) 16 h	607	88	T-S	38	1.5	25	77	75	426	125	114
						–196	–320	67	385	123	112
						–269	–452	61	350	118	107
900 °C (1650 °F) 5 h, OQ, 718 °C (1325 °F) 20 h	822	119	...	12.7	0.5	24	75	121	692	161	146
						–269	–452	143	815	180	163

WQ, water quenched; OQ, oil quenched. Source: Ref 161

°F) were the same as those in water at 100 °C (212 °F) (Fig. 55). At lower cyclic frequencies, the fatigue crack growth rates were higher than at 40 Hz at ΔK levels above 20 MPa√m (18 ksi√in.). For tests in the 1.0 *M* sodium chloride solution at 100 °C (212 °F), fatigue crack growth rates were the same as for water at the same temperature (Fig. 56). At 100 °C (212 °F), fatigue crack growth rates in 1.0 *M* sodium phosphate solution at pH 10 and 10 and 40 Hz and in 1.0 *M* sodium silicate at pH 10 and 10 Hz were practically the same as those in air.

Type 422 stainless steel contains nickel, molybdenum, and tungsten, as well as 12% Cr to improve properties. The effects of sodium chloride solutions and elevated temperatures on fatigue crack growth rates were determined by Eisenstadt and Rajan in tests of notched round rotating beam specimens in which the numbers of test cycles were marked by minor stress interruptions that produced marking rings (Ref 181). Calculations for maximum stress-intensity factors were based on equations for solid round bars subjected to bending loads. The material for these tests apparently had been heat treated to a yield strength of approximately 827 MPa (120 ksi). The specimens were 25 mm (1 in.) in diameter in the test sections. Each specimen was rotated at 600 cycles per minute (10 Hz) while at constant load with the salt water solution flowing over the notched section. Tests with several concentrations of salt solution indicated that the maximum corrosive effect was obtained with the 4.5% solution. Results of tests with specimens in the 4.5% sodium chloride solution at room temperature, 57 °C (135 °F) and 71 °C (160 °F), are shown in Fig. 57. Increasing the temperature of the solution substantially increased the fatigue crack growth rates.

Precipitation-Hardening Stainless Steels

As described earlier in this article, PH steels are classified as either martensitic, semiaustenitic, or austenitic grades. Representative data for each of these PH types are presented in this section. Additional data are available in Ref 161.

Martensitic PH Stainless Steels. Typical K_{Ic} data for 15-5PH, 17-4PH, PH13-8 Mo, and Custom 455 martensitic PH stainless steels are presented in Table 24, and data for PH13-8 Mo from the B-1 program are given in Table 25. For each of these steels, the fracture toughness increases as the aging temperature is increased. The aging temperature, in °F, is indicated by the condition designated in the table (see Table 20 for more detailed information). Of these four steels, Custom 455 has the highest strength in the H900 and H950 conditions. For forged and rolled bars in the H1000 condition, however, the strength and toughness of Custom 455 are comparable to those of PH13-8 Mo. For many applications, either the H1000 or the RH1000 condition represents the best combination of strength and toughness.

Semiaustenitic PH Stainless Steels. Only limited fracture toughness data have been published on the semiaustenitic PH stainless steels. Typical K_{Ic} data are presented in Table 26. The highest toughness was obtained for specimens of AM355 (SCT1000) at a yield strength of 1170 MPa (170 ksi). Increasing the aging temperature from 455 °C (850 °F) to 540 °C (1000 °F) reduced the yield strength only slightly but increased the fracture toughness substantially.

Threshold stress-corrosion cracking (K_{ISCC}) data also are presented in Table 26 for these steels. The semiaustenitic PH steels have relatively low resistance to crack growth in aqueous sodium chloride solutions. The highest value for K_{ISCC} in this series was obtained for the AM355 (SCT1000) specimens.

Austenitic PH Stainless Steels. The main representative in this classification is A-286 stainless steel. Because of the high toughness of A-286 stainless steel, even at –269 °C (–452 °F), available fracture toughness data have been obtained only by the *J*-integral method. Results are presented in Table 27.

ACKNOWLEDGMENTS

The information in this article is largely taken from:

- S.D. Washko and G. Aggen, Wrought Stainless Steels, *Properties and Selection: Irons, Steels, and High-Performance Alloys,* Vol 1, *ASM Handbook* (formerly 10th ed., *Metals Handbook*), ASM International, 1990, p 841-907
- G.F. Vander Voort, Embrittlement of Steels, *Properties and Selection: Irons, Steels, and High-Performance Alloys,* Vol 1, *ASM Handbook* (formerly 10th ed., *Metals Handbook*), ASM International, 1990, p 689-736
- G. Krauss, Stainless Steels, *Steels: Heat Treatment and Processing Principles,* ASM International, 1990, p 351-399
- D.J. Kotecki, Welding of Stainless Steels, *Welding, Brazing, and Soldering,* Vol 6, *ASM Handbook,* ASM International, 1993, p 677-707
- D.N. Noble, Selection of Wrought Duplex Stainless Steels, *Welding, Brazing, and Soldering,* Vol 6, *ASM Handbook,* ASM International, 1993, p 471-481
- B. Pollard, Selection of Wrought Precipitation-Hardening Stainless Steels, *Welding, Brazing, and Soldering,* Vol 6, *ASM Handbook,* ASM International, 1993, p 482-494

REFERENCES

1. *Engineering Properties of Steel,* P. Harvey, Ed., American Society for Metals, 1982, p 243-429
2. *Steel Products Manual: Stainless and Heat Resisting Steels,* Iron and Steel Society, Nov 1990
3. *Stainless Steel,* R. Lula, Ed., American Society for Metals, 1986
4. R.A. Lula, Ed., *Toughness of Ferritic Stainless Steels,* STP 706, ASTM, 1980
5. W.C. Leslie, *The Physical Metallurgy of Steels,* McGraw-Hill, 1981
6. J.F. Grubb, R.N. Wright, and P. Farrar, Jr., Micromechanisms of Brittle Fracture in Titanium-Stabilized and α′-Embrittled Ferritic Stainless Steels, *Toughness of Ferritic Stainless Steels,* R.A. Lula, Ed., STP 706, ASTM, 1980, p 56-76
7. M.K. Veistinen and V.K. Lindroos, Cleavage Fracture Strength of a 26 Cr-1 Mo Ferritic Stainless Steel, *New Developments in Stainless Steel Technology,* R.A. Lula, Ed., American Society for Metals, 1985, p 29-43
8. R.Q. Barr, Ed., *Stainless Steel '77,* Climax Molybdenum Company, 1977
9. A.H. Eichelman, Jr. and F.C. Hull, The Effect of Composition on the Temperature of Spontaneous Transformation of Austenite to Martensite in 18-8 Type Stainless Steel, *Trans. ASM,* Vol 45, 1953, p 77-104
10. C.J. Novak, Structure and Constitution of Wrought Austenitic Stainless Steels, *Handbook of Stainless Steels,* McGraw-Hill, 1977, p 4-1 to 4-78
11. E.P. Butler and M.G. Burke, Preferential Formation of Martensite in Type 304 Stainless Steel: A Microstructural and Compositional Investigation, *Solid-Solid Phase Transformations,* H.J. Aaronson et al., Ed., TMS-AIME, 1982, p 1403-1407
12. S.R. Thomas and G. Krauss, Cyclic Martensitic Transformation and the Structure of a Commercial 18 Cr-8 Ni Stainless Steel, *Trans. TMS-AIME,* Vol 239, 1967, p 1136-1142
13. R.P. Reed, The Spontaneous Martensitic Transformation in 18 pct Cr, 8 pct Ni Steels, *Acta Metall.,* Vol 10, 1962, p 865-877
14. M.C. Mataya, M.J. Carr, and G. Krauss, The Bauschinger Effect in a Nitrogen-strengthened Austenitic Stainless Steel, *Mater. Sci. Eng.,* Vol 57 (No. 2), 1983, p 205-222
15. T. Angel, Formation of Martensite in Austenitic Stainless Steels, *J. Iron Steel Inst.,* Vol 177, 1954, p 165-174
16. R.M. Vennett and G.S. Ansell, The Effect of High-Pressure Hydrogen upon the Tensile Properties and Fracture Behavior of 304L Stainless Steel, *Trans. ASM,* Vol 60, 1967, p 242-251
17. K.G. Brickner, Stainless Steels for Room and Cryogenic Temperatures, *Selection of Stainless Steels,* American Society for Metals, 1968, p 1-29
18. J.P. Bressanelli and A. Moskowitz, Effects of Strain Rate, Temperature and Composition on Tensile Properties of Metastable Austenitic Stainless Steels, *Trans. ASM,* Vol 59, 1966, p 223-239
19. G.L. Huang, D.K. Matlock, and G. Krauss, Martensite Formation, Strain Rate Sensitivity, and Deformation Behavior of Type 304 Stainless Steel Sheet, *Metall. Trans. A,* Vol 20A, 1989, p 1239-1246
20. S.S. Hecker, M.G. Stout, K.P. Staudhammer, and J.L. Smith, Effects of Strain State and Strain Rate on Deformation-Induced Transformation in 304 Stainless Steel: Part I and Part II, *Metall. Trans. A,* Vol 13A, 1982, p 619-626, 627-635
21. G.B. Olson, Transformation Plasticity and the Stability of Plastic Flow, *Deformation, Processing and Structure,* G. Krauss, Ed., American Society for Metals, 1984, p 391-424
22. R.M. Davison and J.D. Redmon, Practical Guide to Using 6Mo Austenitic Stainless Steel, *Materials Performance,* Dec, 1988
23. B. Larsson and B. Lundqvist, "Fabricating Ferritic-Austenitic Stainless Steels," Sandvik Steel Trade Literature, Pamphlet S-51-33-ENG, Oct 1987
24. S. Bernhardsson, The Corrosion Resistance of Duplex Stainless Steels, *Duplex Stainless Steels Conf. Proc.,* Les Editions de Physique, Les Ulis Cedex, Oct 1991, p 185-210
25. L. van Nassau, H. Meelker, and J. Hilkes, "Welding Duplex and Super-Duplex Stainless Steels—A Guide for Industry," Document 01463, Lincoln Norweld, July 1992
26. J. Charles, Super Duplex Stainless Steel: Structure and Properties, *Duplex Stainless Steels Conf. Proc.,* Vol 1, Les Editions de Physique, Les Ulis Cedex, Oct 1991, p 3-48
27. D. Fruytier, Industrial Experiences with Duplex Stainless Steel, *Stainl. Steel Eur.,* Vol 3 (No. 13), Dec 1991
28. B. Wallen and S. Henrikson, Effect of Chlorination on Stainless Steels in Seawater, Paper 403, *Corrosion '86,* National Association of Corrosion Engineers, 1986
29. J. Harston, E. Hutchins, and S. Sweeney, The Development and Construction of Duplex Stainless Steel Pipelines for Use Offshore in the Southern North Sea, *Proc. 3rd Int. Conf. Welding and Performance of Pipelines,* The Welding Institute, 1986
30. V. Seetharaman et al., Precipitation Hardening in a PH13-8 Mo Stainless Steel, *Mater. Sci. Eng.,* Vol 47, Jan 1981, p 1-11
31. H.J. Rack and D. Kalish, The Strength, Fracture Toughness and Low Cycle Fatigue Behavior of 17-4PH Stainless Steel, *Metall. Trans. A,* Vol 5A, July 1974, p 1595-1605
32. K.C. Anthony, Aging Reactions in Precipitation Hardenable Stainless Steel, *J. Met.,* Vol 15, Dec 1963, p 922-927
33. M. Henthorne, T.A. Debold, and R.J. Yinger, "Custom 450-A New Higher Strength Stainless Steel," Paper 53, *Corrosion '72,* National Association of Corrosion Engineers, 1972
34. J.E. McBride, Jr. and G.N. Maniar, *Metallography as a Quality Control Tool,* Plenum Publishing, 1980, p 279
35. S. Widge, "A Study of the Effects of Varying Solution Treatment on the Toughness of a Stainless Maraging Alloy," Ph.D. dissertation, Lehigh University, 1984
36. E.E. Underwood, A.E. Austin, and G.K. Manning, The Mechanism of Hardening in 17-7 Ni-Cr Precipitation-Hardening Stainless Steel, *J. Iron Steel Inst.,* Vol 200, Aug 1962, p 644-651
37. H.C. Burnett, R.H. Duff, and H.C. Vacher, Identification of Metallurgical Reactions and Their Effect on Mechanical Properties of 17-7PH Steel, *J. Res. Natl. Bur. Stand.—Eng. Instrumentation,* Vol 66C, 1962, p 113-119
38. E.G. Feldgandler and M.V. Pridantsev, Phase Transformation in Kh 17 N7 Yu Stainless Steel, *Metalloved. Term. Obrab. Met.,* Nov 1960, p 2-7
39. J.C. Wilkens and R.E. Pence, A Study of the Microstructure of Precipitation Hardening Stainless Steel Sheet, *Advances in Electron Metallography and Electron Probe Mi-*

croanalysis, STP 317, ASTM, 1962, p 140-149

40. J.C. Wilkens, in Precipitation from Iron-Base Alloys, *Proceedings of an AIME Symposium,* American Institute of Mining, Metallurgical, and Petroleum Engineers, 1963, p 98

41. G. Aggen, "Phase Transformations and Heat Treatment Studies of a Controlled Transformation Stainless Steel Alloy," Dr. Eng. Sc. thesis, Rensselaer Polytechnic Institute, Aug 1963

42. D.R. Muzyka, in *The Metallurgy of Nickel-Iron Alloys, The Superalloys,* C.T. Sims and W.C. Hagel, Ed., John Wiley & Sons, 1972, p 113-143

43. A.W. Thompson and J.A. Brooks, The Mechanism of Precipitation Strengthening in an Iron-Base Superalloy, *Acta Metall.,* Vol 30, Dec 1982, p 2197-2203

44. T.J. Headley, M.M. Karnousky, and W.R. Sorenson, Effect of Composition and High Energy Rate Forging on the Onset of Precipitation in an Iron-Base Superalloy, *Metall. Trans. A,* Vol 13A, March 1982, p 345-353

45. "Armco 17-4PH Stainless Steel Bar and Wire," Product Data Bulletin S-24, Armco, Inc., Sept 1966

46. "Armco PH13-8Mo Stainless Steel," Product Data Bulletin S-24, Armco, Inc., Oct 1986

47. "Carpenter Custom 450," Product Data Bulletin, Carpenter Technology Corp., 1971

48. "Carpenter Custom 455," Product Data Bulletin, Carpenter Technology Corp., 1971

49. "Armco 17-7PH and PH15-7Mo Stainless Steel Sheet and Strip," Product Data Bulletin, Armco, Inc., Jan 1975

50. B. Strauss et al., Carbide Precipitation in the Heat Treatment of Stainless Non-Magnetic Chromium-Nickel Steels, *Zh. Anorg. Allg. Chem.,* Vol 188, 1930, p 309-324

51. E.C. Bain et al., The Nature and Prevention of Intergranular Corrosion in Austenitic Stainless Steels, *Trans. ASST,* Vol 21, June 1933, p 481-509

52. K.G. Caroll et al., Chromium Distribution around Grain Boundary Carbides Found in Austenitic Stainless Steel, *Nature,* Vol 184, 1959, p 1479-1480

53. C.W. Weaver, Grain-Boundary Precipitation in Nickel-Chromium-Base Alloys, *J. Inst. Met.,* Vol 90, 1961-1962, p 404

54. S. Alm and R. Kiessling, Chromium Depletion around Grain-Boundary Precipitates in Austenitic Stainless Steel, *J. Inst. Met.,* Vol 91, 1962-1963, p 190

55. R.J. Hodges, Intergranular Corrosion in High Purity Ferritic Stainless Steels: Effect of Cooling Rate and Alloy Composition, *Corrosion,* Vol 17, March 1971, p 119-127

56. A.B Kinzel, Chromium Carbide in Stainless Steel, *Trans. AIME,* Vol 194, May 1952, p 469-488

57. R. Stickler and A. Vinckier, Electron Microscope Investigation of the Intergranular Corrosion Fracture Surfaces in a Sensitized Austenitic Stainless Steel, *Corros. Sci.,* Vol 3, 1963, p 1-8

58. M.A. Streicher, General and Intergranular Corrosion of Austenitic Stainless Steels in Acids, *J. Electrochem. Soc.,* Vol 106, March 1959, p 161-180

59. K.T. Aust et al., Heat Treatment and Corrosion Resistance of Austenitic Type 304 Stainless Steel, *Trans. ASM,* Vol 59, 1966, p 544-556

60. K.T. Aust et al., Intergranular Corrosion and Electron Microscopic Studies of Austenitic Stainless Steels, *Trans. ASM,* Vol 60, 1967, p 360-372

61. K.T. Aust et al., Intergranular Corrosion and Mechanical Properties of Austenitic Stainless Steels, *Trans. ASM,* Vol 61, 1968, p 270-277

62. K.T. Aust, Intergranular Corrosion of Austenitic Stainless Steels, *Trans. AIME,* Vol 245, Oct 1969, p 2117-2126

63. J.S. Armijo, Impurity Adsorption and Intergranular Corrosion of Austenitic Stainless Steel in Boiling HNO_3-$K_2Cr_2O_7$ Solutions, *Corros. Sci.,* Vol 7, 1967, p 143-150

64. J.S. Armijo, Intergranular Corrosion of Nonsensitized Austenitic Stainless Steels, *Corrosion,* Vol 24, Jan 1968, p 24-30

65. T.M. Devine et al., Mechanism of Intergranular Corrosion of 316L Stainless Steel in Oxidizing Acids, *Scr. Metall.,* Vol 14, 1980, p 1175-1179

66. A. Joshi and D.F. Stein, Chemistry of Grain Boundaries and Its Relation to Intergranular Corrosion of Austenitic Stainless Steel, *Corrosion,* Vol 28, Sept 1972, p 321-330

67. C.L. Briant, The Effects of Sulfur and Phosphorus on the Intergranular Corrosion of 304 Stainless Steel, *Corrosion,* Vol 36, Sept 1980, p 497-509

68. C.L. Briant, The Effect of Alloying Elements on Impurity Induced Intergranular Corrosion, *Corrosion,* Vol 38, April 1982, p 230-232

69. C.L. Briant, Grain Boundary Segregation of Phosphorus and Sulfur in Types 304L and 316L Stainless Steel and Its Effect on Intergranular Corrosion in the Huey Test, *Metall. Trans. A,* Vol 18A, April 1987, p 691-699

70. C.S. Pande et al., Direct Evidence of Chromium Depletion Near the Grain Boundaries in Sensitized Stainless Steels, *Scr. Metall.,* Vol 11, 1977, p 681-684

71. P. Rao and E. Lifshin, Microchemical Analysis in Sensitized Austenitic Steel, *Proceedings of the 8th Annual Conference of the Microbeam Analysis Society,* 1977, p 118A-118F

72. R.A. Mulford et al., Sensitization of Austenitic Stainless Steels: II, Commercial Purity Alloys, *Corrosion,* Vol 39, April 1983, p 132-143

73. E.L. Hall and C.L. Briant, Chromium Depletion in the Vicinity of Carbides in Sensitized Austenitic Stainless Steels, *Metall. Trans. A,* Vol 15A, May 1984, p 793-811

74. C.L. Briant and E.L. Hall, A Comparison between Grain Boundary Chromium Depletion in Austenitic Stainless Steel and Corrosion in the Modified Strauss Test, *Corrosion,* Vol 42, Sept 1986, p 522-531

75. S.M. Bruemmer and L.A. Charlot, Development of Grain Boundary Chromium Deple-

tion in Type 304 and 316 Stainless Steels, *Scr. Metall.,* Vol 20, 1986, p 1019-1024

76. E.P. Butler and M.G. Burke, Chromium Depletion and Martensite Formation at Grain Boundaries in Sensitized Austenitic Stainless Steel, *Acta Metall.,* Vol 34, March 1986, p 557-570

77. C. Stawström and M. Hillert, An Improved Depleted-Zone Theory of Intergranular Corrosion of 18-8 Stainless Steel, *J. Iron Steel Inst.,* Vol 207, Jan 1967, p 77-85

78. C.S. Tedmon, Jr. et al., Intergranular Corrosion of Austenitic Stainless Steel, *J. Electrochem. Soc.,* Vol 118, Feb 1971, p 192-202

79. R.L. Fullman, A Thermodynamic Model of the Effects of Composition on the Susceptibility of Austenitic Stainless Steels to Intergranular Stress Corrosion Cracking, *Acta Metall.,* Vol 30, 1982, p 1407-1415

80. G.S. Was and R.M. Kruger, A Thermodynamic and Kinetic Basis for Understanding Chromium Depletion in Ni-Cr-Fe Alloys, *Acta Metall.,* Vol 33, May 1985, p 841-854

81. S.M. Bruemmer, Sensitization Development in Austenitic Stainless Steel: Measurement and Prediction of Thermochemical History Effects, *Corrosion,* Vol 44, July 1988, p 427-434

82. E.M. Mahla and N.A. Nielsen, Carbide Precipitation in Type 304 Stainless Steel—An Electron Microscope Study, *Trans. ASM,* Vol 43, 1951, p 290-322

83. R. Stickler and A. Vinckier, Morphology of Grain-Boundary Carbides and Its Influence on Intergranular Corrosion of 304 Stainless Steel, *Trans. ASM,* Vol 54, 1961, p 362-380

84. F.R. Beckitt and B.R. Clark, The Shape and Mechanism of Formation of $M_{23}C_6$ Carbide in Austenite, *Acta Metall.,* Vol 15, Jan 1967, p 113-129

85. L.K. Singhal and J.W. Martin, The Growth of $M_{23}C_6$ Carbide on Grain Boundaries in an Austenitic Stainless Steel, *Trans. AIME,* Vol 242, May 1968, p 814-819

86. C. Da Casa et al., $M_{23}C_6$ Precipitation in Unstabilized Austenitic Stainless Steel, *J. Iron Steel Inst.,* Vol 207, Oct 1969, p 1325-1332

87. W.O. Binder et al., Resistance to Sensitization of Austenitic Chromium-Nickel Steels of 0.03% Max. Carbon Content, *Trans. ASM,* Vol 41, 1949, p 1301-1370

88. S. Danyluk et al., Intergranular Fracture, Corrosion Susceptibility, and Impurity Segregation in Sensitized Type 304 Stainless Steel, *J. Mater. Energy Syst.,* Vol 7, June 1985, p 6-15

89. R.A. Lula et al., Intergranular Corrosion of Ferritic Stainless Steels, *Trans. ASM,* Vol 46, 1954, p 197-230

90. A.P. Bond, Mechanisms of Intergranular Corrosion in Ferritic Stainless Steels, *Trans. AIME,* Vol 245, Oct 1969, p 2127-2134

91. R.J. Hodges, Intergranular Corrosion in High Purity Ferritic Stainless Steels: Isothermal Time-Temperature Sensitization Measurements, *Corrosion,* Vol 27, April 1971, p 164-167

92. J.J. Demo, Mechanism of High Temperature Embrittlement and Loss of Corrosion Resis-

tance in AISI Type 446 Stainless Steel, *Corrosion*, Vol 27, Dec 1971, p 531-544

93. J.A. Davis et al., Intergranular Corrosion Resistance of a 26Cr-1Mo Ferritic Stainless Steel Containing Niobium, *Corrosion*, Vol 36, May 1980, p 215-220

94. T.M. Devine et al., Influence of Heat Treatment on the Sensitization of 18Cr-2Mo-Ti Stabilized Ferritic Stainless Steel, *Metall. Trans. A*, Vol 12A, Dec 1981, p 2063-2069

95. T.M. Devine and A.M. Ritter, Sensitization of 12 Wt Pct Chromium, Titanium-Stabilized Ferritic Stainless Steel, *Metall. Trans. A*, Vol 14A, Aug 1983, p 1721-1728

96. P. Payson, Prevention of Intergranular Corrosion in Corrosion-Resistant Chromium-Nickel Steels, *Trans. AIME*, Vol 100, 1932, p 306-333

97. T.M. Devine, Mechanism of Intergranular Corrosion of Austenitic and Duplex 308 Stainless Steel, *J. Electrochem. Soc.*, Vol 126, March 1979, p 374-385

98. T.M. Devine, Jr., Influence of Carbon Content and Ferrite Morphology on the Sensitization of Duplex Stainless Steel, *Metall. Trans. A*, Vol 11A, May 1980, p 791-800

99. F.M. Becket, On the Allotropy of Stainless Steels, *Trans. AIME*, Vol 131, 1938, p 15-36

100. G. Reidrich and F. Loib, Embrittlement of High Chromium Steels within Temperature Range of 570-1100 °F, *Arch. Eisenhüttenwes.*, Vol 15, Oct 1941, p 175-182

101. W. Dannöhl, Discussion of Ref 183 (and The Embrittlement of High-Alloy Chrome Steels in the Temperature Range About 500°, by G. Bandel and W. Tofaute, *Arch. Eisenhüttenwes.*, Vol 15, 1942, p 307-320), *Arch. Eisenhüttenwes.*, Vol 15, 1942, p 319

102. H.D. Newell, Properties and Characteristics of 27% Chromium Iron, *Met. Prog.*, Vol 49, May 1946, p 977-1028

103. J.J. Heger, 885 °F Embrittlement of the Ferritic Chromium-Iron Alloys, *Met. Prog.*, Vol 60, Aug 1951, p 55-61

104. A.J. Lena and M.F. Hawkes, 475 °C (885 °F) Embrittlement in Stainless Steels, *Trans. AIME*, Vol 200, May 1954, p 607-615

105. C.A. Zapffe, Fractographic Pattern for 475 °C Embrittlement in Stainless Steel, *Trans. AIME*, Vol 191, March 1951, p 247-248

106. H. Masumoto et al., The Anomaly of the Specific Heat at High Temperatures in α-Phase Alloys of Iron and Chromium, *Sci. Rep. Inst., Tôhuko Univ. A*, Vol 5, 1953, p 203-207

107. S. Takeda and N. Nagai, Experimental Research on Superlattices in Iron-Chromium System, *Mem. Fac. Eng., Nagoya Univ.*, Vol 8, 1956, p 1-28

108. R.M. Fisher et al., Identification of the Precipitate Accompanying 885 °F Embrittlement in Chromium Steels, *Trans. AIME*, Vol 197, May 1953, p 690-695

109. R.O. Williams and H.W. Paxton, The Nature of Aging of Binary Iron-Chromium Alloys Around 500 °C, *J. Iron Steel Inst.*, Vol 185, March 1957, p 358-374

110. G.F. Tisinai and C.H. Samans, Some Observations of 885 °F Embrittlement, *Trans. AIME*, Vol 209, Oct 1957, p 1221-1226

111. M.J. Blackburn and J. Nutting, Metallography of an Iron-21% Chromium Alloy Subjected to 475 °C Embrittlement, *J. Iron Steel Inst.*, Vol 202, July 1964, p 610-613

112. M.J. Marcinkowski et al., Effect of 500 °C Aging on the Deformation Behavior of an Iron-Chromium Alloy, *Trans. AIME*, Vol 230, June 1964, p 676-689

113. R. Lagneborg, Metallography of the 475 °C Embrittlement in an Iron-30% Chromium Alloy, *Trans. ASM*, Vol 60, 1967, p 67-78

114. R. Lagneborg, Deformation in an Iron-30% Chromium Alloy Aged at 475 °C, *Acta Metall.*, Vol 15, Nov 1967, p 1737-1745

115. T. DeNys and P.M. Gielen, Spinodal Decomposition in the Fe-Cr System, *Metall. Trans.*, Vol 2, May 1971, p 1423-1428

116. P.J. Grobner, The 885 °F (475 °C) Embrittlement of Ferritic Stainless Steels, *Metall. Trans.*, Vol 4, Jan 1973, p 251-260

117. R.O. Williams, Further Studies of the Iron-Chromium System, *Trans. AIME*, Vol 212, Aug 1958, p 497-502

118. P.J. Grobner and R.F. Steigerwald, Effect of Cold Work on the 885 °F (475 °C) Embrittlement of 18Cr-2Mo Ferritic Stainless Steels, *J. Met.*, Vol 29, July 1977, p 17-23

119. T.J. Nichol et al., Embrittlement of Ferritic Stainless Steels, *Metall. Trans. A*, Vol 11A, April 1980, p 573-585

120. W. Hoaquan et al., Influence of Annealing and Aging Treatments on the Embrittlement of Type 446 Ferritic Stainless Steel, *J. Mater. Eng.*, Vol 9, 1987, p 51-61

121. W. Trietschke and G. Tammnann, The Alloys of Iron and Chromium, *Zh. Anorg. Chem.*, Vol 55, 1907, p 402-411

122. E.C. Bain and W.E. Griffiths, An Introduction to the Iron-Chromium-Nickel Alloys, *Trans. AIME*, Vol 75, 1927, p 166-213

123. P. Chevenard, Experimental Investigations of Iron, Nickel, and Chromium Alloys, *Trav. Mem., Bur. Int. Poids et Mesures*, Vol 17, 1927, p 90

124. F. Wever and W. Jellinghaus, The Two-Component System: Iron-Chromium, *Mitt. Kaiser-Wilhelm Inst.*, Vol 13, 1931, p 143-147

125. D.C. Ludwigson and H.S. Link, Further Studies of the Formation of Sigma in 12 to 16 Per Cent Chromium Steels, *Advances in the Technology of Stainless Steels and Related Alloys*, STP 369, ASTM, 1965, p 299-311

126. J.H.G. Monypenny, The Brittle Phase in High-Chromium Steels, *Metallurgia*, Vol 21, 1939-1940, p 143-148

127. F.B. Foley, The Sigma Phase, *Alloy Cast. Bull.*, July 1945, p 1-9

128. D.A. Oliver, The Sigma Phase in Stainless Steels, *Met. Prog.*, Vol 55, May 1949, p 665-667

129. G.V. Smith, Sigma Phase in Stainless: What, When and Why, *Iron Age*, Vol 166, 30 Nov 1950, p 63-68; 7 Dec 1950, p 127-132

130. A.J. Lena, Sigma Phase—A Review, *Met. Prog.*, Vol 66, July 1954, p 86-90; Aug 1954, p 94-99; Sept 1954, p 122-126, 128

131. F.B. Foley and V.N. Krivobok, Sigma Formation in Commercial Ni-Cr-Fe Alloys, *Met. Prog.*, Vol 71, May 1957, p 81-86

132. F.B. Pickering, The Formation of Sigma in Austenitic-Stainless Steels, *Precipitation Processes in Steels*, Special Report 64, Iron and Steel Institute, 1959, p 118-124

133. E.O. Hall and S.H. Algie, The Sigma Phase, *Metall. Rev.*, Vol 11, 1966, p 61-88

134. E.R. Jette and F. Foote, The Fe-Cr Alloy System, *Met. Alloys*, Vol 7, Aug 1936, p 207-210

135. A.J. Lena and W.E. Curry, The Effect of Cold Work and Recrystallization on the Formation of the Sigma Phase in Highly Stable Austenitic Stainless Steels, *Trans. ASM*, Vol 47, 1955, p 193-210

136. P. Duhaj et al., Sigma-Phase Precipitation in Austenitic Steels, *J. Iron Steel Inst.*, Vol 206, Dec 1968, p 1245-1251

137. B. Weiss and R. Stickler, Phase Instabilities during High Temperature Exposure of 316 Austenitic Stainless Steel, *Metall. Trans.*, Vol 3, April 1972, p 851-866

138. M.T. Shehata et al., A Quantitative Metallographic Study of the Ferrite to Sigma Transformation in Type 316 Stainless Steel, *Microstruct. Sci.*, Vol 111, Elsevier, 1983, p 89-99

139. J.K.L. Lai et al., Precipitate Phases in Type 316 Austenitic Stainless Steel Resulting from Long-Term High Temperature Service, *Mater. Sci. Eng.*, Vol 49, 1981, p 19-29

140. J. Barcik and B. Brzycka, Chemical Composition of σ Phase Precipitated in Chromium-Nickel Austenitic Steels, *Met. Sci.*, Vol 17, May 1983, p 256-260

141. T. Andersson and B. Lundberg, Effect of Mo on the Lattice Parameters and on the Chemical Composition of Sigma Phase and $M_{23}C_6$ Carbide in an Austenitic 25Cr-20Ni Steel, *Metall. Trans. A*, Vol 8A, May 1977, p 787-790

142. G.N. Emanuel, Sigma Phase and Other Effects of Prolonged Heating at Elevated Temperatures on 25 Per Cent Chromium-20 Per Cent Nickel Steel, *Symposium on the Nature, Occurrence, and Effects of Sigma Phase*, STP 110, ASTM, 1951, p 82-99

143. G. Aggen et al., Microstructures versus Properties of 29-4 Ferritic Stainless Steel, *MiCon 78: Optimization of Processing, Properties, and Service Performance through Microstructural Control*, STP 672, ASTM, 1979, p 334-366

144. J.J. Gilman, Hardening of High-Chromium Steels by Sigma Phase Formation, *Trans. ASM*, Vol 43, 1951, p 161-192

145. G.J. Guarnieri et al., The Effect of Sigma Phase on the Short-Time High Temperature Properties of 25 Chromium-20 Nickel Stainless Steel, *Trans. ASM*, Vol 42, 1950, p 981-1007

146. J.H. Jackson, The Occurrence of the Sigma Phase and Its Effect on Certain Properties of Cast Fe-Ni-Cr Alloys, *Symposium on the Na-*

---

ture, Occurrence, and Effects of Sigma Phase, STP 110, ASTM, 1951, p 101-127

147. L.P. Stoter, Thermal Aging Effects in AISI Type 316 Stainless Steel, *J. Mater. Sci.,* Vol 16, 1981, p 1039-1051

148. R.G. Ellis and G. Pollard, The Observation of Sigma Phase after Short Aging Times in a Duplex Steel, *J. Iron Steel Inst.,* Vol 208, Aug 1970, p 783-784

149. H.D. Solomon and T.M. Devine, Influence of Microstructure on the Mechanical Properties and Localized Corrosion of a Duplex Stainless Steel, *MiCon 78: Optimization of Processing, Properties, and Service Performance through Microstructural Control,* STP 672, ASTM, 1979, p 430-461

150. Y. Maehara et al., Effects of Alloying Elements on σ Phase Precipitation in δ-γ Duplex Phase Stainless Steels, *Met. Sci.,* Vol 17, Nov 1983, p 541-547

151. L.D. Roth et al., Ultrasonic Fatigue Testing, *Mechanical Testing,* Vol 8, *ASM Handbook* (formerly 9th ed., *Metals Handbook*), ASM International, 1985, p 240-258

152. L.F. Coffin, Jr., *Met. Eng. Quart.,* Vol 3, 1963, p 22

153. R.W. Smith, M.H. Hirschberg, and S.S. Manson, NASA Report TN D-1574, NASA, April 1963

154. S.S. Manson and M.H. Hirschberg, *Fatigue: An Interdisciplinary Approach,* Syracuse University Press, 1964, p 133

155. L.F. Coffin, Jr., *Trans. ASME,* Vol 76, 1954, p 931

156. J.F. Tavernelli and L.F. Coffin, Jr., *Trans. ASM,* Vol 51, 1959, p 438

157. R.W. Hertzberg, *Deformation and Fracture Mechanics of Engineering Materials,* 2nd ed., John Wiley & Sons, 1983, p 503-507

158. J.T. Berling and T. Slot, Effect of Temperature and Strain Rate on Low-Cycle Fatigue Resistance of AISI 304, 316, and 348 Stainless Steels, *Fatigue at High Temperatures,* STP 459, ASTM, 1969, p 3

159. J. Goodman, *Mechanics Applied to Engineering,* Longman, Green and Co., 1899

160. W.Z. Gerber, Bestimmung der Zulosigne Spannagen in Eisen Constructionen, *Bayer.*

Archit. Ing. Ver., Vol 6, 1874, p 101 (in German)

161. J.E. Campbell, Fracture Properties of Wrought Stainless Steels, *Application of Fracture Mechanics for Selection of Metallic Structural Materials,* J.E. Campbell, W.W. Gerberich and J.H. Underwood, Ed., American Society for Metals, 1982, p 105-167

162. L.A. James and E.B. Schwenk, Fatigue Crack Propagation Behavior of Type 304 Stainless Steel at Elevated Temperatures, *Metall. Trans.,* Vol 2 (No. 2), Feb 1971, p 491-496

163. L.A. James, Effect of Thermal Aging upon the Fatigue Crack Propagation of Austenitic Stainless Steels, *Metall. Trans.,* Vol 5 (No. 4), Apr 1974, p 831-838

164. P. Shahinian, H.H. Smith, and H.E. Watson, Fatigue Crack Growth Characteristics of Several Austenitic Stainless Steels at High Temperatures, STP 520, ASTM, 1974, p 387-400

165. M. Cahn and J. Shively, The Effects of Temperature, Composition, and Carbide Morphology on Crack Growth in Type 304 Stainless Steel, Report AI-73-12, Atomics International Div., Rockwell International Corp., 12 March 1973

166. L.A. James, Frequency Effects in the Elevated Temperature Crack Growth Behavior of Austenitic Stainless Steels—A Design Approach, *J. Pressure Vessel Tech.,* Vol 101 (No. 2), May 1979, p 171-176

167. L.A. James, The Effect of Frequency upon the Fatigue-Crack Growth of Type 304 Stainless Steel at 1000 °F, STP 513, ASTM, 1972, p 218-229

168. L.A. James, Hold Time Effects on the Elevated Temperature Fatigue-Crack Propagation of Type 304 Stainless Steel, *Nuclear Technology,* Vol 16 (No. 3), Dec 1972, p 521-530

169. P. Shahinian, Creep-Fatigue Crack Propagation in Austenitic Stainless Steel, *J. Pressure Vessel Tech.,* Vol 98, 1976, p 166-172

170. P. Shahinian, H.E. Watson, and H.H. Smith, Fatigue Crack Growth in Selected Alloys for Reactor Applications, *J. Mater.,* Vol 7 (No. 4), Dec 1972, p 527-535

171. D.J. Michel and H.H. Smith, Effect of Hold Time and Thermal Aging on Elevated Temperature Fatigue Crack Propagation in Austentic Stainless Steels, Report NRL-MR-3627, Naval Research Laboratory, Oct 1977

172. W.H. Bamford, Fatigue Crack Growth of Stainless Steel Piping in a Pressurized Water Reactor Environment, *J. Pressure Vessel Tech.,* Vol 101 (No. 1), Feb 1979, p 73-79

173. P. Shahinian, Fatigue and Creep Crack Propagation in Stainless Steel Weld Metal, *Weld. J.,* Vol 57 (No. 3), March 1978, p 87-s to 92-s

174. D.T. Raske and C.F. Cheng, Fatigue Crack Propagation in Types 304 and 308 Stainless Steels at Elevated Temperatures, *Nucl. Tech.,* Vol 34, June 1977, p 101-110

175. P. Shahinian, H.H. Smith, and H.E. Watson, Fatigue Crack Growth in Type 316 Stainless Steel at High Temperature, *J. Eng. Ind.,* Series B, Vol 93 (No. 4), Nov 1971, p 976-980

176. L.A. James, Fatigue Crack Growth in 20% Cold-Worked Type 316 Stainless Steel at Elevated Temperatures, *Nucl. Tech.,* Vol 16 (No. 1), Oct 1972, p 316-322

177. P. Shahinian, Fatigue Crack Propagation in Fast Neutron Irradiated Stainless Steels and Welds, STP 570, ASTM, 1976, p 191-204

178. M.W. Mahoney and N.E. Paton, The Influence of Gas Environments on Fatigue Crack Growth Rates in Types 316 and 321 Stainless Steel, *Nucl. Tech.,* Vol 23 (No. 3), Sept 1974, p 290-297

179. W.A. Logsdon, An Evaluation of the Crack Growth and Fracture Properties of AISI 403 Modified 12 Cr Stainless Steel, *Eng. Fract. Mech.,* Vol 7 (No. 1), March 1975, p 23-40

180. L. Abergo and J.A. Begley, "Fatigue Crack Propagation of 403 Stainless Steel in Aqueous Solutions at 100 °C," Paper 235, International Corrosion Forum (Chicago), 3-7 March 1980

181. R. Eisenstadt and K.M. Rajan, Effect of Salt Water Temperature on Crack Growth Characteristics of 12 Chrome Steel, *J. Eng. Mater. Tech.,* Vol 96 (No. 2), 1974, p 81-87

182. R.R. Ferguson and R.C. Berryman, Fracture Mechanics Evaluation of B-1 Materials, Report AFML-TR-76-137 (I and II), Rockwell International Corp., B-1 Div., 1976

Metallurgy and Properties of Cast Stainless Steels

CAST STAINLESS STEELS are widely used for their corrosion resistance in aqueous media at or near room temperature and for service in hot gases and liquids at elevated temperatures. These high-alloy cast steels generally have more than 10% Cr and primarily consist of stainless steel. Stainless steel castings are usually classified as either corrosion-resistant castings (which are used in aqueous environments below 650 °C, or 1200 °F) or heat-resistant castings (which are suitable for service temperatures above 650 °C, or 1200 °F). However, this line of demarcation in terms of application is not always distinct, particularly for steel castings used in the range from 480 to 650 °C (900 to 1200 °F). The usual distinction between heat-resistant and corrosion-resistant cast steels is based on carbon content, with the heat-resistant grades normally having higher carbon contents.

In general, the cast and wrought stainless steels possess equivalent resistance to corrosive media, and they are frequently used in conjunction with each other. Important differences do exist, however, between some cast stainless steels and their wrought counterparts. One significant difference is in the microstructure of cast austenitic stainless steels. There is usually a small amount of ferrite present in austenitic stainless steel castings, in contrast to the single-phase austenitic structure of the wrought alloys. The presence of ferrite in the castings is desirable for facilitating weld repair, but ferrite also increases resistance to stress-corrosion cracking (SCC). There have been only a few SCC failures with cast stainless steels in comparison to the approximately equivalent wrought compositions. The principal reasons for this resistance are apparently

that silicon added for fluidity gives added benefit from the standpoint of SCC, and that sand castings are usually tumbled or sandblasted to remove molding sand and scale, which probably tends to put the surface in compression.

Wrought and cast stainless steels may also differ in mechanical properties, magnetic properties, and chemical content. Because of the possible existence of large dendritic grains, intergranular phases, and alloy segregation, typical mechanical properties of cast stainless steels may vary more and generally are inferior to those of any wrought structure.

Grade Designations and Compositions

Cast stainless steels are most often specified on the basis of composition using the designation system of the High Alloy Product Group of the Steel Founders' Society of America. (The High Alloy Product Group has replaced the Alloy Casting Institute, or ACI, which formerly administered these designations.) The first letter of the designation indicates whether the alloy is intended primarily for liquid corrosion service (C) or high-temperature service (H). The second letter denotes the nominal chromium-nickel type of the alloy (Fig. 1). As nickel content increases, the second letter of the designation is changed. The numeral or numerals following the first two letters indicate maximum carbon content (percentage × 100) of the alloy. Finally, if further alloying elements are present, these are indicated by the addition of one or more letters as a suffix. Thus, the designation of CF-8M refers to an alloy for corrosion-resistant service (C) of the 19Cr-9Ni type (Fig. 1), with a maximum carbon content 0.08% and containing molybdenum (M).

Some of the high-alloy cast steels exhibit many of the same properties of cast carbon and low-alloy steels. Some of the mechanical properties of these grades (for example, hardness and tensile strength) can be altered by a suitable heat treatment. The cast high-alloy grades that contain more than 20 to 30% Cr plus nickel, however, do not show the phase changes observed in plain carbon and low-alloy steels during heating or cooling between room temperature and the melting point. These materials are therefore nonhardenable, and their properties depend on composition rather than heat treatment. Therefore, special consideration must be given to each grade of high-alloy cast

steel with regard to casting design, foundry practice, and subsequent thermal processing (if any).

Compositions of C-Type (Corrosion-Resistant) Steel Castings. The C-type steel castings for liquid corrosion service are often classified on the basis of composition, although it should be recognized that classification by composition often involves microstructural distinctions (see the section "Composition and Microstructure" in this article).

Table 1 lists the compositions of the commercial cast corrosion-resistant alloys. Alloys are grouped as chromium steels, chromium-nickel steels (in which chromium is the predominant alloying element), and nickel-chromium steels (in which nickel is the predominant alloying element).

The serviceability of cast corrosion-resistant steels depends greatly on the absence of carbon, and especially precipitated carbides, in the alloy microstructure. Therefore, cast corrosion-resistant alloys are generally low in carbon (usually lower than 0.20% and sometimes lower than 0.03%).

All cast corrosion-resistant steels contain more than 11% Cr, and most contain from 1 to 30% Ni (a few have less than 1% Ni). About two-thirds of the corrosion-resistant steel castings produced in the United States are of grades that contain 18 to 22% Cr and 8 to 12% Ni.

In general, the addition of nickel to iron-chromium alloys improves ductility and impact strength. An increase in nickel content increases resistance to corrosion by neutral chloride solutions and weakly oxidizing acids.

The addition of molybdenum increases resistance to pitting attack by chloride solutions. It also extends the range of passivity in solutions of low oxidizing characteristics.

The addition of copper to duplex (ferrite in austenite) nickel-chromium alloys produces alloys that can be precipitation hardened to higher strength and hardness. The addition of copper to single-phase austenitic alloys greatly improves their resistance to corrosion by sulfuric acid. In all iron-chromium-nickel stainless alloys, resistance to corrosion by environments that cause intergranular attack can be improved by lowering the carbon content. Information on the corrosion characteristics and mechanical properties of the C-type steel castings is provided in the section "Corrosion-Resistant Steel Castings" in this article.

Compositions of H-Type (Heat-Resistant) Steel Castings. Castings are classified as heat resistant if they are capable of sustained operation

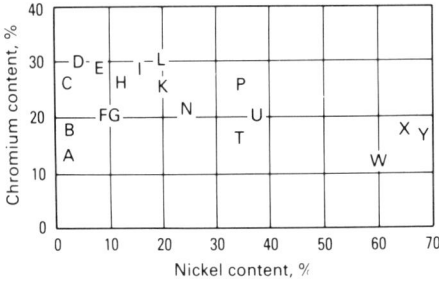

Fig. 1 Chromium and nickel contents in ACI standard grades of heat- and corrosion-resistant steel castings. See text for details.

Table 1 Compositions and typical microstructures of corrosion-resistant cast steels

ACI type	Wrought alloy type(a)	ASTM specifications	Most common end-use microstructure	Composition, %(b)					
				C	Mn	Si	Cr	Ni	Others(c)
Chromium steels									
CA-15	410	A 743, A 217, A 487	Martensite	0.15	1.00	1.50	11.5-14.0	1.0	0.50Mo(d)
CA-15M	...	A 743	Martensite	0.15	1.00	0.65	11.5-14.0	1.0	0.15-1.00Mo
CA-40	420	A 743	Martensite	0.40	1.00	1.50	11.5-14.0	1.0	0.5Mo(d)
CA-40F	...	A 743	Martensite	0.2-0.4	1.00	1.50	11.5-14.0	1.0	...
CB-30	431, 442	A 743	Ferrite and carbides	0.30	1.00	1.50	18.0-22.0	2.0	...
CC-50	446	A 743	Ferrite and carbides	0.30	1.00	1.50	26.0-30.0	4.0	...
Chromium-nickel steels									
CA-6N	...	A 743	Martensite	0.06	0.50	1.00	10.5-12.5	6.0-8.0	...
CA-6NM	...	A 743, A 487	Martensite	0.06	1.00	1.00	11.5-14.0	3.5-4.5	0.4-1.0Mo
CA-28MWV	...	A 743	Martensite	0.20-0.28	0.50-1.00	1.00	11.0-12.5	0.50-1.00	0.9-1.25Mo; 0.9-1.25W; 0.2-0.3V
CB-7Cu-1	...	A 747	Martensite, age hardenable	0.07	0.70	1.00	15.5-17.7	3.6-4.6	2.5-3.2Cu; 0.20-0.35Nb; 0.05N max
CB-7Cu-2	...	A 747	Martensite, age hardenable	0.07	0.70	1.00	14.0-15.5	4.5-5.5	2.5-3.2Cu; 0.20-0.35 Nb; 0.05N max
CD-4MCu	...	A 351, A 743, A 744, A 890	Austenite in ferrite, age hardenable	0.04	1.00	1.00	25.0-26.5	4.75-6.0	1.75-2.25Mo; 2.75-3.25Cu
CE-30	312	A 743	Ferrite in austenite	0.30	1.50	2.00	26.0-30.0	8.0-11.0	...
CF-3(e)	304L	A 351, A 743, A 744	Ferrite in austenite	0.03	1.50	2.00	17.0-21.0	8.0-12.0	...
CF-3M(e)	316L	A 351, A 743, A 744	Ferrite in austenite	0.03	1.50	2.00	17.0-21.0	8.0-12.0	2.0-3.0 Mo
CF-3MN	...	A 743	Ferrite in austenite	0.03	1.50	1.50	17.0-21.0	9.0-13.0	2.0-3.0Mo; 0.10-0.20N
CF-8(e)	304	A 351, A 743, A 744	Ferrite in austenite	0.08	1.50	2.00	18.0-21.0	8.0-11.0	...
CF-8C	347	A 351, A 743, A 744	Ferrite in austenite	0.08	1.50	2.00	18.0-21.0	9.0-12.0	Nb(f)
CF-8M	316	A 351, A 743, A 744	Ferrite in austenite	0.08	1.50	2.00	18.0-21.0	9.0-12.0	2.0-3.0Mo
CF-10	...	A 351	Ferrite in austenite	0.04-0.10	1.50	2.00	18.0-21.0	8.0-11.0	...
CF-10M	...	A 351	Ferrite in austenite	0.04-0.10	1.50	1.50	18.0-21.0	9.0-12.0	2.0-3.0Mo
CF-10MC	...	A 351	Ferrite in austenite	0.10	1.50	1.50	15.0-18.0	13.0-16.0	1.75-2.25Mo
CF-10SMnN	...	A 351, A 743	Ferrite in austenite	0.10	7.00-9.00	3.50-4.50	16.0-18.0	8.0-9.0	0.08-0.18N
CF-12M	316	...	Ferrite in austenite or austenite	0.12	1.50	2.00	18.0-21.0	9.0-12.0	2.0-3.0Mo
CF-16F	303	A 743	Austenite	0.16	1.50	2.00	18.0-21.0	9.0-12.0	1.50Mo max; 0.20-0.35Se
CF-20	302	A 743	Austenite	0.20	1.50	2.00	18.0-21.0	8.0-11.0	...
CG-6MMN	...	A 351, A 743	Ferrite in austenite	0.06	4.00-6.00	1.00	20.5-23.5	11.5-13.5	1.50-3.00Mo; 0.10-0.30Nb; 0.10-30V; 0.20-40N
CG-8M	317	A 351, A 743, A 744	Ferrite in austenite	0.08	1.50	1.50	18.0-21.0	9.0-13.0	3.0-4.0Mo
CG-12	...	A 743	Ferrite in austenite	0.12	1.50	2.00	20.0-23.0	10.0-13.0	...
CH-8	...	A 351	Ferrite in austenite	0.08	1.50	1.50	22.0-26.0	12.0-15.0	...
CH-10	...	A 351	Ferrite in austenite	0.04-0.10	1.50	2.00	22.0-26.0	12.0-15.0	...
CH-20	309	A 351, A 743	Austenite	0.20	1.50	2.00	22.0-26.0	12.0-15.0	...
CK-3MCuN	...	A 351, A 743, A 744	Ferrite in austenite	0.025	1.20	1.00	19.5-20.5	17.5-19.5	6.0-7.0V; 0.18-0.24N; 0.50-1.00Cu
CK-20	310	A 743	Austenite	0.20	2.00	2.00	23.0-27.0	19.0-22.0	...
Nickel-chromium steel									
CN-3M	...	A 743	Austenite	0.03	2.00	1.00	20.0-22.0	23.0-27.0	4.5-5.5Mo
CN-7M	...	A 351, A 743, A 744	Austenite	0.07	1.50	1.50	19.0-22.0	27.5-30.5	2.0-3.0Mo; 3.0-4.0Cu
CN-7MS	...	A 743, A 744	Austenite	0.07	1.50	3.50(g)	18.0-20.0	22.0-25.0	2.5-3.0Mo; 1.5-2.0Cu
CT-15C	...	A 351	Austenite	0.05-0.15	0.15-1.50	0.50-1.50	19.0-21.0	31.0-34.0	0.5-1.5V

(a) Type numbers of wrought alloys are listed only for nominal identification of corresponding wrought and cast grades. Composition ranges of cast alloys are not the same as for corresponding wrought alloys; cast alloy designations should be used for castings only. (b) Maximum unless a range is given. The balance of all compositions is iron. (c) Sulfur content is 0.04% in all grades except: CG-6MMN, 0.030% S (max); CF-10SMnN, 0.03% S (max); CT-15C, 0.03% S (max); CK-3MCuN, 0.010% S (max); CN-3M, 0.030% S (max); CA-6N, 0.020% S (max); CA-28MWV, 0.030% S (max); CA-40F, 0.20-0.40% S; CB-7Cu-1 and -2, 0.03% S (max). Phosphorus content is 0.04% (max) in all grades except: CF-16F, 0.17% P (max); CF-10SMnN, 0.060% P (max); CT-15C, 0.030% P (max); CK-3MCuN, 0.045% P (max); CN-3M, 0.030% P (max); CA-6N, 0.020% P (max); CA-28MWV, 0.030% P (max); CB-7Cu-1 and -2, 0.035% P (max). (d) Molybdenum not intentionally added. (e) CF-3A, CF-3MA, and CF-8A have the same composition ranges as CF-3, CF-3M, and CF-8, respectively, but have balanced compositions so that ferrite contents are at levels that permit higher mechanical property specifications than those for related grades. They are covered by ASTM A 351. (f) Nb, 8 × %C min (1.0% max); or Nb + Ta × %C (1.1% max). (g) For CN-7MS, silicon ranges from 2.50 to 3.50%.

while exposed, either continuously or intermittently, to operating temperatures that result in metal temperatures in excess of 650 °C (1200 °F). Heat-resistant steel castings resemble high-alloy corrosion-resistant steels except for their higher carbon content, which imparts greater strength at elevated temperatures. The higher carbon content and, to a lesser extent, alloy composition ranges distinguish cast heat-resistant steel grades from their wrought counterparts. Table 2 summarizes the compositions of standard cast heat-resistant grades and three grade variations (HK30, HK40, HT30) specified in ASTM A 351 for elevated-temperature and corrosive service of pressure-containing parts. The three principal categories of

Table 2 Compositions of heat-resistant casting alloys

ACI designation	UNS number	ASTM specifications(a)	Composition, %(b)			
			C	Cr	Ni	Si (max)
HA	...	A 217	0.20 max	8-10	...	1.00
HC	J92605	A 297, A 608	0.50 max	26-30	4 max	2.00
HD	J93005	A 297, A 608	0.50 max	26-30	4-7	2.00
HE	J93403	A 297, A 608	0.20-0.50	26-30	8-11	2.00
HF	J92603	A 297, A 608	0.20-0.40	19-23	9-12	2.00
HH	J93503	A 297, A 608, A 447	0.20-0.50	24-28	11-14	2.00
HI	J94003	A 297, A 567, A 608	0.20-0.50	26-30	14-18	2.00
HK	J94224	A 297, A 351, A 567, A 608	0.20-0.60	24-38	18-22	2.00
HK30	...	A 351	0.25-0.35	23.0-27.0	19.0-22.0	1.75
HK40	...	A 351	0.35-0.45	23.0-27.0	19.0-22.0	1.75
HL	J94604	A 297, A 608	0.20-0.60	28-32	18-22	2.00
HN	J94213	A 297, A 608	0.20-0.50	19-23	23-27	2.00
HP	...	A 297	0.35-0.75	24-28	33-37	2.00
HP-50WZ(c)	...	...	0.45-0.55	24-28	33-37	2.50
HT	J94605	A 297, A 351, A 567, A 608	0.35-0.75	13-17	33-37	2.50
HT30	...	A 351	0.25-0.35	13.0-17.0	33.0-37.0	2.50
HU	...	A 297, A 608	0.35-0.75	17-21	37-41	2.50
HW	...	A 297, A 608	0.35-0.75	10-14	58-62	2.50
HX	...	A 297, A 608	0.35-0.75	15-19	64-68	2.50

(a) ASTM designations are the same as ACI designations. (b) Rem Fe in all compositions. Manganese content: 0.35 to 0.65% for HA, 1% for HC, 1.5% for HD, and 2% for the other alloys. Phosphorus and sulfur contents: 0.04% (max) for all but HP-50WZ. Molybdenum is intentionally added only to HA, which has 0.90 to 1.20% Mo; maximum for other alloys is set at 0.5% Mo. HH also contains 0.2% N (max). (c) Also contains 4 to 6% W, 0.1 to 1.0% Zr, and 0.035% S (max) and P (max)

H-type cast steels, based on composition, are iron-chromium alloys, iron-chromium-nickel alloys, and iron-nickel-chromium alloys. Information on the properties of H-type grades of steel castings is contained in the section "Heat-Resistant Cast Steels" in this article.

Composition and Microstructure

As shown in Table 1, cast stainless steels can also be classified on the basis of microstructure. Structures may be austenitic, ferritic, martensitic, or ferritic-austenitic (duplex).

The structure of a particular grade is primarily determined by composition. Chromium, molybdenum, and silicon promote the formation of ferrite (magnetic), while carbon, nickel, nitrogen, and manganese favor the formation of austenite (nonmagnetic). For example, a cast extra-low-carbon grade such as 0.03% C (max) cannot be completely nonmagnetic unless it contains 12 to 15% Ni. The wrought grades of these alloys normally contain about 13% Ni. They are made fully austenitic to improve rolling and forging characteristics.

Chromium (a ferrite and martensite promoter) and nickel and carbon (austenite promoters) are particularly important in determining microstructure (see the section "Ferrite Control" in this article). In general, straight chromium grades of high-alloy cast steel are either martensitic or ferritic, the chromium-nickel grades are either duplex or austenitic, and the nickel-chromium steels are fully austenitic.

Ferrite in Cast Austenitic Stainless Steels. Cast austenitic alloys usually have from 5 to 20% ferrite distributed in discontinuous pools throughout the matrix, the percent of ferrite depending on the nickel, chromium, and carbon contents (see the section "Ferrite Control" in this article). The presence of ferrite in austenite may be beneficial or detrimental, depending on the application.

Ferrite is beneficial and intentionally present in various corrosion-resistant cast steels (see some of the CF grades in Table 1, for example) to improve weldability and to maximize corrosion resistance in specific environments. Ferrite is also used for strengthening duplex alloys. The section "Austenitic-Ferritic (Duplex) Alloys" in this article gives further information.

Ferrite can be beneficial in terms of weldability because fully austenitic stainless steels are susceptible to a weldability problem known as hot cracking, or microfissuring. The intergranular cracking occurs in the weld deposit and/or in the weld heat-affected zone and can be avoided if the composition of the filler metal is controlled to produce about 4% ferrite in the austenitic weld deposit. Duplex CF grade alloy castings are immune to this problem.

The presence of ferrite in duplex CF alloys improves the resistance to SCC and generally to intergranular attack. In the case of SCC, the presence of ferrite pools in the austenite matrix is thought to block or make more difficult the propagation of cracks. In the case of intergranular corrosion, ferrite is helpful in sensitized castings because it promotes the preferential precipitation of carbides in the ferrite phase rather than at the austenite grain boundaries, where they would increase susceptibility to intergranular attack. The presence of ferrite also places additional grain boundaries in the austenite matrix, and there is evidence that intergranular attack is arrested at austenite-ferrite boundaries.

It is important to note, however, that not all studies have shown ferrite to be unconditionally beneficial to the general corrosion resistance of cast stainless steels. Some solutions attack the austenite phase in heat-treated alloys, whereas others attack the ferrite. For instance, calcium chloride solutions attack the austenite. On the other hand, a 10° Baumé cornstarch solution, acidified to a pH of 1.8 with sulfuric acid and heated to a temperature of 135 °C (275 °F), attacks the ferrite. Whether corrosion resistance is improved by ferrite and to what degree depends on the specific alloy composition, the heat treatment, and the service conditions (environment and stress state).

Ferrite can be detrimental in some applications. One concern may be the reduced toughness from ferrite, although this is not a major concern, given the extremely high toughness of the austenite matrix. A much greater concern is for applications that require exposure to elevated temperatures, usually 315 °C (600 °F) and higher, where the metallurgical changes associated with the ferrite can be severe and detrimental. In applications requiring that these steels be heated in the range from 425 to 650 °C (800 to 1200 °F), carbide precipitation occurs at the edges of the ferrite pools in preference to the austenite grain boundaries. When the steel is heated above 540 °C (1000 °F), the ferrite pools transform to a σ- or χ-phase. If these pools are distributed in such a way that a continuous network is formed, embrittlement or a network of corrosion penetration may result. Also, if the amount of ferrite is too great, the ferrite may form continuous stringers where corrosion can take place, producing a condition similar to grain boundary attack.

In the lower end of this temperature range, the reductions in toughness observed have been attributed to carbide precipitation or reactions associated with 475 °C (885 °F) embrittlement. The 475 °C (885 °F) embrittlement is caused by the precipitation of an intermetallic phase with a composition of approximately 80Cr-20Fe. The name derives from the fact that this embrittlement is most severe and rapid when it occurs at approximately 475 °C (885 °F).

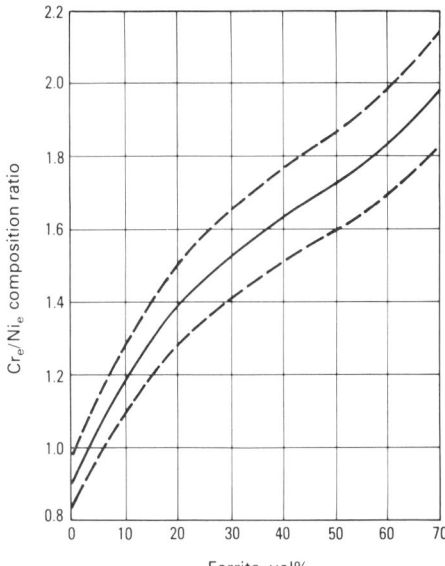

Fig. 2 Schoefer diagram for estimating the ferrite content of steel castings in the composition range of 16 to 26% Cr, 6 to 14% Ni, 4% Mo (max), 1% Nb (max), 0.2% C (max), 0.19% N (max), 2% Mn (max), and 2% Si (max). Dashed lines denote scatter bands caused by the uncertainty of the chemical analysis of individual elements. See text for equations used to calculate Cr_e and Ni_e. Source: Ref 1

At 540 °C (1000 °F) and above, the ferrite phase may transform to a complex iron-chromium-nickel-molybdenum intermetallic compound known as σ-phase, which reduces toughness, corrosion resistance, and creep ductility. The extent of the reduction increases with time and temperature to about 815 °C (1500 °F) and may persist to 925 °C (1700 °F). In extreme cases, Charpy V-notch energy at room temperature may be reduced 95% from its initial value (Ref 1, 2).

At temperatures above 540 °C (1000 °F), austenite also has better creep resistance than ferrite. The weaker ferrite phase may lend better plasticity to the alloy, but after long exposure at temperatures in the 540 to 760 °C (1000 to 1400 °F) range, it may transform to σ- or χ-phase, which reduces resistance to impact. In some instances, the alloy is deliberately aged to form the σ- or χ-phase and thus increase strength. Austenite can transform directly to σ- or χ-phase without going through the ferrite phase.

In weld deposits, the presence of σ- or χ-phase is extremely detrimental to ductility. When welding for service at room temperature or up to 540 °C (1000 °F), 4 to 10% ferrite may be present and will greatly reduce the tendency toward weld cracking. However, for service at temperatures between 540 and 815 °C (1000 and 1500 °F), the amount of ferrite in the weld must be reduced to less than 5% to avoid embrittlement from excessive σ- or χ-phase.

Ferrite Control. From the preceding discussion, it is apparent that ferrite in predominantly austenitic cast stainless steels can offer property advantages in some steels (notably the CF alloys) and disadvantages in other cases (primarily at ele-

vated temperatures). The underlying causes for the dependence of ferrite content on composition are found in the phase equilibria for the iron-chromium-nickel system. These phase equilibria have been exhaustively documented and related to commercial stainless steels.

The major elemental components of cast stainless steels are in competition to promote austenite or ferrite phases in the alloy microstructure. Chromium, silicon, molybdenum, and niobium promote the presence of ferrite in the alloy microstructure; nickel, carbon, nitrogen, and manganese promote the presence of austenite. By balancing the contents of ferrite- and austenite-forming elements within the specified ranges for the elements in a given alloy, it is possible to control the amount of ferrite present in the austenitic matrix. The alloy can usually either be made fully austenitic or be given ferrite contents up to 30% or more in the austenite matrix.

The relationship between composition and microstructure in cast stainless steels permits the foundryworker to predict and control the ferrite content of an alloy, as well as its resultant properties, by adjusting the composition of the alloy. This is accomplished using the Schoefer constitution diagram for cast chromium-nickel alloys (Fig. 2). This diagram was derived from an earlier diagram developed by Schaeffler for stainless steel weld metal (Ref 1). The use of Fig. 2 requires that all ferrite-stabilizing elements in the composition be converted into chromium equivalents and that all austenite-stabilizing elements be converted into nickel equivalents by means of empirically derived coefficients representing the ferritizing or austenitizing power of each element. A composition ratio is then obtained from the total chromium equivalent, Cr_e, and nickel equivalent, Ni_e, calculated for the alloy composition by:

$$Cr_e = \%Cr + 1.5(\%Si) + 1.4(\%Mo) + \%Nb - 4.99 \quad \text{(Eq 1)}$$

$$Ni_e = \%Ni + 30(\%C) + 0.5(\%Mn) + 26(\%N - 0.02) + 2.77 \quad \text{(Eq 2)}$$

where the elemental concentrations are given in weight percent. Although similar expressions have been derived that take into account additional alloying elements and different compositional ranges in the iron-chromium-nickel alloy system, use of the Schoefer diagram has become standard for estimating and controlling ferrite content in stainless steel castings.

The Schoefer diagram possesses obvious utility for casting users and foundryworkers. It is helpful for estimating or predicting ferrite content if the alloy composition is known, and for setting nominal values for individual elements when calculating the furnace charge for an alloy in which a specified ferrite range is desired.

Limits of Ferrite Control. Although ferrite content can be estimated and controlled on the basis of alloy composition only, there are limits to the accuracy with which this can be done. The reasons for this are many. First, there is an unavoidable degree of uncertainty in the chemical analysis of an alloy (note the scatter band in Fig. 2). Second, in addition to composition, the ferrite content depends on thermal history, although to a lesser extent. Third, ferrite contents at different locations in individual castings can vary considerably, depending on section size, ferrite orientation, presence of alloying-element segregation, and other factors.

Both the foundryworker and the user of stainless steel castings should recognize that the factors mentioned above place significant limits on the degree to which ferrite content (either as ferrite number or ferrite percentage) can be specified and controlled. In general, the accuracy of ferrite measurement and the precision of ferrite control diminish as the ferrite number increases. As a working rule, the limit of ferrite control under ordinary circumstances is ±6 about the mean or desired ferrite number, and the limit possible under ideal circumstances is ±3.

Heat Treatment

The heat treatment of stainless steel castings is very similar in purpose and procedure to the thermal processing of comparable wrought materials (see the article "Heat Treating" in this Volume). However, some differences warrant separate consideration here.

Homogenization. Alloy segregation and dendritic structures may occur in castings and may be particularly pronounced in heavy sections. Because castings are not subjected to the high-temperature mechanical reduction and soaking treatments involved in the mill processing of wrought alloys, it is frequently necessary to homogenize some alloys at temperatures above 1095 °C (2000 °F) to promote uniformity of chemical composition and microstructure. The full annealing of martensitic castings results in recrystallization and maximum softness, but it is less effective than homogenization in eliminating segregation. Homogenization is a common procedure in the heat treatment of precipitation-hardening castings.

Sensitization and Solution Annealing of Austenitic and Duplex Alloys. When austenitic or duplex (ferrite in austenite matrix) stainless steels are heated in or cooled slowly through a temperature range of about 425 to 870 °C (800 to 1600 °F), chromium-rich carbides form at grain boundaries in austenitic alloys and at ferrite-austenite interfaces in duplex alloys. These carbides deplete the surrounding matrix of chromium, thus diminishing the corrosion resistance of the alloy. In small amounts, these carbides may lead to localized pitting in the alloy, but if the chromium-depleted zones are extensive throughout the alloy or heat-affected zone (HAZ) of a weld, the alloy may disintegrate intergranularly in some environments.

An alloy in this condition of reduced corrosion resistance due to the formation of chromium carbides is said to be *sensitized,* a situation that is most pronounced for austenitic alloys. In austenitic structures, the complex chromium carbides precipitate preferentially along the grain boundaries. This microstructure is susceptible to intergranular corrosion, especially in oxidizing solutions. In partially ferritic alloys, carbides tend to precipitate in the discontinuous carbide pools; thus, these alloys are less susceptible to intergranular attack.

Solution annealing of austenitic and duplex stainless steels makes these alloys less susceptible to intergranular attack by ensuring the complete solution of the carbides in the matrix. Depending on the specific alloy in question, temperatures between 1040 and 1205 °C (1900 and 2200 °F) will ensure the complete solution of all carbides and phases, such as σ and χ, that sometimes form in highly alloyed stainless steels. Alloys containing relatively high total alloy contents, particularly high molybdenum content, often require the higher solution treatment temperature. Water quenching from the temperature range of 1040 to 1205 °C (1900 to 2200 °F) normally completes the solution treatment. Solution-annealing procedures for all austenitic alloys require holding for a sufficient amount of time to accomplish the complete solution of carbides and quenching at a rate fast enough to prevent reprecipitation of the carbides, particularly while cooling through the range of 870 to 540 °C (1600 to 1000 °F).

A two-step heat-treating procedure can be applied to the niobium-containing CF-8C alloy. The first treatment consists of solution annealing. This is followed by a stabilizing treatment at 870 to 925 °C (1600 to 1700 °F), which precipitates niobium carbides, prevents the formation of damaging chromium carbides, and provides maximum resistance to intergranular attack.

Because of their low carbon content, as-cast CF-3 and CF-3M do not contain enough chromium carbide to cause selective intergranular attack; therefore, these alloys can be used in some environments in this condition. However, for maximum corrosion resistance, these grades require solution annealing.

If the usual quenching treatment is difficult or impossible, holding for 24 to 48 h at 870 to 980 °C (1600 to 1800 °F) and air cooling is helpful for improving the resistance of castings to intergranular corrosion. However, except for alloys of very low carbon content and castings with thin sections, this treatment fails to produce material that is as resistant to intergranular corrosion as properly quench-annealed material.

Corrosion-Resistant Steel Castings

As previously mentioned, various high-alloy steel castings are classified as corrosion resistant (Table 1). These cast steels are widely used in chemical processing and power-generating equipment that requires corrosion resistance in aqueous or liquid-vapor environments at temperatures normally below 315 °C (600 °F). These alloys are also used in special applications with temperatures up to 650 °C (1200 °F).

Compositions

The chemical compositions of various corrosion-resistant cast steels are given in Table 1. These cast steels are specified in the ASTM standards listed in Table 1.

Straight chromium stainless steels contain 10 to 30% Cr and little or no nickel. Although about two-thirds of the corrosion-resistant steel castings produced in the United States are of grades that contain 18 to 22% Cr and 8 to 12% Ni, the straight chromium compositions are also produced in considerable quantity, particularly the steel with 11.5 to 14.0% Cr. Corrosion resistance improves as chromium content is increased. In general, intergranular corrosion is less of a concern in the straight chromium alloys (which are typically ferritic), especially those containing 25% Cr or more. This is attributed to the high bulk chromium contents and the rapid diffusion rates of chromium in ferrite.

Iron-chromium-nickel alloys have found wide acceptance and constitute about 60% of total production of high-alloy castings. They generally are austenitic with some ferrite. The most popular alloys of this type are CF-8 and CF-8M. These alloys are nominally 18-8 stainless steels and are the cast counterparts of wrought types 304 and 316, respectively. The carbon content of each is maintained at 0.08% (max).

Effects of Molybdenum on Corrosion Resistance. Alloys CF-3M and CF-8M are modifications of CF-3 and CF-8 containing 2 to 3% Mo to enhance general corrosion resistance. Their passivity under weakly oxidizing conditions is more stable than that of CF-3 and CF-8. The addition of 2 to 3% Mo increases resistance to corrosion by seawater and improves resistance to many chloride-bearing environments. The presence of 2 to 3% Mo also improves crevice corrosion and pitting resistance compared to the CF-8 and CF-3 alloys. The CF-8M and CF-3M alloys have good resistance to such corrosive media as sulfurous and acetic acids and are more resistant to pitting by mild chlorides. These alloys are suitable for use in flowing seawater, but they will pit under stagnant conditions.

Alloy CG-8M is slightly more highly alloyed than the CF-8M alloys, with the primary addition being increased molybdenum (3 to 4%). The increased amount of molybdenum provides superior corrosion resistance to halide-bearing media and reducing acids, particularly sulfurous and sulfuric acid solutions. The high molybdenum content, however, renders CG-8M generally unsuitable in highly oxidizing environments.

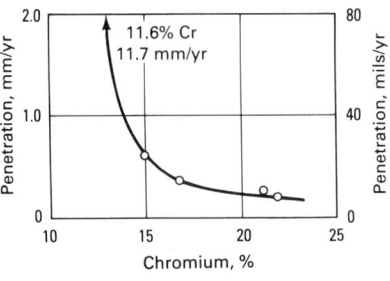
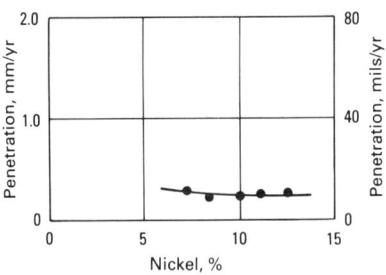
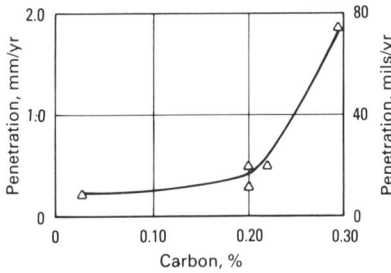
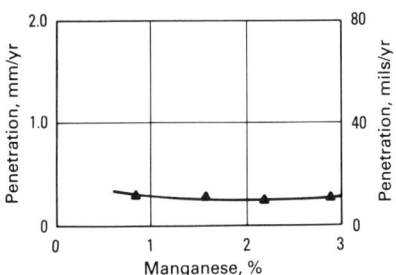
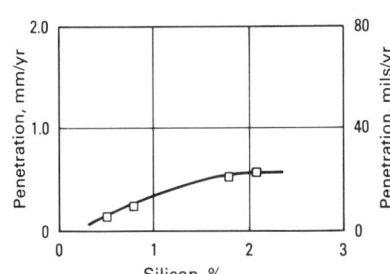
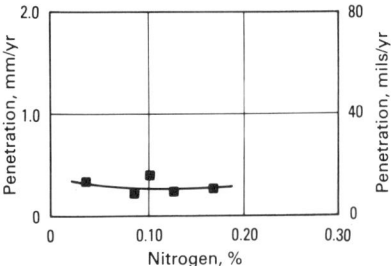

Fig. 3 Effects of various elements in a 19Cr-9Ni casting alloy on corrosion rate in boiling 65% nitric acid. Data were determined for solution-annealed and quenched specimens. Composition of base alloy was 19Cr, 9Ni, 0.09C, 0.8Mn, 1.0Si, 0.04P (max), 0.035 (max), 0.06N.

Table 3 Results of in-plant corrosion testing of CF-8, CF-8M, and CN-7M alloys

Type and composition of corroding solution	Temperature of solution		Alloy	Metal loss on surface		Surface condition by visual examination	Remarks
	°C	°F		μm/yr	mils/yr		
Neutralizer after formation of ammonium sulfate; ammonium sulfate plus small excess of sulfuric acid, ammonia vapor, and steam	100	212	CF-8	665	26.2	Very heavy etch(a)	CF-8M was installed for low corrosion tolerance equipment in this service and performed satisfactorily
			CF-8M	28	1.1	Light tarnish(b)	
			CN-7M	18	0.7	Bright	
Settling tank after neutralizer; ammonium sulfate plus excess of sulfuric acid	50	122	CF-8	385	15.2	Very heavy etch(a)	CF-8 in service showed excessive corrosion rate plus heavy concentration cell attack
			CF-8M	10	0.4	Slight tarnish	
			CN-7M	2.5	0.1	Bright(b)	
Ammonium sulfate processing solution; ammonium sulfate at pH of 8.0	50	122	CF-8	685	27.0	Heavy etch	CF-8M had too high a corrosion rate in service for good valve life, although suitable for equipment of greater corrosion tolerance. CN-7M was installed in this service
			CF-8M	175	6.8	Moderate etch	
			CN-7M	50	2.0	Light etch	
99 to 100% fuming nitric acid	20	68	CF-8	245	9.6	Moderate etch	CF-8 was satisfactory except for low-tolerance equipment such as valves. CN-7M valves performed satisfactorily in service
			CN-7M	79	3.1	Light etch	
			CF-8M	345	13.5	Moderate etch	
Saturated solution of sodium chloride plus 15% sodium sulfate; pH of 4.5	60	140	CF-8M	2.5	0.1	Bright	CF-8M was installed for valves in service
			CF-8	240	9.5	Concentration cell corrosion at various small areas of specimen	

(a) Concentration cell attack under insulating water. (b) Slight concentration cell attack under insulating washer

Molybdenum-bearing alloys are generally not as resistant to highly oxidizing environments (this is particularly true for boiling nitric acid), but for weakly oxidizing environments and reducing environments, molybdenum-bearing alloys are generally superior. Molybdenum may also produce detrimental catalytic reactions. For example, the

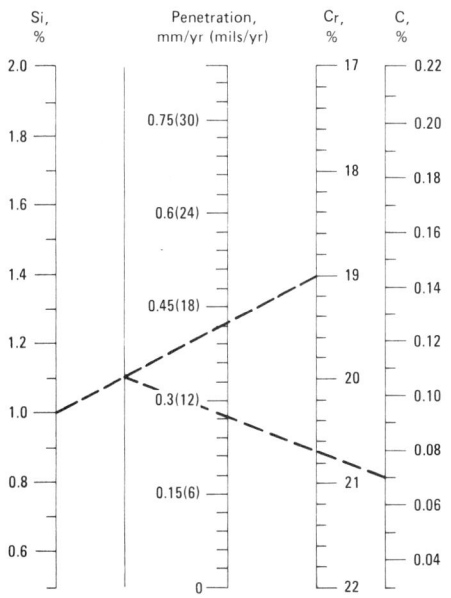

Fig. 4 Nomograph for determining corrosion rate in boiling 65% nitric acid for solution-annealed and quenched type CF casting alloys

residual molybdenum in CF-8 alloy must be held below 0.5% in the presence of hydrazine.

Effects of Chromium, Carbon, and Silicon on Corrosion Resistance. In alloys of the CF type, the effects of composition on rates of general corrosion attack have been studied, and certain definite relationships have been established. Through the use of the Huey test (five 48 h periods of exposure to boiling 65% nitric acid, as described in practice C of ASTM A 262), it has been shown that, in this standardized environment, carbide-free quench-annealed alloys of various nickel, chromium, silicon, carbon, and manganese contents have corrosion rates directly related to these contents.

Figure 3 shows the influences on corrosion rate exerted by various elements in a 19Cr-9Ni casting alloy. Variations in nickel, manganese, and nitrogen contents for the ranges shown have relatively slight influences, but variations in chromium, carbon, and silicon have marked effects. The relationship between composition and corrosion rate for properly heat-treated CF alloys in boiling 65% nitric acid is summarized in the nomograph presented in Fig. 4.

Iron-Nickel-Chromium Alloys. For some types of service, extensive use is made of iron-nickel-chromium alloys that contain more nickel than chromium. Most important among this group is alloy CN-7M, which has a nominal composition of 28% Ni, 20% Cr, 3.5% Cu, 2.5% Mo, and 0.07% C (max). In effect, this alloy is made by adding 20% Ni and 3.5% Cu to alloy CF-8M, which greatly improves resistance to hot, concentrated, weakly oxidizing solutions such as sulfuric

acid and also improves resistance to severely oxidizing media. Alloys of this type can withstand all concentrations of sulfuric acid at temperatures up to 65 °C (150 °F) and many concentrations at temperatures up to 80 °C (175 °F). They are widely used in nitric-hydrofluoric pickling solutions; phosphoric acid; cold dilute hydrochloric acid; hot acetic acid; strong, hot caustic solutions; brines; and many complex plating solutions and rayon spin baths.

Results of in-plant corrosion testing of CF-8, CF-8M, and CN-7M alloys are shown in Table 3. These tests give the specific effect of molybdenum on 19Cr-9Ni alloys in reducing selective attack and pitting, and the overall corrosion rate computed from loss in weight. The higher nickel plus copper and molybdenum in the CN-7M alloy reduce the rate of corrosion to a rate lower than that of the CF-8M alloy.

Microstructures

Although corrosion-resistant cast steels are usually classified on the basis of composition, it should be recognized that classification by composition also often involves microstructural distinctions. Table 1 shows the typical microstructures of various corrosion-resistant cast steels. As noted previously, straight chromium grades of high-alloy cast steel are either martensitic or ferritic, chromium-nickel grades are either duplex or austenitic, and nickel-chromium steels are fully austenitic.

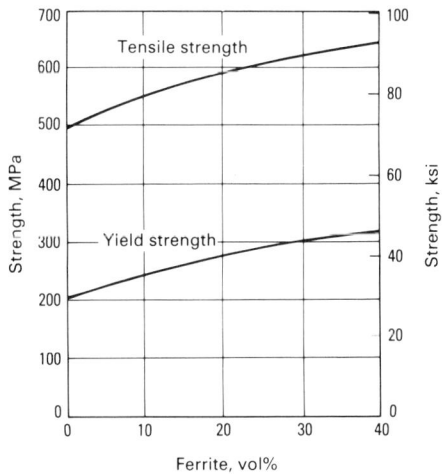

Fig. 5 Yield strength and tensile strength vs. percentage of ferrite for CF-8 and CF-8M alloys. Curves are mean values for 277 heats of CF-8 and 62 heats of CF-8M. Source: Ref 3

Martensitic grades include alloys CA-15, CA-40, CA-15M, and CA-6NM. The CA-15 alloy contains the minimum amount of chromium necessary to make it essentially rustproof. It has good resistance to atmospheric corrosion and to many organic media in relatively mild service. A higher-carbon modification of CA-15, CA-40, can be heat treated to higher strength and hardness levels. Alloy CA-15M is a molybdenum-containing modification of CA-15 that provides improved elevated-temperature strength. Alloy CA-6NM is an iron-chromium-nickel-molybdenum alloy of low carbon content.

Austenitic grades include CH-20, CK-20, and CN-7M. The CH-20 and CK-20 alloys are high-chromium, high-carbon, wholly austenitic compositions in which the chromium content exceeds the nickel content. The more highly alloyed CN-7M, as described earlier in the section "Iron-Nickel-Chromium Alloys," has excellent corrosion resistance in many environments and is often used in sulfuric acid environments. The CN-7MS alloy has a corrosion resistance similar to that of CN-7M. The CN-7MS alloy has outstanding resistance to corrosion from high-strength (>90%) nitric acid.

Ferritic grades include CB-30 and CC-50. Alloy CB-30 is practically nonhardenable by heat treatment. As this alloy is normally made, the balance among the elements in the composition results in a wholly ferritic structure similar to that of wrought type 442 stainless steel. Alloy CC-50 has substantially more chromium than CB-30 and has relatively high resistance to localized corrosion in many environments.

Austenitic-ferritic (duplex) alloys include CE-30, CF-3, CF-3A, CF-8, CF-8A, CF-20, CF-3M, CF-3MA, CF-8M, CF-8C, CF-16F, and CG-8M. The microstructures of these alloys usually contain 5 to 40% ferrite, depending on the particular grade and the balance among the ferrite-promoting and austenite-promoting elements in the chemical composition (see the section "Ferrite Control" in this article). Duplex alloys offer superior strength, corrosion resistance, and weldability.

The use of duplex cast steels has focused primarily on the CF grades, particularly within the power generation industry. Strengthening in the cast CF grade alloys is limited essentially to that which can be gained by incorporating ferrite into the austenite matrix phase. These alloys cannot be strengthened by thermal treatment, as can the cast martensitic alloys, or by hot or cold working, as can the wrought austenitic alloys. Strengthening by carbide precipitation is also out of the question because of the detrimental effect of carbides on corrosion resistance in most aqueous environments. Thus, the alloys are effectively strengthened by balancing the alloy composition to produce a duplex microstructure consisting of ferrite (up to 40 vol%) distributed in an austenite matrix. It has been shown that the incorporation of ferrite into 19Cr-9Ni cast steels improves yield and tensile strengths without substantial loss of ductility or impact toughness at temperatures below 425 °C (800 °F). The magnitude of this strengthening effect for CF-8 and CF-8M alloys at room temperature is shown in Fig. 5. Table 4 shows the effect of ferrite content on the tensile properties of 19Cr-9Ni alloys at room temperature and at 355 °C (670 °F). Table 5 shows the effect of ferrite content on impact toughness.

Other duplex alloys of interest include CD-4MCu and Ferralium. CD-4MCu is the most highly alloyed duplex alloy. Ferralium was developed by Langley Alloys and is essentially CD-4MCu with about 0.15 to 0.20% N added. With high levels of ferrite (about 40 to 50%) and low nickel, the duplex alloys have better resistance to SCC than CF-3M. Alloy CD-4MCu, which contains no nitrogen and has a relatively low molybdenum content, has only slightly better resistance to localized corrosion than CF-3M. Ferralium, which has nitrogen and slightly

Table 4 Effect of ferrite content on tensile properties of 19Cr-9Ni alloys

Ferrite content, %	Tensile strength		Yield strength at 0.2% offset		Elongation in 50 mm (2 in.), %	Reduction in area, %
	MPa	ksi	MPa	ksi		
Tested at room temperature						
3	465	67.4	216	31.3	60.5	64.2
10	498	72.2	234	34.0	61.0	73.0
20	584	84.7	296	43.0	53.5	58.5
41	634	91.9	331	48.0	45.5	47.9
Tested at 355 °C (670 °F)						
3	339	49.1	104	15.1	45.5	63.2
10	350	50.8	109	15.8	43.0	69.7
20	457	66.3	183	26.5	36.5	47.5
41	488	70.8	188	27.3	33.8	49.4

Table 5 Charpy V-notch impact energy, ferrite content, and Cr_e/Ni_e ratio of duplex cast steels

Alloy	Charpy V-notch energy		Ferrite content, %			Cr_e/Ni_e ratio(c)
	J	ft · lbf	Calculated	MG(a)	FS(b)	
CF 3M	197	145	28.5	20	20	1.5
CF 3C	183	135	20.7	12.5	14	1.4
CG 8M	216	159	18	9	10	1.34
CF 3C	>358	>264	15	13	15	1.29
CF 3M	>358	>264	7.7	6	7	1.12

(a) MG, magna gage. (b) FS, ferrite scope. (c) See Eq 1 and 2 for formulas to compute Cr_e and Ni_e.

Table 6 Nominal compositions of first- and second-generation duplex stainless steels

UNS designation	Common name	Composition, %(a)					
		Cr	Ni	Mo	Cu	N	Others
First generation steels							
S31500	3RE60	18.5	4.7	2.7	...	...	1.7Si
S32404	Uranus 50	21	7.0	2.5	1.5	...	...
S32900	Type 329	26	4.5	1.5	...	...	...
J93370	CD-4MCu	25	5	2	3	...	...
Second generation steels							
S31200	44LN	25	6	1.7	...	0.15	...
S31260	DP-3	25	7	3	0.5	0.15	0.3W
S31803	Alloy 2205	22	5	3	...	0.15	...
S32550	Ferralium 255	25	6	3	2	0.20	...
S32950	7-Mo PLUS	26.5	4.8	1.5	...	0.20	...
J93404	Atlas 958, COR 25	25	7	4.5	...	0.25	...

(a) All compositions contain balance of iron.

Table 7 Summary of applications for various corrosion-resistant cast steels

Alloy	Characteristics
CA-15	Widely used in mildly corrosive environments; hardenable; good erosion resistance
CA-40	Similar to CA-15 at higher strength level
CA-6NM	Improved properties over CA-15, especially improved resistance to cavitation
CA-6N	Outstanding combinations of strength, toughness, and weldability with moderately good corrosion resistance
CB-30	Improved performance in oxidizing environments compared to CA-15; excellent resistance to corrosion by nitric acid, alkaline solutions, and many organic chemicals
CB-7Cu-1	Hardenable with good corrosion resistance
CB-7Cu-2	Superior combination of strength, toughness, and weldability with moderately good corrosion resistance
CC-50	Used in highly oxidizing media (hot HNO_3, acid mine waters)
CD-4MCu	Similar to CF-8 in corrosion resistance, but higher strength, hardness, and stress-corrosion cracking resistance; excellent resistance to environments involving abrasion or erosion-corrosion; usefully employed in handling both oxidizing and reducing corrodents
CE-30	Similar to CC-50, but Ni imparts higher strength and toughness levels. A grade available with controlled ferrite
CF-3, CF-8, CF-20, CF-3M, CF-8M, CF-8C, CF-16F	CF types: most widely used corrosion-resistant alloys at ambient and cryogenic temperatures M variations: enhanced resistance to halogen ion and reducing acids C and F variations: used where application does not permit postweld heat treat A grades available with controlled ferrite
CG-8M	Greater resistance to pitting and corrosion in reducing media than CF-8M; not suitable for nitric acids or other strongly oxidizing environments
CH-20	Superior to CF-8 in specialized chemical and paper applications in resistance to hot H_2SO_3, organic acids, and dilute H_2SO_4; the high nickel and chromium contents also make this alloy less susceptible to intergranular corrosion after exposure to carbide-precipitating temperatures
CK-20	Improved corrosion resistance compared to CH-20
CN-7M	Highly resistant to H_2SO_4, H_3PO_4, H_2SO_3, salts, and seawater. Good resistance to hot chloride salt solutions, nitric acid, and many reducing chemicals

higher molybdenum than CD-4MCu, exhibits better localized corrosion resistance than either CF-3M or CD-4MCu.

Improvements in stainless steel production practices (for example, electron beam refining, vacuum and argon-oxygen decarburization, and vacuum induction melting) have also created a second generation of duplex stainless steels. These steels offer excellent resistance to pitting and crevice corrosion, significantly better resistance to chloride SCC than the austenitic stainless steels, good toughness, and yield strengths two to three times higher than those of type 304 or 316 stainless steels.

First-generation duplex stainless steels (e.g., type 329 and CD-4MCu) have been in use for many years. The need for improvement in the weldability and corrosion resistance of these alloys resulted in the second-generation alloys, which are characterized by the addition of nitrogen as an alloying element.

Second-generation duplex stainless steels are usually about a 50-50 blend of ferrite and austenite. The new duplex alloys combine the near immunity to chloride SCC of the ferritic grades with the toughness and ease of fabrication of the austenitics. Among the second-generation duplexes, Alloy 2205 seems to have become the general purpose stainless. Table 6 lists the nominal compositions of first- and second-generation duplex alloys.

Precipitation-Hardening Alloys. Corrosion-resistant alloys capable of being hardened by low-temperature treatment to obtain improved mechanical properties are usually duplex-structure alloys with much more chromium than nickel. The addition of copper enables these alloys to be strengthened by precipitation hardening. These alloys are significantly higher in strength than the other corrosion-resistant alloys, even without hardening.

The alloys CB-7Cu-1 and CB-7Cu-2 have corrosion resistances between those of CA-15 and CF-8. They are widely used for structural components requiring moderate corrosion resis-

tance, as well as for components requiring resistance to erosion and wear.

The alloy CD-4MCu is widely used in many applications where its good corrosion resistance (which often equals or even exceeds that of CF-8M) and excellent resistance to erosion make it the most desirable alloy. The steel CD-4MCu has outstanding resistance to nitric acid and mixtures of nitric acid and organic acids, as well as excellent resistance to a wide range of corrosive chemical process conditions. This alloy is normally used in the solution-annealed condition, but it can be precipitation hardened for carefully selected applications when lower corrosion resistance can be tolerated and when there is no potential for SCC.

Corrosion Characteristics

Table 7 compares the general corrosion resistance of the C-type (corrosion-resistant in liquid service) cast steels. More detailed information on the resistance of cast high-alloy steels to general

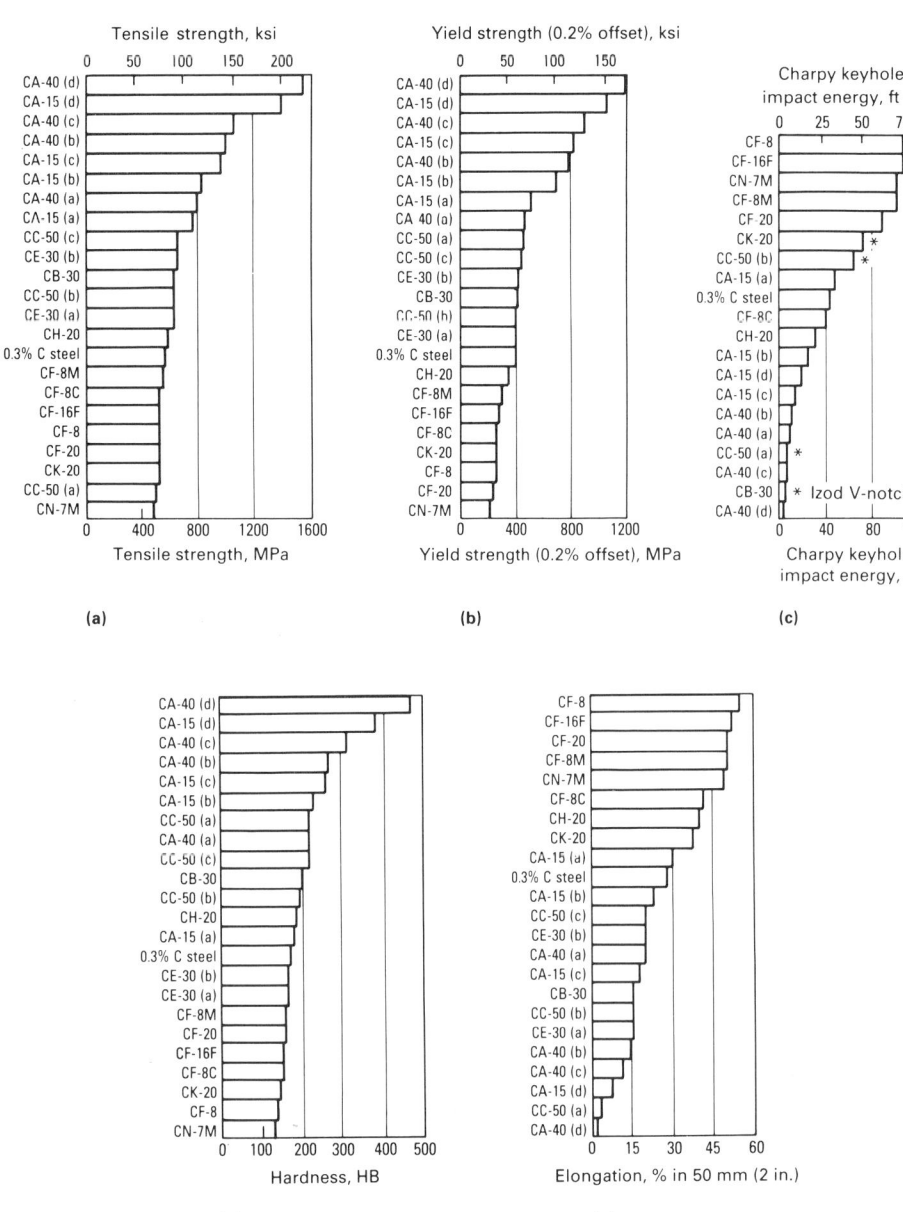

Fig. 6 Mechanical properties of various cast corrosion-resistant steels at room temperature. (a) Tensile strength. (b) 0.2% offset yield strength. (c) Charpy keyhole impact energy. (d) Brinell hardness. (e) Elongation. Also given are the heat treatments used for test materials: AC, air cool; FC, furnace cool; WQ, water quench; A, anneal; T, temper.

Alloy	Heat treatment	Alloy	Heat treatment
CA-15 (a)	AC from 980 °C (1800 °F), T at 790 °C (1450 °F)	CC-50 (a)	As-cast (<1% Ni)
(b)	AC from 980 °C (1800 °F), T at 650 °C (1200 °F)	(b)	As-cast (>2% Ni; >0.15% N)
(c)	AC from 980 °C (1800 °F), T at 595 °C (1100 °F)	(c)	AC from 1040 °C (1900 °F) (>2% Ni; >0.15% N)
(d)	AC from 980 °C (1800 °F), T at 315 °C (600 °F)	CE-30 (a)	As-cast
CA-40 (a)	AC from 980 °C (1800 °F), T at 760 °C (1400 °F)	(b)	WQ from 1065–1120 °C (1950–2050 °F)
(b)	AC from 980 °C (1800 °F), T at 650 °C (1200 °F)	CF-8	WQ from 1065–1120 °C (1950–2050 °F)
(c)	AC from 980 °C (1800 °F), T at 595 °C (1100 °F)	CF-20	WQ from above 1095 °C (2000 °F)
		CF-8M, CF-12M ...	WQ from 1065–1150 °C (1950–2100 °F)
(d)	AC from 980 °C (1800 °F), T at 315 °C (600 °F)	CF-8C	WQ from 1065–1120 °C (1950–2050 °F)
CB-30..............	A at 790 °C (1450 °F), FC to 540 °C (1000 °F), AC	CF-16F	WQ from above 1095 °C (2000 °F)
		CH-20	WQ from above 1095 °C (2000 °F)
		CK-20	WQ from above 1150 °C (2100 °F)
		CN-7M	WQ from above 1065–1120 °C (1950–2050 °F)

corrosion, intergranular corrosion, localized corrosion, corrosion fatigue, and SCC can be found in the article "Corrosion of Cast Stainless Steels" in this Volume.

Corrosion from Chlorine. The influence of contaminants is one of the most important considerations in selecting an alloy for a particular process application. Ferric chloride in relatively small amounts, for example, will cause concentration-cell corrosion and pitting. The buildup of corrosion products in a chloride solution may increase the iron concentration to a level high enough to be destructive. Thus, chlorine salts, wet chlorine gas, and unstable chlorinated organic compounds cannot be handled by any of the iron-base alloys, creating a need for nickel-base alloys.

Mechanical Properties

The importance of mechanical properties in the selection of corrosion-resistant cast steels is established by the casting application. The paramount basis for alloy selection is normally the resistance of the alloy to the specific corrosive media or environment of interest. The mechanical properties of the alloy are usually, but not always, secondary considerations in these applications.

Room-Temperature Mechanical Properties. Representative room-temperature tensile properties, hardness, and Charpy impact values for corrosion-resistant cast steels are given in Fig. 6 and Table 8. These properties are representative of the alloys rather than the specification requirements. Minimum specified mechanical properties for these alloys are given in ASTM A 351, A 743, A 744, and A 747. A wide range of mechanical properties are attainable, depending on the selection of alloy composition and heat treatment. Tensile strengths ranging from 475 to 1310 MPa (69 to 190 ksi) and hardnesses from 130 to 400 HB are available among the cast corrosion-resistant alloys. Similarly, wide ranges exist in yield strength, elongation, and impact toughness.

The straight chromium steels (CA-15, CA-40, CB-30, and CC-50) possess either martensitic or ferritic microstructures in the end-use condition (Table 1). The CA-15 and CA-40 alloys, which contain nominally 12% Cr, are hardenable through heat treatment by means of the martensite transformation and are often selected as much or more for their high strength as for their comparatively modest corrosion resistance.

The higher-chromium CB-30 and CC-50 alloys, on the other hand, are fully ferritic alloys that are not hardenable by heat treatment. These alloys are generally used in the annealed condition and exhibit moderate tensile properties and hardness. Like most ferritic alloys, CB-30 and CC-50 possess limited impact toughness, especially at low temperatures.

Three chromium-nickel alloys, CA-6NM, CB-7Cu, and CD-4MCu, are exceptional in their response to heat treatment and in their resultant mechanical properties. Alloy CA-6NM is balanced compositionally for a martensitic hardening response. This alloy was developed as an alternative to CA-15 and has improved impact toughness and weldability. The CB-7Cu and CD-

Table 8 Room-temperature mechanical properties of cast corrosion-resistant alloys

Alloy	Heat treatment (a)	Tensile strength		Yield strength (0.2% offset)		Elongation in 50 mm (2 in.), %	Reduction in area, %	Hardness, HB	Charpy impact energy		Specimens
		MPa	ksi	MPa	ksi				J	ft · lb	
CA-6NM	>955 °C (1750 °F), AC, T	827	120	689	100	24	60	269	94.9	70	V-notch
CA-15	980 °C (1800 °F), AC, T	793	115	689	100	22	55	225	27.1	20	Keyhole notch
CA-40	980 °C (1800 °F), AC, T	1034	150	862	125	10	30	310	2.7	2	Keyhole notch
CB-7Cu	1040 °C (1900 °F), OQ, A	1310	190	1172	170	14	54	400	33.9	25	V-notch
CB-30	790 °C (1450 °F), AC	655	95	414	60	15	...	195	2.7	2	Keyhole notch
CC-50	1040 °C (1900 °F), AC	669	97	448	65	18	...	210	...	...	...
CD-4MCu	1120 °C (2050 °F), FC to 1040°C (1900 °F), WQ	745	108	558	81	25	...	253	74.6	55	V-notch
	1120 °C (2050 °F), FC to 1040 °C (1900 °F), A	896	130	634	92	20	...	305	35.3	26	V-notch
CE-30	1095 °C (2000 °F), WQ	669	97	434	63	18	...	190	9.5	7	Keyhole notch
CF-3	>1040 °C (1900 °F), WQ	531	77	248	36	60	...	140	149.2	110	V-notch
CF-3A	>1040 °C (1900 °F), WQ	600	87	290	42	50	...	160	135.6	100	V-notch
CF-8	>1040 °C (1900 °F), WQ	531	77	255	37	55	...	140	100.3	74	Keyhole notch
CF-8A	>1040 °C (1900 °F), WQ	586	85	310	45	50	...	156	94.9	70	Keyhole notch
CF-20	>1095 °C (2000 °F), WQ	531	77	248	36	50	...	163	81.4	60	Keyhole notch
CF-3M	>1040 °C (1900 °F), WQ	552	80	262	38	55	...	150	162.7	120	V-notch
CF-3MA	>1040 °C (1900 °F), WQ	621	90	310	45	45	...	170	135.6	100	V-notch
CF-8M	>1065 °C (1950 °F), WQ	552	80	290	42	50	...	170	94.9	70	Keyhole notch
CF-8C	>1065 °C (1950 °F), WQ	531	77	262	38	39	...	149	40.7	30	Keyhole notch
CF-16F	>1095 °C (2000 °F), WQ	531	77	276	40	52	...	150	101.7	75	Keyhole notch
CG-8M	>1040 °C (1900 °F), WQ	565	82	303	44	45	...	176	108.5	80	V-notch
CH-20	>1095 °C (2000 °F), WQ	607	88	345	50	38	...	190	40.7	30	Keyhole notch
CK-20	1150 °C (2100 °F), WQ	524	76	262	38	37	...	144	67.8	50	Izod V-notch
CN-7M	1120 °C (2050 °F), WQ	476	69	214	31	48	...	130	94.9	70	Keyhole notch

(a) AC, air cool; FC, furnace cool; OQ, oil quench; WQ, water quench; T, temper; A, age

4MCu alloys both contain copper and can be strengthened by age hardening. These alloys are initially solution heat treated and then cooled rapidly (usually by quenching in oil or water); thus, the phases that would normally precipitate at slow cooling rates cannot form. The casting is then heated to an intermediate aging temperature at which the precipitation reaction can occur under controlled conditions until the desired combination of strength and other properties is achieved. The CB-7Cu alloy possesses a martensitic matrix, while the CD-4MCu alloy possesses a duplex microstructure, consisting of approximately 40% austenite in a ferritic matrix. Alloy CB-7Cu is applied in the aged condition to obtain the benefit of its excellent combination of strength and corrosion resistance, but alloy CD-4MCu is seldom applied in the aged condition because of its relatively low resistance to SCC in this condition compared to its superior corrosion resistance in the solution-annealed condition.

The CE, CF, CG, CH, CN, and CK alloys are essentially not hardenable by heat treatment. To ensure maximum corrosion resistance, however, it is necessary that castings of these grades receive a high-temperature solution anneal (see "Sensitization and Solution Annealing of Austenitic and Duplex Alloys" in this article). By virtue of their microstructures, which are fully austenitic or duplex without significant carbide precipitation, the alloys exhibit generally excellent impact toughness at low temperatures. The tensile strength range represented by these alloys typically extends from 475 to 670 MPa (69 to 97 ksi). As indicated in the section "Austenitic-Ferritic (Duplex) Alloys" in this article, the alloys with duplex

structures can be strengthened by balancing the composition for higher ferrite levels (Fig. 5). The tensile and yield strengths of CF alloys with a ferrite number of 35 are typically 150 MPa (22 ksi) higher than those of fully austenitic alloys. Tensile ductility (Table 4) and impact toughness (Table 5) decline with increasing ferrite content.

Effects from High Temperatures. Cast corrosion-resistant, high-alloy steels are used extensively at moderately elevated temperatures (up to 650 °C, or 1200 °F). Elevated-temperature properties are important selection criteria for these applications. Table 9 gives the tensile properties of a corrosion-resistant cast steel at various test temperatures. In addition, mechanical properties after long-term exposure at elevated temperatures are increasingly considered because of the aging effect that these exposures may have. For example, cast alloys CF-8C, CF-8M, CE-30A, and CA-15 are currently used in high-pressure service at temperatures up to 540 °C (1000 °F) in sulfurous acid environments in the petrochemical industry. Other uses are in the power generation industry at temperatures up to 565° C (1050 °F).

Room-temperature properties after exposure to elevated service temperatures may differ from those in the as-heat-treated condition because of the microstructural changes that may take place at the service temperature. Microstructural changes in iron-nickel-chromium-(molybdenum) alloys may involve the formation of carbides and such phases as σ, χ, and η (Laves). The extent to which these phases form depends on the composition, as well as the time at elevated temperature.

The martensitic alloys CA-15 and CA-6NM are subject to minor changes in mechanical prop-

erties and SCC resistance in sodium chloride and polythionic acid environments upon exposure for 3000 h at up to 565 °C (1050 °F). In CF-type chromium-nickel-(molybdenum) steels, only negligible changes in ferrite content occur during 10,000 h exposure at 400 °C (750 °F) and during 3000 h exposure at 425 °C (800 °F). Carbide precipitation, however, does occur at these temperatures, and noticeable Charpy V-notch energy losses have been reported. These effects are illustrated in Fig. 7 and 8 for CF-8 cast corrosion-resistant steel.

Above 425 °C (800 °F), microstructural changes in chromium-nickel-(molybdenum) alloys take place at an increased rate. Carbides and -phase form rapidly at 650 °C (1200 °F) at the expense of ferrite (Fig. 9). Tensile ductility and Charpy V-notch impact energy (Fig. 10) are prone to significant losses under these conditions. Density changes, resulting in contraction, have been reported as a result of these high-temperature exposures.

Fatigue Properties and Corrosion Fatigue. The resistance of cast stainless steels to fatigue depends on a sizable number of material, design, and environmental factors. For example, design factors of importance include the stress distribution within the casting (residual and applied stresses), the location and severity of stress concentrators (surface integrity), and the environment and service temperatures. Material factors of importance include strength and microstructure. It is generally found that fatigue strength increases with the tensile strength of a material. Both fatigue strength and tensile strength usually increase with decreasing temperature. Under

Table 9 Short-time tensile properties of peripheral-welded cylinders of CF-8 alloy

Cylinders were 38 mm (1½ in.) thick; specimens were machined with longitudinal axes perpendicular to welded seam and with seam at middle or gage length.

Testing temperature		Tensile strength		Yield strength at 0.2% offset		Proportional limit(a)		Reduction in area,	Elongation in 50 mm	Modulus of elasticity(a)		Location of
°C	°F	MPa	ksi	MPa	ksi	MPa	ksi	%	(2 in.), %	GPa	10⁶ psi	final rupture
Base metal												
Keel block(b)		500	72.5	238	34.5	...	...	59.0	49	...	...	...
Room		500	72.5	261	37.8	179	26	62.1	58	186	27	...
315	600	330	47.8	169	24.5	90	13	54.9	33.5	152	22	...
425	800	339	49.2	167	24.2	59	8.5	58.6	37.5	134	19.5	...
540	1000	291	42.2	140	20.3	55	8	60.8	32.5	117	17	...
595	1100	279	40.4	130	18.8	45	6.5	59.1	38	110	16	...
Welded joint												
Room		490	71.0	247	35.8	148	21.5	70.8	42	186	27	Base metal
315	600	341	49.5	199	28.8	72	10.5	58.3	15.5	152	22	Base metal
425	800	355	51.5	171	24.8	69	10	46.3	24.5	131	19	Base metal
540	1000	326	47.3	188	27.3	62	9	62.8	23.5	114	16.5	Base metal
595	1100	272	39.4	134	19.5	55	8	70.4	31	107	15.5	Base metal

(a) Values of proportional limit and modulus of elasticity at elevated temperatures are apparent values because creep occurs. (b) Separately cast from same heat as cylinders

equivalent conditions of stress, stress concentration, and strength, evidence suggests that austenitic materials are less notch-sensitive than martensitic or ferritic materials.

Corrosion fatigue is highly specific to the environment and alloy. The martensitic materials are degraded the most in both absolute and relative terms. If left to corrode freely in seawater, they have very little resistance to corrosion fatigue. This is remarkable in view of their very high strength and fatigue resistance in air.

Satisfactory properties can be obtained if suitable cathodic protection is applied. However, because these materials are susceptible to hydrogen embrittlement, cathodic protection must be carefully applied. Too large a protective potential will lead to catastrophic hydrogen stress cracking.

Austenitic materials are also severely degraded in corrosion fatigue strength under conditions conducive to pitting, such as in seawater. However, they are easily cathodically protected without fear of hydrogen embrittlement and per-

form well in fresh waters. The corrosion fatigue behavior of duplex alloys has not been widely studied.

Heat-Resistant Cast Steels

As previously mentioned, castings are classified as heat resistant if they are capable of sustained operation while exposed, either continuously or intermittently, to operating tem-

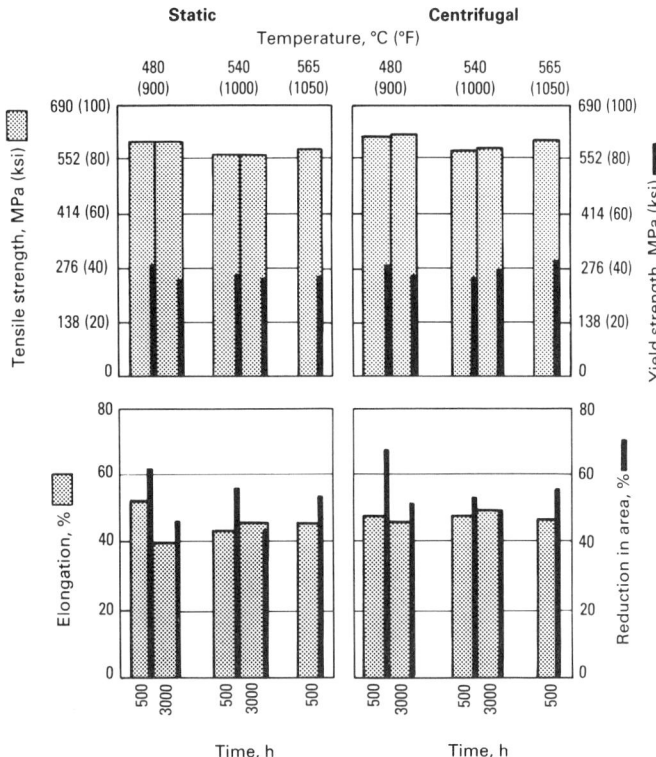

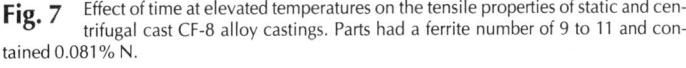

Fig. 7 Effect of time at elevated temperatures on the tensile properties of static and centrifugal cast CF-8 alloy castings. Parts had a ferrite number of 9 to 11 and contained 0.081% N.

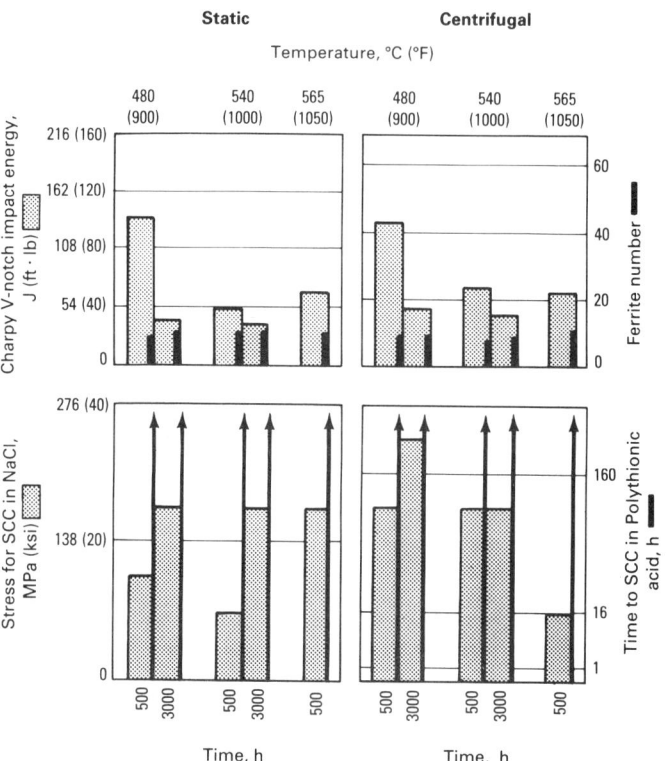

Fig. 8 Effect of time at elevated temperatures on the room-temperature impact strength, ferrite number, and SCC resistance of CF-8 castings with a ferrite number of 9 to 11 and a nitrogen content of 0.081%. Arrows indicate no failure in SCC testing after 336 h.

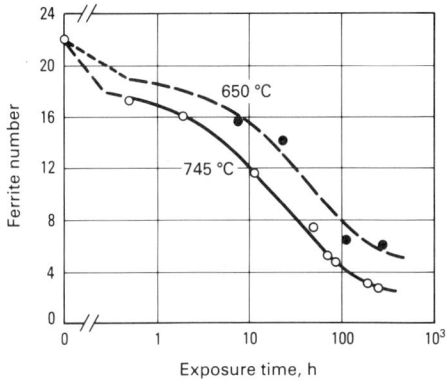

Fig. 9 Transformation of δ-ferrite to austenite and σ-phase upon exposure of a solution-treated CF-8 casting to elevated temperature

peratures that result in metal temperatures in excess of 650 °C (1200 °F). Cast steels for this type of service include iron-chromium (straight chromium), iron-chromium-nickel, and iron-nickel-chromium alloys. In applications of heat-resistant alloys, considerations include resistance to corrosion at elevated temperatures, stability (resistance to warping, cracking, or thermal fatigue), and creep strength (resistance to plastic flow).

Commercial applications of heat-resistant castings include metal treatment furnaces, gas turbines, aircraft engines, military equipment, oil refinery furnaces, cement mill equipment, petrochemical furnaces, chemical process equipment, power plant equipment, steel mill equipment, turbochargers, and equipment used in manufacturing glass and synthetic rubber. Alloys of the iron-chromium and iron-chromium-nickel groups are of the greatest commercial importance.

General Properties

General corrosion and creep properties of heat-resistant steel castings are compared in Table 10. The compositions of these alloys are given in Table 2. Heat-resistant cast steels resemble corrosion-resistant cast steels (Table 1) except for their higher carbon content, which imparts greater strength at elevated temperatures. Typical tensile properties of heat-resistant cast steels are given in Table 11 (properties at room temperature) and 12 (properties at elevated temperatures).

Iron-chromium alloys contain 10 to 30% Cr and little or no nickel. These alloys are useful chiefly for their resistance to oxidation; they have low strength at elevated temperatures. Use of these alloys is restricted to conditions, either oxidizing or reducing, that involve low static loads and uniform heating. Chromium content depends on anticipated service temperature.

Iron-chromium-nickel alloys contain more than 13% Cr and more than 7% Ni (always more chromium than nickel). These austenitic alloys are ordinarily used under oxidizing or reducing conditions similar to those withstood by the ferritic iron-chromium alloys, but in service they have greater strength and ductility than the straight chromium alloys. They are used, therefore, to withstand greater loads and moderate changes in temperature. These alloys also are

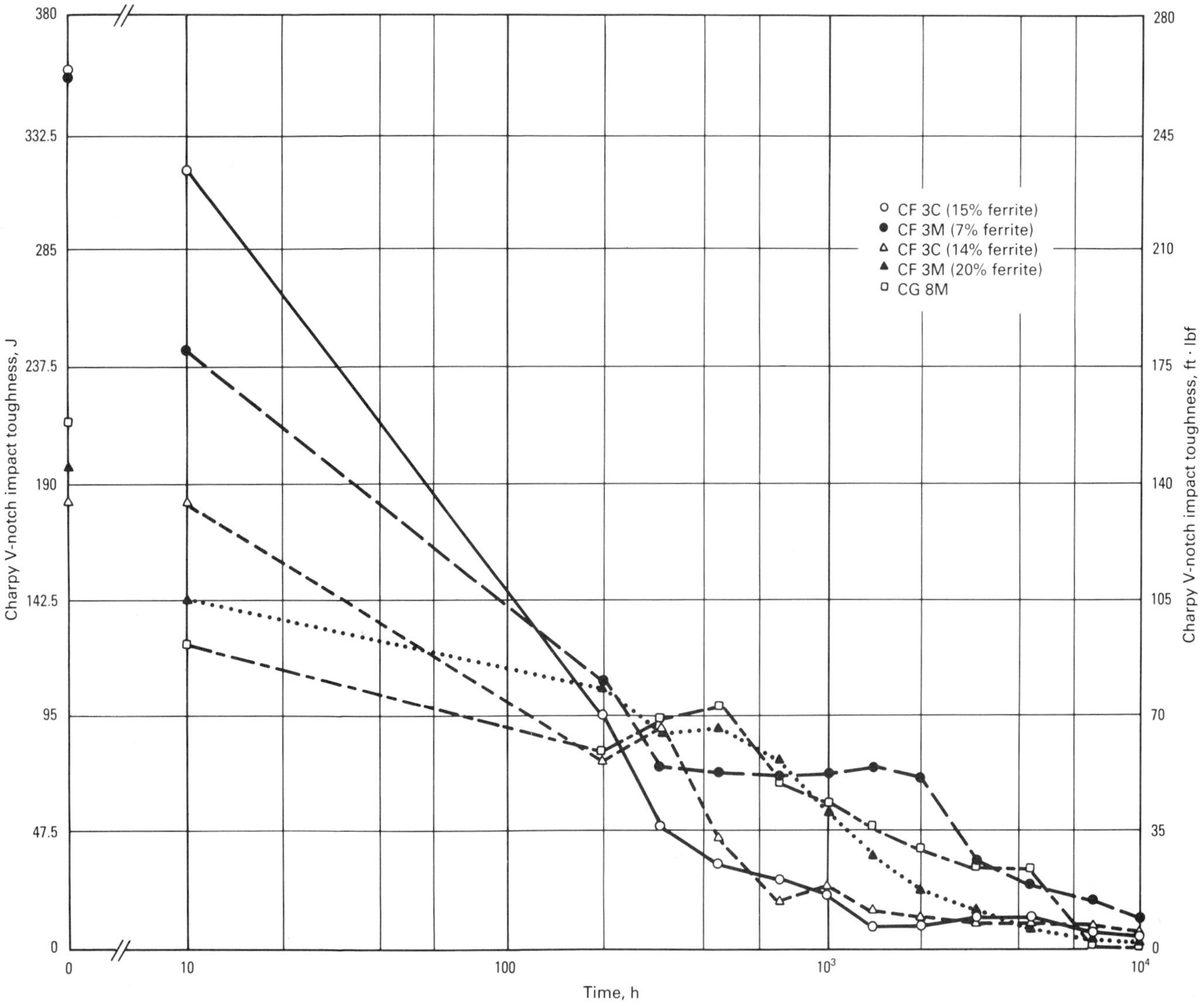

○ CF 3C (15% ferrite)
● CF 3M (7% ferrite)
△ CF 3C (14% ferrite)
▲ CF 3M (20% ferrite)
□ CG 8M

Fig. 10 Charpy V-notch impact energy of three corrosion-resistant cast steels at room temperature after aging at 594 °C (1100 °F). Source: Ref 4

Table 10 General corrosion characteristics of heat-resistant cast steels and typical limiting creep stress values at indicated temperatures

Alloy	Corrosion characteristics	Creep test temperature		Limiting creep stress (0.0001%/h)	
		°C	°F	MPa	ksi
HA	Good oxidation resistance to 650 °C (1200 °F); widely used in oil refining industry	650	1200	21.5	3.1
HC	Good sulfur and oxidation resistance up to 1095 °C (2000 °F); minimal mechanical properties; used in applications where strength is not a consideration or for moderate load bearing up to 650 °C (1200 °F)	870	1600	5.15	0.75
HD	Excellent oxidation and sulfur resistance plus weldability	980	1800	6.2	0.9
HE	Higher temperature and sulfur resistant capabilities than HD	980	1800	9.5	1.4
HF	Excellent general corrosion resistance to 815 °C (1500 °F) with moderate mechanical properties	870	1600	27	3.9
HH(a)	High strength; oxidation resistant to 1090 °C (2000 °F); most widely used	980	1800	7.5 (type I) 14.5 (type II)	1.1 (type I) 2.1 (type II)
HI	Improved oxidation resistance compared to HH	980	1800	13	1.9
HK	Because of its high temperature strength, widely used for stressed parts in structural applications up to 1150 °C (2100 °F); offers good resistance to corrosion by hot gases, including sulfur-bearing gases, in both oxidizing and reducing conditions (although HC, HE, and HI are more resistant in oxidizing gases); used in air, ammonia, hydrogen, and molten neutral salts; widely used for tubes and furnace parts	1040	1900	9.5	1.4
HL	Improved sulfur resistance compared to HK; especially useful where excessive scaling must be avoided	980	1800	15	2.2
HN	Very high strength at high temperatures; resistant to oxidizing and reducing flue gases	1040	1900	11	1.6
HP	Resistant to both oxidizing and carburizing atmospheres at high temperatures	980	1800	19	2.8
HP-50WZ	Improved creep rupture strength at 1090 °C (2000 °F) and above compared to HP	1090	2000	4.8	0.7
HT	Widely used in thermal shock applications; corrosion resistant in air, oxidizing and reducing flue gases, carburizing gases, salts, and molten metals; performs satisfactorily up to 1150 °C (2100 °F) in oxidizing atmospheres and up to 1095 °C (2000 °F) in reducing atmospheres, provided that limiting creep stress values are not exceeded	980	1800	14	2.0
HU	Higher hot strength than HT and often selected for its superior corrosion resistance	980	1800	15	2.2
HW	High hot strength and electrical resistivity; performs satisfactorily to 1120 °C (2050 °F) in strongly oxidizing atmospheres and up to 1040 °C (1900 °F) in oxidizing or reducing products of combustion that do not contain sulfur; resistant to some salts and molten metals	980	1800	9.5	1.4
HX	Resistant to hot-gas corrosion under cycling conditions without cracking or warping; corrosion resistant in air, carburizing gases, combustion gases, flue gases, hydrogen, molten cyanide, molten lead, and molten neutral salts at temperatures up to 1150 °C (2100 °F)	980	1800	11	1.6

(a) Two grades: type I (ferrite in austenite) and type II (wholly austenitic), per ASTM A 447

used in the presence of oxidizing and reducing gases that are high in sulfur content.

Iron-nickel-chromium alloys contain more than 25% Ni and more than 10% Cr (always more nickel than chromium). These austenitic alloys are used for withstanding reducing as well as oxidizing atmospheres, except where sulfur content is appreciable. (In atmospheres containing 0.05% or more hydrogen sulfide, for example, iron-chromium-nickel alloys are recommended.) In contrast with iron-chromium-nickel alloys, iron-nickel-chromium alloys do not carburize rapidly or become brittle and do not take up nitrogen in nitriding atmospheres. These characteristics become enhanced as nickel content is increased, and in carburizing and nitriding atmospheres, casting life increases with nickel content. Austenitic iron-nickel-chromium alloys are used extensively under conditions of severe temperature fluctuations, such as those encountered by fixtures used in quenching and by parts that are not heated uniformly or that are heated and cooled intermittently. In addition, these alloys have characteristics that make them suitable for electrical resistance heating elements.

Metallurgical Structures

The structures of chromium-nickel and nickel-chromium cast steels must be wholly austenitic, or mostly austenitic with some ferrite, if these alloys are to be used for heat-resistant service. Depending on the chromium and nickel content (see the section "Composition and Microstructure" in this article), the structures of these iron-base alloys can be austenitic (stable), ferritic (stable, but also soft, weak, and ductile), or martensitic (unstable). Therefore, chromium and nickel levels should be selected to achieve good strength at elevated temperatures combined with resistance to carburization and hot-gas corrosion.

A fine dispersion of carbides or intermetallic compounds in an austenitic matrix increases high-temperature strength considerably. For this reason, heat-resistant cast steels are higher in carbon content than are corrosion-resistant alloys of comparable chromium and nickel content. By holding at temperatures where carbon diffusion is rapid (such as above 1200 °C) and then rapidly cooling, a high and uniform carbon content is established, and up to about 0.20% C is retained in the austenite. Some chromium carbides are present in the structures of alloys with carbon contents greater than 0.20%, regardless of solution treatment, as described in the section "Sensitization and Solution Annealing of Austenitic and Duplex Alloys" in this article.

Castings develop considerable segregation as they freeze. In standard grades, either in the as-cast condition or after rapid cooling from a temperature near the melting point, much of the carbon is in supersaturated solid solution. Subsequent reheating precipitates excess carbides. The lower the reheating temperature, the slower the reaction and the finer the precipitated carbides. Fine carbides increase creep strength and decrease ductility. Intermetallic compounds such as Ni_3Al have a similar effect if present.

Reheating material containing precipitated carbides in the range between 980 and 1200 °C (1800 and 2200 °F) will agglomerate and spheroidize the carbides, which reduces creep strength and increases ductility. Above 1100 °C (2000 °F), so many of the fine carbides are dissolved or spheroidized that this strengthening mechanism loses its importance. For service above 1100 °C (2000 °F), certain proprietary alloys of the iron-nickel-chromium type have been developed. Alloys for this service contain tungsten to form tungsten carbides, which are more stable than chromium carbides at these temperatures.

Aging at a low temperature, such as 760 °C (1400 °F), where a fine, uniformly dispersed carbide precipitate will form, confers a high level of strength that is retained at temperatures up to those at which agglomeration changes the character of the carbide dispersion (overaging temperatures). Solution heat treatment or quench annealing, followed by aging, is the treatment generally employed to attain maximum creep strength.

Ductility is usually reduced when strengthening occurs, but in some alloys the strengthening treatment corrects an unfavorable grain-boundary network of brittle carbides, and both properties benefit. However, such treatment is costly and may warp castings excessively. Hence, this treatment is applied to heat-resistant castings only for the small percentage of applications for which the need for premium performance justifies the high cost.

Carbide networks at grain boundaries are generally undesirable in iron-base heat-resistant alloys. Grain-boundary networks usually occur in very-high-carbon alloys or in alloys that have cooled slowly through the high-temperature ranges in which excess carbon in the austenite is rejected as grain-boundary networks rather than

Table 11 Typical room-temperature properties of heat-resistant casting alloys

Alloy	Condition	Tensile strength MPa	ksi	Yield strength MPa	ksi	Elongation, %	Hardness, HB
HC	As-cast	760	110	515	75	19	223
	Aged(a)	790	115	550	80	18	...
HD	As-cast	585	85	330	48	16	90
HE	As-cast	655	95	310	45	20	200
	Aged(a)	620	90	380	55	10	270
HF	As-cast	635	92	310	45	38	165
	Aged(a)	690	100	345	50	25	190
HH, type 1	As-cast	585	85	345	50	25	185
	Aged(a)	595	86	380	55	11	200
HH, type 2	As-cast	550	80	275	40	15	180
	Aged(a)	635	92	310	45	8	200
HI	As-cast	550	80	310	45	12	180
	Aged(a)	620	90	450	65	6	200
HK	As-cast	515	75	345	50	17	170
	Aged(b)	585	85	345	50	10	190
HL	As-cast	565	82	360	52	19	192
HN	As-cast	470	68	260	38	13	160
HP	As-cast	490	71	275	40	11	170
HT	As-cast	485	70	275	40	10	180
	Aged(b)	515	75	310	45	5	200
HU	As-cast	485	70	275	40	9	170
	Aged(c)	505	73	295	43	5	190
HW	As-cast	470	68	250	36	4	185
	Aged(d)	580	84	360	52	4	205
HX	As-cast	450	65	250	36	9	176
	Aged(c)	505	73	305	44	9	185

(a) Aging treatment: 24 h at 760 °C (1400 °F), furnace cool. (b) Aging treatment: 24 h at 760 °C (1400 °F), air cool. (c) Aging treatment: 48 h at 980 °C (1800 °F), air cool. (d) Aging treatment: 48 h at 980 °C (1800 °F), furnace cool

as dispersed particles. These networks confer brittleness in proportion to their continuity.

Carbide networks also provide paths for selective attack in some atmospheres and in certain molten salts. Therefore, it is advisable in some salt bath applications to sacrifice the high-temperature strength imparted by high carbon content and gain resistance to intergranular corrosion by specifying that carbon content be no greater than 0.08%.

Straight Chromium Heat-Resistant Castings

Iron-chromium alloys, also known as straight chromium alloys, contain either 9 or 28% Cr. HC and HD alloys are included among the straight chromium alloys, although they contain low levels of nickel.

HA alloy (9Cr-1Mo), a heat treatable material, contains enough chromium to provide good resistance to oxidation at temperatures up to about 650 °C (1200 °F). The 1% Mo is present to provide increased strength. HA alloy castings are widely used in oil refinery service. A higher-chromium modification of this alloy (12 to 14% Cr) is widely used in the glass industry.

HA alloy has a structure that is essentially ferritic; carbides are present in pearlitic areas or as agglomerated particles, depending on prior heat treatment. Hardening of the alloy occurs upon

cooling in air from temperatures above 815 °C (1500 °F). In the normalized-and-tempered condition, the alloy exhibits satisfactory toughness throughout its useful temperature range.

HC alloy (28% Cr) resists oxidation and the effects of high-sulfur flue gases at temperatures up to 1100 °C (2000 °F). It is used for applications in which strength is not a consideration, or in which only moderate loads are involved, at temperatures of about 650 °C (1200 °F). It is also used where appreciable nickel cannot be tolerated, as in very-high-sulfur atmospheres, or where nickel may act as an undesirable catalyst and destroy hydrocarbons by causing them to crack.

Table 12 Representative short-term tensile properties of cast heat-resistant alloys at elevated temperatures

	760 °C (1400 °F) Ultimate tensile strength		Yield strength at 0.2% offset		Elongation, %	870 °C (1600 °F) Ultimate tensile strength		Yield strength at 0.2 % offset		Elongation, %	980 °C (1800 °F) Ultimate tensile strength		Yield strength at 0.2% offset		Elongation, %
Alloy	MPa	ksi	MPa	ksi	%	MPa	ksi	MPa	ksi	%	MPa	ksi	MPa	ksi	%
HA	462(a)	67(a)	220(b)	32(b)	...	...	...	...	...	...	...	...	...	...	...
HD	248	36	...	...	14	159	23	...	...	18	103	15	...	...	40
HF	262	38	172	25	16	145	21	107	15.5	16	...	...	...	...	...
HH (type I)(c)	228	33	117	17	18	127	18.5	93	13.5	30	62	9	43	6.3	45
HH (type II)(c)	258	37.4	136	19.8	16	148	21.5	110	16	18	75	10.9	50	7.3	31
HI	262	38	...	...	6	179	26	...	...	12	...	...	...	...	...
HK	258	37.5	168	24.4	12	161	23	101	15	16	85.5	12.4	60	8.7	42
HL	345	50	...	...	...	210	30.5	...	...	...	129	18.7	...	...	...
HN	...	...	...	...	...	140	20	100	14.5	37	83	12	66	9.6	51
HP	296	43	200	29	15	179	26	121	17.5	27	100	14.5	76	11	46
HT	240	35	180	26	10	130	19	103	15	24	76	11	55	8	28
HU	275	40	...	...	...	135	19.5	...	...	20	69	10	43	6.2	28
HW	220	32	158	23	...	131	19	103	15	...	69	10	55	8	40
HX	310(d)	45(d)	138(d)	20(d)	8(d)	141	20.5	121	17.5	48	74	10.7	47	6.9	40

(a) In this instance, test temperature was 540 °C (1000 °F). (b) Test temperature was 590 °C (1100 °F). (c) Type I and II per ASTM A 447. (d) Test temperature was 650 °C (1200 °F)

HC alloy is ferritic at all temperatures. Its ductility and impact strength are very low at room temperature, and its creep strength is very low at elevated temperatures unless some nickel is present. In a variation of HC alloy that contains more than 2% Ni, substantial improvement in all three of these properties is obtained by increasing the nitrogen content to 0.15% or more.

HC alloy becomes embrittled when heated for prolonged periods at temperatures between 400 and 550 °C (750 and 1025 °F), and it shows low resistance to impact. The alloy is magnetic and has a low coefficient of thermal expansion, comparable to that of carbon steel. It has about eight times the electrical resistivity and about half the thermal conductivity of carbon steel. Its thermal conductivity, however, is roughly double the value for austenitic iron-chromium-nickel alloys.

HD alloy (28Cr-5Ni) is very similar in general properties to HC, except that its nickel content gives it somewhat greater strength at high temperatures. The high chromium content of this alloy makes it suitable for use in high-sulfur atmospheres.

HD alloy has a two-phase, ferrite-plus-austenite structure that is not hardenable by conventional heat treatment. Long exposure at 700 to 900 °C (1300 to 1650 °F), however, may result in considerable hardening and severe loss of room-temperature ductility through the formation of a phase. Ductility may be restored by heating uniformly to 980 °C (1800 °F) or higher and then cooling rapidly to below 650 °C (1200 °F).

Iron-Chromium-Nickel Heat-Resistant Castings

Heat-resistant ferrous alloys in which the chromium content exceeds the nickel content are made in compositions ranging from 20Cr-10Ni to 30Cr-20Ni.

HE alloy (28Cr-10Ni) has excellent resistance to corrosion at elevated temperatures. Because of its higher chromium content, it can be used at higher temperatures than HF alloy and is suitable for applications up to 1100 °C (2000 °F). This alloy is stronger and more ductile at room temperature than the straight chromium alloys.

In the as-cast condition, HE alloy has a two-phase, austenite-plus-ferrite structure containing carbides. HE castings cannot be hardened by heat treatment; however, as with HD castings, long exposure to temperatures near 815 °C (1500 °F) will promote formation of σ-phase and consequent embrittlement of the alloy at room temperature. The ductility of this alloy can be improved somewhat by quenching from about 1100 °C (2000 °F).

Castings of HE alloy have good machining and welding properties. Thermal expansion is about 50% greater than that of either carbon steel or the iron-chromium alloy HC. Thermal conductivity is much lower than for HD or HC, but electrical resistivity is about the same. HE alloy is weakly magnetic.

HF alloy (20Cr-10Ni) is the cast version of 18-8 stainless steel, which is widely used for its outstanding resistance to corrosion. HF alloy is suitable for use at temperatures up to 870 °C (1600 °F). When this alloy is used for applications requiring resistance to oxidation at elevated temperatures, it is not necessary to keep the carbon content at the low level specified for corrosion-resistant castings. Molybdenum, tungsten, niobium, and titanium are sometimes added to the basic HF composition to improve elevated-temperature strength.

In the as-cast condition, HF alloy has an austenitic matrix that contains interdendritic eutectic carbides and, occasionally, a lamellar constituent presumed to consist of alternating platelets of austenite and carbide or carbonitride. Exposure at service temperatures usually promotes precipitation of finely dispersed carbides, which increases room-temperature strength and causes some loss of ductility. If improperly balanced, as-cast HF may be partly ferritic. HF is susceptible to embrittlement due to σ-phase formation after long exposure at 760 to 815 °C (1400 to 1500 °F).

HH Alloy (26Cr-12Ni). Alloys of this nominal composition comprise about one-third of the total production of iron-base heat-resistant castings. Alloy HH is basically austenitic and holds considerable carbon in solid solution, but carbides, ferrite (soft, ductile, and magnetic), and σ-phase (hard, brittle, and nonmagnetic) may also be present in the microstructure. The amounts of the various structural constituents present depend on composition and thermal history. In fact, two distinct grades of material can be obtained within the stated chemical compositional range of the type alloy HH. These grades are defined as type I (partially ferritic) and type II (wholly austenitic) in ASTM A 447.

The partially ferritic (type I) alloy HH is adapted to operating conditions that are subject to changes in temperature level and applied stress. A plastic extension in the weaker, ductile ferrite under changing load tends to occur more readily than in the stronger austenitic phase, thereby reducing unit stresses and stress concentrations and permitting rapid adjustment to suddenly applied overloads without cracking. Near 870 °C (1600 °F), the partially ferritic alloys tend to embrittle from the development of σ-phase, while close to 760 °C (1400 °F), carbide precipitation may cause comparable loss of ductility. Such possible embrittlement suggests that 930 to 1100 °C (1700 to 2000 °F) is the best service temperature range, but this is not critical for steady temperature conditions in the absence of unusual thermal or mechanical stresses.

To achieve maximum strength at elevated temperatures, the HH alloy must be wholly austenitic. Where load and temperature conditions are comparatively constant, the wholly austenitic (type II) alloy HH provides the highest creep strength and permits the use of maximum design stress. The stable austenitic alloy is also favored for cyclic temperature service that might induce σ-phase formation in the partially ferritic type. When HH alloy is heated to between 650 and 870 °C (1200 and 1600 °F), a loss in ductility may be produced by either of two changes within the alloy: precipitation of carbides or transformation of ferrite to σ-phase. When the composition is balanced so that the structure is wholly austenitic, only carbide precipitation normally occurs. In partly ferritic alloys, both carbides and σ-phase may form.

The wholly austenitic (type II) HH alloy is used extensively in high-temperature applications because of its combination of relatively high strength and oxidation resistance at temperatures up to 1100 °C (2000 °F). Typical tensile properties and impact toughness of the type II HH alloy at elevated temperatures are shown in Fig. 11(a). The HH alloy (type I or II) is seldom used for carburizing applications because of embrittlement from carbon absorption. High silicon content (over 1.5%) will fortify the alloy against carburization under mild conditions but will promote ferrite formation and possible σ-embrittlement.

For the wholly austenitic (type II) HH alloy, composition balance is critical in achieving the desired austenitic microstructure (see the section "Composition and Microstructure" in this article). An imbalance of higher levels of ferrite-promoting elements compared to levels of austenite-promoting elements may result in substantial amounts of ferrite, which improves ductility but decreases strength at high temperatures. If a balance is maintained between ferrite-promoting elements (such as chromium and silicon) and austenite-promoting elements (such as nickel, carbon, and nitrogen), the desired austenitic structure can be obtained. In commercial HH alloy castings with the usual carbon, nitrogen, manganese, and silicon contents, the ratio of chromium to nickel necessary for a stable austenitic structure is expressed by:

$$\frac{\%Cr - 16(\%C)}{\%Ni} < 1.7 \qquad \text{(Eq 3)}$$

Silicon and molybdenum have definite effects on the formation of σ-phase. A silicon content in excess of 1% is equivalent to a chromium content three times as great, and any molybdenum content is equivalent to a chromium content four times as great.

Before HH alloy is selected as a material for heat-resistant castings, it is advisable to consider the relationship between chemical composition and operating-temperature range. For castings that are to be exposed continuously at temperatures appreciably above 870 °C (1600 °F), there is little danger of severe embrittlement from either the precipitation of carbide or the formation of -phase, and composition should be 0.50% C (max) (0.35 to 0.40% preferred), 10 to 12% Ni, and 24 to 27% Cr. On the other hand, castings to be used at temperatures from 650 to 870 °C (1200 to 1600 °F) should have compositions of 0.40% C (max), 11 to 14% Ni, and 23 to 27% Cr. For applications involving either of these temperature ranges, that is, 650 to 870 °C (1200 to 1600 °F) or appreciably above 870 °C (1600 °F), composition should be balanced to provide an austenitic structure. For service from 650 to 870 °C (1200 to 1600 °F), for example, a combination of 11% Ni and 27% Cr is likely to produce -phase and its associated embrittlement, which occurs most rapidly around 870 °C (1600 °F). It is preferable, therefore, to avoid using the maximum chromium content with the minimum nickel content.

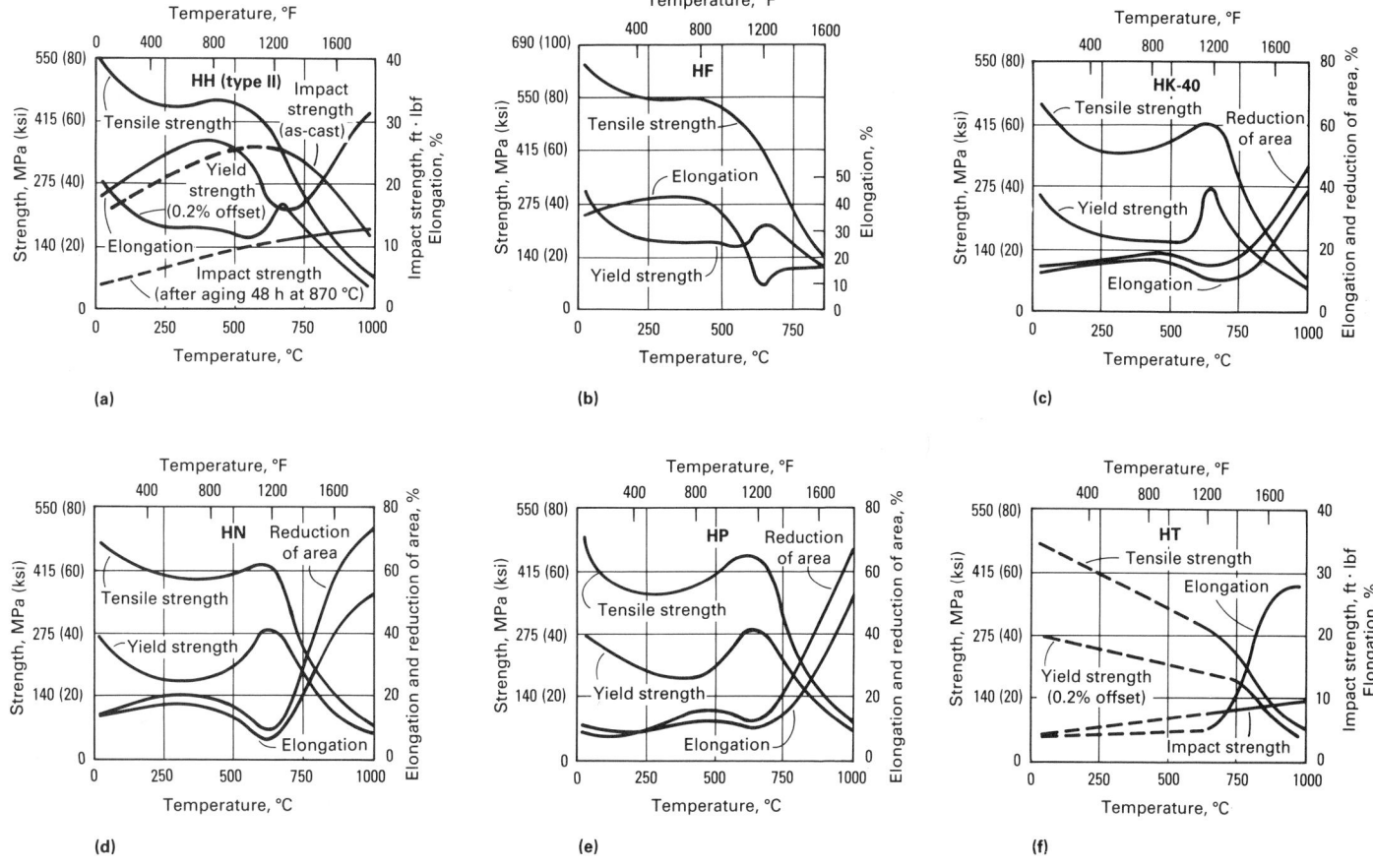

Fig. 11 Effect of short-term elevated-temperature exposure on the tensile properties of wholly austenitic (type II) HH cast steel (a) and of five other heat-resistant cast steels: (b) HF cast steel, (c) HK-40 cast steel, (d) HN cast steel, (e) HP cast steel, and (f) HT cast steel. Long-term elevated-temperature exposure reduces the strengthening effects between 500 to 750 °C (900 to 1400 °F) in (c), (d), and (e). Tensile properties of alloy HT in (f) include extrapolated data (dashed lines) below 750 °C but should be similar to alloy HN in terms of yield and tensile strengths. Source: Ref 5

Short-time tensile testing of fully austenitic HH alloys shows that tensile strength and elongation depend on carbon and nitrogen contents. For maximum creep strength, HH alloy should be fully austenitic in structure (Fig. 12). In the design of load-carrying castings, data concerning creep stresses should be used with an understanding of the limitations of such data. An extrapolated limiting creep stress for 1% elongation in 10,000 h cannot necessarily be sustained for that length of time without structural damage. Stress-rupture testing is a valuable adjunct to creep testing and a useful aid in selecting section sizes to obtain appropriate levels of design stress.

Because HH alloys of wholly austenitic structure have greater strength at high temperatures than partly ferritic alloys of similar composition, measurement of ferrite content is recommended. Although a ratio calculated from Eq 3 that is less than 1.7 indicates wholly austenitic material, ratios greater than 1.7 do not constitute quantitative indications of ferrite content. It is possible, however, to measure ferrite content by magnetic analysis after quenching from about 1100 °C (2000 °F). The magnetic permeability of HH alloys increases with ferrite content. This measurement of magnetic permeability, preferably after holding 24 h at 1100 °C (2000 °F) and then

quenching in water, can be related to creep strength, which also depends on structure.

HH alloys are often evaluated by measuring percentage elongation in room-temperature tension testing of specimens that have been held 24 h at 760 °C (1400 °F). Such a test may be misleading because there is a natural tendency for engineers to favor compositions that exhibit the greatest elongation after this particular heat treatment. High ductility values are often measured for alloys that have low creep resistance, but, conversely, low ductility values do not necessarily connote high creep resistance.

HI alloy (28Cr-15Ni) is similar to HH but contains more nickel and chromium. The higher chromium content makes HI more resistant to oxidation than HH, and the additional nickel serves to maintain good strength at high temperatures. Exhibiting adequate strength, ductility, and corrosion resistance, this alloy has been used extensively for retorts operating with an internal vacuum at a continuous temperature of 1175 °C (2150 °F). It has an essentially austenitic structure that contains carbides and that, depending on the exact composition balance, may or may not contain small amounts of ferrite. Service at 760 to 870 °C (1400 to 1600 °F) results in precipitation of finely dispersed carbides that increase strength

and decrease ductility at room temperature. At service temperatures above 1100 °C (2000 °F), however, carbides remain in solution, and room-temperature ductility is not impaired.

HK alloy (26Cr-20Ni) is somewhat similar to wholly austenitic HH alloy in general characteristics and mechanical properties. Although less resistant to oxidizing gases than HC, HE, or HI, HK alloy contains enough chromium to ensure good resistance to corrosion by hot gases, including sulfur-bearing gases, under both oxidizing and reducing conditions. (See the article "Corrosion of Cast Stainless Steels" in this Volume for high-temperature corrosion data.) The high nickel content of this alloy helps make it one of the strongest heat-resistant casting alloys at temperatures above 1040 °C (1900 °F). Accordingly, HK alloy castings are widely used for stressed parts in structural applications at temperatures up to 1150 °C (2100 °F). As normally produced, HK alloy is a stable austenitic alloy over its entire range of service temperatures. The as-cast microstructure consists of an austenitic matrix containing relatively large carbides in the form of either scattered islands or networks. After the alloy has been exposed to service temperatures, fine, granular carbides precipitate within the grains of austenite and, if the temperature is high enough, undergo

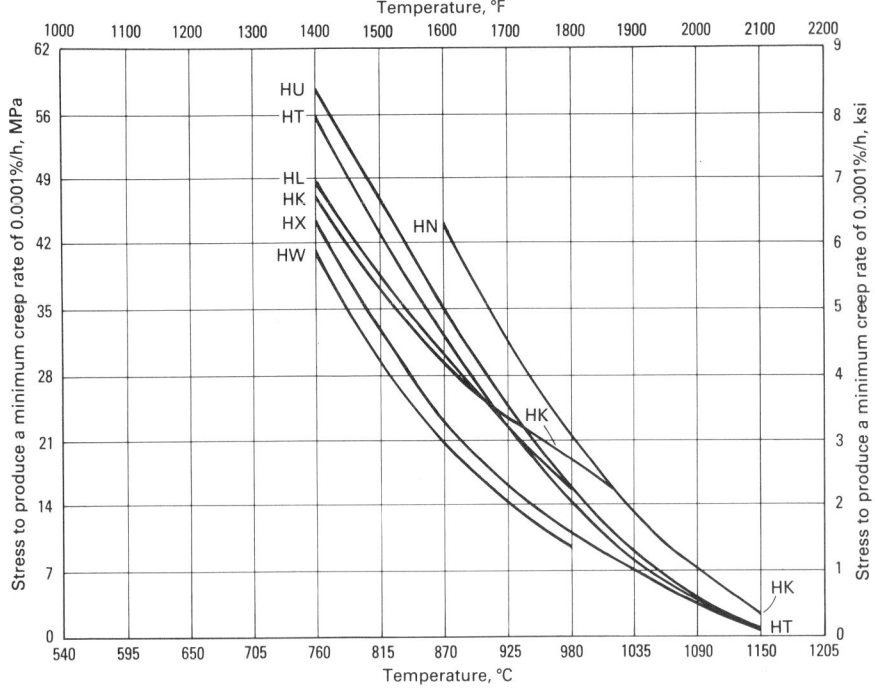

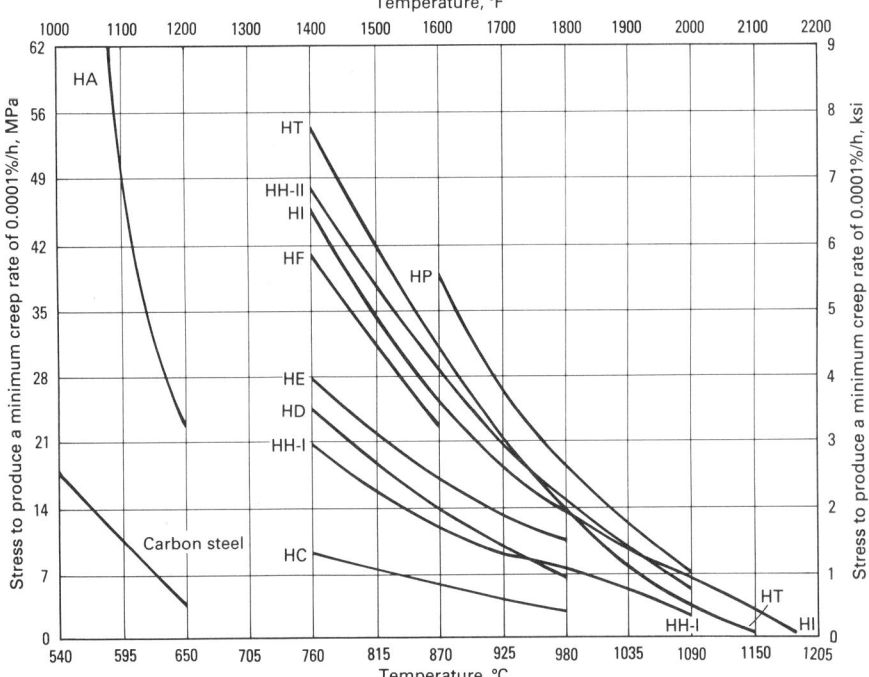

Fig. 12 Creep strength of heat-resistant alloy castings (HT curve is included in both graphs for ease of comparison). Source: Ref 6

The minimum creep rate and average rupture life of HK alloy are strongly influenced by variations in carbon content. Under the same conditions of temperature and load, alloys with higher carbon content have lower creep rates and longer lives than lower-carbon compositions. Room-temperature properties after aging at elevated temperatures are affected also: The higher the carbon, the lower the residual ductility. For these reasons, three grades of HK alloys with carbon ranges narrower than the standard HK alloy in Table 2 are recognized: HK-30, HK-40, and HK-50. In these designations, the number indicates the midpoint of a 0.10% C range. HK-40 (Table 2) is widely used for high-temperature processing equipment in the petroleum and petrochemical industries.

Figure 11(c) shows the effect of short-term temperature exposure on an HK-40 alloy. Figure 13 indicates the statistical spread in room-temperature mechanical properties obtained for an HK alloy. These data were obtained in a single foundry and are based on 183 heats of the same alloy.

HL alloy (30Cr-20Ni) is similar to HK; its higher chromium content gives it greater resistance to corrosion by hot gases, particularly those containing appreciable amounts of sulfur. Because essentially equivalent high-temperature strength can be obtained with either HK or HL, the superior corrosion resistance of HL makes it especially useful for service in which excessive scaling must be avoided. The as-cast and aged microstructures of HL alloy, as well as its physical properties and fabricating characteristics, are similar to those of HK.

Iron-Nickel-Chromium Heat-Resistant Castings

Iron-nickel-chromium alloys generally have more stable structures than iron-base alloys in which chromium is the predominant alloying element. There is no evidence of an embrittling phase change in iron-nickel-chromium alloys that would impair their ability to withstand prolonged service at elevated temperatures. Experimental data indicate that composition limits are not critical; therefore, the production of castings from these alloys does not require the close composition control necessary for making castings from iron-chromium-nickel alloys.

The following general observations should be considered in the selection of iron-nickel-chromium alloys:

- As nickel content is increased, the ability of the alloy to absorb carbon from a carburizing atmosphere decreases.
- As nickel content is increased, tensile strength at elevated temperatures decreases somewhat, but resistance to thermal shock and thermal fatigue increases.
- As chromium content is increased, resistance to oxidation and to corrosion in chemical environments increases.
- As carbon content is increased, tensile strength at elevated temperatures increases.

subsequent agglomeration. These fine, dispersed carbides contribute to creep strength. A lamellar constituent that resembles pearlite, but that is presumed to be carbide or carbonitride platelets in austenite, is also frequently observed in HK alloy.

Unbalanced compositions are possible within the standard composition range for HK alloy, and hence some ferrite may be present in the austenitic matrix. Ferrite will transform to brittle σ-phase if the alloy is held for more than a short time at about 815 °C (1500 °F), with consequent embrittlement upon cooling to room temperature. Direct transformation of austenite to σ-phase can occur in HK alloy in the range of 760 to 870 °C (1400 to 1600 °F), particularly at lower carbon levels (0.20 to 0.30%). The presence of σ-phase can cause considerable scatter in property values at intermediate temperatures.

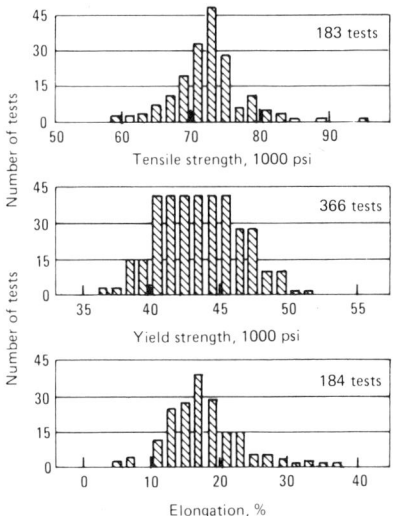

Fig. 13 Statistical spread in mechanical properties of HK alloy. Data are for 183 heats of HK alloy produced in a single foundry. Tests were performed at room temperature on as-cast material.

- As silicon content is increased, tensile strength at elevated temperatures decreases, but resistance to carburization increases somewhat.

HN alloy (25Ni-20Cr) contains enough chromium for good high-temperature corrosion resistance. HN has mechanical properties somewhat similar to those of the much more widely used HT alloy, but it has better ductility (see Fig. 11d and 11f for a comparison of HN and HT tensile properties above 750 °C, or 1400 °F). It is used for highly stressed components in the temperature range of 980 to 1100 °C (1800 to 2000 °F). In several specialized applications (notably, brazing fixtures), it has given satisfactory service at temperatures from 1100 to 1150 °C (2000 to 2100 °F). HN alloy is austenitic at all temperatures: Its composition limits lie well within the stable austenite field. In the as-cast condition it contains carbide areas, and additional fine carbides precipitate with aging. HN alloy is not susceptible to σ-phase formation, and increases in its carbon content are not especially detrimental to ductility.

HP, HT, HU, HW, and HX alloys make up about one-third of the total production of heat-resistant alloy castings. When used for fixtures and trays for heat-treating furnaces, which are subjected to rapid heating and cooling, these five high-nickel alloys have exhibited excellent service life. Because these compositions are not as readily carburized as iron-chromium-nickel alloys, they are used extensively for parts of carburizing furnaces. Because they form an adherent scale that does not flake off, castings of these alloys are also used in enameling applications in which loose scale would be detrimental.

Four of these high-nickel alloys (HT, HU, HW, and HX) also exhibit good corrosion resistance with molten salts and metal. They have excellent corrosion resistance to tempering and to cyaniding salts and fair resistance to neutral salts, with proper control. These alloys exhibit excellent resistance to molten lead, good resistance to molten tin to 345 C (650 F), and good re-

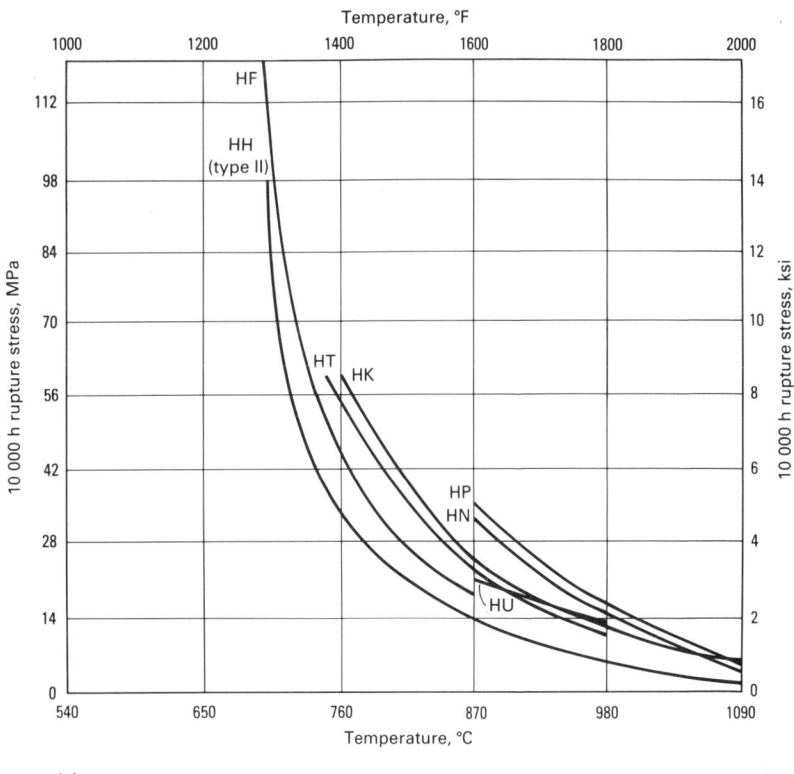

(a)

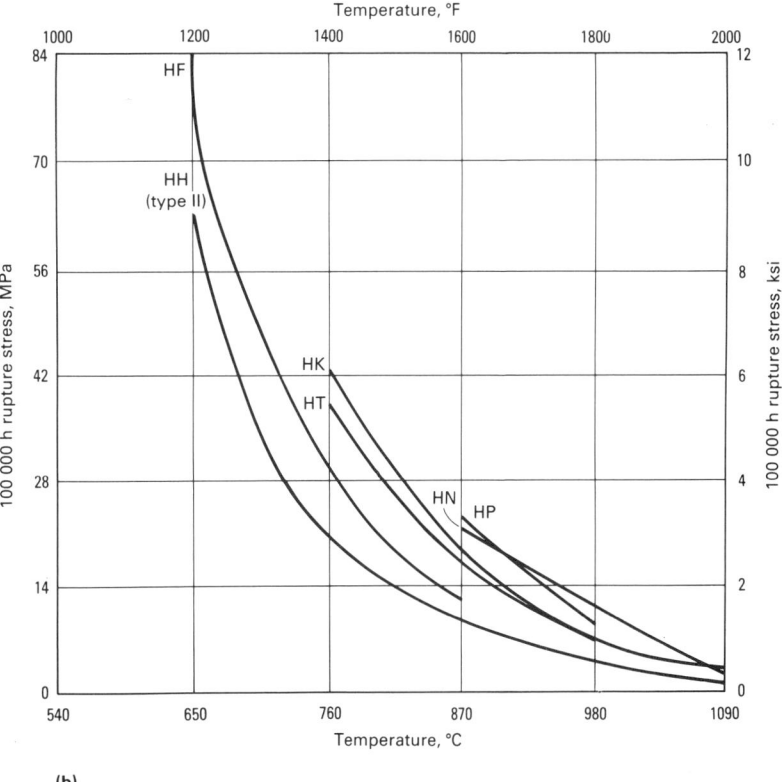

(b)

Fig. 14 Stress-rupture properties of several heat-resistant alloy castings. (a) 10,000 h rupture stress. (b) 100,000 h rupture stress. Source: Ref 6

sistance to molten cadmium to 410 C (775 F). The alloys have poor resistance to antimony, babbitt,

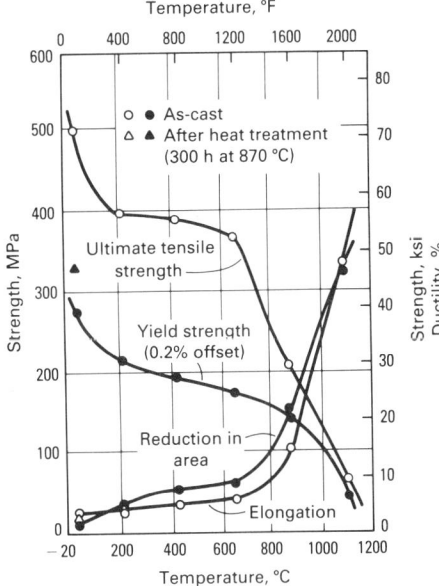

Fig. 15 Tensile properties vs. temperature for heat-resistant alloy HP-50WZ

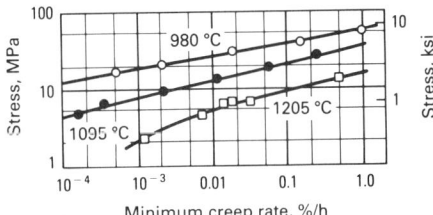

Fig. 16 Minimum creep rate vs. stress and temperature for alloy HP-50WZ

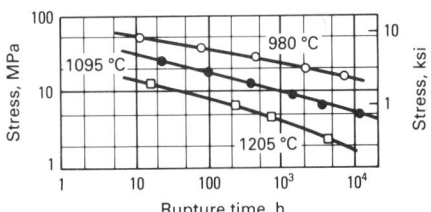

Fig. 17 Rupture time vs. stress and temperature for alloy HP-50WZ

soft solder, and similar metal. In many respects, there are no sharp lines of demarcation among the HP, HT, HU, HW, and HX alloys with respect to service applications.

HP alloy (35Ni-26Cr) is related to HN and HT alloys but is higher in alloy content. It contains the same amount of chromium but more nickel than HK, and the same amount of nickel but more chromium than HT. This combination of elements makes HP resistant to both oxidizing and carburizing atmospheres at high temperatures. It has stress-rupture properties that are comparable to, or better than, those of HK-40 and HN alloys (Fig. 14).

HP alloy is austenitic at all temperatures and is not susceptible to σ-phase formation. Its microstructure consists of massive primary carbides in an austenitic matrix; in addition, fine secondary carbides are precipitated within the austenite grains upon exposure to elevated temperatures. This precipitation of carbides is responsible for the strengthening between 500 and 750 °C (900 and 1400 °F) shown in Fig. 11(e). This strengthening, which is reduced after long-term exposure at high temperatures, also occurs for the cast stainless steels shown in Fig. 11(c) and (d).

HP-50WZ alloy (Table 2) is a modified version of alloy HP with a narrower carbon content range that also contains tungsten for enhanced elevated-temperature performance. Figures 15 to 17 show elevated-temperature properties for alloy HP-50WZ.

HT alloy (35Ni-17Cr) contains nearly equal amounts of iron and alloying elements. Its high nickel content enables it to resist the thermal shock of rapid heating and cooling. In addition, HT is resistant to high-temperature oxidation and carburization and has good strength at the temperatures ordinarily used for heat treating steel. Except in high-sulfur gases, and provided that limiting creep-stress values are not exceeded, it performs satisfactorily in oxidizing atmospheres at temperatures up to 1150 °C (2100 °F) and in reducing atmospheres at temperatures up to 1100 °C (2000 °F).

HT alloy is widely used for highly stressed parts in general heat-resistant applications. It has an austenitic structure containing carbides in amounts that vary with carbon content and thermal history. In the as-cast condition, it has large carbide areas at interdendritic boundaries, but fine carbides precipitate within the grains after exposure to service temperatures, causing a decrease in room-temperature ductility. Increases in carbon content may decrease the high-temperature ductility of the alloy. A silicon content above about 1.6% provides additional protection against carburization, but at some sacrifice in elevated-temperature strength. HT can be made still more resistant to thermal shock by the addition of up to 2% Nb.

HU alloy (39Ni-18Cr) is similar to HT, but its higher chromium and nickel contents give it greater resistance to corrosion by either oxidizing or reducing hot gases, including those that contain sulfur. Its high-temperature strength and resistance to carburization are essentially the same as those of HT alloy, and thus its superior corrosion resistance makes it especially well suited for severe service involving high stress and/or rapid thermal cycling, in combination with an aggressive environment.

HW alloy (60Ni-12Cr) is especially well suited for applications in which wide and/or rapid fluctuations in temperature are encountered. In addition, HW exhibits excellent resistance to carburization and high-temperature oxidation. HW alloy has good strength at steel-treating temperatures, although it is not as strong as HT. HW performs satisfactorily at temperatures up to about 1120 °C (2050 °F) in strongly oxidizing atmospheres and up to 1040 °C (1900 °F) in oxidizing or reducing products of combustion, provided

that sulfur is not present in the gas. The generally adherent nature of its oxide scale makes HW suitable for enameling furnace service, where even small flakes of dislodged scale could ruin the work in process.

HW alloy is widely used for intricate heat-treating fixtures that are quenched with the load and for many other applications (such as furnace retorts and muffles) that involve thermal shock, steep temperature gradients, and high stresses. Its structure is austenitic and contains carbides in amounts that vary with carbon content and thermal history. In the as-cast condition, the microstructure consists of a continuous interdendritic network of elongated eutectic carbides. Upon prolonged exposure at service temperatures, the austenitic matrix becomes uniformly peppered with small carbide particles except in the immediate vicinity of eutectic carbides. This change in structure is accompanied by an increase in room-temperature strength, but there is no change in ductility.

HX alloy (66Ni-17Cr) is similar to HW but contains more nickel and chromium. Its higher chromium content gives it substantially better resistance to corrosion by hot gases (even sulfur-bearing gases), which permits it to be used in severe service applications at temperatures up to 1150 °C (2100 °F). However, it has been reported that HX alloy decarburizes rapidly at temperatures from 1100 to 1150 °C (2000 to 2100 °F). High-temperature strength (Table 12), resistance to thermal fatigue, and resistance to carburization are essentially the same as for HW. Hence HX is suitable for the same general applications in which its corrosion microstructures, as well as its mechanical properties and fabricating characteristics, are similar to those of HW.

Properties of Heat-Resistant Alloys

Elevated-Temperature Tensile Properties. The short-term elevated-temperature test, in which a standard tension test bar is heated to a designated uniform temperature and then strained to fracture at a standardized rate, identifies the stress due to a short-term overload that will cause fracture in uniaxial loading. The manner in which the values of tensile strength and ductility change with increasing temperature is shown in Fig. 11 for selected alloys. Representative tensile properties at temperatures between 760 and 980 C (1400 and 1800 F) are given in Table 12 for several heat-resistant cast steel grades.

Creep and Stress-Rupture Properties. Creep is defined as the time-dependent strain that occurs under load at elevated temperature and is operative in most applications of heat-resistant high-alloy castings at the normal service temperatures. In time, creep may lead to excessive deformation and even fracture at stresses considerably below those determined in room-temperature and elevated-temperature short-term tension tests.

When the rate or degree of deformation is the limiting factor, the design stress is based on the minimum creep rate and design life after allowing for initial transient creep. The stress that produces a specified minimum creep rate of an alloy or a specified amount of creep deformation in a given

Table 13 Composition and elevated-temperature properties of selected cast heat-resistant alloys

Grade	UNS number	Approximate composition, %			Temperature		Creep stress to produce 1% creep in 10,000 h		Stress to rupture in 10,000 h		Stress to rupture in 100,000 h	
		C	Cr	Ni	°C	°F	MPa	ksi	MPa	ksi	MPa	ksi
Iron-chromium-nickel alloys												
HF	J92603	0.20-0.40	19-23	9-12	650	1200	124	18.0	114	16.5	76	11.0
					760	1400	47	6.8	42	6.1	28	4.0
					870	1600	27	3.9	19	2.7	12	1.7
					980	1800	...	...	...	...	...	...
HH	J93503	0.20-0.50	24-28	11-14	650	1200	124	18.0	97	14.0	62	9.0
					760	1400	43	6.3	33	4.8	19	2.8
					870	1600	27	3.9	15	2.2	8	1.2
					980	1800	14	2.1	6	0.9	3	0.4
HK	J94224	0.20-0.60	24-28	18-22	650	1200	...	...	...	...	...	...
					760	1400	70	10.2	61	8.8	43	6.2
					870	1600	41	6.0	26	3.8	17	2.5
					980	1800	17	2.5	12	1.7	7	1.0
Iron-nickel-chromium alloys												
HN	J94213	0.20-0.50	19-23	23-27	650	1200	...	...	...	...	...	...
					760	1400	...	...	...	...	...	...
					870	1600	43	6.3	33	4.8	22	3.2
					980	1800	16	2.4	14	2.1	9	1.3
HT	J94605	0.35-0.75	15-19	33-37	650	1200	...	...	...	...	...	...
					760	1400	55	8.0	58	8.4	39	5.6
					870	1600	31	4.5	26	3.7	16	2.4
					980	1800	14	2.0	12	1.7	8	1.1
HU	...	0.35-0.75	17-21	37-41	650	1200	...	...	...	...	...	...
					760	1400	59	8.5	...	...	...	...
					870	1600	34	5.0	23	3.3	...	...
					980	1800	15	2.2	12	1.8	...	...
HX	...	0.35-0.75	15-19	64-68	650	1200	...	...	...	...	...	...
					760	1400	44	6.4	...	...	...	...
					870	1600	22	3.2	...	...	...	...
					980	1800	11	1.6	...	...	...	...

Note: Some stress values are extrapolated.

time (for example, 1% total creep in 100,000 h) is referred to as the *limiting creep strength,* or *limiting stress*. Tables 10 and 13 (Ref 7) list the creep strengths of various H-type castings at specific temperatures. Figure 12 shows creep rates as a function of temperature.

Stress-rupture testing is a valuable adjunct to creep testing and is used to select the section sizes necessary to prevent creep rupture of a component. Figure 14 compares the creep-rupture strengths of various H-type steel castings at 10,000 and 100,000 h. It should be recognized that long-term creep and stress-rupture values (for example, 100,000 h) are often extrapolated from shorter-term tests. Whether these property values are extrapolated or determined directly often has

little bearing on the operating life of high-temperature parts. The actual material behavior is often difficult to predict accurately because of the complexity of the service stresses relative to the idealized, uniaxial loading conditions in the standardized tests, and because of the attenuating factors such as cyclic loading, temperature fluctuations, and metal loss from corrosion. The de-

Table 14 Thermal conductivity and mean coefficient of linear thermal expansion of heat-resistant cast steels at various temperatures

Alloy	Mean coefficient of linear thermal expansion for a temperature change				Thermal conductivity, W/m · K, at:		
	From 21 to 540 °C (700 to 1000 °F)		From 21 to 1090 °C (70 to 2000 °F)		100 °C (212 °F)	540 °C (1000 °F)	1090 °C (2000 °F)
	mm/mm/°C × 10⁻⁶	in./in./°F × 10⁻⁶	mm/mm/°C × 10⁻⁶	in./in./°F × 10⁻⁶			
HA	12.8	7.1	...	...	26.0	27.2	...
HC	11.3	6.3	13.9	7.7	21.8	31.0	41.9
HD	13.9	7.7	16.6	9.2	21.8	31.0	41.9
HE	17.3	9.6	20.0	11.1	14.7	21.5	31.5
HF	17.8	9.9	19.3	10.7	14.4	21.3	...
HH (type I)(a)	17.1	9.5	19.3	10.7	14.2	20.8	30.3
HH (type II)(a)	17.1	9.5	19.3	10.7	14.2	20.8	30.3
HI	17.8	9.9	19.4	10.8	14.2	20.8	30.3
HK	16.9	9.4	18.7	10.4	13.7	20.4	32.2
HL	16.6	9.2	18.2	10.1	14.2	21.1	33.4
HN	16.7	9.3	18.4	10.2	13.0	19.0	29.4
HP	16.6	9.2	19.1	10.6	13.0	19.0	29.4
HT	15.8	8.8	18.0	10.0	12.1	18.7	28.2
HU	15.8	8.8	17.5	9.7	12.1	18.7	28.2
HW	14.2	7.9	16.7	9.3	12.5	19.2	29.4
HX	14.0	7.8	17.1	9.5	12.5	19.2	29.4

(a) Type I and II specified per ASTM A 447

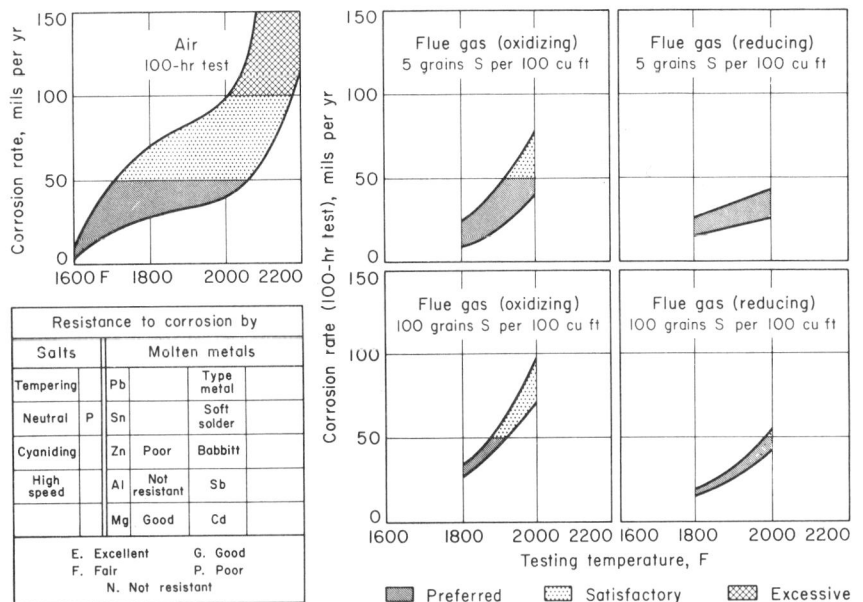

Fig. 18 Corrosion characteristics of alloy HC (Fe-28Cr) castings. Source: Ref 5

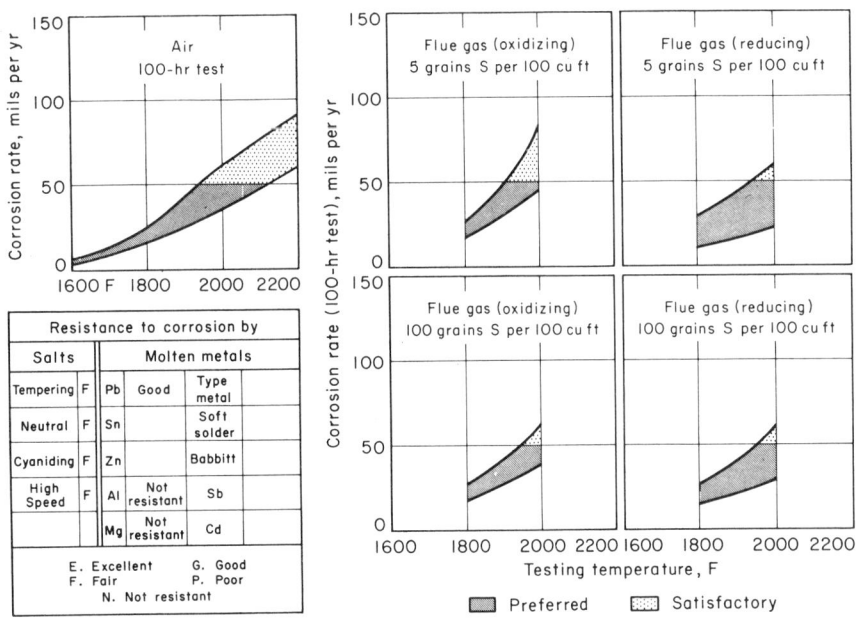

Fig. 19 Corrosion characteristics of alloy HH (Fe-26Cr-12Ni) castings. Source: Ref 5

signer should anticipate the synergistic effects of these variables.

Table 13 includes the nominal composition of heat-resistant alloys and the stress required to produce 1% creep in 10,000 h and rupture in 10,000 h and 100,000 h at temperatures of 650, 760, 870, and 980 °C (1200, 1400, 1600, and 1800 °F). A design stress figure commonly used for uniformly heated parts not subjected to thermal or mechanical shock is 50% of the stress to produce 1% creep in 10,000 h. This should be used carefully and should be verified with the supplier (Ref 7).

Thermal fatigue failure involves cracking caused by heating and cooling cycles. Very little experimental thermal fatigue information is available on which to base a comparison of the various alloys, and no standard test as yet has been adopted. Field experience indicates that resistance to thermal fatigue is usually improved with an increase in nickel content. Niobium-modified alloys have been employed successfully when a high degree of thermal fatigue resistance is desired, such as in reformer outlet headers.

Thermal Shock Resistance. Thermal shock failure may occur as a result of a single, rapid tem-

perature change or as a result of rapid cyclic temperature changes that induce stresses high enough to cause failure. Thermal shock resistance is influenced by the coefficient of thermal expansion and the thermal conductivity of materials. Increases in the thermal expansion coefficient or decreases in thermal conductivity reduce the resistance against thermal shock. Table 14 (Ref 6) lists the thermal conductivities and expansion coefficients for heat-resistant castings at various temperatures. The HA, HC, and HD alloys, because of their predominantly ferritic microstructure, have the lowest thermal expansion coefficients and the highest thermal conductivities.

Corrosion Resistance. Figures 18 to 20 provide typical corrosion data for straight chromium (HC alloy), iron-chromium-nickel (HH alloy), and iron-nickel-chromium (HT alloy) heat-resistant grades. More detailed information can be found in the article "Corrosion of Cast Stainless Steels" in this Volume.

Manufacturing Characteristics

Foundry practices for cast high-alloy steels for corrosion resistance or heat resistance are essentially the same as those used for cast plain carbon steels. Details on melting practice, metal treatment, and foundry practices, including gating, risering, and cleaning of castings, are available in Volume 15 of the *ASM Handbook*.

Iron-base alloys can be cast from heats melted in electric arc furnaces that have either acid or basic linings. When melting is done in acid-lined furnaces, however, chromium losses are high and silicon content is difficult to control, and thus acid-lined furnaces are seldom used. Alloys that contain appreciable amounts of aluminum, titanium, or other reactive metals are melted by induction or electron beam processes under vacuum or a protective atmosphere prior to casting.

Welding. As the alloy content of steel castings is increased to produce a fully austenitic structure, welding without cracking becomes more difficult. The fully austenitic, low-carbon grades tend to form microfissures adjacent to the weld. This tendency toward microfissuring increases as nickel and silicon contents increase and carbon content decreases. Microfissuring is most evident in coarse-grain alloys with a carbon content of approximately 0.10 to 0.20% and a nickel content exceeding 13%. The microfissuring is reduced by an extremely low sulfur content. In welding these grades, low interpass temperatures, low heat inputs, and peening of the weld to relieve mechanical stresses are all effective. If strength is not a great factor, an initial weld deposit or "buttering of the weld" is also occasionally used.

Welding of corrosion-resistant steel castings can be done by shielded metal arc welding, gas-tungsten arc welding, gas-metal arc welding, and electroslag (submerged arc) welding. Austenitic castings are normally welded without preheat and are solution annealed after welding. Martensitic castings require preheating to avoid cracking during welding and are given an appropriate postweld heat treatment. Specific conditions for

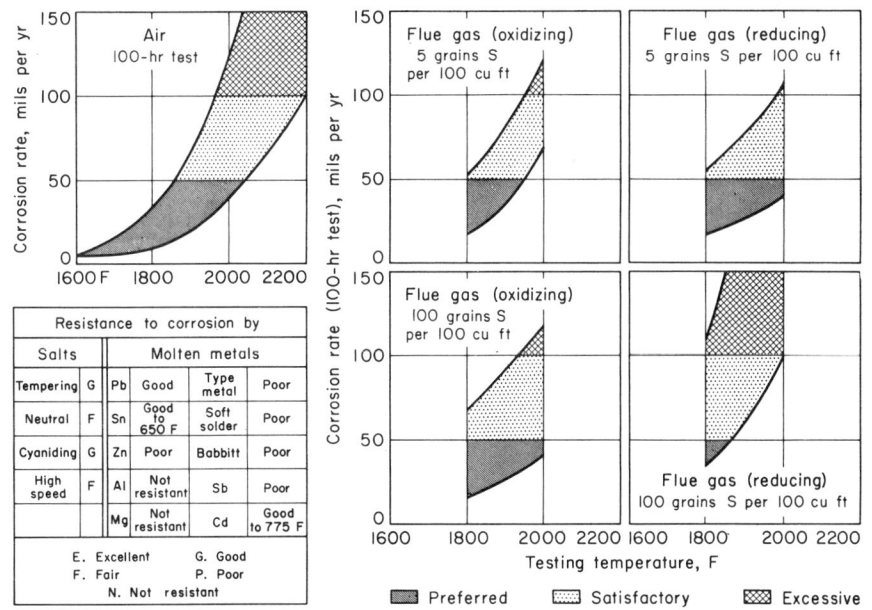

Fig. 20 Corrosion characteristics of alloy HT (Fe-35Ni-17Cr) castings. Source: Ref 5

preheated. In many cases, the weld is cooled with a water spray between passes to reduce the interpass temperature to 150 °C (300 °F) or below.

Any welding performed on the corrosion-resistant grades will affect the corrosion resistance of the casting, but for many applications the castings will perform satisfactorily in the as-welded condition. Where extremely corrosive conditions exist or where SCC may be a problem, complete reheat treatment may be required after welding. Heating the casting above 1065 °C (1950 °F) and then cooling it rapidly redissolves the carbides precipitated during the welding operation and restores corrosion resistance.

When maximum corrosion resistance is desired and postweld heat treatment (solution annealing) cannot be performed, alloying elements can be added to form stable carbides. Although niobium and titanium both form stable carbides, titanium is readily oxidized during the casting operation and therefore is seldom used. The niobium-stabilized grade CF-8C is the most commonly used cast grade. The stability of the niobium carbides prevents the formation of chromium carbides and the consequent chromium depletion of the base metal. This grade may therefore be welded without postweld heat treatment. Another approach to take when postweld heat treatment is undesirable or impossible is to keep the carbon content below 0.03%, as in the CF-3 and CF-3M grades. At this low carbon level, the depletion of the chromium due to carbide precipitation is so slight that the corrosion resistance of the grade is unaffected by the welding opera-

welding specific alloys are listed in Table 15. When welds are properly made, tensile and yield strengths of the welded joint are similar to those of the unwelded castings. Elongation is generally lower for specimens taken perpendicular to the weld bead.

Most of the corrosion-resistant cast steels, such as the CF-8 and CF-8M grades, are readily weldable, especially if their microstructures contain small percentages of δ-ferrite. Because stainless steels can become sensitized and lose their corrosion resistance if subjected to temperatures above 425 °C (800 °F), great care must be taken in welding to make certain that the casting or fabricated component is not heated excessively. For this reason, many stainless steels are almost never

Table 15 Welding conditions for corrosion-resistant steel castings

ACI designation	Type of electrodes used(a)	Preheat °C	Preheat °F	Postweld heat treatment
CA-6NM	Same composition	110-150	212-300	590-620 °C (1100-1150 °F)
CA-15	410	200-315	400-600	610-760 °C (1125-1400 °F), air cool
CA-40	410 or 420	200-315	400-600	610-760 °C (1125-1400 °F), air cool
CB-7Cu	Same composition or 308		Not required	480-590 °C (900-1100 °F), air cool
CB-30	442	315-425	600-800	790 °C (1450 °F) min, air cool
CC-50	446	200-700	400-1300	900 °C (1650 °F), air cool
CD-4MCu	Same composition		Not required	Heat to 1120 °C (2050 °F), cool to 1040 °C (1900 °F), quench
CE-30	312		Not required	Quench from 1090-1120 °C (2000-2050 °F)
CF-3	308L		Not required	Usually unnecessary
CF-8	308		Not required	Quench from 1040-1120 °C (1900-2050 °F)
CF-8C	347		Not required	Usually unnecessary
CF-3M	316L		Not required	Usually unnecessary
CF-8M	316		Not required	Quench from 1070-1150 °C (1950-2100 °F)
CF-12M	316		Not required	Quench from 1070-1150 °C (1950-2100 °F)
CF-16F	308 or 308L		Not required	Quench from 1090-1150 °C (2000-2100 °F)
CF-20	308		Not required	Quench from 1090-1150 °C (2000-2100 °F)
CG-8M	317		Not required	Quench from 1040-1120 °C (1900-2050 °F)
CH-20	309		Not required	Quench from 1090-1150 °C (2000-2100 °F)
CK-20	310		Not required	Quench from 1090-1180 °C (2000-2150 °F)
CN-7M	320	200	400	Quench from 1120 °C (2050 °F)

Note: Metal arc, inert-gas arc, and electroslag welding methods can be used. Suggested electrical settings and electrode sizes for various section thicknesses are:

Section thickness, mm (in.)	Electrode diameter, mm (in.)	Current, A	Maximum arc voltage, V
3.2-6.4 (⅛-¼)	2.4 (³⁄₃₂)	45-70	24
3.2-6.4 (⅛-¼)	3.2 (⅛)	70-105	25
3.2-6.4 (⅛-¼)	4.0 (⁵⁄₃₂)	100-140	25
6.4-13 (¼-½)	4.8 (³⁄₁₆)	130-180	26
≥13 (½)	6.4 (¼)	210-290	27

(a) Lime-coated electrodes are recommended.

tion. For more detailed information on welding of cast stainless steels, see the article "Welding" in this Volume.

Galling

Stainless steel castings are susceptible to galling and seizing when dry surfaces slide or chafe against each other. However, the surfaces of the castings can be nitrided so that they are hard and wear resistant. Tensile properties are not impaired. Nitriding reduces resistance to corrosion by concentrated nitric or mixed acids.

Parts such as gate disks for gate valves are usually furnished in the solution-treated condition, but they may be nitrided to reduce susceptibility to seizing in service. Similar results are obtained by hardfacing with cobalt-chromium-tungsten alloys.

Magnetic Properties

The magnetic properties of high-alloy castings depend on microstructure. The straight chromium types are ferritic and ferromagnetic. All other grades are mainly austenitic, with or without minor amounts of ferrite, and are either weakly magnetic or wholly nonmagnetic.

Cast nonmagnetic parts for applications in radar and in minesweepers require close control of ferrite content. Thicker sections have higher permeability than thinner sections. Therefore, to ensure low magnetic permeability in all areas of a casting, magnetic permeability checks should be made on the thicker sections.

ACKNOWLEDGMENTS

The information in this article is largely taken from:

- M. Blair, Cast Stainless Steels, *Properties and Selection: Irons, Steels, and High-Performance Alloys*, Vol 1, *ASM Handbook* (formerly 10th ed., *Metals Handbook*), ASM International, 1990, p 908-929
- J.M. Svoboda, High-Alloy Steels, *Casting*, Vol 15, *ASM Handbook* (formerly 9th ed., *Metals Handbook*), ASM International, 1988, p 722-735

REFERENCES

1. M. Prager, Cast High Alloy Metallurgy, *Steel Casting Metallurgy*, J. Svoboda, Ed., Steel Founders' Society of America, 1984, p 221-245
2. C.E. Bates and L.T. Tillery, *Atlas of Cast Corrosion-Resistant Alloy Microstructures*, Steel Founders' Society of America, 1985
3. F. Beck, E.A. Schoefer, E. Flowers, and M. Fontana, New Cast High Strength Alloy Grades by Structure Control, *Advances in the Technology of Stainless Steels and Related Alloys*, STP 369, ASTM, 1965, p 159-174
4. S.B. Shendye, "Effect of Long Term Elevated Temperature Exposure on the Mechanical Properties and Weldability of Cast Duplex Steels," Master's thesis, Oregon Graduate Center, 1985
5. High Alloy Data Sheet, Heat Series, *Steel Castings Handbook Supplement 9*, Steel Founders' Society of America
6. "Heat and Corrosion-Resistant Castings," The International Nickel Company, 1978
7. G.Y. Lai, Heat-Resistant Materials for Furnace Parts, Trays, and Fixtures, *Heat Treating*, Vol 4, *ASM Handbook*, ASM International, 1991, p 510-518

SELECTED REFERENCES

- High-Alloy Data Sheets, Corrosion Series, *Steel Castings Handbook Supplement 8*, Steel Founders' Society of America, 1981
- *Steel Castings Handbook*, 5th ed., P.R. Wieser, Ed., Steel Founders' Society of America, 1980

Powder Metallurgy Stainless Steels

STAINLESS STEEL powder metallurgy (P/M) parts represent an important and growing segment of the P/M industry. In the first decade of rapid commercialization of sintered stainless steel, its use increased at a compound annual rate of nearly 20% to reach a consumption of 2000 tons per year in 1973 for the North American market. The annual production of sintered stainless steel parts in North America is presently about 3000 tons (Ref 1).

This article will describe the processing, properties (particularly corrosion properties), and applications of medium-density and high-density P/M stainless steels. Medium-density materials are produced by pressing and sintering prealloyed stainless powders. They achieve densities in the range of 6.4 to 6.6 g/cm^3 (about 80 to 85% of theoretical density). High-density materials are produced by hot isostatic pressing, cold isostatic pressing followed by hot extrusion, or metal injection molding. Densities in these materials approach (95 to 99%) or reach 100% of theoretical density.

Sintered P/M Stainless Steels

All commercial compacting-grade stainless steel powders are produced by atomization. Most powders that are conventionally pressed and sintered are water atomized. This process produces a completely alloyed powder that is characterized by an irregular particle shape (Fig. 1). Gas (nitrogen) atomization is also used to produce spherical powder for high-density applications (Fig. 2). The chemical compositions of the important grades of P/M stainless steels are listed in Table 1.

Processing Sequence

Design and processing of stainless steel P/M parts are subject to the same basic considerations as are other P/M materials. However, compared with low-alloy ferrous powders, stainless steel powders require higher compacting pressures and have lower green strength. Typical compaction characteristics of austenitic and martensitic grades are shown in Fig. 3. Compaction pressures ranging from 550 to 830 MPa (40 to 60 tsi) are common in commercial practice.

The green strength of stainless steel compacts, which is about half that of P/M iron, is influenced by compaction pressure and the type of lubricant. (For the manufacture of P/M structural parts, a lubricant must be used with the prealloyed powder to permit compaction of the powder and the ejection of the part from the die.) Lubricants that provide high green strength, such as stearic acid (Fig. 4), generally cause lower compactibility (Fig. 3). Therefore, lubricant selection is an important factor in determining successful application and fabrication of P/M stainless steels.

Lubricant removal, prior to the actual sinter operation, is vitally important for several reasons. Generally, this removal is accomplished

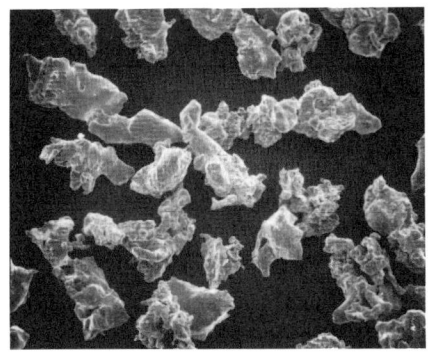

Fig. 1 Scanning electron micrograph of water-atomized type 304L stainless steel (–100 mesh). 150×

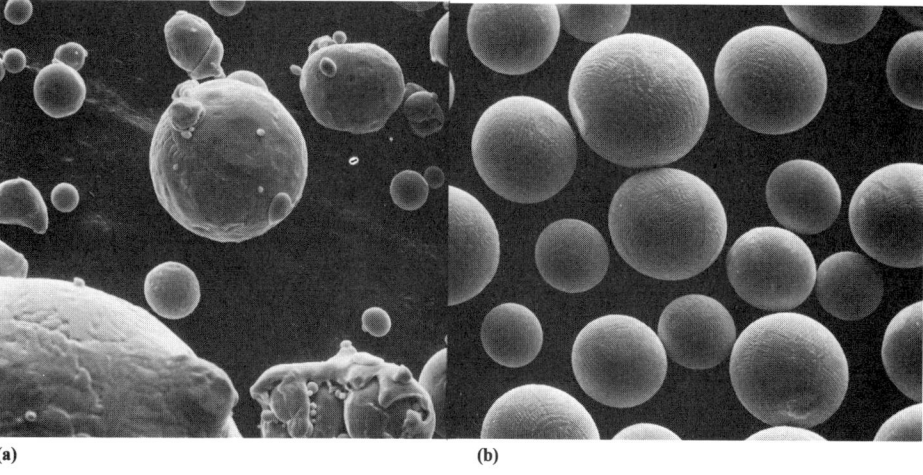

(a)　　　　　　　　　　(b)

Fig. 2 Scanning electron micrographs of gas-atomized stainless steel powders. (a) Type 316 stainless steel powder produced by conventional gas atomization. Note attached satellites. 700×. (b) Type 316L stainless steel powder produced by the rotating electrode process. Shown are nearly perfect spheres with absence of satellite formation. 200×

Table 1　Compositions of standard Metal Powder Industries Federation powder metallurgy stainless steels

MPIF designation	Fe	Cr	Ni	Mn	Si	S	C	P	Mo	N
						Composition, %				
SS-303N1, N2	rem	17.0-19.0	8.0-13.0	0-2.0	0-1.0	0.15-0.30	0-0.15	0-0.20	...	0.2-0.6
SS-303L	rem	17.0-19.0	8.0-13.0	0-2.0	0-1.0	0.15-0.30	0-0.03	0-0.20	...	...
SS-304N1, N2	rem	18.0-20.0	8.0-12.0	0-2.0	0-1.0	0-0.03	0-0.08	0-0.045	...	0.2-0.6
SS-304L	rem	18.0-20.0	8.0-12.0	0-2.0	0-1.0	0-0.03	0-0.03	0-0.045	...	...
SS-316N1, N2	rem	16.0-18.0	10.0-14.0	0-2.0	0-1.0	0-0.03	0-0.08	0-0.045	2.0-3.0	0.2-0.6
SS-316L	rem	16.0-18.0	10.0-14.0	0-2.0	0-1.0	0-0.03	0-0.03	0-0.045	2.0-3.0	...
SS-410	rem	11.5-13.0	...	0-1.0	0-1.0	0-0.03	0-0.25	0-0.04	...	0.2-0.6

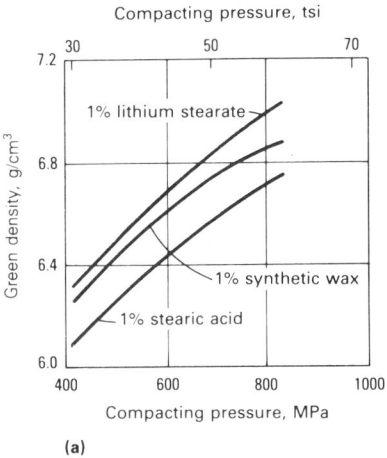

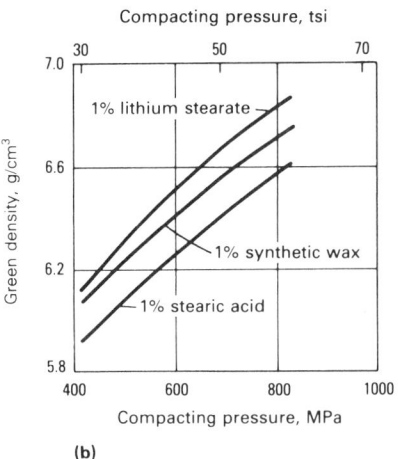

Fig. 3 Compactibility of stainless steel powders. (a) Type 316L austenitic stainless steel. (b) Type 410L martensitic steel

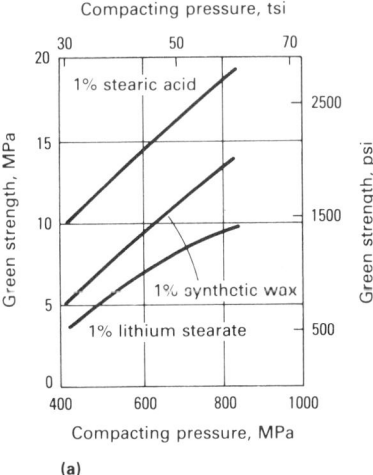

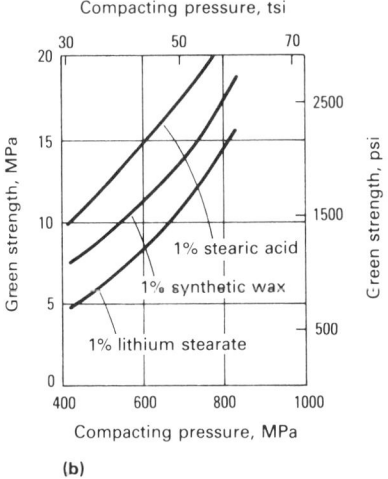

Fig. 4 Effect of lubricant and compacting pressure on green strength of stainless steel powder. (a) Type 316L austenitic stainless steel. (b) Type 410L martensitic stainless steel

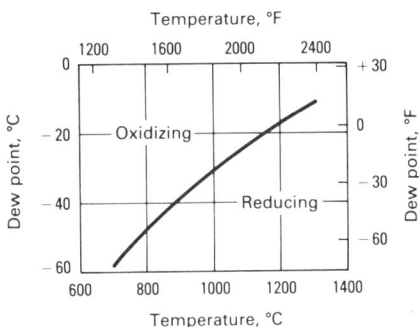

Fig. 5 Oxidation-reduction curve of chromium oxide with hydrogen

during the sintering preheat operation and is referred to as "burn-off." Because residual lubricant carbon deposits have highly adverse effects when stainless steel is sintered, resulting in lowered corrosion resistance, an extensive study was carried out on the burn-off characteristics of common lubricants (lithium stearate, zinc stearate, synthetic waxes) in type 316L powder compacts (Ref 2). Burn-off temperatures of 370, 425, and 480 °C (700, 800, and 900 °F) were used in both air and dissociated ammonia atmospheres. This study revealed that the waxes leave no residue at 425 °C (800 °F) or higher; the stearates, however, leave approximately 15% residue even when burned at temperatures up to 540 °C (1000 °F). Maximum lubricant burn-off is achieved at about 425 °C (800 °F). Burn-off is less controllable in dissociated ammonia, and the amount of lubricant removed decreases as the compacting pressure increases. Carbon burn-off is incomplete when compacts are burned off in dissociated ammonia atmosphere.

Sintering is the most critical step in processing stainless steel parts. During this treatment, the lubricant must be removed, and the particles must bond together. Average temperatures for sintering stainless steels range from 1120 to 1150 °C (2050 to 2100 °F). When improved mechanical properties and corrosion resistance are required, however, temperatures up to 1315 °C (2400 °F) and higher are used.

Continuous mesh belt sintering furnaces are suitable to about 1150 °C (2100 °F). At higher temperatures, manual or automatic pusher, walking beam, or vacuum furnaces are used.

Sintering Atmospheres

The most widely used commercial atmosphere for sintering of stainless steel is dissociated ammonia (75 vol% hydrogen and 25 vol% nitrogen), although nitrogen-base atmospheres that contain 5 to 10% hydrogen are also used with some frequency. The principal alternative to dissociated ammonia and nitrogen-based systems is vacuum. Hydrogen atmospheres, although viable, are not used commercially to a large extent because of higher costs. As will be described below, however, hydrogen atmospheres are used for sintering martensitic P/M stainless steels.

Dissociated Ammonia. When stainless steels are sintered in dissociated ammonia, a dew point of –45 to –50 °C (–50 to –60 °F) is required to prevent oxidation. The oxidation-reduction curve for chromium oxide (Fig. 5) shows that lower dew points are required at lower temperatures if a reducing environment is to be maintained. To ensure that no discoloration occurs during cooling and to allow some latitude in the sintering process, dissociated ammonia is sometimes dried to a dew point of –60 °C (–80 °F) or less before being introduced into the furnace.

Nitrogen-Base Atmospheres. It has been demonstrated that many parts can be sintered successfully in production with as little as 3% hydrogen in the atmosphere, in contrast to the 75% in dissociated ammonia.

Nitrogen content is proportional to the square root of the positive pressure of nitrogen. Thus, sintering in an atmosphere of 90% or more nitrogen results in almost twice the amount of nitrogen as that obtained in dissociated ammonia. Slow cooling results in additional nitrogen pickup, partly because of increasing nitrogen solubility down to a temperature of about 1095 °C (2000 °F) and partly because of reduced nitrogen solubility coupled with chromium nitride precipitation below that temperature.

Vacuum. The principal alternative to dissociated ammonia or nitrogen-base atmospheres is vacuum. The acceptance and wide usage of vacuum sintering is increasing, largely because of energy conservation and ecological considerations. Although conventional cold-wall vacuum furnaces are used, the operation is more properly described as partial pressure sintering. The vapor pressure of some elements (such as chromium) at the sintering temperature is near the pressure that can be achieved in commercial vacuum furnaces equipped only with mechanical pumping systems.

Chromium evaporates if the furnace pressure falls below its vapor pressure, and corrosion resistance is seriously reduced. Chromium content in a stainless steel can be virtually depleted in a typical vacuum sintering cycle if the vacuum level is not properly controlled.

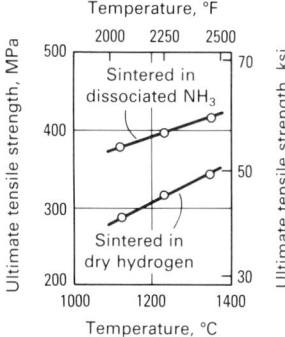
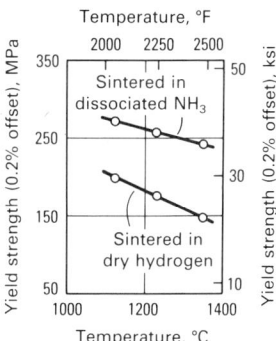
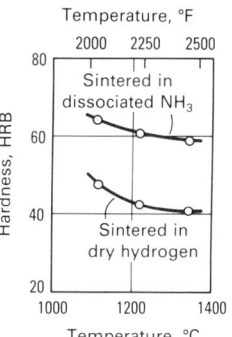

Fig. 6 Effect of sintering temperature on tensile and yield strengths and apparent hardness of type 316L stainless steel. Parts had a density of 6.85 g/cm³ and were sintered for 30 min in various atmospheres.

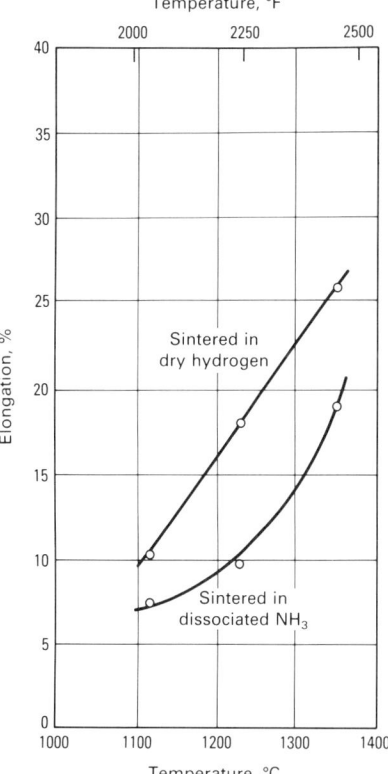
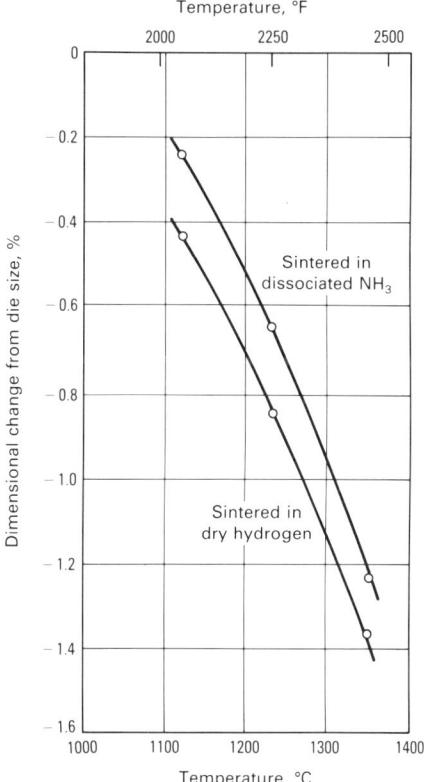

Fig. 7 Effect of sintering temperature on elongation and dimensional change during sintering of type 316L stainless steel. Parts had a density of 6.85 g/cm³ and were sintered for 30 min in various atmospheres.

To maintain reducing conditions in actual practice, a dew point of at least –35 to –40 °C (–30 to –40 °F) is required in the furnace. Because water vapor is formed during reduction, a sufficient flow of gas is required to continually remove this water, as well as the water that is formed by the reaction between the hydrogen and the air introduced with the parts and through furnace openings.

High-temperature sintering in hydrogen atmospheres is sometimes used for processing type 410L martensitic stainless steel. Typical processing conditions call for sintering at 1260 °C (2300 °F) for 45 min in 100% hydrogen at a dew point of –35 °C (–30 °F). Studies have shown that the best combination of mechanical, magnetic, and corrosion properties for antilock brake sensor rings made from type 410L powder were obtained by high-temperature sintering in hydrogen (Ref 3).

Sintering Cycles

Tensile strength increases with sintering temperature and sintering time, whereas yield strength decreases with increasing time and temperature. After surface oxides have been reduced in the initial stage of sintering, the particles bond together by solid-state diffusion. This is followed by a gradual increase in the amount of bonding and an increase in grain size. The two phenomena occur simultaneously, but their rate of growth is influenced differently by sintering time and temperature.

The growth of the bond area depends on both time and temperature, while grain size depends primarily on temperature. As the bond areas increase, yield and tensile strengths increase because of an increase in actual cross-sectional area of the bonds. However, for a given material, yield strength decreases as grain size increases. These two effects combine to increase the tensile strength of sintered material with increasing sintering time and temperature and to increase the yield strength with time, but to decrease it with increased temperature.

Figures 6 and 7 show the effect of sintering temperature and atmosphere on the mechanical properties and the dimensional change (calculated from die size) of type 316L stainless steel. The decrease in yield strength and the increase in tensile strength and ductility are readily apparent. A high degree of shrinkage is apparent when sintering at higher temperatures, especially in hydrogen. Lengthening the sintering time increases all tensile properties and the amount of shrinkage. Figures 8 and 9 illustrate the influence of sintering time on type 316L stainless steel in dissociated ammonia. Sintering in hydrogen or vacuum produces similar curves.

Cooling Rates

Regardless of the sintering atmosphere, the rate of cooling from the sintering temperature has a significant effect on the properties of sintered austenitic stainless steels. The rates of cooling normally used provide the best combination of strength and ductility. All stainless steels contain some carbon, and when dissociated ammonia is used, nitrogen is also present. The amount of

The required control is achieved by backfilling the vacuum vessel with a suitable gas to a partial pressure above the vapor pressure of any of the elements in the alloy. A gas pressure of 25 to 65 Pa (200 to 500 μm Hg) is typical for sintering stainless steel at 1315 °C (2400 °F). If argon is used as backfill gas, mechanical properties are similar to those obtained in hydrogen. When nitrogen is used for backfilling, sintered properties are comparable to those achieved in dissociated ammonia. A circulating gas quench generally is used to provide the desired high cooling rate. Gas composition should be the same as that used for maintaining a partial pressure during heating and soaking.

Hydrogen is the most strongly reducing of all commercially available sintering atmospheres. The principal disadvantage of using hydrogen is higher cost. Typically, the ratio of hydrogen to water vapor determines the extent of surface chromium oxide reduction during sintering and cooling.

The dew point controlling the reduction-oxidation reaction depends on temperature. As the sintering temperature increases, the dew point required for reduction is less critical, as shown in Fig. 5. Theoretically, at 1120 °C (2050 °F), a dew point of less than –22 °C (–8 °F) at the surface of the powder is required for reduction. At 1315 °C (2400 °F), a dew point of –11 °C (+13 °F) is satisfactory.

these elements normally present is beyond the limits of room-temperature solubility. On cooling, carbides and nitrides tend to precipitate in the form of fine particles. With extremely slow cooling, such as furnace cooling, precipitation occurs preferentially at grain boundaries. As a result, there is a noticeable increase in strength and loss of ductility, even though the amount of the precipitate is minimal.

However, carbide precipitation is detrimental to corrosion resistance (see the section below on "Corrosion Resistance of Sintered Stainless Steels"). With the normal rates of cooling (10 to 30 min) used in typical P/M production, less precipitation occurs at grain boundaries. Consequently, strength is lower, but ductility is higher. Rapid cooling, such as is obtained by water quenching, suppresses the precipitation of carbides and nitrides, which produces maximum ductility.

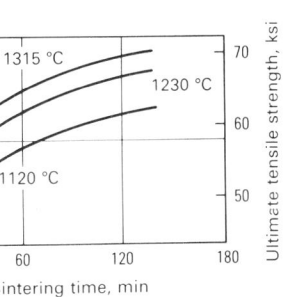
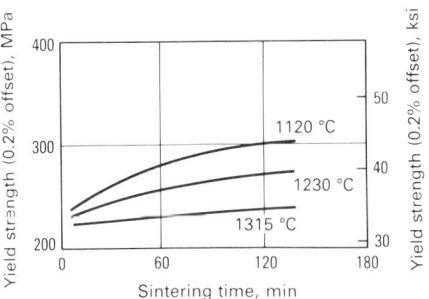

Fig. 8 Effect of sintering time on tensile and yield strengths of type 316L stainless steel. Parts were pressed to 6.85 g/cm³ and sintered at various temperatures in dissociated ammonia.

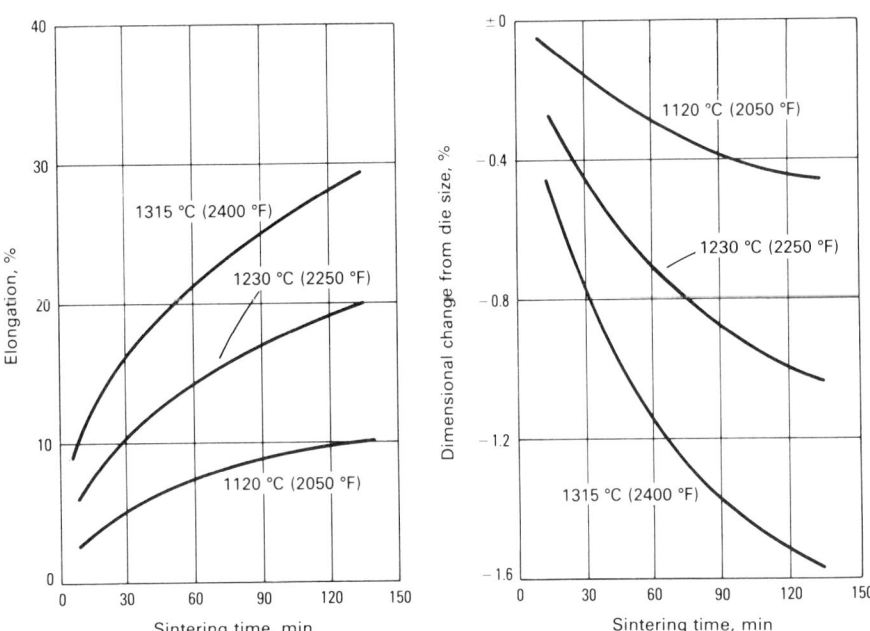

Fig. 9 Effect of sintering time on elongation and dimensional change during sintering of type 316L stainless steel. Parts were pressed to 6.85 g/cm³ and sintered at various temperatures in dissociated ammonia.

Control of Carbon Content

Austenitic grades of stainless steel powders are made with less than 0.03% C (Table 1). To retain this low carbon content after sintering, which ensures maximum corrosion resistance, weldability, and machinability, carbon pickup must be avoided.

The solid lubricant used for pressing must be completely removed by presintering (burn-off), because stearates and waxes are a source of carbon. Frequently, small loads can be sintered directly by using excessive flow of atmosphere to flush away the volatilized lubricant. Generally, however, a two-step sintering process (burn-off plus sintering) is the most efficient practice.

Other common sources of carbon include soot, residual lubricant in the furnace, and traces of previous furnace atmosphere. Dissociated ammonia or hydrogen atmospheres develop a carburizing potential when small amounts of residual carbonaceous materials are present in the furnace. Care must be taken to ensure that the furnace is clean and that the atmosphere is pure.

Properties of Sintered Stainless Steels

Mechanical properties of austenitic stainless steels depend on the atmosphere in which they are sintered. As mentioned above, the most common commercial atmosphere for sintering stainless steel is dissociated ammonia. Sintering in this atmosphere introduces as much as 0.3% nitrogen into the composition, which increases

Table 2 Minimum and typical mechanical properties of powder metallurgy stainless steels

Material designation code(a)	Ultimate strength MPa	ksi	0.2% offset yield strength MPa	ksi	Elongation in 25 mm (1 in.), %	0.1% compressive yield strength MPa	ksi	Transverse rupture strength MPa	ksi	Unnotched Charpy impact energy J	ft · lbf	Apparent hardness	Density, g/cm³
SS-303N1-25(b)	270	39	220	32	0.5	262	38	593	86	4.7	3.5	62 HRB	6.4
SS-303N2-35(b)	380	55	290	42	5	317	46	675	98	26	19	63 HRB	6.5
SS-303L-12(b)	270	39	115	17	17.5	145	21	565	82	...	...	21 HRB	6.6
SS-304N1-30(b)	295	43	260	38	0.5	262	38	772	112	5.5	4	61 HRB	6.4
SS-304N2-33(b)	393	57	275	40	10	324	47	875	127	34	25	62 HRB	6.5
SS-304L-13(b)	295	43	125	18	23	152	22	...	...	...	...	...	6.6
SS-316N1-25(b)	283	41	235	34	0.5	248	36	745	108	6.8	5	59 HRB	6.4
SS-316N2-33(b)	415	60	270	39	10	303	44	860	125	38	28	62 HRB	6.5
SS-316L-15(b)	283	41	138	20	18.5	152	22	550	80	47	35	20 HRB	6.6
SS-410-90HT(c)	725	105	(e)	(e)	<0.5	641	93	780	113	3.5	2.5	23 HRC(d)	6.5

Notes: Minimum strength values (in ksi) are specified by the numerical suffix in the first column of the table. Typical values are given in the remaining columns. (a) Codes for the stainless steel designations: N1, nitrogen alloyed with good strength and low elongation, sintered at 1150 °C (2100 °F) in dissociated ammonia; N2, nitrogen alloyed with high strength and medium elongation, sintered at 1290 °C (2350 °F) in dissociated ammonia; L, low carbon with lower strength and highest elongation, sintered at 1290 °C (2350 °F) in partial vacuum and cooled to avoid nitrogen absorption; HT, martensitic grade that is heat treated for highest strength, sintered at 1150 °C (2100 °F) in dissociated ammonia. (b) The numerical suffix represents the minimum yield strength in ksi. (c) The numerical suffix represents the ultimate tensile strength in ksi. (d) Or a matrix (converted) hardness of 55 HRC. (e) Yield and ultimate tensile strengths in heat-treated materials are approximately the same. Source: Metal Powder Industries Federation Standard 35, "Materials Standards for P/M Structural Parts" (1990-1991 edition)

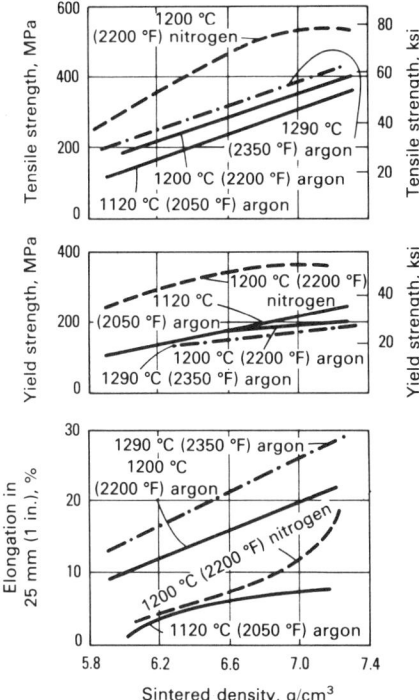

Fig. 10 Tensile properties of standard type 316L stainless steel Metal Powder Industries Federation tensile bars. Bars were sintered in vacuum for 2 h using argon and nitrogen as backfilling gases. A partial pressure of 400 μm mercury was used to prevent vaporization of chromium.

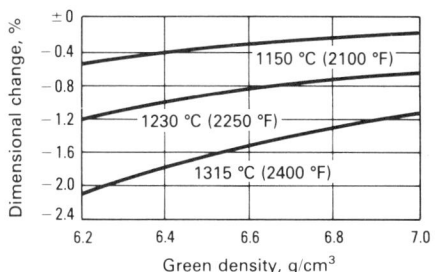

Fig. 11 Dimensional changes for type 304L stainless steel. Dimensional changes were determined on transverse-rupture bars sintered for 45 min in dissociated ammonia (dew point –40 °C, or –40 °F) and were calculated from die size.

Table 3 Applications for powder metallurgy stainless steels

Part	Alloy	Part	Alloy
Aerospace		**Hardware**	
Seatback tray slides	316L	Lock components	304L, 316L
Galley latches	316L	Threaded fasteners	303L
Jet fuel refueling impellers	316L	Fasteners	316L
Foam generators	316L	Quick-disconnect levers	303L, 316L
Agriculture		**Industrial**	
Fungicide spray equipment	316L	Water and gas meter parts	316L
		Filters, liquid and gas	316L-Si
Appliances		Recording fuel meters	303L
Automatic dishwasher components	304L	Fuel flow meter devices	410L
Automatic washer components	304L	Pipe flange clamps	316L
Garbage disposal components	410L	High polymer filtering	316L-Si
Pot handles	316L	**Jewelry**	
Coffee filters	316L-Si	Coins, medals, medallions	316L
Electric knives	316L	Watch cases	316L
Blenders	303L	Watch band parts	316L
Can opener gears	410L		
Automotive		**Marine**	
Rearview mirror mounts	316L, 434L	Propeller thrust hubs	316L
Brake components	434L	Cam cleats	304L
Seat belt locks	304L	**Medical**	
Windshield wiper pinions	410L	Centrifugal drive couplings	316L
Windshield wiper arms	316L	Dental equipment	304L
Manifold heat control valves	304L	Hearing aids	316L
Building and construction		Anesthetic vaporizers	316L
Plumbing fixtures	303L	**Office equipment**	
Spacers and washers	316L	Nonmagnetic card stops	316L
Sprinkler system nozzles	316L	Dictating machine switches	316L
Shower heads	316L	Computer knobs	316L
Window hardware	304L, 316L	**Recreation and leisure**	
Thermostats	410L	Fishing rod guides	304L, 316L
Chemical		Fishing rod gear ratchets	316L
Filters	304L-Si, 316L	Photographic equipment	316L
High corrosion resistance filters	830	Soft drink vending machines	830, 316L
Cartridge assemblies	316L-Si	Travel trailer water pumps	316L
Electrical and electronic			
Limit switches	410L		
G-frame motor sleeves	303L		
Rotary switches	316L		
Magnetic clutches	410L, 440A		
Battery nuts	830		
Electrical testing probe jaws	316L		

strength but lowers ductility. Typical tensile properties of stainless steels sintered in dissociated ammonia are given in Table 2.

The effect of sintered part density, sintering temperature, and atmosphere on the tensile strength of vacuum-sintered type 316L stainless steel is illustrated in Fig. 10. Strength increases as part density and sintering temperature increases when argon is used as the backfilling gas. In addition, the use of nitrogen as the backfilling gas has almost a doubling effect on strength, especially at lower densities. Therefore, sintered density is not the sole factor to be considered when designing a type 316L stainless steel P/M part in which strength is a critical factor. Both sintering temperature and atmosphere must be known in order to determine tensile strength.

The effect of sintering parameters on yield strength is also shown in Fig. 10. In this case, the effect of sintering temperature is not as pronounced as for tensile strength. However, the strengthening effect of nitrogen in austenitic stainless steel is evident. Note also the flattening of yield strength above 6.8 g/cm^3 under the nitrogen sintering conditions.

Sintering conditions have the most significant effect on the ductility of type 316L stainless steel, as shown in Fig. 10. Although the influence of final part density is recognized as a controlling factor in determining ductility, the effect of sintering temperature has not been emphasized. In comparing the ductility curves in Fig. 10, ductility at 7.2 g/cm^3 for a 1120 °C (2050 °F) sinter cycle was less than for a 6.0 g/cm^3 part sintered at 1200 °C (2200 °F). Note also the dramatic rise in ductility for the 1290 °C (2350 °F) sinter cycle above the 7.0 g/cm^3 level. At these densities, ductility begins to approach that of wrought stock. The nitrogen backfill limits ductility, especially at lower densities. However, just as the yield strength flat-

tens above 6.8 g/cm^3, ductility begins to rise rapidly above this density level and approaches ductility for the 1200 °C (2200 °F) argon cycle. At higher densities, nitrogen diffusion is limited to bulk diffusion rates and can no longer enter the alloy through the decreasing interconnected porosity network.

Dimensional Changes. Stainless steels exhibit greater shrinkage during sintering than do P/M irons. The dimensional change for type 304L sintered in dissociated ammonia is shown in Fig. 11, in which it can be seen that shrinkage increases with increasing temperature. Sintering in either hydrogen or vacuum results in greater shrinkage. Additional data on dimensional changes occurring in stainless steels during the sintering process are shown in Fig. 7 and 9.

Application and Selection of Sintered P/M Stainless Steels

In the absence of detailed and reliable corrosion data, tentative selection of a P/M stainless steel for a specific application is made by following the same principles developed for cast and wrought stainless steels. Thus, for better corrosion resistance, the austenitic grades are preferred. However, type 410L stainless steel is often used for its good abrasion resistance and for its good combination of mechanical, magnetic, and corrosion properties. One such example of the latter is the use of type 410L for antilock brake sensor rings (Ref 3). Because the corrosion resistance of sintered stainless steels depends so much on powder quality and parts-processing details, appropriate field testing is advisable to ensure compliance with specifications.

Table 3 provides an overview of market segments and applications for sintered stainless steels. The 300-series austenitic grades account for about two-thirds of total usage, and among the austenitic grades, type 316L is the most important. In terms of market distribution, automotive applications constitute the largest volume, followed by hardware and tools, filters, appliances, office machines, and a large segment of miscellaneous uses. Typical examples of P/M stainless steel parts are shown in Fig. 12.

Porous Parts. One of the major applications for P/M stainless steels is in the fabrication of porous mediums. Porosity generally is an undesirable, although tolerable, characteristic of P/M parts for structural applications. However, for porous mediums, this porosity is an advantage. Applications include liquid retention (as in bearings), filtering, metering of liquids or gases, and sound attenuation in telephones, microphones, and hearing aids.

The most common commercial composition of porous stainless steel parts is type 316L. From a manufacturing standpoint, however, any of the austenitic grades (300 series) of stainless steel may be used.

The methods used for making stainless steel filter materials depend on the final shape of the filter. For making sheet, loose powder mixed with resin is spread in a mold and lightly pressed at a temperature that cures the resin, and the resulting sheet is sintered. During sintering, the resin decomposes. The porous sheet is densified by repressing and is then resintered. It may be subsequently formed into hollow cylinders and seam welded. Another method for fabricating porous P/M parts is cold isostatic pressing followed by sintering. Examples of cold isostatically pressed porous stainless steel parts, including hollow tubular products, are shown in Fig. 13. More detailed information can be found in the article "Cold Isostatic Pressing" in Volume 7 of the *ASM Handbook*.

Appliances. Parts for appliances represent another sizable market for P/M stainless steels. Figure 14 shows a type 316L steel ejector pad that is used for a refrigerator automatic icemaker. The ejector pad is pressed to a density of 6.6 g/cm^3 and has a hardness of 65 HRB. After the part is pressed, it is sintered at 1260 °C (2300 °F) or higher in dissociated ammonia and is coined or restruck to attain straightness.

The complex shape (five individual pads joined by a thin rail) requires precise part flatness

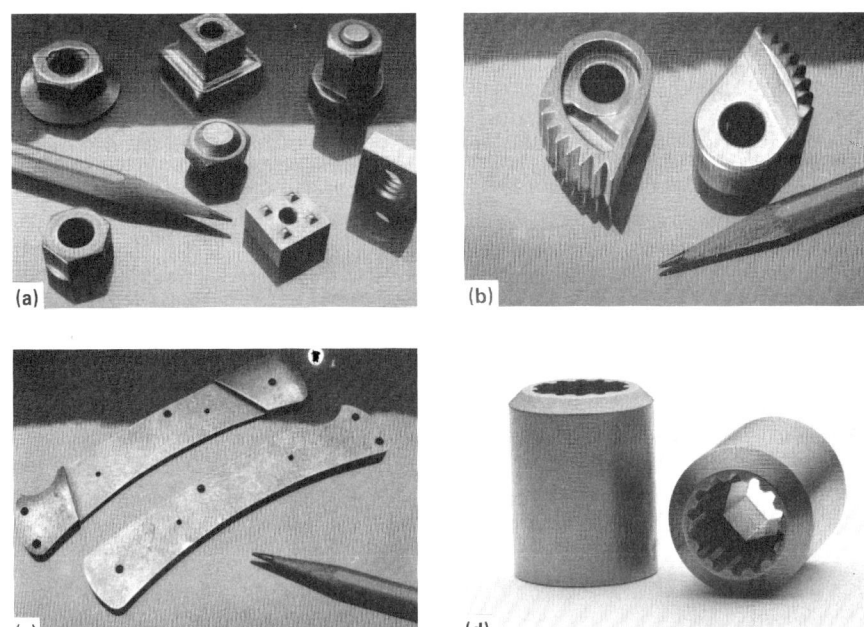

Fig. 12 Powder metallurgy parts produced from stainless steel powder. (a) Specialty fasteners made from type 303L powder. (b) Sailboat cleats made from type 316L powder. (c) Hunting knife handles made from type 316L powder. (d) Splined coupling for pump made from type 304L powder

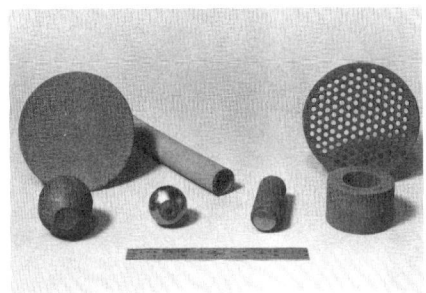

Fig. 13 Porous powder metallurgy parts made by cold isostatic pressing

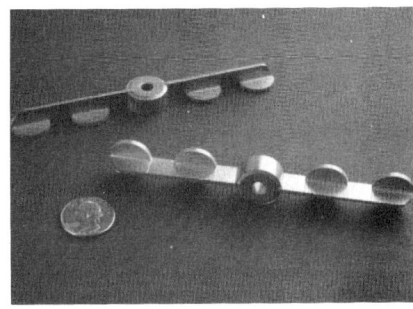

Fig. 14 Type 316L stainless steel ejector pad for refrigerator automatic icemaker

Fig. 15 Garbage disposal part made from type 410L stainless powder

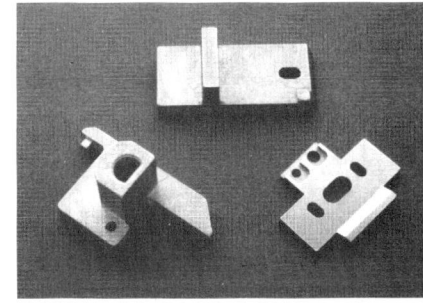

Fig. 16 Copier machine parts made from type 316L powder

and straightness. The bottom of the center pad must be parallel with the bottom of the other pads within 0.254 mm (0.010 in.) from center pad to end pad. It must be straight within 0.127 mm (0.005 in.) maximum from the theoretical centerline through the pads over a part length of 140 mm (5.514 in.).

The improved straightness allows a tighter fit in the mating die casting, resulting in improved ice cube ejection. Barrel finishing to a smooth surface texture prevents ice cubes from sticking when freezing.

Figure 15 shows a garbage disposal part made from type 410L stainless steel powder. This

Table 4 Corrosion resistance of wrought and sintered type 316L stainless steel

Corrodent	Wrought type 316L	P/M type 316L(a)
5% aqueous NaCl salt spray, 100 h(b)	Clean	Profuse, voluminous corrosion product and pitting
5% aqueous NaCl immersion(c)	>1000 h(d)	5 to 500 h(d)
10% aqueous FeCl₃, 25 °C (75 °F)(e)	70 g/m²/h	70 g/m²/h
10% aqueous HNO₃, 20 °C (70 °F)	<0.1 g/m²/h	0.001 to 0.4 g/m²/h

(a) 85% of theoretical density. (b) Per ASTM B 117. (c) Per ASTM G 31. (d) Time in hours at which 90% of specimens had 1% of surface covered by stain. (e) Per ASTM G 48. Source: Ref 4

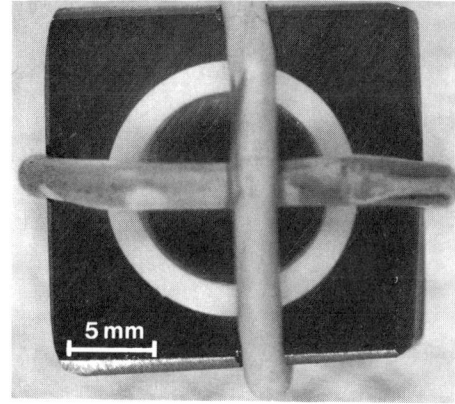

(a)

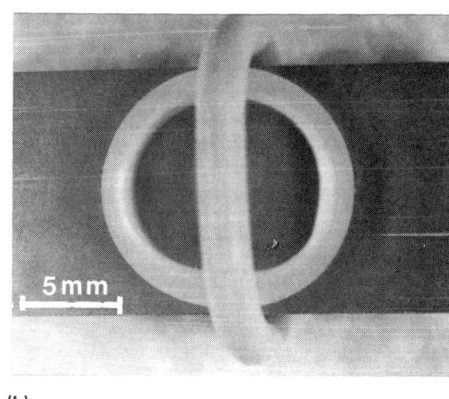

(b)

(d)

(c)

martensitic grade of stainless steel powder is intended for use in the manufacture of hard, wear-resistant P/M parts. Type 410L powder contains less than 0.03% C, but sufficient hardening is obtained by sintering in dissociated ammonia. When maximum hardness and wear resistance are required, carbon in the form of graphite can be added to the mix to give added hardenability.

Business Machines. Figure 16 shows a variety of P/M stainless steel parts used in copier machines. More than 90 metric tonnes (100 tons) of stainless steel powder are used annually in the manufacture of business machine parts. Use of stainless steel powder pressed to near-net shape eliminates the expensive machining operations required when using wrought bar stock.

Corrosion Resistance of Sintered Stainless Steels

Although powder and processing requirements for improving corrosion resistance are now better defined and improved stainless steel powders are available, the basic understanding of corrosion as well as corrosion data development for sintered stainless steels are both still in their early stages. There are many factors that distinguish sintered stainless steel from cast and wrought stainless steel. Complicating the issue is the fact that the corrosion resistance of sintered stainless steels depends as much on the sintering process as it does on the properties of the powder. Neither guidelines nor standards relating to corrosion behavior exist for most of the critical composition and process parameters. Furthermore, much of the published literature on specific corrosion data of sintered stainless steels is nearly obsolete because of the lack of information on process conditions. Therefore, emphasis in the following discussion will be placed on summarizing recent basic and practical information on powder selection and on sintering process control for maximizing corrosion resistance.

Comparing Wrought and P/M Stainless Steels. Table 4 compares the corrosion resistance of sintered type 316L stainless steel of 85% of theoretical density with that of wrought stainless steel of similar composition in a 5% aqueous so-

Fig. 17 Comparison of wrought and sintered type 316L stainless steels before and after testing in 10% aqueous FeCl₃. (a) Assembled crevice corrosion test specimen of wrought type 316L (100% dense). (b) Assembled crevice corrosion test specimen of sintered type 316L (85% dense). (c) Wrought specimen after test showing severe attack at four crevices under rubber bands and under Teflon ring. (d) Sintered specimen after test showing slight attack under Teflon ring. Source: Ref 5

lution of sodium chloride (NaCl) after a 100 h 5% aqueous NaCl salt spray test in 10% ferric chloride (FeCl₃) and in 10% nitric acid (HNO₃) solutions (Ref 4). For both HNO₃ and dilute FeCl₃, sintered type 316L performed similarly to wrought type 316L. For chloride environments, however, the P/M product is inferior. Because NaCl is probably the single most important corrodent for sintered stainless steels, a summary of recent investigations is presented below. Most of the data are for type 316L, but the general conclusions should also be valid for other stainless steel grades of the 300 and 400 series.

The limited corrosion resistance of sintered stainless steels, particularly in a chloride environment, is commonly thought to derive from the presence of residual pores that give rise to crevice corrosion as a result of oxygen depletion within the pores. There is evidence, however, that factors other than porosity often determine corrosion life. For example, despite similar pore volumes, pore sizes, and pore shapes, type 316L parts prepared from various powder lots and sintered under varying conditions had corrosion resistances in 5%

aqueous NaCl that varied between 5 and 500 h for a specified degree of corrosion (Table 4) (Ref 4, 5). Furthermore, a comparison of wrought and sintered (85% of theoretical density) type 316L for susceptibility to crevice corrosion in 10% FeCl₃ showed that the wrought part was even more severely attacked than the porous P/M part (Fig. 17). Lastly, surface analyses of water-atomized stainless steel powders showed the presence of large amounts of oxidized silicon concurrent with a severe depletion of chromium (Ref 5). The surface composition of a sintered part depended on its sintering conditions.

It is clear that the factors of critical importance for the corrosion resistance of sintered stainless steels include control of iron contamination, carbon, nitrogen, oxygen, and sintered part density (Ref 4-8). The effects of these variables are discussed in the following sections and are summarized in Table 5. In addition, the precautions necessary for maximizing corrosion resistance differ with the sintering atmosphere.

Effect of Iron Contamination. Contamination of stainless steel powder with iron or iron-

Table 5 Effect of iron, carbon, nitrogen, and oxygen on corrosion resistance of sintered austenitic stainless steels in NaCl

Variable	Origin of problem	Effect on corrosion resistance	Suggested solutions	Ref
Iron	Contamination of prealloyed powder with iron or iron-base powder at powder or parts producer's facility	Lowering of corrosion resistance by more than 99% due to galvanic corrosion	Utmost cleanliness at both powder and parts producer's manufacturing facilities, preferably separate and dedicated equipment and facilities	4
Carbon	Inadequate lubricant removal; carburizing sintering atmosphere; soot in sintering furnace; high-carbon powder	Inferior resistance to intergranular corrosion	Use L-grade designation of stainless steel powder. Ensure adequate lubricant removal (before sintering). Use clean soot-free sintering furnace and carbon-free sintering atmospheres; carbon content of sintered part should be ≤0.03%.	4, 5
Nitrogen	Sintering in dissociated NH_3 or other nitrogen-containing atmosphere combined with slow cooling	Inferior resistance to intergranular corrosion	Reduce percentage of nitrogen in sintering atmosphere. Use fast cooling of parts preferably >150 to 200 °C/min (270 to 360 °F/min) through critical temperature range (700 to 1000 °C, or 1290 to 1830 °F). Use higher sintering temperature. Use intermediate dew points (–37 to –45 °C, or –35 to –50 °F) in cooling zone of furnace. Use tin-modified stainless steel powders.	4, 6, 7, 8, 9
Oxygen	Excessive oxygen in powder; excessive dew point of sintering atmosphere; slow cooling after sintering	Inferior resistance to general corrosion	Use low-oxygen content powder, preferably <2000 ppm. Control dew point within sintering furnace to ensure reducing conditions. Fast cooling, preferably >200 °C/min (360 °F/min) For nitrogen-containing atmospheres, use dew point of –37 to –45 °C (–35 to –50 °F) in cooling zone. For sintering in H_2, ensure that water vapor content of atmosphere is below 50 ppm.	4, 6, 9
Density of sintered part	High sintered density	Inferior resistance to crevice corrosion	Use lower density to increase pore size and circulation of corrodent. In acidic environments, corrosion resistance improves with increasing density due to a decrease of specific surface area.	4, 6, 10, 11, 12

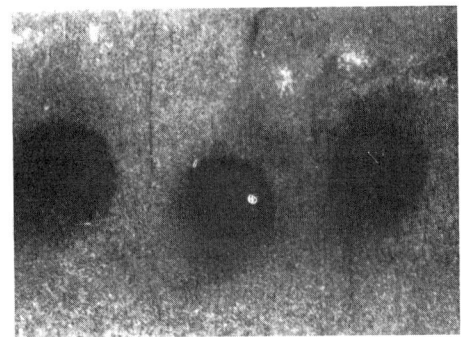

Fig. 18 Small circles of rust around iron particles embedded in the surface of sintered type 316L stainless steel after testing in 5% aqueous NaCl. 35×. Source: Ref 4

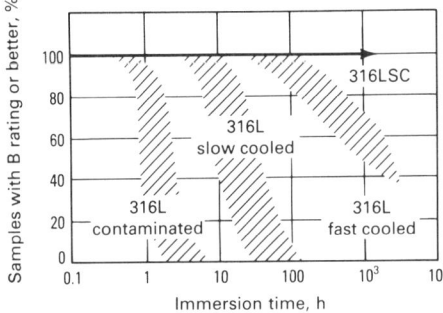

Fig. 19 Typical corrosion behavior of regular and copper-tin-modified (type 316LSC) sintered type 316L stainless steel sintered in dissociated ammonia under various conditions of cooling and contamination. The "B" rating indicates that <1% of the specimen surface is covered by stain. Testing of the modified stainless steel was terminated after 1500 h. Source: Ref 4

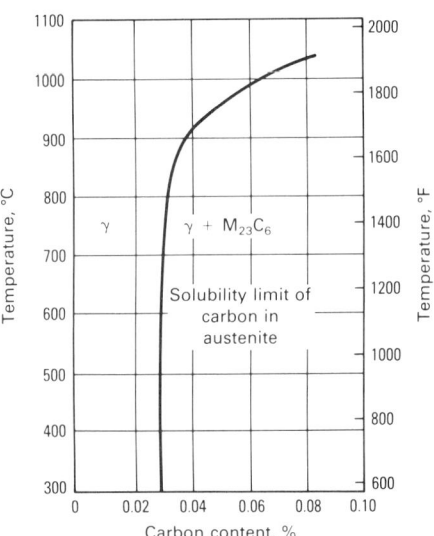

Fig. 20 Solid solubility of carbon in an austenitic stainless steel. Source: Ref 13

base powder may originate at the powder producer or the part manufacturer. Even extremely small amounts of iron contamination have a disastrous effect on the corrosion resistance of sintered parts in a saline environment. Utmost cleanliness, for example, through the use of separate production facilities and dedicated equipment, is mandatory. In saline solutions, active iron or iron-base powder particles form galvanic couples with the passive stainless steel and corrode anodically in preference to the stainless steel. Figure 18 shows this type of corrosion for iron particles embedded in the surface of a pressed-and-sintered type 316L part. Rusting occurs within minutes after exposure. The buildup of the initial corrosion product forms a crevice in which oxygen depletion causes acidification of the solution inside the part and further corrosion.

Because of its severity, iron contamination overshadows the other factors that affect corro-

sion resistance (Fig. 19). Active iron or iron alloy particles present in stainless steel powder or on the surface of a sintered stainless steel part will be revealed by placing the powder or part in a concentrated aqueous solution of copper sulfate ($CuSO_4$). The dissolved copper plates out on the iron particles within minutes, making them easy to identify with a low-magnification microscope. The powder must be tested in the unlubricated condition because lubricant will prevent the solution from wetting the powder. Experiments with very fine iron powder particles combined with high-temperature (>1260 °C, or 2300 °F) sintering have shown that this type of corrosion can be avoided if the sintering conditions result in complete alloying of the iron particles with the stainless steel matrix (Ref 4).

Effect of Carbon. Water-atomized austenitic and ferritic grades of stainless steel powders have low (<0.03%) carbon contents in order to resist intergranular corrosion from sensitization during cooling of the sintered part. However, in P/M sintering there are additional sources of potential carbon contamination, and because stabilization with titanium, niobium, and tantalum is not practiced due to the excessive oxidation of these elements during water atomization, the phenomenon of sensitization will be discussed as it applies to sintered stainless steels.

Because of the decreasing carbon solubility with decreasing temperature (Fig. 20), grain-

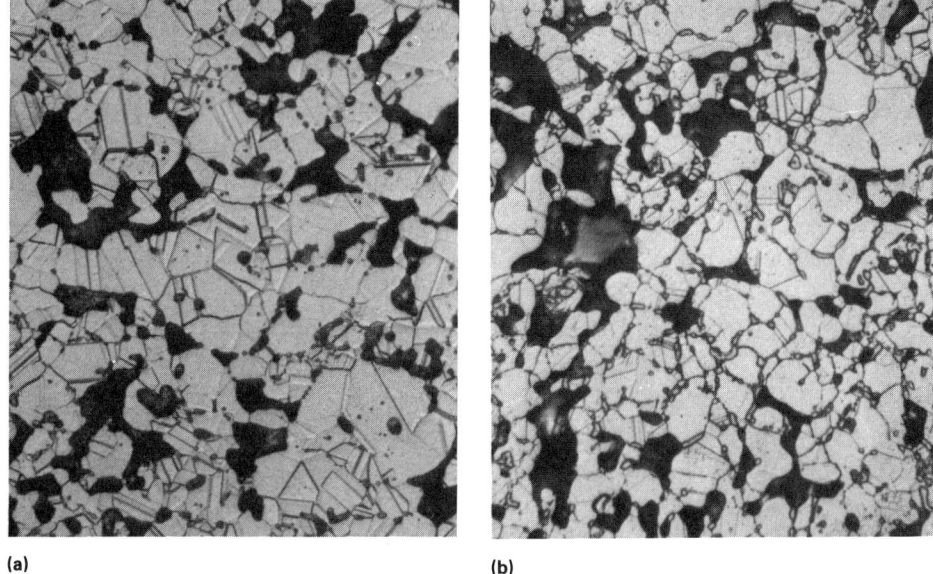

Fig. 21 Microstructures of type 316L stainless steel sintered in hydrogen at 1150 °C (2100 °F). (a) Low carbon content. (b) Excessive carbon content. Both 400×

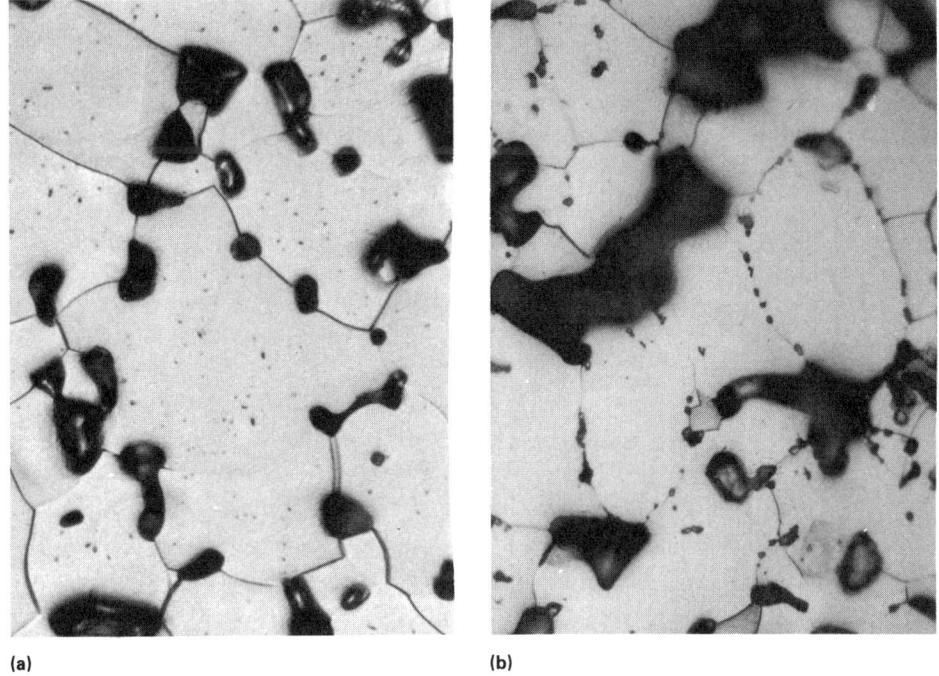

Fig. 22 Cross sections of vacuum-sintered (30 min at 1330 °C, or 2430 °F) type 430L stainless steel. (a) No oxides are present in grain boundaries after addition of 0.2% C. (b) Small, gray, rounded oxide particles are present in grain boundaries.

boundary precipitation of carbon as chromium-rich carbide ($M_{23}C_6$) with attendant chromium depletion occurs during cooling in the sintering furnace for materials with carbon contents exceeding 0.03%. The chromium-depleted regions will exhibit interior corrosion resistance.

Figure 21 shows the microstructures of two sintered type 316L parts with carbon contents below and above the critical concentration of 0.03%. The low-carbon material has clean, thin grain boundaries, but the high-carbon material has

grain boundaries with heavy precipitates of chromium-rich carbides.

As described above, the two main sources of carbon contamination of sintered stainless steels are: (a) the organic lubricant present in prelubricated powder or added by the part manufacturer (typically 0.5 to 1%) to minimize die wear during powder compaction; and (b) carbon (soot) contaminated sintering furnaces. Adequate lubricant removal is accomplished by a so-called lubricant burn-off, or dewaxing, process (Ref 10), which

consists of heating the green parts in air or nitrogen to 425 to 540 °C (800 to 1000 °F). Length of heating should take into consideration the size (mass) of the parts. The oxygen absorbed during dewaxing in air will be reduced during sintering in a low-dew-point reducing atmosphere but not when sintering is done in a vacuum furnace.

A soot-containing sintering furnace, that is, a furnace used with a low-dew-point endothermic atmosphere, can carburize stainless steel parts when soot that adheres loosely to furnace walls falls onto the stainless steel parts. Moisture from the sintering atmosphere or moisture formed by reduction of oxides can react with soot to form carbon monoxide and carburize the stainless steel.

For vacuum sintering of stainless steels, it may actually be beneficial to use powders with carbon contents exceeding 0.03%. With correct processing, the excessive carbon will be used up for the reduction of some of the oxides of the water-atomized stainless steel powders (typically 0.2 to 0.3% oxygen) and thus improve the mechanical strength, ductility, and corrosion resistance of the sintered part. This phenomenon is illustrated in Fig. 22 for a vacuum-sintered ferritic stainless steel. Both parts were processed identically except for an addition of 0.2% graphite to one of the powders for the purpose of reducing its oxygen content. As expected, the graphite-containing material (Fig. 22a) produced clean grain boundaries, indicating the absence of both carbides and oxides, but the graphite-free powder (Fig. 22b) showed a heavy decoration of the grain boundaries with oxides, with an accompanying deterioration of corrosion resistance. Grain-boundary corrosion due to carbide sensitization, although somewhat less severe than the type of corrosion discussed above, still severely limits the attainment of adequate corrosion resistance of sintered P/M stainless steels.

Remedies such as heat treatment to rediffuse chromium back into the chromium-depleted austenite and the use of carbide stabilizers (titanium, vanadium, and niobium) are not practiced in the P/M industry. Such remedies are unnecessary if carbon pickup during sintering is avoided, because the various powders are available as low-carbon grades.

Effect of Nitrogen. As with carbon, the key to understanding the effect of nitrogen on the corrosion resistance of sintered stainless steels is the solubility of nitrogen in the stainless steel matrix. Under certain conditions, dissolved nitrogen will precipitate as chromium nitride (Cr_2N), with accompanying chromium depletion and deterioration of corrosion resistance. Under industrial conditions of sintering in dissociated ammonia, in synthetic nitrogen-base atmospheres (typically 5 to 10% H_2, rem N_2) or in a vacuum with a partial pressure of nitrogen, the stainless steel part absorbs nitrogen in accordance with known phase equilibria (Fig. 23). The amount of nitrogen absorbed during sintering decreases with increasing sintering temperature and with decreasing chromium concentration of the stainless steel. Also, absorption follows Sievert's law; that is, absorption is proportional to the square root of the partial pressure of nitrogen in the sintering atmosphere.

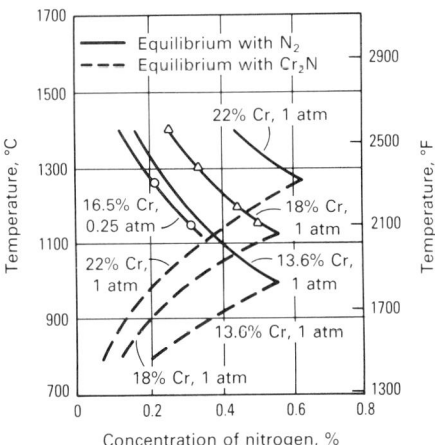

Fig. 23 Solubility of nitrogen in austenitic stainless steel in equilibrium with gaseous nitrogen or Cr_2N. Source: Ref 4

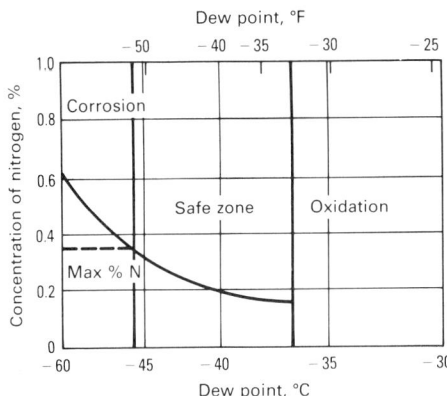

Fig. 24 Safe operating parameters with respect to dew point can be developed for a specific set of operating conditions and quality requirements. The safe zone here is for sintering in an atmosphere of 30% H_2-70% N_2 at 1035 °C (1900 °F). Source: Ref 9

This nitrogen absorption provides significant strengthening (Fig. 6). Upon completion of sintering, when the part enters the cooling zone of the furnace, the solubility of nitrogen decreases sharply with temperature (Fig. 23). As a result, Cr_2N begins to precipitate at the temperature at which the nitrogen content crosses the solubility limits. More important, below about 1150 °C (2100 °F), additional nitrogen is absorbed from the sintering atmosphere, leading to more Cr_2N precipitation and chromium depletion along the grain boundaries. The net result is inferior corrosion resistance due to grain-boundary corrosion.

The rate of this detrimental nitrogen absorption increases with decreasing part density and with decreasing dew point. A high dew point, however, leads to the problem of excessive oxidation. The basic relationship of this phenomenon is shown in Fig. 24. The data in Fig. 24, which were developed for the bright annealing of stainless steel in dissociated ammonia atmospheres, show the extent of nitrogen and oxygen absorption as a function of dew point. At high dew points (higher than about –37 °C, or –35 °F, depending on part size), the rate of oxidation is severe enough to produce a dull surface. At dew points of about –45 °C (–50 °F) or lower, nitrogen absorption increases so much that the corrosion resistance deteriorates because of excessive Cr_2N formation. Thus, optimum bright annealing of austenitic stainless steels must be done within a narrow dew-point range. Although Shay et al. (Ref 9) caution against applying these findings to sintered stainless steels, based on the unexplained higher nitrogen contents found for their parts sintered in dissociated ammonia, it should be noted that such higher nitrogen contents are expected on the basis of known solubility data for nitrogen in type 316L (Fig. 23), considering the differing methods of nitrogen analysis used.

Chromium nitride sensitization may in some cases be limited to a very shallow surface depth of the part. With very slow cooling, however, absorption and precipitation proceed toward the interior of the porous part. Figure 25 shows Cr_2N precipitates in the grain boundaries of parts that were sintered under conditions that produced nitrogen contents from 55 to 6650 ppm. Increasing nitrogen content correlates with increasing amounts of precipitation and

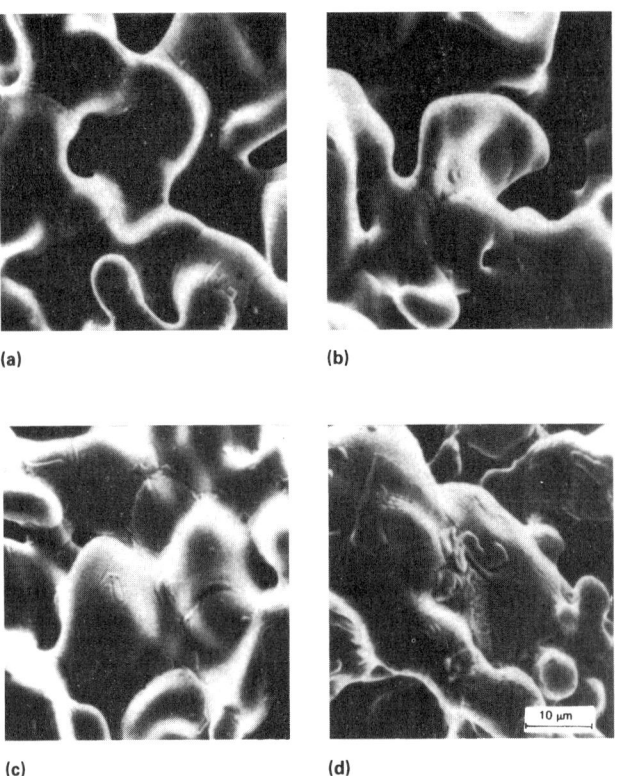

Fig. 25 Scanning electron micrographs of type 316L stainless steel. (a) Sintered 45 min in 100% H_2 at 1350 °C (2460 °F); 66 ppm N. (b) Sintered 45 min in 75% H_2 at 1350 °C (2460 °F); 3100 ppm N. (c) Sintered 45 min in 25% H_2 at 1350 °C (2460 °F); 4300 ppm N. (d) Sintered 45 min in 25% H_2 at 1150 °C (2100 °F); 6650 ppm N. The amount of intergranular precipitate increases with nitrogen content. Source: Ref 8

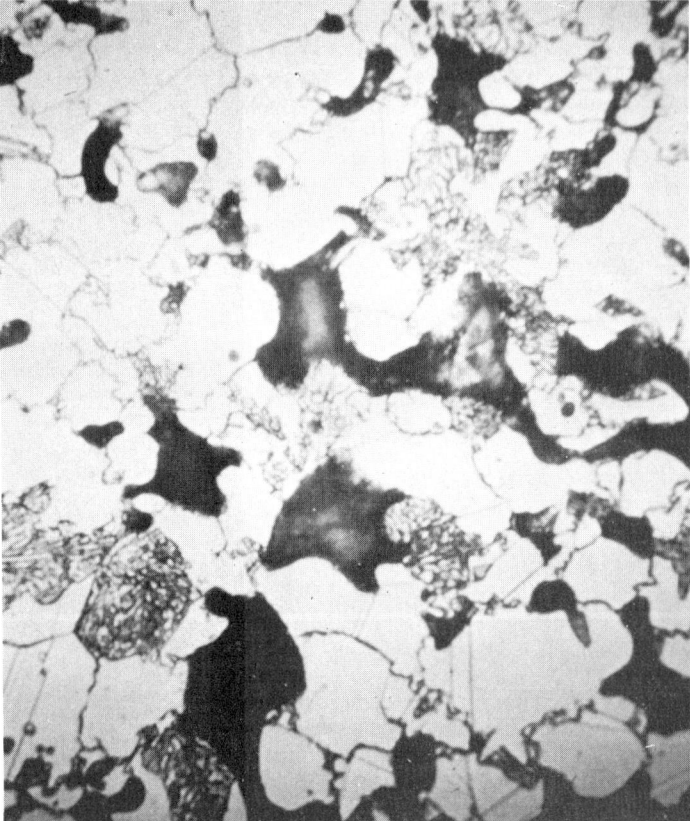

Fig. 26 Micrograph showing the lamellar structure of Cr_2N and low-chromium austenite in sintered type 316L that was slowly cooled in dissociated ammonia. Etched with Marble's reagent. 700x. Source: Ref 4

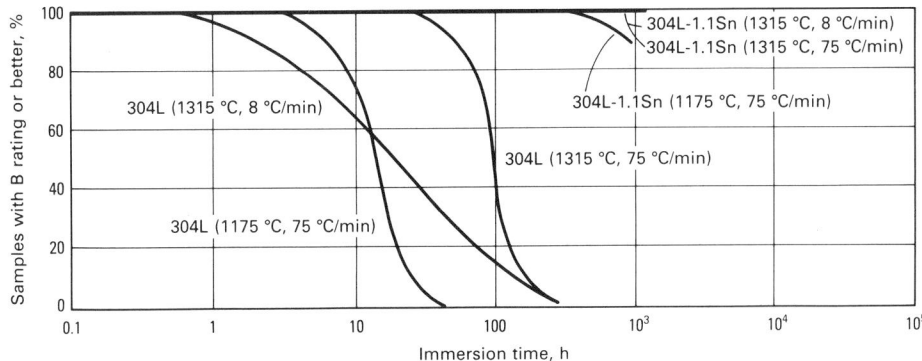

Fig. 27 Effect of composition, cooling rate, and sintering temperature on corrosion resistance of type 304L and tin-modified type 304L powder metallurgy stainless steels (sintered density 6.5 g/cm³, sintering atmosphere dissociated ammonia) in 5% aqueous NaCl. The "B" rating indicates that <1% of the specimen surface is covered by stain. Parenthetical values designate sintering temperature and cooling rate, respectively. Source: Ref 14

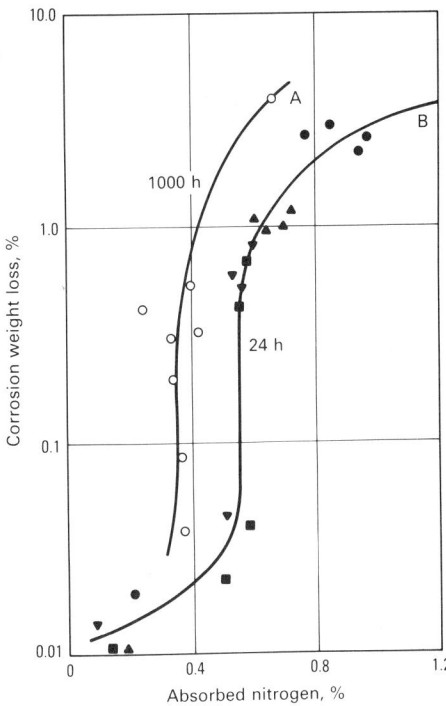

Fig. 28 Weight loss of austenitic stainless steel in 10% aqueous HNO_3 as a function of absorbed nitrogen content. Curve A: sintered in dissociated ammonia at 1150 °C (2100 °F) with a dew point of –43 °C (–45 °F). Density: 5.10 to 5.20 g/cm³. Curve B: sintered in various atmospheres with different dew points. Density: 5.2 to 5.8 g/cm³. Source: Ref 14

increasing localized corrosion. Figure 26 shows the microstructure of a type 316L part that was sintered in dissociated ammonia and cooled very slowly. Slow cooling produced a lamellar structure of Cr_2N and low-chromium austenite of very poor corrosion resistance.

Corrosion resistance data for sintered types 304L and 316L in NaCl solutions and in 10% HNO_3, reflecting the effect of Cr_2N precipitation, are shown in Fig. 19, 27, and 28. Figures 19 and 27 show that a higher sintering temperature, fast cooling rates (75 °C/min, or 135 °F/min, vs. 8 °C/min, or 14 °F/min), and the use of type 316L rather than type 304L provide better corrosion resistance. That these measures are beneficial follows directly from the austenite-nitrogen phase diagram (Fig. 23).

Figure 29 shows potentiodynamic corrosion curves for sintered type 316L in 10% HNO_3. The corrosion current density in the passive range increases and the corrosion potential decreases under conditions that promote Cr_2N precipitation, that is, lower sintering temperature, slower cooling rate, and high nitrogen concentration of the sintering atmosphere. Figure 30 is similar to Fig. 29 except that internal rather than external cross sections were used. The significantly lower corrosion currents of the internal surface confirm that Cr_2N precipitation is most severe on the surface of a sintered part.

Recently developed tin-containing (~1.0% Sn) grades of type 304L and 316L stainless steels have shown less sensitivity to nitride precipitation and correspondingly improved corrosion resistance (Fig. 19 and 27). The beneficial effect of tin has been confirmed in several studies (Ref 4, 5, 11, 14-17) and has been attributed to an enrichment of the surfaces of both the water-atomized powder and the sintered part with tin, presumably as a result of the low solubility of tin in solid stainless steel (Ref 5). Tin may also form stable acid-resistant passive films in a crevice and may cause cathodic surface poisoning, but its major beneficial effect is believed to lie in its formation of an effective barrier to nitrogen (and possibly also to oxygen) diffusion. This reduces the rate at which nitrogen is absorbed on the surface of the sintered part as it enters the cooling zone of the furnace. Auger composition depth profiles of regular and 1.5% tin-containing type 316L parts sintered in dissociated ammonia (Fig. 31) show that the presence of tin on the surface effectively suppresses nitrogen absorption. In addition, on the basis of potentiodynamic polarization tests in 10% HNO_3

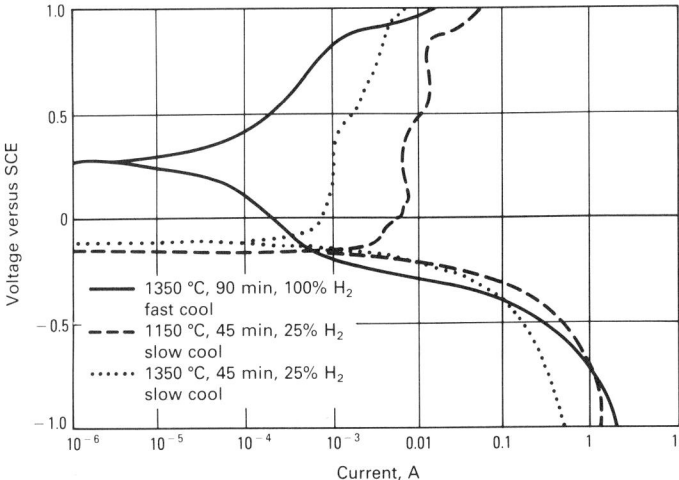

Fig. 29 Forward scan potentiodynamic corrosion curves for external surfaces of three sintered type 316L stainless steel samples in 10% HNO_3 at 25 °C (75 °F). Note the increasing corrosion currents in the range of 0 to 1 V and the decreasing corrosion potential with nitrogen additions to the atmosphere, slow cooling, and lower sintering temperatures. SCE, saturated calomel electrode. See also Fig. 30. Source: Ref 15

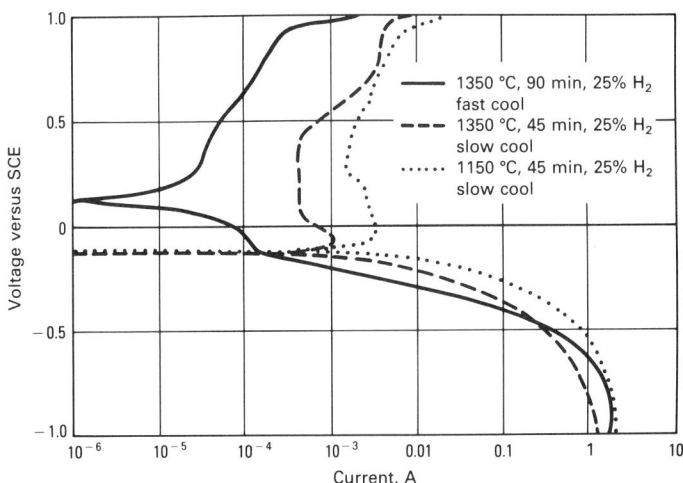

Fig. 30 Forward scan potentiodynamic corrosion curves of the internal microstructure (metallographic cross section) for type 316L stainless steel samples sintered in 25% H_2. Corrosion susceptibility in 10% HNO_3 at 25 °C (75 °F) increases with a lower sintering temperature and slow cooling. Cr_2N precipitation is most severe on the surface of a sintered part. See also Fig. 29. Source: Ref 15

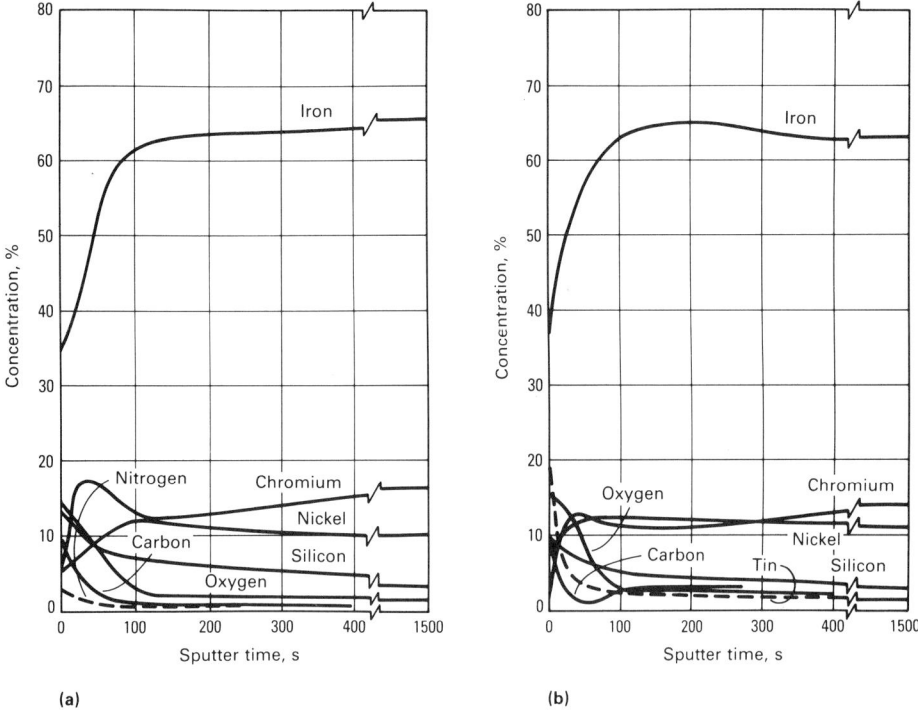

Fig. 31 Auger composition depth profiles of powder metallurgy type 316L stainless steel parts sintered in dissociated ammonia at 1175 °C (2150 °F). (a) Type 316L. (b) Tin-modified type 316L. Source: Ref 4

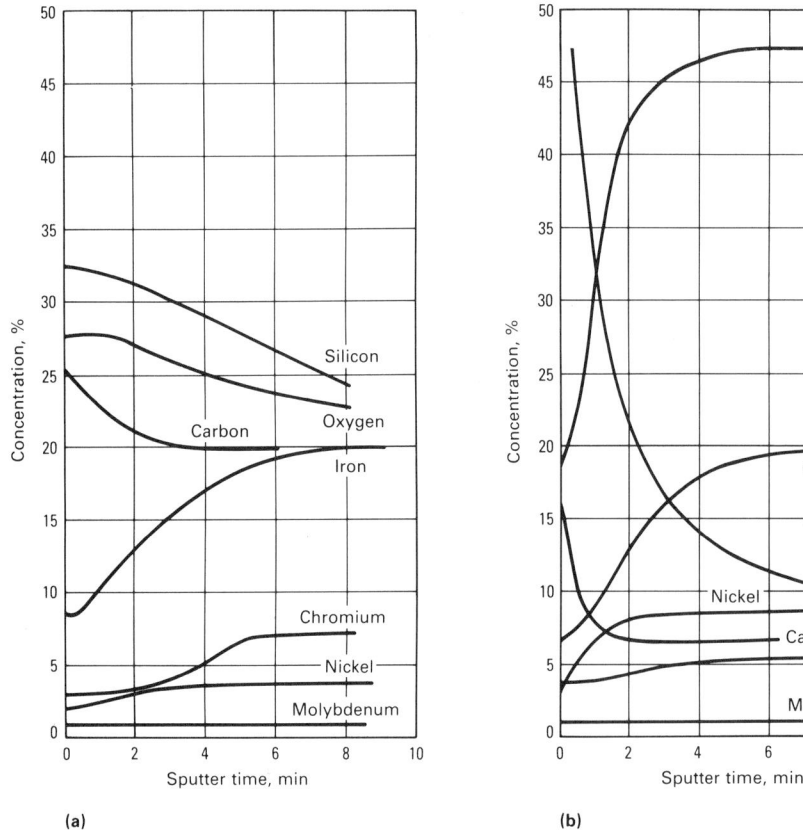

Fig. 32 Auger composition depth profiles of powder metallurgy type 316L stainless steel. (a) Green part. (b) Sintered part

and 5 N H$_2$SO$_4$, improvement in corrosion resistance has also been reported due to the presence of tin (Ref 15, 17).

The effect of oxygen on the corrosion resistance of sintered stainless steels is probably the most complex and least understood variable, for several reasons. First, commercial water-atomized compactible stainless steel powders have typical oxygen contents of about 2000 ppm or more. Although much of this oxygen resides on the surfaces of individual powder particles as oxidized silicon (Fig. 32a), the exact nature and distribution of the oxides depend on atomizing conditions. Second, with typical industrial sintering practice, the reduction of these oxides remains incomplete and depends on many process parameters. Lastly, as a sintered part enters the cooling zone of the furnace, certain elements will oxidize upon reaching the temperature for the oxide-metal equilibrium of the high-oxygen-affinity elements (Fig. 33). Thus, a sintered part still reflects the history of its powdermaking process, compaction, and sintering. Figure 32(b) shows the Auger composition depth profile of a type 316L part after sintering in hydrogen at 1260 °C (2300 °F). It is apparent that much of the oxidized silicon present in the green part has become reduced and that severely depleted chromium has been replenished.

An empirical correlation between the saltwater corrosion resistance of sintered type 316L and the oxygen content of the sintered parts suggests that sintering conditions resulting in lower oxygen contents provide better corrosion resistance (Fig. 34). With excessive dew points (> –34 °C, or –30 °F), the oxygen content of a sintered part may increase considerably. The microstructure (Fig. 35) of such a part shows a lack of particle bonding (compare with Fig. 21a for low oxygen content), and its mechanical strength and corrosion resistance are both inferior.

For optimum corrosion resistance, it appears that the following precautions are beneficial:

- Use of a powder with low-oxygen content
- Sintering conditions that ensure a high degree of oxide removal
- Fast cooling through the high-temperature range after sintering

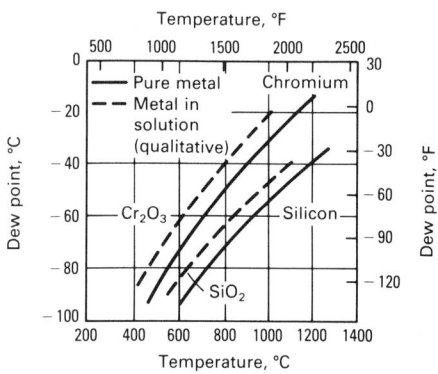

Fig. 33 Redox curves for chromium and silicon alone and in solution. Source: Ref 4

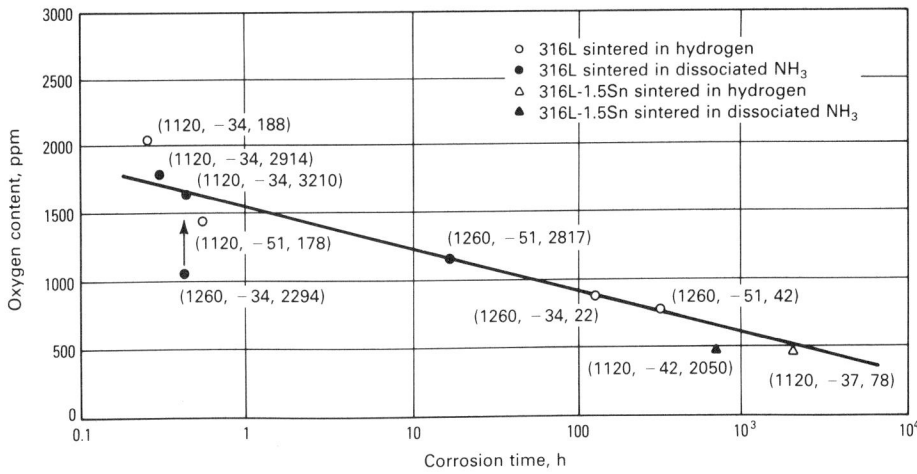

Fig. 34 Effect of oxygen content on corrosion resistance of sintered type 316L and tin-modified type 316L (sintered density 6.65 g/cm³, cooling rate: 75 °C/min, or 135 °F/min). Parenthetical values are sintering temperature (°C), dew point (°C), and nitrogen content (ppm), respectively. Time indicates when 50% of specimens showed first sign of corrosion in 5% aqueous NaCl. Source: Ref 5

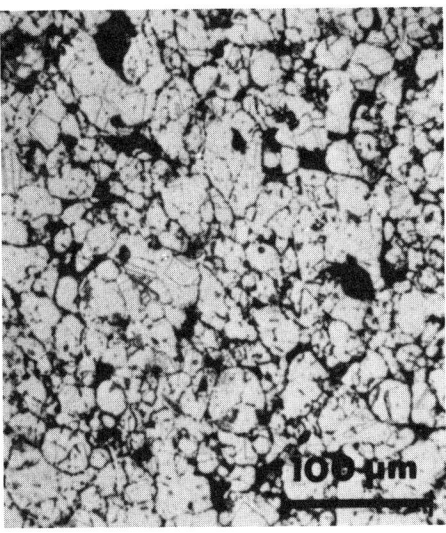

Fig. 35 Microstructure of type 316L stainless steel sintered in a high-dew-point atmosphere. Oxygen content 5100 ppm, sintered density 7.5 g/cm³. Etched with Marble's reagent. 200×. Source: Ref 4

Cooling in a hydrogen atmosphere should be done with a water vapor content of less than 50 ppm (Ref 7). Cooling in a nitrogen-containing atmosphere should be done with a dew point between about –37 and –45 °C (–35 and –50 °F) (Ref 9).

Effect of Sintered Density. Applications of sintered stainless steels cover a wide density spectrum. Low densities of about 5 g/cm³ may be typical of filters, but densities of 6.5 g/cm³ or greater are typical of structural parts. It is therefore of interest to know the effect of density on corrosion resistance. Corrosion studies of sintered austenitic stainless steels have shown that corrosion resistance improves significantly with increasing density in acidic environments, such as dilute sulfuric acid (H_2SO_4), hydrochloric acid (HCl), and HNO_3. Figure 36 illustrates this behavior for three austenitic stainless steels (18Cr-11Ni to 18Cr-14Ni) that were vacuum sintered 1 h at 1150 and 1250 °C (2100 and 2280 °F) and tested in boiling 40% HNO_3.

For saline solutions, some investigators have found the effect of increasing density to be beneficial (Ref 15), whereas others have found it to be detrimental (Ref 5, 11, 18). This lack of agreement is perhaps not surprising considering that concentration changes in several of the critical variables, such as oxygen, carbon, and nitrogen, also depend on the density of a part. It should be noted, however, that the positive relationship between density and corrosion resistance was derived from short-term potentiodynamic polarization measurements (Ref 15), whereas the negative relationships were all derived from longer-term salt immersion tests.

Table 6 summarizes recent results on the effect of density on the salt corrosion resistance (immersion in 5% aqueous NaCl) of vacuum-sintered type 316L parts. Unlike sintering in a reducing atmosphere, vacuum sintering does not lower the oxygen content with decreasing density. Thus, an improvement in corrosion resistance with de-

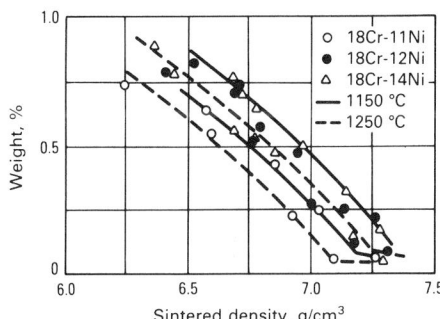

Fig. 36 Relationship between sintered density and weight decrease of three austenitic stainless steels in 40% HNO_3 solution. Source: Ref 18

Table 6 Effect of density on corrosion performance of vacuum-sintered type 316L stainless steel

Compacting pressure		Sintering temperature		Sintering time, min	Sintered density, g/cm³	Median pore size of pore volume(a)	Corrosion rating(b) for four specimens, each immersed in 5% aqueous NaCl, h											
MPa	tsi	°C	°F				1	3	19	27	46	91	140	210	314	380	558	525
276	20	1205	2200	45	5.67	9	A	A	A	A	A	B	B	B	A	B	B	B
							A	A	A	B	B	B	B	B	B	B	B	C
							A	A	B	B	B	B	B	B	B	B	C	C
							A	A	B	B	B	B	B	B	C	C	C	C
552	40	1205	2200	45	6.53	5	A	B	B	B	C	C	D	...	...	...	...	...
							A	B	...	B	B	C	C	C	D	...	...	...
							A	A	B	B	C	C	C	C	D	...	...	...
							A	A	B	C	C	C	C	D	...	...	...	...
276	20	1315	2400	45	5.86	8	A	A	A	A	B	B	B	B	B	B	B	B
							A	A	A	A	B	B	B	B	B	B	B	B
							A	A	A	A	B	B	B	B	B	B	B	B
							A	A	A	A	B	B	B	B	B	B	B	B
552	40	1315	2400	45	6.57	5	A	A	B	B	B	B	B	C	C	C	D	...
							A	A	B	C	C	C	C	D	...	...	...	...
							A	A	B	C	C	C	C	D	...	...	...	...
							A	A	A	A	B	B	B	C	C	D	...	...

(a) Determined by mercury porosimetry. (b) A, sample free from any corrosion; B, ≤1% of surface covered by stain; C, 1 to 25% of surface covered by stain with slight corrosion product; D, >25% of surface covered by stain with heavy corrosion product

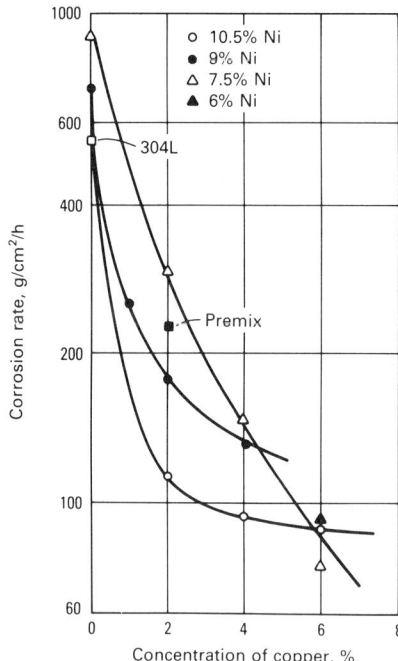

Fig. 37 Effect of nickel and copper additions on the corrosion rate of sintered austenitic stainless steel compacts exposed to boiling H_2SO_4 for 6 h. Relative sintered density is 88%. Source: Ref 12

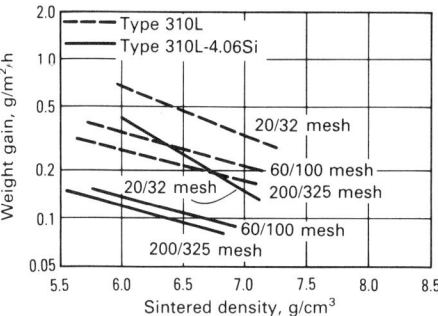

Fig. 38 Weight gain vs. sintered density curves for materials prepared from powders of various particle sizes. Parts were sintered 1 h at 1250 °C (2280 °F). Source: Ref 19

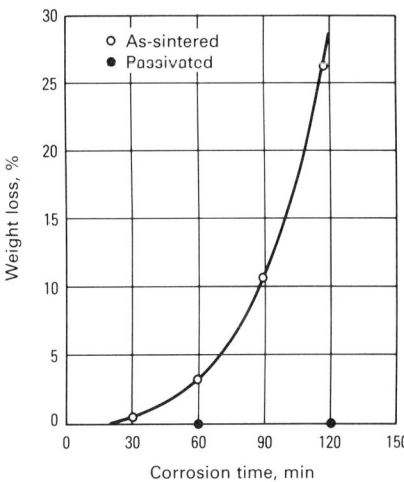

Fig. 39 Relationship between weight loss and corrosion time of vacuum-sintered type 304L stainless steel in 5% H_2SO_4

creasing density, as shown in Table 6, should not be attributed to a lower oxygen content, but is perhaps better explained in terms of reduced crevice corrosion as a result of the improved circulation of the corrodent through large pores (Ref 4). The average pore diameters of the parts pressed at the lower compacting pressures (Table 6), as measured by mercury porosimetry, were 60 to 80% larger than the size of the pores of the higher-density parts. The standard deviations of the pore size distributions were similar and were around 2. Therefore, sintered stainless steel parts with densities from about 60 to 90% of theoretical have average pore sizes from about 10 to 2 or 3 μm that are likely to affect the circulation of the corrodent and thus its resistance to crevice corrosion.

Effect of Copper Additions to Type 304L. One study found that the corrosion resistance of copper-containing type 304L vacuum-sintered parts (1 h at 1200 °C, or 2190 °F; 88% dense) improved with increasing copper content (Ref 12). Figure 37 shows the weight loss of the parts kept for 6 h in boiling 5% H_2SO_4. Higher nickel content is also beneficial. Salt spray testing for 24 h with 5% NaCl solution resulted in almost no pitting. The effect of copper in P/M stainless steels is said to be identical to that observed in cast stainless steels.

Oxidation Resistance. Sintered stainless steels are not widely used for elevated-temperature service. Thus, information on elevated-temperature oxidation resistance is scarce.

For type 310L stainless steel parts that were vacuum sintered 1 h at 1250 °C (2280 °F), Fig. 38 shows the weight gain in air at 700 °C (1290 °F) as a function of sintered density, mesh size of powder used, and sintering temperature. This initial weight

gain did not always show a parabolic course of oxidation. Within the density range studied, oxidation increased almost exponentially with decreasing density. Silicon-modified (4.06% Si) type 310L stainless steel showed weight gains that were less than 50% of those of regular type 310L. The increased oxidation of the parts made from the finer powder fraction is due to their large internal surface area. Higher sintering temperature and higher compacting pressure (higher densities) reduce surface porosity and specific pore surface area, thus lessening internal oxidation through early pore closure. The maximum recommended operating temperature for sintered austenitic stainless steels is 700 °C (1290 °F).

Higher-Alloyed Stainless Steels. Although the common stainless steel grades used in industry have maximum chromium and nickel contents of 20 and 14%, respectively (Table 1), higher-alloyed stainless steels have been used in the past to obtain improved corrosion resistance. Such steels are available from powder producers. In one investigation, a high-nickel/chromium/molybdenum austenitic stainless steel P/M material (SS-100) performed comparably to wrought type 216, 316, or 317 in 16 h salt solution immersion tests (Ref 20).

Other Approaches to Improving the Corrosion Resistance of Sintered Stainless Steels. If the corrosion resistance of sintered stainless steel parts remains inadequate after composition and process optimization, passivation and coating treatments are sometimes used. Chemical and thermal passivation treatments for sintered type 316L, effective in dilute H_2SO_4, are described in Ref 21. Chemical passivation with HNO_3 solutions similar to those applied to wrought stainless steels is not suitable for every material. On the basis of rest potential measurements of sintered type 316L, thermal passivation by heating the sintered parts for 20 to 30 min in air at temperatures of 400 to 500 °C (750 to 930 °F) is recommended.

In another study, the corrosion resistance of vacuum-sintered type 304L (6.9 g/cm³) in 5% H_2SO_4 was improved by activating the parts in a mixture of 13 to 15% HNO_3, 2% hydrofluoric acid (HF), and 0.3% HCl, followed by passivation for 30 min in 30% HNO_3 at 70 °C (160 °F) (Ref 22). After testing for 2 h in 5% H_2SO_4 (Fig. 39), the passivated specimens showed no weight loss,

whereas the as-sintered specimens rapidly lost weight and turned the solution green. In addition, Ref 23 describes a phosphate-based passivating treatment for sintered stainless steels that is effective in acetic acid.

Improvement of the corrosion resistance of sintered stainless steel through the use of chromium diffusion coatings is discussed in Ref 24. The chromium was applied onto sintered stainless steel parts by pack cementation. In such situations considerable infilling of the pores with chromium takes place; pores 50 μm thick with diameters of up to 50 μm may become sealed. Immersion of coated and uncoated specimens in 5 and 10% H_2SO_4 solutions for 168 h at room temperature showed significant attack of the uncoated specimens and no noticeable attack of the coated specimens. Electrochemical testing in 5% H_2SO_4 gave similar results, and a 3% salt spray test at room temperature showed many local sites of corrosion for the uncoated specimen and no corrosion after 250 h for the coated specimen. Sealing or coating of the pores of a sintered stainless steel part with an organic resin (Ref 20) is sometimes recommended, but performance data proving the effectiveness of this treatment are lacking.

High-Density P/M Stainless Steels

As stated in the introduction to this article, high-density (full-density) P/M stainless steels are those with densities approaching or reaching 100% of theoretical density. Processing methods used to achieve such density levels include hot isostatic pressing (HIPing), a combination of cold isostatic pressing (CIPing) and hot extrusion, and metal injection molding (MIM). Each of these processes and the resulting properties of high-density stainless steels will be briefly described below.

Hot Isostatic Pressing. Manufacturing processes used to produce HIPed parts from nitrogen-atomized stainless steel powders (Fig. 2) consist of the following steps. A shaped container pre-

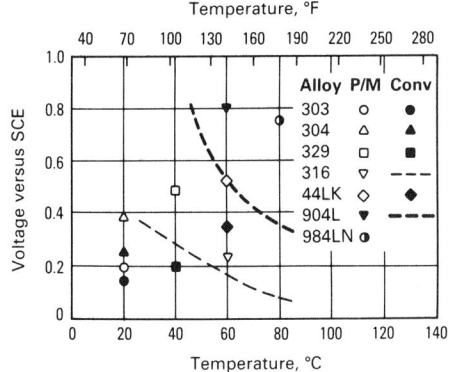

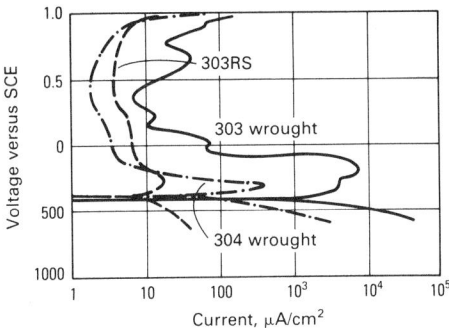

Alloy	— Nominal composition, % —					
	C(max)	Fe	Cr	Ni	Mo	Others
303........	0.10	rem	18	8.5	...	...
304........	0.05	rem	18.5	8.5	...	...
329........	0.05	rem	26	5	1.5	...
316........	0.05	rem	17	11.5	2.2	...
44LK......	0.03	rem	25	6	1.6	...
904L......	0.02	rem	20	25	4.5	Cu
984LN.....	0.05	rem	20	33	2.2	Cu,N

Fig. 40 Comparison of pitting resistance of powder metallurgy and conventional stainless steels. Source: Ref 26

Fig. 41 Potentiodynamic polarization curves for conventional type 303 and 304 stainless steels and for rapidly solidified type 303 in deaerated 1 M H$_2$SO$_4$ at 30 °C (85 °F). Source: Ref 29

pared from low-carbon steel sheet is carefully cleaned and filled with stainless steel powder. The container is then vacuum outgassed and sealed to maintain a vacuum in the container. Hot isostatic pressing of the powder-filled container to full density is then accomplished. Typical temperatures are 1100 to 1200 °C (2000 to 2200 °F), and typical pressures are 100 to 150 MPa (15 to 20 ksi). Argon is used as the pressure medium. Heat treatment, inspection of the near-net-shape part, and machining to final shape complete the manufacturing sequence. The carbon steel container is removed by machining or acid pickling. More detailed information on HIPing can be found in the article " Hot Isostatic Pressing" in Volume 7 of the *ASM Handbook.*

A variety of HIPed duplex stainless steel parts have been produced for off-shore applications (Ref 25). For HIPed UNS S31803 (22Cr-5Ni-3Mo-0.15N) used for such applications, ultimate tensile strengths range from 750 to 770 MPa (109 to 112 ksi), yield strengths range from 520 to 570 MPa (75 to 83 ksi), and elongations range from 29 to 31%. Corrosion properties are similar to conventionally processed wrought alloys.

Cold Isostatic Pressing Plus Hot Extrusion. Since the 1980s, seamless stainless steel tubes for offshore applications have been produced from gas-atomized powders. The P/M method is said to offer a competitive alternative to conventional production methods due to (Ref 26):

- Efficient use of raw materials
- Low energy consumption
- Short total production time
- High flexibility (less material in process; short delivery times)
- The ability to make difficult compositions

The process consists of cold isostatic compaction of the encapsulated nitrogen-atomized powder, followed by heating to the extrusion temperature and hot extrusion. The capsule material is removed by decladding. Standard grades include most of the common austenitic stainless steels as well as some superaustenitic, duplex, and ferritic stainless steels.

In comparison to conventional material, the CIPed-and-extruded P/M products possess a more homogeneous structure with reduced microsegregation due to the rapid cooling of the powder particles. Also, the grain size is somewhat finer, slag inclusions (particularly sulfides) are smaller, and the nitrogen content is somewhat higher (900 vs. 500 ppm for wrought type 316).

Attributed to the above differences are slightly higher yield strength and tensile strength (Table 7) without a loss in elongation. Mechanical properties at elevated temperatures are practically identical to those of conventionally produced materials. The impact toughness of the P/M material, although good, is lower than that of conventional material when tested in the longitudinal direction. Creep strength is similar to that of conventional material.

No difference between P/M and conventional material has been found regarding the resistance to intergranular corrosion according to practice C and practice E of ASTM A 262 (Ref 27). Figure 40 shows that the resistance to pitting attack, as measured by the pitting corrosion breakthrough potential, is superior for several P/M grades compared to those of the corresponding conventional grades. Table 8 gives the general and selective corrosion information from tests according to ASTM A 262, practice C (Ref 27) for 724L (17.5Cr-14Ni-2.7Mo) and 725LN (25Cr-22Ni-2.2 Mo plus nitrogen) austenitic P/M grades. The improved corrosion resistance of the P/M grades is attributed to their lower segregation rate, their finer and more uniform distribution of inclusions, and their finer grain size.

The enhancement of the corrosion resistance of stainless steel parts made from rapidly solidified powders has been confirmed by several investigators. For example, the significantly superior oxidation resistance of type 303 stainless steel, made by extrusion of rapidly solidified powder, was attributed to the elevated-temperature grain-growth-inhibiting effect of uniformly dispersed manganese sulfide (MnS) particles (Ref 28). Figure 41 shows that this material maintains its good corrosion performance in aqueous environments, and potentiodynamic polarization curves in 1 M H$_2$SO$_4$ indicate that the P/M material exhibits the lowest corrosion rate at the corrosion potential. Finally, although wrought type 303 was highly susceptible to pitting, the P/M alloy showed no obvious pits on the surface

Table 7 Typical mechanical properties of cold-worked and annealed stainless steel tubes cold isostatically pressed and hot extruded from powders

Grade	Type(a)	Number of samples	Yield strength, 0.2% offset		Tensile strength		Elongation, %
			MPa	ksi	MPa	ksi	
Type 304L	C	84	302	44	582	84	57
	P/M	18	325	47	609	88	58
Type 304	C	133	321	46	600	87	57
	P/M	72	350	51	660	96	55
Type 316L	C	90	319	46	604	88	53
	P/M	128	336	49	632	92	52
Type 316	C	134	306	44	584	85	54
	P/M	125	346	50	649	94	51
Type 940L	C	49	334	48	651	94	45
	P/M	112	382	55	681	99	43

(a) C, conventional production; P/M, powder metallurgy. Source: Ref 26

Table 8 Huey test (ASTM A 262, practice C) corrosion data for two powder metallurgy cold isostatically pressed and hot extruded stainless steels

Grade	Number of samples	Corrosion rate, μm/48 h		Selective attack, μm	
		Average	Specific	Average	Specific
Type 725LN	14	0.57-0.69	1.5 max	<50	100 max
Type 724L	14	1.48-1.79	3.3 max	<30	200 max

Source: Ref 26

and only a low pit density within the material. The pits were related to the presence of sulfide stringers in the wrought material, from which it was concluded that P/M steels with lower sulfur contents and with spherical sulfide morphology, such as type 304 and 316, might exhibit improved pitting resistance.

Metal Injection Molding (MIM) Technology. When 60 vol% of fine (average particle size ~10 μm) metal powder is blended with 40 vol% lubricant and binder, the resulting mixture can be injection molded, much like a conventional plastic (Ref 30, 31). Any shape that can be molded in plastic can be molded in metal powder. The use of paraffin waxes and thermoplastics such as polyethylene or polypropylene provides the rheological basis for allowing the mixture to flow around corners and into undercuts in a way that is impossible in the uniaxial pressing of binder-free metal powders. An alternative process uses methylcellulose as a binder, along with small amounts of water, glycerine, and boric acid. The methylcellulose dissolves in cold water to form a binder.

Individual process steps in injection molding are selection and production of metal powders, mixing of metal powder and binder, molding, debinding, and sintering. Debinding, perhaps the most critical step in the injection molding sequence, is accomplished by solvent extraction/thermal degradation in a two-step process or by a one-step thermal debinding process. The latter is carried out in microprocessor-controlled single-stage vacuum furnaces to evaporate and thermally remove all binders and lubricants from injection molded parts. Stainless steel compacts are debinderized in hydrogen atmospheres. The time taken from molding to produce debinderized compacts can range from 15 to 55 h, depending on the cross section thickness/weight of the parts (Ref 32). The injection-molded parts are then sintered at temperatures of 1100 to 1300 °C (2000 to 2400 °F).

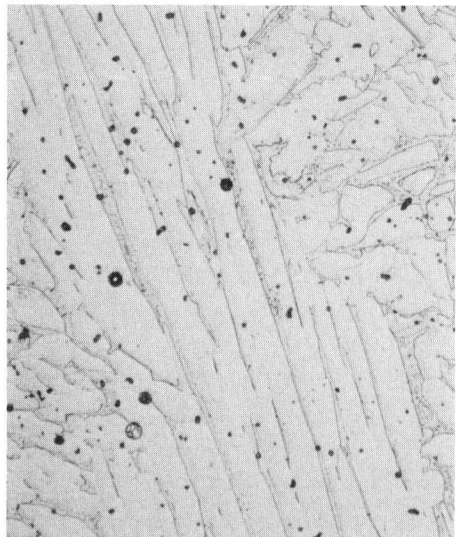

Fig. 42 Microstructure of injection-molded 17-4 PH stainless steel showing rounded porosity typical of injection-molded materials. 200×. Courtesy of J.R. Merhar, Parmatech Corp.

The 60% dense as-molded parts shrink 14 to 20% during sintering and achieve near-full density (>95% dense). Injection-molded parts are limited to section sizes of 9.5 to 13 mm (0.375 to 0.5 in.) and have tolerances of ±0.003 mm/mm (±0.003 in./in.).

Sintering to near-full density gives excellent toughness, elongation, and other dynamic properties. This is aided by the presence of fine spheroidized porosity versus the sharp, stress-raiser porosity of conventional P/M parts. Figure 42 shows the rounded porosity in an injection-molded 17-4 PH stainless steel.

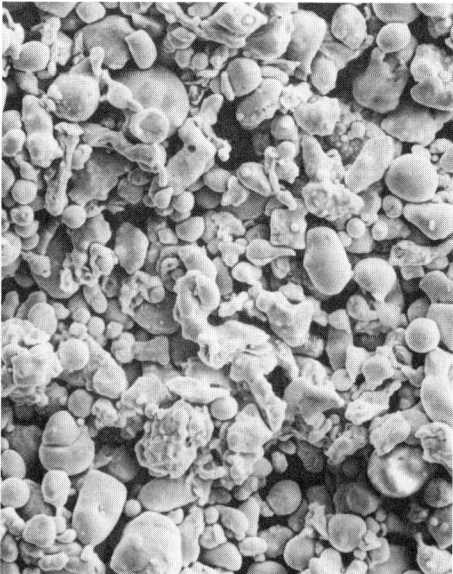

Particle size, μm(a)	Percent finer
62	100
44	99-100
31	90-100
22	78-88
16	55-75
11	32-53
5.5	7-16
3.9	2-6

(a) Obtained using a Microtrac particle size analyzer

Fig. 43 Water-atomized 17-4 PH stainless steel metal injection molding powder. Such powders have apparent densities ranging from 2.30 to 2.90 g/cm^3 and tap densities of 3.50 to 4.50 g/cm^3. The particle size distribution is listed in the accompanying table. Courtesy of J.H. Reinshagen, Ametek Specialty Metal Products Division

Table 9 Compositions of standard (MPIF) injection-molded stainless steels

| MPIF designation | Composition, wt%(a) | | | | | | | |
	Fe	Ni	Cr	Mo	C	Cu	Nb + Ta	Other(b)
MIM-316L	rem	10.0-14.0	16.0-18.0	2.0-3.0	0.03	...	...	2.0
MIM-Duplex (316L)	rem	7.5-8.5	19.0-21.0	1.5-2.5	0.03	...	...	2.0
MIM-17-4 PH	rem	3.0-5.0	15.5-17.5	...	0.07	3.0-5.0	0.15-0.45	2.0

MPIF, Metal Powder Industries Federation. (a) Single values are maximum values unless otherwise stated. (b) Other elements not specified in standard. Source: MPIF Standard 35, "Materials Standards for Metal Injection Molded Parts" (1993-1994 edition)

Table 10 Minimum and typical properties for standard (MPIF) injection-molded stainless steels

| Material designation/condition | Minimum values | | | | | Typical values | | | | | Density, g/cm^3 | Apparent hardness |
| | Ultimate strength | | 0.2% yield strength | | Elongation in 25 mm (1 in.), % | Ultimate strength | | 0.2% yield strength | | Elongation in 25 mm (1 in.), % | | |
	MPa	ksi	MPa	ksi		MPa	ksi	MPa	ksi			
MIM-316L, as-sintered	448	65	138	20	40	517	75	172	25	50	7.6	67 HRB
MIM-Duplex, as-sintered	469	68	179	26	33	538	78	228	33	43	7.6	84 HRB
MIM-17-4 PH, as-sintered	793	115	648	94	4	896	130	731	106	6	7.5	27 HRC
MIM-17-4 PH, solution treated and aged	1069	155	965	140	4	1186	172	1089	158	6	7.5	33 HRC

MPIF, Metal Powder Industries Federation. MIM, metal injection molding. Source: MPIF Standard 35, "Materials Standards for Metal Injection Molded Parts" (1993-1994 edition)

Fig. 44 Dental bracket components made from injection-molded stainless steel. These parts weigh 0.040 to 0.20 g. Courtesy of Parmatech Corp.

Stainless steel powders that are most commonly injection molded include austenitic, duplex, and precipitation-hardening grades. These powders are either water atomized (Fig. 43) or are mixtures of gas-atomized and water-atomized materials. Compositions and properties of standardized injection-molded stainless steels are listed in Tables 9 and 10, respectively. In addition to these standard grades, type 410 martensitic stainless steel is also injection molded. Typical properties for injection-molded type 410 in the heat-treated condition are:

- *Density:* 7.4 to 7.5 g/cm^3
- *Tensile strength:* 1172 to 1213 MPa (170 to 176 ksi)
- *Yield strength:* 917 to 965 MPa (133 to 140 ksi)
- *Elongation:* 5 to 7%
- *Hardness:* 35 to 47 HRC

Applications for injection-molded stainless steels include dental bracket components (Fig. 44), disk drive components, firing pins, blades for crimping/cutting tools used for telephone terminal wire connections, and assorted automotive components.

ACKNOWLEDGMENTS

The information in this article is largely taken from:

- E. Klar, Corrosion of Powder Metallurgy Materials, *Corrosion,* Vol 13, *ASM Handbook* (formerly 9th ed., *Metals Handbook*), ASM International, 1987, p 823-845
- R.W. Stevenson, P/M Stainless Steels, *Powder Metallurgy,* Vol 7, *ASM Handbook* (formerly 9th ed., *Metals Handbook*), ASM International, 1984, p 728-732
- L.F. Pease, Ferrous Powder Metallurgy Materials, *Properties and Selection: Irons, Steels, and High-Performance Alloys,* Vol 1, *ASM Handbook* (formerly 10th ed., *Metals Handbook*), ASM International, 1990, p 801-821

REFERENCES

1. E. Klar, M. Svilar, C. Lall, and H. Tews, Corrosion Resistance of Austenitic Stainless Steels Sintered Commercial Furnaces, *Advances in Powder Metallurgy and Particulate Materials,* Vol 5, Metal Powder Industries Federation, 1992, p 411-426
2. C.B. Thompson, Lubrication of Metal Powders, *Powder Metallurgy,* Vol 7, *ASM Handbook* (formerly 9th ed., *Metals Handbook*), ASM International, 1984, p 190-193
3. S. Shah, P. Samal, and E. Klar, "Properties of 410-L P/M Stainless Steel Antilock Brake Sensor Rings," Technical Paper 930449, SAE International, March 1993, p 1-11
4. M.A. Pao and E. Klar, Corrosion Phenomena in Regular and Tin-modified P/M Stainless Steels, *Progress in Powder Metallurgy,* H.S. Nayar, S.M. Kaufman, and K.E. Meiners, Ed., Metal Powder Industries Federation, 1984, p 431-444
5. D. Ro and E. Klar, Corrosive Behavior of P/M Austenitic Stainless Steels, *Modern Developments in Powder Metallurgy,* Vol 13, H.H. Hausner and P.W. Taubenblat, Ed., Metal Powder Industries Federation, 1980, p 247-287
6. R.L. Sands, G.F. Bidmead, and D.A. Oliver, The Corrosion Resistance of Sintered Stainless Steels, *Modern Developments in Powder Metallurgy,* Vol 2, H.H. Hausner, Ed., Plenum Press, 1966, p 73-85
7. H.S. Nayar, R.M. German, and W.R. Johnson, The Effect of Sintering on the Corrosion Resistance of 316L Stainless Steel, *Progress in Powder Metallurgy,* Vol 37, Metal Powder Industries Federation, 1981, p 255-265
8. G. Lei, R.M. German, and H.S. Nayar, Influence of Sintering Variables on the Corrosion Resistance of 316L Stainless Steel, *Powder Metall. Int.,* Vol 15 (No. 2), 1983, p 70-76
9. R.H. Shay, T.L. Ellison, and K.R. Berger, Control of Nitrogen Absorption and Surface Oxidation of Austenitic Stainless Steels in H-N Atmospheres, *Progress in Powder Metallurgy,* Vol 39, H.S. Nayar, S.M. Kaufman, and K.E. Meiners, Ed., Metal Powder Industries Federation, 1983, p 411-430
10. K.H. Moyer, The Burn-Off Characteristics of Common Lubricants in 316L Powder Compacts, *Int. J. Powder Metall.,* Vol 7 (No. 3), 1971, p 33-43
11. S.K. Chatterjee, M.E. Warwick, and D.J. Maykuth, The Effect of Tin, Copper, Nickel, and Molybdenum on the Mechanical Properties and Corrosion Resistance of Sintered Stainless Steel (AISI 304L), *Modern Developments in Powder Metallurgy,* Vol 16, E.N. Aqua and C.I. Whitman, Ed., Metal Powder Industries Federation, 1984, p 277-293
12. T. Kato, K. Kusaka, and T. Hisada, Influence of Cu Addition on Some Properties of SUS 304L Stainless Steel Powders, *Denki Seiko (Electro. Furn. Steel),* Vol 51 (No. 4), Nov 1980, p 252-263
13. A.J. Sedriks, *Corrosion of Stainless Steels,* John Wiley & Sons, 1979, p 15
14. M.A. Pao and E. Klar, *On the Corrosion Resistance of P/M Austenitic Stainless Steels,* Proceedings of the International Powder Metallurgy Conference (Florence, Italy), Associazone Italiano di Metallurgia, 1982
15. G. Lei, R.M. German, and H.S. Nayar, Corrosion Control in Sintered Austenitic Stainless Steels, *Progress in Powder Metallurgy,* Vol 39, H.S. Nayar, S.M. Kaufman, and K.E. Meiners, Ed., Metal Powder Industries Federation, 1984, p 391-410
16. K. Kusaka, T. Kato, and T. Hisada, Influence of S, Cu, and Sn Additions on the Properties of AISI 304L Type Sintered Stainless Steel, *Modern Developments in Powder Metallurgy,* Vol 16, E.N. Aqua and C.I. Whitman, Ed., Metal Powder Industries Federation, 1984, p 247-259
17. D. Itzhak and S. Harush, The Effect of Sn Addition on the Corrosion Behaviour of Sintered Stainless Steel in H$_2$SO$_4$, *Corros. Sci.,* Vol 25 (No. 10), 1985, p 883-888
18. F.M.F. Jones, The Effect of Processing Variables on the Properties of Type 316L Powder Compacts, *Progress in Powder Metallurgy,* Vol 30, Metal Powder Industries Federation, 1970, p 25-50
19. T. Kato and K. Kusaka, On Some Properties of Sintered Stainless Steels at Elevated Temperatures, *Powder Metall.,* Vol 27 (No. 5), July 1980, p 2-8
20. O.W. Reen and G.O. Hughes, Evaluating Stainless Steel Powder Metal Parts, *Precis. Met.,* Vol 35 (No. 8), Aug 1977, p 53-54
21. M.H. Tikkanen, Corrosion Resistance of Sintered P/M Stainless Steels and Possibilities for Increasing It, *Scand. J. Metall.,* Vol 11, 1982, p 211-215
22. T. Takeda and K. Tamura, Compacting and Sintering of Chrome-Nickel Austenitic Stainless Steel Powders, H.B. Trans. 8311 from *Powder and Powder Metallurgy* (Japan), Vol 17 (No. 2), 1970, p 70-76
23. T.J. Treharne, "Corrosion Inhibition in Sintered Stainless Steel," U.S. Patent 4,536,228, 20 Aug 1985
24. A. Kempster, J.R. Smith, and C.C. Hanson, "Chromium Diffusion Coatings on Sintered Stainless Steel," Metal Powder Report, MPR Publishing Services Ltd., England, June 1986, p 455-460
25. M. Lindenmo, P/M-HIP Produced Components of Duplex Stainless Steels for Offshore and Other Demanding Applications, *Duplex Stainless Steels '91,* Vol 2, Editions de Physique, 1992, p 1289-1296

26. C. Tornberg, "The Manufacture of Seamless Stainless Steel Tubes from Powder," Paper 8410-013, presented at the 1984 ASME International Conference on New Developments in Stainless Steel Technology (Detroit, MI), American Society of Mechanical Engineers, 1984, p 1-6

27. "Standard Practices for Detecting Susceptibility to Intergranular Attack in Austenitic Stainless Steels," A 262, *Annual Book of ASTM Standards,* ASTM

28. G.S. Yurek, D. Eisen, and A.J. Garrat-Reed, *Metall. Trans. A,* Vol 13A, 1982, p 473

29. P.C. Searson and R.M. Latanision, The Corrosion and Oxidation Resistance of Iron- and Aluminum-Based Powder Metallurgical Alloys, *Corros. Sci.,* Vol 25 (No. 10), 1985, p 947-968

30. R.L. Billiet, Net-Shape Full Density P/M Parts by Injection Molding, *International Journal of Powder Metallurgy and Technology*, Vol 21 (No. 2), 1985, p 119-129

31. L.F. Pease, Metal Injection Molding: The Incubation Is Over, *International Journal of Powder Metallurgy*, Vol 24 (No. 2), 1988, p 123-127

32. B. Williams, Parmatech Shapes Metals Like Plastic, *Metal Powder Report*, Vol 44 (No. 10), Oct 1989, p 1-5

Stainless Steel Cladding and Weld Overlays

A STAINLESS-STEEL-CLAD metal or alloy is a composite product consisting of a thin layer of stainless steel in the form of a veneer integrally bonded to one or both surfaces of the substrate. The principal object of such a product is to combine, at low cost, the desirable properties of the stainless steel and the backing material for applications where full-gage alloy construction is not required. While the stainless cladding furnishes the necessary resistance to corrosion, abrasion, or oxidation, the backing material contributes structural strength and improves the fabricability and thermal conductivity of the composite. Stainless-steel-clad metals can be produced in plate, strip, tube, rod, and wire form.

The principal cladding techniques include hot roll bonding, cold roll bonding, explosive bonding, centrifugal casting, brazing, and weld overlaying, although adhesive bonding, extrusion, and hot isostatic pressing have also been used to produce clad metals. With casting, brazing, and welding, one of the metals to be joined is molten when a metal-to-metal bond is achieved. With hot/cold roll bonding and explosive bonding, the bond is achieved by forcing clean oxide-free metal surfaces into intimate contact, which causes a sharing of electrons between the metals. Gaseous impurities diffuse into the metals, and nondiffusible impurities consolidate by spheroidization. These non-melting techniques involve some form of deformation to break up surface oxides, to create metal-to-metal contact, and to heat in order to

accelerate diffusion. They differ in the amount of deformation and heat used to form the bond and in the method of bringing the metals into intimate contact.

This article will review each of the processes commonly associated with stainless-steel-clad metal systems as well as the stainless steels used. Design considerations and the welding of stainless-steel-clad carbon and low-alloy steels are also addressed. Additional information can be found in Ref 1 to 3.

Hot Roll Bonding (Ref 3)

The hot roll bonding process, which is also called *roll welding,* is the most important commercially because it is the major production method for stainless-clad steel plates. Hot roll bonding accounts for more than 90% of the clad plate production worldwide (Ref 1). It is known also as the *heat and pressure process* because the principle involves preparing the carefully cleaned cladding components in the form of a pack or sandwich, heating to the plastic range, and bringing the stainless and backing material into intimate contact, either by pressing or by rolling. A product so formed is integrally bonded at the interface. The clad surface is in all respects (corrosion resistance, physical properties, and mechanical properties) the equal of the parent stainless steel. It can be polished and worked in the same manner as solid stainless steel.

Table 1 lists the clad combinations that have been commercially produced on a large scale. As this table indicates, stainless steels can be joined to a variety of ferrous and nonferrous alloys. On a tonnage basis, however, the most common clad systems are carbon or low-alloy steels clad with 300-series austenitic grades. The types of austenitic stainless steel cladding commonly available in plate forms are:

- Type 304 (18-8)
- Type 304 L (18-8 low carbon)
- Type 309 (25-12)
- Type 310 (25-20)
- Type 316 (17-12 Mo)
- Type 316 Cb (17-12 Nb stabilized)
- Type 316 L (17-12 Mo low carbon)
- Type 317 (19-13 Mo)
- Type 317 L (19-13 Mo low carbon)
- Type 321 (18-10 Ti)
- Type 347 (18-11 Nb)

The carbon or low-alloy steel/stainless steel plate rolling sequence is normally followed by heat treatment, which is usually required to restore the cladding to the solution-annealed condition and to bring the backing material into the correct heat-treatment condition. Table 2 lists typical mill heat treatments.

The cladding thickness is normally specified as a percentage of the total thickness of the composite plate. It varies from 5 to 50%, depending on the end use. For most commercial applications in-

Table 1 Selected dissimilar metals and alloys that can be roll bonded (hot or cold) into clad-laminate form

Base metal No. 1/No. 2	Weldability rating(a)																		
	Ag	Al	Al alloys	Au	Carbon steel	Co	Cu	Mn	Mn-Ni	Nb	Ni	Pt	Stainless steel	Steel	Sn	Ta	Ti	U	Zr
Ag	...	...	...	...	...	...	A	B	...	...	...	...	...	B	...	...	...	...	...
Al	...	...	A	C	B	C	B	...	...	...	B	...	B	...	...	...	...	...	C
Alfesil	D	D	D	D	D	D	D	D	D	D	D	D	D	D	D	D	D	D	D
Be	D	D	D	D	D	D	D	D	D	D	D	D	D	D	D	D	D	D	D
Carbon steel	...	B	...	...	...	...	...	...	...	...	...	...	B	...	...	...	B	...	...
Cu	A	B	...	A	...	...	...	B	B	B	A	B	B	A	A	B	B	...	B
Mn	B	...	...	...	...	...	B	...	...	...	A	B	...	...	...	...	...	...	...
Ni	...	B	...	A	...	...	A	...	...	...	...	B	...	B	A	...	...	...	...
Nb	...	...	...	...	...	...	B	...	...	...	...	...	...	...	...	B	...	...	...
Stainless steel	...	B	...	...	B	...	B	...	...	...	...	...	...	...	...	...	B	...	B
Steel	B	...	...	...	...	...	A	...	...	...	B	...	...	...	...	...	...	...	B
U	...	...	...	...	...	...	...	...	...	...	...	...	...	...	...	...	...	...	B

(a) A, easy to weld; B, difficult but possible to weld; C, impractical to weld; D, impossible to weld. Source: Ref 2

Table 2 Typical mill heat treatments for stainless clad carbon and low-alloy steels

Type of cladding material	Type of ASTM-grade backing material	Heat treatment(a)
304, 304L, 309, 310, 316, 316Cb, 316L, 317, 321, or 347	A285, A201, A212 (up to 50 mm, or 2 in., gage)	Anneal 1065 to 1175 °C (1950 to 2150 °F), air quench
304L, 316L, 316Cb, 317L, 321, or 347	A201, A 212 (over 50 mm, or 2 in., gage)	Anneal 1065 to 1175 °C (1950 to 2150 °F), air quench, normalize 870 to 900 °C (1600 to 1650 °F) 1 hr per 25 mm (1 in.) thickness, air quench(b)
304, 304L, 309, 310, 316, 316Cb, 316L, 317, 321, or 347	A204, A 302 (up to 50 mm, or 2 in., gage)	Anneal 1065 to 1175 °C (1950 to 2150 °F), air quench
304L, 316L, 316Cb, 317L, 321, or 347	A204, A 302 (over 50 mm, or 2 in., gage). A301 (all gages)	Anneal 1065 to 1175 °C (1950 to 2150 °F), air quench, normalize 870 to 900 °C (1600 to 1650 °F) 1 hr per 25 mm (1 in.) thickness, air quench(b)

(a) Heat treatments listed are generally correct for the material combinations shown. Deviations may be made to meet specific requirements. Procedure selected will be one favorable for both cladding and backing material. (b) Stabilized or low-carbon types of stainless steel should be used when this double heat treatment is involved. Source: Ref 3

volving carbon or low-alloy steel/stainless steel combinations, cladding thickness generally falls in the 10 to 20% range.

Hot roll bonding has also been used to clad high-strength low-alloy (HSLA) steel plate with duplex stainless steels (Ref 4, 5). The microalloyed base metals contain small amounts of copper (0.15% max), niobium (0.03% max), and nitrogen (0.010% max) and have mechanical properties comparable to those of duplex stainless steels. Typically these HSLA base metals have yield strengths of 500 MPa (72.5 ksi) and impact values of 60 J (44 ft·lbf) at –60 °C (–75 °F). The shear strength of the cladding bond can be as high as 400 MPa (58 ksi).

Other metals and alloys commonly roll bonded to stainless steels include aluminum, copper, and nickel. Table 3 lists properties and applications of roll-bonded clad laminates.

Cold Roll Bonding

The cold roll bonding process, which is shown schematically in Fig. 1, involves three basic steps:

- The mating surfaces are cleaned by chemical and/or mechanical means to remove dirt, lubricants, surface oxides, and any other contaminants.
- The materials are joined in a bonding mill by rolling them together with a thickness reduction that ranges from 50 to 80% in a single pass. Immediately afterwards, the materials have an incipient, or green, bond created by the massive cold reduction.
- The materials then undergo sintering, a heat treatment during which the bond at the interface is completed. Diffusion occurs at the atomic level along the interface and results in a metallurgical bond that is due to a sharing of atoms between the materials. The resulting bond can exceed the strength of either of the parent materials.

Upon completion of this three-step process, the resultant clad material can be treated in the same way as any other conventional monolithic metal. The clad material can be worked by any of the traditional processing methods for strip metals. Rolling, annealing, pickling, and slitting are typically performed to produce the finished strip to specific customer requirements, so that the material can be roll formed, stamped, or drawn into the required part.

Clad steels prepared by this method show substantially the same microstructures as those that have been bonded by hot roll bonding processes. Because of the high power requirement in the initial reduction, the cold bonding process is not practical for producing clad plates of any appreciable size.

The single largest application for cold-roll-bonded materials is stainless-steel-clad aluminum for automotive trim (Table 3 and Fig. 2) (Ref 6). The stainless steel exterior surface provides corrosion resistance, high luster, and abrasion and dent resistance, and the aluminum on the inside provides sacrificial protection for the painted auto body steel and for the stainless steel.

Explosive Bonding (Ref 1)

Explosive bonding uses the very-short-duration, high-energy impulse of an explosion to drive two surfaces of metal together, simultaneously cleaning away surface oxide films and creating a metallic bond. The two surfaces do not collide instantaneously but rather progressively over the in-

Table 3 Typical properties of roll-bonded stainless steel

Materials system	Composite ratio, %	Thickness mm	Thickness in.	Width mm	Width in.	Tensile strength MPa	Tensile strength ksi	Yield strength MPa	Yield strength ksi	Elongation, %	Applications
Type 434 stainless/5052 aluminum	40:60	0.56-0.76	0.022-0.030	≤610	≤24	395	57	360	52	12	Widely used for automotive body moldings, drip rails, rocker panels, and other trim components, often replacing solid stainless steel or aluminum. Stainless steel provides bright appearance; the hidden aluminum base provides cathodic protection, corroding sacrificially to the body steel.
C1008 steel/type 347 stainless steel/C1008 steel	45:10:45	0.36	0.014	305	12	393	57	195	28	35	Used in hydraulic tubing in vehicles, replacing terne-coated carbon steel tubing. The outer layer of carbon steel cathodically protects the stainless core of the tube, extending its life significantly.
Nickel 201/type 304 stainless steel/nickel 201	7.5:85:7.5	0.20-2.41	0.008-0.095	25-64	1-2.5	…	…	310	45	40	Used in formed cans for transistor and button cell batteries, replacing solid nickel at a lower cost
Copper 10300/type 430 stainless steel/copper 10300	17:66:17, 20:60:20, 33:34:33	0.10-0.15	0.004-0.006	12.7-150	0.5-6	415(a)	60(a)	275	40	20(a)	Replaces heavier gages of copper and bronze in buried communications cable. The stainless steel provides resistance to gnawing by rodents, which is a serious problem in underground installations.

(a) 20/60/20 three-layer laminate. Source: Ref 2

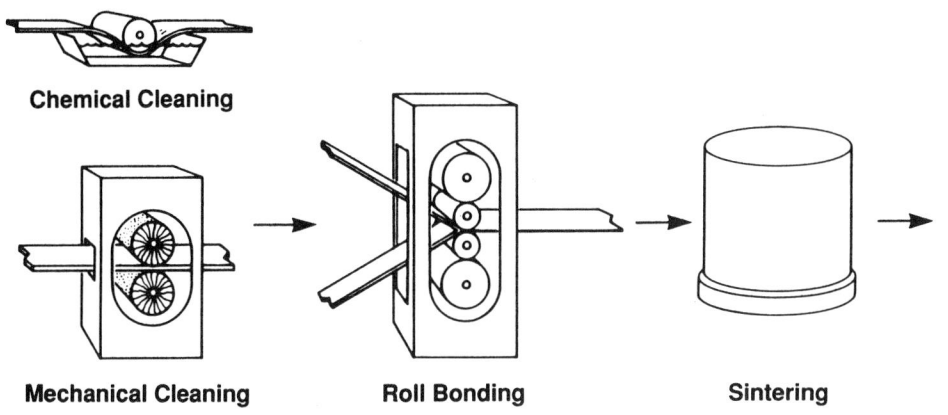

Chemical Cleaning

Mechanical Cleaning   **Roll Bonding**   **Sintering**

Fig. 1   Process steps in cold roll bonding

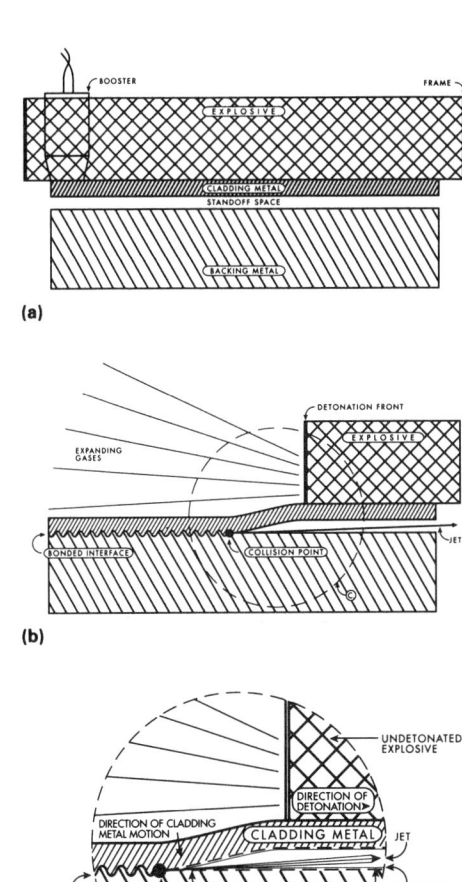

(a)

(b)

(c)

Fig. 4   Parallel-plate explosion welding process. (a) Explosion-cladding assembly before detonation. (b) Explosion-cladding assembly during detonation. (c) Closeup of (b) showing mechanism for jetting away the surface layer from the parent layer

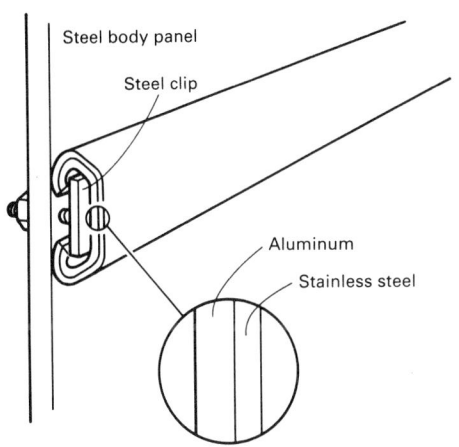

Fig. 2   Stainless-steel-clad aluminum automotive trim provides sacrificial corrosion protection to the auto body while maintaining a bright corrosion-resistant exterior surface.

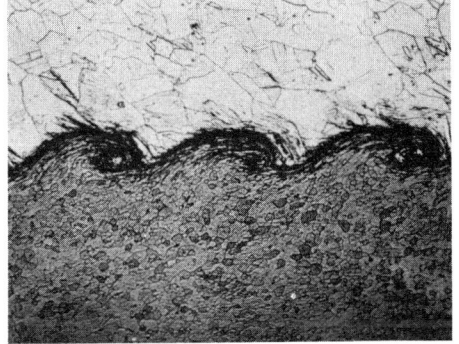

Fig. 3   Bond zone pattern typical of explosion-clad metals. Materials are type 304L stainless steel and medium-carbon steel. 20×

terface area. The pressure generated at the resulting collision front is extreme and causes plastic deformation of the surface layers. In this way, the surface layers and any contaminating oxides present are removed in the form of a jet projected ahead of the collision front. This leaves perfectly clean surfaces under pressure to form the bond. Figure 3 illustrates the wavy interface that characterizes most explosive bonds.

Two basic geometric configurations of the explosive bonding process are commonly used: angle bonding and parallel-plate bonding. Angle bonding is normally used for bonding sheet components and tubes, where the required bond width does not exceed 20 times the flyer plate thickness. The more commonly used parallel-plate geometry (Fig. 4) is applicable for welding larger flat areas, plate, and concentric cylinders.

The energy of bonding typically creates sufficient deformation that flattening or straightening is required prior to further processing. Flattening is performed with equipment of the same design used in plate and sheet manufacture.

Explosive bonding is an effective joining method for virtually any combination of metals.

The only metallurgical limitation is sufficient ductility and fracture toughness to undergo the rapid deformation of the process without fracture. Generally accepted limits are 10% and 30 J (22 ft·lbf) minimum, respectively. Figure 5 lists the combinations that are useful in industry. More detailed information on explosive bonding is available in Ref 7 to 9.

Centrifugal Casting (Ref 1)

An entirely different approach to clad seamless pipe production uses horizontal centrifugal casting technology. First, well-refined molten steel is poured into a rotating metal mold with flux. After casting, the temperature of the outer shell is monitored. At a suitable temperature after solidification the molten stainless steel is introduced. The selection of the flux, the temperature of the outer shell when the molten stainless steel is introduced, and the pouring temperature of the stainless steel are the most important factors in achieving a sound metallurgical bond. By controlling these various parameters it is possible to achieve minimum mixing at the interface and maintain homogenous cladding thickness and wall thickness.

Centrifugal casting is followed by heat treatment to solution anneal the cladding and quench and tem-

per the outer pipe to achieve the required mechanical properties. Finally, the pipe is machined externally and internally to remove the shallow interdendritic porosity in the bore and achieve the required dimensions and surface finish.

Centrifugal cast pipe is available with the outer steel made of API 5L X52, X60, or X65 grades and internal cladding made of type 316L stainless steel. Sizes range from 100 to 400 mm (4 to 16 in.) in diameter, wall thickness from 10 to 90 mm (0.4 to 3.5 in.) (minimum 3 mm, or 0.12 in. cladding), and lengths typically from 4 to 5 m (13 to 16 ft), with longer lengths above 200 mm (8 in.) in diameter.

Brazing

In furnace brazing, the stainless steel cladding and the backing material, in their respective final gages, are assembled as a multilayer sandwich, with a brazing alloy placed between each pair of surfaces to be bonded. The sandwich is heated under continuous vacuum to a temperature at which

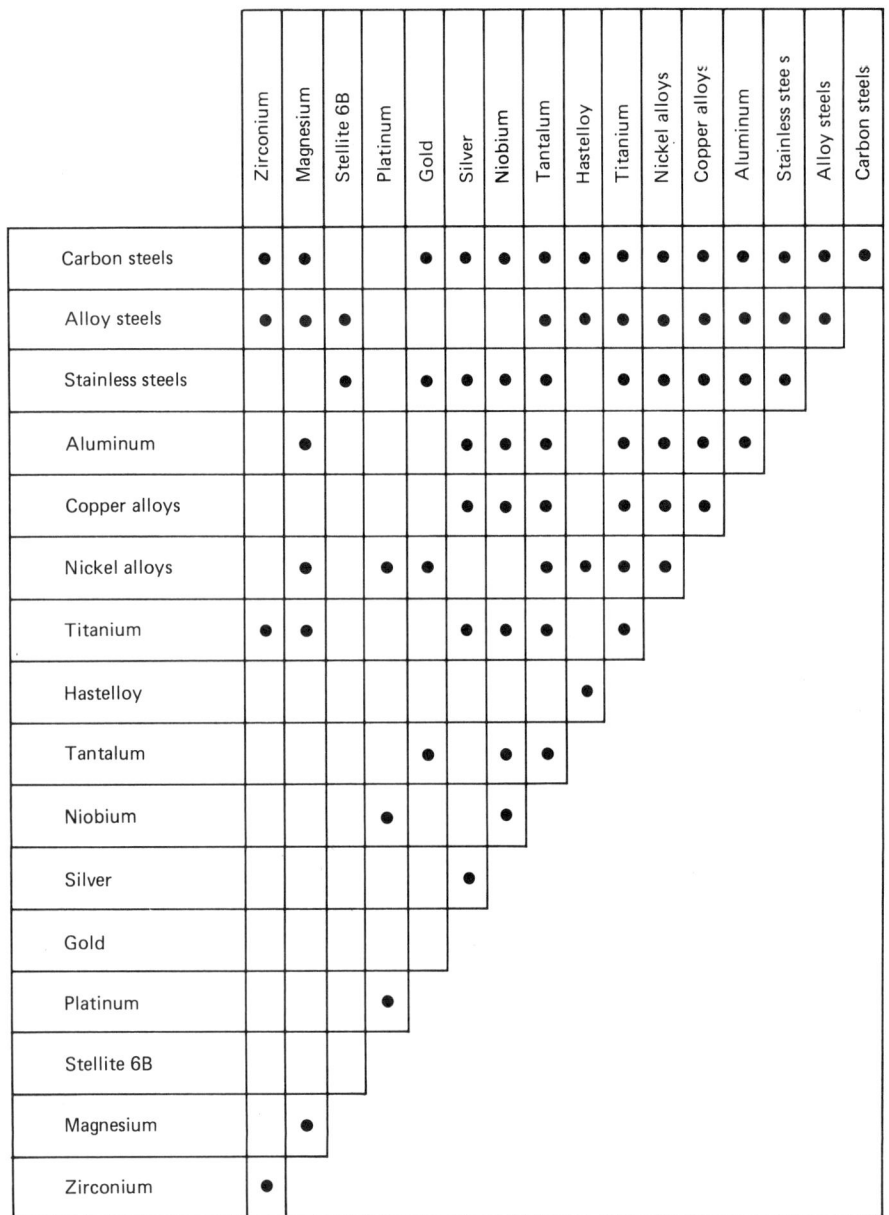

Fig. 5 Commercially available explosion-clad metal combinations

	Zirconium	Magnesium	Stellite 6B	Platinum	Gold	Silver	Niobium	Tantalum	Hastelloy	Titanium	Nickel alloys	Copper alloys	Aluminum	Stainless steels	Alloy steels	Carbon steels
Carbon steels	•	•			•	•	•	•	•	•	•	•	•	•	•	•
Alloy steels	•	•	•				•	•	•	•	•	•	•	•	•	
Stainless steels			•		•	•	•	•		•	•	•	•	•		
Aluminum		•				•	•	•		•	•	•	•			
Copper alloys						•	•	•			•	•				
Nickel alloys		•		•	•			•	•	•	•					
Titanium	•	•				•	•	•		•						
Hastelloy									•							
Tantalum					•		•	•								
Niobium				•			•									
Silver						•										
Gold																
Platinum				•												
Stellite 6B																
Magnesium		•														
Zirconium	•															

the brazing alloy liquefies and forms an intermetallic alloying zone at the interface of the stainless and backing material (normally carbon steels). A wide range of brazing filler metals can be used to join stainless steels to carbon or low-alloy steels. The most commonly used are silver-base alloys. More detailed information on brazing of stainless steels can be found in the article "Brazing, Soldering, and Adhesive Bonding" in this Volume.

Weld Overlays

Weld overlaying refers to the deposition of a filler metal on a base metal (substrate) to impart some desired property to the surface that is not intrinsic to the underlying base metal. There are several types of weld overlays: weld claddings, hardfacing materials, buildup alloys, and buttering alloys.

A weld clad is a relatively thick layer of filler metal applied to a carbon or low-alloy steel base metal for the purpose of providing a corrosion-resistant surface. Hardfacing is a form of weld surfacing that is applied for the purpose of reducing wear, abrasion, impact, erosion, galling, or cavitation. The term *buildup* refers to the addition of weld metal to a base metal surface for the restoration of the component to the required dimensions. Buildup alloys are generally not designed to resist wear, but to return the worn part back to, or near, its original dimensions, or to provide adequate support for subsequent layers of true hardfacing materials. Buttering also involves the addition of one or more layers of weld metal to the face of the joint or surface to be welded. It differs from buildup in that the primary purpose of buttering is to satisfy some metallurgical consideration. It is used primarily for the joining of dissimilar metal base metals, as described in the section "Welding Austenitic-Stainless-Clad Carbon or Low-Alloy Steels" in this article. An extensive review of the weld processes and materials associated with weld overlays can be found in the article "Hardfacing, Weld Cladding, and Dissimilar Metal Joining," in Volume 6 of the *ASM Handbook* (Ref 10).

Weld Cladding

The term *weld cladding* usually denotes the application of a relatively thick layer (≥3 mm, or $^1/_8$ in.) of weld metal for the purpose of providing a corrosion-resistant surface. Hardfacing produces a thinner surface coating than a weld cladding and is normally applied for dimensional restoration or wear resistance. Typical base metal components that are weld-cladded include the internal surfaces of carbon and low-alloy steel pressure vessels, paper digesters, urea reactors, tubesheets, nuclear reactor containment vessels, and hydrocrackers. The cladding material is usually an austenitic stainless steel or a nickel-base alloy. Weld cladding is usually performed using submerged arc welding. However, flux-cored arc welding (either self-shielded or gas-shielded), plasma arc welding, and electroslag welding can also produce weld claddings. Figure 6 compares deposition rates obtainable with different welding processes. Filler metals are available as covered electrodes, coiled electrode wire, and strip electrodes. For very large areas, strip welding with either submerged arc or electroslag techniques is the most economical. Table 4 lists some of the filler metals for stainless steel weld claddings.

Application Considerations. Weld cladding is an excellent way to impart properties to the surface of a substrate that are not available from that of a base metal, or to conserve expensive or difficult-to-obtain materials by using only a relatively thin surface layer on a less expensive or abundant base material. Several inherent limitations or possible problems must be considered when planning for weld cladding. The thickness of the required surface must be less than the maximum thickness of the overlay that can be obtained with the particular process and filler metal selected.

Welding position also must be considered when selecting an overlay material and process. Certain processes are limited in their available welding positions (e.g., submerged arc welding can be used only in the flat position). In addition, when using a high-deposition-rate process that exhibits a large liquid pool, welding vertically or overhead may be difficult or impossible. Some alloys exhibit eutectic solidification, which leads to large molten pools that solidify instantly, with no "mushy" (liquid plus solid) transition. Such materials are also difficult to weld except in the flat position.

Dilution Control. The economics of stainless steel weld cladding are dependent on achieving the specific chemistry at the highest practical deposition rate in a minimum number of layers. The fabricator selects the filler wire and welding process, whereas the purchaser specifies the sur-

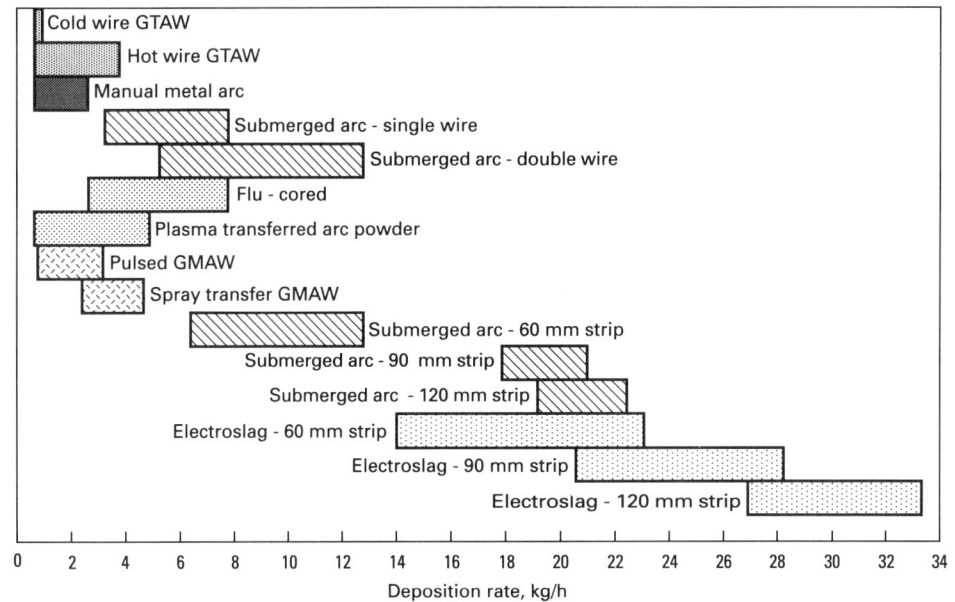

Fig. 6   Comparison of deposition rates for various weld cladding processes. To obtain equivalent deposition rates in pounds per hour, multiply the metric value by 2.2. Source: Ref 1

face chemistry and thickness, along with the base metal. The most outstanding difference between welding a joint and depositing an overlay is the percentage of dilution:

$$\% \text{ dilution} = \frac{x}{x+y} \times 100$$

where x is the amount of base metal melted and y is the amount of filler metal added.

For stainless steel cladding, a fabricator must understand how the dilution of the filler metal with the base metal affects the composition and metallurgical balance, such as the proper ferrite level to minimize hot cracking, absence of martensite at the interface for bond integrity, and

carbon at a low level to ensure corrosion resistance. The prediction of the microstructures and properties (such as hot cracking and corrosion resistance) for the austenitic stainless steels has been the topic of many studies. During the last two decades, four microstructure prediction diagrams have found the widest application. These include the Schaeffler diagram, the DeLong diagram, and the Welding Research Council (WRC) diagrams (WRC-1988 and WRC-1992). Each of these is described in Ref 10 and the article "Welding" in this Volume.

Although each weld cladding process has an expected dilution factor, experimenting with the welding parameters can minimize dilution. A value between 10 and 15% is generally considered opti-

mum. Less than 10% raises the question of bond integrity, and greater than 15% increases the cost of the filler metal. Unfortunately, most welding processes have considerably greater dilution.

Because of the importance of dilution in weld cladding as well as hardfacing applications, each welding parameter must be carefully evaluated and recorded. Many of the parameters that affect dilution in weld cladding applications are not so closely controlled when arc welding is performed:

- *Amperage*: Increased amperage (current density) increases dilution. The arc becomes hotter, it penetrates more deeply, and more base metal melting occurs.
- *Polarity*: Direct current electrode negative (DCEN) gives less penetration and resulting lower dilution than direct current electrode positive (DCEP). Alternating current results in a dilution that lies between that provided by DCEN and DCEP.
- *Electrode size*: The smaller the electrode, the lower the amperage, which results in less dilution.
- *Electrode extension*: A long electrode extension for consumable electrode processes decreases dilution. A short electrode extension increases dilution.
- *Travel speed*: A decrease in travel speed decreases the amount of base metal melted and increases proportionally the amount of filler metal melted, thus decreasing dilution.
- *Oscillation*: Greater width of electrode oscillation reduces dilution. The frequency of oscillation also affects dilution: The higher the frequency of oscillation, the lower the dilution.
- *Welding position*: Depending on the welding position or work inclination, gravity causes the weld pool to run ahead of, remain under, or run behind the arc. If the weld pool stays ahead of or under the arc, less base metal penetration and resulting dilution will occur. If the pool is too far ahead of the arc, there will be insuffi-

Table 4   Stainless steel filler metals for weld cladding applications

Weld overlay type	First layer		Subsequent layers	
	Covered electrode(a)	Bare rod or electrode(b)	Covered electrode(a)	Bare rod or electrode(b)
304	E309	ER309	E308	ER308
304L	E309L E309Cb	ER309L	E308L	ER308L
321	E309Cb	ER309Cb	E347	ER347
347	E309Cb	ER309Cb	E347	ER347
309	E309	ER309	E309	ER309
310	E310	ER310	E310	ER310
316	E309Mo	ER309Mo	E316	ER316
316L	E309MoL E317L	E309MoL ER317L	E316L	ER316L
317	E309Mo E317	ER309Mo ER317	E317	ER317
317L	E309MoL E317L	ER309MoL ER317L	E317L	ER317L
20 Cb	E320	ER320	E320	ER320

Note: Columbium (Cb) is also referred to as niobium (Nb). (a) Refer to AWS specification A5.4. (b) Refer to AWS specification A5.9.

Fig. 7   Weld cladding of a 1.8 m (6 ft) inner diameter pressure vessel shell with 50 mm (2 in.) wide, 0.64 mm (0.025 in.) thick stainless steel strip. Courtesy of J.J. Barger, ABB Combustion Engineering

Fig. 8 Closeup view of the 25 mm (1 in.) wide by 0.64 mm (0.025 in.) thick stainless steel strip used to clad a 300 mm (12 in.) inner diameter pressure vessel nozzle. Courtesy of J.J. Barger, ABB Combustion Engineering

Hardfacing Alloys

Hardfacing materials include a wide variety of alloys, carbides, and combinations of these alloys. Conventional hardfacing alloys are normally classified as carbides (WC-Co), nickel-base alloys, cobalt-base alloys, and ferrous alloys (high-chromium white irons, low-alloy steels, austenitic manganese steels, and stainless steels). Stainless steel hardfacing alloys include martensitic and austenitic grades, the latter having high manganese (5 to 10%) and/or silicon (3 to 5%) contents. As will be described below, both cobalt-containing and cobalt-free austenitic stainless steel hardfacing alloys have been developed.

Hardfacing alloy selection is guided primarily by wear and cost considerations. However, other manufacturing and environmental factors must also be considered, such as base metal; deposition process; and impact, corrosion, oxidation, and thermal requirements. Usually, the hardfacing process dictates the hardfacing or filler metal product form.

Hardfacing alloys usually are available as bare rod, flux-coated rod, long-length solid wires, long-length tube wires (with and without flux), or powders. The most popular processes, and the forms most commonly associated with each process, are:

Hardfacing process	Consumable form
Oxyfuel/oxyacetylene (OFW/OAW)	Bare cast or tubular rod
Shielded metal arc (SMAW)	Coated solid or tubular rod (stick electrode)
Gas-tungsten arc (GTAW)	Bare cast or tubular rod
Gas-metal arc (GMAW)	Tubular or solid wire
Flux-cored open arc	Tubular wire (flux cored)
Submerged arc (SAW)	Tubular or solid wire
Plasma transferred arc (PTA)	Powder
Laser beam	Powder

cient melting of the surface of the base metal, and coalescence will not occur.

- *Arc shielding*: The shielding medium, gas or flux, also affects dilution. The following list ranks various shielding mediums in order of decreasing dilution: granular flux without alloy addition (highest), helium, carbon dioxide, argon, self-shielded flux-cored arc welding, and granular flux with alloy addition (lowest).
- *Additional filler metal*: Extra metal (not including the electrode), added to the weld pool as powder,

wire, strip, or with flux, reduces dilution by increasing the total amount of filler metal and reducing the amount of base metal that is melted.

For weld cladding the inside surfaces of large pressure vessels, as shown in Fig. 7 and 8, wide beads produced by oscillated multiple-wire systems or strip electrodes have become the means to improve productivity and minimize dilution while offering a uniformly smooth surface. Welding parameters for stainless steel strip weld overlays are described in Ref 10.

Table 5 Characteristics of welding processes used in hardfacing

Welding process	Mode of application	Form of hardfacing alloy	Weld-metal dilution, %	Deposition kg/h	Deposition lb/h	Minimum thickness(a) mm	Minimum thickness(a) in.	Deposit efficiency, %
OAW	Manual	Bare cast rod, tubular rod	1-10	0.5-2	1-4	0.8	1/32	100
	Manual	Powder	1-10	0.5-2	1-4	0.8	1/32	85-95
	Automatic	Extra-long bare cast rod, tubular wire	1-10	0.5-7	1-15	0.8	1/32	100
SMAW	Manual	Flux-covered cast rod, flux-covered tubular rod	10-20	0.5-5	1-12	3.2	1/8	65
Open arc	Semiautomatic	Alloy-cored tubular wire	15-40	2-11	5-25	3.2	1/8	80-85
	Automatic	Alloy-cored tubular wire	15-40	2-11	5-25	3.2	1/8	80-85
GTAW	Manual	Bare cast rod, tubular rod	10-20	0.5-3	1-6	2.4	3/32	98-100
	Automatic	Various forms(b)	10-20	0.5-5	1-10	2.4	3/32	98-100
SAW	Automatic, single wire	Bare tubular wire	30-60	5-11	10-25	3.2	1/8	95
	Automatic, multiwire	Bare tubular wire	15-25	11-27	25-60	4.8	3/16	95
	Automatic, series arc	Bare tubular wire	10-25	11-16	25-35	4.8	3/16	95
PAW	Automatic	Powder(c)	5-15	0.5-7	1-15	0.8	1/32	85-95
	Manual	Bare cast rod, tubular rod	5-15	0.5-4	1-8	2.4	3/32	98-100
	Automatic	Various forms(b)	5-15	0.5-4	1-8	2.4	3.32	98-100
GMAW	Semiautomatic	Alloy-cored tubular wire	10-40	0.9-5	2-12	1.6	1/16	90-95
	Automatic	Alloy-cored tubular wire	10-40	0.9-5	2-12	1.6	1/16	90-95
Laser	Automatic	Powder	1-10	(d)	(d)	0.13	0.005	85-95

(a) Recommended minimum thickness of deposit. (b) Bare tubular wire; extra-long (2.4 m, or 8 ft) bare cast rod; tungsten carbide powder with cast rod or bare tubular wire. (c) With or without tungsten carbide granules. (d) Varies widely depending on powder feed rate and laser input power

Typical dilution percentages, deposition rates, and minimum deposit thicknesses for different welding processes, along with various forms, compositions, and modes of application of hardfacing alloys, are given in Table 5. More detailed information on the selection of hardfacing alloys and processes can be found in Ref 10.

The buildup alloys include low-alloy pearlitic steels, austenitic manganese (Hadfield) steels, and high-manganese austenitic stainless steels. For the most part, these alloys are not designed to resist wear but to return a worn part back to, or near, its original dimensions and to provide adequate support for subsequent layers of true hardfacing materials. However, austenitic manganese steels are used as wear-resistant materials under mild wear conditions. Typical examples of applications where buildup alloys are used for wearing surfaces include tractor rails, railroad rail ends, steel mill table rolls, and large slow-speed gear teeth. The stainless steel included in this category is AWS EFeMn-Cr, which has a hardness value of 24 HRC and the following chemical composition:

Element	Composition, wt%
Carbon	0.5
Chromium	15.0
Manganese	15.0
Silicon	1.3
Nickel	1.0
Molybdenum	2.0
Iron	bal

Martensitic air-hardening steels (including stainless steels) are metal-to-metal wear alloys that, with care, can be applied (without cracking) to wearing areas of machinery parts. Hence, these materials are commonly referred to as *machinery hardfacing alloys*. Typical applications of this alloy family include undercarriage components of tractors and power shovels, steel mill work rolls, and crane wheels. The stainless steel in this category is AWS ER420, which has a hardness value of 45 HRC and the following chemical composition:

Element	Composition, wt%
Carbon	0.3
Chromium	12.0
Manganese	2.0
Silicon	1.0
Iron	bal

Cobalt-free austenitic stainless steels have been developed to replace cobalt-base hardfacing alloys (Stellite grades) in nuclear power plant applications. Cobalt-base alloys have been traditionally used for hardfacing nuclear plant valves (check valves, seat valves, and control valves), because they generally show high corrosion resistance and superior tribological behavior under sliding conditions. However, even the (usually low) corrosion and sliding-wear rates of these hardfacings lead to a release of particles with a high cobalt content. The particles are entrained in the coolant flow through the core, and Co^{60}, which is a strong emitter of gamma radiation, is

produced. The activated particles are incorporated into the oxide layers of primary system components and contribute considerably to the occupational radiation exposure of maintenance personnel during the inspection, repair, or replacement of components. Additionally, material loss has been found for cobalt-base hardfacings used for control or throttle valves that are exposed to high flow velocities, indicating that this type of alloy has a limited resistance to erosion-corrosion and cavitation attack.

Detailed investigations of candidate replacement cobalt-free, iron-base alloys have been performed since the late 1960s. In the U.S., the Electric Power Research Institute has developed cobalt-free NOREM alloys (U.S. Patent 4,803,045, Feb. 7, 1989). These alloys can be deposited successfully on stainless and carbon steel substrates with gas-tungsten arc welding, in any position and with no preheat, using controlled heat input techniques. Nominal compositions of the NOREM alloys are as follows:

Element	Composition, wt%
Carbon	0.7-1.0
Chromium	24-26
Manganese	4.0-5.2
Silicon	2.5-3.2
Nickel	5.0-9.0
Molybdenum	1.7-2.3
Nitrogen	0.05-0.15
Iron	bal

NOREM alloys are characterized by high wear resistance and antigalling properties, and they have a microstructure consisting of an austenitic matrix containing eutectic alloy carbides. The NOREM alloys meet or surpass the performance of cobalt alloys with respect to corrosion, material loss due to wear, and maintenance of the valve's sealing function. Galling wear data for various NOREM and cobalt-base alloys are given in Table 6. Chemical compositions of the alloys tested are provided in Table 7. Additional information on these alloys can be found in Ref 11 to 14.

Considerable work has also been carried out in Europe on cobalt-free, iron-base hardfacing alloys. Everit 50 (47 to 53 HRC), Fox Antinit DUR 300 (28 to 32 HRC), and Cenium Z 20 (42 to 48 HRC) are tradenames used by Thyssen Edelstahlwerke Bochum (Germany), Vereinigte Edelstahlwerke Kapfenberg (Austria), and L.A.M.E.F. Rueil-Malmaison (France), respectively. Compositions of these alloys are given in Table 8. Studies have demonstrated that these alloys have tribological, corrosion, and mechanical properties comparable to those of cobalt-base Stellite 6 (Ref 15).

Cobalt-containing austenitic stainless steels have been developed by Hydro-Québec for the repair of the cavitation erosion damage of its hydraulic turbines. *Cavitation* refers to the formation of vapor bubbles, or cavities, in a fluid that is moving across the surface of a solid component.

Table 6 Galling wear of gas-tungsten arc weld overlays made from cobalt-free NOREM alloys

Alloy/form	Surface damage, μm, at indicated tests in air			Stress, MPa (ksi) tests in water		
	140 (20)	275 (40)	415 (60)	140 (20)	275 (40)	415 (60)
NOREM 01/solid	0.4	0.9	1.1	0.3	0.4	0.4
NOREM 01/solid	0.7	1.6	2.8	nt	nt	nt
NOREM 01/metal-core	0.7	0.4	0.6	0.7	1.1	1.3
NOREM 01/metal-core	1.9	2.3	4.7	1.2	1.3	1.5
NOREM 01/metal-core	0.3	0.5	1.4	0.3	0.5	0.7
NOREM 04/metal-core	0.6	0.7	1.0	nt	nt	nt
Stellite 21/solid	1.3	1.9	2.4	0.5	1.0	1.5
Stellite 6/solid	2.2	2.6	2.8	1.1	1.7	1.6

Source: H. Ocken, Electric Power Research Institute

Table 7 Chemical compositions of the NOREM hardfacing alloys listed in Table 6

Alloy/Vendor	Nominal composition, wt%(a)								
	C	Mn	Si	Cr	Ni	Mo	P	S	Other
NOREM 01/Stoody	1.3	9.7	3.3	25	4.2	2	0.02	0.01	0.1N
NOREM 01/Cartech	1.27	6.15	3.17	25.5	4.47	2.03	0.006	0.009	0.12N, 0.02Cu, 0.01Co
NOREM 04/Anval	1.17	12.2	5.13	25.3	8.19	1.81	0.029	0.01	0.22N, 0.05Cu, 0.068Co
NOREM A/Anval	1.22	7.5	4.7	26.5	4.9	2.21	0.018	0.015	0.236N, 0.03Nb, 0.007Ti, 0.07Co

(a) Single values are maximum values. Source: H. Ocken, Electric Power Research Institute

Table 8 European-developed cobalt-free hardfacing alloys

| | Chemical composition, wt%(a) | | | | | | |
Alloy	C	Mn	Si	Cr	Ni	Mo	Other
Everit 50	2.5	≤1.0	≤0.5	25.0	...	3.2	0.5V
Fox Antinit Dur 300	0.12	6.5	5.0	21.0	8.0	...	...
Cenium Z 20	0.3	NR(b)	NR(b)	27	18	...	2.0 W, unspecified other elements ≤5

(a) Single values are maximum values. (b) NR, not reported. Source: Ref 15

These vapor bubbles are caused by localized reductions in the dynamic pressures of the fluid. The collapse of these vapor cavities produces extremely high compressive shocks, which leads to local elastic and/or plastic deformation of the metallic surfaces. These repeated collapses (compressive shocks) in a localized area cause surface tearing or fatigue cracking, which leads to the removal of small metallic particles from the exposed surface. This eventually results in serious erosion damage to the metallic surfaces and is a major problem in the efficient operation of hydraulic equipment, such as hydroturbines, runners, valves, pumps, ship propellers, and so on. The damage caused by cavitation erosion frequently contributes to higher maintenance and repair costs, excessive downtime and lost revenue, use of replacement power (which is very expensive), reduced operating efficiencies, and shortened equipment service life.

The outstanding cavitation erosion resistance of cobalt-containing austenitic stainless steels comes from a patented chemistry formulated to yield the highest work-hardening rate, with a high interstitial carbon and nitrogen content. For the same reason, and in order to stabilize a fully austenitic structure, nickel has been replaced by manganese and cobalt, which are balanced with silicon and chromium to give good corrosion resistance. The nominal composition for these alloys is:

Element	Composition, wt%
Carbon	0.2
Chromium	17
Manganese	9.5
Silicon	2.5
Cobalt	9
Nitrogen	0.2
Iron	bal

Studies by Simoneau (Ref 16 and 17) at the Institut de Recherche d'Hydro-Québec have determined that the elements most favorable to cavitation resistance, in decreasing order, are carbon, nitrogen, cobalt, and silicon. The combination of carbon and nitrogen has an equivalent effect, whereas chromium and manganese show a neutral effect within the 8 to 12% Co range. Nickel is detrimental. Figure 9 presents the effect of carbon plus nitrogen, and Fig. 10 presents the effect of cobalt concentration, on the steady-state rate of cavitation erosion. These results allow the formulation of alloys with the appropriate amount of austenitizer (carbon, nitrogen, cobalt, manganese) and ferritizer elements (chromium, silicon, molybdenum) to stabilize the austenite phase at room temperature. Cobalt alone is not sufficient as an austenitizer, because it only very slightly lowers the martensitic transformation temperature. Thus, it must be supplemented with manganese, carbon, or nitrogen. In order to increase the ductility and the corrosion resistance, carbon can be replaced by nitrogen.

The composition of cobalt-containing austenitic stainless steels provides a balance of elements in such a way that an essentially austenitic γ phase with a low stacking fault energy is obtained in an as-welded and solidified weld overlay. This metastable face-centered cubic (fcc) γ-phase transforms under stress to a body-centered cubic (bcc) α-martensitic phase exhibiting fine deformation twins. The phase transformation and twinning absorb the energy of the shock waves generated by the collapsing of the vapor bubbles. Such behavior is similar to that of cavitation-resistant high-cobalt alloys, which exhibit a transformation from a fcc γ-phase to a hexagonal close-packed (hcp) ε-phase in addition to twinning.

In the "incubation" period of the alloy surface under a cavitation condition, the hardness increases as deformation twins form on the surface. The metal loss during this period is generally minimal, and the surface is smooth and hardened. Unlike the case for other alloys, such as 300-series stainless steels, this incubation period is long and high hardness levels (450 HV) are reached in the steady state.

After the surface is fully hardened, further cavitation causes damage by initiating fatigue cracks and subsequent detachment of particulates at the intersections of the deformation twins. Because the twins are relatively small and the metal particles also small, the result is a uniform and slow degradation of the metal surface.

The main effect of these chemical composition modifications on the mechanical properties of austenitic stainless steels is illustrated by the tensile curves shown in Fig. 11. The work- or strain-hardening coefficient increases markedly when going from 304 to 301, and in particular for the cobalt-containing stainless steel. Decreasing the nickel and replacing it with cobalt results in a decrease in yield strength and in an important increase in ultimate tensile strength. Although the initial strain-hardening coefficient for these steels is quite similar, it increases to a very high value at larger strains (up to 1.26) for cobalt-containing stainless steels. This larger strain hardening is as-

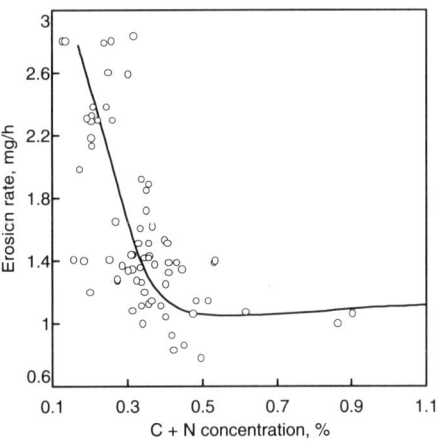

Fig. 9 Effect of carbon plus nitrogen additions on cavitation erosion of cobalt-containing alloys. Source: Ref 17

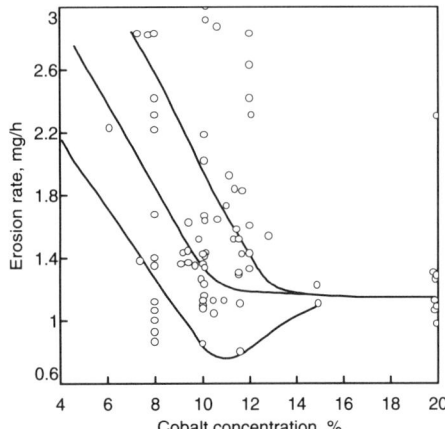

Fig. 10 Effect of cobalt additions on cavitation erosion of austenitic stainless steels. Source: Ref 17

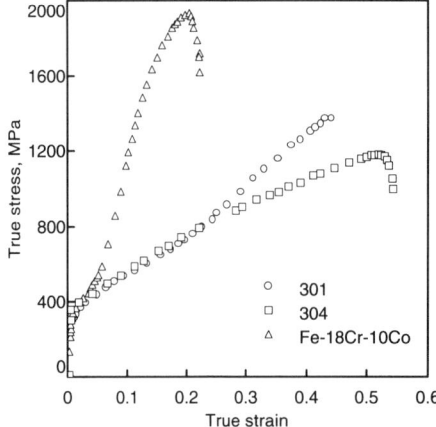

Fig. 11 Tensile stress-strain curves of 308, 301, and cobalt-containing stainless steels. Source: Ref 18

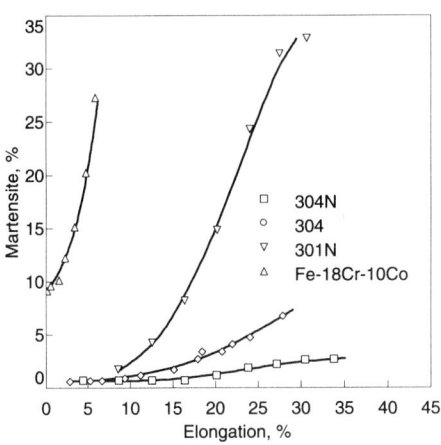

Fig. 12 Deformation-induced martensitic transformation measured in tensile tests. Source: Ref 18

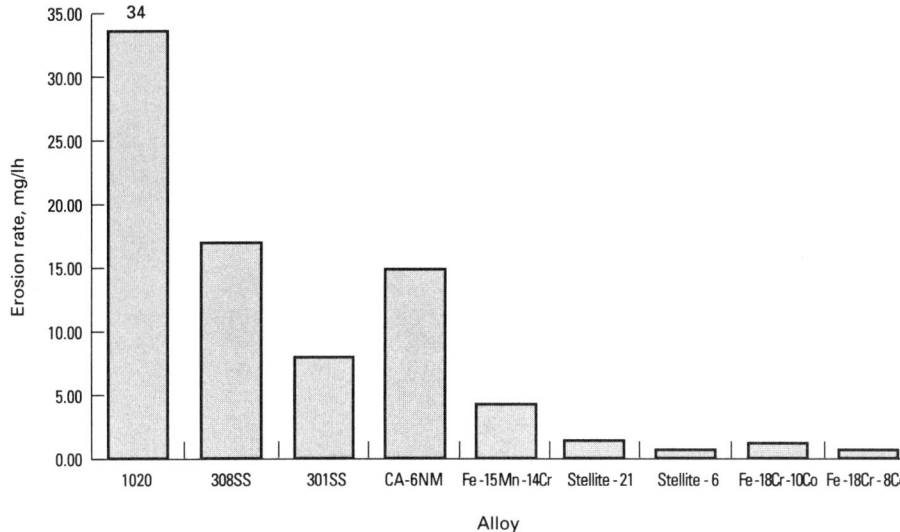

Fig. 14 Comparison of cavitation erosion rate of various materials. Source: Ref 18

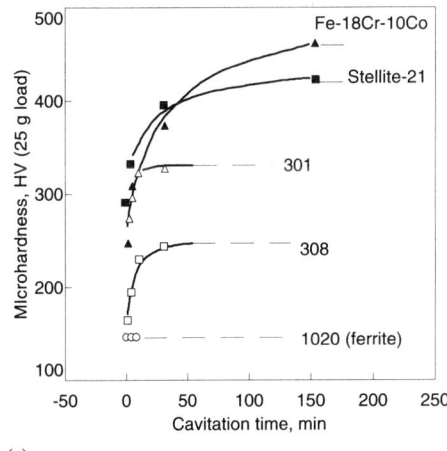

(a)

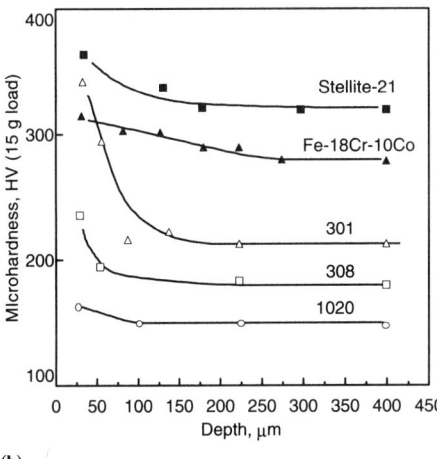

(b)

Fig. 13 Cavitation-induced surface (a) and cross-section (b) hardening in various materials.
Source: Ref 18

sociated with a faster initial martensitic transformation, $\gamma \rightarrow \alpha'$, of the less stable austenite phase, as shown in Fig. 12. The higher the cavitation resistance, the less the plastic deformation required to transform the fcc γ-austenitic phase to the bcc α'-martensitic phase. For the cobalt-containing steel, only 5% elongation is required to produce some 25% transformation.

Figure 13 presents the actual hardness values reached by the material surface exposed to cavitation. Almost no cavitation-deformation hardening could be detected for 1020 carbon steel, whereas substantial strain hardening was measured for austenitic stainless steels and the cobalt-base alloy, in good correlation with their ultimate tensile strength and cavitation resistance. The hardness values measured on the surfaces exposed to cavitation also correspond quite well to values equivalent to their ultimate strength. It appears to be not so much the initial hardness or the strain energy (area under the stress-strain curve) that controls cavitation resistance, but rather the strain-hardening capability under cavitation exposure (Ref 18). Figure 13(b) shows that strain hardening is restricted to a very thin surface layer (< 50 μm), which is even thinner for the cobalt-containing alloys.

Cobalt-containing austenitic stainless steels are about ten times more resistant to cavitation erosion than the standard 300-series stainless steels (Fig. 14). Although cobalt-containing stainless steels may become less ductile because of their high work-hardening coefficient, their ductility is good enough to be welded or cast without cracking. The as-welded hardness is around 25 HRC, with work-hardened materials reaching 50 HRC. With a tensile elongation between 10 and 55%, the annealed yield strength is around 350 MPa, and the ultimate strength can exceed 1000 MPa (145 ksi). The corrosion resistance is fair, comparable to that of type 301 stainless steel, being somewhat limited by the higher carbon content. Nevertheless,

the materials are adequate for most applications in flowing river or tap waters.

The original experimental cobalt-containing stainless steels were named IRECA to denote *Improved REsistance to CAvitation*. The currently commercially available welding consumables that can be deposited on stainless and carbon steel substrates are 1.2 mm (0.045 in.) and 1.6 mm (1/16 in.) gas-metal arc welding wires and 3.2 mm (1/8 in.) and 4.0 mm (5/32 in.) shielded metal arc welding electrodes. The name for these consumables is Hydroloy HQ913, which is a tradename of Thermodyne Stoody. Additional information on cobalt-containing stainless steel hardfacing alloys can be found in Ref 16 to 23 and in the article "Tribological Properties" in this Volume.

Designing with Clad Metals (Ref 6)

The choice of a material for a particular application depends on such factors as cost, availability, appearance, strength, fabricability, electrical or thermal properties, mechanical properties, and cor-

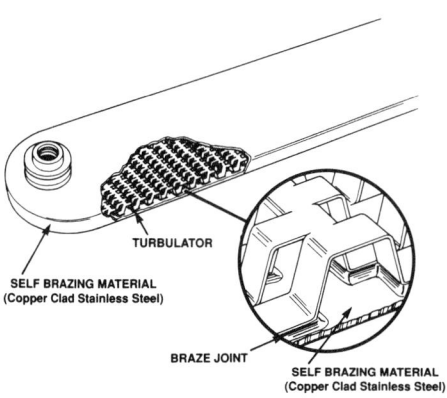

Fig. 15 Heat exchanger fabricated using clad brazing ("self-brazing") materials

Table 9 Properties of copper-clad stainless steel brazing alloys

Material system	Layer thickness ratio	Tensile		0.2% yield strength		Elongation in 50 mm (2 in.), %
		MPa	ksi	MPa	ksi	
Two-layer systems						
C12200/304LSS	6/94	590	86	255	37	55
	13.5/86.5	650	94	300	43	55
C12200/409SS	15/85	400	58	215	31	36
Three-layer systems						
C12200/304LSS/	10/80/10	600	87	310	45	55
C12200	13/74/13	575	83	290	42	53
	32/34/32	380	55	170	25	48
C12200/409SS/	10/80/10	385	56	205	30	37
C12200	15/80/5	385	56	205	30	37

Source: Ref 25

rosion resistance. Clad metals provide a means of designing into a composite material specific properties that cannot be obtained in a single material.

Self-brazing materials, such as copper-clad stainless steel (Cu/SS or Cu/SS/Cu), provide an example of the unique properties designed into a clad material. Clad brazing materials are produced as strips, using the cold roll bonding technique. The strips comprise a base metal that is clad with a brazing filler metal on either one or both sides. These products are used primarily in high-volume manufacturing operations, such as the production of heat exchangers, brazed bellows, and honeycomb structures. The use of a self-brazing sheet reduces the total part count, simplifies the assembly operation (because the brazing filler metal is always present on the core material), and reduces assembly time and, therefore, cost. In addition, there is no need for the application of flux or for its subsequent removal. This not only saves the initial purchase cost of the flux, but also the waste-management cost associated with the disposal of the spent material.

Figure 15 depicts an automotive transmission fluid cooler that was assembled using clad brazing materials. A turbulator is brazed to a copper-clad stainless steel base and cover. The base and cover are formed from a stainless steel strip containing copper braze on one side. After brazing, the dimensional changes in this part are minimal,

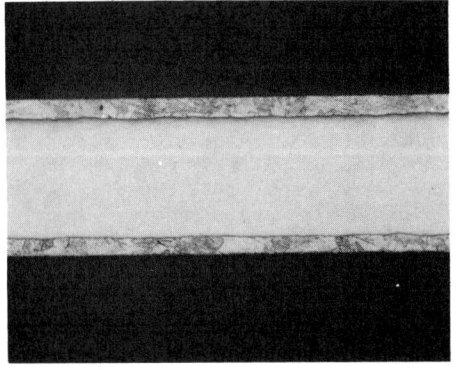

Fig. 16 Photomicrograph of typical clad brazing material, C12200 copper clad to 304L stainless steel

which is important when making a hermetically sealed heat exchanger. Figure 16 shows a typical clad brazing strip of copper-clad stainless steel. Properties of two-layer and three-layer brazing strips are listed in Table 9. Additional material on clad brazing alloys can be found in Ref 24 and 25.

Designing Clad Metals for Corrosion Control (Ref 6)

Clad metals designed for corrosion control can be categorized as follows:

- Noble metal clad systems
- Corrosion barrier systems
- Sacrificial metal systems
- Transition metal systems
- Complex multilayer systems

Proper design is essential for providing maximum corrosion resistance with clad metals. This section will discuss the basis for designing clad metals for corrosion resistance.

Noble metal clad systems are materials having a relatively inexpensive base metal covered with a corrosion-resistant metal. Selection of the substrate metal is based on the properties required for a particular application. For example, when strength is required, steel is frequently chosen as the substrate. The cladding metal is chosen for its corrosion resistance in a particular environment, such as seawater, sour gas, high temperature, and motor vehicles.

A wide range of corrosion-resistant alloys clad to steel substrates have been used in industrial applications. One example is type 304 stainless steel on steel. Figure 17 shows cross sections of this material. The uniformity of the bond interface is apparent in Fig. 17(a), and in the polished-and-etched condition (Fig. 17b), the metallographic structure of the stainless steel is clearly visible. The grain structure is analogous to that of annealed stainless steel strip.

Clad metals of this type are typically used in the form of strip, plate, and tubing. The noble metal cladding ranges from commonly used stainless steels, such as type 304, to high-nickel alloys, such as Inconel 625. These clad metals find various applications in the marine, chemical process-

(a)

(b)

Fig. 17 Photomicrographs of cross sections of type 304 stainless-steel-clad carbon steel. (a) As-polished. 300×. (b) Polished and etched. 500×

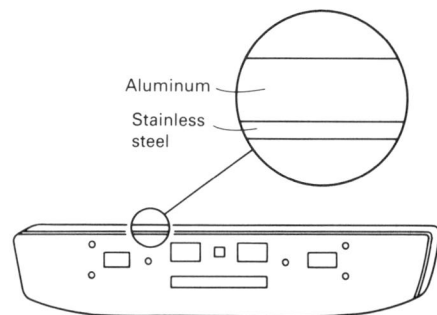

Fig. 18 Stainless-steel-clad aluminum truck bumper material that combines the corrosion resistance of stainless steel with lightweight aluminum

ing, power, and pollution control industries. Specific uses include heat exchangers, reaction and pressure vessels, furnace tubes, and tubes and

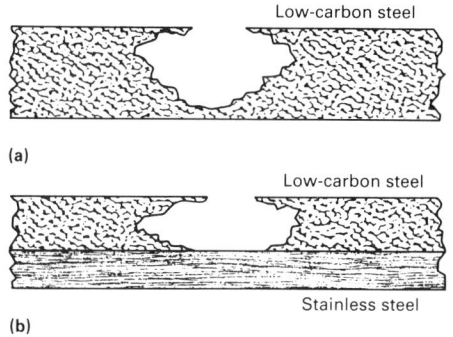

Fig. 19 Illustrations of the corrosion barrier principle. (a) Solid carbon steel. (b) Carbon-steel-clad stainless steel

tube elements for boilers, scrubbers, and other systems involved in the production of chemicals.

Another group of commonly used noble metal clad metals uses aluminum as a substrate. For example, in stainless-steel-clad aluminum truck bumpers (Fig. 18), the type 302 stainless steel cladding provides a bright corrosion-resistant surface that also resists the mechanical damage (stone impingement) encountered in service. The aluminum provides a substrate with a high strength-to-weight ratio.

Corrosion Barrier Systems. The combination of two or more metals to form a corrosion barrier system is most widely used where perforation caused by corrosion must be avoided (Fig. 19). Low-carbon steel and stainless steel are susceptible to localized corrosion in chloride-containing environments and may perforate rapidly. When steel is clad over the stainless steel layer, the corrosion barrier mechanism prevents perforation. Localized corrosion of the stainless steel is prevented: The stainless steel is protected galvanically by the sacrificial corrosion of the steel in the metal laminate. Therefore, only a thin pore-free layer is required.

The example shown in Fig. 20 of carbon steel clad to type 304 stainless steel demonstrates how this combination prevents perforation in seawater, while solid type 304 stainless steel does not. This material can be used for tubing and for wire in applications requiring strength and corrosion resistance.

Carbon steel cannot be used when increased general corrosion resistance of the outer cladding is required. A low-grade stainless steel with good resistance to uniform corrosion but poor resistance to localized corrosion can be selected. In seawater service, type 304 stainless steel that is clad to a thin layer of Hastelloy C-276 provides a substitute for solid Hastelloy C-276. In this corrosion barrier system, localized corrosion of the type 304 stainless steel is arrested at the C-276 alloy interface.

The most widely used clad metal corrosion barrier material is copper-clad stainless steel (Cu/430 SS/Cu) for telephone and fiber optic cable shielding. In environments in which the corrosion rate of copper is high, such as acidic or sulfide-containing soils, the stainless steel acts as a corrosion barrier and thus prevents perforation, while the inner copper layer maintains high electrical conductivity of the shield.

Sacrificial metals, such as magnesium, zinc, and aluminum, are in the active region of the galvanic series and are extensively used for corrosion protection. The location of the sacrificial metal in the galvanic couple is an important consideration in the design of a system. By cladding, the sacrificial metal may be located precisely for efficient cathode protection, as described for the stainless-steel-clad aluminum automotive trim shown in Fig. 2.

Transitional Metal Systems. A clad transitional metal system provides an interface between two incompatible metals. It not only reduces galvanic corrosion where dissimilar metals are joined, but also allows welding techniques to be used when direct joining is not possible.

Complex Multilayer Systems. In many cases, materials are exposed to dual environments; that is, one side is exposed to one corrosive medium, and the other side is exposed to a different one. A single material may not be able to meet this requirement, or a critical material may be required in large quantity.

In small battery cans and caps, copper-clad, stainless-steel-clad nickel (Cu/SS/Ni) is used where the external nickel layer provides atmospheric-corrosion resistance and low contact resistance. The copper layer on the inside provides the electrode contact surface as well as compatible

cell chemistry. The stainless steel layer provides strength and resistance to perforation corrosion.

Welding Austenitic-Stainless-Clad Carbon or Low-Alloy Steels (Ref 26)

To preserve its desirable properties, stainless-clad plate can be welded by either of the two following methods, depending on plate thickness and service conditions:

- The unclad sides of the plate sections are beveled and welded with carbon or low-alloy steel filler metal. A portion of the stainless steel cladding is removed from the back of the joint, and stainless steel filler metal is deposited.
- The entire thickness of the stainless-clad plate is welded with stainless steel filler metal.

When the nonstainless portion of the plate is comparatively thick, as in most pressure vessel applications, it is more economical to use the first method. When the nonstainless portion of the plate is thin, the second method is often preferred. When welding components for applications involving elevated or cyclic temperatures, the differences in the coefficients of thermal expansion of the base plate and the weld should be taken into consideration.

All stainless steel deposits on carbon steel should be made with filler metal of sufficiently high alloy content to ensure that normal amounts of dilution by carbon steel will not result in a brittle weld. In general, filler metals of type 308, 316, or 347 should not be deposited directly on carbon or low-alloy steel. Deposits of type 309, 309L, 309Cb, 309Mo, 310, or 312 are usually acceptable, although type 310 is fully austenitic and is susceptible to hot cracking when there is high restraint in a welded joint. Thus, welds made with type 310 filler metal should be carefully inspected. Welds made with types 309 and 312 filler metals are partially ferritic and therefore are highly resistant to hot cracking.

The procedure most commonly used for making welded joints in stainless-clad carbon or low-alloy steel plate is shown in Fig. 21. Stainless steel filler metal is deposited only in that portion of the weld where the stainless steel cladding has been removed, and carbon or low-alloy steel filler metal is used for the remainder. The backgouged por-

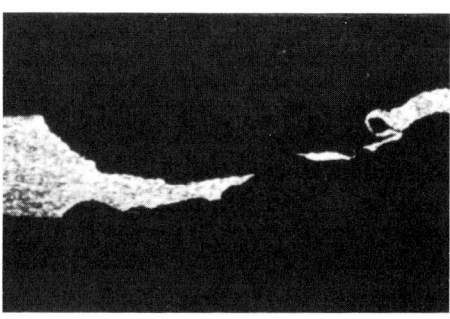

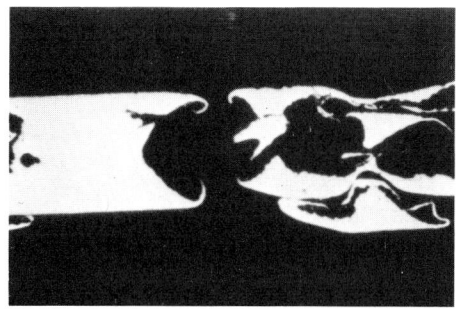

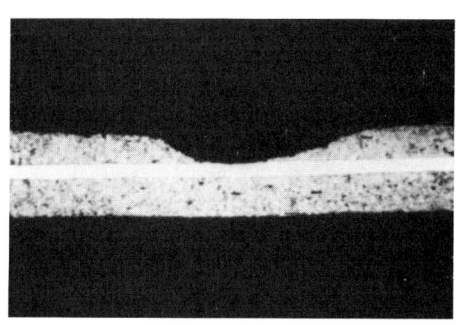

Fig. 20 Photomicrographs of cross sections of materials after 18 months of immersion in seawater at Duxbury, MA. (a) Low-carbon steel. (b) Type 304 stainless steel. (c) Carbon-steel-clad type 304 stainless steel

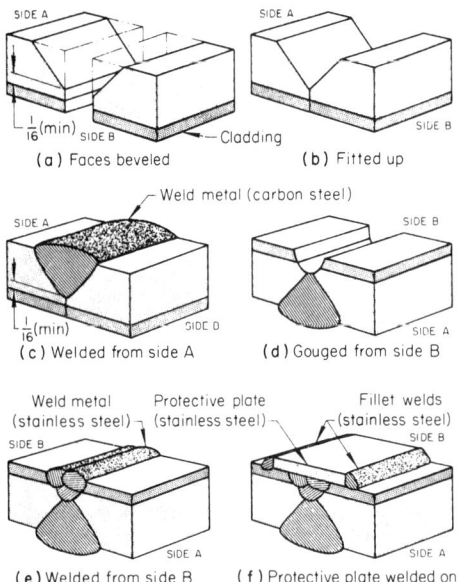

Fig. 21 Procedure for welding stainless-clad carbon and low-alloy steel, using stainless steel filler metal only in portion of joint from which cladding was removed. (a) and (b) The clad plates are machined for a tight fitup, with the bottom of the weld groove not less than 1.6 mm (1/16 in.) above the stainless steel cladding. (c) Carbon steel filler metal is deposited from side A (a low-hydrogen filler metal is used for the first pass), taking care not to penetrate closer than 1.6 mm (1/16 in.) to the cladding. (d) Stainless steel cladding on side B is backgouged until sound carbon steel weld metal is reached. (e) The backgouged groove is filled with stainless steel weld metal in a minimum of two layers. (f) When required for severely corrosive service, a protective strip of stainless steel plate may be fillet welded to the cladding to cover the weld zone.

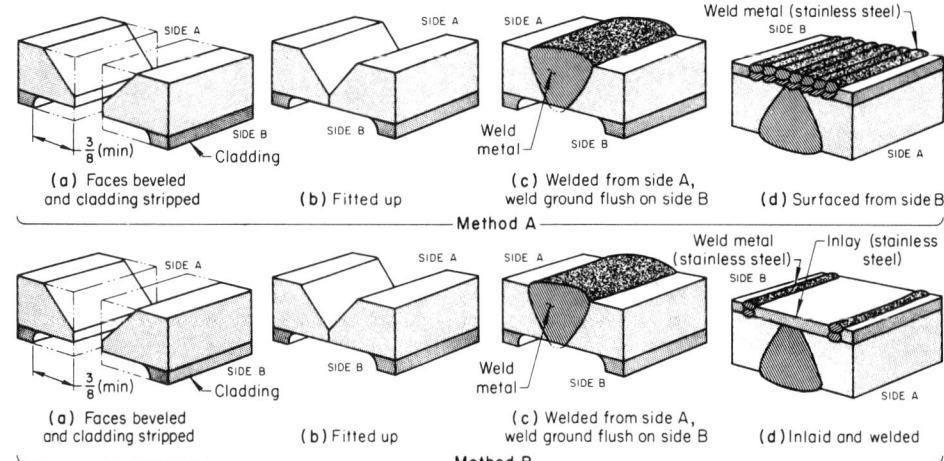

Fig. 22 Alternative procedures for joining stainless-clad carbon and low-alloy steel plate involving different techniques for replacing portions of the stainless steel cladding removed before welding the carbon or low-alloy steel side. The joint is prepared by beveling side A and removing a portion of the stainless steel cladding from side B to a minimum width of 9.5 mm (3/8 in.) from each side of the joint, and the joint is fitted up in position for welding. Use of a root gap (not shown) is permissible (a and b, methods A and B). Carbon steel filler metal is deposited, and the root of the weld is ground flush with the underside of the carbon steel plate (c, methods A and B). The area from which cladding was removed is surfaced with at least two layers of stainless steel weld metal (d, method A), or an inlay of wrought stainless steel can be welded in place (d, method B).

tion of the stainless steel cladding should be filled with a minimum of two layers of stainless steel filler metal (Fig. 21e); an additional layer is recommended if a high weld reinforcement at the cladding surface can be tolerated.

If the cladding is of type 304 stainless steel, the first layer of stainless steel weld metal should be of type 309 or 312. Subsequent layers of weld metal can be of type 308. If the cladding is of type 316, the first layer is deposited with type 309 Mo filler metal and the subsequent layers with type 316. When the cladding is of type 304L or 347, the welding procedure must be carefully controlled to obtain the desired weld metal composition in the outer layers of the weld. Chemical analysis of sample welds should be made before joining clad plates intended for use under severely corrosive conditions.

In some applications, a narrow protective plate of wrought stainless steel of the same composition as the cladding is welded over the completed weld (Fig. 21f) to ensure uniformity of corrosive resistance. The fillet welds joining the protective plate to the cladding should be carefully inspected after deposition. These welds, of course, are made with stainless steel filler metal.

Figure 22 illustrates an alternative method (method A) of welding clad plate, in which a carbon or low-alloy steel weld joins the carbon steel portion of the plate, and the use of stainless steel filler metal is limited to replacement of the cladding that was removed prior to making the carbon or low-alloy steel weld. This method is more expensive than the method described in Fig. 21 because of the cost of removing a larger portion of the cladding and depositing more stainless steel filler metal. Because there is no danger of alloy contamination from the cladding layer, method A in Fig. 22 permits the use of faster welding processes, such as submerged arc welding, in depositing the carbon steel weld.

In depositing the stainless steel weld metal, the first layer must be sufficiently high in alloy content to avoid cracking as a result of normal dilution by the carbon steel base metal. A stringer bead technique should be employed; penetration must be held to a minimum. If the proper weld metal composition is not achieved after the second layer has been deposited, a portion of the second layer should be ground off and additional filler metal should be deposited to obtain the desired composition. Figure 22(d) of method B shows an alternative procedure in which the exposed carbon steel weld on side B is covered by welding an inlay of wrought stainless steel to the edges of the cladding.

The most common method of joining stainless-steel-clad carbon or low-alloy steel plate with a weld that consists entirely of stainless steel is shown in Fig. 23. This method is most frequently used for joining thin sections of stainless-clad plate. The same basic welding procedure is followed for both the butt and corner joints shown in Fig. 23. After the plate has been beveled and fitted up for welding, a stainless steel weld is deposited from the carbon steel side, using a filler metal sufficiently high in alloy content to minimize difficulties (such as cracking) resulting from weld dilution and joint restraint. Types 309 and 312 filler metals are suitable for this application.

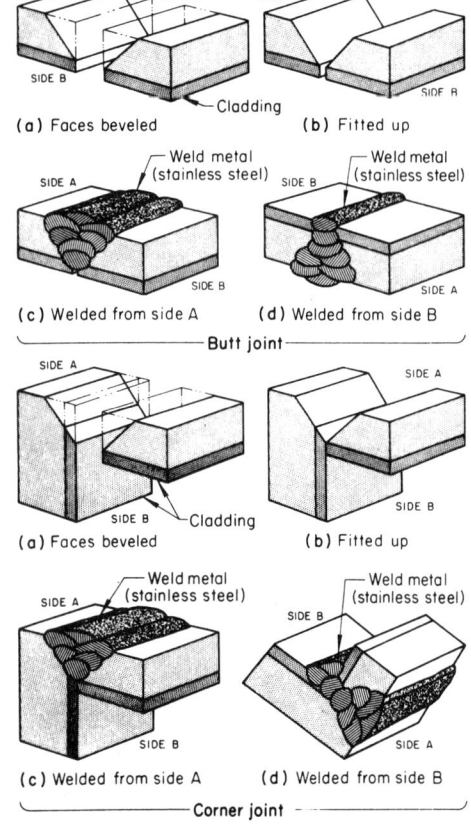

Fig. 23 Procedures for welding V-groove butt and corner joints in stainless-clad carbon or low-alloy steel plate, using stainless steel filler metal exclusively. The clad plates are beveled and fitted up (a and b, butt and corner joints). The root of the weld is cleaned and gouged, if necessary, before depositing stainless weld metal from the stainless steel side (d, butt and corner joints).

After the stainless steel weld has been deposited from the carbon steel side (Fig. 23c), the root of the weld is cleaned by brushing, chipping, or grinding, as required, and one or more layers of stainless steel filler metal are deposited (Fig. 23d). The filler metal composition should correspond to that normally employed to weld the type of stainless steel used for cladding. If the cladding is type 304, the final layer of weld metal should be type 308. If the cladding is type 316, it may be necessary to backgouge before deposition of the final weld metal layers to ensure that the proper weld metal composition is obtained at the surface of the weld.

ACKNOWLEDGMENTS

The editor thanks Howard Ocken, Project Manager, Electric Power Research Institute (EPRI) and Raynald Simoneau, Vice-Présidence Technologie, Institut de Recherche d'Hydro-Québec (IREQ), for their significant contributions to this article. Mr. Ocken supplied material on cobalt-free NOREM alloys developed at EPRI. Mr. Simoneau contributed material on cobalt-containing IRECA alloys that he developed at IREQ.

REFERENCES

1. L.M. Smith, "Engineering with Clad Steel," NiDI Technical Series No. 10,064, Nickel Development Institute, 1992
2. R.G. Delati, "Designing with Clad Metals," Metallurgical Materials Division of Texas Instruments, Inc.
3. "Stainless Clad Steels," The International Nickel Company, Inc., 1963
4. H. Enöckl, U. Malina-Altzinger, and H. Ornig, Advantages of Duplex Clad Plates, *Duplex Stainless Steels '91*, Volume 1, J. Charles and S. Bernhardsson, Ed., les éditions de physique, 1992, p 649-655
5. J. Charles et al., UR 45N and UR 47N Duplex Stainless Steel Clad Plates: Heat Treatment, Weldability, Forming, Procedures and Uses, *Duplex Stainless Steels '91*, Volume 1, J. Charles and S. Bernhardsson, Ed., les éditions de physique, 1992, p 657-665
6. R. Baboian and G. Haynes, Corrosion of Clad Metals, *Corrosion,* Vol 13, *ASM Handbook,* ASM International, 1987, p 887-890
7. J.G. Banker and E.G. Reinke, Explosion Welding, *Welding, Brazing, and Soldering,* Vol 6, *ASM Handbook,* ASM International, 1993, p 303-305
8. V.D. Linse, Procedure Development and Process Considerations for Explosion Welding, *Welding, Brazing, and Soldering,* Vol 6, *ASM Handbook,* ASM International, 1993, p 896-900
9. R.A. Patterson, Fundamentals of Explosion Welding, *Welding, Brazing, and Soldering,* Vol 6, *ASM Handbook,* ASM International, 1993, p 160-164
10. J.R. Davis, Hardfacing, Weld Cladding, and Dissimilar Metal Joining, *Welding, Brazing, and Soldering,* Vol 6, *ASM Handbook,* ASM International, 1993, p 789-829
11. "Welding of NOREM Iron-Base Hardfacing Alloy Wire Products—Procedures for Gas Tungsten Arc Welding," Report TR-101094, Electric Power Research Institute, Sept 1992
12. "Endurance Tests of Valves with Cobalt-Free Hardfacing Alloys—PWR Phase Final Report," Report TR-100601, Electric Power Research Institute, May 1992
13. "Endurance Tests of Valves with Cobalt-Free Hardfacing Alloys—BWR Phase Final Report," Report TR-101847, Electric Power Research Institute, Jan 1993
14. "NOREM Wear-Resistant, Iron-Based Hard-Facing Alloys," Report NP-6466-SD, Electric Power Research Institute, July 1989
15. "Laboratory Evaluations of Iron-Based Hard-Facing Alloys—A European Study," Report NP-5874, Electric Power Research Institute, June 1988
16. R. Simoneau, A New Class of High Strain-Hardening Austenitic Stainless Steels to Fight Cavitation Erosion, *Proc. IAHR Symposium* (Montreal, Canada), Sept 1986
17. R. Simoneau, Cavitation Erosion and Deformation Mechanisms of Ni and Co Austenitic Stainless Steels, *Proc. ELSI VII* (Cambridge, United Kingdom), Sept 1987
18. C.J. Heathcock, B.E. Protheroe, and A. Ball, Cavitation Erosion of Stainless Steels, *Wear,* Vol 81, 1982
19. R. Simoneau and Y. Mossoba, Field Experience with Ultra-High Cavitation Resistance Alloys in Francis Turbines, *Proc. IAHR Symposium* (Trondheim, Norway), June 1988
20. R. Simoneau, Vibratory, Jet, and Hydroturbine Cavitation Erosion, Cavitation and Multiphase Flow Forum, *First Joint ASME-JSME Fluids Engineering Conf.* (Portland, Oregon), June 1991
21. P.A. March, O.F. Karr, and L.L. Corvin, Laboratory and Field Comparisons of Cavitation Erosion Resistance for Base Materials, Weld Overlays, and Coatings, *Proc. IAHR Symposium* (Trondheim, Norway), June 1988
22. R. Simoneau and Y. Mossoba, "Recent Results Obtained with High Cavitation Resistance Alloys in Hydraulic Turbines," paper presented at Canadian Electrical Association Spring Meeting (Montreal, Canada), March 1988
23. R. Simoneau, The Optimum Protection of Hydraulic Turbines Against Cavitation Erosion, *Proc. IAHR Symposium* (Stirling, United Kingdom), Sept 1984
24. S. Jha, M. Karavolis, K. Dunn, and J. Forster, Brazing with Clad Brazing Materials, *Welding, Brazing, and Soldering,* Vol 6, *ASM Handbook,* ASM International, 1993, p 347-350
25. M. Karavolis, S. Jha, J. Forster, and K. Meeking, Application of Clad Brazing Materials, *Welding, Brazing, and Soldering,* Vol 6, *ASM Handbook,* ASM International, 1993, p 961-963
26. J.G. Feldstein, Dissimilar Welds with Stainless Steels, *Welding, Brazing, and Soldering,* Vol 6, *ASM Handbook,* ASM International, 1993, p 500-504

Melting and Refining Methods

MELTING AND REFINING of stainless steels is most commonly accomplished by electric arc furnace/argon oxygen decarburization (EAF/AOD). In fact, about 90% of all stainless steel produced in the United States and nearly 75% of stainless steel produced worldwide is processed by EAF/AOD (Ref 1). The EAF/AOD process involves melting the charge in a basic-lined electric arc furnace. The charge is comprised of stainless steel scrap compatible with the grade to be produced, carbon steel scrap, high-carbon ferrochromium alloy, and possibly a nickel or molybdenum source. Carbon electrodes extending through the roof of the furnace (Fig. 1) contact the charge, and a three-phase alternating current flows through the metal between the electrodes. Once the charge has been melted, the molten metal is transferred to the AOD converter vessel. Detailed information on electric-furnace steelmaking can be found in Ref 2 and 3.

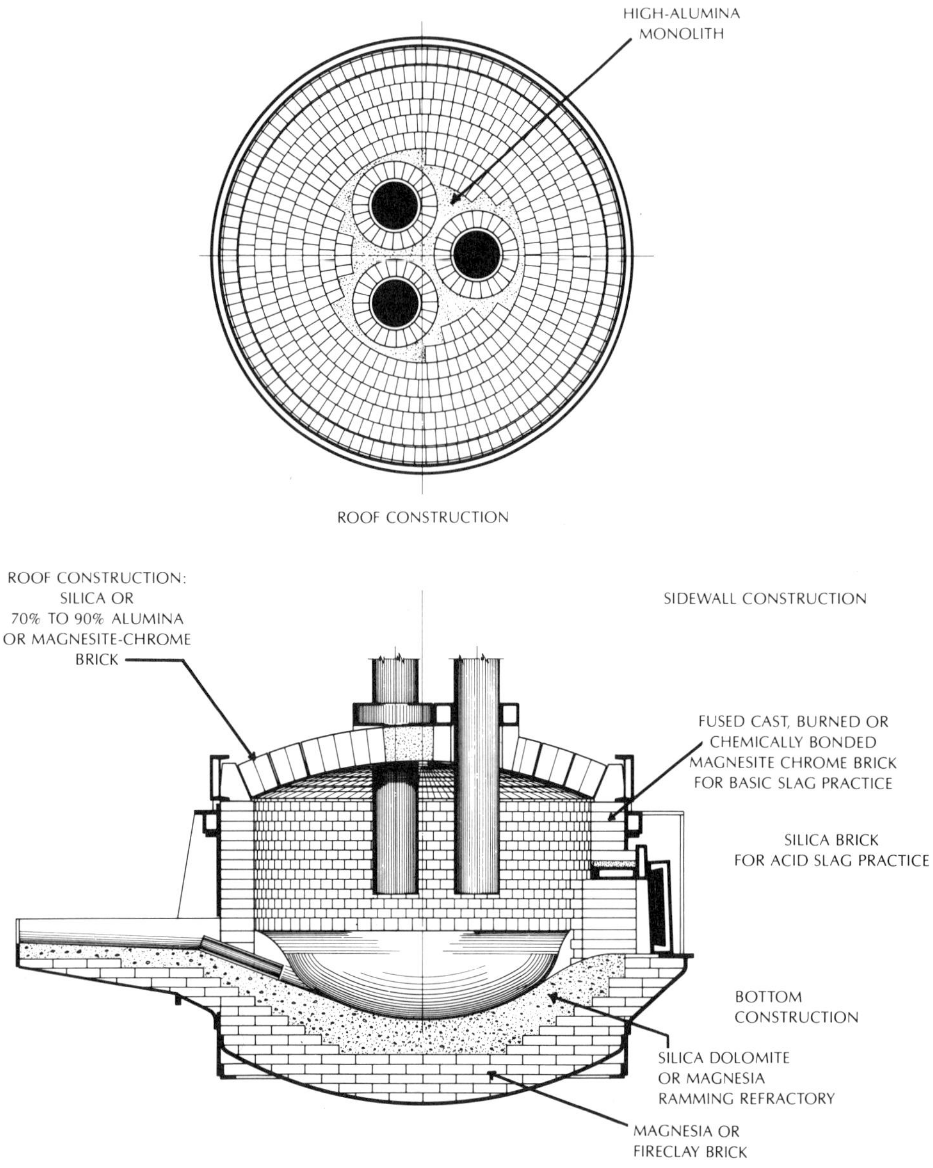

Industry-wide acceptance of EAF/AOD since the 1970s and the installation of continuous casters have not only reduced the cost of producing stainless steels and improved their quality but have also made possible the production of a variety of new types of stainless steels. These alloys provide significant improvements in resistance to chloride pitting and crevice corrosion compared with the conventional austenitic types 304 and 316.

The new alloys that were developed because of EAF/AOD include:

- Ferritic iron-chromium-molybdenum compositions with 18 to 30% Cr, 1 to 4% Mo, and 4% Ni max
- High-nickel (25 to 35%) austenitic stainless steels with 3 to 6% Mo and about 20 to 22% Cr
- Duplex alloys with a near 50-50 distribution of austenite and ferrite resulting from combinations of chromium (18 to 26%), molybdenum (1.5 to 3.5%), and nickel (5 to 6%)

Another major development made possible by EAF/AOD has been the use of 0.1 to 0.25% N to control the ferrite-austenite ratio in duplex stainless steels; to suppress the formation of brittle second phases in high-nickel, molybdenum-bearing austenitic alloys; to increase the strength of very low carbon types 304L and 316L steels; to enhance resistance to chloride pitting, crevice corrosion, and certain acids; and to retard sensitization.

Alternative melting/refining methods for stainless steels, which will also be described briefly in this article, include vacuum oxygen decarburization, vacuum induction melting, vacuum arc remelting, electroslag remelting, and electron beam melting and remelting.

Argon Oxygen Decarburization

AOD is a secondary refining process that was originally developed to reduce material and operating costs and to increase the productivity of stainless steel production. In addition to its economic merits, AOD offers improved metal cleanliness, which is measured by low unwanted residual element and gas contents; this ensures superior mechanical properties. AOD is duplexed, with molten metal supplied from a separate melting source to the AOD refining unit (vessel). The source of the molten metal is usually an electric arc furnace or a coreless induction furnace. Foundries and integrated steel mills use vessels ranging

HIGH-ALUMINA MONOLITH

ROOF CONSTRUCTION

ROOF CONSTRUCTION:
SILICA OR
70% TO 90% ALUMINA
OR MAGNESITE-CHROME
BRICK

SIDEWALL CONSTRUCTION

FUSED CAST, BURNED OR
CHEMICALLY BONDED
MAGNESITE CHROME BRICK
FOR BASIC SLAG PRACTICE

SILICA BRICK
FOR ACID SLAG PRACTICE

BOTTOM
CONSTRUCTION

SILICA DOLOMITE
OR MAGNESIA
RAMMING REFRACTORY

MAGNESIA OR
FIRECLAY BRICK

Fig. 1 Typical electric arc furnace for stainless steel production

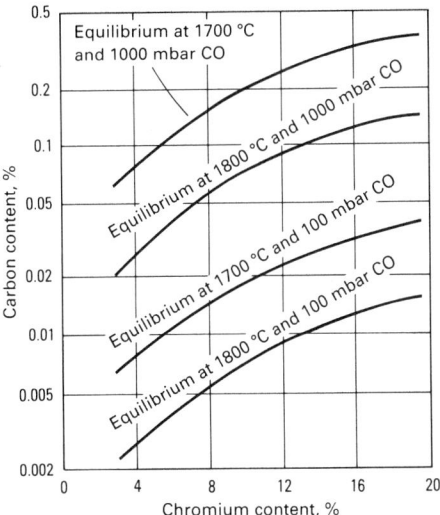

Fig. 2 Carbon-chromium equilibrium curves

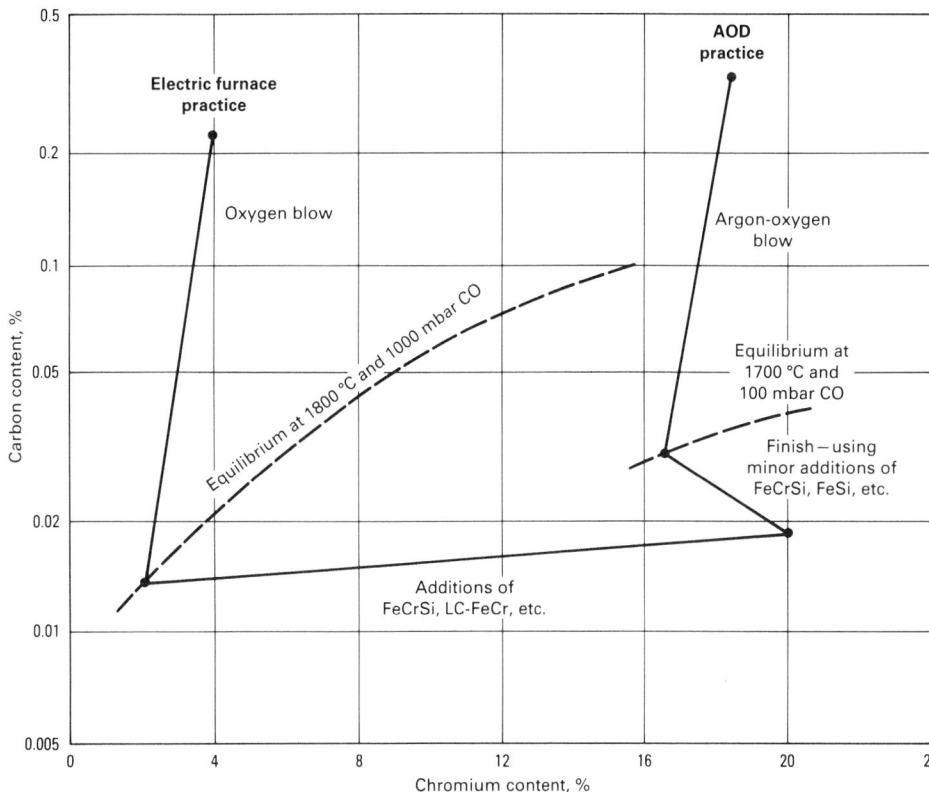

Fig. 3 Composition changes in refining type 304L stainless steel using electric arc furnace practice and argon oxygen decarburization

in nominal capacity from 1 to 160 metric tonnes (1 to 175 tons).

Although the process was initially targeted for stainless steel production, AOD is used in refining a wide range of alloys, including tool steels, silicon (electrical) steels, high-temperature alloys and superalloys, and carbon steels, low-alloy steels, and high-strength low-alloy steels.

Fundamentals

In AOD, oxygen, argon, and nitrogen are injected into a molten metal bath through submerged, side-mounted tuyeres. The primary aspect of AOD is the shift in the decarburization thermodynamics that is afforded by blowing with mixtures of oxygen and inert gas as opposed to pure oxygen. References 4 to 6 contain detailed discussions of the thermodynamics and the dilution principle and its influence on the refining of chromium-bearing steel.

To understand AOD, it is necessary to examine the thermodynamics governing the reactions that occur in the refining of stainless steel, that is, the relationships among carbon, chromium, chromium oxide (Cr_3O_4), and carbon monoxide (CO). The overall reaction in the decarburization of chromium-containing steel can be written as:

$$\tfrac{1}{4} Cr_3O_4 + \underline{C} \leftrightarrow \tfrac{3}{4} \underline{Cr} + CO(g) \qquad \text{(Eq 1)}$$

The equilibrium constant, K, is given by:

$$\underline{K} = \frac{(a_{Cr})^{3/4} (P_{CO})}{(a_{Cr_3O_4})^{1/4}(a_C)} \qquad \text{(Eq 2)}$$

where a and P represent the activity and partial pressure, respectively.

At a given temperature, there is a fixed, limited amount of chromium that can exist in the molten bath that is in equilibrium with carbon. By examining Eq 2, one can see that by reducing the partial pressure of CO, the quantity of chromium that can exist in the

molten bath in equilibrium with carbon increases. The partial pressure of CO can be reduced by injecting mixtures of oxygen and inert gas during the decarburization of stainless steel. Figure 2 illustrates the relationships among carbon, chromium, and temperature for a partial pressure of CO equal to 1 and 0.10 atm (1000 and 100 mbar, or 760 and 76 torr). The data shown in Fig. 2 indicate that diluting the partial pressure of CO allows lower carbon levels to be obtained at higher chromium contents with lower temperatures.

In refining stainless steel, it is generally necessary to decarburize the molten bath to less than 0.05% C. Chromium is quite susceptible to oxidation; therefore, prior to the introduction of AOD, decarburization was accomplished by withholding most of the chromium until the bath had been decarburized by oxygen lancing. After the bath was fully decarburized, low-carbon ferrochromium and other low-carbon ferroalloys were added to the melt to meet chemical specifications.

Dilution of the partial pressure of CO allows the removal of carbon to low levels without excessive chromium oxidation. This practice enables the use of high-carbon ferroalloys in the charge mix, avoiding the substantially more expensive low-carbon ferroalloys. Figure 3 compares the refining steps in the two processes.

Equally important, however, are the processing advantages offered by submerged blowing. These include excellent slag/metal and gas/metal contact, superior decarburization kinetics, and 100% use of the injected oxygen by reaction with

the bath. In addition, submerged injection allows accurate control of end-point nitrogen and the removal of dissolved gases (nitrogen and hydrogen) and nonmetallic inclusions.

Equipment

The processing vessel consists of a refractory-lined steel shell mounted on a tiltable trunnion ring

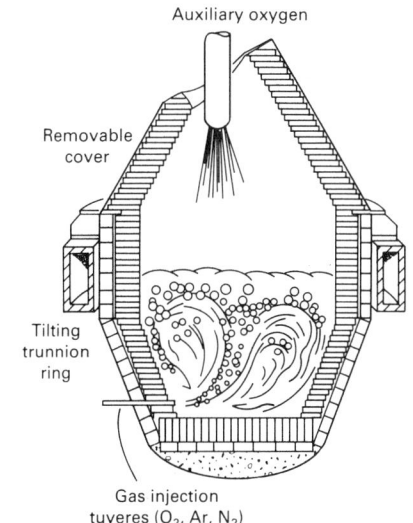

Fig. 4 Schematic of argon oxygen decarburization vessel

Table 1 Processing parameters for argon oxygen decarburization refining of type 304 stainless steel
Total gas flow rate: ~1.5 m³/min/tonne (3500 ft³/h/ton)

| Carbon level, % | Gas ratios | | | Partial pressures, atm | | | CRE, %(a) | CRR, ppm/min(b) | Temperature | |
	O₂	N₂	Ar	Ar	N₂	CO			°C	°F
3.0-0.7	4	1	...	...	0.14	0.86	80	1200	1510	2750
1-0.25	3	1	...	...	0.20	0.80	65	830	1700	3100
0.25-0.12	1	1	...	...	0.53	0.47	45	430	1700	3100
0.12-0.04	1	...	3	0.83	...	0.17	30	133	1730	3150
0.04-0.01	1	...	8	0.96	...	0.04	15	26	1730	3150

(a) CRE, carbon removal efficiency. (b) CRR, carbon removal rate

Table 2 Composition control of type 316 stainless steel refined by argon oxygen decarburization

Element	Target, %	Standard deviation, %
Carbon	0.040	0.003
Manganese	1.40	0.03
Silicon	0.40	0.04
Sulfur	<0.010	0.002
Chromium	18.08	0.06
Nickel	8.03	0.04
Molybdenum	2.03	0.02

Source: Praxair, Inc.

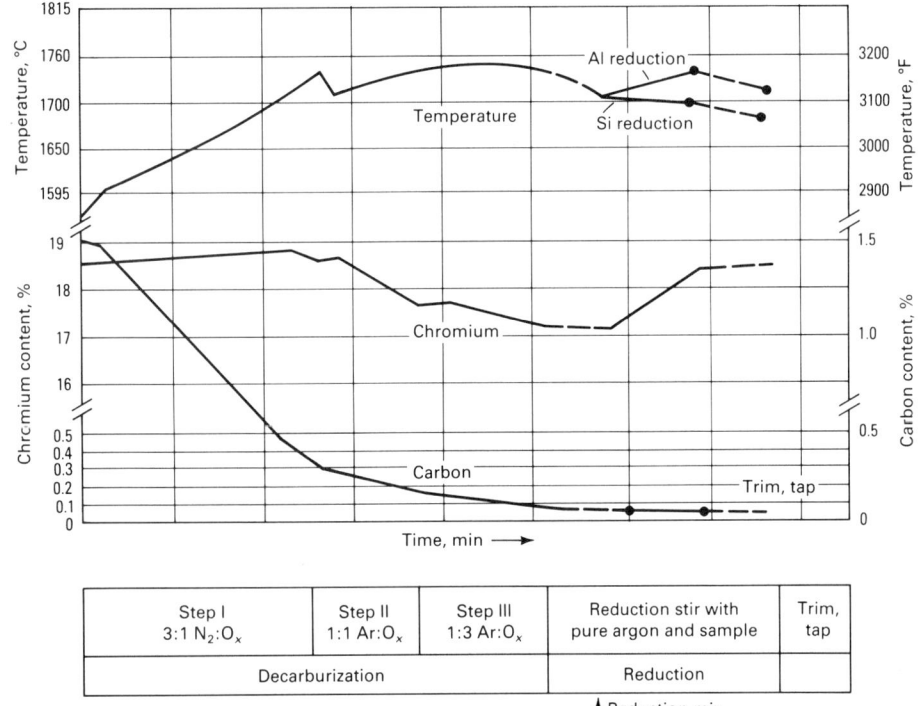

| Step I 3:1 N₂:Oₓ | Step II 1:1 Ar:Oₓ | Step III 1:3 Ar:Oₓ | Reduction stir with pure argon and sample | Trim, tap |
| Decarburization | | | Reduction | |

↑ Reduction mix

Fig. 5 Schematic of stainless steel refining cycle for small (< 27 metric tonne, or 30 ton) vessels showing the relationship between carbon and chromium contents as a function of time and temperature

fully automated. Most installations are equipped with a computer to assist in process control by calculating the required amount of oxygen as well as alloying additions. Some installations have computer control systems capable of sending set points and flow rates to the gas control systems.

Processing

Charge materials (scrap and ferroalloys) are melted in the melting furnace. The charge is usually melted with the chromium, nickel, and manganese concentrations at midrange specifications. The carbon content at meltdown can vary from 0.50 to 3.0%, depending on the scrap content of the charge. Once the charge is melted down, the heat is tapped and the slag is removed and weighed before the AOD vessel is charged.

In the refining of stainless steel grades, oxygen and inert gas are injected into the bath in a stepwise manner. The ratio of oxygen to inert gas injected decreases (3:1, 1:1, 1:3) as the carbon level decreases. Typically, for a type 409 stainless steel containing 11% Cr, an oxygen-argon ratio of 3:1 is used down to 0.2% C, and then a 1:3 ratio to 0.003% C. For an 18% Cr steel, an oxygen-argon ratio of 3:1 is used to 0.6% C, then a 1:1 ratio to 0.4% C, and finally a 1:3 ratio to 0.003% C.

Once the target carbon level is obtained, a reduction mix (silicon, aluminum, and lime) is added. If extra-low sulfur levels are desired, a second desulfurization can be added. Both of these steps are followed by an argon stir. After reduction, a complete chemistry sample is usually taken and trim additions are made following analysis. Figure 5 illustrates the relationships among carbon, chromium, temperature, and the various processing steps for refining a typical type 304 stainless steel using AOD.

Another critical aspect of AOD refining is the ability to predict when to change from nitrogen to argon to obtain the target nitrogen specification. Table 1 lists the process parameters, carbon removal efficiencies, and carbon removal rates for AOD refining of type 304 stainless steel. The point during refining when the oxygen-to-inert-gas ratio is lowered is based on carbon content and temperature. The ratios and carbon switch points are designed to provide optimum carbon removal efficiency without exceeding a bath temperature of 1730 °C (3150 °F).

(Fig. 4). With a removable, conical cover in place, the vessel outline is sometimes described as pear-shaped. Several basic refractory types and various quality levels of the refractories have gained widespread acceptance (Ref 7, 8). Dolomite refractories are used in most AOD installations; magnesite chromium refractories are predominant in small (< 9 metric tonne, or 10 ton) installations and are used almost exclusively in Japan.

As seen in Fig. 4, process gases are injected through submerged, side-mounted tuyeres. The number and relative positioning of tuyeres are determined in part by vessel size, range of heat sizes, process gas flow rates, and the types of alloys refined. Process gases are oxygen, nitrogen, argon, and in some cases carbon dioxide. The most recent AOD installations include the use of top-blown oxygen (one-third of all AOD installations have this capability). Oxygen top- and bottom-

blowing converters are described in a subsequent section in this article.

The specific volume of AOD vessels ranges from 0.4 to 0.8 m³/tonne (16 to 32 ft³/ton). The gas control system supplies the process gases at nominal rates of 0.5 to 3 m³/min/tonne (1500 to 6000 ft³/h/ton). The system accurately controls the flow rates and monitors the amount of gas injected into the bath to enable the operator to control the process and keep track of the total oxygen injected.

Normally, a shop has three interchangeable vessels. At any given time, one of the vessels is in a tiltable trunnion ring refining steel, a second vessel is at a preheating station, and the third vessel is being relined. The vessel in the trunnion ring can be replaced with a preheated vessel in less than 1 h.

The control of process gases, vessel activities, and ancillary equipment can range from manual to

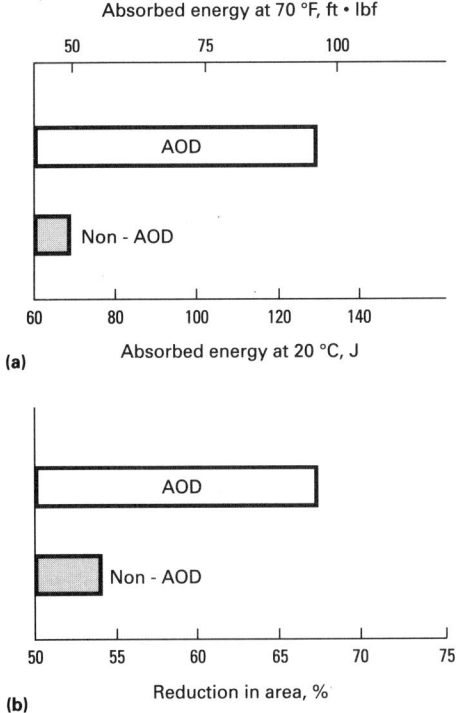

(a)

(b)

Fig. 6 Comparison of Charpy V-notch toughness values (a) and ductility (b) of CA6NM stainless steel processed with and without argon oxygen decarburization (AOD). Source: Ref 10

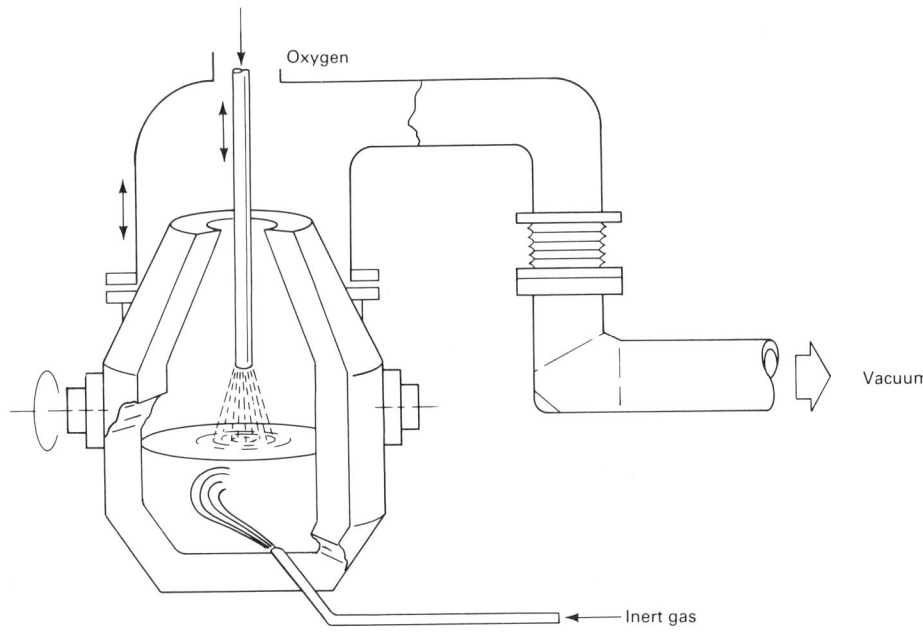

Fig. 7 Schematic of a vacuum oxygen decarburization converter

Decarburization. In both stainless and low-alloy steels, the dilution of oxygen with inert gas results in increased carbon removal efficiencies without excessive metallic oxidation. In stainless grades, carbon levels of 0.01% are readily obtained.

Chemistry Control. The excellent compositional control of AOD-refined steel is indicated in Table 2 for a ten-heat series of type 316 stainless steel. The injection of a known quantity of oxygen with a predetermined bath weight enables the steelmaker to obtain very tight chemical specifications.

Desulfurization. Sulfur levels of 0.01% or less are routinely achieved, and levels less than 0.005% can be achieved with single slag practice. When extra-low sulfur levels are required, a separate slag treatment for 3 min is sufficient. Double slag treatments result in sulfur levels as low as 0.001%.

Slag Reduction. During oxygen injection for carbon removal, there is some metallic oxidation. Efficient slag reduction with stoichiometric amounts of silicon or aluminum permits overall recoveries of 97 to 100% for most metallic elements. Chromium recovery averages approximately 97.5%, and nickel and molybdenum recoveries are approximately 100%.

Nitrogen Control. Degassing during AOD is achieved by inert gas sparging. Each argon and CO bubble leaving the bath removes a small amount of dissolved nitrogen and hydrogen. Final nitrogen content can be accurately controlled by substituting nitrogen for argon during refining. Nitrogen levels as low as 25 to 30 ppm can be obtained in carbon and low-alloy steels, and 60 ppm N can be obtained in

stainless steels. The ability to obtain target nitrogen levels substantially reduces the need to use nitrided ferroalloys for alloy specification, and this also minimizes the use of argon. Hydrogen levels as low as 1.5 ppm can be obtained.

Advantages of AOD

Some of the advantages of AOD process that led to its rapid adoption are (Ref 9):

• Lower capital cost and higher productivity. The addition of an AOD converter can be equivalent to adding another electric furnace.
• Ability to use lower-cost, high-carbon ferrochromium in the charge
• Better recovery of chromium
• Increased precision of compositions via computer control. A spectrograph reading of the AOD melt can be directly fed into a desktop computer system equipped with floppy disk memory storage, which then issues processing instructions to the AOD operator. To ensure accuracy in determining the extremely low levels of carbon and sulfur, a combustion carbon-sulfur digital analyzer supplements the spectrograph. Digital readout gas analyzers to determine oxygen-nitrogen and hydrogen contents are also used during processing to improve control over melt quality.
• Uniformity of composition ensured by argon stirring
• Low levels of oxide inclusions and of sulfur, lead, and other contaminating elements
• Capability of producing low levels of carbon and nitrogen in new high-chromium ferritic alloys
• Excellent coupling of AOD vessels to continuous casting machines in terms of timing and quality of metal. No vacuum degassing is required.

The subsequent introduction of continuous casting resulted in further advances in cast metal uniformity and cost reduction: yields are increased from 80 to 90%, and there are energy savings and fewer processing delays.

Property Improvements. It has been well documented that AOD-refined steels exhibit significantly improved ductility and toughness (Fig. 6), along with impact energy increases of over 50% (Ref 10-13). These improved properties result from a decrease in the number and size of inclusions. The capability to produce low-gas-content steel with exceptional microcleanliness, along with alloy savings, is the primary factor in the growth of AOD for refining stainless, carbon, and low-alloy steels.

Oxygen Top and Bottom Blowing

Oxygen top and bottom blowing (OTB), also referred to as *combined blowing,* is an extension of AOD technology for refining steel. During OTB, oxygen is injected into the molten steel through a top lance during carbon removal, and inert gases, such as argon, nitrogen, or carbon dioxide, are injected with oxygen through submerged tuyeres or alternate forms of gas injectors such as canned bricks, porous bricks, or thin pipes set in the refractory brick. The top-blown oxygen can react with the bath, reducing refining times, or with CO. The combustion of CO above the surface of the bath increases the thermal efficiency of the refining process and decreases the quantity of silicon and aluminum required for reduction of metallic oxides.

If the top-blown oxygen system is designed so that more than 65% of the oxygen reacts with the bath, the system is referred to as *hard blown;* if less than 65% of the oxygen reacts with the bath,

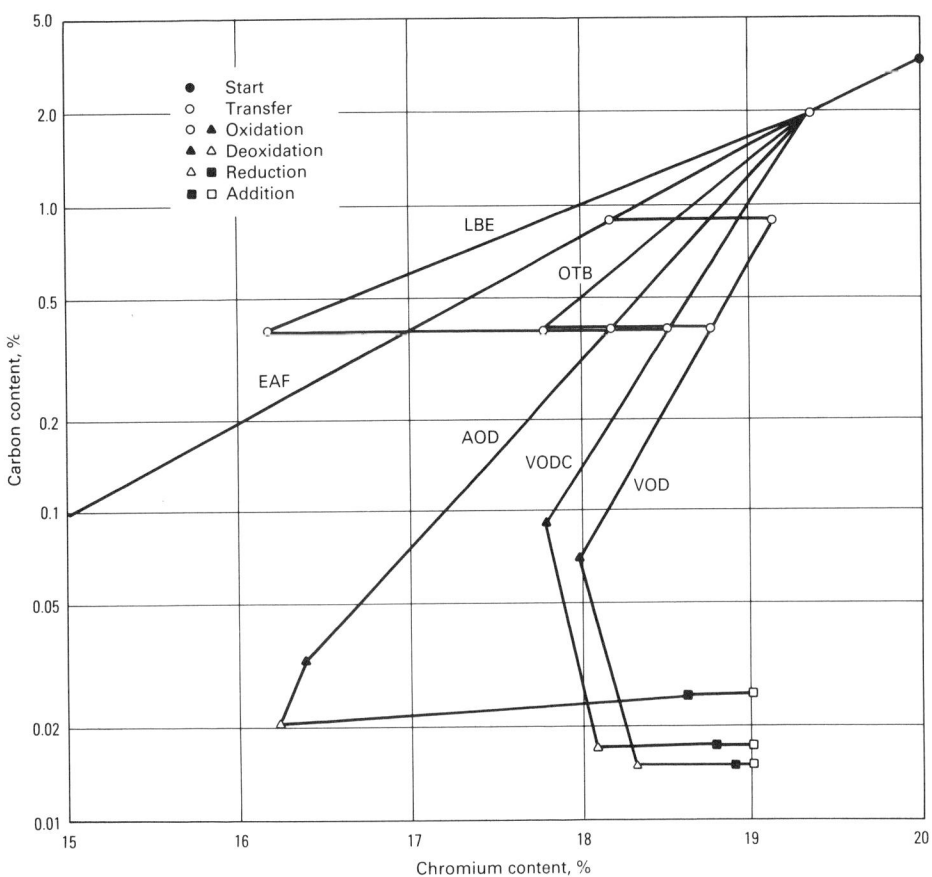

Technique	Total gas flow		Inert gas, %
	m³/min/Mg	ft³/min/ton	
Electric arc furnace (EAF)...................................	1.2	46	0
Lance bubbling equilibrium (LBE)........................	2.5	95	1
Oxygen top blowing (OTB)................................	2.0	77	10
Argon oxygen decarburization (AOD)...................	1.0	40	20–90
Vacuum oxygen decarburization converter (VODC).........	0.7	27	2–5
Vacuum oxygen decarburization (VOD-ladle)..............	0.4	15	0.5–4

Fig. 8 Processing steps for achieving proper chromium and carbon levels in stainless steel using various refining techniques with varying gas blow rates and inert gas additions

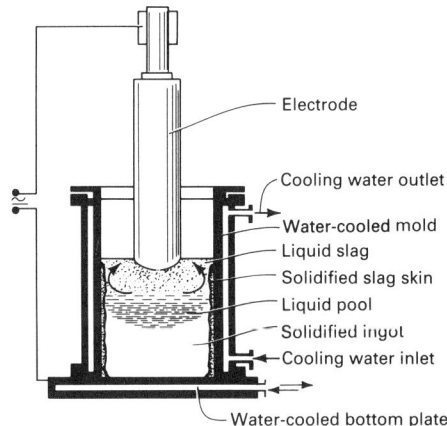

Fig. 9 Schematic of the electroslag remelting process

it is referred to as *soft blown*. As a general guideline, a top-blown oxygen system installed in AOD vessels with a nominal capacity greater than 45 metric tonnes (50 tons) will be hard blown and smaller vessels will be soft blown. In hard-blown systems, the flow rate of oxygen through the top lance will be between 50 and 150% of the oxygen injected through tuyeres or injectors. In soft-blown systems, the top oxygen flow rate is between 50 and 100% of the oxygen flow through the tuyeres or injectors.

Because foundry AOD vessels have a nominal capacity less than 45 metric tonnes (50 tons), the top-blown oxygen systems are designed to be soft blown. This design maximizes the thermal efficiency of the smaller AOD vessels, reducing the quantity of fuel and reduction material required during refining. Top-blown oxygen flow rates in foundry AOD vessels range from 50% of the bottom oxygen flow rate to 120%. More detailed information on OTB technology can be found in Ref 14 and 15.

Vacuum Oxygen Decarburization

Vacuum oxygen decarburization (VOD) converters are similar to AOD and OTB converters in terms of design and the tilting device used. Bottom blowing is, however, restricted to the introduction of small amounts of inert gas through simple pipes, thus avoiding the special erosion-resistant refractory material used around AOD tuyeres. Flue gas handling is easier and is incorporated into the vacuum system. In terms of vessel design, the conical converter top is closed by a vacuum hood with an oxygen lance feedthrough and vacuum addition lock (Fig. 7).

Because the VOD system is closed and no air enters the vessel, control of the decarburization rate and the carbon level in the bath can be maintained and monitored with a flue gas analyzing device (Ref 16, 17). Pollution control for CO and dust is also incorporated into the system.

Figure 8 shows the relationship between the oxygen blow rates and the inert gas additions for

various refining techniques, as well as the resulting chromium and carbon levels achieved at specific process steps. Figure 8 also shows the extent to which decarburization is accompanied by chromium oxidation. Using the VOD process, carbon and nitrogen levels below 100 ppm are achieved with corresponding chromium yields of over 95% before reduction and 98% after reduction (Ref 18, 19). Sulfur levels are at 10 to 30 ppm for any grade of steel without any sacrifice in the degassing effect. As with AOD, the cleanliness of VOD-processed melts results in significant improvements in mechanical properties of both cast and wrought stainless steels.

Special Melting Processes (Ref 20)

Several special melting methods can be used to produce stainless steels of higher purity and lower nonmetallic inclusion content than conventional EAF/AOD/VOD product when the demands of the application justify the added cost (for example, precipitation-hardenable stainless steels used for critical aerospace components). Selected charge materials may be melted entirely under high vacuum to prevent oxidation in melting and remove any volatile impurities. Vacuum induction melting (VIM) is the most commonly used method, but electron beam melting may also be used. Conventionally melted or vacuum-melted material my be refined further by consumable electrode remelting. In this process, the starting stock is progressively melted and allowed to drip into a cooled metal mold where it is solidified to form an ingot. This can be done under vacuum (vacuum arc remelting, VAR, or electron beam remelting) or under a blanket of molten slag (electroslag remelting, ESR).

A schematic view of an ESR furnace is shown in Fig. 9. The material (electrode) to be refined is remelted by passing a current through it into the molten slag, which is resistively heated and which, in turn, melts the electrode. Molten metal droplets form on the end of the electrode and fall through the slag, forming an ingot in the water-cooled copper crucible. The process continues until the electrode is consumed and the ingot is formed. Additional information on VIM, VAR, ESR, and electron beam melting/remelting can be found in Volume 15 of the *ASM Handbook*.

ACKNOWLEDGMENTS

The information in this article is largely taken from:

- I.F. Masterson, Argon Oxygen Decarburization, *Casting*, Vol 15, *ASM Handbook* (formerly 9th ed., *Metals Handbook*), ASM International, 1988, p 426-429
- W. Burgmann, Vacuum Oxygen Decarburization, *Casting*, Vol 15, *ASM Handbook* (formerly 9th ed., *Metals Handbook*), ASM International, 1988, p 429-431

REFERENCES

1. J. Feinstein, Praxair, Inc., private communication, 1994
2. Electric-Furnace Steelmaking, *The Making, Shaping and Treating of Steel*, 10th ed., Association of Iron and Steel Engineers, 1985, p 627-669
3. N. Wukovich, Electric Arc Furnaces, *Casting*, Vol 15, *ASM Handbook* (formerly 9th ed., *Metals Handbook*), ASM International, 1988, p 356-368
4. F.D. Richardson and W.E. Dennis, Effect of Chromium on the Thermodynamic Activity of Carbon in Liquid Iron-Chromium-Carbon Metals, *J. Iron Steel Inst.*, Nov 1953, p 257-263
5. R.J. Choulet, F.S. Death, and R.N. Dokken, Argon-Oxygen Refining of Stainless Steel, *Can. Metall. Q.*, Vol 10 (No. 2), 1971, p 129-136
6. R.B. Aucott, D.W. Gray, and C.G. Holland, The Theory and Practice of the Argon-Oxygen Decarburizing Process, *J.W. Scot. Iron Steel Inst.*, Vol 79 (No. 5), 1971-1972, p 98-127
7. D.A. Whitworth, F.D. Jackson, and F.F. Patrick, Fused Basic Refractories in the Argon-Oxygen Decarburization Process, *Ceram. Bull.*, Vol 53 (No. 11), 1974
8. D. Brosnan and R.J. Marr, "The Use of Direct Burned Dolomite Brick in the AOD Vessel," paper presented at the Electric Furnace Conference (Detroit, MI), Iron and Steel Society, Dec 1977
9. M.A. Streicher, New Stainless Steels for the Process and Power Industries, *Metal Progress*, Oct 1985, p 29-42
10. C.S. Nalbone, "The Effect of AOD Refining on the Mechanical Properties and Sulfide Stress Cracking of CA6NM," STP 756, ASTM, 1982, p 315-331
11. P.A. Tichauer and L.J. Venne, AOD, a New Process for Steel Foundries, Promises Better Properties, Less Repair, *33 Magazine*, April 1977, p 35-38
12. D. Heckel, J.P. Weincek, and N. Netoskie, "Metallurgical Aspects of the AOD," paper presented at the Electric Furnace Conference (Detroit, MI), Iron and Steel Society, Dec 1977
13. F.J. Andreini and S.K. Mehlman, "Quality Aspects of Foundry AOD," paper presented at the Electric Furnace Conference (Detroit, MI), Iron and Steel Society, Dec 1979
14. S.K. Mehlman, Ed., *Mixed Gas Blowing*, Proceedings of the Fourth Process Technology Conference, Iron and Steel Society of AIME, American Institute of Mechanical Engineers, 1984
15. L.G. Kuhn, Ed., Mixed Gas Blowing—A New Era of Pneumatic Steelmaking, *Iron and Steel Maker*, Aug 1983
16. R. Heinke and S. Köhle, Computer Control of the VOD Process, *Proceedings of the Seventh International Conference on Vacuum Metallurgy* (Tokyo), Section 34-2, Iron and Steel Institute of Japan, 1982, p 1356-1363
17. L. Tolnay, I. Sziklavari, and G. Karolyk, Method of Regulating the Endpoint of the Vacuum Decarburization Process Developed for the Production of Acid Resistant Steel Grades with Extra Low Carbon Content in ASEA-SKF Ladle Metallurgy Plant, *Proceedings of the Eighth International Vacuum Metallurgy Conference* (Linz), M1.3, Eisenhütte Osterreich, 1985, p 606-615
18. P. Tennilae, M. Kaivola, and M. Walter, Systems Technology and Operating Results of VODC Converter, *Proceedings of the First Electric Steel Congress* (Aachen), F4, Verein Deutscher Eisenhütterleute, 1983, p 1-12
19. W. Burgmann, O. Wiessner, and G. Reese, Vacuum Converter Technology for the Production of Superalloys, Stainless and Low Alloy Steels, *Proceedings of the Vacuum Metallurgy Conference on Special Metals and Melting Processes* (Pittsburgh, PA), Iron and Steel Society, 1985, p 3-10
20. *Stainless and Heat Resisting Steels*, Iron and Steel Society, Nov 1990, p 6

Recycling Technology

RECYCLING, the use of a material over and over again, has many benefits, including the conservation of natural resources and reductions in energy consumption and in the amount of disposable waste. Recycled scrap is a major raw material for stainless steel production, supplying more than one-third of the stainless steel market in the United States (Ref 1).

Because stainless steel scrap is almost always used to produce more stainless steel, demand for stainless scrap is largely a function of the demand for stainless steel itself. A general increase over time is therefore expected as manufacturers increase their use of stainless steels to improve product performance. However, general industrial production, which is driven by the overall economy, is the primary factor that influences demand. High demand for stainless steel in 1987 through 1989, following a period of low demand, resulted in sharply increased demand for stainless steel scrap. Demand is heightened by tight world markets for both chromium and nickel. Fortunately, increased demand also raises the value of scrap, which enables more to be recycled. As a major producer and consumer of stainless steel, the United States usually has excess stainless steel scrap, which is exported.

Stainless steels are recycled to produce the same metal whenever possible. For example, type 316 stainless steel is recycled to produce more type 316. It is the responsibility of the scrap processor to ensure that the metal producer receives the desired scrap, as needed, and in the desired form.

The most critical step in stainless steel recycling, therefore, is the identification and sorting of alloys into groups of similar materials (Ref 2). Scrap stainless steels are typically identified by skilled sorters using a number of physical and chemical tests. These tests rely on object recognition, color, apparent density, magnetic properties, nature of spark patterns when ground on an abrasive wheel (see the section "Spark Testing" in this article), chemical reaction to reagents or quantitative chemical analysis (see the section "Chemical Identification" in this article), and spectroscopic analysis (see the next section in this article). Valid and rapid identification techniques are necessary because a penalty is exacted for contamination of a scrap product. Figure 1 lists common identification tests for presorting metal scrap, including stainless steel.

Spark Testing

Spark testing is a fast and economical method of separating stainless scrap. Experienced operators can use this method to identify 200-, 300-, and 400-series materials with reasonable accuracy.

Spark testing is not intended as a substitute for chemical analysis. Each spark stream from a number of parts supposedly of the same composition should have the same spark characteristics. If one or more of the parts exhibits a spark stream having characteristics that differ from the other parts being tested, a different composition is indicated. In such instances, chemical or spectrochemical analysis can be used for positive identification of the unknown composition.

An advantage of spark testing is that it can be applied to alloys in forms representing almost any form of scrap. Because spark testing is performed

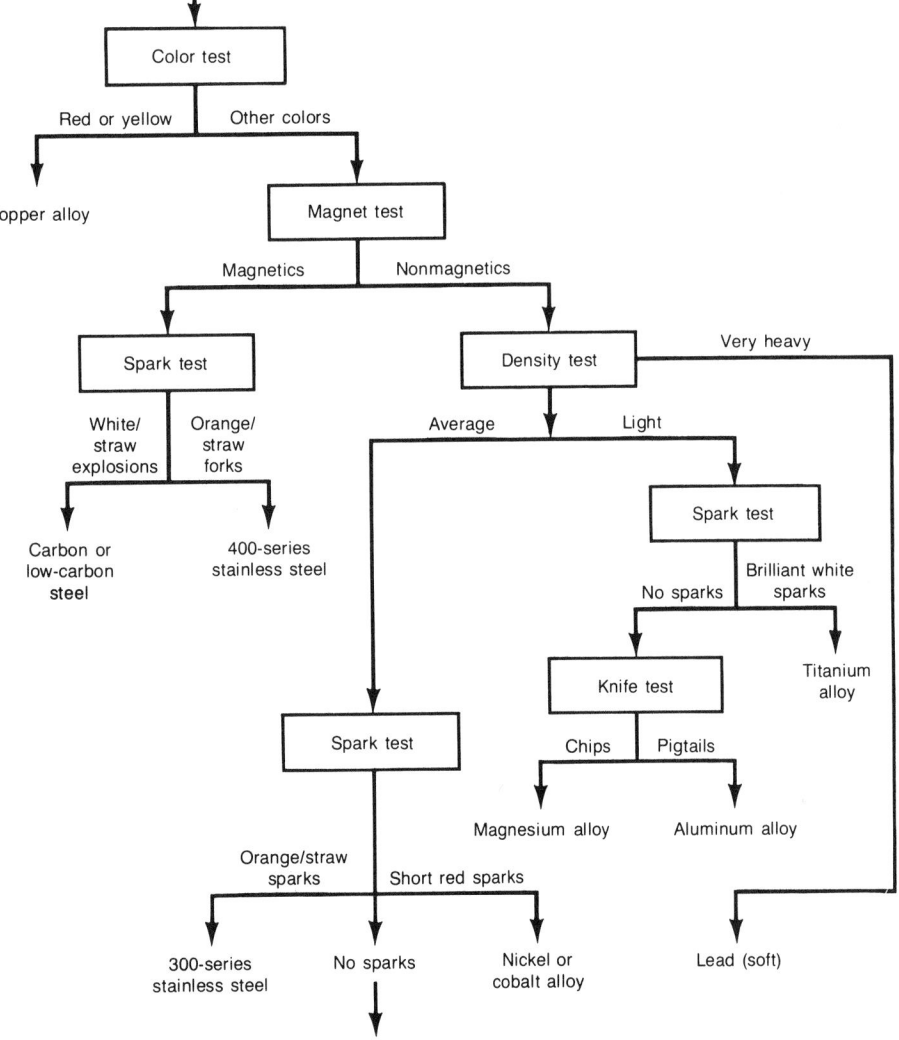

Fig. 1 Simple flowchart for presorting metallic scrap

directly on scrap pieces, expensive sampling methods are avoided.

Equipment. The minimum apparatus necessary for spark testing is either a portable or a stationary grinding machine and a suitable grinding wheel. A stationary grinder suitable for sharpening tools can be used to test scrap that can be transported to the machine. Where it is impractical to move a part or component to the grinding machine, portable grinding equipment can be used. To provide spark stream that is satisfactory for examination, the grinder should provide a peripheral wheel speed of not less than 23 m/s (4500 sfm), and preferably higher. Speeds of 38 to 58 m/s (7500 to 11,500 sfm) are considered optimum in most plants.

Grinding wheels should be coarse and very hard. Aluminum oxide or carborundum wheels are suggested for general-purpose use on stainless steel scrap.

The examination of spark streams under nearly ideal conditions can be done in a spark-test cabinet. A cabinet about 100 cm (40 in.) long, 90 cm (36 in.) wide, and 90 cm (36 in.) deep is suitable for spark testing. The inside of the cabinet should be painted a flat black and should be equipped for artificial illumination. The spark-test cabinet should be located where no direct light will strike either the operator's eyes or the inside of the cabinet. The grinding machine may be mounted at the left front of the cabinet and should throw a spark stream across the front of the cabinet at right angles to the operator's line of vision.

Protection of the eyes during spark testing is very important, both to avoid injury from abrasive particles of metal and to minimize the effect of certain rays of light. Several optical companies have developed goggles that satisfy the requirements of spark testing.

Spark Classification. The spark stream may be divided into three equal sections: the wheel sparks, which are in the spark stream nearest the wheel; the center area; and the tail sparks, which are in the spark stream farthest from the wheel.

The components of a spark stream to be observed are the carrier lines, the spark bursts, and the "characteristic sparks." The carrier lines vary in length, width, color, and number. The spark bursts vary in intensity, size, number, shape, and distance from the grinding wheel or from the end of the carrier lines. Carrier lines are the incandescent streaks that trace the trajectory of every glowing particle and are closely related to characteristic sparks. Spark characteristics of stainless steels are compared with those of carbon steels and nickel- and cobalt-base superalloys in Table 1.

Test Reliability. The reliability of spark testing depends on the ability of the test operator to visually differentiate the various spark patterns produced. Skilled personnel are therefore required for dependable results. Test conditions, including lighting conditions, background (preferably dark), and the pressure used to hold the specimen against the wheel, should be uniform. In addition, the wheel must be frequently dressed to remove the metal particles that adhere to it during tests. The use of standards, or samples of known

Table 1 Spark characteristics of various metals and alloys

Material	Spark characteristic
Normal carbon steel	Heavy, dense sparks 455-610 mm (18-24 in.) long that travel completely around the grinding wheel. Sparks are white to straw colored with main burst throughout.
400-series chromium stainless steel	Sparks are not as heavy or dense as those of normal carbon steel. Sparks are 355-455 mm (14-18 in.) long, travel completely around the grinding wheel, and are orange to straw colored, ending with a forked tongue. Preliminary bursts and few main bursts
300-series stainless steel	Sparks are not as heavy or as dense as those of normal carbon steel. Sparks are 305-455 mm (12-18 in.) long, travel completely around the grinding wheel, and are orange to straw colored, ending in a straight line with few if any bursts.
310-series 25-20 stainless steel	The spark stream is thin and 100-150 mm (4-6 in.) long. Sparks are orange to red in color and do not travel around the grinding wheel; there are no bursts.
Nickel and cobalt high-temperature alloys	The spark stream is thin and about 50 mm (2 in.) long. The sparks are dark red in color and do not travel around the grinding wheel; there are no bursts.

Source: Ref 3

composition, is desirable if positive identification of the alloy is required.

Automated Spark Testing. To avoid reliance on operator skills and experience for spark testing, methods have been developed to classify spark test results using optical spectroscopy, optical spectrometry, and other methods (Ref 4, 5). Preliminary results reported in Ref 5 indicate that the methods can distinguish even stainless materials with spark patterns that appear similar to the naked eye, such as those of AISI type 304 and 316 stainless steels.

Chemical Identification

There are two main types of chemical identification: qualitative chemical spot testing and quantitative wet chemical analysis. Spot testing is commonly used to provide rapid identification and sorting of stainless scrap. Spot testing is the main technique used in sorting of stainless steel scrap and is the only chemical method described in this article. Information on quantitative chemical identification can be found in the article "Classical Wet Analytical Chemistry" in Volume 10 of the *ASM Handbook*.

Chemical spot testing is a relatively simple, qualitative method that can be used for rapid laboratory or field identification of metals and alloys. Information on the chemical composition of the testpiece is gained by observing the color change occurring during a chemical reaction taking place on one spot on the test piece, on filter paper, or on a spot plate. The test method is not dependent on the use of auxiliary optical magnification.

An important part of chemical spot testing is the manipulation of drops of test or reagent solutions. The success of the test method derives from the nature of the reagents used, together with the advantageous use of reactive conditions, so that the desired sensitivity and selectivity can be obtained with a minimum of physical and chemical operations. Tests ordinarily are performed by using one of the following techniques (Ref 6):

- Bringing together a few drops of the test solution and of the reagent on porous or nonporous supporting surfaces such as paper, glass, or porcelain
- Placing a few drops of test solution on a medium (filter paper or gelatin) impregnated with appropriate reagents
- Placing a drop or two of reagent on a small quantity of the solid specimen (the most common technique for sorting and identification of scrap)
- Subjecting a drop of reagent or a strip of reagent paper to the action of liberated gases from a drop of the test solution or from a small quantity of the solid specimen
- Adding a drop of test solution to a larger volume (0.5 to 2 mL) of reagent solution and then extracting the reaction products with organic solvents

The successful application of spot-testing procedures is enhanced by: (a) a knowledge of the chemical basis of the test used, so that every step of the procedure is understood and executed intelligently; (b) strict observance of the experimental conditions; (c) cleanness of the laboratory or test site and equipment; and (d) use of the purest reagents available. If possible, tests should be repeated to ensure reproducibility, and tests on unknown materials should be compared with tests on known materials.

Although chemical spot testing should be conducted in a laboratory using laboratory equipment and conditions, portable kits can be assembled that contain the necessary chemicals and equipment for field testing. These are often used for quick, preliminary identification of stainless steel scrap materials.

Specific Tests for Stainless Scrap. Tests for identifying specific types of austenitic and precipitation-hardening stainless steels are described in Ref 7. The following is information on general spot tests used to sort and identify stainless steel scrap.

Nitric Acid Test. Stainless steels are noted for their inherent resistance to attack by either concentrated or dilute solutions of nitric acid. This characteristic makes it easy to separate them from most other metals or alloys. However, the higher-carbon types (420 and 440) may be attacked slightly by nitric acid. In contrast, carbon and alloy steels are vigorously attacked by dilute nitric acid.

Copper Sulfate Test. One of the simplest methods for differentiating quickly between carbon or alloy steels and all types of stainless steel is a spot test using a solution with 5 to 10% copper sulfate (blue vitriol) in water.

Before running the spot test, the areas to be tested should be thoroughly cleaned of grease or any foreign substances, and a mild abrasive should be used on a small area before the test solution is applied on the clean area with a drop bottle. Ordinary carbon steel or iron will become coated with metallic copper in a few seconds,

whereas stainless steel will show no deposit or copper color.

Sulfuric Acid Tests. An immersion test in heated sulfuric acid can be used to distinguish types 316 and 317 from types 302 and 304 stainless steel. The cut edges of samples should be honed; then the pieces should be cleaned and passivated in 3 *M* nitric acid or 6 *M* nitric acid for ½ h at 60 to 65 °C (140 to 150 °F).

The test solution consists of 10% sulfuric acid heated to 70 °C (160 °F). When types 302 and 304 are immersed in this hot solution, attack is rapid, as evidenced by the vigorous rising of bubbles, and the pieces become dark in a few minutes. Samples of type 316 or 317 will show either no attack or a very slow reaction (small number of bubbles), and the pieces will not change color during a short testing period of 10 to 15 min. The test can be made more accurate by simulta-

neously testing samples of known compositions for close comparison.

Alternatively, types 302 and 304 may be distinguished from types 316 and 317 by applying drops of 3 *M* sulfuric acid to surfaces that have been activated by grinding, filing, scouring, or rough polishing. A few drops of the acid solution are applied to each of the activated surfaces. Types 302 and 304 will show vigorous attack and darkened surfaces under the solution; a dark-brown or black color will appear under the acid, and later greenish crystals will form from the solution. Type 316 is attacked slowly and gradually turns tan in color but later may darken to brown, and finally some dark crystals with a slight greenish tinge may form. The reaction progresses more slowly with type 317.

Phosphoric Acid Test. To separate chromium-nickel stainless steel from chromium-nickel-moly-

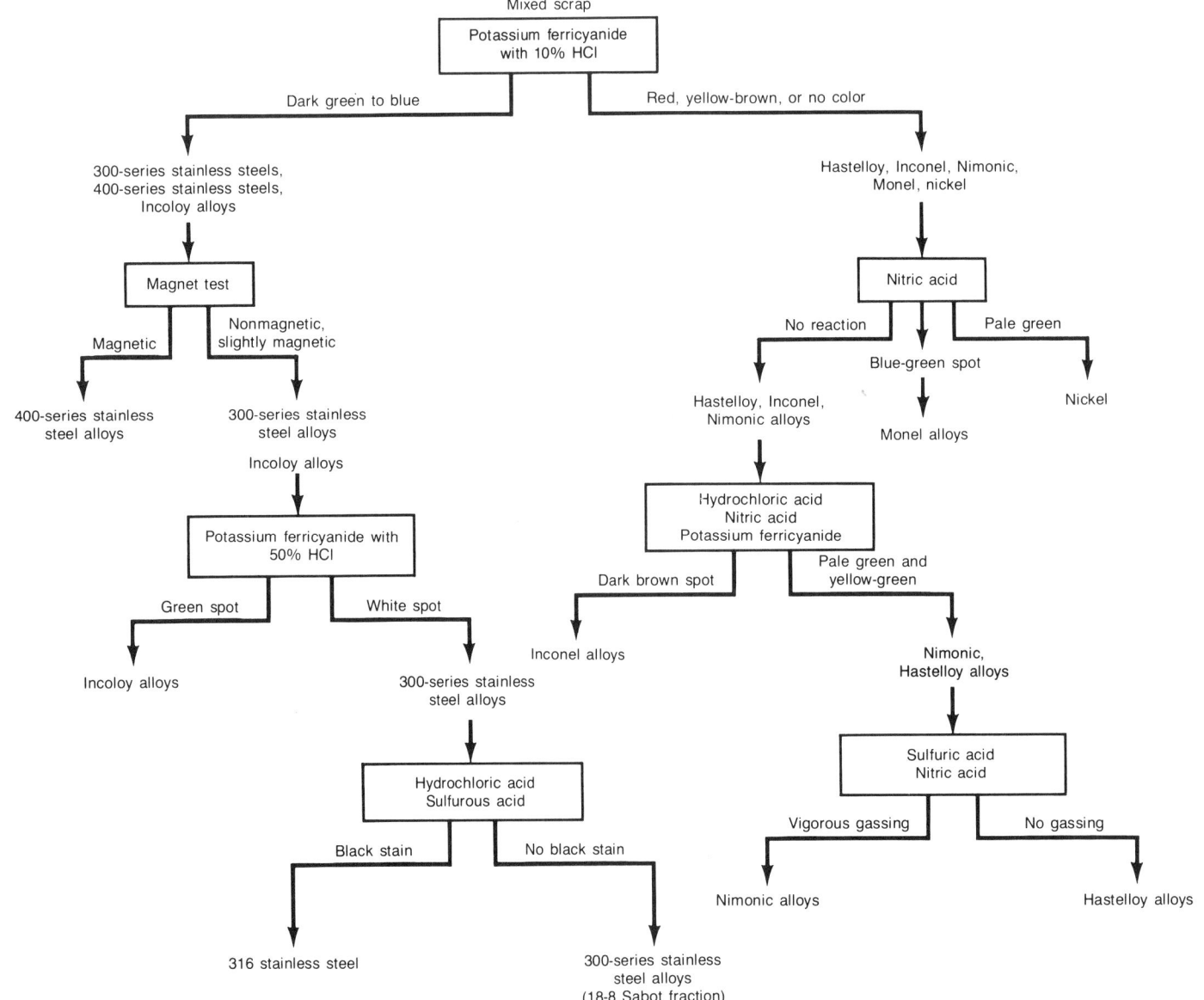

Fig. 2   Chemical test identification techniques for nickel-base alloys and stainless steels

bdenum types, a solution consisting of 0.5% sodium fluoride added to concentrated phosphoric acid is heated to 60 to 65 °C (140 to 150 °F). Samples are immersed in this hot solution. Type 316 or 317 will show no reaction; gas bubbles will evolve slowly from chromium-nickel types such as 302 and 304.

Hydrochloric acid tests may be used to separate lower-chromium types 403, 410, 416, and 420 from types 430, 431, 440, and 446, which contain more chromium. Equal weights of sample drillings are dissolved in 6 *M* hydrochloric acid, and the color intensities of the solutions are compared. A more pronounced greenish color is an indication of higher chromium content.

Separation tests may also be conducted by means of acid reaction with drillings of types 302, 303(Se), 410, and 416. A few grams of clean drillings from each sample are placed in separate test tubes; then an equal amount of 6 *M* hydrochloric acid is poured into each tube. The reactions of the steels with the acid, and the colors of the solutions after 3 min, are as follows:

Type	Reaction	Solution color
302	Fairly rapid	Pale blue-green
303(Se)	Garlic odor	Light amber
410	Vigorous	Darker green than for 302
416	Very rapid; rotten-egg odor	Dark, muddy green

Types 301, 304, 310, 316, and 347 will react similarly to type 302 or will slowly produce a pale bluish-green color without garlic odor. The results of chemical spot tests for identifying stainless steel and superalloy scrap are summarized in Fig. 2.

Spectroscopic Analysis

As the number and complexity of stainless steels have increased, the need of the scrap metal processor to more accurately quantify and qualify the metals present has also increased. Spectroscopic analysis has been developed as an analytical tool and is in general use by scrap processors. The basic principle of this analytical technique is that an element, upon being energized, will re-emit energy in characteristic wavelengths. Measuring these emissions from the sample and comparing them to a standard permits a quick and accurate analysis of most metals.

In optical spectroscopes, an electrical discharge is used to vaporize a small quantity of metal from the surface of a specimen. The heat provided is sufficient to cause the vaporized metal to luminesce as well. The light emitted is broken down into individual wavelengths, and the individual elements are then identified by the presence of their characteristic wavelengths. Although this type of analysis is very useful in discovering the presence of an element, it is not always accurate in determining the precise quantity that is present.

X-ray spectroscopy is another technique for identifying the elements present in an alloy; it is also useful in quantifying the elements present. In principle, a sample is bombarded with x-rays and then radiates back characteristic x-rays, which are used to identify the elements present by comparing the emissions with emissions from known standards. A potential problem occurs when elements with close atomic numbers are being analyzed, because resolution at low concentrations is often difficult, although not always impossible.

Available spectroscopic equipment ranges from portable, simple-to-use instruments (Fig. 3) to highly sophisticated and precise equipment. This equipment is most frequently used by scrap processors to identify and sort scrap with a high alloy content; the unit value of the scrap must be high enough to warrant the use of such equipment. Considerable experience and knowledge of the equipment are required. The results, however, can be obtained relatively quickly, which helps make this type of analytical equipment practical.

Other Identification Techniques

When two different metals at two different temperatures are in contact, they generate an electric potential known as the Seebeck effect. Thermoelectric devices use this effect to identify and sort scrap. These devices contain two probes made of the same metal, one heated and one at ambient temperature. When they contact another piece of metal, the scrap, a potential difference between the two probes is generated and is measured by a voltmeter. The potential difference is characteristic of the metal being tested. Calibration against standards enables identification of various alloys.

The magnitude of this change in potential is small for stainless steels, usually less than 1%. An extreme example is 304 stainless steel; the instrument reading increases 6% when the cold work increases from 0 to 75%. In this case, the austenite structure is being transformed by the cold work into a structure like martensite. This effect is fairly small when compared with the changes in instrument readings that occur with changes in composition from alloy to alloy. Thermoelectric measurements for several common stainless steels are (Ref 8):

Material	Average thermoelectric response(a)
201	585
301	597
303	603
304	602
316	587
321	591
347	586

(a) Copper-tipped base probe. Arbitrary units based on type 302 stainless steel standard

Reference 8 compares the effectiveness of various spectroscopic and other techniques, including the thermoelectric method, in the sorting of mixed stainless and superalloy scrap. The researchers used 27 stainless and superalloy samples to determine the relative usefulness of thermoelectric, x-ray spectro-

Fig. 3 Portable x-ray spectroscope. Source: Ref 8

graphic, and optical emission techniques as well as combined methods.

The research resulted in a flow chart showing instrumental identification techniques for stainless and superalloy scrap (Fig. 4). Also, a combined thermoelectric/optical spectroscopic technique was identified that had equipment costs less than half those for an x-ray analyzer.

Melting and Refining of Stainless Scrap (Ref 9)

Very clean, segregated stainless steel scrap can be sheared into small pieces, descaled using grit or steel blasting, and sent to foundries for remelting. Handling and processing equipment, including balers, presses, crushers, and shears, is identical to the equipment used in recycling plain carbon steels.

Stainless scrap is purchased entirely by stainless and special alloy producers. All stainless steel melters use both scrap and virgin materials in production. The

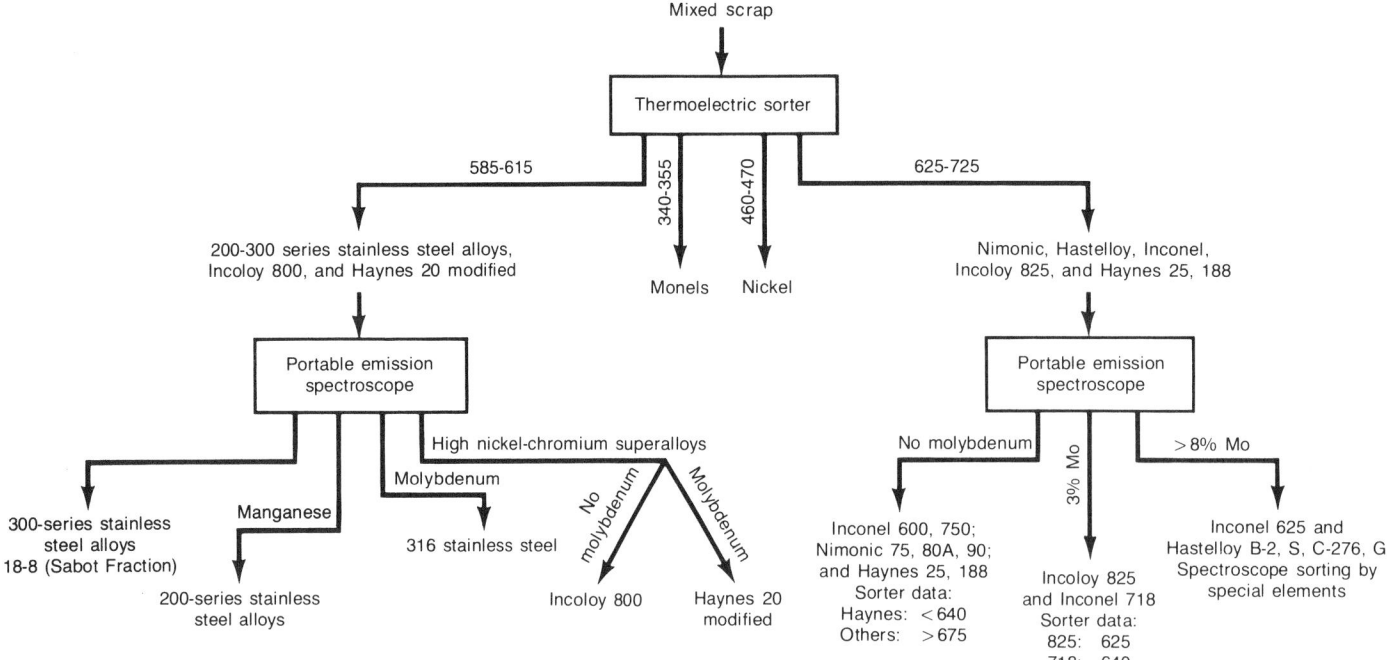

Fig. 4 Flow chart of instrumental identification techniques for sorting mixed stainless steel and superalloy scrap. Source: Ref 8

proportions of scrap and new materials are calculated for each heat based on the lowest cost per heat.

The major process for making stainless steel is a duplex method involving melting and initial refining in an electric arc furnace, followed by refining in an argon-oxygen decarburization (AOD) vessel. Small quantities of stainless (less than 10% of the total produced) are still made entirely in the electric furnace. Electric furnace processing is a relatively inefficient production method, requiring considerably longer heat time and thus consuming more energy than AOD processing. Lower chromium recoveries, less flexibility in scrap usage, and greater ferrosilicon consumption are other drawbacks of using electric furnace processing alone.

Induction furnaces also are used to produce small amounts of stainless from scrap. Generally used in foundries, induction melting is used only for melting scrap and virgin materials in proportions usually dictated by customer specifications and other market conditions.

For more information on stainless steel melting and refining processes, see the article "Melting and Refining Methods" in this Volume.

REFERENCES

1. Iron and Steel, *Recycled Metals in the 1980's,* National Association of Recycling Industries, 1982, p 89-97
2. W.D. Riley, R.E. Brown, and D.M. Soboroff, Rapid Identification and Sorting of Scrap Metals, *Conserv. Recycl.,* Vol 6 (No. 4), 1983, p 181-192
3. W.D. Riley, R.D. Brown, Jr., and J.M. Larrain, Large-Scale Metals Identification and Sorting Using Instrumental Techniques, *J. Test. Eval.,* Vol 15 (No. 4), July 1987, p 239-247
4. W.D. Riley, B.W. Dunning, Jr., and D.M. Soboroff, "Spectral Characteristics of Grinding Sparks Used for Identification of Scrap Metals," Bureau of Mines Report RI-8932, U.S. Department of the Interior, 1985
5. J.M. Larrain, W.D. Riley, and R.D. Brown, Jr., Spark Testing in the Identification of Stainless Steel and Superalloy Scrap, Recycle and Secondary Recovery of Metals, Proceedings of the International Symposium on Recycle and Secondary Recovery of Metals, TMS-AIME, 1985
6. F. Feigl and U. Anger, *Spot Tests in Inorganic Analysis,* 6th ed., Elsevier, 1972
7. "Nondestructive Rapid Identification of Metals and Alloys by Spot Tests," STP 550, ASTM, 1974
8. R.D. Brown, Jr., W.D. Riley, and C.A. Zieba, "Rapid Identification of Stainless Steel and Superalloy Scrap," Bureau of Mines Report RI-8858, U.S. Department of the Interior, 1984
9. C.L. Kusik and C.B. Kenahan, "Energy Use Patterns for Metal Recycling," Bureau of Mines Information Circular IC-8781, U.S. Department of the Interior, 1978, p 112

Contents

Atmospheric and Aqueous Corrosion

STAINLESS STEELS, as defined throughout this Volume, are iron-base alloys that contain at least 11% Cr. With increasing chromium content and the presence or absence of some 10 to 15 other elements, stainless steels can provide an extraordinary range of corrosion resistance. Various grades have been used for many years in environments as mild as open air in architectural applications and as severe as the chemically active product streams in the chemical-processing industries. Stainless steels are categorized in five distinct families according to their crystal structure and strengthening precipitates (see the "General Introduction" in this Volume). Each family exhibits its own general characteristics in terms of mechanical properties and corrosion resistance. Within each family, there is a range of grades that vary in composition, corrosion resistance, and cost.

Stainless steels are susceptible to several forms of localized corrosive attack. The avoidance of such localized corrosion is the focus of most of the effort involved in selecting stainless steels. Furthermore, the corrosion performance of stainless steels can be strongly affected by practices of design, fabrication, surface conditioning, and maintenance.

Selection of a suitable stainless steel for a specific environment requires consideration of several criteria. The first is corrosion resistance. Alloys are available that provide resistance to mild atmospheres (for example, type 430) or to many food-processing environments (for example, type 304). Chemicals and more severe corrodents require type 316 or a more highly alloyed material, such as 20Cb-3. Factors that affect the corrosivity of an environment include the concentration of chemical species, pH, aeration, flow rate (velocity), impurities (such as chlorides), and temperature, including effects from heat transfer.

The second criterion is mechanical properties, or strength. High-strength materials often sacrifice resistance to some form of corrosion, particularly stress-corrosion cracking (SCC).

Third, fabrication must be considered, including such factors as the ability of the steel to be machined, welded, or formed. Resistance of the fabricated article to the environment must be considered—for example, the ability of the material to resist attack in crevices that cannot be avoided in the design.

Fourth, total cost must be estimated, including initial alloy price, installed cost, and the effective life expectancy of the finished product. Finally, consideration must be given to product availability.

This article describes the corrosion of stainless steels in various atmospheres and aqueous media. Emphasis is placed on the selection and corrosion resistance of wrought alloys for service in harsh chemical environments (acids, chlorine, alkalis, etc.). Discussion of the corrosion resistance of powder metallurgy and cast stainless steels can be found in the articles "Powder Metallurgy Stainless Steels" and "Corrosion of Cast Stainless Steels," respectively, in this Volume.

Mechanism of Corrosion Resistance

The mechanism of corrosion protection for stainless steels differs from that for carbon steels, alloy steels, and most other metals. In these other cases, the formation of a barrier of true oxide separates the metal from the surrounding atmosphere. The degree of protection afforded by such an oxide is a function of the thickness of the oxide layer, its continuity, its coherence and adhesion to the metal, and the diffusivities of oxygen and metal in the oxide. In high-temperature oxidation, stainless steels use a generally similar model for corrosion protection. However, at low temperatures, stainless steels do not form a layer of true oxide. Instead, a passive film is formed. One mechanism that has been suggested is the formation of a film of hydrated oxide, but there is not total agreement on the nature of the oxide complex on the metal surface. However, the oxide film should be continuous, nonporous, insoluble, and self-healing if broken in the presence of oxygen.

Passivity exists under certain conditions for particular environments. The range of conditions over which passivity can be maintained depends on the precise environment and on the family and composition of the stainless steel. When conditions are favorable for maintaining passivity, stainless steels exhibit extremely low corrosion rates. If passivity is destroyed under conditions that do not permit restoration of the passive film, then stainless steel will corrode much like a carbon or low-alloy steel.

The presence of oxygen is essential to the corrosion resistance of a stainless steel. The corrosion resistance of stainless steel is at its maximum when the steel is boldly exposed and the surface is maintained free of deposits by a flowing bulk environment. Covering a portion of the surface—for example, by biofouling, painting, or installing a gasket—produces an oxygen-depleted region under the covered region. The oxygen-depleted region is anodic relative to the well-aerated boldly exposed surface, and a higher level of alloy content in the stainless steel is required to prevent corrosion.

With appropriate grade selection, stainless steel will perform for very long times with minimal corrosion, but an inadequate grade can corrode and perforate more rapidly than a plain carbon steel will fail by uniform corrosion. Selection of the appropriate grade of stainless steel is then a balancing of the desire to minimize cost and the risk of corrosion damage by excursions of environmental conditions during operation or downtime.

Confusion exists regarding the meaning of the term *passivation*. It is not necessary to chemically treat a stainless steel to obtain the passive film; the film forms spontaneously in the presence of oxygen. Most frequently, the function of passivation is to remove free iron, oxides, and other surface contamination. For example, in the steel mill, the stainless steel may be pickled in an acid solution, often a mixture of nitric and hydrofluoric acids (HNO_3-HF), to remove oxides formed in heat treatment. Once the surface is cleaned and the bulk composition of the stainless steel is exposed to air, the passive film forms immediately. Additional information on passivation treatments can be found in the article "Surface Engineering" in this Volume.

Effects of Composition

Chromium is the one element essential in forming the passive film. Other elements can influence the effectiveness of chromium in forming or maintaining the film, but no other element can, by itself, create the properties of stainless steel. The film is first observed at about 10.5% Cr, but it is rather weak at this composition and affords only mild atmospheric protection. Increasing the chromium content to 17 to 20%, as typical of the austenitic stainless steels, or to 26 to 29%, as possible in the newer ferritic stainless steels, greatly increases the stability of the passive film. However, higher chromium may adversely affect mechanical properties, fabricability, weldability, or suitability for applications involving certain thermal exposures. Therefore, it is often more efficient to improve corrosion resistance by altering other elements, with or without some increase in chromium.

Nickel, in sufficient quantities, will stabilize the austenitic structure; this greatly enhances mechanical properties and fabrication characteristics. Nickel is effective in promoting repassivation, especially in reducing environments. Nickel is particularly useful in resisting corrosion in mineral acids. Increasing nickel content to about 8 to 10% decreases resistance to SCC, but further increases begin to restore SCC resistance. Resistance to SCC in most service en-

Table 1 Chemical compositions of superaustenitic 6% Mo grades

UNS No.	Common name	Producers	Chemical composition, wt%(a)					
			Cr	Ni	Mo	Cu	N	C
S31254	254 SMO(b)	Avesta	19.50-20.50	17.50-18.50	6.00-6.50	0.50-1.00	0.18-0.22	0.020 max
J93254	Cast 254 SMO(b); CK-3MCuN	Various licensees	19.50-20.50	17.50-18.50	6.00-6.50	0.50-1.00	0.18-0.22	0.020 max
N08366	AL-6X(c)	Allegheny Ludlum	20.00-22.00	23.50-25.50	6.00-7.00	...	...	0.035 max
N08367	AL-6XN(c)	Allegheny Ludlum	20.00-22.00	23.50-25.50	6.00-7.00	0.75 max	0.18-0.25	0.030 max
N08925	1925 hMo; 25-6MO	VDM Technologies; Inco Alloys International	19.00-21.00	24.00-26.00	6.0-7.0	0.8-1.5	0.10-0.20	0.020 max
N08026	20Mo-6(d)	Carpenter Technology	22.00-26.00	33.00-37.20	5.00-6.70	2.00-4.00	...	0.03 max

(a) ASTM composition limits. (b) Registered trademark and patented alloy of Avesta AB. (c) Registered trademark and patented alloy of Allegheny Ludlum Corp. (d) Registered trademark and patented alloy of Carpenter Technology Corp.

vironments is achieved at about 30% Ni. In the newer ferritic grades, in which the nickel addition is less than that required to destabilize the ferritic phase, there are still substantial effects. In this range, nickel increases yield strength, toughness, and resistance to reducing acids, but it makes the ferritic grades susceptible to SCC in concentrated magnesium chloride ($MgCl_2$) solutions.

Manganese in moderate quantities and in association with nickel additions will perform many of the functions attributed to nickel. However, total replacement of nickel by manganese is not practical. Very-high-manganese steels have some unusual and useful mechanical properties, such as resistance to galling. Manganese interacts with sulfur in stainless steels to form manganese sulfides. The morphology and composition of these sulfides can have substantial effects on corrosion resistance, especially pitting resistance.

Molybdenum in combination with chromium is very effective in terms of stabilizing the passive film in the presence of chlorides. Molybdenum is especially effective in increasing resistance to the initiation of pitting and crevice corrosion.

Carbon is useful to the extent that it permits hardenability by heat treatment, which is the basis of the martensitic grades, and that it provides strength in the high-temperature applications of stainless steels. In all other applications, carbon is detrimental to corrosion resistance through its re-

action with chromium. In the ferritic grades, carbon is also extremely detrimental to toughness.

Nitrogen is beneficial to austenitic stainless steels in that it enhances pitting resistance, retards the formation of the chromium-molybdenum phase, and strengthens the steel. Nitrogen is essential in the newer duplex grades for increasing the austenite content, diminishing chromium and molybdenum segregation, and raising the corrosion resistance of the austenite phase. Nitrogen is highly detrimental to the mechanical properties of the ferritic grades and must be treated as comparable to carbon when a stabilizing element is added to the steel.

Corrosion Characteristics of Stainless Steel Families

As described in the "General Introduction" to this Volume, stainless steels are classified into the following five families:

- Austenitic stainless steels
- Ferritic stainless steels
- Martensitic stainless steels
- Duplex stainless steels
- Precipitation-hardening (PH) stainless steels

This section will summarize the general corrosion characteristics of each of these families. Although some chemical composition tables are provided, particularly for more specialized grades, the reader is referred to the "General Introduction" and the article "Metallurgy and Properties of Wrought Stainless Steels" in this Volume for more extensive listings of chemical compositions. The latter article also describes the physical metallurgy and properties associated with wrought stainless steels.

Austenitic Stainless Steels

The austenitic stainless steels were developed for use in both mild and severe corrosive conditions. They are also used at temperatures that range from cryogenic temperatures, where they exhibit high toughness, to elevated temperatures of nearly 600 °C (1110 °F), where they exhibit

good oxidation resistance. Because the austenitic materials are nonmagnetic, they are sometimes used in applications where magnetic materials are not acceptable. These desirable properties, combined with ease of fabrication, have made the austenitic grades, especially type 304, the most common of the stainless grades. (In fact, most of the austenitic grades have been developed from the basic 18Cr-8Ni type 304—see Fig. 1 in the "General Introduction" to this Volume.) Processing difficulties tend to limit increases in chromium content; therefore, improved corrosion resistance is usually obtained by adding molybdenum. The use of nitrogen as an intentional alloy addition stabilizes the austenite phase, particularly with regard to the precipitation of intermetallic compounds. With the nitrogen addition, it is possible to produce austenitic grades with up to 6% Mo for improved corrosion resistance in chloride environments (see the discussion below on "superaustenitics"). Other special grades include the high-chromium grades for high-temperature applications and the high-nickel grades for inorganic acid environments.

The austenitic stainless steels can be sensitized to intergranular corrosion by welding or by longer-term thermal exposure. These thermal exposures lead to the precipitation of chromium carbides in grain boundaries and to the depletion of chromium adjacent to these carbides. Sensitization can be greatly delayed or prevented by the use of lower-carbon grades (< 0.03% C) or stabilized grades, such as types 321 and 347, which include additions of carbide-stabilizing elements (titanium and niobium, respectively).

The common austenitic grades, types 304 and 316, are especially susceptible to chloride SCC. All austenitic stainless steels exhibit some degree of susceptibility, but several of the high-nickel, high-molybdenum grades are satisfactory with respect to stress-corrosion attack in most engineering applications.

Superaustenitics are high-alloy austenitic stainless steels that contain 6% Mo and 0.15 to 0.3% N. The leading 6% Mo austenitic stainless steels are listed in Table 1, along with their common names, corresponding UNS numbers, and ASTM composition ranges.

As mentioned above, the primary corrosion environments for the application of the 6% Mo austenitics are chlorides. Table 2 shows the critical crevice temperature (CCT) in 10% $FeCl_3$ · $6H_2O$ (pH 1) for several of the 6% Mo austenitics and some of the more common stainless steels. For a particular environment and crevice geometry, each stainless steel will have a critical temperature above which crevice corrosion initiates. Comparing the 6% Mo austenitics to some common austenitics, a dramatic improvement in corrosion resistance is noted by increasing molybdenum and nitrogen. Among the 6% Mo grades, nitrogen has a powerful effect, but nickel and copper seem to have almost no effect.

Ferritic Stainless Steels

The simplest stainless steels contain only iron and chromium. Chromium is a ferrite stabilizer;

Table 2 Critical crevice temperature (CCT) for selected 6% Mo and other common austenitic stainless steels

UNS No.	Grade	CCT in 10% $FeCl_3$ · H_2O (pH 1)	
		°C	°F
S31254	254 SMO	32.5	90.5
N08366	AL-6X	17.5	63.5
N08367	AL-6XN	32.5	90.5
S30403	Type 304L	<−2.5	<27.5
S31603	Type 316L	−2.5	27.5
N08904	Alloy 904L	0	32

Source: Ref 1

Table 3 Chemical compositions of superferritic stainless steels

UNS No.	Common name	Composition, %(a)								
		C	Mn	P	S	Si	Cr	Ni	Mo	Others
S44627	E-Brite	0.01	0.40	0.02	0.02	0.40	25.0-27.0	0.50	0.75-1.50	0.05-0.2Nb, 0.2Cu, 0.015N
S44635	MONIT	0.025	1.00	0.04	0.03	0.75	24.5-26.0	3.50-4.50	3.50-4.50	0.035N, Nb + Ti: 0.20 + 4(C + N)-0.80
S44660	Sea-Cure	0.025	1.00	0.04	0.03	1.00	25.0-27.0	1.50-3.50	2.50-3.50	0.035N, Nb + Ti: 0.20 + 4(C + N)-0.80
S44735	AL-29-4C	0.03	1.00	0.04	0.03	1.00	28.0-30.0	1.00	3.60-4.20	0.045N, Nb + Ti:6(C + N)
S44473S	Usinor 290 Mo	0.03	1.00	0.04	0.03	1.00	28.0-30.0	1.00	3.60-4.20	0.045N, Nb + Ti:6(C + N)
S44800	AL-29-4-2	0.01	0.30	0.025	0.02	0.20	28.0-30.0	2.0-2.5	3.50-4.20	0.15Cu, 0.02N, C + N:0.025 max

(a) Maximum unless otherwise stated

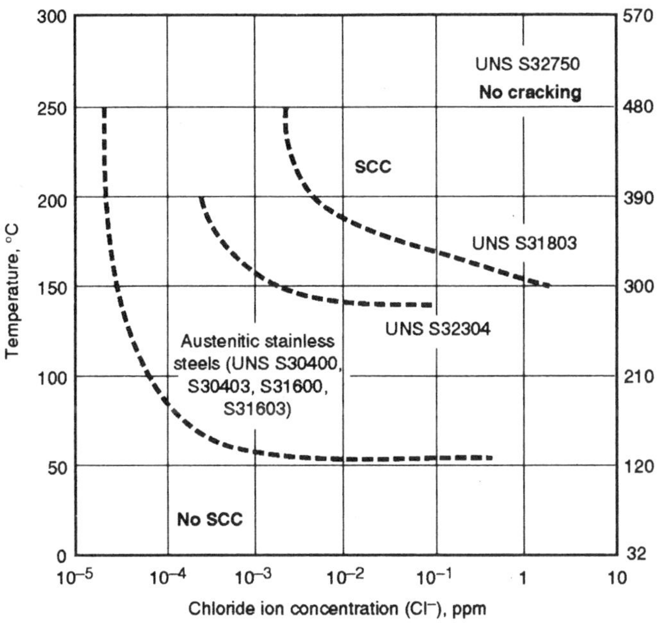

Fig. 1 Stress-corrosion cracking resistance of selected duplex stainless steels (S31803, S32304, and S32750) relative to that of austenitic stainless steels (S30400, S30403, and S31603) as a function of temperature and chloride concentration in neutral O_2-bearing solutions (approximately 8 ppm). Test duration was 1000 h. Applied stress was equal to yield strength. Source: Ref 2

therefore, the stability of the ferritic structure increases with chromium content. Ferrite has a body-centered cubic crystal structure, and it is characterized as magnetic and relatively high in yield strength but low in ductility and work hardenability. Ferrite shows an extremely low solubility for such interstitial elements as carbon and nitrogen. The ferritic grades exhibit a transition from ductile to brittle behavior over a rather narrow temperature range. At higher carbon and nitrogen contents, especially at higher chromium levels, this ductile-to-brittle transition can occur above ambient temperature. This possibility severely limited the use of ferritic grades before the use of argon-oxygen decarburization (AOD). The ferritic family was then limited to type 446 for oxidation-resistance applications and to types 430 and 434 for such corrosion applications as automotive trim. The fact that these grades were readily sensitized to intergranular corrosion as a result of welding or thermal exposure further limited their use.

With AOD, it was possible to reduce the levels of carbon and nitrogen significantly. The activity of carbon and nitrogen could be further reduced by the use of stabilizers, which are highly reactive elements (e.g., titanium and niobium) that precipitate the remaining interstitials. This newer generation of ferritic stainless steels includes type 444 and the more highly alloyed superferritic grades shown in Table 3. With control of interstitial elements, it is possible to produce grades with unusually high chromium and molybdenum contents. At these low effective carbon levels, these grades are tougher and more weldable than the first generation of ferritic stainless steels. Nevertheless, their limited toughness generally restricts use of these grades to sheet or lighter-gage tubulars.

Ferritic stainless steels are highly resistant and in some cases immune to chloride SCC. These grades are frequently considered for thermal transfer applications.

The same properties and advantages are also responsible for the extraordinary development of

the lowest-alloyed grade of the ferritics, type 409. This grade, developed for automotive muffler and catalytic converter service, has gained in technical sophistication. It is increasingly used in automotive exhaust systems and in other moderately severe atmospheric-exposure applications.

Martensitic Stainless Steels

With lower chromium levels and relatively high carbon levels, it is possible to obtain austenite at elevated temperatures and then, with accelerated cooling, to transform this austenite to martensite, which has a body-centered tetragonal structure. Just as with plain carbon and low-alloy steels, this strong, brittle martensite can be tempered to favorable combinations of high strength and adequate toughness. Because of the ferrite-stabilizing character of chromium, the total chromium content, and thus the corrosion resistance, of the martensitic grades is somewhat limited. They have far lower corrosion resistance than the austenitic grades and in most instances somewhat lower resistance than the ferritic grades, particularly the superferritic alloys. In recent years, nitrogen, nickel, and molybdenum additions at somewhat lower carbon levels have produced martensitic stainless steels of improved toughness and corrosion resistance.

Duplex Stainless Steels

Duplex stainless steels are two-phase alloys based on the iron-chromium-nickel system. These materials typically comprise approximately equal proportions of ferrite and austenite phases in their microstructure and are characterized by their low carbon contents (<0.03 wt%) and additions of molybdenum, nitrogen, tungsten, and copper. Typical chromium and nickel contents are 20 to 30% and 5 to 10%, respectively. The specific advantages offered by duplex stainless steels over conventional 300-series stainless steels are strength (about twice that of austenitic stainless steels), chloride SCC resistance (Fig. 1), and pitting corrosion resistance. These materials are used in the intermediate-temperature range (about –60 to 300 °C, or –75 to 570 °F) where resistance to acids and aqueous chlorides is required.

The current commercial duplex grades can be divided into four generic types. Listed in terms of increasing corrosion resistance, these are:

Table 4 Composition and pitting resistance equivalent (PRE) values of selected wrought duplex stainless steels

| UNS number | Composition, %(a) | | | | | | | | | | PRE range(b) |
	C	Mn	S	P	Si	Cr	Ni	Mo	N₂	Other	
S31200	0.03	2.00	0.03	0.045	1.00	24.0-26.0	5.5-6.5	1.2-2.0	0.14-0.20	...	30.2-35.8
S31260	0.03	1.00	0.030	0.030	0.75	24.0-26.0	5.5-7.5	2.5-3.5	0.10-0.30	0.10-0.50 W, 0.20-0.80 Cu	33.9-42.4
S31500	0.03	1.2-2.0	0.03	0.03	1.4-2.0	18.0-19.0	4.25-5.25	2.5-3.0	0.05-0.10	...	27.1-30.5
S31803	0.03	2.00	0.02	0.03	1.00	21.0-23.0	4.5-6.5	2.5-3.5	0.08-0.20	...	30.5-37.8
S32304	0.03	2.5	0.04	0.04	1.0	21.5-24.5	3.0-5.5	0.05-0.60	0.05-0.20	0.05-0.60 Cu	22.5-29.7
S32550	0.03	1.5	0.03	0.04	1.0	24.0-27.0	4.5-6.5	2.9-3.9	0.10-0.25	1.5-2.5 Cu	35.2-43.9
S32750	0.03	1.2	0.02	0.035	1.0	24.0-26.0	6.0-8.0	3.0-5.0	0.24-0.32	0.5 Cu	37.7-47.6
S32760	0.03	1.0	0.01	0.03	1.0	24.0-26.0	6.0-8.0	3.0-4.0	0.30	0.5-1.0 Cu, 0.5-1.0 W	40(c)
S32900	0.06	1.00	0.03	0.04	0.75	23.0-28.0	2.5-5.0	1.0-2.0	(d)	...	26.3-34.6
S32950	0.03	2.00	0.01	0.035	0.60	26.0-29.0	3.5-5.2	1.0-2.5	0.15-0.35	...	...

(a) Single values are maximum. (b) PRE = %Cr + 3.3(%Mo) + 16(%N). (c) Minimum value. (d) Not specified

- Fe-23Cr-4Ni-0.1N
- Fe-22Cr-5.5Ni-3Mo-0.15N
- Fe-25Cr-5Ni-2.5Mo-0.17N-Cu
- Fe-25Cr-7Ni-3.5Mo-0.25N-W-Cu

As with 18-8 austenitic stainless steels, duplex grades are also frequently referred to by their chromium and nickel contents to describe the alloy class. The alloys listed above are then described as 2304, 2205, 2505, and 2507, respectively. The last alloy class is also frequently termed "super" duplex stainless steel.

As with all stainless steels, composition also plays a major role in the corrosion resistance of duplex stainless steels. Pitting corrosion resistance is most easily affected. To determine the extent of pitting corrosion resistance offered by the material, the pitting resistance equivalent (PRE) is commonly used. This concept was proposed in the 1970s to characterize alloy resistance to pitting in chloride solutions. The PRE is calculated by adding the weight percentages of elements that affect pitting corrosion resistance—namely, chromium, molybdenum, and nitrogen—and then normalizing them with respect to the effect of 1% Cr. There are several formulas, which principally vary in the coefficient used for nitrogen, from 13 to 30. The PRE may also include negative coefficients for sulfur and phosphorus. The most commonly used formula for pitting resistance equivalent is:

$$PRE = \%Cr + 3.3(\%Mo) + 16(\%N) \qquad (Eq~1)$$

The four types of duplex stainless steels can also be classified by their PRE values. These range from 24 for the Fe-23Cr-4Ni-0.1N steel without molybdenum to greater than 40 for the Fe-25Cr-7Ni-3.5Mo-0.25N-Cu-W "super" grades. A minimum PRE value of 40 is often used to define the "super" duplex grades. Table 4 lists PRE values for various duplex stainless steels.

Precipitation-Hardening Stainless Steels

The PH stainless steels are chromium-nickel grades that can be hardened by an aging treatment at a moderately elevated temperature. These grades may have austenitic, semiaustenitic, or martensitic crystal structures. Semiaustenitic structures are transformed from a readily for-

mable austenite to martensite by a high-temperature austenite-conditioning treatment. Some grades use cold work to facilitate transformation. The strengthening effect is achieved by adding such elements as copper and aluminum, which form intermetallic precipitates during aging. In the solution-annealed condition, these grades have properties similar to those of the austenitic grades and are therefore readily formed. Hardening is achieved after fabrication within a relatively short time at 480 to 620 °C (900 to 1150 °F). The PH grades must not be subjected to further exposure to elevated temperature by welding or environment, because the strengthening can be lost by overaging of the precipitates. The PH grades have corrosion resistance generally comparable to that of the chromium-nickel grades and superior to that of the hardenable 400-series stainless steels.

Effects of Processing, Design, Fabrication, and External Treatments

Corrosion failures in stainless steels can often be prevented by suitable changes in design or process parameters and by use of the proper fabri-

cation technique or treatment. The solution to a corrosion problem is not always to upgrade the stainless steel. It is, of course, very important to establish the types of corrosion that may occur in a given service environment, and, if failure does occur, it is important to establish the type of corrosion that caused the failure in order that the proper preventive measures can be implemented.

Heat Treatment

Improper heat treatment can produce deleterious changes in the microstructure of stainless steels. The most troublesome problems are carbide precipitation (sensitization) and precipitation of various intermetallic phases, such as σ, χ, and Laves (η).

Sensitization, or carbide precipitation at grain boundaries, can occur when austenitic stainless steels are heated for a period of time in the range of about 425 to 870 °C (800 to 1600 °F). Time at temperature will determine the amount of carbide precipitation. When the chromium carbides precipitate in grain boundaries, the area immediately adjacent is depleted of chromium. When the precipitation is relatively continuous,

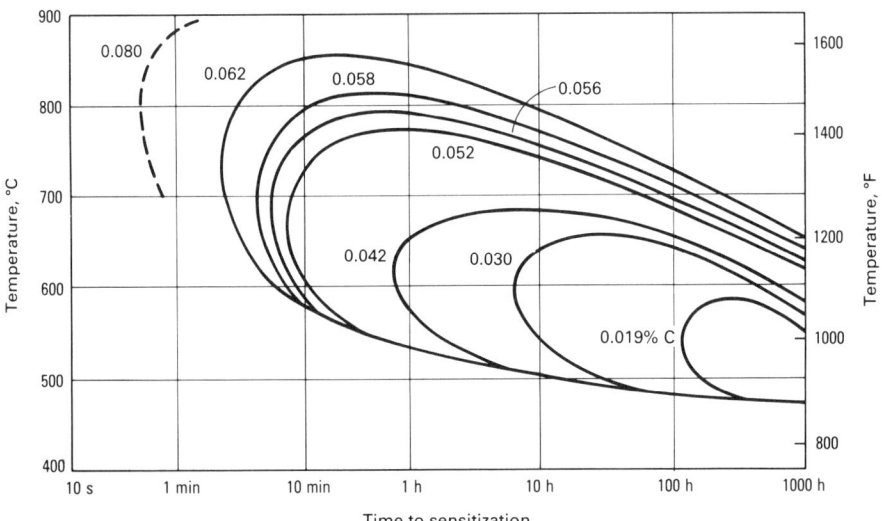

Fig. 2 Time-temperature-sensitization curves for type 304 stainless steel in a mixture of CuSO₄ and H₂SO₄ containing free copper. Curves show the times required for carbide precipitation in steels with various carbon contents. Carbides precipitate in the areas to the right of the various carbon-content curves.

the depletion renders the stainless steel susceptible to intergranular corrosion, which is the dissolution of the low-chromium layer or envelope surrounding each grain. Sensitization also lowers resistance to other forms of corrosion, such as pitting, crevice corrosion, and SCC.

Time-temperature-sensitization curves are available that provide guidance for avoiding sensitization and that illustrate the effect of carbon content on this phenomenon (Fig. 2). The curves shown in Fig. 2 indicate that a type 304 stainless steel with 0.062% C would have to cool below 595 °C (1100 °F) within about 5 min to avoid sensitization, but a type 304L with 0.030% C could take about 20 h to cool below 480 °C (900 °F) without becoming sensitized. These curves are general guidelines and should be verified before they are applied to various types of stainless steels.

Another method of avoiding sensitization is to use stabilized steels. Such stainless steels contain titanium and/or niobium. These elements have an affinity for carbon and form carbides readily; this allows the chromium to remain in solution even for extremely long exposures to temperatures in the sensitizing range. Type 304L can avoid sensitization during the relatively brief exposure of welding, but it will be sensitized by long exposures.

Annealing is the only way to correct a sensitized stainless steel. Because different stainless steels require different temperatures, times, and quenching procedures, the user should contact the material supplier for such information. A number of tests can detect sensitization resulting from carbide precipitation in austenitic and ferritic stainless steels. The most widely used tests are described in ASTM A 262 and A 763 (Ref 3, 4). More detailed information on sensitization of stainless steels can be found in the sections in this article on intergranular corrosion.

Precipitation of Intermetallic Phases. Sigma-phase precipitation and precipitation of other intermetallic phases also increase susceptibility to corrosion. Sigma phase is a chromium-molybdenum-rich phase that can render stainless steels susceptible to intergranular corrosion, pitting, and crevice corrosion. It generally occurs in higher-alloyed stainless steels (high-chromium, high-molybdenum stainless steels). Sigma phase can occur at a temperature range between 540 and 900 °C (1000 and 1650 °F). Like sensitization, it can be corrected by solution annealing. Precipitation of intermetallic phases in stainless steels is also covered in detail in the sections in this article on intergranular corrosion.

Cleaning Procedures. Any heat treatment of stainless steel should be preceded and followed by cleaning. Steel should be cleaned before heat treating to remove any foreign material that may be incorporated into the surface during the high-temperature exposure. Carbonaceous materials on the surface could result in an increase in the carbon content on the surface, causing carbide precipitation. Salts could cause excessive intergranular oxidation.

After heat treatment, unless an inert atmosphere was used during the process, the stainless steel surface will be covered with an oxide film.

Such films are not very corrosion resistant and must be removed to allow the stainless steel to form its passive film and provide the corrosion resistance for which it was designed. Numerous cleaning methods can be used before and after heat treating. An excellent guide is ASTM A 380 (Ref 5).

Welding

The main problems encountered in welding of stainless steels are the same as those seen in heat treatment. The heat of welding (portions of the base metal adjacent to the weld may be heated to 430 to 870 °C, or 800 to 1600 °F) can cause sensitization and formation of intermetallic phases, thus increasing the susceptibility of stainless steel weldments to intergranular corrosion, pitting, crevice corrosion, and SCC. These phenomena often occur in the heat-affected zone (HAZ) of the weld. Sensitization and intermetallic phase precipitation can be corrected by solution annealing after welding. Alternatively, low-carbon or stabilized grades may be used.

Another problem in high-heat-input welds is grain growth, particularly in ferritic stainless steels. Excessive grain growth can increase susceptibility to intergranular attack and reduce toughness. Thus, when welding most stainless steels, it is wise to limit weld heat input as much as possible. More detailed information on welding of stainless steels and the problems encountered can be found in the sections in this article on intergranular corrosion and in the articles "Corrosion of Weldments" and "Welding" in this Volume.

Cleaning Procedures. Before any welding begins, all materials—chill bars, clamps, hold-down bars, work tables, electrodes, and wire, as well as the stainless steel—must be cleaned of all foreign matter. Moisture can cause porosity in the weld that would reduce corrosion resistance. Organic materials, such as grease, paint, and oils, may result in carbide precipitation. Copper contamination may cause cracking. Other shop dirt can cause weld porosity and poor welds in general. Information on cleaning is available in Ref 5.

Weld design and procedure are very important in producing a sound, corrosion-resistant weld. Good fit and minimal out-of-position welding will minimize crevices and slag entrapment. The design should not place welds in critical flow areas. When attaching such devices as low-alloy steel supports and ladders on the exterior of a stainless steel tank, a stainless steel intermediate pad should be used. In general, stainless steels with higher alloy content than type 316 should be welded with weld metal richer in chromium, nickel, and molybdenum than the base metal. Every attempt should be made to minimize weld spatter.

After welding, all weld spatter, slag, and oxides should be removed by brushing, blasting, grinding, or chipping. All finishing equipment must be free of iron contamination. It is advisable to follow the mechanical cleaning and finishing with a chemical cleaning. Such a cleaning will remove any foreign particles that may have been embedded in the surface during mechanical

cleaning without attacking the weldment. Procedures for cleaning and descaling are given in Ref 5 and in the article "Surface Engineering" in this Volume.

Surface Condition

To ensure satisfactory service life, the surface condition of stainless steels must be given careful attention. Smooth surfaces, as well as freedom from surface imperfections, blemishes, and traces of scale and other foreign material, reduce the probability of corrosion. In general, a smooth, highly polished, reflective surface has greater resistance to corrosion. Rough surfaces are more likely to catch dust, salts, and moisture, which tend to initiate localized corrosive attack.

Oil and grease can be removed by using hydrocarbon solvents or alkaline cleaners, but these cleaners must be removed before heat treatment. Hydrochloric acid (HCl) formed from residual amounts of trichloroethylene, which is used for degreasing, has caused severe attack of stainless steels. Surface contamination may be caused by machining, shearing, and drawing operations. Small particles of metal from tools become embedded in the steel surface and, unless removed, may cause localized galvanic corrosion. These particles are best removed by the passivation treatments described below. Additional information on cleaning and descaling of stainless steel is available in Ref 5 and the article "Surface Engineering" in this Volume.

Shot blasting or sandblasting should be avoided unless iron-free silica is used; metal shot, in particular, will contaminate the stainless steel surface. If shot blasting or shot peening with metal grit is unavoidable, the parts must be cleaned after blasting or peening by immersing them in an HNO_3 solution.

Passivation Techniques

During handling and processing operations, such as machining, forming, tumbling, and lapping, particles of iron, tool steel, or shop dirt may be embedded in or smeared on the surfaces of stainless steel components. These contaminants may reduce the effectiveness of the natural oxide (passive) film that forms on stainless steels exposed to oxygen at low temperatures. (The formation of these passive films is discussed in the section "Mechanism of Corrosion Resistance" in this article.) If allowed to remain, these particles may corrode and produce rustlike spots on the stainless steel. To prevent this condition, semifinished or finished parts are given a passivation treatment. This treatment consists of cleaning and then immersing stainless steel parts in a solution of HNO_3 or of HNO_3 plus oxidizing salts. The treatment dissolves the embedded or smeared iron, restores the original corrosion-resistant surface, and maximizes the inherent corrosion resistance of the stainless steel.

Cleaning. Each workpiece to be passivated must be cleaned thoroughly to remove grease, coolant, or other shop debris (Ref 6). A worker will sometimes eliminate the cleaning step based

Table 5 Passivating solutions for stainless steels (non-free-machining grades)

Grade	Passivation treatment
Austenitic 300-series grades Grades with ≥ 17% Cr (except 440 series)	20 vol% HNO_3 at 50-60 °C (120-140 °F) for 30 min
Straight chromium grades (12-14% Cr) High-carbon/high-chromium grades (440 series)	20 vol% HNO_3 plus 22 g/L (3 oz/gal) $Na_2Cr_2O_7 \cdot 2H_2O$ at 50-60 °C (120-140 °F) for 30 min or
Precipitation-hardening grades	50 vol% HNO_3 at 50-60 °C (120-140 °F) for 30 min

Source: Ref 6

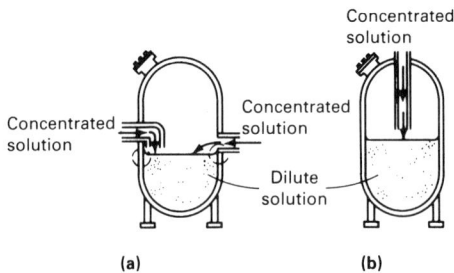

Fig. 3 Poor (a) and good (b) designs for vessels used for mixing concentrated and dilute solutions. Poor design causes concentration and uneven mixing of incoming chemicals along the vessel wall (circled areas). Good design allows concentrated solutions to mix away from vessel walls.

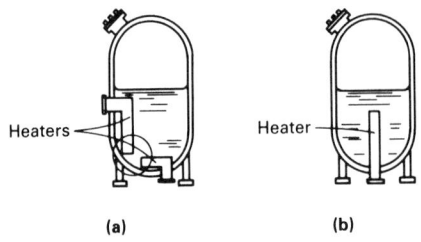

Fig. 4 Poor (a) and good (b) designs for heating of solutions. Poor design creates hot spots (circled area) that may induce boiling under the heater at the bottom of the vessel or may cause deposits to form between heaters and vessel walls. Good design avoids hot spots and pockets in which small volumes of liquid can become trapped between the heater and the vessel wall.

on the reasoning that the cleaning and passivation of a grease-laden part will occur simultaneously by immersing it in an HNO_3 bath. This assumption is mistaken. The grease will react with the HNO_3 to form gas bubbles, which collect on the surface of the workpiece and interfere with passivation. Also, contamination of the passivating solution (particularly with high levels of chlorides) can cause flash attack, which results in a gray or black appearance and deterioration of the surface.

To avoid such problems, each part should be wiped clean of any large machining chips or other debris. More tenacious deposits should be removed by brushing with a stainless steel wire brush, grinding, polishing with an iron-free abrasive, or sand-

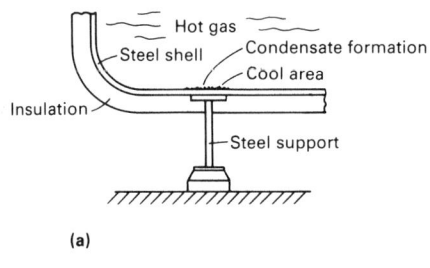

(a)

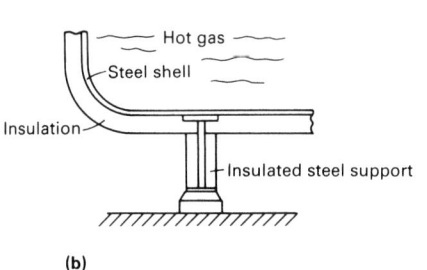

(b)

Fig. 5 Design to prevent localized cooling. In the poor design (a), the uninsulated steel support radiates heat, which causes a cool area on the steel shell. In (b), the steel support is insulated to prevent temperature decrease at the base of the shell.

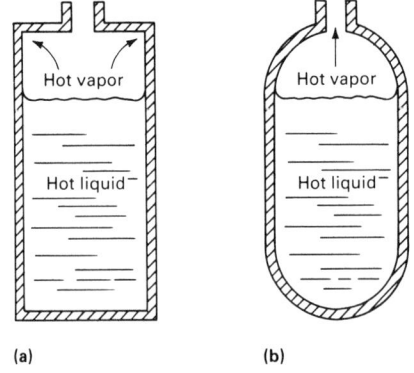

Fig. 6 Poor (a) and good (b) designs for vessels holding both liquid and vapor phases. Sharp corners and the protruding outlet end in (a) allow hot gases to become trapped in the vapor space. This is avoided in (b) by using rounded corners and mounting the vessel outlet pipe flush.

blasting. Tools and materials used for these processes should be clean and used only for stainless steels. Machining, forming, or grinding oils must be removed in order for passivation to be effective. Cleaning should begin with solvent cleaning, which may be followed by alkaline soak cleaning and thorough water rinsing. Optimum results are obtained in passivation when the parts to be treated are as clean as they would have to be for plating. When large parts or bulky vessels are to be cleaned, it may be necessary to apply cleaning liquids by means of pressure spray; exterior surfaces may be cleaned by immersion or swabbing.

Passivating. After cleaning, the workpiece can be immersed in the passivating acid bath. As shown in Table 5, the composition of the acid bath depends on the grade of stainless steel. The 300-

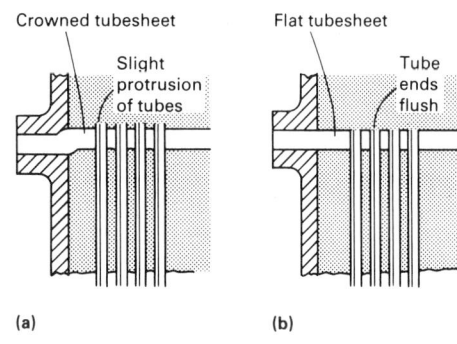

Fig. 7 Poor (a) and good (b) designs for tube/tubesheet assemblies. Crowned tubesheet and protruding tubes in (a) allow buildup of corrosive deposits; in (b), tubesheet is flat and tubes are mounted flush.

series stainless steels can be passivated in 20 vol% HNO_3. A sodium dichromate ($Na_2Cr_2O_7 \cdot 2H_2O$) addition or an increased concentration of HNO_3 is used for less corrosion-resistant stainless steels to reduce the potential for flash attack.

The procedure suggested for passivating free-machining stainless steels is somewhat different from that used for non-free-machining grades (Ref 6). This is because sulfides of sulfur-bearing free-machining grades, which are totally or partially removed during passivation, create microscopic discontinuities in the surface of the machined part. Even normally efficient water rinses can leave residual acid trapped in these discontinuities after passivation. This acid can then attack the surface of the part unless it is neutralized or removed. For this reason, a special passivation process, referred to as the *alkaline-acid-alkaline method*, is suggested for free-machining grades.

The following steps should be followed when passivating free-machining stainless steels with the alkaline-acid-alkaline technique:

1. After degreasing, soak the parts for 30 min in 5 wt% sodium hydroxide (NaOH) at 70 to 80 °C (160 to 180 °F).
2. Water rinse.
3. Immerse the part for 30 min in 20 vol% HNO_3 plus 22 g/L (3 oz/gal) $Na_2Cr_2O_7 \cdot 2H_2O$ at 50 to 60 °C (120 to 140 °F).
4. Water rinse.
5. Immerse for 30 min in 5 wt% NaOH at 70 to 80 °C (160 to 180 °F).
6. Water rinse and dry.

Testing is often performed to evaluate the passivated surface. For example, 400-series, precipitation-hardening, and free-machining stainless steels are often tested in a cabinet capable of maintaining 100% humidity at 35 °C (95 °F) for 24 h. Material that is properly passivated will be virtually free of rust, although light staining may occur (Ref 3). Austenitic 300-series grades can be evaluated using a technique given in ASTM A380 (Ref 5). This test consists of swabbing the part with a copper sulfate ($CuSO_4 \cdot 5H_2O$)/sulfuric acid (H_2SO_4) solution; wetness should be maintained for 6 min (Ref 6). Free iron, if present, plates out the copper from the solution, and the surface develops a copper cast or color. Precau-

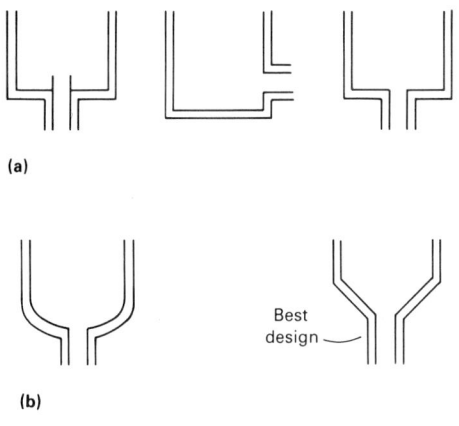

Fig. 8 Examples of poor (a) and good (b) designs for drainage, corners, and other dead spaces in vessels. Sharp corners and protruding outlet pipes in (a) can cause buildup of corrosive deposits and crevice corrosion; these design features are avoided in (b).

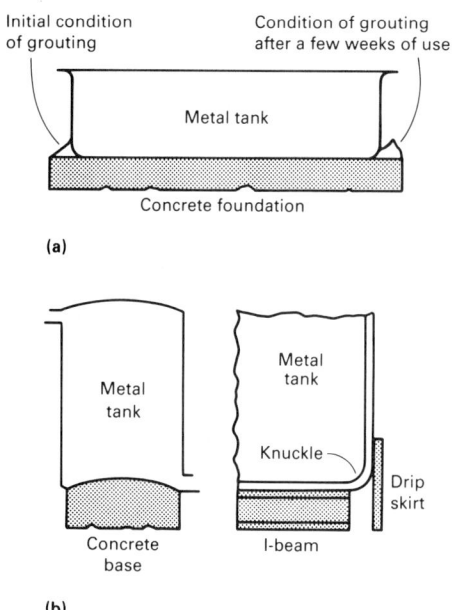

Fig. 9 Design for preventing external corrosion from spills and overflows. (a) Poor design. (b) Good designs

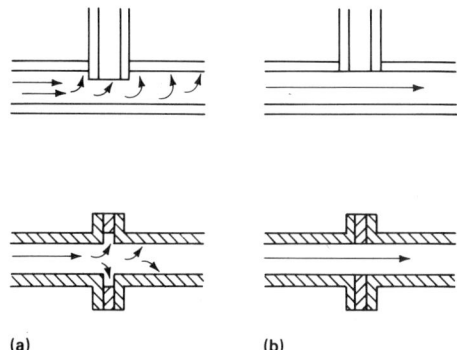

Fig. 10 Designs for preventing excessive turbulence. (a) Poor designs (both top and bottom figures). (b) Good designs (both top and bottom figures)

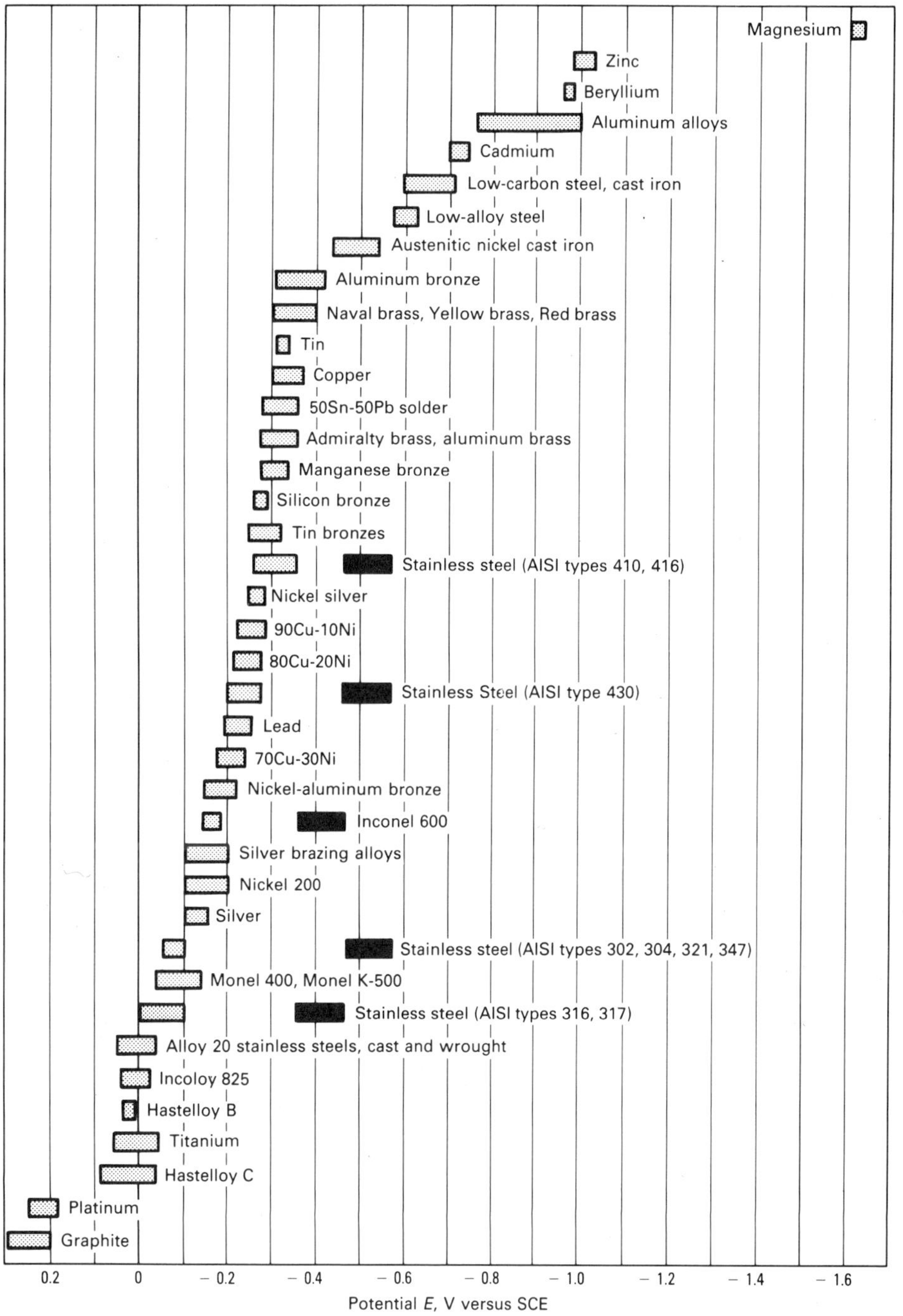

Fig. 11 Corrosion potentials of various metals and alloys in flowing seawater at 10 to 25 °C (50 to 80 °F). Flow rate was 2.5 to 4 m/s (8 to 13 ft/s); alloys are listed in order of the potential vs. a saturated calomel electrode (SCE) that they exhibited. Those metals and alloys indicated by a black bar may become active and exhibit a potential near –0.5 V (SCE) in low-velocity or poorly aerated water and in shielded areas.

tions for this procedure and details on additional tests for detecting the presence of iron on passivated surfaces are outlined in Ref 5 and 6. Information on passivation treatments for corrosion-resistant steels is also available in Federal Specification QQ-P-35B (Ref 7).

Design

Corrosion can often be avoided by suitable changes in design without changing the type of steel. The factors to be considered include joint design, surface continuity, and concentration of stress. Designs that tend to concentrate corrosive media in a small area should be avoided. For example, tank inlets should be designed such that concentrated solutions are mixed and diluted as they are introduced (Fig. 3). Otherwise, localized pockets of concentrated solutions can cause excessive corrosion.

Poor design of heaters can create similar problems, such as those that cause hot spots and thus

Fig. 12   Two views of deep pits in a type 316 centrifuge head due to exposure to CaCl₂ solution

accelerate corrosion. Heaters should be centrally located (Fig. 4). If a tank is to be heated externally, heaters should be distributed over as large a surface area as possible, and circulation of the corrosive medium should be encouraged, if possible.

Hot gases that are not corrosive to stainless steel may form corrosive condensates on the cold portions of a poorly insulated unit. Proper design or insulation can prevent such localized cooling (Fig. 5). Conversely, vapors from noncorrosive liquids may cause attack; exhausts and overflows should be designed to prevent hot vapor pockets (Fig. 6). In general, the open ends of inlets, outlets, and tubes in heat exchangers should be flush with tank walls or tubesheets to avoid buildup of harmful corrodents, sludges, and deposits (Fig. 7). This is also true of tank bottom and drainage designs (Fig. 8).

Tanks and tank supports should be designed to prevent or minimize corrosion due to spills and overflows (Fig. 9). A tank support structure may not be as corrosion resistant as the tank itself, but it is a very important part of the unit and should not be made vulnerable to spilled corrodents.

Designs that increase turbulence or result in excessive flow rates should be avoided where erosion-corrosion may be a problem (Fig. 10). Gaskets in flanges should fit properly, intrusions in a flow stream should be avoided, and elbows should be given a generous radius. Finally, crevices should be avoided. Where crevices cannot be avoided, they should be sealed by welding, soldering, or the use of caulking compounds or sealants. Additional information is available in the article "Design Details to Minimize Corrosion" in Volume 13 of the *ASM Handbook*.

Forms of Corrosion

The forms of corrosive attack that most affect stainless steels include general (uniform) corrosion, galvanic corrosion, pitting corrosion, crevice corrosion, intergranular corrosion, stress-corrosion cracking, erosion-corrosion, and high-temperature corrosion. Each of these forms of corrosion is described below. Additional information can be found in Volume 13 of the *ASM Handbook*.

General Corrosion

General corrosion refers to corrosion dominated by uniform thinning that proceeds without appreciable localized attack. Weathering steels and copper alloys are good examples of materials that typically exhibit general attack, while passive materials, such as stainless steels, are generally subject to localized attack. Under specific conditions, however, stainless steels are also susceptible to general corrosion. This is particularly true when stainless steels are subjected to high-temperature corrosive environments.

General corrosion can be divided into seven specific types of corrosion. *Atmospheric corrosion* is probably the most common form of corrosion and may well be the most costly. *Galvanic corrosion* is an electrochemical form of corrosion that protects cathodic areas at the expense of anodic areas. *Stray-current corrosion* is similar to galvanic corrosion but does not rely on electrochemically induced driving forces to cause rapid attack. *Biological corrosion* is a microbial-assisted form of attack that can manifest itself in a general or a localized form. *Molten-salt corrosion* and *liquid-metal corrosion* have become more of a concern as the demand for higher-temperature heat-transfer fluids increases. *High-temperature (gaseous) corrosion* is of great concern, particularly for the industrial sector. Of these seven types of general corrosion, atmospheric, galvanic, and high-temperature corrosion are of greatest concern for stainless steels. Each of these types of general corrosion is discussed in subsequent sections in this article.

Galvanic Corrosion

Galvanic corrosion results when two dissimilar metals are in electrical contact in a corrosive medium. As a highly corrosion-resistant metal, stainless steel can act as a cathode when in contact with a less noble metal, such as steel. The corrosion of steel parts—for example, steel bolts in a stainless steel construction—can be a significant problem. However, the effect can be used in a beneficial way for

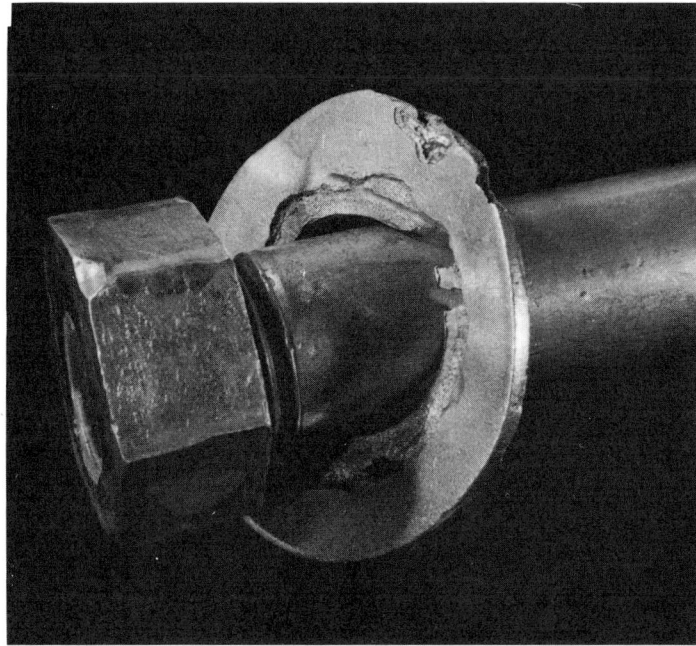

Fig. 13 Crevice corrosion at a metal-to-metal crevice site formed between components of a type 304 fastener in seawater

Table 6 Comparison of critical crevice temperature (CCT) for duplex and austenitic stainless steels
See also Table 2.

UNS No.	Alloy nsame	CCT in 10% FeCl₃ · 6H₂O, pH = 1, 24-h exposure	
		°C	°F
Duplex grades			
S32900	Type 329	5	41
S31200	44LN	5	41
S31260	DP-3	10	50
S32950	7-Mo PLUS	15	60
S31803	2205	17.5	63.5
S32250	Ferralium 255	22.5	72.5
Austenitic grades			
S30400	Type 304	<−2.5	<27.5
S31600	Type 316	−2.5	27.5
S31703	Type 317L	0	32
N08020	20Cb-3	0	32

Source: Ref 8

protecting critical stainless steel components within a larger steel construction.

Galvanic corrosion behavior of stainless steels is difficult to predict because of the influence of passivity. In the common galvanic series, a noble position is assumed by stainless steels in the passive state, while a more active position is assumed in the active state (Fig. 11). This dual position in galvanic series in chloride-bearing aqueous environments has been the cause of some serious design errors. More precise information on the galvanic behavior of stainless steels can be obtained by using polarization curves, critical potentials, and the mixed potential of the galvanic couple. In chloride-bearing environments, galvanically induced localized corrosion of many stainless steels occurs in couples with copper or nickel and their alloys and with other more noble materials. However, couples of stainless and copper alloys are often used in freshwater cooling systems. Iron and steel tend to protect stainless steel in aqueous environments when galvanically coupled. The passive behavior of stainless steels makes them easy to polarize; thus, galvanic effects on other metals or alloys tend to be minimized. However, galvanic corrosion of steel can be induced by stainless, particularly in aqueous environments and with adverse surface area ratios.

Pitting Corrosion

Pitting is a localized attack that can produce penetration of a stainless steel with almost negligible weight loss to the total structure. Pitting is associated with a local discontinuity of the passive film. It can be a mechanical imperfection, such as an inclusion or surface damage, or it can be a local chemical breakdown of the film. Chloride is the most common agent for initiation of pitting. Once a pit is formed, it in effect becomes a crevice; the local chemical environment is substantially more aggressive than the bulk environment. This explains why very high flow rates over a stainless steel surface tend to reduce pitting corrosion; the high flow rate prevents the concentration of corrosive species in the pit. The stability of the passive film with respect to resistance to pitting initiation is controlled primarily by chromium and molybdenum. Minor alloying elements can also have an important effect by influencing the amount and type of inclusions (for example, sulfides) in the steel that can act as pitting sites.

Pitting initiation can also be influenced by surface condition, including the presence of deposits, and by temperature. For a particular environment, a grade of stainless steel may be characterized by a single temperature, or a very narrow range of temperatures, above which pitting will initiate and below which pitting will not initiate. It is therefore possible to select a grade that will not be subject to pitting attack if the chemical environment and temperature do not exceed the critical levels. If the range of operating conditions can be accurately characterized, a meaningful laboratory evaluation is possible. Formation of deposits in service can reduce the pitting temperature.

In environments containing appreciable concentrations of chloride (Cl⁻) or bromide (Br⁻), most stainless steels tend to corrode at specific areas and to form deep pits. Figure 12 shows deep pits that formed in a type 316 stainless steel centrifuge head from a calcium chloride ($CaCl_2$) solution. Ions such as thiosulfate ($SO_2O_3^{2-}$) may also induce pitting of stainless steels. In the absence of passivity, such as in deaerated alkali-metal chlorides and nonoxidizing metal chlorides (for example, stannous chloride, $SnCl_2$, or nickel chloride, $NiCl_2$), pitting does not occur, although general or uniform corrosion may be appreciable in such environments.

Although chloride is known to be the primary agent of pitting attack, it is not possible to establish a single critical chloride limit for each grade. The corrosivity of a particular concentration of chloride solution can be profoundly affected by the presence or absence of various other chemicals species that may accelerate or inhibit corrosion. Chloride concentration may increase where evaporation or deposits occur. Because of the nature of pitting attack—rapid penetration with little total weight loss—it is rare that any significant amount of pitting will be acceptable in practical applications.

Crevice Corrosion

Crevice corrosion can be considered a severe form of pitting. Any crevice, whether the result of a metal-to-metal joint (Fig. 13), a gasket, fouling, or deposits, tends to restrict oxygen access, resulting in attack. In practice, it is extremely difficult to prevent all crevices, but every effort should be made to do so. Higher-chromium and, in particular, higher-molybdenum grades are more resistant to crevice attack. Just as there is a critical pitting temperature for a particular environment, there is also a critical crevice temperature. This temperature is specific to the geometry and nature of the crevice and to the precise corrosion environment for each grade. The CCT can be useful in selecting an adequately resistant grade for particular applications. Table 2 lists the CCT for various austenitic stainless steels. Table 6 compares the CCT for duplex and standard austenitic stainless steel grades.

In cases in which the bulk environment is particularly aggressive, general corrosion may preclude localized corrosion at a crevice site. Figure 14 compares the behavior of type 304 and 316 stainless steels exposed in different zones of a model sulfur dioxide (SO_2) scrubber. In the aggressive acid condensate zone, type 304 incurred severe general corrosion of the exposed surfaces,

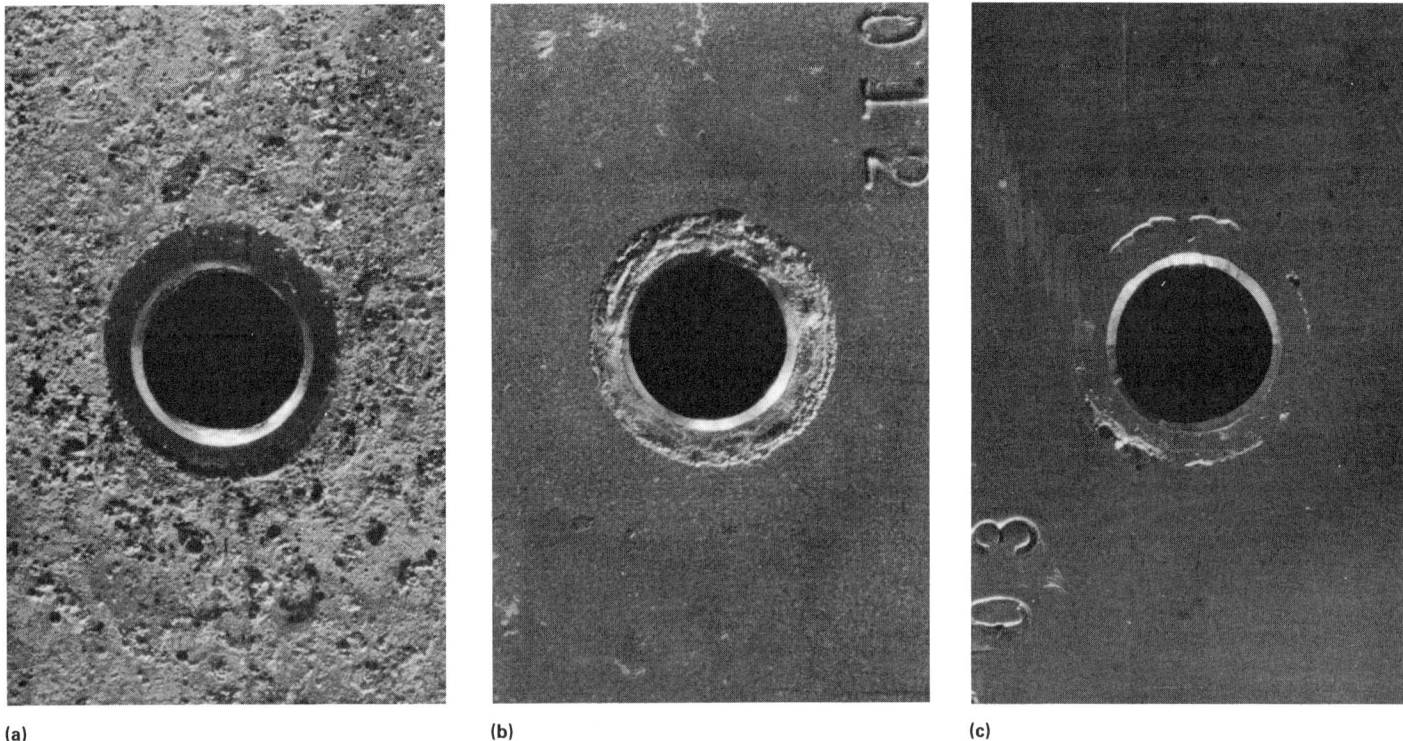

Fig. 14 Variation in stainless steel corrosion resistance in model SO$_2$ scrubber environments. (a) Type 304 in acid condensate. (b) Type 316 in acid condensate. (c) Type 304 in limestone slurry zone

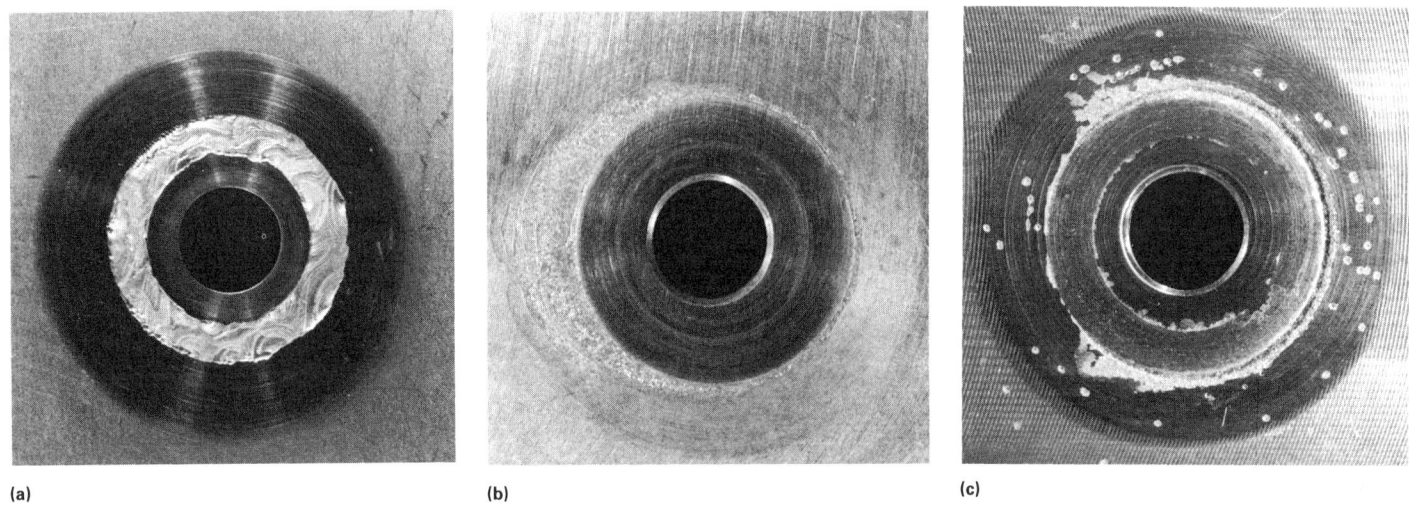

Fig. 15 Crevice-related corrosion for different alloys in natural seawater. Type 904L stainless steel after 30 days. (b) 70Cu-30Ni after 180 days. (c) Alloy 400 (70Ni-30Cu) after 45 days

while the more resistant type 316 suffered attack beneath a polytetrafluoroethylene insulating spacer. In the higher-pH environment of the limestone slurry zone, type 304 was resistant to general corrosion but was susceptible to crevice corrosion.

In seawater, localized corrosion of copper and its alloys at crevices is different from that of stainless materials because the attack occurs outside the crevice rather than within. In general, the degree of crevice-related attack increases as the resistance to general corrosion increases. Figure 15 compares the crevice corrosion behavior for several different materials exposed to ambient-tem-

perature seawater for various periods. In each case, a nonmetallic washer created the crevice. The more classical form of crevice corrosion (that is, beneath the crevice former) is shown for type 904L stainless steel (20Cr-25Ni-4.5Mo-1.5Cu) after only 30 days of exposure (Fig. 15a). For 70Cu-30Ni, corrosion occurred just outside the crevice mouth and was found to be quite shallow after six months (Fig. 15b). In contrast, crevice-related corrosion of alloy 400 (70Ni-30Cu) was more severe after only 45 days (Fig. 15c). In some cases, corrosion may occur within as well as outside the crevice.

Factors Influencing Crevice Corrosion. For stainless steels, numerous interrelated metallurgical, geometrical, and environmental factors affect both crevice corrosion initiation and propagation (Ref 9). A number of these factors are indicated in Table 7, and a more thorough discussion of the mechanism can be found in Ref 10. In short, however, the release of metal ions, particularly chromium, in the crevice produces an acidic condition as a result of a series of hydrolysis reactions. To effect charge neutrality with excess H$^+$ ions, Cl$^-$ ions migrate and concentrate from the bulk environment. If the concentration of acid and chloride

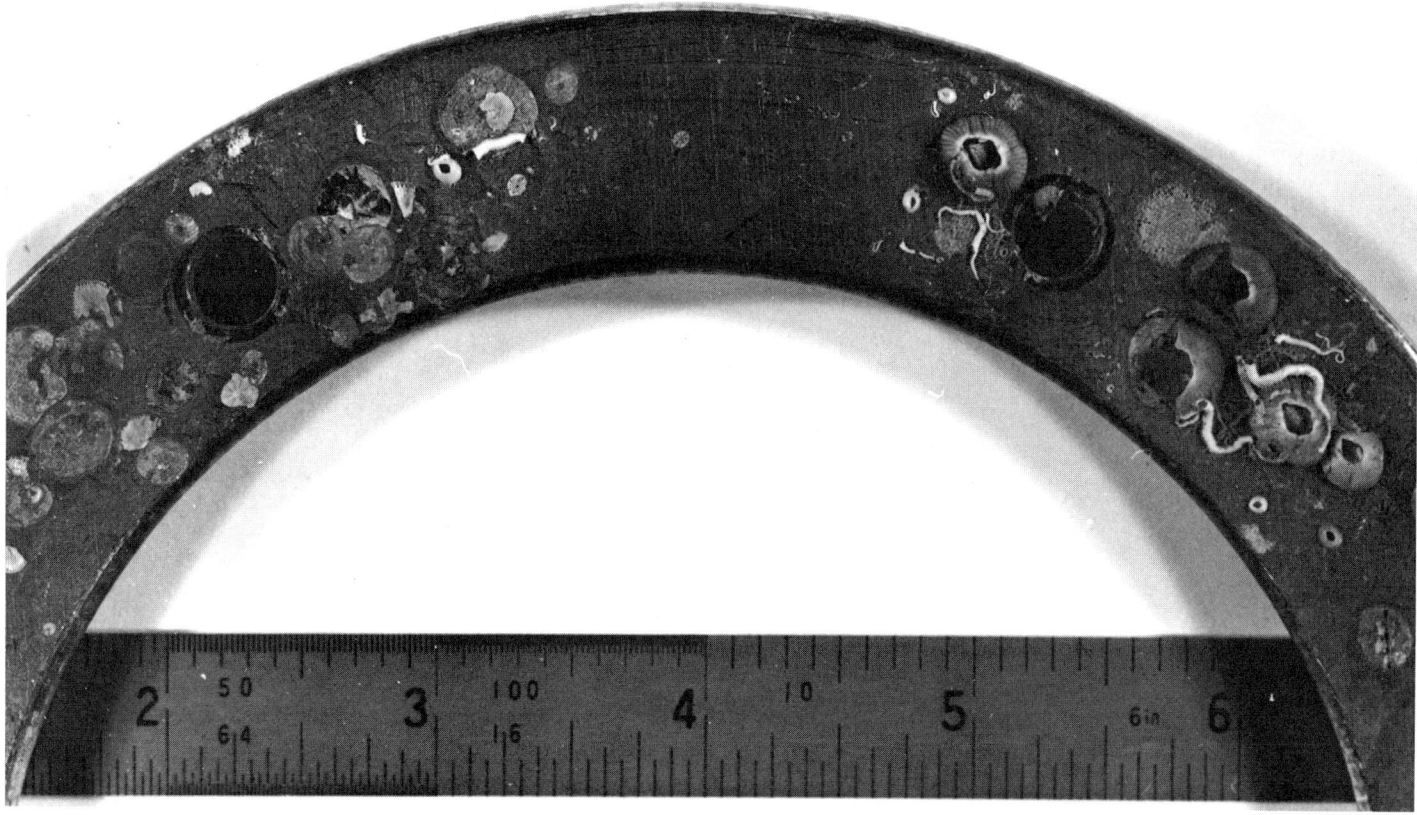

Fig. 16 Biological corrosion under a scatter of individual barnacles on a stainless steel surface

Table 7 Factors that can affect the crevice corrosion resistance of stainless steels

Geometrical

Type of crevice:
    metal to metal
    nonmetal to metal
Crevice gap (tightness)
Crevice depth
Exterior to interior surface area ratio

Environmental

Bulk solution:
    O_2 content
    pH
    chloride level
    temperature
    agitation
Mass transport, migration
Diffusion and convection
Crevice solution: hydrolysis equilibria
Biological influences

Electrochemical reactions

Metal dissolution
O_2 reduction
H_2 evolution

Metallurgical

Alloy composition:
    major elements
    minor elements
    impurities
Passive film characteristics

in the crevice solution becomes sufficiently aggressive to cause breakdown of the passive film, crevice corrosion initiation occurs. Although

natural seawater, for example, is typically pH 8 and contains about 0.5 M Cl^-, crevice solutions may attain a pH of 1 or less and contain 5 to 6 M Cl^- (saturated) (Ref 10).

Biological Corrosion

Biological corrosion is the deterioration of metals as a result of the metabolic activity of the biological organisms present in virtually all natural aqueous environments. In seawater environments, such as tidal bays, estuaries, harbors, and coastal and open ocean seawaters, a great variety of organisms are present. Some of these are large enough to observe with the naked eye (for example, barnacles), while others are microscopic. In freshwater environments, both natural and industrial, the large organisms are missing, but there is still a great variety of microorganisms, such as bacteria and algae.

Most of the documented cases in which biological organisms are the sole cause of, or an accelerating factor in, corrosion involve localized forms of attack. One reason for this is that organisms often do not form in a continuous film on the metal surface.

The large fouling organisms in marine environments settle as individuals, and it is often a period of months or even years before a complete cover is built up. A scatter of individual barnacles on a stainless steel surface will create oxygen concentration cells. The portion of the metal surface covered by the barnacle shell is shielded from dis-

solved oxygen in the water and thus becomes the anode. The result is crevice corrosion under the base of the barnacles, as shown in Fig. 16. As described in the article "Corrosion of Weldments" in this Volume, biological corrosion can also result in severe pitting of stainless steels.

Intergranular Corrosion

Intergranular corrosion is a preferential attack at the grain boundaries of a stainless steel. It is generally the result of sensitization. This condition occurs when a thermal cycle leads to grain-boundary precipitation of a carbide, nitride, or intermetallic phase without providing sufficient time for chromium diffusion to fill the locally depleted region. A grain-boundary precipitate is not the point of attack; instead, the low-chromium region adjacent to the precipitate is susceptible.

Sensitization is not necessarily detrimental unless the grade is to be used in an environment capable of attacking the region. For example, elevated-temperature applications for stainless steel can operate with sensitized steel, but concern for intergranular attack must be given to possible corrosion during downtime when condensation might provide a corrosive medium. Because chromium provides corrosion resistance, sensitization also increases the susceptibility of chromium-depleted regions to other forms of corrosion, such as pitting, crevice corrosion, and SCC. The thermal exposures required to sensitize a steel can be rela-

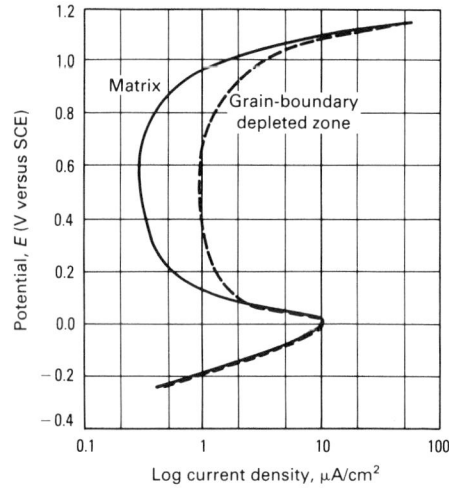

Fig. 17 Anodic polarization behavior of an active-passive alloy with grain-boundary depleted zones

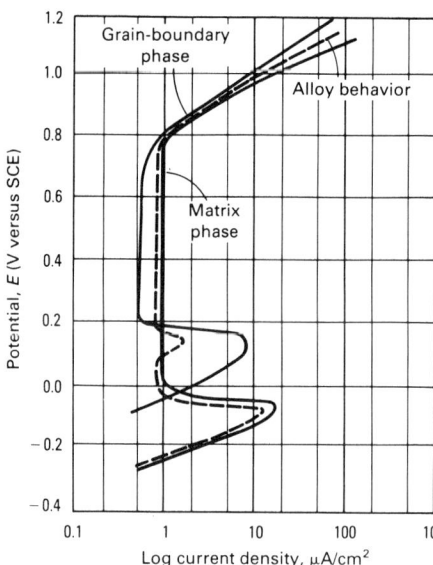

Fig. 18 Anodic polarization behavior of a two-phase active-passive alloy

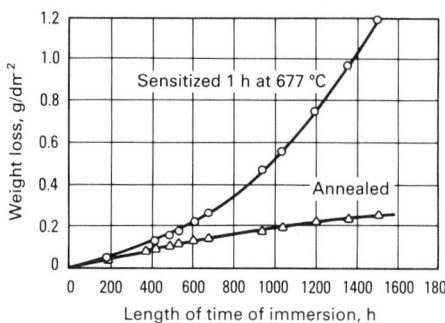

Fig. 19 Corrosion of type 304 in inhibited boiling 10% H_2SO_4. Inhibitor: 0.47 g Fe^{3+}/L of solution added as $Fe_2(SO_4)_3$. Source: Ref 11

tively brief, as in welding, or very long, as in high-temperature service.

Mechanisms of Intergranular Corrosion. Intergranular corrosion takes place when the corrosion rate of the grain-boundary areas of an alloy exceeds that of the grain interiors. This difference in corrosion rate is generally the result of differences in composition between the grain boundary and the interior.

The differences in corrosion rate may be caused by a number of reactions. A phase may precipitate at

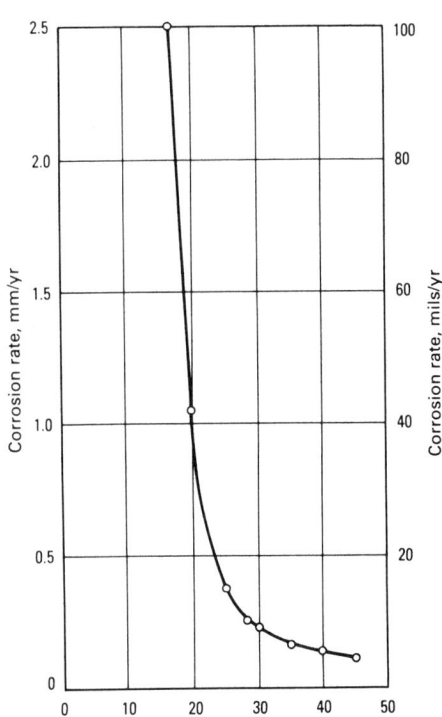

Fig. 20 Effect of chromium content on the corrosion behavior of iron-chromium alloys in boiling 50% H_2SO_4 with $Fe_2(SO_4)_3$. Source: Ref 12

a grain boundary and deplete the matrix of an element that affects its corrosion resistance. A grain-boundary phase may be more reactive than the matrix. Various solute atoms may segregate to the grain boundaries and locally accelerate corrosion. The metallurgical changes that lead to intergranular corrosion are not always observable in the microstructure; therefore, corrosion tests may sometimes be the most sensitive indication of metallurgical changes (see, for example, the section "Corrosion Testing" in this article).

Figure 17 illustrates the electrochemistry of intergranular corrosion. Polarization curves are shown for the grain-boundary and matrix areas. The system chosen is one that exhibits active-passive behavior, for example, an iron-chromium-nickel stainless steel in H_2SO_4. Several points must be noted. The difference in corrosion rate varies with potential. The rates are close or the same in the active and transpassive ranges and vary considerably with potential in the passive range.

Intergranular corrosion is usually not the result of active grain boundaries and a passive matrix. The corroding surface is at one potential. Differences in composition produce different corrosion rates at the same potential in the passive region. When more than one metallic phase is present in an alloy, its polarization behavior will be the volume average sum of the behavior of each phase (Fig. 18). Active-passive surfaces are possible in this case.

When an alloy is undergoing intergranular corrosion, its rate of weight loss usually accelerates with time. As the grain-boundary area dissolves, the unaffected grains are undermined and fall out; this increases the weight loss. Typical weight-loss-versus-time curves for an alloy undergoing intergranular corrosion are shown in Fig. 19.

Intergranular Corrosion and Other Forms of Corrosion. Susceptibility to intergranular cor-

rosion cannot be taken as a general indication of increased susceptibility to other forms of corrosion, such as pitting or general corrosion. The environments that cause intergranular corrosion for a particular alloy system are often very specific. Susceptibility to intergranular corrosion may mean susceptibility to intergranular SCC, but some nickel-base alloys are actually more resistant to SCC when they are sensitized to intergranular corrosion.

Although intergranular corrosion can occur in many alloy systems, it has been most widely investigated in stainless steels. In the following sections, intergranular corrosion of austenitic, ferritic, and duplex stainless steels will be discussed.

Intergranular Corrosion of Austenitic Stainless Steels

At temperatures above about 1035 °C (1900 °F), chromium carbides are completely dissolved in austenitic stainless steels. However, when these steels are slowly cooled from these high temperatures or reheated into the range of 425 to 815 °C (800 to 1500 °F), chromium carbides are precipitated at the grain boundaries. These carbides contain more chromium than the matrix contains.

The precipitation of the carbides depletes the matrix of chromium adjacent to the grain boundary. The diffusion rate of chromium in austenite is slow at the precipitation temperatures; therefore, the depleted zone persists, and the alloy is sensitized to intergranular corrosion. This sensitization occurs because the depleted zones have higher corrosion rates than the matrix in many environments. Figure 20 illustrates how the chromium content influences the corrosion rate of iron-chromium alloys in boiling 50% H_2SO_4 containing ferric sulfate ($Fe_2(SO_4)_3$). In all cases, the alloys are in the passive state. The wide differences in the corrosion rate are the result of the differences in the chromium content.

If the austenitic stainless steels are cooled rapidly to below about 425 °C (800 °F), the carbides do not precipitate, and the steels are immune to intergranular corrosion. Reheating the alloys to 425 to 815 °C (800 to 1500 °F), as for stress relief, will cause carbide precipitation and sensitivity to intergranular corrosion. The maximum rate of carbide precipitation occurs at about 675 °C (1250

Fig. 21 Weld decay (sensitization) in austenitic stainless steel and methods for its prevention. Panels of four different 300-series stainless steels were joined by welding and exposed to hot HNO_3 + HF solution. The weld decay evident in the type 304 panel was prevented in the other panels by reduction in carbon content (type 304L) or by addition of carbide-stabilizing elements (titanium in type 321 and niobium in type 347). Source: Ref 11

°F). Because this is a common temperature for the stress relief of carbon and low-alloy steels, care must be exercised in selecting stainless steels to be used in dissimilar-metal joints that are to be stress relieved.

Welding is the common cause of the sensitization of stainless steels to intergranular corrosion (see the article "Corrosion of Weldments" in this Volume). Although the cooling rates in the weld itself and the base metal immediately adjacent to it are sufficiently high to avoid carbide precipitation, the weld thermal cycle will bring part of the HAZ into the precipitation range. Carbides will precipitate, and a zone somewhat removed from the weld will become susceptible to intergranular corrosion (see Fig. 15 in the article "Corrosion of Weldments" in this Volume). Welding does not always sensitize austenitic stainless steels. In thin sections, the thermal cycle may be such that no part of the HAZ is at sensitizing temperatures long enough to cause carbide precipitation. Once the precipitation has occurred, it can be removed by reheating the alloy to above 1035 °C (1895 °F) and cooling it rapidly.

Avoiding Intergranular Corrosion. Susceptibility to intergranular corrosion in austenitic stainless steels can be avoided by controlling their carbon contents or by adding elements whose carbides are more stable than those of chromium. For most austenitic stainless steels, restricting their carbon contents to 0.03% or less will prevent sensitization during welding and most heat treatment. This method is not effective for eliminating sensitization that would result from long-term service exposure at 425 to 815 °C (800 to 1500 °F).

Titanium and niobium form more stable carbides than chromium and are added to stainless steels to form these stable carbides, which remove carbon from solid solution and prevent precipitation of chromium carbides. The most common of these stabilized grades are types 321 and 347. Type 321 contains a minimum of $[5 \times (C + N)]\%$ titanium, and type 347 a minimum of $(8 \times C)\%$ niobium. Nitrogen must be considered when titanium is used as a stabilizer, not because the precipitation of chromium nitride is a problem in austenitic steels, but because titanium nitride is very stable. Titanium will combine with any

available nitrogen; therefore, this reaction must be considered when determining the total amount of titanium required to combine with the carbon.

The stabilized grades are more resistant to sensitization by long-term exposure at 425 to 815 °C (800 to 1500 °F) than the low-carbon grades, and the stabilized grades are the preferred materials when service involves exposure at these temperatures. For maximum resistance to intergranular corrosion, these grades are given a stabilizing heat treatment at about 900 °C (1650 °F). The purpose of the treatment is to remove carbon from solution at temperatures where titanium and niobium carbides are stable but chromium carbides are not. Such treatments prevent the formation of chromium carbide when the steel is exposed to lower temperatures.

Figure 21 illustrates how both carbon control and stabilization can eliminate intergranular corrosion in as-welded austenitic stainless steels. It also shows that the sensitized zone in these steels is somewhat removed from the weld metal.

Knife-Line Attack. Stabilized austenitic stainless steels may become susceptible to a localized form of intergranular corrosion known as knife-line attack or knife-line corrosion. During welding, the base metal immediately adjacent to the fusion line is heated to temperatures high enough to dissolve the stabilizing carbides, but the cooling rate is rapid enough to prevent carbide precipitation. Subsequent welding passes reheat this narrow area into the temperature range in which both the stabilizing carbide and the chromium carbide can precipitate. The precipitation of chromium carbide leaves the narrow band adjacent to the fusion line susceptible to intergranular corrosion. Knife-line attack can be avoided by the proper choice of welding variables and by the use of stabilizing heat treatments.

Intergranular SCC. Austenitic stainless steels that are susceptible to intergranular corrosion are also subject to intergranular SCC. This topic is covered in greater depth in the article "Stress-Corrosion Cracking and Hydrogen Embrittlement" in this Volume. The problem of the intergranular SCC of sensitized austenitic stainless steels in boiling high-purity water containing oxygen has received a great deal of study. This seemingly benign environment has led to cracking of sensitized stainless steels in many boiling water reactors.

Sensitized stainless alloys of all types crack very rapidly in the polythionic acid that forms during the shutdown of desulfurization units in petroleum refineries. Because this service involves long-term exposure of sensitizing temperatures, the stabilized grades should be used.

Effect of Ferrite and Martensite. Phases other than carbides can also influence the corrosion behavior of austenitic stainless steels. Ferrite, which is the result of an unbalanced composition, appears to reduce the pitting resistance of the steels. The presence of martensite may render the steels susceptible to hydrogen embrittlement under some conditions. The martensite can be produced by the deformation of unstable austenite. Although this phenomenon can occur in a number of commercial stainless steels, it is most common in the lower-nickel steels such as type 301, in which the transformation is used to increase formability.

Effect of Sigma Phase. The effect of σ-phase on the corrosion behavior of austenitic stainless steel has received considerable attention. This hard, brittle intermetallic phase precipitates in the same temperature range as chromium carbide and may produce susceptibility to intergranular corrosion in some environments.

Because it is hard and brittle, σ-phase affects mechanical as well as corrosion properties. Although it is often associated with δ-ferrite, it can form directly from austenite.

The effects of σ-phase on the corrosion behavior of austenitic stainless steels are most serious in highly oxidizing environments. The problem is of practical concern only if the phase is continuous. Although discrete particles of σ-phase may be attacked directly, such corrosion does not seem to contribute significantly to the penetration of the steel.

The most important corrosion problem with σ-phase in austenitic stainless steels occurs before it is microscopically resolvable. When the low-

carbon, molybdenum-containing austenitic stainless steels (such as types 316L and CF3M) or the stabilized grades (such as types 321 and 347) are exposed at 675 °C (1245 °F), they may become susceptible to intergranular corrosion in HNO_3 and, in some cases, $Fe_2(SO_4)_3$-H_2SO_4. This susceptibility cannot be explained by carbide precipitation, and σ-phase usually cannot be found in the optical microstructure. However, because some of the susceptible steels do exhibit continuous networks of σ-phase, it has been assumed that this constituent is the cause of the intergranular corrosion. The hypothesis is that even when σ-phase is not visible in the optical microstructure its effects are felt through some precursor or invisible phase. Invisible σ-phase must be considered when testing for susceptibility to intergranular corrosion, but it seems to affect corrosion resistance only in very oxidizing environments, such as HNO_3.

Unsensitized austenitic stainless steels (that is, solution-annealed material containing no carbides or other deleterious phases) are subject to intergranular corrosion in very highly oxidizing environments, such as HNO_3 containing hexavalent chromium. None of the regularly controlled metallurgical variables influences this type of intergranular attack. More detailed information on σ-phase in austenitic stainless steels can be found in the article "Metallurgy and Properties of Wrought Stainless Steels" in this Volume.

Intergranular Corrosion of Ferritic Stainless Steels

The mechanism for intergranular corrosion in ferritic stainless steels is largely accepted as being the same as that in austenitic stainless steels. Chromium compounds precipitate at grain boundaries, and this causes chromium depletion in the grains immediately adjacent to the boundaries. This lowering of the chromium content leads to increased corrosion rates in the oxidizing solutions usually used to evaluate intergranular corrosion.

There are several differences between the sensitization of ferritic and austenitic stainless steels to intergranular corrosion. The first is that the solubility of nitrogen in austenite is great enough that chromium nitride precipitation is not a significant cause of intergranular corrosion in austenitic steels. It is, however, a significant cause in ferritic stainless steels. The second is the temperature at which it occurs. Sensitization in austenitic steels is produced by heating between 425 and 815 °C (800 and 1500 °F). In conventional ferritic alloys, sensitization is caused by heating above 925 °C (1700 °F). This difference is the result of the relative solubilities of carbon and nitrogen in ferrite and austenite.

Because the sensitization temperatures are different for austenitic and ferritic steels, it is not surprising that the welding of susceptible steels produces different zones of intergranular corrosion. In austenitic steels, intergranular corrosion occurs at some distance from the weld, where the peak temperature reached during welding is approximately 675 °C (1250 °F). Because the sensitization of ferritic stainless steels occurs at higher

temperatures, the fusion zone and the weld itself are the most likely areas for intergranular corrosion. Detailed information on sensitization and corrosion of ferritic stainless steel welds is available in the article "Corrosion of Weldments" in this Volume.

The mere presence of chromium carbides and nitrides in ferritic stainless steels does not ensure that they will be subject to intergranular corrosion. On the contrary, the usual annealing treatment for conventional ferritic stainless steels is one that precipitates the carbides and nitrides at temperatures (700 to 925 °C, or 1300 to 1700 °F) at which the chromium can diffuse back into the depleted zones. These same treatments would of course sensitize austenitic stainless steels because of the much slower rate of diffusion of chromium in austenite.

Avoiding Intergranular Corrosion. Clearly, the most straightforward method of preventing intergranular attack in ferritic stainless steels is to restrict their interstitial contents. The results shown in Table 8 give an indication of the levels of carbon and nitrogen required to avoid intergranular corrosion of iron-chromium-molybdenum alloys in boiling 16% H_2SO_4-copper/copper sulfate ($CuSO_4$) solutions. Evaluation was by bending. The samples that passed had no cracks.

For 18Cr-2Mo alloys to be immune to intergranular corrosion, it appears that the maximum level of carbon plus nitrogen is 60 to 80 ppm; for 26Cr-1Mo steels, this level rises to around 150 ppm. The notation of partial failure for the 26Cr-1Mo steel containing 0.004% C and 0.010% N indicates that only a few grain boundaries opened upon bending and that it probably represents the limiting composition. Using the 50% H_2SO_4-$Fe(SO_4)_3$ test, it was determined that the interstitial limits for the 29Cr-4Mo steel were 0.010% C (max) and 0.020% N (max), with the additional restriction that the combined total not exceed 250 ppm (Ref 14). As their alloy contents increase, the iron-chromium-molybdenum steels seem to grow more tolerant of interstitials with regard to intergranular corrosion.

The levels of carbon and nitrogen that are needed to keep 18Cr-Mo alloys free of intergranular corrosion are such that very-low-interstitial versions of 18% Cr alloys have received little

Table 8 Results of ASTM A 763, Practice Z, on representative as-welded ferritic stainless steels

Welds were made using the gas tungsten arc welding technique with no filler metal added.

Alloy	Interstitial content, wt%		Result
	C	N	
18Cr-2Mo	0.002	0.004	Pas
	0.010	0.004	Fail
	0.002	0.009	Fail
26Cr-1Mo	0.002	0.005	Pass
	0.004	0.010	Partial failure
	0.003	0.016	Fail
	0.013	0.006	Fail

Source: Ref 13

Table 9 Corrosion rates of 26% Cr ferritic stainless steels containing 0 to 3% Mo that were annealed for 15 min at 900 °C (1650 °F), water quenched, annealed for increasing times at 620 °C (1150 °F), then water quenched

Testing was performed according to recommendations in ASTM A 763, Practice X (Fe$_2$(SO$_4$)$_3$-H$_2$SO$_4$ test).

Alloy	900-°C (1650-°F) anneal	Corrosion rate, mg/dm^2/d Annealing time at 620 °C (1150 °F)					
		10 min	30 min	1 h	2 h	4 h	5 h
26-0	50	15,700	270	62	81	85	43
		15,600	264	50	67	85	43
26-1	43	5,950(a)	8,030(a)	990	50	40	53
	37	8,220(a)	12,400(a)	890	50	37	50
26-2	78	15,600	940	138	80	74	270
	77	15,500	500	132	80	70	226
26-3	50	104	214	258	98	102	58
	50	95	160	96	93	97	58

(a) 56 h in test solution. Source: Ref 15

commercial attention. The 26Cr-1Mo and 29Cr-4Mo steels have been made in considerable quantity with very low interstitials, for example, 20 ppm C and 100 ppm N.

The low-interstitial ferritic stainless steels respond to heat treatment in a manner somewhat similar to that of austenitic stainless steels. As the results of welding in Table 8 show, rapid cooling from high temperature will preserve resistance to intergranular corrosion. However, depending on alloy content and interstitial levels, these alloys may be sensitive to a cooling rate from temperatures above about 600 °C (1110 °F). Less pure iron-chromium-molybdenum alloys can also be affected by a cooling rate from around 800 °C (1470 °F), but at higher temperatures, it is impossible to quench them fast enough to avoid intergranular attack.

Isothermal heat treatments can also produce sensitivity to intergranular corrosion in low-interstitial ferritic stainless steels. For example, the effects of annealing at 620 °C (1150 °F) on the intergranular corrosion of 26% Cr alloys with 0 to 3% Mo were studied. The alloys contained 0.007 to 0.013% C and 0.020 to 0.024% N. As little as 10 min at temperature can lead to intergranular corrosion; however, continuing the treatment for 1 to 2 h can cure the damage (Table 9). Increasing the

molybdenum content delays the onset of sensitization and makes it less severe. It does, however, delay recovery.

The very low levels of interstitials needed to ensure that ferritic stainless steels are immune to intergranular corrosion suggest that stabilizing elements might offer a means of preventing this type of corrosion without such restrictive limits on the carbon and nitrogen. Both titanium and niobium can be used, and each has its advantages. In general, weld ductility is somewhat better in the titanium-containing alloys, but the toughness of the niobium steels is better. As noted above, titanium-stabilized alloys are not recommended for service in HNO$_3$, but the niobium-containing steels can be used in this environment. Additional information on materials selection for HNO$_3$ environments is available in the section "Corrosion by Nitric Acid" in this article.

Table 10 shows the results of Cu/CuSO$_4$-16% H$_2$SO$_4$ tests on 26Cr-1Mo and 18Cr-2Mo steels with additions of either titanium or niobium. Inspection of the data suggests that the required amount of titanium cannot be described by a simple ratio as it is in austenitic steels. The amount of titanium or niobium required for ferritic stainless steels to be immune to intergranular corrosion in the CuSO$_4$-16% H$_2$SO$_4$ test has been investigated

(Ref 16). It has been determined that for 26Cr-1Mo and 18Cr-2Mo alloys, the minimum stabilizer is given by:

$$Ti + Nb = 0.2 + 4 (C + N) \qquad (Eq 2)$$

According to Ref 16, these limits are valid for combined carbon and nitrogen contents in the range of 0.02 to 0.05%. It should be emphasized that the limits set in Eq 2 are truly minima and are needed in the final product if intergranular attack is to be avoided.

This guideline is empirical and cannot be explained on the basis of stoichiometry. The alloys in the study (Ref 16) were fully deoxidized with aluminum before the stabilizing additions were made. Therefore, it is unlikely that the excess stabilizer is required because it reacts with oxygen.

The susceptibility of titanium-stabilized steels to intergranular attack in HNO$_3$ has been noted earlier. Because there is evidence that titanium carbide can be directly attacked by HNO$_3$, this mechanism is usually in titanium-containing steels. Another explanation that could be advanced about the intergranular attack of titanium-bearing steels under highly oxidizing conditions is an invisible σ-phase such as that encountered in type 316L and discussed above.

Effects of Austenite and Martensite. The austenitic and martensitic phases are discussed together for ferritic stainless steels because they are interrelated; one can occur as the result of the other.

High-purity iron-chromium alloys are ferritic at all temperatures up to the melting point if they contain more than about 12% Cr. However, the γ-loop in iron-chromium alloys can be greatly expanded by the addition of carbon and nitrogen. For example, it has been found that the ferrite-austenite boundary is extended to 29% Cr in alloys that contain 0.05% C and 0.25% N.

Although the formation of austenite in ferritic stainless steels can be avoided by restricting their interstitial contents or by combining the interstitials with such elements as titanium or niobium, many of the ferritic stainless steels that are produced commercially will undergo partial transformation to austenite. Once the austenite is formed, the question is then what it will transform into. In one study, for example, the transformation products were dependent on chromium content and cooling rate (Ref 17). Slow cooling led to the transformation of austenite into ferrite and carbides in all of the steels examined, but quenching either produced martensite or retained the austenite.

In addition, the martensite start (M$_s$) temperature for a 17% Cr steel was measured at 176 °C (349 °F), and it was found that the transformation was 90% complete at 93 °C (199 °F) (Ref 17). The M$_s$ for a 21% Cr steel was −160 °C (−255 °F), and martensite did not form in quenched 25% Cr alloys. Untempered martensite obviously reduces the toughness and ductility of ferritic stainless steels, and its presence is one cause of the poor ductility of welded type 430. In discussing this work (Ref 17), other researchers observed that welded type 430 (17% Cr) had poor ductility but

Table 10 Results of ASTM A 763, Practice Z, tests on as-welded ferritic stainless steels with titanium or niobium

Welds were made using gas tungsten arc welding with no filler metal added.

Alloy	(C + N), wt%	Ti, wt%	Nb, wt%	$\frac{Ti \text{ or } Nb}{(C + N)}$, %	Result
18Cr-2Mo	0.022	0.16	...	7.3	Fail
	0.028	0.19	...	6.8	Fail
	0.027	0.23	...	8.5	Pass
	0.057	0.37	...	6.5	Pass
	0.079	0.47	...	5.9	Pass
18Cr-2Mo	0.067	...	0.32	4.8	Fail
	0.067	...	0.61	9.1	Pass
	0.030	...	0.19	6.3	Pass
26Cr-1Mo	0.026	0.17	...	6.5	Fail
	0.026	0.22	...	8.5	Fail
	0.026	0.26	...	10.0	Pass
26Cr-1Mo	0.026	...	0.17	6.5	Fail
	0.025	...	0.33	13.2	Pass

Source: Ref 13

Table 11 Effect of crystal structure on the corrosion behavior of an Fe-47Cr alloy

Solution	Corrosion rate, g/dm^2/d		
	Ferrite	σ phase	Ratio(a)
Reducing			
10% HCl boiling	1461	7543	5.2
10% H$_2$SO$_4$ boiling	2939	7422	2.5
50% H$_2$SO$_4$ boiling	5088	5280	1.04
Oxidizing			
50% H$_2$SO$_4$ + Fe$_2$(SO$_4$)$_3$ boiling	0.0195	0.196	10
50% H$_2$SO$_4$ + CuSO$_4$ boiling	0.0170	0.415	24
65% HNO$_3$ boiling	0.0205	0.861	42
HNO$_3$ + HF at 65 °C (150 °F)	0.00	0.06	...
Pitting			
10% FeCl$_3$ · 6H$_2$O at room temperature	0.00	2.5	...

(a) Corrosion rate of σ-phase + corrosion rate of ferrite. Source: Ref 20

that welded type 442 (21% Cr) had good ductility (Ref 18). These findings were attributed to the transformation of austenite to martensite in the lower-chromium steel but not in the 21% Cr steel. Both weldments were subject to intergranular corrosion, however.

The austenite retained in the higher-chromium steels is saturated with carbon, and when it is heated into the carbide precipitation region to, for example, 760 °C (1400 °F), it loses carbon and becomes unstable enough to transform to martensite upon cooling. This transformation product must then be tempered to restore ductility.

Another study found that martensite in type 430 corroded at a higher rate than the surrounding ferrite in boiling 50% H$_2$SO$_4$ + Fe$_2$(SO$_4$) (Ref 13). This difference was attributed to the partitioning of chromium between ferrite and austenite at high temperatures. Because the austenite is lower in chromium, the martensite that forms from it would also be lower in chromium. The 50% H$_2$SO$_4$-Fe$_2$(SO$_4$) test is quite sensitive to changes in chromium content in the 12 to 18% Cr range (Fig. 20). The test is less sensitive at higher chromium contents; therefore, no preferential attack was noted in austenite formed in type 446. This same austenite was preferentially attacked by boiling 5% H$_2$SO$_4$, presumably because of its higher interstitial content.

These corrosion experiments help to elucidate the effect of metallurgical factors on the corrosion behavior of ferritic stainless steels. However, these experiments describe situations rarely encountered in practice, because the mechanical properties of steels with such microstructures limit their usefulness.

Effect of Sigma and Related Phases. In contrast to the case of austenitic steels, the occurrence of σ-phase in most commercial ferritic stainless steels can be predicted from the iron-chromium phase diagram. Fortunately, the kinetics of σ formation are very sluggish, and σ-phase is not normally encountered in the processing of commercial ferritic stainless steels.

The formation of σ-phase in the Fe-Cr system has been thoroughly researched, and the literature

has been well summarized (Ref 19). The phase has the nominal composition of FeCr, but it can dissolve about 5% of either iron or chromium. It forms congruently from ferrite at 815 °C (1500 °F). The sluggishness of the reaction makes it difficult to define the low-temperature limits of the σ-phase field, but the ferrite/ferrite + σ-phase boundary has been estimated at 9.5% Cr at 480 °C (895 °F). Cold work accelerates the precipitation of σ-phase.

There is relatively little information on how σ-phase affects the corrosion behavior of ferritic stainless steels; however, continuous networks would be expected to be more troublesome than isolated colonies. Because σ-phase contains more chromium than ferrite, its presence could also affect the corrosion behavior by either local or general depletion of the chromium content of the matrix.

One study investigated the corrosion behavior of an Fe-47Cr alloy that was heat treated so that it was either entirely ferrite or entirely σ-phase (Ref 20). These data are given in Table 11. The types of environments studied induced reducing (active), oxidizing (passive), and pitting corrosion conditions. The differences were greatest in the oxidizing and pitting environments. These results indicate that σ-phase is more likely to corrode than ferrite in many instances and that no chromium-depletion mechanism need be invoked to explain how σ-phase can reduce the corrosion resistance.

In molybdenum-containing ferritic steels, χ-phase, which is closely related to σ-phase, can be found. It occurs in the temperature range of 550 to 950 °C (1020 to 1740 °F). It has the nominal composition Fe$_2$CrMo, but there are deviations from stoichiometry. In an investigation of the effect of heat treatment on the microstructure of 29Cr-4Mo alloys, both χ- and σ- phase were found in material held in the 700 to 925 °C (1290 to 1695 °F) range (Ref 21). Long-term aging of the 29Cr-4Mo steel did not render it susceptible to intergranular corrosion in the boiling 50% H$_2$SO$_4$ + Fe$_2$(SO$_4$)$_3$ solution.

This work also included 29Cr-4Mo-2Ni alloys, and χ- and σ-phase were seen to form much more quickly in these steels than in nickel-free materials. This observation is consistent with earlier results that nickel additions up to about 2% can accelerate the formation of σ-phase in iron-chromium alloys (Ref 22). At higher levels, nickel decreases the rate of σ-phase precipitation. Sigma and χ reduce the ductility of the 29Cr-4Mo-2Ni alloys but do not cause it to undergo intergranular corrosion. However, long-term aging at 815 °C (1500 °F) did render them susceptible to crevice corrosion in 10% hydrated ferric chloride (FeCl$_3$ · 6H$_2$O) at 50 °C (120 °F). In this case, the ferrite was preferentially attacked—perhaps because it was depleted in chromium and molybdenum by precipitation of the second phase.

There is some evidence that the invisible χ- or σ-phase may affect the properties of stabilized 18Cr-2Mo ferritic stainless steels aged at approximately 620 °C (1150 °F). For example, it has been shown that aging for even relatively short times can produce extensive intergranular corrosion in 18Cr-2Mo-Ti steels exposed to boiling 50%

H$_2$SO$_4$ + Fe$_2$(SO$_4$)$_3$. The steels were not subject to intergranular attack in 10% HNO$_3$ + 3% HF or in boiling 16% H$_2$SO$_4$ + 6% CuSO$_4$ + Cu, and both of these solutions are known to produce intergranular attack in improperly stabilized ferritic stainless steels. Similar behavior has been noted in niobium-stabilized 18Cr-2Mo steels. In neither case was χ- or σ-phase clearly present in the grain boundaries.

Intergranular Corrosion of Duplex Stainless Steels

Duplex stainless steels are those that are composed of a mixture of austenite and ferrite. The common cast stainless steels, such as CF-8 and CF-8M, are mostly austenite with some ferrite. These alloys are often considered to be simple analogs of wrought alloys with similar compositions; however, they do not always have the same response to heat treatment. Additional information on cast duplex stainless steels can be found in the article "Corrosion of Cast Steels" in this Volume.

Wrought duplex stainless steels contain approximately equal amounts (50:50) of austenite and ferrite. The modern alloys are produced with low carbon contents, usually less than 0.03%, and intergranular corrosion resulting from carbide precipitation generally has not been a practical problem.

These alloys are usually high in chromium (25 to 27%) and molybdenum (2 to 4%). As a result, these alloys are prone to the formation of intermetallic phases such as σ and χ if they are not cooled rapidly through the 900 to 700 °C (1650 to 1290 °F) range. Although these intermetallic compounds do affect the corrosion resistance of the alloys, they have a more drastic effect on mechanical properties. If a duplex alloy has satisfactory mechanical properties, it probably will not experience intergranular corrosion. In both wrought and cast alloys, it appears that the high rate of diffusion of chromium in the ferrite generally minimizes depleted zones and, therefore, intergranular corrosion.

Stress-Corrosion Cracking

Stress-corrosion cracking is a corrosion mechanism in which the combination of a susceptible alloy, sustained tensile stress, and a particular environment leads to cracking of the metal. Stainless steels are particularly susceptible to SCC in chloride environments; temperature and the presence of oxygen tend to aggravate chloride SCC of stainless steels. Most ferritic and duplex stainless steels are either immune or highly resistant to SCC. All austenitic grades, especially types 304 and 316, are susceptible to some degree. The highly alloyed austenitic grades are resistant to sodium chloride (NaCl) solutions but crack readily in MgCl$_2$ solutions. Although some localized pitting or crevice corrosion probably precedes SCC, the amount of pitting or crevice attack may be so small as to be undetectable. Stress corrosion is difficult to detect while in progress, even when pervasive, and can lead to rapid catastrophic failures of pressurized equipment.

Fig. 22 Erosion-corrosion of CN-7M stainless steel pump components that pumped hot H_2SO_4 with some solids present. Note the grooves, gullies, waves, and valleys common to erosion-corrosion damage.

Table 12   Atmospheric corrosion of austenitic stainless steels at two industrial sites

Type(a)	New York City (industrial)		Niagara Falls (industrial-chemical)	
	Exposure time, years	Specimen surface evaluation	Exposure time, years	Specimen surface evaluation
302	5	Free from rust stains	<²⁄₃	Rust stains
302	26	Free from rust stains	...	...
304	26	Free from rust stains	<1	Rust stains
304	...	...	6	Covered with rust spots and pitted
347	26	Free from rust stains	...	...
316	23	Free from rust stains	<²⁄₃	Slight stains
316	...	...	6	Slight rust spots, slightly pitted
317	...	...	<²⁄₃	Slight stains
317	...	...	6	Slight stains
310	...	...	<1	Rust stains
310	...	...	6	Rust spots; pitted

(a) Solution-annealed sheet, 1.6 mm (¹⁄₁₆ in.) thick

It is difficult to alleviate the environmental conditions that lead to SCC. The level of chlorides required to produce stress corrosion is very low. In operation, there can be evaporative concentration or a concentration in the surface film on a heat-rejecting surface. Temperature is often a process parameter, as in the case of a heat exchanger. Tensile stress is one parameter that might be controlled. However, the residual stresses associated with fabrication, welding, or thermal cycling, rather than design stresses, are often responsible for SCC, and even stress-relieving heat treatments do not completely eliminate these residual stresses. More detailed information on SCC of stainless steels can be found in the article "Stress-Corrosion Cracking and Hydrogen Embrittlement" in this Volume.

Erosion-Corrosion

Corrosion of a metal or alloy can be accelerated when there is an abrasive removal of the protective oxide layer. This form of attack is especially significant when the thickness of the oxide layer is an important factor in determining corrosion resistance. In the case of a stainless steel, erosion of the passive film can lead to some acceleration of attack.

Material selection is an important consideration for erosion-corrosion resistance. Alloy hardness has also been shown to be a factor. Generally, soft alloys are more susceptible to erosion-corrosion than their harder counterparts, but the relative hardness properties of the alloy can be misleading, because the hardening mechanism affects resistance to erosion-corrosion. For example, solid-solution hardening has been found to offer greater resistance than that provided by conventional heat treatment. One example of this is the cast precipitation-hardening alloy ACI CD-4MCu, which outperforms alloy 20 (CN-7M) and austenitic stainless steels in many applications. Erosion-corrosion of an ACI CN-7M stainless steel cast impeller after exposure to hot concentrated H_2SO_4 with solids present is shown in Fig. 22.

High-Temperature Corrosion

High-temperature corrosion involves the degradation of metals and alloys in hot gases, liquid metals, and molten salts. Each of these corrosive mediums is briefly described below. More detailed information can be found in the article "High-Temperature Corrosion" in this Volume.

Oxidation. Because of their high chromium contents, stainless steels tend to be very resistant to oxidation. Important factors to be considered in the selection of stainless steels for high-temperature service are the stability of the composition and microstructure of the grade upon thermal exposure and the adherence of the oxide scale upon thermal cycling. Many of the stainless steels used for high temperatures are austenitic grades with relatively high nickel contents; increased nickel minimizes spalling when temperature cycling occurs.

Contamination of the air with water and carbon dioxide (CO_2) often increases corrosion at elevated temperatures. Increased attack can also occur because of sulfidation as a result of SO_2, hydrogen sulfide (H_2S), or sulfur vapor.

Carburization of stainless steels can occur in carbon monoxide (CO), methane (CH_4), and other hydrocarbons. Carburization can also occur when stainless steels contaminated with oil or grease are annealed without sufficient oxygen to burn off the carbon. This can occur during vacuum or inert gas annealing as well as during open-air annealing of oily parts with shapes that restrict air access. Chromium, silicon, and nickel are useful in combating carburization.

Nitridation can occur in dissociated ammonia (NH_3) at high temperatures. Resistance to nitriding depends on alloy composition as well as NH_3 concentration, temperature, and pressure. Stainless steels are readily attacked in pure NH_3 at about 540 °C (1000 °F).

Liquid Metals. The 18-8 stainless steels are highly resistant to liquid sodium or sodium-potassium alloys. Mass transfer is not expected up to 540 °C (1000 °F) and remains at moderately low levels up to 870 °C (1600 °F). Accelerated attack of stainless steels in liquid sodium occurs with oxygen contamination, with a noticeable effect occurring at about 0.02% oxygen by weight.

Exposure to molten lead under dynamic conditions often results in mass transfer in common stainless alloy systems. Particularly severe corrosion can occur in strongly oxidizing conditions. Stainless steels are generally attacked by molten aluminum, zinc, antimony, bismuth, cadmium, and tin.

Molten salts are commonly used as a medium for heat treating of metals and alloys as well as a heat-transfer medium in nuclear energy systems. The most prevalent molten salts in use are nitrates for heat-treat salt baths and fluorides for nuclear reactor cooling systems. Stainless steels perform well in molten nitrates but can exhibit void formation and chromium depletion in molten fluorides.

Atmospheric Corrosion

The atmospheric contaminants most often responsible for the rusting of structural stainless steels are chlorides and metallic iron dust. Chloride contamination may originate from the $CaCl_2$ used to make concrete or from exposure in marine or industrial locations. Iron contamination may occur during fabrication or erection of the structure. Contamination should be minimized, if possible.

The corrosivity of different atmospheric exposures can vary greatly and can dictate application of different grades of stainless steel. Rural atmospheres, uncontaminated by industrial fumes or coastal salt, are extremely mild in terms of corrosivity for stainless steel, even in areas of high humidity. Industrial or marine environments can be considerably more severe.

Table 12 demonstrates that resistance to staining can depend on the specific exposure. For example, several 300-series stainless steels showed no rust during long-term exposures in New York City. On the other hand, staining was observed after much shorter exposures at Niagara Falls in a severe industrial-chemical environment near plants producing chlorine or HCl.

Although marine environments can be severe, stainless steels often provide good resistance. Table 13 compares several AISI 300-series stainless steels after a 15-year exposure to a marine atmosphere 250 m (800 ft) from the ocean at Kure

Table 13 Corrosion of AISI 300-series stainless steels in a marine atmosphere
Based on 15-year exposures 250 m (800 ft) from the ocean at Kure Beach, NC

AISI type	Average corrosion rate		Average depth of pits		Appearance(a)
	mm/yr	mils/yr	mm	mils	
301	$< 2.5 \times 10^{-5}$	<0.001	0.04	1.6	Light rust and rust stain on 20% of surface
302	$< 2.5 \times 10^{-5}$	<0.001	0.03	1.2	Spotted with rust stain on 10% of surface
304	$< 2.5 \times 10^{-5}$	<0.001	0.028	1.1	Spotted with slight rust stain on 15% of surface
321	$< 2.5 \times 10^{-5}$	<0.001	0.067	2.6	Spotted with slight rust stain on 15% of surface
347	$< 2.5 \times 10^{-5}$	0.001	0.086	3.4	Spotted with moderate rust stain on 20% of surface
316	$< 2.5 \times 10^{-5}$	<0.01	0.025	1.0	Extremely slight rust stain on 15% of surface
317	$< 2.5 \times 10^{-5}$	<0.001	0.028	1.1	Extremely slight rust stain on 20% of surface
308	$< 2.5 \times 10^{-5}$	<0.001	0.04	1.6	Spotted by rust stain on 25% of surface
309	$< 2.5 \times 10^{-5}$	<0.001	0.028	1.1	Spotted by slight rust stain on 25% of surface
310	$< 2.5 \times 10^{-5}$	<0.001	0.01	0.4	Spotted by slight rust stain on 20% of surface

(a) All stains easily removed to reveal bright surface. Source: Ref 23

Beach, NC. Materials containing molybdenum exhibited only extremely slight rust staining, and all grades were easily cleaned to reveal a bright surface. Type 304 may provide satisfactory resistance in many marine applications, but more highly alloyed grades are often selected when the stainless is sheltered from washing by the weather and is not cleaned regularly.

Types 302 and 304 stainless steel have had many successful architectural applications. Type 430 has been used in many locations, but there have been problems. For example, type 430 rusted in sheltered areas after only a few months' exposure in an industrial environment. Type 302, used as a replacement, provided satisfactory service. In more aggressive environments, such as marine or severely contaminated atmospheres, type 316 is especially useful.

Stress-corrosion cracking is generally not a concern when austenitic or ferritic stainless steels are used in atmospheric exposures. Several austenitic stainless steels were exposed to a marine atmosphere at Kure Beach, NC. Annealed and quarter-hard wrought types 201, 301, 302, 304, and 316 were not susceptible to SCC. In the as-welded condition, only type 301 experienced failure. Following sensitization at 650 °C (1200 °F) for 1.5 h and furnace cooling, failures were obtained only for materials with carbon contents of 0.043% or more.

Stress-corrosion cracking must be considered when quench-hardened martensitic stainless steels or PH grades are used in marine environments or in marine environments where chlorides are present. Several hardenable stainless grades were exposed as U-bends 25 m (80 ft) from the ocean at Kure Beach, NC. Most samples were cut longitudinally, and two alloys received different heat treatments to produce different hardness or strength levels. The results of the study (Table 14) indicated that Custom 450 stainless and stainless alloy 355 resisted cracking. Stainless alloy 355 failed in this type of test when fully hardened; resistance was imparted by the 540 °C (1000 °F) temper. Precipitation-hardenable grades are expected to exhibit improved corrosion resistance when higher aging temperatures (lower strengths) are used.

Resistance to SCC is of particular interest in the selection of high-strength stainless steels for fastener applications. Cracking of high-strength fasteners is possible and often results from hydrogen generation due to corrosion or contact with a less noble material, such as aluminum. Resistance to SCC can be improved by optimizing the heat treatment, as noted above.

Fasteners for atmospheric exposure have been fabricated from a wide variety of alloys. Type 430 and unhardened type 410 have been used when moderate corrosion resistance is required in a lower-strength material. Better-than-average corrosion resistance has been obtained by using type 305 and Custom Flo 302 HQ when lower strength is acceptable.

Corrosion in Waters

Waters may vary from extremely pure water to chemically treated water to highly concentrated chloride solutions, such as brackish water or seawater, further concentrated by recycling. This chloride content poses the danger of pitting or crevice attack of stainless steels. When the application involves moderately increased temperatures, even as low as 45 °C (110 °F), and particularly when there is heat transfer into the chloride-containing medium, there is the possibility of SCC. It is useful to consider water with two general levels of chloride content: freshwater, which can have chloride levels up to approximately 600 ppm, and seawater, which encompasses brackish and severely contaminated waters. The corrosivity of a particular level of chloride can be strongly affected by the other chemical constituents present, making the water either more or less corrosive.

Permanganate ion (MnO_4^-), which is associated with the dumping of chemicals, has been related to pitting of type 304. The presence of sulfur compounds and oxygen or other oxidizing agents can affect the corrosion of copper and copper alloys but does not have very significant effects on stainless steels at ambient or slightly elevated temperatures (up to approximately 250 °C, or 500 °F).

In freshwater, type 304 has provided excellent service for such items as valve parts, weirs, fasteners, and pump shafts in water and wastewater treatment plants. Custom 450 stainless steel has been used as shafts for large butterfly valves in potable water. The higher strength of a PH stainless steel permits reduced shaft diameter and increased flow. Type 201 has seen service in revetment mats to reduce shoreline erosion in freshwater. Type 316 has been used as wire for microstrainers in tertiary sewage treatment and is suggested for waters containing minor amounts of chloride.

Seawater is a very corrosive environment for many materials. Stainless steels are more likely to be attacked in low-velocity seawater or at crevices resulting from equipment design or attachment of barnacles.

Types 304 and 316 suffer deep pitting if the seawater flow rate decreases below about 1.5 m/s (5 ft/s) because of the crevices produced by fouling organisms. However, in one study, type 316 stainless steel provided satisfactory service as tubing in the

Table 14 Stress-corrosion cracking of U-bend test specimens 25 m (80 ft) from the ocean at Kure Beach, NC

Alloy	Final heat treatment	Hardness, HRC	Specimen orientation	Time to failure of each specimen, days(a)
Custom 450	Aged at 480 °C (900 °F)	42	Transverse	NF, NF, NF, NF, NF
Type 410	Tempered at 260 °C (500 °F)	45	Longitudinal	379, 379, 471
	Tempered at 550 °C (1025 °F)	35	Longitudinal	4, 4
Alloy 355	Tempered at 540 °C (1000 °F)	38	Longitudinal	NF, NF, NF
15Cr-7Ni-Mo	Aged at 510 °C (950 °F)	49	Longitudinal	1, 1, 1
17Cr-4Ni	Aged at 480 °C (900 °F)	42	Longitudinal	93, 129, NF
	Aged at 620 °C (1150 °F)	32	Longitudinal	93, 129, NF
14Cr-6Ni	Aged at 480 °C (900 °F)	39	Longitudinal	93, 872, NF

(a) NF, no failure in over 4400 days for Custom 450 and 1290 days for the other materials. Source: Ref 24

Table 15 Crevice corrosion indexes of several alloys in tests in filtered seawater
Mill-finished panels exposed for 30, 60, and 90 days to seawater at 30 °C (85 °F) flowing at <0.1 m/s (<0.33 ft/s); crevice washers tightened to 2.8 or 8.5 N · m (25 or 75 in. · lb)

Alloy	UNS Designation	Number of sides (S) attacked(a)	Maximum pit depth (D)		Crevice corrosion index (S × D)
			mm	mils	
AL 29-4C	S44735	0	nil	nil	0
MONIT	S44635	3	0.01	0.4	0.03
Ferralium 255	S32550	1	0.09	3.5	0.09
Alloy 904L	N08904	3	0.37	14.6	1.1(b)
254SMO	S31254	6	0.19	7.5	1.1
Sea-Cure	S44660	14	0.11	4.3	1.5
AL-6X	N08366	8	0.34	13.4	2.7
JS777	...	6	2.3	90.6	14(b)
JS700	N08700	14	1.8	70.9	24
AISI type 329	...	17	1.6	63	28(c)
Nitronic 50	S20910	17	1.2	47.2	20

(a) Total number of sides was 18. (b) Also showed tunneling attack perpendicular to the upper edge, or attack at edges. (c) Perforated by attack from both sides. Source: Ref 26

heat-recovery section of a desalination test plant with relatively high flow rates (Ref 25).

The choice of stainless steel for seawater service can depend on whether or not stagnant conditions can be minimized or eliminated. For example, boat shafting of 17Cr-4Ni stainless steel has been used for trawlers where stagnant exposure and the associated pitting would not be expected to be a problem. When seagoing vessels are expected to lie idle for extended periods of time, more resistant boat shaft materials, such as 22Cr-13Ni-5Mn stainless steel, are considered. Boat shafts with intermediate corrosion resistance are provided by 18Cr-2Ni-12Mn and high-nitrogen type 304 (type 304F HN) stainless steels.

The most severe exposure conditions are often used in seawater test programs. In one example of such data, flat-rolled specimens of 11 commercially available alloys with several mill finishes were exposed to seawater (Table 15). Triplicate samples were prepared with plastic multiple-crevice washers, each containing 20 plateaus or crevices. These washers were affixed to both sides of each panel by using a torque of either 2.8 or 8.5 N · m (25 or 75 in. · lb). The panels were exposed for up to 90 days in filtered seawater flowing at a velocity of less than 0.1 m/s (0.33 ft/s).

The results given in Table 15 show the number of sides that experienced crevice attack and the maximum attack depth at any crevice for that alloy. A crevice corrosion index (CCI) was calculated by multiplying the maximum attack depth times the number of sides attacked. This provided a ranking system that accounts for both initiation and growth of attack. Lower values of the CCI imply improved resistance.

Attack in the above test does not mean that materials with high CCIs cannot be used in seawater. For example, 22Cr-13Ni-5Mn stainless steel with a CCI of 20 has proved to be a highly resistant boat shaft alloy. Some of the more resistant materials in the above tests have been used for utility condenser tubing. These alloys include MONIT, AL 29-4C, 254SMO, Sea-Cure, and AL-6XN.

The possibility of galvanic corrosion must be considered if stainless steel is to be used in contact with other metals in seawater. Figure 11 provides corrosion potentials in flowing seawater for several materials. Preferably, only those materials that exhibit closely related electrode potentials should be coupled to avoid attack of the less noble material. Galvanic differences have been used to advantage in the cathodic protection of stainless steel in seawater. Crevice corrosion and pitting of austenitic types 302 and 316 have been prevented by cathodic protection, but types 410 and 430 develop hydrogen blisters at current densities below those required for complete protection.

Other factors that should be noted when applying stainless steels in seawater include the effects of high velocity, aeration, and temperature. Stainless steels generally show excellent resistance to high velocities, impingement attack, and cavitation in seawater. Also, stainless steels provide optimum service in aerated seawater because a lack of aeration at a specific site often leads to crevice attack. Very little oxygen is required to maintain the passive film on a clean stainless surface. Increasing the temperature from ambient to about 50 °C (120 °F) often reduces attack of stainless steels, possibly because of differences in the amount of dissolved oxygen, changes in the surface film, or changes in the resistance of the boldly exposed sample area. Further temperature increases can result in increased corrosion, such as SCC.

Corrosion in Chemical Environments

Selection of stainless steels for service in chemicals requires consideration of all forms of corrosion, along with impurity levels and degree of aeration. When an alloy with sufficient general corrosion resistance has been selected, care must be taken to ensure that the material will not fail by pitting or SCC due to chloride contamination. Aeration may be an important factor in corrosion, particularly in cases of borderline passivity. If dissimilar-metal contact or stray currents occur, the possibility of galvanic attack or hydrogen embrittlement must be considered.

Alloy selection also depends on fabrication and operation details. If a material is to be used in the as-welded or stress-relieved condition, it must resist intergranular attack in service after these thermal treatments. In chloride environments the possibility of crevice corrosion must be considered when crevices are present because of equipment design or the formation of adherent deposits. Higher flow rates may prevent the formation of deposits, but in extreme cases may also cause accelerated attack due to erosion or cavitation. Increased operating temperatures generally increase corrosion. In heat-transfer applications, higher metal wall temperatures result in higher rates than expected from the lower temperature of the bulk solution. These and other items may require consideration in the selection of stainless steels, yet suitable materials continue to be chosen for a wide variety of chemical plant applications, as will be described below.

Some generalizations can be made regarding the performance of various categories of stainless steels in certain types of chemical environments. These observations relate to the compositions of the grades. For example, the presence of nickel and copper in some austenitic grades greatly enhances resistance to H_2SO_4 compared to the resistance of the ferritic grades. However, combinations of chemicals that are encountered in practice can be either more or less corrosive than might be expected from the corrosivity of the individual components. Testing in actual or simulated environments is always recommended as the best procedure for selecting a stainless steel grade. Additional information describing service experience is available from alloy suppliers. Another excellent source of information is the *Handbook of Corrosion Data* published by ASM International.

Corrosion by Sulfuric Acid

Sulfuric acid is the largest-volume inorganic acid currently in use and is generally considered to be the most important industrial chemical. The corrosiveness of H_2SO_4 depends on many factors, particularly temperature and concentration. Strong, hot conditions present the greatest problems. The presence of oxidizing or reducing contaminants, velocity effects, solids in suspension, and galvanic effects also can alter the serviceability of a particular material of construction.

It is unwise to select materials of construction for equipment that will handle H_2SO_4 solely on the basis of published corrosion data unless the conditions involved are adequately and specifically covered by the reference data. Seemingly minor differences in impurities or environmental conditions may significantly affect actual service corrosion rates. Impurities such as halides generally increase corrosion. Aeration or the presence of oxidizing agents generally reduces corrosion of stainless alloys, but the extent of this effect depends on specific conditions. Hot-wall effects are frequently overlooked, and heating coils made of the same material as the containing vessel can corrode rapidly while the condition of the vessel itself remains satisfactory.

It is thus advisable to consider all general corrosion data only as an indicator of relative resis-

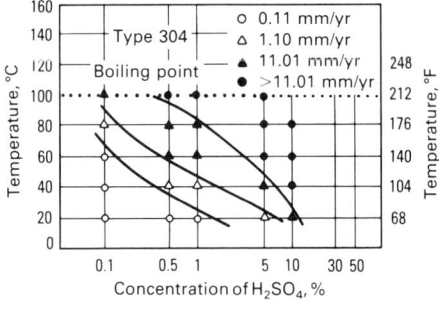

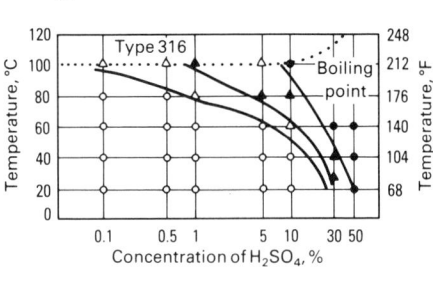

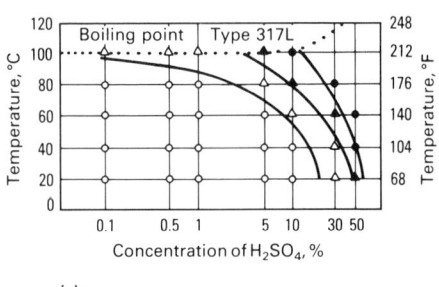

Fig. 23 Isocorrosion diagrams for (a) type 304, (b) type 316, and (c) type 317L stainless steels in aerated H_2SO_4 up to 50% concentration. Source: Ref 28

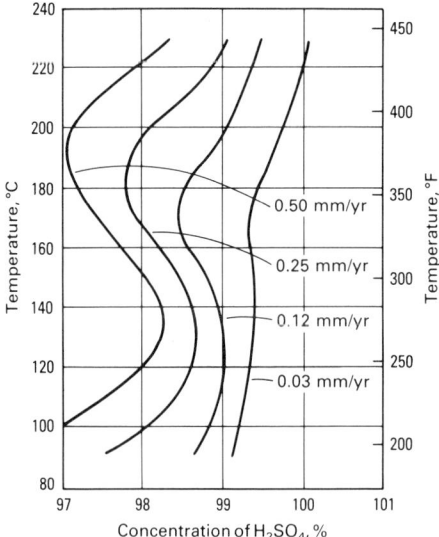

Fig. 24 Isocorrosion diagram for type 304 stainless steel in highly concentrated H_2SO_4. Source: Ref 29

tance and as a guide by which the limiting conditions of materials may be further reviewed. Final selection of materials for specific equipment depends, of course, on such factors as allowable corrosion rate, desired mechanical and physical properties, fabrication requirements, availability, and cost.

Austenitic Stainless Steels. The resistance of austenitic stainless steels to H_2SO_4 is complex due to the active-passive nature of the alloys. An excellent summary that includes corrosion rate data is provided in Ref 27.

Mechanism of Protection. Stainless steels depend on electrochemical passivity for resistance to corrosion in H_2SO_4 solutions. Stable passivity is achieved at ambient temperatures in the very low and very high concentrations and in oleum (fuming H_2SO_4).

Corrosion Resistance. At ambient temperatures, austenitic stainless steels (e.g., type 304) exhibit stable passivity in H_2SO_4 above 93% concentration and are frequently used for piping and tankage where product purity is desirable. The corrosion rates are essentially nil as compared with 0.15 to 1.0 mm/yr (5.9 to 39 mils/yr) for steel. Molybdenum stretches the passive region,

making types 316 and 317 acceptable above 90% concentration at ambient temperature. The upper temperature limit for stable passivity for types 304 and 316 in 93% H_2SO_4 is believed to be around 40 °C (105 °F). For 98.5% H_2SO_4, the upper stable passive limit is believed to be above 70 °C (160 °F). As concentration increases above 99%, corrosivity decreases rapidly, allowing the use of stainless steels above 100 °C (210 °F).

In dilute acid, only the molybdenum grades, such as types 316 or 317, are useful, although type 304 may be used when only a trace of acid is present. Figure 23 shows corrosion data for these alloys in as-mixed and refluxed (aerated) H_2SO_4 solutions. Stainless steels have poor resistance to deaerated dilute solutions. Type 310, with 25% Cr and no intentionally added molybdenum, is more resistant than the molybdenum-bearing grades when oxidizing agents are present. This is attributed to the higher chromium content of type 310.

Effect of Velocity. If a stainless steel exhibits solidly passive behavior, velocity appears to have little effect. Laboratory tests of type 304L with velocities to 6 m/s (20 ft/s) in 93% H_2SO_4 at ambient temperature have shown stable passive behavior. However, once the alloy drops to active-passive behavior, usually because of increasing temperature, velocity has a major effect. Under abrasive conditions, cast stainless steels have shown active-passive behavior in 96% H_2SO_4 even at ambient temperatures.

Effect of Aeration and Oxidants. Highly aerated solutions are much more suitable for these alloys than air-free ones. Similarly, the presence of oxidizing impurities stabilizes the passive film, and the resistance to H_2SO_4 of austenitic stainless steels improves markedly. Cations that are easily reducible, such as Fe^{3+}, Cu^{2+}, stannic (Sn^{4+}), and cerric (Ce^{4+}) ions, are oxidizing agents that can inhibit the attack of stainless steels in H_2SO_4 solutions. It has been found that 0.19 g/L of Fe^{3+} ion is sufficient to cause passivity and low corrosion

rates in boiling 10% H_2SO_4, but 0.115 g/L does not give inhibition.

Other oxidizing agents, such as H_2CrO_4 and HNO_3, have been shown to be effective in reducing corrosion rates. Nitric acid concentrations as low as 1.5% have been found to inhibit the corrosion of stainless steel over a wide range of H_2SO_4 concentrations at ambient and elevated temperatures. Oxidants in sufficient quantities reduce the corrosivity of H_2SO_4 on stainless steel by shifting the corrosion potential from an active to a passive state.

Effect of SO_3. In strong H_2SO_4 (above 97% concentration) and in oleum, the increased SO_3 content has a strong oxidizing effect, and corrosion rates are reduced dramatically. Figure 24 shows an isocorrosion diagram generated for type 304L stainless steel in an absorption tower environment. Most stainless steels and nickel-base alloys likely have similar reductions in corrosion rates with increasing concentration. However, the molybdenum-containing alloys are distinctly inferior unless the chromium content is high, as is the case with E-Brite stainless steel (Table 16).

Extreme care must be taken when using stainless steels in the 98 to 100% concentration at high temperatures; velocity conditions, reductions in acid concentration, or changes in oxidant levels may initiate high corrosion rates. For contrast, compare the corrosion data generated in flowing 98.7% H_2SO_4 at 100 °C (210 °F) shown in Table 17 with the data in Table 16. In the oleum range, stainless steels are free from the concerns about minor concentration variations and corrosion resistance is extended well in excess of 100 °C (210 °F).

Anodic protection is a practical method of extending the useful temperature and concentration range for stainless steels in H_2SO_4. With anodic protection, a stainless steel component (anode) is

Table 16 Corrosion rates of various metals in 99% H_2SO_4 at 100-120 °C (212-250 °F)

Alloy	Corrosion rate	
	mm/yr	mils/yr
Steel	>2.4	94.5
Cast iron	0.12	4.7
Ductile iron	0.25	9.8
Type 304L	0.02	0.8
Type 316L	0.06	2.4
Alloy 904L	0.19	7.5
Alloy 20Cb-3	0.08	3.1
Alloy C-276	0.33	13.0
Alloy B-2	2.3	90.6
A-611	0.04	1.6
E-Brite 26-1	<0.01	0.4

Table 17 Corrosion tests in flowing 98.7% H_2SO_4 at 100 °C (212 °F)

Alloy	Corrosion rate	
	mm/yr	mils/yr
Type 304	0.5	19.7
Type 316	3.44	135.0
Alloy 904L	2.3	90.6

Source: Ref 30

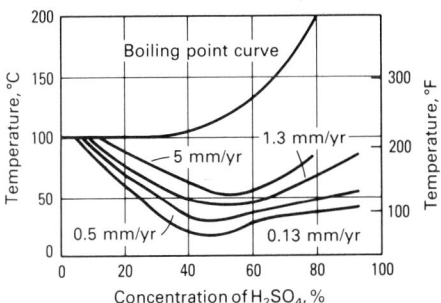

Fig. 25 Isocorrosion diagram for CD-4MCu in H_2SO_4. Source: Ref 27

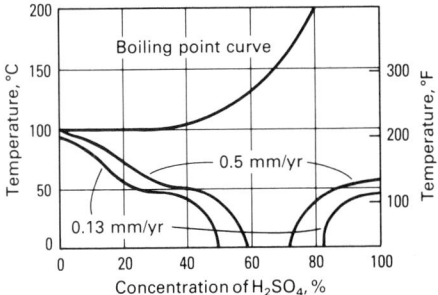

Fig. 26 Isocorrosion diagram for Hastelloy M-532 in H_2SO_4. Source: Ref 27

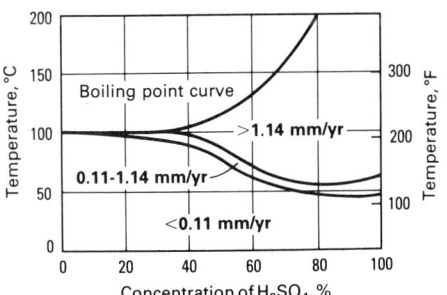

Fig. 27 Isocorrosion diagram for alloy 904L in H_2SO_4. Source: Ref 27

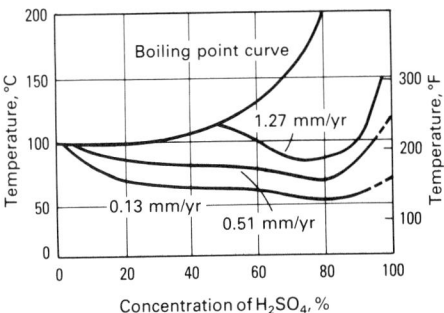

Fig. 28 Isocorrosion diagram for CN-7M in H_2SO_4. Source: Ref 27

held in the passive condition by an impressed current from a cathode.

Fortunately, H_2SO_4 is a good conductor of electricity and therefore has good throwing power. Complex shell sides of stainless steel shell-and-tube coolers handling concentrated H_2SO_4 can be easily protected using Hastelloy C-276 cathodes that extend the full length of the tube bundle. Piping is more difficult to protect because a cathode must throw the current a greater distance from the cathodes, which are typically located every 4.5 to 6 m (15 to 20 ft). Stainless steel may be protected in 93% H_2SO_4 up to 70 °C (160 °F) and in 98% H_2SO_4 up to 120 °C (250 °F). Corrosion rates can be reduced to 0.01 to 0.1 mm/yr (0.4 to 4 mils/yr). Approximately 400 anodically protected coolers have been installed in acid recirculation loops in H_2SO_4 plants throughout the world.

Silicon Stainless Steels. Austenitic stainless steels containing 5 to 6% Si have interesting corrosion characteristics in concentrated H_2SO_4 service. Cast and wrought versions are available. The cast version has a typical composition of Fe-5Si-21Cr-16Ni-0.02C. The wrought version of this alloy, A-611, has a typical composition of Fe-5.3Si-18Cr-18Ni-0.02C. The A-611 alloy has useful corrosion resistance in 99% H_2SO_4 up to 120 °C (250 °F) without anodic protection. Corrosion protection is obtained by the formation of a tenacious silicon-rich film formed on the surface during the initial days of corrosion. Corrosion resistance of the cast alloy is similar. Piping, distributors, and pump tanks handling hot 98 to 99% H_2SO_4 have been made from the A-611 alloy.

Cast stainless steels have essentially the same corrosion resistance to H_2SO_4 as their wrought counterparts. Because the cast versions contain second-phase ferrite for castability, care must be taken that proper heat treatment is performed for maximum corrosion resistance. Preferential corrosion as the result of the duplex structure has been shown to be a problem. However, properly cast and heat-treated duplex materials perform well.

One cast alloy that does not have a close wrought counterpart is ACI CD-4MCu. Corrosion resistance lies between 20Cb-3 stainless steel and type 316. Figure 25 shows the isocorrosion diagram for this alloy. Corrosion resistance of CD-4MCu in H_2SO_4 extends over the entire concentration range at ambient temperatures, and the alloy is suitable above 100 °C (210 °F) in oleum service.

Higher Austenitic Stainless Steels. Similar to that of the austenitic stainless steels, the corrosion resistance of the higher austenitic stainless steels is complex. However, the range of passivity and corrosion resistance is extended because of the higher alloy content. Like the stainless steels, active and active-passive behavior are the modes of corrosion. Resistance is achieved in the passive state.

Iron-base nickel-chromium-molybdenum alloys contain approximately 25% Ni, 20% Cr, and 4.5% Mo; copper, titanium, and niobium are sometimes added as stabilizing elements. Alloys in this category that do not contain copper are generally more corrosion resistant than type 316 and include Hastelloy M532 and alloy JS-700 (Fe-25Cr-20Ni-3Mn-3Mo). Figure 26 shows an isocorrosion diagram of Hastelloy M-532. The temperature and concentration range of this alloy has been extended beyond that for type 316 as the result of the increased alloy content.

The copper-bearing alloys in this class are more resistant in H_2SO_4 than the copper-free alloys. Figure 27 shows an isocorrosion diagram for a 25Ni-20Cr-4.5Mo-1.5Cu alloy such as alloy 904L. The copper additions make the alloy suitable for the entire concentration range at ambient temperature.

The 20-Type alloys are usually the first considered when an H_2SO_4 environment is too corrosive for the use of steel, 300-series stainless steels, or cast iron. This group contains both wrought (20Cb-3) and cast alloys (ACI CN-7M) that are roughly equivalent in resistance to H_2SO_4.

Figure 28 shows an isocorrosion diagram for cast ACI CN-7M. This alloy is generally suitable to 80 °C (175 °F) at concentrations to 50%. For higher concentrations, good corrosion resistance is expected to 65 °C (150 °F).

The wrought counterpart to cast ACI CN-7M was developed in 1947. In 1948, niobium was added to this alloy for stabilization against sensitization and intergranular attack. In 1963, the nickel content was raised to 33 to 35% in order to give greater resistance to chloride SCC and to improve resistance to boiling H_2SO_4 under heat-transfer conditions. Minor changes were subsequently made to impart greater resistance to intergranular corrosion. This alloy is now known as 20Cb-3. A typical composition is Fe-34Ni-20Cr-3.3Cu-2.5Mo. Corrosion resistance of 20Cb-3 is similar to that of CN-7M. Figure 29 shows an isocorrosion diagram for 20Cb-3.

Corrosion by Nitric Acid

Nitric acid is typically produced by the air oxidation of NH_3. This catalyzed reaction takes place at very high temperatures. The gaseous oxidation product is condensed to an aqueous liquid of about 65% concentration. During the high-temperature oxidation, corrosion of the plant materials is of secondary concern. The elevated operating temperatures dictate that the high-temperature properties of the materials are the primary design consideration. Corrosion considerations prevail during and after condensation and at lower temperatures.

The concentration of HNO_3 up to 99% requires secondary processing to remove excess water. This involves mixing 65% HNO_3 with another substance having a greater affinity for water

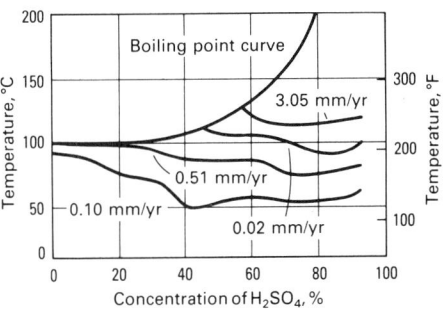

Fig. 29 Isocorrosion diagram for alloy 20Cb-3 in H_2SO_4. Source: Ref 27

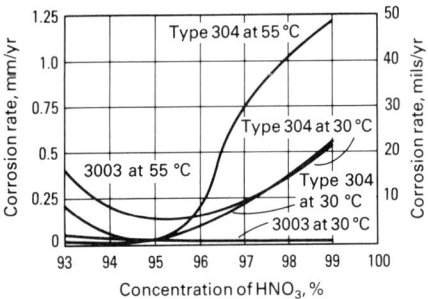

Fig. 30 Comparison of corrosion of aluminum alloy 3003 and type 304 stainless steel in HNO_3

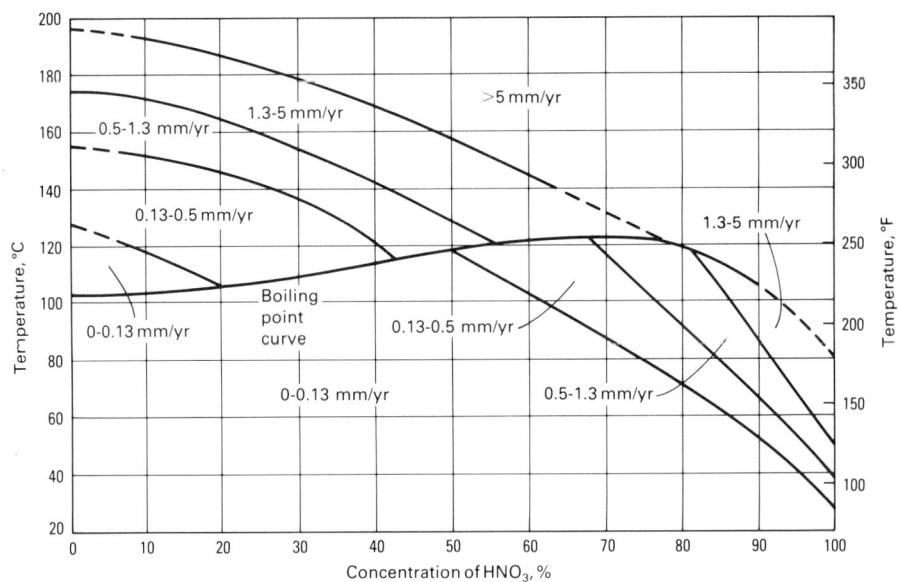

Fig. 31 Isocorrosion diagram for annealed type 304 in HNO_3. Source: Ref 31

(such as H_2SO_4), then separating the mixed acids by distillation and condensation processes.

Commercially produced HNO_3 is available in concentrations from 52 to 99%. Nitric acid over 86% is described as *fuming*. Nitric acid up to 95% is stored and shipped in type 304 stainless steel. Concentrated acid above 95% is handled in aluminum alloy 1100 or 3003. Figure 30 shows the reason for this; the corrosion rate of type 304 increases rapidly above 95% concentration, while that of aluminum 3003 remains essentially constant to 100%. A new stainless steel containing 4% Si—alloy A-610—shows excellent resistance to concentrated HNO_3; unfortunately, this advantage does not extend to lower concentrations.

Nitric acid is a strong oxidizing agent and attacks most metals, such as iron, by oxidizing the metal to the oxide. A secondary effect of oxidation is the generation of hydrogen at the metal-acid interface, which can cause hydrogen embrittlement of some materials. Metals and alloys that are able to form adherent oxide films, such as austenitic stainless steels, are protected by their oxide films from corrosion by HNO_3.

Austenitic Stainless Steels. The basic corrosion data for the austenitic (300-series) stainless steels have been reduced to the isocorrosion diagram format. Figure 31 shows the effect of temperature and HNO_3 concentration on the corrosion of type 304. Increasing either or both raises the corrosion rate; nevertheless, there is a large useful area extending from 0 to 90% concentration and up to the boiling point below 50% concentration in which the predicted corrosion rate is less than 0.13 mm/yr (5 mils/yr).

Experience has shown that, although all austenitic stainless steels behave in this fashion, types 304 and 304L, when welded, are clearly superior to the others. Therefore, they are the most popular grades for HNO_3 service.

Figure 31 also applies in general to the cast equivalents of wrought stainless steels. However, the generally higher carbon contents of cast alloys and the propensity of castings to have high-carbon surfaces often lead to selective intergranular corrosion in strong HNO_3.

Although austenitic stainless steels are commonly used in HNO_3, they are not without problems. One of the most prevalent is selective corrosion associated with chromium carbides precipitated around grain boundaries in the weld HAZ. Because few pieces of industrial equipment

are made without welding, this is a serious shortcoming. There are three methods for avoiding this problem:

- Use low or extra-low carbon content (Fig. 32).
- Add carbide stabilizers to the alloy, as in types 321 and 347.
- Solution anneal after welding to reduce the chromium carbide gradient.

Of these alternatives, solution annealing is frequently not practical, and the choice of stabilized alloys is not always an option. Therefore, when welding is planned, use of low-carbon stainless steels is the most popular alternative.

Sensitization of stainless steel refers to the precipitation of chromium carbides and the resultant depletion of the matrix of chromium as a result of heating from 480 to 760 °C (900 to 1400 °F). Figure 33 shows that the effect of such heating on corrosion rate in 65% HNO_3 is detrimental in all cases. Sigma phase, which may also form during prolonged heating of austenitic stainless steels, is preferentially and rapidly attacked by 65% HNO_3. Solution heat treating the alloy will restore corrosion resistance.

The corrosion of austenitic stainless steels in HNO_3 is accompanied by the formation of hexavalent chromium (Cr^{6+}), a complex chromium compound that increases the corrosivity of HNO_3 solutions. The effect of Cr^{6+} buildup is shown in Fig. 34 to be clearly detrimental. In general, the presence of chlorides and fluorides in HNO_3 solutions tends to increase the corrosion rate of stainless steels.

Selective corrosion along grain boundaries is common in austenitic stainless steels exposed to HNO_3, especially strong acid. There is some evidence to support the view that this cannot be entirely prevented; however, maintaining low carbon and avoiding sensitization will help.

For very concentrated acid (>95%), the addition of silicon to austenitic stainless steels is beneficial. Recently, two new stainless alloys of 4 and 6% Si—alloys A-610 and A-611—have been produced. These new alloys have remarkable resistance to HNO_3 above 95% (Fig. 35). At lower concentrations, they offer no advantage over type 304.

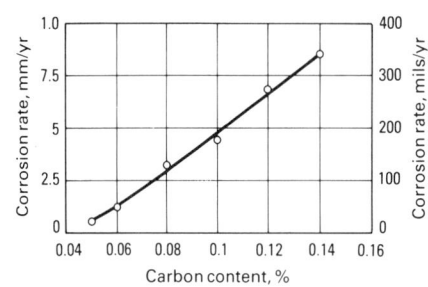

Fig. 32 Effect of carbon content on corrosion rate of type 304 in boiling 65% HNO_3. Source: Ref 32

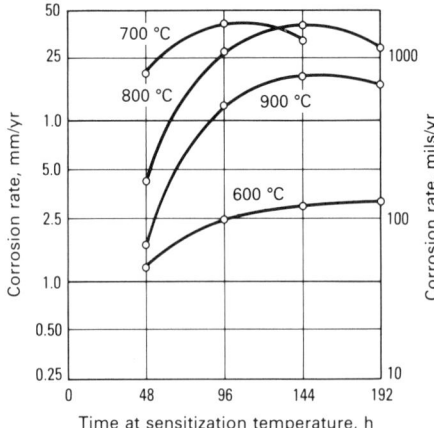

Fig. 33 Effect of sensitization time and temperature on the corrosion of type 304 in boiling HNO_3. Source: Ref 33

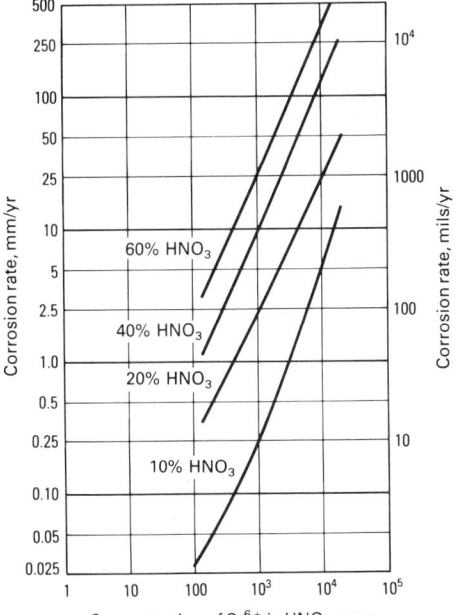

Fig. 34 Effect of hexavalent Cr^{6+} contamination on the corrosion rate of type 304 in HNO_3. Test duration: 40 h. Source: Ref 34

Corrosion by Phosphoric Acid

Conventional straight-chromium stainless steels have very limited general corrosion resistance in phosphoric acid (H_3PO_4) and exhibit lower rates only in very dilute or more highly concentrated solutions. Conventional austenitic stainless steels provide useful general corrosion resistance over the full range of concentrations up to about 65 °C (150 °F); use at temperatures up to the boiling point is possible for acid concentrations up to about 40%.

In commercial applications, however, wet-process H_3PO_4 environments include impurities derived from the phosphate rock, such as chlorides, fluorides, and H_2SO_4. These three impurities accelerate corrosion, particularly pitting or crevice corrosion in the presence of the halogens. Higher-alloyed materials than the conventional austenitic stainless steels are required to resist

wet-process H_3PO_4. Candidate materials include alloy 904L, alloy 28, 20Cb-3, 20Mo-4, and 20Mo-6 stainless steels.

Corrosion by Sulfurous Acid

Although sulfurous acid (H_2SO_3) is a reducing agent, several stainless steels have provided satisfactory service in H_2SO_3 environments. Conventional austenitic stainless steels have been used in sulfite digestors, and type 316, type 317, 20Cb-3, and cast alloys CF-8M and CN-7M have seen service in wet SO_2 and H_2SO_3 environments. Service life is improved by eliminating crevices, including those from settling of suspended solids, or by using molybdenum-containing grades. In some environments, SCC is also a possibility.

Corrosion by Organic Acids

Organic acids constitute a group of the most important chemicals currently in use in industry. The acids are produced more as precursors for other chemicals than for end use as organic acids. Acetic acid is the best known member of the group and is produced in the largest volume, but the other organic acids are also important for the preparation of compounds used in daily life—compounds from aspirin to plastics and fibers.

The subject of corrosion by organic acids is complicated not only by the numerous acids to be considered but also because the acids typically are not handled as pure chemicals but as process mixtures with inorganic acids, organic solvents, salts, and mixtures of several organic acids. They are even used as solvents for other chemical reactions.

This section will present some of the corrosion characteristics shared by the organic acids, will detail information on corrosion by formic acid (HCOOH), acetic acid (CH_3COOH), and propionic acid (CH_3CH_2COOH), and will provide selected data on longer-chain organic acids.

Corrosion Characteristics. Organic acids are weak acids, but they provide sufficient protons to act as true acids toward most metals. Most organic acids are neither oxidizing nor reducing to metals. In organic acids, the corrosion behavior of the 400-series or type 304 stainless steels, which

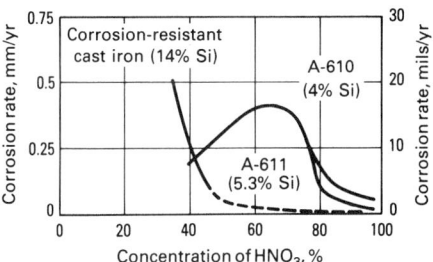

Fig. 35 Effect of silicon content on the corrosion of iron and iron-chromium-nickel alloys in boiling HNO_3. Source: Ref 35

are protected by oxide films, is mixed. This makes contaminants extremely important, because they tend to shift the oxidizing capacity of the acid mixture. The presence of chlorides can have disastrous effects on stainless steels.

Truly anhydrous organic acids are usually much more corrosive to stainless steels than organic acids containing even traces of water. Corrosion rates reported for glacial (concentrated) acids often reflect this effect, because the acids may be truly anhydrous or may contain small amounts of water.

Formic acid is the most highly ionized of the common organic acids and therefore the most corrosive. It reacts readily with many oxidizing and reducing compounds and is somewhat unstable as the concentration approaches 100%, decomposing to carbon monoxide and water.

The 400-series stainless steels are usually not resistant to HCOOH, except for very dilute, cool solutions, and they are seldom used in HCOOH service. Type 304 has excellent resistance to HCOOH at all concentrations at ambient temperatures, and it is the preferred material of construction for storage of the acid. However, type 304 is resistant to only 1 or 2% HCOOH at the atmospheric boiling temperature, and corrosion tests are advisable whenever type 304 is considered for handling HCOOH at elevated temperatures. Table 18 shows typical rates of attack on various stainless steels in several concentrations of HCOOH at the atmospheric boiling temperature.

Type 316 shows excellent resistance to HCOOH in all concentrations at ambient tem-

Table 18 Corrosion of stainless steel by HCOOH
96-h laboratory tests at atmospheric boiling temperature

Acid concentration, %	Type 304(a)		Type 316(a)		Type 316(b)		20Cb-3(c)		UNS S44627(c)(d)	
	mm/yr	mils/yr	mm/yr	mils/yr	mm/yr	mils/yr	mm/yr	mils/yr	mm/yr	mils/yr
1.0	0.17	6.8	0.09	3.5	…	…	…	…	…	…
5.0	0.79	31.1	0.04	1.5	…	…	…	…	< 0.03	<1.0
10.0	1.35	53.0	0.27	10.5	…	…	…	…	…	…
20.0	1.93	75.9	0.28	10.9	…	…	…	…	…	…
40.0	3.45	136	0.20	7.8	…	…	…	…	…	…
50.0	4.26	168	0.51	20.0	0.38	15.0	0.03	1.0	…	…
60.0	3.45	136	0.47	18.5	…	…	…	…	…	…
70.0	4.04	159	0.50	19.5	0.33	13.0	…	…	< 0.03	<1.0
80.0	4.29	169	0.47	18.7	…	…	…	…	…	…
90.0	3.28	129	0.42	16.5	0.15	6.0	0.10	4.0	…	…
100.0	…	…	…	…	0.10	4.0	…	…	…	…

(a) Oxygen not controlled. (b) Deaerated. (c) 48-h exposure. (d) Low-carbon molybdenum-bearing version of type 446

peratures and is resistant to at least 5% HCOOH acid at the atmospheric boiling temperature. However, type 316 can be seriously attacked by intermediate strengths of HCOOH at higher temperatures, and corrosion tests are advisable.

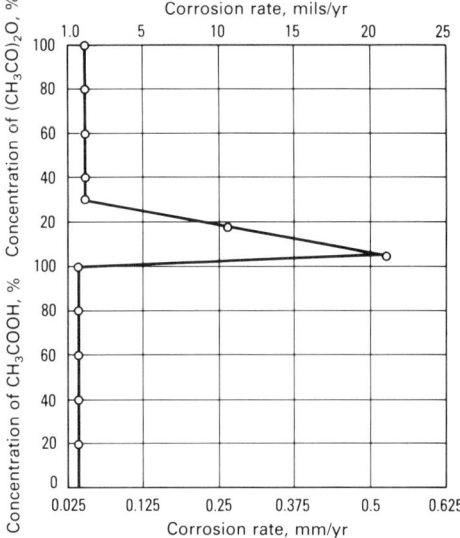

Fig. 36 Corrosion of type 316 in CH₃COOH and in CH₃COOH-(CH₃CO)₂O mixtures

The 20-type alloys, such as 20Cb-3, are more resistant than type 316 to HCOOH, and their use should be considered in higher concentrations at higher temperatures. Other alloys with chromium and nickel contents higher than those of type 316 also show superior resistance to mixtures of HCOOH and CH₃COOH and would be expected to perform better in HCOOH itself. Duplex alloys are also reported to be superior to type 316. Weld overlays of 20-type alloys have been used to alleviate the crevice corrosion of type 316—for example, under gaskets.

A low-carbon, niobium-bearing variant of type 446—alloy S44627—appears to have exceptional corrosion resistance to HCOOH in preliminary laboratory studies and plant usage. This alloy should be considered for handling HCOOH.

Acetic acid, as well as its derivatives, is produced in large quantities. It is the most important organic acid and is frequently encountered as a contaminant in other organic chemical processes. Acetic acid is even used as a solvent for some organic reactions. Consequently, knowledge of its corrosivity is essential. Acetic acid is classified as a weak acid, but the effective acidity in aqueous streams increases rapidly with concentration.

The chromium stainless steels of the 400 series occasionally exhibit low corrosion rates in laboratory tests in dilute CH₃COOH. However, because field experience with these materials indicates high corrosion rates and pitting attack, they are rarely used for CH₃COOH production equipment. Type

304 is the lowest grade commonly used. Exceptions include the high-purity ferritic stainless steels, which show good resistance.

Type 304 finds wide application in dilute CH₃COOH and in the shipment and storage of concentrated CH₃COOH. Data show that glacial CH₃COOH can be handled in type 304 to a temperature of about 80 °C (175 °F) and that type 304 has been satisfactory for lower concentrations to the boiling point of the acid. At temperatures above 60 °C (140 °F), use of the low-carbon type 304L is advisable for welded construction in order to prevent intergranular attack of HAZs.

Type 316 is the alloy most commonly used in CH₃COOH processing equipment. It will resist glacial acid to temperatures above the atmospheric boiling point. As with type 304, the low-carbon grade (type 316L) is required for higher-temperature application.

Acetic anhydride was produced as a coproduct in the old acetaldehyde oxidation process for CH₃COOH and is found in other acid streams. When CH₃COOH is truly anhydrous or contains small quantities of (CH₃CO)₂O, the rate of attack on type 316 increases dramatically. Experience has shown that the introduction of a few tenths of a percent of water will reduce the corrosion. Figure 36 illustrates the reduction in corrosion rate as (CH₃CO)₂O is added.

Contamination with chloride can cause pitting, rapid SCC, and accelerated corrosion of type 316. Up to 20 ppm of chloride can be tolerated,

Table 19 Corrosion of metals in refined organic acids

	Corrosion rate									
	Steel		Copper		Silicon-bronze		Type 304 stainless steel		Type 316 stainless steel	
Acid	mm/yr	mils/yr	mm/yr	mils/yr	mm/yr	mils/yr	mm/yr	mils/yr	mm/yr	mils/yr
50% acrylic in an ether at 88 °C (190 °F)	...	...	...	...	...	...	< 0.02	<1	< 0.02	<1
90% benzoic at 138 °C (280 °F)	...	...	...	...	...	...	0.38	15	0.13	5
Butyric										
Room temperature	0.15	6	0.05	2	0.05	2	< 0.02	<1	< 0.02	<1
115 °C (240 °F)	...	...	...	...	...	...	0.08	3	0.08	3
Boiling (163 °C, or 325 °F)	...	...	...	...	...	...	1.42	56	0.12	5
Crotonic (crude product), 92 °C (20 °F)	...	...	...	...	...	...	< 0.02	1	< 0.02	1
2-ethylbutyric										
Room temperature	0.18	7	0.02	1	0.02	1	< 0.02	<1	< 0.02	<1
150 °C (300 °F)	0.86	34	0.41	16	0.23	9	0.53	21	< 0.02	<1
2-ethylhexoic										
Room temperature	0.02	1	< 0.02	<1	< 0.02	<1	< 0.00	<1	< 0.02	<1
190 °C (375 °F)	1.27	50	< 0.02	<1	< 0.02	<1	0.20	8	< 0.02	<1
Heptanedionic (pimelic), 225 °C (435 °F)	...	...	...	...	...	...	0.94	37	0.18	7
Hexadienoic (sorbic) as water slurry, 88 °C (190 °F)	...	...	...	...	...	...	< 0.02	<1	< 0.02	<1
Iso-octanoic										
Room temperature	< 0.02	<1	< 0.02	<1	< 0.02	<1	< 0.02	<1	< 0.02	<1
190 °C (375 °F)	0.89	35	< 0.02	<1	< 0.02	<1	0.20	8	< 0.02	<1
Iso-decanic										
Room temperature	< 0.02	<1	< 0.02	<1	< 0.02	<1	< 0.02	<1	< 0.02	<1
190 °C (375 °F)	0.84	33	< 0.02	<1	< 0.02	<1	0.20	8	< 0.02	<1
2-methylpentanoic										
Room temperature	0.02	1	0.08	3	0.10	4	< 0.02	<1	<0.02	<1
150 °C (300 °F)	0.53	21	0.30	12	0.08	3	< 0.02	<1	< 0.02	<1
Pentanedioic (gluloric), 210 °C (410 °F)	...	...	...	...	...	...	0.68	27	0.20	<1
Pentanoic (valeric)										
Room temperature	0.05	2	0.05	2	0.05	2	< 0.02	<1	< 0.02	<1
114 °C (237 °F)	1.37	54	0.68	27	0.13	5	< 0.02	<1	< 0.02	<1

but higher concentrations are likely to cause rapid equipment failure.

Transferring heat through a metal wall, as in heat exchangers, can drastically alter the corrosion characteristics of the metal. Higher alloys, such as 20Cb-3 and Incoloy 825, show better resistance to CH_3COOH than does type 316.

Propionic acid has corrosion characteristics very similar to, but somewhat less aggressive than, those of acetic acid. The 400-series stainless steels are not used in CH_3CH_2COOH because of their propensity for pitting. They should be thoroughly tested in the exact environment for which their use is proposed. Type 304 shows good resistance to CH_3CH_2COOH at room temperature and to aqueous solutions up to about 50% concentration at boiling temperature. Between 80 and 100% concentration, type 304 shows borderline passivity at the boiling temperature and should not be considered for such service.

Type 316 is the preferred material for handling hot concentrated CH_3CH_2COOH solutions. The low-carbon grade (type 316L) should be used to avoid possible intergranular attack, unless corrosion tests in the exact environment show that intergranular attack is not a problem.

Other Organic Acids. It is impossible to cover each of the remaining hundreds of organic acids. However, Table 19 lists the corrosion rates of various metals in several of the longer-chain aliphatic acids and aromatic acids and some dicarboxylic acids.

Type 304 has excellent resistance to the higher-molecular-weight organic acids at room temperature and at lower concentrations at high temperatures. With the concentrated acids, type 304 is sometimes severely corroded. Type 316 is then required and is usable in almost all of the acids, even at elevated temperatures.

Corrosion by Hydrogen Chloride and Hydrochloric Acid

Hydrochloric acid is an important mineral acid with many uses, including acid pickling of steel, acid treatment of oil wells, chemical cleaning, and chemical processing. It is made by ab-sorbing hydrogen chloride in water. Most acid is the byproduct of chlorinations. Pure acid is produced by burning chlorine and hydrogen. Hydrochloric acid is available in technical, recovered, food-processing, and reagent grades. Reagent grade is normally 37.1%. Hydrochloric acid is a corrosive, hazardous liquid that reacts with most metals to form explosive hydrogen gas and causes severe burns and irritation of eyes and mucous membranes.

The commonly used austenitic stainless steels, such as types 304 and 316, are nonresistant to HCl at any concentration and temperature. At ambient temperatures and above, corrosion rates are high. Nickel, molybdenum, and, to a lesser extent, copper impart some resistance to dilute acid, but pitting, local attack, and SCC may result. Subambient temperatures will slow the corrosion rate but will invite SCC. Type 316 has been known to crack in 5% HCl at 0 °C (32 °F). At high corrosion rates (>0.25 mm/yr, or 10 mils/yr), SCC is unlikely to occur. However, the corrosion products, particularly $FeCl_3$, will cause cracking. Chlorides can penetrate and destroy the passivity (oxide film) that is responsible for the corrosion resistance of stainless steels, and the corrosion engineer should resist every attempt to use stainless steels in environments containing chlorides.

The standard ferritic stainless steels, such as types 410 and 430, should not be considered, because their corrosion resistance to HCl is lower than that of carbon steel. An exception is 29-4-2 stainless steel, which reportedly resists up to 1.5% HCl to the boiling point and remains passive. However, it is not suitable at higher concentrations, and the alloy is susceptible to SCC, although its resistance is reported to be high.

Some stainless steels—such as 20Cb-3, with its high nickel content (31 to 38%), 1 to 3% Mo, and 3 to 4% Cu—resist dilute HCl at ambient temperatures. However, 20Cb-3 is susceptible to pitting and crevice attack in acid chlorides and should be used with caution.

Hydrogen Chloride Gas. The recommended upper temperature limits for various metals in HCl gas are shown in Table 20. These guidelines were developed from short-term tests. Because corrosion rates generally decrease with time as films and scales form, these limits have proved to be conservative. Temperature versus design corrosion rates for carbon steel, 18-8 stainless, and several other alloys are shown in Fig. 37.

The addition of water vapor to HCl gas has little effect on upper temperature limits. The addition of 0.2% water vapor by weight has been found to have no effect. However, water vapor has a severe effect at lower temperatures.

Corrosion by Hydrogen Fluoride and Hydrofluoric Acid

Anhydrous hydrogen fluoride (AHF) and aqueous HF are of great industrial importance. Anhydrous HF is the foundation of the multi-billion-dollar fluorocarbon industry, which encompasses essentially all refrigerants, a fire-extinguishing agent, ultrasonic cleaning fluids, fluorocarbon plastics, and fluorocarbon elastomers. A popular process for alkylation of petroleum to enhance yields of gasoline depends on the use of AHF. Aqueous HF is used in large quantities to pickle stainless steels, to acid treat wells, and to etch glass.

Aqueous HF and AHF are hazardous chemicals. Fluoride salts, although added to potable waters to prevent tooth decay, are toxic in higher concentrations. Painful, persistent burns result from contact with aqueous HF or AHF, and inhalation of high concentrations of the vapors causes lung damage.

Austenitic stainless steels have good resistance to liquid AHF at somewhat elevated temperatures (Table 21). Unpublished data show corrosion rates of less than 0.13 mm/yr (5 mils/yr) for type 304 at 100 °C (210 °F) but high corrosion rates at 150 °C (300 °F). Type 304 has good resis-

Table 20 Suggested upper temperature limits for continuous service in dry HCl gas

Material	Temperature	
	°C	°F
Platinum	1200	2190
Gold	870	1600
Nickel 201	510	950
Inconel 600	480	900
Hastelloy B	450	840
Hastelloy C	450	840
Type 316 stainless steel	430	805
Type 310Cb stainless steel	430	805
Type 304 stainless steel	400	750
Carbon steel	260	500
Monel 400	230	445
Silver	230	445
Cast iron	200	390
Copper C11000	90	195

Source: Ref 36

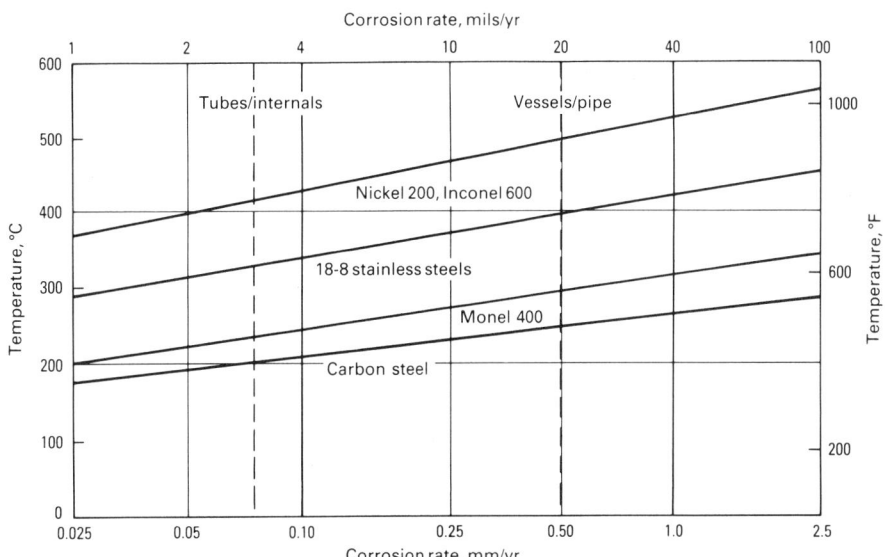

Fig. 37 Maximum temperature limits for various alloys in HCl service. Source: Ref 37

Table 21 Corrosion of metals and alloys in anhydrous hydrogen fluoride
Exposure for 6 to 40 days

Metal	Corrosion rate at temperature, °C (°F)											
	15-25 (60-80)		25-40 (80-100)		40-95 (100-200)		55 (130)		70 (160)		80-90 (180-190)	
	mm/yr	mils/yr	mm/yr	mils/yr	mm/yr	mils/yr	mm/yr	mils/yr	mm/yr	mils/yr	mm/yr	mils/yr
Carbon steel	0.07	2.8	0.16	6.2	...	...	0.35	14	...	...	2.3	89
Low-alloy steel	0.15	6	0.14	5.9	...	...	...	...	...	...	2	78
Austenitic stainless steel	0.16	6.2	0.12	4.8	...	...	...	...	...	...	0.06	2.4
Monel 400	0.08	3.2	0.02	0.9	0.12	4.7	...	...	...	...	...	...
Copper	0.33	12.9	...	...	...	...	...	...	...	...	...	...
Nickel 200	0.06	2.5	...	...	...	...	...	...	0.12	4.6	...	...
70-30 copper-nickel	...	...	0.05	2	...	...	0.008	0.3	...	...	0.25	10
80-20 copper-nickel	...	...	0.13	5.2	...	...	...	...	...	...	...	...
Red brass	0.76	30	0.4	16	...	...	...	...	...	...	1.3	50
Admiralty brass	0.25	10	0.33	12.8	...	...	0.01	0.4	...	...	0.5	20
Aluminum-bronze	0.37	14.4	...	...	...	...	...	...	...	...	...	...
Phosphorus-bronze	0.5	20	0.48	18.8	...	...	...	...	...	...	1.5	60
Inconel 600	...	...	0.067	2.6	...	...	...	...	...	...	...	...
Duriron	...	...	1.1	45	...	...	...	...	...	...	...	...
Aluminum	0.52	20.4	...	...	...	...	...	...	...	...	24.8	976
Magnesium	0.13	5.2	0.43	17.1	...	...	nil	nil	...	...	nil	nil

Source: Ref 38

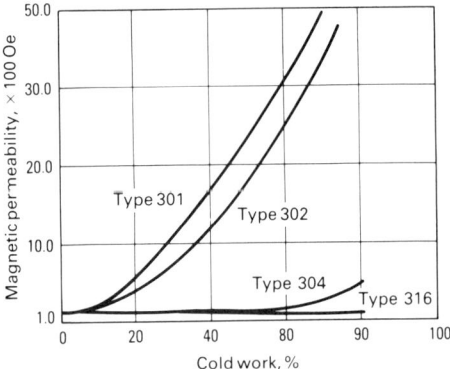

Fig. 38 Effect of cold work on the magnetic permeability of austenitic stainless steels

tance to AHF gas to 200 °C (390 °F). Cast ACI CF-8M stainless steel is used for AHF pumps. However, both type 304 and carbon steel have been known to fail by direct impingement of AHF streams.

Austenitic stainless steels have limited resistance to dilute HF. Type 304 has poor resistance to any significant concentration, but type 316 has useful resistance at ambient temperatures and concentrations below 10%.

Cold-worked type 303 failed rapidly when used as a fastener material in an HF plant. Cold-worked type 304 fasteners (ASTM A 193, grade B8, class 2) had few failures. The failed fasteners were strongly magnetic. It is believed that α-martensite is the susceptible phase. Alpha-martensite is formed when such alloys as type 301, type 303, and, to a lesser extent, type 304 are cold worked. Figure 38 shows the effect of cold work on the magnetic permeability of common

austenitic stainless steels. Type 316 is metallurgically stable but type 304 is only marginally so.

Annealed austenitic stainless steels are resistant but not immune to SCC by HF. In one study, types 304 and 316 both failed from transgranular cracking in impure 12% HF at 70 °C (160 °F); type 304 failed in hot 40 to 50% HF (Ref 38). However, these conditions are more severe than are reasonable for the use of stainless steels in HF. This study also reported that cold-worked 18-8 stainless steel did not suffer SCC in a seven-day test in AHF at 70 °C (150 °F). Another study showed that the threshold Cl⁻ ion concentration necessary to cause intergranular SCC of sensitized type 304 was greatly reduced by the presence of fluorides (Ref 39).

Higher alloys such as 20Cb-3 stainless steel and Incoloy 825 have good resistance to all concentrations of HF at ambient temperatures and to 0 to 10% concentrations at 70 °C (160 °F). Corro-

Table 22 Corrosion of nickel stainless steels and chromium-nickel-molybdenum-iron alloys in aqueous hydrogen fluoride
Laboratory tests with no aeration or agitation (except boiling tests)

Concentration HF, %	Temperature		Test duration, days	Corrosion rate									
	°C	°F		Type 304		Type 316		Type 309Cb		Alloy 20Cb-3		Incoloy 825	
				mm/yr	mils/yr	mm/yr	mils/yr	mm/yr	mils/yr	mm/yr	mils/yr	mm/yr	mils/yr
0.05	60	140	10	0.3	12	...	...	0.25	10	...	...	...	...
0.1	60	140	10	0.64	25	...	...	0.69	27	...	...	...	...
0.15	60	140	10	1.2	47	...	...	1.1	44	...	...	...	...
0.2	60	140	10	1.6	62	...	...	1.4	54	...	...	...	...
10	16	60	30	0.01	0.4	<0.002	<0.1	...	...	...	...	...	...
20	102	215	3	...	...	...	...	...	...	...	...	1.04	41
38	110	230	2	...	...	51	2000	...	...	...	...	...	...
38	Boiling	Boiling	4	...	...	...	...	...	...	...	...	0.25	10
48	Boiling	Boiling	4	...	...	...	...	...	...	...	...	0.23	9
50	60	140	35	...	...	...	...	...	...	...	...	0.05	2
65	60	140	35	...	...	...	...	...	...	...	...	0.13	5
70	60	140	35	...	...	...	...	...	...	...	...	0.13	5
70	21	70	42	...	...	1.24	49	...	...	0.38	15	0.35	14
90	4	40	0.2	0.9	35	...	...	...	...	...	...	...	...
90	21	70	1	0.76	30	...	...	...	...	...	...	...	...
90	21	70	1	0.28	11(a)	...	...	...	...	...	...	...	...
98	38-44	95-110	3.5	...	...	0.05	2	...	...	...	...	...	...

(a) Velocity: 0.14 to 0.43 m/s (0.4 to 1.4 ft/s)

Table 23 Corrosion of metals and alloys by gaseous anhydrous hydrogen fluoride at elevated temperatures
Exposure for approximately 4 h

| | Corrosion rate at temperature, °C (°F) | | | | | |
| | 500 (930) | | 550 (1020) | | 600 (1110) | |
Metal	mm/yr	mils/yr	mm/yr	mils/yr	mm/yr	mils/yr
Nickel 200	0.9	36	...	...	0.9	36
Monel 400	1.2	48	1.2	48	1.8	72
Copper	1.5	60	...	...	1.2	48
Inconel 600	1.5	60	...	...	1.5	60
Aluminum alloy 1100	4.9	192	...	...	14.6	576
Magnesium G	13.8	542	...	...	...	...
1020 steel	15.5	612	14.6	576	7.6	300
Type 430 stainless steel	1.5	60	9.1	360	11.6	456
Type 304 stainless steel	...	...	...	...	13.4	528
Type 347 stainless steel	183	7,200	457	18,000	177	6,960
Type 309Cb stainless steel	5.8	228	42.7	1,680	168	6,600
Type 310 stainless steel	12.2	480	100.6	3,960	305	12,000

Source: Ref 40

sion data are shown in Table 22. The preferred material for pumps and valves for 70% HF at ambient temperatures and for valve trim for AHF is CN-7M casting alloy.

High-Temperature Gas. A series of short-term corrosion tests was conducted on the rate of attack of hot, gaseous AHF on various metals; results are given in Table 23. Nickel 200, Monel 400, and Inconel 600 all have useful resistance to gaseous AHF at temperatures to 600 °C (1110 °F). Austenitic stainless steels are inferior to carbon steel in this regard. Although corrosion rates are exaggerated and distorted by the short 3 to 15 h test periods, other data confirm the general ranking of the materials.

Corrosion by Chlorine

Dry chlorine is not corrosive to stainless steels at ambient temperatures. Austenitic stainless steels have been shown to be significantly more resistant to dry chlorine than steel, aluminum, or copper. Types 304 and 316 may be used up to 300 °C (570 °F). Moisture is reported to accelerate attack below 370 °C (700 °F) but to exert little effect or even decrease attack above that temperature. The presence of moisture also increases the possibility of SCC.

Table 24 gives approximate temperatures at which various corrosion rates occur in dry chlorine for type 304, type 316, and other metals. Suggested upper design limits for type 304 and some other alloys in dry chlorine are shown in Fig. 39, based on corrosion rates of approximately 0.08 mm/yr (3 mils/yr) for tubes and internals, and 0.5 mm/yr (20 mils/yr) for vessels and pipes.

Moist Chlorine. Many industrial chlorine environments contain substantial water, particularly those in chlorine manufacture prior to the drying operation. Wet chlorine gas is extremely corrosive at temperatures below the dew point because the condensate is a very acidic and oxidizing mixture. Wet chlorine gas can be handled at room temperatures with stainless steels similar to alloy 20 if condensation is not too great and if corrosion rates up to 1.3 mm/yr (50 mils/yr) are tolerable.

Moisture has a significant effect on the corrosion of type 304 stainless steel in chlorine. In tests conducted in chlorine containing 0.4% H_2O, rates of approximately 30.5 mm/yr (1200 mils/yr) were found at 40 °C (105 °F), versus an estimated 0.3 mm/yr (12 mils/yr) at 100 °C (210 °F) in dry chlorine. Corrosion in wet chlorine decreased with increasing temperature until about 370 °C (700 °F), at which point the corrosion was about 4.6 mm/yr (180 mils/yr) and the effect of the moisture disappeared. The detrimental effect of moisture at low temperatures is believed to exist for chromium and austenitic stainless steels in general.

Several alloys were tested in water-saturated chlorine gas for six weeks at room temperature. The results, given in Table 25, show substantially higher rates than in dry chlorine. The data support the view that moisture in room-temperature chlorine gas increases corrosion rates on stainless steels, including cast stainless steels.

Chlorine-Water. Chlorine dissolved in water forms a mixture of HCl and hypochlorous acid (HClO). The latter is very oxidizing, which makes the mixture extremely corrosive. Relatively little information is available on corrosion in water containing substantial levels of chlorine, especially near saturation.

Corrosion of several alloys in chlorine-saturated water at 25 °C (75 °F) was investigated (Ref 42). The results, presented in Table 26, show that

Table 25 Corrosion of cast alloys by water-saturated chlorine gas
Exposure for 6 weeks at room temperature

| Alloy | Wrought version | Corrosion rate | |
		mm/yr	mils/yr
ACI CF-8M	Type 316	0.79	31
ACI CN-7M	...	1.04	41
ACI CD-4MCu	Duplex stainless steel	1.24	49
ACI CW-12M	Hastelloy C	0.056	2.2

Source: Ref 42

Table 24 Approximate temperatures at which the indicated corrosion rates occur in dry chlorine

| | Temperature for corrosion rate, mm/yr (mils/yr) | | | | | | | | | | | |
| | 0.76 (30) | | 1.5 (60) | | 3 (120) | | 15 (600) | | 30 (1200) | | Maximum(a) | |
Alloy	°C	°F	°C	°F	°C	°F	°C	°F	°C	°F	°C	°F
Nickel 201	510	950	540	1000	590	1100	650	1200	680	1250	540	1000
Inconel 600	510	950	540	1000	565	1050	650	1200	680	1250	540	1000
Hastelloy B	510	950	540	1000	590	1100	650	1200	...	...	540	1000
Hastelloy C	480	900	540	1000	560	1050	650	1200	...	...	510	950
Magnesium	450	850	480	900	510	950	540	1000	565	1050	450	850
Ni-20Cr-1Si	425	800	480	900	540	1000	620	1150	...	...	450	850
Monel 400	400	750	450	850	480	900	540	1000	540	1000	420	800
Type 316 stainless steel	310	600	345	650	400	750	450	850	480	900	340	650
Type 304 stainless steel	290	550	315	600	340	650	400	750	450	850	310	600
Platinum	480	900	510	950	540	1000	560	1050	560	1050	260	500
Hastelloy D	205	400	230	450	290	550	...	...	...	...	205	400
Deoxidized copper	180	350	230	450	260	500	260	500	290	550	205	400
Carbon steel	120	250	180	350	205	400	230	450	230	450	205	400
Cast iron	90	200	120	250	180	350	230	450	230	450	180	350
Aluminum alloy 1100	120	250	150	300	150	300	180	350	180	350	120	250
Gold	120	250	150	300	180	350	200	400	200	400	...	...
Silver	40	100	65	150	120	250	230	450	260	500	...	...

(a) Suggested upper temperature limit for continuous service. Source: Ref 41

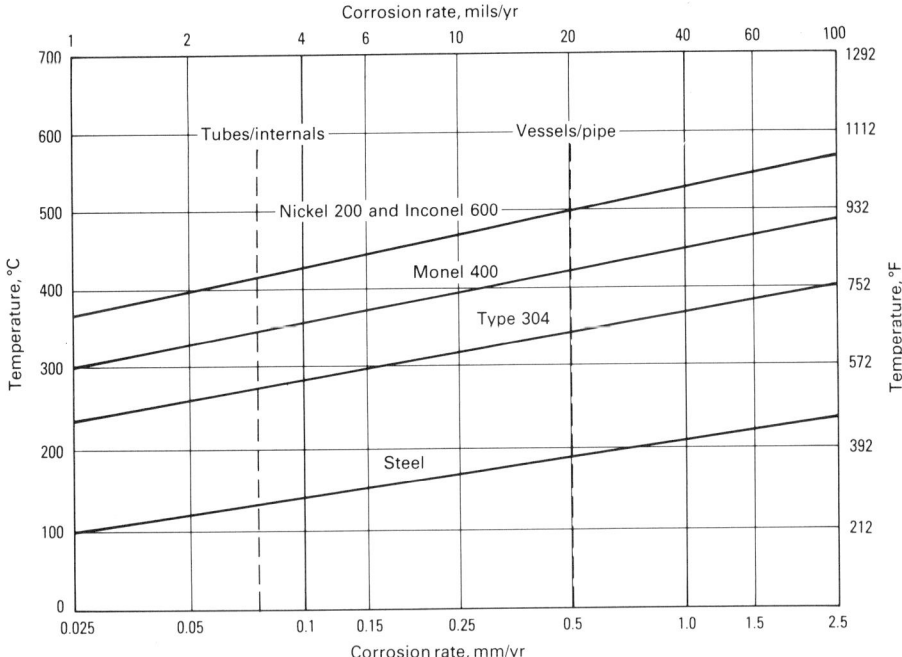

Fig. 39 Design guidelines for use in dry chlorine. Source: Ref 37

Table 26 Corrosion of alloys in chlorine-saturated water
Temperature: 25 °C (75 °F)

Alloy	Test duration, days	Corrosion rate	
		mm/yr	mils/yr
ACI CF-8M	42	0.013	0.50(a)
Type 316	56	0.008	0.30
ACI CN-7M	42	0.05	1.8(a)
20Cb-3	56	0.008	0.30
ACI CD-4MCu	42	0.06	2.5(a)
ACI CW-12M	42	0.023	0.90
Hastelloy C-276	56	0.0025	0.10
Monel 400	56	24	948
Titanium, grade 2	56	0.0005	0.02

(a) Crevice corrosion. Source: Ref 42

Table 27 Corrosion of alloys in chlorine-ice
147-day tests at –20 °C (–4 °F)

Alloy	Corrosion rate	
	µm/yr	mils/yr
Steel	38	1.5
ACI CF-8	0.25	0.01
ACI CF-8M	0.25	0.01
ACI CN-7M	<0.25	<0.01
ACI CD-4MCu	0.25	0.01
Alloy 255	<0.25	<0.01
N-12M	76	3.01
ACI CW-12M	3.8	0.15
M-35	29	1.15

Source: Ref 42

rates are generally low for the chromium-containing alloys tested. No large difference in performance between cast alloys and their wrought equivalents was found, except for crevice attack on CF-8M, CN-7M, and CD-4MCu.

Related tests were performed in chlorine ice at –20 °C (–4 °F). The results, given in Table 27, show that corrosion rates for chromium-containing alloys are below 0.0025 mm/yr (0.1 mil/yr), except for CW-12M at 0.0038 mm/yr (0.15 mil/yr). Higher, but not unacceptable, rates were found for steel, N-12M, and M-35. These alloys are sensitive to oxidants in acidic environments, which explains their poorer performance.

Corrosion by Alkalis and Hypochlorite

Caustic soda (NaOH), caustic potash (potassium hydroxide, KOH), and soda ash (Na$_2$CO$_3$) are true alkaline chemicals. Technically, hypochlorites are alkaline oxidizing salts, but they exhibit behavior that is much different from alkalis.

Sodium hydroxide, or caustic soda, is the most widely used and available alkaline chemi-

cal. Most NaOH is produced as a coproduct of chlorine through the use of electrolytic cells; the cells are of the diaphragm, mercury, or membrane type. Some NaOH is marketed as produced in the cells; most is evaporated and sold in 50 or 73% solutions or as anhydrous beads. Most caustic end uses require solutions of relatively low concentrations. Tables 28 to 33 provide resistance data for many metals. Table 31 relates specifically to corrosivity relationships of diaphragm and mercury cell caustic.

No discussion of materials of construction for NaOH would be complete without stressing the need to consider safety in every application. Caustic solutions, especially when hot, are extremely damaging to the human body. Exposure can cause immediate and severe burns; eyes are an especially sensitive area. Frequently, materials selection decisions must account for potential personnel exposure and dictate a more costly but completely reliable material.

Austenitic and ferritic stainless steels are often used to fill an economic slot in what could be termed intermediate ranges of caustic service.

Austenitic stainless steels, primarily types 304 and 316, are very resistant to caustic in concentrations up to 50% and temperatures to about 95 °C (200 °F) (Tables 28, 30-32, and 34). Usage in these ranges has increased in recent years for economic reasons, even though some potential problems must be addressed.

Figure 40 shows corrosion rates and a stress-corrosion boundary for austenitic stainless steels exposed to NaOH solutions. No distinction is made between types 304 and 316, because their behaviors are so similar. Of significance is the SCC zone, based on known failures, which indicates potential cracking problems above about 105 °C (220 °F). It is generally accepted that this caustic SCC mechanism occurs regardless of

Table 28 Corrosion of metals and alloys in NaOH at various concentrations
Laboratory tests at room temperature

Material	Corrosion rate in NaOH							
	5%		15%		25%		35%		45%	
	mm/yr	mils/yr	mm/yr	mils/yr	mm/yr	mils/yr	mm/yr	mils/yr	mm/yr	mils/yr
Aluminum-bronze	0.09	3.8	0.018	0.7	0.008	0.3	0.01	0.4	0.005	0.2
Deoxidized copper	0.086	3.4	0.008	0.3	0.008	0.3	0.025	1	0.005	0.2
Monel	<0.0025	<0.1	<0.0025	<0.1	<0.0025	<0.1	<0.0025	<0.1	<0.0025	<0.1
Nickel	<0.0025	<0.1	<0.0025	<0.1	<0.0025	<0.1	<0.0025	<0.1	<0.0025	<0.1
Type 304 stainless steel	0.0025	0.1	<0.0025	<0.1	<0.0025	<0.1	<0.0025	<0.1	<0.0025	<0.1

Source: Ref 43

Table 29 Corrosion of metals and alloys in 30-50% NaOH

16-day exposure in a single-effect evaporator concentrating NaOH from 30 to 50%. Average temperature: 80 °C (180 °F)

Material	Corrosion rate	
	mm/yr	mils/yr
Nickel	0.0025	0.1
Monel	0.005	0.2
Copper-nickel-zinc (75-20-5)	0.013	0.5
Copper	0.06	2.3
Low-carbon steel	0.09	3.7
Cast iron	0.18	7
Chromium steel (14Cr)	0.84	33

Source: Ref 44

austenitic alloy type (304 vs. 316). Cracking is affected by stress level and temperature. To provide a measure of insurance, the suggested maximum service temperature is 95 °C (200 °F). Microscopic stress cracking has been reported in laboratory testing at concentrations as low as 10% with temperatures of 100 °C (210 °F).

Although the austenitic stainless steels crack readily in neutral and acid chlorides above 60 °C (140 °F), the effect of chlorides in an alkaline solution seems to be nil. As long as the solution remains alkaline, the mode of stress cracking is that of caustic embrittlement and continues to occur only in the range indi-

cated in Fig. 40. A solution of 0.5 g/L NaOH with a pH of 12 is sufficiently alkaline. The concern for chloride contamination in caustic when using stainless steel equipment is not well founded.

More important concerns are those extraneous to the caustic solution. Failures resulting from such factors as external exposure, faulty insulation, contaminated test water, and improper cleaning and storage have produced more problems than handling caustic.

Because chloride pitting and/or chloride stress cracking are often primary concerns, alloy selection should consider relative performance in these areas. Although types 304 and 316 perform com-

Table 30 Corrosion of metals and alloys in 50% NaOH at various temperatures

Material	Corrosion rate at temperature, °C (°F)							
	40 (100)(a)		60 (135)(b)		55-75 (130-165)(c)		150 (300)(d)	
	mm/yr	mils/yr	mm/yr	mils/yr	mm/yr	mils/yr	mm/yr	mils/yr
Titanium	0.00025	0.01	0.013	0.5	...	...	...	...
Zirconium	0.0023	0.09	0.002	0.08	...	...	...	...
Nickel	0.00023	0.009	0.0005	0.02	0.0005	0.02	0.013	0.5
Inconel	0.0002	0.008	0.0005	0.02	0.0008	0.03	...	...
Monel	0.0005	0.02	0.0005	0.02	0.0008	0.03	0.013	0.5
70-30 copper-nickel	...	...	...	...	0.0013	0.05	...	...
Deoxidized copper	...	...	...	...	...	...	0.14	5.5
Aluminum bronze	...	...	0.025	1	...	...	0.08	3
Type 304 stainless steel	...	...	...	...	0.0025	0.1	1.2	47
Low-carbon steel	0.018	0.7	0.13	5	0.2	8	...	...
Ni-Resist I	...	...	...	...	0.05	2	...	...
Cast iron	...	...	...	...	0.27	10.5	...	...

(a) 162-day exposure (Ref 45). (b) 135-day exposure (Ref 45). (c) 30-day exposure (Ref 44). (d) Laboratory test (Ref 43)

Table 31 Comparison of corrosiveness of NaOH manufactured in diaphragm cells and mercury cells

Material	Diaphragm cell corrosion rate				Mercury cell corrosion rate			
	50% NaOH at 35-90 °C (95-190 °F)		73% NaOH at 100-125 °C (212-260 °F)		50% NaOH at 40-80 °C (100-180 °F)		73% NaOH at 115 °C (240 °F)	
	mm/yr	mils/yr	mm/yr	mils/yr	mm/yr	mils/yr	mm/yr	mils/yr
Nickel 200	<0.0025	<0.1	<0.005	<0.2	<0.0025	<0.1	0.008	0.3
Inconel 600	<0.0025	<0.1	0.005	0.2	<0.0025	0.1	0.005	0.2
Monel 400	<0.0025	<0.1	0.01	0.4	0.0025	<0.1	0.013	0.5
Incoloy 800	<0.0025	<0.1	0.04	1.6	<0.0025	<0.1	0.008	0.3
20Cb-3	<0.0025	<0.1	0.02	0.8	<0.0025	<0.1	0.01	0.4
Cast alloy 20	<0.0025	<0.1	0.09	3.5	<0.0025	<0.1	0.01	0.4
Ni-Resist type 3	0.0064	0.25	0.094	3.7	0.0025	0.1	0.03	1.2
Type 316 stainless steel	0.017	0.65	0.24	9.3	0.0025	0.1	0.25	10
Type 304 stainless steel	0.005	0.2	0.4	15.8	0.019	0.75	0.38	15
Type 430 stainless steel	0.01	0.4	>0.97	>38	>0.14	>5.4	1.5	60
Low-carbon steel	0.12	4.7	>0.87	>34.2	0.09	3.4	1.8	71
Cast iron	0.11	4.2	1.06	41.7	0.08	3.3	2.1	82
Ductile cast iron	0.1	3.9	1.7	65.7	0.06	2.4	2.6	103

Source: Ref 46, originally from NACE Task group T-5A round-robin testing

Table 32 Corrosion of metals and alloys in 70-73% NaOH at various temperatures

Material	Corrosion rate at temperature, °C (°F)							
	110 (230)(a)		90-115 (190-240)(b)		120 (240)(c)		130 (265)(d)	
	mm/yr	mils/yr	mm/yr	mils/yr	mm/yr	mils/yr	mm/yr	mils/yr
Nickel	0.0025	0.1	0.0025	0.1	0.005	0.2	0.025	1
Monel	0.0025	0.1	0.028	1.1	0.013	0.5	0.023	0.9
Inconel	0.0025	0.1	0.008	0.3	0.005	0.2	0.025	1
Zirconium	0.02	0.8	...	...	...	...	0.05	2
Titanium	0.05	2	...	...	...	...	0.18	7
Aluminum-bronze	0.023	0.9	...	...	0.15	6.1	...	...
Type 304 stainless steel	...	...	0.69	27	0.26	10.2	...	...
Steel	0.99	39	1.45	57	...	...	>2	>80(e)

(a) 126-day exposure (Ref 45). (b) 90-day exposure (Ref 44). (c) 180-day exposure (Ref 43). (d) 200-day exposure (Ref 45). (e) Duplicate specimens consumed during test

Table 33 Corrosion of metals and alloys in caustic fusion process

Material	Corrosion rate			
	Laboratory test(a)		Plant test(b)	
	mm/yr	mils/yr	mm/yr	mils/yr
Silver	0.13	5.3	...	...
Nickel	1.3-1.8	52-72	6.6	260
Zirconium	...	...	2.8	110
Cast iron	3.3	130	5.3	210
Ni-Resist type 3	3.3	130	...	...
Ni-Resist type 2	3.8	150	...	...
Monel	6.6	260	9.7	380
Low-carbon steel	...	...	12.7	500
Inconel	...	...	49	1930
Type 302 stainless steel	45.7	1800	...	...
Chromium steel (18.5% Cr)	68.6	2700	...	...

Table 34 Corrosion of stainless steel in NaOH solutions

Type	Concentration of NaOH, %	Temperature		Test duration, days	Corrosion rate	
		°C	°F		mm/yr	mils/yr
302	20	50-60	120-140	134	<0.0025	<0.1
304	22	50-60	120-140	133	<0.0025	<0.1
309	20	50-60	120-140	134	<0.0025	<0.1
310	20	50-60	120-140	134	<0.0025	<0.1
410	20	50-60	120-140	134	0.0025	0.1
430	20	50-60	120-140	134	0.0025	0.1
304	72(a)	120-125	245-255	119	0.09	3.7
316	72(a)	120-125	245-255	119	0.08	3.1
329	72(a)	120-125	245-255	119	0.0025	0.1
21Cr-4Ni-0.5Cu	72(a)	120-125	245-255	119	0.15	6
410	72(a)	120-125	245-255	119	0.8	32
302	73(b)	100-120	210-245	88	0.97	38
304	73(b)	100-120	210-245	88	1.1	45

(a) Solution moderately agitated. (b) No aeration. Source: Ref 47

parably in caustic and in standard stress-cracking tests, type 316 shows improved overall performance because of its pitting resistance (the role of dissolved oxygen may be significant in this regard). In addition, the low-carbon grades

perform marginally better because of their resistance to sensitization. This suggests that type 316L(molybdenum-containing low-carbon type 316) should be used unless significant controls are to be placed on the total exposure of the equipment. Painting the exteriors of stainless equipment is also recommended, especially if insulation will be applied.

Applications of stainless steel for caustic services include piping, valves, pumps, and equipment. Transfer piping applications are quite common. Problems rarely occur whenever 10 to 20% solutions are involved, because cleanout and freezing considerations are minimal.

Another possible hazard involves introduction of mercury as a contaminant in mercury cell caustic. This can contribute to cracking or pitting of austenitic stainless with mercury concentrations as low as a few parts per million. Also, there are cases in which stainless steels cannot be used because of concern in returning Cr^{6+} ions to a mercury cell operation.

Cast stainless pumps and valves have performed very well in caustic applications. The nature of cast surfaces minimizes SCC problems, and castings are usually acceptable in situations considerably beyond the capabilities

of wrought products. Corrosion rates are similar to those of the wrought products.

One other practical application of stainless steel in caustic service is in evaporation processes, in which high-purity alloy 26-1 (a low-carbon version of type 446 containing niobium and molybdenum) heat-exchanger tubing has been used. Some high-temperature applications have proved effective where corrosion rates on nickel are excessive. This is probably due to the presence of hypochlorite or chlorate contaminants. The debate between nickel and ferrous alloys continues, yet both materials have shown satisfactory performance. The 26-1 alloy is useful up to 175 °C (350 °F), depending on the caustic, chloride, and contaminant concentrations. When 26-1 is attacked, the normal failure mode seems to be intergranular. At this time, there are no specific criteria to provide recommendations regarding the use of ferritic stainless steel. Decisions should be governed by economics, taking into account the impact of heat-transfer coefficients as well as the cost of tubing.

A comprehensive summary of criteria for selection of stainless steel for process equipment is given in Ref 48. There probably are good applications for the new ferritic and duplex steels; however, little testing has been completed.

Potassium hydroxide, also known as caustic potash, has a higher boiling point than NaOH at equal concentrations. Consequently, it is rarely evaporated above a 90% strength. It is very similar to NaOH in corrosion behavior as well as safety requirements.

Corrosion and degradation of metals is the same in KOH as in NaOH. Indications are that KOH is slightly more aggressive, but this generally relates to its higher boiling point and the increased likelihood of higher-temperature exposure.

Sodium carbonate, or soda ash, is an alkaline salt. This chemical has been extensively used in alkaline processes to supply sodium oxide (Na_2O) equivalence. Over the years, some uses have been replaced with caustic. At one time, Na_2CO_3 was primarily synthetically produced using an ammonia-soda (Solvay) process. Current production is largely of the natural ash, which is mined and refined.

When in solution, Na_2CO_3 creates less alkalinity than the hydroxide. A 0.1% solution creates a pH of 11; a fully saturated solution is 35%, which has a pH of 12.5. The related bicarbonates (sodium bicarbonate, $NaHCO_3$) are less alkaline, but they will convert to carbonates at high temperatures and increase the pH of the solution. The safety requirements for Na_2CO_3 can be considered less demanding because of its lower alkalinity.

Soda ash solutions can be handled easily in anything that is suitable for caustic. As with other alkaline solutions, the presence of carbonate ions (CO_3^{2-}) usually provides an inhibiting effect on metals.

When nil corrosion rates are deemed necessary, the stainless steels perform very effectively. Stainless steel has an SCC range similar to that in caustic, but at considerably elevated temperatures.

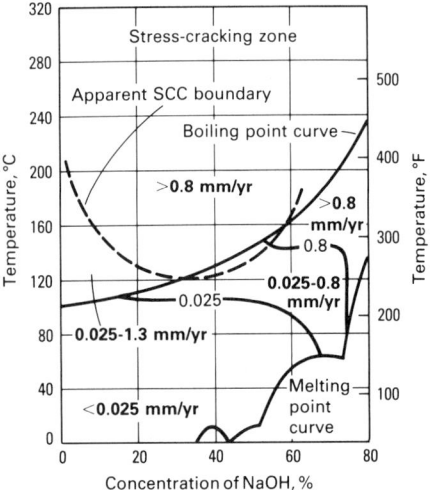

Fig. 40 Isocorrosion diagram for types 304 and 316 in NaOH

Table 35 Corrosion of metals and alloys in NaOCl solutions at elevated temperatures

Material	Corrosion rate at 65-95 °C (150-200 °F)(a)		Relative corrosion rate at 50 °C (120 °F)(b)	
	mm/yr	mils/yr	mm/yr	mils/yr
Titanium	0.0025	0.1	0.000025	0.001
Remanit 2800	...	...	0.000025	0.001
E-Brite	...	...	0.00025	0.01
2Mo-0.4Cu stainless steel	...	...	0.00025	0.01
Type 317 stainless steel	...	...	0.00025	0.01
Inconel 600	...	...	0.005	0.02
Zirconium	0.1	4	...	...
Durichlor	0.18	7	...	...
Duriron	0.3	12	...	...
Incoloy 825	...	...	0.005	0.2
Hastelloy C	1.2	46	0.005	0.2
Type 316 stainless steel	>2.5	100 (consumed)	0.008	0.3
Type 304 stainless steel	...	...	0.025	1.0
Low-carbon steel	>5	>200 (consumed)	0.025	1.0

(a) 72-day test in 1.5-4% NaOCl with 12-15% NaCl and 1% NaOH (Ref 45). (b) NaOCl solution (pH 9) with 500 ppm active chlorine and 1.2% NaCl (Ref 49)

Table 36 Corrosion of metals and alloys in Ca(OCl)$_2$
204-day test in 18-20% Ca(OCl)$_2$ at 20-24 °C (70-75 °F)

Material	Corrosion rate		Pitting
	mm/yr	mils/yr	
Titanium	nil	nil	none
Zirconium	0.025	1(a)	none
Hastelloy C	< 0.0025	< 0.1	none
Chlorimet 3	0.025	1	none
Type 316 stainless steel	0.25	10(a)	severe

(a) Severe attack under spacer

Hypochlorites. These alkaline oxidizing salts are among the most corrosive salts. Sodium hypochlorite (NaOCl), is produced as a liquid by chlorinating 20% NaOH. Resulting soda bleach solutions contain about 15% NaOCl, with some residual NaOH to aid stability. These industrial-strength bleaches are diluted to concentrations of about 5% for household use. To enhance stability further, the NaOH used should not contain heavy metals, and the NaOCl should be stored in dark or polyethylene bottles at temperatures below 30 °C (85 °F). Sodium hypochlorite does not exist as a stable solid.

The solid hypochlorites include lithium, calcium, strontium, and barium, although the only major applications are for calcium hypochlorite (Ca(OCl)$_2$). Solid Ca(OCl)$_2$ will decompose rapidly at high temperatures (175 °C, or 350 °F), releasing chlorine. It also reacts vigorously with many oxidizable organic compounds. Calcium hypochlorite solutions are encountered during production and in other chemical processes for bleaching, sanitizing, or deodorizing. The solid product is often dissolved in water to form dilute solutions used for bleaching operations and water purification.

Sodium Hypochlorite. The hypochlorite ion (OCl⁻) is similar to wet chlorine gas in its effects on materials. Not many metals show good resistance, even at low temperatures and concentrations. Because hypochlorite solutions are unstable at neutral and lower pHs, they normally contain excess alkali, which modifies the aggressiveness somewhat. High iron-chromium-nickel alloys, such as 20Cb-3, have been used, especially as pump materials, in the less aggressive environments.

Sodium hypochlorite is usually maintained at low temperatures to prevent decomposition. The effect of higher temperature, even in the dilute solutions, is reflected by corrosion rates (Table 35). The presence of heavy-metal ions, especially in the case of higher solution concentrations, often causes instability with decomposition. This potential may rule against metals that might otherwise be acceptable, because the occurrence of decomposition often triggers a corrosion reaction.

Some of the newer super stainless steel materials indicate useful resistance in certain NaOCl solutions, and successful performance of a high-alloy duplex stainless (Ferralium 255) in a NaOCl scrubber has been reported (Ref 50). When stainless steels are attacked in NaOCl, the mode is usually pitting and/or crevice corrosion.

Calcium Hypochlorite. Although produced as a solid, the reactions of Ca(OCl)$_2$ in solution are very similar to those of NaOCl. In general, the recommended temperature levels for Ca(OCl)$_2$ are slightly higher, probably owing to the higher decomposition temperature. Like NaOCl, the calcium product is unstable at lower pH, but it can be concentrated to a higher degree. Corrosion rates for type 316 and several other metals are shown in Table 36.

Corrosion in Pulp and Paper Plant Environments

In the kraft process, paper is produced by digesting wood chips with a mixture of sodium sulfite (Na$_2$S) and NaOH (white liquor). The product is transferred to the brown stock washers to remove the liquor (black liquor) from the brown pulp. After screening, the pulp may go directly to the paper mill to produce unbleached paper, or it may be directed first to the bleach plant to produce white paper.

The digester vapors are condensed, and the condensate is pumped to the brown stock washers. The black liquor from these washers is concentrated and burned with sodium sulfate (Na$_2$SO$_4$) to recover Na$_2$CO$_3$ and Na$_2$S. After dissolution in water, this green liquor is treated with calcium hydroxide (Ca(OH)$_2$) to produce NaOH to replenish the white liquor. Pulp bleaching involves treating with various chemicals, including chlorine, chlorine dioxide (ClO$_2$), NaClO, Ca(ClO)$_2$, peroxide, caustic soda, quicklime, or oxygen.

The sulfite process uses a liquor in the digester that is different from that used in the kraft process. This liquor contains free SO$_2$ dissolved in water, along with SO$_2$ as a bisulfite. The compositions of the specific liquors differ, and the pH can range

from 1 for an acid process to 10 for alkaline cooking. Sulfur dioxide for the cooking liquor is produced by burning elemental sulfur, cooling rapidly, absorbing the SO$_2$ in a weak alkaline solution, and fortifying the raw acid.

Various alloys are selected for the wide range of corrosion conditions encountered in pulp and paper mills. Paper mill headboxes are typically fabricated from type 316L plate with superior surface finish and are sometimes electropolished to prevent scaling, which may affect pulp flow. The blades used to remove paper from the drums have been fabricated from types 410 and 420 and from cold-reduced 22Cr-13Ni-5Mn stainless steel.

Evaporators and reheaters must deal with corrosive liquors and must minimize scaling to provide optimum heat transfer. Type 304 ferrite-free welded tubing has been used in kraft black liquor evaporators. Cleaning is often performed with HCl, which attacks ferrite. In the sulfite process, types 316 and 317 have been used in black liquor evaporators. Digester liquor heaters in the kraft and sulfite processes have used 7-Mo stainless for resistance to caustic or chloride SCC.

Bleach plants have used types 316 and 317 and are upgrading to austenitic grades containing 4.5 and 6% Mo in problem locations. Tightening of environmental regulations has generally increased temperature, chloride level, and acidity in the plant, and this requires grades of stainless steel that are more highly alloyed than those used in the past. Tall oil units have shifted from types 316 and 317 to such candidate alloys as 904L or 20Mo-4 and most recently to 254SMO and 20Mo-6 stainless steels. Alloy selection criteria and corrosion-control methods for bleach plant environments are discussed below.

Tests including higher-alloyed materials have been coordinated by the Metals Subcommittee of the Technical Association of the Pulp and Paper Industry (TAPPI) Corrosion and Materials Engineering Committee. Racks of test samples, which included crevices at polytetrafluoroethylene spacers, were submerged in the vat below the washer in the C (chlorination), D (chlorine dioxide), and H (hypochlorite) stages of several paper mills. The sum of the maximum attack depth on all samples for each alloy—at crevices and remote from crevices—is shown in Fig. 41. It should be noted that the vertical axes are different in Fig. 41(a), (b), and (c). Additional information on corrosion in this industry is available in the article

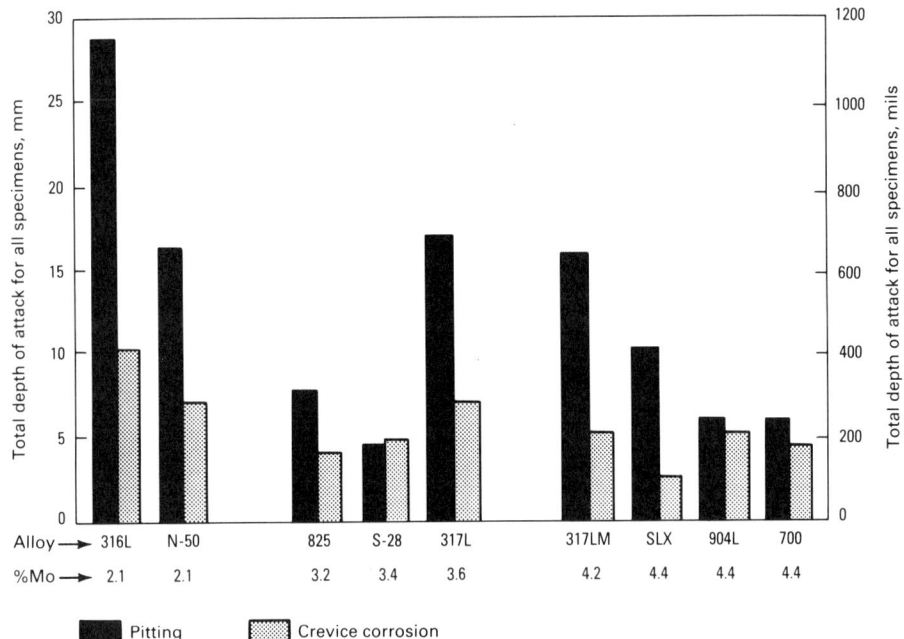

Fig. 41(a) Resistance of austenitic stainless steels containing 2.1 to 4.4% Mo to localized corrosion in paper mill bleach plant environment. Total depth of attack has been divided by 4 because there were four crevice sites per specimen. See also Fig. 41(b) and 41(c). Source: Ref 51

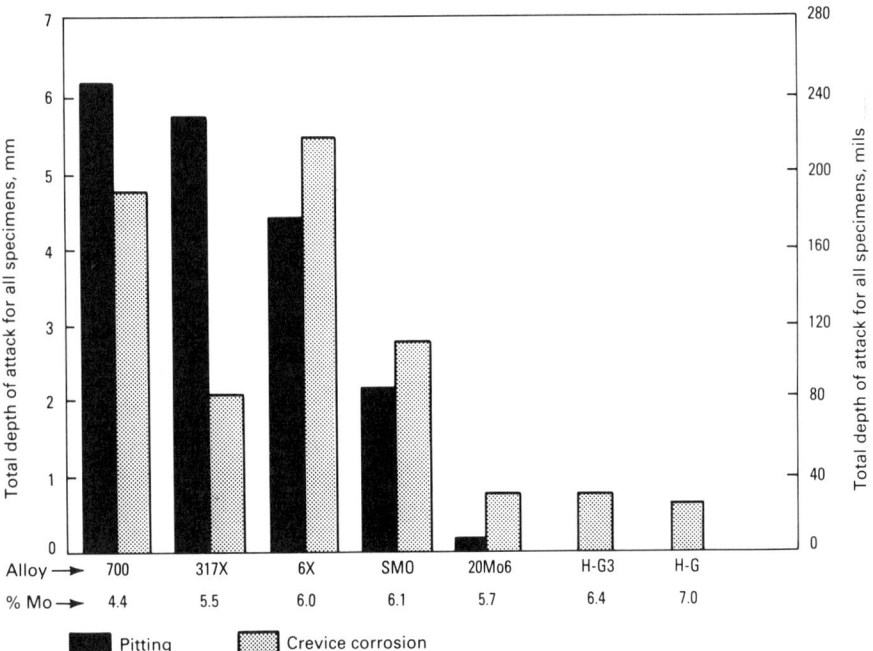

Fig. 41(b) Resistance of austenitic stainless steels containing 4.4 to 7.0% Mo to localized corrosion in paper mill bleach plant environment. Total depth of attack has been divided by 4 because there were four crevice sites per specimen. See also Fig. 41(a) and 41(c). Source: Ref 51

"Corrosion in the Pulp and Paper Industry" in Volume 13 of the *ASM Handbook.*

Corrosion Control in Pulp Bleach Plants

Pulp mill bleach plants have traditionally used austenitic stainless steels because of their combination of good corrosion resistance and weldability. Type 317L (18Cr-14Ni-3.5Mo) has been the typical bleach plant alloy for oxidizing acid chloride environments. However, bleach plants have become more corrosive over the past 20 years as mills have closed washwater systems and reduced effluent volumes. In modern closed bleach plants, type 317L is no longer adequate for long-term service, and many mills have turned to higher-alloy stainless steels, nickel-base alloys, and titanium for better corrosion resistance. Metals are chosen over nonmetals for moving equipment, such as washers. Metals are stronger, tougher, have better fatigue properties, and, if they have sufficient corrosion resistance, require virtually no maintenance. However, the more corrosion-resistant alloys are more costly, and the challenge is to choose an alloy with just enough resistance to avoid corrosion problems.

A wide selection of alloys is available for bleach plant applications. The list includes three families of stainless steels (austenitic, ferritic, and duplex), whose differing merits are outlined in Table 37. Table 38 outlines the influence of each alloy component on bleach plant corrosion resistance.

Austenitic stainless steels, including the 300 series and enriched variations of these steels, are tough and easy to weld. Their corrosion resistance ranges from fair to excellent, depending on the alloy content (Table 37).

Ferritic stainless steels in the 400 series are not used in bleach plants because of their poor corrosion resistance, particularly after welding. However, there is a new generation of extra-low carbon and nitrogen (low-interstitial) grades that retain postweld corrosion resistance. As with austenitic stainless steels, the corrosion resistance of these ferritic stainless steels ranges from fair to excellent, depending on alloy content. However, steels such as 29-4 have not been used in the bleach plant because of problems with embrittling precipitation in thicker sections (>3 mm, or 0.12 in.) and because of the special precautions required to avoid nitrogen contamination during welding.

In contrast to the ferritic grades, the properties of austenitic and duplex stainless steels are enhanced by nitrogen. As a result, duplex stainless steels such as 2205 and Ferralium 255 have recently been developed with improved corrosion resistance.

Laboratory Assessment of Candidate Alloys. The relative corrosion resistance of stainless steels and nickel-base alloys can be assessed with the ferric chloride ($FeCl_3$) test. The relative resistance to pitting corrosion of a range of commercial stainless steels is shown in Fig. 42. A critical temperature has been measured for each alloy below which no pitting will occur in $FeCl_3$. The higher the cited pitting temperature, the more resistant the steel is to pitting. Types 316L and 317L, for example, have comparatively poor pitting resistance. The 904L-type alloys with about 4.5% Mo provide somewhat better pitting resistance, and the 6% Mo steels, such as 254SMO, are remarkably resistant. Based on these results, one might predict that the duplex steel, Ferralium 255, and the manganese-substituted austenitic, Nitronic 50, should outperform type 317L in the bleach plant.

Generally, similar conclusions can be drawn from crevice corrosion tests in $FeCl_3$. Such data are presented in Fig. 43. The critical temperatures for crevice corrosion are lower than those for pitting, indicating that crevice corrosion is more readily initiated. If equipment is not designed to avoid crevice corrosion, then this will be the mode of failure. An example of this form of attack is presented in Fig. 44, which shows a type 317L corru-

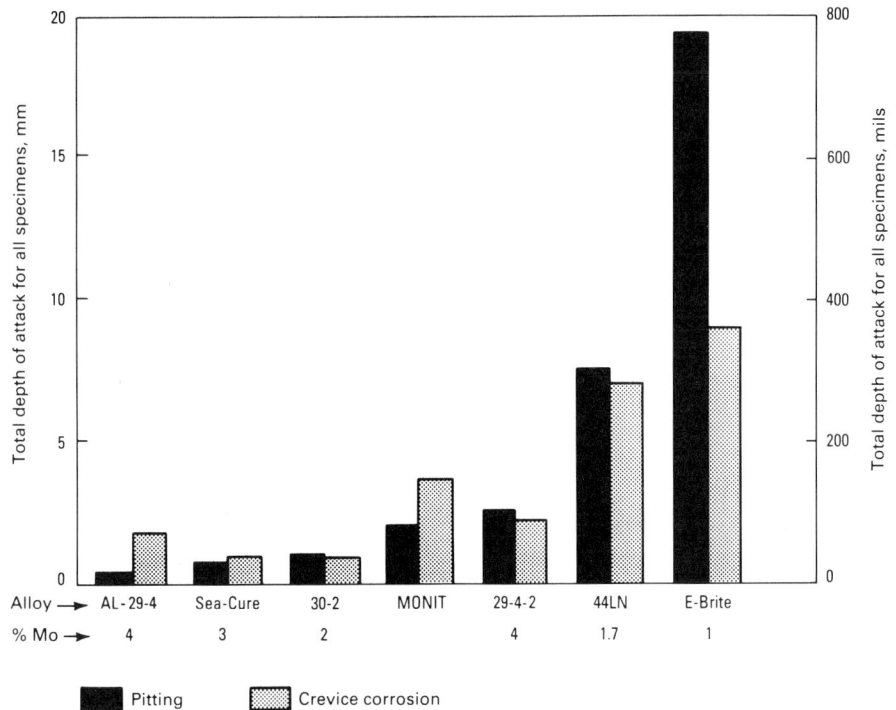

Fig. 41(c) Resistance of ferritic and duplex stainless steels to localized corrosion in paper mill bleach plant environment. Total depth of attack has been divided by 4 because there were four crevice sites per specimen. See also Fig. 41(a) and 41(b). Source: Ref 51

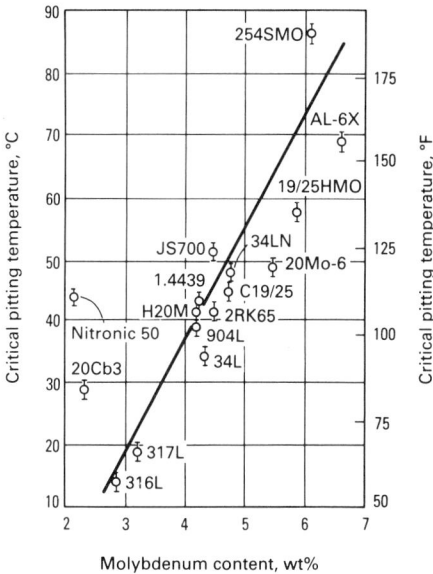

Fig. 42 Effect of molybdenum content on the $FeCl_3$ critical pitting temperature of commercial stainless steels. The more resistant steels have tighter critical pitting temperatures.

Table 37 Characteristics of three families of stainless steels for bleach plant service

Family	Examples	Characteristics	Comments
Austenitics	316L 317L 904L 254SMO AL-6XN	Tough, ductile, readily welded without loss of corrosion resistance; corrosion resistance related to alloy content	Bleach plant steels traditionally chosen from this group
	Nitronic 50	As above, with better pitting resistance than type 317L	Manganese-substituted austenitic, may be better value than type 317L; not common at present
Ferritics			
Low-interstitial type	29-4-2 29-4	Not as tough as austenitics, particularly after welding thicker sections. Special precautions needed for welding to avoid N_2 pickup. Corrosion resistance, related to alloy content, can be very good.	Higher alloys have remarkable corrosion resistance. Thin-section (<3 mm, or 0.120 in.) may find applications as corrugated deck or tubing; not common at present. (C + N) ≤ 0.025%
Ti- or Ti + Nb stabilized type	29-4C NYBY MONIT SEA-CURE	0.02% C max versions	Less expensive 0.02% C version of low-interstitial ferritics, for thin-section weldments (≤1.14 mm, or 0.045 in.)
Duplex	2205 Ferralium 255	Tough, ductile, should be weldable without significant loss in corrosion resistance	Combines toughness and corrosion resistance of austenitics and ferritics. Can be made highly resistant to SCC

gated deck from a C-stage washer that failed because of crevice corrosion.

Field testing of candidate alloys has been performed by a number of researchers (Ref 52-56). An early study measured pitting attack on a range of welded alloys in comparatively benign Nordic bleach plants (Ref 53). Pitting and crevice attack were later tested in more closed (more corrosive) Canadian bleach plants. This program focused on a few representative alloys, examined the selection of welding electrodes, and compared gaseous and liquid exposure in C- and D-stage washers (Ref 52). Figure 45 shows the corrosion products covering stainless steel test coupons that were exposed to a D-stage washer environment.

Two other exposure programs of note were carried out by the TAPPI Corrosion and Materials Engineering Committee in U.S. and Canadian mills. Unwelded alloys were tested in the first program (Ref 54), while the second program tested welded alloys (Ref 55, 56). The alloys tested included almost all available choices for bleach plant applications. However, alloy development has been such an active field in recent years that other promising steels, such as Ferralium 255, AL-6XN, and 29-4C, have been commercialized since the comprehensive TAPPI exposure programs.

Data from all these test rack programs can be interpreted as follows:

- *The premium bleach plant alloy of the future*: It will probably be chosen from 254SMO, Hastelloy alloy G-3, Sanicro 28, or 20Mo-6; VDM Cronifer 19/25 HMO, AL-6XN, and 29-4C (thin section) were not tested, but they should also be competitive.
- *Attractive alloys close to the type 317L cost level*: Nitronic 50 and 1.4439 (317LMN) are promising alternatives to type 317L. Ferralium 255 was not tested but should also be competitive.
- *Alloys with less competitive price or performance*: Titanium, Hastelloy alloy C-276, Inconel alloy 625, and 29-4-2 all performed exceptionally well but are expensive; 904L and related alloys appear to perform slightly below the level required for a premium alloy.

Bleach Plant Environments. Residual oxidants, such as Cl_2 and ClO_2, are the primary cause of corrosion in the bleach plant. The corrosive influence of Cl_2 has been demonstrated with coupon testing at higher Cl_2 levels (Fig. 46); other work has indirectly identified 25 ppm Cl_2 or ClO_2 as the level above which corrosion reactions are driven by residual oxidants. It seems probable that the 25 ppm of Cl_2 determined by iodine titration is close to zero actual Cl_2, because the titration is

Table 38 Effect of alloy components on the corrosion resistance of stainless steels in bleach plant applications

Element	Effect	Comments
Beneficial alloy additions		
Chromium	Enhances resistance to initiation of pitting and crevice corrosion	Steel must have more than 11% Cr to exhibit stainless property
Nickel	Enhances resistance to propagation of pitting and crevice corrosion	Higher levels of nickel enable partly corroded component to remain functional; little or no nickel in ferritic grades
Molybdenum	Enhances resistance to initiation and propagation of pitting and crevice corrosion	Over three times more effective than chromium against pitting and crevice attack, but has solubility limit of about 7% in stainless steels
Nitrogen	Enhances pitting resistance, particularly in combination with molybdenum	Used in austenitic and duplex grades only; increases strength of the steel
Detrimental residual elements		
Carbon	More than 0.03% can cause sensitization, making heat-affected zones of welds less corrosion resistant.	Oxidized out of steel during refining, down to limit set by simultaneous, costly, chromium oxidation
Phosphorus	Can cause hot cracking, that is, cracks formed in weld metal upon cooling. Hot cracks are sites for crevice corrosion, which looks like pitting attack.	Can only be controlled by use of low-phosphorus charge materials. Less than 0.015% P is respectable.
Sulfur	As with phosphorus, can cause hot cracking	Can be controlled to very low levels (<0.005% S) by good steelmaking practice. Less than 0.015% S is respectable. Less than 0.005% S is excellent

Note: Silicon, manganese, and copper are added for steelmaking reasons or sulfuric acid resistance (copper).

Table 39 Typical environmental conditions for bleach plant washers

Environment	Chlorination	Chlorine dioxide	Hypochlorite
Oxidant	30 ppm Cl_2	30 ppm ClO_2	30 ppm NaOCl
pH	2	4	9
Temperature, °C (°F)	45 (115)	65 (150)	40 (105)
Chloride ion (Cl^-), ppm	1500	1000	2000
Electrochemical potentials, mV_{SCE}			
Redox potential	1000	500	...
Washer potential	750	500	...

Note: SCE, saturated calomel electrode

Effect of Temperature, Chlorides, and pH. Temperatures and chloride ion concentrations are raised after bleach plant closure. The influence of these two changes on corrosion, although significant, is usually far overshadowed by the corrosive effect of residual oxidants. Typical environmental conditions for bleach plant washers are given in Table 39.

Recycling can lower pH in all acidic washing stages. Lower pH will create a corrosion problem only during the last stage of bleach plant closure—namely, when C-stage filtrate is used for C-stage lower dilution. With this practice, lower pH can give the pulp the viscosity protection required for the consequent higher-temperature chlorination. However, when pH decreases to 1.5 or 1.2 as compared to the normal pH 2, stainless steel corrosion rates increase dramatically. It is probable that for any given stainless, a critical lower-limit pH exists below which corrosion rates are high, but such limits have not yet been identified with any degree of certainty. What can be assumed is that more highly alloyed materials should have lower limiting pHs and that nickel and molybdenum should be the most influential alloying elements.

Vapor-Phase Corrosion. The corrosion of nonwetted components, such as shower pipes and metal vats above the stock level, is a major problem in C-stage washers. This attack is caused by excess chlorination, in which gaseous chlorine from the filtrate makes small droplets of condensation highly corrosive. Chlorination-stage gas-phase attack is probably the most aggressive in all the bleach plant. Methods of avoiding this problem include improving chlorine control, using titanium or nonmetallic-coated shower pipes, and, for stainless steel vats, cladding with 6% Mo stainless or nickel-base alloys to just below the liquid level or lining the whole vat with nonmetallic coating (good design and workmanship are essential).

The vapor space above D-stage washers is not very corrosive unless SO_2 is used in excess, is poorly controlled, or is badly mixed. When both SO_2 and ClO_2 are present in the vapor space, any condensation will contain HCl and H_2SO_4, mixtures of which are very corrosive to stainless steel.

D-Stage Washer Corrosion. Sodium hydroxide or SO_2 additions are made to bleached pulp before the pulp machine in order to improve drainage and to limit brightness reversion. Such

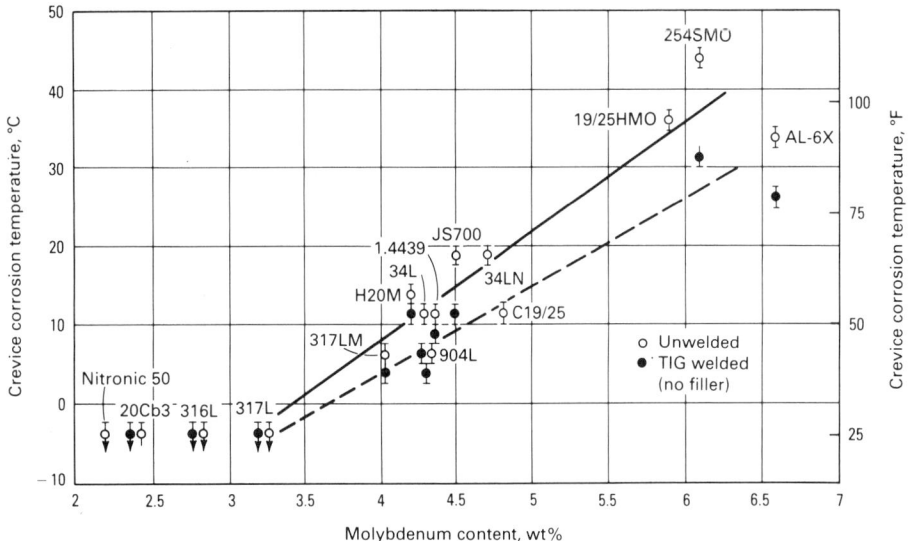

Fig. 43 Effect of molybdenum content on the crevice corrosion temperature of commercial stainless steels. The more resistant steels have higher crevice corrosion temperatures in the $FeCl_3$ test.

also sensitive to traces of oxidizing organics present in C-stage filtrates.

Any steps that can be taken to lower residual oxidants to below 25 ppm will lower corrosion rates. Options include automatic chlorine control, chlorine dioxide sensor/controls, SO_2 antichlor, and NaOH additions (ClO_2 is not very corrosive at pH 7, and NaOH additions to a pH 4 filtrate will transform ClO_2 to ClO_2^- after a few hours).

Recycling of filtrates can compound corrosion problems. For example, ClO_2 can be recycled with a D2-stage filtrate to the D1-stage washer showers; therefore, an increase from 50 to 150 ppm ClO_2 has been measured in a D1-stage filtrate when D2-stage SO_2 additions were cut off during high ClO_2 use. Recycling of D1- or D2-stage filtrate to the C-stage washer should be avoided completely, because the more acidic C-stage filtrate (pH 2) regenerates ClO_2 from chlorite ions, thus rendering the shower water highly corrosive to stainless steels. Many C-stage washers were lost because of this practice when recycling was first carried out.

Fig. 44 Failure of corrugated type 317L washer-deck commonly associated with crevice corrosion

Fig. 45 Stainless steel coupons of types 316L, 317L, and 904L on a rack exposed below the incoming stock of a D-stage washer. Profuse ferrous oxide corrosion products cover the coupons.

additions are often made before the D2 washer so that the washer may also be protected from residual-related corrosion. In some cases, SO_2 additions are made before the D1-stage washer for corrosion protection, and in Nordic countries, SO_2 is even added before some C-stage washers. Sulfur dioxide additions are an effective (if costly) way of limiting corrosion; they work because SO_2 reacts irreversibly with the residual oxidant to form nonoxidizing reaction products, for example, with ClO_2:

$$2ClO_2 + 5SO_2 + 6H_2O \rightarrow 2HCl + 5H_2SO_4 \qquad \text{(Eq 3)}$$

The amount of acid formed by this reaction has a negligible effect on washer corrosion, and sufficient SO_2 should be used to maintain a trace of residual SO_2 at all times. Sulfur dioxide control can be automatic or manual; in the latter case a target maximum pH of 3 is often used for additions before the D2-stage washer.

If SO_2 additions are discontinued—for example, because of SO_2 shortage—rust nodules or "barnacles" may appear within a few weeks on the washer (Fig. 45). Residual ClO2 (present because SO2 was discontinued) has caused the iron oxide [FeO(OH)] corrosion deposits to form. The deposits are insoluble above pH 3.5, and their presence exacerbates the corrosion problem, because additional underdeposit formation occurs. Deposits can be avoided by increasing the pH to above 5.5 (target pH 7) with NaOH and by holding residual ClO_2 to less than 25 ppm.

When a D-stage washer drum has been in operation for a number of years, it is not advisable to change to C-stage service if there is any evidence of rust deposit. The deposits may plug corrosion pits, and in C-stage washing at pH 2 the deposits will be dissolved quickly, causing the washer to leak.

Hypochlorite, Oxygen, and Peroxide. Because bleaching with hypochlorite, oxygen, and peroxide is usually carried out under alkaline conditions, stainless steels are much less subject to pitting and crevice corrosion. Hypochlorite washers are commonly made of type 316L to resist crevice attack. Oxygen reactors are often made of high-nickel stainless steels such as 20Cb3 to guard against chloride SCC, which can occur at higher temperatures in pressure vessels. Some lower alloys have been used in this latter application, apparently without problems, although type 304 has failed by chloride SCC. However, chloride pitting corrosion can also occur in oxygen reactors, and alloys containing higher molybdenum levels may be necessary. Alkaline peroxide is used to brighten mechanical pulps in newsprint production without any corrosion consequences. Peroxide has also been used in place of ClO_2 in chemical pulp bleach plants and appears to present no more corrosion problems than ClO_2.

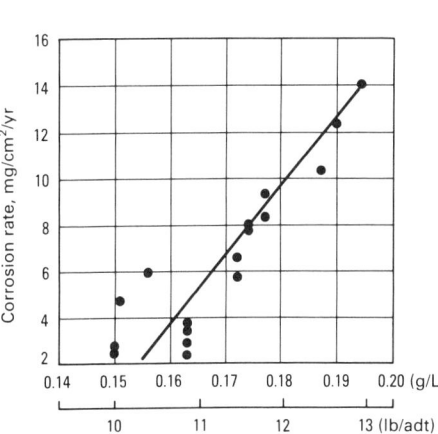

Fig. 46 Effect of residual chlorine on the corrosion rate of test coupons in a C-stage washer

[Graph: y-axis "Corrosion rate, mg/cm²/yr" from 2 to 16; x-axis "Top-of-the-tower residual Cl₂ concentration" with upper scale 0.14, 0.15, 0.16, 0.17, 0.18, 0.19, 0.20 (g/L) and lower scale 10, 11, 12, 13 (lb/adt)]

Table 40 Principal causes of corrosion of austenitic stainless steel weldments

Attack site and mode		Reason for attack	When is it a problem?	How to avoid
Weld metal				
	Pitting	Welding with no filler	All molybdenum-containing austenitics(a)	Use appropriate filler.
		Welding with underalloyed filler	3 to 6% Mo austenitics(a)	Use appropriate filler, for example, IN112.
	Crevice corrosion	Microfissures in weld metal create sites for crevice corrosion (looks like pitting).	In ferrite-free stainless steel weld metal, for example, fillers commonly recommended for 904L(a)	Use IN112 electrode for 3 to 6% Mo austenitics.
		Lack of penetration	In one-side or stitched butt-weld joints	Ensure full penetration, and do not use stitchwelds on process side.
		Entrapped welding flux	Shielded metal arc welded joints	Use electrode with good flux detachment.
Heat-affected zone		Precipitation of carbides during welding	When steel has over 0.03% C	Use steel with 0.03% C max.
Fusion line		Unmixed zone formed at fusion line	With high-alloy steels close to their corrosion limits	Use lower heat input on final pass.
		Precipitation of carbides at fusion line (knife-line attack)	In niobium- or titanium-stabilized steels	A very rare problem. Niobium- and titanium-stabilized steels not common

(a) Particularly after high heat input welding

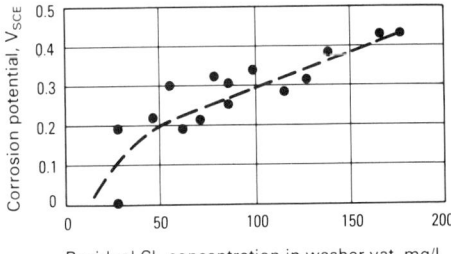

Fig. 47 Effect of residual Cl₂ concentration in a washer vat on the free-corrosion potential of a type 317L bleach plant washer. Source: Ref 57

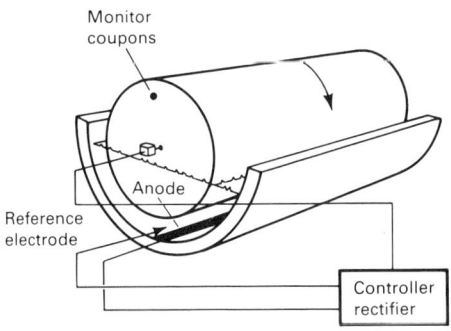

Fig. 48 Components of a washer electrochemical protection system

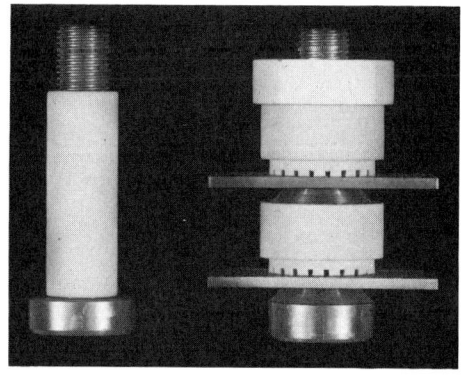

Fig. 49 Crevice corrosion monitor assembly

Corrosion of Welds. Stainless steel washers fail occasionally because of weld-related corrosion. The principal causes of weld-related corrosion are detailed in Table 40.

Welding without filler metal creates a preferential attack site on austenitic stainless steel and should be avoided in washer construction. It is important to select a filler metal that gives a deposit that is no less corrosion resistant than the base metal. For type 316L, the American Welding Society standard filler is adequate. However, for type 317L and the more highly alloyed materials, a filler metal with a composition similar to that of the base metal can have much lower pitting resistance.

The optimal weld metal for all 4.5 to 6% Mo austenitic stainless steels is Inconel alloy 112 or an equivalent (for example, Inconel alloy 625 or Avesta alloy P12). Inconel alloy 112 is a good choice because:

- It is metallurgically compatible with all austenitic stainless steels.
- As-welded Inconel alloy 112 is highly resistant to pitting and crevice corrosion.
- There is no significant galvanic effect between Inconel alloy 112 and austenitic stainless steels in bleach plant liquors.
- If microfissures or hot cracks occur in the weld metal, they will not be preferentially attacked by crevice corrosion. This is a particular problem for most ferrite-free stainless steel fillers.

Microfissuring or hot cracking is a phenomenon associated with thermal stresses during welding. These stresses usually cause small cracks to form in the weld metal or HAZ of a stainless steel or nickel-base alloy weldment. Higher-nickel-content alloys, which have a greater coefficient of thermal expansion, are more susceptible to hot cracking. Cracking is more likely to occur because of higher phosphorus (>0.015% P) and sulfur (>0.015% S) in the alloy or contamination of the weld area. It is most commonly seen in the HAZ in the previous pass of a multiple-pass weld. Hot cracking rarely has a detrimental effect on the mechanical properties or structural integrity of a fabrication. However, it can be very detrimental to the corrosion properties of a weldment. Microfissures form crevice corrosion sites that are readily attacked.

Recent laboratory tests have shown that other fillers can be used for 904L, such as Sanicro 27.31.4L CuR, Smitweld NiCro 31/27, and Ther-

manit 30/40 E. These fillers would be appropriate for microfissure-free shop construction. However, contaminated weldments are best repaired with Inconel alloy 112 or an equivalent filler.

Another common problem with stainless steel weldments—sensitization in the HAZ—is avoided in bleach plants by the use of low-carbon steels (0.03% C max for austenitics). Similarly, fusion-line attack (sometimes called knife-line attack) due to precipitation of carbides at the fusion line in niobium- and titanium-stabilized austenitic steels is rarely seen, because these steels have been made obsolescent by new steelmaking technology.

However, attack at the fusion line is possible when overalloyed fillers such as Inconel alloy 112 are used with high-heat-input welding. Such welding can create zones consisting of melted base metal that is not mixed with weld filler—called unmixed zones—at the fusion line. Cases of unmixed zone corrosion have occasionally been observed in the bleach plant. In practice, this can be minimized by the use of lower heat input on the final weld passes.

Electrochemical Protection. The discussion thus far has centered on the selection of material or the control of the environment to minimize corrosion. A third approach has recently become available with the development of electrochemical protection for bleach plant washers.

The life of a stainless steel washer can be greatly extended if the washer is cathodically polarized from the oxidizing potentials imposed by residual oxidants such as chlorine (Fig. 47) to a more negative, passive potential by the use of a rectifier and a platinized anode mounted in the washer vat (Fig. 48). Electrical contact to the washer is made through a rotating mercury contactor; the washer potential is measured with a reference electrode and is automatically controlled with a feedback-controlled rectifier to a potential set point or window that minimizes corrosive attack.

A detailed description of the principle of electrochemical protection is provided in Ref 57. However, the essential feature of the technique is the use of the electron as an antichlor for corrosion protection. Electrons are fed from the rectifier to the washer in the form of electric current. At the washer surface, they react with chlorine:

$$Cl_2 + 2e^- \rightarrow 2Cl^- \tag{Eq 4}$$

Therefore, like SO₂, electrons react with the corrosive oxidant (chlorine) to form relatively harmless chloride ions. For corrosion protection, the electron has a clear advantage over SO₂: It can be delivered to the cathodic reaction site. For this reason, comparatively few electrons are needed. The required current is low, and running costs are negligible.

Because of the comparatively low cost of electrochemical protection and the ease of retrofitting to existing washers, commercialization of the technique has found wide acceptance. The first successful operation of one of these systems was in Nova Scotia, Canada, in 1978. By the end of 1986, there were about 90 installations worldwide.

The corrosion rate of each protected washer is monitored with coupons, using a technique designed for comparison of protected and unprotected coupons. A mounting bolt is welded to the end face of the rotating washer as shown in Fig. 48, and two coupons, together with segmented crevicing disks, are mounted so that one is in electrical contact with the washer and the other is isolated, with all other mounting details being identical (Fig. 49). The degree of protection is assessed by comparing the corrosion of protected and unprotected coupons after a 60-day exposure period (Fig. 50).

Both weight loss and depth of attack measurements have been made on coupons to assess the comparative severity of pitting or crevice corrosion. The ratio of unprotected and protected coupon weight loss is used as a measure of protection. Table 41 lists protection ratios measured for washers that have been protected for up to five years (6 washer types/212 test coupons). These results show that protection lowers corrosion rates. On the average, unprotected coupons lose six times more weight than protected coupons.

Improved performance with protection can be compared with improved performance after alloy upgrading in the absence of protection. The results of an extensive bleach plant exposure program, which involved 880 coupons, 40 test racks, 10 mills, and no electrochemical protection, were reexamined to obtain the average weight loss ratios (using type 317L as a base case) for alloys 904L and 254SMO. These data are given in Table 42; greater ratios indicate better performance. Type 317L coupons lose 5.5 times as much weight as 254SMO coupons. Therefore, the improved

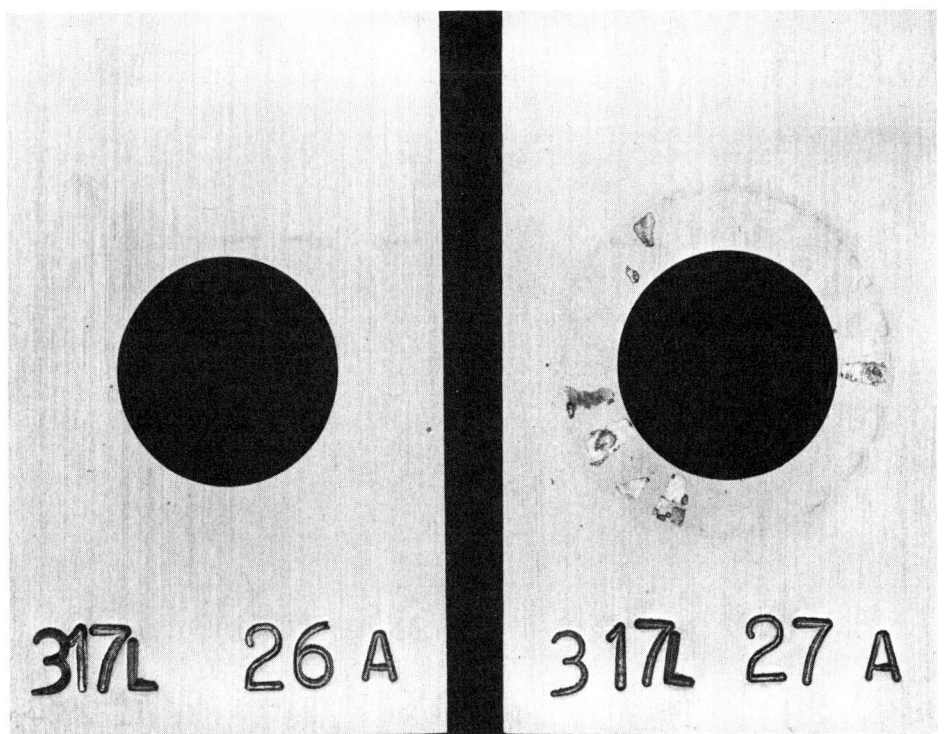

Fig. 50 Type 317L monitor coupons after a 60-day exposure attached to a C-stage washer. The coupon on the left was in electrical contact with the washer and was therefore protected. The coupon on the right was isolated and unprotected. Substantial crevice corrosion occurred on the right-hand coupon at seven of the 20 possible crevicing sites.

from Volume 13 of the *ASM Handbook* that are referenced throughout this section.

Food and Beverage Industry

Stainless steels have been relied on in food and beverage applications because of the lack of corrosion products that could contaminate the process environment and because of the superior cleanability of the stainless steels. The corrosion environment often involves moderately to highly concentrated chlorides on the process side, often mixed with significant concentrations of organic acids. The water side can range from steam heating to brine cooling. Purity and sanitation standards require excellent resistance to pitting and crevice corrosion.

Food Applications. Foods such as vegetables represent milder environments and can generally be handled by using type 304. Sauces and pickle liquors, however, are more aggressive and can pit even type 316. For improved pitting resistance, such alloys as 22Cr-13Ni-5Mn, 904L, 20Mo-4, 254SMO, AL-6XN, and MONIT stainless steels should be considered.

At elevated temperatures, materials must be selected for resistance to pitting and SCC in the presence of chlorides. Stress corrosion must be avoided in heat-transfer applications, such as steam jacketing for cooking or processing vessels or in heat exchangers. Cracking may occur from the process or water side or may initiate outside the unit under chloride-containing insulation.

Stainless steel equipment should be cleaned frequently to prolong its service life. The equipment should be flushed with fresh water, scrubbed with a nylon brush and detergent, then rinsed. On the other hand, consideration should be given to the effect of very aggressive cleaning procedures on the stainless steels, as in the chemical sterilization of commercial dishwashers. In some cases, it may be necessary to select a more highly alloyed stainless steel grade to deal with these brief exposures to highly aggressive environments.

Conventional AISI grades provide satisfactory service in many food and beverage applications. Type 304 is widely used in the dairy industry, and type 316 finds application as piping and tubing in breweries. These grades, along with type 444 and Custom 450, have been used for chains to transfer food through processing equipment. Machined parts for beverage-dispensing equipment have been fabricated from types 304, 304L, 316, 316L, 303Al Modified, 302HQ-FM, and 303BV. When the free-machining grades are used, it is important to passivate and rinse properly before service in order to optimize corrosion resistance.

Food-handling equipment should be designed without crevices in which food can become lodged. In more corrosive food products, extra-low-carbon stainless steels should be used whenever possible. Improved results have been obtained when equipment is finished with a 2B (general-purpose cold-rolled) finish rather than No. 4 (general-purpose polished) finish. Alternatively, an electropolished surface may be considered.

performance achieved by the electrochemical protection of type 317L appears to be very close to that gained by upgrading type 317L to unprotected 254SMO.

The installation and operating costs of electrochemical protection systems are small compared to the resulting cost savings. Capital cost savings are such that if the life of a washer is extended from five to ten years by protection, the protection system will have a payback period of about one year.

Even this substantial saving can be overshadowed by savings in chemical costs in mills that add NaOH or SO_2 to pulp before washing. Experience has shown that, in general, SO_2 additions need not be made ahead of a protected washer to protect it from corrosion. If pulp souring is still required, then this can be done immediately after the washer,

where much less SO_2 will be needed. Additional savings can be realized by eliminating SO_2 use in a closed bleach plant, because SO_2-free recycled filtrate used for tower dilution consumes much less unreacted ClO_2. Protection systems have been installed on washers made from types 316L, 317L, and 904L, and 254SMO stainless steels. A protected 254SMO washer probably represents the state of the art for corrosion control in the most severe washer environments.

Materials Selection for Other Industrial Applications

Every industry features a variety of applications encompassing a range of corrosion environments. This section will characterize the experience of each industry according to the corrosion problems most frequently encountered and will suggest appropriate grade selections. More detailed information can be found in the articles

Table 41 Type 317L test coupon data from the first six electrochemical protection systems

Washer	Protection period, years	Average protection ratio(a)
C-stage	5.4	4.9
D2-stage	4.0	2.6
D2-stage	3.3	12.3
D1-stage	2.9	8.2
D2-stage	2.9	1.9
D1-stage	1.8	6.2
General average		6.0

(a) Unprotected ÷ protected type 317L coupon weight loss (larger ratios indicate better performance)

Table 42 Test rack weight loss data for unprotected steels

Steel	Average weight loss ratio(a)
Type 317L	1
904L	2.5
254SMO	5.5

(a) This ratio is obtained, for example, by determining the average weight loss for type 317L coupons ÷ average weight loss for 904L coupons (larger ratios indicate better performance).

Brewery Applications. Most of the brewery equipment currently being installed is fabricated from type 304 and includes kettles, tanks, tubs, plate coolers, and even some pasteurizers. Stainless steel hot water tanks have been a problem; there has been some major SCC of heavy-wall vessels holding up to 500 barrels. The problem has been one of Cl⁻ concentration due to evaporation under hot conditions and cracking of shaped plate sections at the bottom of the tanks. Remedial measures have consisted of treated water plus complete drainage and flushing.

Stress-corrosion failures in stainless steel thin-wall piping have been common. Stress-corrosion cracking has taken place where low-chloride water leaking from valve stems saturated insulation and concentrated at temperatures as low as 70 °C (160 °F). Remedial measures have consisted of replacing the piping, coating the exposed stainless steel with a chloride-free coating, and maintaining better valve maintenance.

Stress-corrosion cracking has also been observed where heavy scaling has occurred because of hard water conditions, with chloride concentration in the hardness salt deposits. Remedial action has involved acid treating the water to remove carbonates. Type 444 ferritic stainless steel has been successfully used where SCC problems have occurred because of deposit formation.

Pharmaceutical and Medical Applications

Pharmaceutical Industry. The production and handling of drugs and other medical applications require exceedingly high standards for preserving the sterility and purity of process streams. Process environments can include complex organic compounds, strong acids, chloride solutions comparable to seawater, and elevated processing temperatures. Higher-alloy grades, such as type 316 or higher, may be necessary instead of type 304 in order to prevent even superficial corrosion. Electropolishing may be desirable to reduce or prevent adherent deposits and the possibility of underdeposit corrosion. Superior cleanability and ease of inspection make stainless steel the preferred material.

The 18-8 stainless grades have been used for a wide variety of applications—from pill punches to operating tables. However, care is required in selecting stainless steels for pharmaceutical applications, because small amounts of contamination can be objectionable. For example, stainless steel has been used to process vitamin C, but copper must be eliminated because copper in aqueous solutions accelerates the decomposition of vitamin C. Also, stainless steel is not used to handle vitamin B_6 hydrochloride, even though corrosion rates may be low, because trace amounts of iron are objectionable.

The effects of temperature and chloride concentration must be considered. At ambient temperature, chloride pitting of 18Cr-8Ni stainless steel may occur, but SCC is unlikely. At about 65 °C (150 °F) or above, SCC of austenitic grades must be considered. Duplex alloys, such as 7-Mo PLUS, alloy 2205, and Ferralium 255, possess improved resistance to SCC in elevated-temperature chloride environments. Ferritic grades with lower nickel content, such as 18Cr-2Mo, provide another means of avoiding chloride SCC. Additional information on the use of stainless steels in the pharmaceutical industry is available in the article "Corrosion in the Pharmaceutical Industry" in Volume 13 of the *ASM Handbook*.

Orthopedic Implants. Stainless steels have also found application as orthopedic implants. Material is required that is capable of moderately high strength and resistance to wear and fretting corrosion, along with pitting and crevice attack. Vacuum-melted type 316L has been used for temporary internal fixation devices, such as bone plates, screws, pins, and suture wire. Higher purity improves electropolishing, and increased chromium (17 to 19%) improves corrosion resistance.

In permanent implants, such as artificial joints, very high strength and resistance to wear, fatigue, and corrosion are essential. Cobalt- or titanium-base alloys are used for these applications. More information on this subject is available in the article "Corrosion of Metallic Implants and Prosthetic Devices" in Volume 13 of the *ASM Handbook*.

Oil and Gas Industry

Stainless steels were not frequently used in oil and gas production until the tapping of sour reservoirs (those containing H_2S) and the use of enhanced recovery systems in the mid-1970s. Sour environments can result in sulfide stress cracking (SSC) of susceptible materials. This phenomenon generally occurs at ambient or slightly elevated temperatures; it is difficult to establish an accurate temperature maximum for all alloys. Factors affecting SSC resistance include material variables, pH, H_2S concentration, total pressure, maximum tensile stress, temperature, and time. A description of some of these factors, along with information on materials that have demonstrated resistance to SSC, is available in the article "Stress-Corrosion Cracking and Hydrogen Embrittlement" in this Volume.

The resistance of stainless steels to SSC improves with reduced hardness. Conventional materials, such as types 410, 430, and 304, exhibit acceptable resistance at hardnesses below 22 HRC. Specialized grades, such as 22Cr-13Ni-5Mn, Custom 450, 20Mo-4, and some duplex stainless steels, have demonstrated resistance at higher hardnesses. Duplex alloy 2205 has been used for its strength and corrosion resistance as gathering lines for CO_2 gas before gas cleaning. Custom 450 and 22Cr-13Ni-5Mn stainless steels have seen service as valve parts. Other grades used in these environments include 254SMO and alloy 28, particularly for chloride and sulfide resistance, respectively.

In addition to the lower-temperature SSC, resistance to cracking in high-temperature environments is required in many oil field applications. Most stainless steels, including austenitic and duplex grades, are known to be susceptible to elevated-temperature cracking, probably by a mechanism similar to chloride SCC. Failure appears to be accelerated by H_2S and other sulfur compounds. Increased susceptibility is noted in material of higher yield strength, for example, because of the high residual tensile stresses imparted by some cold-working operations.

The above discussion is pertinent to the production phase of a well. However, drilling takes place in an environment of drilling mud, which usually consists of water, clay, weighting materials, and an inhibitor (frequently an oxygen scavenger). Chlorides are also present when drilling through salt formations. Austenitic stainless steels containing high manganese (15 to 18%) and nitrogen (0.45 to 0.50%) have found use in this environment as nonmagnetic drill collars, as weight for the drill bit, and as housings for measurement-while-drilling (MWD) instruments. Nonmagnetic materials are required for operation of these instruments, which are used to locate the drill bit in directional-drilling operations. Nonstandard stainless steels used as drill collars or MWD components include type 316LN (high nitrogen), 18-8 Plus (Fe-0.12C-18Mn-18Cr-0.45N), 15-15LC (Fe-0.03C-15Mn-16Cr-0.40N), and AN618 (Fe-0.07C-15Mn-17Cr-0.5N). More information on corrosion during petroleum production is available in the article "Corrosion in Petroleum Production Operations" in Volume 13 of the *ASM Handbook*.

In refinery applications, the raw crude contains such impurities as sulfur, water, salts, organic acids, and organic nitrogen compounds. These and other corrosives and their products must be considered in providing stainless steels for the various refinery steps.

Raw crude is separated into materials from petroleum gas to various oils by fractional distillation. These materials are then treated to remove impurities, such as CO_2, NH_3, and H_2S, and to optimize product quality. Refinery applications of stainless steels often involve heat exchangers. Duplex and ferritic grades have been used in this application for their improved SCC resistance. Type 430 and type 444 exchanger tubing has been used for resisting hydrogen, chlorides, and sulfur and nitrogen compounds in oil refinery streams. The article "Corrosion in Petroleum Refining and Petrochemical Operations" in Volume 13 of the *ASM Handbook* contains detailed information on corrosion of materials in these applications.

Severe naphthenic acid corrosion has been experienced primarily in the vacuum towers of crude distillation units in the temperature zone of 290 to 345 °C (550 to 650 °F) and sometimes as low as 230 °C (450 °F). (Naphthenic acids are organic acids that are present in many crude oils, especially those from California, Venezuela, Eastern Europe, and Russia.) Damage is in the form of pitting and localized (lake-type) attack of tray components and vessel walls. Attack is often limited to the undersides of tray floors and to the inside and very top of the outside surfaces of bubble caps, as shown in Fig. 51. These areas are normally not covered by a layer of liquid, which suggests that the attack is caused by impinging droplets of the condensing acids. No corrosion damage is found at temperatures above 345 °C (650 °F), probably because a protective coke

Fig. 51 Naphthenic acid corrosion on top of 150 mm (6 in.) bubble caps made from type 317 containing 2.95% Mo. Tray temperature was 305 °C (580 °F).

layer is formed. Naphthenic acid corrosion is most easily controlled by blending crude oils having high neutralization numbers with other crude oils.

Stress-corrosion cracking of stainless steels under thermal insulation has been a great concern to the operators of gas- and petrochemical-processing plants for many years. The collection and concentra-tion of chlorides on austenitic stainless steels can lead to rapid failure of expensive equipment. Table 43 summarizes the possible methods of pre-vention that apply to each causative agent. As can be seen, application of a suitable protective coat-ing system is generally the most economical method, although other methods are included and may be practical under certain circumstances.

Power Industry

Stainless steels are used in the power industry for generator components, feedwater heaters, boiler applications, heat exchangers, condenser tubing, flue gas desulfurization systems, and nu-clear power applications.

Generator blades and vanes have been fabri-cated of modified 12% Cr stainless steel, such as types 615 (UNS S41800) and 616 (UNS S42200). In some equipment, Custom 450 has replaced types 410 and 616.

Heat Exchangers. Stainless steels have been widely used in tubing for surface condensers and feedwater heaters. Both of these are shell-and-tube heat exchangers that condense steam from the tur-bine on the shell side. In these heat exchangers, the severity of the corrosion increases with higher tem-peratures and pressures. Stainless steels resist failure by erosion and do not suffer SCC in NH_3 (from de-composition of boiler feedwater additives), as do some nonferrous materials.

Stainless steels must be chosen to resist chloride pitting. The amount of chloride that can be tolerated is expected to be higher with higher pH and cleaner stainless steel surfaces, that is, surfaces without deposits. For example, type 304 may resist pitting in chloride levels of 1000 ppm or higher in the absence of fouling, crevices, or stagnant conditions. The presence of one or more of these conditions can allow chlorides to concentrate at the metal surface and initiate pits. Several high-performance stainless steels have been used to resist chloride pitting in brackish water or seawater. High-per-formance austenitic grades have been useful in

Table 43   Guidelines for preventing stress-corrosion cracking of stainless steels under thermal insulation

Causative agent	Preventive method	Comments	Evaluation
Austenitic stainless steel	Change to SCC-resistant alloy	Stainless steel alloys with >30% Ni and the duplex stainless alloys are alternative choices, but cost considerably more and may not be readily available.	Extra cost compared to other preventive methods makes this an unwise choice.
Tensile stress	Thermal treatment (anneal or stress relieve)	Annealing at 1065 °C (1950 °F), followed by water quenching will distort and scale equipment severely. Stress relieving at 955 °C (1750 °F) and slow cooling will sensitize the grain structure and cause some warpage and scaling. Note: A stress-relieved vessel or pipe will be subjected to tensile stresses in assembly and under operating conditions. May override the thermal treatment	Generally not practical for piping and vessels; may be used for small individual components
	Shot peen	Shot peening converts the surface stresses to compressive stress and is a proven SCC preventive method. It is a delicate process requiring specific skills and experience. May be costly or difficult to apply in the field	Should be considered, but may be more costly and difficult to obtain than other prevention methods.
Chlorides	Remove or eliminate Cl⁻ ion	Because of their widespread occurrence, highly soluble chloride salts are difficult to avoid or keep off of equipment.	Not practical
	Apply barrier coating to stainless steel	Use of a protective coating on the stainless steel surface can prevent Cl⁻ contact with the alloy.	This is a practical and proven preventive method.
		Wrap stainless steel with aluminum foil, which serves as both a barrier coating and cathodic protection anode.	Being used with success; extended life of the aluminum has not been determined.
Water	Improve waterproofing to prevent water entry	No type of coating, cementing, or wrapping of insulation can keep air and water from entering the insulation system, except for constructing an external pressure shell. Note: The application and maintenance of a weather barrier is important to good insulation performance and should have a high maintenance priority.	Not practical to expect a wrap or coating to keep water out
	Apply barrier coating to stainless steel	A carefully selected protective coating can provide long-term protection for stainless steel equipment.	This is a practical and proven preventive method.
		Use of aluminum foil wrap as above	Limited use, but with success

Note: Use of inorganic zinc primer or paint system is not safe due to the possibility of liquid-metal embrittlement upon subsequent welding or exposure to extreme heat.

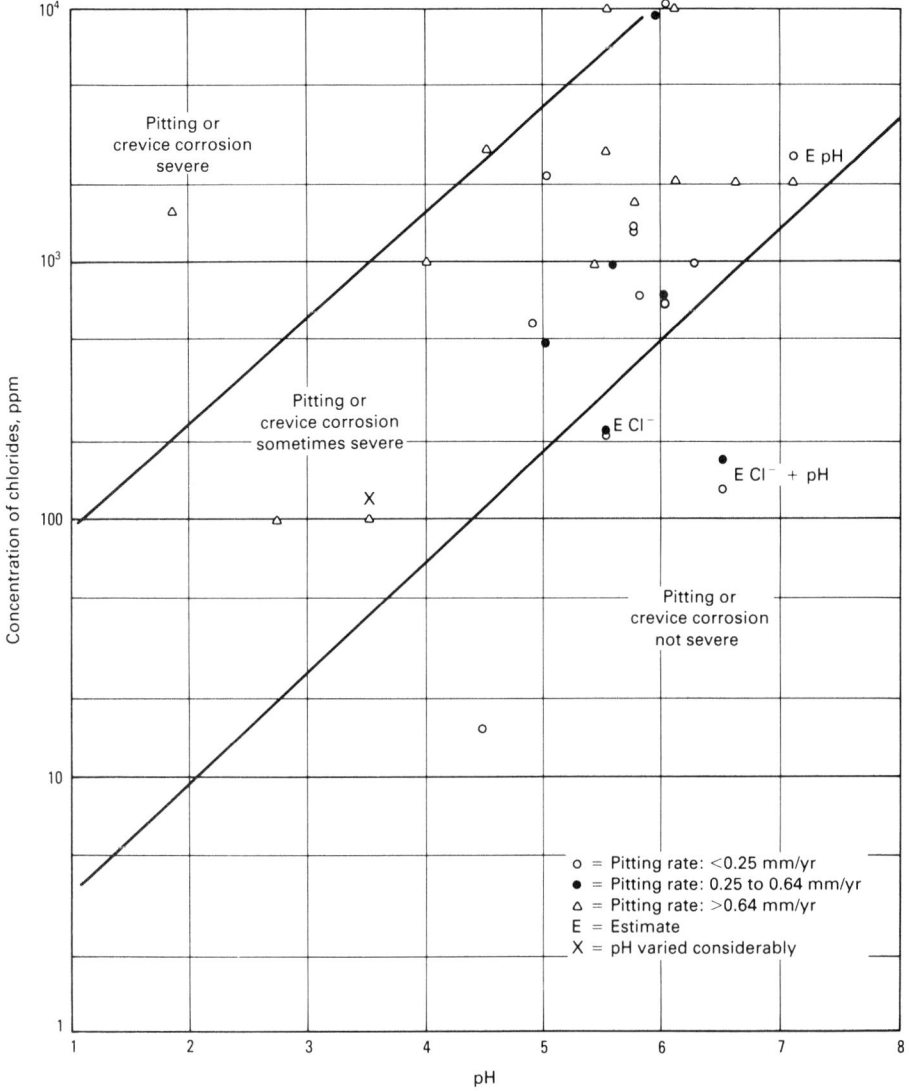

Fig. 52 Pitting of type 316L in flue gas desulfurization scrubber environments. Solid lines indicate zones of differing severity of corrosion; because the zones are not clearly defined, the lines cannot be precisely drawn.

feedwater heaters, although duplex stainless steels may also be considered because of their high strength. Ferritic stainless steels have proved to be economically competitive in exchangers and condensers. High-performance austenitic and ferritic grades have been satisfactory for seawater-cooled units. These grades include MONIT, AL-29-4C, Usinor 290 Mo, Sea-Cure, AL-6X, AL-6XN, and 254SMO.

Compatibility of materials and good installation practice are required. Tubes of materials such as those listed above have been installed in tube-sheets fabricated of alloy 904L, 20Mo-4, and 254SM. Crevice corrosion can occur when some tube materials are rolled into type 316 tubesheets.

Flue Gas Desulfurization. A wide variety of alloys have been used in scrubbers, which are located between the boiler and smokestack of fossil fuel power plants to treat effluent gases and to remove SO$_2$ and other pollutants. Typically, fly ash is removed, and the gas travels through an inlet gas duct, followed by the quencher section. Next, SO$_2$ is removed in the absorber section, most often using either a lime or limestone system. A mist eliminator is employed to remove suspended droplets, and the gas proceeds to the treated-gas duct, reheater section, and the stack.

Two important items for consideration in selecting stainless steels for resistance to pitting in scrubber environments are pH and chloride level. Stainless steels are more resistant to higher pH and lower chloride levels, as shown in Fig. 52 for type 316L. Environments that cause pitting or crevice attack of type 316 can be handled by using higher-alloy materials, for example, those with increased molybdenum and chromium.

Some of the materials being considered and specified for varying chloride levels are listed in Table 44, which shows the results for samples exposed to several scrubber environments. The maximum depth of localized corrosion and pit density are given for the stainless steels tested. Exposure at the quencher spray header (above slurry) was more severe than expected, probably because of wet-dry concentration effects. Severe attack also occurred in the outlet duct. Samples in this area were exposed to high chlorides, high temperatures, and low pH during the 39 days on bypass operation. More information on corrosion in fossil fuel power plants is available in the article "High-Temperature Corrosion" in this Volume and the articles "Corrosion in Fossil Fuel Power Plants" and "Corrosion of Emission-Control Equipment" in Volume 13 of the *ASM Handbook*.

Nuclear Power Applications. Type 304 piping has been used in boiling water nuclear reactor power plants. The operating temperature of these reactors is about 290 °C (550 °F), and a wide range of conditions can be present during startup, operation, and shutdown. Because these pipes are joined by welding, there is a possibility of sensitization. This can result in intergranular SCC in chloride-free high-temperature water that contains small amounts of oxygen, for example, 0.2 to 8 ppm.

Type 304 with additions of boron (about 1%) has been used to construct spent-fuel storage units, dry storage casks, and transportation casks. The high boron level provides neutron-absorbing properties. More information on nuclear applications is available in the articles "Stress-Corrosion Cracking and Hydrogen Embrittlement" (see the discussion of irradiation-assisted SCC) and "Corrosion in the Nuclear Power Industry" in Volume 13 of the *ASM Handbook*.

Transportation Industry

Automotive Applications. Stainless steels are used in a wide range of components in transportation that are both functional and decorative. Bright automobile parts, such as trim, fasteners, wheel covers, mirror mounts, and windshield wiper arms, have generally been fabricated from 17Cr or 18Cr-8Ni stainless steel or similar grades. Example alloys include types 430, 343, 304, and 305. Type 302HQ-FM remains a candidate for such applications as wheel nuts, and Custom 455 stainless has been used as wheel lock nuts. Use of type 301 for wheel covers has diminished with the weight-reduction programs of the automotive industry.

Stainless steels also serve many nondecorative functions in automotive design. Small-diameter shafts of type 416 and, occasionally, type 303 have been used in connection with power equipment, such as windows, door locks, and antennas. Solenoid grades, such as type 430 FR, have also found application. Type 409 has been used for mufflers and catalytic converters for many years, but it is now being employed throughout the exhaust system. Figure 53 shows the stainless steels currently used or under development for automotive exhaust systems.

Railroad Cars, Trucks, and Buses. In railroad cars, external and structural stainless steels provide durability, low-cost maintenance, and superior safety through crashworthiness. The fire resistance of stainless steel is a significant safety advantage. Modified type 409 is used as a structural component in buses. Types 430 and 304 are

Table 44 Pitting of stainless steel spool test specimens in a flue gas desulfurization system
The slurry contained 7000 ppm dissolved Cl⁻; test duration was 6 months, with 39 days on bypass.

Spool location(a)	pH	Maximum temperature °C	°F	Maximum chloride concentration, Type ppm	Type 304	Type 316L	Type 317L	Incoloy 317LM	825	JS700	JS777	904L	20Mo-6
Wet/dry line at inlet duct	1-2(b)	60-170	140-335	7000(b)	>1.25 (>49) Profuse	>0.91 (>36) Profuse	0.53 (21) Sparse	0.53 (21) Sparse	0.74 (29) Profuse	0.33 (13) Sparse	0.33 (13) Profuse	0.43 (17) Sparse	(c)
Quencher sump (submerged; 1.8-m, or 6 ft, level)	4.4	60	140	7000	>1.19 (>47) Sparse	>0.91 (>36) Sparse	0.28 (11)	0.1 (4) Single	<0.02 (<1)	nil	nil	nil	nil
Quencher sump (submerged; 3.4-m, or 11-ft, level)	4.4	60	140	7000	>1.2 (>48) Profuse	>0.9 (>36) Sparse	<0.03 (<1)	0.05 (2)	0.25 (10)	nil	nil	nil	nil
Quencher spray header, above slurry	4.4	60	140	100	>1.19 (>47) Profuse	0.58 (23) Profuse	0.61 (24) Profuse	0.46 (18) Profuse	0.66 (26) Profuse	0.33 (13) Sparse	0.61 (24) Profuse	0.25 (10) Sparse	0.15 (6) Sparse
Absorber, spray area	6.2	60	140	100	0.58 (23) Sparse	0.10 (4)	nil	nil	nil	nil	nil	nil	nil
Outlet duct	2-4(d)	55	130(d)	100(d)	>1.19 (>47)	>0.91 (>36)	0.58 (23)	0.58 (23)	0.48 (19)	0.18 (7)	0.51 (20)	0.53 (21)	0.36 (14)
	1.5(e)	170	335(e)	82,000(e)	Profuse	Profuse	Profuse	Profuse	Profuse	Single	Profuse	Profuse	IG etch

used for exposed functional parts on buses. Type 304 has provided economical performance in truck trailers. For tank trucks, type 304 has been the most frequently used stainless steel, but type 316 and higher-alloyed grades have been used where appropriate to carry more corrosive chemicals safely over the highways.

Chemical Tanker Ships. Stainless steels are used for seagoing chemical tankers, with types 304, 316, and 317 and alloy 2205 being selected according to the corrosivity of the cargoes being carried. Conscientious adherence to cleaning procedures between cargo changeovers has allowed these grades to give many years of service with a great variety of corrosive cargoes.

In aerospace, quench-hardenable and PH stainless steels have been used in varying applications. Heat treatments are chosen to optimize fracture toughness and resistance to SCC. Stainless steel grades 15-5PH and PH13-8Mo have been used in structural parts, and A-286 and PH3-8Mo stainless steels have served as fasteners. Parts in cooler sections of the engine have been fabricated from type 410 or A-286. Custom 455, 17-4PH, 17-7PH, and 15-5PH have been used in the space shuttle program (see the articles "Corrosion in the Aircraft Industry" and "Corrosion in the Aerospace Industry" in Volume 13 of the *ASM Handbook*).

Corrosion Testing

The physical and financial risks involved in selecting stainless steels for particular applications can be reduced through consideration of corrosion tests. However, care must be taken when selecting a corrosion test. The test must relate to the type of corrosion possible in the application. The steel should be tested in the condition in which it will be applied. The test conditions should be representative of the operating conditions and all reasonably anticipated excursions of operating conditions.

Corrosion tests vary in their degree of simulation of operation in terms of the design of the specimen and the selection of medium and test conditions. Standard tests use specimens of defined nature and geometry exposed in precisely defined media and conditions. Standard tests can confirm that a particular lot of steel conforms to the level of performance expected of a standard grade. Standard tests can also rank the performance of standard and proprietary grades. The relevance of test results to performance in particular applications increases as the specimen is made to resemble more closely the final fabricated structure—for example, bent, welded, stressed, or creviced. Relevance also increases as the test medium and conditions more closely approach the most severe operating conditions. However, many types of failures occur only after extended exposures to operating cycles. Therefore, there is often an effort to accelerate testing by increasing the severity of one or more environmental factors, such as temperature, concentration, aeration, and pH. Care must be taken that the altered conditions do not give spurious results. For example, an excessive temperature may either introduce a new failure mode or prevent a failure mode relevant to the actual application. The effects of minor constituents or impurities on corrosion are of special concern in simulated testing.

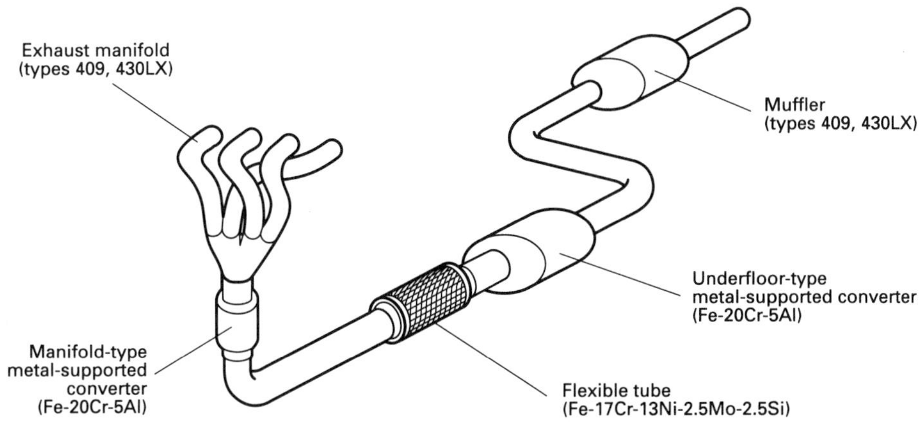

Fig. 53 Currently used or newly developed stainless steels for automotive exhaust systems

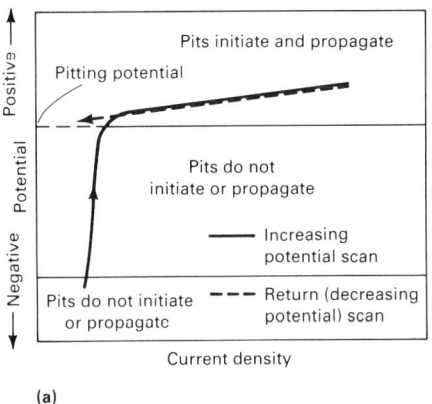

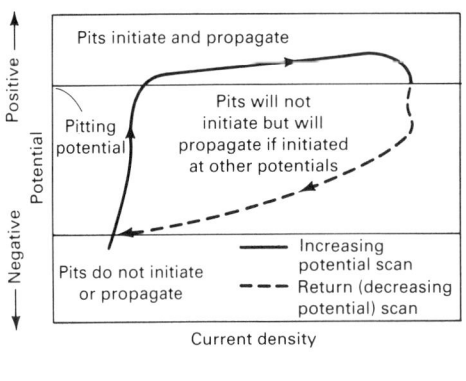

Fig. 54 Schematics showing how electrochemical tests can indicate the susceptibility to pitting of a material in a given environment. (a) Specimen has good resistance to pitting. (b) Specimen has poor resistance to pitting. In both cases, attack occurs at the highest potentials.

Fig. 55 Serrated washers used for multiple-crevice assembly testing

Pitting Corrosion

Pitting is a form of localized corrosion that is often a concern in applications involving passivating metals and alloys in aggressive environments. It is a very damaging form of corrosion that is not readily evaluated by the methods used for uniform corrosion. Therefore, special accelerated tests have been devised for the evaluation of the relative resistance to pitting corrosion of passive alloys.

Pitting and corrosion is readily tested in the laboratory by using small coupons and controlled-temperature conditions. ASTM G 48 (Ref 58) covers procedures for determining the pitting (and crevice) corrosion resistance of stainless steels and related alloys when exposed to an oxidizing chloride environment—namely, 6% FeCl$_3$ at 22 or 50 ± 2 °C (70 or 120 ± 3.5 °F). Method A is a 72 h total-immersion test of small coupons that is designed to determine the relative pitting resistance of stainless steels and nickel-base, chromium-bearing alloys. Method B is a crevice test under the same exposure conditions, and it can be used to determine both the pitting and crevice corrosion resistance of these alloys. These tests can be used for determining the effects of alloying additions, heat treatments, and surface finishes on pitting and crevice corrosion resistance. The coupons may be evaluated in terms of weight loss, pit depth, pit density, and appearance. Several suggestions for methods of pitting evaluation are given in ASTM G 46 (Ref 59).

Laboratory media do not necessarily have the same response of corrosivity as a function of temperature as do engineering environments. For example, the ASTM G 48 solution is thought to be roughly comparable to seawater at ambient temperatures. However, the corrosivity of FeCl$_3$ increases steadily with temperature. The response of seawater to increasing temperature is quite complex, relating to such factors as concentration of oxygen and biological activity. Also, although the various families of stainless steels are internally consistent, they differ from one another in response to a particular medium.

Pitting corrosion can also be evaluated by electrochemical techniques. When immersed in a particular medium, a metal coupon will assume a potential that can be measured relative to a standard reference electrode. It is then possible to impress a potential on the coupon and observe the corrosion as measured by the resulting current. Various techniques of scanning the potential range provide extremely useful data on corrosion resistance. Figure 54 demonstrates a simplified view of how these tests may indicate the corrosion resistance for various materials and media.

Crevice Corrosion

Evaluation of crevice corrosion involves a variety of immersion tests and electrochemical test methods. The most commonly used immersion tests are the ferric chloride test, the Materials Technology Institute (MTI) tests, and multiple-crevice assembly testing; the last method is described in greater detail in this section.

The FeCl$_3$ test described in ASTM G 48 involves exposure to a highly oxidizing acid chloride environment (Ref 58). Crevices are created at sites of contact with tetrafluoroethylene-fluorocarbon blocks secured by rubber bands. A test is generally conducted at 22 or 50 ± 2 °C (72 or 120 ± 3.5 °F) for 72 h.

Two MTI methods address resistance to crevice corrosion. Method MTI-2 proposes alloy ranking on the merits of increased critical crevice temperature. This method, which originates from ASTM G 48, also involves the use of a 6% FeCl$_3$ solution for determining the relative resistance of alloys to crevice corrosion in oxidizing chloride environments. In the MTI procedure, crevices are formed by the application of two serrated tetrafluoroethylene washers, each having 12 plateaus or contact sites in which corrosion may initiate.

Method MTI-4 uses increases in neutral bulk Cl$^-$ concentration at eight levels ranging from 0.1 to 3.0% NaCl to establish a minimum (critical) Cl$^-$ concentration in order to produce crevice corrosion at room temperature (20 to 24 °C, or 68 to 75 °F).

Multiple-Crevice Assembly Testing. Since its inception in the mid-1970s, the multiple-crevice assembly test has been one of the most popular and most controversial procedures available for evaluating the crevice corrosion resistance of stainless steels and related alloys. Although frequently cited in the literature, its present status is that of an acknowledged test method covered by ASTM G 78 (Ref 60). Multiple-crevice assembly devices generally consist of two serrated washers that provide a number of plateau-contact sites when fastened to a sheet or plate specimen. The acetal resin washer multiple-crevice assembly shown in Fig. 55 contains 20 plateaus, thus producing a total of 40 sites on each specimen. Typically, triplicate sheet or plate specimens are tested. Other multiple-crevice assemblies may have fewer plateaus of somewhat different size. Procedures generally call for attachment with an insulated, corrosion-resistant fastener and tightening in a reproducible manner with a calibrated torque wrench. The actual level of tightness may vary as a function of initial torque, crevice-forming material (i.e., washer), and any relaxation. The fastener can also be used to attach the specimen to a suitable support and thus prevent the creation of any other undesirable crevice sites.

Multiple-crevice assemblies were developed as a rapid and economical screening tool for establishing resistance to crevice corrosion in natural seawater. Testing was specifically intended to be severe enough to produce some measure of alloy behavior before other factors, such as fouling and seasonal variation in temperature, could come into play. It was also desirable that the multiple-crevice assembly demonstrate recognized differences in alloy capabilities, such as those between types 304 and 316, as well as the exceptional degree of performance expected of highly corrosion-resistant alloys. Unlike other crevice corrosion tests, the multiple-crevice assembly test relied solely on naturally occurring processes and required neither outside electrochemical nor chemical stimulation.

Because crevice corrosion appeared to be random in its occurrence, the creation of a number of identical crevice sites on a given set of specimens

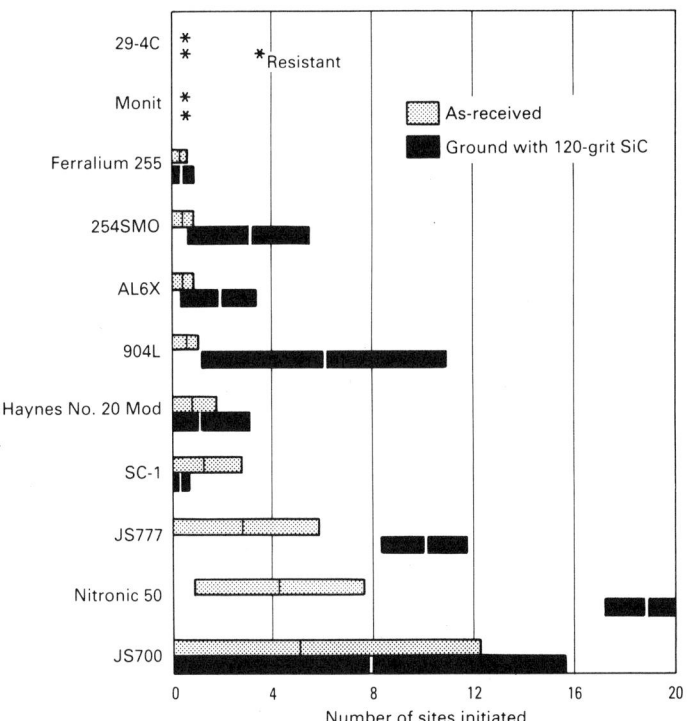

Fig. 56 Summary of the number of initiated crevice sites beneath multiple-crevice assembly washers for a series of alloys tested in natural seawater. Bar graphs represent the mean value (plus and minus one standard deviation) for replicate 30-day tests of both as-received and ground (120-grit SiC) specimens. Assembly torque: 8.5 N · m (75 in. · lb)

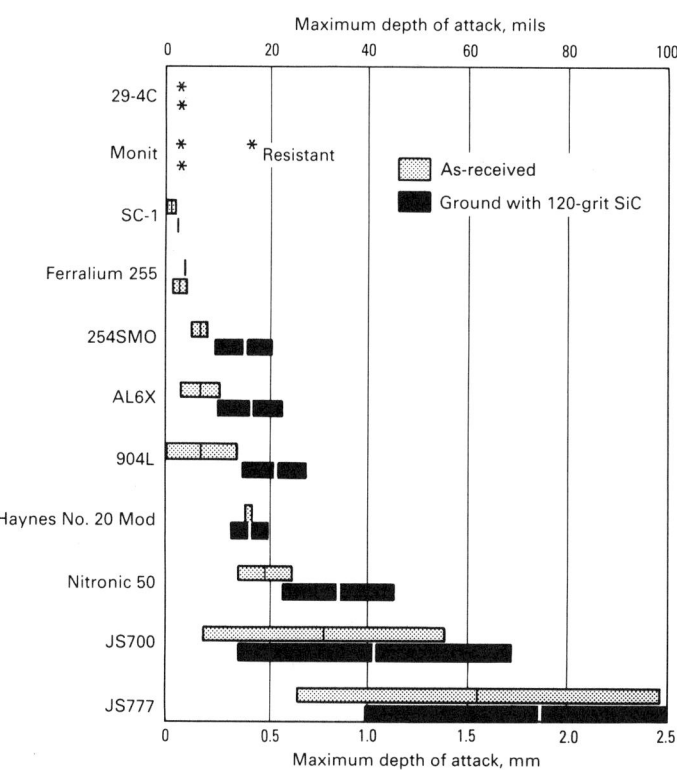

Fig. 57 Summary of maximum depth of attack beneath multiple-crevice assembly washers for a series of alloys tested in natural seawater. Bar graphs represent the mean values (plus and minus one standard deviation) for 30-day replicate tests on both as-received and ground (120-grit SiC) specimens. Assembly torque: 8.5 N · m (75 in. · lb)

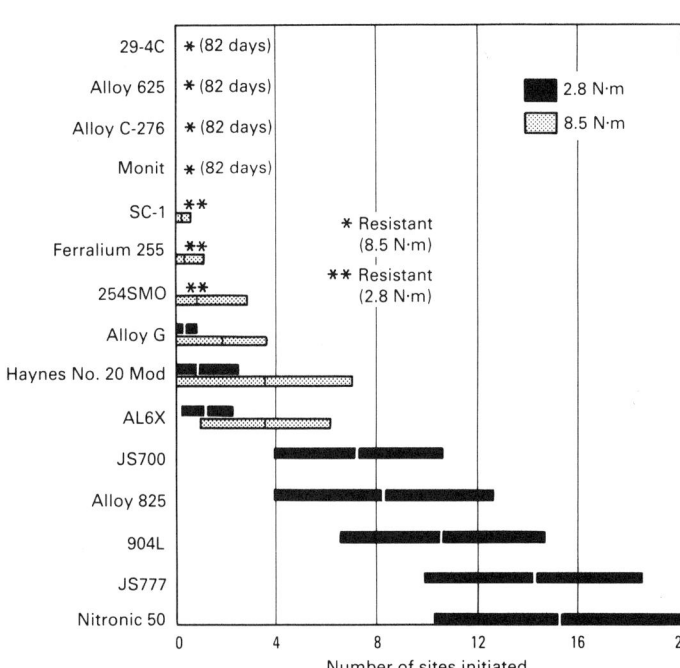

Fig. 58 Summary of the number of initiated crevice sites beneath multiple-crevice assembly washers for a series of alloys tested in natural seawater. Bar graphs represent mean values (plus and minus one standard deviation) for replicate 60-day tests using an assembly torque of either 2.8 or 8.5 N · m (25 or 75 in. · lb). All specimen surfaces were ground with 120-grit SiC.

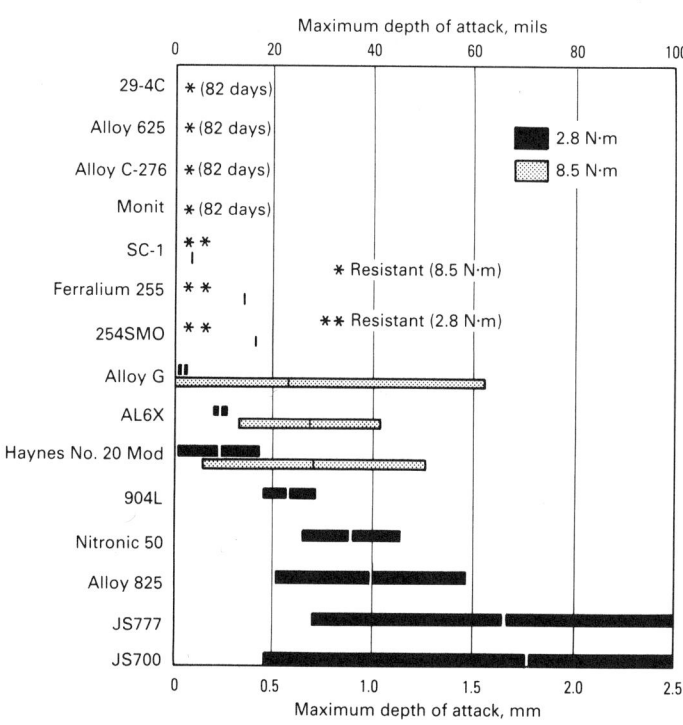

Fig. 59 Summary of maximum depth of attack beneath multiple-crevice assembly washers for a series of alloys tested in natural seawater. Bar graphs represent the mean values (plus and minus one standard deviation) for 60-day replicate tests conducted using an assembly torque of either 2.8 or 8.5 N · m (25 or 75 in. · lb). All specimen surfaces were ground with 120-grit SiC.

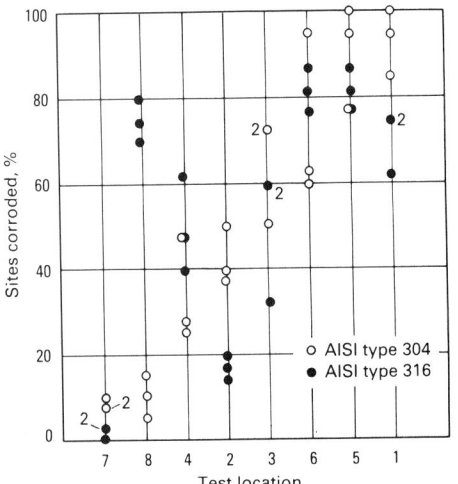

Fig. 60 Crevice corrosion initiation results from 30-day multiple-crevice assembly tests on triplicate specimens in natural seawater at various test sites (ASTM round robin). Source: Ref 60

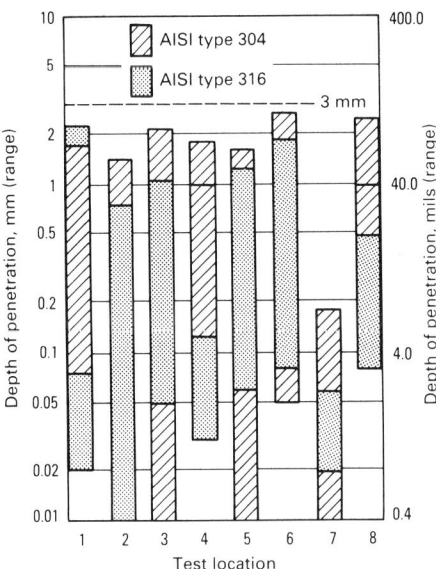

Fig. 61 Crevice corrosion propagation results from 30-day multiple-crevice assembly tests on triplicate specimens in natural seawater at various test sites (ASTM round robin)

would provide the basis for statistical analysis. Therefore, the multiple-crevice design and the use of the probability concept gained appeal. Early concerns with geometrical factors primarily addressed the size of the specimen in terms of boldly exposed area (cathode) to shielded or crevice area (anode). Subsequent research, especially through mathematical modeling, showed that the occurrence of crevice corrosion was dependent on a number of interrelated factors, but the probability concept suggested only a material (i.e., alloy) property. Because such crevice geometry factors as crevice tightness could be overriding considerations, proponents and users of the multiple-crevice assembly generally abandoned the probability concept in describing the occurrence of crevice corrosion.

The multiple-crevice assembly remains popular because it enables the investigator to report results in terms of initiation and propagation. For example, resistance to initiation can be expressed as the number of sides or sites or the percentage thereof exhibiting attack in a given test period. Because attack, when it occurs, is located at specific sites, penetration measurements can be made at each site and can be reported as a maximum depth. This can be accomplished by using an appropriate dial depth gage or microscope.

Other methods of data presentation have been used to describe crevice corrosion initiation and propagation behavior. Figures 56 to 59 show multiple-crevice assembly results plotted in bar graph form as mean values plus and minus one standard deviation of the percentage of sites initiated and maximum depth of attack. Figures 56 and 57 provide a ranking of alloys based on their resistance to crevice corrosion when tested in their respective mill conditions and with a common surface finish (120-grit SiC, wet ground). The second examples (Fig. 58 and 59) are used to illustrate the influence of the initial crevice assembly torque level. Observations on different materials responding to differences in crevice tightness help to explain further the apparent variability in mul-

tiple-crevice assembly tests and in other types of crevice tests. Because of the criticality of crevice geometry, some degree of variability should be expected in data not only from different sources but also from a single location or a single investigator.

Figure 60 shows a plot of the percentage of crevice sites that incurred visible attack after 30 days. Each data point represents a single specimen with 40 crevice sites. Test locations are identified on the basis of ascending order of initiation for type 304. Although results showed considerable variation from some locations to others, repeatability at each site was generally good to excellent in most cases. Three of the test locations (1, 2, and 7) ranked type 316 as more resistant than type 304, as is typically assumed. Two other locations (3 and 5) showed mixed behavior, but still favored type 316; the opposite is shown by results from locations 4 and 6. Results from location 8 actually showed greater initiation resistance for type 304.

Figure 61 shows the range of penetration incurred by both alloys at all eight test locations. With the exception of location 7, which consistently reported low incidences of attack, the range of penetration measured elsewhere was more or less comparable, considering the variation of two orders of magnitude in site-to-site propagation. On the basis of maximum depth of penetration, seven of eight participants reported greater resistance for type 316.

Electrochemical Tests. The *Annual Book of ASTM Standards* identifies two practices for investigating localized corrosion. ASTM G 61 is recommended primarily for iron-, nickel-, or cobalt-base alloys (Ref 61). Crevices are formed on a 16 mm (0.63 in.) diameter disk electrode by a tetrafluoroethylene-fluorocarbon gasket/mounting assembly. The electrode is made the anodic

member of a polarization cell containing a deaerated 3.5% NaCl solution. (This procedure has been used for other environments of interest.) After a 1-h period of free corrosion, the crevice electrode potential is increased in the noble direction at a scan rate of 0.6 V/h. The current measured and the potential charge are both continuously plotted (or data are collected by computer for subsequent analysis). Upon reaching a current of 5 mA, the scan direction is reversed and continued to its potential of origin. Susceptibility to crevice corrosion is identified by the occurrence of hysteresis during the reverse scan. Relative alloy resistance can be established by comparing the forward and reverse scan potential-current domains with alloy C-276 and type 304 stainless steel standards.

A potentiostatic test procedure identified with the Santron CTD 400 potentiostat is discussed in Ref 62. This technique, like the MTI procedure, identifies alloy crevice corrosion resistance according to an established critical crevice temperature. Tests have been conducted in neutral NaCl solution and synthetic seawater under constant applied potentials, for example, +600 mV (saturated calomel electrode). In this automated test, the equipment is programmed to increase the solution temperature in 5 °C (9 °F) increments if a specific critical current level is not reached in a given period, for example, 15 to 20 min.

Test results obtained with the above method using 12-serration multiple-crevice assemblies are summarized in Table 45. Also given in Table 45 is a ranking determined in 72 h FeCl₃ tests according to ASTM G 48 (rubber band test) and another ranking based on the total number of sites initiated in 30-day natural seawater multiple-crevice assembly (20 serrations) tests. The three procedures provided the same order of merit for only three of the 12 materials, numbers 1, 2, and 6. In several of the cases, at least two procedures provided the same ranking for a given alloy. In the Santron test, the noble potential is intended to mimic the redox potential of FeCl₃. In natural seawater, such potentials would never be achieved without chemical stimulation. Nickel-base chromium-molybdenum alloys, for example, may reach potentials of only +350 mV (saturated calomel electrode) in ambient-temperature seawater. Other electrochemical tests are described in the article "Evaluation of Crevice Corrosion" in Volume 13 of the *ASM Handbook*.

Intergranular Corrosion

Most alloys are susceptible to intergranular attack when exposed to specific environments. This is because grain boundaries are sites for precipitation and segregation, which makes them chemically and physically different from the grains themselves. Intergranular attack is defined as the selective dissolution of grain boundaries, or closely adjacent regions, without appreciable attack of the grains themselves. This is caused by potential differences between the grain-boundary region and any precipitates, intermetallic phases, or impurities that form at the grain boundaries. The actual mechanism differs with each alloy system.

Table 45 Initiation of crevice corrosion in immersion tests in seawater, FeCl₃, and synthetic seawater

All specimens were ground with 120-grit SiC.

Alloy	Filtered seawater(a) Number of sites	Rank	FeCl₃(b) Failure temperature °C	°F	Rank	Synthetic seawater Failure temperature °C	°F	Rank
29-4C	0	1	55	131	1	90.0	195	1
Monit	0	2	47	117	2	67.5	155	2
SC-1	1	3	45	113	4	60.0	140	5
Ferralium 255	2	4	37	99	5	60.0	140	4
Haynes No. 20 Mod	6	5	28	82	8	47.5	120	7
AL6X	11	6	37	99	6	57.5	135	6
254SMO	18	7	46	115	3	62.5	145	3
904L	36	8	22	72	10	42.5	110	9
JS700	47	9	31	88	7	45.0	115	8
JS777	60	10	14	57	12	30.0	85	12
AISI type 329	73	11	25	77	9	40.0	105	11
Nitronic 50	112	12	15	59	11	40.0	105	10

(a) 30-day test at 30 °C (85 °F). (b) 72-h test in 10% FeCl₃ · 6H₂O. (c) Santron test; 20-min measuring time

Precipitates that form as a result of the exposure of metals at elevated temperatures (for example, during production, fabrication, and welding) often nucleate and grow preferentially at grain boundaries. If these precipitates are rich in alloying elements that are essential for corrosion resistance, the regions adjacent to the grain boundary are depleted of these elements. The metal is thus sensitized and is susceptible to intergranular attack in a corrosive environment. For example, in austenitic stainless steels such as type 304, the cause of intergranular attack is the precipitation of chromium-rich carbides [(Cr, Fe)₂₃C₆] at grain boundaries. These chromium-rich precipitates are surrounded by metal that is depleted in chromium; therefore, they are more rapidly attacked at these zones than on undepleted metal surfaces.

Corrosion tests for evaluating the susceptibility of an alloy to intergranular attack are typically classified as either simulated-service or accelerated tests. The first laboratory tests for detecting intergranular attack were simulated-service exposures. These were first observed and used in 1926 when intergranular attack was detected in an austenitic stainless steel in a CuSO₄-H₂SO₄ pickling tank.

Over the years, specific tests have been developed and standardized for evaluating the susceptibility of various alloys to intergranular attack. For example, tests for the low-alloy austenitic stainless steels have been standardized by ASTM A 262, with its various practices (A to E) (see Table 46). Practice A is a screening test that uses an electrolytic oxalic acid etch combined with metallographic examination. The other practices involve exposing the material (possibly after a sensitizing treatment) to boiling solutions of 65% HNO₃, acidified Fe₂(SO₄)₃ solution, HNO₃-HF solution, or acidified CuSO₄ solution, depending on the specific alloy and its application. Similar

ASTM tests have been developed for other higher-alloyed stainless steels and ferritic stainless steels (Table 47).

The austenitic and ferritic stainless steels are generally supplied in a heat-treated condition such that they are free of carbide precipitates that are detrimental to corrosion resistance. However, these alloys are susceptible to sensitization from welding, improper heat treatment, and service in the sensitizing temperature range.

Because sensitized alloys may inadvertently be used, acceptance tests are implemented as a quality control check to evaluate stainless steels when:

- Different alloys, or regular carbon types of the specified alloy, are substituted for the low-carbon grades (for example, type 316 substituted for type 316L) and are involved in welding or heat treating.
- An improper heat treatment during fabrication results in the formation of intermetallic phases.
- The specified limits for carbon and/or nitrogen contents of an alloy are inadvertently exceeded.

Some standard tests include acceptance criteria, but others do not. Some type of criterion is needed that can clearly separate material susceptible to intergranular attack from that resistant to attack. Table 47 lists evaluation tests and acceptance criteria for various stainless steels that have been used by the DuPont Company, the U.S. Department of Energy, and others in the chemical-processing industry. Identifying such rates still leaves the buyer and seller free to agree on a rate that meets their particular needs.

Stress-Corrosion Cracking

The term *stress-corrosion cracking* refers to all types of corrosion involving the combined action of tensile stress and corrodent. Important variables include the level of stress, the presence of oxygen, the concentration of corrodent, temperature, and the conditions of heat transfer. It is important to recognize the type of corrodent likely to produce cracking in a particular family of steel.

The environments causing SCC that are encountered in the chemical industry are specific and are limited primarily to chloride and caustic solutions at elevated temperatures and sulfide environments at ambient temperatures. In seawater at or near room temperature, austenitic and ferritic steels do not experience SCC. Fully ferritic stainless steels are highly resistant to SCC in chloride and caustic environments; such environments, however, cause austenitic stainless steels to crack (Table 48). However, laboratory studies have shown that small additions of nickel or copper to ferritic steels may render them susceptible to SCC in severe environments.

It is important to realize that corrosion tests are designed to single out one particular corrosion mechanism. Therefore, determining the suitability of a stainless steel for a particular application will usually require consideration of more than one type of test. No single chemical or electrochemical test has been shown to be an all-purpose measure of corrosion resistance.

Table 46 ASTM standard tests for susceptibility to intergranular corrosion in stainless alloys

ASTM test method	Test medium and duration	Alloys	Phases detected
A 262, practice A	Oxalic acid etch; etch test	AISI types 304, 304L, 316, 316L, 317L, 321, 347 casting alloys	Chromium carbide
A 262, practice B	Fe₂(SO₄)₃-H₂SO₄; 120 h	Same as above	Chromium carbide, σ-phase(a)
A 262, practice C	HNO₃ (Huey test); 240 h	Same as above	Chromium carbide, σ-phase(b)
A 262, practice D	HNO₃-HF; 4 h	AISI types 316, 316L, 317, 317L	Chromium carbide
A 262, practice E	CuSO₄-16% H₂SO₄, with copper contact; 24 h	Austenitic stainless steels	Chromium carbide
A 708 (formerly A 393)	CuSO₄-16% H₂SO₄, without copper contact; 72 h	Austenitic stainless steels	Chromium carbide
G 28	Fe₂(SO₄)₃-H₂SO₄; 24-120 h	Hastelloy alloys C-276 and G; 20Cb-3; Inconel alloys 600, 625, 800, and 825	Carbides and/or intermetallic phases(c)
A 763, practice X	Fe₂(SO₄)₃-H₂SO₄; 24-120 h	AISI types 403 and 446; E-Brite, 29-4, 29-4-2	Chromium carbide and nitride intermetallic phases(d)
A 763, practice Y	CuSO₄-50% H₂SO₄; 96-120 h	AISI types 446, XM27, XM33, 29-4, 29-4-2	Chromium carbide and nitride
A 763, practice Z	CuSO₄-16% H₂SO₄; 24 h	AISI types 430, 434, 436, 439, 444	Chromium carbide and nitride

(a) There is some effect of σ-phase in type 321 stainless steel. (b) Detects σ phase in AISI types 316, 316L, 317, 317L, and 321. (c) Carbides and perhaps other phases detected, depending on the alloy system. (d) Detects χ- and σ-phases, which do not cause intergranular attack in unstabilized iron-chromium-molybdenum alloys

Table 47 Appropriate evaluation tests and acceptance criteria for wrought stainless steels

UNS number	Alloy name	Applicable tests (ASTM standards)	Sensitizing treatment	Exposure time, h	Criteria for passing, appearance or maximum allowable corrosion rate, mm/month (mils/month)
S43000	Type 430	Ferric sulfate (A 763-X)	None	24	1.14 (45)
S44600	Type 446	Ferric sulfate (A 763-X)	None	72	0.25 (10)
S44625	26-1	Ferric sulfate (A 763-X)	None	120	0.05 (2) and no significant grain dropping
S44626	26-1S	Cupric sulfate (A 763-Y)	None	120	No significant grain dropping
S44700	29-4	Ferric sulfate (A 763-X)	None	120	No significant grain dropping
S44800	29-4-2	Ferric sulfate (A 763-X)	None	120	No significant grain dropping
S30400	Type 304	Oxalic acid (A 262-A)	None	…	(a)
		Ferric sulfate (A 262-B)		120	0.1 (4)
S30403	Type 304L	Oxalic acid (A 262-A)	1 h at 675 °C (1250 °F)	…	(a)
		Nitric acid (A 262-C)		240	0.05 (2)
S30908	Type 309S	Nitric acid (A 262-C)	None	240	0.025 (1)
S31600	Type 316	Oxalic acid (A 262-A)	None	…	(a)
		Ferric sulfate (A 262-B)		120	0.1 (4)
S31603	Type 316L	Oxalic acid (A 262-A)	1 h at 675 °C (1250 °F)	…	(a)
		Ferric sulfate (A 262-B)		120	0.1 (4)
S31700	Type 317	Oxalic acid (A 262-A)	None	…	(a)
		Ferric sulfate (A 262-B)		120	0.1 (4)
S31703	Type 317L	Oxalic acid (A 262-A)	1 h at 675 °C (1250 °F)	…	(a)
		Ferric sulfate (A 262-B)		120	0.1 (4)
S32100	Type 321	Nitric acid (A 262-C)	1 h at 675 °C (1250 °F)	240	0.05 (2)
S34700	Type 347	Nitric acid (A 262-C)	1 h at 675 °C (1250 °F)	240	0.05 (2)
N08020	20Cb-3	Ferric sulfate (G 28-A)	1 h at 675 °C (1250 °F)	120	0.05 (2)
N08904	904L	Ferric sulfate (G 28-A)	None	120	0.05 (2)

(a) See ASTM A 262, practice A.

Table 48 Stress-corrosion cracking resistance of stainless steels

	Stress-corrosion cracking test(a)		
Grade	Boiling 42% MgCl$_2$	Wick test	Boiling 25% NaCl
AISI type 304	F(b)	F	F
AISI type 316	F	F	F
AISI type 317	F	[P(c) or F](d)	(P or F)
Type 317LM	F	(P or F)	(P or F)
Alloy 904L	F	(P or F)	(P or F)
AL-6XN	F	P	P
254SMO	F	P	P
20Mo-6	F	P	P
AISI type 409	P	P	P
Type 439	P	P	P
AISI type 444	P	P	P
E-Brite	P	P	P
Sea-Cure	F	P	P
MONIT	F	P	P
AL 29-4	P	P	P
AL 29-4-2	F	P	P
AL 29-4C	P	P	P
3RE60	F	NT	NT
2205	F	NT	(P or F)(c)
Ferralium	F	NT	(P or F)(e)

(a) U-bend tests, stressed beyond yielding. (b) Fails, cracking observed. (c) Passes, no cracking observed. (d) Susceptibility of grade to SCC determined by variation of composition within specified range. (e) Susceptibility of grade to SCC determined by variation of thermal history. Source: Ref 63

Testing in Boiling Magnesium Chloride Solution. ASTM G 36 (Ref 64) is applicable to wrought, cast, and welded austenitic stainless steels and related nickel-base alloys. This method determines the effects of composition, heat treatment, surface finish, microstructure, and stress on the susceptibility of these materials to chloride SCC. Although this test can be performed with various concentrations of magnesium chloride (MgCl$_2$), ASTM G 36 specifies a test solution of approximately 45% MgCl$_2$ maintained at a constant boiling temperature of 155 ± 1 °C (311 ± 1.8 °F). Also described is a test apparatus capable of maintaining solution concentration and temperature within the recommended limits for extended periods of time. Typical exposure times are up to 1000 h. However, historically, most of the SCC data on austenitic stainless steels were obtained by using a boiling 42% MgCl$_2$ solution (boiling point: 154 °C, or 309 °F). For this reason, much current testing is still done at the lower concentration.

Most chloride cracking testing has been carried out in accelerated test media such as boiling MgCl$_2$. All austenitic stainless steels are susceptible to chloride cracking, as shown in Fig. 62. It is noteworthy, however, that the higher-nickel types 310 and 314 were appreciably more resistant than the others (Fig. 63). Although this solution causes rapid cracking, it does not necessarily simulate the cracking observed in field applications.

Other ions in addition to chloride can cause cracking. Of all halogen ions, chlorides cause the most cases of SCC in austenitic stainless steels. Known cases of fluoride and bromide SCC are few, and iodide is not known to produce SCC. In addition, cations, such as Li$^+$, Ca^{2+}, Zn^{2+}, NH$_4^+$, Ni^{2+}, and Na$^+$, affect test results to varying degrees. Although chloride SCC occurs primarily at temperatures above about 90 °C (190 °F), acidified chloride solutions can produce SCC at low temperatures. Therefore, in diagnosing service failures, it is necessary to establish which ions (and other environmental and stress conditions as well) have caused the failure. In this manner, an appropriate test procedure can be designed for the evaluation of alternative materials.

Reference 67 discusses laboratory reproduction of an environment that caused SCC at the top of a distillation tower in a crude-oil refinery. The service environment consisted of a very dilute HCl solution (36 ppm chloride) with a pH of 3 saturated with H$_2$S gas at 80 °C (175 °F). In this test environment, austenitic stainless steels such as types 304 or 316 failed, but the ferritic types 430 and 434 did not.

Testing in Polythionic Acids. Petrochemical refinery equipment is subject to polythionic acid cracking, which may occur after shutdown. Polythionic acid forms by the decomposition of sulfides on metal walls in the presence of oxygen and water. ASTM G 35 (Ref 64) describes procedures for preparing and conducting exposures to polythionic acids (H$_2$S$_n$O$_6$, where n is usually 2 to 5) at room temperature to determine the relative

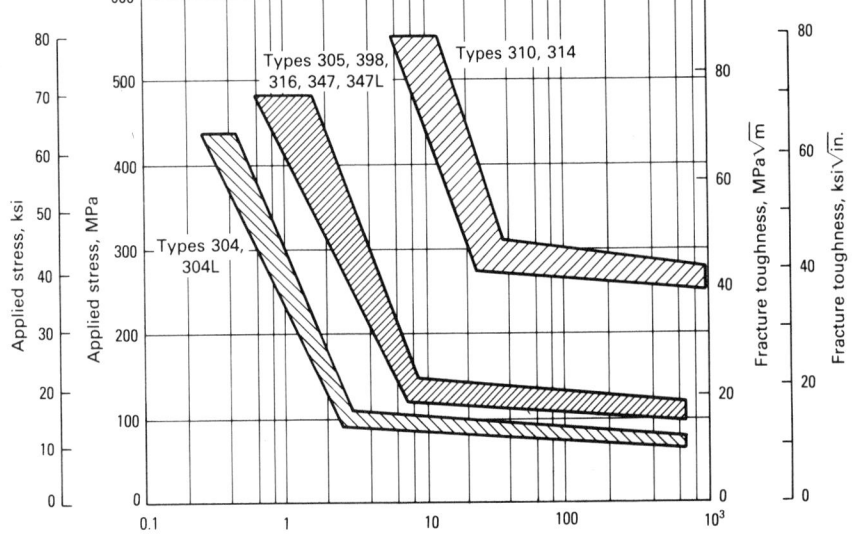

Fig. 62 Relative SCC behavior of austenitic stainless steels in boiling MgCl$_2$. Source: Ref 65

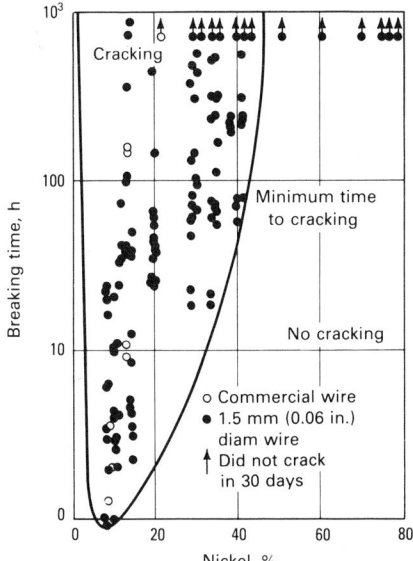

Fig. 63 Effect of nickel additions to a 17 to 24% Cr steel on resistance to SCC in boiling 42% MgCl₂. 1.5 mm (0.06 in.) diam wire specimens dead-weight loaded to 228 or 310 MPa (33 or 45 ksi). Source: Ref 66

susceptibility of sensitized stainless steels or related materials (high nickel-chromium-iron alloys) to intergranular SCC.

This test method can be used to evaluate stainless steels or other materials in the as-received condition or after high-temperature service (480 to 815 °C, or 900 to 1500 °F) for prolonged periods of time. Wrought products, castings, and weldments of stainless steels or other related materials used in environments containing sulfur or sulfides can also be evaluated. Other materials that are capable of being sensitized can also be tested.

A variety of smooth SCC test specimens, surface finishes, and methods of applying stress can be used. Stressed specimens are immersed in the polythionic acid solution, which can be prepared by passing a slow current of H_2S gas for 1 h through a fritted glass tube into a flask containing chilled (0 °C, or 32 °F) 6% H_2SO_3, after which the liquid is kept in a stoppered flask for 48 h at room temperature. Solutions can also be prepared by passing a slow current of SO_2 gas through a fritted glass bubbler submerged in a container of distilled water at room temperature. This is continued until the solution becomes saturated. The H_2S gas is then slowly bubbled into the H_2SO_3 solution.

Prior to use, the polythionic acid solution should be filtered to remove elemental sulfur and then tested for acid content. This can be done by analytical tests or by using a control test specimen of sensitized type 302 stainless steel. The control should fail by cracking in less than 1 h.

The wick test can be used to evaluate the chloride cracking characteristics of thermal insulation for applications in the chemical process industry. ASTM C 692 (Ref 64) covers the methodology and apparatus used to conduct this procedure. When a dilute aqueous solution is transmitted to a metal surface by capillary action through an absorbent fibrous material, the process is called *wicking*. Cracking occurs at much lower temperatures when alternate wetting and drying is used than when the specimens are kept wet continuously.

Other Testing Media. Hot concentrated caustic solutions are another type of environment encountered in chemical industries that causes SCC of stainless steels. However, the conditions leading to caustic cracking are more restrictive than those leading to chloride cracking, and caustic environments have not received the attention that chlorides have. There is little difference in the susceptibilities among types 304, 304L, 316, 316L, 347, and USS 18-18-2 austenitic steels. All of these alloys crack rapidly in solutions of 10 to 50% NaOH at 150 to 370 °C (300 to 700 °F).

Certain strong acid solutions containing chlorides, such as 5 N H_2SO_4 plus 0.5 N NaCl, 3 N $HClO_4$ plus 0.5 N NaCl, and 0.5 N to 1.0 N HCl, are capable of causing SCC in austenitic stainless steels at room temperature. Cracking in these environments is similar to the type of cracking that occurs in hot chloride environments.

Electrochemical Polarization. Stress-corrosion cracking in austenitic and ferritic stainless steels can be delayed or prevented by the application of cathodic current; however, if ferritic steels are overprotected by relatively large cathodic current, they are apt to blister or crack due to the hydrogen discharged by the cathodic protection action. Anodic polarization significantly accelerates the initiation of SCC but appears to have a smaller accelerating effect on crack propagation.

ACKNOWLEDGMENTS

The information in this article is largely taken from:

- R.M. Davison, T. DeBold, and M.J. Johnson, Corrosion of Stainless Steels, *Corrosion,* Vol 13, *ASM Handbook* (formerly 9th ed., *Metals Handbook*), ASM International, 1987, p 547-565
- T.F. Degnan et al., Corrosion in the Chemical Processing Industry, *Corrosion,* Vol 13, *ASM Handbook* (formerly 9th ed., *Metals Handbook*), ASM International, 1987, p 1134-1185
- A. Garner et al., Corrosion in the Pulp and Paper Industry, *Corrosion,* Vol 13, *ASM Handbook* (formerly 9th ed., *Metals Handbook*), ASM International, 1987, p 1186-1220
- R. Steigerwald, Metallurgically Influenced Corrosion, *Corrosion,* Vol 13, *ASM Handbook* (formerly 9th ed., *Metals Handbook*), ASM International, 1987, p 123-135
- D.O. Sprowls, Evaluation of Stress-Corrosion Cracking, *Corrosion,* Vol 13, *ASM Handbook* (formerly 9th ed., *Metals Handbook*), ASM International, 1987, p 245-282
- R.M. Kain, Evaluation of Crevice Corrosion, *Corrosion,* Vol 13, *ASM Handbook* (formerly 9th ed., *Metals Handbook*), ASM International, 1987, p 303-310

REFERENCES

1. R.M. Davison and J.D. Redmond, Practical Guide to Using 6Mo Austenitic Stainless Steel, *Mater. Perform.,* Dec 1988
2. B. Larsson and B. Lundqvist, "Fabricating Ferritic-Austenitic Stainless Steels," Sandvik Steel Trade Literature, Pamphlet S-51-33-ENG, Oct 1987
3. "Standard Practices for Detecting Susceptibility to Intergranular Corrosion Attack in Austenitic Stainless Steels," A 262, *Annual Book of ASTM Standards,* ASTM
4. "Standard Practices for Detecting Susceptibility to Intergranular Attack in Ferritic Stainless Steels," A 763, *Annual Book of ASTM Standards,* ASTM
5. "Standard Recommended Practice for Cleaning and Descaling Stainless Steel Parts, Equipment, and Systems," A 380, *Annual Book of ASTM Standards,* ASTM
6. T. DeBold, Passivating Stainless Steel Parts, *Mach. Tool Blue Book,* Nov 1986
7. "Passivation Treatments for Corrosion-Resisting Steels," Federal Specification QQ-P-35B, U.S. Government Printing Office, April 1973
8. J.D. Redmon, Selecting Second Generation Duplex Stainless Steels, *Chem. Eng.,* Vol 93 (No. 20), 1986, p 153-155; and Vol 93 (No. 22), 1986, p 103-105
9. T.S. Lee, R.M. Kain, and J.W. Oldfield, "Factors Influencing the Crevice Corrosion Behavior of Stainless Steels," Paper 69, presented at Corrosion/83, National Association of Corrosion Engineers, 1983
10. J.W. Oldfield and W.H. Sutton, *Br. Corros. J.,* Vol 13, 1978, p 13
11. M.A. Streicher, in *Intergranular Corrosion of Stainless Alloys,* STP 656, R.F. Steigerwald, Ed., ASTM, 1978, p 3-84
12. R.F. Steigerwald, *Metall. Trans.,* Vol 5, 1974, p 2265-2269
13. R.F. Steigerwald, *Metalloved. Term. Obrab. Met.,* No. 7, 1973, p 16-20
14. M.A. Streicher, *Corrosion,* Vol 29, 1973, p 337-360
15. C.R. Rarey and A.H. Aronson, *Corrosion,* Vol 28, 1972, p 255-258
16. H.J. Dundas and A.P. Bond, in *Intergranular Corrosion of Stainless Alloys,* STP 656, R.F. Steigerwald, Ed., ASTM, 1978, p 154-178
17. A.E. Nehrenberg and P. Lillys, *Trans. ASM,* Vol 46, 1954, p 1176-1213
18. A.J. Lena, R.A. Lula, and G.C. Kiefer, *Trans. ASM,* Vol 46, 1954, p 1203-1205
19. D.C. Ludwigson and H.S. Link, in *Advances in the Technology of Stainless Steels and Related Alloys,* STP 369, ASTM, 1965, p 249-310
20. R.F. Steigerwald and M.A. Streicher, paper presented at the Annual Meeting (St. Louis), National Association of Corrosion Engineers, 1965
21. M.A. Streicher, *Corrosion,* Vol 30, 1974, p 115-125
22. A.J. Lena, *Met. Prog.,* Vol 66 (No. 1), 1954, p 86-90

23. Corrosion Resistance of the Austenitic Chromium-Nickel Stainless Steels in Atmospheric Environments, International Nickel Co., Inc., 1963

24. M. Henthorne, T.A. DeBold, and R.J. Yinger, "Custom 450—A New High Strength Stainless Steel," Paper 53, presented at Corrosion/72, National Association of Corrosion Engineers, 1972

25. *The Role of Stainless Steels in Desalination,* American Iron and Steel Institute, 1974

26. M.A. Streicher, Analysis of Crevice Corrosion Data from Two Sea Water Exposure Tests on Stainless Alloys, *Mater. Perform.,* Vol 22, May 1983, p 37-50

27. "Corrosion Resistance of Nickel-Containing Alloys in Sulfuric Acid and Related Compounds," Corrosion Engineering Bulletin I, International Nickel Co., Inc., 1983

28. H. Abo, M. Ueda, and S. Noguchi, *Boshoku Gijutso,* Vol 23, 1974, p 341-346 (in Japanese)

29. D.R. McAlister, et al., "A Major Breakthrough in Sulfuric Acid," paper presented at AIChE 1986 Annual Meeting (New Orleans), American Institute of Chemical Engineers, April 1986

30. M. Renner, et al., "Corrosion Resistance of Stainless Steels and Nickel Alloys in Concentrated Sulfuric Acid," Paper 189, presented at Corrosion/86, National Association of Corrosion Engineers, 1986

31. M.G. Fontana and N.D. Greene, *Corrosion Engineering,* McGraw-Hill, 1967

32. R.S. Stewart, *Met. Prog.,* Vol 52, Dec 1947

33. J.E. Slater and R.W. Staehle, "A Study of the Mechanism of Stress Corrosion Cracking in the Iron-Nickel-Chromium Alloy System in Chloride Environments," Contract AT(11-1)2069, U.S. Atomic Energy Commission, 30 Sept 1970

34. M.W. Wilding and B.E. Paige, "Idaho National Engineering Laboratory Survey on Corrosion of Metals and Alloys in Solutions Containing Nitric Acid," Report N77-32302, National Technical Information Service, Dec 1976

35. "Product Information on Stainless Steel for the Nitric Acid Industry," TOK31/08.82, Vereinigte Edel Stahlwerke

36. M.H. Brown, W.B. DeLong, and J.R. Auld, *Ind. Eng. Chem.,* Vol 39 (No. 7), 1947, p 839-844

37. C.M. Schillmoller, *Chem. Eng.,* Vol 87 (No. 5), 10 March 1980, p 161

38. "Hydrofluoric Acid Alkylation," Phillips Petroleum Co., 1946

39. M. Takemoto, T. Shonohara, M. Shirai, and T. Shinogaya, *Mater. Perform.,* Vol 24 (No. 6), 1985, p 26

40. W.R. Myers and W.B. DeLong, *Chem. Eng. Prog.,* Vol 44, 1948, p 359

41. M.H. Brown, W.B. DeLong, and J.R. Auld, *Ind. Eng. Chem.,* Vol 39 (No. 7), 1947, p 839

42. E.L. Liening, Report ME-4242, Dow Chemical Co., April 1980

43. Ampco Metal Div., Ampco-Pittsburgh, unpublished research, 1951

44. "Corrosion Resistance of Nickel and Nickel-Containing Alloys in Caustic Soda and Other Alkalies," Corrosion Engineering Bulletin CEB-2, International Nickel Co., Inc., 1973

45. P.J. Gegner and W.L. Wilson, *Corrosion,* Vol 15 (No. 7), 1959

46. P.J. Gegner, "Corrosion Resistance of Materials in Alkalies and Hypochlorites," Paper 27, Process Industries Corrosion Short Course, National Association of Corrosion Engineers, 1974

47. F.L. LaQue and H.R. Copson, *Corrosion Resistance of Metals and Alloys,* Reinhold, 1963

48. E.C. Hoxie, "Some Considerations in the Selection of Stainless Steel for Pressure Vessels and Piping," International Nickel Co., Inc., 1975

49. S.R. Seagle, *Pulp Paper,* Vol 53 (No. 10), Sept 1979

50. *Cabot Dig.,* Vol 36 (No. 5), Sept 1985

51. A.H. Tuthill, Resistance of Highly Alloyed Materials and Titanium to Localized Corrosion in Bleach Plant Environments, *Mater. Perform.,* Vol 24, Sept 1985, p 43-49

52. A. Garner, *Pulp Paper Can.,* Vol 82 (No. 12), 1981, p T414

53. B. Wallen, in *Pulp and Paper Industry Corrosion Problems,* Vol 2, National Association of Corrosion Engineers, 1977, p 43

54. A.H. Tuthill, J.D. Rushton, J.J. Geisler, R.H. Heasley, and L.L. Edwards, *TAPPI J.,* Vol 62 (No. 11), 1979, p 49

55. A.H. Tuthill, in *Pulp and Paper Industry Corrosion Problems,* Vol 4, Swedish Corrosion Institute, 1983

56. J. Hill, in *Pulp and Paper Industry Corrosion Problems,* Vol 4, Swedish Corrosion Institute, 1983

57. A. Garner, *Mater. Perform.,* Vol 21 (No. 5), 1982, p 43

58. "Standard Test Methods for Pitting and Crevice Corrosion Resistance of Stainless Steels and Related Alloys by the Use of Ferric Chloride Solution," G 48, *Annual Book of ASTM Standards,* ASTM

59. "Standard Recommended Practice for Examination and Evaluation of Pitting Corrosion," G 46, *Annual Book of ASTM Standards,* ASTM

60. "Standard Guide for Crevice Corrosion Testing of Iron-Base and Nickel-Base Stainless Alloys in Seawater and Other Chloride Containing Aqueous Environments," G 78, *Annual Book of ASTM Standards,* ASTM

61. "Standard Practice for Conducting Cyclic Potentiodynamic Polarization Measurements for Localized Corrosion," G 61, *Annual Book of ASTM Standards,* ASTM

62. S. Bernhardsson, Paper 85, presented at Corrosion/80, National Association of Corrosion Engineers, 1980

63. R.M. Davison, et al., A Review of Worldwide Developments in Stainless Steels in Specialty Steels and Hard Materials, Pergamon Press, 1983, p 67-85

64. *Metal Corrosion, Erosion, and Wear,* Vol 03.02, Section 3, *Annual Book of ASTM Standards,* ASTM

65. E. Denard, Effect of Composition and Heat Treatment on the Stress Corrosion Cracking of Austenitic Stainless Steels, *Corrosion,* Vol 16 (No. 7), 1960, p 131-141

66. H.R. Copson, Effect of Composition on Stress Corrosion Cracking of Some Alloys Containing Nickel, *Physical Metallurgy of Stress Corrosion Fracture,* T.N. Rhodin, Ed., Interscience, 1959, p 247-272

67. S. Takemura, M. Onoyama, and T. Ooka, Stress Corrosion Cracking of Stainless Steels in Hydrogen Sulfide Solutions, *Corrosion,* Vol 16 (No. 7), 1960, p 338-348

Stress-Corrosion Cracking and Hydrogen Embrittlement

STRESS-CORROSION CRACKING (SCC) is a generic term describing the initiation and propagation of cracks in a material under the combined action of tensile stresses (applied and/or residual) and a corrosive environment. Because the susceptibility to SCC of stainless steels depends on alloy composition, structure, and thermal history (Ref 1), these alloys exhibit widely varying susceptibilities in different environments. For example, the austenitic (300 series) stainless steels can be susceptible to SCC in certain chloride environments, whereas the ferritic and martensitic grades (400 series) can be susceptible to hydrogen embrittlement. However, there is still lack of agreement about the mechanisms of cracking in many stainless steel/environment systems (Ref 2). In fact, the multiplicity of proposed mechanisms and the disagreement as to which mechanisms are operative (Ref 2) have led to the evolution of a simplistic nomenclature that describes SCC in terms of the environments that cause it. The terms *chloride SCC, caustic SCC,* and *polythionic acid SCC* are often used to describe SCC of stainless steels in those types of environments. The term *high-temperature water SCC* usually denotes SCC in simulated boiling water reactor (BWR) and pressurized water reactor (PWR) coolant environments. The term *irradiation-assisted SCC* refers to SCC in nuclear power station core components that are subjected to heavy doses of radiation within the core as well as to coolant water. The term *sulfide SCC* usually denotes hydrogen embrittlement, with the sulfide ion acting as a hydrogen ion recombination poison, promoting entry of hydrogen into the metal.

The extent to which these variously described forms of SCC are manifestations of the same process remains a matter of continuing debate that is not likely to be settled in the near future. Accordingly, in this article the various forms of SCC are discussed under the environment-related descriptors noted above. When considering the SCC of stainless steels, it is also useful to distinguish between cracking in sensitized and nonsensitized materials. Sensitization is particularly detrimental to the stress-corrosion resistance of austenitic stainless steels in a variety of environments, and in many cases the elimination of sensitization will eliminate SCC susceptibility. In view of the importance of sensitization to SCC, it is worthwhile to describe it here in some detail. Additional information on sensitization can be found in the articles "Metallurgy and Properties of Wrought Stainless Steels," "Atmospheric and Aqueous Corrosion," and "Corrosion of Weldments" in this Volume.

Sensitization

Considerable effort has gone into producing stainless steel grades that resist sensitization. It is now widely accepted that this phenomenon is related to the precipitation of carbide at austenite grain boundaries. To understand this phenomenon in terms of microstructure, it is instructive to examine the equilibrium relationships and carbon solubility in the Fe-18Cr-8Ni alloy, illustrated in Fig. 1 (Ref 3). This figure shows that in alloys containing between about 0.03 and 0.7% C, the equilibrium structure should contain austenite, α-ferrite, and carbide ($M_{23}C_6$) at room temperature.

In commercial alloys containing various austenite stabilizers, the reaction $\gamma + M_{23}C_6 \rightarrow \gamma + \alpha + M_{23}C_6$ (at line SK in Fig. 1) is too sluggish to take place at practical rates of cooling from elevated temperatures. The same applies to the reaction $\gamma \rightarrow \alpha + M_{23}C_6$ at carbon contents below approximately 0.03%.

For commercial-purity materials, the transformation of austenite to α-ferrite is ignored in practice, and in considering carbon solubility in austenite, the simplified diagram (Ref 4) shown in Fig. 2 is often regarded as representative of real (i.e., nonequilibrium) situations. In terms of this simplified diagram, up to 0.03% C should be soluble in austenite at temperatures up to 800 °C (1470 °F). Austenite that contains more than 0.03% C should precipitate $M_{23}C_6$ on cooling below the solubility line. However, at relatively rapid rates of cooling, this reaction is partially

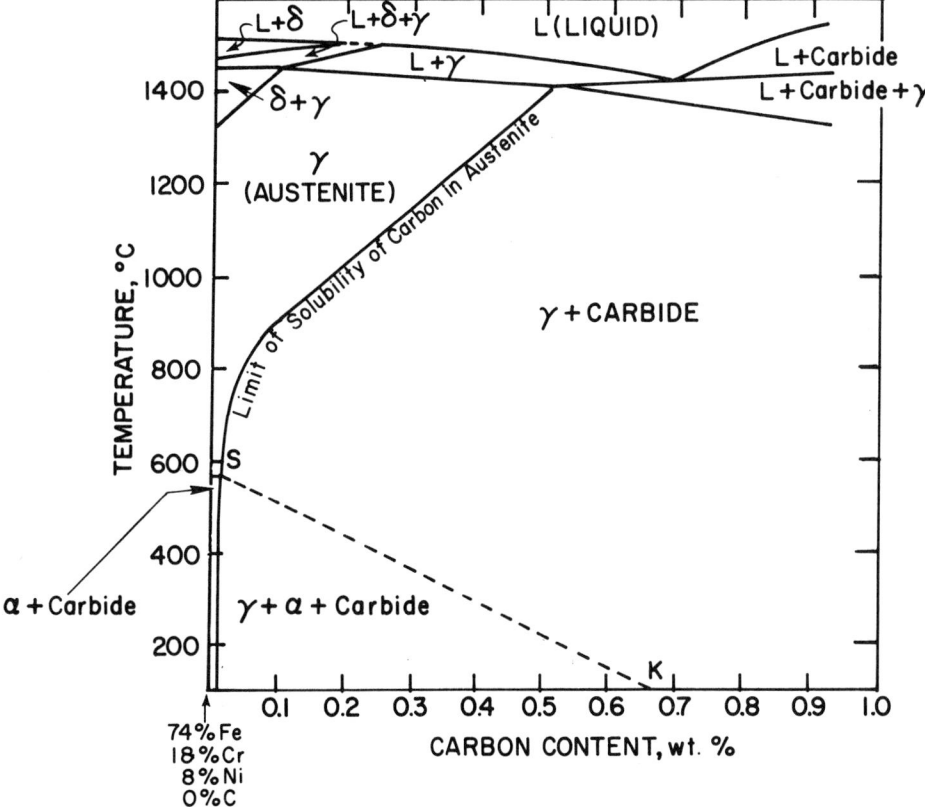

Fig. 1 Pseudobinary phase diagram for an Fe-18Cr-8Ni alloy with varying carbon content. Source: Ref 3

suppressed. This is the case in practice when type 304 stainless steel containing more than 0.03% C is heat treated at 1050 °C (1920 °F) to remove the effects of cold working or hot working and is cooled at a fairly rapid rate to room temperature. While some carbide may have precipitated on cooling, the room-temperature austenite is still largely supersaturated with respect to carbon.

If this supersaturated austenite is reheated to elevated temperatures within the $\gamma + M_{23}C_6$ field, further precipitation of the chromium-rich $M_{23}C_6$ will take place at the austenite grain boundaries. Certain time-temperature combinations will be sufficient to precipitate this chromium-rich carbide, but insufficient to rediffuse chromium back into the austenite near the carbide. This will result in the formation of envelopes of chromium-depleted austenite around the carbide (Ref 5, 6). Because the carbides precipitate along grain boundaries, the linking of the chromium-depleted envelopes provides a continuous path of lower corrosion resistance along the grain boundaries for the propagation of SCC. This type of structure is known as *sensitized,* irrespective of whether the chromium depletion has been caused by slow cooling, heat treatment, elevated-temperature service, or welding. Sensitization also occurs in ferritic and martensitic stainless steels (Ref 1). The metallurgical remedies for reducing sensitization in austenitic stainless steels include:

- The use of low-carbon (0.03% maximum) grades of stainless steel (for example, types 304L, 316L, and 317L)
- Postweld heat treatment to rediffuse chromium back into the impoverished austenite
- The addition of titanium (type 321) or niobium plus tantalum (type 347) to precipitate the carbide at higher temperatures so that little carbon is left to precipitate as the chromium-rich grain-boundary carbide during cooling. Types 321 and 347 are sometimes given a stabilizing treatment at 900 to 925 °C (1650 to 1695 °F) to ensure maximum precipitation of carbon as titanium or niobium carbide.

All of these remedies have certain advantages and disadvantages. Thus, postweld heat treatment is not always practicable in large structures. The stabilized grades can suffer another form of corrosive attack known as knife-line attack (Ref 1), and the low-carbon grades have lower strength.

To compensate for the lower strength of the low-carbon grades, the nuclear power industry has supported the development of nitrogen-strengthened nuclear grade (NG) stainless steels (Ref 7). These are designated as types 304NG and 316NG. They have the low carbon levels of the low-carbon grades (i.e., < 0.03 wt% C), but they contain added nitrogen at levels of $0.06 < N < 0.1$ wt% to increase strength. Sensitized types 304NG and 316NG have exhibited resistance to intergranular SCC when tested in high-purity water at elevated temperatures (Ref 7). However, other studies (Ref 8) have shown that sensitized type 316NG exhibits transgranular SCC when tested

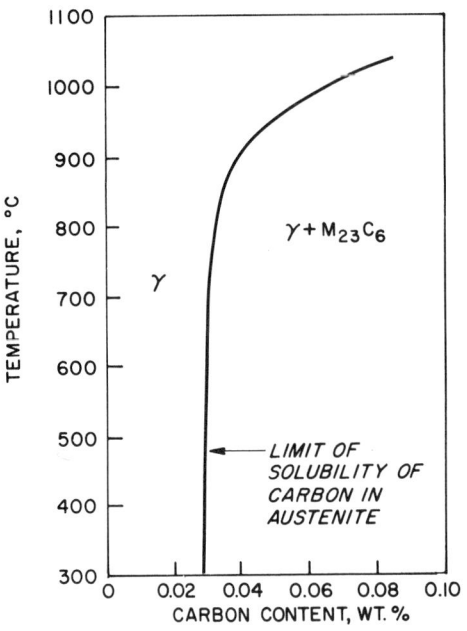
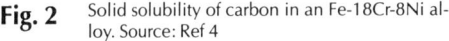

Fig. 2 Solid solubility of carbon in an Fe-18Cr-8Ni alloy. Source: Ref 4

in simulated BWR environments that contain sulfate ions as an impurity.

Other recent sensitization studies related to the nuclear power industry suggest that at BWR operating temperatures of about 288 °C (550 °F), radiation itself can cause chromium depletion at the grain boundaries in type 304 stainless steel and nickel-base alloys (Ref 9). In this radiation-induced phenomenon, there is no precipitation of chromium carbide and the chromium depletion is thought to occur by a process known as radiation-induced segregation. During the irradiation of an alloy, some constituents of the alloy migrate toward point defect sinks, such as grain boundaries or dislocation lines, and other constituents migrate away. This nonequilibrium segregation during irradiation was predicted in 1971 (Ref 10) and has subsequently received considerable attention. In austenitic steels, this segregation causes a depletion in the chromium levels and an enhancement in the nickel levels near grain boundaries during irradiation. Minor alloying elements are also redistributed; for example, silicon and phosphorus migrate toward the grain boundaries (Ref 9). These compositional changes occur in narrow regions close to grain boundaries. For example, the chromium depletion profiles suggest that the depletion widths are less than 20 nm (Ref 11). Cracking associated with this radiation-induced segregation is known as irradiation-assisted stress-corrosion cracking (IASCC) (Ref 12, 13) and has been shown to be dependent on temperature and radiation fluence. IASCC of solutionized stainless steel is reported (Ref 9) to occur in service at fluences above 5×10^{20} n/cm^2 and at temperatures above 150 °C (300 °F) (Ref 14). Maximum radiation-induced segregation is reported to occur in the temperature range of 400 to 500 °C (750 to 930 °F) (Ref

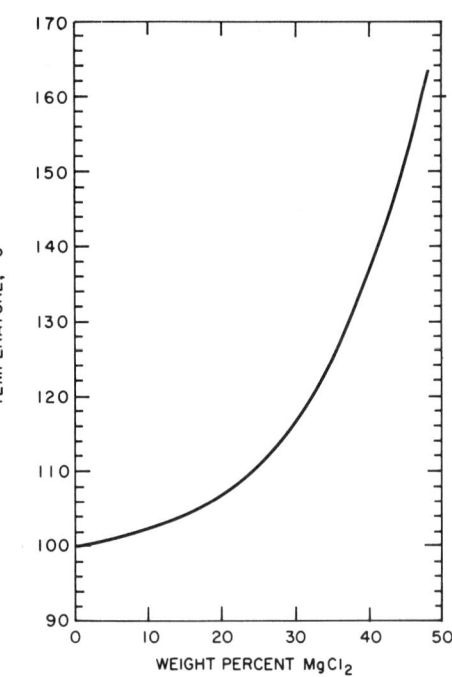

Fig. 3 Boiling points of aqueous magnesium chloride solutions at 1 atm as a function of concentration. Source: Ref 17

12). Additional information on IASCC can be found later in this article.

Chloride SCC

Chloride SCC in stainless steels was first widely studied using austenitic stainless steels in boiling magnesium chloride solutions. Nickel-free ferritic stainless steels are highly resistant to SCC in boiling magnesium chloride and sodium chloride solutions. Hence, a misleading impression has emerged that all ferritic stainless steels are immune to all chloride environments. As will be discussed below, there is no immunity associated with the body-centered cubic (bcc) ferrite lattice, and, as in the case of austenitics, susceptibility of ferritic and duplex stainless steels to chloride SCC depends on alloy composition and structure and on environmental parameters. Also, the danger of chloride SCC in austenitic stainless steels should not be minimized. It is reassuring to see the supplier literature (e.g., Ref 15) using the caution "may be susceptible to chloride stress-corrosion cracking" when describing all variants of the austenitic types 304, 316, 317, 321, 347, and 348, and the austenitic high-manganese/high-nitrogen grades, UNS S21904 and S20910.

Austenitic Stainless Steels

The Magnesium Chloride Test. Because chloride SCC was first noted in the more widely used austenitic stainless steels, these materials have received the greatest amount of study. Most early evaluations employed boiling magnesium chloride solutions, which are very severe environments. Nevertheless, the magnesium chloride test

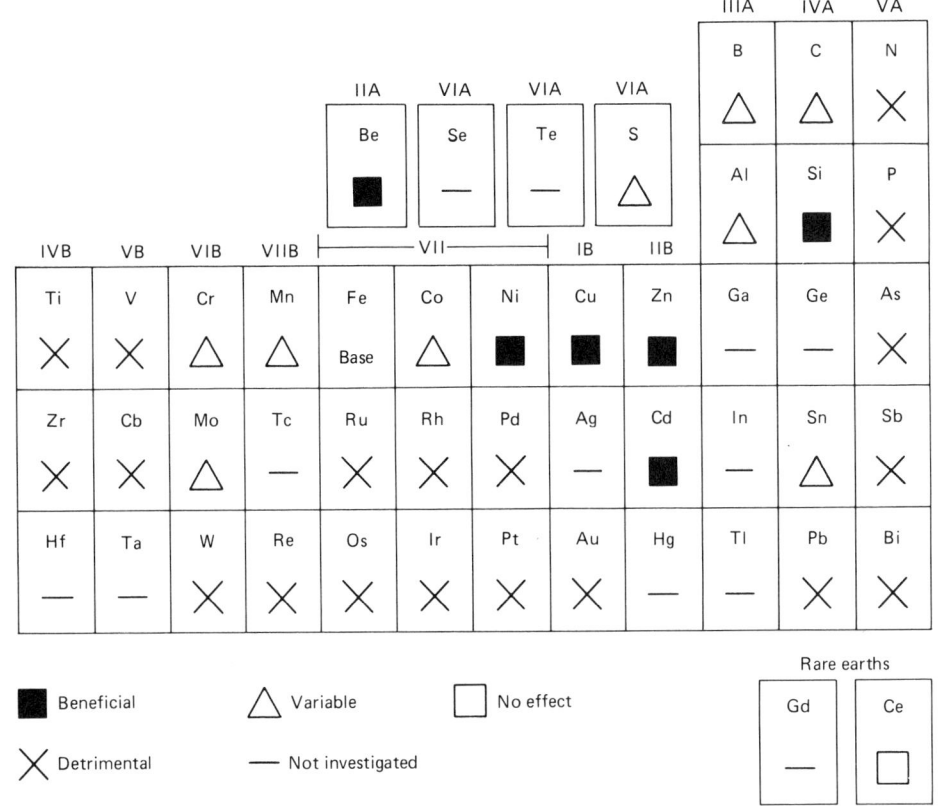

Beneficial ■   Variable △   No effect ☐

Detrimental ✕   Not investigated —

Rare earths

Fig. 4 Effect of various elements on resistance of austenitic stainless steels to stress-corrosion cracking in chloride solutions

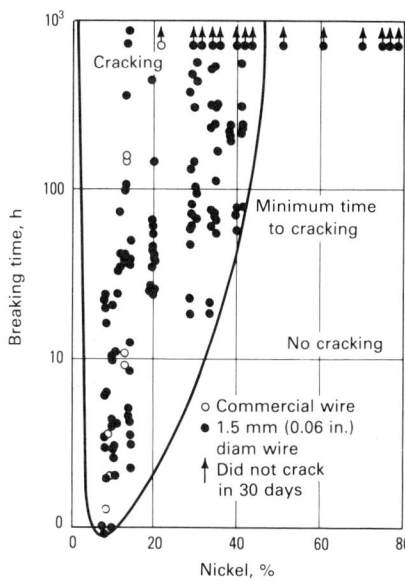

Fig. 5 Effect of nickel content on stress-corrosion cracking susceptibility of stainless steel wires containing 18 to 20% Cr in a magnesium chloride solution boiling at 154 °C (309 °F). Source: Ref 23

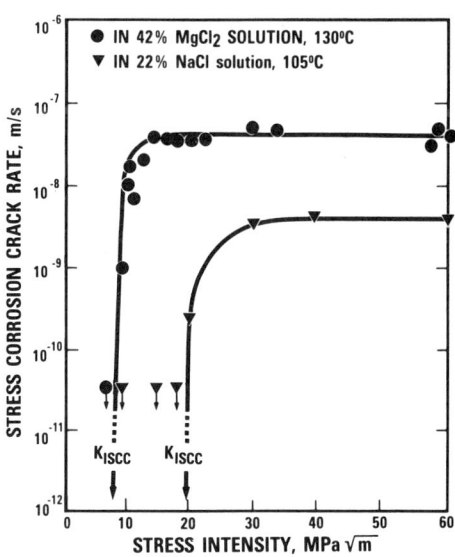

Fig. 6 Effect of stress intensity on the growth rate of stress-corrosion cracks in type 304L stainless steel exposed to magnesium chloride and sodium chloride solutions. Source: Ref 27

is still used because of its severity and the belief among end-users that stainless alloys that can survive lengthy periods of exposure to concentrated boiling magnesium chloride are not likely to exhibit chloride cracking in service. It is also used by researchers, because it is simple and rapid and allows comparison among tests performed in different laboratories.

The boiling magnesium chloride test was first described in 1945 (Ref 16). It has now been standardized as ASTM G 36. The boiling point of magnesium chloride solution is strongly dependent on concentration, as shown in Fig. 3 (Ref 17), and ASTM G 36 recommends the use of a test solution that boils at 155° C ± 1 °C (311 °F ± 1.8 °F). It is important to make alloy comparisons under the same conditions, because significant differences in the relative susceptibilities of types 304 and 316 are found at different temperatures or concentrations (Ref 18).

Other studies (Ref 19) using a 40% MgCl$_2$ solution have shown that keeping the solution at or near the boiling point for long periods of time causes it to become more alkaline. This increased alkalinity is reported to cause changes in the chloride SCC susceptibility of type 304, with different behaviors observed in freshly prepared and in aged (preboiled) solutions (Ref 19). The increased alkalinity reduces the transgranular crack-propagation rate and changes the potential dependence of the cracking process (Ref 19).

ASTM G 36 notes that any type of stress-corrosion test specimen can be used in the magnesium chloride test. A comprehensive discussion of the various types of test specimens used for SCC tests in magnesium chloride solutions can be found in Ref 20. One of the most popular is the U-bend specimen (described in ASTM G 30), which contains large elastic and plastic strains and provides one of the most severe configurations available for smooth (as opposed to notched or fatigue precracked) specimens. It is also simple and relatively inexpensive to make and use. Additional information on U-bend specimens, as well as alternative SCC test sample configurations, can be found in the article "Evaluation of Stress-Corrosion Cracking" in Volume 13 of the *ASM Handbook*.

Effects of Composition. As noted before, there has been extensive research, often employing boiling magnesium chloride environments, on the effects of alloying additions on the chloride SCC resistance of stainless steels. The results, summarized in Fig. 4, have been taken largely from Ref 21 and 22. It is evident from Fig. 4 that many alloying additions appear to be detrimental to chloride SCC, but there are also those that can be categorized as *beneficial* and *variable*. Those designated *beneficial* in Fig. 4 are nickel, cadmium, zinc, silicon, beryllium, and copper. It should be emphasized that the beneficial effect of nickel relates only to austenitic stainless steels. When present in relatively small quantities in ferritic stainless steels, nickel is detrimental to chloride SCC resistance. The beneficial effect of nickel on chloride SCC resistance of austenitic stainless steels and

higher alloys has been extensively studied and is well documented (Ref 23-26).

Figure 5 (Ref 23) shows the effect of nickel content on the susceptibility to chloride SCC of stainless steel wire specimens tested in boiling magnesium chloride. The data of Fig. 5 suggest that very high nickel contents (about 50%) would be required for resistance to chloride SCC. This is at variance with general industrial experience, which is that chloride SCC is not usually observed at nickel contents at or above 42%. In fact, Alloy 825 (42% Ni), Alloy G (44% Ni), and 20Cb3 (33% Ni) are often specified for applications

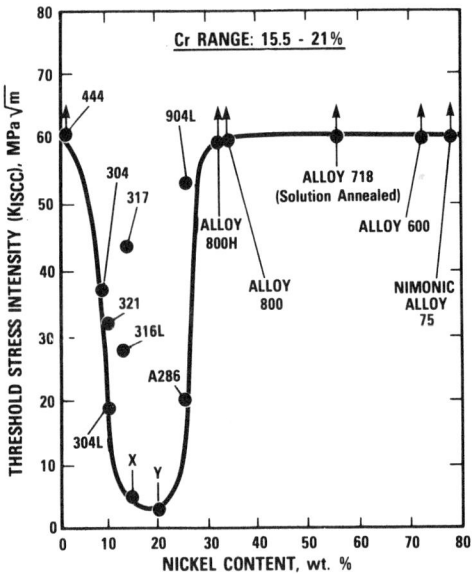

Fig. 7 Effect of nickel content on the stress-corrosion threshold stress intensity of various alloys in an aerated aqueous 22% NaCl solution at 105 °C (220 °F). Alloys X and Y are German heat-resistant grades. Source: Ref 27

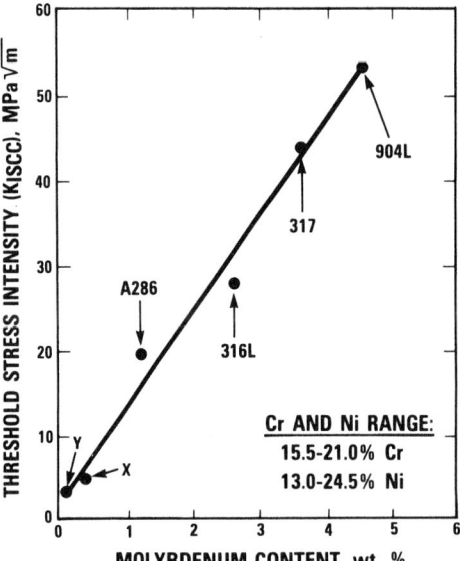

Fig. 8 Effect of molybdenum content on the stress-corrosion threshold stress intensity of Fe-Cr-Ni-Mo alloys in an aerated aqueous 22% NaCl solution at 105 °C (220 °F). Alloys X and Y are German heat-resistant grades. Source: Ref 27

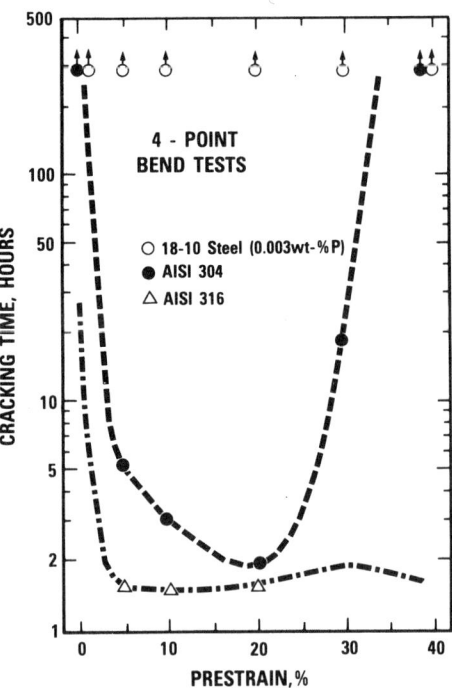

Fig. 9 Effect of phosphorus content on the cracking time of an 18Cr-10Ni-0.003P stainless steel and types 304 and 316 in magnesium chloride solutions boiling at 154 °C (309 °F) under an applied tensile stress of 196 MPa (28 ksi). Source: Ref 39

requiring resistance to chloride SCC. Recent evaluations (Ref 27) using precracked fracture-mechanics specimens support the view that magnesium chloride is a much more severe environment than sodium chloride (Fig. 6), and they suggest that the nickel level required for lack of susceptibility to SCC in sodium chloride may be between 30 and 40% (Fig. 7). In these tests, absence of crack propagation at a stress intensity of 60 MPa√m (55 ksi√in.) is equated with resistance to SCC.

Additions of cadmium and zinc are also designated as beneficial (Fig. 4). Actually, there is very little information about the effects of these alloying elements. A 0.2% Cd addition to type 304 inhibited cracking in a vapor test that readily cracked type 304 (Ref 28), and a 1% Zn addition to an Fe-20Cr-15Ni alloy led to a fivefold improvement in SCC resistance (Ref 29). Therefore, the designation of these elements as beneficial must be regarded as tentative.

Alloying with silicon has been shown to be beneficial to chloride SCC resistance in boiling 42% MgCl₂ (Ref 30). However, other studies (Ref 31), summarized in Table 1, have shown that the beneficial effect of silicon noted in magnesium

chloride tests is barely detectable, if at all, in sodium chloride solutions at higher temperatures. Beryllium and copper alloying additions have been shown to be beneficial (Ref 32), although the effect of copper is slight.

The elements designated in Fig. 4 as having a variable effect on chloride SCC can be divided into the three categories shown in Table 2. Boron, aluminum, and cobalt appear to be detrimental in small quantities but beneficial in larger amounts (Ref 29, 32-36); tin and manganese appear to have no effect in certain ranges and beneficial or detrimental effects in other ranges (Ref 21, 36); carbon and chromium show minimal effect on chloride SCC resistance (Ref 21, 37). The effect of molybdenum appears to depend on the test environment. The magnesium chloride data suggest that molybdenum additions first decrease and then increase resistance to cracking, with a minimum resistance at about 1.5% Mo (Ref 37). No such pattern is in evidence in sodium chloride tests (Fig. 8) (Ref 27), which show cracking resistance increasing with increasing molybdenum content.

The foregoing survey of the effects of alloying additions on the chloride SCC resistance of

austenitic stainless steels pertains to materials made by conventional melting practice, which contain many impurities. In this regard it has been shown that austenitic (as well as ferritic) stainless steels of very high purity are highly resistant to SCC in boiling magnesium chloride. Two examples are Fe-16Cr-20Ni (Ref 36) and Fe-18Cr-14Ni (Ref 38) high-purity alloys. In the latter case, the total metallic impurities were quoted at 1 ppm and the total nonmetal impurities (oxygen, nitrogen, sulfur, and phosphorus) at 10 ppm, the material having been prepared by plasma furnace melting. Other studies (Ref 39) have shown that decreasing the phosphorus content of an Fe-18Cr-10Ni stainless steel down to 0.003 wt% produces a material that is highly resistant to chloride SCC in a magnesium chloride solution boiling at 154 °C (309 °F) (Fig. 9). It has been suggested (Ref 40) that these high-purity alloys are resistant because their corrosion potentials are outside the potential range where SCC occurs.

Table 1 Effect of silicon on SCC resistance of austenitic stainless steels in various chloride media

							Time to failure, h		
		Analysis, wt%(a)				Ferrite content, %	42% MgCl₂ at boiling point(b)	100 ppm NaCl at 250 °C (480 °F)	1000 ppm NaCl at 250 °C (480 °F)
C	Si	Mn	Cr	Ni	N				
0.020	0.46	0.83	18.28	15.10	0.07	0.5	219	28	10
0.022	0.80	0.77	18.54	15.20	0.08	0.5	292	24	5
0.031	2.48	0.83	18.58	15.23	0.07	1	1000 NF	92	32
0.031	3.69	0.88	18.46	15.20	0.07	1	1000 NF	81	15
0.031	4.53	0.86	18.42	15.28	0.08	2.5	1000 NF	54	50

(a) Balance iron. (b) 1000 NF, no failure in 1000 h. Source: Ref 31

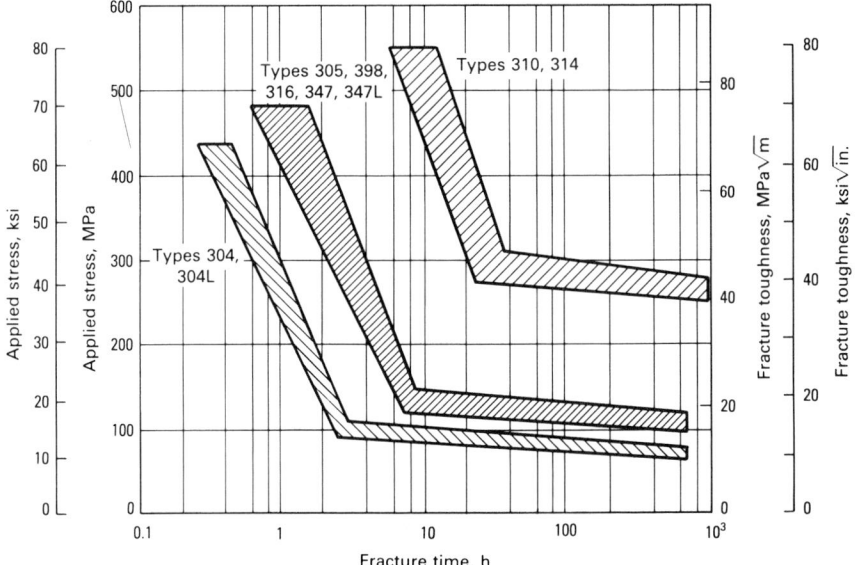

Fig. 10 Effect of applied stress on the times to failure of various alloys tested in a magnesium chloride solution boiling at 154 °C (309 °F). Source: Ref 41

Table 2 Effects of various elements on resistance of austenitic stainless steels to chloride cracking

Element	Beneficial	Detrimental
Boron	>0.1%	0.01%
Aluminum	0.1%	0.04%
Cobalt	>1.8%	1.50%
Tin	0.001-0.02%	No effect at 0.4%
Manganese	No effect at 0-2%	>2%
Minimum in cracking resistance at:		
Carbon	0.06-0.1%	
Molybdenum	~1.5%	
Chromium	12-25%	

Effects of Stress. As shown in Fig. 10 (Ref 41), decreasing the applied stress increases time to failure, and at low stresses a runout (threshold) stress is indicated. Figure 10 also shows that the family of curves shift to greater SCC resistance with increased nickel content. The 304 and 304L alloys contained 9% Ni; the 305, 309, 316, 347, and 347L alloys contained from 10.5 to 13.9% Ni; and the 310 and 314 alloys contained from 24.5 and 19.7% Ni, respectively. Careful studies (Ref 42) using solution-annealed type 347 electropolished tensile specimens have established a threshold stress for this material at approximately 160 MPa (23 ksi), as indicated in Fig. 11. Threshold stress intensities (K_{ISCC}) obtained using precracked fracture-mechanics specimens in boiling magnesium chloride and sodium chloride solutions have been measured for various stainless steels, as shown in Fig. 6 to 8 (Ref 27). These threshold stress intensities should be regarded as stress-intensity factors below which the rate of cracking in a given environment is very low, rather than as absolute thresholds.

The method of increasing resistance to chloride SCC by reducing stress level has been studied. Stress, however, is a difficult parameter to control, and while it is obviously good practice to minimize applied (design) stresses, the presence of tensile residual stresses in the material can negate any benefit. The only sure way to control stresses is by stress-relief annealing the fully assembled structure. Full stress relief can be attained by annealing in the range of 800 to 900 °C (1470 to 1650 °F), because this causes a recrystallization of the deformed (internally stressed) grains. Unfortunately, this is often an option only for small components. For larger components, it is sometimes possible to achieve partial stress relief by heating to 400 to 600 °C (750 to 1110 °F), and it is believed, particularly in Europe, that even

such partial stress relief can significantly improve resistance to chloride SCC. However, the benefits of any such procedure should be carefully weighed against potential sensitization problems. Compressive residual stresses, such as may be introduced by careful shot peening, have been shown to increase resistance to chloride SCC (Fig. 12) (Ref 43).

The effects of various surface finishes (which can produce stress variations due to local work hardening, martensitic transformation, residual stresses, and embedded material from abrasives and machining equipment, or provide stress raisers such as deep grooves or notches) are virtually impossible to quantify. All that can be said is that comparative evaluation of chloride SCC resistance should be carried out with nominally identical surface finishes. In particular, predictive laboratory evaluations should be performed using surface finishes identical to those encountered in service.

Effects of Microstructure. A schematic of the microstructural features found in stainless steels is shown in Fig. 13 (Ref 44), and many of these features have an effect on chloride SCC, as noted below.

The presence of δ-ferrite in austenitic stainless steels generally improves resistance to chloride SCC. An example of this for several cast austenitic stainless steels is shown in Fig. 14 (Ref 45). The beneficial effect of δ-ferrite is generally at-

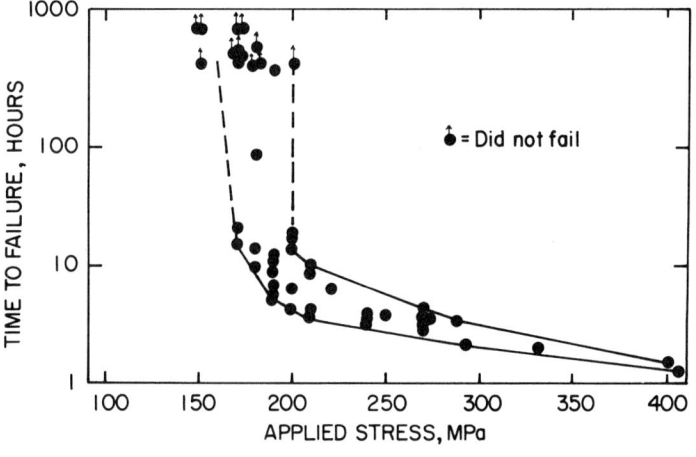

Fig. 11 Effect of applied stress on the time to failure of solution-annealed and electropolished type 347, tested in a magnesium chloride solution boiling at 145 °C (293 °F). Source: Ref 42

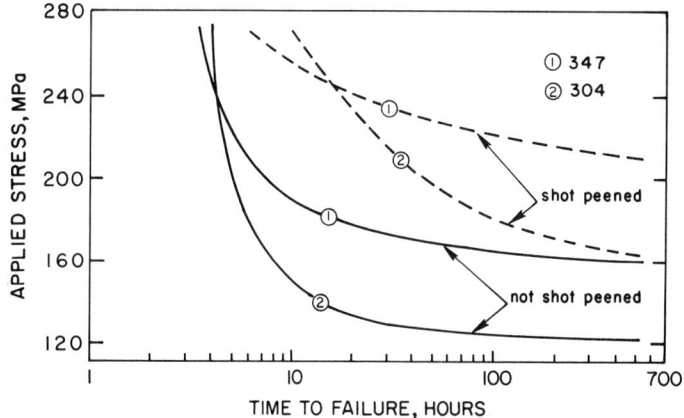

Fig. 12 Effect of peening with 40 to 80 μm glass shot on the times to failure of types 304 and 347 in a boiling 42% MgCl₂ solution. Source: Ref 43

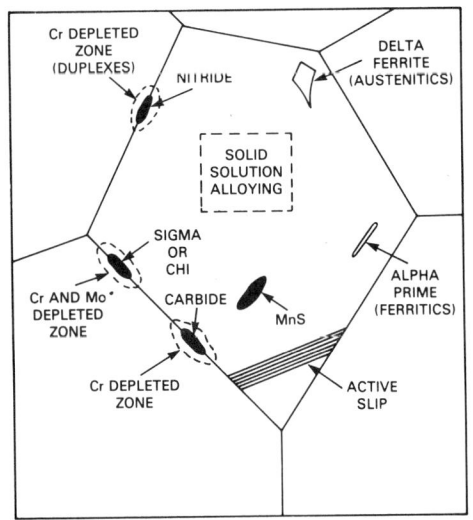

Fig. 13 Schematic of microstructural features found in stainless steels. Source: Ref 44

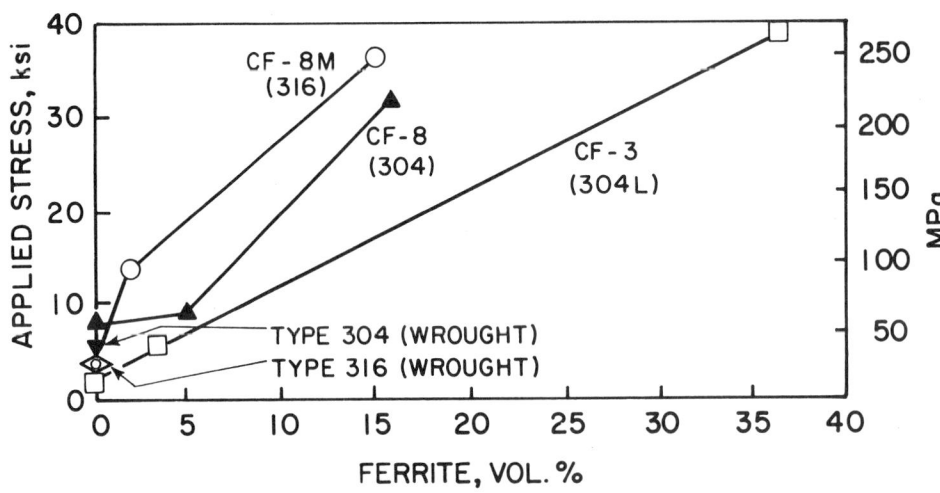

Fig. 14 Effect of ferrite content on the stress required to induce chloride stress-corrosion cracking in various cast stainless steels. Materials exposed for 8 h in condensate from an 875 ppm chloride solution at 204 °C (400 °F). Source: Ref 45

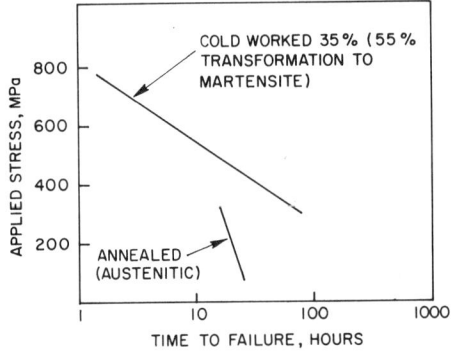

Fig. 15 Effect of cold work on the stress-corrosion cracking susceptibility of type 301 in a boiling 40% CaCl₂ solution. Source: Ref 49

tributed to its interference with the propagation of cracks across the austenite matrix. To obtain significantly improved resistance, however, considerable quantities of ferrite must be present, such as those found in duplex stainless steels. These are discussed in the section "Duplex Stainless Steels" in this article.

Regarding σ-phase, few attempts have been made to evaluate its effect on chloride SCC resistance. A metallographic study (Ref 46) has shown that the transgranular cracks produced in boiling 42% MgCl₂ avoid or bypass σ-phase produced in high-silicon types 316 and 317 by heating for 4 h at 870 °C (1600 °F).

Studies (Ref 46, 47) have failed to identify any relationship between sulfide stringers and the transgranular cracks produced in boiling magnesium chloride environments. The cracks appear to ignore the sulfide stringers. Other studies suggest that there may be an association between crack initiation and sulfides (Ref 48).

Plastic deformation of austenitic stainless steels results in both work hardening and partial transformation to α- and ε-martensites. Therefore, it is very difficult to separate effects caused by cold work (slip) from those caused by transfor-

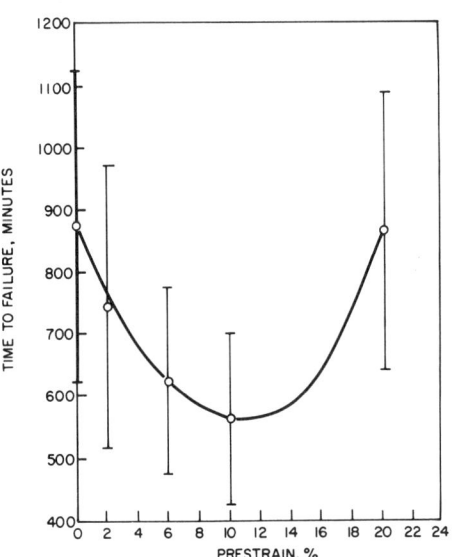

Fig. 16 Effect of prestrain on the time to failure of type 310 exposed to a magnesium chloride solution boiling at 154 °C (309 °F) and stressed at 90% of the yield stress. Source: Ref 50

mation to martensites. Studies (Ref 49) using type 301, which readily transforms to martensites on cold working, show that at comparable applied stresses (e.g., 300 MPa, or 43.5 ksi) the cold-worked and partially transformed material exhibits longer times to failure than the untransformed material (Fig. 15). However, the deformed material has a higher yield stress. Studies (Ref 50) using prestrained wires of type 310, which shows little tendency for transformation to martensites, suggest a minimum at 10% prestrain (Fig. 16). Other reports of the observation of such minima have been compiled in Ref 21. An exception appears to be type 316 (Fig. 9), which shows a sharp decrease with strain but no increase at higher strains (Ref 39). Current understanding of this phenomenon can be summarized by stating that,

in general, significant cold work (e.g., 35%) increases time to failure, as shown by the data for type 321 in Fig. 17 (Ref 49).

Sensitization is very detrimental to chloride SCC resistance, and in many cases it appears to cause SCC. As shown in Table 3 (Ref 51), sensitization can cause many stainless steels to become susceptible to intergranular cracking in chloride environments such as marine atmosphere. Sensitization is also reported (Ref 52) to cause intergranular chloride SCC of types 304 and 316 in synthetic seawater and in 0.1 M NaCl solutions at 80 °C (175 °F). More quantitative tests using fracture-mechanics test specimens have shown that the threshold stress-intensity factor for SCC susceptibility, K_{ISCC}, of type 304 stainless steel tested in a 22% NaCl solution at 105 °C (220 °F) is decreased from a value above 35 MPa√m (32 ksi√in.) to a value below 9 MPa√m (8 ksi√in.) as a result of sensitization (Ref 27).

Stress-corrosion cracking in sensitized stainless steels generally propagates along an intergranular crack path, whereas nonsensitized materials exhibit predominantly transgranular cracking in environments such as boiling magnesium chloride. However, exceptions occur, and the factors determining the selection of a crack path require further research. Sensitization-induced SCC in the high-temperature water environments of nuclear light-water reactors is discussed later in this article.

Grain size differences can influence SCC resistance. Studies have shown that increasing the grain size accelerates SCC, although the effect is not large, except at low applied stresses (Ref 53). Figure 18 shows the time to failure for type 302 wires in boiling magnesium chloride as a function of the applied stress, expressed as a percentage of the yield strength and for grain sizes of ASTM No. 5 and 9.

Effects of Environmental Variables. The susceptibility of austenitic stainless steels to chloride SCC is greatly influenced by environmental variables such as temperature, chloride concentration,

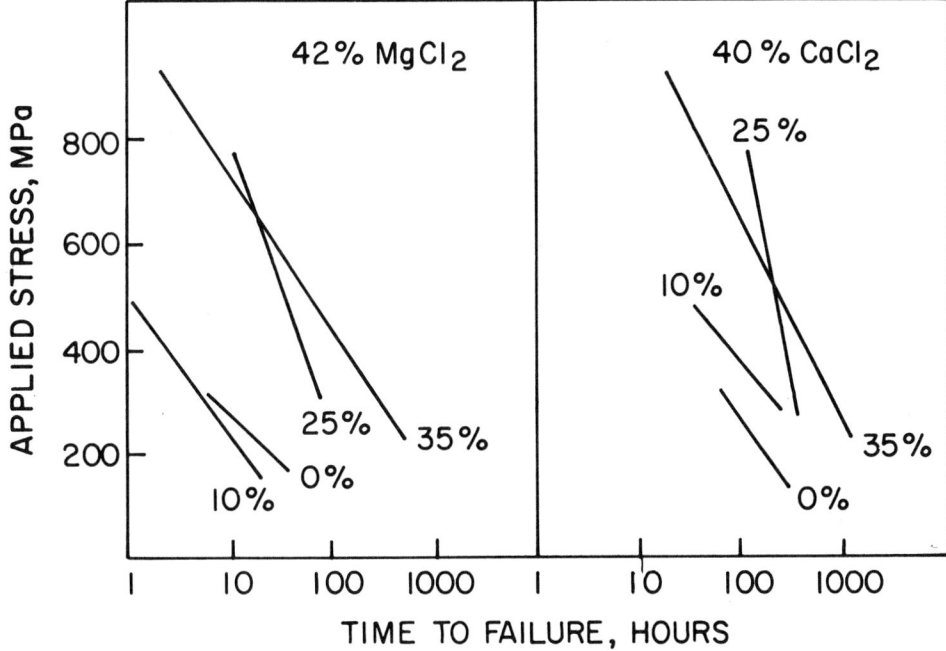

Fig. 17 Effect of cold work (%) on the stress-corrosion cracking susceptibility of type 321 in boiling magnesium chloride and calcium chloride solutions. Source: Ref 49

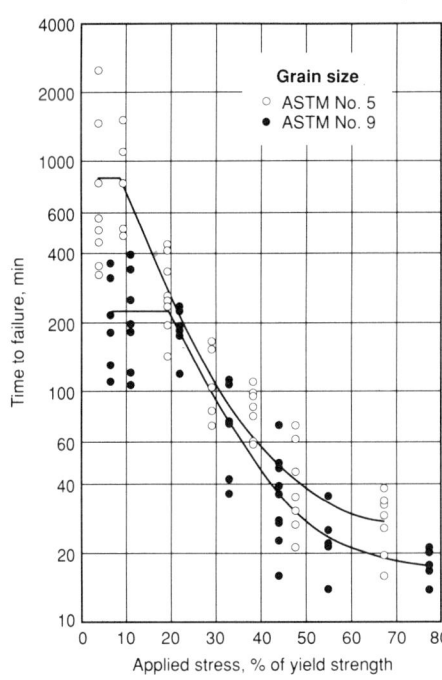

Fig. 18 Effect of austenite grain size and applied stress as a percentage of the yield strength (311.7 MPa and 358.5 MPa, or 45.2 and 52 ksi) for specimens with grain sizes ASTM No. 5 and No. 9, respectively, on the time to failure for type 302 wires in boiling 42% MgCl₂. Source: Ref 53

Table 3 Results of SCC tests in which U-bend specimens were exposed for 5 years to marine atmosphere in the 25 m (80 ft) lot at Kure Beach

Material	Condition(a)			
	Annealed	Welded	Cold worked, ¼ hard	Sensitized, 650 °C/1.5 h/FC
201	NF	NF	NF	IGA
301	NF	IGA	NF	IGA
302	NF	NF	NF	IGA
304	NF	NF	NF	IGA
304L	NF	NF	NF	NF
309	NF	NF	…	IGA
310	NF	NF	…	NF
316	NF	NF	NF	IGA
Carpenter 20Cb3	NF	NF	…	NF
Incoloy alloy 825	NF	NF	…	NF
Incoloy alloy 800	NF	NF	…	NF
Inconel alloy 600	NF	NF	…	NF

(a) NF, no failure in 5 years; IGA, intergranular attack; FC, furnace cooled. Source: Ref 51

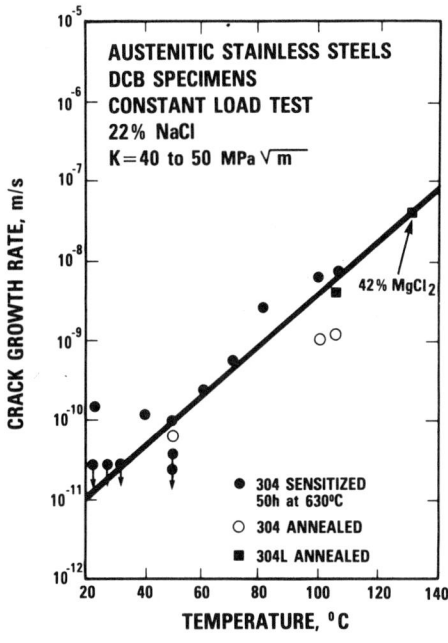

Fig. 19 Effect of temperature on stress-corrosion cracking velocity for austenitic stainless steels in concentrated chloride solutions. Source: Ref 27

pH, electrode potential, cathodic protection, and inhibitors. Each of these is described below.

Temperature is an important variable in determining whether chloride SCC will occur. The traditional engineering viewpoint, based on practical experience (Ref 54), has been that chloride SCC does not occur in nonsensitized austenitic stainless steels at temperatures below about 60 °C (140 °F) in near-neutral chloride solutions. Under the severe conditions encountered in a fracture-mechanics SCC test, this minimum temperature can be lowered to 50 °C (120 °F) for annealed type 304 and to temperatures approaching ambient for sensitized type 304 (Fig. 19) (Ref 27).

Instances of transgranular chloride SCC in service in nonsensitized austenitic stainless steels at ambient temperature have been reported to occur in atmospheres above indoor swimming pools (Ref 55, 56) and in the marine atmosphere (Ref 57, 58). The swimming pool atmospheres have caused chloride SCC in ceiling support rods made from type 304, type 316, and a German titanium-stabilized type 316 (DIN 1.4571). The mechanism of these swimming pool atmosphere failures is not understood, and their occurrence was not predicted (Ref 55).

Marine atmospheres have caused transgranular chloride SCC in type 303 (free-machining grade) nuts after 14 years of service (Ref 57), in type 304L heater sheaths and dished ends (Ref 58), and in type 304 pipe for an emergency cooling system (Ref 58). Common factors in the marine atmosphere failures were the presence of a hot, humid coastal atmosphere, contamination of the stainless steel by iron that rusted, and residual stresses from fabrication and fitup. Reference 59

outlines procedures for identifying and removing iron contaminants from stainless steel equipment.

Ambient-temperature chloride SCC of type 304 stainless steel has also been reported in solutions containing sulfuric acid and sodium chloride (Ref 60-62), and in hydrochloric acid

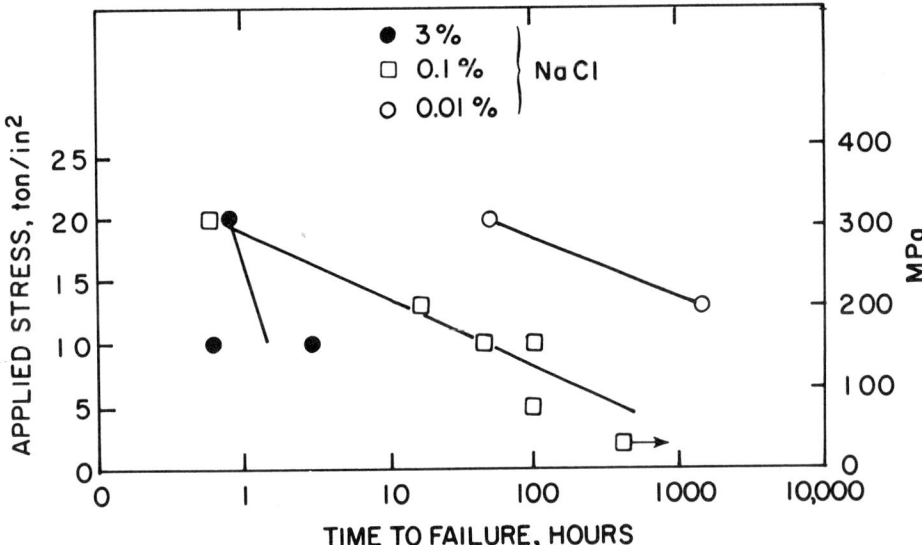

Fig. 20 Effect of chloride concentration on the stress-corrosion cracking susceptibility of type 347 in oxygen-containing sodium chloride solutions at 250 °C (480 °F). Source: Ref 65

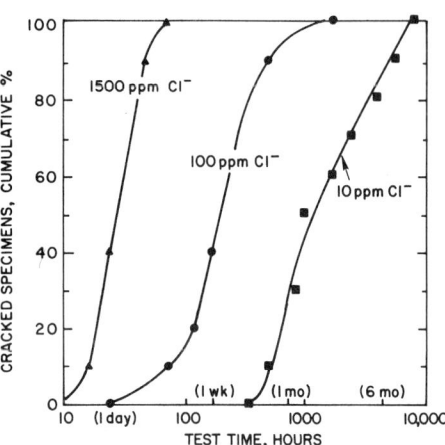

Fig. 21 Effect of chloride concentration on the stress-corrosion cracking susceptibility of type 304 exposed at 100 °C (212 °F) under the concentrating conditions of the wick test. Source: Ref 66

solutions (Ref 60, 63). Type 304 U-bend specimens exposed to a 10 N H_2SO_4 + 0.5 N NaCl solution at 28 °C (82 °F) for 300 h exhibited primarily intergranular cracking, with only short transgranular cracks developing (Ref 60). However, type 316 tested under similar exposure conditions showed entirely transgranular cracking (Ref 60). Exposure of U-bend specimens of types 304 and 316 to a 5% HCl solution held at –5 °C (23 °F) for 742 h resulted in transgranular cracking (Ref 60). This form of acid-induced SCC occurs at potentials in the active region (Ref 63). Chloride SCC of stainless steels has also been reported (Ref 56) to occur on exposure to hydrogen chloride vapor at –4 °C (25 °F).

Chloride Concentration. Under immersion conditions, chloride SCC is facilitated by increased chloride concentrations, presence of oxygen, and lowered pH. The relationship between chloride concentration and SCC susceptibility is not simple, and in elevated-temperature environments it is linked with oxygen concentration. The presence of oxygen is not necessary to cause SCC in concentrated chloride solutions boiling at atmospheric pressure, since their oxygen contents should approach zero. However, the introduction of oxygen into such solutions by bubbling accelerates SCC (Ref 64).

There is some evidence to suggest that in oxygen-containing, higher-temperature sodium chloride solutions, susceptibility to SCC decreases with decreasing chloride concentration, as indicated in Fig. 20 (Ref 65). However, the maintenance of low chloride levels cannot ensure freedom from SCC under conditions in which chloride can concentrate in crevices or shielded areas. The effect of temperature on chloride SCC susceptibility of type 304 under concentrating conditions is shown in Fig. 21 (Ref 66). In the wick test used to obtain the data of Fig. 21, a porous insulating material was used to draw the salt solution to the heated surface of a stressed specimen, where chloride can concentrate (Ref 20, 66, 67).

pH Effects. Regarding pH, it has been determined (Ref 68) that the pH of the solution at the tip of a crack in type 304 undergoing SCC in magnesium chloride is between 1.2 and 2.0. This suggests that, as in the case of pitting and crevice corrosion, acidification may be occurring by the hydrolysis of metal ions. In the case of pitting, increase in the bulk pH of the solution increases pitting resistance (Ref 69), and a similar improvement with increasing pH has been reported for chloride SCC resistance. Figure 22 shows the influence of pH on the time to fracture for type 304 in magnesium chloride and calcium chloride at 125 °C (255 °F) (Ref 70). The specimens were loaded in tension at 345 MPa (50 ksi). Variations in the pH had a greater effect on magnesium chloride than on calcium chloride, and the former was a much more severe environment than the latter. However, as noted later, caustic SCC may occur in stronger caustic solutions. Acidity may also explain (Ref 56) why magnesium chloride and calcium chloride, which dissolve to form acidic solutions (Ref 19), cause chloride SCC.

Electrode potential has a major effect on susceptibility to chloride SCC. Detailed studies (Ref 71), summarized in Fig. 23, have established the relationships among applied potential, applied stress, and time to failure for type 304 stainless steel in boiling 42% $MgCl_2$. Increasing the potential in the noble direction facilitates cracking, whereas increasing the potential in the active direction reduces susceptibility until a cathodic protection potential is attained.

Cathodic Protection. Regarding cathodic protection, it has been shown (Ref 72) that both impressed currents and sacrificial anodes can be used to prevent chloride SCC of type 304 in boiling 42% $MgCl_2$. Cathodic protection is also effective for preventing crack initiation in sensitized type 304 in sodium chloride solutions at 80 °C (175 °F) (Ref 73). Some researchers regard the cathodic protection potential as a critical cracking

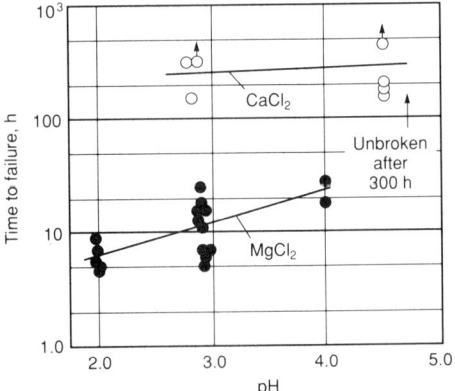

Fig. 22 Effect of solution pH on the time to failure for type 304 in magnesium chloride and calcium chloride at 125 °C (255 °F) with an applied load of 345 MPa (50 ksi). Source: Ref 70

potential and equate it with the repassivation potential for crevice corrosion (Ref 74).

Inhibitors of chloride SCC have been extensively studied (Ref 72, 75-80). Silicates, nitrates, phosphates, carbonates, iodides, and sulfites have all proved to effectively inhibit chloride SCC if present in certain concentrations. Cadmium sulfate effectively inhibits chloride SCC of sensitized type 304 in 4 N NaCl solution acidified to a pH 2.3 with HCl at 100 °C (212 °F) (Ref 81).

Ferritic Stainless Steels

The high resistance to chloride SCC of types 405 and 430 ferritic stainless steels was first demonstrated in 1945 (Ref 16) and was confirmed in subsequent studies (Ref 72, 82). More recent studies have also demonstrated the SCC resistance of some of the newer ferritic grades tested as U-bend specimens (Ref 83) and precracked fracture-mechanics specimens (Ref 27). In the frac-

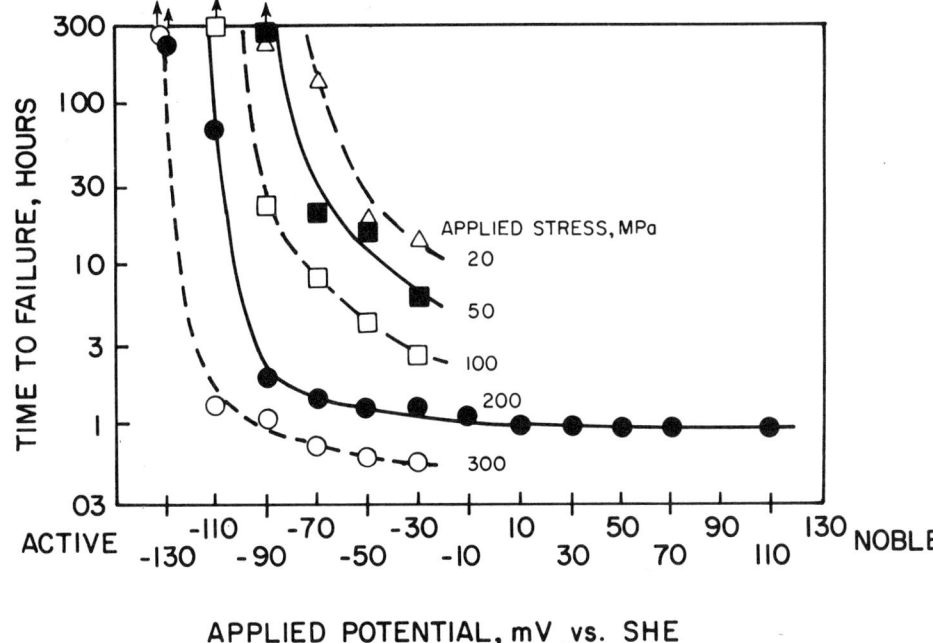

Fig. 23 Relationship among applied potential, applied stress, and time to failure of solution-annealed type 304 in a 42% MgCl₂ solution at 144 °C (291 °F). Source: Ref 71

Table 4   SCC resistance of stainless steels

Material	SCC test(a) Boiling 42% MgCl₂	Wick test	Boiling 25% NaCl
AISI type 304	F(b)	F	F
AISI type 316	F	F	F
AISI type 317	F	(P or F)(d)	(P or F)
Type 317LM	F	(P or F)	(P or F)
Alloy 904L	F	(P or F)	(P or F)
AL-6XN	F	P	P
254SMO	F	P	P
20Mo-6	F	P	P
AISI type 409	P(c)	P	P
Type 439	P	P	P
AISI type 444	P	P	P
E-Brite	P	P	P
Sea-Cure	F	P	P
Monit	F	P	P
AL29-4	P	P	P
AL29-4-2	F	P	P
AL29-4C	P	P	P
3RE60	F	NT(e)	NT
2205	F	NT	(P or F)(f)
Ferralium	F	NT	(P or F)(f)

(a) U-bend tests, stressed beyond yielding. (b) Fails, cracking observed. (c) Passes, no cracking observed. (d) Susceptibility of grade to SCC determined by variation of composition within specified range. (e) Not tested. (f) Susceptibility of grade to SCC determined by variation of thermal history. Source: Ref 83

ture-mechanics tests (Ref 27), the ferritic grades UNS S44400 (Remanit 4522) and S44800 (Remanit 4575) were fully resistant to chloride SCC at stress-intensity levels of 60 MPa√m (55 ksi√in.) in 22% NaCl solutions at 105 °C (220 °F). The U-bend test data are shown in Table 4 (Ref 83), with types 409, 439, and 444 exhibiting resistance to chloride SCC in all three test environments.

The tests noted above have led to the misleading impression that all ferritic stainless steels are immune to SCC in all chloride environments. However, SCC of the ferritics has been reported in several instances: for type 434, type 430, and Fe-18Cr-2Mo in lithium chloride solutions (Ref 84), for sensitized type 446 in boiling magnesium chloride and sodium chloride solutions (Ref 85), for type 430F in the marine atmosphere (Ref 86), and for the nickel-containing superferritics AL 29-4-2 (UNS S44800), Monit (UNS S44635), and Sea-Cure (UNS S44660) in boiling magnesium

chloride (Ref 83). Data for the superferritics are shown in Table 4. The producers of AL 29-4C (UNS S44735), which is shown to be SCC-resistant in Table 4, caution that the addition of 1% Ni to the alloy composition will introduce susceptibility to chloride SCC in boiling magnesium chloride environments (Ref 87).

Factors that have so far been identified as detrimental to the chloride SCC resistance of ferritic stainless steels include the presence of certain alloying elements, sensitization (induced by heat treatment or welding), cold work, high-temperature embrittlement, and the precipitation of α'(475 °C, or 885 °F, embrittlement as described in the article "Metallurgy and Properties of Wrought Stainless Steels" in this Volume). Because of the metallurgical complexity of ferritic stainless steels, it is not known whether all of these factors are related to the phenomenon identified as chloride SCC in austenitic stainless steels or also represent manifestations of other phenomena, such as hydrogen embrittlement and stress-aided intergranular corrosion along sensitized grain boundaries. However, for the purpose of the present discussion, it is assumed that effects that can be detected in boiling magnesium chloride tests relate to chloride SCC.

Effects of Composition. Alloying elements that have been identified as detrimental to the chloride SCC resistance of ferritic stainless steels include copper, nickel, molybdenum (in the presence of nickel), cobalt (in the presence of molybdenum), ruthenium, and carbon. Sulfur, either in the alloy or as sulfur-containing gases in the environment, may also facilitate SCC in chloride environments.

The copper and nickel levels that introduce susceptibility to SCC in magnesium chloride environments in annealed and in welded Fe-18Cr-2Mo alloy are shown in Fig. 24 (Ref 88). The detrimental effect of molybdenum in the presence of nickel is shown in Fig. 25 (Ref 89). The detrimental effect of cobalt is noted in Ref 89. Because molybdenum can be an alloying addition, and copper, nickel, and cobalt can be present if scrap is used in the melt charge, these effects could become technologically significant. The reported detrimental effect of ruthenium (Ref 90) is of more academic interest, because significant amounts of this element are not generally found as an impurity in stainless steels. Regarding carbon, it has been shown (Ref 85) that, for a 28.5Cr-4.0Mo stainless steel, increasing the carbon content from 20 to 171 ppm leads to SCC in a magnesium chloride solution boiling at 155 °C (310 °F). The detrimental effect of sulfur was suggested by the report (Ref 86) that type 430F (0.15% S, min) can exhibit cracking in the marine atmosphere.

Effects of Microstructure. It is probably true that the presence of structural features that reduce the ductility of ferritic stainless steels increases their susceptibility to chloride SCC. Ductility is reduced by the precipitation of carbonitrides (high-temperature embrittlement), by α'(475 °C, or 885 °F, embrittlement), and, to some degree, by cold work. The detrimental effects of these three factors on chloride SCC resistance are noted in Ref 88, 91, and 88, respectively. There do not appear to have been any systematic investigations of the effect of σ-phase or of sulfide inclusions on chloride SCC resistance. The detrimental effects of furnace sensitization of 28.5Cr-4.2Mo ferritic stainless steels that contain small amounts of copper and nickel have been reported and discussed in Ref 85 and 92.

Effects of Environmental Variables. The importance of the test environment in determining whether chloride SCC will occur is strikingly illustrated in Table 4. Several points emerge from these data. The first is that the boiling magnesium chloride test environment is much more severe than the boiling sodium chloride test environment. The second is that while the nickel alloying addition in the ferritic stainless steels (Sea-Cure, Monit, and AL 29-4-2 contain nickel) introduces SCC susceptibility in magnesium chloride solutions, it does not do so in the sodium chloride solution or in the wick test, which also uses sodium chloride. It is estimated (Ref 56) that 95% of the industrial and service occurrences of chloride SCC are due to sodium chloride. In a geothermal brine that contained alkali and alkaline earth chlorides, heavy-metal chlorides and sulfides, silica, and dissolved gases, both type 430 and E-Brite 26-1 ferritic stainless steels exhibited SCC (Ref 93).

Studies employing applied potentials show that, as in the case of austenitic stainless steels, chloride SCC of ferritic stainless steels can be prevented by cathodic protection. This is illustrated in Fig. 26 (Ref 94), which shows that a cathodic protection potential range (i.e., –250 to –650 mV, standard hydrogen electrode, SHE) exists for an Fe-18Cr-1.5Ni alloy in a 42% $MgCl_2$ solution at 143 °C (289 °F). Figure 26 also shows that at applied potentials active to –650 mV (SHE), another cracking region exists, possibly caused by hydrogen embrittlement. Hydrogen embrittlement of ferritic stainless steels is discussed later in this article.

Duplex Stainless Steels

Stainless steels with 18 to 28% Cr and 4 to 8% Ni contain both austenite and ferrite and thus are known as duplex. Commercial practice is to process or heat treat these alloys at temperatures in the range from 1050 to 1150 °C (1920 to 2100 °F) and to water quench to maintain a structure of about 50% austenite and 50% ferrite. An attractive feature of the duplexes is their higher strength. For example, the 0.2% offset yield strengths of the austenitic type 304, the ferritic type 430, and the duplex type 329 are 241, 310, and 551 MPa (35, 45, and 80 ksi), respectively.

As shown in Table 4, the duplex grades 3RE60, 2205, and Ferralium are susceptible to chloride SCC in boiling magnesium chloride. However, the threshold stresses for chloride SCC generally are higher for the duplex stainless steels than for the austenitics. An example of this is shown in Fig. 27 (Ref 95), where the threshold stresses for duplex stainless steels are about three times higher than that for an austenitic stainless steel. In fracture-mechanics tests (Ref 27) using precracked fatigue specimens in a 22% NaCl solution at 105 °C (220 °F), two variants of type 329 duplex stainless steel were found to be resistant to

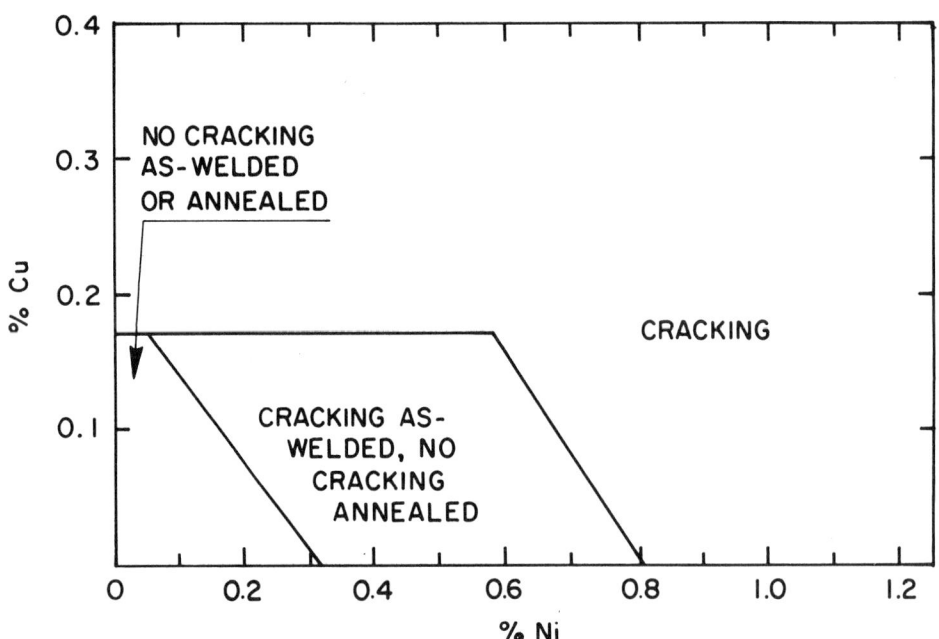

Fig. 24 Effect of copper and nickel contents on the stress-corrosion cracking resistance of U-bend specimens of ferritic Fe-18Cr-2Mo-0.35Ti-0.015C-0.015N stainless steels exposed to a magnesium chloride solution boiling at 140 °C (284 °F). Source: Ref 88

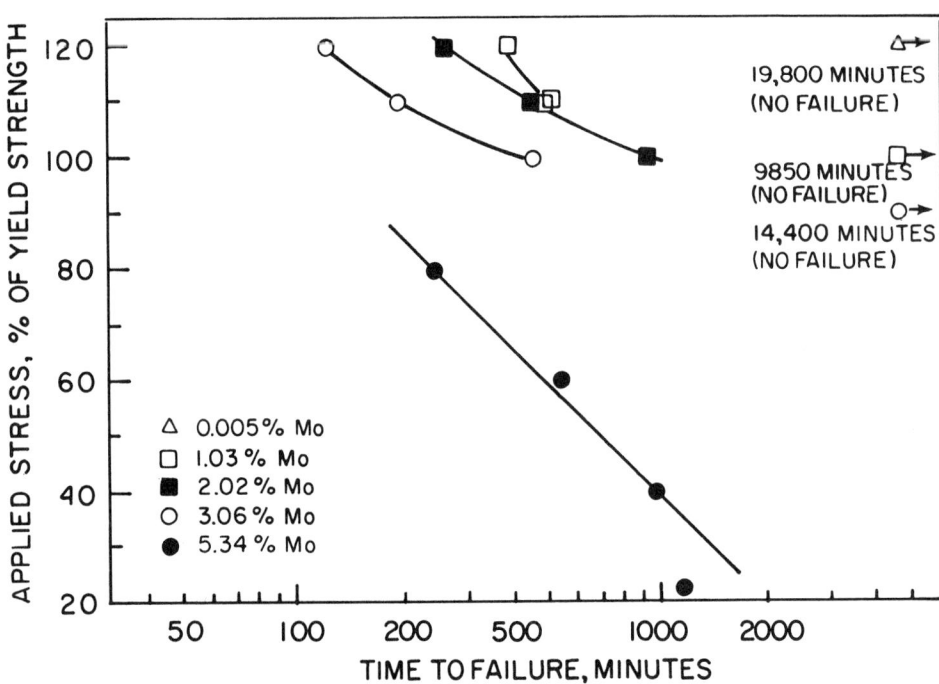

Fig. 25 Effect of applied stress on the times to failure of tensile specimens of experimental ferritic Fe-17Cr-1Ni stainless steels containing various amounts of molybdenum in a magnesium chloride solution boiling at 140 °C (284 °F). Source: Ref 89

chloride SCC at stress-intensity levels of 60 MPa√m (55 ksi√in.).

Effects of Microstructure. Among the microstructural parameters that have been examined in relation to chloride SCC susceptibility are the presence of σ-phase and the ferrite content. The presence of σ-phase has been shown (Ref 95) to be detrimental to chloride SCC resistance in boiling 35% $MgCl_2$ at 125 °C (255 °F). As illustrated in Fig. 28, ferrite content has also been shown to influence chloride SCC resistance in boiling 42% $MgCl_2$, with resistance reaching a maximum at

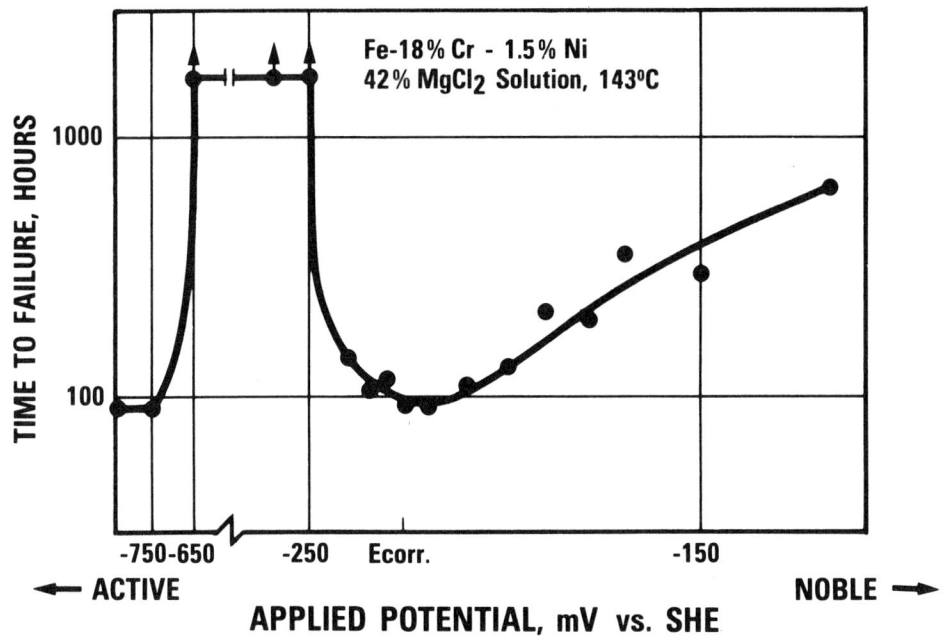

Fig. 26 Effect of applied potential on the times to failure of a ferritic stainless steel in a magnesium chloride solution. Source: Ref 94

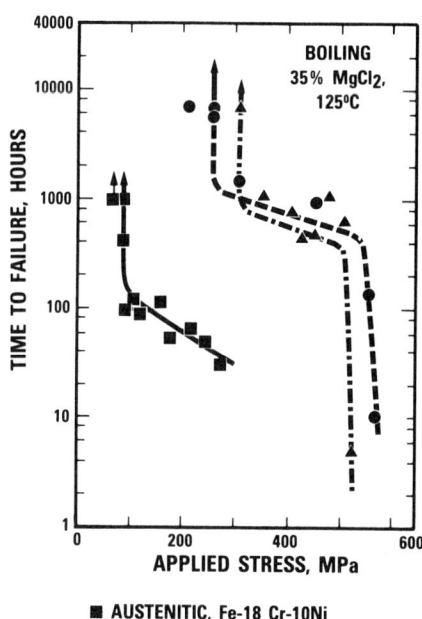

Fig. 27 Effect of applied stress on the times to failure of various stainless steels in a magnesium chloride solution. Source: Ref 95

40% ferrite and decreasing on either side of this value (Ref 96-98). Ferrite formed by welding can also reduce resistance to chloride SCC (Ref 1, 95). From a metallurgical viewpoint, welding will destroy the duplex structure of an annealed material, creating continuous regions of ferrite in the heat-affected zone (HAZ), and, as discussed in the previous section, the precipitation of carbonitrides (high-temperature embrittlement), the precipitation of α′ (475°C, or 885 °F, embrittlement), and sensitization can increase the susceptibility of ferrite to chloride SCC. Significantly, SCC has been reported in the ferrite portion of the HAZ of welds in a duplex stainless steel when welded U-bend specimens were exposed in the vapor phase above a 3% NaCl solution at 95 °C (205 °F) (Ref 1). Stress-corrosion cracking has also been observed in the HAZ of a welded duplex stainless steel when exposed as U-bend specimens to the marine atmosphere and a chemical plant atmosphere contaminated with traces of phosphoric and sulfuric acids (Ref 99). Tungsten-inert gas welding is reported (Ref 95) to cause a much greater loss in chloride SCC resistance than manual arc welding. The latter is thought to provide larger heat input and longer cooling times, enabling some of the newly formed ferrite to transform back to austenite, thereby producing the more SCC-resistant duplex structure (Ref 95).

Effects of Composition. There have been no reports of systematic studies of the effects of single-alloying-element additions on chloride SCC for duplex stainless steels. There are, however, significant variations in chloride SCC resistance among the different commercial grades (Fig. 29) (Ref 100). The data of Fig. 29 suggest that increasing the total chromium, nickel, molybdenum, and nitrogen contents results in increased chloride SCC resistance. These data do not differentiate between effects due to individual alloying elements.

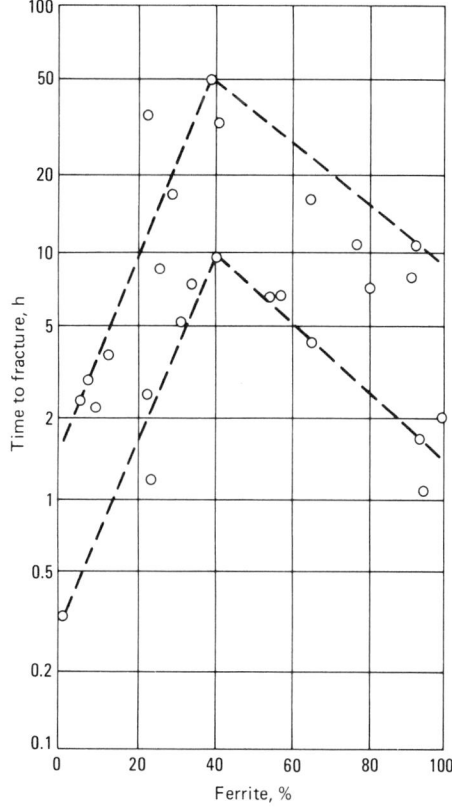

Fig. 28 Effect of ferrite content on the time to failure for duplex stainless steels in boiling 42% MgCl$_2$ under an applied stress of 240 MPa (35 ksi). Source: Ref 97

Effects of Environmental Variables. Studies of environmental variables have been somewhat more extensive. It has been established that, as in the case of austenitic and ferritic stainless steels,

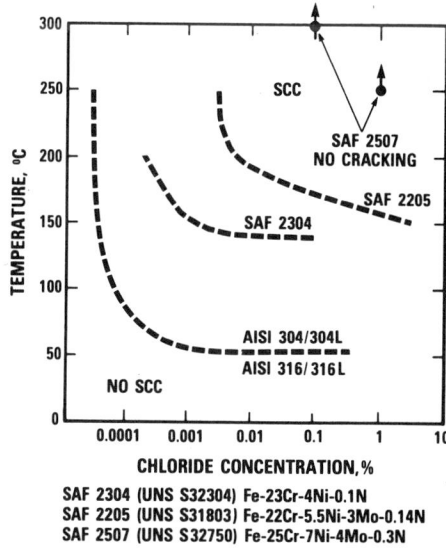

SAF 2304 (UNS S32304) Fe-23Cr-4Ni-0.1N
SAF 2205 (UNS S31803) Fe-22Cr-5.5Ni-3Mo-0.14N
SAF 2507 (UNS S32750) Fe-25Cr-7Ni-4Mo-0.3N

Fig. 29 Stress-corrosion cracking susceptibility of various stainless steels as a function of temperature and chloride concentration. Materials designated as 2304, 2205, and 2507 are duplex grades. Source: Ref 100

chloride SCC in duplex stainless steels can be prevented by cathodic protection. Figure 30 (Ref 95) shows that the cathodic protection potentials of an austenitic and a duplex stainless steel are similar, despite the fact that the two steels were stressed at their widely differing ambient-temperature yield strengths during the SCC tests.

In addition to exhibiting SCC in concentrated chloride solutions such as boiling magnesium chloride, duplex stainless steels exhibit SCC in

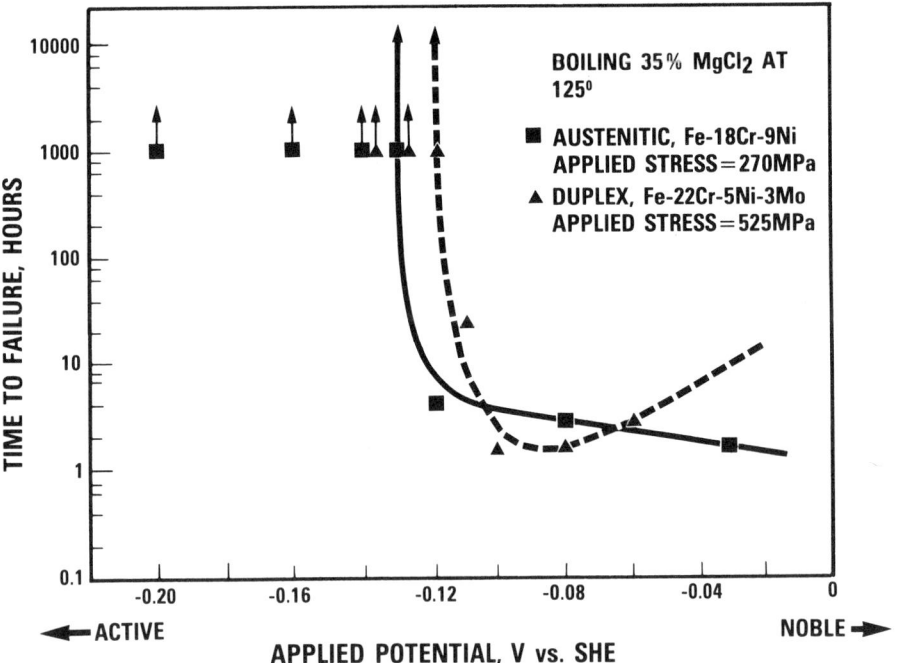

Fig. 30   Effect of applied potential on the times to failure of an austenitic and a duplex stainless steel in a magnesium chloride solution. Source: Ref 95

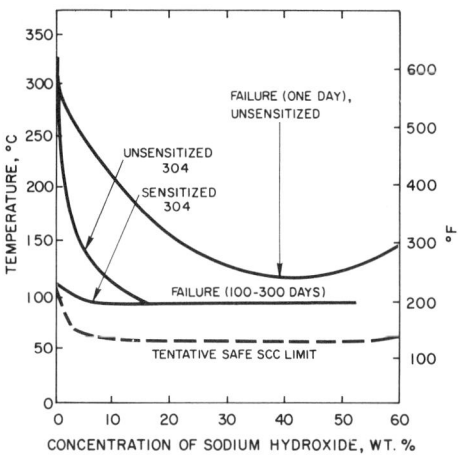

Fig. 31   Temperature and concentration limits for caustic stress-corrosion cracking of types 304, 347, 316, and 321. Source: Ref 113

sour gas environments that contain chloride and hydrogen sulfide (Ref 101-104). Materials for use in sour-gas environments are often evaluated using NACE Standard Test TM-01-77 (Ref 105). This test employs a 5% NaCl + 0.5% CH_3COOH solution, saturated with hydrogen sulfide by continuous bubbling after nitrogen deaeration, which has a pH of 2.7 to 2.8. The test is sometimes modified by raising the temperature to 80 °C (175 °F) (Ref 104), bubbling with a gas mixture containing 90% CO_2 + 10% H_2S (Ref 103), or applying potentials (Ref 101). It has been found that in these environments, increasing temperature (to 80 °C, or 175 °F) increases susceptibility to SCC (Ref

102) and that SCC is more severe in transverse specimens than in longitudinal specimens (Ref 102). Mechanistic assessments suggest that the environmentally induced cracking process of duplex stainless steels in sour-gas environments comprises an anodic chloride SCC step in which the crack is initiated in the austenite phase and a hydrogen-embrittlement propagation step in which the crack propagates through the ferrite phase (Ref 102, 104). Susceptibility to SCC can be reduced by lowering the hydrogen sulfide concentration to below 0.1 g/L or decreasing the applied stress level to below 60% of the yield stress (Ref 106). High-temperature annealing treat-

ments designed to increase ferrite content do not affect SCC susceptibility in sulfide-containing environments (Ref 107).

Martensitic and Precipitation Hardening Stainless Steels

The martensitic and precipitation-hardening stainless steels are used in heat-treated conditions that give high strength. As noted by Brown (Ref 86), the modern view, arising from extensive studies, is that most of the service failures involving high-strength steels, including high-strength stainless steels, are caused by hydrogen embrittlement. This topic is discussed in the last major section of this article.

Caustic SCC

The handling and containment of caustic soda (sodium hydroxide) do not pose technological problems, because adequate materials are readily available. For example, the low-carbon grade of unalloyed nickel, Nickel 201 (0.02% C maximum), can handle caustic soda, without SCC, at all concentrations and temperatures of current technological interest (Ref 108). General corrosion resistance in caustic is almost directly proportional to the nickel content of a given alloy, and the nickel-containing austenitic stainless steels are used in some applications involving moderate-temperature caustic at concentrations of 50% or less (Ref 109, 110). However, it has been known for some time that at certain combinations of caustic concentration and temperature, stainless steels can exhibit caustic SCC (Ref 111, 112).

The 1970s witnessed increased interest in caustic SCC as a result of the use of austenitic alloys in heat-exchanger systems of water-cooled nuclear power plants. It is well known from conventional boiler technology that boiling and steam blanketing at heat-transfer surfaces can give rise to very high local concentrations of caustic. Apart from the power industry, caustic SCC resistance is also of interest in the chemical, petro-

Table 5   Cracking behavior of various stainless steels in deaerated 10% NaOH solution at 332 °C (630 °F) C-ring specimens stressed at 90% of the yield strength

Material	Condition(a)	Observation(b)
Type 304 (austenitic)	Mill annealed	NC
	10 h/650 °C	NC
Type 405 (ferritic)	Mill annealed	NC, GC
	1 h/1010 °C/FC	NC, GC
Fe-18Cr-2Mo-0.5Ti (ferritic)	Mill annealed	NC, IGA
	1 h/1010 °C/FC	C
	3 h/475 °C	C
	20 h/475 °C	C
E-BRITE 26-1 (ferritic)	Mill annealed	NC
	1 h/1010 °C/FC	C
	100 h/475 °C	NC
	300 h/475 °C	C
3RE60 (duplex)	Mill annealed	NC, GC, IGA
	10 h/650 °C	NC, GC, IGA
	100 h/475 °C	C
	300 h/475 °C	C
Type 410 (martensitic)	Mill annealed	NC, GC
	Tempered 650 °C (28 HRC)	NC, GC
	Tempered 565 °C (41 HRC)	NC, GC
	Tempered 480 °C (50 HRC)	C

(a) FC, furnace cooled. (b) NC, no cracking in 4800 h; C, cracking during 4800 h; GC, heavy general corrosion; IGA, intergranular attack. Source: Ref 91

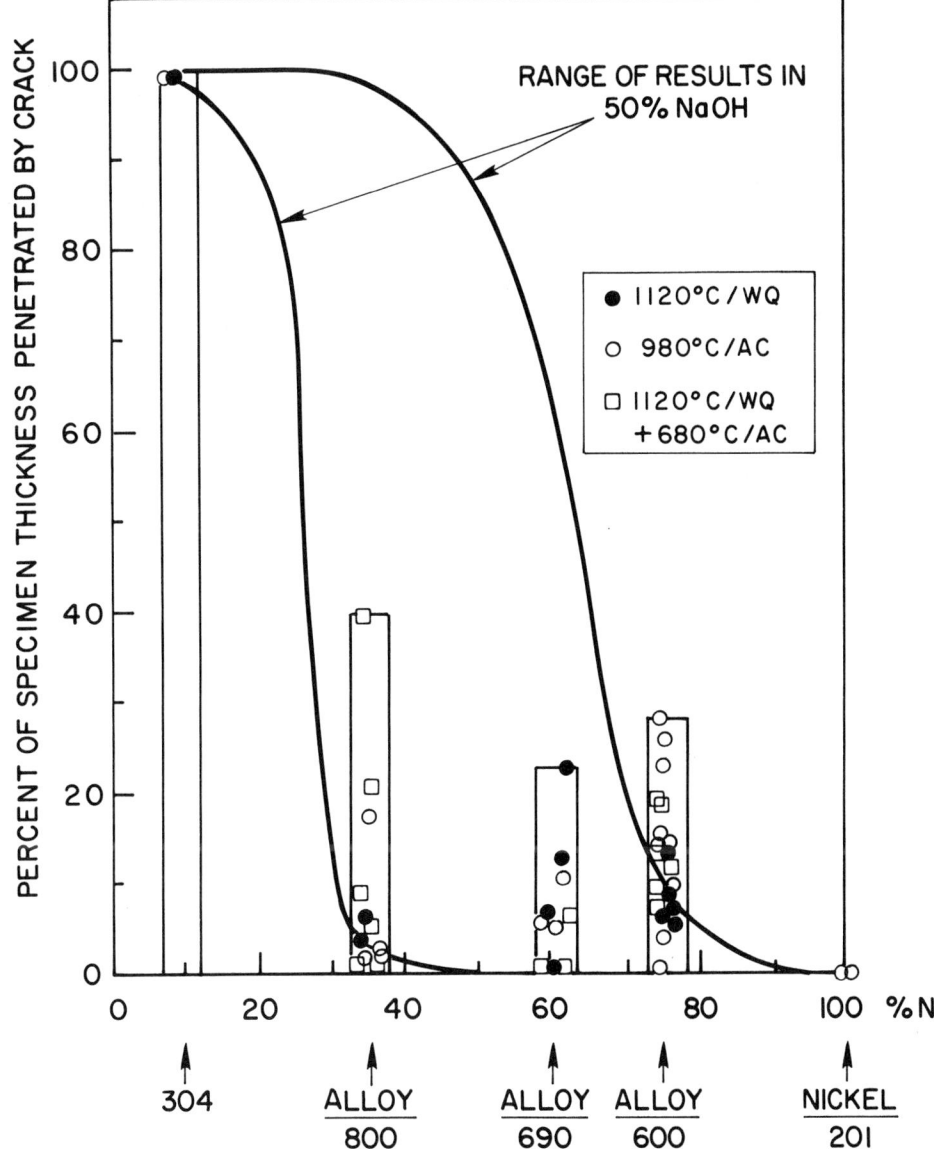

Fig. 32 Caustic stress-corrosion cracking behavior of U-bend specimens of various alloys in deaerated 10% and 50% NaOH solutions at 316 °C (600 °F). Exposure time of 6 weeks. Source: Ref 116

114). The presence of molybdenum as an alloying element does not improve SCC resistance in deaerated 50% NaOH (Ref 115). Figure 32 also shows that at lower caustic concentrations (e.g., 10% NaOH), the beneficial effect of nickel is less pronounced, with all three high-nickel alloys (Alloys 800, 690, and 600) exhibiting comparable SCC resistance.

In aerated (oxygen-containing) solutions of sodium hydroxide, high levels of both nickel and chromium appear to be necessary for resistance to caustic cracking, as indicated in Fig. 33 (Ref 115) and Fig. 34 (Ref 111). Figure 35 (Ref 65) illustrates that in oxygenated caustic solutions, times to failure increase with decreasing applied stress. This suggests that stress-relief annealing could be a remedy. However, it has been reported (Ref 115) that annealing stressed U-bend specimens of type 304 stainless steel for 4 h at 595 °C (1100 °F) did not prevent cracking on subsequent exposure to deaerated 50% NaOH at 284 and 332 °C (543 and 630 °F). This, together with the observation that no meaningful threshold stress intensity could be determined for type 304 in this environment (Ref 114), poses questions both as to the effectiveness of stress-relief annealing for stainless steels in deaerated caustic solutions and the mechanism of cracking. The mitigation of caustic SCC by the addition of phosphate has received much more attention. Water treatments employing phosphate additions to prevent the development of free caustic have been known for several decades and have been used to prevent caustic SCC of stainless steels in boiler water (Ref 117-119). Chlorides (Ref 120) and chromates (Ref 121) have also been reported to inhibit the caustic SCC of austenitic stainless steels.

Ferritic, Duplex, and Martensitic Stainless Steels

The most extensive investigation of commercial stainless steels other than austenitics is probably that described in Ref 91. This investigation examined the caustic SCC behavior of ferritic, duplex, and martensitic stainless steels under conditions insufficiently severe to crack type 304 (i.e., at 90% of the yield strength). The data are shown in Table 5 (Ref 91). Heat treatments designed to cause sensitization and 475 °C (885 °F) embrittlement were detrimental to the caustic SCC resistance of the higher-chromium ferritic stainless steels. Low-chromium type 405 exhibited heavy general corrosion. Heat treatments designed to produce 475 °C (885 °F) embrittlement in the duplex stainless steel were also detrimental. Martensitic type 410 exhibited SCC after tempering at 480 °C (900 °F), which produces a hardness of 50 HRC.

In other studies of ferritic stainless steels, it was reported (Ref 122) that types 430 and 434 exhibited uniform corrosion or intergranular corrosion on exposure to boiling 25% NaOH, rather than SCC. However, SCC of type 446 and E-Brite 26-1 heat treated at 870 °C (1600 °F) was reported (Ref 115) after exposure to deaerated 50% NaOH at 315 °C (600 °F).

In the case of duplex stainless steels, no SCC was reported in U-bend specimens of annealed

chemical, and pulp and paper industries, although few publications attest to this fact.

Austenitic Stainless Steels

A summary (Ref 113) of available caustic SCC data for types 304, 347, 316, and 321 is shown in Fig. 31. While there is some uncertainty about the position of the conservative line designated "tentative safe SCC limit," the data show that there is an inherent danger of caustic SCC in strong caustic solutions when the temperature approaches 100 °C (212 °F). Sensitization appears to be detrimental at lower caustic concentrations. Figure 31 shows that at nuclear power plant steam generator temperatures of approximately 300 °C (570 °F), these steels could exhibit rapid cracking. This is a fact well recognized by steam generator designers, who use higher-nickel alloys with im-

proved caustic and chloride SCC resistance for these applications.

When considering factors that affect caustic SCC resistance, careful attention must be paid to the oxygen level of the caustic solution. While there is no evidence that oxygen is necessary to cause caustic SCC, major changes in the ranking of alloys can occur, depending on whether or not oxygen is present. Studies (Ref 114, 115) show that in deaerated concentrated (50%) sodium hydroxide solutions, cracking resistance increases with increasing nickel content of the alloy, with Nickel 201 exhibiting complete resistance (Fig. 32) (Ref 116). The data shown in Fig. 32 were obtained using U-bend specimens, which measure the effects of both crack initiation and propagation. Tests using precracked (wedge-opening-load) fracture-mechanics specimens have shown that the beneficial effect of nickel is also reflected in increasing threshold stress intensities (Ref

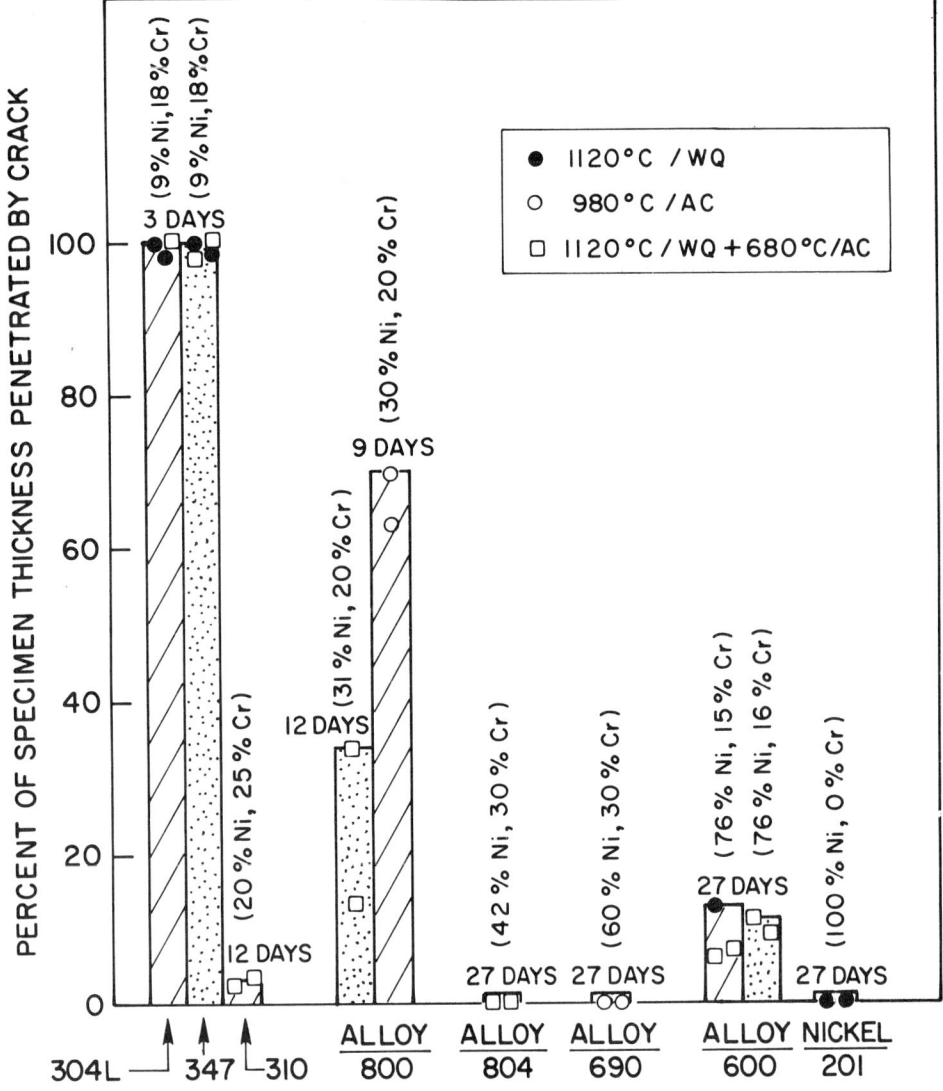

Fig. 33 Caustic stress-corrosion cracking behavior of U-bend specimens of various alloys in an aerated 50% NaOH solution at 300 °C (570 °F). Source: Ref 115

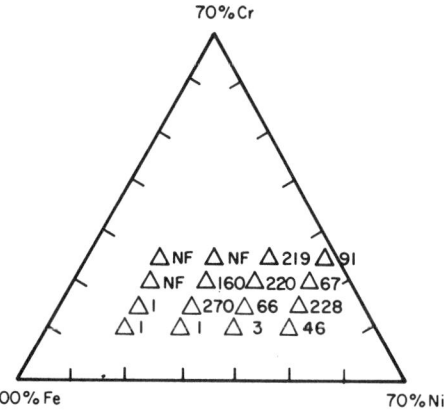

Fig. 34 Times to failure (hours) of various Fe-Cr-Ni alloys in a 50% NaOH solution at 300 °C (570 °F) with 14 MPa (2 ksi) oxygen. Specimens stressed at 140 MPa (20 ksi). NF, no failure. Source: Ref 111

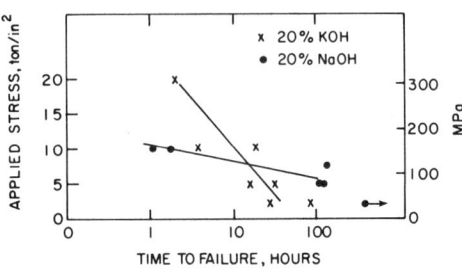

Fig. 35 Effect of applied stress on the times to failure of type 347 in oxygenated sodium hydroxide and potassium hydroxide solutions at 300 °C (570 °F). Source: Ref 65

IN-744 after a 15-day exposure to 90% NaOH at 300 °C (570 °F) (Ref 1). Other studies (Ref 123) have shown that introduction of the austenite phase into a ferritic matrix improves the caustic SCC resistance of experimental 25% Cr stainless steels (see Table 6), although general corrosion resistance is decreased.

High-Temperature Water SCC

As noted in the introduction to this article, *high-temperature water SCC* denotes SCC in the cooling water of nuclear reactors and has been used to describe the SCC of weld HAZ in type 304 piping exposed to oxygenated BWR coolants. In the 1970s and early 1980s, more articles were written about the SCC of sensitized type 304 in BWR environments than about any other corrosion topic, and several detailed reviews are available (Ref 124-127). A compilation of test data from 17 test programs carried out in the 1970s is

shown in Fig. 36 (Ref 113). The data clearly indicate that at dissolved oxygen contents of between 0.15 and 0.3 ppm and chloride contents of between 0.02 and 0.5 ppm, which span the BWR operating ranges (Ref 124), sensitized type 304 can undergo SCC.

The effect of stress level on the time to failure of sensitized austenitic stainless steels has also been studied in detail, and a well-defined dependence of stress on time to cracking has been found (Ref 128). Figure 37 shows this relationship for furnace-sensitized (24 h at 650 °C, or 1200 °F) type 304 stainless steel in 0.2 ppm oxygen (O_2) BWR-type water. As expected, the lower the tensile stress, the longer the time to cracking.

Considerable research has gone into understanding the mechanism of intergranular SCC of type 304 BWR piping, and a quantitative and predictive model has been developed (Ref 129-131). The model is based on the slip-dissolution/film-rupture model and relates crack advance to the oxidation reactions that are occurring at the crack

tip, where a thermodynamically stable oxide (or protective film) is ruptured by an increase in the strain in the underlying matrix. The amount of subsequent crack propagation is related via Faraday's law to the oxidation charge density associated with both dissolution and oxide growth on the bare surface. Such an environmentally controlled mode of crack advance is sustained by a further increment in matrix strain, which ruptures the oxide after a certain time. This model successfully predicts, to within a factor of 2, the environmentally controlled crack-propagation rates for stainless steel in water at 288 °C (550 °F). The model is used in the nuclear power industry as a crack-propagation prediction tool (Ref 128).

Several preventive measures have been developed for the intergranular SCC of BWR piping, including materials solutions such as the adoption of niobium-stabilized type 347L and of types 304NG and 316NG (described in the section "Sensitization" in this article), solution treatment, cladding with types 308 and 308L, and weld overlays. Minimizing tensile stresses by procedures such as heat-sink welding and altering the water chemistry of the BWR coolant are also remedies. Reference 128 provides a comprehensive description of all these preventive measures.

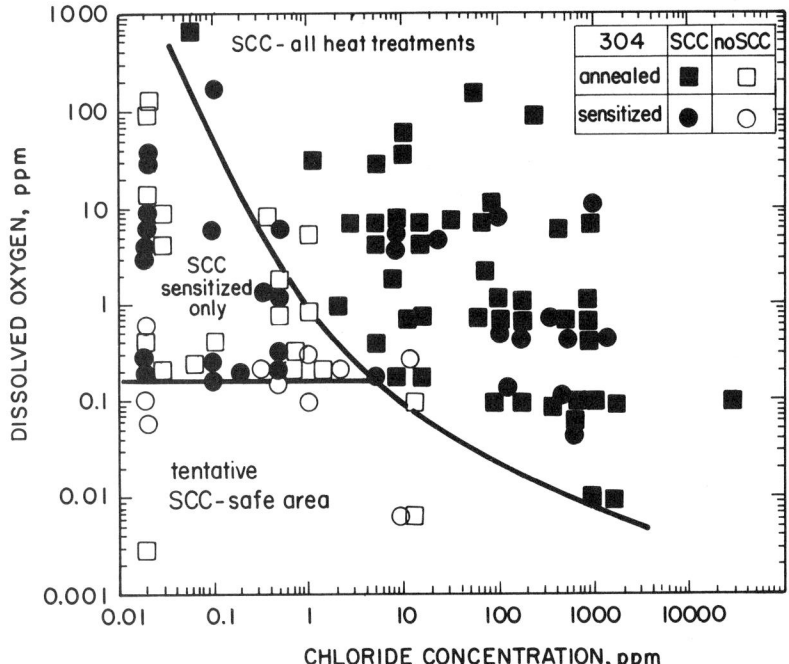

Fig. 36 Concentration ranges of dissolved oxygen and chloride that may lead to stress-corrosion cracking of type 304 in water at temperatures ranging from 260 to 300 °C (500 to 570 °F). Applied stresses in excess of yield strength and test times in excess of 1000 h, or strain rates greater than 10⁻⁵/s. Source: Ref 113

Polythionic Acid SCC

In the 1950s a form of intergranular SCC became recognized as a technological problem in catalytic reformers used in the petroleum industry. Earlier studies (Ref 132, 133) showed that this form of attack occurred in the aqueous condensates of reforming furnaces when polythionic acids (H_2SxO_6, where x = 3, 4, or 5) were present. Subsequently, this form of attack became known as polythionic acid SCC. More recent studies (Ref 134) have shown that of all the polythionic acids, only tetrathionic acid ($H_2S_4O_6$) induces SCC in sensitized type 304. Tetrathionic acid has also

been shown to be the critical species causing SCC of sensitized type 304 in tests employing sulfurous acid solutions (Ref 135).

A laboratory test for resistance to polythionic acid cracking has been standardized as ASTM G 35. The solution is prepared by bubbling sulfur dioxide and then hydrogen sulfide through distilled water. Stressed U-bend specimens are often used in such tests, although any type of SCC test specimen can be used. Excellent correlation has been shown (Ref 133) between polythionic acid cracking resistance as determined by ASTM G 35 and intergranular corrosion resistance as determined by the Strauss test (ASTM A 393) for a dozen dif-

ferent austenitic stainless steels and higher alloys. An example of this correlation in terms of a tearing topography surface diagram is shown in Fig. 38 (Ref 133). As a result of this study, it is now generally accepted that polythionic acid cracking is a form of intergranular SCC linked to sensitization. Accordingly, attempts to mitigate this form of attack have included the metallurgical remedies used to minimize sensitization.

The technological problem encountered in the petroleum industry is essentially as follows. Stainless steel components are used at operating temperatures that may be high enough to sensitize the material. On subsequent shutdown of a refinery unit, polythionic acids may form by the interaction of sulfur compounds, moisture, and air at low temperatures and attack the chromium-depleted boundaries. A combination of operational procedures and metallurgical remedies has been used to minimize polythionic acid cracking during shutdowns. The operational procedures are described in NACE Recommended Practice P-0170-85 and are based on preventing the condensation of water vapor or maintaining an alkaline environment by additions of ammonia or sodium carbonate.

Among the metallurgical remedies that have been tried are the use of low-carbon grades (e.g., type 304L), the use of stabilized grades (type 321 or 347), and the use of higher-nickel-content alloys such as Incoloy alloy 801. However, the stabilized and the low-carbon grades of stainless steel can be sensitized at certain time-temperature combinations (Ref 1). Accordingly, it has been recommended that low-carbon grades be used for operating temperatures below 400 °C (750 °F), and that stabilized grades be thermally treated at temperatures of 900 to 925 °C (1650 to 1700 °F) to ensure maximum precipitation of carbon as titanium or niobium carbides prior to service (Ref 136). In cases where welding is necessary, a British practice has been to weld the thermally stabilized (920 °C, or 1690 °F) type 321 and to locally anneal the welds at 920 °C (1690 °F) (Ref 1). Higher-nickel-content alloys, such as the titanium-stabilized Incoloy alloy 801, have been used in the United States (Ref 137). Weld overlays, in the as-deposited state, of several austenitic stainless steels have been reported to be resistant to polythionic acid SCC (Ref 138).

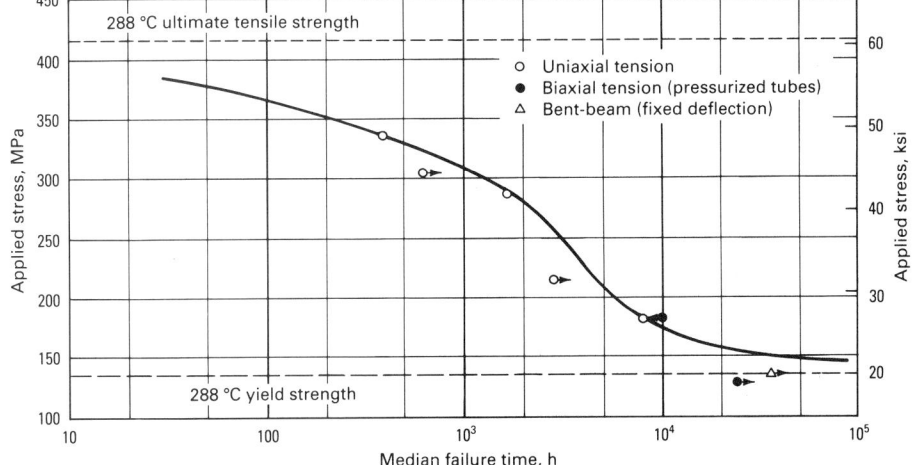

Fig. 37 Stress dependence of intergranular stress-corrosion cracking of sensitized type 304 in 288 °C (550 °F) water with 0.2 ppm O₂. Source: Ref 128

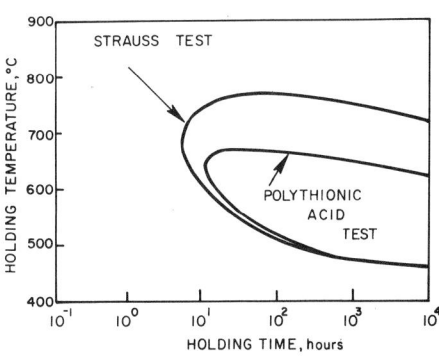

Fig. 38 Effect of heat treatment on the resistance of type 304 (0.04% C) in polythionic acid during the Strauss tests. Source: Ref 133

Table 6 Caustic cracking resistance of various experimental stainless steels tested as bent-beam specimens in boiling 30% NaOH at 119 °C (246 °F) for 300 h

Alloy composition, wt%					0.5 h/900 °C/WQ		0.5 h/1100 °C/WQ		0.16 h/1300 °C/WQ	
Cr	Ni	Mo	C	N	Phases(a)	Result(b)	Phases(a)	Result(b)	Phases(a)	Result(b)
24.6	0.05	2.07	0.023	0.018	α	NF	α	C	α	C
24.9	0.50	2.11	0.029	0.020	α	NF	α	C	α	C
25.2	0.96	2.09	0.027	0.019	α	NF	α	C	α	C
24.9	1.95	2.09	0.030	0.018	α	NF	α	C	α	C
25.2	3.38	2.03	0.027	0.021	α + γ	NF	α	C	α	C
25.2	4.41	2.14	0.032	0.024	α + γ	NF	α + γ	C	α	C
24.9	5.92	2.09	0.027	0.017	...	...	α + γ	NF	α	C
24.8	7.63	2.10	0.024	0.014	...	...	α + γ	NF	α	NF
24.9	9.50	2.10	0.024	0.019	...	...	α + γ	NF	α	NF

(a) α, ferrite; γ, austenite. (b) NF, no failure; C, intergranular caustic cracking. Source: Ref 123

Table 7 Reported IASCC failures of reactor components

Component	Material	Reactor type	Possible sources of stress
Fuel cladding	304 SS	BWR	Fuel swelling
Fuel cladding	304 SS	PWR	Fuel swelling
Fuel cladding(a)	20Cr-25Ni-Nb	AGR	Fuel swelling
Fuel-cladding ferrules	20Cr-25Ni-Nb	SGHWR	Fabrication
Neutron source holders	304 SS	BWR	Welding, Be swelling
Instrument dry tubes	304 SS	BWR	Fabrication
Control-rod absorber tubes	304 SS	BWR	B4C swelling
Fuel-bundle cap screws	304 SS	BWR	Fabrication
Control-rod follower rivets	304 SS	BWR	Fabrication
Control-blade handle	304 SS	BWR	Low stress
Control-blade sheath	304 SS	BWR	Low stress
Control blades	304 SS	PWR	Low stress
Plate-type control blades	304 SS	BWR	Low stress
Various bolts(b)	A-286	PWR, BWR	Service
Steam separator dryer bolts(b)	A-286	BWR	Service
Shroud-head bolts(b)	600	BWR	Service
Various bolts	X-750	BWR, PWR	Service
Guide-tube support pins	X-750	PWR	Service
Jet-pump beams	X-750	BWR	Service
Various springs	X-750	BWR, PWR	Service
Various springs	718	PWR	Service

(a) Cracking in advanced gas-cooled reactor (AGR) fuel occurred during storage in spent fuel pond. (b) Cracking of core internals occurs away from high neutron and gamma fluxes.

SCC in the Presence of Other Sulfur Species

In addition to SCC in the presence of hydrogen sulfide and polythionic acids, SCC caused by thiosulfate, thiocyanate, and sulfate solutions has been investigated. Stress-corrosion cracking of sensitized type 304 in thiosulfate solutions at ambient temperatures is of interest to the nuclear industry. Borate solutions are stored in stainless steel tanks in containment buildings for use as sprays in case of nuclear accidents. In addition to borate, the solutions contain thiosulfate anions that would react with iodine fission products. Following earlier reports of SCC of sensitized austenitic stainless steels in these borate solutions (Ref 139), thiosulfate was identified as the critical species causing SCC (Ref 140). Laboratory tests showed that SCC could occur with very low concentrations of $Na_2S_2O_3$, although in the presence of boric acid higher concentrations were required (Ref 140). Cathodic protection was shown to prevent SCC (Ref 140).

Thiosulfate solutions have been used in recent work related to a percolation model of intergranular SCC in sensitized alloys (Ref 141). Essentially, this model states that a continuous path of susceptible grain boundaries must be present for a crack to propagate macroscopic distances, and that the percentage of sensitized grain-boundary facets required to achieve this can be derived from a percolation model. A percolation threshold (p_c) of about 24% was derived for a model lattice of boundaries, and approximate correspondence to this was achieved in slow-strain-rate tests of material heat treated for various lengths of time. Below p_c, small cracks initiated but ran out of susceptible grain boundaries. A percolation model may explain (Ref 142) the extremely abrupt onset of SCC with increasing sensitization time.

Heavily sensitized type 304 stainless steel has been found (Ref 143) to be susceptible to SCC in thiocyanate solutions at concentrations greater than 10^{-4} mol/L.

Stress-corrosion cracking of tempered (sensitized) type 403 martensitic stainless steel is of interest to the power industry, because the martensitic grades are used as blade materials in steam turbines. The impurities found in the steam include sulfate. Tempered martensitic type 403 has been found (Ref 144) to suffer pitting corrosion and intergranular SCC in 0.01 M Na_2SO_4 at temperatures of 75 and 100 °C (165 and 212 °F), but not at the lower temperatures of 25 and 50 °C (75 and 120 °F). Significant sulfate contamination of the passive film from solution was found, but the level of contamination could not be correlated with the SCC susceptibility of the alloy. Nonmetallic inclusions (MnS) and carbide precipitates were found to act as nucleation sites for corrosion pits, which in turn gave rise to SCC (Ref 144).

Stress-corrosion cracking has been noted (Ref 54) in a 26Cr-1Mo low-interstitial ferritic stainless steel in 130 °C (270 °F) water containing chloride, hydrogen sulfide, ammonia, and traces of oil, thiocyanates, and organic acids. The possibility that this failure may be due to hydrogen embrittlement cannot be ruled out.

Irradiation-Assisted SCC

Irradiation-assisted stress-corrosion cracking describes premature cracking of material/environment systems exposed to ionizing irradiation. This broad interpretation attributes to IASCC all instances of environmental cracking accelerated by radiation, whether acting singly or conjointly in altering water chemistry, material microchemistry, material hardness, creep behavior, and so on. While initially interpreted as inducing a form of cracking that would not occur in its absence, radiation is now more broadly viewed as an accelerate of the environmental cracking process.

From a practical perspective, IASCC is principally associated with intergranular cracking of austenitic alloys in high-temperature water under neutron-irradiation exposure, which alters many material properties and produces radiolysis of water. Classic examples of the neutron-fluence dependence of IASCC of austenitic stainless steel are shown in Fig. 39(a) (Ref 145, 146) for control-blade sheath cracking in high-conductivity BWRs and in Fig. 39(b) (Ref 147) for laboratory tests on preirradiated material. In both instances, a characteristic rise in intergranular cracking occurs for fluences above approximately 5×10^{20} n/cm^2 (energy >1 MeV), which corresponds to nearly 0.7 lattice displacements per atom. The contribution of oxidizing water chemistries produced by radiolysis is also indicated by the strong dependence of cracking on dissolved oxygen at a fluence of approximately 3×10^{21} n/cm² in Fig. 39(b).

Overview of Service Experience. Initial concern for aggressive high radiation conditions was reflected in the specification of solution-annealed materials for most light water reactor (LWR) core components. Nevertheless, IASCC was first observed in the early 1960s in fuel elements where high stresses associated with fuel swelling were considered an essential and unusual ingredient. However, IASCC was later reported in a variety of high- and low-stress core components and in situ test specimens in BWRs, commercial pressurized water reactors (PWRs), U.S. Navy test PWRs, and steam-generating heavy water reactors (SGHWRs), although there is not complete consensus on whether cracking is properly attributed to IASCC in all instances. While IASCC is of primary interest in light water reactor core materials, it is also of concern in applications such as fusion reactors and high-level radioactive waste containers. Reported failures of various reactor internal components are summarized in Table 7.

The effects of radiation damage on material properties have been widely recognized and studied for decades. Radiation damage is induced by a variety of high-energy particles that cause lattice atoms to be displaced to interstitial sites, leaving behind vacancies. These radiation-induced interstitials (primarily iron, chromium, and nickel) should be distinguished from elements such as carbon and nitrogen, which normally occupy interstitial sites.

The motion of vacancies and interstitials formed during displacement damage causes nonequilibrium segregation at grain boundaries and other vacancy/interstitial sites. This nonequilibrium segregation is referred to as radiation-induced segregation (RIS). This migration of defects can also result in the formation of defect clusters; those consisting of interstitials can evolve into dislocation loops, while vacancy clusters can develop into microvoids or cavities (Fig. 40). The formation of these clustered defects causes an increase in hardness, yield strength, and ultimate tensile strength, a loss of ductility and fracture toughness, and an increased susceptibility to corrosion and SCC. More detailed information on IASCC, including an extensive bibliography on this subject, can be found in Ref 148.

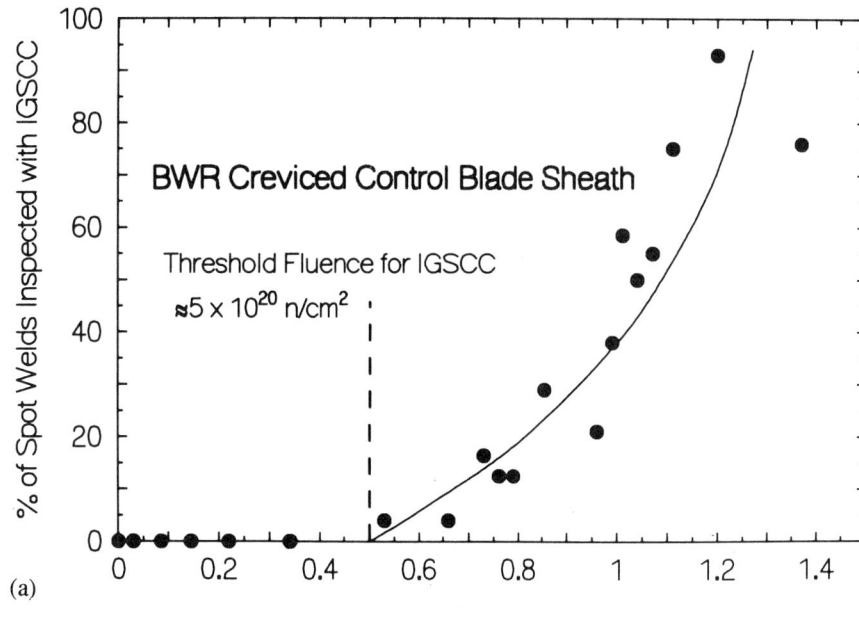

(a)

Neutron Fluence, n/cm² x 10²¹ (E>1MeV)

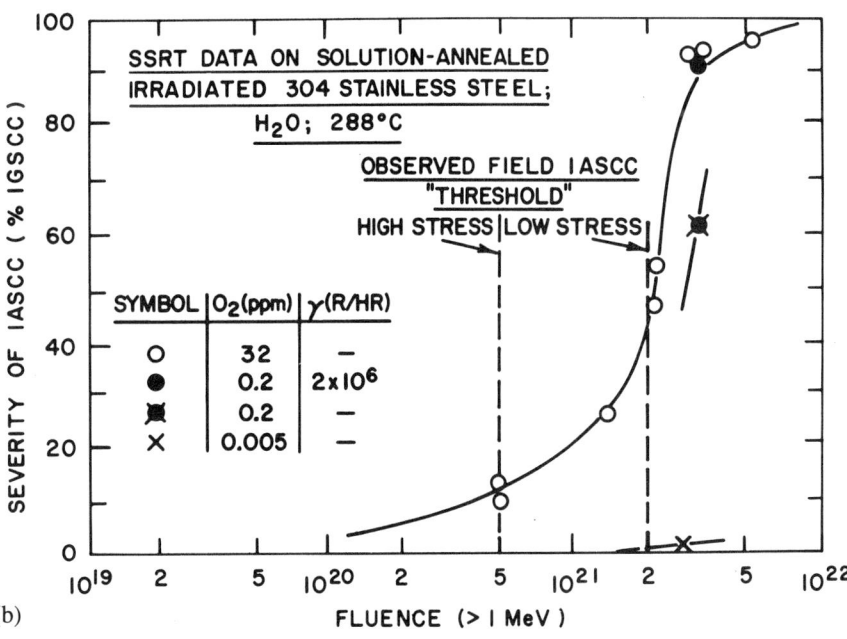

(b)

Fig. 39 Dependence of intergranular stress-corrosion cracking on fast neutron fluence for (a) creviced control-blade sheath in high conductivity BWRs (Source: Ref 145, 146) and (b) as measured in slow-strain-rate tests at 3.7 ×10⁻⁷/s on preirradiated type 304 in 288 °C (550 °F) water (Source: Ref 147). The effect of corrosion potential via changes in dissolved oxygen is shown at a fluence of approximately 2×10^{21} n/cm².

Hydrogen Embrittlement

For SCC in aqueous environments, such as saline solutions, two mechanisms have been discussed in the literature. The earlier discussions (Ref 149) distinguished between SCC that is accelerated by the application of anodic currents and SCC that is accelerated by cathodic currents. An example of this behavior is shown in Fig. 41 (Ref 150) for an Fe-12Cr-1Mo-0.33V-0.25C martensitic stainless steel in a neutral salt solution.

Subsequent studies (Ref 151) demonstrated that hydrogen enters steel when it is in contact with a neutral sodium chloride solution at both anodic and cathodic potentials. It is now widely accepted (Ref 95, 96) that in high-strength stainless steels, hydrogen embrittlement is the crack-propagation mechanism under both anodic and cathodic conditions. Anodic dissolution may, however, contribute to the initiation of the crack nucleus by

processes such as pitting. It should also be noted that the presence of the chloride ion is not necessary to cause hydrogen embrittlement in the high-strength stainless steels (Ref 149).

It has been customary to compare the cracking of high-strength stainless steels in sulfide and sulfide-free service environments that contain sulfides and in environments that do not contain sulfides. Sulfide environments are of particular

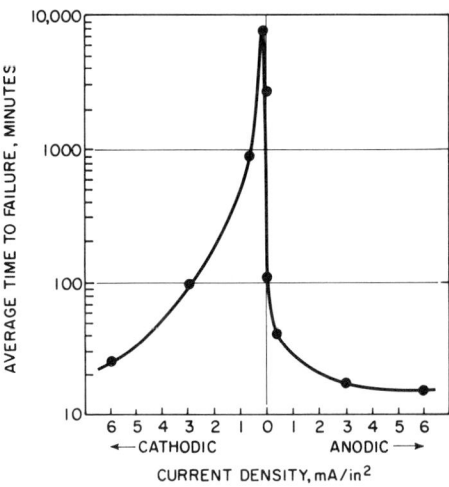

Fig. 41 Effect of applied current on the time to failure of an Fe-12Cr-1Mo-0.33V-0.25C martensitic stainless steel in an oxygenated 3% NaCl solution at pH 6.5. Source: Ref 150

0.25 μm

Fig. 40 Cavities (indicated as the white rectangles and circles) formed in type 316 stainless steel irradiated to 60 displacements per atom at 600 °C (1110 °F) in the high-flux isotope reactor. Courtesy of Oak Ridge National Laboratory

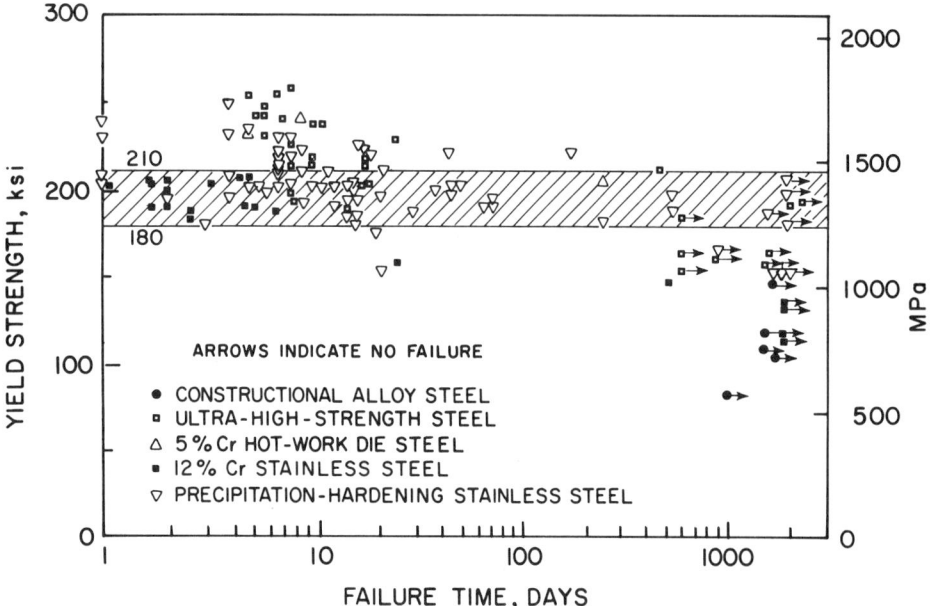

Fig. 42 Effect of yield strength on the times to failure of various steels exposed to a marine atmosphere at 75% of the yield stress. Source: Ref 152

interest to the oil industry, and there is a large measure of agreement with the view that cracking in sulfide environments (known as sulfide SCC) is a form of hydrogen embrittlement. Sulfide is a hydrogen-ion recombination poison that promotes the entry of hydrogen into a metal.

Martensitic and Precipitation-Hardening Stainless Steels

Hydrogen Embrittlement in Sulfide-Free Environments. Most evaluations of the resistance of high-strength stainless steels in sulfide-free environments have been carried out either in natural marine atmospheres or in chloride solutions. Among the parameters that determine hydrogen-embrittlement resistance, yield strength has been identified as having a dominant effect. Hydrogen embrittlement can occur quite readily in most high-strength materials irrespective of composition or structure. This is illustrated by the data presented in Fig. 42 (Ref 152) for a variety of high-strength materials. It is evident that martensitic and precipitation-hardening stainless steels can exhibit hydrogen embrittlement in marine atmosphere at yield strengths above 1035 MPa (150 ksi). This applies to smooth specimens. In notched or precracked specimens, hydrogen embrittlement may occur at lower yield strengths.

Tempering, in the case of martensitic stainless steels, and overaging, in the case of precipitation-hardening stainless steels, can significantly lower the yield strength and hence increase resistance to hydrogen embrittlement. An example of the effect of tempering on the yield strength and hydrogen embrittlement resistance of a martensitic stainless steel in marine atmosphere is presented in Fig. 43 (Ref 153). The relationship between yield strength and K_{ISCC} of a number of precipitation-hardening stainless steels in a 3.5% NaCl solution is shown in Table 8 (Ref 154). Other studies (Ref 27) employing fracture-mechanics specimens have shown that for type 431 martensitic stainless steel, the untempered (as-quenched) martensite exhibits much faster crack-growth rates and much lower K_{ISCC} values than the quenched and tempered material. Accordingly, it has become accepted practice to define resistance to hydrogen embrittlement in terms of yield strength, hardness, or heat-treatment conditions. For example, the Marshall Space Flight Center permits the use of precipitation-hardening stainless steels in space vehicles and associated equipment only in certain conditions of heat treatment known to improve resistance to hydrogen embrittlement, as outlined in Table 9 (Ref 155).

Table 8 K_{ISCC} values for several precipitation-hardening stainless steels determined using 3.5% NaCl solution

Material	Yield strength		K_{IC}		K_{ISCC}	
	MPa	ksi	MPa√m	ksi√in.	MPa√m	ksi√in.
17-4 PH	1215	176	56	51	56	51
17-4 PH	1090	158	131	119	131	119
15-5 PH	1210	175	106	96	85	77
15-5 PH	1090	158	132	120	132	120
PH 13-8 Mo	1435	208	81	74	81	74
AM-362	1360	197	33	30	11	10
AM-362	1210	175	44	40	30	27
Custom 455	1695	246	79	72	79	72

Source: Ref 154

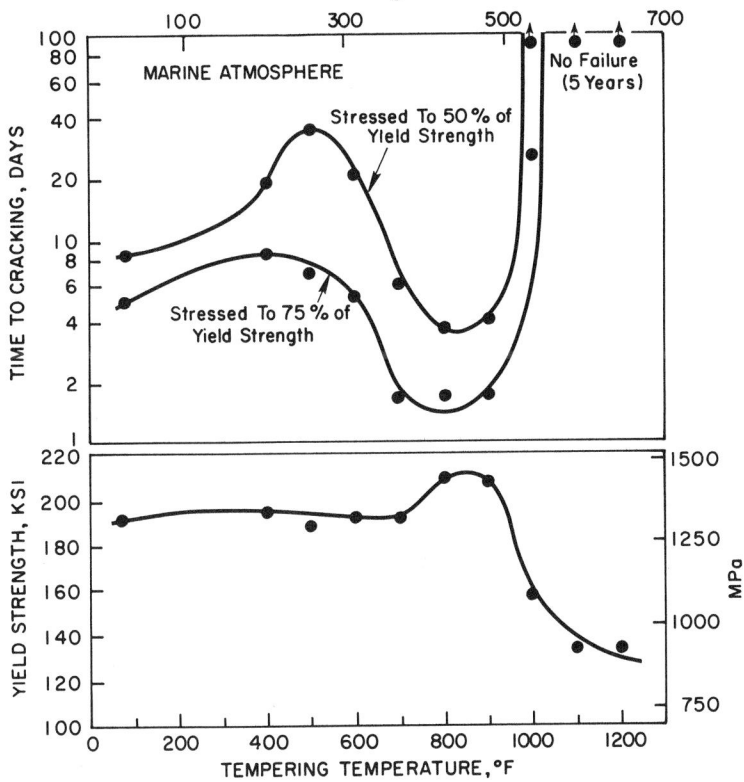

Fig. 43 Effect of tempering temperature on the cracking resistance and yield strength of an Fe-12Cr-1Mo-0.33V-0.25C martensitic stainless steel. Source: Ref 153

Table 9 Precipitation-hardening stainless steels with high resistance to hydrogen embrittlement as determined by the Marshall Space Flight Center

Material	Condition
A-286	All
AM-350	SCT 1000 and above
AM-355	SCT 1000 and above
ALMAR 362	H1000 and above
Custom 455	H1000 and above
15-5 PH	H1000 and above
PH 14-8 Mo	CH900 and SRH950 and above
PH 15-7 Mo	CH900
17-7 PH	CH900

Source: Ref 155

Regarding environmental factors, it has been shown (Ref 150) that pH can have an important effect on cracking resistance. For a martensitic stainless steel heat treated to give a yield strength of 1400 MPa (203 ksi), no hydrogen embrittlement was observed at a pH higher than 11.5, whereas rapid cracking was found at a low pH (Ref 150). However, the acidification of the solution within the crack could lead to hydrogen embrittlement not anticipated from tests in neutral solutions.

Resistance to hydrogen embrittlement can be improved by alloying with niobium (Ref 96) and introducing δ-ferrite into the structure (Ref 156).

Detrimental features are manganese sulfide inclusions, which provide pits that can act as crack-initiation sites (Ref 157), and certain surface-machining procedures that generate localized subsurface cold-worked regions at which cracking can initiate (Ref 158).

Hydrogen Embrittlement in Sulfide-Containing Environments. It is well known that the presence of hydrogen sulfide in various environments decreases the hydrogen embrittlement resistance of high-strength stainless steels. This problem became prominent in the 1950s as a result of failures in the oil industry and has received considerable attention. Most

of the studies have dealt with steels other than high-strength stainless steels; however, there is sufficient information about the latter, because many evaluations have included some of these materials. The first extensive investigation (Ref 159), which included the precipitation-hardening stainless steels AM-350, AM-355, A-286, and 17-4PH, led to the conclusion that in sulfide-containing environments none of the steels tested completely resisted hydrogen embrittlement at yield strengths above 690 MPa (100 ksi). It was also established (Ref 159) that there exists a minimum hardness below which cracking does not occur for a given applied stress, and that this minimum hardness increases with decreasing hydrogen sulfide concentration. Numerous subsequent studies, covering a wide range of materials, have led to the issuance of NACE Standard MR-01-75 (Ref 160). It lists metallic material requirements for resistance to hydrogen embrittlement for petroleum production, drilling, gathering, and flowline equipment, and it lists field processing facilities to be used in hydrogen sulfide service. This standard is revised annually. The part of the listing that relates to stainless steels is summarized in Table 10. Factors such as low pH, an increase in temperature and hydrogen sulfide concentration, galvanic coupling to anodic materials, an increase in yield strength, and cold work facilitate hydrogen embrittlement, and com-

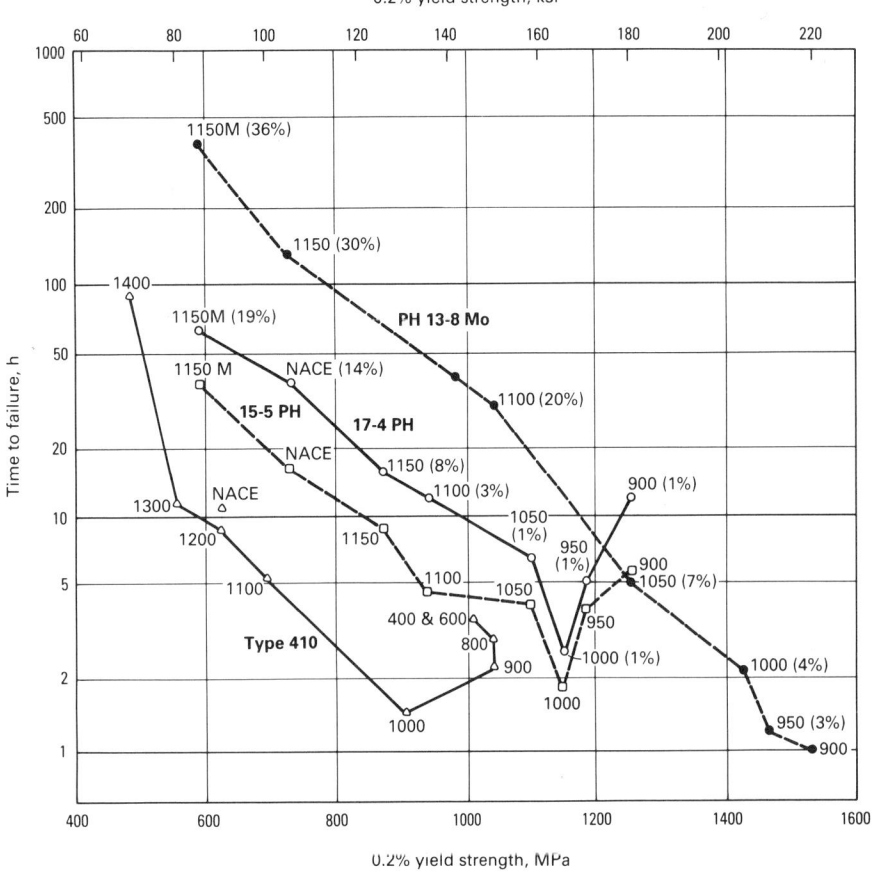

Fig. 44 Time to failure of various stainless steels as a function of yield strength when tested under 345 MPa (50 ksi) of applied stress in saturated hydrogen sulfide. Numbers adjacent to data points represent tempering or aging treatments; parenthetical values indicate approximate amounts of austenite. Source: Ref 162

Table 10 Stainless steels listed in NACE Standard MR-01-75(a) as acceptable for sulfide environments

Stainless steel type	Acceptable grades
Austenitic(b)	302, 304, 304L, 310, 316, 316L, 317, 321, 347, Carpenter 20Cb3
Ferritic(c)	405, 430
Martensitic(d)	410, CA15, CA15M
Precipitation-hardening	A-286(e), 17-4 PH(f)

(a) Revised annually. Reader should consult Technical Practices Committee of NACE for considered modifications. Some of the materials listed may be susceptible to chloride cracking in certain environments. (b) Annealed condition, not strengthened by cold work. (c) Annealed condition, hardness of 22 HRC (max). (d) Double tempered to hardness of 22 HRC (max). (e) Aged to hardness of 35 HRC (max). (f) Aged to hardness of 33 HRC (max)

pliance with NACE Standard MR-01-75 may not be adequate to prevent failures under all conditions. In this regard, hydrogen-embrittlement failures have been reported (Ref 161) in type 410 (UNS S41000) and 17-4PH (UNS S17400) stainless steel tubing hangers in wellhead equipment, even though the hanger material met NACE Standard MR-01-75 hardness requirements. Figure 44 compares several grades of precipitation-hardening stainless steel with type 410 martensitic stainless tested in an aqueous environment saturated with hydrogen sulfide (Ref 162). The numbers adjacent to each data point represent the tempering or aging treatment. Generally, the same trend of decreasing time to failure with increasing yield strength is observed as for low-alloy steels (Ref 163).

Ferritic Stainless Steels

Hydrogen embrittlement was identified (Ref 164, 165) as a potential problem for superferritic stainless steel condenser tubes for seawater-cooled power plant condensers in the mid-1980s. In many instances, these tubes are used in conjunction with copper alloy tubesheets and cast iron or steel waterboxes, and the latter materials require cathodic protection by impressed-current systems. Cathodic protection at about –0.8 V satu-

rated calomel electrode (SCE) is necessary to protect the tubesheets and waterboxes from corrosive attack. Both superferritics, 29-4C (UNS S44735) and Sea-Cure (UNS S44660), exhibit hydrogen embrittlement when they are cathodically polarized to potentials in the range of –0.9 to –1.4 V (SCE). The data for 29-4C are shown in Fig. 45 (Ref 164), which demonstrates that overprotection at potentials more negative than –0.8 V (SCE) must be carefully avoided. Because hydrogen can also be picked up from annealing in hydrogen atmospheres or acid pickling, these processes should be avoided for superferritic stainless steels. It is also claimed that the loss in ductility of the superferritics that results from hydrogen charging can be eliminated by outgassing the alloy at slightly elevated temperatures (Ref 165). Recently the UNS S44660 (Sea-Cure) alloy composition has been modified to contain %C + %N = 0.02 max, and the titanium stabilizing addition has been replaced by niobium (Ref 165). The new developmental alloy, designated by the trade name Sea-Cure Hy-Resist, reportedly can be cathodically protected to –2.0 V (SCE) without exhibiting hydrogen embrittlement (Ref 166).

Prior to the discovery of hydrogen embrittlement of superferritic stainless steels at cathodic potentials in seawater, most of the investigations of hydrogen embrittlement of ferritic stainless

steels had been done under conditions of cathodic charging in sulfuric acid solutions containing arsenic (Ref 167-170). Applied stresses at or above the yield stress and the presence of a hydrogen-ion recombination poison (e.g., an arsenic compound) in the sulfuric acid solutions are required for hydrogen embrittlement to occur (Ref 170). Increasing the heat-treatment temperature and increasing the molybdenum content of the ferritic stainless steel reduce resistance to hydrogen embrittlement (Ref 170), as does applying test stresses perpendicular to the cold-rolling direction of the steel (Ref 168). The crack path of hydrogen embrittlement in the ferritic steels is transgranular (Ref 98, 170), with some evidence of intergranular cracking at the crack-initiation stage (Ref 98).

Austenitic Stainless Steels (Ref 163)

The response of austenitic stainless steels to hydrogen-bearing environments is also basically related to their strength level.

Austenitic stainless steels are highly resistant to hydrogen cracking in the annealed or lightly cold-worked condition, but they can become quite susceptible when heavily cold worked. This increased susceptibility to hydrogen cracking due to a higher yield strength from cold working is similar to the dependence of carbon and low-alloy steels on strength. Decreased resistance to hydrogen for highly cold-worked austenitic stainless steels is largely attributed to the deformation-induced formation of martensite. For those austenitic stainless steels having a very stable austenite phase and high yield strength (such as 21Cr-6Ni-9Mn) susceptibility is considered to be solely a function of yield strength, similar to the behavior of low-alloy steels.

Other factors that may affect the susceptibility of austenitic stainless steels to hydrogen damage are the possible formation of a metastable hydride phase that would produce a hydride-based fracture path and the interaction of hydrogen with stacking faults to reduce stacking fault energy in the austenite, leading to planar slip and brittle

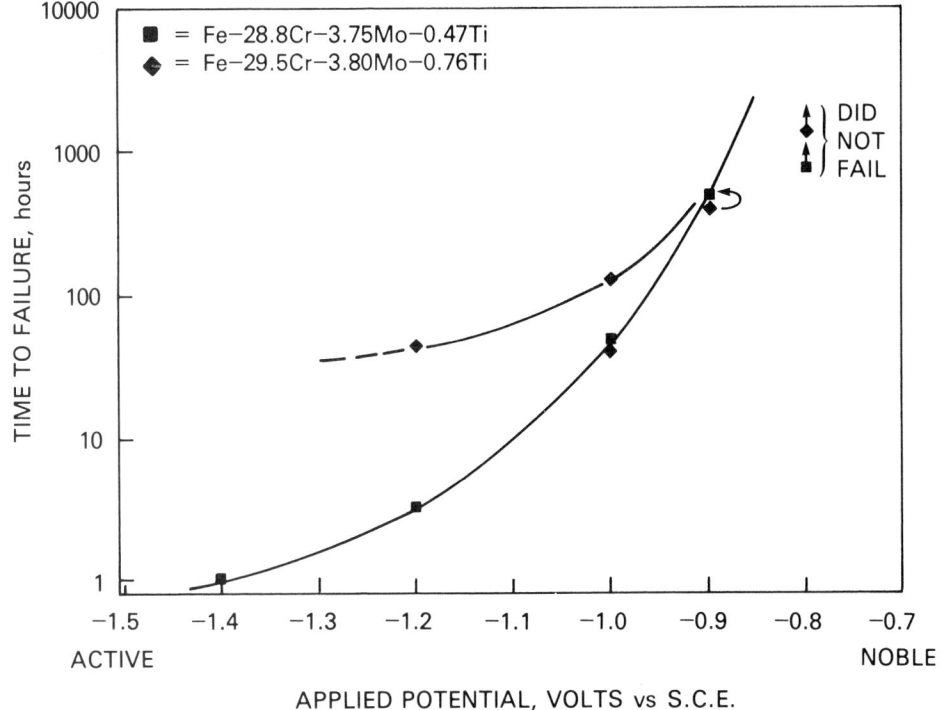

Fig. 45 Time to failure by hydrogen embrittlement of two heats of as-welded Al 29-4C stainless steel in ambient-temperature synthetic seawater as a function of applied potential. Source: Ref 164

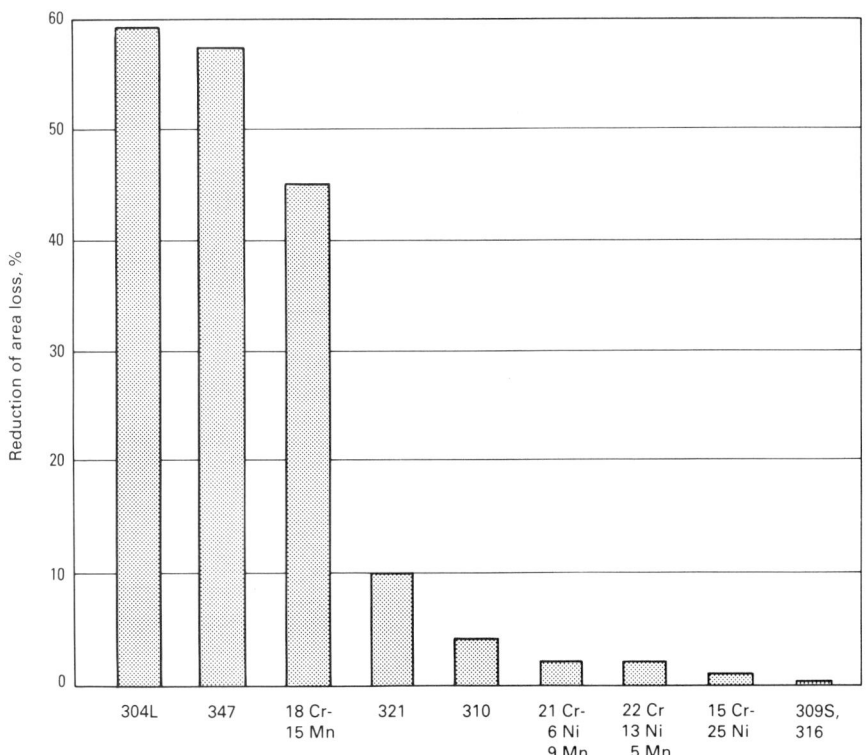

Fig. 46 Ductility loss for several austenitic stainless steels in high-pressure hydrogen. Source: Ref 171

area for several austenitic stainless steels in high-pressure hydrogen (Ref 171). It is apparent that a wide variation in hydrogen damage exists between these various austentic alloys. Type 304L is the most susceptible to loss in tensile ductility, and the stable austenitic alloys, such as 15Cr-25Ni, are almost unaffected.

ACKNOWLEDGMENTS

The information in this article is largely taken from:

- A.J. Sedriks, Stress-Corrosion Cracking of Stainless Steels, *Stress-Corrosion Cracking—Materials Performance and Evaluation*, R.H. Jones, Ed., ASM International, 1992, p 91-130
- P.L. Andresen, Irradiation-Assisted Stress-Corrosion Cracking, *Stress-Corrosion Cracking—Materials Performance and Evaluation*, R.H. Jones, Ed., ASM International, 1992, p 181-210
- G.F. Vander Voort, Embrittlement of Steels, *Properties and Selection: Irons, Steels, and High-Performance Alloys*, Vol 1, *ASM Handbook*, ASM International, 1990, p 689-736
- R.L. Klueh, Effect of Neutron Irradiation on Properties of Steels, *Properties and Selection: Irons, Steels, and High-Performance Alloys*, Vol 1, *ASM Handbook*, ASM International, 1990, p 653-661
- B. Craig, Hydrogen Damage, *Corrosion*, Vol 13, *ASM Handbook*, (formerly 9th ed. *Metals Handbook*), ASM International, 1987, p 163-172
- B.M. Gordon and G.M. Gordon, Corrosion in Boiling Water Reactors, *Corrosion*, Vol 13, *ASM Handbook*, (formerly 9th ed. *Metals Handbook*), ASM International, 1987, p 927-937

REFERENCES

1. A.J. Sedriks, *Corrosion of Stainless Steels*, John Wiley and Sons, 1979
2. Environment-Induced Cracking of Metals, R.P. Gangloff and M.B. Ives, Ed., National Association of Corrosion Engineers, 1990
3. V.N. Krivobok, *The Book of Stainless Steels*, E.E. Thum, Ed., American Society for Steel Treating, 1933
4. C. Husen and C.H. Samans, *Chem. Eng.*, 27 Jan 1969, p 178
5. B. Strauss, H. Schottky, and J. Hinnuber, *Z. Anorg. Chem.*, Vol 188, 1930, p 309
6. E.C. Bain, R.H. Abom, and J.B. Rutheford, *Trans. Am. Soc. Steel Treat.*, Vol 21, 1933, p 481
7. J.E. Alexander, "Alternative Alloys for BWR Piping Applications," Final Report, NP-2671-LD, General Electric Co., Oct 1982
8. P.S. Maiya and W.J. Shack, *Corrosion*, Vol 41, 1985, p 630
9. P.L. Andresen, F.P. Ford, S.M. Murphy, and J.M. Perks, State of Knowledge of Radiation Effects on Environmental Cracking in Light Water Reactor Core Materials, *Proc. 4th Int. Conf. Environmental Degradation of Materials in Nuclear Power Systems—Water Reac-*

fracture. The degree of participation of any of these factors has not been fully established.

Just as a similarity exists between austenitic stainless steels and low-alloy steels at the high-strength end of the spectrum, the lower-strength austenitics behave in the same manner as the low-alloy steels in hydrogen by a reduction in ductility. Figure 46 shows the loss in reduction of

tors, National Association of Corrosion Engineers, 1990

10. T.R. Anthony, Solute Segregation and Stresses around Growing Voids in Metals, *Proc. Radiation-Induced Voids in Metals and Alloys,* J.W. Corbet and L.C. Laniello, Ed., U.S. Atomic Energy Commission Symp. Series 26, CONF 710601, 1971, p 630
11. S.M. Bruemmer, L.A. Charlot, and E.P. Simonen, "Grain Boundary Chemistry Effects on Irradiation-Assisted Stress Corrosion Cracking," Paper 506, presented at Corrosion/90, National Association of Corrosion Engineers, 1990
12. A.J. Jacobs and G.P. Wozadlo, *J. Mater. Eng.,* Vol 9 (No. 4), 1988, p 345
13. R.H. Jones, Some Radiation Damage-Stress Corrosion Synergisms in Austenitic Stainless Steels, *Proc. 2nd Int. Symp. Environmental Degradation of Materials in Nuclear Power Systems—Water Reactors,* American Nuclear Society, 1985, p 173
14. G.R. Caskey, R.S. Ondrejcin, P. Aldred, R.B. Davis, and S.A. Wilson, "Effects of Irradiation on Intergranular Stress Corrosion Cracking of Type 304 Stainless Steel," Paper 504, presented at Corrosion/90, National Association of Corrosion Engineers, 1990
15. "Stainless Steel and High Alloy Tubing and Pipe," Trent Tube, 1990
16. M.A. Scheil, in *Symposium on Stress Corrosion Cracking of Metals,* STP 64, ASTM, 1945, p 395
17. I.B. Casale, *Corrosion,* Vol 23, 1967, p 314
18. M. Kowaka and T. Kudo, *Trans. Jpn. Inst. Met.,* Vol 16, 1975, p 385
19. I.A. Maier, C. Manfredi, and J.R. Galvele, *Corros. Sci.,* Vol 25 (No. 1), 1985, p 15
20. A.J. Sedriks, *Stress Corrosion Cracking Test Methods,* National Association of Corrosion Engineers, 1990
21. R.M. Latanision and R.W. Staehle, *Proc. Conf. Fundamental Aspects of Stress Corrosion Cracking,* National Association of Corrosion Engineers, 1969, p 214
22. G.J. Theus and R.W. Staehle, *Stress Corrosion Cracking and Hydrogen Embrittlement of Iron Base Alloys,* National Association of Corrosion Engineers, 1977, p 845
23. H.R. Copson, Physical Metallurgy of Stress Corrosion Fracture, *Interscience,* 1959, p 247
24. R.W. Staehle, *Trans. Inst. Chem. Eng.,* Vol 47, 1969, p T-227
25. A.J. Sedriks, *J. Inst. Met.,* Vol 101, 1973, p 225
26. A.J. Sedriks, *Corrosion,* Vol 31, 1975, p 339
27. M.O. Speidel, *Metall. Trans. A,* Vol 12, 1981, p 779
28. R.L. Beauchamp, M.S. thesis, Ohio State University, 1963
29. J.J. Royuela and R.W. Staehle, unpublished results quoted in Ref 21
30. J. Hochman and J. Bourrat, *Compt. Rend. Acad. Sci.,* Vol 255, 17 Dec 1962
31. J.E. Truman, Brown-Firth Research Laboratories, Sheffield, U.K., private communication
32. R.W. Staehle, J.J. Royuela, T.L. Raredon, E. Serrate, C.R. Morin, and R.W. Farrar, *Corrosion,* Vol 26, 1970, p 451

33. H.H. Uhlig and R.A. White, *Trans. ASM,* Vol 52, 1960, p 830
34. F.S. Lang, *Corrosion,* Vol 18, 1962, p 378t
35. D.G. Tufanov, *Metalloved. Term. Obrabotka Met.,* 15 April 1964
36. D. van Rooyen, in *Proc. 1st Int. Conf. Stress Corrosion Cracking,* Butterworths, 1961
37. J.G. Hinees and E.R.W. Jones, *Corros. Sci.,* Vol 1, 1961, p 88
38. M. da Cunha Belo and J. Montuelle, in *Proc. NATO Conf. Theory of Stress Corrosion Cracking in Alloys,* March 1971 (Ericeiria, Portugal)
39. M. Kowaka and H. Fujikawa, *Sumitomo Search,* No. 7, 1972, p 10
40. H.E. Hanninen, *Int. Met. Rev.,* Vol 24 (No. 3), 1979, p 85
41. E.E. Denhard, Jr., Effects of Composition and Heat Treatment on the Stress-Corrosion Cracking of Austenitic Stainless Steels, *Corrosion,* Vol 16, July 1960, p 359t-369t
42. H. Spahn, G.H. Wagner, and U. Steinhoff, Methods to Prevent Stress Corrosion Cracking, *Techn. Ueberwachung,* Vol 14, 1973, p 292
43. K. Fassler, *Korrosionum,* H. Grafen, F. Kahl, and A. Rahmel, Ed., Vol 1, Verlag Chemie, 1974, p 136
44. A.J. Sedriks, *Corrosion,* Vol 42 (No. 7), 1986, p 376
45. M.G. Fontana, F.H. Beck, and J.W. Flowers, *Met. Prog.,* Vol 80 (No. 6), 1961, p 99
46. D. Warren, "Microstructure and Corrosion Resistance of Austenitic Stainless Steels," Sixth Annual Liberty Bell Corrosion Course, National Association of Corrosion Engineers, Sept 1968
47. F.S. Lang, *Corrosion,* Vol 18, 1962, p 378t
48. R.F. Overman, *Corrosion,* Vol 22, 1966, p 48
49. J.E. Truman, The Effects of Composition and Structure on the Resistance to Stress Corrosion Cracking of Stainless Steels, *British Nuclear Energy Society Symposium on Effects of Environment on Material Properties in Nuclear Systems,* Paper 10, Institute of Civil Engineers, July 1971
50. R.W. Cochran and R.W. Staehle, *Corrosion,* Vol 11, 1968, p 369
51. K.L. Money and W.W. Kirk, *Mater. Perform.,* Vol 17 (No. 7), July 1978, p 28
52. F. Zucchi, G. Trabanelli, G. Rocchini, and G. Perboni, *Corros. Sci.,* Vol 29 (No. 4), 1989, p 417
53. V.L. Barnwell et al., Effect of Grain Size on Stress Corrosion of Type 302 Austenitic Stainless Steel, *Corrosion,* Vol 22, Sept 1966, p 261-264
54. E.C. Hoxie, Some Corrosion Considerations in the Selection of Stainless Steel for Pressure Vessels and Piping, *Pressure Vessels and Piping: A Decade of Progress,* Vol 3, American Society of Mechanical Engineers, 1977
55. J.W. Oldfield and B. Todd, *Mater. Perform.,* Vol 29 (No. 12), 1990, p 57
56. C.P. Dillon, *Mater. Perform.,* Vol 29 (No. 12), 1990, p 66
57. R.M. Kain, *Mater. Perform.,* Vol 29 (No. 12), 1990, p 60

58. J.B. Gnanamoorthy, *Mater. Perform.,* Vol 29 (No. 12), 1990, p 63
59. J.Q. Lackey and M.A. Streicher, *J. Mater.,* Vol 3 (No. 4), 1968, p 983
60. N.A. Nielsen, *Corrosion,* Vol 27 (No. 5), 1971, p 173
61. J.P. Harston and J.C. Scully, *Corrosion,* Vol 25, 1969, p 493
62. S.J. Acello and N.D. Greene, *Corrosion,* Vol 18, 1962, p 286
63. S. Torchio, *Corros. Sci.,* Vol 20, 1980, p 555; A.I. Maier, C. Manfredi, and J.R. Galvele, *Corros. Sci.,* Vol 25, 1985, p 15
64. H. Grafen, *Corros. Sci.,* Vol 7, 1967, p 177
65. J.E. Truman, Methods Available for Avoiding SCC of Austenitic Stainless Steels in Potentially Dangerous Environments, *Stainless Steels,* ISI Publication 117, Iron and Steel Institute, 1969, p 101
66. D. Warren, Chloride-Bearing Cooling Water and the Stress Corrosion Cracking of Austenitic Stainless Steel, *Proc. 15th Annual Purdue Industrial Waste Conference,* Purdue University, May 1960, p 1
67. A.W. Dana and W.B. DeLong, *Corrosion,* Vol 12 (No. 7), 1956, p 309t
68. H.R. Baker, M.C. Bloom, R.N. Bolster, and C.R. Singleberry, *Corrosion,* Vol 26, 1970, p 420
69. Z. Szklarska-Smialowska, *Corrosion,* Vol 27, 1971, p 223
70. K.C. Thomas et al., Stress Corrosion of Type 304 Stainless Steel in Chloride Environments, *Corrosion,* Vol 20, March 1964, p 89t-92t
71. E. Brauns and H. Temes, *Werkst. Korros.,* Vol 19, 1968, p 1
72. A.S. Couper, *Mater. Protect.,* Vol 8, 1969, p 17
73. Y. Ogayu and T. Shoji, Cathodic Protection of Stress Corrosion Cracking of Austenitic Stainless Steels in Dilute NaCl Solutions, in *Proc. Life Prediction of Corrodible Structures,* 5-8 Nov 1991 (Hawaii), National Association of Corrosion Engineers
74. R.L. Shamakian, A.R. Troiano, and R.F. Hehemann, *Corrosion,* Vol 36, 1980, p 279
75. J.H. Phillips and W.J. Singely, *Corrosion,* Vol 15, 1959, p 450t
76. S.P. Rideout, W.C. Rion, and J. Wade, *Trans. Am. Nucl. Soc.,* Vol 7, 1964, p 419
77. H.H. Uhlig, *J. Electrochem. Soc.,* Vol 116, 1969, p 173
78. M.L. Holzworth and A.E. Symonds, *Corrosion,* Vol 25, 1969, p 287
79. P.P. Snowden, *Nucl. Eng.,* Vol 6, 1961, p 409
80. S.A. Balezin and N.I. Podovaev, *J. Appl. Chem. USSR,* Vol 33, June 1990, p 1287
81. C.S. O'Dell, B.F. Brown, and R.T. Foley, *Corrosion,* Vol 36 (No. 4), 1980, p 183
82. C. Edeleanu, *J. Iron Steel Inst.,* Vol 173, 1953, p 140
83. R.M. Davison, T. DeBold, and M.J. Johnson, *Corrosion,* 9th ed., Vol 13, *Metals Handbook,* ASM International, 1987, p 547
84. L. Bednar, *Corrosion,* Vol 35, 1979, p 96
85. M.A. Streicher, "Stress Corrosion of Ferritic Stainless Steels," Paper 68, presented at Corrosion/75, National Association of Corrosion Engineers, 1975

86. B.F. Brown, "Stress Corrosion Cracking Control Measures," NBS Monograph 156, 1977, p 55

87. "Stainless Steel: Allegheny Ludlum AL 29-4C," Allegheny Ludlum Corp., 1990

88. R.F. Steigerwald, A.P. Bond, H.J. Dundas, and E.A. Lizlovs, *Corrosion,* Vol 33, 1977, p 279

89. A.P. Bond and H.J. Dundas, *Corrosion,* Vol 24, 1968, p 344

90. M.A. Streicher, *Platinum Met. Rev.,* Vol 21, 1977, p 51

91. I.L.W. Wilson, F.W. Pement, and R.G. Aspden, "Stress Corrosion Studies on Some Stainless Steels in Elevated Temperature Aqueous Environments," Paper 136, presented at Corrosion/77, National Association of Corrosion Engineers, 1977

92. M.A. Streicher, *Corrosion,* Vol 30, 1974, p 77

93. J.P. Carter and S.D. Cramer, *Mater. Perform.,* Sept 1980, p 13

94. S. Matsushima and T. Ishihara, *Trans. Natl. Res. Inst. Met.,* Vol 17, 1975, p 14

95. H. Spaehn, *Environment-Induced Cracking of Metals,* R.P. Gangloff and M.B. Ives, Ed., National Association of Corrosion Engineers, 1990, p 449

96. J.E. Truman, *Int. Met. Rev.,* Vol 26 (No. 6), 1981, p 301

97. T. Suzuki, H. Hasegawa, and M. Watanabe, *Nippon Kinzaku Gakaishi,* Vol 32, 1968, p 1171

98. S. Shimodaira, M. Takano, Y. Takizawa, and H. Kamide, *Stress Corrosion Cracking and Hydrogen Embrittlement of Iron Base Alloys,* R.W. Staehle, J. Hochmann, R.D. McCright, and J.E. Slater, Ed., National Association of Corrosion Engineers, 1977, p 1003

99. D.B. Anderson and C.J. Novak, "Stress Corrosion Cracking of High Strength Stainless and Low Alloy Steels in Chemical Plant Atmospheres," Paper 152, presented at Corrosion/76, National Association of Corrosion Engineers, 1976

100. "Sandvik SAF 2507: A High Performance Duplex Stainless Steel," Sandvik Steel, Sweden, March 1990

101. R. Oltra, A. Desestret, E. Mirabal, and F.P. Bizouaird, *Corros. Sci.,* Vol 27, 1987, p 1251

102. K. van Gelder, J.G. Erlings, J.W.M. Damen, and A. Visser, *Corros. Sci.,* Vol 27, 1987, p 1271

103. A. Cigada, T. Pastore, P. Pedeferri, and B. Vicentini, *Corros. Sci.,* Vol 27, 1987, p 1213

104. M. Baireri, F. Mancia, A. Tamba, and G. Montagna, *Corros. Sci.,* Vol 27, 1987, p 1239

105. "Testing of Metals for Resistance to Sulfide Stress Cracking at Ambient Temperatures," NACE Standard TM-01-77-86, National Association of Corrosion Engineers, 1986

106. G. Herbsleb and R.F. Poepperling, *Corrosion,* Vol 36 (No. 11), 1980, p 611

107. S.M. Wilhelm and R.D. Kane, *Corrosion,* Vol 40 (No. 8), 1984, p 431

108. "Corrosion Resistance of Nickel and Nickel-Containing Alloys in Caustic Soda and Other Alkalis," Corrosion Eng. Bull. CEB-2, International Nickel Co., 1976

109. M.G. Fontana and N.D. Greene, *Corrosion Engineering,* McGraw-Hill, 1978

110. J.K. Nelson, *Corrosion,* 9th ed., Vol 13, *Metals Handbook,* ASM International, 1987, p 1174

111. J.E. Truman and R. Perry, *Br. Corros. J.,* Vol 1, 1966, p 60

112. H. Nathorst, Welding Research Council Bull. No. 6, Oct 1950, p 6

113. M.O. Speidel, "Stress Corrosion Cracking of Austenitic Stainless Steels," Ohio State University Report to the Advanced Research Projects Agency, ARPA Order 2616, Contract N00014-75-C-0703, Aug 1977

114. A.F. Sedriks, S. Floreen, and A.R. McIlree, *Corrosion,* Vol 32, 1976, p 157

115. A.R. McIlree and H.T. Michels, *Corrosion,* Vol 33, 1977, p 60

116. A.J. Sedriks, J.W. Schultz, and M.A. Cordovi, *Corros. Eng. (Boshoku Gijutsu),* Vol 28, 1979, p 82

117. M. Hecht, E.P. Partridge, W.C. Schraeder, and S.F. Hall, *The Corrosion Handbook,* H.H. Uhlig, Ed., John Wiley and Sons, 1963, p 520

118. G.C. Wheeler and E. Howells, *Power,* Sept 1960, p 86

119. E. Howells, *Corros. Technol.,* 1960, p 368

120. A.V. Ryabchenkov, V.I. Gerasimov, and V.P. Sidorov, *Prot. Met. (USSR),* Vol 2, May-June 1966, p 217

121. R.W. Staehle and A.K. Agrawal, "Corrosion, Stress Corrosion Cracking, and Electrochemistry of the Fe and Ni Base Alloys in Caustic Environments," Ohio State University, Report to ERDA, Contract E(11-1)-2421, 1976

122. A.P. Bond, J.D. Marshall, and H.J. Dundas, in *Stress Corrosion Testing,* STP 425, ASTM, 1967, p 116

123. M. Kowaka and T. Kudo, "Stress Corrosion Cracking Behavior of Ferritic and Duplex Stainless Steels in a Caustic Solution," paper presented at the Spring Meeting of the Japan Society of Corrosion Engineering, May 1977 (Tokyo)

124. B.M. Gordon, *Mater. Perform.,* Vol 19, 1980, p 29

125. S. Szklarska-Smialowska and G. Cragnolino, *Corrosion,* Vol 36, 1980, p 653

126. P.M. Scott, *Corros. Sci.,* Vol 25 (No. 8-9), 1985, p 583

127. J.C. Danko, *Corrosion,* 9th ed., Vol 13, *Metals Handbook,* ASM International, 1987, p 927

128. B.M. Gordon and G.M. Gordon, *Corrosion,* 9th ed., Vol 13, *Metals Handbook,* ASM International, 1987, p 927

129. F.P. Ford, D. Taylor, P.L. Andresen, and R.G. Ballinger, "Environmentally Controlled Cracking of Stainless and Low Alloy Steels in Light Water Reactors," Final Report, EPRI Contract RP 2006-6, Electric Power Research Institute, 1986

130. F.P. Ford and M. Silverman, *Corrosion,* Vol 36 (No. 10), 1980, p 558

131. F.P. Ford and P.L. Andresen, "The Theoretical Prediction of the Effect of System Variables on the Cracking of Stainless Steel and Its Use in Design," Paper 83, presented at Corrosion/87, National Association of Corrosion Engineers, 1987

132. A. Dravnieks and C. Samans, *Proc. Am. Pet. Inst.,* Vol 37 (No. 111), 1957, p 100

133. C. Samans, *Corrosion,* Vol 20 (No. 8), 1964, p 256t

134. S. Ahmad, M.L. Mehta, S.K. Saraf, and I.P. Saraswat, *Corrosion,* Vol 38 (No. 6), 1982, p 347

135. S. Ahmad, M.L. Mehta, S.K. Saraf, and I.P. Saraswat, *Corrosion,* Vol 37 (No. 7), 1981, p 412

136. C. Husen and C.H. Samans, *Chem. Eng.,* 27 Jan 1969, p 178

137. C.D. Stephens and R.C. Scarberry, "Relationship of Polythionic Acid Cracking Susceptibility to Sensitization in Inconel Alloy 800 and 801," Paper 10, presented at Corrosion/69, National Association of Corrosion Engineers, 1969

138. E. Lendvai-Lintner, *Mater. Perform.,* March 1979, p 10

139. U.S. NRC I.E. Circular No. 76-06, 26 Nov 1976

140. H.S. Isaacs, B. Vyas, and M.W. Kendig, *Corrosion,* Vol 38 (No. 3), 1982, p 130

141. J. Stewart, P.M. Scott, D.B. Wells, and A.W. Herbert, "The Use of Percolation Theory to Predict the Probability of Failure of Sensitized Austenitic Stainless Steels by Intergranular Stress Corrosion Cracking," Paper 289, presented at Corrosion/88, National Association of Corrosion Engineers, 1988

142. R.C. Newman and A. Mehta, *Environment-Induced Cracking of Metals,* R.P. Gangloff and M.B. Ives, Ed., National Association of Corrosion Engineers, 1990, p 489

143. P.M. Perillo and G.S. Duffo, *Corrosion,* Vol 46 (No. 7), 1990, p 545

144. B. Bavarian, Z. Szklarska-Smialowska, and D.D. Macdonald, *Corrosion,* Vol 38 (No. 12), 1982, p 604

145. G.M. Gordon and K.S. Brown, Dependence of Creviced BWR Component IGSCC Behavior on Coolant Chemistry, *Proc. 4th Int. Conf. Environmental Degradation of Materials in Nuclear Power Systems—Water Reactors,* National Association of Corrosion Engineers, 1990, p 14-46 to 14-62

146. K.S. Brown and G.M. Gordon, Effects of BWR Coolant Chemistry on the Propensity for IGSCC Initiation and Growth in Creviced Reactor Internal Components, *Proc. Environmental Degradation of Materials in Nuclear Power Systems—Water Reactors,* AIME, 1987, p 243-248

147. A.J. Jacobs, D.A. Hale, and M. Siegler, unpublished data, GE Nuclear Energy, San Jose, CA, Jan 1986

148. P.L. Andresen, Irradiation-Assisted Stress-Corrosion Cracking, *Stress-Corrosion Cracking—Materials Performance and Evaluation,* R.H. Jones, Ed., ASM International, 1992, p 181-210

149. E.H. Phelps, *Fundamental Aspects of Stress Corrosion Cracking,* R.W. Staehle, A.J. Forty, and D. van Rooyen, Ed., National Association of Corrosion Engineers, 1969, p 398

150. H.J. Bhatt and E.H. Phelps, *Corrosion,* Vol 17, 1961, p 430t

151. B.E. Wilde, *Corrosion,* Vol 27, 1971, p 328
152. R.J. Schmitt and E.H. Phelps, *J. Met.,* March 1970, p 47
153. J.F. Bates and A.W. Loginow, *Corrosion,* Vol 20, 1964, p 189t
154. C.S. Carter et al., *Corrosion,* Vol 27, 1971, p 190
155. D.B. Franklin, *Design Criteria for Controlling Stress Corrosion Cracking,* Marshall Space Flight Center Doc. MSFC-SPEC-522A, Nov 1977
156. P. Lillys and A.E. Nehrenberg, *Trans. ASM,* Vol 48, 1956, p 327
157. M.G. Fontana, "Stress Corrosion Cracking in Type 403 Stainless Steel," WADC Techn. Rep. 56-242, ASTIA Doc. AD-97215, Aug 1956
158. G.T. Murray, H.H. Honegger, and T. Mousel, *Corrosion,* Vol 40, 1984, p 146
159. C.M. Hudgins, R.L. McGlasson, P. Mehdizadeh, and W.R. Rosborough, *Corrosion,* Vol 22, 1966, p 238
160. "Sulfide Stress Cracking Resistant Metallic Materials for Oilfield Equipment," NACE Standard MR-01-75-91, National Association of Corrosion Engineers, 1991
161. R.M. Thompson, G.B. Kohut, D.R. Canfield, and W.R. Bass, *Corrosion,* Vol 47, 1991, p 216
162. R.R. Gaugh, "Sulfide Stress Cracking of Precipitation Hardening Stainless Steels," Paper 109, presented at Corrosion/77, National Association of Corrosion Engineers, 1977
163. B. Craig, Hydrogen Damage, *Corrosion,* 9th ed., Vol 13, *Metals Handbook,* ASM International, 1987, p 163-172
164. J.F. Grubb and J.R. Maurer, "Use of Cathodic Protection With Superferritic Stainless Steels," Paper 28, presented at Corrosion/84, National Association of Corrosion Engineers, 1984
165. L.S. Redmerski, J.J. Eckenrod, K.E. Pinnow, and C.W. Kovach, "Cathodic Protection of Seawater Cooled Power Plant Condensers Operating with High Performance Ferritic Stainless Steel Tubing," Paper 208, presented at Corrosion/85, National Association of Corrosion Engineers, 1985
166. Crucible Materials Corporation, U.S. Patent No. 4942922
167. R.T. Newberg and H.H. Uhlig, *J. Electrochem. Soc.,* Vol 119, 1972, p 981
168. H.H. Uhlig and R.T. Newberg, *Corrosion,* Vol 28, 1972, p 337
169. J. Marquez, I. Matushima, and H.H. Uhlig, *Corrosion,* Vol 26, 1970, p 215
170. A.P. Bond and H.J. Dundas, in *Stress Corrosion Cracking and Hydrogen Embrittlement of Iron Base Alloys,* R.W. Staehle, J. Hochmann, R.D. McCright, and J.E. Slater, Ed., National Association of Corrosion Engineers, 1977, p 1136
171. A.W. Thompson, "Hydrogen Embrittlement of Stainless Steels and Carbon Steels," paper presented at the Midyear Meeting 1978 (Toronto, Canada), American Petroleum Institute

High-Temperature Corrosion

HIGH-TEMPERATURE CORROSION plays an important role in the selection of material for construction of industrial equipment ranging from gas turbines to heat treating retorts. The principal modes of high-temperature corrosion frequently responsible for equipment problems are (Ref 1):

- Oxidation
- Carburization and metal dusting
- Sulfidation
- Nitridation
- Halogen gas corrosion
- Ash/salt deposit corrosion
- Molten salt corrosion
- Molten metal corrosion

The industries that face these high-temperature corrosion problems include:

- Aerospace
- Heat treating
- Mineral and metallurgical processing
- Chemical processing
- Petroleum refining and petrochemical processing
- Ceramic, electronic, and glass manufacturing
- Automotive
- Pulp and paper
- Waste incineration
- Fossil fuel power generation
- Coal gasification
- Nuclear

Following a brief discussion that provides general background information on high-temperature corrosion, this article will review each mode of corrosion with emphasis placed on the properties of stainless steels in these environments. To enhance understanding of materials selection in these environments, data comparing stainless steels to alternative materials, such as nickel-base alloys, are also provided. Although information on the general principles associated with each mode of high-temperature corrosion is presented, the thermodynamics and reaction kinetics associated with elevated-temperature corrosive reactions, as well as the fundamental mechanisms of scale formation, will not be addressed in detail. Such information can be found in the cited references and the selected references listed at the conclusion of this article.

General Background (Ref 1)

The important environments and principal modes of high-temperature corrosion encoun-

tered in various industrial processes are briefly described below. These are summarized schematically in Fig. 1, which illustrates that in each corrosion mode there will be interactions between oxygen activity and a principal corrodent activity.

Oxidation is the most important high-temperature corrosion reaction. In most industrial environments, oxidation often participates in the high-temperature corrosion reaction, regardless of the predominant mode of corrosion. In fact, alloys often rely on the oxidation reaction to develop a protective oxide scale to resist corrosion attack such as sulfidation, carburization, and ash/salt deposit corrosion.

Environments are frequently classified, in terms of oxygen activity, as either *oxidizing* or *re-*

ducing. An oxidizing atmosphere is an environment that contains molecular oxygen (O_2), such as air or a combustion atmosphere with excess "free" oxygen. Oxygen activity in this case is very high and is controlled by the concentration of molecular oxygen. A reducing atmosphere is generally produced by combustion under stoichiometric or substoichiometric conditions with no excess oxygen. The oxygen activity is very low in this case and is controlled by CO/CO_2 or H_2/H_2O ratios. The reducing atmosphere is generally more corrosive for many corrosion modes, such as sulfidation, carburization, nitridation, and ash/salt deposit corrosion.

Sulfidation. When an environment has a high sulfur activity (or sulfur potential), the corrosion

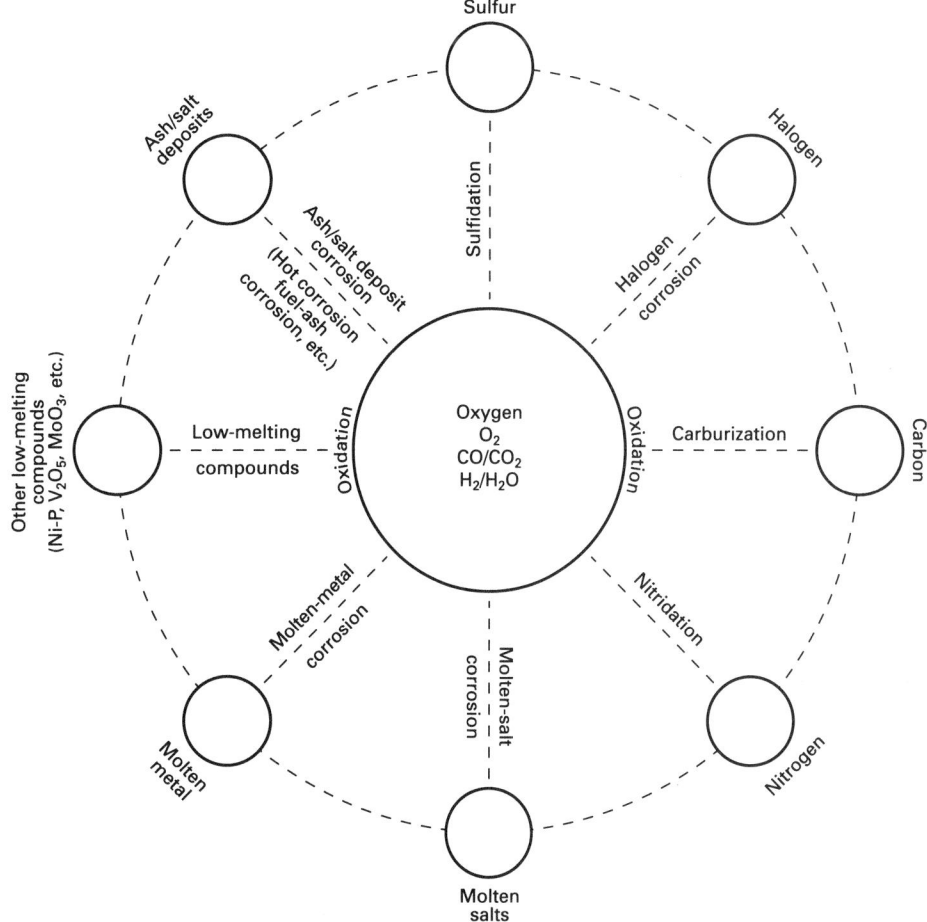

Fig. 1   Schematic showing the principal modes of high-temperature corrosion in industrial environments, as well as the interaction between oxygen activity and a principal "corrodent" activity. Source: Ref 1

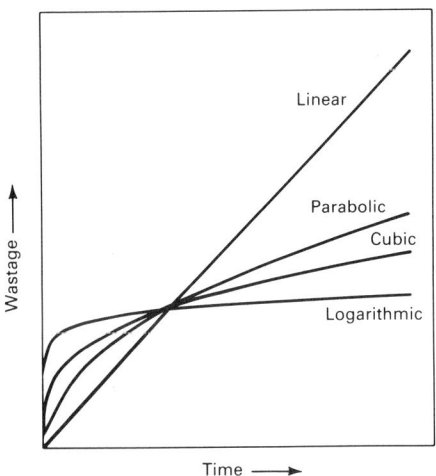

Fig. 2 Forms of kinetic curves that represent various thermal degradation processes

reaction will more likely be dominated by sulfidation. The reaction will also be influenced by oxygen activity. Lowering the oxygen activity tends to make the environment more sulfidizing, resulting in increased domination by sulfidation. Conversely, increasing the oxygen activity generally results in a less sulfidizing environment. The reaction is then increasingly dominated by oxidation. Thus, sulfidation is controlled by both sulfur and oxygen activities.

Carburization and Nitridation. Carburization behaves in a similar fashion. The reaction is controlled by both carbon and oxygen activities. Lowering the oxygen activity tends to make the environment more carburizing, and vice versa. Nitridation is the same in that the reaction becomes more severe when the environment is reducing.

In halogen corrosion, oxygen activity influences the reaction differently. For example, high-temperature corrosion in chlorine-bearing environments is generally attributed to the formation of volatile metallic chlorides. Oxidizing environments cause some alloys with high levels of molybdenum and tungsten to suffer significantly higher corrosion rates, presumably by forming very volatile oxychlorides. Reducing environments often are less corrosive. Nevertheless, the reaction is controlled by both halogen and oxygen activities.

Ash/Salt Deposits. Many industrial environments may contain several corrosive contaminants that tend to form ash/salt deposits on metal surfaces during high-temperature exposure. These ash/salt deposits can play a significant role in the corrosion reaction. "Hot corrosion" of gas-turbine components is a good example. Sulfur from the fuel and NaCl from the ingested air may react during combustion to form salt vapors, such as Na_2SO_4. These salt vapors may then deposit at lower temperatures on metal surfaces, resulting in accelerated corrosion attack. In fossil-fuel-fired power generation, ash/salt deposits are also very common because of sulfur and vanadium in the fuel oil, particularly low-grade fuels, and alkali metals, chlorine, and sulfur in the coal. The accelerated corrosion due to ash/salt deposits in this case is frequently referred to as *fuel ash corrosion*. Both hot corrosion and fuel ash corrosion are generally believed to be related to liquid salt deposits, which destroy the protective oxide scale on the metal surface. Waste incineration generates very complex ash/salt deposits, which often contain sulfur, sodium, potassium, chlorine, zinc, lead, phosphorus, and other elements. Ash/salt deposits are common in waste-heat recovery systems for industrial processes, such as aluminum remelting operations and pulp and paper recovery boilers, and are also common in calcining operations for various chemical products. This mode of corrosion is referred to as *ash/salt deposit corrosion*.

Effect of Low-Melting Compounds. There are other types of low-melting compounds that can form on the metal surface during the high-temperature reaction. The most common ones include V_2O_5, MoO_3, and nickel-phosphorus compounds. These liquid phases can easily destroy the protective oxide scale and result in accelerated corrosion attack. When V_2O_5 or MoO_3 is involved, the attack is referred to as *catastrophic oxidation*. When the environment contains phosphorus, high-nickel alloys may react with it to form low-melting nickel-phosphorus eutectics, which then destroy the protective oxide scale. The subsequent oxidation or other mode of attack is thus accelerated.

Molten salt and molten metal corrosion are two other important high-temperature corrosion modes. Oxygen activity may still play an important role in the corrosion reaction for both environments. For example, in a molten salt pot the worst attack frequently occurs at the air-salt interface, presumably because that is where oxygen activity is highest.

Oxidation (Ref 1)

Oxidation is the most important high-temperature corrosion reaction. Metals or alloys are oxidized when heated to elevated temperatures in air or highly oxidizing environments, such as a combustion atmosphere with excess air or oxygen. Oxidation can also take place in reducing environments (i.e., low oxygen potentials). Most industrial environments have sufficient oxygen activities to allow oxidation to participate in the high-temperature corrosion reaction regardless of the predominant mode of corrosion. In fact, the alloy often relies on the oxidation reaction to develop a protective oxide scale to resist corrosion attack, such as sulfidation, carburization, ash/salt deposit corrosion, and so forth.

Oxidation in air occurs in many industrial processes. Heat-treating furnaces and chemical reaction vessels are often heated by electrical resistance in air. Under these conditions, the alloy is oxidized by oxygen.

For many other industrial processes, heat is generated by combustion, accomplished in many cases by using air and relatively "clean" fuels such as natural gas or No. 1 or No. 2 fuel oil. These fuels generally have low concentrations of contaminants, such as sulfur, chlorine, alkali metals, and vanadium. Many high-temperature processes use excess air to ensure complete combustion of the fuel. The combustion products thus consist primarily of O_2, N_2, CO_2, and H_2O. Although alloys in these environments are oxidized by oxygen, other combustion products, such as H_2O and CO_2, may play an important role in affecting oxidation behavior.

General Principles of Oxidation (Ref 2)

When metal is exposed to an oxidizing gas at elevated temperatures, corrosion can occur by direct reaction with the gas, without the need for the presence of a liquid electrolyte. This type of corrosion is referred to as *tarnishing, high-temperature oxidation,* or *scaling*. The rate of attack increases substantially with temperature. The surface film typically thickens as a result of reaction at the scale-gas or metal-scale interface due to cation or anion transport through the scale, which behaves as a solid electrolyte. For continuous, nonporous scales, ionic transport through the scale is the rate-controlling process. The thermodynamic stability, the ionic defect structure, and certain morphological features of the scale formed are key factors in determining the resistance of an alloy to a specific environment.

Initial film growth is usually very rapid. If the scale is a nonporous solid and completely covers the metal surface, the reaction rate will decrease when the thickness reaches a few thousand angstroms as the transport of reactive species through

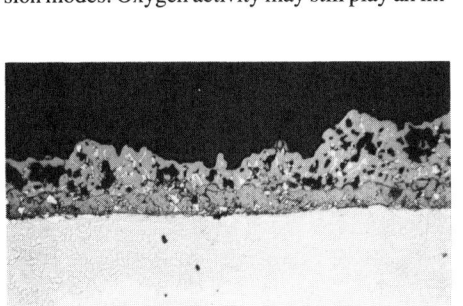

Fig. 3 Protective and nonprotective scales formed on Alloy 800. (a) Cr_2O_3-base protective oxide scale formed in sulfur-free oxidizing gas. (b) Sulfide-oxide scale formed in reducing conditions containing hydrogen sulfide

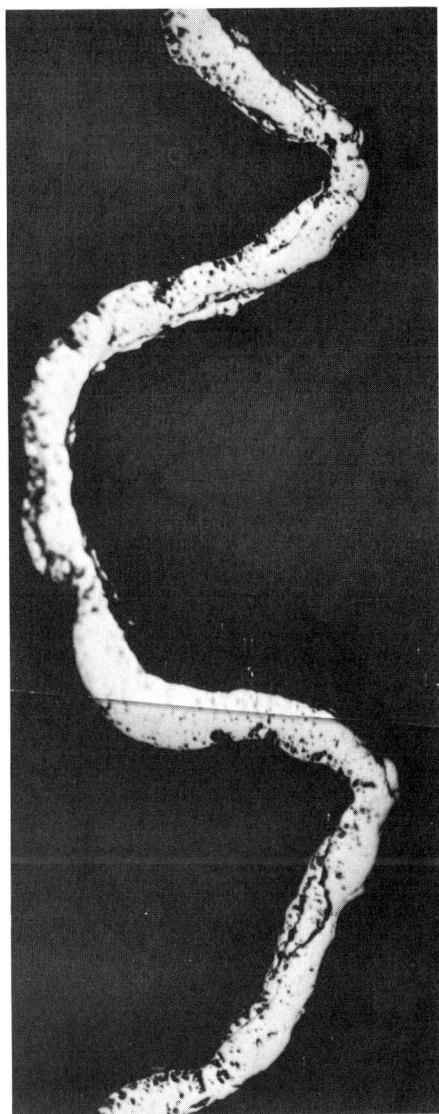

Fig. 4 Cr₂O₃ scale formed on pure chromium at 1100 °C (2012 °F). A Pilling-Bedworth ratio of 2.0 results in high compressive stress in the scale, which is relieved by buckling and spalling.

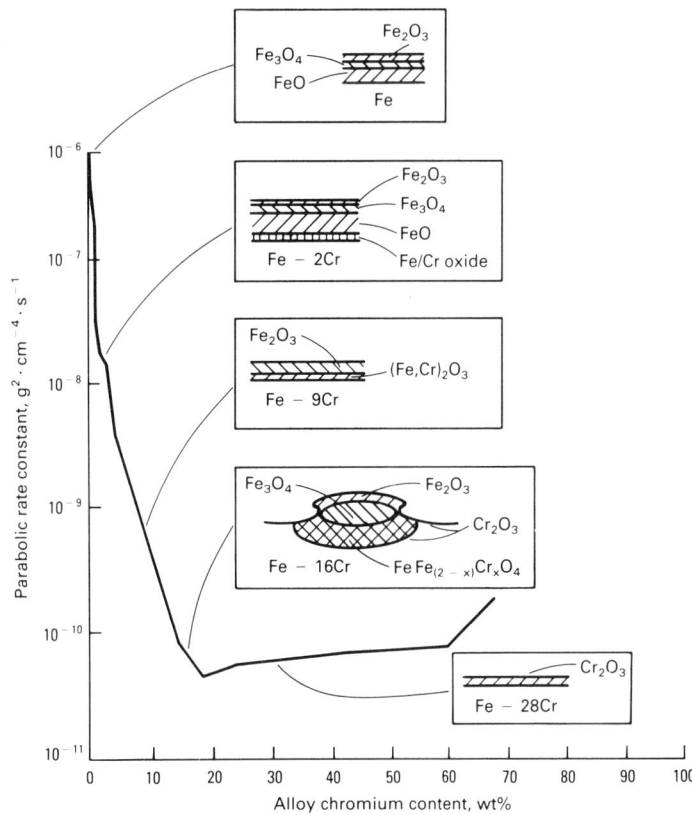

Fig. 5 Schematic of the variation of the oxidation rate and oxide scale structure with alloy chromium content (based on isothermal studies at 1000 °C, or 1830 °F, in 0.13 atm oxygen)

the film becomes rate controlling. The subsequent corrosion rate depends on the details of this transport mechanism, which may be due to electrical potential or concentration gradients or to migration along preferential paths, and so may correspond to any of several rate laws, as shown in Fig. 2. Where a diffusion process is rate controlling, the kinetics usually follow a parabolic rate law, in which the rate progressively decreases with time. Figure 3(a) illustrates the compact, continuous protective scale of essentially chromium oxide (Cr₂O₃) formed on an iron-nickel-chromium alloy (Alloy 800 or UNS N08800). If the scale is porous, is formed as a vapor species, or does not completely cover the metal surface, a linear rate is usually experienced.

The latter circumstance can be assessed from the Pilling-Bedworth ratio described in Ref 3, which is the ratio of the volumes of oxide produced to the metal consumed by oxidation. Values of 1.0 or greater result in complete surface coverage by oxide and, usually, protective behavior. This is not a complete or foolproof measure for assessing the likelihood of protective scaling behavior. At high temperatures, the growth of nominally protective oxides may be sufficiently rapid that the compressive stresses resulting from a Pilling-Bedworth ratio greater than 1 become sufficiently great that the scale (or alloy) deforms and possibly spalls as a relief mechanism. In some cases, the protection offered by such scales may be low at this point, as shown in Fig. 4.

The desired characteristics for a protective oxide scale include the following:

- High thermodynamic stability (highly negative Gibbs free energy of formation) so that it forms preferentially to other possible reaction products
- Low vapor pressure so that the oxide forms as a solid and does not evaporate into the atmosphere
- Pilling-Bedworth ratio greater than 1.0 so that the oxide completely covers the metal surface
- Low coefficient of diffusion of reactant species (metal cations, the corrodent anions) so that the scale has a slow growth rate
- High melting temperature
- Good adherence to the metal substrate, which usually involves a coefficient of thermal expansion close to that of the metal, and sufficient high-temperature plasticity to resist fracture from differential thermal expansion stresses

High-temperature scales are usually thought of as oxides, but they may also be sulfides, carbides, or mixtures of these species. Oxides and sulfides are nonstoichiometric compounds and semiconductors. There are essentially two types of semiconductors: p-type (or positive carrier), which may have vacancies in its metal lattice, or an excess of anions contained interstitially, and n-type (or negative carrier), which may have an excess of metal ions contained interstitially, or vacant anion lattice sites. For diffusion-controlled scaling, the rate of scale growth can be altered by modification of the concentration of the particular defects involved. For example, p-type oxides exhibit increased cationic transport rates (increased oxidation rates) at increased oxygen pressures, while transport in n-type oxides is essentially independent of oxygen pressure. Both types of oxide can be doped by the addition of specific ions to the oxide lattice. For p-type metal deficit oxides, for example, the addition of cations of higher valence than the native cations results in an increase in the number of cation vacancies and therefore an increase in the oxidation rate, while lower-valence cation additions have the opposite effect.

Sulfides typically exhibit an intrinsically greater rate of transport of anions and cations than the oxides of the same metal and so provide scales that are significantly less protective than oxides. Detailed information on the kinetics of high-temperature corrosion in gases and the thermodynamic stability of oxide/sulfide scales can be found in Ref 4.

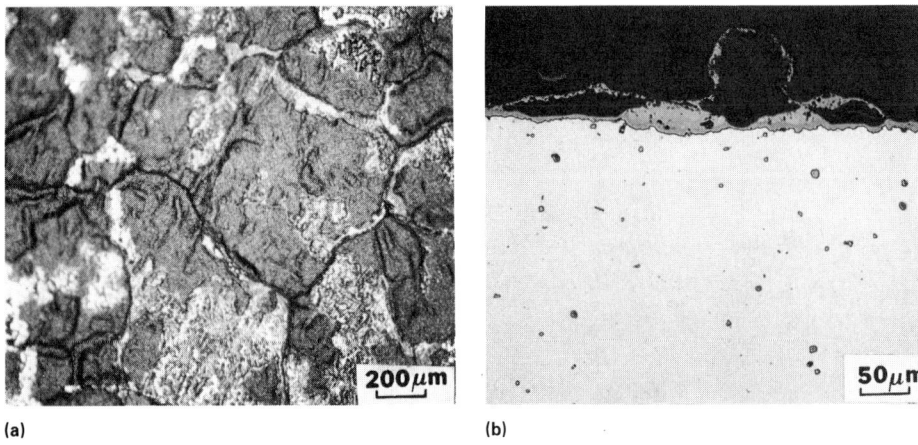

(a)   (b)

Fig. 6 Topography (a) and cross section (b) of oxide scale formed on Fe-18Cr alloy at 1100 °C (2012 °F). The bright areas on the alloy surface (a) are areas from which scale has spalled. The buckled scale and locally thickened areas (b) are iron-rich oxide. The thin scale layer adjacent to the alloy is Cr_2O_3, which controls the oxidation rate.

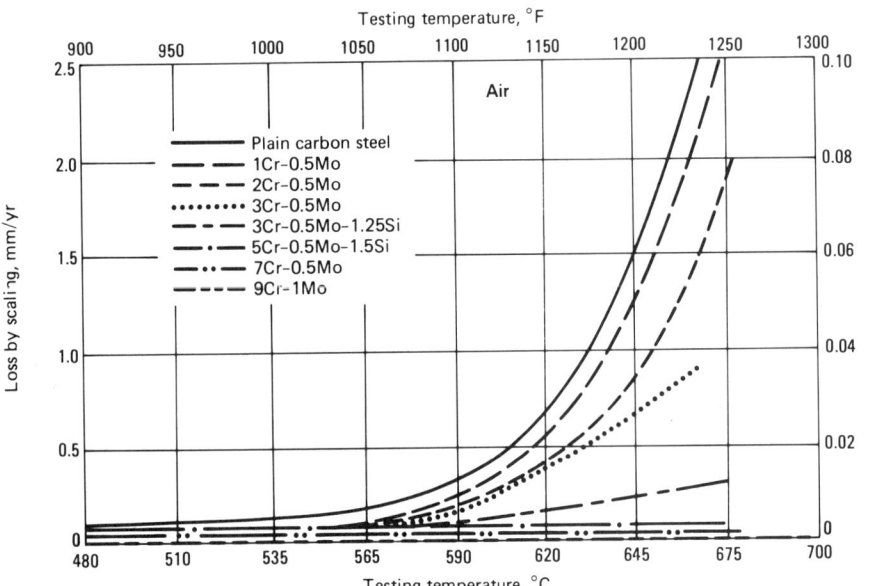

Fig. 7 Effect of temperature and chromium content on metal loss from scaling for several carbon and low-alloy steels in air

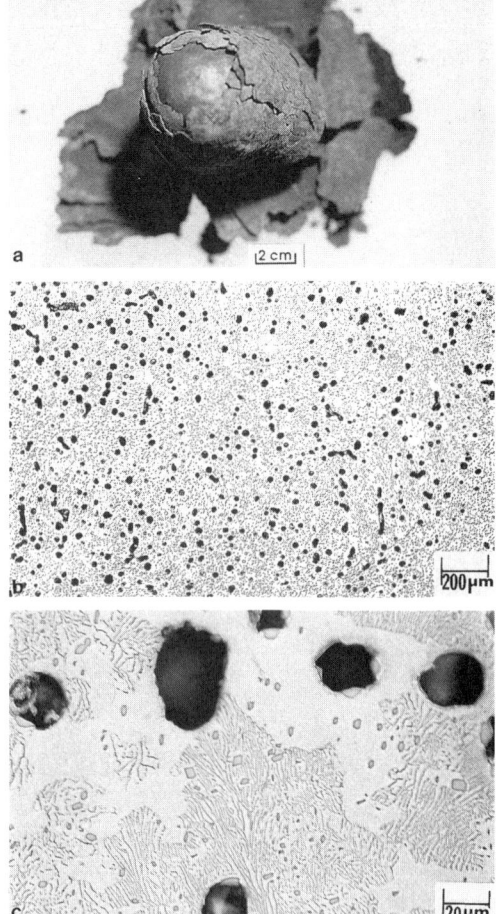

Fig. 8 25Cr-10Ni steel that suffered catastrophic oxidation in a natural gas-fired furnace operating at temperatures up to 1230 °C (2250 °F), which are above the upper temperature limit of the alloy for long-term applications. The alloy suffered not only extensive scaling (a), but also extensive internal void formation (b and c). Source: Ref 1

Alloys intended for high-temperature applications are designed to have the capability of forming protective oxide scales. Alternatively, where the alloy has ultrahigh-temperature strength capabilities (which is usually synonymous with reduced levels of protective scale-forming elements), it must be protected by a specially designed coating. The only oxides that effectively meet the criteria for protective scales listed above and can be formed on practical alloys are Cr_2O_3, alumina (Al_2O_3), and possibly silicon dioxide (SiO_2). The Cr_2O_3 scale is applicable to stainless steels.

Alloying requirements for the production of specific oxide scales have been translated into minimum levels of the scale-forming elements, or combinations of elements, depending on the base alloy composition and the intended service temperature. Figure 5 schematically represents the oxidation rate of iron-chromium alloys (1000 °C, or 1830 °F, in 0.13 atm oxygen) and depicts the types of oxide scale associated with various alloy types. As Fig. 5 indicates, a minimum chromium content of approximately 20 wt% is needed to develop a continuous Cr_2O_3 scale against further oxidation in this environment.

In assessing the potential high-temperature oxidation behavior of an alloy, a useful guide is the reservoir of scale-forming element contained by the alloy in excess of the minimum level (around 20 wt% for iron-chromium alloys at 1000 °C, or 1830 °F, according to Fig. 5). The greater the reservoir of scale-forming element required in the alloy for continued protection, the more likely it is that service conditions will cause repeated loss of the protective oxide scale. Extreme cases require chromizing or aluminizing to enrich the surface regions of the alloy or the provision of an external coating rich in the scale-forming elements.

The breakdown of protective scales based on Cr_2O_3 appears, in the majority of cases, to originate through mechanical means. The most common is spallation as a result of thermal cycling, or loss through impact or abrasion. Typical scale structures on an Fe-18Cr alloy after thermal cycling are shown in Fig. 6. Cases in which the scales have been destroyed chemically are usually related to reactions occurring beneath deposits, especially where these consist of molten species. An additional mode of degradation of protective Cr_2O_3 scale is through oxidation to the volatile chromium trioxide (CrO_3), which becomes prevalent above about 1010 °C (1850 °F) and is greatly accelerated by high gas flow rates.

Because these protective oxide scales form wherever the alloy surface is exposed to the ambient environment, they form at all surface discontinuities. Therefore, the possibility exists that notches of oxide will form at occluded angles in the surface and may eventually initiate or propagate cracks under thermal cycling conditions. The ramifications of stress-assisted oxidation (and of oxidation assisting the applied stress) are not well understood, but stress-assisted oxidation is an important consideration in practical failure analysis.

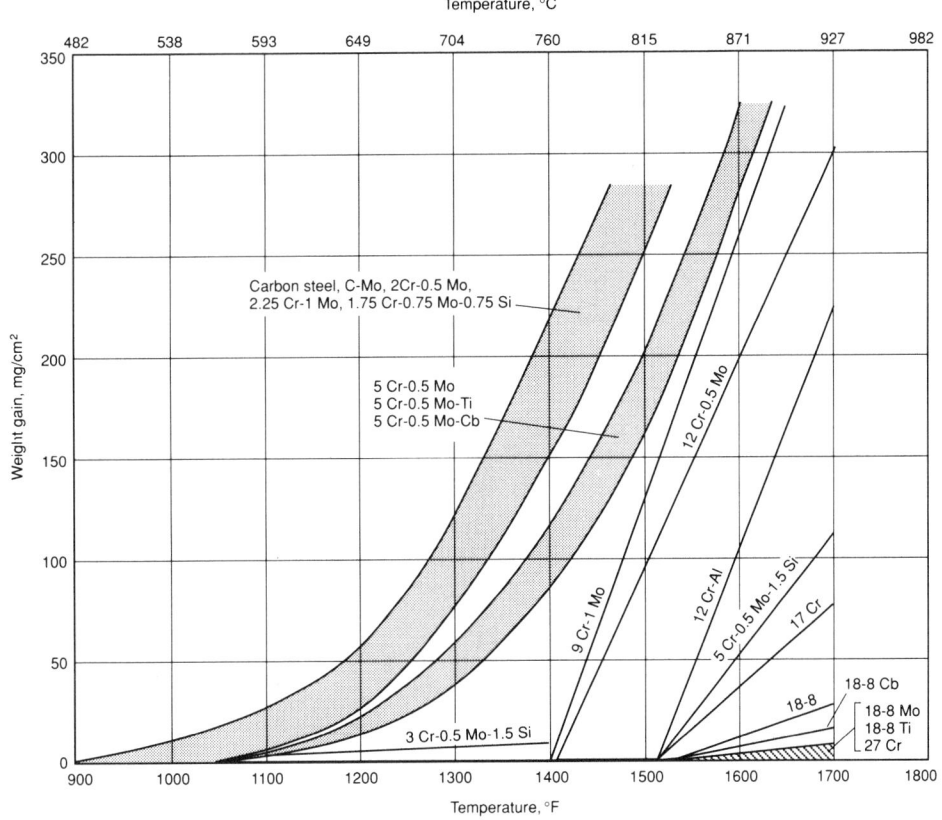

Fig. 9 Oxidation resistance of carbon, low-alloy, and stainless steels in air after 1000 h at temperatures from 590 to 930 °C (1100 to 1700 °F). Source: Ref 5

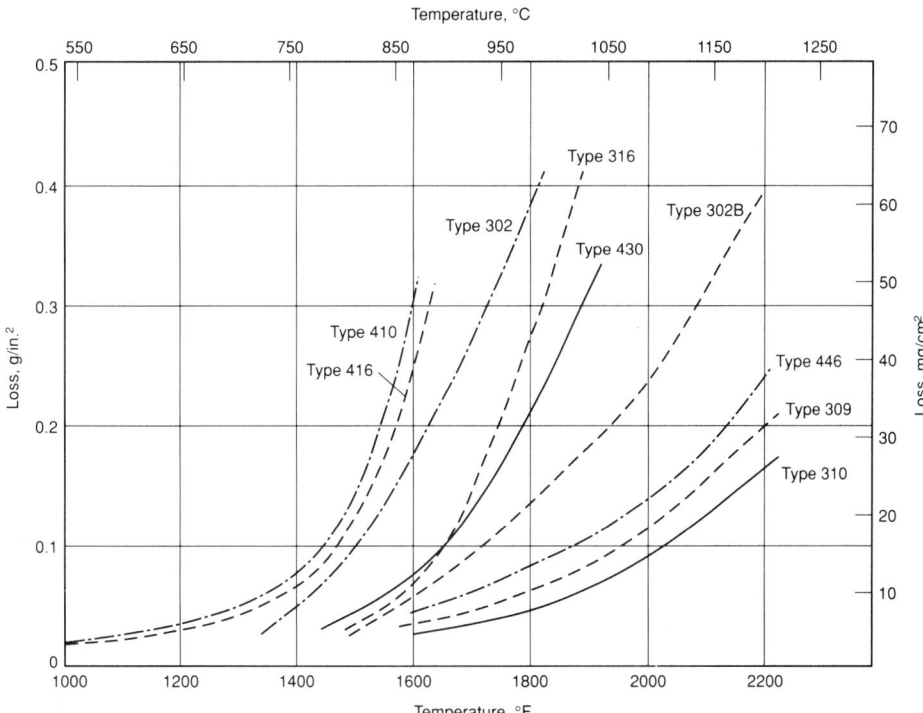

Fig. 10 Oxidation resistance of several stainless steels as a function of temperature. Source: Ref 6

Oxidation Resistance of Stainless Steels (Ref 1)

Engineering alloys available for intermittent or continuous service in different temperature ranges, in order of *increasing* oxidation resistance, include:

- Carbon steels (used at temperatures below approximately 540 °C, or 1000 °F)
- Low-alloy ferritic chromium-molybdenum steels (used at maximum temperatures ranging from approximately 600 to 700 °C, or 1100 to 1300 °F, depending on chromium content, as shown in Fig. 7)
- Stainless steels (used at maximum temperatures ranging from 600 to 1000 °C, or 1100 to 1800 °F, depending on the alloying content, the effect of atmosphere, the presence of low-melting-point compounds, etc., as described below)
- Nickel-base alloys (used at maximum temperatures ranging from 1000 to 1200 °C, or 1800 to 2200 °F)

Many oxidation problems result from the use of an alloy in a temperature region exceeding the capability of that alloy. Figure 8 illustrates a typical example of an alloy selected for applications at temperatures well above its upper temperature limit. The 25Cr-10Ni stainless steel suffered catastrophic oxidation in a natural gas-fired furnace operating at temperatures of 1090 to 1230 °C (2000 to 2250 °F). In addition to excessive scaling, the alloy suffered extensive internal void formation. Both scaling and internal void formation can significantly lower the load-bearing capability of an alloy.

This section covers oxidation data for austenitic 300-series and martensitic and ferritic 400-series stainless steels. Additional information on carbon and low-alloy steels and nickel-base alloys can be found in Ref 1 and in Volumes 1 and 13 of the *ASM Handbook*.

Martensitic and Ferritic Grades. The superior oxidation resistance of martensitic and ferritic stainless steels to that of carbon and low-alloy chromium-molybdenum steels is illustrated in Fig. 9 (Ref 5). As chromium content in the straight chromium steels increases from 9 to 27%, resistance to oxidation improves significantly. The ferritic 27% Cr steel (type 446) is the most oxidation resistant among the 400-series stainless steels, due to the development of a continuous Cr_2O_3 scale on the metal surface.

Cyclic oxidation studies conducted by Grodner (Ref 6) also revealed that type 446 was the best performer in the 400-series stainless steels, followed by types 430, 416, and 410 (Fig. 10). Another ferritic stainless steel, 18SR (about 18% Cr), was found to be as good as, and sometimes better than, type 446 (27% Cr), as shown in Tables 1 and 2 (Ref 7). This was attributed to the addition of 2% Al and 1% Si to the alloy. Furthermore, 18SR and type 446 showed better cyclic oxidation resistance than some austenitic stainless steels, such as types 309 and 310, when cycled to 980 to 1040 °C (1800 to 1900 °F), as shown in Tables 1 and 2.

Table 1 Cyclic oxidation resistance of several stainless steels in air cycling to 870 to 930 °C (1600 to 1700 °F) temperature range
15 min in furnace and 15 min out of furnace

Alloy	Specimen weight changes after indicated cycles, mg/cm^2			
	288 cycles	480 cycles	750 cycles	958 cycles
409 + Al	Destroyed	...	...	...
430	9.9	Destroyed	...	...
22-13-5	0.5	−3.0	−18.8	−35.7
442	0.7	1.2	1.5	1.5
446	0.3	0.4	0.2	0.1
309	0.3	−4.6	−23.7	−32.6
18SR	0.3	0.4	0.5	0.6

Source: Ref 7

Table 2 Cyclic oxidation resistance of several stainless steels in air cycling to 980 to 1040 °C (1800 to 1900 °F) temperature range
15 min in furnace and 15 min out of furnace

Alloy	Specimen weight changes after indicated cycles, mg/cm^2				
	130 cycles	368 cycles	561 cycles	753 cycles	1029 cycles
446	0.4	0.5	−0.2	7.0	−19.4
18SR	0.7	1.1	1.5	2.2	3.0
309	−24.2	−77.5	−178.3	−242	−358
310	1.5	−11.3	−29.3	−62.8	−107

Source: Ref 7

Austenitic Grades. When the service temperature is above 640 °C (1200 °F), ferritic stainless steels, which have a body-centered cubic crystal structure, drastically lose their strengths. At these temperatures, alloys with a face-centered cubic (fcc) crystal structure are preferred because of their higher creep strengths. Nickel is added to iron-chromium steels to stabilize the fcc austenitic structure. The austenitic structure is inherently stronger and more creep resistant than ferrite (Ref 8). The 300-series austenitic stainless steels have been widely used for high-temperature applications in various industries. These alloys exhibit higher elevated-temperature strengths than ferritic stainless steels. Furthermore, they do not suffer 475 °C (885 °F) embrittlement and ductility problems in thick sections and in heat-affected zones, as do ferritic stainless steels. Nevertheless, some austenitic stainless steels can suffer significant ductility loss or embrittlement upon long-term exposure to intermediate temperatures (540 to 800 °C, or 1000 to 1500 °F) due to σ-phase formation. Embrittlement of stainless steels is described in the article "Metallurgy and Properties of Wrought Stainless Steels" in this Volume.

The oxidation resistance of several austenitic stainless steels is illustrated in Fig. 11 (Ref 9). Nickel improves the resistance of alloys to cyclic oxidation. Similar results have also been observed by Grodner (Ref 6) (Fig. 10) and by Moccari and Ali (Ref 10). Brasunas et al. (Ref 11) studied the oxidation behavior of about 80 experimental Fe-Cr-Ni alloys exposed to an air-H$_2$O mixture at 870 to 1200 °C (1600 to 2190 °F) for 100 and 1000 h. They observed that increases in nickel in excess of 10% in alloys containing 11 to 36% Cr improved the oxidation resistance of the alloys. Figure 11 also shows several high-nickel alloys that exhibited better oxidation resistance than austenitic stainless steels.

Comparative Data from Engine Atmospheres. Oxidation studies have been carried out by Kado et al. (Ref 12) and Michels (Ref 13) to evaluate materials for automobile emission-control devices, such as thermal reactors and catalytic converters. In cyclic oxidation tests performed by Kado et al. (Ref 12) in still air at 1000 °C (1830 °F) for 400 cycles (30 min in the furnace and 30 min out of the furnace), types 409 (12% Cr), 420 (13% Cr), and 304 (18Cr-8Ni) suffered severe attack. Type 420 was completely oxidized after only 100 cycles, although the sample did not show any weight changes. Alloys that performed well under these conditions were types 405 (14% Cr), 430 (17% Cr), 446 (27% Cr), 310 (25Cr-20Ni), and DIN 4828 (19Cr-12Ni-2Si steel), as illustrated in Fig. 12. When cycled to 1200 °C (2190 °F) for 400 cycles (30 min in the furnace and 30 min out of the furnace), all the alloys tested except F-1 alloy (Fe-15Cr-4Al) suffered severe oxidation attack (Fig. 13). This illustrates the superior oxidation resistance of alumina formers (i.e., alloys that form Al$_2$O$_3$ scales when oxidized at elevated temperatures). Two familiar alumina-forming, ferritic alloys are Kanthal A (5% Al) and Fecralloy (4.7% Al and 0.3% Y).

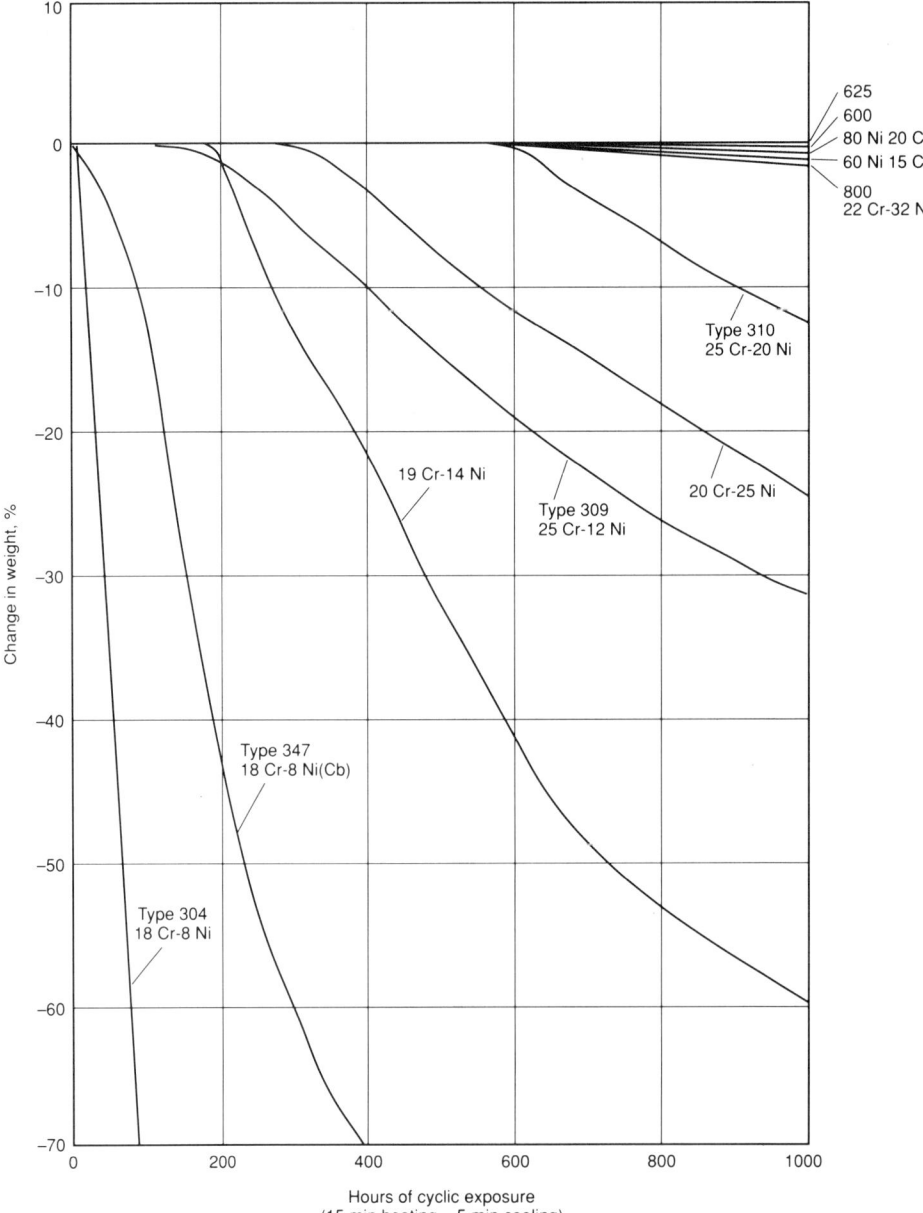

Fig. 11 Cyclic oxidation resistance of several stainless steels and nickel-base alloys in air at 980 °C (1800 °F). Source: Ref 9

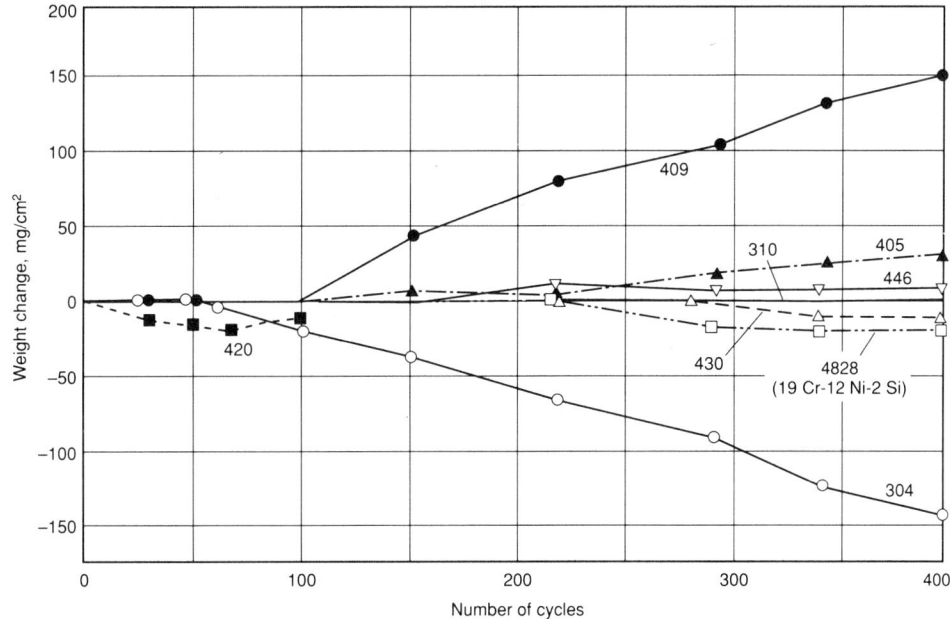

Fig. 12 Cyclic oxidation resistance of several ferritic and austenitic stainless steels in still air at 1000 °C (1830 °F) for up to 400 cycles (30 min in furnace and 30 min out of furnace). Source: Ref 12

Kado et al. (Ref 12) also investigated oxidation behavior in a combustion environment that simulated a gasoline engine. Their test involved air-to-fuel ratios of 9 to 1 and 14.5 to 1 and regular gasoline that contained 0.01 wt% S and 0.04 L/kL Pb. Exhaust gas taken from the exhaust manifold was mixed with air before being piped into a furnace retort where the tests were performed. Test specimens were exposed to the mixture of exhaust gas and air. The gas mixture coming from the combustion environment with an air-to-fuel ratio of 14.5 to 1 consisted of 72.4% N_2, 9.7% H_2O, 9.93% O_2, 8% CO_2, and 507 ppm NO_x, while that coming from the combustion environment with an air-to-fuel ratio of 9 to 1 consisted of 70.6% N_2, 13.7% H_2O, 3.21% O_2, 12.5% CO_2, and 34 ppm NO_x. Test results and air oxidation data are summarized in Fig. 14.

There were no significant differences between air and exhaust gas test environments when tested at 800 °C (1470 °F). All the alloys tested showed negligible attack. When the test temperature was increased to 1000 °C (1830 °F), all the 400-series stainless steels with less than 17% Cr (i.e., types 405, 409, 410, and 430) and type 304 exhibited significant oxidation attack. Type 310, type 446, DIN 4828 (Fe-19Cr-12Ni-2Si), F-1 alloy (Fe-15Cr-4Al), A-1 alloy (Fe-16Cr-13Ni-3.5Si), and A-2 alloy (Fe-20Cr-13Ni-3.5Si) performed well. At 1200 °C (2190 °F), all the alloys tested suffered severe oxidation attack. At both 1000 and 1200 °C (1830 and 2190 °F), the exhaust gas test environment was found to be more aggressive than air. The authors attributed the enhanced attack to the presence of sulfur in the exhaust gas environment, although low-sulfur (0.01%) gasoline was used for testing. Sulfur segregation to the scale-metal interface was detected.

In another study (Ref 13), an engine combustion atmosphere was also found to be significantly more corrosive than an air-10% H_2O environment. The engine combustion exhaust gas contained about 10% H_2O along with 2% CO, 0.33 to 0.55% O_2, 0.05 to 0.24% hydrocarbon, and 0.085% NO_x. The balance was presumably N_2 (not reported in the paper). The engine exhaust gas was piped into a furnace retort where the tests were performed. The results generated in both the air-10H_2O environment and the engine exhaust environment are shown in Fig. 15. After exposure to the air-10H_2O environment at 980 °C (1800 °F) for 102 h, type 309, type 310, 18SR, alloy OR-1 (Fe-13Cr-3Al), Alloy 800, and Alloy 601 were all relatively unaffected. On the other hand, only 18SR and Alloy 601 were relatively unaffected by the engine exhaust gas environment. Alloy OR-1, type 309, type 310, and Alloy 800 suffered severe oxidation attack. The sulfur content in the gasoline used in this test was not reported. The relatively high gas velocity, about 6 to 9 m/s (20 to 30 ft/s), was considered one of the possible factors responsible for accelerated oxidation attack (Ref 13).

Oxidation data generated in combustion atmospheres is relatively limited. No systematic studies have been reported that varied combustion conditions, such as air-to-fuel ratios. In combustion atmospheres, the oxidation behavior of metals or alloys is not controlled by just oxygen. The combustion products, such as H_2O, CO, CO_2, hydrocarbon, and others, are expected to influence oxidation behavior. Water vapor, for example, has been found to be detrimental to the oxidation resistance of austenitic stainless steels.

Figure 16 illustrates the effect of moist air on the oxidation of types 302 and 330. Type 302 undergoes rapid corrosion in wet air at 1095 °C (2000 °F), whereas a protective film is formed in dry air. The higher-nickel type 330 is less sensitive to the effects of moisture, so it is assumed that increased chromium and nickel permit higher operating temperatures in moist air (Ref 14).

Catastrophic Oxidation (Ref 1)

As temperature increases, metals and alloys generally suffer increasingly higher rates of oxidation. When the temperature is excessively high, stainless steels can suffer catastrophic oxidation.

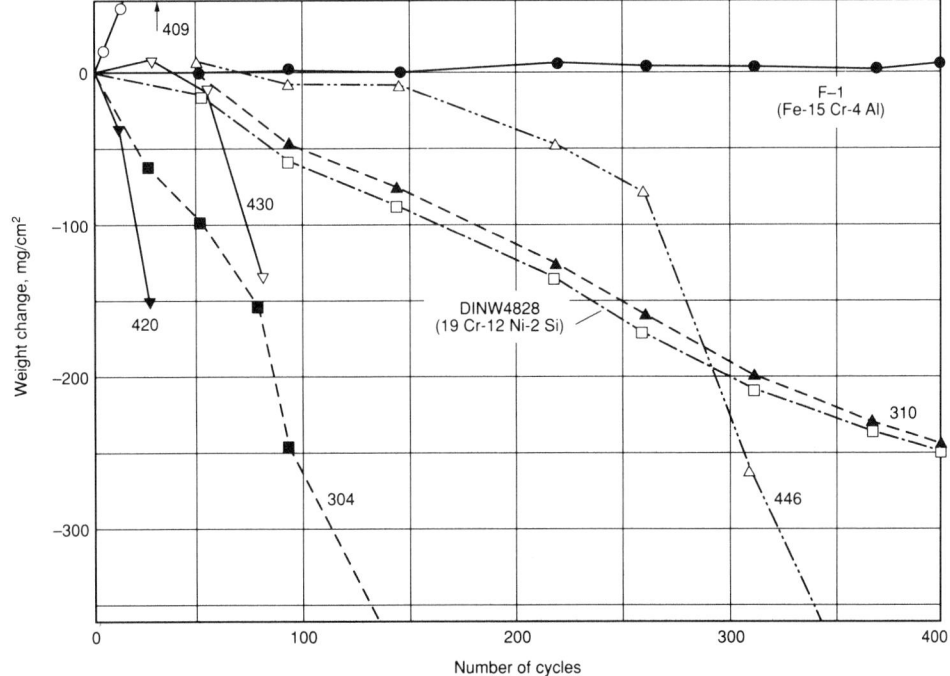

Fig. 13 Cyclic oxidation resistance of several ferritic and austenitic stainless steels in still air at 1200 °C (2190 °F) for up to 400 cycles (30 min in furnace and 30 min out of furnace). Source: Ref 12

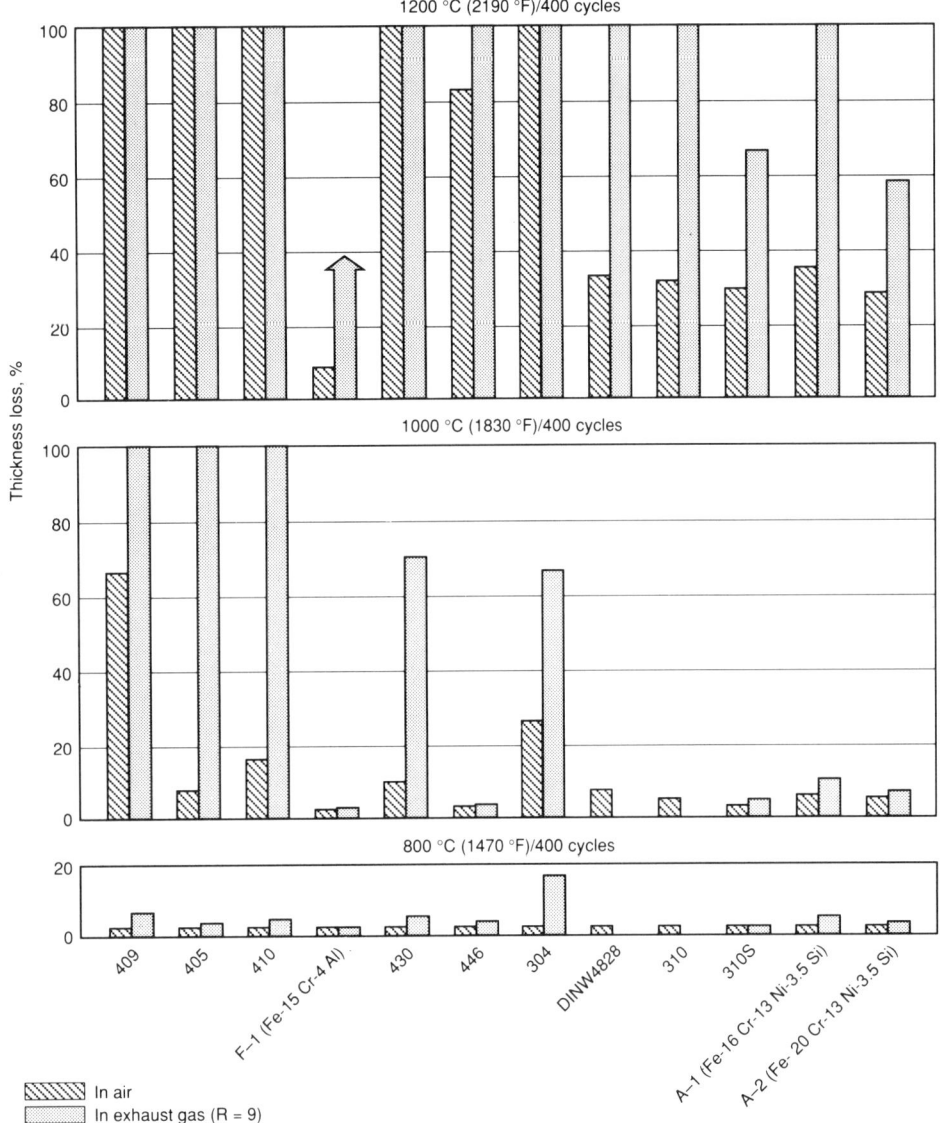

Fig. 14 Comparison of cyclic oxidation resistance between air and gasoline engine exhaust gas environments at 800, 1000, and 1200 °C (1470, 1830, and 2190 °F) for 400 cycles (30 min in hot zone and 30 min out of hot zone). Alloy F-1 suffered localized attack at 1200 °C in engine exhaust gas. Source: Ref 12

An example of this is shown in Fig. 8 for austenitic Fe-25Cr-10Ni steel.

There is, however, another mode of rapid oxidation that takes place at relatively lower temperatures. This mode, also referred to as *catastrophic oxidation,* is generally associated with the formation of a liquid oxide that disrupts and dissolves the protective oxide scale, causing the alloy to suffer catastrophic oxidation. Leslie and Fontana (Ref 15) observed an unusually rapid oxidation for Fe-25Ni-16Cr alloy containing 6% Mo when heated to 900 °C (1650 °F) in static air. The same alloy exhibited good oxidation resistance when heated to the same temperature in flowing air. The authors postulated that the rapid oxidation was due to the accumulation of gaseous MoO_3 on the metal surface and the thermal dissociation of MoO_3 into MoO_2 and O. However, Meijering and Rathenau (Ref 16), Brasunas and Grant (Ref 17), and Brennor (Ref 18) attributed

this to the presence of a liquid oxide phase. The MoO_3 oxide melts at about 795 °C (1463 °F). The 19Cr-9Ni steel suffered catastrophic oxidation attack in the presence of MoO_3 at 770 °C (1420 °F) in air (Ref 19). This temperature was very close to the eutectic temperature of MoO_2-MoO_3-Cr_2O_3.

Other oxides, such as PbO and V_2O_5, can also cause metals or alloys to suffer catastrophic oxidation in air at intermediate temperatures of 640 to 930 °C (1200 to 1700 °F) (Ref 1). PbO and V_2O_5 melt at 888 °C (1630 °F) and 690 °C (1270 °F), respectively. The deleterious effect of lead oxide is believed to be related to exhaust-valve failures in gasoline engines. Gasoline additives are a primary source for lead compounds. Vanadium is an important contaminant in residual or heavy fuel oils. Therefore, V_2O_5 plays a significant role in oil-ash corrosion.

Sawyer (Ref 20) indicated that accelerated oxidation of type 446 stainless steel in the pres-

ence of lead oxide can proceed at temperatures where the liquid phase does not exist. Experiments carried out by Brasunas and Grant (Ref 21) showed that 16-25-6 alloy specimens placed adjacent to, but not in contact with, 0.5 g samples of WO_3 oxides suffered accelerated oxidation attack when tested in air at 868 °C (1585 °F), which is well below the melting point of WO_3 (1473 °C, or 2683 °F). However, there are no reported data on mixed oxides involving WO_3.

Sulfidation (Ref 1)

Because sulfur is one of the most common corrosive contaminants in high-temperature industrial environments, sulfidation is second only to oxidation in frequency of occurrence (Ref 22). Sulfur is generally present as an impurity in fuels or feedstocks. Typically, fuel oils are contaminated with sulfur varying from fractions of 1% (No. 1 or No. 2 fuel oil) to about 3% (No. 6 fuel oil). U.S. coal may contain from 0.5 to 5%, depending on where it is mined. Feedstocks for calcining operations in mineral and chemical processing are frequently contaminated with various amounts of sulfur.

When combustion takes place with excess air to ensure complete combustion of fuel for generating heat in many industrial processes, such as coal- and oil-fired power generation, sulfur in the fuel reacts with oxygen to form sulfur dioxide (SO_2) and sulfur trioxide (SO_3). An atmosphere of this type is generally oxidizing. Oxidizing environments are usually much less corrosive than reducing environments, where sulfur is in the form of hydrogen sulfide (H_2S). However, sulfidation in oxidizing environments (as well as in reducing environments) is frequently accelerated by other fuel impurities, such as sodium, potassium, and chlorine, which may react among themselves and/or with sulfur during combustion to form salt vapors. These salt vapors may then deposit at lower temperatures on metal surfaces, resulting in accelerated sulfidation attack. Corrosion of this type (e.g., fuel ash corrosion in fossil-fuel-fired boilers) is discussed in the section "Ash/Salt Deposit Corrosion" in this article.

Oxidizing environments that contain high concentrations of SO_2 can be produced by the chemical process used to manufacture sulfuric acid. In this case, sulfur is used as a feedstock. Combustion of sulfur with excess air takes place in a sulfur furnace at about 1150 to 1200 °C (2100 to 2200 °F). The product gas typically contains about 10 to 15% SO_2 along with 5 to 10% O_2 (balance N_2), which is then converted to SO_3 for sulfuric acid.

In many industrial processes, combustion is carried out under stoichiometric or substoichiometric conditions in order to convert feedstocks to process gases consisting of H_2, CO, methane (CH_4), and other hydrocarbons. Sulfur is converted to H_2S. The environment, in this case, is reducing and is characterized by low oxygen potentials. Coal gasification, which converts coal to substitute natural gas or medium- and low-Btu fuel gases, is a common example of a process that

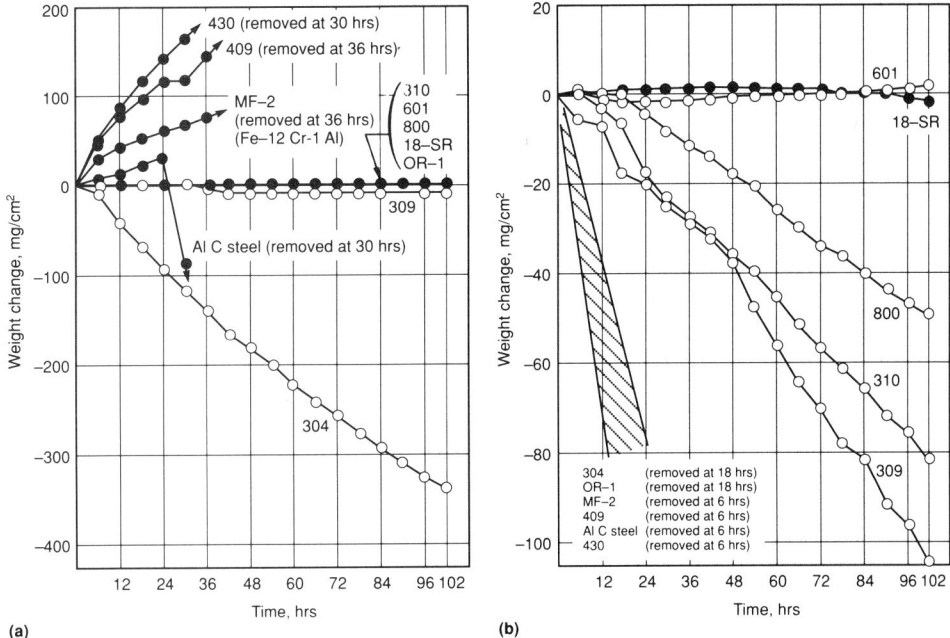

Fig. 15 Cyclic oxidation resistance of several ferritic and austenitic stainless steels in (a) air-10% H_2O at 980 °C (1800 °F), cycled every 2 h, and (b) gasoline engine exhaust gas at 980 °C (1800 °F), cycled every 6 h. Source: Ref 13

generates this type of atmosphere. Reducing conditions may also prevail in localized areas (in some cases, even when combustion is taking place with excess air). Furthermore, ash deposits on the metal surface can sometimes turn an oxidizing condition in the gaseous environment into a reducing condition beneath the deposits.

In most cases, metals and alloys rely on oxide scales to resist sulfidation attack; most high-temperature alloys rely on chromium oxide scales. In oxidizing environments, oxide scales form much more readily because of high oxygen activities. Thus, oxidation is likely to dominate the corrosion reaction.

When the environment is reducing (i.e., has low oxygen potentials), the corrosion reaction becomes a competition between oxidation and sulfidation. Thus, lowering the oxygen activity tends to make the environment more sulfidizing, resulting in increased domination by sulfidation. Conversely, increasing the oxygen activity generally results in a less sulfidizing environment with increased domination by oxidation. Sulfidation is thus controlled by both sulfur and oxygen activities. When corrosion involves more than one mode, including sulfidation, sulfidation generally dictates materials selection.

General Principles of Sulfidation (Ref 2)

When the sulfur activity (partial pressure, concentration) of the gaseous environment is sufficiently high, sulfide phases, instead of oxide phases, can be formed. The mechanisms of sulfide formation in gaseous environments and beneath molten-salt deposits have been determined in recent years. In the majority of environments encountered in practice by oxidation-resistant stainless steel alloys, Cr_2O_3 should form in preference to any sulfides, and destructive sulfidation

attack occurs mainly at sites where the protective oxide has broken down. The role of sulfur, once it has entered the alloy, appears to tie up the chromium as sulfides, effectively redistributing the protective scale-forming elements near the alloy surface and thus interfering with the process of formation or re-formation of the protective scale. If sufficient sulfur enters the alloy so that all immediately available chromium is converted to sulfides, then the less stable sulfides of the base metal may form because of morphological and kinetic reasons. These base metal sulfides are often responsible for the observed accelerated attack, because they grow much faster than the oxides or sulfides of chromium. In addition, they have relatively low melting points, so that molten slag phases are often possible. Figure 3 compares a protective (oxide) scale and a nonprotective (sulfide) scale formed on Alloy 800.

Sulfur can transport across continuous protective scales of Cr_2O_3 under certain conditions, with the result that discrete sulfide precipitates can be observed immediately beneath the scales on alloys that are behaving in a protective manner. For reasons indicated above, as long as the amount of sulfur present as sulfides is small, there is little danger of accelerated attack. However, once sulfides have formed in the alloy, there is a tendency for the sulfide phases to be preferentially oxidized by the encroaching reaction front and for the sulfur to be displaced inward, forming new sulfides deeper in the alloy, often in grain boundaries or at the sites of other chromium-rich phases, such as carbides. In this way, fingerlike protrusions of oxide/sulfide can be formed from the alloy surface inward, which may act to localize stress or otherwise reduce the load-bearing section. Such attack of an austenitic stainless steel experienced in a coal gasifier product gas is shown in Fig. 17.

Sulfidation Resistance of Stainless Steels

As with oxidation, resistance to sulfidation relates to chromium content. Unalloyed iron will be converted rather rapidly to iron sulfide scale, but when iron is alloyed with chromium, sulfidation resistance is enhanced, as illustrated in Fig. 18. Silicon also affords some protection against sulfidation.

The low-melting-point nickel/nickel sulfide eutectic, however, may be formed on the austenitic stainless steels containing more than 25% Ni even in the presence of high chromium. The occurrence of molten phases during high-temperature service can lead to catastrophic destruction of the alloy.

In addition to the usual factors of time, temperature, and concentration, sulfidation depends upon the form in which the sulfur exists. Of particular interest are the effects of sulfur dioxide, sulfur vapor, hydrogen sulfide, and flue gases.

Reaction with Sulfur Dioxide. Stainless steels containing more than 18 to 20% Cr are resistant to dry sulfur dioxide (Ref 23). In 24 h tests over the temperature range 590 to 870 °C (1100 to 1600 °F), only a heavy tarnish was formed on type 316 in atmospheres varying from 100% O_2 to 100% SO_2. The corrosion rate of type 316 in SO_2-O_2-N_2 atmospheres was 0.12 mm/yr (4.9 mils/yr)

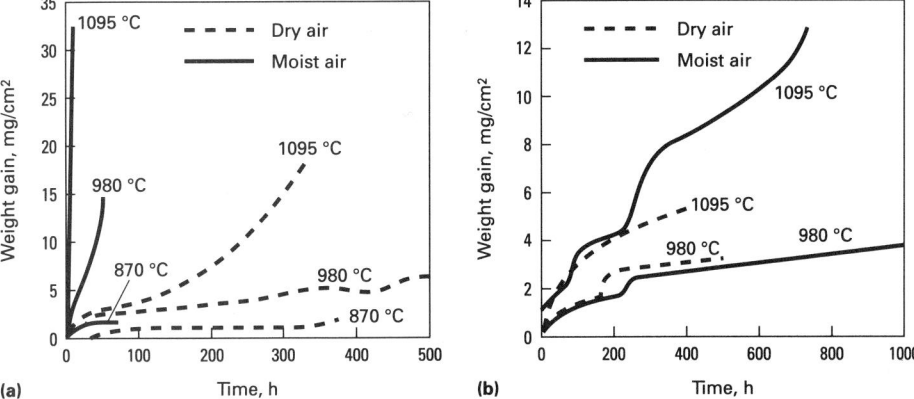

Fig. 16 Oxidation rates of types 302 (a) and 330 (b) in moist and dry air. Source: Ref 14

at 640 to 655 °C (1185 to 1210 °F). Fe-15Cr (types 430, 440), Fe-30Cr (~ type 446), and Fe-18Cr-8Ni (type 304) show increasing resistance to sulfur dioxide, in the order indicated.

Reaction with Sulfur Vapor. Sulfur vapor readily attacks the austenitic grades. In tests, the following relatively high corrosion rates were encountered in flowing sulfur vapor at 570 °C (1060 °F) (Ref 23):

Type	Corrosion rate(a)	
	mm/yr	mils/yr
314	0.43	16.9
310	0.48	18.9
309	0.57	22.3
304	0.69	27.0
302B	0.76	29.8
316	0.79	31.1
321	1.39	54.8

(a) Corrosion rate based on 1295 h tests

In liquid sulfur, most austenitic grades are resistant up to 200 °C (400 °F), with the stabilized types 321 and 347 showing satisfactory service up to 445 °C (830 °F) (Ref 22).

Reaction with Hydrogen Sulfide. The rate of corrosion in hydrogen sulfide depends on concentration, temperature, pressure, and permeability of the sulfide scale. The presence of chromium in the steel helps to stabilize the scale and slow the diffusion process. However, at high pressure and temperature when hydrogen is present, the attack is more aggressive, to the extent that low-chromium steels are not adequate.

Hydrogen-hydrogen sulfide (H_2-H_2S) mixtures are characteristic of the gas stream in catalytic reforming units (Ref 24). Catalytic reforming is used in petroleum refineries to upgrade the octane number of gasoline (Ref 25). A large amount of hydrogen is present in catalytic reforming, and sulfur in the naphtha charge reacts with hydrogen to form hydrogen sulfide (Ref 25). Severe corrosion attack on processing equipment by hydrogen sulfide has been encountered in several catalytic reforming and desulfurizing units (Ref 24-26).

Sorell (Ref 24) reported hydrogen sulfide corrosion data generated by various refinery operators in laboratory tests, pilot plant testing, field testing in commercial units, and inspection of commercial operating equipment. Austenitic stainless steels (18Cr-8Ni) were most resistant, followed by straight chromium stainless steels (12 to 16% Cr). Low-chromium steels (0 to 9% Cr) were worst. It is interesting to note that adding a moderate amount of nickel to iron-chromium alloys significantly improves the alloy sulfidation resistance of the alloy in H_2-H_2S environments (Fig. 19).

Sulfidation of alloys in H_2-H_2S mixtures has been described by isocorrosion rate curves that show corrosion rate as a function of H_2S concentration and temperature (Ref 27). The isocorrosion curves in Fig. 20 show the effects of

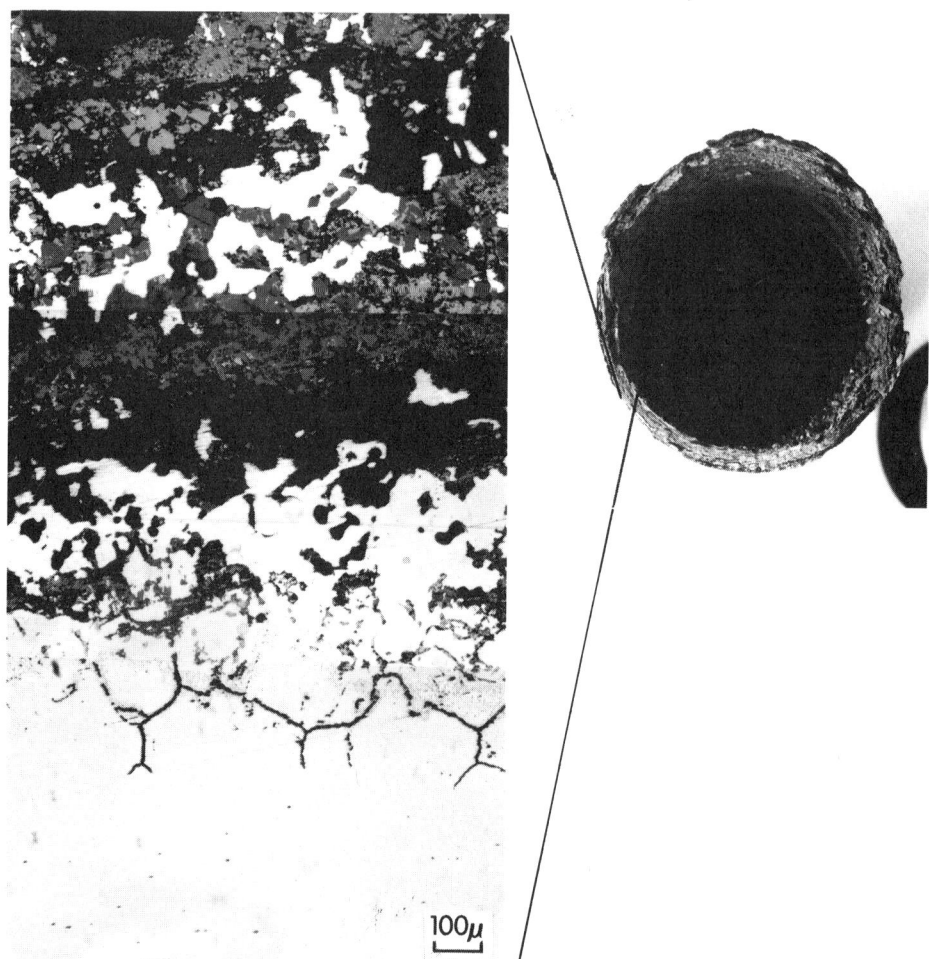

Fig. 17 Example of high-temperature sulfidation attack in a type 310 heat-exchanger tube after ~100 h at 705 °C (1300 °F) in coal gasifier product gas

hydrogen sulfide and temperature on the sulfidation resistance of austenitic stainless steels.

Effect of Sulfur in Flue and Process Gases. It is extremely difficult to generalize corrosion rates in flue and process gases, because gas composition and temperature may vary considerably within the same process unit. Combustion gases normally contain sulfur compounds; sulfur dioxide is present as an oxidizing gas along with carbon dioxide, nitrogen, carbon monoxide, and excess oxygen. Protective oxides are generally formed, and depending on exact conditions, the

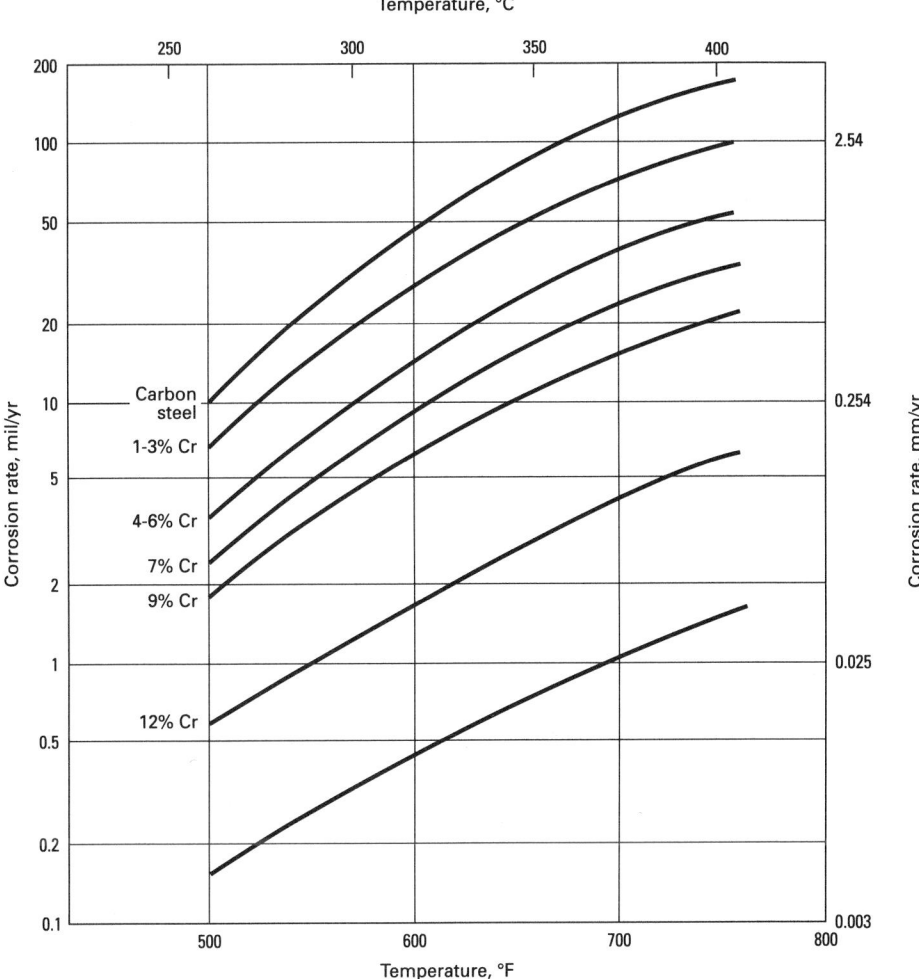

Fig. 18 Effect of chromium content on the sulfidation resistance of iron-base alloys in a hydrogen-free environment. Source: Ref 22

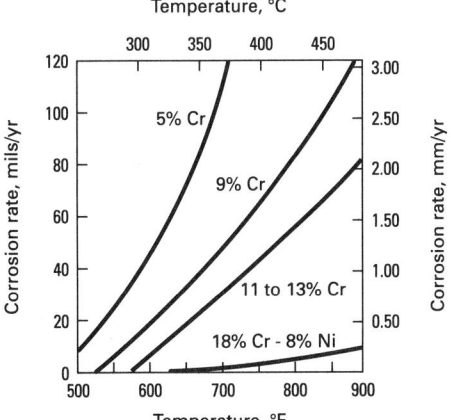

Fig. 19 Corrosion rates of Fe-Cr and Fe-Cr-Ni alloys in H_2-H_2S environments (H_2S concentrations above 1 mol%). Source: Ref 22

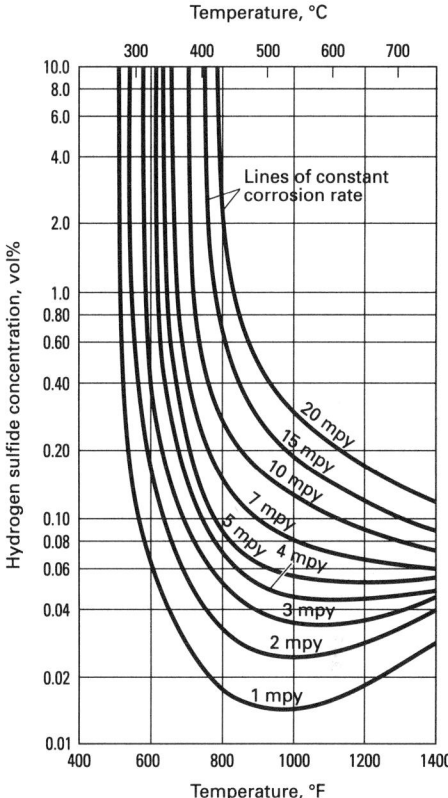

Fig. 20 Isocorrosion diagram showing the effect of hydrogen sulfide concentration on corrosion rate (in mils per year, or mpy) of austenitic stainless steels in hydrogen atmospheres at 1200 to 3450 kPa (175 to 500 psig). Exposure time was longer than 150 h. Source: Ref 27

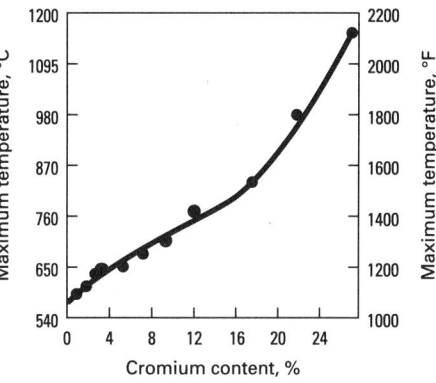

Fig. 21 Effect of chromium on the maximum oxidation resistance temperature for iron-chromium alloys in a normal combustion atmosphere. Source: Ref 23

corrosion rate may be approximately the same as in air or slightly greater. The resistance of stainless steels to normal combustion gases is increased by successive increments in chromium content, as shown in Fig. 21. Table 3 indicates the beneficial effect of chromium and the influence of fuel source.

Reducing flue gases contain varying amounts of hydrogen sulfide, hydrogen, carbon monoxide, carbon dioxide, and nitrogen. The corrosion rates encountered in these environments are sensitive to hydrogen sulfide content and temperature, and satisfactory material selection often necessitates service tests. Table 4 illustrates the effect of sulfur content on the corrosion of types 309, 310, and 330 in oxidizing and reducing flue gases. The deleterious effect of high nickel content is apparent (type 330).

Carburization and Metal Dusting (Ref 1)

Metals or alloys are generally susceptible to carburization when exposed to an environment containing CO, CH_4, or other hydrocarbon gases, such as propane (C_3H_8), at elevated temperatures. Carburization attack generally results in the formation of internal carbides, which often cause the alloy to suffer embrittlement as well as degradation of other mechanical properties.

Carburization problems are quite common to heat-treating equipment, particularly furnace retorts, baskets, fans, and other components used for case hardening of steels by gas carburizing. A common commercial practice for gas carburizing is to use an endothermic gas as a carrier enriched

Table 3 Corrosion rates of stainless steels after 3-mo exposure to flue gases

Type	Corrosion rate, mm/yr (mils/yr)		
	Coke oven gas at 815 °C (1500 °F)	Coke oven gas at 980 °C (1800 °F)	Natural gas at 815 °C (1500 °F)
430	2.31 (91)	6.0 (236)(b)	0.3 (12)
446 (26Cr)	0.76 (30)	1.0 (40)	0.1 (4)
446 (28Cr)	0.68 (27)	0.36 (14)	0.07 (3)
302B	2.6 (104)	5.7 (225)(b)	...
309S	0.94 (37)(a)	1.14 (45)	0.07 (3)
310S	0.96 (38)(a)	0.64 (25)	0.07 (3)
314	0.58 (23)(a)	2.39 (94)	0.07 (3)

(a) Pitted specimens—average pit depth. (b) Specimen destroyed. Source: Ref 23

with one of the hydrocarbon gases, such as CH_4, C_3H_8, and so on. An endothermic gas enriched with about 10% natural gas (CH_4) is a commonly used atmosphere. The typical endothermic gas consists of 39.8% N_2, 20.7% CO, 38.7% H_2, and 0.8% CH_4, with a dew point of –20 to –4 °C (–5 to +25 °F). Gas carburizing is typically performed at temperatures of 840 to 930 °C (1550 to 1700 °F). Furnace equipment and components repeatedly subjected to these service conditions frequently suffer brittle failures as a result of carburization attack.

In the petrochemical industry, carburization is one of the major modes of high-temperature cor-

rosion for processing equipment. Pyrolysis furnace tubes for the production of ethylene and olefins are a good example. Ethylene is formed by cracking petroleum feedstocks, such as ethane and naphtha, at temperatures up to 1150 °C (2100 °F). This generates strong carburizing environments inside the tubes. Carburization was found to be a major mode of tube failure in a survey of ethylene and olefins pyrolysis furnaces conducted by Moller and Warren (Ref 28).

Production of carbon fibers also generates carburizing atmospheres in a furnace. As a result, the furnace retorts, fixtures, and other components require frequent replacement because of carburization attack.

General Principles (Ref 2). As in the case of sulfide penetration, carburization of high-temperature alloys is thermodynamically unlikely except at very low oxygen partial pressures, because the protective oxides of chromium are generally more likely to form than the carbides. While carburization can occur kinetically in many carbon-containing environments, carbon transport across continuous nonporous scales of Cr_2O_3 is very slow. Furthermore, the alloy pretreatments that are likely to promote such scales, such as initially smooth surfaces or preoxidation, have generally been effective in decreasing carburization attack. In practice, the scales formed on high-temperature alloys often consist of multiple layers of oxides resulting from localized bursts of oxide

formation in areas where the original scale was broken or lost. The protection is derived from the innermost layer, which is usually richest in chromium. Concentration of gaseous species, such as carbon monoxide, in the outer porous oxide layers appears to be one means by which sufficiently high carbon activities can be generated at the alloy surface for carburization to occur in otherwise oxidizing environments. The creation of localized microenvironments is also possible under deposits that create stagnant conditions not permeable by the ambient gas.

Once inside the alloy, the detrimental effects of the carbon depend on the location, composition, and morphology of the carbides formed. Austenitic steels should carburize more readily than ferritic steels because of the high solubility of carbon in austenite. Iron-chromium alloys containing less than about 13% Cr contain various amounts of austenite, depending on temperature, and should be susceptible to carburization, while alloys with 13 to 20% Cr will form austenite as a result of absorption of small amounts of carbon. Iron-chromium alloys containing more than ~20% Cr can absorb considerable amounts of carbon before austenite forms, becoming principally $(CrFe)_{23}C_6$ and ferrite. An example of rapid high-temperature carburization attack of an austenitic stainless steel is shown in Fig. 22.

Carburization Resistance. Stainless steels are widely used for processing equipment to resist

Table 4 Corrosion rates of cast stainless steels in air and oxidizing and reducing flue gases

Type	Corrosion rate, mm/yr (mils/yr)					
	Air		Oxidizing flue gas at 1095 °C (2000 °F)		Reducing flue gas at 1095 °C (2000 °F)	
	1095 °C (2000 °F)	1200 °C (2200 °F)	5 gr S(a)	100 gr S(a)	5 gr S(a)	100 gr S(a)
309	1-2.3 (40-90)	1.5 (60)	1.3-1.8 (50-70)	1-2.5 (40-100)	0.5-1.3 (20-50)	0.76 (30)
310	1 (40)	1.3-2 (50-80)	1.3 (50)	1 (40)	0.5-1.3 (20-50)	0.76 (30)
330	1.3 (50)	2.5-25 (100-1000)	1.5-7.6 (60-300)	2.5-12.7 (100-500)	1.3-5 (50-200)	7.6-20 (300-800)

(a) Grains of sulfur per 100 ft^3. Source: Ref 23

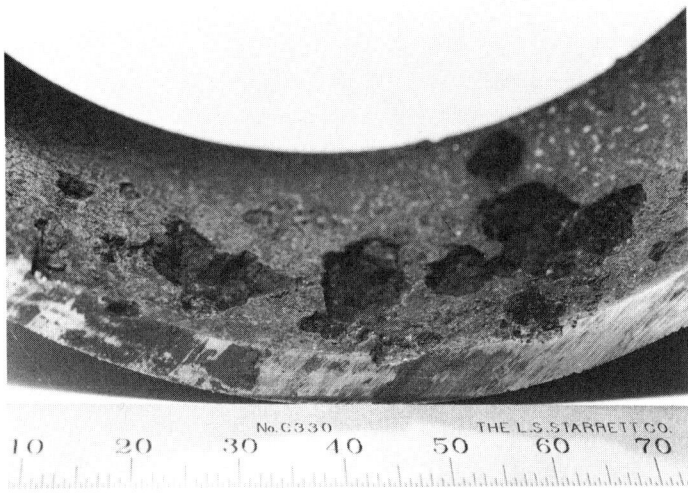

(a)

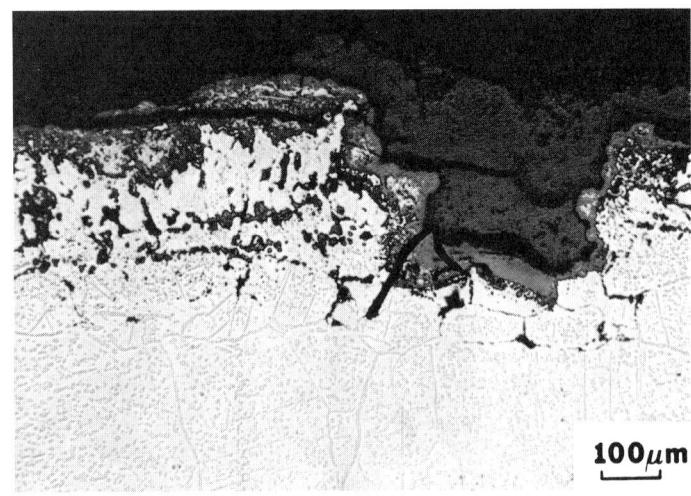

(b)

Fig. 22 Example of high-temperature carburization attack pitting in a type 310 reactor wall after ~4000 h exposure to coal gasification product gas. The pits were formed during operation under conditions of high carbon activity in the gas. (a) Overall view of pitting. (b) Section through a pit

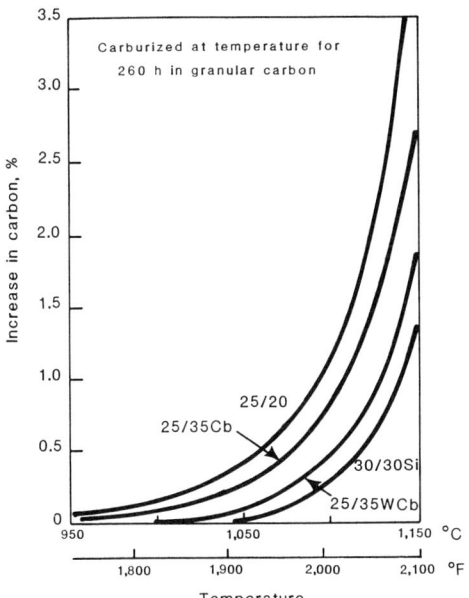

Fig. 23 Carburization resistance of HK (25Cr-20Ni) and several HP alloys (Cr-Ni) as a function of temperature. Source: Ref 29

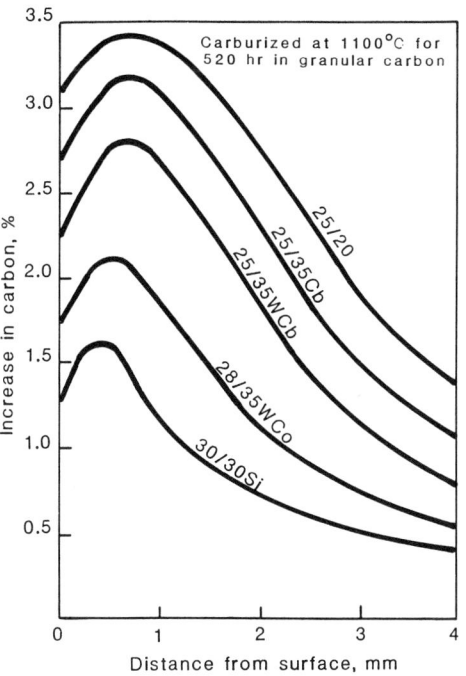

Fig. 24 Carbon concentration profiles for HK (25Cr-20Ni) and several HP alloys (Cr-Ni) carburized at 1100 °C (2010 °F) for 520 h in granular carbon. Source: Ref 29

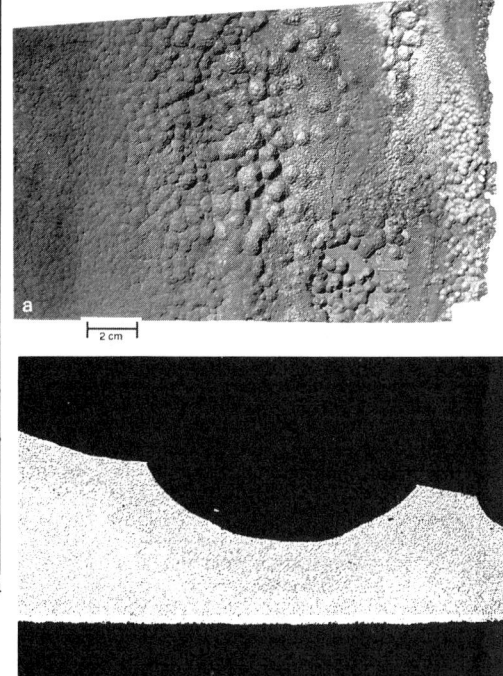

Fig. 25 Type 310 stainless steel component suffering metal dusting in a furnace used in manufacturing carbon fibers. (a) General view. (b) Cross section of the sample showing pitting attack

carburization in the petrochemical industry. The cast 25Cr-20Ni alloy, HK-40, has been the workhorse of pyrolysis furnace tubes in ethylene cracking operations. Many modifications of HK-40 have been developed that have improved carburization resistance. These modified alloys use small additions of niobium, tungsten, molybdenum, and/or silicon, as well as increases in nickel and/or chromium. Among these alloying elements, silicon is the most effective in improving carburization resistance. This is attributed to the formation of SiO_2 scale, which is more impervious to carbon ingress than Cr_2O_3 scale. Increasing nickel in Fe-Cr-Ni alloys also improves carburization resistance, because nickel reduces the diffusivity of carbon. Figures 23 and 24 illustrate the carburization resistance of some of these modified alloys compared to that of HK-alloy.

Metal dusting is a form of carburization attack that generally results in metal wastage, such as pitting and/or thinning. The environment is highly carburizing, with enrichment of H_2, CO, or hydrocarbons. A stagnant atmosphere is particularly conducive to metal dusting. Metal dusting occurs between 430 and 900 °C (800 and 1650 °F) and has been encountered in heat treating, refining and petrochemical processing, and other operations. Figure 25 shows a stainless steel component that was subjected to metal dusting in a furnace used to manufacture carbon fibers.

Nitridation (Ref 1)

Stainless steels are generally susceptible to nitridation attack when exposed to ammonia-bearing environments at elevated temperatures. Nitrogen-base atmospheres can also be nitriding, particularly when the environments are reducing (i.e., have low oxygen potentials). As the environment becomes more oxidizing, nitridation attack generally becomes less severe. Highly oxidizing combustion atmospheres or air normally do not result in nitridation attack. During nitridation, the alloy absorbs nitrogen from the environment. When nitrogen in the alloy exceeds its solubility limit, nitrides precipitate out in the matrix as well as at grain boundaries. As a result, the alloy can become embrittled.

Ammonia is a commonly used nitriding gas for case hardening of steel, typically performed at temperatures from 500 to 590 °C (925 to 1100 °F). Furnace equipment and components repeatedly subjected to these service conditions frequently suffer brittle failures as a result of nitridation attack.

Carbonitriding is another important method of case hardening that produces a surface layer of both carbides and nitrides. The process is typically carried out at 700 to 900 °C (1300 to 1650 °F) in ammonia, with additions of carbonaceous gases, such as CH_4. Thus, the heat-treat retort, fixtures, and other furnace equipment are subject to both nitridation and carburization.

Cracked ammonia (ammonia that is completely dissociated into H_2 and N_2) provides an economical protective atmosphere for processing metals and alloys. Many bright annealing operations for stainless steels use a protective atmosphere consisting of N_2 and H_2, generated by dissociation of ammonia. Once nitrogen molecules are formed from the dissociation of ammonia, the potential for nitriding the metal is significantly reduced. With three parts H_2 and one part N_2 produced in cracked ammonia, heat-treating equipment is generally less susceptible to nitridation attack.

Nitrogen atmospheres are becoming increasingly popular as a protective atmosphere in heat-treating and sintering operations. Although molecular nitrogen is less reactive than ammonia, it can be severely nitriding when the temperature is sufficiently high. Long-term exposure to a nitrogen atmosphere at high temperatures may cause metallic equipment to suffer premature failure.

In the chemical processing industry, nitriding environments are generated by processes employed for production of ammonia, nitric acid, melamine, and nylon 6/6. Ammonia is produced by reacting nitrogen with hydrogen over a catalyst, typically at temperatures of 500 to 550 °C (930 to 1020 °F) and pressures of 200 to 400 atm.

Production of nitric acid involves the oxidation of ammonia over a platinum catalyst at temperatures of about 900 °C (1650 °F). The catalyst grid support structure and other processing components in contact with ammonia may also be susceptible to nitridation attack.

Nitridation Resistance. Nitridation attack is different from other modes of high-temperature corrosion in that metals or alloys do not suffer metal loss or metal wastage. Nitrogen from the environment is absorbed on the metal surface and then diffuses into the interior. Once nitrogen exceeds its solubility limit, nitrides precipitate out. When the temperature is low, such as 500 °C (930 °F), the diffusion of nitrogen is slow. Nitridation at these temperatures generally results in the formation of a surface nitride layer (Fig. 26a and b). At higher temperatures (e.g., 1000 °C, or 1830

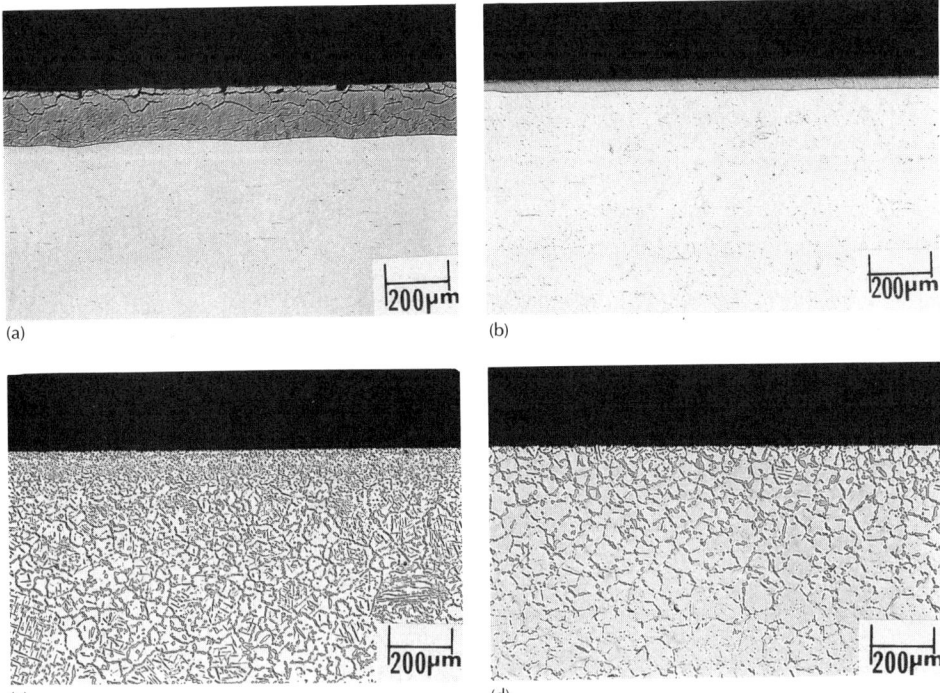

(a)   (b)

(c)   (d)

Fig. 26 Typical morphology of nitrides formed in ammonia at 650 °C (1200 °F) for 168 h for (a) type 310 stainless steel and (b) Alloy X, and at 1090 °C (2000 °F) for 168 h for (c) type 310 and (d) Alloy X

Table 5 Corrosion behavior of various alloys in an ammonia converter and plant ammonia line

Alloy	Nickel content, %	Corrosion rate, mm/yr (mils/yr) Ammonia converter(a)	Plant ammonia line(b)
430	...	0.022 (0.90)	...
446	...	0.028 (1.12)	4.18 (164.5)
302B	10	0.019 (0.73)	...
304	9	0.015 (0.59)	2.53 (99.5)
316	13	0.012 (0.47)	>13.21 (>520)
321	11	0.012 (0.47)	...
309	14	0.006 (0.23)	2.41 (95)
314	20	0.003 (0.10)	...
310	21	0.004 (0.14)	...
330 (0.47Si)	36	0.002 (0.06)	...
330 (1.00Si)	36	0.001 (0.02)	0.43 (17.1)
Alloy 600	76	...	0.16 (6.3)
80Ni-20Cr	80	...	0.19 (7.4)
Ni	100	...	2.01 (79.0)

Source: Ref 30

Table 6 Corrosion of stainless steels in chlorine
Chlorine pressure was approximately 1.0 atm.

Alloy	Temperature °C	°F	Flow rate, L/min	Linear rate constant(a), μm/min	Corrosion rate(b) mm/yr	mils/yr
Ferritic stainless (Fe-17Cr)	300	572	15	4×10^{-4}	0.2	7.9
	360	680	15	3.8×10^{-3}	2	79
	440	824	15	6.7×10^{-2}	40	1.6 in.
	540	1004	15	1.35	700	28 in.
Austenitic stainless (Fe-18Cr-9Ni-Ti)	418	784	15	1.1×10^{-3}	0.6	24
	450	842	15	4.3×10^{-2}	20	787
	480	896	15	0.13	70	2.8 in.
	535	995	15	0.47	200	7.9 in.
	640	1184	15	46	20,000	787 in.
Austenitic stainless (Fe-18Cr-8Ni-Mo)	315	599	28	1.4×10^{-3}	0.8	31
	340	644	28	2.9×10^{-3}	1.5	59
	400	752	28	5.9×10^{-3}	3	118
	450	842	28	2.9×10^{-2}	15	590
	480	896	28	5.9×10^{-2}	30	1.2 in.
Austenitic stainless (Fe-18Cr-8Ni)	290	554	28	1.5×10^{-3}	0.8	31
	315	599	28	2.9×10^{-3}	1.5	59
	340	644	28	5.9×10^{-3}	3	118
	400	752	28	2.9×10^{-2}	15	590
	450	842	28	5.9×10^{-2}	30	1.2 in.

(a) Duration of these tests was 60 to 360 min for the first two alloys and 120 to 1200 min for the last two alloys. (b) Estimated metal loss after one year of exposure. Source: Ref 31

°F), the diffusion of nitrogen is rapid. In this case nitridation leads to the formation of internal nitrides in the matrix and at grain boundaries (Fig. 26c and d). With either a surface nitride or internal nitrides, the metal or alloy can become brittle.

For stainless steels, increasing the nickel content increases resistance to nitridation. Table 5 shows the effect of nickel content on corrosion behavior in an ammonia converter and plant ammonia line. If conditions are too hostile for stainless steels because of higher tem-

peratures and/or higher ammonia concentration, nickel-base alloys should be used.

Halogen Gas Corrosion (Ref 1)

Many metals react readily with halogen gases at elevated temperatures to form volatile metal halides. Many metal halides also exhibit low melting points. Some metal halides even sublime at relatively low temperatures. As a result, alloys containing elements that form volatile halides can suffer severe high-temperature corrosion.

Industrial environments often contain halogen gases. Because of the high vapor pressures of many metal chlorides, the chlorination process is an important step in processing metallurgical ores for production of titanium, zirconium, tantalum, niobium, and tungsten. Chlorination is also used for extraction of nickel from iron laterites and for detinning of tin plate. Production of TiO$_2$ and SiO$_2$ involves processing environments containing Cl$_2$ and/or HCl, along with O$_2$ and other combustion products. Calcining operations for production of lanthanum, cerium, and neodymium for electronic and magnetic materials, as well as for production of ceramic ferrites for permanent magnets, frequently generate environments contaminated with chlorine. In the chemical processing industry, many processing streams also contain chlorine. Manufacturing of ethylene dichloride (EDC), which is an intermediate for the production of vinyl chloride monomer, generates chlorine-bearing environments. The reactor vessels, calciners, and other processing equipment for the above operations require alloys resistant to high-temperature chlorination attack.

In the manufacture of fluorine-containing compounds, such as fluorocarbon plastics, refrigerants, and fire-extinguishing agents, the processing equipment requires alloys with good resistance to corrosion by fluorine and hydrogen fluorides at elevated temperatures. During the re-

Table 7 Corrosion of selected alloys in Ar-$20O_2$-$2Cl_2$ at 900 °C (1650 °F) for 8 h

Alloy	Metal loss		Average metal affected(a)	
	mm	mils	mm	mils
214	0	0	0.012	0.48
R-41	0.004	0.16	0.028	1.12
600	0.012	0.48	0.035	1.36
310SS	0.012	0.48	0.041	1.60
S	0.053	2.08	0.063	2.48
X	0.020	0.80	0.071	2.80
C-276	0.079	3.12	0.079	3.12
6B	0.014	0.56	0.098	3.84
188	0.014	0.56	0.116	4.56

(a) Metal loss + average internal penetration. Source: Ref 32

Table 8 Corrosion of alloys in dry HCl
Based on short-term laboratory tests

Alloy	Approximate temperature, °C (°F), at which given corrosion rate is exceeded			
	0.8 mm/yr (30 mils/yr)	1.5 mm/yr (60 mils/yr)	3.0 mm/yr (120 mils/yr)	15 mm/yr (600 mils/yr)
Nickel	455 (850)	510 (950)	565 (1050)	675 (1250)
600	425 (800)	480 (900)	538 (1000)	675 (1250)
B	370 (700)	425 (800)	480 (900)	650 (1200)
C	370 (700)	425 (800)	480 (900)	620 (1150)
D	288 (550)	370 (700)	455 (850)	650 (1200)
18-8Mo	370 (700)	370 (700)	480 (900)	593 (1100)
25-12Cb	345 (650)	400 (750)	455 (850)	565 (1050)
18-8	345 (650)	400 (750)	455 (850)	593 (1100)
Carbon steel	260 (500)	315 (600)	400 (750)	565 (1050)
Ni-resist	260 (500)	315 (600)	370 (700)	538 (1000)
400	230 (450)	260 (500)	345 (650)	480 (900)
Cast iron	205 (400)	260 (500)	315 (600)	455 (850)
Copper	93 (200)	148 (300)	205 (400)	315 (600)

Source: Ref 33

fining operation in the production of uranium, UO_2 is fluorinated at elevated temperatures (e.g., 500 to 600 °C, or 930 to 1110 °F) with HF to produce UF_4 or UF_6 for separation of U_{235}. The materials of construction for this processing equipment must resist corrosion by HF at both high and low temperatures.

Resistance to Halogen Gas Corrosion. In Cl_2- and HCl-bearing environments, the corrosion behavior of various alloy systems is strongly dependent on whether the environment is oxidizing or reducing. For Cl_2-bearing environments with no measurable O_2, iron and steel are very susceptible to chlorination attack. Adding chromium and/or nickel to iron improves the corrosion resistance of the alloy. Thus, ferritic and austenitic stainless steels can resist chlorination attack at higher temperatures than cast iron and carbon steels. Nickel and nickel-base alloys, including Ni-Cr-Fe, Ni-Cr-Mo, and Ni-Mo alloys, are significantly more resistant to chlorination attack than stainless steels and Fe-Ni-Cr alloys such as 800-type alloys. Table 6 lists the corrosion resistance of stainless steels in chlorine.

In oxidizing environments containing both Cl_2 and O_2, molybdenum and tungsten are detrimental to the resistance of the alloy to chlorination attack, presumably due to the formation of highly volatile oxychlorides, such as WO_2Cl_2 and MoO_2Cl_2. Thus, nickel-base alloys containing

high levels of tungsten or molybdenum, such as Alloy 188 (14% W) and Alloy C-276 (16% Mo, 4% W), suffer higher rates of corrosion attack than Fe-Ni-Cr and Ni-Cr-Fe alloys, such as type 310 stainless steel and Alloy 600. The addition of aluminum improves the chlorination resistance of nickel-base alloys such as Alloy 214 (Ni-Cr-Al). Table 7 compares the corrosion rates of nickel-base alloys and stainless steels in an O_2-Cl_2 -containing environment.

In reducing environments containing HCl, nickel and nickel-base alloys are generally more resistant than iron-base alloys, such as austenitic stainless steels. Table 8 compares the corrosion rates of various materials, including stainless steels, in dry HCl.

Stainless steels are very susceptible to corrosion in fluorine gas at temperatures as low as 300 °C (570 °F) or even lower (Table 9). Commercially pure nickel probably has the best resistance to fluorine corrosion at elevated temperatures, attributable to the formation of an adherent nickel fluoride scale. Many nickel-base alloys are significantly worse than nickel.

Stainless steels also exhibit poor resistance to fluorination attack in hydrogen fluoride environments. As shown in Table 10, pure nickel and

nickel-base alloys such as Alloy 400 and Alloy 600 are far more resistant to hydrogen fluoride attack than stainless steels.

Ash/Salt Deposit Corrosion (Ref 1)

Deposition of ashes and salts on the surfaces of process components is quite common in some industrial environments, such as fossil-fuel-fired power plants and waste incineration plants. The corrosion process under these conditions involves both the deposit and the corrosive gases. The deposit may alter the thermodynamic potentials of the environment on the metal surface beneath the deposit. In an environment with both oxygen and sulfur activities, for example, the deposit tends to lower the oxygen activity and raise the sulfur activity beneath the deposit. As a result, formation of a protective oxide scale on the metal surface may become more difficult for most alloys. In most cases, the deposit involves some type of salt. This may lead to chemical reactions between the protective oxide scale and the salt, resulting in the breakdown of the scale. A salt deposit that becomes liquid is particularly damaging.

Table 9 Corrosion of several alloys in fluorine
Tests were conducted in flowing fluorine.

Alloy	Exposure time, h	Corrosion rate, mm/yr (mils/yr)		
		200 °C (400 °F)	370 °C (700 °F)	540 °C (1000 °F)
400	5	0.013 (0.5)	0.048 (1.9)	0.76 (29.8)
	24	0.013 (0.5)	0.043 (1.7)	0.29 (11.3)
	120	0.003 (0.1)	0.031 (1.2)	0.18 (7.2)
Ni-200	5	0.084 (3.3)	0.043 (1.7)	0.62 (24.5)
	24	0.013 (0.5)	0.031 (1.2)	0.41 (16.1)
	120	0.003 (0.1)	0.010 (0.4)	0.35 (13.8)
304	5	0.155 (6.1)	40 (1565)	...
304L	24	0.191 (7.5)	153 (6018)	...
	120	0.65 (25.4)	...	...
347	5	0.102 (4.0)	108 (4248)	...
Illium R	5	0.152 (6.0)	0.32 (12.7)	103 (4038)
600	5	0.015 (0.6)	2.0 (78.0)	88 (3451)

Source: Ref 34

Table 10 Corrosion of various metals and alloys in anhydrous HF

Material	Corrosion rate, mm/yr (mils/yr)		
	500 °C (930 °F)	550 °C (1020 °F)	600 °C (1110 °F)
Nickel	0.9 (36)	...	0.9 (36)
400	1.2 (48)	1.2 (48)	1.8 (72)
600	1.5 (60)	...	1.5 (60)
Copper	1.5 (60)	...	1.2 (48)
Aluminum	4.9 (192)	...	14.6 (576)
Magnesium	12.8 (504)	...	...
Carbon steel (1020)	15.5 (612)	14.6 (576)	7.6 (300)
304	...	...	13.4 (528)
347	183 (7200)	457 (18,000)	177 (6960)
309Cb	5.8 (228)	43 (1680)	168 (6600)
310	12.2 (480)	100 (3960)	305 (12,000)
430	1.5 (60)	9.1 (360)	11.6 (456)

Source: Ref 35

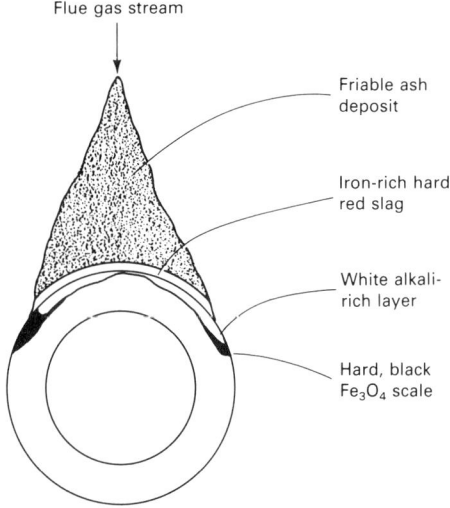

Fig. 27 Deposit layers on a corroding superheater or reheater tube. The deposit may be several inches thick. Source: Ref 36

The term *hot corrosion*, introduced previously, refers to high-temperature corrosion of hot-section gas-turbine components, such as nozzle guide vanes and rotor blades, due to salt deposits, principally sodium sulfate. Because gas-turbine components are generally made from nickel-base superalloys, this form of corrosion will not be addressed in this section.

Another term introduced previously, *fuel ash corrosion,* refers to fireside corrosion of components such as superheaters and reheaters in fossil-fuel-fired boilers. This type of corrosion is related to alkali-iron trisulfates for coal-fired boilers and vanadium salts (a mixture of vanadium pentoxide and sodium oxide or sodium sulfate) for oil-fired boilers. Corrosion in waste incinerators is not very well understood. The principal corrosive contaminants typically found in deposits and corrosion products include sulfur, chlorine, zinc, lead, and potassium. It is believed that the corrosion reaction is also related to salt deposits formed on metal surfaces.

Materials Performance. Fireside corrosion in coal-fired boilers involves the corrosion of furnace walls and superheaters/reheaters. Corrosion of furnace wall tubes is believed to be enhanced by the establishment of localized reducing conditions in the vicinity of furnace walls. This tends to result in high sulfur potentials and low oxygen potentials at the localized furnace wall surface, thus promoting sulfidation attack. The formation of low-melting-point salt deposits may also be responsible. Figure 27 illustrates the deposit formed on superheater tubes. Corrosion may be further accelerated by the presence of hydrogen chloride gas. Austenitic stainless steels (as an outer layer of a coextruded tube) are more resistant to furnace wall corrosion than carbon steels. Higher-chromium austenitic stainless steels appear to be better cladding material for coextruded tubes in terms of furnace wall corrosion. For example, type 310 stainless steel is more corrosion resistant than type 304.

Corrosion of superheater/reheater tubes may be related to the formation of molten alkali metal-iron-trisulfate, $(Na,K)_3Fe(SO_4)_3$. The corrosion rate exhibits a bell-shape curve with respect to temperature (Fig. 28). Austenitic stainless steels are more corrosion resistant than carbon steels and chromium-molybdenum steels. Higher-chromium austenitic stainless steels and nickel-base alloys (e.g., type 310 and Alloy 671) make better outer-diameter cladding materials for coextruded tubes in terms of superheater/reheater corrosion.

Fireside corrosion can be a severe problem in oil-fired boilers or furnaces when low-grade fuels with high concentrations of vanadium, sulfur, and sodium are used for firing. This corrosion is frequently referred to as *oil/ash corrosion*. Accelerated attack by oil/ash corrosion is related to the formation of low-melting-point molten vanadium pentoxide and sodium sulfate eutectics, which flux the protective oxide scale from the metal surface.

Uncooled components, such as tube supports and spacers, can suffer severe corrosion attack at temperatures higher than 650 °C (1200 °F). High-chromium alloys generally perform better. For example, 50Ni-50Cr alloy (e.g., Alloy 657) is significantly more corrosion resistant than 25Cr-12Ni steel (HH alloy) or 25Cr-20Ni steel (HK alloy).

Superheater/reheater tubes, with much lower temperatures than tube supports, are also susceptible to oil/ash corrosion. Results of a long-term field test performed at temperatures of 605 °C (1200 °F) and lower suggest that chromium-molybdenum steels (e.g., 2.25Cr-1Mo, 9Cr, and 12Cr steels) are significantly more corrosion resistant than austenitic stainless steels, such as types 316, 321, 347, and 310 (Fig. 29). As outer-diameter cladding materials for coextruded tubes, type 446 and Alloy 671 (high-chromium alloys) are better than 300-series austenitic stainless steels, such as types 347 and 310.

Injecting additives, such as $Mg(OH)_2$, into the fuel to raise the melting point of the oil/ash deposit is another effective means of combatting oil/ash corrosion problems.

Molten Salt Corrosion

Molten salt technology plays an important role in various industries. In the heat-treating industry, molten salts are commonly used as a medium for heat treatment of metals and alloys (e.g., annealing, tempering, hardening, quenching, and cleaning) as well as for surface treatment (e.g., case hardening). In nuclear energy systems, they have been used as a medium for heat transfer and energy storage. Other applications include extraction of aluminum, magnesium, sodium, and other reactive metals, refining of refractory metals, and high-temperature batteries and fuel cells.

Mechanisms of Molten Salt Corrosion (Ref 38)

Two general mechanisms of corrosion can exist in molten salts. One is the metal dissolution caused by the solubility of the metal in the melt. This dissolution is similar to that in molten met-

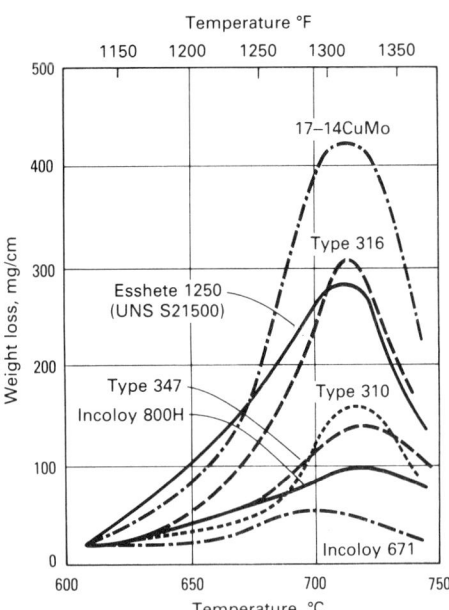

Fig. 28 Corrosion rates of alloys in a laboratory test using synthetic ash (37.5 mol% Na_2SO_4, 37.5 mol% K_2SO_4, and 25 mol% Fe_2O_3) in a synthetic flue gas (80% nitrogen, 15% CO_2, 4% oxygen, and 1% SO_2 saturated with water). Exposure time: 50 h. Source: Ref 36

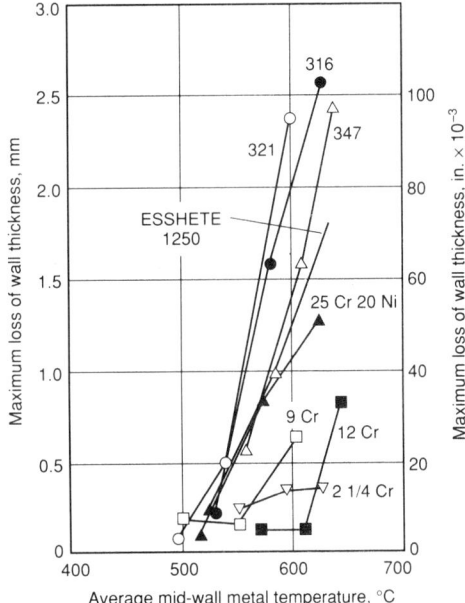

Fig. 29 Results of a 10,000 h field test in the superheater inlet zone (horizontal position) in an oil-fired boiler. Source: Ref 37

als, but it is not common. The second and most common mechanism is the oxidation of the metal to ions, similar to aqueous corrosion. For this reason, molten salt corrosion has been identified as an intermediate form of corrosion between molten metal and aqueous corrosion.

General, or uniform, metal oxidation and dissolution is a common form of molten salt corrosion, but it is not the only form seen. Selective

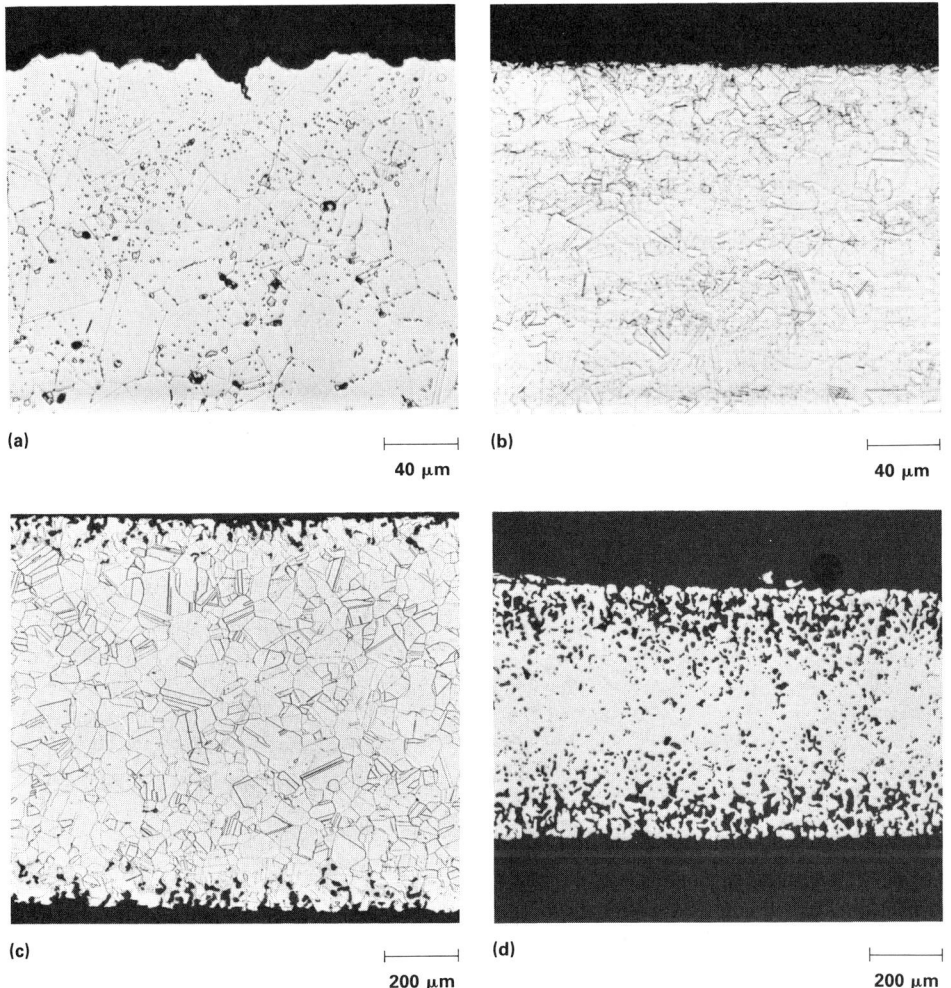

(a)

40 μm

(b)

40 μm

(c)

200 μm

(d)

200 μm

Fig. 30 Effect of molten salt corrosion on nickel-base and stainless steel alloys. In all four examples, chromium depletion (dealloying) was the result of prolonged exposure. Accompanying chromium depletion was the formation of subsurface voids that did not connect with the surface or with each other. As chromium was leached from the surface of the metal, a concentration (activity) gradient resulted and caused chromium atoms from the underlying region to diffuse toward the surface, leaving behind a zone enriched with vacancies. These vacancies would then agglomerate at suitable sites, primarily at grain boundaries and impurities. The vacancies became visible as voids, which tended to agglomerate and grow with increasing time and temperature. (a) Microstructure of Hastelloy alloy N exposed to $LiF-BeF_2-ThF_4-UF_4$ (68, 20, 11.7, and 0.3 mol%, respectively) for 4741 h at 700 °C (1290 °F). (b) Microstructure of Hastelloy alloy N after 2000 h exposure to $LiF-BeF_2-ThF_4$ (73, 2, and 25 mol%, respectively) at 676 °C (1249 °F). (c) Microstructure of type 304L stainless steel exposed to $LiF-BeF_2-ZrF_4-ThF_4-UF_4$ (70, 23, 5, 1, and 1 mol%, respectively) for 5700 h at 688 °C (1270 °F). (d) Microstructure of type 304L stainless steel exposed to $LiF-BeF_2-ZrF_4-ThF_4-UF_4$ (70, 23, 5, 1, and 1 mol%, respectively) for 5724 h at 685 °C (1265 °F)

transfer reaction that is typical of aqueous systems. Molten-salt systems operate at higher temperatures than aqueous systems, which leads to different forms of corrosion attack.

In aqueous systems in which specific elements are removed from alloys (dealloying corrosion), it is not clear whether the nobler element is oxidized at some stage in the process and is subsequently plated out or whether the element agglomerates by a surface diffusion mechanism. In both cases, bulk diffusion is unlikely to play a major role. In high-temperature molten-salt systems, dissolution of the less noble element is the most probable mechanism and will occur even if the element is present at low concentration. Unlike the case in aqueous systems, the rate of dissolution is therefore related to the bulk diffusion of the selectively leached element.

Because molten salt corrosion reactions are reduction/oxidation controlled, the relative nobilities of the salt melts and the metals are important. The corrosion potential of the melt is often controlled by impurities in the melt or gas phase, which increases the cathodic reaction rate or changes the acidic or basic nature of the melt. The aggressiveness of the salt melts is typically governed by its redox equilibria.

Thermal gradients in the melt can cause dissolution of metal at hot spots and metal deposition at cooler spots. The result is very similar to aqueous galvanic corrosion, and as in aqueous galvanic corrosion, a continuous electrical path is necessary between the hot and cold areas. Crevice corrosion has been observed, and "washline attack" caused by oxygen concentration corrosion is not uncommon at the interface of metal, molten salt, and air.

High-temperature corrosion in molten salts often exhibits selective attack and internal oxidation. Chromium depletion in iron-chromium-nickel alloy systems can occur by the formation of a chromium compound at the surface and by the subsequent removal of chromium from the matrix, leaving a depleted zone (Fig. 30). Thus, the selectively removed species move out, while vacancies move inward and eventually form voids. The voids tend to form at grain boundaries in most chromium-containing metals, but in some high-nickel alloys they form in the grains. Specific examples of the types of corrosion expected for the different metal-fused salt systems are given below.

Types of Molten Salts (Ref 38)

Molten Fluorides. Fluoride melts are important because of their use in nuclear reactor cooling systems. Corrosion in many fluoride molten salt melts is accelerated because no protective surface films are formed. In fact, the fluoride salts act as excellent fluxes and dissolve the various corrosion products.

Typically, nickel-base alloys show better corrosion resistance in molten fluoride salts than do iron-base alloys. Studies have also shown that most nickel- and iron-base alloys that contain varying amounts of chromium show void formation to varying depths. In nonisothermal flow systems, the metallic material shows void formation

leaching is very common at higher temperatures, as are pitting and crevice corrosion at lower temperatures. All the forms of corrosion observed in aqueous systems, including stress-assisted corrosion, galvanic corrosion, erosion-corrosion, and fretting corrosion, have been seen in fused salts.

Electrochemically, the molten salt/metal surface interface is very similar to the aqueous solution/metal surface interface. Many of the principles that apply to aqueous corrosion also apply to molten salt corrosion, such as anodic reactions leading to metal dissolution and cathodic reduction of an oxidant.

The acid and base behavior of the melt is very similar to that of its aqueous counterpart. The corrosion process is mainly electrochemical in nature because of the excellent ionic conductivity of most molten salts. Some investigators feel that

dissolved water enhances the electrochemical corrosion nature of the molten salts.

Even though their corrosion mechanisms are similar, there are major differences between molten salt and aqueous corrosion. The differences arise mainly from the fact that molten salts are partially electronic conductors as well as ionic conductors, so that reduction reactions take place in the melt as well as the metal-melt interface. This behavior also allows an increase in the frequency of cathodic reactions, and the corrosion rate may be substantially higher than that of a similar electrochemically controlled aqueous system, especially if the corrosion media contain very few oxidants. Because of property differences between water and molten salt, the rate-controlling step in most molten-metal systems is ion diffusion into the bulk solution, not the charge

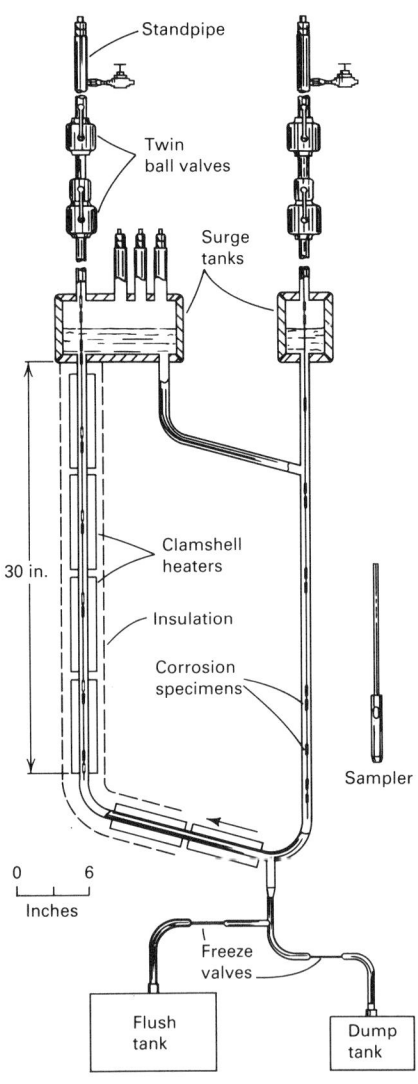

Fig. 31 Thermal convection loop used to study molten salt corrosion of metals and alloys

in the hot section and deposits in the cold section. In most alloys that contain chromium, depletion of the chromium accompanies the void formation. Analysis of the attacked metal and salt clearly shows that selective removal and outward diffusion of chromium result from oxidation by the fluoride mixture.

Inconel alloy 600 and certain stainless steels become magnetic after exposure to molten fluoride salt. This magnetism is caused by the selective removal of the chromium and the formation of a magnetic iron-nickel alloy covering the surface. The conditions of the melt need to be controlled to minimize the selective removal of the alloying elements. This control can be done by maintaining the melt in a reducing condition. Addition of beryllium metal to the melt is one way to slow the corrosion rate. Figure 30 shows examples of microstructures of nickel-base and stainless steels as a result of exposure to molten fluoride salts.

Corrosion studies on molten fluoride salts, as well as all other types of fused salts, are conducted in thermal convection or forced convection loops. These apparatuses allow determination of the effects of thermal gradients, flow, chemistry changes, and surface area changes. These loops can also include electrochemical probes and gas monitors. A thermal convection loop is shown in Fig. 31. Test results from these loops are summarized below (Ref 39).

Lithium fluoride-beryllium fluoride salts containing UF_4 or ThF_4 and tested in thermal convection loops showed temperature gradient mass transfer, as noted by weight losses in the hot leg and weight gains in the cold leg of a type 316 stainless steel specimen (Fig. 32).

A type 304L stainless steel exposed to a fluoride fuel salt for 9.5 years in a type 304L stainless steel loop showed a maximum uniform corrosion rate of 22 μm/yr (0.86 mil/yr). Voids extended into the matrix for 250 μm (10 mils), and chromium depletion was found (Fig. 33 and 34).

Type 316 stainless steel exposed to a fluoride fuel salt in a type 316 stainless steel loop showed a maximum uniform corrosion rate of 25 μm/yr (1 mil/yr) for 4298 h. Mass transfer did occur in the system.

For selected nickel- and iron-base alloys, a direct correlation was found between corrosion resistance in molten fluoride salt and the chromium and iron contents of an alloy. The more chromium and iron in the alloy, the less the corrosion resistance.

Chloride Salts. Molten salts consisting of chlorides are important, but they have been studied less than fluoride system. In general, chloride salts attack steels very rapidly, with preferential attack of the carbides. Aluminum coatings on steels are not effective, while the addition of nickel to steel is beneficial. Nickel-base alloys decrease in resistance with increased oxygen partial pressure. In the chloride salts, no protective oxide scale is formed on the nickel-base alloys. The attack of metal surfaces in pure sodium chloride has been observed at temperatures above 600 °C (1110 °F).

In most cases with iron-nickel-chromium alloys, the corrosion takes the form of intergranular attack. An increase of chromium in the alloy from 10 to 30% increases the corrosion rate by a factor of seven, while changes in nickel content have no effect. Thus, the intergranular attack is probably selective with respect to chromium. The chromium removal begins at the grain boundary and continues with diffusion of the chromium from within the grain to the boundary layer, gradually enlarging the cavity in the metal. The gross corrosive attack is probably caused by the free chlorine, which is highly oxidizing material, attacking the highly active structure-sensitive sites, such as dislocations and grain boundaries.

Molten nitrates are commonly used for heat-treatment baths, so a great deal of material compatibility information exists. Plain carbon and low-alloy steels form protective iron oxide films that effectively protect the metal surface to approximately 500 °C (930 °F). Chromium additions increase the corrosion resistance of the steel, and hydroxide additions to the melt further increase the resistance of chromium-containing steels. Table 11 compares the corrosion rates of various metals and alloys in molten $NaNO_3$-KNO_3 salt.

Molten Sulfates. High-temperature alloys containing chromium perform well in sulfate salts because they form a protective scale. If the chromium content is not sufficient, the alloy will suffer severe external corrosion and internal sulfidation.

Hydroxide Melts. Stainless steels perform poorly in hydroxide melts because of selective oxidation of the chromium, which leads to pore formation in the metal. Nickel is more resistant than stainless steels or unalloyed steels.

Carbonate Melts. Austenitic stainless steels perform well in carbonate melts up to 500 °C (930 °F). If temperatures to 600 °C (1110 °F) are required, nickel-base alloys containing chromium are needed. For temperatures to 700 °C (1290 °F), high-chromium alloys containing at least 50% Cr are required. Above 700 °C (1290 °F), the passive films that form at lower temperatures will break down and preclude the use of metals.

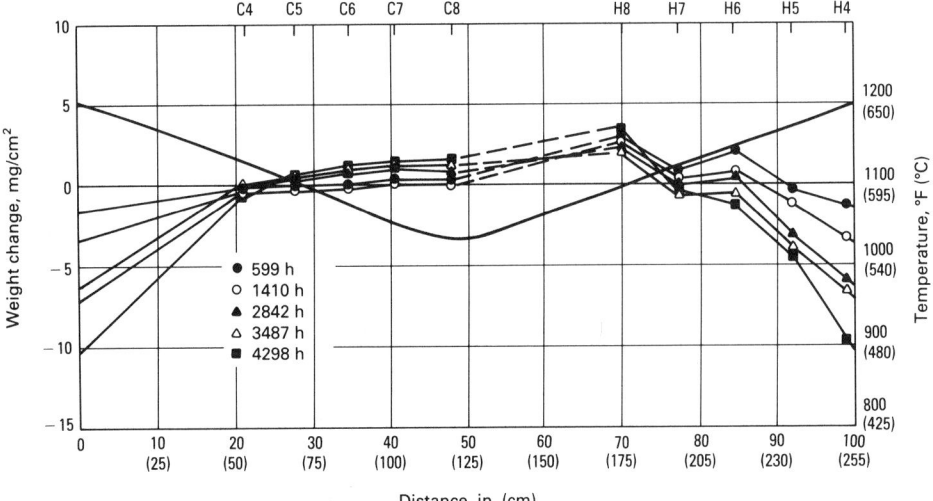

Fig. 32 Weight changes of type 316 stainless steel specimens exposed to LiF-BeF$_2$-ThF$_4$-UF$_4$ (68, 20, 11.7, and 0.3 mol%, respectively) as a function of position and temperature in a thermal convection loop

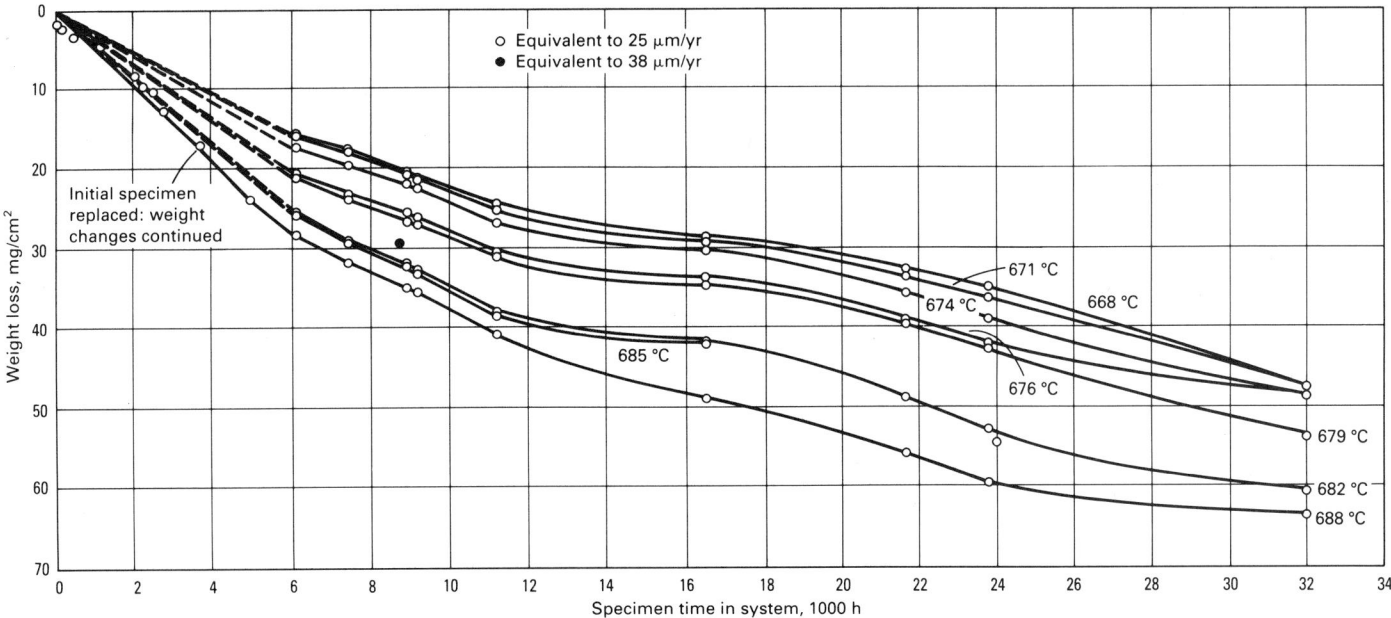

Fig. 33 Weight changes of type 304L stainless steel specimens exposed to LiF-BeF$_2$-ZrF$_4$-ThF$_4$-UF$_4$ (70, 23, 5, 1, and 1 mol%, respectively) for various times and temperatures

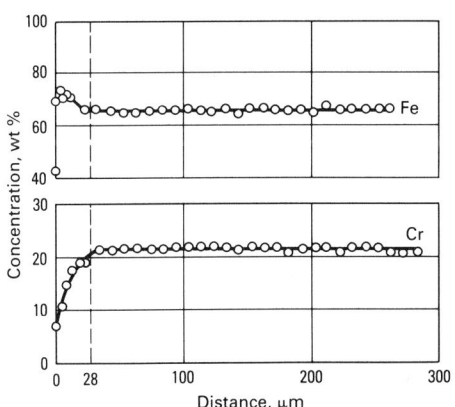

Fig. 34 Chromium and iron concentration gradient in a type 304L stainless steel specimen exposed to LiF-BeF$_2$-ZrF$_4$-ThF$_4$-UF$_4$ (70, 23, 5, 1, and 1 mol%, respectively) for 5700 h at 688 °C (1270 °F)

Table 11 **Corrosion rates of selected metals and alloys in molten NaOH$_3$-KNO$_3$**

Alloy	Temperature		Corrosion rate	
	°C	°F	mm/yr	mils/yr
Carbon steel	460	860	0.120	4.7
2.25Cr-1Mo	460	860	0.101	4.0
	500	932	0.026	1.0
9Cr-1Mo	550	1020	0.006	0.2
	600	1110	0.023	0.9
Aluminized Cr-Mo steel	600	1110	<0.004	<0.2
12Cr steel	600	1110	0.022	0.9
304SS	600	1110	0.012	0.5
316SS	600	1110	0.007-0.010	0.3-0.4
	630	1170	0.106	4.2
800	565	1050	0.005	0.2
	600	1110	0.006-0.01	0.2-0.4
	630	1170	0.075	3.0
600	600	1110	0.007-0.01	0.3-0.4
	630	1170	0.106	4.2
Nickel	565	1050	>0.5	>20
Titanium	565	1050	0.04	1.6
Aluminum	565	1050	<0.004	<0.2

Source: Ref 40

Liquid Metal Corrosion (Ref 41)

Liquid metals have long been considered for the improvement of efficiency in heat transfer systems. A recent example is the work that has been performed around the world on the sodium-cooled fast breeder reactor. This concept led to large-scale research and development programs that have continued through more than two decades. The result is a vast wealth of knowledge related to sodium corrosion behavior in all its varied aspects. The body of information greatly overshadows the corrosion data compiled for other liquid metals. This type of reactor is now in commercial operation in France and the former Soviet Union for power generation. Development reactors are operating in the United Kingdom, Germany, Japan, India, and the United States.

Liquid lithium systems have been designed for two widely different areas: space nuclear power and fusion reactors. These two applications draw on the unique properties of this liquid metal and have led to studies with a wide range of containment materials and operating conditions. Space power reactors require low mass and therefore high-temperature operation. Lithium, with its low melting point, high boiling point, and high specific heat, is an ideal heat transfer medium. Refractory metal alloy containment is essential for these reactors, which may have design operating temperatures as high as 1500 °C (2730 °F).

Liquid lithium in fusion reactor concepts is selected because here the neutronics allow tritium fuel to be bred from the lithium. This is essential in order to make the economics of the reactor viable. Containment temperatures are below 700 °C (1290 °F); therefore, iron-base alloys can be used for construction.

Liquid mercury, potassium, and cesium have also been used for space and terrestrial applications. In some cases, these have involved two-phase systems in which corrosion considerations became significantly altered. Lead, lead-bismuth, and lead-lithium alloys have received attention for topping cycle heat extraction systems, heat exchangers, reactor coolants, and, more recently, fusion reactor designs.

Other applications for liquid metals include heat-treatment baths (molten lead) and hot dip galvanizing baths (molten zinc or zinc-aluminum).

Liquid metal corrosion can be divided into several categories:

- Dissolution from a surface by (a) direct dissolution, (b) surface reaction involving solid metal atom(s), the liquid metal, and an impurity

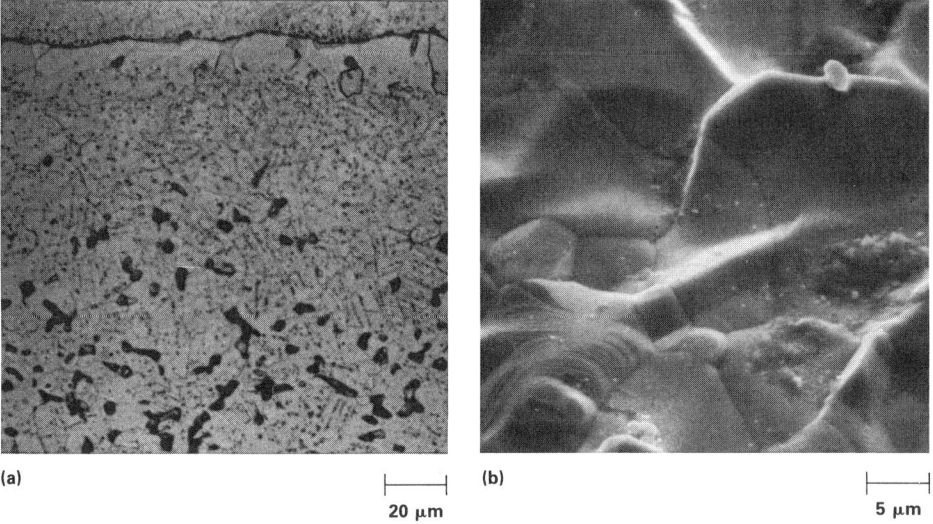

(a)

|← 20 μm →|

(b)

|← 5 μm →|

|← 2 μm →|

Fig. 35 Corrosion of type 316 stainless steel exposed to liquid sodium for 8000 h at 700 °C (1290 °F); hot leg of circulating system. Surface regression is uniform; a 10-15 μm layer of ferrite (>95% Fe) has formed. Total damage depth: 27 μm. (a) Light micrograph of wall section showing σ-phase (etched black) suppressed by composition changes to a depth of ~50 μm. (b) Scanning electron microscopy micrograph of surface

Fig. 37 Typical surface appearance of a stabilized stainless steel (X10CrNiMoTi 15 15) after 5000 h of exposure to flowing sodium at 700 °C (1290 °F). Cavities are formed at the grain corners; coral-like particles of a MoFe phase are on the grain surfaces.

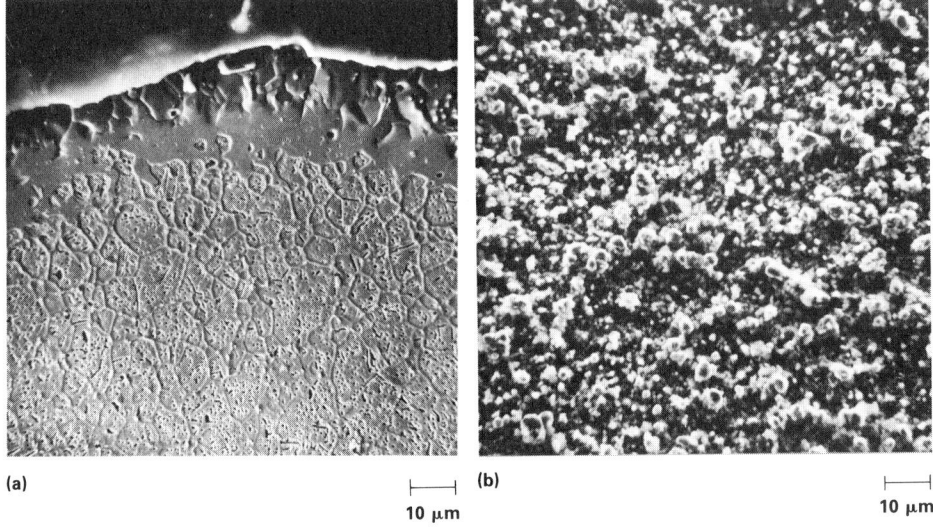

(a)

|← 10 μm →|

(b)

|← 10 μm →|

Fig. 36 Corrosion of X8CrNiMoVNb 16 13 stainless steel exposed to flowing sodium. (a) Ferrite formation in the surface layer and grain boundaries after 5000 h at 700 °C (1290 °F). Scanning electron microscopy (SEM) micrograph. Oxalic acid etch. (b) SEM micrograph of the deposition layer formed on the same steel after exposure to flowing sodium at 590 °C (1095 °F). Specimen taken downstream from the 700 °C (1290 °F) hot leg specimen shown in (a). The dark particles are rich in chromium and oxygen; some of the bright crystals are rich in calcium.

element present in the liquid metal, or (c) intergranular attack
- Impurity and interstitial reactions
- Alloying
- Compound reduction

All the variables present in the system play a part in the form and rate of corrosion that is established. Ten key factors that have a major influence on the corrosion of metals and alloys by liquid metal or liquid vapor metal coolants are:

- Composition, impurity content, and stress condition of the metal or alloy
- Exposure temperature and temperature range

- Impurity content of the liquid metal
- Circulating or static inventory
- Heating/cooling conditions
- Single or two-phase coolant
- Liquid metal velocity
- Presence/control of corrosion inhibition elements
- Exposure time
- Monometallic or multialloy system components

These factors have a varied influence, depending on the combination of containment material and liquid metal or liquid metal alloy. In most cases, the initial

period of exposure (of the order of 100 to 1000 h, depending on temperature and liquid metal involved), is a time of rapid corrosion that eventually reaches a much slower steady-state condition as factors related to solubility and activity differences in the system approach a dynamic equilibrium. In some systems, this eventually leads to the development of a similar composition on all exposed corroding surfaces. High-nickel alloys and stainless steel exposed together in the high-temperature region of a sodium system will, for example, all move toward a composition that is more than 95% Fe.

Compatibility of a liquid metal and its containment varies widely, as shown in Fig. 35 to 40. For a pure metal, surface attrition may proceed in an orderly, planar fashion, being controlled by either dissolution or a surface reaction. For a multicomponent alloy, selective loss of certain elements may lead to a phase transformation. For example, loss of nickel from austenitic stainless steel exposed to sodium may result in the formation of a ferritic surface layer (Fig. 35 and 36a). In high-nickel alloys, the planar nature of the corroding surface may be lost altogether, and a porous, spongelike layer may develop (Fig. 38b). A more insidious situation can produce intergranular attack. Liquid lithium, for example, will penetrate deep into refractory metals if precautions are not taken to ensure that the impurity element oxygen is in an oxide form more stable than Li_2O or LiO solutions and is not left free in solid solution.

Three factors should be evaluated collectively in any liquid metal system: surface attrition, depth of depleted zone (for an alloy), and the presence of intergranular attack. The assessment of total damage may be presented as either a rate or a cumulative allowance that must be made for the exposure of a given material over a given time. A large body of literature exists in which rate relationships for numerous liquid metal/containment

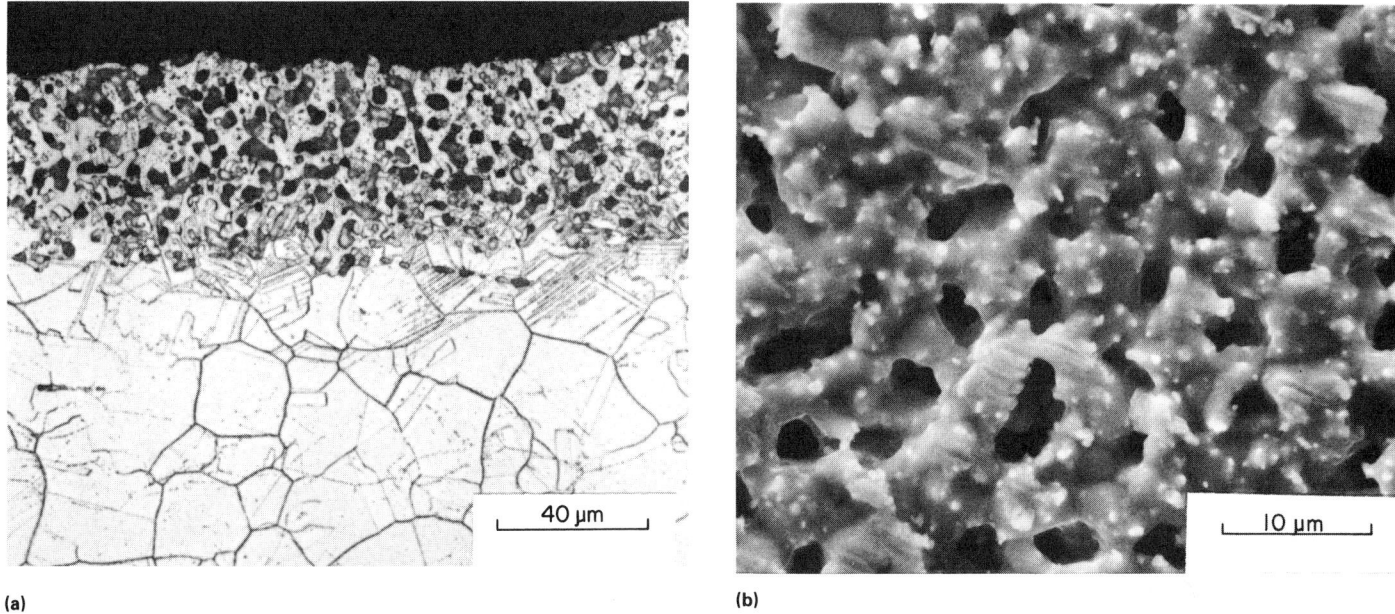

Fig. 38 Corrosion of type 316 stainless steel exposed to thermally convective lithium for 7488 h at the maximum loop temperature of 600 °C (1110 °F). (a) Light micrograph of polished and etched cross section. (b) SEM micrograph showing the top view of the porous surface

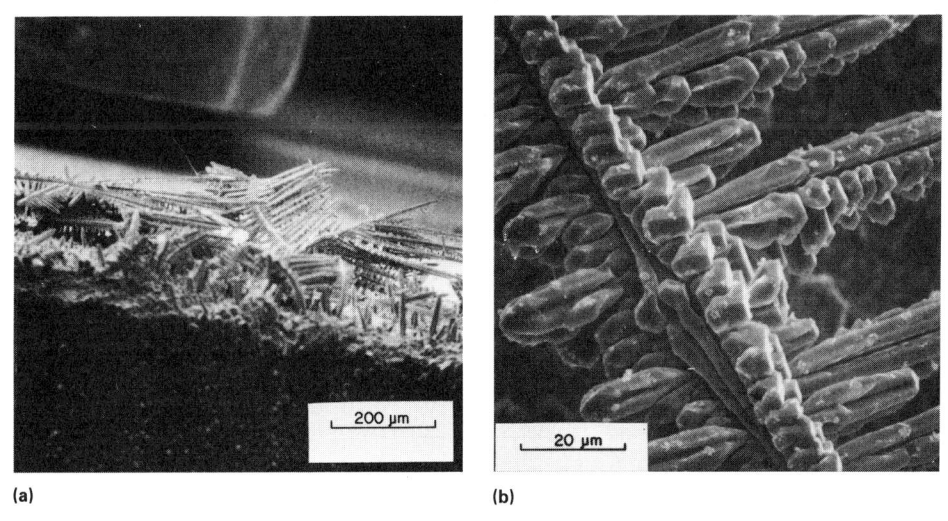

Fig. 39 SEM micrographs of chromium mass transfer deposits found at the 460 °C (860 °F) position in the cold leg of a lithium/type 316 stainless steel thermal convection loop after 1700 h. Mass transfer deposits are often a more serious result of corrosion than wall thinning. (a) Cross section of specimen on which chromium was deposited. (b) Top view of surface

Table 12 Results of corrosion tests in molten lithium at 704 to 816 °C (1300 to 1500 °F) in a forced-convection loop

Alloy	Exposure time, h	Maximum depth of attack(a), + deposits, mm	mils	Maximum thickness of mm	(mils)
Iron(b)	108-138	IG 0.0 ML 0.05-0.11	0.0 2.0-4.5	0.32-0.38	12.5-15.0
Iron	138-187	IG 0.0-0.02 ML 0.13-0.17	0.0-0.6 5.0-6.6	0.36-0.46	14.0-18.0
304	105-138	IG 0.03-0.13 ML 0.10-0.15	1.0-5.0 3.8-6.0	0.47-0.51	18.5-20.0
310	64-96	IG 0.08-0.10 ML 0.06-0.12	3.0-4.0 2.2-4.7	0.49-0.61	19.5-24.0
321	69-200	IG 0.0-0.05 ML 0.15-0.16	0.0-2.0 6.2-6.4	0.64-0.81	25.0-32.0
347	82-160	IG 0.01-0.02 ML 0.11-0.12	0.5-0.6 4.3-4.9	0.84-1.02	33.0-40.0

(a) ML, metal loss due to apparent solution attack, decrease in wall thickness; IG, intergranular attack. (b) Titanium getter in lithium flow stream. Source: Ref 43

combinations have been established. The more basic principles of liquid metal corrosion are outlined in Ref 42 and in the Selected References that follow this article.

One vitally important aspect of liquid metal corrosion that is often overlooked is deposition. Corrosion itself is very often not a factor of major concern, because surface recession rates in regions of maximum attack are often of the order of microns per year. What can be serious are the formation of compounds in the circulating liquid metal and the accumulation of deposits in localized regions where there is a drop in temperature, a change in flow rate or flow direction, or an induced change in surface roughness. If these de-

posits do not succeed in restricting flow channels completely, their nature is often such that they are only loosely adherent to deposition surfaces and may be dislodged by vibrations or thermal shock in the system, thus creating a major coolant flow restriction in a high-temperature region. Most deposits have a very low packing density; therefore, deposit growth can proceed at a rate that outstrips corrosion by several orders of magnitude. Examples of loosely adherent deposits are shown in Fig. 36(b) and 39.

As with other forms of corrosion, preventing liquid metal corrosion involves an appreciation for the source of corrosion in any system and an understanding of how potential sinks will operate

on the corrosion burden. This is particularly true if the liquid metal is not static but is circulated in a heat-transfer system either by pumping or by thermal convection.

Considerations in Materials Selection. The liquid metal corrosion reactions mentioned above must be considered in materials selection for liquid metal containment. In many cases, particularly at low temperatures or with less aggressive liquids (such as molten steel), liquid metal corrosion is not an important factor, and many materials, both metals and ceramics, will suffice. Under more severe conditions, however, an understanding of the various types of liquid metal corrosion is necessary to select or develop a compatible containment material. For example, for applications in high-temperature molten lithium, most oxides would be unstable, low-chro-

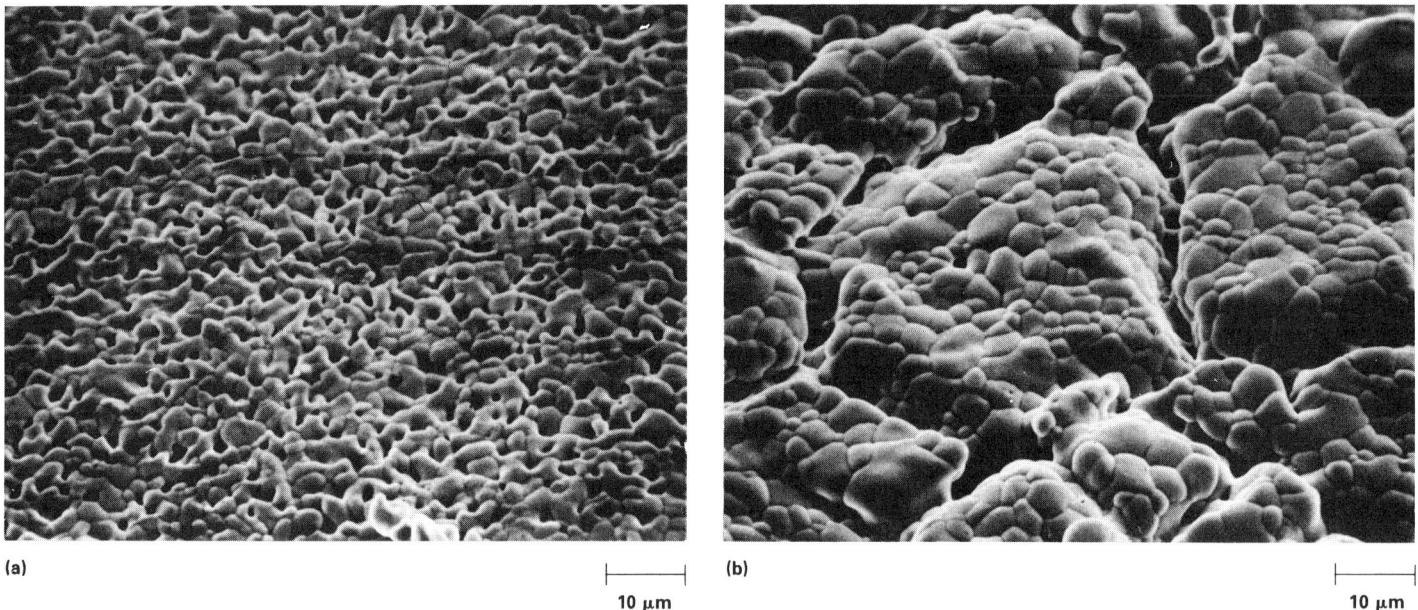

Fig. 40 Changes in surface morphology along the isothermal hot leg of a type 304 stainless steel pumped lithium system after 2000 h at 538 °C (1000 °F). Composition changes transform the exposed surface from austenite to ferrite, containing approximately 86% Fe, 11% Cr, and 1% Ni. (a) Inlet. (b) 7.7 m (25 ft) downstream

mium steels would decarburize, and alloys containing large amounts of nickel or manganese would suffer extensive preferential dissolution and irregular attack. Materials selection would then be limited to higher-chromium ferritic/martensitic steels or high-purity refractory metals and alloys. Tables 12 and 13 summarize the corrosion rates of stainless steels in liquid lithium and sodium, respectively.

A general summary of the most common corrosion reactions and guidelines for materials selection and/or development are given in Table 14, which also includes typical examples for each category. Because two or more concurrent corrosion reactions are possible, and because consideration of all of the applicable materials consequences may lead to opposite strategies, materials selection for liquid metal environments can become quite complex and may require optimization of several factors rather than minimization of any particular one. In addition, an assessment of the suitability of a given material for liquid metal service must be based on the knowledge of its total corrosion response. As in many corrosive environments, a simple numerical rate is not an accurate measurement of the susceptibility of a material when reaction with the liquid metal results in more than one mode of attack. Under such circumstances, a measurement reflecting total corrosion damage is much more appropriate for judging the ability of a material to resist corrosion by a particular liquid metal.

ACKNOWLEDGMENT

The information in this article is largely taken from:

- G.Y. Lai, *High-Temperature Corrosion of Engineering Alloys*, ASM International, 1990

Table 13 Corrosion of carbon steel, chromium-molybdenum steels, and stainless steels in liquid sodium(a) under isothermal conditions

Materials	Test temperature °C	Test temperature °F	Exposure time, h	Test system	Weight change rate, mg/cm^2 per month
1010 steel	593	1100	1000	Flowing	−0.49
	593	1100	1000	Static	−0.37
2.25Cr-1Mo	552	1026	943	Flowing	−0.12
	556	1033	902	Static	−0.12
	593	1100	1000	Flowing	−0.14
	593	1100	1000	Static	−0.09
5Cr-0.5Mo	552	1026	943	Flowing	+0.22
	566	1033	1913	Static	−0.06
	593	1100	500	Flowing	+0.23
	593	1100	500	Static	−0.08
9Cr-1Mo	552	1026	943	Flowing	+0.35
	566	1033	902	Static	−0.05
	593	1100	500	Flowing	+0.70
	593	1100	500	Static	+0.29
410	593	1100	1000	Flowing	+0.38
	593	1100	1000	Static	+0.35
420	593	1100	1000	Flowing	+0.33
	593	1100	1000	Static	+0.31
304	593	1100	1000	Flowing	+0.17
	593	1100	1000	Static	+0.15
310	593	1100	500	Flowing	+0.75
	593	1100	500	Static	+0.27
316	593	1100	1000	Flowing	+0.10
	593	1100	1000	Static	+0.13
347	593	1100	500	Flowing	+1.46
	593	1100	500	Static	+0.22
410	1000	1830	400	Static	+29.8
430	1000	1830	400	Static	+46.8
446	1000	1830	400	Static	+28.2
304	1000	1830	400	Static	+25.5
316	1000	1830	400	Static	+29.6
310	1000	1830	400	Static	+28.2
347	1000	1830	400	Static	+44.2
600	1000	1830	400	Static	+18.7

(a) Containing a maximum of 100 ppm oxygen. Source: Ref 44

Table 14 Guidelines for materials selection and/or alloy development based on liquid-metal corrosion reactions

Corrosion reaction	Guidelines	Example
Direct dissolution	Lower activity of key elements.	Reduce nickel in lithium, lead, or sodium systems.
Corrosion product formation	Lower activity of reacting elements.	Reduce chromium and nitrogen in lithium systems.
	In case of protective oxide, add elements to promote formation.	Add aluminum or silicon to steel exposed to lead.
Elemental transfer	Increase (or add) elements to decrease transfer tendency.	Increase chromium content in steels exposed to sodium or lithium.
	Minimize element being transferred.	Reduce oxygen content in metals exposed to lithium.
Alloying	Avoid systems that form stable compounds.	Do not expose nickel to molten aluminum.
	Promote formation of corrosion-resistant layers by alloying.	Add aluminum to lithium to form surface aluminides.
Compound reduction	Eliminate solids that can be reduced by liquid metal.	Avoid bulk oxide-lithium couples.

- I.G. Wright, High-Temperature Corrosion, *Corrosion,* Vol 13, *ASM Handbook* (formerly 9th ed., *Metals Handbook*), ASM International, 1987, p 97-101
- J.W. Koger, Molten-Salt Corrosion, *Corrosion,* Vol 13, *ASM Handbook* (formerly 9th ed., *Metals Handbook*), ASM International, 1987, p 88-91
- C. Bagnall and W.F. Brehm, Corrosion in Liquid Metals, *Corrosion,* Vol 13, *ASM Handbook* (formerly 9th ed., *Metals Handbook*), ASM International, 1987, p 91-96
- P.F. Tortorelli, Fundamentals of High-Temperature Corrosion in Liquid Metals, *Corrosion,* Vol 13, *ASM Handbook* (formerly 9th ed., *Metals Handbook*), ASM International, 1987, p 56-60
- J. Stringer, Corrosion of Superheaters and High-Temperature Air Heaters, *Corrosion,* Vol 13, *ASM Handbook* (formerly 9th ed., *Metals Handbook*), ASM International, 1987, p 998-999

REFERENCES

1. G.Y. Lai, *High-Temperature Corrosion of Engineering Alloys,* ASM International, 1990
2. I.G. Wright, High-Temperature Corrosion, *Corrosion,* Vol 13, *ASM Handbook* (formerly 9th ed., *Metals Handbook*), 1987, p 97-101
3. N.B. Pilling and R.E. Bedworth, The Oxidation of Metals at High Temperatures, *J. Inst. Met.,* Vol 29, 1923, p 529-582
4. S.A. Bradford, Fundamentals of Corrosion in Gases, *Corrosion,* Vol 13, *ASM Handbook* (formerly 9th ed., *Metals Handbook*), ASM International, 1987, p 61-76
5. *The Making, Shaping and Treating of Steel,* H.E. McGarrow, Ed., United States Steel Corp., 1971, p 1136
6. A. Grodner, *Weld. Res. Counc. Bull.,* No. 31, 1956
7. S.B. Lasday, *Ind. Heat.,* March 1979, p 12
8. O.D. Sherby, *Acta Metall.,* Vol 10, 1962, p 135
9. H.E. Eiselstein and E.N. Skinner, in STP No. 165, 1954, p 162
10. A. Moccari and S.I. Ali, *Br. Corros. J.,* Vol 14 (No. 2), 1979, p 91
11. A. de S. Brasunas, J.T. Gow, and O.E. Harder, *Proc. ASTM,* Vol 46, 1946, p 870
12. S. Kado, T. Yamazaki, M. Yamazaki, K. Yoshida, K. Yabe, and H. Kobayashi, *Trans. Iron Steel Inst. Jpn.,* Vol 18 (No. 7), 1978, p 387
13. H.T. Michels, *Met. Eng. Quart.,* Aug 1974, p 23
14. "Design Guidelines for the Selection and Use of Stainless Steel," Document 9014, Nickel Development Institute
15. W.C. Leslie and M.C. Fontana, Paper 26, 30th Annual Convention of the American Society for Metals (Philadelphia), 25-29 Oct 1948
16. J.K. Meijering and G.W. Rathenau, *Nature,* Vol 165, 11 Feb 1950, p 240
17. A.D. Brasunas and N.J. Grant, *Iron Age,* 17 Aug 1950, p 85
18. S.S. Brennor, *J. Electrochem. Soc.,* Vol 102 (No. 1), Jan 1955, p 16
19. G.W. Rathenau and J.L. Meijering, *Metallurgia,* Vol 42, 1950, p 167
20. J.C. Sawyer, *Trans. TMS-AIME,* Vol 221, 1961, p 63
21. A. de S. Brasunas and N.J. Grant, *Trans. ASM,* Vol 44, 1950, p 1133
22. "High-Temperature Characteristics of Stainless Steels," Document 9004, Nickel Development Institute
23. L.A. Morris, Corrosion Resistance of Stainless Steels at Elevated Temperatures, *Selection of Stainless Steels,* American Society for Metals, 1968, p 30-47
24. G. Sorell, "Compilation and Correlation of High Temperature Catalytic Reformer Corrosion Data," Tech. Comm. Rep., Publication 58-2, National Association of Corrosion Engineers, 1957
25. E.B. Backensto, R.E. Drew, J.E. Prior, and J.W. Sjoberg, "High-Temperature Hydrogen Sulfide Corrosion of Stainless Steels," Tech. Comm. Rep., Publication 58-3, National Association of Corrosion Engineers, 1957
26. E.B. Backensto, "Corrosion in Catalytic Reforming and Associated Processes," Summary Report of the Panel on Reformer Corrosion to the Subcommittee on Corrosion, 22nd Midyear Meeting (Philadelphia), 13 May 1957, Division of Refining, American Petroleum Institute
27. E.B. Backensto and J.W. Sjoberg, "Iso-Corrosion Rate Curves for High Temperature Hydrogen-Hydrogen Sulfide," Tech. Comm. Rep., Publication 59-10, National Association of Corrosion Engineers, Houston, 1958
28. G.E. Moller and C.W. Warren, Paper 237, presented at Corrosion/81, National Association of Corrosion Engineers
29. C.M. Schillmoller, *Chem. Eng.,* 6 Jan 1986, p 87
30. J.J. Moran, J.R. Mihalisin, and E.N. Skinner, *Corrosion,* Vol 17 (No. 4), 1961, p 191t
31. P.L. Daniel and R.A. Rapp, *Advances in Corrosion Science and Technology,* Vol 5, M.G. Fontana and R.W. Staehle, Ed., Plenum Press, 1970
32. S. Baranow, G.Y. Lai, M.F. Rothman, J.M. Oh, M.J. McNallan, and M.H. Rhee, Paper 16, Corrosion/84, National Association of Corrosion Engineers
33. M.H. Brown, W.B. DeLong, and J.R. Auld, *Ind. Eng. Chem.,* Vol 39 (No. 7), 1947, p 839
34. R.B. Jackson, "Corrosion of Metals and Alloys by Fluorine," NP-8845, Allied Chemical Corp., 1960
35. W.R. Myers and W.B. DeLong, *Chem. Eng. Prog.,* Vol 44 (No. 5), 1948, p 359
36. J. Stringer, Corrosion of Superheaters and High-Temperature Air Heaters, *Corrosion,* Vol 13, *ASM Handbook* (formerly 9th ed., *Metals Handbook*), ASM International, 1987, p 998-999
37. J.C. Parker and D.F. Rosborough, *J. Inst. Fuel,* Feb 1972, p 95
38. J.W. Koger, Molten-Salt Corrosion, *Corrosion,* Vol 13, *ASM Handbook* (formerly 9th ed., *Metals Handbook*), ASM International, 1987, p 88-91
39. J.W. Koger, Fundamentals of High-Temperature Corrosion in Molten Salts, *Corrosion,* Vol 13, *ASM Handbook* (formerly 9th ed., *Metals Handbook*), ASM International, 1987, p 50-53
40. R.W. Bradshaw and R.W. Carling, "A Review of the Chemical and Physical Properties of Molten Alkali Nitrate Salts and Their Effect on Materials Used for Solar Central Receivers," SAND 87-8005, Sandia National Laboratories, April 1987
41. C. Bagnall and W.F. Brehm, Corrosion in Liquid Metals, *Corrosion,* Vol 13, *ASM Handbook* (formerly 9th ed., *Metals Handbook*), ASM International, 1987, p 91-96
42. P.F. Tortorelli, Fundamentals of High-Temperature Corrosion in Liquid Metals, *Corrosion,* Vol 13, *ASM Handbook* (formerly 9th ed., *Metals Handbook*), ASM International, 1987, p 56-60
43. M.S. Freed and K.J. Kelly, "Corrosion of Columbium Base and Other Structural Alloys in High Temperature Lithium," Report PWAC-355, Pratt and Whitney Aircraft—CANEL, Division of United Aircraft Corp., June 1961 (declassified in June 1965)
44. W.E. Berry, *Corrosion in Nuclear Applications,* John Wiley & Sons, 1971

SELECTED REFERENCES

High-Temperature Corrosion in Gases

- E.F. Bradley, Ed., *Source Book on Materials for Elevated Temperature Applications,* American Society for Metals, 1979

- B.R. Cooper and W.A. Ellingson, Ed., *The Science and Technology of Coal and Coal Utilization,* Plenum Press, 1984
- D.L. Douglass, Ed., *Oxidation of Metals and Alloys,* American Society for Metals, 1971
- U.R. Evans, *The Corrosion and Oxidation of Metals—First Supplementary Volume,* St. Martin's Press, 1968
- A.B. Hart and A.J.B. Cutler, Ed., *Deposition and Corrosion in Gas Turbines,* John Wiley & Sons, 1973
- U.L. Hill and H.L. Black, Ed., *The Properties and Performance of Materials in the Coal Gasification Environment,* Materials/Metalworking Technology Series, American Society for Metals, 1981
- D.R. Holmes and A. Rahmel, Ed., *Materials and Coatings to Resist High-Temperature Corrosion,* Applied Science, 1978
- *Hot Corrosion Problems Associated with Gas Turbines,* STP 421, ASTM, 1967
- O. Kubaschewski and B.E. Hopkins, *Oxidations of Metals and Alloys,* 2nd ed., Academic Press, 1962
- D.B. Meadowcroft and M.I. Manning, Ed., *Corrosion-Resistant Materials for Coal Conversion Systems,* Applied Science, 1983
- S. Mrowec and T. Werber, *Gas Corrosion of Metals,* W. Bartoszewski, Trans., Foreign Science Publications, Department of the National Center for Scientific, Technical and Economic Information, available from National Technical Information Service, 1978
- R.A. Rapp, Ed., *High-Temperature Corrosion,* Publication 8, National Association of Corrosion Engineers, 1983
- M.F. Rothman, Ed., *High Temperature Corrosion in Energy Systems,* The Metallurgical Society, 1985
- H. Schmalzried, *Solid State Reactions,* A.D. Pelton, Trans., Academic Press, 1974

- I.G. Wright, Ed., *Corrosion in Fossil Fuel Systems,* Vol 83-5, Conference Proceedings, The Electrochemical Society, 1983

Molten Salt Corrosion

- M.G. Fontana and N.D. Greene, *Corrosion Frequency,* McGraw-Hill, 1978
- G.J. Janz and R.P.T. Tomkins, *Corrosion,* Vol 35, 1979, p 485
- J.W. Koger, *Advances in Corrosion Science and Technology,* Vol 4, Plenum Press, 1974
- D.G. Lovering, Ed., *Molten Salt Technology,* Plenum Press, 1982
- A. Rahmel, Corrosion, *Molten Salt Technology,* Plenum Press, 1982
- L.L. Sheir, Ed., *Corrosion,* Vol 1, Newnes-Butterworths, 1979, p 2.10

Corrosion in Liquid Metals

- C.C. Addison, *The Chemistry of the Liquid Alkali Metals,* John Wiley & Sons, 1984
- *Alkali Metal Coolants,* Symposium Proceedings (Vienna), International Atomic Energy Agency, 1967
- C. Bagnall and D.C. Jacobs, "Relationships for Corrosion of Type 316 Stainless Steel in Sodium," WARD-NA-3045-23, National Technical Information Service, 1974
- W.E. Berry, *Corrosion in Nuclear Applications,* John Wiley & Sons, 1971
- H.U. Borgstedt, Ed., *Proc. Conf. Material Behavior and Physical Chemistry in Liquid Metal Systems,* Plenum Press, 1982
- H.U. Borgstedt and C.M. Matthews, *Applied Chemistry of the Alkali Metals,* Plenum Press, 1986
- M.H. Cooper, Ed., *Proc. Int. Conf. Liquid Metal Technology in Energy Production,* CONF-760503, P1 and P2, National Technical Information Service, 1977

- J.M. Dahlke, Ed., *Proceedings of the Second International Conference on Liquid Metal Technology in Energy Production,* CONF-300401-P1 and P2, National Technical Information Service, 1981
- J.E. Draley and J.R. Weeks, Ed., *Corrosion by Liquid Metals,* Plenum Press, 1970
- R.L. Eichelberger and W.F. Brehm, "Effect of Sodium on Breeder Reactor Components," Paper 106, Corrosion/78, National Association of Corrosion Engineers, 1978
- S.A. Jannson, Ed., *Chemical Aspects of Corrosion and Mass Transfer in Liquid Metals,* The Metallurgical Society, 1973
- C.J. Klamut, D.G. Schweitzer, J.G.Y. Chow, R.A. Meyer, O.F. Kammerer, J.R. Weeks, and D.H. Gurinsky, Material and Fuel Technology for an LMFR, *Progress in Nuclear Engineering Series IV, V2-Technology Engineering and Safety,* Pergamon Press, 1960
- *Proc. Int. Conf. Liquid Alkali Metals,* British Nuclear Energy Society, Thomas Telford Ltd., 1973
- *Proc. Int. Conf. Sodium Technology and Large Fast Reactor Design,* ANL-7520, Part I, National Technical Information Service, 1969
- *Proc. 3rd Int. Conf. Liquid Metal Engineering and Technology,* British Nuclear Energy Society, Thomas Telford Ltd., 1985
- M.C. Rowland et al., "Sodium Mass Transfer XV: Behavior of Selected Steels Exposed in Flowing Sodium Test Loops," GEAP-4831, National Technical Information Service, 1965
- P.F. Tortorelli and J.H. DeVan, Corrosion of Fe-Cr-Mn Alloys in Thermally Convective Lithium and Corrosion of Ferrous Alloys Exposed to Thermally Convective Pd-17at.% Li, *J. Nucl. Mater.,* Vol 141-143, 1986, p 579-583, 592-598; Proc. 2nd Int. Conf. Fusion Reactor Materials (Chicago), April 1976

Corrosion of Cast Stainless Steels

STEEL CASTING COMPOSITIONS are generally divided into the categories of carbon, low-alloy, corrosion-resistant (C-type), or heat-resistant (H-type), depending on alloy content and intended service. The latter two high-alloy categories are considered cast stainless steels and will be the focus of this article. More detailed information on the compositions, alloy designation systems, microstructures, and properties (including corrosion properties) of high-alloy ferrous castings can be found in the article "Metallurgy and Properties of Cast Stainless Steels" in this Volume. Typical and atypical microstructures of these alloys are shown in the article "Metallography and Microstructures of Cast Stainless Steels" in this Volume.

Corrosion resistance is a relative term that depends on the particular environment to which a specific alloy is exposed. Carbon and low-alloy steels are considered resistant only to very mild corrosives, but the various high-alloy grades are applicable for mild to severe service, depending on the particular conditions involved.

It is often misleading to list the comparative corrosion rates of different alloys exposed to the same corroding medium. In this article, no attempt will be made to recommend alloys for specific applications, and the data supplied should be used only as a general guideline. Alloy casting users will find it helpful to consult materials and corrosion specialists when selecting alloys for a particular application. The factors that must be considered in material selection include:

- The principal corrosive agents and their concentrations
- Known or suspected impurities, including abrasive materials and their concentration
- Average operating temperature, including variations even if encountered only for short periods
- Presence (or absence) of oxygen or other gases in solution
- Continuous or intermittent operation
- Fluid velocity

Each of these can have a major effect on the service life of both cast and wrought equipment, and such detailed information usually must be provided. Many rapid failures are traceable to these details being overlooked—often when the information was available.

Selection of the most economical alloy is often made by the judicious use of corrosion data. However, discretion is suggested in evaluating the relative corrosion rates of various high-alloy steels

because of the uncertainties of the actual test or service conditions. Corrosion rates determined in controlled laboratory tests should be applied cautiously when considering actual service. The best information is obtained from equipment used under similar operating conditions. However, exposing samples to service conditions will also provide valuable information.

Composition and Microstructure of Cast Stainless Steels

The principal alloying element in the high-alloy family is usually chromium, which, through the formation of protective oxide films, is the first step for these alloys in achieving stainless quality. For all practical purposes, stainless behavior requires at least 12% Cr. As will be discussed later, corrosion resistance further improves with additions of chromium to at least the 30% level. Nickel and lesser amounts of molybdenum and other elements are often added to the iron-chromium matrix.

Although chromium is a ferrite and martensite promoter, nickel is an austenite promoter. By varying the amounts and ratios of these two elements (or their equivalents), almost any desired combination of microstructure, strength, or other properties can be achieved. Equally important is heat treatment. Temperature, time at temperature,

and cooling rate must be controlled to obtain the desired results.

It is useful to think of the compositions of high-alloy steels in terms of the balance between austenite promoters and ferrite promoters. This is done on the widely used Schaeffler-type diagrams (Fig. 1). The phases shown are those that persist after cooling to room temperature at rates normally used in fabrication (Ref 1, 2).

The empirical correlations shown in Fig. 1 can be understood from the following. The field designated as martensite encompasses such alloys as CA-15, CA-6NM, and even CB-7Cu. These alloys contain 12 to 17% Cr, with adequate nickel, molybdenum, and carbon to promote high hardenability (i.e., the ability to transform completely to martensite when cooled at even the moderate rates associated with the air cooling of heavy sections). High alloys have low thermal conductivities and cool slowly. To obtain the desired properties, a full heat treatment is required after casting, meaning that the casting is austenitized by heating to 870 to 980 °C (1600 to 1800 °F), cooled to room temperature to produce the hard martensite, and then tempered at 595 to 760 °C (1100 to 1400 °F) until the desired combination of strength, toughness, ductility, and resistance to corrosion or stress corrosion is obtained (Ref 1, 2).

Increasing the nickel equivalent (moving vertically in Fig. 1) eventually results in an alloy that

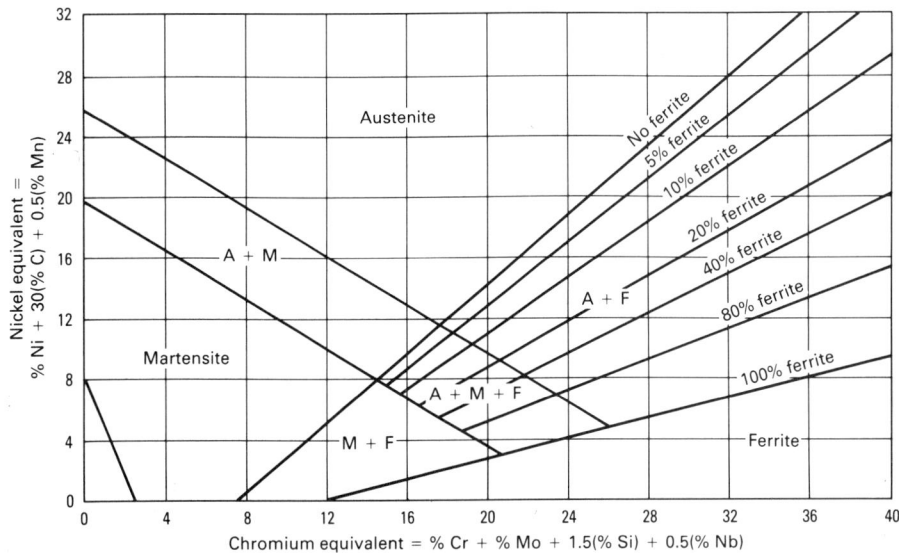

Fig. 1 Schaeffler diagram showing the amount of ferrite and austenite present in weldments as a function of chromium and nickel equivalents. Source: Ref 1

Table 1 Corrosion resistance of heat-resistant cast steels at 980 °C (1800 °F) in 100 h tests in various atmospheres

Alloy	Air	Oxidizing flue gas(b)	Reducing flue gas(b)	Reducing flue gas(c)	Reducing flue gas (constant temperature)(d)	Reducing flue gas cooled to 150 °C (300 °F) every 12 h(d)
HA	U	U	U	U	U	U
HC	G	G	G	S	G	G
HD	G	G	G	S	G	G
HE	G	G	G	...	G	...
HF	S	G	S	U	S	S
HH	G	G	G	S	G	G
HI	G	G	G	S	G	G
HK	G	G	G	U	G	G
HL	G	G	G	S	G	G
HN	G	G	G	U	S	S
HP	G	G	G	G	G	...
HT	G	G	G	U	S	U
HU	G	G	G	U	S	U
HW	G	G	G	U	U	U
HX	G	G	G	S	G	U

(a) G, good (corrosion rate $r <1.27$ mm/yr, or 50 mils/yr); S, satisfactory ($r <2.54$ mm/yr, or 100 mils/yr); U, unsatisfactory ($r >2.54$ mm/yr, or 100 mils/yr). (b) Contained 2 g of sulfur/m³ (5 grains S/100 ft³). (c) Contained 120 g/S/m³ (300 grains S/100 ft³). (d) Contained 40 g/S/m³ (100 grains S/100 ft³)

Table 2 Approximate rates of corrosion for heat-resistant casting alloys in air and in flue gas

Alloy	Oxidation rate in air, mm/yr			Corrosion rate, mm/yr, at 980 °C (1800 °F) in flue gas with sulfur content of:			
	870 °C (1600 °F)	980 °C (1800 °F)	1090 °C (2000 °F)	0.12 g/m³		2.3 g/m³	
				Oxidizing	Reducing	Oxidizing	Reducing
HB	0.63–	6.25–	12.5–	2.5+	12.5	6.25–	12.5
HC	0.25	1.25	1.25	0.63–	0.63+	0.63	0.63–
HD	0.25–	1.25–	1.25–	0.63–	0.63–	0.63–	0.63–
HE	0.13–	0.63–	0.88–	0.63–	0.63–	0.63–	0.63–
HF	0.13–	1.25+	2.5	1.25+	2.5+	1.25+	6.25
HH	0.13–	0.63–	1.25	0.63–	0.63	0.63	0.63–
HI	0.13–	0.25+	0.88–	0.63–	0.63–	0.63–	0.63–
HK	0.25–	0.25–	0.88–	0.63–	0.63–	0.63–	0.63–
HL	0.25+	0.63–	0.88	0.63–	0.63–	0.63	0.63–
HN	0.13	0.25+	1.25–	0.63–	0.63–	0.63–	0.63
HP	0.63–	0.63	1.25	0.63–	0.63–	0.63–	0.63–
HT	0.13–	0.25+	1.25	0.63	0.63–	0.63	2.5
HU	0.13–	0.25–	0.88–	0.63–	0.63–	0.63–	0.63
HW	0.13–	0.25–	0.88	0.63	0.63–	1.25–	6.25
HX	0.13–	0.25–	0.88–	0.63–	0.63–	0.63–	0.63–

is fully austenitic, such as CH-20, CK-20, or CN-7M. These alloys are extremely ductile, tough, and corrosion resistant. On the other hand, the yield and tensile strengths may be relatively low for the fully austenitic alloys. Because these high-nickel alloys are fully austenitic, they are nonmagnetic. Heat treatment consists of a single step: water quenching from a relatively high temperature at which carbides have been taken into solution. Solution treatment may also homogenize the structure, but because no transformation occurs, there can be no grain refinement. The solutionizing step and rapid cooling ensure maximum resistance to corrosion. Temperatures between 1040 and 1205 °C (1900 and 2200 °F) are usually required (Ref 1, 2).

Adding chromium to the lean alloys (proceeding horizontally in Fig. 1) stabilizes the δ-ferrite that forms when the casting solidifies. Examples are CB-30 and CC-50. With high chromium content, these alloys have relatively good resistance to corrosion, particularly in sulfur-bearing atmospheres. However, being single-phase, they are nonhardenable, have moderate-to-low strength,

and are often used as-cast or after only a simple solutioning treatment. Ferritic alloys also have poor toughness (Ref 1, 2).

Between the fields designated M, A, and F in Fig. 1 are regions indicating the possibility of two or more phases in the alloys. Commercially, the most important of these alloys are the ones in which austenite and ferrite coexist, such as CF-3, CF-8, CF-3M, CF-8M, CG-8M, and CE-30. These alloys usually contain 3 to 30% ferrite in a matrix of austenite. Predicting and controlling ferrite content is vital to the successful application of these materials. Duplex alloys offer superior strength, weldability, and corrosion resistance. Strength, for example, increases directly with ferrite content. Achieving specified minimums may necessitate controlling the ferrite within narrow bands. These duplex alloys should be solution treated and rapidly cooled before use to ensure maximum resistance to corrosion (Ref 1, 2).

The presence of ferrite is not entirely beneficial. Ferrite tends to reduce toughness, although this is not of great concern given the extremely

high toughness of the austenite matrix. However, in applications that require exposure to elevated temperatures, usually 315 °C (600 °F) and higher, the metallurgical changes associated with the ferrite can be severe and detrimental. At the low end of this temperature range, the reductions in toughness observed have been attributed to carbide precipitation or reactions associated with 475 °C (885 °F) embrittlement. The 475 °C (885 °F) embrittlement is caused by precipitation of an intermetallic phase with a composition of approximately 80Cr-20Fe. The name derives from the fact that this embrittlement is most severe and rapid when it occurs at approximately 475 °C (885 °F). At 540 °C (1000 °F) and above, the ferrite phase may transform to a complex iron-chromium-nickel-molybdenum intermetallic compound known as s phase, which reduces toughness, corrosion resistance, and creep ductility. The extent of the reduction increases with time and temperature to about 815 °C (1500 °F) and may persist to 925 °C (1700 °F). In extreme cases, Charpy V-notch energy at room temperature may be reduced 95% from its initial value (Ref 1, 2).

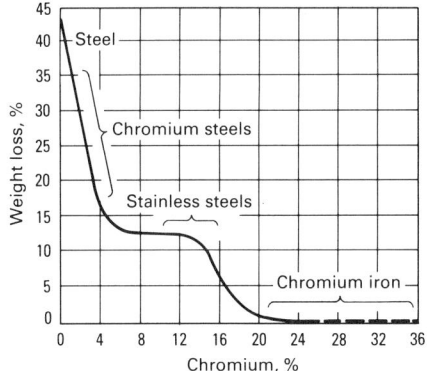

Fig. 2 Effect of chromium on oxidation resistance of cast steels. Specimens (13 mm, or 0.5 in., cubes) were exposed for 48 h at 1000 °C (1830 °F). Source: Ref 2

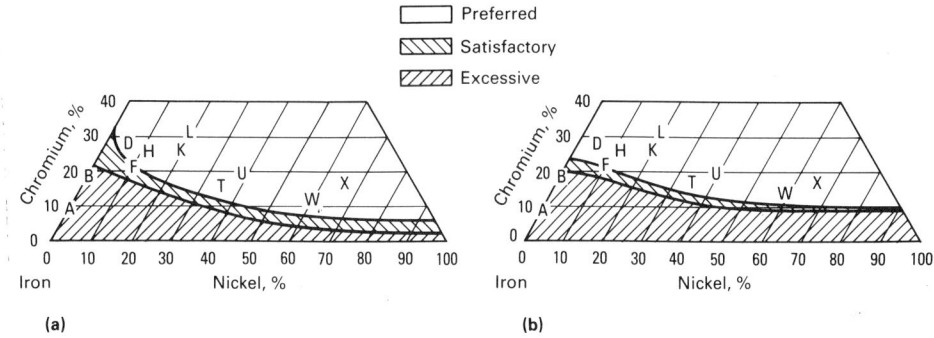

Fig. 3 Corrosion behavior of H-type (heat-resistant) alloy castings in air (a) and in oxidizing flue gases containing 5 grains of sulfur per 2.8 m³ (100 ft³) of gas (b). Letters represent the nickel content of the alloy with A denoting the lowest nickel content and X the highest. See the article "Metallurgy and Properties of Cast Stainless Steels" in this Volume for details on grade designations. Source: Ref 2

Corrosion Behavior of H-Type Alloys

The heat-resistant (H-type) alloys must be able to withstand temperatures exceeding 1095 °C (2000 °F) in the most severe high-temperature service. An important factor pertaining to the corrosion behavior of these alloys is chromium content. Chromium imparts resistance to oxidation and sulfidation at high temperatures by forming a passive oxide film. Heat-resistant casting alloys must also have good resistance to carburization.

The atmospheres most commonly encountered by heat-resistant cast steels are air, flue gases, and process gases. Such gases may be either oxidizing or reducing, and they may be sulfidizing or carburizing if sulfur and carbon are present. The corrosion of heat-resistant alloys by the environment at elevated temperatures varies significantly with alloy type, temperature, velocity, and the nature of the specific environment to which the part is exposed. Table 1 presents a general ranking of the standard cast heat-resistant grades in various environments at 980 °C (1800 °F). Corrosion rates at other temperatures are given in Table 2 (Ref 3).

Oxidation. Resistance to oxidation increases directly with chromium content (Fig. 2). For the most severe service at temperatures above 1095 °C (2000 °F), 25% or more chromium is required. Additions of nickel, silicon, manganese, and aluminum promote the formation of relatively impermeable oxide films that retard further scaling. Thermal cycling is extremely damaging to oxidation resistance because it leads to breaking, cracking, or spalling of the protective oxide film. The best performance is obtained with austenitic alloys containing 40 to 50% combined nickel and chromium. Figure 3 illustrates the corrosion behavior of H-type grades in air and oxidizing flue gases.

Sulfidation environments are becoming increasingly important. Petroleum processing, coal conversion, utility and chemical applications, and waste incineration have heightened the need for alloys resistant to sulfidation attack in relatively weak oxidizing or reducing environments. Fortunately, high chromium and silicon contents increase resistance to sulfur-bearing environments. On the other hand, nickel has been found to be detrimental in the presence of the most aggressive

gases. The problem is attributable to the formation of low-melting nickel-sulfur eutectics. These produce highly destructive liquid phases at temperatures even below 815 °C (1500 °F). Once formed, the liquid may run onto adjacent surfaces and rapidly corrode other metals. The behavior of H-type grades in sulfidation environments is represented in Fig. 4.

Carburization. High alloys are often used in nonoxidizing atmospheres in which carbon diffusion into metal surfaces is possible. Depending on chromium content, temperature, and carburizing potential, the surface may become extremely rich in chromium carbides, rendering it hard and possibly susceptible to cracking. Silicon and nickel enhance resistance to carburization.

Corrosion Behavior of C-Type Alloys

The C-type (for liquid corrosion service) stainless steels must resist corrosion in the various

environments in which they regularly serve. Temperatures for these environments are generally below 650 °C (1200 °F). In this section, the general principles and important highlights of corrosion behavior will be discussed as it is influenced by the metallurgy of these materials. Topics include general corrosion, intergranular corrosion, localized corrosion, corrosion fatigue, and stress-corrosion cracking (SCC). Additional information on these forms of corrosion can be found in the other articles contained in the Section "Corrosion Behavior" in this Volume.

General Corrosion of Martensitic Alloys. The martensitic grades include CA-15, CA-15M, CA-6NM, CA-6NM-B, CA-40, CB-7Cu-1, and CB-7Cu-2. These alloys are generally used in applications requiring high strength and some corrosion resistance.

Alloy CA-15 typically exhibits a microstructure of martensite and ferrite. This alloy contains the minimum amount of chromium required for it to be considered a stainless steel (11 to 14% Cr), and as

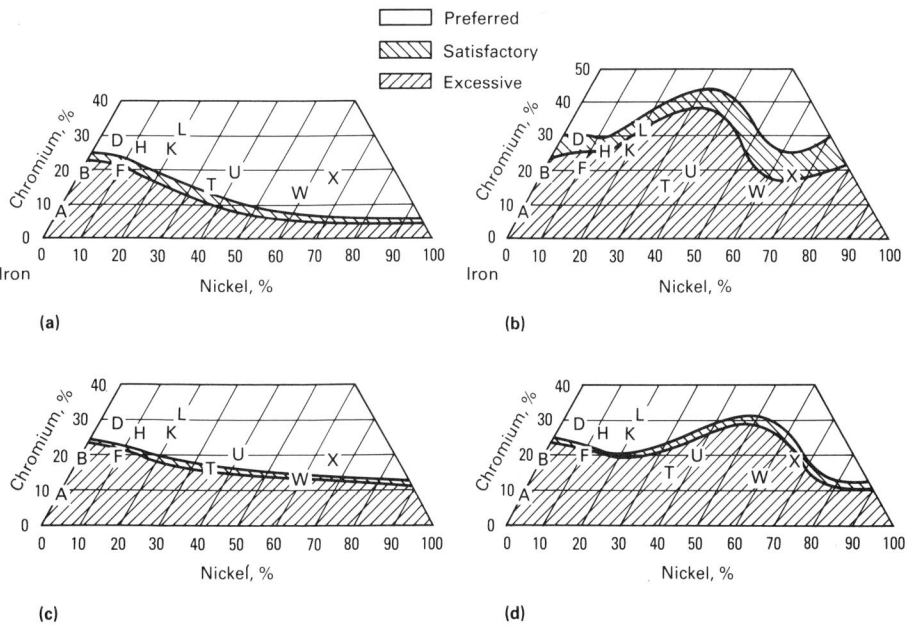

Fig. 4 Corrosion behavior of H-type alloys in 100 h tests at 980 °C (1800 °F) in reducing sulfur-bearing gases. (a) Gas contained 5 grains of sulfur per 2.8 m³ (100 ft³) of gas. (b) Gas contained 300 grains of sulfur per 2.8 m³ (100 ft³) of gas. (c) Gas contained 100 grains of sulfur per 2.8 m³ (100 ft³) of gas; test at constant temperature. (d) Same sulfur content as gas in (c), but cooled to 150 °C (300 °F) each 12 h

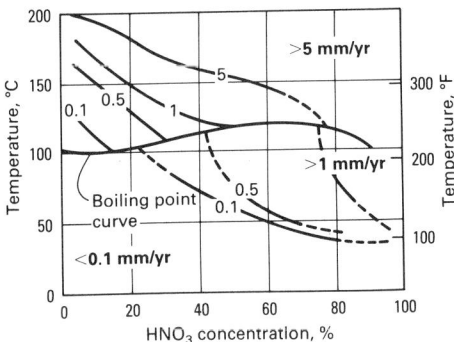

Fig. 5 Isocorrosion diagram for CB-30 in HNO₃. Castings were annealed at 790 °C (1450 °F), furnace cooled to 540 °C (1000 °F), and then air cooled to room temperature.

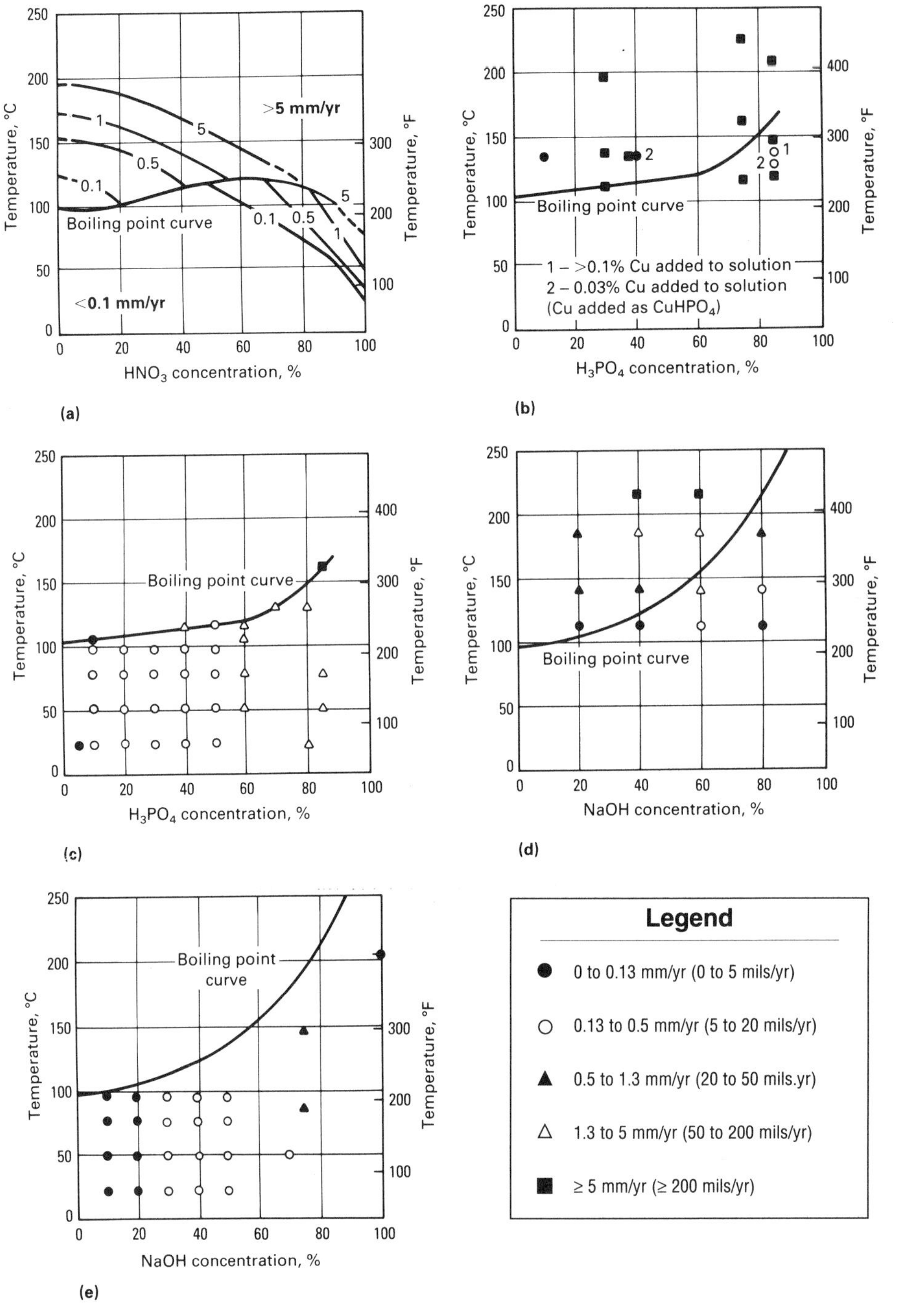

Fig. 6 Isocorrosion diagrams for CF-8 in HNO₃ (a), H₃PO₄ (b and c), and NaOH solutions (d and e). Tests for (b) and (d) were performed in a closed container at equilibrium pressure. Tests for (c) and (e) were performed at atmospheric pressure.

such, it may not be used in aggressive environments. It does, however, exhibit good atmospheric-corrosion resistance, and it resists staining by many organic environments. Alloy CA-15M may contain slightly more molybdenum than CA-15 (up to 1% Mo), and it therefore may have improved general corrosion resistance in relatively mild environments. Alloy CA-6NM is similar to CA-15M except that it contains more nickel and molybdenum, which improves its general corrosion resistance. Alloy CA-6NM-B is a lower-carbon version of this alloy. The lower strength level promotes resistance to sulfide stress cracking. Alloy CA-40 is a higher-strength version of CA-15, and it also exhibits excellent atmospheric-corrosion resistance after a normalize-and-temper heat treatment. Microstructurally, the CB-7Cu alloys usually consist of mixed martensite and ferrite, and because of the increased chromium and nickel levels compared to the other martensitic alloys, they offer improved corrosion resistance to seawater and some mild acids. These alloys also have good atmospheric-corrosion resistance. The CB-7Cu alloys are hardenable and offer the possibility of increased strength and improved corrosion resistance among the martensitic alloys.

General Corrosion of Ferritic Alloys. Alloys CB-30 and CC-50 are higher-carbon and higher-chromium alloys than the CA alloys previously mentioned. Each alloy is predominantly ferritic, although a small amount of martensite may be found in CB-30. Alloy CB-30 contains 18 to 21% Cr and is used in chemical-processing and oil-refining applications. The chromium content is sufficient to have good corrosion resistance to many acids, including nitric acid (HNO₃). Figure 5 shows an isocorrosion diagram for CB-30 in HNO₃. Alloy CC-50 contains substantially more chromium (26 to 30%) and offers relatively high resistance to localized corrosion and high resistance to many acids, including dilute sulfuric acid (H₂SO₄) and such oxidizing acids as HNO₃.

General Corrosion of Austenitic and Duplex Alloys. Alloy CF-8 typically contains approximately 19% Cr and 9% Ni and is essentially the cast equivalent of AISI type 304 wrought alloy. Alloy CF-8 may be fully austenitic, but it more commonly contains some residual ferrite (3

to 30%) in an austenite matrix. In the solution-treated condition, this alloy has excellent resistance to a wide variety of acids. It is particularly resistant to highly oxidizing acids, such as boiling HNO₃. Figure 6 shows isocorrosion diagrams for CF-8 in HNO₃, phosphoric acid (H₃PO₄), and sodium hydroxide (NaOH). The duplex nature of the microstructure of this alloy imparts additional resistance to SCC compared to its wholly austenitic counterparts. Alloy CF-3 is a reduced-carbon version of CF-8 with essentially identical corrosion resistance except that CF-3 is much less sus-

ceptible to sensitization (Fig. 7). For applications in which the corrosion resistance of the weld heat-affected zone (HAZ) may be critical, CF-3 is a common material selection.

Alloys CF-8A and CF-3A contain more ferrite than their CF-8 and CF-3 counterparts. Because the higher ferrite content is achieved by increasing the chromium-nickel equivalent ratio, the CF-8A and CF-3A alloys may have slightly higher chromium or slightly lower nickel contents than the low-ferrite equivalents. In general, the corrosion resistance is very similar, but the strength in-

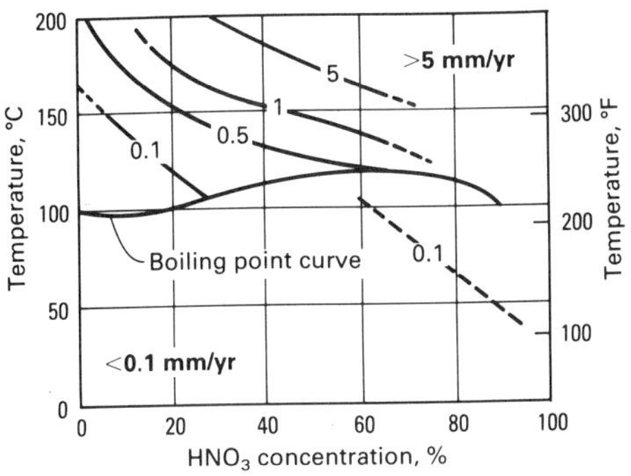

Fig. 7 Isocorrosion diagram for solution-treated quenched and sensitized CF-3 in HNO_3

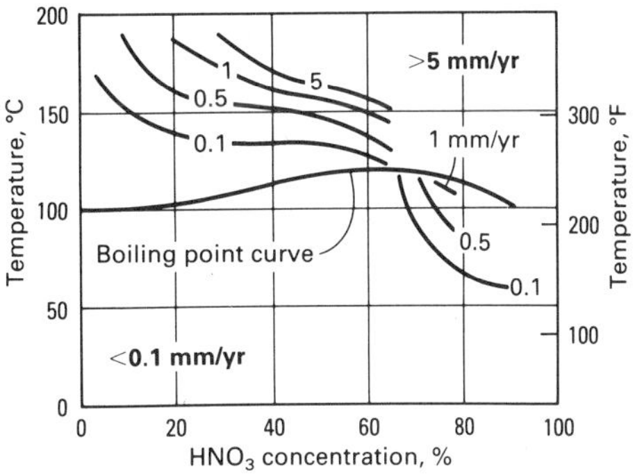

Fig. 8 Isocorrosion diagram for CD-4MCu in HNO_3. The material was solution treated at 1120 °C (2050 °F) and water quenched.

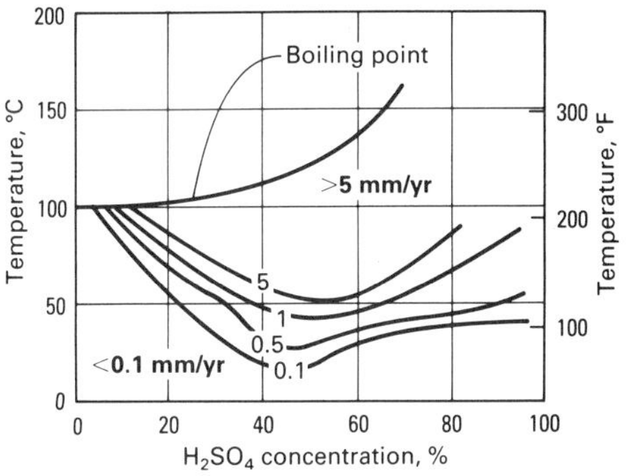

Fig. 9 Isocorrosion diagram for CD-4MCu in H_2SO_4. The material was solution annealed at 1120 °C (2050 °F) and water quenched.

creases with ferrite content. Because of the high ferrite content, service should be restricted to temperatures below 400 °C (750 °F) due to the possibility of severe embrittlement. Alloy CF-8C is the niobium-stabilized grade of the CF-8 alloy class. This alloy contains small amounts of niobium, which tend to form carbides preferentially over chromium carbides and improve intergranular corrosion resistance in applications involving relatively high service temperatures.

Alloys CF-8M, CF-3M, CF-8MA, and CF-3MA are molybdenum-bearing (2 to 3%) versions of the CF-8 and CF-3 alloys. The addition of 2 to 3% Mo increases resistance to corrosion by seawater and improves resistance to many chloride-bearing environments. The presence of 2 to 3% Mo also improves crevice corrosion and pitting resistance compared to that of the CF-8 and CF-3 alloys. Molybdenum-bearing alloys are generally not as resistant to highly oxidizing environments (this is particularly true for boiling HNO_3), but for weakly oxidizing environments and reducing environments, molybdenum-bearing alloys are generally superior.

Alloy CF-16F is a selenium-bearing, free-machining grade of cast stainless steel. Because CF-16F nominally contains 19% Cr and 10% Ni, it has adequate corrosion resistance to a wide range of corrodents, but the large number of selenide inclusions makes surface deterioration and pitting definite possibilities.

Alloy CF-20 is a fully austenitic, relatively high-strength corrosion-resistant alloy. The 19% Cr content provides resistance to many types of oxidizing acids, but the high carbon content makes it imperative that this alloy be used in the solution-treated condition for environments known to cause intergranular corrosion.

Alloy CE-30 is a nominally 27Cr-9Ni alloy that normally contains 10 to 20% ferrite in an austenite matrix. The high carbon and ferrite contents provide relatively high strength. The high chromium content and duplex structure act to minimize corrosion because of the formation of chromium carbides in the microstructure. This particular alloy is known for good resistance to sulfurous acid (H_2SO_3) and H_2SO_4, and it is extensively used in the pulp and paper industry (see the article "Atmospheric and Aqueous Corrosion" in this Volume).

Alloy CG-8M is slightly more highly alloyed than the CF-8M alloys, with the primary addition being increased molybdenum (3 to 4%). The increased amount of molybdenum provides superior corrosion resistance to halide-bearing media and reducing acids, particularly H_2SO_3 and H_2SO_4 solutions. The high molybdenum content, however, renders CG-8M generally unsuitable in highly oxidizing environments.

Alloy CD-4MCu is the most highly alloyed material in this group of alloys; it has a nominal composition of Fe-26Cr-5Ni-2Mo-3Cu. The chromium-nickel equivalent ratio for this alloy is quite high, and a microstructure containing approximately equal amounts of ferrite and austenite is common. The low carbon content and high chromium content render the alloy relatively immune to intergranular corrosion. High chromium and molybdenum contents provide a high degree of localized corrosion resistance (resistance to crevices and pitting), and the duplex microstructure provides SCC resistance in many environments. This alloy can be precipitation hardened to provide strength and is also relatively resistant to abrasion and erosion corrosion. Figures 8 and 9 show isocorrosion diagrams for CD-4MCu in HNO_3 and H_2SO_4, respectively.

Fully Austenitic Alloys. Alloys CH-10 and CH-20 are fully austenitic and contain 22 to 26% Cr and 12 to 15% Ni. The high chromium content minimizes the tendency toward the formation of chromium-depleted zones due to sensitization. These alloys are used for handling paper pulp solutions and are known for good resistance to dilute H_2SO_4 and HNO_3.

Alloy CK-20 contains 23 to 27% Cr and 19 to 22% Ni. It is less susceptible than CH-20 to intergranular corrosion attack in many acids after brief exposures to the chromium-carbide-formation temperature range. Maximum corrosion resistance is achieved by solution treatment. Alloy CK-20 possesses good corrosion resistance to many acids and, because of its fully austenitic structure, can be used at relatively high temperatures.

Alloy CN-7M, with a nominal composition of Fe-29Ni-20Cr-2.5Mo-3.5Cu, exhibits excellent corrosion resistance in a wide variety of environments and is often used for H_2SO_4 service. Figure 10 shows isocorrosion diagrams for CN-7M in H_2SO_4, HNO_3, H_3PO_4, and NaOH. Relatively high resistance to intergranular corrosion and SCC makes this alloy attractive for many applications. Although relatively highly alloyed, the fully austenitic structure of CN-7M may lead to SCC susceptibility for some environments and stress states.

Intergranular Corrosion of Austenitic and Duplex Alloys. The optimum corrosion resistance for austenitic and duplex alloys is developed by solution treatment. Depending on the specific alloy in question, temperatures between 1040 and 1205 °C (1900 and 2200 °F) are required to ensure complete solution of all carbides and phases, such as σ and χ, that sometimes form in highly alloyed stainless steels. Alloys with a relatively high total alloy content, particularly a high molybdenum content, often require the higher solution treatment temperature. Water quenching from the temperature range of 1040 to 1205 °C (1900 to 2200 °F) normally completes the solution treatment.

Failure to solution treat a particular alloy, or an improper solution treatment, may seriously compromise the observed corrosion resistance in service. Inadvertent or unavoidable heat treatment in the temperature range of 480 to 820 °C (900 to 1500 °F)—for example, welding—may destroy the intergranular corrosion resistance of the alloy. When austenitic or duplex (ferrite in austenite matrix) stainless steels are heated in or cooled slowly through this temperature range, chromium-rich carbides form at grain boundaries in austenitic alloys and at ferrite-austenite interfaces in duplex alloys. These carbides deplete the surrounding matrix of chromium, thus diminishing the corrosion resistance of the alloy. An alloy in this condition of reduced corrosion resistance due to the formation of chromium carbides is said to be sensitized. In small amounts, these carbides may lead to localized pitting in the alloy, but if the chromium-depleted zones are extensive throughout the alloy or HAZ of a weld, the alloy may disintegrate intergranularly in some environments.

If solution treatment of the alloy after casting and/or welding is impractical or impossible, the metallurgist has several tools from which to choose to minimize potential intergranular corrosion problems. The low-carbon grades CF-3 and CF-3M are commonly used as a solution to the sensitization incurred during welding. The low carbon content (0.03% C maximum) of these al-

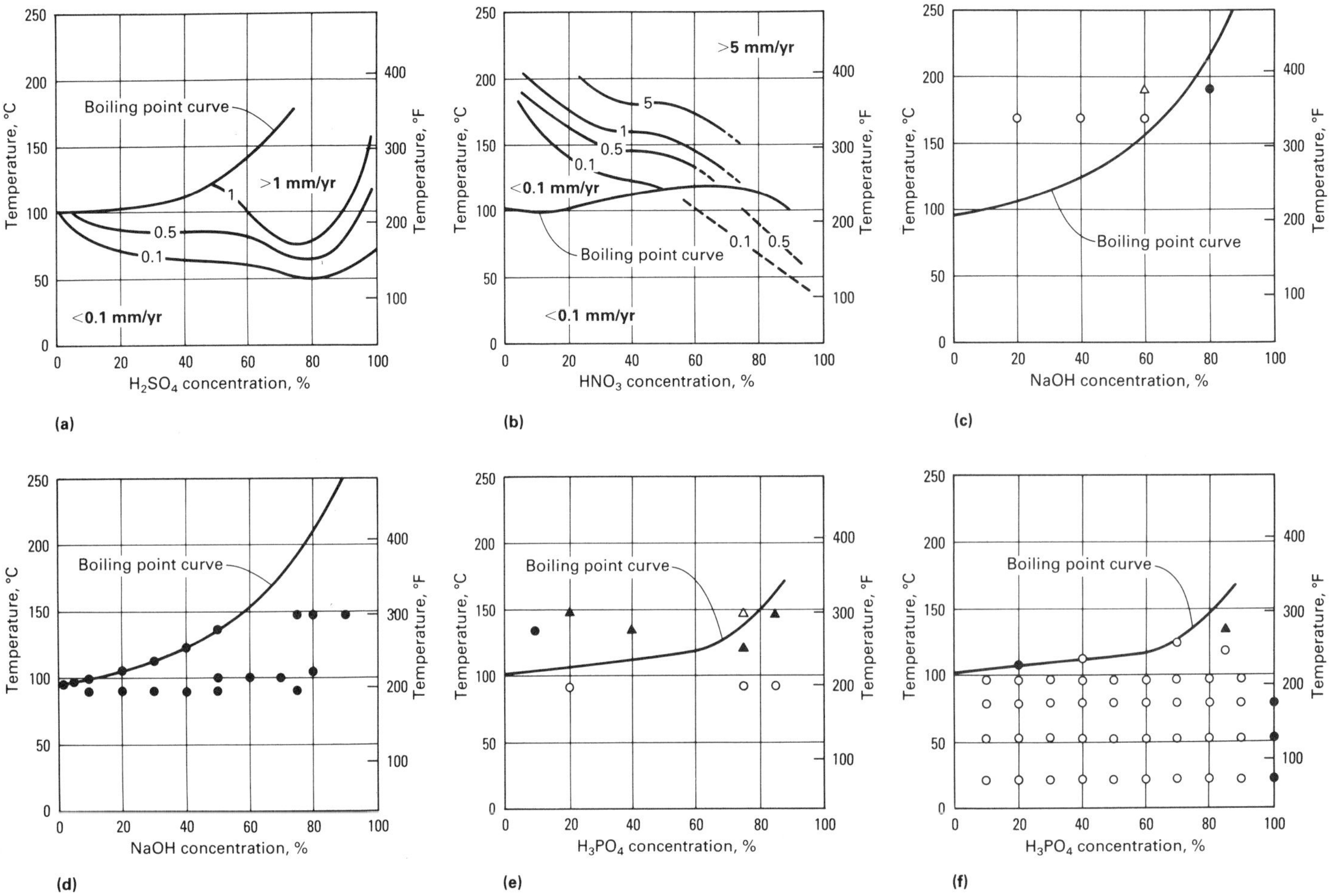

Fig. 10 Isocorrosion diagrams for solution-annealed and quenched CN-7M in H_2SO_4, HNO_3, NaOH, and H_3PO_4. Tests for (a), (b), (d), and (f) were performed at atmospheric pressure. Tests for (c) and (e) were performed at equilibrium pressure in a closed container. See Fig. 6 for legend.

loys precludes the formation of an extensive number of chromium carbides. In addition, these alloys normally contain 3 to 30% ferrite in an austenitic matrix. By virtue of rapid carbide precipitation kinetics at ferrite-austenite interfaces compared to austenite-austenite interfaces, carbide precipitation is confined to ferrite-austenite boundaries in alloys containing a minimum of about 3 to 5% ferrite (Ref 4, 5). If the ferrite network is discontinuous in the austenite matrix (depending on the amount, size, and distribution of ferrite pools), then extensive intergranular corrosion will not be a problem in most of the environments to which these alloys would be subjected.

An example of attack at the ferrite-austenite boundaries is shown in Fig. 11. These low-carbon alloys need not sacrifice significant strength compared to their high-carbon counterparts, because nitrogen may be added to increase strength. However, a large amount of nitrogen will begin to reduce the ferrite content, which will cancel some of the strength gained by interstitial hardening. Appropriate adjustment of the chromium-nickel equivalent ratio is beneficial in such cases. Fortunately, nitrogen is also beneficial to the corrosion resistance of austenitic and duplex stainless steels (Ref 6). Nitrogen seems to retard sensitization

and improve the resistance to pitting and crevice corrosion of many stainless steels.

The standard practices of ASTM A 262 (Ref 7) are commonly implemented to predict and measure the susceptibility of austenitic and duplex stainless steels to intergranular corrosion. Table 3 indicates some representative results for CF-type alloys as tested according to practices A, B, and C of Ref 7 as well as two electrochemical tests described in Ref 10 and 11. Table 4 lists the compositions of the alloys investigated. The data indicate the superior resistance of the low-carbon alloys to intergranular corrosion. Table 3 also indicates that for highly oxidizing environments (represented here by A 262C, boiling HNO_3), the CF-3 and CF-3M alloys are equivalent in the solution-treated condition, but that subsequent heat treatment causes the corrosion resistance of the CF-3M alloys to deteriorate rapidly for service in oxidizing environments (Ref 9). In addition, the degree of chromium depletion necessary to cause susceptibility to intergranular corrosion appears to increase in the presence of molybdenum (Ref 5). The passive film stability imparted by molybdenum may offset the loss of solid-solution chromium for mild degrees of sensitization.

Intergranular Corrosion of Ferritic and Martensitic Alloys. Ferritic alloys may also be

sensitized by the formation of extensive chromium carbide networks, but because of the high

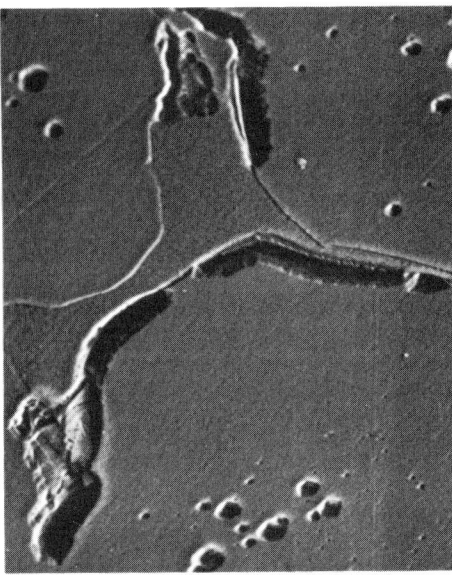

Fig. 11 Ferrite-austenite grain-boundary ditching in as-cast CF-8. This specimen contained 3% ferrite. Scanning electron micrograph. 4550×. Source: Ref 5

Table 3 Intergranular corrosion test results for corrosion-resistant casting alloys
See Table 4 for compositions of alloys listed.

Metallurgical condition	Test(a)	Alloy(b)/Test results(c)											
		CF-8 (4)	CF-8 (11)	CF-8 (20)	CF-8M (5)	CF-8M (11)	CF-8M (20)	CF-3 (2)	CF-3 (5)	CF-3 (8)	CF-3M (5)	CF-3M (9)	CF-3M (16)
Solution treated	A 262A	P	P	P	P	P	P	P	P	P	P	P	P
	A 262B	P	P	P	P	P	P	P	P	P	P	P	P
	A 262C	P	P	P	P	P	P	P	P	P	P	P	P
	EPR	P	P	P	P	P	P	P*	P*	P*	P	P	P
	JEPR	P	P	P	P	P	P	P	P	P	P	P	P
Simulated weld repair	A 262A	X	X	X	X	X	X	P	P	P	P	P	P
	A 262B	X	X	X	X	X	X	P	P	P	P	P	P
	A 262C	X	X	X	X	X	X	P	P	P	P	P	P
	EPR	X	X	X	P	P	P	P*	P*	P*	P	P	P
	JEPR	X	X	X	P	P	P	P	P	P	P	P	P
Solution treated, held 1 h at 650 °C (1200 °F)	A 262A	X	X	X	X	X	X	X	X	X	X	X	X
	A 262B	X	X	X	X	X	X	P	P	P	P	P	P
	A 262C	X	X	X	X	X	X	P	P	P	X	X	X
	EPR	X	X	X	X	X	X	X/P*	X/P*	X/P*	X/P	P	P
	JEPR	X	X	X	P	X	X	P	P	P	P	P	P
As-cast	A 262A	X	X	X	X	X	X	X	X	X	X	X	X
	A 262B	X	X	X	X	X	X	P	P	P	P	X	P
	A 262C	X	X	X	X	X	X	P**	P**	P**	X	X	X
	EPR	X	X	X	X	X	X	X/P*	X/P*	X/P*	X/P	X/P	P
	JEPR	X	X	X	X	X	X	X/P	P	P	P	P	P

(a) See Ref 7 for details of ASTM A 262 practices. EPR, electrochemical potentiokinetic reactivation test; see Ref 10 for details. JEPR, Japanese electrochemical potentiokinetic reactivation test; see Ref 11 for details. (b) Parenthetical value is the percentage of ferrite. See Table 8 for alloy compositions. (c) P, pass; X, fail, based on the following criteria: A 262A ditching, <10% = pass; A 262B, penetration rate <0.64 m/yr (25 mils/yr) = pass; A 262C, penetration rate <0.46 mm/yr (18 mils/yr) and not increasing = pass; EPR, peak current density <100 $\mu A/cm^2$ (645 $\mu A/in.^2$) = pass; JEPR, ratio <1% = pass. P*, pass, but matrix pitting complicates test results. X/P, near pass. X/P*, likely pass; small EPR indication complicated by matrix pitting. P**, pass; actual heat treatment 4 h at 650 °C (1200 °F) after solution treatment rather than as-cast. Source: Ref 5, 8, 9

Table 4 Composition of alloys tested for intergranular corrosion
See Table 3 for test results.

Material	Ferrite number(a)	Element, %								
		C	Mn	Si	P	S	Cr	Ni	Mo	N
CF-8 LO	4	0.058	0.60	1.52	0.012	0.013	18.53	9.98	0.02	0.02
CF-8 INT	11	0.086	0.84	1.10	0.031	0.012	19.90	8.73	0.50	0.02
CF-8 HI	20	0.066	0.79	1.25	0.031	0.011	20.81	8.85	0.45	0.02
CF-8M LO	5	0.063	0.94	1.21	0.011	0.014	18.26	11.17	2.28	0.02
CF-8M INT	11	0.083	1.20	1.20	0.030	0.013	19.78	9.53	2.21	0.02
CF-8M HI	20	0.071	1.19	1.16	0.030	0.011	19.92	9.40	1.95	0.02
CF-3 LO	2	0.016	0.98	1.12	0.010	0.008	17.36	10.10	0.10	0.04
CF-3 INT	5	0.023	0.68	1.24	0.011	0.009	19.35	10.27	0.10	0.06
CF-3 HI	8	0.015	0.67	1.09	0.013	0.006	19.82	8.73	0.10	0.04
CF-3M LO	5	0.027	0.96	0.85	0.011	0.010	17.55	12.00	2.18	0.04
CF-3M INT	9	0.027	1.04	1.02	0.009	0.009	18.78	10.79	2.12	0.03
CF-3M HI	16	0.022	0.94	1.14	0.012	0.007	19.85	10.08	2.26	0.02

(a) This value is the percentage of ferrite.

bulk chromium content and rapid diffusion rates of chromium in ferrite, the formation of carbides can be tolerated if the alloy has been slowly cooled from a solutionizing temperature of 780 to 900 °C (1435 to 1650 °F). The slow cooling allows replenishment of the chromium adjacent to carbides. Martensitic alloys normally do not contain sufficient bulk chromium to be used in applications in which intergranular corrosion is likely to be of concern. Typical chromium contents for martensitic alloys may be as low as 11 to 12%.

Localized Corrosion. Austenitic and martensitic alloys display a tendency toward localized corrosion. Conditions conducive to this behavior may be found in any situation where flow is restricted and an oxygen concentration cell may be established. Duplex alloys

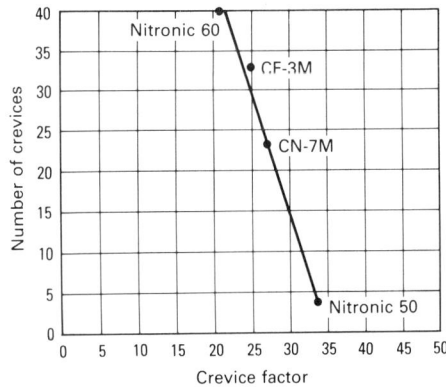

Fig. 12 Crevice corrosion resistance of various alloys in 5-day test in FeCl₃ at room temperature. See text and Ref 12 for explanation of crevice factor. Source: Ref 12

Table 5 Critical crevice temperatures for several common cast and wrought alloys

Alloy	Structure	CCT °C	CCT °F	Ref
Wrought AISI type 317L	Austenitic	2	35	13
Cast CF-3M	90% austenite, 10% ferrite	2	35	12
Cast CN-7M	Austenitic	−1.1	30	12
Cast CF-8M	90% austenite, 10% ferrite	−2.5	28	15
Wrought AISI type 316L	Austenitic	−2.5	28	14
Wrought AISI type 316	Austenitic	−3	27	13

Note: See text and Ref 12 for information on CCTs.

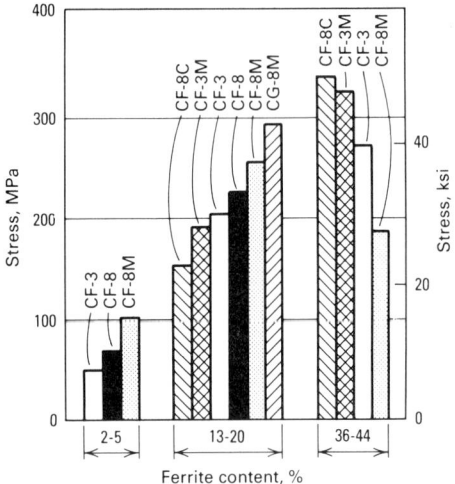

Fig. 13 Stress required to produce stress-corrosion cracking in several corrosion-resistant cast steels with varying amounts of ferrite

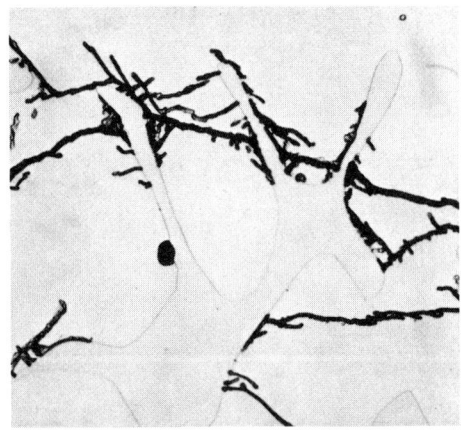

Fig. 14 Ferrite pools blocking the propagation of stress-corrosion cracks in a cast stainless steel

have been found to be less susceptible. Localized corrosion is particularly acute in environments containing chloride ion (Cl-) and in acidic solutions.

Increasing the alloy content improves resistance to localized corrosion. Molybdenum has long been recognized as effective in reducing localized corrosion, although it is not a total solution. Excellent results have been obtained with CG-8M, but the CF-3M or CN-7M alloys are readily attacked. Nitrogen is also effective at retarding localized corrosion.

It has been suggested that resistance to pitting is good when a crevice factor [%Cr + 3(%Mo) + 15(%N)] exceeds 35 (Fig.12). Another technique for comparing alloy composition resistance to localized corrosion is to ascertain the critical crevice temperature (CCT). This involves determining the maximum temperature at which no crevice attack occurs during a 24 h testing period. These tests have been conducted on a number of cast stainless alloys; the results are given in Table 5. Although the CCT has been shown to correlate well with tests in aerated seawater (Ref 16), it must not be used as the maximum operating temperature in seawater or other chloride-containing media. The ferric chloride (FeCl₃) test environment is a very severe, highly oxidizing environment containing about 39,000 ppm Cl⁻ at a pH of about 1.4. Therefore, the FeCl₃ CCT is lower than that normally found in aerated seawater (Ref 16), which contains about 20,000 ppm Cl⁻ with a pH of about 7.5 to 8.0.

Corrosion fatigue is one of the most destructive and unpredictable corrosion-related failure mechanisms. Behavior is highly specific to the environment and alloy. The martensitic materials are degraded the most in both absolute and relative terms. If left to corrode freely in seawater, they have very little resistance to corrosion fatigue. This is remarkable in view of their very high strength and fatigue resistance in air.

Properties can be protected if suitable cathodic protection is applied. However, because these materials are susceptible to hydrogen embrittlement, cathodic protection must be carefully applied. Too large a protective potential will lead to catastrophic hydrogen-stress cracking.

Austenitic materials are also severely degraded in terms of corrosion fatigue strength under conditions conducive to pitting, such as in seawater. However, they are easily cathodically protected without risk of hydrogen embrittlement, and they perform well in fresh water. The corrosion fatigue behavior of duplex alloys has not been widely studied.

Stress-Corrosion Cracking. The SCC of cast stainless steels has been investigated for only a limited number of environments, heat treatments, and test conditions. From the limited information available, the following generalizations apply.

First, SCC resistance seems to improve as the composition is adjusted to provide increasingly greater amounts of ferrite in an austenite matrix. This trend continues to a certain level, apparently near 50% ferrite (Fig. 13 and 14). Second, lower nickel content tends to improve SCC resistance in cast duplex alloys, possibly because of its effect on ferrite content (Ref 17). Third, ferrite appears to be involved in a keying action in discouraging SCC. At low and medium stress levels, the ferrite tends to block the propagation of stress-corrosion cracks. This may be due to a change in composition and/or crystal structure across the austenite-ferrite boundary (Fig. 14). As the stress level increases, crack propagation may change from austenite-ferrite boundaries to transgranular propagation (Ref 17, 18). Finally, reducing the carbon content of cast stainless alloys, thus reducing the susceptibility to sensitization, improves SCC resistance. This is also true for wrought alloys (Ref 17, 19-21).

ACKNOWLEDGMENT

The information in this article is largely taken from:

- R.W. Monroe and S.J. Pawel, Corrosion of Cast Steels, *Corrosion*, Vol 13, *ASM Handbook* (formerly 9th ed. *Metals Handbook*),ASM International, 1987, p 573-582
- M. Blair, Cast Stainless Steels, *Properties and Selection: Irons, Steels, and High-Performance Alloys*, Vol 1, *ASM Handbook* (formerly 10th ed. *Metals Handbook*), ASM International, 1990, p 908-929

REFERENCES

1. M. Prager, Cast High Alloy Metallurgy, *Steel Casting Metallurgy*, J. Svoboda, Ed., Steel Founders' Society of America, 1984, p 221-245
2. C.E. Bates and L.T. Tillery, *Atlas of Cast Corrosion-Resistant Alloy Microstructures*, Steel Founders' Society of America, 1985
3. A. Brasunas, J.T. Glow, and O.E. Harder, Resistance of Fe-Ni-Cr Alloys to Corrosion in

Air at 1600 to 2200 °F, *Proceedings of the ASTM Symposium for Gas Turbines,* ASTM, 1946, p 129-152

4. T.M. Devine, Mechanism of Intergranular Corrosion and Pitting Corrosion of Austenitic and Duplex 308 Stainless Steel, *J. Electrochem. Soc.,* Vol 126 (No. 3), 1979, p 374

5. E.E. Stansbury, C.D. Lundin, and S.J. Pawel, Sensitization Behavior of Cast Stainless Steels Subjected to Simulated Weld Repair, in *Proceedings of the 38th SFSA Technical and Operating Conference,* Steel Founders' Society of America, 1983, p 223

6. S.J. Pawel, Literature Review on the Role of Nitrogen in Austenitic Steels, *Steel Founders' Res. J.,* Issue 5, First Quarter, 1984

7. "Standard Practices for Detecting Susceptibility to Intergranular Attack in Austenitic Stainless Steel," A 262, *Annual Book of ASTM Standards,* ASTM

8. S.J. Pawel, "The Sensitization Behavior of Cast Stainless Steels Subjected to Weld Repair," MS thesis, University of Tennessee, June 1983

9. S.J. Pawel, E.E. Stansbury, and C.D. Lundin, Evaluation of Post Weld Repair Requirements for CF3 and CF3M Alloys—Exposure to Boiling Nitric Acid, *First International Steel Foundry Congress Proceedings,* Steel Founders' Society of America, 1985, p 45

10. W.L. Clarke, R.L. Cowan, and W.L. Walker, Comparative Methods for Measuring Degree of Sensitization in Stainless Steel, *Intergranular Corrosion of Stainless Alloys,* STP 656, R.F. Steigerwald, Ed., American Society for Testing and Materials, 1978, p 99

11. M. Akashi et al., Evaluation of IGSCC Susceptibility of Austenitic Stainless Steels Using Electrochemical Methods, *Boshoku Gijutsu (Corros. Eng.),* Vol 29, 1980, p 163 (BTSITS trans.)

12. J.A. Larson, 1984 SCRATA Exchange Lecture: New Developments in High Alloy Cast Steels, *Proceedings of the 39th SFSA T & O Conference,* Steel Founders' Society of America, 1984, p 229-239

13. R. Maurer and J.R. Kearns, "Enhancing the Properties of a 6% Molybdenum Austenitic Alloy With Nitrogen," Paper 172, presented at Corrosion/85, National Association of Corrosion Engineers, 1985

14. A.P. Bond and H.J. Dundas, "Resistance of Stainless Steels to Crevice Corrosion in Seawater," Paper 26, presented at Corrosion/84, National Association of Corrosion Engineers, 1984

15. A. Poznansky and P.J. Grobner, "Highly Alloyed Duplex Stainless Steels," Paper 8410-026, presented at the International Conference on New Developments in Stainless Steel Technology, Detroit, MI, American Society for Metals, Sept 1984

16. A. Garner, Crevice Corrosion of Stainless Steels in Seawater: Correlation of Field Data With Laboratory Ferric Chloride Tests, *Corrosion,* Vol 37 (No. 3), March 1981, p 178-184

17. S. Shimodaira et al., Mechanisms of Transgranular Stress Corrosion Cracking of Duplex and Ferrite Stainless Steels, *Stress Corrosion Cracking and Hydrogen Embrittlement in Iron Base Alloys,* NACE Reference Book 5, National Association of Corrosion Engineers, 1977

18. P.L. Andresen and D.J. Duquette, The Effect of Cl⁻ Concentration and Applied Potential on the SCC Behavior of Type 304 Stainless Steel in Deaerated High Temperature Water, *Corrosion,* Vol 36 (No. 2), 1980, p 85-93

19. J.N. Kass et al., Stress Corrosion Cracking of Welded Type 304 and 304L Stainless Steel Under Cyclic Loading, *Corrosion,* Vol 36 (No. 6), 1980, p 299-305

20. J.N. Kass et al., Comparative Stress Corrosion Behavior of Welded Austenitic Stainless Steel Pipe in High Temperature High Purity Oxygenated Water, *Corrosion,* Vol 36 (No. 12), 1980, p 686-698

21. G. Cragnolino et al, Stress Corrosion Cracking of Sensitized Type 304 Stainless Steel in Sulfate and Chloride Solutions at 250 and 100 °C, *Corrosion, Vol 37 (No. 6), 1981, p 312-319*

Corrosion of Weldments

WELDMENTS exhibit special microstructural features that need to be recognized and understood in order to predict the acceptable corrosion service life of welded structures. It is not unusual to find that, although the wrought form of a metal or alloy is resistant to corrosion in a particular environment, the welded counterpart is not. Further, welds can be made with the addition of filler metal or can be made autogenously (without filler metal). However, there are also many instances in which the weld exhibits corrosion resistance superior to that of the unwelded base metal. There also are times when the weld behaves in an erratic manner, displaying both resistance and susceptibility to corrosive attack. Corrosion failures of welds occur in spite of the fact that the proper base metal and filler metal have been selected, industry codes and standards have been followed, and welds have been deposited that possess full weld penetration and have proper shape and contour.

It is sometimes difficult to determine why welds corrode; however, one or more of the following factors often are implicated:

- Weldment design
- Fabrication technique
- Welding practice
- Welding sequence
- Moisture contamination
- Organic or inorganic chemical species
- Oxide film and scale
- Weld slag and spatter
- Incomplete weld penetration or fusion
- Porosity
- Cracks (crevices)
- High residual stresses
- Improper choice of filler metal
- Final surface finish

The aforementioned welding parameters and their influence on weldment integrity and mechanical properties are described in greater detail in the article "Welding" in this Volume. The present article will discuss welding parameters and weld filler metal selection only as they influence the corrosion behavior of welds.

Metallurgical Factors

The cycle of heating and cooling that occurs during the welding process affects the microstructure and surface composition of welds and adjacent base metal. Consequently, the corrosion resistance of autogenous welds and welds made with matching filler metal may be inferior to that of properly annealed base metal because of:

- Microsegregation
- Precipitation of secondary phases
- Formation of unmixed zones
- Recrystallization and grain growth in the weld heat-affected zone (HAZ)
- Volatilization of alloying elements from the molten weld pool
- Contamination of the solidifying weld pool

Corrosion resistance can usually be maintained in the welded condition by:

- Balancing alloy compositions to inhibit certain precipitation reactions
- Shielding molten and hot metal surfaces from reactive gases in the weld environment
- Removing chromium-enriched oxides and chromium-depleted base metal from thermally discolored (heat tinted) surfaces
- Choosing the proper welding parameters (Ref 1)

Weld Solidification. During the welding process, a number of important changes occur that can significantly affect the corrosion behavior of the weldment. Heat input and welder technique obviously play important roles. The way in which the weld solidifies is equally important to understanding how weldments may behave in corrosive environments (Ref 2).

A metallographic study has shown that welds solidify into various regions, as illustrated in Fig. 1. The composite region, or fusion zone, essentially consists of filler metal that has been diluted with material melted from the surrounding base metal. Next to the composite region is the unmixed zone where the base metal is melted and then quickly solidified to produce a composition similiar to that of the base metal (Ref 4). For example, when type 304 stainless steel is welded using a filler metal with high chromium-nickel content, steep concentration gradients of chromium and nickel are found in the fusion zone,

whereas the unmixed zone has a composition similar to the base metal (Fig. 2). The weld interface is the surface bounding the region within which complete melting occurred during welding, and it is evidenced by the presence of a cast structure. Beyond the weld interface is the partially melted zone, which is a region of the base metal within which the proportion melted ranges from 0 to 100%. Lastly, the true HAZ is that portion of the base metal within which microstructural change has occurred in the absence of melting. Although the various regions of a weldment shown in Fig. 1 are for a single-pass weld, similar solidification patterns and compositional differences can be expected to occur in underlying weld beads during multipass applications.

Corrosion of Austenitic Stainless Steel Weldments

The corrosion problems commonly associated with welding of austenitic stainless steels are related to precipitation effects and chemical segregation. These problems can be eliminated or minimized through control of base metal metallurgy, control of the welding practice, and selection of the proper filler metal.

Preferential Attack Associated with Weld Metal Precipitates. In austenitic stainless steels, the principal weld metal precipitates are δ-ferrite, σ-phase, and $M_{23}C_6$ carbides. Small amounts of M_6C carbide may also be present. Sigma phase is often used to describe a range of chromium- and molybdenum-rich precipitates, including χ and laves (η) phases. These phases may precipitate directly from weld metal, but they are most readily formed from weld metal δ-ferrite in molybdenum-containing austenitic stainless steels.

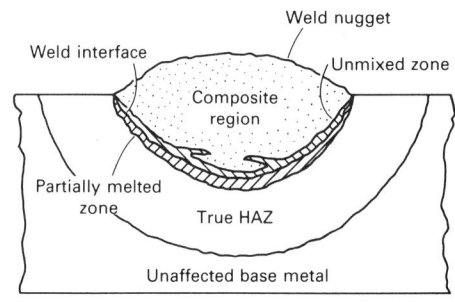

Fig. 1 Schematic of a weld cross section. Source: Ref 3

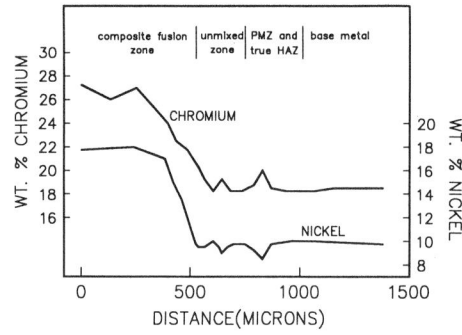

Fig. 2 Concentration profile of chromium and nickel across the weld fusion boundary region of type 304 stainless steel. Source: Ref 4

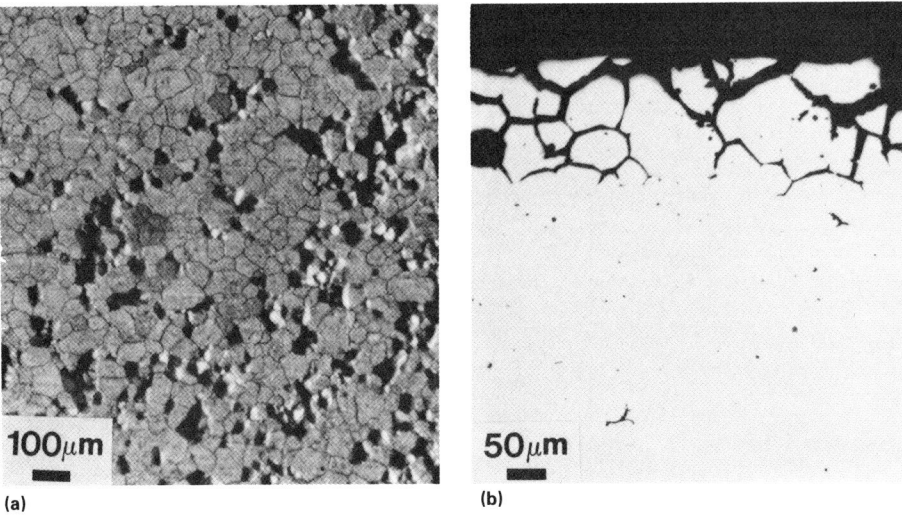

(a)   (b)

Fig. 3 Planar (a) and cross-sectional (b) views of intergranular corrosion (grain dropping) in a sensitized austenitic stainless steel. As-polished. (a) 50×. (b) 100×. Courtesy of G.F. Vander Voort, Carpenter Technology Corporation

Fig. 4 Corroded type 316 stainless steel pipe from a black liquor evaporator. Two forms of attack are evident: preferential attack of the weld metal ferrite, suffered during HCl acid cleaning, and less severe attack in the sensitized HAZ center. Source: Ref 5

The δ-ferrite transforms into brittle intermetallic phases, such as σ and χ, at temperatures ranging from 500 to 850 °C (930 to 1560 °F) for σ and 650 to 950 °C (1200 to 1740 °F) for χ. The precipitation rate for σ and χ phases increases with the chromium and molybdenum contents. Continuous intergranular networks of a phase reduce the toughness, ductility, and corrosion resistance of austenitic stainless steels.

It is extremely difficult to discriminate between fine particles of σ and χ phases by using conventional optical metallographic techniques; hence the designation σ/χ phase. The use of more sophisticated analytical techniques to identify either phase conclusively is usually not justified when assessing corrosion properties, because the precipitation of either phase depletes the surrounding matrix of crucial alloying elements. Grain-boundary regions that are depleted in chromium and/or molybdenum are likely sites for attack in oxidizing and chlorine-bearing solutions. The damage caused by preferential corrosion of alloy-depleted regions ranges from the loss of entire grains (grain dropping) to shallow pitting at localized sites, depending on the distribution and morphology of the intermetallic precipitate particles at grain boundaries. Figure 3 shows two views of an austenitic stainless steel exhibiting intergranular corrosion. Figure 3(a) shows the surface of the sample. The grain structure is visible due to the attack, and some grains have fallen out (grain dropping). The cross-sectional view (Fig. 3b) shows the depth of penetration of the attack along the grain boundaries.

Because these precipitates are usually chromium- and molybdenum-rich, they are generally more corrosion resistant than the surrounding austenite. However, there are some exceptions to this rule.

Preferential attack associated with δ-ferrite and σ can be a problem when a weldment is being used close to the limit of corrosion resistance in environments represented by three types of acidic media:

- Mildly reducing (e.g., hydrochloric acid, HCl)
- Borderline active-passive (e.g., sulfuric acid, H_2SO_4)
- Highly oxidizing (e.g., nitric acid, HNO_3)

Acid cleaning of type 304 and 316 stainless steel black liquor evaporators in the pulp and paper industry with poorly inhibited HCl can lead to weld metal δ-ferrite attack (Fig. 4 and 5). Attack is avoided by adequate inhibition (short cleaning times with sufficient inhibitor at low enough temperature) and by specification of full-finished welded tubing (in which the δ-ferrite networks within the weld metal structure are altered by cold work and a recrystallizing anneal). The latter condition can easily be verified with laboratory HCl testing, and such a test can be specified when ordering welded tubular products.

Sulfuric acid attack of σ phase or of chromium- and molybdenum-depleted regions next to σ-phase precipitates is commonly reported. However, it is difficult to predict because the strong influence of tramp oxidizing agents, such as ferric (Fe^{3+}) or cupric (Cu^{2+}) ions, can inhibit preferential attack. Type 316L weld filler metal has been formulated with higher chromium and lower molybdenum to minimize σ-phase formation, and filler metals for more highly alloyed materials such as 904L (Fe-22Cr-26Ni-4.5Mo) are balanced to avoid δ-ferrite precipitation and thus minimize σ-phase.

Highly oxidizing environments such as those found in bleach plants could conceivably attack δ-ferrite networks and σ phase. However, this mode of attack is not often a cause of failure, probably because free-corrosion potentials are generally lower (less oxidizing) than that required to initiate attack. Preferential attack of δ-ferrite in type 316L weld metal is most often reported after prolonged HNO_3 exposure, as in nuclear fuel reprocessing or urea production. For these applications, a low corrosion rate in the Huey test (ASTM A 262, practice C) is specified (Ref 7).

Pitting Corrosion. Under moderately oxidizing conditions, such as a pulp and paper

bleach plant, weld metal austenite may suffer preferential pitting in alloy-depleted regions. This attack is independent of any weld metal precipitation and is a consequence of microsegregation or coring in weld metal dendrites. Preferential pitting is more likely:

- In autogenous (no filler) gas-tungsten arc (GTA) welds (Fig. 6)
- In 4 to 6% Mo alloys (Table 1)

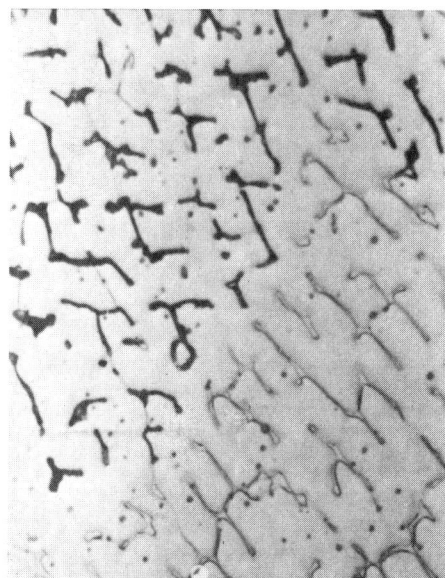

Fig. 5 Preferential corrosion of the vermicular ferrite phase in austenitic stainless steel weld metal. Discrete ferrite pools that are intact can be seen in the lower right; black areas in upper left are voids where ferrite has been attacked. Electrolytically etched with 10% ammonium persulfate. 500×. Source: Ref 6

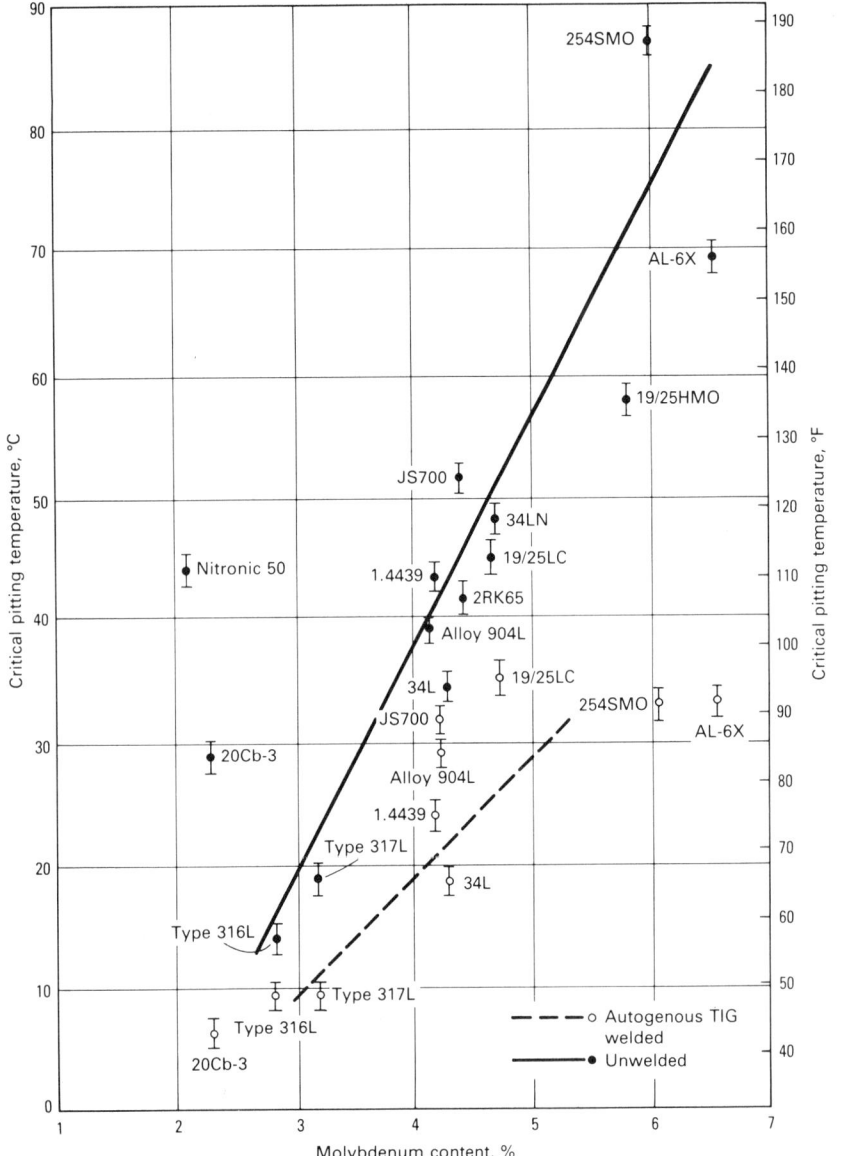

Fig. 6 Critical pitting temperature vs. molybdenum content for commercial austenitic stainless steels tested in 10% FeCl₃. Resistance to pitting, as measured by the critical pitting temperature, increases with molybdenum content and decreases after autogenous tungsten inert gas welding. Source: Ref 5

- When the recommended filler metal has the same composition as the base metal (Fig. 7)
- When higher-heat-input welding leaves a coarse microstructure with surface-lying dendrites (Fig. 8). Such a microstructure is avoided by use of a suitably alloyed filler metal (Fig. 7)

Filler metals with pitting resistance close to or better than that of corresponding base metals include:

Base metal	Filler metals
Type 316L	316L, 317L, 309MoL
Type 317	317L, 309MoL
Alloy 904	Sandvik 27.31.4.LCuR
	Thermanit 30/40 E, Nicro 31/27, Fox CN 20 25 M, IN-112, Avesta P12, Hastelloy alloy C-276
Avesta 254 SMO	Avesta P12, IN-112, Hastelloy alloy C-276

Even when suitable fillers are used, preferential pitting attack can still occur in an unmixed zone of weld metal. High-heat-input welding can leave bands of melted base metal close to the fusion line. The effect of these bands on corrosion resistance can be minimized by welding techniques that bury unmixed zones beneath the surface of the weldment.

When the wrong filler metal is used, pitting corrosion can readily occur in some environments. In the example shown in Fig. 9, the type 316L base metal was welded with a lower-alloy filler metal (type 308L). Tap water was the major environmental constituent contributing to crust formation on the weld joint. The type 316L base metal on either side of the joint was not affected.

Crevice Corrosion. Defects such as residual welding flux and microfissures create weld metal crevices that are easily corroded, particularly in chloride-containing environments. Some flux formulations on coated shielded metal arc electrodes produce easily detached slags, and others give slags that are difficult to remove completely, even after gritblasting. Slags from rutile (titania-base) coatings are easily detached and give good bead shape. In contrast, slags from the basic-coated electrodes for out-of-position welding can be difficult to remove; small particles of slag may remain on the surface, providing an easy initiation site for crevice attack (Fig. 10).

Microfissures or their larger counterparts, hot cracks, also provide easy initiation sites for crevice attack, which will drastically reduce the corrosion resistance of a weldment in the bleach plant. Microfissures are caused by thermal contraction stresses during weld solidification and are a problem that plagues austenitic stainless steel fabrications. These weld metal cracks are more likely to form when phosphorus and sulfur levels are higher (i.e., >0.015% P and >0.015% S), with high-heat-input welding, and in austenitic weld metal in which the δ-ferrite content is low (<3%).

Small-scale microfissures are often invisible to the naked eye, and their existence can readily explain the unexpectedly poor pitting performance of one of a group of weldments made with filler metals of apparently similar general composition. The microfissure provides a crevice, which is easily corroded because stainless alloys are more susceptible to crevice corrosion than to pitting. However, microfissure-crevice corrosion is often mistakenly interpreted as self-initiated pitting (Fig. 11 and 12).

Crevice corrosion sites can also occur at the beginning or end of weld passes, between weld passes, or under weld spatter areas. Weld spatter is most troublesome when it is loose or poorly adherent. A good example of this type of crevice condition is the type 304 stainless system shown in Fig. 13.

Microfissure corrosion in austenitic stainless steel weldments containing 4 to 6% Mo is best avoided with the nickel-base Inconel 625, Inconel 112, or Avesta P12 filler metals, which are very resistant to crevice attack. Some stainless electrodes are suitable for welding 4% Mo steels, but they should be selected with low phosphorus and sulfur to avoid microfissure problems.

Hot tap water is not thought to be particularly aggressive; however, Fig. 14 shows what can happen to a weld that contains a lack-of-fusion defect in the presence of chlorides. In this case, the base metal is type 304 stainless steel, and the weld metal is type 308.

Sensitization. The best known weld-related corrosion problem in stainless steels is weld decay (sensitization) caused by carbide precipitation in the weld HAZ. Sensitization occurs in a zone subject to a critical thermal cycle in which chromium-rich carbides precipitate and in which chromium diffusion is much slower than that of carbon. The carbides are precipitated on grain boundaries that are consequently flanked by a thin chromium-depleted layer. This sensitized microstructure is much less corrosion resistant, because the chromium-depleted layer and the precipitate

Table 1 Amounts of principal alloying elements in stainless steels tested for pitting resistance
Test results are shown in Fig. 6 and 7.

| Alloy | Composition, % | | | |
	Cr	Ni	Mo	N
Base metals				
Type 316L	16	13	2.8	...
Type 317L	18	14	3.2	...
34L	17	15	4.3	...
34LN	18	14	4.7	...
1.4439	18	14	4.3	0.13
Nitronic 50	21	14	2.2	0.20
20Cb-3	20	33	2.4	...
Alloy 904L	20	25	4.2	...
2RK65	20	25	4.5	...
JS700	21	25	4.5	...
19/25LC	20	25	4.8	...
AL-6X	20	24	6.6	...
254SMO	20	18	6.1	0.20
19/25HMO	21	25	5.9	0.15
Filler metals				
Type 316L	19	12	2.3	...
Type 317L	19	13	3.8	...
309MoL	23	14	2.5	...
Batox Cu	19	24	4.6	...
254SLX	20	24	5.0	...
SP-281	20	25	4.6	...
Jungo 4500	20	26	4.4	...
Nicro 31/27	28	30	3.5	...
Thermanit 30/40E	28	35	3.4	...
SAN 27.31.4.LCuR	27	31	3.5	...
Incoloy alloy 135	27	31	3.5	...
Hastelloy alloy G	22	38	3.7	...
P 12	21	61	8.6	...
Inconel alloy 112	21	61	8.7	...
Hastelloy alloy C-276	15	58	15.4	...

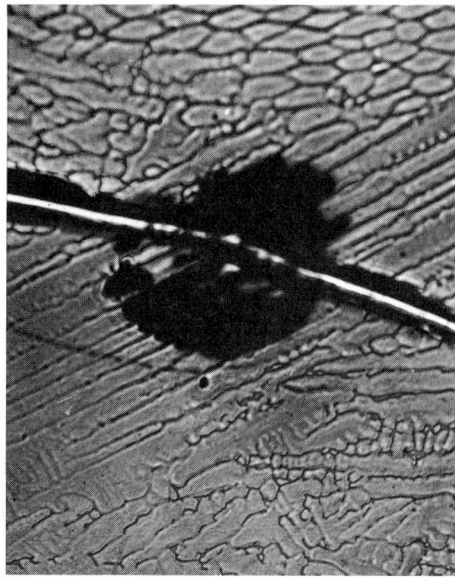

Fig. 8 A scratch-initiated pit formed in type 317L weld metal at 190 mV vs. SCE in 0.6 N NaCl (pH 3) at 50 °C (120 °F). Pitting occurred at a grain with primary dendrites lying parallel to the surface rather than in grains with dendrites oriented at an angle to the surface.

can be subject to preferential attack (Fig. 15 and 16). In North America, sensitization is avoided by the use of low-carbon grades such as type 316L (0.03% C max) in place of sensitization-susceptible type 316 (0.08% C max). In Europe, it is more common to use 0.05% C (max) steels, which are still reasonably resistant to sensitization, particularly if they contain molybdenum and nitrogen; these elements appear to raise the tolerable level of carbon and/or heat input. However, low-carbon

stainless steels carry a small cost premium and so are not universally specified.

Thiosulfate $(S_2O_3^{2-})$ pitting corrosion will readily occur in sensitized HAZs of type 304 weldments in paper machine white-water service (Fig. 17). This form of attack can be controlled by limiting sources of $S_2O_3^{2-}$ contamination; the principal one is the brightening agent sodium hyposulfite $(Na_2S_2O_4)$. However, nonsensitized type 304 will also be attacked. Consequently, type

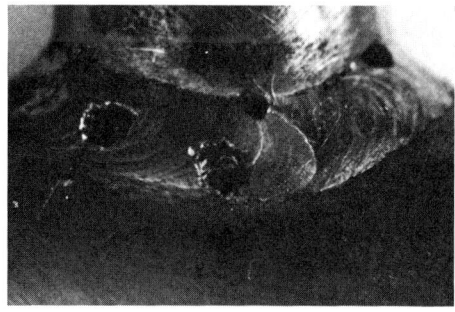

Fig. 9 Pitting of underalloyed (relative to base metal) type 308L weld metal. The type 316L stainless steel base metal is unaffected. About 2.5×

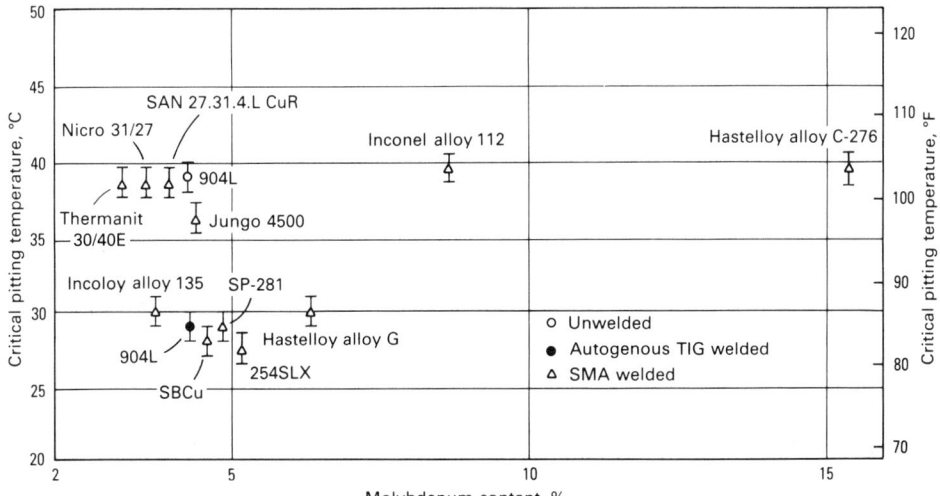

Fig. 7 Effects of various welding techniques and filler metals on the critical pitting temperature of alloy 904L. Data for an unwelded specimen are included for comparison. Source: Ref 5

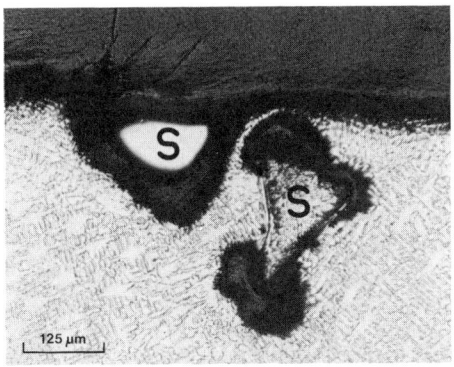

Fig. 10 Crevice corrosion under residual slag (S) in IN-135 weld metal after bleach plant exposure. Etched with glycergia. Source: Ref 5

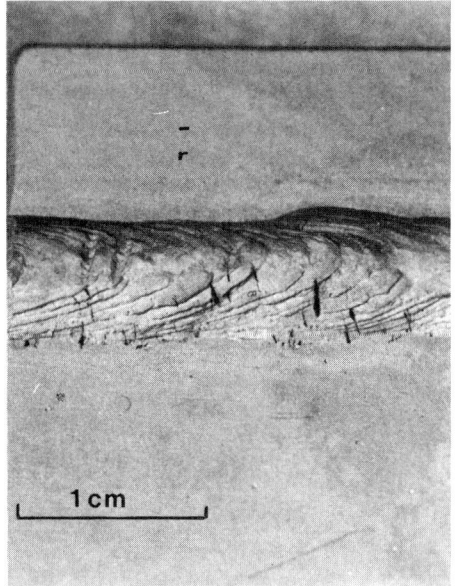

Fig. 11 Microfissure corrosion on IN-135 weld metal on an alloy 904L test coupon after bleach plant exposure. See also Fig. 12. Source: Ref 5

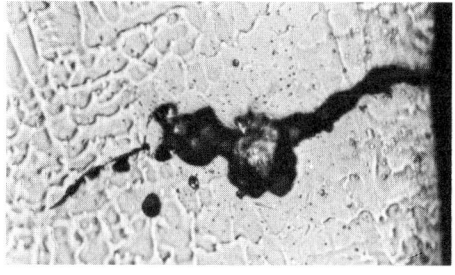

Fig. 12 Section from the bleach plant test coupon in Fig. 11 showing crevice corrosion that has almost obliterated evidence of a microfissure. This form of attack is often mistakenly interpreted as self-initiating pitting; more often, crevice corrosion originates at a microfissure. Etched with glycergia. Source: Ref 5

Fig. 13 Cross section of a weldment showing crevice corrosion under weld spatter. Oxides (light gray) have formed on the spatter and in the crevice between spatter and base metal.

316L is the preferred grade of stainless steel that should be specified for paper machine service.

At higher solution temperatures, sensitized type 304 and type 316 are particularly susceptible to stress-corrosion cracking (SCC), whether caused by chlorides, sulfur compounds, or caustic. For example, type 304 or 316 kraft black liquor evaporators and white liquor tubing are subject to SCC in sensitized HAZs. In many cases cracking occurs after HCl acid cleaning. Although the initial crack path may be intergranular, subsequent propagation can have the characteristic branched appearance of transgranular chloride SCC. Intergranular SCC caused by sulfur compounds can also occur during the acid cleaning of sensitized stainless steels in kraft liquor systems.

Sigma Precipitation in HAZs. When the higher molybdenum alloys such as 904L, AL-6XN, and 254SMO were first developed, one of the anticipated corrosion problems was attack of single-phase precipitates in weld HAZs. This form of attack has subsequently proved to be either superficial or nonexistent in most applications, probably because the compositions of the alloys have been skillfully formulated to minimize a phase-related hot-rolling problems.

More recently, nitrogen has been added to molybdenum-bearing austenitic stainless steels to retard the precipitation of chromium- and molybdenum-rich intermetallic compounds (σ or χ phases). The incubation time for intermetallic precipitation reactions in Fe-Cr-Ni-Mo stainless alloys is significantly increased by raising the alloy nitrogen content. This has allowed the commercial production of thick plate sections that can be fabricated by multipass welding operations. In addition to suppressing the formation of deleterious phases, nitrogen, in cooperation with chromium and molybdenum, has a beneficial effect on localized corrosion resistance in oxidizing acid-chloride solutions.

Corrosion Associated with Postweld Cleaning. Postweld cleaning is often specified to remove the heat-tinted metal formed during welding. Recent work has shown that cleaning by stainless steel wire brushing can lower the corrosion resistance of a stainless steel weldment (Fig. 18). This is a particular problem in applications in which the base metal has marginal corrosion resistance. The effect may be caused by inadequate heat-tint removal, by the use of lower-alloy stainless steel brushes such as type 410 or 304, or by the redeposition of abraded metal or oxides.

Any cleaning method may be impaired by contamination or by lack of control. Results of a study in bleach plants suggest that pickling and glass bead blasting can be more effective than stainless wire brushing and that brushing is more difficult to perform effectively in this case.

Corrosion Associated with Weld Backing Rings. Backing rings are sometimes used when welding pipe. In corrosion applications, it is important that the backing ring insert be consumed during the welding process to avoid a crevice. In the example shown in Fig. 19, the wrong type of backing ring was used, which left a crevice after welding. The sample was taken from a leaking brine cooling coil used in the production of nitroglycerin. The cooling coils contained calcium chloride ($CaCl_2$) brine inhibited with chromates. Coils were made by butt welding sections of seamless type 304L stainless steel tubing. This failure was unusual because several forms of corrosion had been observed.

A metallographic examination of a small trepanned sample revealed the following:

- *Microstructure:* The base metal and weld metal microstructures appeared satisfactory.
- *Pitting:* Irregular corrosion pits were seen on the inside tube surface at crevices formed by the tube and the backing ring adjacent to the tube butt weld. The deepest pits extended 0.1 to 0.2 mm (4 to 8 mils) into the 1.65 mm (0.065 in.) thick tube wall.
- *Cracking:* There were numerous brittle, branching transgranular cracks originating on

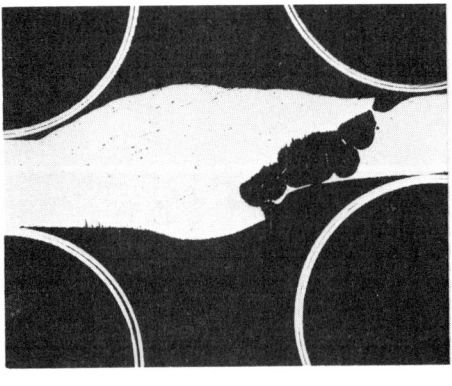

(a)

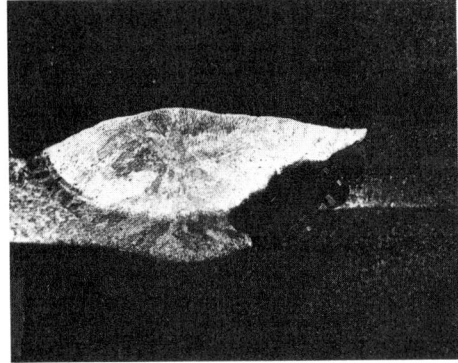

(b)

Fig. 14 Unetched (a) and etched (b) cross sections of a type 304 stainless steel weldment showing chloride pitting attack along a crevice by a lack-of-fusion defect. Service environment: hot tap water

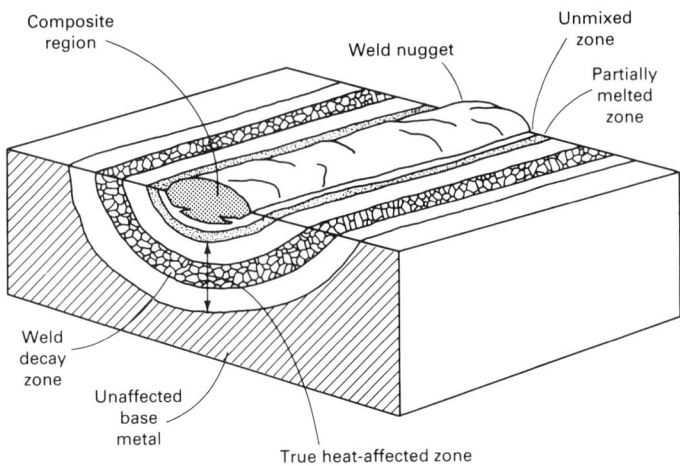

Fig. 15 Schematic diagram of weld decay (sensitization) in an austenitic stainless steel weldment. Source: Ref 3

Labels on figure: Composite region, Weld nugget, Unmixed zone, Partially melted zone, Weld decay zone, Unaffected base metal, True heat-affected zone

Fig. 16 Weld decay and methods for its prevention. The four different panels were joined by welding and then exposed to a hot solution of HNO₃/HF. Weld decay, such as that shown for the type 304 steel (bottom right), is prevented by reduction of the carbon content (type 304L, top left) or by stabilizing with titanium (type 321, bottom left) or niobium (type 347, top right). Source: Ref 2

the inside surface at the crevice under the backing ring.

- *Preferential weld corrosion:* Extensive preferential corrosion of the ferrite phase (vermicular morphology) in the tube weld had occurred and penetrated almost completely through the tube wall. Corrosion originated on the outside surface of the tube.

It was concluded that the preferential weld corrosion from the process side was the most probable cause of the actual leak in the nitrator coil. The preferential corrosion of ferrite in nitrating mixtures of HNO₃ and H₂SO₄ is well known. Whether this corrosion causes a serious problem depends on the amount of ferrite present in the weld. If the amount of ferrite is small and the particles are not interconnected, the overall corrosion rate is not much higher than that of a completely austenitic material. If the

particles are interconnected, as in this case, there is a path for fairly rapid corrosion through the weld, causing failure to occur.

To minimize this problem, two possible solutions were considered. The first was to weld the coils with a filler metal that produces a fully austenitic deposit, and the second was to solution anneal at 1065 °C (1950 °F) after welding to dissolve most of the ferrite. It would also help to select stainless steel base metal by composition (e.g., high nickel, low chromium content) to minimize the production of ferrite during welding. Welding with a fully austenitic filler metal was considered to be the best approach.

Cracking on the brine side was caused by chloride SCC. The cracking probably did not happen during operation at 15 °C (60 °F) or lower. It is thought that the cracking most likely occurred

while the coil was being decontaminated at 205 to 260 °C (400 to 500 °F) in preparation for weld repairing of the leak. Brine trapped in the crevice between the tube wall and the backing ring was boiled to dryness. Under these conditions, SCC would occur in a short time.

There probably were stress cracks behind all of the backing rings. Because the future life of this coil was questionable, a new coil was recommended.

The pitting corrosion caused by the brine was not considered to be as serious as it first appeared. If this had been the only corrosion (and the sample had been representative of the coil), the coil would not have failed for a considerable length of time. The decontamination process, which evaporated the trapped brine, produced some of the observed corrosion and made the pitting appear worse than it was before decontamination.

Because chromates are anodic inhibitors, they can also greatly increase the corrosion (usually by pitting) in the system if insufficient quantities are used. This might have occurred in the crevices in the nitrator coil butt welds, regardless of the bulk solution concentration. The best solution to this problem was to eliminate the crevices, that is, not to use backing rings.

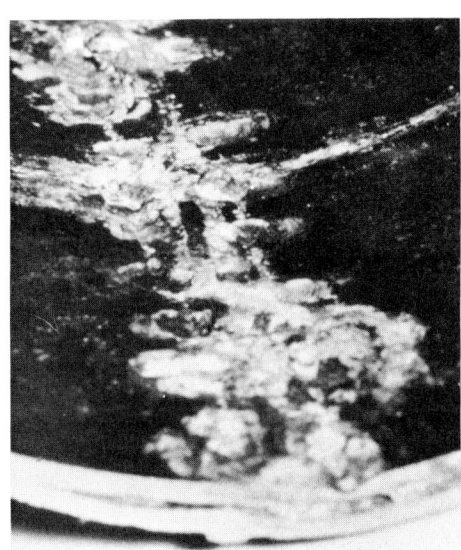

Fig. 17 Thiosulfate pitting in the HAZ of a type 304 stainless steel welded pipe after paper machine white-water service. 2×. Source: Ref 5

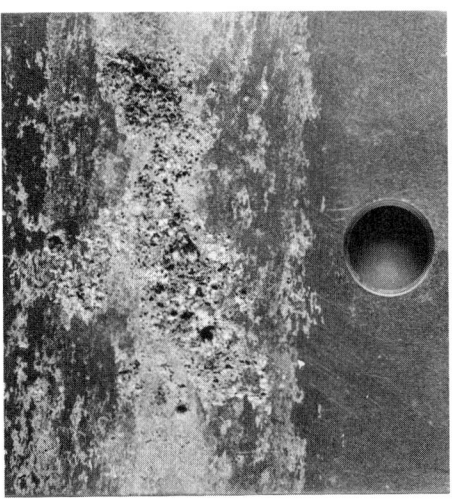

Fig. 18 Pitting corrosion associated with stainless steel wire brush cleaning on the back of a type 316L stainless steel test coupon after bleach plant exposure. Source: Ref 5

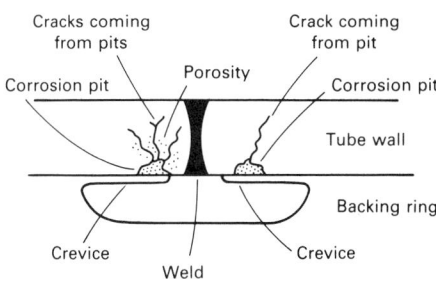

Fig. 19 Schematic of a stainless steel nitrator cooling coil weld joint. Failure was caused by improper design of the backing ring, which was not consumed during welding and left a crevice. Source: Ref 8

Labels on figure: Cracks coming from pits, Crack coming from pit, Corrosion pit, Porosity, Corrosion pit, Tube wall, Backing ring, Crevice, Weld, Crevice

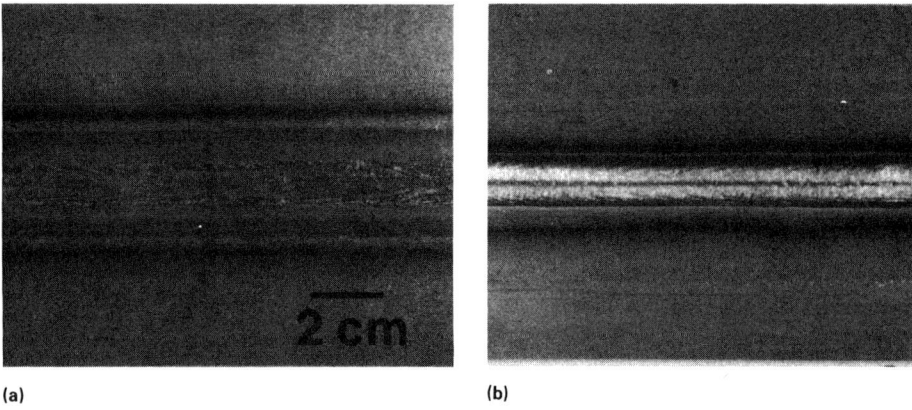

(a)

(b)

Fig. 20 Examples of properly shielded (a) and poorly shielded (b) autogenous gas-tungsten arc welds in type 304 stainless steel strip. Source: Ref 8

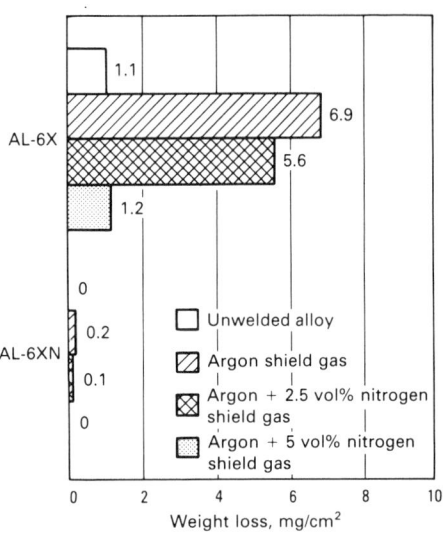

Fig. 21 Effect of gas-tungsten arc weld shielding gas composition on the corrosion resistance of two austenitic stainless steels. Welded strip samples were tested according to ASTM G 48; test temperature was 35 °C (95 °F). Source: Ref 8

Effects of GTA Weld Shielding Gas Composition. The chromium in a stainless steel has a strong chemical affinity for oxygen and carbon. Weld pools formed by electric arc processes must be shielded from the atmosphere to prevent slag formation and oxidation (Fig. 20), to maintain a stable arc, and to reduce contamination of the molten metal by the weld environment. Argon or argon plus helium gas mixtures are commonly used in GTA welding processes to create a barrier between the solidifying weld and the atmosphere. In other cases, nitrogen is commonly used as a backing gas to protect the backside of the root pass.

The composition of a shielding gas can be modified to improve the microstructure and properties of GTA welds in austenitic stainless steels. More specifically, the use of argon mixed with small volumes of nitrogen (10 vol% N_2 or less) in a GTA welding process enhances the corrosion resistance of Fe-Cr-Ni-Mo-N stainless alloys in oxidizing acid chloride solutions (Fig. 21). In certain nonoxidizing solutions, argon-nitrogen shielding gas reduces the δ-ferrite content of weld metal and influences weld metal solidification behavior.

The nitrogen content of weld metal increases with the partial pressure of nitrogen in the GTA weld shielding gas. The increase in weld metal nitrogen content is greater when nitrogen is mixed with an oxidizing gas, such as carbon dioxide (CO_2), than with either a reducing (hydrogen) or a neutral (argon) gas. Porosity and concavity are observed in austenitic stainless steel weld metals when more than 10 vol% nitrogen is added to an argon shielding gas. Although solid-solution additions of nitrogen are not detrimental to the SCC resistance of unwelded molybdenum-containing austenitic stainless steels, an increased weld metal nitrogen content tends to increase susceptibility to SCC.

Effects of Heat-Tint Oxides on Corrosion Resistance. Under certain laboratory conditions, a mechanically stable chromium-enriched oxide layer can be formed on a stainless steel surface that enhances corrosion resistance. In contrast, the conditions created by arc-welding operations produce a scale composed of elements that have been selectively oxidized from the base metal. The region near the surface of an oxidized stainless steel is depleted in one or more of the elements that have reacted with the surrounding atmosphere to form the scale. The rate of oxidation for a stainless steel, and consequently the degree of depletion in the base metal, are independent of the alloy composition. They are controlled by diffusion through the oxide.

The oxidized, or heat-tinted, surface of a welded stainless steel consists of a heterogeneous oxide composed primarily of iron and chromium above a chromium-depleted layer of base metal. The properties of such a surface depend on:

• The time and temperature of the thermal exposure

• The composition of the atmosphere in contact with the hot metal surface

• The chemical composition of the base metal beneath the heat-tint oxide

• The physical condition of the surface (contamination, roughness, thermomechanical history) prior to heat tinting

• The adherence of the heat-tint oxide to the base metal

The defects, internal stresses, and composition of the heat-tint oxide make it a poor barrier to any corrosive media that might initiate localized corrosion in the chromium-depleted layer of base metal.

The severity of localized corrosion at heat-tinted regions exposed to oxidizing chloride solutions is directly related to the temperature of the hot metal surface during welding. A heat-tint oxide on an austenitic stainless steel exposed in air first becomes obvious at approximately 400 °C (750 °F). As the surface temperature is increased, differently colored oxides develop that appear to be superimposed on the oxides formed at lower temperatures. Table 2 shows the relationship between welding conditions and heat-tint color (Ref 9). Dark blue heat-tint oxides are the most susceptible to localized corrosion. Gas-shielded surfaces do not form the same distinctly colored oxides as surfaces exposed to air during welding, but gas-shielded surfaces can also be susceptible to preferential corrosion.

Whether a weld heat tint should be removed prior to service depends on the corrosion behavior of the given alloy when exposed to the particular environment in question. Preferential corrosion at heat-tinted regions is most likely to occur on an alloy that performs near the limit of its corrosion resistance in service, but certain solutions do not affect heat-tinted regions. Even when heat-tinted regions are suspected of being susceptible to accelerated corrosion in a particular environment, the following factors should be considered:

Table 2 Welding conditions and corrosion resistance of heat-tinted UNS S31726 stainless steel plate

Welding conditions(a)				Corrosion test results(b)		
Heat input		Welding current, A	Centerline heat-tint color	Maximum pit depth,		Number of pits on heat-tinted surface
kJ/mm	kJ/in.			mm	mils	
0.3	7.525	50	None	0.1	4	2
0.59	15.050	100	Straw	0.7	28	10
0.89	22.576	150	Rose	0.8	31	50
1.19	30.101	200	Blue	0.7	28	>70
1.48	37.626	250	White	0.9	35	>70

(a) Single-pass autogenous bead-on-plate GTA welds were made to heat tint the root surface of 6.4-mm (1/4-in.) thick plate samples. (b) Duplicate coupons, each with one 25- × 51-mm (1- × 2-in.) heat-tinted surface, were exposed to 10% $FeCl_3$ solutions at 50 °C (120 °F). The weld face and edges of each coupon were covered with a protective coating.

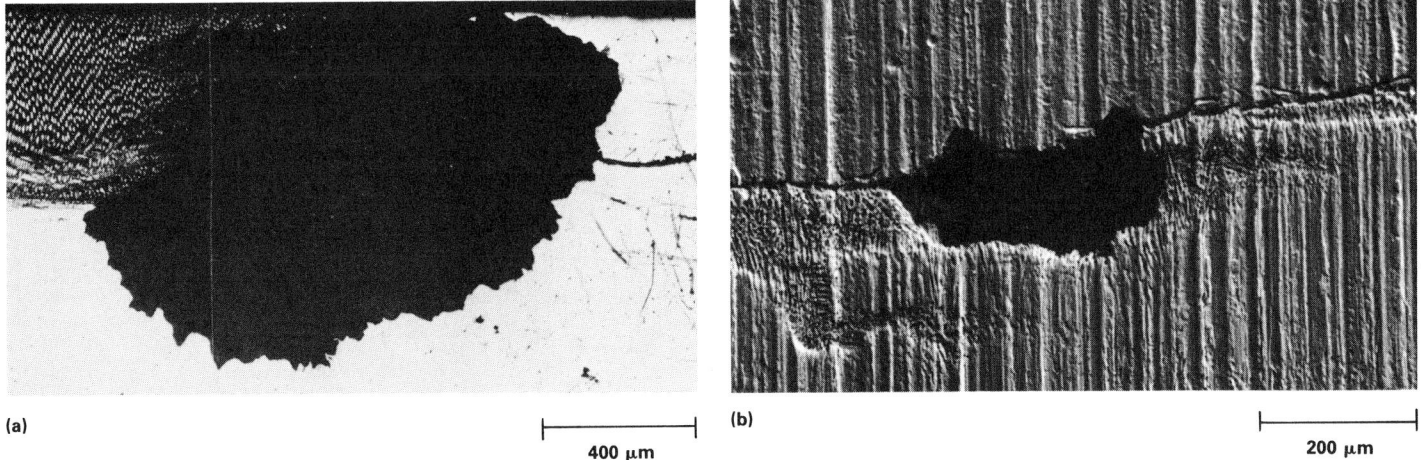

Fig. 22 Optical (a) and scanning electron (b) micrographs of pitting in the unmixed zone of Fe-Cr-Ni-Mo stainless steel plates that were gas-tungsten arc welded with an overalloyed filler metal. The unmixed zones were preferentially attacked in an oxidizing acid chloride solution at elevated temperature.

• The rate at which pits, once initiated in the chromium-depleted surface layer, will propagate through sound base metal
• The hazards associated with the penetration of a process unit due to localized corrosion
• The cost and effectiveness of an operation intended to repair a heat-tinted stainless steel surface

The corrosion resistance of heat-tinted regions can be restored in three stages. First, the heat-tint oxide and chromium-depleted layer are removed by grinding or wire brushing. Second, the abraded surface is cleaned with an acid solution or a pickling paste (a mixture of HNO_3 and HF suspended in an inert paste or gel) to remove any surface contamination and to promote the reformation of a passive film. Third, after a sufficient contact time, the acid cleaning solution or pickling paste is thoroughly rinsed with water, preferably demineralized or with a low chloride ion (Cl^-) content.

Grinding or wire brushing might not be sufficient to repair a heat-tinted region. Such abrading operations may only smear the heat-tint oxide and embed the residual scale into the surface, expose the chromium-depleted layer beneath the heat-tint oxide, and contaminate the surface with ferrous particles

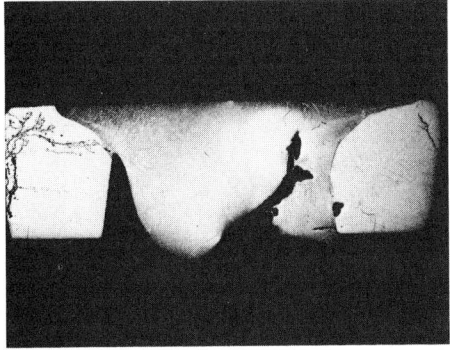

Fig. 23 Selective attack of a type 317L stainless steel weldment and chloride stress-corrosion cracking of the adjacent 317L base metal. The environment was a bleaching solution (7 g/L Cl_2) at 70 °C (160 °F).

that were picked up by the grinding wheel or wire brush. A stainless steel surface should never be abraded with a wheel or brush that has been used on a carbon or low-alloy steel; wire brushes with bristles that are not made of a stainless steel of similar composition should also be avoided. Conversely, attempting to repair a heat-tinted region with only a pickling paste or acid solution can stain or even corrode the base metal if the solution is overly aggressive or is allowed to contact the surface for an extended time. If the acid is too weak, a chromium-depleted scale residue could remain on a surface, even if the chromium-depleted layer were completely removed by a grinding operation. Mechanically ground surfaces generally have inferior corrosion resistance compared to properly acid-pickled surfaces.

Unmixed Zones. All methods of welding stainless steel with a filler metal produce a weld fusion boundary consisting of base metal that has been melted but not mechanically mixed with filler metal and a partially melted zone in the base metal. The weld fusion boundary lies between a weld composite consisting of filler metal diluted by base metal and an HAZ in the base metal (Fig. 1). The width of the unmixed zone depends on the local thermal conditions along the weld fusion line. For a GTA welding process, the zone is most narrow at the weld face and most broad near the middle of the weld thickness.

An unmixed zone has the composition of base metal but the microstructure of an autogenous weld. The microsegregation and precipitation phenomena characteristic of autogenous weldments decrease the corrosion resistance of an unmixed zone relative to the parent metal. Unmixed zones bordering welds made from overalloyed filler metals can be preferentially attacked when exposed on the weldment surface (Fig. 22). The potential for preferential attack of unmixed zones can be reduced by minimizing the heat input to the weld and/or by flowing molten filler metal over the surface of the unmixed zone to form a barrier to the service environment. Care must be taken in this latter operation to avoid cold laps and lack-of-fusion defects. In both cases, preferential attack is avoided as long as the sur-

face of the unmixed zone lies beneath the exposed surface of the weldment.

Chloride SCC. Welds in the 300-series austenitic stainless steels, with the exception of types 310 and 310Mo, contain a small amount of δ-ferrite (usually less than 10%) to prevent hot cracking during weld solidification. In hot, aqueous chloride environments, these duplex weldments generally show a marked resistance to cracking, while their counterparts crack readily (Fig. 23). The generally accepted explanation for this behavior is that the ferrite phase is resistant to chloride SCC and impedes crack propagation through the austenite phase. Electrochemical effects may also play a part; however, under sufficient tensile stress, temperature, and chloride concentration, these duplex weldments will readily crack. An example is shown in Fig. 24.

Caustic Embrittlement (Caustic SCC). Susceptibility of austenitic stainless steels to this form of corrosion usually becomes a problem when the caustic concentration exceeds approximately 25% and temperatures are above 100 °C (212 °F). Because welding is involved in most fabrications, the weld joint becomes the focus of attention because of potential stress raiser effects and because of high residual shrinkage stresses. Cracking occurs most often in the weld HAZ.

In one case, a type 316L reactor vessel failed repeatedly by caustic SCC in which the process fluids contained 50% sodium hydroxide (NaOH) at 105 °C (220 °F). Failure was restricted to the weld HAZ adjacent to bracket attachment welds used to hold a steam coil. The stresses caused by the thermal expansion of the Nickel 200 steam coil at 1034 kPa (150 psig) aggravated the problem. Figure 25 shows the cracks in the weld HAZ to be branching and intergranular. Because it was not practical to reduce the operating temperature below the threshold temperature at which caustic SCC occurs, it was recommended that the vessel be weld overlayed with nickel or that the existing vessel be scrapped and a replacement fabricated from Nickel 200.

Microbiologically Induced Corrosion (MIC). Microbiological corrosion in the process

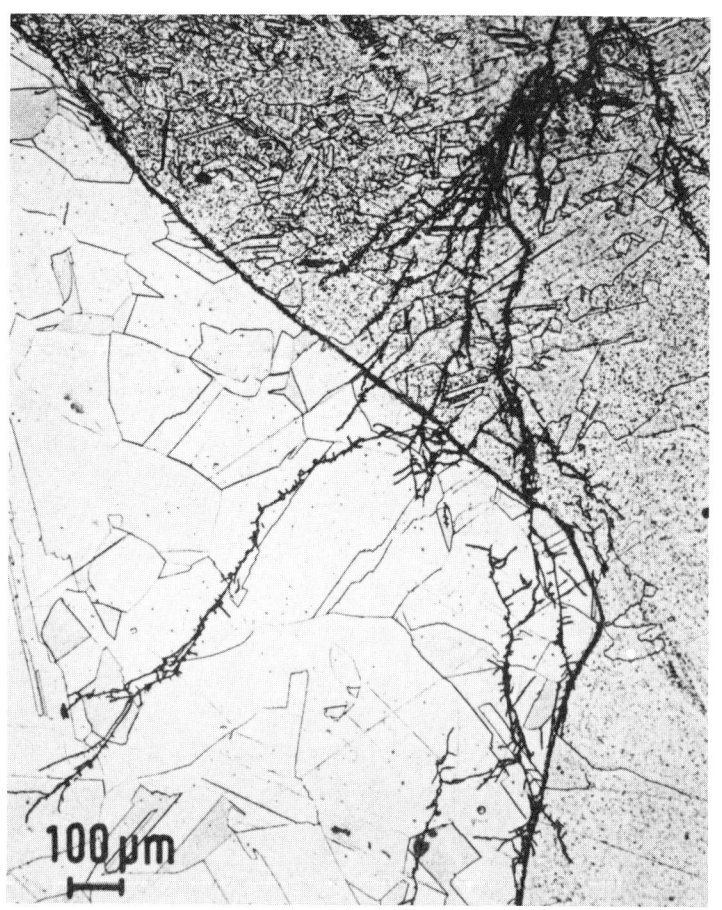

Fig. 24 Chloride stress-corrosion cracking of type 304 stainless steel base metal and type 308 weld metal in an aqueous chloride environment at 95 °C (200 °F). Cracks are branching and transgranular.

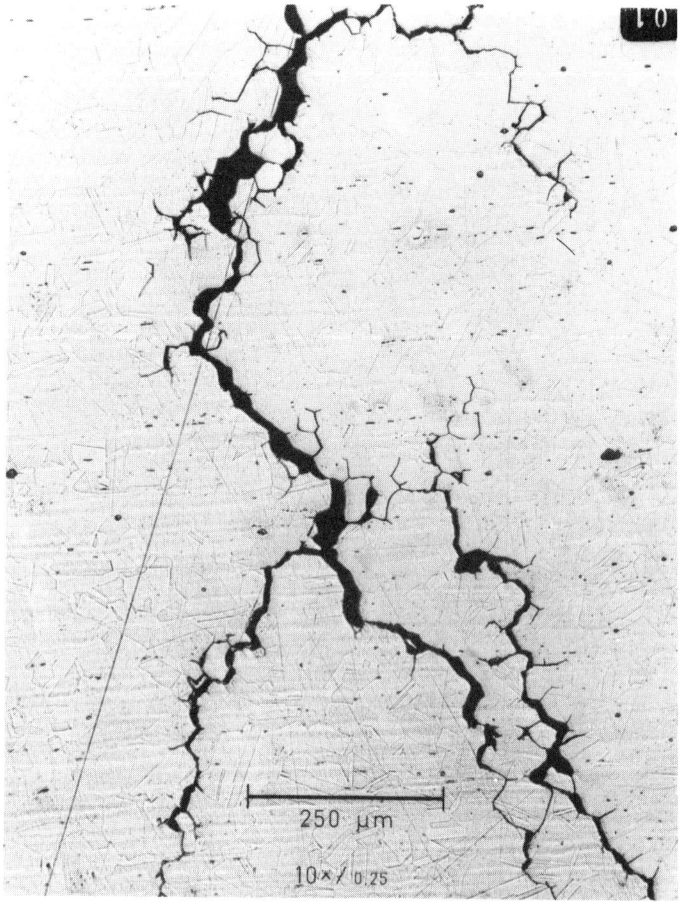

Fig. 25 Caustic stress-corrosion cracking in the heat-affected zone of a type 316L stainless steel NaOH reactor vessel. Cracks are branching and intergranular.

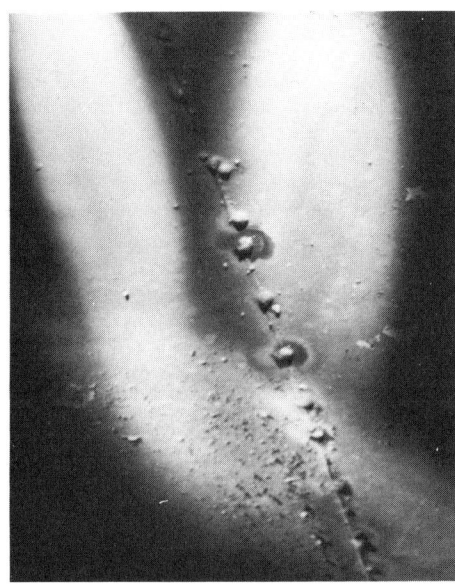

Fig. 26 Moundlike microbiological deposits along a weld seam in the bottom of a type 304L stainless steel tank after several months of exposure to well water at ambient temperature. Source: Ref 10

industries is most often found in three areas: cooling water systems, aqueous waste treatment, and groundwater left in new equipment or piping systems after testing. Nearly all confirmed cases of MIC have been accompanied by characteristic deposits. These are usually discrete mounds. Deposit color can also be an indication of the types of microorganisms that are active in the system. For example, iron bacteria deposits on stainless steel, such as those produced by *Gallionella,* are often reddish.

Investigators have shown that in almost all cases the environment causing the damage was a natural, essentially untreated water containing one or more culprit species of microbiological organisms. In the case of austenitic stainless steel weldments, corrosion generated by bacteria takes a distinctive form, that is, subsurface cavities with only minute pinhole penetration at the surface. The following case history illustrates these characteristics (Ref 10).

Case History 1: Well Water in Texas. New production facilities at one plant site required austenitic stainless steels, primarily types 304L and 316L, for resistance to HNO_3 and organic acids and for maintaining product purity. The piping was shop fabricated, field erected, and then hydrostatically tested. All of the large (>190,000 L, or 25,000 gal) flat-bottom storage tanks were field erected and hydrostatically tested. During the early stages of construction, sodium-softened plant well water (also used for drinking) containing 200 ppm of chlorides was used for testing.

No attempts were made to drain the pipelines after testing. Tanks were drained, but then refilled to a depth of approximately 0.5 to 1 m (2 to 3 ft) for ballast because of a hurricane threat. The water was left in the tanks to evaporate.

The problem became evident when water was found dripping from butt welds in type 304L and 316L piping (nominal wall thickness 3.2 mm, or $\frac{1}{8}$ in.) approximately 1 and 4 months, respectively, after the hydrotest. Internal inspection showed pits in and adjacent to welds under reddish brown deposits. Tank manways were uncovered, and similar conditions were found. As shown in Fig. 26, moundlike deposits were strung out along weld seams in the tank bottoms.

Figure 27 shows a closeup view of a typical deposit still wet with test water. The brilliantly colored deposit was slimy and gelatinous in appearance and to the touch, and it measured 75 to 100 mm (3 to 4 in.) in width. At one point during the investigation, a similar deposit on a weld that was covered with about 150 mm (6 in.) of water was thoroughly dispersed by hand. Twenty-four hours later, the deposit had returned in somewhat diminished form at exactly the same location.

Figure 28 shows a nearly dry deposit. After wiping the deposit clean, a dark ring-shape stain outlining the deposit over the weld was noted (Fig. 29). There was, however, no evidence of pitting or other corrosion, even after light sanding with emery. Finally, probing with an icepick revealed a large, deep pit at the edge of the weld, as shown in Fig. 30. Figure 31, a radiograph of this weld seam, shows the large pit that nearly consumed the entire width of the weld bead, as well as several smaller pits. A cross section through a large pit in a 9.5 mm ($3/8$ in.) thick type 304L tank bottom is shown in Fig. 32.

The characteristics of this mode of corrosion were a tiny mouth at the surface and a thin shell of metal covering a bottle-shape pit that had consumed both weld and base metal. There was no evidence of intergranular or interdendritic attack of base or weld metal. However, pitted welds in a type 316L tank showed preferential attack of the δ-ferrite stringers (Fig. 33).

This type 316L tank was left full of hydrotest water for 1 month before draining. The bottom showed severe pitting under the typical reddish-

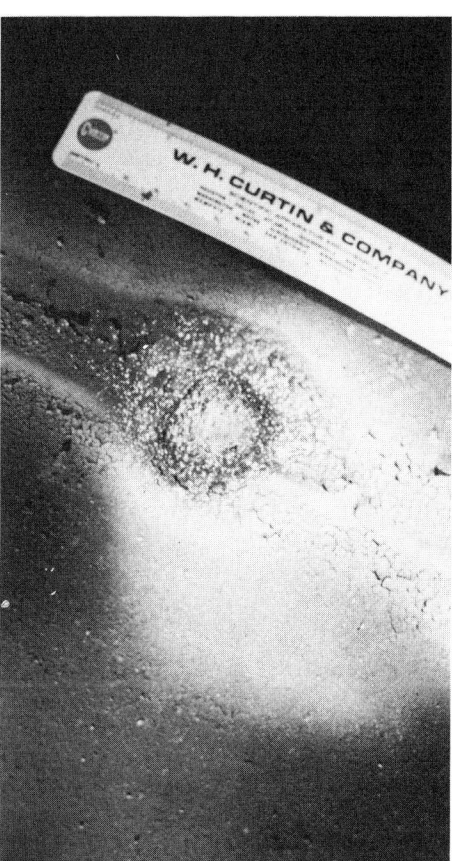

Fig. 27 Closeup of a wet deposit as shown in Fig. 26. Source: Ref 10

Fig. 28 Closeup of a dry deposit. See also Fig. 26 and 27. Source: Ref 10

Fig. 29 Ring-shape stain left around a weld after removal of the type of deposit shown in Fig. 26 to 28. Source: Ref 10

Fig. 30 Large pit (center) at the edge of the weld shown in Fig. 29. The pit was revealed by probing with an icepick. Source: Ref 10

Fig. 31 Radiograph of a pitted weld seam in a type 304L stainless steel tank bottom. Source: Ref 10

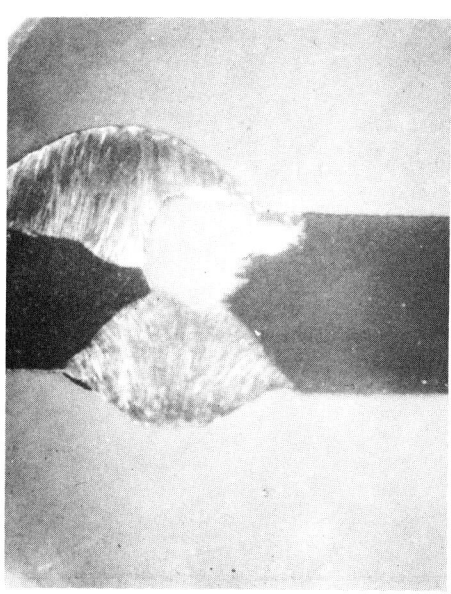

Fig. 32 Cross section through a pitted weld seam from a type 304L tank showing a typical subsurface cavity. Source: Ref 10

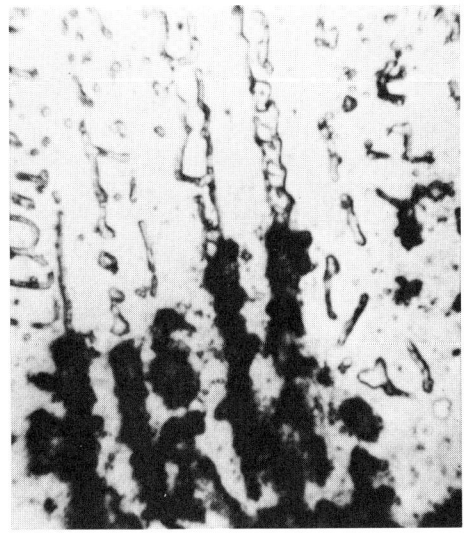

Fig. 33 Micrograph showing preferential attack of δ-ferrite stringers in type 316 stainless steel weld metal. 250×. Source: Ref 10

Fig. 34 Rust-colored streaks transverse to horizontal weld seams in the sidewall of a type 316L stainless steel tank. Source: Ref 10

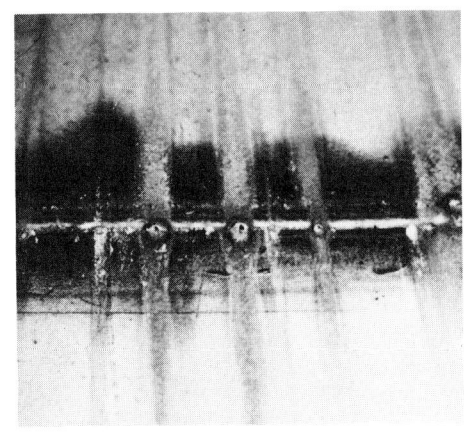

Fig. 35 Closeup of the rust-colored streaks shown in Fig. 34. Source: Ref 10

brown deposits along welds. In addition, vertical rust-colored streaks (Fig. 34) were found above and below the sidewall horizontal welds, with deep pits at the edges of the welds associated with each streak (Fig. 35).

Analyses of the well water and the deposits showed high counts of iron bacteria (*Gallionella*) and iron-manganese bacteria (*Siderocapsa*). Both sulfate-reducing and sulfur-oxidizing bacteria were absent. The deposits also contained large amounts (thousands of parts per million) of iron, manganese, and chlorides.

As indicated, nearly all biodeposits and pits were found at the edges of, or very close to, weld seams. It is possible that the bacteria in stagnant well water were attracted by an electrochemical phenomenon or surface imperfections (oxide or slag inclusions, porosity, ripples, and so on) typically associated with welds. A sequence of events for the corrosion mechanism in this case might be the following:

1. Attraction and colonization of iron and iron-manganese bacteria at welds
2. Microbiological concentration of iron and manganese compounds, primarily chlorides, because Cl⁻ was the predominant anion in the well water
3. Microbiological oxidation to the corresponding ferric and manganic chlorides, which either singly or in combination are severe pitting corrodents of austenitic stainless steel
4. Penetration of the protective oxide films on the stainless steel surfaces that were already weakened by oxygen depletion under the biodeposits

All affected piping was replaced before the new facilities were placed in service. The tanks were repaired by sandblasting to uncover all pits, grinding out each pit to sound metal, and then welding with the appropriate stainless steel filler metal. Piping and tanks have been in corrosive service for about 19 years to date with very few leaks, indicating that the inspection, replacement, and repair program was effective.

Corrosion of Ferritic Stainless Steel Weldments

Conventional 400-series ferritic stainless steels such as types 430, 434, and 446 are susceptible to intergranular corrosion and to embrittlement in the as-welded condition. Corrosion in the weld area generally encompasses both the weld metal and weld HAZ. Early attempts to avoid some of these problems involved the use of austenitic stainless steel filler metals; however, failure by corrosion of the HAZ usually occurred even when exposure was to rather mild media for relatively short periods of time.

Figure 36 shows an example of a saturator tank used to manufacture carbonated water at room temperature that failed by leakage through the weld HAZ of the base metal after only 2 months of service. This vessel, fabricated by welding with a type 308 stainless steel welding electrode, was placed in service in the as-welded condition. Figure 37 shows

Fig. 36 As-welded type 430 stainless steel saturator tank used in the manufacture of carbonated water that failed after two months of service. The tank was shielded metal arc welded using type 308 stainless steel filler metal. Source: Ref 11

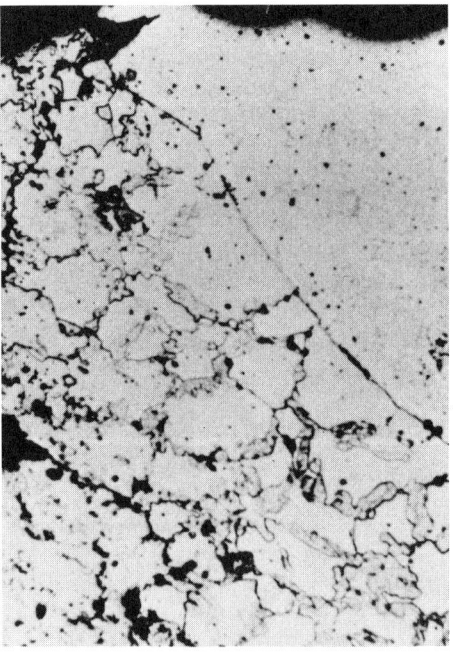

Fig. 37 Micrograph of the outside surface of the saturator tank in Fig. 36 showing intergranular corrosion at the fusion line. Source: Ref 11

Fig. 38 Top view of a longitudinal weld in 6.4 mm (¹⁄₄ in.) E-Brite ferritic stainless steel plate showing intergranular corrosion. The weld was made with matching filler metal. About 4×

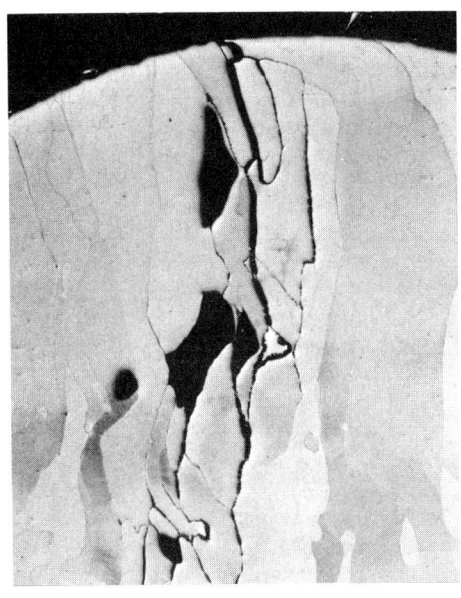

Fig. 39 Intergranular corrosion of a contaminated E-Brite ferritic stainless steel weld. Electrolytically etched with 10% oxalic acid. 200×

a photomicrograph of the weld/base metal interface at the outside surface of the vessel; corrosion initiated at the inside surface. Postweld annealing—at 785 °C (1450 °F) for 4 h in the case of type 430 stainless steel—restores weld area ductility and resistance to corrosion equal to that of the unwelded base metal.

To overcome some of these earlier difficulties and to improve weldability, several of the standard grade ferritic stainless steels have been modified. For example, type 405, containing nominally 11% Cr, is made with lower carbon and a small aluminum addition of 0.20% to restrict the formation of austenite at high temperature so that hardening is reduced during welding. For maximum ductility and corrosion resistance, however, postweld annealing is necessary. Recommendations for welding include either a 430- or a 309-type filler metal, the latter being used where increased weld ductility is desired.

Superferritic Stainless Steels. In the late 1960s and early 1970s, researchers recognized that a new generation of high Cr-Mo-Fe ferritic stainless steels, commonly referred to as *superferritics,* possess a desirable combination of good mechanical properties and resistance to general corrosion, pitting, and SCC. These properties make them attractive alternatives to the austenitic stainless steels commonly plagued by chloride SCC.

It was reasoned that the formation of martensite (as well as the need for preheat and postweld heat treatment) could be eliminated by controlling the interstitial element (carbon, oxygen, and nitrogen) content of these new ferritic alloys, either by ultrahigh purity or by stabilization with titanium or niobium. The welds would thus be corrosion resistant, tough, and ductile in the as-welded condition. To achieve these results, electron beam

vacuum refining, vacuum and argon-oxygen decarburization, and vacuum induction melting processes were used. From this beginning, two basic ferritic alloy systems evolved:

- *Ultrahigh purity:* The (C + N) interstitial content is less than 150 ppm (Ref 12)
- *Intermediate purity:* The (C + N) interstitial content exceeds 150 ppm (Ref 12)

Chromium contents in these alloys generally range from 25 to 28% with ≥3% Mo (some alloys, however, contain less molybdenum). Nickel additions are also used with a maximum level of 4%. Although not usually mentioned in the alloy chemistry specifications, oxygen and hydrogen are also harmful, and these levels must be carefully restricted.

The unique as-welded properties of the superferritic stainless steels have been made possible by obtaining very low levels of impurities (including carbon, nitrogen, hydrogen, and oxygen, in the case of the alloys described as ultralow interstitials) and by obtaining a careful balance of niobium and/or titanium to match the carbon content in the case of the alloys with intermediate levels of interstitials. For these reasons, every precaution must be taken, and welding procedures that optimize gas shielding and cleanliness must be selected to avoid pickup of carbon, nitrogen, hydrogen, and oxygen.

To achieve maximum corrosion resistance, as well as maximum toughness and ductility, the GTA welding process with a matching filler metal is usually specified; however, dissimilar high-alloy weld metals have also been successfully used. In this case, the choice of dissimilar filler metal must ensure the integrity of the ferritic metal system. Regardless of which of the new generation of ferritic stainless steels is to be welded, the following precautions are considered essential:

- The joint groove and adjacent surfaces must be thoroughly degreased with a solvent, such as acetone, that does not leave a residue. This will prevent pickup of impurities, especially carbon, before welding. The filler metal must also be handled carefully to prevent it from picking up impurities. Solvent cleaning is also recommended. *Caution: Under certain conditions, when using solvents, a fire hazard or health hazard may exist.*
- A welding torch with a large nozzle inside diameter, such as 19 mm (³⁄₄ in.), and a gas lens (inert gas calming screen) is necessary. Pure, welding-grade argon with a flow rate of 28 L/min (60 ft³/h) is required for this size nozzle. In addition, the use of a trailing gas shield is beneficial, especially when welding heavy-gage materials. Use of these devices will drastically limit the pickup of nitrogen and oxygen during welding. Back gas shielding with argon is also essential. *Caution: Procedures for welding austenitic stainless steels often recommend the use of nitrogen backing gas. Nitrogen must not be used when welding ferritic stainless steels. Standard GTA welding procedures used to weld stainless steels are inadequate and therefore must be avoided.*
- Overheating and embrittlement by excessive grain growth in the weld and HAZ should be avoided by minimizing heat input. In multipass welds, overheating and embrittlement should be avoided by keeping the interpass temperature below 95 °C (200 °F).
- To avoid embrittlement further, preheating (except to remove moisture) or postweld heat treating should not be performed. Postweld heat treatment is used only with the conventional (less highly alloyed) ferritic stainless alloys.

The following example illustrates the results of not following proper procedures.

Case History 2: Leaking Welds in a Ferritic Stainless Steel Wastewater Vaporizer. A nozzle in a wastewater vaporizer began leaking after approximately 3 years of service with acetic and formic acid wastewaters at 105 °C (225 °F) and 414 kPa (60 psig).

Investigation. The shell of the vessel was weld fabricated in 1972 from 6.4 mm (¹⁄₄ in.) E-Brite (UNS S44627, Fe-26Cr-1Mo+Nb) stainless steel plate. The shell measured 1.5 m (58 in.) in diameter and 8.5 m (28 ft) in length. Nondestructive examination included 100% radiography, dye-penetrant inspection, and hydrostatic testing of all E-Brite welds.

An internal inspection of the vessel revealed that portions of the circumferential and longitudinal seam welds, in addition to the leaking nozzle weld, displayed intergranular corrosion. At the point of leakage, there was a small intergranular crack. Figure 38 shows a typical example of a corroded weld. A transverse cross section through this weld will characteristically display intergranular corrosion with grains dropping out (Fig. 39). It was also noted that the HAZ next to the weld fusion line also experienced intergranular

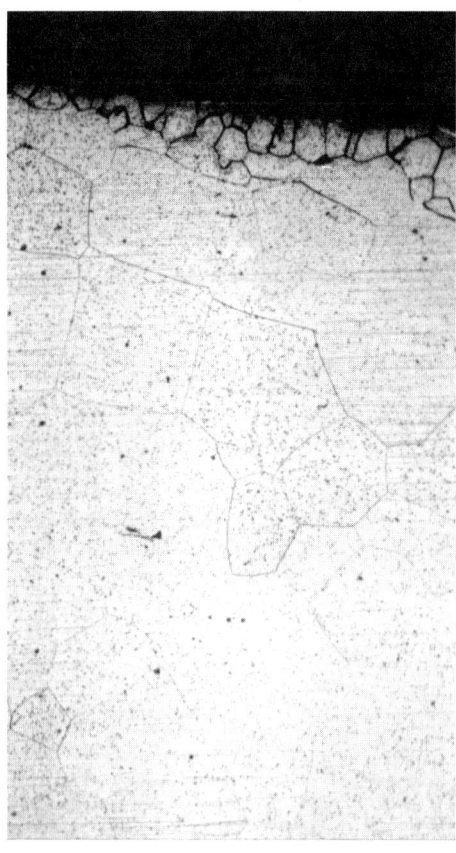

Fig. 40 Intergranular corrosion of the inside surface heat-affected zone of E-Brite stainless steel adjacent to the weld fusion line. Electrolytically etched with 10% oxalic acid. 100×

corrosion a couple of grains deep as a result of sensitization (Fig. 40).

The evidence indicated weldment contamination; therefore, effort was directed at finding the levels of carbon, nitrogen, and oxygen in the various components present before and after welding. The averaged results were as follows:

Base plate
C = 6 ppm
N = 108 ppm (C + N = 114 ppm)
O = 57 ppm

Corroded longitudinal weld
C = 133 ppm
N = 328 ppm (C + N = 461 ppm)
O = 262 ppm

Corroded circumferential weld
C = 34 ppm
N = 169 ppm (C + N = 203 ppm)
O = 225 ppm

Weld wire
C = 3 ppm
N = 53 ppm (C + N = 56 ppm)
O = 55 ppm

Sound longitudinal weld
C = 10 ppm
N = 124 ppm (C + N = 134 ppm)
O = 188 ppm

Sound circumferential weld
C = 20 ppm
N = 106 ppm (C + N = 126 ppm)
O = 85 ppm

These results confirmed suspicions that failure was due to excessive amounts of nitrogen, carbon, and oxygen. To characterize the condition of the vessel further, Charpy V-notch impact tests were run on the unaffected base metal, the HAZ, and the uncorroded (sound) weld metal. These tests showed the following ductile-to-brittle transition temperatures:

Specimen	Ductile-to-brittle transition temperature	
	°C	°F
Base metal	40 ± 3	105 ± 5
HAZ	85 ± 3	180 ± 5
Weld	5 ± 3	40 ± 5

Comparison of the interstitial levels of the corroded welds, sound welds, base metal, and filler wire suggested that insufficient joint preparation (carbon pickup) and faulty gas shielding were probably the main contributing factors that caused this weld corrosion failure. Discussions with the vendor uncovered two discrepancies. First, the welder was using a large, 19 mm (¾ in.) inside diameter ceramic nozzle with a gas lens, but was flowing only 19 L/min (40 ft³/h) of argon; this was the flow rate previously used with a 13 mm (½ in.) inside diameter gas lens nozzle. Second, a manifold system was used to distribute pure argon welding gas from a large liquid argon tank to various satellite welding stations in the welding shop. The exact cause for the carbon pickup was not determined.

Conclusions. Failure of the nozzle weld was the result of intergranular corrosion caused by the pickup of interstitial elements and subsequent precipitation of chromium carbides and nitrides. Carbon pickup was believed to have been caused by inadequate joint cleaning prior to welding. The increase in the weld nitrogen level was a direct result of inadequate argon gas shielding of the molten weld pool. Two areas of inadequate shielding were identified: improper gas flow rate for a 19 mm (¾ in.) diameter gas lens nozzle; and contamination of the manifold gas system.

In order to preserve the structural integrity and corrosion performance of the more highly alloyed ferritic stainless steels, it is important to avoid the pickup of the interstitial elements carbon, nitrogen, oxygen, and hydrogen. In this particular case, the vendor used a flow rate intended for a smaller welding torch nozzle. The metal supplier recommended a flow rate of 23 to 38 L/min (50 to 60 ft³/min) of argon for a 19 mm (¾ in.) gas lens nozzle. The gas lens collect body is an important and necessary part of the torch used to weld these alloys. Failure to use a gas lens will result in a flow condition that is turbulent enough to aspire air into the gas stream, thus contaminating the weld and destroying its mechanical and corrosion properties.

The manifold gas system also contributed to this failure. When this system is first used, it is necessary to purge the contents of the manifold of any air to avoid oxidation and contamination. When that is done, the system functions satisfactorily; however, when it is shut down overnight or

for repairs, air reinfiltrates, and a source of contamination is reestablished. Manifold systems are never fully purged, and leaks are common.

The contaminated welds were removed, and the vessels were rewelded and put back into service. Some rework involved the use of covered electrodes of dissimilar composition. No problems have been reported to date.

Recommendations:

- To ensure proper joint cleaning, solvent washing and wiping with a clean lint-free cloth should be performed immediately before welding. The filler wire should be wiped with a clean cloth just prior to welding. *Caution: Solvents are generally flammable and can be toxic. Ventilation should be adequate. Cleaning should continue until cloths are free of any residues.*

- When GTA welding, a 19 mm (¾ in.) diameter ceramic nozzle with a gas lens collect body is recommended. An argon gas flow rate of 28 L/min (60 ft³/min) is optimum. Smaller nozzles are not recommended. Argon back gas shielding is mandatory at a slight positive pressure to avoid disrupting the flow of the welding torch.

- The tip of the filler wire should be kept within the torch shielding gas envelope to avoid contamination and pickup of nitrogen and oxygen. (They embrittle the weld.) If the tip becomes contaminated, welding should be stopped, the contaminated weld area should be ground out, and the tip of the filler wire that has been oxidized should be snipped off before proceeding with welding.

- A manifold gas system should not be used to supply shielding and backing gas. Individual argon gas cylinders have been found to provide optimum performance. A weld button spot test should be performed to confirm the integrity of the argon cylinder and all hose connections. In this test, the weld button sample should be absolutely bright and shiny. Any cloudiness is an indication of contamination. It is necessary to check for leaks or to replace the cylinder.

- Corrosion resistance is not the only criterion when evaluating these new ferritic stainless steels. Welds must also be tough and ductile, and these factors must be considered when fabricating welds.

Lastly, dissimilar weld filler metals can be successfully used. To avoid premature failure, the dissimilar combination should be corrosion tested to ensure suitability for the intended service.

Corrosion of Duplex Stainless Steel Weldments

In the wrought condition, duplex stainless steels have microstructures consisting of a fairly even balance of austenite and ferrite. The new generation of duplex alloys, which have a composition centered around Fe-26Cr-6.5Ni-3.0Mo, are now being produced with low carbon and a nitrogen addition. These alloys are useful because of their good resistance to chloride SCC, pitting cor-

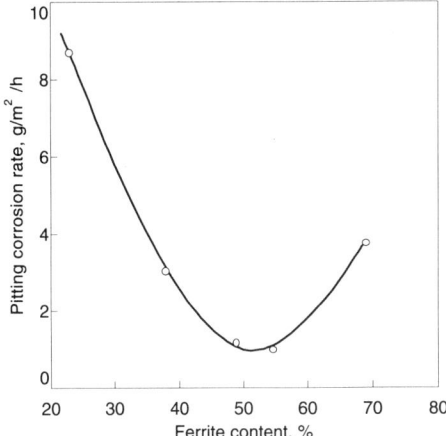

Fig. 41 Effect of ferrite-austenite balance on pitting resistance of Fe-22Cr-5.5Ni-3.0Mo-0.12N gas-tungsten arc stainless steel welds. Source: Ref 13

rosion, and intergranular corrosion in the as-welded condition.

The distribution of austenite and ferrite in the weld and HAZ is known to affect the corrosion properties and the mechanical properties of duplex stainless steels. Figure 41 shows the effect of the ferrite-austenite balance on the pitting resistance of a duplex stainless steel. To achieve a satisfactory balance in properties, it is essential that both base metal and weld metal be of the proper composition. For example, without nickel enrichment in the filler rod, welds can be produced with ferrite levels in excess of 80%. Such microstructures have very poor ductility and inferior corrosion resistance. For this reason, autogenous welding (without the addition of filler metal) is not recommended unless postweld solution annealing is performed, which is not always practical. To achieve a balanced weld microstructure, a low carbon content (~0.02%) and the addition of nitrogen (0.1 to 0.2%) should be specified for the base metal. Low carbon helps to minimize the effects of sensitization, and the nitrogen slows the precipitation kinetics associated with the segregation of chromium and molybdenum during the welding operation. Nitrogen also enhances the reformation of austenite in the HAZ and weld metal during cooling.

Because these duplex alloys have been used in Europe for many years, guidelines relating to austenite-ferrite phase distribution are available. It has been shown that to ensure resistance to chloride SCC, welds should contain at least 25% ferrite. To maintain a good phase balance for corrosion resistance and mechanical properties (especially ductility and notch toughness) comparable to those of the base metal, the average ferrite content of the weld should not exceed 60%. This means using welding techniques that minimize weld dilution, especially in the root pass. Conditions that encourage mixing of the lower-nickel base metal with the weld metal reduce the overall nickel content. Weld metal with a lower nickel content will have a higher ferrite content, with reduced mechanical and corrosion properties. Once duplex base metal and welding consumables have been selected, it is then necessary to select joint designs and weld parameters that will produce welding heat inputs and cooling rates so as to produce a favorable balance of austenite and ferrite in the weld and HAZ.

Researchers have shown that the high-ferrite microstructures that develop during welding in lean (low-nickel) base metal and weld metal compositions can be altered by adjusting welding heat input and cooling rate. In these cases, a higher heat input that produces a slower cooling rate can be used to advantage by allowing more time for ferrite to transform to austenite. There are, however, some practical aspects to consider before applying higher heat inputs indiscriminately. For example, as heat input is increased, base metal dilution increases. As the amount of lower-nickel base metal in the weld increases, the overall nickel content of the deposit decreases. This increases the potential for more ferrite, with a resultant loss in impact toughness, ductility, and corrosion resistance. This would be another case for using an enriched filler metal containing more nickel than the base metal. Grain growth and the formation of embrittling phases are two other negative effects of high heat inputs. When there is uncertainty regarding the effect that welding conditions will have on corrosion performance and mechanical properties, a corrosion test is advisable.

The influence of different welding conditions on various material properties of alloy 2205 (UNS S31803, Fe-22Cr-5.5Ni-3.0Mo-0.15N) has been studied (Ref 14). Chemical compositions of test materials are given in Table 3, and the results of the investigation are detailed in the following sections.

Intergranular Corrosion. Despite the use of very high arc energies (0.5 to 6 kJ/mm, or 13 to 150 kJ/in.) in combination with multipass welding, the Strauss test (ASTM A 262, practice E) (Ref 7) failed to uncover any signs of sensitization after bending through 180°. The results of Huey tests (ASTM A 262, practice C) on submerged-arc welds showed that the corrosion rate increased slightly with arc energy in the studied range of 0.5 to 6.0 kJ/mm (13 to 150 kJ/in.). For comparison, the corrosion rate for parent metal typically varies between 0.15 and 1.0 mm/yr (6 and 40 mils/yr), depending on surface finish and heat treatment cycle.

Similar results were obtained in Huey tests of specimens from bead-on-tube welds produced by GTA welding. In this case, the corrosion rate had a tendency to increase slightly with arc energy up to 3 kJ/mm (75 kJ/in.).

Pitting tests were conducted in 10% ferric chloride ($FeCl_3$) at 25 and 30 °C (75 and 85 °F) in accordance with ASTM G 48 (Ref 15). Results of tests on submerged-arc test welds did not indicate any significant change in pitting resistance when the arc energy was increased from 1.5 to 6 kJ/mm (38 to 150 kJ/in.). Pitting occurred along the boundary between two adjacent weld beads. Attack was caused by slag entrapment in the weld; therefore, removal of slag is important.

Gas-tungsten arc weld test specimens (arc energies from 0.5 to 3 kJ/mm, or 13 to 75 kJ/in.) showed a marked improvement in pitting resistance with increasing arc energy. In order for duplicate specimens to pass the $FeCl_3$ test at 30 °C (85 °F), 3 kJ/mm (75 kJ/in.) of arc energy was required. At 25 °C (75 °F), at least 2 kJ/mm (50 kJ/in.) was required to achieve immunity. Welds made autogenously (no nickel enrichment) were somewhat inferior; improvements were achieved by using higher arc energies.

For comparison with a different alloy, Fig. 42 shows the effect of heat input on the corrosion resistance of Ferralium alloy 255 (UNS S32550, Fe-25.5Cr-5.5Ni-3.0Mo-0.17N) welds made autogenously and tested on $FeCl_3$ at 15 °C (60

Table 3 Chemical compositions of alloy 2205 specimens tested and filler metals used in Ref 14

Specimen size and configuration	Element, %									
	C	Si	Mn	P	S	Cr	Ni	Mo	Cu	N
Parent metals										
48.1-mm (1.89-in.) OD, 3.8-mm (0.149-in.) wall tube	0.015	0.37	1.54	0.024	0.003	21.84	5.63	2.95	0.09	0.15
88.9-mm (3.5-in.) OD, 3.6-mm (0.142-in.) wall tube	0.017	0.28	1.51	0.025	0.003	21.90	5.17	2.97	0.09	0.15
110-mm (4.3-in.) OD, 8-mm (0.31-in.) wall tube	0.027	0.34	1.57	0.027	0.003	21.96	5.62	2.98	0.09	0.13
213-mm (8.4-in.) OD, 18-mm (0.7-in.) wall tube	0.017	0.28	1.50	0.026	0.003	21.85	5.77	2.98	0.10	0.15
20-mm (3/4-in.) plate	0.019	0.39	1.80	0.032	0.003	22.62	5.81	2.84	...	0.13
Filler metals										
1.2 mm (0.047 in.) diam wire 1.6 mm (0.063 in.) diam rod 3.2 mm (0.125 in.) diam wire	0.011	0.48	1.61	0.016	0.003	22.50	8.00	2.95	0.07	0.13
3.25 mm (0.127 in.) diam covered electrode	0.020	1.01	0.82	0.024	0.011	23.1	10.4	3.06	...	0.13
4.0 mm (0.16 in.) diam covered electrode	0.016	0.94	0.78	0.015	0.011	23.0	10.5	3.13	...	0.11

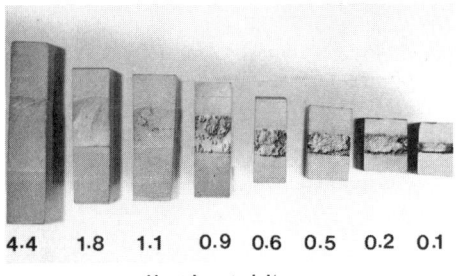

Fig. 42 Effect of welding heat input on the corrosion resistance of autogenous gas-tungsten arc welds in Ferralium alloy 255 in 10% FeCl₃ at 10 °C (40 °F). The base metal was 25 mm (1 in.) thick. Source: Ref 16

°F). Preferential corrosion of the ferrite phase is shown in Fig. 43. In a different test, Ferralium alloy 255 was welded autogenously and tested in a neutral chloride solution according to ASTM D 1141 (Ref 17) at 60 to 100 °C (140 to 212 °F). In this case, preferential attack of the austenite phase was observed. An example is shown in Fig. 44. Similar results would be expected for alloy 2205.

A study of the alloy 2205 weld microstructures (Ref 14) revealed why high arc energies were found to be beneficial to pitting resistance. Many investigations have indicated that the presence of chromium nitrides in the ferrite phase lowers the resistance to pitting of the weld metal and the HAZ in duplex stainless steels. In this study, both weld metal and HAZ produced by low arc energies contained an appreciable amount of chromium nitride (Cr₂N) (Fig. 45). The nitride precipitation vanished when an arc energy of 3 kJ/mm (75 kJ/in.) was used (Fig. 46).

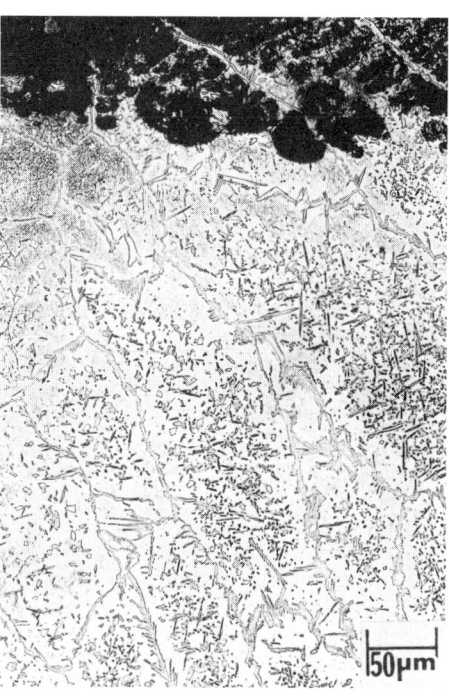

Fig. 43 Preferential corrosion of the ferrite phase in the weld metal of Ferralium alloy 255 gas-tungsten arc welds in 10% FeCl₃ at room temperature. Base metal was 3.2 mm (⅛ in.) thick.

The results of FeCl₃ tests on submerged-arc welds showed that all top weld surfaces passed the test at 30 °C (85 °F) without pitting attack, irrespective of arc energy in the range of 2 to 6 kJ/mm (50 to 150 kJ/in.). Surprisingly, the weld metal on the root side, which was the first to be deposited, did not pass the same test temperature.

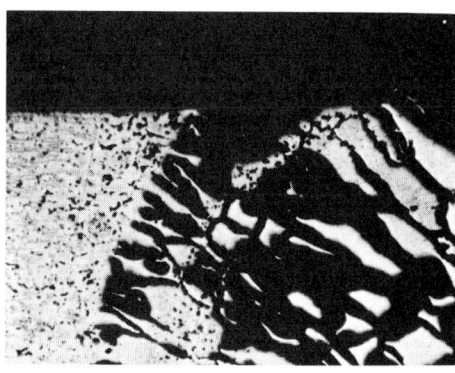

Fig. 44 Preferential attack of the continuous austenite phase in an autogenous gas-tungsten arc weld in Ferralium alloy 255. Crevice corrosion test was performed in synthetic seawater according to ASTM D 1141 (Ref 17) at 100 °C (212 °F). Etched with 50% HNO₃. 100×

The deteriorating effect of high arc energies on the pitting resistance of the weld metal on the root side was unexpected. Potentiostatic tests carried out in 3% sodium chloride (NaCl) at 400 mV versus saturated calomel electrode confirmed these findings. Microexamination of the entire joint disclosed the presence of extremely fine austenite precipitates, particularly in the second weld bead (Fig. 47) but also in the first or root side bead. The higher the arc energy, the more austenite of this kind was present in the first two weld beads. Thus, nitrides give rise to negative effects on the pitting resistance, as do fine austenite precipitates that were presumably re-

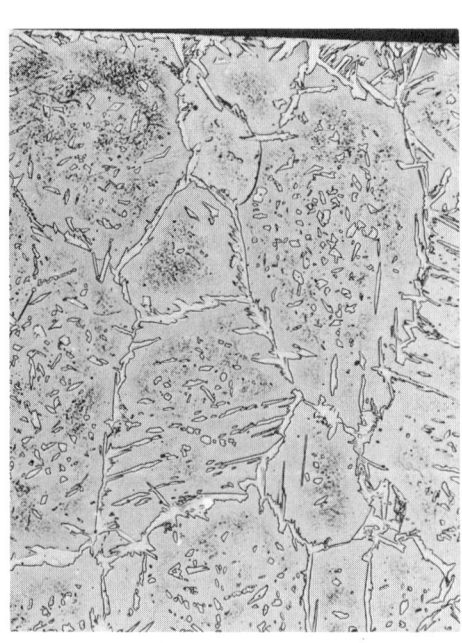

Fig. 45 Microstructure of bead-on-tube weld made by autogenous gas-tungsten arc welding with an arc energy of 0.5 kJ/mm (13 kJ/in.). Note the abundance of chromium nitrides in the ferrite phase. See also Fig. 46. 200×. Source: Ref 14

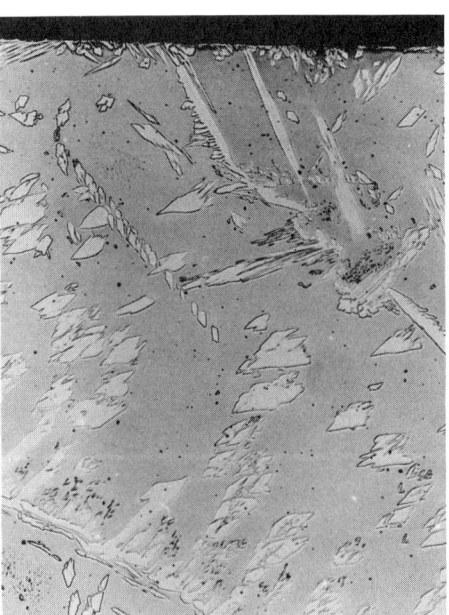

Fig. 46 Microstructure of bead-on-tube weld made by autogenous gas-tungsten arc welding with an arc energy of 3 kJ/mm (76 kJ/in.). Virtually no chromium nitrides are present, which results in adequate pitting resistance. 200×. Source: Ref 14

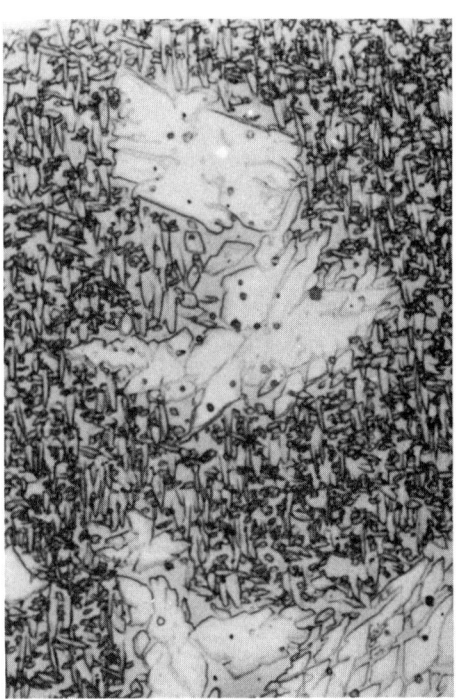

Fig. 47 Microstructure of the second weld bead of a submerged-arc weld joint in 20 mm (¾ in.) duplex stainless steel plate. The extremely fine austenite precipitate was formed as a result of reheating from the subsequent weld pass, which used an arc energy of 6 kJ/mm (150 kJ/in.). 1000×. Source: Ref 14

Table 4 Corrosion resistance of Ferralium alloy 255 weldments using various nickel-base alloy fillers and weld techniques

3.2-mm (0.125-in.) plates tested in 10% FeCl₃ for 120 h

| | Critical pitting temperature | | | | | |
| | Gas tungsten arc | | Gas metal arc | | Submerged arc | |
Filler metal	°C	°F	°C	°F	°C	°F
Hastelloy alloy G-3	30-35	85-95(a)	30	85(a)	30-35	85-95(b)
IN-112	30	85(a)	...	...	35-40	95-105(b)
Hastelloy alloy C-276	...	...	...	...	25-30	75-85(a)
Hastelloy alloy C-22	30	85(a)	...	...	35-40	95-105(a)

(a) HAZ. (b) HAZ plus weld metal

formed at as low a temperature as approximately 800 °C (1470 °F).

Therefore, the resistance of alloy 2205 to pitting corrosion is dependent on several factors. First, chromium nitride (Cr_2N) precipitation in the coarse ferrite grains upon rapid cooling from temperatures above about 1200 °C (2190 °F) causes the most severe impairment to pitting resistance. This statement is supported by a great number of $FeCl_3$ tests as well as by potentiostatic pitting tests. Generally, it seems difficult to avoid Cr_2N precipitation in welded joints completely, particularly in the HAZ, the structure of which can be controlled only by the weld thermal cycle. From this point of view, it appears advisable to employ as high an arc energy as practical in each weld pass. In this way, the cooling rate will be slower (but not slow enough to encounter 475 °C, or 885 °F, embrittlement), and the re-formation of austenite will clearly dominate over the precipitation of Cr_2N.

In addition, if there were no restriction on maximum interpass temperature, the heat produced by previous weld passes could be used to decrease the cooling rate further in the critical temperature range above about 1000 °C (1830 °F). Preliminary tests with preheated workpieces have shown the significance of temperature in suppressing Cr_2N precipitation. Currently, the maximum recommended interpass temperature for alloy 2205 is 150 °C (300 °F). This temperature limit does not appear to be critical, and it is suggested that this limit could be increased to 300 °C (570 °F). The maximum recommended interpass temperature for Ferralium alloy 255 is 200 °C (390 °F). Excessive grain growth as a result of too much heat input must also be considered to avoid loss of ductility and impact toughness.

Second, the fine austenite precipitates found in the reheated ferrite when high arc energies and multipass welding were combined are commonly referred to as γ_2 in the literature. The harmful influence of γ_2 on the pitting resistance has been noted with isothermally aged specimens, but as far as is known, it has never been observed in connection with welding. It is felt, however, that γ_2 is less detrimental to pitting than Cr_2N. Moreover, γ_2 formation is believed to be beneficial to mechanical properties, such as impact strength and ductility.

A third factor that lowers pitting resistance is oxide scale. Where possible, all surface oxides should be removed by mechanical means or, preferably, by pickling. Root surfaces (in pipe), how-ever, are generally inaccessible, and pitting resistance must rely on the protection from the backing gas during GTA welding. It is therefore advisable to follow the current recommendation for stainless steels, which is a maximum of 25 ppm oxygen in the root backing gas.

Stress-Corrosion Cracking. The SCC resistance of alloy 2205 in aerated, concentrated chloride solutions is very good. The effect of welding on the SCC resistance is negligible from a practical point of view. The threshold stress for various welds, as well as for unwelded parent metal in the calcium chloride ($CaCl_2$) test, is as high as 90% of the tensile strength at the testing temperature. This is far above all conceivable design limits.

Also, in environments containing both hydrogen sulfide (H_2S) and chlorides, the resistance of welds is almost as high as for the parent metal. In this type of environment, however, it is important to avoid too high a ferrite content in weld metal and the HAZ. For normal welding of joints, the resulting ferrite contents should not cause any problems. For weld repair situations, however, care should be taken so that extremely high ferrite contents (>75%) are avoided. To preserve the high degree of resistance to SCC, the ferrite content should not be less than 25% (Ref 18).

Another reason to avoid coarse weld microstructures (generated by excessive welding heat) is the resultant nonuniform plastic flow, which can locally increase stresses and induce preferential corrosion and cracking effects.

Use of High-Alloy Filler Metals. In critical pitting or crevice corrosion applications, the pitting resistance of the weld metal can be enhanced by the use of high Ni-Cr-Mo alloy filler metals. The corrosion resistance of such weldments in Ferralium alloy 255 is shown in Table 4. For the same weld technique, it can be seen that using high-alloy fillers does improve corrosion resistance. If high-alloy fillers are used, the weld metal will have better corrosion resistance than the HAZ and the fusion line. Therefore, again, proper selection of welding technique can improve the corrosion resistance of the weldments.

ACKNOWLEDGMENTS

The information in this article is largely taken from:

• K.F. Krysiak, et al., Corrosion of Weldments, *Corrosion,* Vol 13, *ASM Handbook* (formerly 9th ed. *Metals Handbook)*, ASM International, 1987, p 344-367
• D.L. Olson, et al., Corrosion of Weldments, *Welding, Brazing, and Soldering,*Vol 6, *ASM Handbook,* ASM International, 1993, p 1065-1069

REFERENCES

1. F.C. Brautigam, Welding Practices That Minimize Corrosion, *Chem. Eng.,* 17 Jan 1977, p 145-147
2. M.A. Streicher, Theory and Application of Evaluation Tests for Detecting Susceptibility to Intergranular Attack in Stainless Steels and Related Alloys—Problems and Opportunities, in *Intergranulur Corrosion of Stainless Alloys,* STP 656, American Society for Testing and Materials, 1978, p 70
3. W.F. Savage, New Insight into Weld Cracking and a New Way of Looking at Welds, *Weld. Des. Eng.,* Dec 1969
4. W.A. Baeslack III, J.C. Lippold, and W.F. Savage, Unmixed Zone Formation in Austenitic Stainless Steel Weldments, *Weld. J.,* Vol 58 (No. 6), 1979, p 168s-176s
5. A. Garner, How Stainless Steel Welds Corrode, *Met. Prog.,* Vol 127 (No. 5), April 1985, p 31
6. K.F. Krysiak, "Cause and Prevention of Unusual Failures of Materials," Paper 19, presented at Corrosion/83, Anaheim, CA, National Association of Corrosion Engineers, April 1983
7. "Standard Practices for Detecting Susceptibility to Intergranular Attack in Austenitic Stainless Steels," A 262, *Annual Book of ASTM Standards,* American Society for Testing and Materials
8. J.R. Kearns and H.E. Deverell, "The Use of Nitrogen to Improve Fe-Cr-Ni-Mo Alloys for the Chemical Process Industries," Paper 188, presented at Corrosion/86, Houston, TX, National Association of Corrosion Engineers, March 1986
9. J.R. Kearns, "The Corrosion of Heat Tinted Austenitic Stainless Alloys," Paper 50, presented at Corrosion/85, Boston, MA, National Association of Corrosion Engineers, March 1985
10. G. Kobrin, Corrosion by Microbiological Organisms in Natural Waters, *Mater. Perform.,* Vol 15 (No. 7), 1976
11. R.H. Espy, "How Corrosion and Welding Conditions Affect Corrosion Resistance of Weldments in Type 430 Stainless Steel," Paper 22, presented at Corrosion/68, Houston, TX, National Association of Corrosion Engineers, 1968
12. K.F. Krysiak, Welding Behavior of Ferritic Stainless Steels—An Overview, *Weld. J.,* Vol 65 (No. 4), April 1986, p 37-41
13. T.G. Gooch, Corrosion Resistance of Welds in Duplex Stainless Steels, *Duplex Stainless Steels '91,* Vol 1, *Les Editions de Physique,* 1991, p 325-346
14. B. Lundquist, P. Norberg, and K. Olsson, "Influence of Different Welding Conditions on Mechanical Properties and Corrosion Resistance of Sandvik SAF 2205 (UNS S31803),"

Paper 10, presented at the Duplex Stainless Steels '86 Conference, the Hague, Netherlands, Oct 1986

15. "Standard Test Methods for Pitting and Crevice Corrosion Resistance of Stainless Steels and Related Alloys by the Use of Ferric Chloride Solution," G 48, *Annual Book of ASTM Standards,* American Society for Testing and Materials

16. N. Sridhar, L.H. Flasche, and J. Kolts, Effect of Welding Parameters on Localized Corrosion of a Duplex Stainless Steel, *Mater. Perform.,* Dec 1984, p 52-55

17. "Standard Specification for Substitute Ocean Water," D 1141, *Annual Book of ASTM Standards, American Society for Testing and Materials*

18. E. Perteneder, J. Tosch, and G. Rabensteiner, "New Welding Filler Metals for the Welding of Girth Welds on Pipelines of Corrosion-Resistant Cr-Ni-Mo-N-Duplex Steels," paper presented at the International Conference on Welding in Energy Related Projects, Toronto, Canada, Welding Institute of Canada, Sept 1983

Contents

Forming

STAINLESS STEELS are blanked, pierced, formed, and drawn using basically the same press tools and machines as those used for other metals. However, because stainless steels have higher strength and are more prone to galling than low-carbon steels, and because they have a surface finish that often must be preserved, the techniques used in the fabrication of sheet metal parts from stainless steels are more exacting than those used for low-carbon steels. In general, stainless steels have the following characteristics, as compared with those of carbon steels:

- Greater strength
- Greater susceptibility to work hardening
- Higher propensity to weld or gall to tooling
- Lower heat conductivity

This article reviews a variety of forming processes applicable to stainless steels. More detailed information on these processes can be found in Volume 14 of the *ASM Handbook*.

Alloy Selection

The properties and selection of stainless steels used in forming operations are discussed in the article "Metallurgy and Properties of Wrought Stainless Steels" in this Volume. General ratings of the relative suitability of the commonly used austenitic, martensitic, and ferritic types of stainless steels for various methods of forming are given in Table 1. These ratings are based on formability and on the power required for forming.

As Table 1 shows, the austenitic and ferritic steels are, almost without exception, well suited to all of the forming methods listed. Of the martensitic steels, however, only types 403, 410, and 414 are generally recommended for cold-forming applications. Because the higher carbon content of the remaining martensitic types severely limits their cold formability, these steels are sometimes formed warm. Warm forming can also be used to advantage with other stainless steels in difficult applications.

Formability. The characteristics of stainless steel that affect its formability include yield strength, tensile strength, ductility (and the effect of work hardening on these properties), and the r value. The composition of stainless steel is also an important factor in formability. Figure 1 compares the effect of cold work on the tensile strength and yield strength of type 301 (an austenitic alloy), types 409 and 430 (ferritic alloys), and 1008 low-carbon steel sheet.

Formability of Austenitic Types. Type 301 stainless steel has the lowest nickel and chromium contents of the standard austenitic types; it also has the highest tensile strength in the annealed condition. The extremely high rate of work hardening of type 301 results in appreciable increases in tensile strength and yield strength with each increase in the amount of cold working, as measured by cold reduction (Fig. 1). This response to work hardening is particularly important for structural parts, including angles and channel sections, which are expected to have additional strength and stiffness after fabrication. On the other hand, for deep-drawing applications, a lower rate of work hardening is usually preferable and can be obtained in the austenitic alloys that have higher nickel contents, notably types 304, 304L, and 305.

In general, the austenitic alloys are more difficult to form as the nickel content or both the nickel and the chromium contents are reduced, as in type 301. Such alloys show increased work-hardening rates and are less suitable for deep drawing or multiple forming operations. The higher carbon content and the presence of the stabilizing elements niobium, titanium, and tantalum also exert an adverse effect on the forming characteristics of the austenitic stainless steels. Therefore, the

Table 1 Relative suitability of stainless steels for various methods of forming

Suitability ratings are based on comparison of the steels within any one class; therefore, it should not be inferred that a ferritic steel with an A rating is more formable than an austenitic steel with a C rating for a particular method. A, excellent; B, good; C, fair; D, not generally recommended

Steel	0.2% yield strength, 6.89 MPa (1 ksi)	Blanking	Piercing	Press-brake forming	Deep drawing	Spinning	Roll forming	Coining	Embossing
Austenitic steels									
201	55	B	C	B	A-B	C-D	B	B-C	B-C
202	55	B	B	A	A	B-C	A	B	B
301	40	B	C	B	A-B	C-D	B	B-C	B-C
302	37	B	B	A	A	B-C	A	B	B
302B	40	B	B	B	B-C	C	...	C	B-C
303, 303(Se)	35	B	B	D(a)	D	D	D	C-D	C
304	35	B	B	A	A	B	A	B	B
304L	30	B	B	A	A	B	A	B	B
305	37	B	B	A	B	A	A	A-B	A-B
308	35	B	...	B(a)	D	D	...	D	D
309, 309S	40	B	B	A(a)	B	C	B	B	B
310, 310S	40	B	B	A(a)	B	B	A	B	B
314	50	B	B	A(a)	B-C	C	B	B	B-C
316	35	B	B	A(a)	B	B	A	B	B
316L	30	B	B	A(a)	B	B	A	B	B
317	40	B	B	A(a)	B	B-C	B	B	B
321, 347, 348	35	B	B	A	B	B-C	B	B	B
Martensitic steels									
403, 410	40	A	A-B	A	A	A	A	A	A
414	95	A	B	A(a)	B	C	C	B	C
416, 416(Se)	40	B	A-B	C(a)	D	D	D	D	C
420	50	B	B-C	C(a)	C-D	D	C-D	C-D	C
431	95	C-D	C-D	C(a)	C-D	D	C-D	C-D	C-D
440A	60	B-C	...	C(a)	C-D	D	C-D	D	C
440B	62	...	...	...	...	D	...	D	D
440C	65	...	...	...	...	D	...	D	D
Ferritic steels									
405	40	A	A-B	A(a)	A	A	A	A	A
409	38	A	A-B	A(a)	A	A	A	A	A
430	45	A	A-B	A(a)	A-B	A	A	A	A
430F, 430F(Se)	55	B	A-B	B-C(a)	D	D	D	C-D	C
442	...	A	A-B	A(a)	B	B-C	A	B	B
446	50	A	B	A(a)	B-C	C	B	B	B

(a) Severe sharp bends should be avoided.

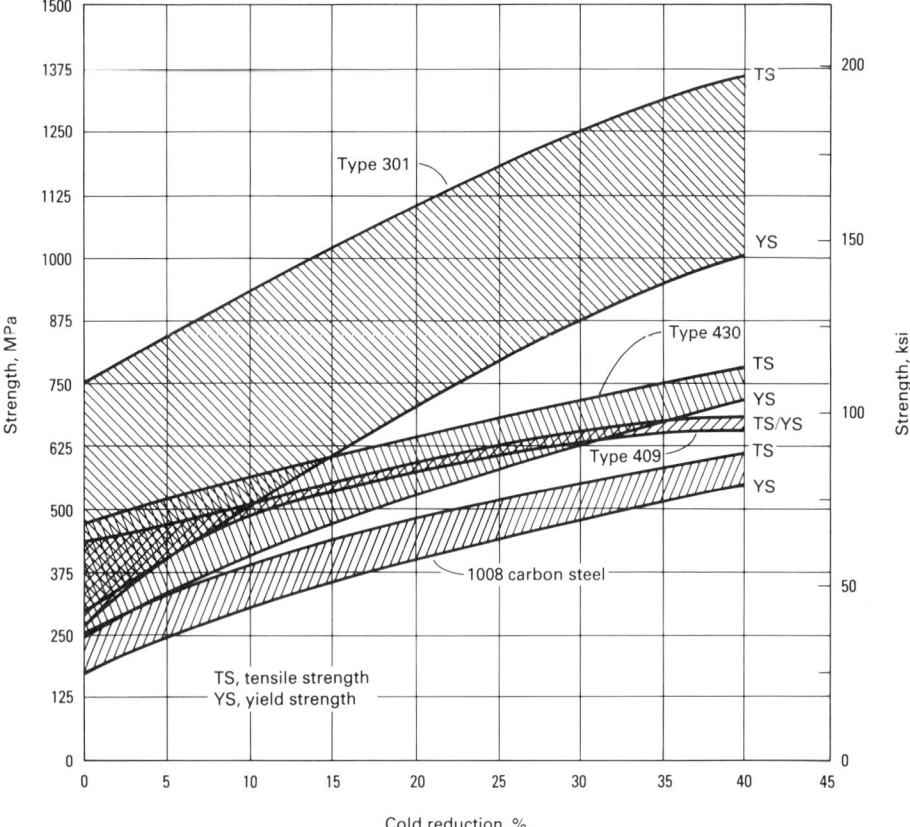

Fig. 1 Comparison of work-hardening qualities of type 301 austenitic stainless steel, types 409 and 430 ferritic stainless steels, and 1008 low-carbon steel

Table 2 Forming and heat treatment temperatures for three duplex stainless steels

Grade	Forming temperature		Annealing temperature		Soaking time, min/mm	Cooling
	°C	°F	°C	°F		
S32304	850/1100	1560/2010	1000	1830	1	Thickness: <15 mm (0.6 in.) air; >15 mm (0.6 in.) water
S31803	900/1150	1650/2100	1040	1905	1	Thickness: <15 mm (0.6 in.) air; >15 mm (0.6 in.) water
S32550	950/1150	1740/2100	1080	1975	2	Water cooling recommended

forming properties of types 321 and 347 stainless steel are less favorable than those of types 302, 304, and 305.

Formability of Ferritic Types. The range between yield strength and tensile strength of types 409 and 430 narrows markedly as cold work increases, as shown in Fig. 1. This response is typical of the ferritic alloys and limits their formability (ductility) when compared to the austenitic alloys. Nevertheless, types 409 and 430, although lacking the formability of type 302, are widely used in applications that require forming by blanking, bending, drawing, or spinning. One of the most important applications for type 430 stainless steel is in automotive trim or molding. Type 409 stainless steel has found wide acceptance as the material of choice in automotive exhaust systems.

Formability of Duplex Types. Duplex stainless steels have about twice the yield strength of most austenitic stainless steels. Their elongation, toughness, and work-hardening rates are generally intermediate compared to those of the usual austenitic and ferritic grades.

Duplex stainless steels can be cold formed and expanded. Their higher strength relative to their austenitic counterparts necessitates greater loads in cold-forming operations. Because elongation is less, they should be formed to more generous radii than fully austenitic materials. Heavily cold-formed (>15%) sections should be fully annealed and quenched whenever applications for the alloy present the possibility of stress-corrosion cracking in the service environment. Full annealing is conducted in the temperature range of 1010 to 1100 °C (1850 to 2010 °F), followed by a rapid cooling.

Hot-forming operations are usually performed in the temperature range of 980 to 1260 °C (1800 to 2300 °F); the preferred temperature range is dictated by the specific alloy composition. The temperature range of about 370 to 925 °C (700 to 1700 °F) should be avoided to preclude the precipitation of such deleterious phases as σ and α'. These phases can adversely affect mechanical properties and corrosion resistance. As with cold forming, hot-formed parts must also be annealed between 950 and 1120 °C (1740 and 2050 °F), depending on the grade, and quenched rapidly in fast-cooling water or forced air (Table 2).

Comparison with Carbon Steel. Curves for 1008 low-carbon steel are included in Fig. 1 as a reference for the evaluation of stainless steels. The decrease in the formability of 1008 steel with cold work appears to fall between that of types 409 and 430 and that of the more formable type 301. Figure 1 also shows that cold work does not increase the strength of 1008 as rapidly as it does that of type 301 and the ferritic alloys.

Stress-Strain Relations. Figure 2 shows load-elongation curves for six types of stainless steel: four austenitic (202, 301, 302, and 304), one martensitic (410), and one ferritic (430). The type of failure in cup drawing of the austenitic types was different from that of types 410 and 430, as shown in Fig. 2. The austenitic types broke in a fairly clean line near the punch nose radius, almost as if the bottom of the drawn cup were blanked out; types 410 and 430 broke in the sidewall in sharp jagged lines, showing extreme brittleness as a result of the severe cold work.

As suggested by the data in Fig. 2, the force required to form type 301 exceeds that required by the other austenitic alloys. In addition, type 301 will develop maximum elongation before failing. Types 410 and 430 require considerably less power to form, but they fail at comparatively low elongation levels.

Forming-limit diagrams, also known as *forming-limit curves,* are direct and useful representations of the formability of stainless steel sheet. These diagrams illustrate the biaxial combinations of strain that can occur without failure.

To construct forming-limit diagrams, an array of circles, often 2.5 mm (0.1 in.) in diameter, is first imprinted by photoprinting, photoetching, or electroetching on the surface of the sheet metal before forming. The individual circles become ellipses wherever deformation occurs, except in areas where pure biaxial stretching occurs. The major and minor axes of the ellipses are compared with the circles of the original grid to determine the major and minor strains at each location. The areas immediately adjacent to failures are of particular concern in evaluating the forming capabilities of the metal. Failure can be defined by several criteria, but the onset of visible necking is the most widely used. The loci of strain combinations that produce failures define the forming-limit curve. The area below this curve encompasses all the combinations of strain that the metal can withstand.

A forming-limit diagram for a variety of stainless steels is shown in Fig. 3. More information on the construction and use of forming-limit dia-

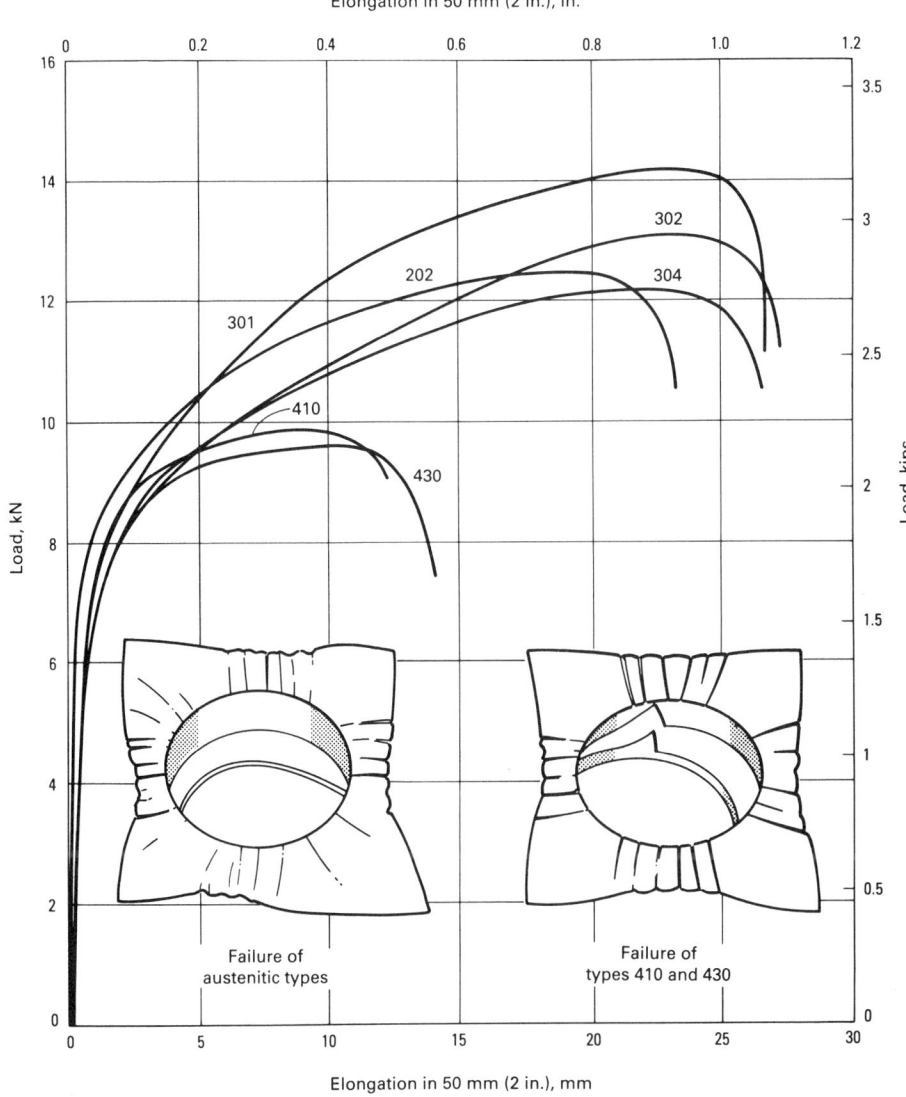

Fig. 2 Comparison of ductility of six stainless steels and of the types of failure resulting from deep drawing

Elongation in 50 mm (2 in.), in.

Elongation in 50 mm (2 in.), mm

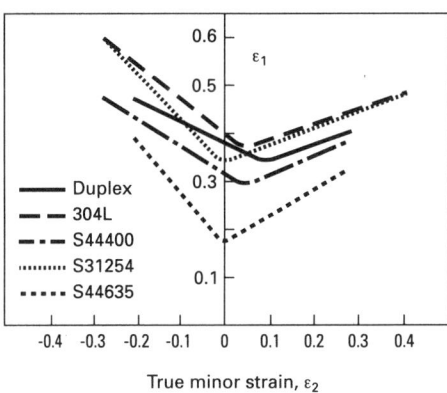

Fig. 3 Forming-limit diagram for five stainless steels

True minor strain, ε_2

Among stainless steel lubricants for severe drawing applications, the extreme-pressure additive types are the most desirable. Additives of chlorine or sulfur tend to react chemically with the steel surface at higher temperatures and form a readily shearable compound. Chlorine is the more popular additive, because sulfur tends to react with some steel tooling.

Mineral oils, soap solutions, and water emulsions of general-purpose soluble oils are omitted because they are ineffective in most forming of stainless. The recommended lubricants are discussed further in the sections of this article that deal with individual forming processes.

As a precaution, all lubricants should be removed and the parts thoroughly dried after completion of the sheet metalworking operation. Most lubricants must be removed before the formed parts are heat treated; this applies particularly to those containing insoluble solids, sulfur, or chlorine. In addition, certain metastable austenitic stainless alloys can react with their lubricant and cause delayed cracking in heavily strained areas. Rapid removal of the lubricant is thus desirable.

grams is available in the article "Process Modeling and Simulation for Sheet Forming" in Volume 14 of the *ASM Handbook*.

Power requirements for the forming of stainless steel, because of its high yield strength, are greater than those for low-carbon steel. In general, twice as much power is used in forming stainless steel. Because the austenitic steels work harden rapidly in cold-forming operations, the need for added power after the start of initial deformation is greater than that for the ferritic steels. The ferritic steels behave much like plain carbon steels once deformation begins, although higher power is also needed to start plastic deformation.

Lubrication

Lubrication requirements are more critical in forming stainless steels than in forming carbon and alloy steels, because of the general need to preserve the high-quality surface on stainless steels and because of their higher strength, greater

hardness, lower thermal conductivity, and higher coefficient of friction. In forming stainless steels, galling and spalling occur more readily, and higher temperatures are reached in a larger volume of the workpiece. Local or general overheating can change the properties of the work metal and lubricant.

Table 3 lists the lubricants ordinarily used in forming stainless steel by various processes. Except for the special-purpose lubricants graphite and molybdenum disulfide, the lubricants are listed in the approximate order of increasing ability to reduce galling and friction. The ratings in Table 3 also consider other suitability factors such as cleanliness and ease of removal. The desirable characteristics of a lubricant include the ability to reduce friction and wear, heat dissipation, durability, nonreactiveness with the base steel, and ease of removal. The higher temperatures generated when forming stainless alloys, particularly the austenitic varieties, frequently lead to breakdown of the polar lubricant molecules.

Blanking and Piercing

The shear strength of stainless steel is about twice that of low-carbon steel. Therefore, the available force for the blanking or piercing of stainless steel should be 50 to 100% higher than that for equivalent work on carbon steel.

Tools and power can be saved if the stock can be blanked at about 175 °C (350 °F). The finish will be better as well. Power requirements can also be reduced by using angular shear on the punch or the die.

Die Materials. Cutting edges must be of a hard, strong material. Recommended die materials, in order of suitability for increasing quantities, include O1, A2, D2, and D4 tool steels and carbide. The use of carbide for high-volume production in applications that do not require the impact resistance of tool steels is illustrated in the following example.

Example 1: Use of a Carbide Die to Form a Miniature Piece. The cathode shown in Fig. 4 was produced in a three-stage progressive carbide

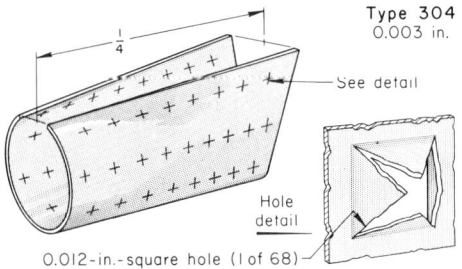

Fig. 4 Cathode produced in a progressive die with carbide tools. Dimensions given in inches

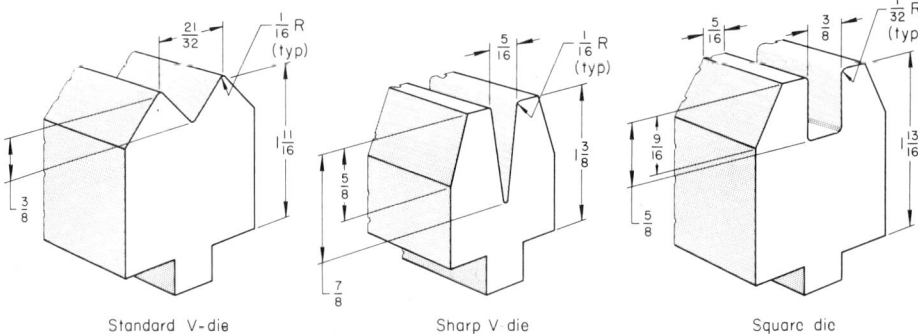

Fig. 5 Typical dies for press-brake forming of stainless steel sheet up to 0.9 mm (0.035 in.) thick. Dimensions given in inches

die by piercing, blanking, and forming. The piece was trough-shaped, 6.4 mm (¼ in.) long, and it was made of 0.08 mm (0.003 in.) thick type 304 stainless steel. One end was rounded, and the other was V-shape. The difference in contour of the two ends kept the pieces from stacking. Before forming, the blank was 9.5 mm (⅜ in.) wide. The piece was pierced with 68 holes, each 0.31 mm (0.012 in.) square. In this operation, the material was displaced by a pointed punch instead of being removed by a flat-nose punch. The pieces were cut from 152 mm (6 in.) wide strip, producing 16 pieces at a stroke. The 130 kN (15 tonf) mechanical press ran at 240 strokes/minute.

Clearance between punch and die should be about the same as that for the blanking and piercing of cold-rolled low-carbon steel. Some manufacturers use less than 0.03 mm (0.001 in.) per side; others specify 5 to 10% of stock thickness per side for sheet and 10 to 15% of stock thickness for plates and bars. Studies have shown, however, that larger clearances—12.5 to 13.5%, and even up to 42%, of stock thickness—have resulted in increased die life.

Cutting edges should be carefully aligned, sharp, clean, and free of burrs. The importance of sharp cutting edges cannot be overemphasized.

Deburring. Generally, stainless steel does not shear clean; shearing leaves a rough work-hardened edge that is dangerous to handle and may adversely affect subsequent operations. Flat pieces can be rolled or pressed between dies adjusted exactly to the thickness of the stock, or the burrs can be removed by grinding, stoning, or filing.

Lubrication. The blanking and piercing of stainless is often done dry, but the lubricants indicated in Table 3 are sometimes used to prolong die life. Lubricants containing sulfur or chlorine are the most effective for this purpose. Emulsions are used for high-speed work.

Dimensions. Pierced holes should not be smaller than the thickness of the stock. Holes larger than 3.18 mm (⅛ in.) should be spaced so that the distance between centers is not less than 1½ times the hole diameter. Small holes should have a distance between centers of at least 1¾ times the diameter of the holes. Holes should never be closer together than one stock thickness, nor should the edge of a blank be less than one stock thickness from the edge of the stock. For progressive-die operation, edge distances should be between 1½ and 2 times the stock thickness.

Nibbling. In some applications, an irregular contour is cut out by punching a series of overlapping holes along the contour. This process is called nibbling. A variety of unusual shapes can be cut at 300 to 900 strokes/min by a press equipped with either a round or rectangular punch.

Press-Brake Forming

All of the austenitic stainless steels in the soft condition can be bent 180° over one stock thickness, but they need up to 50% more power to form than that required by low-carbon steel. Springback is more severe with austenitic stainless steels than with low-carbon steel and must be allowed for. Work-hardened austenitic steel can be press-brake formed only to a very limited degree. If austenitic stainless steel is heated to about 65 °C (150 °F), it can be formed with appreciably less power than that required when it is cold, and yet it can be handled easily.

The straight-chromium grades of stainless steels vary in their response to press-brake forming. The low-carbon stainless steels containing 12 to 17% Cr bend readily, but, like the austenitic steels, they need more power for bending than that required for low-carbon steel. High-chromium, low-carbon types, such as 446, bend better when heated to 175 to 205 °C (350 to 400 °F). The heating of these high-chromium, low-carbon grades tends to lower the yield strength but can simultaneously aid in allowing the forming to be done above the brittle-to-ductile transition temperature. For these alloys, that temperature can be at or above room temperature, depending on thickness. In room-temperature forming, the highly alloyed ferritic stainless steels have been known to benefit from slower bend speeds, which minimize the possibility of an impactlike load and resultant brittle fracture. High-carbon heat-treatable stainless steels are not recommended for press-brake forming, even if in the annealed condition.

Typical bending limits for the major stainless steels are shown in Table 4. A completely flat bend can generally be made in the 18-8 and similar alloys.

Dies. Press brakes can use dies with cross sections such as those shown in Fig. 5 for forming

Table 3 Suitability of various lubricants for use in the forming of stainless steel

Ratings consider effectiveness, cleanliness, ease of removal, and other suitability factors. A, excellent; B, good; C, acceptable; NR, not recommended

Lubricant	Blanking and piercing	Press-brake forming	Press forming	Multiple-slide forming	Deep drawing	Spinning	Drop-hammer forming	Contour roll forming	Embossing
Fatty oils and blends(a)	C	B	C	A	C	A	C	B	B
Soap-fat pastes(b)	NR	NR	C	A	B	B	C	B	C
Wax-base pastes(b)	B	B	B	A	B	B	C	B	A
Heavy-duty emulsions(c)	B	NR	B	A	B	B	NR	A	B
Dry film (wax, or soap plus borax)	B	B	B	NR	B	A	B	NR	A
Pigmented pastes(b)(d)	B	NR	A	B	A	C	NR	NR	NR
Sulfurized or sulfochlorinated oils(e)	A	A	B+	A	C	NR	A	B	A
Chlorinated oils or waxes(b)									
High-viscosity types(g)	A(h)	NR	A	NR	A	NR	A(j)	A	NR
Low-viscosity types(k)	B+	A	A	A	B	NR	A(j)	A	A
Graphite or molybdenum disulfide(m)	NR	(n)	(n)	NR	(n)	NR	(n)	NR	NR

(a) Vegetable or animal types: mineral oil is used for blending. (b) May be diluted with water. (c) Water emulsions of soluble oils; contain a high concentration of extreme-pressure sulfur or chlorine compounds. (d) Chalk (whiting) is commonest pigment: others sometimes used. (e) Extreme-pressure types; may contain some mineral or fatty oil. (f) Extreme-pressure chlorinated mineral oils or waxes; may contain emulsifiers for ease of removal in water-base cleaners. (g) Viscosity of 4000 to 20 000 SUS (Saybolt Universal seconds, see ASTM D 2161 for more detailed information). (h) For heavy plate. (j) For cold forming only. (k) Viscosity (200 to 1000 SUS) is influenced by base oil or wax, degree of chlorination, and additions of mineral oil. (m) Solid lubricant applied from dispersions in oil, solvent, or water. (n) For hot-forming applications only

Table 4 Typical bending limits for six commonly formed stainless steels

	Minimum bend radius		
	Annealed to 4.75 mm (0.187 in.) thick (180° bend)	Quarter hard, cold rolled	
Type		To 1.27 mm (0.050 in.) thick (180° bend)	1.30-4.75 mm (0.051-0.187 in.) thick (90° bend)
301, 302, 304	$\frac{1}{2}t$	$\frac{1}{2}t$	$1t$
316	$\frac{1}{2}t$	$1t$	$1t$
410, 430	$1t$	...	...

t, stock thickness

Table 5 Springback of three austenitic stainless steels bent 90° to various radii

	Springback for bend radius of:		
Steel and temper	$1t$	$6t$	$20t$
302 and 304, annealed	2°	4°	15°
301, half-hard	4°	13°	43°

t, stock thickness

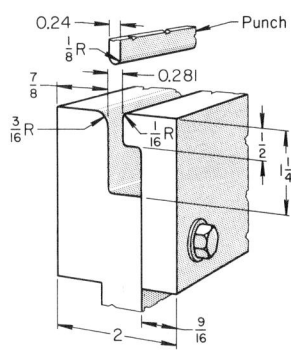

Fig. 6 Adjustable press-brake die for forming 180° bends in stainless steel sheet. Setup can be used for forming bends to 3.2 mm (0.12 in.) inside radius in sheet 0.30 to 0.46 mm (0.012 to 0.018 in.) thick, and it will produce 4.0 mm ($\frac{5}{32}$ in.) radius bends in half-hard stainless steel. The detachable side of die can be shimmed for bending thicker sheet or for bending with larger-radius punches. Dimensions given in inches

stainless steel in sheets up to 0.89 mm (0.035 in.) thick. An adjustable die, such as that shown in Fig. 6, can be used for forming 180° bends in stainless steel sheet 0.30 to 0.46 mm (0.012 to 0.018 in.) thick.

Springback is a function of the strength of the material, the radius and angle of bend, and the thickness of the stock; the thicker the stock, the less severe the problem. Table 5 shows the relationship between radius of bend and springback for three austenitic stainless steels. Ferritic steels usually exhibit less springback than austenitic steels, because the rate of work hardening of ferritic steels is lower. As a practical guide, the amount of springback is normally proportional to (0.2YS + UTS)/2 where YS is the abbreviation for *yield strength* and UTS is the abbreviation for *ultimate tensile strength*.

Springback can be controlled by reducing the punch radius, by coining the line of bend (if the shape of the die is such that bottoming is feasible), and by overbending. For overbending, it is sometimes necessary only to make the punch angle smaller than the desired final angle of the workpiece, as in the following example.

Example 2: Setting a Flange Angle in a Press Brake. The bracket shown in Fig. 7 was preformed in a U-die from a developed blank of type 302 stainless steel, half-hard and 1.0 mm (0.040 in.) thick. Only the punch angle needed to be reduced to set the angle on the flange.

As the bracket came from the U-die, the springback in each flange was 15°. To correct this spread, the piece was put in a restrike die in a press brake, which set each angle separately. The restrike die angle was 90° with a 3.2 mm ($\frac{1}{8}$ in.) radius. The restrike punch was made to an angle of 86° with a 2.4 mm ($\frac{3}{32}$ in.) radius to coin the bend, so that the flanges would form to 90 ± 1°.

The lubricant was a water-soluble pigmented drawing compound. The workpiece was degreased after forming.

Lubricants. For ordinary press-brake operations (chiefly bending and simple forming), lubricants are not used as frequently as with higher-speed press operations. Convenience of use is a major factor in selecting lubricants for this type of press-brake forming. Pigmented lubricants are not favored, and cooling effectiveness is of little significance at low production rates. For severe forming and for operations that would ordinarily be done in a press, if available, the recommendations in the "Press-brake forming" column in Table 3 apply.

Applications of press-brake forming are described in the following examples. Repetitive bends, as in corrugated stock, are frequently made one at a time in a press brake if the quantity of production is not sufficient to warrant a special die, as in the example below.

Example 3: Press-Brake Forming of Corrugations. The corrugated sheet shown in Fig. 8 was formed from 0.41 mm (0.016 in.) thick, full-hard type 302 stainless steel. The finished sheets,

after bending, were 419 mm (16$\frac{1}{2}$ in.) long, as shown, but the width, w, varied according to the use of the piece.

The corrugations were made one at a time by air bending in the tooling shown at the lower right in Fig. 8. Pilot holes in the workpiece and locating pins in the punch helped to keep the workpiece aligned. Deviation from flatness in the pieces was corrected by restriking some of the bends.

Irregular contours on long, narrow parts are conveniently produced by bending in a press brake. Because of the strength of stainless steels, the forming often must be divided among several successive operations, as in the example below.

Example 4: Forming of Stainless Steel Handrails in a Press Brake. Figure 9 illustrates the shapes produced in five successive operations that were required for forming a handrail from 1.57 mm (0.062 in.) thick type 304 stainless steel. Because of flatness requirements and the resistance of the metal to bending, a 3600 kN (400 tonf) press brake was used.

Forming the 1.6 mm ($\frac{1}{16}$ in.) radius beads (operation 1, Fig. 9) was particularly troublesome because of the difficulty in retaining flatness. A

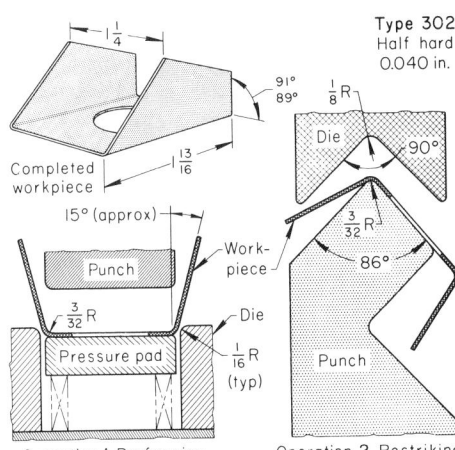

Fig. 7 Production of a U-shape bracket from a developed blank by preforming, and restriking to set flange angles, in a press brake. Dimensions given in inches

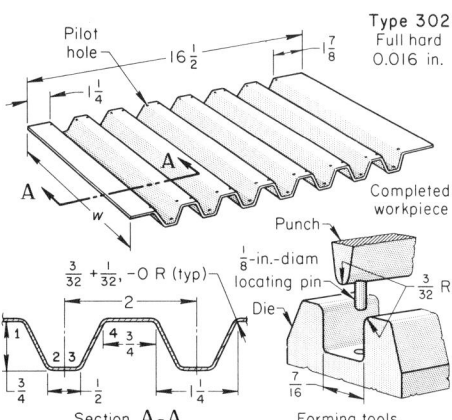

Fig. 8 Corrugated sheet in which corrugations were formed one at a time in a press brake, using tools shown. Dimensions given in inches

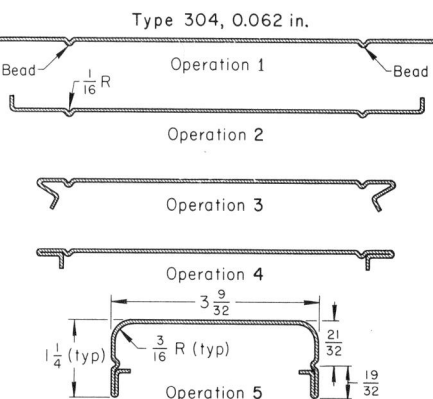

Fig. 9 Shapes progressively produced in the five-operation forming of a handrail in a 3600 kN (400 tonf) press brake. Dimensions given in inches

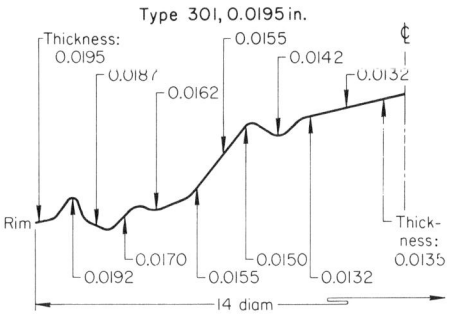

Fig. 10 Profile of a press-formed automobile wheel cover showing thinning purposely produced by severe stretching. Dimensions given in inches

force of 5300 kN (600 tonf), which exceeded the rating of the press brake, was used to form the beads.

The second and third operations presented no problems, but the fourth operation was difficult because the workpiece had to be held without marring the polished surface. Similar parts were produced from low-carbon steel without difficulty.

Press Forming

Stainless steels are press formed with the same kind of equipment as that used in the forming of low-carbon steel. However, although all stainless steels are not the same in strength or ductility, they all require more power for forming than do carbon steels. In general, presses should have the capacity for 100% more ram force than that needed for equivalent work in low-carbon steel, and frames should have the rigidity and bulk necessary to withstand this greater force.

Dies. In addition to wearing out faster, dies may fracture more readily when used with stainless steel than when used with low-carbon or medium-carbon steel. This is because of the greater forces needed for the working of stainless steel.

For the longest service in mass production, the wearing parts of the dies should be made of carbide, D2 tool steel, or high-strength aluminum bronze. Carbide can last ten times as long as most tool steels, but it is more expensive and does not have the shock resistance of tool steels and aluminum bronze. Tool steels such as D2 are preferred when resistance to both shock and wear is required.

Aluminum bronze offers the most protection against galling and scuffing of the workpiece. An oil-hardening tool steel such as O2 can be used for short production runs.

Austenitic Alloys. Workpieces can be stretched by applying high blankholder pressures to the flange areas to prevent metal from flowing into the die. This causes severe thinning, but work hardening may cause the thinned metal to be as strong as or stronger than the thicker unworked sections. Figure 10 shows a section of an automobile wheel cover made of type 301 stainless steel; the central portion was purposely thinned and work hardened by stretching. In the following example, one of the principal reasons for stressing

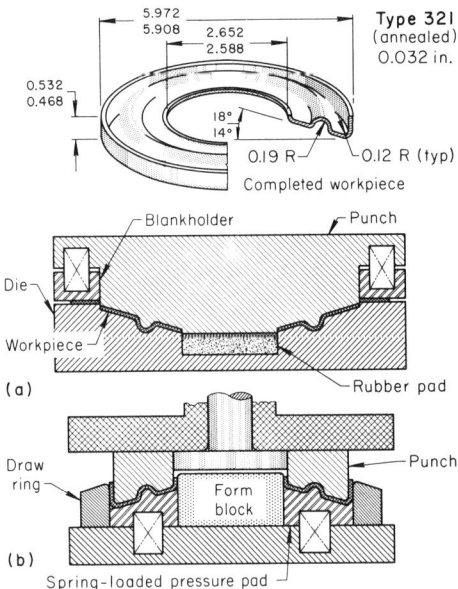

Fig. 11 Severe forming of an austenitic stainless steel aircraft muffler header to produce work hardening that would increase the rigidity and fatigue strength of the part. Dimensions given in inches

the workpiece to the limits of formability was to work harden it for increased strength.

Example 5: Severe Forming for Intentional Work Hardening. The material for a muffler header (Fig. 11) for a small aircraft engine was intentionally stressed nearly to the limits of formability to increase rigidity and to impart the necessary fatigue strength. The headers were made in two operations in a 530 kN (60 tonf) open-back-inclinable mechanical press having a 127 mm (5 in.) stroke. Each operation used a tool steel die hardened to 59 to 62 HRC. Production was 400 pieces/month.

The first die (Fig. 11a) was a compound die that formed the dish of the part, formed the bead in the dish, and blanked the inside and outside diameters. The blankholder at the outer edge of the workpiece was spring loaded, and a rubber pad supported the inner surface of the workpiece against the center blanking punch. The sequence was programmed so that the forming was completed before the outside and inside diameters were blanked, thus making the flange dimensions more accurate and concentric than would have otherwise been possible. Die life was approximately 20,000 pieces.

The second die (Fig. 11b) formed both the inner (stretch) flange and the outer (compression) flange. A spring-loaded pressure pad maintained the correct gripping pressure against the muffler-header body during this operation.

The blank was annealed type 321 stainless steel 0.81 mm (0.032 in.) thick, sheared to 216 mm (8½ in.) square. The bead formed in the first die was used as a locating surface in the second die. The dies were brushed with oil between pieces.

The production rate for both operations was seven pieces/min. Setup time for the first operation was 0.17 h; for the second operation, 0.31 h.

Stretching. Stainless steel has high ductility but wrinkles easily in compression. Therefore, if

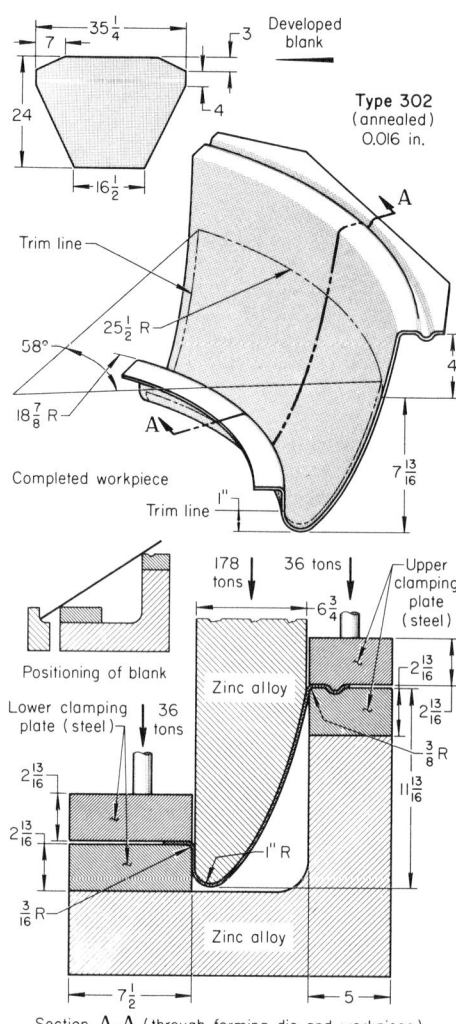

Fig. 12 Tools and clamping plates for controlling metal flow in press forming the part shown. Dimensions given in inches

there is a choice in the direction of metal flow during forming, a better part is likely to be produced by stretching than by compression, as described in the following example.

Example 6: Use of Clamping Plates and Bead to Control Metal Flow. The dome section shown in Fig. 12 was formed from a tapered blank of annealed type 302 stainless steel in a 2200 kN (250 tonf) double-action hydraulic press. It was desirable to maximize metal flow from the narrow end of the blank in order to cause stretching rather than contraction in the metal and thus avoid wrinkles.

The dies could not be oriented to let the blank lie flat, because of the necessity for forming the reentrant angle next to the lower clamping plates. Both the upper and the lower edges of the blank were held between steel plates during forming. The clamping force on each pair of plates was 320 kN (36 tonf). Because the upper plates were twice as long as the lower and two-thirds as wide, the clamping force was distributed over a larger area and could have permitted most of the metal flow from the larger end, with attendant wrinkling of

Table 6 Production rates and labor time for making a severely drawn shell

Operation	Production, pcs/h	Labor per 100 pcs, h
Blank and draw(a)	922	0.108
Restrike(a)	1429	0.070
Pierce center hole; trim(b)	845	0.118
Pierce side holes(c)	786	0.127

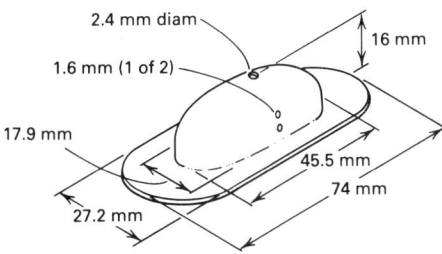

(a) In a compound die, in a 400 kN (45 tonf) mechanical press with an air cushion. (b) In a 200 kN (22 tonf) mechanical press. (c) In a horn die in a 200 kN (22 tonf) mechanical press

the work metal. The addition of a bead to the upper clamping plates improved holding at that end and caused most of the metal flow to occur at the small end of the blank. The application of a fatty-acid-type, nonpigmented drawing compound to the lower plates further encouraged metal flow from the small end of the blank. Scrap loss because of tearing over the relatively sharp lower die radius was 3%.

Ferritic Alloys. The formability of ferritic stainless steels, particularly the higher-chromium types, can be improved by warm forming at 120 to 200 °C (250 to 400 °F), rather than cold forming. The metal is more ductile at the higher temperatures, and less power is needed in forming. Some pieces that cannot be made by cold forming can be successfully made by warm forming.

Lubrication. The lubricant used most often in the press forming of stainless steel is the chlorinated type. It has unexcelled chemical extreme-pressure activity, and its ability to adjust this activity and viscosity independently over an extremely wide range makes it the most versatile lubricant for this purpose. All chlorinated lubricants are readily removable by degreasers or solvents, and emulsifiers can be added to them for easy removal by water-based cleaners.

As shown in Table 3, pigmented pastes, sulfurized or sulfochlorinated oils, and dry wax or soap-borax films are also highly effective lubricants for press forming but are less convenient to use. Heavy-duty emulsions, because of their superior characteristics as coolants, are preferred for high-speed operations. In the following example, high chlorine content and high viscosity were needed to produce acceptable parts. (See also Example 15, in which a low-viscosity, chlorine-base lubricant replaced a viscous mineral oil.)

Example 7: Increase in Chlorine Content and Viscosity of a Lubricant That Improved Forming Results. A wheel cover was made from a type 302 stainless steel blank, 457 mm (18 in.) in diameter by 0.71 mm (0.028 in.) thick, in two operations: draw, then trim and pierce. At first, a lightly chlorinated oil (10% Cl) of medium viscosity (1500 SUS [Saybolt Universal seconds], at 40 °C, or 100 °F) was used in drawing. Even though the draw was shallow, 12% of the wheel covers were rejected for splits and scratches.

A change was made to a highly chlorinated oil (36% Cl) of much higher viscosity (4000 SUS at 40 °C, or 100 °F). As a result, the rejection rate decreased to less than 1%.

Combined Operations in Compound and Progressive Dies

Both compound and progressive dies must be made of die materials that are hard enough to

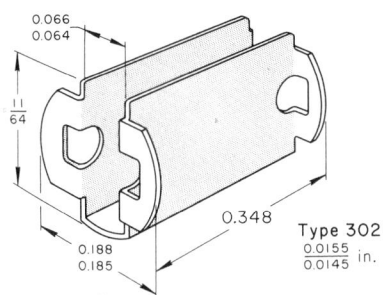

Fig. 13 Bracket that was made by hand feeding stock into a progressive die to avoid the jamming that would have been likely from automatic feeding. Dimensions given in inches

withstand the most severe demands of blanking and tough enough for the most severe forming or coining operations. The lubricant must have enough body for the most severe draw, yet it must be light enough not to interfere with the production of coined or embossed details or to gum up cutting edges. In a compound die in a double-action press, two draws can be made in stainless steel if the press capacity is not exceeded. The following example demonstrates the near-maximum severity of forming that can be achieved in a blank-and-draw compound die.

Example 8: Blanking and Severe Drawing in One Operation in a Compound Die. The shell illustrated in Table 6 was blanked and drawn in a severe forming operation in a compound die at the rate of 16,000 pieces/year. The die was used in a 400 kN (45 tonf) mechanical press with an air cushion. The formed piece was restruck in the same die to sharpen the draw radius and to flatten the flange within 0.15 mm (0.006 in.). The die was made of A2 tool steel and had a life of 50,000 pieces/grind. An emulsified chlorinated concentrate was used as a lubricant.

After forming, the piece was moved to a 200 kN (22 tonf) mechanical press, in which the 2.4

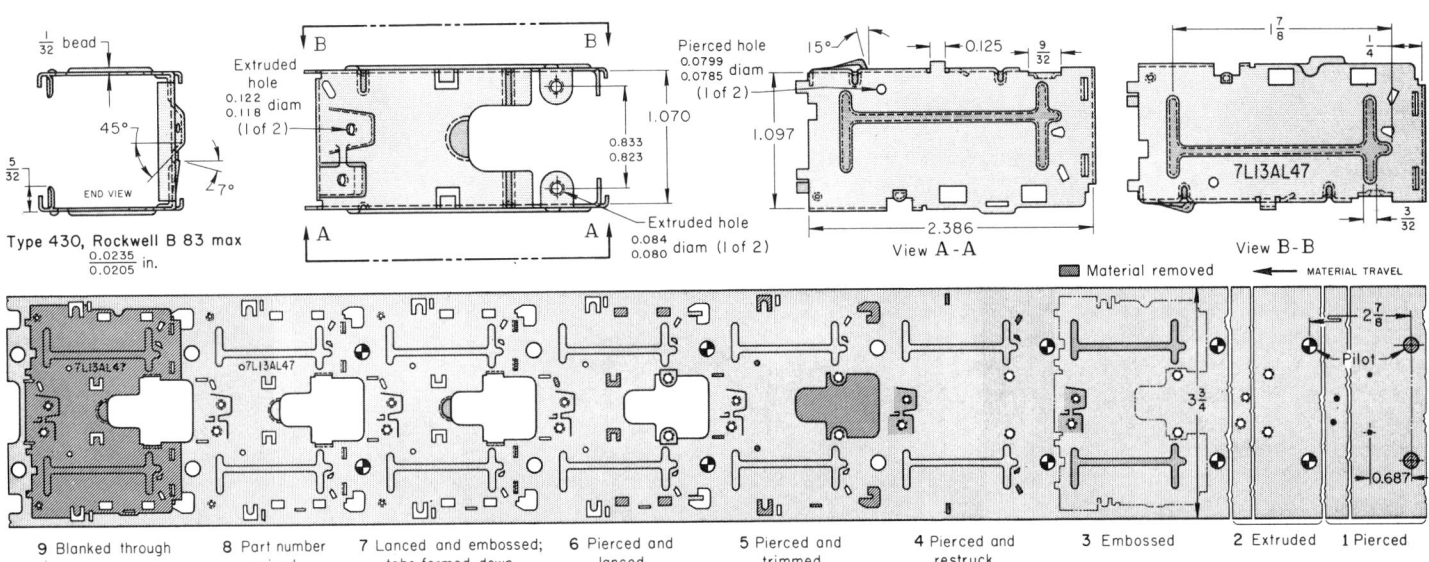

Fig. 14 Frame produced in a nine-station progressive die in the sequence of operations indicated on the strip development shown. Final forming was done in separate dies. Dimensions given in inches

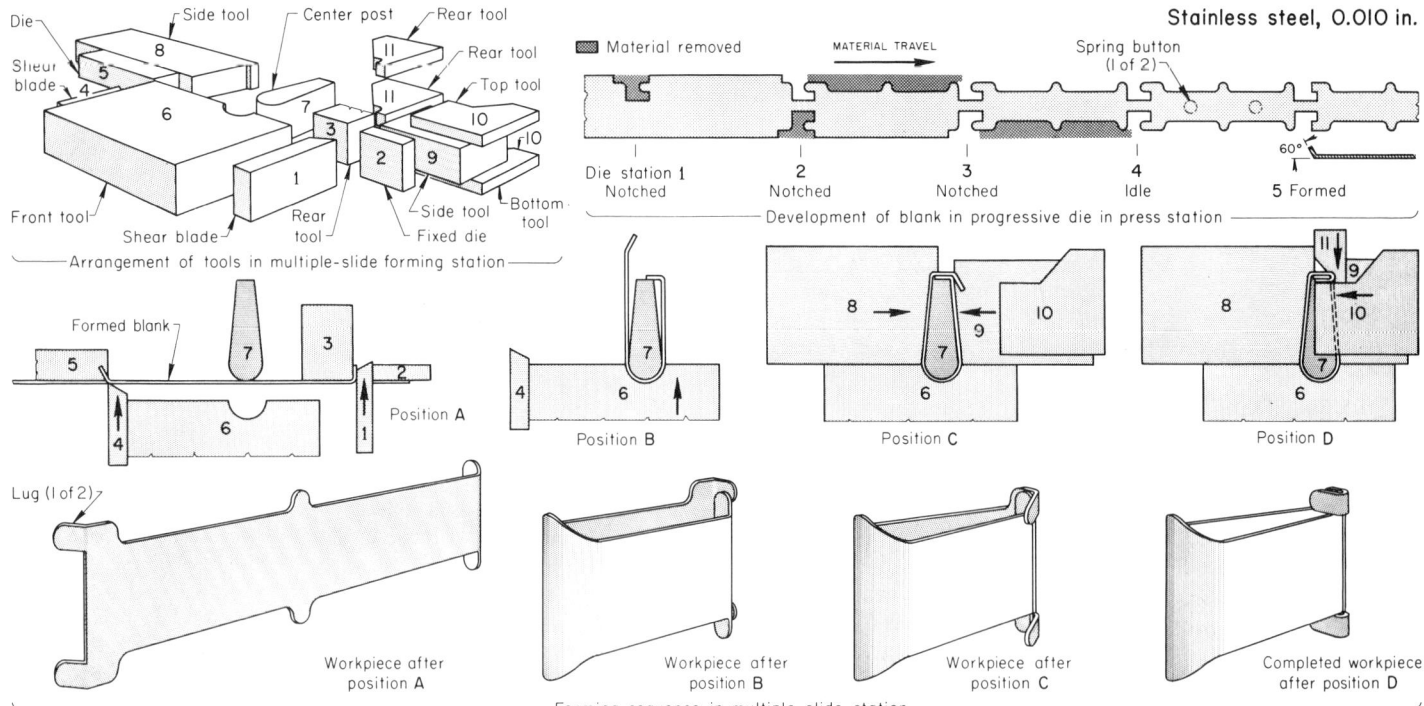

Fig. 15 Operations in the forming of a wristband link in a multiple-slide machine

mm (0.093 in.) diameter hole was pierced and the flange was trimmed to an oval shape. A second piercing operation, in a horn die in a 200 kN (22 tonf) mechanical press, pierced two 1.6 mm (0.062 in.) diameter holes in the side of the shell. Air ejection was used in all operations except the final piercing, where the piece was picked off.

The material was type 302 stainless steel, 0.94 mm (0.037 in.) thick and 57 mm (2¼ in.) wide, which had been annealed. Table 6 lists the production rate and labor time for each of the four operations.

Small, complex parts that must be made in large quantities are well suited to production in progressive or transfer dies. A transfer die uses a minimum of material and can accept coil stock, loose blanks, or partially formed parts. Scrap removal problems are lessened. A progressive die is preferred when the piece can remain attached to the strip.

In the following example, piercing, blanking, and forming were combined in a seven-stage progressive die. Although progressive, it was hand fed—a rather unusual combination.

Example 9: Producing a Small Bracket in a Progressive Die with Hand Feeding. The small bracket shown in Fig. 13 was made in a seven-station progressive die from 9.5 mm (⅜ in.) wide stock that was hand fed into the 50 kN (6 tonf) press. Hand feeding was done because close operator attention was required to prevent jamming, which would have damaged the frail dies. The sequence of operations was as follows:

- Feed strip to finger stop; pierce
- Feed to notch-die opening; pierce
- Notch and trim lugs
- Form lugs

- Form and cut off
- Unload by blast of air

The parts were barrel finished to remove burrs and to provide a smooth finish and high luster. The production rate was 2175 pieces/h. Annual production was 2 million pieces. A chlorinated and inhibited oil was used as a lubricant.

Progressive Dies versus Simple Dies. There is often a choice as to whether a stainless steel piece is to be made in a progressive die or in a series of single-operation (simple) dies. Deep forming usually presents difficulties in designing and constructing efficient and long-life progressive dies. The cost and delay involved in developing progressive tooling was justified for producing the frame described in the following example in quantities of 100,000 or more per year.

Example 10: Use of Progressive Dies for High-Quantity Production of Frames. The frame shown in Fig. 14 was made of 0.56 mm (0.022 in.) thick type 430 stainless steel coil stock, 95.3 mm (3¾ in.) wide. The maximum hardness was 83 HRB.

A nine-station progressive die was used to pierce and flange the holes, to emboss the stiffening beads on the two legs, to trim and form the tabs, to coin identification data, and to blank the part from the strip. Stops were then lanced and formed, and bottom flanges were formed in a forming die. A final forming die was used for the deep side flanges.

The progressive die was run in a 670 kN (75 tonf) mechanical press at a rate of 5000 pieces/h. The first and second forming dies were run in a 270 kN (30 tonf) press at speeds of 984 and 936 pieces/h, respectively.

Annual production was 90,000 frames, and demand was expected to increase. This, in addition to the short press time (0.2284 h/100 pieces, compared to an estimated 0.6665 h/100 pieces if produced in eight separate dies) and the greater accuracy obtainable in the progressive die, justified the higher tooling cost for the progressive-die method (60% higher when compared to separate dies).

The dies were made of A2 tool steel and had a life of 50,000 to 75,000 pieces between regrinds. The lubricant was an emulsifiable chlorinated oil concentrate.

Multiple-Slide Forming

Small high-production stainless steel parts can sometimes be formed in multiple-slide machines with the same kinds of tools as those used for the forming of low-carbon steel. The following example describes the forming of a link for a flexible expanding wristband.

Example 11: Multiple-Slide Forming of a Wristband Link. The workpiece shown in Fig. 15, a link for an expanding wristband, was formed in a multiple-slide machine from stainless steel strip 0.25 mm (0.010 in.) thick by 8.99 mm (0.354 in.) wide, and it was locked in shape by bent lugs. The production rate was 6000 pieces/h.

The blank for the link was made in a five-station progressive die mounted in the press station of the machine. As shown in the upper-right corner of Fig. 15, the strip was notched in stations 1, 2, and 3 by four small heeled punches. For support against side thrust, the heels entered the die before engaging the stock. An air blast entering through holes in the punches removed the scrap in order to protect the die and the feed mechanisms. In the fifth die station, two lugs on the blank were bent 60°. Spring-actuated lifters stripped the blank from the bending section of the die after the lugs were bent. The workpieces were held together by a narrow strip of stock that was left to index the workpiece through the stations of the progressive die.

The blank was then fed to the forming station so that it was edge-up between the center post (7) and the front tool (6), as shown in position A in Fig. 15. As the blank entered the forming station, the center post moved upward into the forming position. The shear blade (1) then moved forward against the fixed die (2) to trim off the joining strip. The shear blade (1) also bent the end of the blank against the auxiliary rear tool (3), which then retracted. The other end of the blank was cut off by the shear blade (4) against the die (5). After the blank was cut off by the shear blade (4), the front tool (6) bent the workpiece around the center post (7), as shown in position B in Fig. 15.

In position C, the workpiece was formed on the center post by the side tools (8 and 9) while still being held by the front tool (6). The front tool was wide enough to form the full width of the workpiece, including the lugs, but the side tools (8 and 9) were narrower, leaving exposed the top and bottom lugs that had been formed in the last press-die station.

In position D, the front and side tools (6, 8, and 9) held the part against the center post (7), while the rear tools (11) flattened the top and bottom lugs against the center post. The center post was then lowered from the workpiece. The side tool (9), which was spring loaded, slid between the top and bottom tools (10), permitting them to advance to form the top and bottom lugs into a U-shape. The side tool (9) held the workpiece against the front and side tools (6 and 8), while the top tools (10) tucked in the lugs.

With all the other tools holding the closed position against the workpiece, the rear tools (11) moved slightly to press the lugs closed against the top tools (10). As the tools opened, the completed link was then ejected by an air jet.

Deep Drawing

The percentages of reduction obtainable in deep drawing range from 40 to 60% for the chromium-nickel (austenitic) stainless steels of best drawability and from 40 to 55% for the straight-chromium (ferritic) grades (percentage of reduction = $[(D - d)/D] \times 100$, where D is the diameter of the blank and d is the inside diameter of the drawn piece). The amount of reduction obtainable varies greatly with the radius of the die and to a lesser extent with the radius of the punch nose. As the die radius decreases, the drawability decreases, as shown in Table 7 for austenitic stainless steel. Typically used punch and die radii are five to ten times the metal thickness. With the ferritic grades, drawability and ductility usually decrease with increasing chromium content. To offset this, steels with high chromium contents are often warmed moderately before drawing.

Table 7 Effect of die radius on percentage of reduction obtainable in the deep drawing of austenitic stainless steel

Percentage of reduction = $[(D - d)/D] \times 100$, where D is the diameter of blank, and d is the inside diameter of the drawn piece

Die radius(a)	Reduction in drawing, %
15t	50-60
10t	40-50
5t	30-40
2t	0-10

(a) t, stock thickness

Presses used for the deep drawing of stainless steel differ only in power and rigidity from those used for low-carbon steel. Because of the higher work-hardening rate of stainless steel and its inherent higher strength, presses used for the deep drawing of stainless steel often need 100% more ram force and the necessary frame stiffness to support this greater force.

Dies for drawing stainless steel must be able to withstand the high force and resist galling. For ordinary service, D2 tool steel dies give a good combination of hardness and toughness. On long runs, carbide draw rings have exceptionally long life. Where friction and galling are the principal problems, draw rings are sometimes made of high-strength aluminum bronze. The following example describes an application in which the selection of tool material was critical in order to avoid scoring of the workpiece and to obtain acceptable die life in drawing.

Example 12: Use Of A Carbide Blank-and-Draw Ring. An orifice cup, 25 mm (1 in.) in diameter by 11 mm ($^7/_{16}$ in.) deep, was blanked and drawn in one operation. A 1.35 mm (0.053 in.) diameter orifice was pierced in the cup in a second operation. The specifications called for the sides of the cup to be free of score marks from the die. The blank was 40.0 mm (1.575 in.) in diameter, cut from 0.97 mm (0.038 in.) thick type 302 stainless steel strip 50 mm (2 in.) wide.

The blank-and-draw tooling shown in Fig. 16 was originally made of tool steel of a grade no longer used. It produced fewer than 50 pieces without scoring the workpieces. The combination blanking punch and draw ring was chromium plated in an attempt to increase its durability. Adhesion of the plating was not satisfactory; the chromium started to peel after 180 pieces had been produced. A draw ring of graphitic tool steel was then tried, but this also scored the workpieces.

Finally, a new draw ring was made of sintered carbide consisting of 81% tungsten carbide, 15% Co, and 4% Ta, a composition especially recommended for draw dies. The new ring, used with a chlorinated oil-base lubricant, withstood the heat and pressure generated by the severe blank-and-draw operation and produced mar-free parts. Maintenance was negligible, and after three years the carbide draw ring had produced 180,000 pieces, with little evidence of wear.

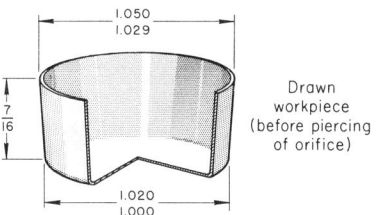

Type 302, 0.038 in.

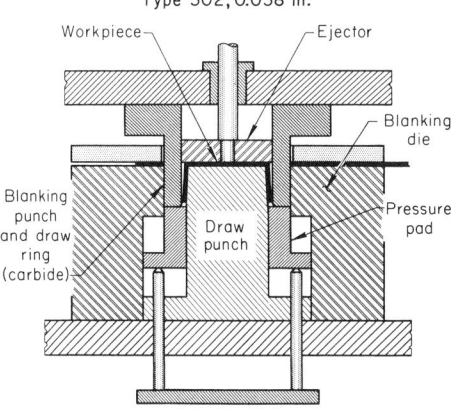

Fig. 16 Forming an orifice cup in a blank-and-draw die with a carbide punch and draw ring. Orifice was pierced in a second operation. Annual production was 60,000 pieces. Rate of blanking and drawing was 670 pieces per hour. Rate of piercing was 153 pieces per hour. Dimensions given in inches

The blanking punch-to-die clearance was 0.05 mm (0.002 in.) per side. The drawing punch-to-die clearance was 0.851 mm (0.335 in.) plus 3° taper per side on the draw punch. The punch nose radius was 0.38 mm (0.015 in.), and the draw radius was 2.4 mm (0.093 in.).

Effect of Worn Draw Rings. The following example shows how the gradual wear of carbide draw rings in severe drawing affects the outside diameter of drawn shells.

Example 13: Effect of Wear of a Carbide Draw Ring on the Diameter of a Drawn Shell. The carbide draw ring used in deep drawing a shell for pens and pencils made more than 225,000 pieces before it was replaced. Measurements of the pieces were made at production intervals, as shown in Fig. 17.

Shortly after 225,000 pieces had been drawn, shells began to be produced that would no longer enter the "go" ring gage freely, because of wear on the draw ring. The worn draw ring, which per-

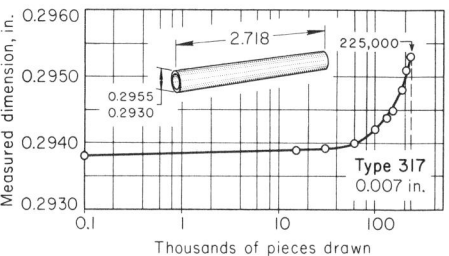

Fig. 17 Variation in diameter of a deep-drawn steel that resulted from wear of the carbide draw ring used. Dimensions given in inches

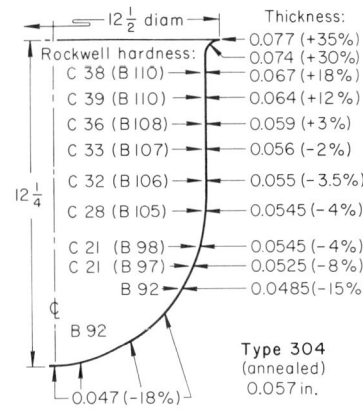

Fig. 18 Profile of a shell drawn from an austenitic stainless steel showing variations in hardness and thickness produced by drawing. Dimensions given in inches

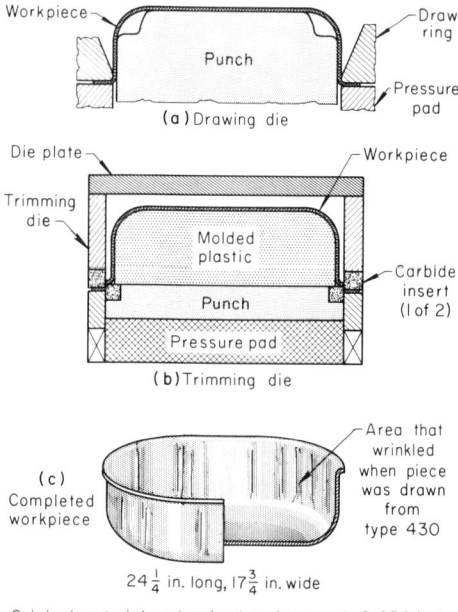

Original material: galvanized carbon steel, 0.050 in.; changed to type 430, 0.031 in.; then to type 302, 0.031 in.

Fig. 19 Setups for drawing and trimming a basin. Die clearance (1.40 mm, or 0.055 in., per side) and drawing radius (6.4 mm, or ¼ in.) were not changed when 0.79 mm (0.031 in.) thick type 430 was substituted for 1.27 mm (0.050 in.) thick galvanized carbon steel as the work metal, and wrinkles resulted in drawing. Dimensions given in inches

Table 8 Effect of die clearance and draw ring radius on noncylindrical draws of stainless steel

Stock thickness, t		Carbon steel		Type 430		Types 302 and 304	
mm	in.	mm	in.	mm	in.	mm	in.
1.27	0.050	1.40	0.055	1.40	0.055	2.29	0.090
0.76	0.030	0.84	0.033	0.84	0.033	1.37	0.054

(Die clearance per side)

Stock thickness, t		Carbon steel		Type 430		Types 302 and 304
mm	in.	mm	in.	mm	in.	
1.27	0.050	6.4-9.5	¼–⅜	6.4-9.5	¼–⅜	4t min
0.76	0.030	4.8-7.9	3/16–5/16	4.8-7.9	3/16–5/16	4t min

(Draw ring radius)

mitted excessive springback, was replaced before the beginning of the next production run.

The shell was drawn from a blank of type 317 stainless steel 48.4 mm (1.906 in.) in diameter and 0.18 mm (0.007 in.) thick to a finished depth of 69.0 mm (2.718 in.) using chromium-plated punches. The shell was made in eight single-station dies, seven drawing and one end forming, at a rate of 600/h. The punches had a 2.29 mm (0.090 in.) nose radius, and the draw dies had a 90° conical entrance angle with a 1.52 mm (0.060 in.) radius blending the corners. A mixture of three parts inhibited hydraulic oil and one part chlorinated oil was used as lubricant.

Die clearance for heavy draws is 35 to 40% greater than the original metal thickness for austenitic alloys. For the ferritic alloys, which thicken less, 10 to 15% is generally adequate.

Figure 18 shows a profile of an austenitic stainless steel drawn part that illustrates the thickening pattern observed in drawing a cup from this material. If the process is one of stretching more than drawing, the clearances need not compensate for natural thickening.

Clearances of less than the metal thickness are generally not used with stainless steel, because they result in ironing (squeezing of the metal between the punch and die). The austenitic stainless steels are not suited to ironing, because their high rate of work hardening promotes scoring and rapid wear of the dies. In addition, any substantial ironing in the drawing of austenitic stainless steels greatly increases the likelihood of fracturing the workpiece.

The example below describes an application in which the work metal was changed from galvanized carbon steel to a thinner ferritic stainless steel without a revision of die clearance. The resultant problems were solved by substituting an austenitic stainless steel that was better suited to the original clearance even though it had the same thickness as the ferritic steel.

Example 14: Matching Work Metal to Die Clearance. Using the tooling shown in Fig. 19, basins were made at the rate of 10,000 to 15,000 pieces/year from galvanized carbon steel, 1.27 mm (0.050 in.) thick. The press was an 8900 kN (1000 tonf) hydraulic press with an air-over-oil pressure pad and a draw rate of 152 mm (6 in.) in 5 s. The punch, draw ring, and pressure pad for the drawing die (Fig. 19a) were hardened cast iron. Carbide inserts were used as cutting edges on the trimming punch and die (Fig. 19b). The locator on the trimming die was molded plastic, and the die plate was cast iron. Both dies were used side by side in the press at the same time, because the press had enough capacity to draw and trim in one stroke. Therefore, a finished piece was produced with each stroke of the press, using manual transfer.

To produce a more corrosion-resistant basin, type 430 stainless steel was substituted for the galvanized carbon steel. The type 430 was only 0.79 mm (0.031 in.) thick in order to minimize the increase in material costs. However, the same tooling was used because the relatively low annual quantity did not warrant the cost of retooling. Because the holddown forces were not suitable for the ferritic stainless steel, several hundred pieces out of the first run were fractured in drawing.

When the holddown pressure was adjusted to a level suitable for a ferritic stainless steel, contraction wrinkles formed where the material entered the throat of the die (Fig. 19c), because the die clearance was too great. The corners of the blank were cropped, the viscosity of the lubricant was changed, and the holddown pressures were more closely adjusted in an effort to control wrinkling.

The data given in Table 8 for noncylindrical draws provide an explanation for the difficulties encountered in changing the work metal as well as guidance for the selection of a suitable stainless steel. According to these data, the thickness of type 430 stock that could best be formed by the die would be the same as that of the carbon steel previously formed. In addition, if the stock thickness was reduced, an austenitic steel such as type 302 could be used. The die clearance was 1.4 mm (0.055 in.) per side, and the draw ring radius was 6.4 mm (¼ in.). Therefore, the die was suitable for the 1.27 mm (0.050 in.) thick carbon steel, but not for the 0.79 mm (0.031 in.) thick type 430. However, 0.79 mm (0.031 in.) thick type 302 would be closely matched to the die capacity.

A change was made to type 302 stainless steel, 0.79 mm (0.031 in.) thick, with no further difficulty. A change to 1.27 mm (0.050 in.) thick stock of type 430 also might have been successful.

Speed of drawing has an important bearing on the success of the draw. A rate of 6 to 7.5 m (20 to 25 ft) per minute is a good compromise between the rate of work hardening and the uniform distribution of stress. With proper forming techniques, the rate of fracture at this speed is often less than 2%.

Lubricants. Ordinarily, both sides of the workpiece need to be lubricated for each draw. If too little lubricant is used, tools may accumulate enough heat during a production run to cause the work metal to fracture because of galling. In tests with a minimum of lubricant, failures occurred after 25 draws.

The chemical type and the viscosity of the lubricant are both important. Either chemical or mechanical extreme-pressure activity is needed for the severe deep drawing of stainless steel.

Viscosity or pigment loading must not be too high or too low. Too thick a lubricant can cause wrinkling of compressed metal; too thin a lubricant can cause seizing or galling. The ability to readily remove a lubricant is also important. In general, the higher the viscosity, the more difficult the lubricant is to apply and remove.

The same characteristics that make chlorinated oils and waxes useful for the press forming of stainless steel (see the section "Lubrication" in this article) also make them useful for the deep drawing of these alloys. Table 3 lists other lubricants used in the deep drawing of stainless steel. Pigmented pastes and dry films are also effective (and in some cases superior) in deep drawing.

In Example 15, changing from a viscous mineral oil to a low-viscosity mineral oil blend of a chlorinated wax eliminated wrinkling and galling. Sometimes, however, there is no substitute for the physical separation and equalization of pressure provided by pigments, as discussed in Example 16.

Example 15: Effect of Reducing Viscosity and Adding Chlorinated Wax to Mineral Oil Lubricant in Deep Drawing. A coffeepot was deep drawn from a type 302 stainless steel blank, 355 mm (14 in.) in diameter by 0.81 mm (0.032 in.) thick, in two deep draws and one bulging operation. At first, the blanks were lubricated by brushing both sides with mineral oil having a viscosity of 6000 SUS at 40 °C (100 °F). The workpiece wrinkled in the first draw, and it galled in the second draw and in bulging.

The lubricant was replaced with a thinner mineral oil (viscosity of 500 SUS at 40 °C, or 100 °F) that was fortified with a chlorinated wax. The lubricant was brushed on, as before. Not only did the use of the modified lubricant eliminate the wrinkles in the first draw, but enough lubricant remained on the surface to prevent galling in the two other operations. Even though a fluid of much lower viscosity was used, the tenacity imparted by the chlorinated wax permitted the retention of sufficient lubricant for the subsequent bulging and deep-drawing operations.

Example 16: Pigmented Paste versus Chlorinated Oil for Deep Drawing. For easy cleaning in a vapor degreaser, highly fortified oils were specified for the deep drawing of a rectangular shell from 0.89 mm (0.035 in.) thick type 304 stainless steel. Chlorinated and sulfochlorinated oils with viscosities of 4000 to 20,000 SUS at 40 °C (100 °F) failed to eliminate welding to the dies and splitting of the workpiece at the corners. The shell, a well for a steam table, was deep drawn from a rectangular blank measuring 760 by 585 mm (30 by 23 in.) with corners trimmed at 45°. The shell was drawn in one operation, and the flange was then trimmed. Interior dimensions of the drawn shell were 510 by 305 by 150 mm (20 by 12 by 6 in.). Bottom corners had 16 mm ($\frac{5}{8}$ in.) radii; vertical corners had 29 mm ($1\frac{1}{8}$ in.) radii, and the flange had a 6.4 mm ($\frac{1}{4}$ in.) radius. The shell had an approximately 3° taper on each side. The clearance between the punch and die was equal to the stock thickness.

The oil-type lubricant was replaced with a highly pigmented water-miscible fatty paste, diluted with two parts of water, which was applied to both sides of each blank by rollers. This lubricant eliminated the welding and allowed enough metal flow to prevent splitting. The drawn parts were cleaned with hot alkaline solution in a soak tank.

Lubricant Location. The location of the lubricant on the blank is also critical to the successful fabrication of a drawn part. Because all draws are made up of a combination of stretching and deep drawing, the lubricant location often depends on which type of forming is dominant. In a stretch condition, lubricant should especially be applied on the steel surface contacting the punch so that friction is minimized and the steel slips over the punch surface during stretching and thinning. Under deep-draw conditions, the steel surface contacting the die is definitely lubricated in order to allow ease of movement into the die cavity. However, whether stretch or deep drawing dominates, some lubricant is necessary on both steel surfaces to minimize the galling tendencies of stainless alloys.

Drawing Cylindrical Parts. When a part is made in several drawing operations, the amount of reduction in redrawing is related to the condition of the metal in the first drawing operation (cupping). If the material is highly stressed because of excessive blankholder pressure or because of small die radius, very little reduction can be made in the second operation.

General practice on the more formable grades of austenitic stainless steel is to allow 40 to 45% reduction in the first operation, followed by a maximum of 30% in the second operation, if the workpiece is not annealed between draws. With an anneal, the second reduction is usually 30 to 40%. On some parts, it may be preferable to spread the reduction over four draws before annealing (e.g., successive reductions of 35, 30, 20, and 10%).

There is usually a decrease in drawability upon redrawing, and the greatest total reduction in a two-draw operation is most often produced by having the first-stage reduction as large as possible. During redrawing, it is advisable to use a tapered or rounded-end internal blankholder or sleeve to allow easy flow of metal into the die. An internal blankholder with small-radius 90° corners causes the metal to be bent severely through two 90° bends before flowing into the die.

Optimal drawability is available at ram speeds of not more than 6 to 9 m (20 to 30 ft) per minute. Because of the strain-rate sensitivity of most stainless steels, work hardening of these alloys is minimized by slow forming.

The following example describes an application in which small shells were deep drawn in several steps to reduce the amount of work done in a single operation. Because production quantities were small, individual dies were more economical than a transfer die.

Example 17: Seven-Step Deep Drawing of a Fountain-Pen Cap. Fountain-pen caps of various closely related designs were made on the same production line by one blanking and cupping operation and six redraws. A flat blank of type 302 stainless steel having a hardness of 83 to 88 HR15-T was used. The first five draws were usually the same for any of the caps made on the line. Therefore, to set up for a different size of cap, only the compound blank-and-cup die and the last die (or, for some caps, the last two dies) needed to be changed. As a result, the changeover time was only about 45 min.

In the first operation, which was done in a 160 kN (18 tonf) mechanical press, a compound blank-and-cup die equipped with a rubber die cushion was used to cut circular blanks from 0.267 to 0.279 mm (0.0105 to 0.0110 in.) thick strip and to draw them into a cup. To make a typical cap 90 mm ($3\frac{1}{2}$ in.) long by 8.55 to 8.57 mm (0.3365 to 0.3375 in.) in outside diameter, a blank 55.9 mm (2.200 in.) in diameter was cut from stock 57 mm ($2\frac{1}{4}$ in.) wide and was drawn into a cup 19 mm ($\frac{3}{4}$ in.) deep by 31.8 mm (1.250 in.) in diameter—a 43% reduction in diameter. Reductions in the subsequent redraws were 27, 22, 18, 18, 16, and 15%, respectively. All except the last redraw were done in 35 kN (4 tonf) hydraulic presses with 152 mm (6 in.) strokes. The final redraw was made in a 55 kN (6 tonf) hydraulic press with a 305 mm (12 in.) stroke.

The draw dies were carbide inserts 13 to 16 mm ($\frac{1}{2}$ to $\frac{5}{8}$ in.) thick. The die openings had a 4.8 mm ($\frac{3}{16}$ in.) radius blending with a 1.6 mm ($\frac{1}{16}$ in.) wide land. There was a 2° relief per side below the land. The high-speed steel punches had a 2.4 mm ($\frac{3}{32}$ in.) nose radius and were chromium plated for smoothness and wear characteristics. The workpiece was pushed through the die and stripped from the punch by a split stripper plate under the draw die. The strippers were closed by cam action from the press stripper rod.

Because production quantities of any one part were small, this technique was preferable to making a transfer die for each of the several caps produced on this line. Operations were set up in machines in the line as they were needed and as the machines became available.

The final draw, which was the deepest, governed the final production rate of 575 pieces/h. However, when there was a backlog of pieces, this operation was set up on two machines at the same time.

The blank-and-cup die made about 45,000 pieces before resharpening. The draw rings were used for 150,000 to 200,000 pieces before wear was too great. Dies in the first few draws were allowed to wear over a fairly wide range. As the die opening increased, clearance was maintained by increasing the thickness of the chromium plating on the punch. When the die openings were 0.10 to 0.13 mm (0.004 to 0.005 in.) oversize, the dies were replaced, and punches were returned to the original size by stripping, polishing, and replating.

The lubricant was a mixture of one part sulfur-free chlorinated oil with three parts inhibited hydraulic oil having a viscosity of 250 SUS at 40 °C (100 °F). This lubricant was furnished to all presses through a central pumping system.

Critical tolerances on these fountain-pen caps were ±0.02 mm (±0.001 in.) on the outside diameter and ±0.01 mm (±0.0005 in.) on the inside diameter. Holding the clearance between the draw

Table 9 Force required for drawing two stainless steels and low-carbon steel of 1.27 mm (0.050 in.) thickness to various diameters

Diameter of piece		Approximate drawing force required					
		Austenitic stainless steel, type 18-8		Ferritic stainless steel, 17% Cr		Low-carbon steel	
mm	in.	kN	tonf	kN	tonf	kN	tonf
125	5	350	39	180	20	160	18
255	10	700	78	520	59	350	39
510	20	1400	157	1040	117	700	78

die and punch to 10% greater than stock thickness helped to maintain these tolerances.

Steel Drawing Forces. Estimates of the maximum drawing forces necessary to form cups from an austenitic stainless steel, a ferritic stainless steel, and a low-carbon steel are compared in Table 9. These drawing forces, in tons of force, are based on the formula $S\pi Dt$, where S is the tensile strength of the metal in tons of force per square inch, D is the cup diameter in inches, and t is the metal thickness in inches.

Blankholding pressures for the austenitic alloys must be much higher than those for the ferritic types or low-carbon steels. For austenitic alloys the pressure, P, on the metal under the blankholder is usually about 6.9 MPa (1.0 ksi); for the ferritic alloys it is 1.4 to 3.4 MPa (0.2 to 0.5 ksi). Thinner material and larger flange areas generally require greater pressure.

Drawing Hemispherical Parts. The drawing of hemispherical, or dome-shape, parts demands special attention to blankholder pressure to prevent wrinkling, because so much of the metal surface is not in contact with any die surface for most of the draw. Only the very tip of the punch is in contact with the work at the start of the stroke, and the surface between the tip and the blankholder draws or stretches free until the punch descends far enough to contact it. An undersize punch can sometimes be used to draw or stretch the blank into a preform before the dome-shape punch makes the final draw, as in the following example.

Example 18: Two-Stage Drawing of a Stepped-Diameter Hemisphere. One of the critical points in the production of the vacuum-bottle top shown in Fig. 20 was the forming of the shoulder at the large end of the dome-shaped top. The stepped inside diameter of this shoulder had to be an exact fit with the body of the vacuum-bottle jacket. The pierced hole at the small end also had to be accurately formed to conform to the mouth of the inner container.

The stock was 289 mm (11.375 in.) wide annealed type 304 stainless steel strip, 1.1 mm (0.042 in.) thick. A single-action mechanical press with a spring-loaded pressure pad was used to cut 280 mm ($11\frac{1}{8}$ in.) diameter blanks from the strip, leaving 3.2 mm ($\frac{1}{8}$ in.) minimum scrap on each side of the strip.

The first draw was made in a 2200 kN (250 tonf) double-action mechanical press. The punch was 83 mm ($3\frac{1}{4}$ in.) in diameter; therefore, much of the surface of the dome was drawn free (operation 2, Fig. 20). This required careful control of the blankholder pressure to prevent puckers and wrinkles. Blankholder pressure had to be adjusted for every lot of steel; it varied from 5.5 to 6.9 MPa (0.8 to 1.0 ksi). The die radius also had to be held closely (5.2 times the stock thickness). The first draw produced a cup 175 mm ($6\frac{7}{8}$ in.) in diameter with a 235 mm ($9\frac{1}{4}$ in.) diameter flange.

The second draw was also made in the 2200 kN (250 tonf) double-action press. The punch for the second draw was shaped to the required inner contour of the part, including the step at the base of the dome, which was formed as the press bottomed at the end of the second draw stroke (operation 3, Fig. 20). This operation formed the dome shape of the bottle top by reshaping (mostly by stretching) the cup formed in the first draw. The metal for the cylindrical area above the step was drawn from the flange metal remaining after the first draw.

In the fourth operation, the hole in the top of the dome was pierced, and an internal stretch flange was formed around the hole. This was done with a spring-loaded piercing die, which gave sufficient resistance to let the piercing punch shear the material and then retreat under pressure from the flange-forming part of the punch. Both ends of the part were later trimmed in a lathe.

Drawing Rectangular Parts. During the deep drawing of a box-shape part, the metal in the corners of the part and in the flange around the corners undergoes a change much like that which takes place when a round shell is drawn from a circular blank. Metal is compressed at the corners, and significant thickening occurs where the metal flows into the corners. The sides of the box undergo essentially no thickening, because there is no compression of the metal in the flange areas as it flows or bends over the die radius.

Clearances in the sides between the punch and die are ordinarily about 10% greater than the metal thickness, to compensate for gage variations and allow for metal flow. At the corners, punch-to-die clearances are similar to those used for cylindrical parts to allow for thickening.

Blankholding devices are almost always used in producing deeply recessed box-shape parts in order to control the metal movement, particularly in the corners. The corners are under severe strain because of the intense compression of the flange metal, and most fracturing, if it does occur, takes place in the lower wall corner sections.

Punch and die radii are generally the same for rectangular draws as for circular draws. Some fabricators prefer to make the punch and die radii at the corners larger than along the sides in order to equalize the stress in the metal at the corners. The top surface of the draw die and the draw radii should be polished smooth (free of grind marks

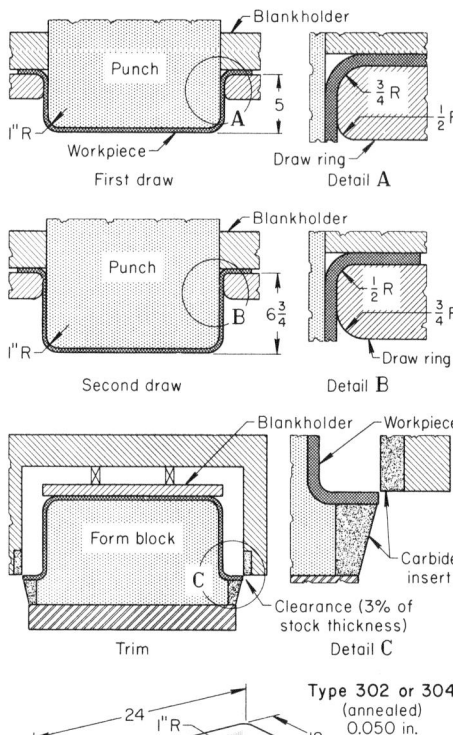

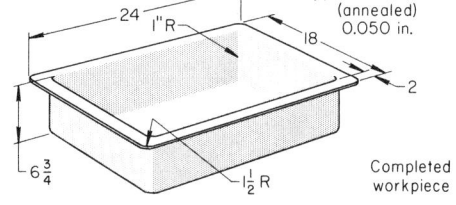

Fig. 21 Production of a flat-flanged sink basin by drawing and redrawing (using a two-radius reversible draw ring) and trimming. Dimensions given in inches

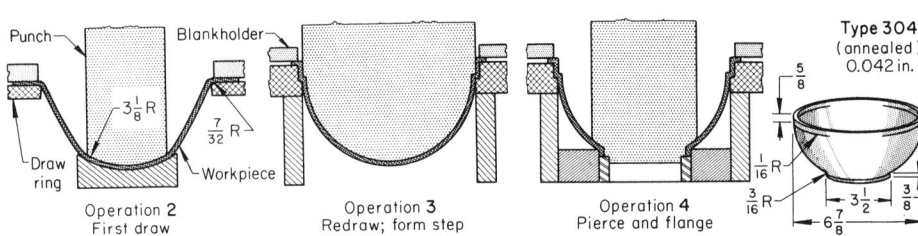

Fig. 20 Production of a stepped-diameter flanged hemisphere, in which a narrow punch was used in predrawing the dome. The piece was drawn from a 280 mm (11 in.) diam blank produced in operation 1 (not shown). Dimensions given in inches

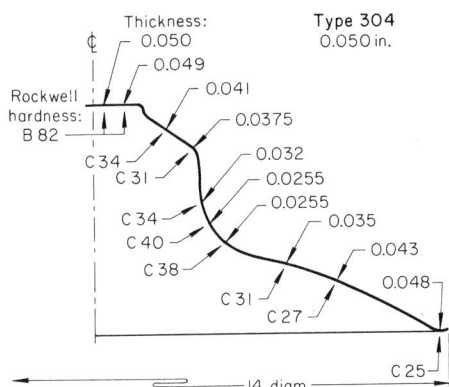

Fig. 22 Profile of shape, hardness, and thickness of a manually spun part that often fractured in its thinnest section. Dimensions given in inches

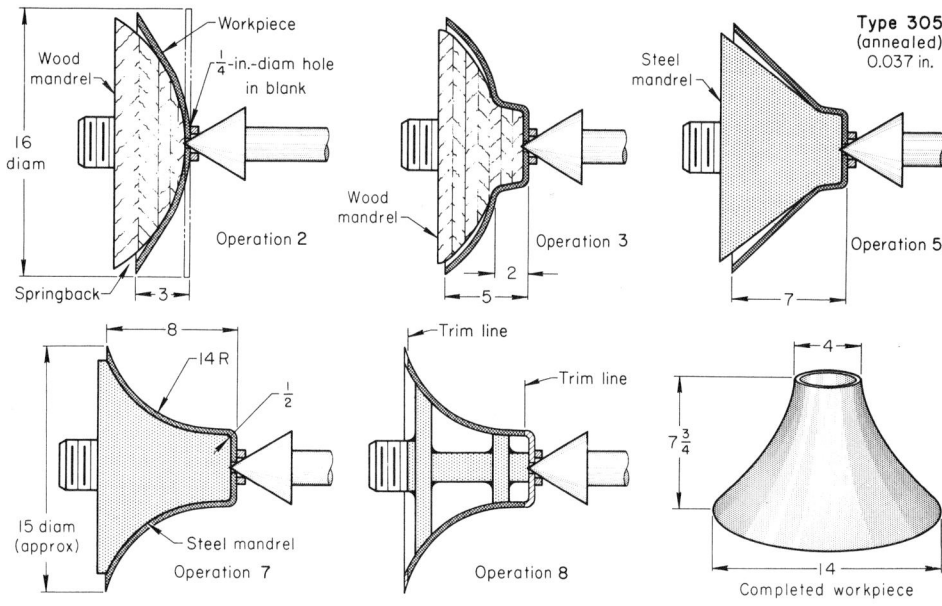

Sequence of operations

1. Drill a 6.4 mm (¼ in.) diam center hole in a 405 mm (16 in.) diam blank 0.94 mm (0.037 in.) thick.
2. Spin to 75 mm (3 in.) depth on a laminated hardwood mandrel at 300 rpm, applying manual pressure on lever and roller.
3. Spin to 125 mm (5 in.) depth on a second laminated hardwood mandrel to within 25 mm (1 in.) of edge.
4. Anneal in hydrogen atmosphere at 1040 °C (1900 °F); air cool.
5. Spin to 178 mm (7 in.) depth on a steel mandrel to within 25 mm (1 in.) of edge.
6. Anneal as in operation 4.
7. Spin to 205 mm (8 in.) depth and final shape on a steel mandrel.
8. Lathe-trim top and bottom ends to 195 mm (7¾ in.) final height of cone.

Fig. 23 Production of a stainless steel cone by four-pass manual spinning. Dimensions given in inches

and well blended) to prevent localized retardation of metal flow with resultant uneven drawing of the metal. Burrs and bent edges on the blank often restrict metal flow or movement along the blank-holder surface to such a degree that vertical wall fractures can occur.

Semideveloped blanks usually produce better results than rectangular ones. There are a number of patterns for trimming the corners, ranging from a simple 45° trim to patterns with a carefully developed area containing the optimal volume and area of metal.

The economic success of the run is related to tool wear and scrap rate. The following example describes a combination of tool materials that has given satisfactory performance in terms of parts or draws per regrind and redress. The same tooling can be used for both drawing operations, with the draw ring reversed to present a different radius for the second draw.

Example 19: Use of a Reversible Two-Radius Draw Ring for Drawing and Redrawing of a Flanged Rectangular Shell. The flat-flanged single-sump kitchen sink shown in Fig. 21 was formed in four operations: blank, draw, redraw, and trim. Forming of the part was a combined draw-and-stretch operation. Because several different models, with drain holes in various locations, were made from the same drawn part, the drain hole was not pierced in the trimming operation but was made separately. The production rate was 50,000 to 100,000 pieces/year.

The material was annealed type 302 or 304 stainless steel coil stock, 735 mm (29 in.) wide and 1.27 mm (0.050 in.) thick, with a No. 2D sheet finish. Blanks 635 mm (25 in.) long were sheared from the coil at the rate of 40/min in a single-action mechanical press. Corners of the blanks were trimmed at 45°, removing 50 mm (2 in.) from each edge of the blank at each corner. Clearance for this trimming was kept at less than 5% of metal thickness to minimize edge distortion and burrs.

The draws were made in a 3600 kN (400 tonf) double-action mechanical press with 2200 kN (250 tonf) available for blank holding. The draw punch was made of alloy tool steel, and the blankholder was made of alloy cast iron. The reversible draw ring (Fig. 21) was made of hard aluminum bronze and had a 19 mm (¾ in.) draw radius on one side for the first draw and a 13 mm (½ in.) draw radius on the other side for the redraw. The workpiece was annealed in an inert atmosphere at 1065 °C (1950 °F) between the first and second draws and then air cooled rapidly to room temperature.

The depth of the sink after the first draw was 127 mm (5 in.); after the second draw it was 170 mm (6¾ in.). Draws were made at a punch speed of approximately 6.4 m (21 ft) per minute, with less than 2% of the workpieces fracturing.

A similar 3600 kN (400 tonf) press was used to trim the piece. Carbide inserts provided shearing edges for the trimming operation. The sink was held on a form block of molded plastic or cast iron for trimming.

The second draw operation sharpened the bottom and flange corner radii and stretched the bottom surface and the side walls to remove any loose metal. Little or no metal was drawn into the part from the flange during the second draw.

Spinning

Stainless steel parts such as cups, cones, and dished heads can be readily formed by manual or power spinning, although more power is required than for the spinning of low-carbon steel.

Manual Spinning. The amount of thinning that occurs during manual spinning is related to the severity of the formed shape. A cross section is shown in Fig. 22 of a manually spun piece that thinned out to such a degree that it often fractured. This piece was excessively worked, and the mid-center area was work hardened beyond the capacity of the material, causing the workpiece to fracture. The piece was later made by press drawing the dome-shape cup and spinning the broad flared flange.

The approximate limits of stretch in manual spinning are given in Table 10. These are for 1.57 mm (0.062 in.) thick fully annealed stock. The second stretch after annealing is about 8% less than the first. The amount of stretch is not necessarily uniform over the entire part; it varies with the severity of the form.

Table 10 Approximate limits of stretch in the manual spinning of stainless steels 1.57 mm (0.062 in.) thick

Type	Stretch (max), %	Type	Stretch (max), %	Type	Stretch (max), %
305	45	321	35	202	25
302	40	309	30	301	25
304	40	310	30	405	25
302B	35	317	30	446	25
316	35	430	30	403	20
316L	35	201	25	410	20

These limits for stretching during one spinning pass; after being annealed, the metal can be respun to 8% less than the first stretch.

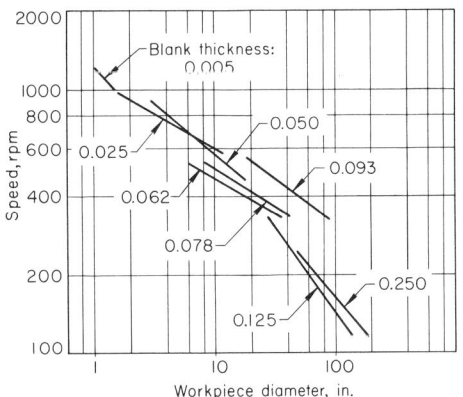

Fig. 24 Effect of workpiece diameter and blank thickness on rotational speed for the manual spinning of austenitic stainless steel. Dimensions given in inches

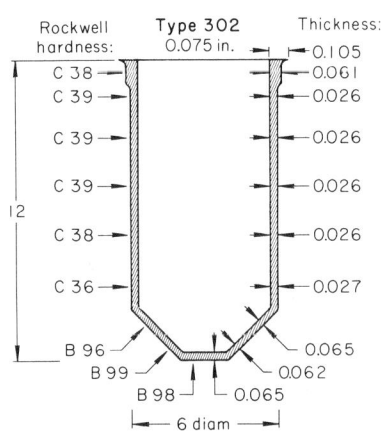

Fig. 25 Variations in hardness and thickness of a shell that was power spun from a preform drawn from stainless steel 1.9 mm (0.075 in.) thick. Dimensions given in inches

300-Series Stainless Steels. Although 300-series stainless steels can be formed by spinning, types 302, 304, and 305 can be spun to greater reductions than other stainless steels before intermediate annealing becomes necessary. All anneals must be followed by pickling to remove oxides, thus restoring the clean, smooth surface. The No. 1 strip or No. 2D sheet finish is best for severe applications because the metal is in the softest stress-free condition and will take the greatest amount of working. The following example demonstrates the spinnability of type 305 stainless steel.

Example 20: Four-Pass Manual Spinning of a Cone from Type 305 Stainless Steel. The 355 mm (14 in.) diameter cone shown in Fig. 23 was produced in eight operations, including four manual spinning passes, from a 405 mm (16 in.) diameter blank of 0.94 mm (0.037 in.) thick annealed type 305 stainless steel that had a No. 2D sheet finish or a No. 1 strip finish. Other types of austenitic stainless steel could have been used, but the reduction per pass would have been lower, in proportion to the increase in rate of work hardening.

As shown in Fig. 23, the mandrels for spinning were made of wood or steel. The spinning roller was made of hardened steel. Pressure was applied to the entire blank in the first spinning pass. In the three other passes, the outer 25 mm (1 in.) of the blank was not spun. This caused the edge to thicken to 1.78 mm (0.070 in.) and helped hold the outer shape. Thinning was greatest at the middle of the cone, to about 0.69 mm (0.027 in.) wall thickness (28% reduction). The surface area of the piece was increased 40%. The drastic working that accompanied the thinning and the increase in area made two anneals necessary (see sequence of operations, Fig. 23). Annual production quantity was 500 pieces.

The 400-series stainless steels, because of their relatively low ductility, do not adapt readily to manual spinning, especially when the deformation is severe. The high pressure of the forming tool causes wear of the work metal, resulting in early thinning and fracturing.

The surface of severely spun parts is often very rough because of the action of the tools on the metal, and the production of a buffed or highly polished finish on a part spun from a 400-series stainless steel can be expensive. It is generally necessary to rough grind the material to smooth out the irregularities before polishing and buffing.

Typical stock thicknesses of stainless steel for manual spinning are 0.30 to 3.18 mm (0.012 to 0.125 in.), although stainless steels as thin as 0.13 mm (0.005 in.) and as thick as 6.35 mm (0.250 in.) have been spun by hand. The corner radius should be at least five times the thickness of the work metal. Allowance must be made in the size and shape of mandrels for springback and for heat-induced dimensional changes. Figure 24 shows the relationship between workpiece size (thickness and diameter) and rotational speed during manual spinning.

Power spinning is used for severe reductions and for work that cannot be done by hand. Stainless steels in both the 300 and 400 series are readily formed by power spinning, but the low-work-hardening types 302 and 305 are superior. Much larger reductions of type 430 can be made by power spinning than by manual spinning.

Spinning can be done hot or cold, although the severe reduction accompanying power spinning may cause so much heat that the spinning that began cold becomes warm spinning. Hot spinning, done only above 790 °C (1450 °F), is commonly used for work 4.8 to 13 mm (³⁄₁₆ to ½ in.) thick. The need for careful control of temperature makes it difficult to hot spin metal that is less than 6.4 mm (¼ in.) thick. Thicker stainless steel can be hot spun as easily as low-carbon steel.

Cracking at the edge is the main problem in the power spinning of austenitic stainless steels. It may be necessary to grind the edge of the blank smooth to prevent cracking. A generous trim allowance is helpful so that the cracked edge can be cut off. Cracking and distortion can be prevented by keeping a narrow flange on the work. If the size of the spun piece is not correct after it cools (because of springback and heat expansion), the piece can be annealed and spun to size while it is still above 150 °C (300 °F).

Considerable thinning can be produced by power spinning, as indicated by the cross section of a deeply spun vessel shown in Fig. 25. The thickness of the vessel was reduced from 1.90 to 0.66 mm (0.075 to 0.026 in.) in one spinning operation. A preformed cup 152 mm (6 in.) in diameter and 75 mm (3 in.) deep, drawn on a conventional press, was used as the starting shape. The top of the vessel is much thicker than the wall. Thickening of the rim occurred during drawing, and it remained thick because there was essentially no deformation in this region during spinning.

The surfaces of power-spun pieces are rough, and extensive finishing is required to make them smooth and bright. The spun surface is rough because the roller usually imparts a spiral or helical groove to the surface as the roller is fed into the metal while it rotates. Except for this disadvantage, power spinning is an excellent way of forming pieces from stainless steel.

Lubricants (see Table 3) are used to reduce friction, to minimize galling and tool drag, and to provide cooling. For manual spinning, firmly adherent lubricants are preferred; for power spinning, coolant action is more important. Lubricants containing sulfur or chlorine are usually avoided; they are difficult to remove completely and have harmful effects on heated stainless surfaces.

Rubber-Pad Forming

Annealed austenitic stainless steels types 301, 302, 304, 305, 321, and 347—are rubber-pad formed in thicknesses to 1.3 mm (0.050 in.). Most of the operations are straight flanging, especially in thicker workpieces. With auxiliary devices, such as wedges or rollers, pieces up to 2.0 mm (0.078 in.) thick can be formed. Flanges must be wide enough to develop adequate forming force from the unit pressure on their surfaces. For annealed stainless steels, the following minimum flange widths beyond the bend radius are recommended for successful forming:

Thickness		Flange width	
mm	in.	mm	in.
0.41	0.016	6.35	0.250
0.51	0.020	6.86	0.270
0.64	0.025	7.37	0.290
0.81	0.032	8.38	0.330
1.02	0.040	9.14	0.360
1.30	0.051	10.0	0.410
1.63	0.064	12.2	0.480
1.83	0.072	13.0	0.510

In quarter-hard temper, types 301 and 302 up to 0.81 mm (0.032 in.) thick can be flanged if the flange is at least 16 mm (⅝ in.) wide.

The rubber-pad forming of contoured flanges in stainless steel requires more powerful equipment than that used for flat flanges. Most forming of contoured flanges is done on annealed stainless steel, but a limited amount is done on quarter-hard stock.

Stretch flanges are readily formed on annealed stainless steel up to 1.3 mm (0.050 in.) thick. Rubber-pad-formed stretch flanges of thin metal are generally smoother and more accurately formed than those formed by single-action dies.

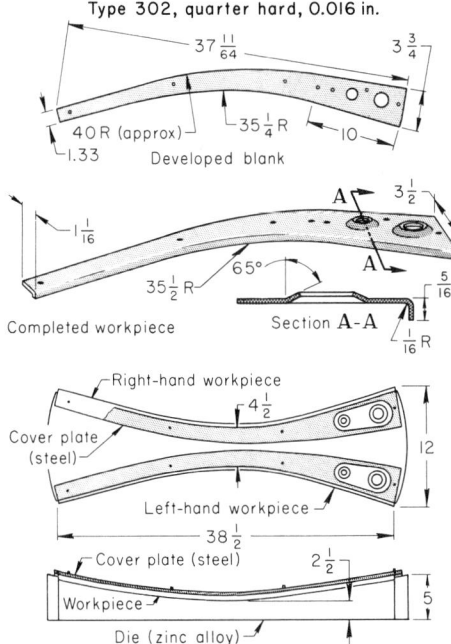

Fig. 26 Long narrow strut with a contoured stretch flange that was made by rubber-pad forming in a curved die with cover plates to prevent springback. Dimensions given in inches

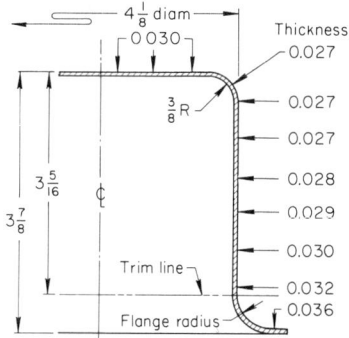

Fig. 27 Profile of a shell that was deep drawn from 0.76 mm (0.030 in.) thick stainless steel by the rubber-pad method showing the relatively uniform wall thickness obtained. Dimensions given in inches

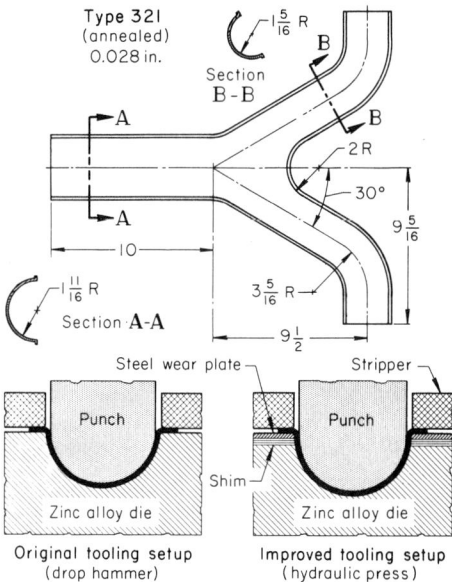

Fig. 28 Aircraft tailpipe half that was formed by the drop hammer and hydraulic press tooling setups shown. Dimensions given in inches

Die-formed flanges often curl outward, requiring considerable hand work for correction.

The hydraulic presses used in the Guerin process develop forming pressures to 34.5 MPa (5 ksi). Narrow stretch flanges that require pressures greater than 34.5 MPa (5 ksi) are formed with the aid of auxiliary devices, such as traps and wedge blocks, that raise the forming pressure locally.

Thin metal can be formed by means of a simple form block, but if the web is narrow, the workpiece should be protected by a cover plate to avoid distortion.

Example 21: Use of a Curved Die with Cover Plates in Rubber-Pad Forming. The strut shown in Fig. 26 had a 7.9 mm (⁵⁄₁₆ in.) wide stretch flange and external 65° flanges on two lightening holes at the large end. It was rubber-pad formed from a quarter-hard type 302 stainless steel blank 0.41 mm (0.016 in.) thick.

The zinc alloy die used was made with a curve to offset the springback of the flange (Fig. 26). Right-hand and left-hand pieces were flanged at the same time in the same die. A steel cover plate protected the thin web of each piece from distortion during forming. No lubricant was used. The pressure developed by the rubber was 10.3 MPa (1.5 ksi).

The following example demonstrates the limits of rubber-pad forming of stretch flanges in stainless steel:

- The stock was quarter-hard type 302.
- The workpiece had a narrow web and therefore required the use of a cover plate in forming.
- The workpiece had external hole flanges.
- The stretch flange was only 7.9 mm (⁵⁄₁₆ in.) wide.

- The curved workpiece was nearly 965 mm (38 in.) long.

If a stainless steel part of this shape is more than 610 mm (24 in.) long, it is almost impossible to prevent the springback of the flange material from bowing the part unless curved dies are used.

Deep Drawing. If the rubber-pad and rubber-diaphragm processes are used, stainless steels in both the 300 and the 400 series can be deep drawn to greater reductions than can be achieved with conventional methods. For extremely deep sections, the lower-work-hardening austenitic types 302 and 305 are recommended.

Two characteristics of rubber-pad methods make this great depth of draw possible. The first is controlled, continuously adjustable pressure on the blankholder or holddown mechanism, and the second is the continuously variable draw ring radius. There is no draw ring as such, but the rubber that forms around the workpiece functions as a draw ring and conforms to the radius that will apply equal pressure to the entire surface of the workpiece. This minimizes both thinning at the punch radius and work hardening as the flange metal is drawn into the cup.

Figure 27 illustrates the relatively uniform wall thickness that can be produced by drawing using the rubber-pad method. For comparison, Fig. 18 shows the much greater variation in wall thickness produced by conventional deep drawing.

Drop Hammer Forming. A wide variety of sizes and shapes can be formed in thin stainless steel by drop hammer forming. The advantages of this method include high impact energy (which often means that a piece can be formed by one blow, as compared to four or five by other processes) and suitability to low-volume and experimental production.

Dies. Die material for drop hammer forming is less critical than for press forming. The dies are made of steel, plastic, zinc alloy, and lead. Zinc alloy is widely used.

Punches are often made of lead, because it can be cast directly on the lower die and because its weight adds energy to the stroke of the drop hammer. Although the lead is reusable, the number of pieces that can be made from each cast punch is small, about 200. Plastic punches and dies impart

a finish to formed parts that would otherwise be difficult to obtain. Steel dies are used for high production and for coining and sizing.

Die designs are generally similar to those for press forming, with the same punch and die radii to reduce stress on the work metal. Die design for the forming of beads and methods of relieving entrapment to ensure good metal flow in drop hammer forming are also similar to those used in press forming.

Quality of Product. The dimensions of workpieces formed in a drop hammer are less consistent than those made by other processes, because the degree of impact is subject to operator skill and because the punch can shift under localized high loads. However, springback is less pronounced in drop hammer forming than in other forming methods because of the high impact and forming speed.

Lubrication. The lubricants that can be used in drop hammer forming are listed in Table 3. If working is severe enough to require annealing between stages, contaminants such as graphite or sulfur (from the lubricant) or zinc or lead (from the die) must be removed from the work surface. If these contaminants are left on the surface of the stainless steel when it is heated, they can cause serious surface deterioration.

Comparison with Press Forming. Press forming, although done rapidly, is inherently an operation in which ram speed and holding pressures can be closely controlled. However, in drop hammer forming, the only way to form a part is by sudden impact. In some applications, production difficulties are overcome by the high rate of energy release in a drop hammer. In others, especially those in which blankholder pressure is critical, press forming produces better parts more economically if the die is properly made, as in the following example.

Example 22: Change from Drop Hammer to Press Forming That Eliminated Wrinkling

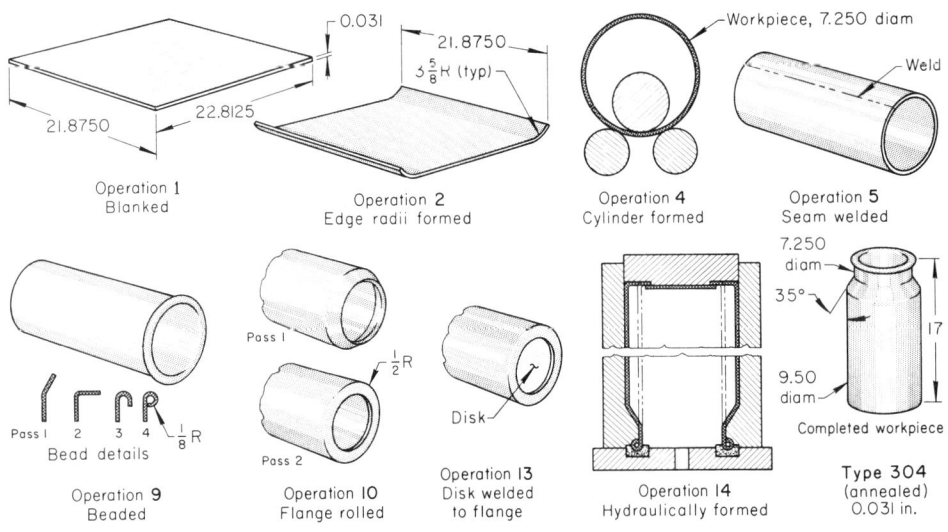

Operation 1
Blanked

Operation 2
Edge radii formed

Operation 4
Cylinder formed

Operation 5
Seam welded

Operation 9
Beaded

Operation 10
Flange rolled

Operation 13
Disk welded
to flange

Operation 14
Hydraulically formed

Completed workpiece

Type 304
(annealed)
0.031 in.

Sequence of operations

1. Blank in die, in single-action press.
2. Form edge radii on blank, in a press brake.
3. Vapor degrease, to remove lubricant used in operations 1 and 2.
4. Roll cylinder, in three-roll former.
5. Weld cylinder seam, in automatic Heliarc setup using starting and stop-off tabs.
6. Trim tabs.
7. Hammer weld to induce compressive stress, using an air hammer at 310 kPa (45 psi).

8. Restore roundness of cylinder by rerolling several times in three-roll former.
9. Form bead on one end of cylinder, in four passes in an edger.
10. Roll flange on opposite end of cylinder, in two passes.
11. Trim flange.
12. Vapor degrease.
13. Weld (Heliarc) disk to inside of flange.
14. Expand and form to final shape (30% reduction in wall thickness), in a hydraulic expansion die (final pressure: 4800 kPa, or 700 psi).

Fig. 29　Use of three-roll forming in conjunction with press forming and hydraulic expansion forming, in the 14-operation production of a container for liquids. Dimensions given in inches

and Reduced Cost. The tailpipe half shown at the top in Fig. 28 was originally produced in a drop hammer, using the tooling setup shown at the lower left in Fig. 28. The operation was unsatisfactory, however, because wrinkles occurred at the intersection of the 30° risers, and six operations totaling nearly 2 min/piece were required to complete each piece.

The tools were redesigned for use in a 4400 kN (500 tonf) hydraulic press (lower right, Fig. 28). The zinc alloy die used in the drop hammer was reused in the press. To make it resistant to the abrasion of press forming with stainless steel, the die was faced off, and a low-carbon steel wear plate was installed. The 43 mm ($1^{11}/_{16}$ in.) radius had formed well in the drop hammer with very little springback, but springback in the press made it necessary to deepen the die. This was done by inserting shims between the die and the wear plate.

The press produced pieces that were completely free of wrinkles at the rate of two pieces/min. This saved $1^{1}/_{2}$ min/piece.

The blank for both methods was annealed type 321 stainless steel measuring 510 by 610 mm (20 by 24 in.) and 0.71 mm (0.028 in.) thick. No lubricant was required for drop hammer forming; a wax emulsion was used for the press operation. Trimming after forming was done in a second press.

A drop hammer is ordinarily used for prototypes, and a press, using the prototype or improved dies, is used for mass production. If the quality of the prototype die is good, the drop hammer can be used for low-volume production.

Three-Roll Forming

The three-roll forming of stainless steel is, in general, similar to the three-roll forming of other metals. Springback is a major problem with austenitic stainless steels, primarily because of the large radii involved and work hardening. It is important that the equipment be set up so that the desired curvature can be made in one pass. Because of the high rate of work hardening of austenitic stainless steels, subsequent passes are sometimes difficult to accomplish and control unless heavy equipment is used. The response of annealed ferritic stainless steel to three-roll forming is quite similar to that of hot-rolled low-carbon steel.

Three-roll and two-roll formers can be put in sequence with contour-roll formers to make a cross-sectional shape and to bend or coil it, all in one production line. The following example describes an application in which three-roll forming was combined with press forming and hydraulic expansion forming.

Example 23: Use of Three-Roll Forming in the Production of a Container for Liquid. Figure 29 shows eight of the 14 operations entailed in the production of a container for liquids by press forming and hydraulic expansion forming of a

welded cylinder made from a radiused flat blank by three-roll forming in pyramid-type rolls. The six other operations are identified in the table that accompanies Fig. 29. These containers were produced in annual quantities of 10,000 to 100,000 pieces from annealed type 304 stainless steel coil stock 0.79 mm (0.031 in.) thick and 585.8 mm (23.0625 in.) wide.

Blanking the rectangular sheets for three-roll forming gave the workpiece the uniform square edges needed for maintaining the welded seam of the tube in axial alignment. The blanking tools were hardened high-carbon high-chromium tool steel; clearance was 0.08 mm (0.003 in.) per side. The stock was lubricated for blanking and edge radiusing, but the blanks were vapor degreased before three-roll forming.

Contour Roll Forming

Stainless steel is ordinarily contour roll formed in the annealed condition. Types 410 and 430 are usually roll formed on equipment similar to that used for carbon steel, with a No. 2 finish generally specified. Speeds are usually in the range of 7.6 to 30 m (25 to 100 ft) per minute, with the heavier gages and more difficult sections being roll formed at the slower speeds.

Stainless steels in hard tempers, such as quarter-hard and half-hard type 301, are also frequently roll formed. Increased power over that used for forming the same steels in the annealed condition is necessary because of the higher initial strength of the strip. Springback must be compensated for by adequate overbending. Longitudinal cracking can be a problem with the hard tempers if adequate radii are not included in the design of the part.

Distortion or warpage of straight sections causes the greatest problem in roll forming the 300-series steels, particularly when the steel is thick. The distortion can be minimized by using more sets of rolls, or more passes, for greater control during each stage of bending. However, the skill of the operator is all-important in controlling distortion. Various straightening devices are usually attached or used on the last pass as the section emerges from the machine. In some applications, sections are deliberately curved.

With the chromium-nickel stainless steels, pickup on the rolls and galling of the strip sometimes occur. Highly polished rolls or bronze rolls are used with lubrication to minimize this problem when high pressure is needed. Heavy-duty emulsions containing chlorine offer the best combination of chemical extreme-pressure and coolant activity (Table 3). Chlorinated oils or waxes are easy to use but are less effective as coolants. For severe forming, the cushioning effect of pigments is sometimes needed (as in the next example), as well as efficient cooling.

Example 24: Nine-Station Contour Roll Forming of Annealed 304 Stainless Steel. Figure 30 shows the sectional shapes progressively produced in the nine-station roll forming of a sheave track from annealed type 304 stainless steel strip 67.3 mm (2.648 in.) wide by 0.79 mm (0.031 in.)

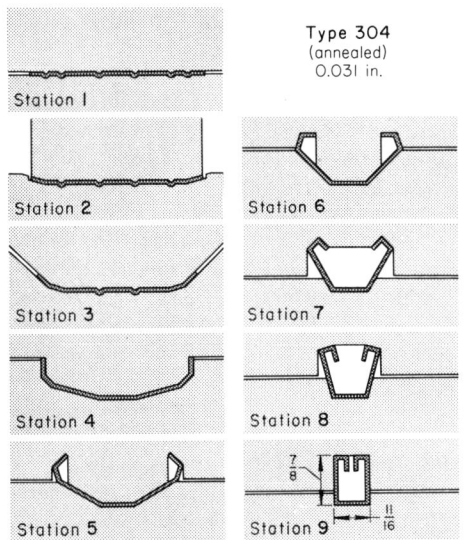

Fig. 30 Contour roll forming of a sheave track in nine stations. Dimensions given in inches

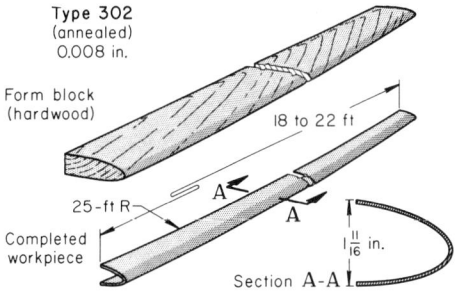

Fig. 31 Airfoil on which the leading edge was stretch formed to a long convex shape without lubricant in a radial-draw former

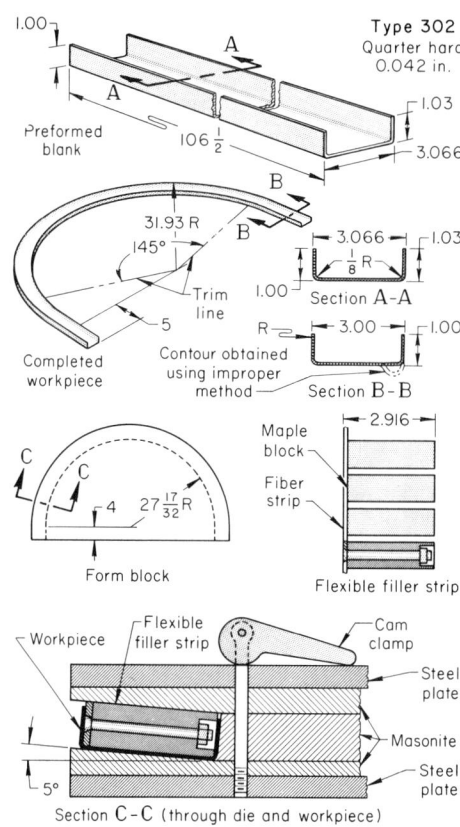

Fig. 32 Channel section that was stretch formed from a preform produced in a press brake, and details of tooling used in stretch forming, which provided reverse twist to compensate for springback. Dimensions given in inches

thick, with a No. 2 finish. In a tenth station, the formed track was straightened. As the track left the tenth station, it was clamped to a moving table that conveyed it to an abrasive wheel for cutoff into lengths of 3 to 6 m (10 to 20 ft). The material weighed 0.414 kg/m (0.278 lb/ft); annual production was 180 Mg (400,000 lb).

During forming, the developed width of the section measured along the neutral axis increased only 1.02 mm (0.040 in.) to 68.2 mm (2.688 in.), corresponding to only 1.5% stretch. The stretch was limited because the metal was restrained by the six pinch beads that were rolled into the strip before it was bent (stations 1, 2, and 3, Fig. 30). Each bead, 1.6 mm ($\frac{1}{16}$ in.) wide by 0.8 mm (0.030 in.) deep, permitted a sharp bend at that point without tearing or breaking the steel. The 50 to 55% elongation property of austenitic 304 stainless steel made it unlikely that the metal would break in bending. The strip was rolled with the slitting burr down so that the burr was flattened by the shoulders of the bottom roll of station 2.

The forming rolls were made of hardened steel, and the straightening rolls of hard bronze, for a good finish. Rolling speed was 17 m (55 ft) per minute. The lubricant was a pigmented water-soluble oil.

Plastic protective coatings are sometimes applied to the strip to minimize or prevent scratches and scuffing when high pressures are used and surface finish requirements are critical. On light-gage material (especially type 430), such protection is generally unnecessary if the fabricator is experienced in processing stainless steel.

Stretch Forming

Machines used for the stretch forming of stainless steel require 60 to 100% more power than that needed for similar operations on low-carbon steel of the same thickness. Because of the abrasiveness of stainless steels, forming tools must be especially abrasion resistant. Wiping dies, wiping shoes, mandrels, and wear plates must be made of wear-resistant tool steel, carbide, or a bearing grade of bronze in order to avoid galling and welding.

Although the 300-series stainless steels are especially suitable for stretch forming because of their high work-hardening rate and their ability to take large elongations, the 400-series steels are usable only for shallow stretched shapes. Type 301 is the austenitic steel that is best suited to stretch forming. Because of its high rate of work hardening, forming should be done slowly to derive maximum benefit from the ductility of type 301.

Maximum percentages of stretch for one-directional forming of various kinds of austenitic stainless steels are as follows:

- Annealed types 301, 302, 304, 305, 316, 321, and 347: 20% typical; possibly 30% on symmetrical and solid sections
- Quarter-hard types 301 and 302: 15% typical; possibly 20% on optimum sections
- Half-hard types 301 and 302: 5% typical; possibly 10% on optimum sections
- Full-hard type 301: possibly 2% on optimum sections

These figures should not be confused with permissible stretch in bending, nor are they the limits to which these stainless steels will stretch (which are considerably greater). Instead, these percentages, which determine the possible curvature of stretch-formed sectional shapes of stainless steel, are based on the distortion susceptibility of severely stretched stainless steel.

The upper limits can be extended by very slow stretching and forming, especially with hardened metal. In addition, to obtain maximum stretch from the harder tempers, workpieces should be carefully deburred. Automatic programming is valuable in applying continuously increasing tension to overcome the continuously increasing strength as work hardening takes place during stretch forming.

Lubricants. If there is little or no movement after contact between workpiece and form block, as in stretch wrapping or single-die draw forming, little or no lubricant need be used except when deformation is severe. A low-viscosity chlorinated oil or wax provides excellent chemical EP action and convenience of use. If there is considerable movement of the work metal against the dies (such as against the wiper shoe in radial-draw forming), pigmented lubricants are sometimes used. The following example describes an application in which no lubricant was used in the stretch forming of a sharply contoured part.

Example 25: Dry Stretch Forming of an Airfoil Leading Edge. The leading edge of an airfoil was stretch formed dry from a type 302 stainless steel blank, 0.20 mm (0.008 in.) thick, 115 mm ($4\frac{1}{2}$ in.) wide, and 5.5 to 6.7 m (18 to 22 ft) long, that had been roll formed to the airfoil contour shown in section A-A in Fig. 31. The blank had been annealed before roll forming, and it was stretch formed, without further annealing, to a 7.6 m (25 ft) radius with the heel of the contour pointing out (Fig. 31).

The airfoil was stretch formed in a radial-draw former over a hard-maple form block with the airfoil contour carved into its surface (Fig. 31). Lubricant was not used, because it had previously caused local variations in friction. Time for forming was 10 min/piece with three workers. Setup time was 2 h. A typical production lot was 100 pieces.

The rolled contour had to be held within ±0.1 mm (±0.005 in.) after stretch forming. The envelope tolerance on the stretch-formed shape was 0.76 mm (0.030 in.).

Springback. In sharply contoured pieces that have a relatively deep, wide cross section, some springback cannot be avoided, even in annealed metal. During severe stretch forming, considerably higher strength, and therefore appreciably higher elastic recovery, is developed in the more highly stressed convex surface.

Springback in regular, symmetrical sections can usually be offset by overbending the piece. Dimensional variations in workpieces are primarily caused by variations in springback, which are in turn caused by variations in mechanical properties from sheet to sheet.

If the workpiece is irregular in cross section, if preformed flanges are to be held to a certain angular position, or if the curve of the form varies in severity, springback may cause twist or irregular distortion of the workpiece. Various methods of blocking, pretwisting, or overforming are used to prevent or correct this distortion. In the following example, an asymmetrical cross section was twisted during forming to offset the twist caused by springback.

Example 26: Use of Twisting to Compensate for Springback in Stretch Forming. The curved channel section shown in Fig. 32 was stretch formed from quarter-hard type 302 stainless steel strip, 1.07 mm (0.042 in.) thick, that had been preformed in a press brake. Although the channel fit closely in the groove of the form block, springback caused considerable twist in the finished piece.

Elastic recovery of the outer flange and the metal near the outer edge of the web caused buckling and twisting in the part as forming tension was released. To overcome this, the part was canted by the form block, and tension on the part was gradually increased during forming.

To establish a compensating initial reverse twist in the workpiece, spacers were added to the builtup form block to wedge the section to a 5° angle, as shown in Fig. 32. At the same time, a fiber filler strip with maple filler blocks was closely fitted into the channel to hold the cross-sectional contour. Details of the tooling are shown in Fig. 32.

The applied tension during stretch forming was 83.2 kN (18,700 lbf) at the start, 87.0 kN (19,550 lbf) at 45° bend, 90.7 kN (20,400 lbf) at 90°, 94.5 kN (21,250 lbf) at 135°, and 98.3 kN (22,100 lbf) upon completion of the bend. A nonpigmented fatty acid was used as the forming lubricant. After forming, the workpiece was trimmed to a 145° arc with a band saw.

Equalizing Stretch. In the stretch forming of sheets to a curvature in two directions (especially in stretching tempered material when the limits of stretch are very close), the quality of the product can be controlled much better if the stretch is uniform across the workpiece. One means of obtaining uniform stretch is to provide compensating contours (which are later trimmed off) at the end of the form block.

Bending of Tubing

Austenitic stainless steel tubing can be bent to a centerline radius of $1\frac{1}{2}$ times tube diameter. As the ratio of tube diameter to wall thickness, D/t, increases, it becomes increasingly necessary to provide both internal and external support to keep

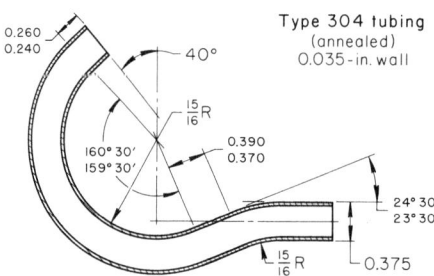

Fig. 33 Aerospace component that was bent from stainless steel tubing with the use of a low-melting alloy as a filler during bending. Dimensions given in inches

the tube from collapsing as it is bent. When D/t is greater than 30, the tube is classed as a thin-wall tube. Interlocked tooling, as well as bending machines of a greater capacity than that required for thick-wall tubes, is strongly recommended for thin-wall tubing.

For the bending of stainless steel tubing, wiper dies and mandrels are often made of aluminum bronze or a chromium-plated tool steel. Lubricants for the mandrel should be fairly heavy. Viscous or pigmented oil-base lubricants containing emulsifiers for ease of removal are used. Only the very lightest of lubricants should be used between the wiper die and the tube. A thin application of very light chlorinated mineral oil can be used in some bending operations without causing wrinkling. The following example describes techniques used in the bending of stainless steel tubing.

Example 27: Bending Difficult-to-Form Tubing into an Aerospace Component. The bent tube shown in Fig. 33, used in an aerospace assembly, was difficult to form within the specified tolerances (dimensions within ±0.25 mm, or ±0.010 in.; angles within ±½°; and flattening of the tube at bends not more than 0.05 mm, or 0.002 in.). The piece was produced from type 304 stainless steel tubing in nine operations in the following sequence (times shown are for the production of 100-piece lots):

- Cut tubing into lengths of 160 mm ($6\frac{1}{4}$ in.) with an abrasive cutoff wheel; deburr roughly (3 h).
- Fill each workpiece with low-melting alloy (8 h).
- Make 160° bend in powered draw bender; gage the bend (5 h).
- Make 24° bend in hand bender; gage the bend (5 h).
- Trim ends to length in a cutoff fixture using an abrasive wheel (3 h).
- Melt out the filler (6 h).
- Deburr by hand, using a grinder and a drill (3 h).
- Passivate in a chemical dip (1 h).
- Inspect 100% with gage and by rolling an accurate ball through the completed part (2 h).

Springback in bending, about 5°, was corrected by overbending to a degree established in trial bends.

Other Forming Operations on Tubing

Stainless steel tubing can be easily flared to increase the diameter 25 to 30% if it is annealed. The diameter can be reduced by rotary swaging, or it can be reduced by bulging or beading. Rubber punches are often used for this purpose.

Tubing of austenitic stainless steel can be hot formed by heating to 1175 to 1260 °C (2150 to 2300 °F). Work should be halted when the tube has cooled to 925 °C (1700 °F), and the tube should then be cooled rapidly to minimize the precipitation of carbides.

Because austenitic stainless steel tubing is stronger than carbon steel tubing and work hardens rapidly, warm forming (below the recrystallization temperature) is also used on this material. The temperature for warm forming should be kept below 425 °C (800 °F) to prevent the formation of carbides.

Tubing of ferritic stainless steels, such as types 430 and 446, is less easily formed than similar tubing of austenitic stainless steels. Ferritic tubing is hot formed at 1035 to 1095 °C (1900 to 2000 °F), and forming is stopped when the tubing cools to 815 °C (1500 °F). For best results, the range from 815 to 980 °C (1500 to 1800 °F) should be avoided, because ductility and notch toughness are progressively impaired as the tube cools through that range. Hot shortness may be encountered in the upper part of the range. Tubing of ferritic stainless steels is warm formed at 120 to 205 °C (250 to 400 °F).

Steel producers have studied the cold formability of 11% Cr (type 409) and 17% Cr (type 439 or 18% Cr-Nb) tubing materials, primarily because of requests from the automotive industry to use titanium or Ti + Nb stabilized ferritic alloys in exhaust systems. Such alloys are normally used in high-frequency welded or gas-tungsten arc welded (autogenous) and annealed tubing. Traditionally, the gas-tungsten arc welded and annealed tubes had more formability because of the elimination of the 8 to 15% cold work induced in forming the tube.

As these ferritic alloys were subjected to the demands of high-speed vector bending, particularly in making tubular exhaust manifolds, breakage rates increased to more than 50%. In response, stainless steel producers borrowed technology from low-carbon steel production practices and developed a line of high-performance ferritic alloys with improved elongations and higher r values (>1.5).

Such alloys have permitted the greater use of high-frequency welded and unannealed tubes for thin-wall bends with a centerline bend radius less than twice the tube diameter. Furthermore, such bends can be made at room temperature, although care should be exercised in cold weather not to fabricate sub-room-temperature tubing. Finally, through tighter control of both melt chemistry and processing parameters, ferritic tube alloys with excellent welding and bending reproducibility from heat to heat have been developed.

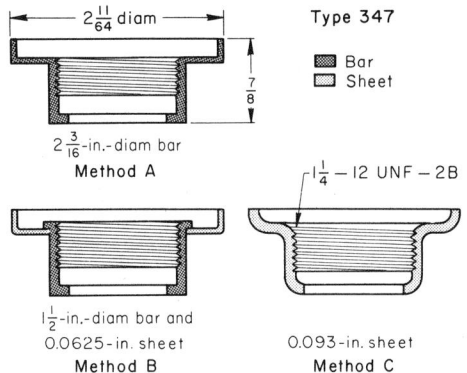

Fig. 34 Machining vs. press forming for producing a cap. In method A, the cap was completely machined from bar stock. In method B, the cap (redesigned) combined components that were press formed from sheet and machined from bar stock. In method C, the entire cap (again redesigned) was press formed from sheet and then partly machined. Dimensions given in inches

Forming versus Machining

Although forming ordinarily requires expensive tooling and bulky equipment, it is a high-speed process, and for most parts that can be formed from sheet it is more economical than machining for mass production. The following example shows how production techniques can vary with the size of the production lot to make the best use of each technique.

Example 28: Influence of Change in Quantity of Production Method and Product Design. A threaded cap was made from type 347 stainless steel by three different methods. Each method involved a change in design, as illustrated in Fig. 34.

The original order was for 100 caps, with an anticipated design change on future orders. The quickest and most economical production method was to machine the cap in one piece from bar stock (method A, Fig. 34).

The next order was for 1000 caps. The design and manufacturing methods were revised so that the cap was produced as an assembly of two components, one press formed from sheet and the other machined from bar stock (method B, Fig. 34).

When requirements increased to 5000 caps, a cost reduction was essential to obtain the order against a competitor's bid. The part was redesigned for production entirely from sheet by press forming and partial machining (method C, Fig. 34). Overall cost was reduced nearly 50% as compared to methods A and B.

The press-formed part of method B was made in a 400 kN (45 tonf) open-back-inclinable mechanical press at a rate of 200 to 250 pieces/h. The die was made of oil-hardening tool steel. Method C used an air-hardening tool steel die and a 530 kN (60 tonf) open-back-inclinable mechanical press that made 300 to 350 pieces/h. Mineral oil was used as a lubricant in both methods.

ACKNOWLEDGMENT

The information in this article is largely taken from J.A. Douthett, Forming of Stainless Steel, *Forming and Forging*, Vol 14, *ASM Handbook*, ASM International, 1988, p 759-778.

SELECTED REFERENCES

- J.A. Ferree, Forming Sheet, Strip, and Plate, *Handbook of Stainless Steels*, D. Peckner and I.M. Bernstein, Ed., McGraw-Hill, 1977, p 27-1 to 27-8
- H. Giraud and B. Baroux, Deep Drawing Properties of Stainless Steels, *Stainless Steels*, P. Lacombe, B. Baroux, and G. Beranger, Ed., Les Éditions de Physique, 1993, p 696-731

Forging and Extrusion

STAINLESS STEEL SHAPES can be produced by a variety of hot and cold bulk deformation processes, including rolling, forging (hot), cold or warm heading, and extrusion (hot or cold). In bulk forming, the input material is in billet, rod, or slab form, and the surface-to-volume ratio in the formed part increases considerably under largely compressive loading. In sheet forming, on the other hand, a piece of sheet metal is plastically deformed by tensile loads into a three-dimensional shape, often without significant changes in sheet thickness or surface characteristics. This article addresses processing parameters for forging, heading, and extrusion of stainless steels. Sheet forming operations are described in the article "Forming" in this Volume.

Hot Forging

In terms of forging pressure and load requirements, stainless steels are considerably more difficult to forge than carbon or low-alloy steels, primarily because of their greater strength at elevated temperatures and the limitations on the maximum temperatures at which they can be forged without incurring microstructural damage. Forging load requirements and forgeability vary widely among stainless steels of different types and compositions; the most difficult alloys to forge are those with the greatest strength at elevated temperatures.

Forging Methods

Open-die forging, closed-die forging, upset forging, roll forging, and ring rolling are among the most common methods used to forge stainless steel. As in the forging of other metals, two of these methods are sometimes used in sequence to produce a desired shape. More detailed information on each of these forging methods can be found in Volume 14 of the *ASM Handbook*.

Open-die forging (hand forging) is often used for smaller quantities for which the cost of closed dies cannot be justified and in cases in which delivery requirements dictate shortened lead times. Generally, products include round bars, blanks, hubs, disks, thick-wall rings, and square or rectangular blocks or slabs in virtually all stainless grades. Forged stainless steel round bar can also be produced to close tolerances on radial forge machines.

Although massive forgings are normally associated with open-die forging, most stainless steel open-die forgings are produced in the range of 10 to 900 kg (25 to 2000 lb). The relative open-die forgeabilities of various metals, including stainless steels, are as follows:

Most forgeable

Aluminum alloys
Magnesium alloys
Copper alloys
Carbon and low-alloy steels
Martensitic stainless steels
Maraging steels
Austenitic stainless steels
Nickel alloys
Semiaustenitic PH stainless steels
Titanium alloys
Iron-base superalloys
Cobalt-base superalloys
Niobium alloys
Tantalum alloys
Molybdenum alloys
Nickel-base superalloys
Tungsten alloys
Beryllium alloys

Least forgeable

Closed-die forging is extensively applied to stainless steel to produce blocker-type, conventional, and close-tolerance forgings.

Blocker-type forgings are produced in relatively inexpensive dies, but their weight and dimensions are somewhat greater than those of corresponding conventional closed-die forgings. A blocker-type forging approximates the general shape of the final part, with relatively generous finish allowance and radii. Such forgings are sometimes specified when only a small number of forgings are required and the cost of machining parts to final shape is not excessive.

Conventional closed-die forgings are the most common and are produced to comply with commercial tolerances. These forgings are characterized by design complexity and tolerances that fall within the broad range of general forging practice. They are made closer to the shape and dimensions of the final part than are blocker-type forgings; therefore, they are lighter and have more detail.

Close-tolerance forgings are usually held to smaller dimensional tolerances than conventional forgings. Little or no machining is required after forging, because close-tolerance forgings are made with less draft, less material, and thinner walls, webs, and ribs. These forgings cost more and require higher forging pressures per unit of plan area than conventional forgings. However, the higher forging cost is sometimes justified by a reduction in machining cost.

Selection from the above closed-die types invariably depends on the quantity and cost of the finished part.

Upset forging is sometimes the only suitable forging process when a large amount of stock is needed in a specific location of the workpiece. For many applications, hot upset forging is used as a preforming operation to reduce the number of operations, to save metal, or both when the forgings are to be completed in closed dies.

The rules that apply to the hot upset forging of carbon and alloy steels are also applicable to stainless steel; that is, the unsupported length should never be more than $2\frac{1}{2}$ times the diameter (or, for a square, the distance across flats) for single-blow upsetting. Beyond this length, the unsupported stock may buckle or bend, forcing metal to one side and preventing the formation of a concentric forging. Exceeding this limitation also causes grain flow to be erratic and nonuniform around the axis of the forging and encourages splitting of the upset on its outside edges. The size of an upset produced in one blow also should not exceed $2\frac{1}{2}$ diameters (or, for a square, $2\frac{1}{2}$ times the distance across flats). This varies to some extent, depending on the thickness of the upset. For extremely thin upsets, the maximum size may be only two diameters or even less. Without reheating and multiple blows, it is not possible to produce an upset in stainless steel that is as thin or has corner radii as small as that which can be produced with a more forgeable metal such as carbon steel.

Roll forging can be used to forge specific products, such as tapered shafts. The principle involved in reducing the cross-sectional area of the work metal in roll forging is essentially the same as that employed in rolling mills to reduce billets to bars. Roll forging is also used as a stock-gathering operation prior to forging in closed dies.

Ring rolling is used to produce some ringlike parts from stainless steel at lower cost than by closed-die forging. The techniques used are essentially the same as those for the ring rolling of carbon or alloy steel. More power is required to roll stainless steel, and it is more difficult to fill corners. A large ring mill capable of rolling carbon steel rings with a face height of 2 m (80 in.) can roll stainless steel rings up to about 1.25 m (50 in.) in height. Because stainless steel is more costly than carbon or alloy steel, the savings that result from using ring rolling are proportionately greater for stainless steel.

Ingot Breakdown

In discussing the forgeability of the stainless steels, it is critical to understand the types of primary mill practices available to the user of semifinished billet or bloom product.

Primary Forging and Ingot Breakdown. Most stainless steel ingots destined for the forge shop are melted by the electric arc furnace-argon oxygen decarburization (EAF-AOD) process, as described in the article "Melting and Refining Methods" in this Volume. They usually weigh between 900 and 13,500 kg (2000 to 30,000 lb), depending on the shop and the size of the finished piece. Common ingot shapes are round, octagonal, or fluted; less common ingot shapes include squares. Until recently, all of these ingots would have been top poured. Increasing numbers of producers are now switching to the bottom-poured ingot process. This process is slightly more expensive, but it more than pays for itself in extended mold life and greatly improved ingot surface.

Some stainless steel grades, such as the precipitation-hardening (PH) steels used in the aircraft and aerospace industries, are double melted. The first melt is done with the EAF-AOD process or vacuum induction melting, and these "electrodes" are then remelted by a vacuum arc remelting or electroslag remelting process. This remelting under a vacuum or a slag tends to give a much cleaner product with better hot workability. For severe forging applications, the use of remelt steels can sometimes be a critical factor in producing acceptable parts. These double-melted ingots are round and vary in diameter from 450 to 900 mm (18 to 36 in.). In some cases, they weigh in excess of 11,000 kg (25,000 lb). The breakdown of ingots is usually done on large hydraulic presses (13,500 kN, or 1500 tonf). A few shops, however, still use large hammers, and the four-hammer radial forging machine is increasingly often used for ingot breakdown.

Heating is the single most critical step in the initial forging of ingots. The size of the ingot and the grade of the stainless steel dictate the practice necessary to reduce thermal shock and to avoid unacceptable segregation levels. It is essential to have accurate and programmable control of the furnaces used to heat stainless steel ingots and large blooms.

Primary forging or breakdown of an ingot is usually achieved using flat dies. However, some forgers work the ingot down as a round using "V"

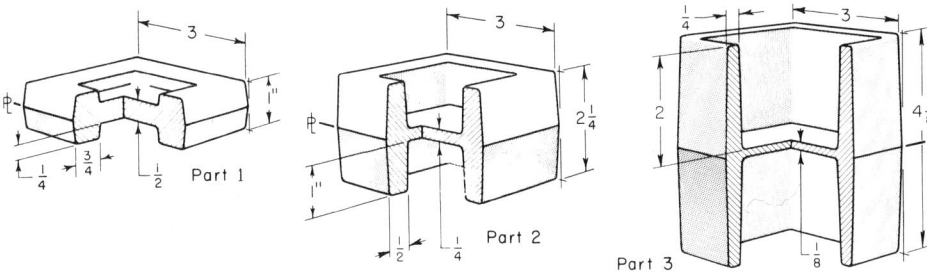

Fig. 1 Three degrees of forging severity. Dimensions given in inches

or swage dies. Because of the high hot hardness of stainless steel and the narrow range of working temperatures for these alloys, a series of light reductions, or saddening, is the preferred initial step in the forging of the entire surface of the ingot. (During saddening an ingot is given a succession of light reductions in a press or rolling mill, or under a hammer, to break down the skin and overcome the initial fragility that is due to the coarse crystalline structure.)

Once saddening is complete, normal reductions of 50 to 100 mm (2 to 4 in.) can be taken. If the chemistry of the heat is in accordance with specifications and if heating practices have been followed and minimum forging temperatures observed, no problems should be encountered in making the bloom and other semifinished product.

If surface tears occur, the forging should be stopped and the workpiece should be conditioned. Some forgers use hot powder scarfing, but this presents environmental problems. The most common method is to grind out the defect. The ferritic, austenitic, and nitrogen-strengthened austenitic stainless steels can be air cooled, ground, and reheated for reforging. The martensitic and PH grades must be slow cooled and overaged before grinding and reheating. The ingot surface is important, and many producers find it advantageous to grind the ingots before forging to ensure good starting surfaces.

Billet and Bloom Product. Forgers buy bars, billets, or blooms of stainless steel for subsequent forging on hammers and presses. Forged stainless steel billet and bloom products tend to have better internal integrity than rolled product, especially with larger-diameter sections (>180 mm, or 7 in.). Correctly conditioned billet and bloom product should yield acceptable finished forgings if good heating practices are followed and if attention is paid to the minimum temperature requirements. Special consideration must be given to sharp corners and thin sections, because these tend to cool very rapidly. Precautions should be taken when forging PH or nitrogen-strengthened austenitic grades.

Forgeability

Closed-Die Forgeability. The relative forging characteristics of stainless steels can be most easily depicted through examples of closed-die forgings. The forgeability trends these examples establish can be interpreted in light of the grade, type of part, and forging method to be used.

Stainless steels of the 300 and 400 series can be forged into any of the hypothetical parts illustrated in Fig. 1. However, the forging of stainless steel into shapes equivalent to part 3 in severity may be prohibited by shortened die life (20 to 35% of that obtained in forging such a shape from carbon or low-alloy steel) and by the resulting high cost. For a given shape, die life is shorter in forging stainless steel than in forging carbon or low-alloy steel.

Forgings of mild severity, such as part 1 in Fig. 1, can be produced economically from any stainless steel with a single heating and about five blows. Forgings approximating the severity of part 2 can be produced from any stainless steel with a single heating and about ten blows. For any type of stainless steel, die life in the forging of part 1 will be about twice that in the forging of part 2.

Part 3 represents the maximum severity for forging all stainless steels and especially those with high strength at elevated temperature, namely types 309, 310, 314, 316, 317, 321, and 347. Straight-chromium types 403, 405, 410, 416, 420, 430, 431, and 440 are the easiest to forge into a severe shape such as part 3 (although type 440, because of its high carbon content, would be the least practical). Types 201, 301, 302, 303, and 304 are intermediate between the two previous groups.

One forge shop has reported that part 3 would be practical and economical to produce in the higher-strength alloys if the center web were increased from 3 to 6 mm ($\frac{1}{8}$ to $\frac{1}{4}$ in.) and if all fillets and radii were increased in size. It could then be forged with 15 to 20 blows and one reheating, dividing the number of blows about equally between the first heat and the reheat.

Table 1 compares the closed-die forgeability of various alloy groups and their respective forging temperatures. As this table indicates, stainless steels are more difficult to forge than carbon and alloy steels but have superior forgeability when compared to titanium alloys, superalloys, and refractory alloys.

Hot Upsetting. Forgings of the severity represented by hypothetical parts 4, 5, and 6 in Fig. 2 can be hot upset in one blow from any stainless steel. However, the conditions are similar to those encountered in hot die forging. First, with a stainless steel, die wear in the upsetting of part 6 will be several times as great as in the upsetting of part 4. Second, die wear for the forming of any shape will increase as the elevated-temperature strength of the alloy increases. Therefore, type 410, with about the lowest strength at high temperature,

Table 1 Classification of alloys in order of increasing forging difficulty

Alloy group	Approximate forging temperature range	
	°C	°F
Least difficult		
Aluminum alloys	400-550	750-1020
Magnesium alloys	250-350	480-660
Copper alloys	600-900	1110-1650
Carbon and low-alloy steels	850-1150	1560-2100
Martensitic stainless steels	1100-1250	2010-2280
Maraging steels	1100-1250	2010-2280
Austenitic stainless steels	1100-1250	2010-2280
Nickel alloys	1000-1150	1830-2100
Semiaustenitic PH stainless steels	1100-1250	2010-2280
Titanium alloys	700-950	1290-1740
Iron-base superalloys	1050-1180	1920-2160
Cobalt-base superalloys	1180-1250	2160-2280
Niobium alloys	950-1150	1740-2100
Tantalum alloys	1050-1350	1920-2460
Molybdenum alloys	1150-1350	2100-2460
Nickel-base superalloys	1050-1200	1920-2190
Tungsten alloys	1200-1300	2190-2370
Most difficult		

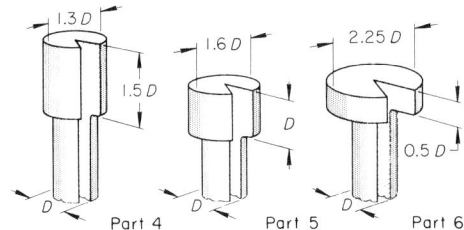

Fig. 2 Three degrees of upsetting severity

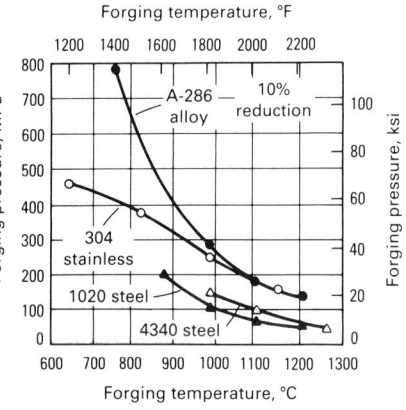

(a)

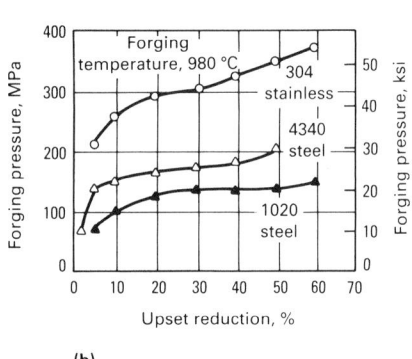

(b)

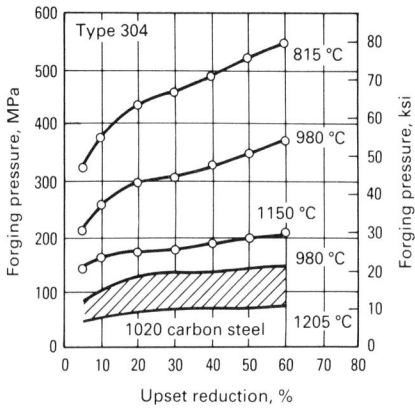

Fig. 3 Effect of upset reduction on forging pressure for various temperatures. Source. Ref 1

Fig. 4 Forging pressure required for upsetting vs. (a) forging temperature and (b) percentage of upset reduction. Source: Ref 2

would be the most economical stainless steel for forming any of the parts, particularly part 6. Conversely, type 310 would be the least economical.

Upset Reduction versus Forging Pressure. The effect of percentage of upset reduction (upset height vs. original height) on forging pressure for low-carbon steel and for type 304 stainless steel at various temperatures is illustrated in Fig. 3. Temperature has a marked effect on the pressure required for any given percentage of upset, and at any given forging temperature and percentage of upset, type 304 stainless requires at least twice the pressure required for 1020 steel.

The effects of temperature on forging pressure are further emphasized in Fig. 4(a). These data, based on an upset reduction of 10%, show that at 760 °C (1400 °F), type 304 stainless steel requires only half as much pressure as A-286 (an austenitic PH alloy), although the curves for forging pressure for the two metals converge at 1100 °C (2000 °F). However, at a forging temperature of 1100 °C (2000 °F), the pressure required for a 10% upset reduction on type 304 is more than twice that required for a carbon steel (1020) and about 60% more than that required for 4340 alloy steel. Figure 4(b) shows the differences in forgeability, based on percentage of upset reduction and forging pressure, between type 304 stainless steel, 1020, and 4340 at the same temperature (980 °C, or 1800 °F).

Austenitic Stainless Steels

The austenitic stainless steels are more difficult to forge than the straight-chromium types but are less susceptible to surface defects. Most of the austenitic stainless steels can be forged over a wide range of temperatures above 930 °C (1700 °F). Because they do not undergo major phase transformation at elevated temperatures, they can

be forged at higher temperatures than the martensitic types (Tables 1 and 2). Exceptions occur when the composition of the austenitic stainless steel promotes the formation of δ-ferrite, as in the case of the 309S, 310S, or 314 grades. At temperatures above 1100 °C (2000 °F), these steels, depending on their composition, may form appreciable amounts of δ-ferrite. Figure 5 depicts these compositional effects in terms of nickel equivalent (austenitic-forming elements) and chromium

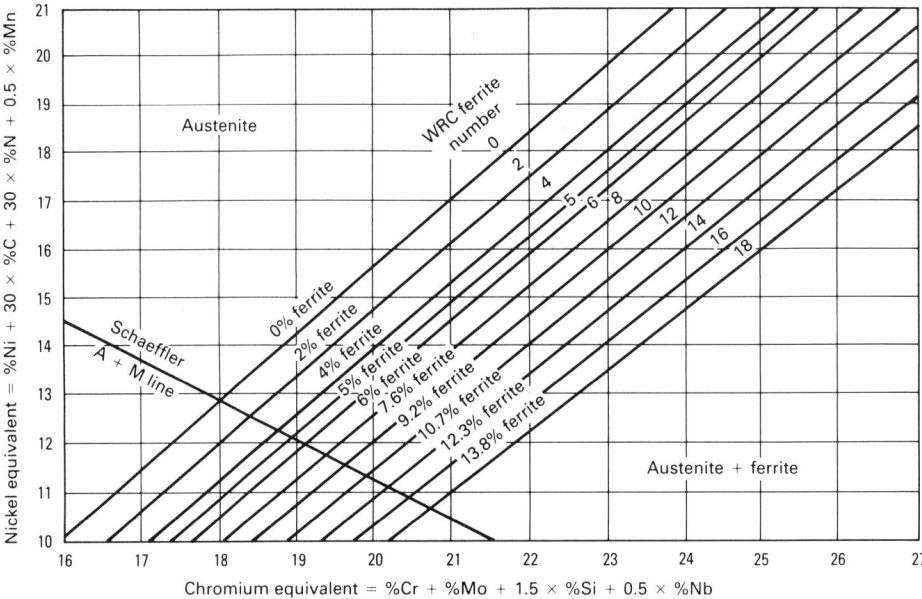

Fig. 5 Schaeffler (constitution) diagram used to predict the amount of δ-ferrite that will be obtained during elevated-temperature forging or welding of austenitic/ferritic stainless steels. A, austenite; M, martensite. WRC, Welding Research Council. Source: Ref 4

Table 2 Typical compositions and forging temperature ranges of high-temperature alloys

Alloy	C	Cr	Ni	Mo	Co	Other	Temperature °C	°F
More difficult to hot work								
Carpenter 41	0.09	19.0	Bal	10.0	11.0	3.1 Ti, 1.5 Al, 0.005 B	1040-1175	1900-2145
Pyromet 718	0.10	18.0	55.0	3.0	...	1.3 Ti, 0.6 Al, 5.0 Nb	925-1120	1700-2050
M252	0.15	18.0	38.0	3.2	20.0	2.8 Ti, 0.2 Al	980-1175	1800-2145
Waspaloy	0.07	19.8	Bal	4.5	13.5	3.0 Ti, 1.4 Al, 0.005 B	1010-1175	1850-2145
Pyromet 860	0.1	14.0	45.0	6.0	4.0	3.0 Ti, 1.3 Al, 0.01 B	1010-1120	1850-2050
Carpenter 901	0.05	12.5	42.5	6.0	...	2.7 Ti, 0.2 Al, 0.015 B	1010-1120	1850-2050
N155	0.12	21.0	20.0	3.0	19.5	2.4 W, 1.2 Nb, 0.13 N	1040-1150	1900-2100
V57	0.05	15.0	27.0	1.3	...	3.0 Ti, 0.2 Al, 0.01 B, 0.3 V	955-1095	1750-2000
A-286	0.05	15.0	25.0	1.3	...	2.1 Ti, 0.2 Al, 0.004 B, 0.3 V	925-1120	1700-2050
Carpenter 20Cb-3	0.05	20.0	34.0	2.5	...	3.5 Cu	980-1230	1800-2245
Pyromet 355	0.12	15.5	4.5	3.0	...	0.10 N	925-1150	1700-2100
Type 440F	1.0	17.0	...	0.5	...	0.15 Se	925-1150	1700-2100
Type 440C	1.0	17.0	...	0.5	...	...	925-1150	1700-2100
19-9DL/19DX	0.32	18.5	9.0	1.5	...	1.4 W plus Nb or Ti	870-1150	1600-2100
Types 347 and 348	0.05	18.0	11.0	...	...	0.07 Nb	925-1230	1700-2245
Type 321	0.05	18.0	10.0	...	...	0.40 Ti	925-1260	1700-2300
AMS 5700	0.45	14.0	14.0	...	...	2.5 W	870-1120	1600-2050
Type 440B	0.85	17.0	...	0.5	...	...	925-1175	1700-2145
Type 440A	0.70	17.0	...	0.5	...	...	925-1200	1700-2200
Type 310	0.15	25.0	20.0	...	...	...	980-1175	1800-2145
Type 310S	0.05	25.0	20.0	...	...	...	980-1175	1800-2145
17-4 PH	0.07	17.0	4.0	...	...	3.0-3.5 Cu, 0.3 Nb + Ta	1095-1175	2000-2145
15-5 PH	0.07	15.0	5.0	...	...	3.5 Cu, 0.3 Nb + Ta	1095-1175	2000-2145
13-8 Mo	0.05	13.0	8	2.25	...	0.90-1.35 Al	1095-1175	2000-2145
Type 317	0.05	19.0	13.0	3.5	...	...	925-1260	1700-2300
Type 316L	0.02	17.0	12.0	2.5	...	...	925-1260	1700-2300
Type 316	0.05	17.0	12.0	2.5	...	...	925-1260	1700-2300
Type 309S	0.05	23.0	14.0	...	...	...	980-1175	1800-2145
Type 309	0.10	23.0	14.0	...	...	...	980-1175	1800-2145
Type 303	0.08	18.0	9.0	...	...	0.30 S	925-1260	1700-2300
Type 303Se	0.08	18.0	9.0	...	...	0.30 Se	925-1260	1700-2300
Type 305	0.05	18.0	12.0	...	...	...	925-1260	1700-2300
Easier to hot work								
Types 302 and 304	0.05	18.0	9.0	...	...	...	925-1260	1700-2300
UNS S21800	0.06	17	8.5	...	...	8.0 Mn, 0.12 N	1095-1175	2000-2145
No. 10	0.05	16.0	18.0	...	...	...	925-1230	1700-2245
Lapelloy	0.30	11.5	0.30	2.8	...	0.3 V	1040-1150	1900-2100
Lapelloy C	0.20	11.5	0.40	2.8	...	2.0 Cu, 0.08 N	1040-1150	1900-2100
636	0.23	12.0	0.8	1.0	...	0.3 V, 1.0 W	1040-1175	1900-2145
H46	0.17	12.0	0.5	0.8	...	0.4 Nb, 0.07 N, 0.3 V	1010-1175	1850-2145
AMS 5616 (Greek Ascoloy)	0.17	13.0	2.0	0.2	...	3.0 W	955-1175	1750-2145
Type 431	0.16	16.0	2.0	...	...	...	900-1200	1650-2200
Type 414	0.12	12.5	1.8	...	...	...	900-1200	1650-2200
Type 420F	0.35	13.0	...	...	...	0.2 S	900-1200	1650-2200
Type 420	0.35	13.0	...	...	...	...	900-1200	1650-2200
Pyromet 600	0.08	16.0	74.0	...	...	8.0 Fe	870-1150	1600-2100
Type 416	0.1	13.0	...	...	...	0.3 S	925-1230	1700-2245
Type 410	0.1	12.5	...	...	...	...	900-1200	1650-2200
Type 404	0.04	11.5	1.8	...	...	...	900-1150	1650-2100
Type 501	0.2	5.0	...	0.5	...	...	980-1200	1800-2200
Type 502	0.05	5.0	...	0.5	...	...	980-1200	1800-2200
HiMark 300	0.02	...	18.0	4.8	9.0	0.7 Ti, 0.1 Al	815-1260	1500-2300
HiMark 250	0.02	...	18.0	4.8	7.5	0.4 Ti, 0.1 Al	815-1260	1500-2300
Carpenter 7-Mo (Type 329)	0.08	28.0	5.8	1.6	...	...	925-1095	1700-2000
Type 446	0.1	25.0	...	...	...	...	900-1120	1650-2050
Type 443	0.1	21.0	...	...	...	1.0 Cu	900-1120	1650-2050
Type 430F	0.08	17.0	...	...	...	0.3 S	815-1150	1500-2100
Type 430	0.06	17.0	...	...	...	...	815-1120	1500-2050

Source: Ref 3

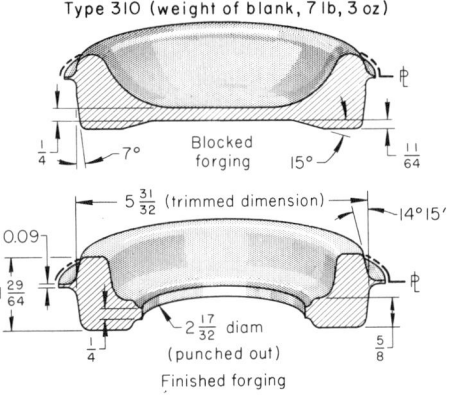

Type 310 (weight of blank, 7 lb, 3 oz)

Sequence of operations

1—Upset on flat portion of die to approximately 115 mm (4½ in.) in diameter. 2—Forge in blocker impression. 3—Forge in finisher impression. 4—Hot trim (900 to 925 °C, or 1650 to 1700 °F) and punch out center. 5—Air cool. 6—Clean (shot blast)

Processing conditions

```
Blank preparation . . . . . . . . . . . . . . . . . . . . . Cold sawing
Stock size . . . . . . . . . . . . . . 90 mm (3½ in.) in diameter
Blank weight . . . . . . . . . . . . . . . . . . . . 3.25 kg (7 lb, 3 oz)
Heating method . . . . . Gas-fired, slot-front box furnace
Heating time . . . . . . . . . . . . . . . . . . . . . . . . . . . . . . . . . . 1 h
Atmosphere . . . . . . . . . . . . . . . . . . . . . . Slightly oxidizing
Die material . . . . . . . . . . . . . . . . . . 6G at 388–429 HB(a)
Die life, total . . . . . . . . . . . . . . . . 507–2067 forgings(b)
Die lubricant . . . . . . . . . . . . . . . . . . . . . . . . . . . Graphite-oil
Production rate . . . . . . . . . . . . . 50 forgings per hour(c)
```

(a) Inserts at this hardness were used in die blocks of the same material, but softer (341–375 HB). (b) Average life was 1004 forgings. Life to rework and total life were the same, because worn die inserts were not reworked. (c) Based on a 50 min working hour

Fig. 6 Typical procedure for forging a ringlike part from an austenitic stainless steel. Dimensions given in inches

about 1065 °C (1950 °F) is generally advised for nonstabilized austenitic stainless steel forgings in order to retain the chromium carbides in solid solution.

Finishing temperatures for austenitic stainless steels become more critical where section sizes increase and ultrasonic testing requirements are specified. During ultrasonic examination, coarse-grain austenitic stainless steels frequently display excessive sweep noise due to a coarse-grain microstructure. The degree of sound attenuation normally increases with section size and may become too great to permit detection of discontinuities. Careful control of forging conditions, including final forge reductions of at least 5%, can assist in the improvement of ultrasonic penetrability.

A typical procedure for the hammer forging of one of the more difficult-to-forge austenitic steels (type 310) is given in the following example.

Example 1: Forging a Ringlike Part from Type 310 Steel. The ringlike part shown in Fig. 6 was forged in a 13,500 N (3000 lbf) steam hammer by upsetting a piece of round bar and completing the shape in one blocking and one finishing impression. Because of its small size and symmetrical shape, the workpiece could be handled rapidly and completed without reheating. The effect of forging severity, however, is re-

equivalent. Delta-ferrite formation adversely affects forgeability, and compensation for the amount of ferrite present can be accomplished with forging temperature restrictions.

Equally important restrictions in forging the austenitic stainless steels apply to the finishing temperatures. All but the stabilized types (321, 347, 348) and the extra-low-carbon types should

be finished at temperatures above the sensitizing range (~815 to 480 °C, or 1500 to 900 °F) and cooled rapidly from 870 °C (1600 °F) to a black heat. The highly alloyed grades, such as 309, 310, and 314, are also limited with regard to finishing temperature because of their susceptibility at lower temperatures to hot tearing and σ formation. A final annealing by cooling rapidly from

flected in the short die life. Die life and other forging details are given in the table in Fig. 6.

The stabilized or extra-low-carbon austenitic stainless steels, which are not susceptible to sensitization, are sometimes strain hardened by small reductions at temperatures well below the forging temperature. Strain hardening is usually accomplished at 535 to 650 °C (1000 to 1200 °F) (referred to as *warm working* or *hot-cold working*). When minimum hardness is required, the forgings are solution annealed.

Sulfur or selenium can be added to austenitic stainless steel to improve machinability. Selenium, however, is preferred because harmful stringers are less likely to exist. Type 321, stabilized with titanium, may also contain stringers of segregate that will open as surface ruptures when the steel is forged. Type 347, stabilized with niobium, is less susceptible to stringer segregation and is the stabilized grade that is usually specified for forgings.

When the austenitic stainless steels are heated, it is especially desirable that a slightly oxidizing furnace atmosphere be maintained. A carburizing atmosphere or an excessively oxidizing atmosphere will impair corrosion resistance, either by harmful carbon pickup or by chromium depletion. In types 309 and 310, chromium depletion can be especially severe.

Nitrogen-strengthened austenitic stainless steels are iron-base alloys containing chromium and manganese. Varying amounts of nickel, molybdenum, niobium, vanadium, and/or silicon are also added to achieve specific properties. Nitrogen-strengthened austenitic stainless steels provide high strength, excellent cryogenic properties and corrosion resistance, low magnetic permeability (even after cold work or subzero temperature), and higher elevated-temperature strengths as compared to the 300-series stainless steels. These alloys are summarized as follows:

- *UNS S24100 (Nitronic 32) ASTM XM-28:* High work hardening while remaining nonmagnetic, plus has twice the yield strength of type 304 with equivalent corrosion resistance
- *UNS S24000 (Nitronic 33) ASTM XM-29:* Has twice the yield strength of type 304, low magnetic permeability after severe cold work, high resistance to wear and galling as compared to standard austenitic stainless steels, and good cryogenic properties
- *UNS S21904 (Nitronic 40) ASTM XM-11:* Has twice the yield strength of type 304 with good corrosion resistance, low magnetic permeability after severe cold working, and good cryogenic properties
- *UNS S20910 (Nitronic 50) ASTM XM-19:* Has corrosion resistance greater than type 316L with twice the yield strength, good elevated-temperature and cryogenic properties, and low magnetic permeability after severe cold work
- *UNS S21800 (Nitronic 60):* Has galling resistance, corrosion resistance equal to that of type 304, along with twice the yield strength, good oxidation resistance, and cryogenic properties

A forgeability comparison as defined by dynamic hot hardness, is provided in Fig. 7.

Martensitic Stainless Steels

Martensitic stainless steels have high hardenability to the extent that they are generally air hardened. Therefore, precautions must be taken in cooling forgings of martensitic steels, especially those with high carbon content, in order to prevent cracking. The martensitic alloys are generally cooled slowly to about 590 °C (1100 °F), either by burying in an insulating medium or by temperature equalizing in a furnace. Direct water sprays, such as might be employed to cool dies, should be avoided, because they would cause cracking of the forging.

Forgings of the martensitic steels are often tempered in order to soften them for machining. They are later quench hardened and tempered.

Maximum forging temperatures for these steels need to be kept low enough to avoid the formation of δ-ferrite. If δ-ferrite stringers are present at forging temperatures, cracking is likely to occur. Delta-ferrite usually forms at temperatures from 1095 to 1260 °C (2000 to 2300 °F). Care must be exercised so as not to exceed this temperature during forging and to avoid rapid metal movement that might result in local overheating. Surface decarburization, which promotes ferrite formation, must be minimized.

The δ-ferrite formation temperature decreases with increasing chromium content, and small amounts of δ-ferrite reduce forgeability significantly. As the δ-ferrite increases above about 15% (Fig. 5), forgeability improves gradually until the structure becomes entirely ferritic. Finishing temperatures are limited by the allotropic transformation, which begins near 815 °C (1500 °F). However, forging of these steels is usually done at about 925 °C (1700 °F), because

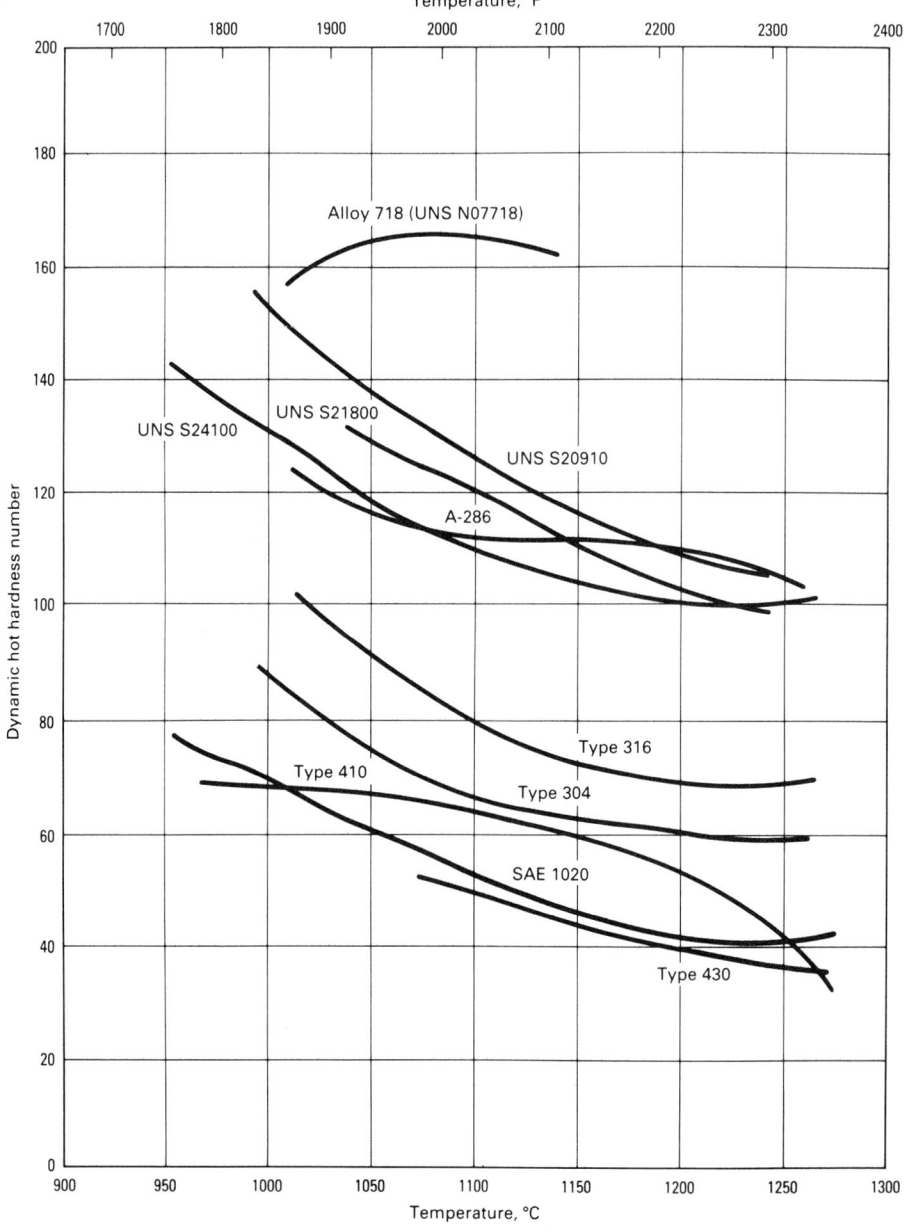

Fig. 7 Comparative dynamic hot hardness vs. temperature (forgeability) for various ferrous alloys

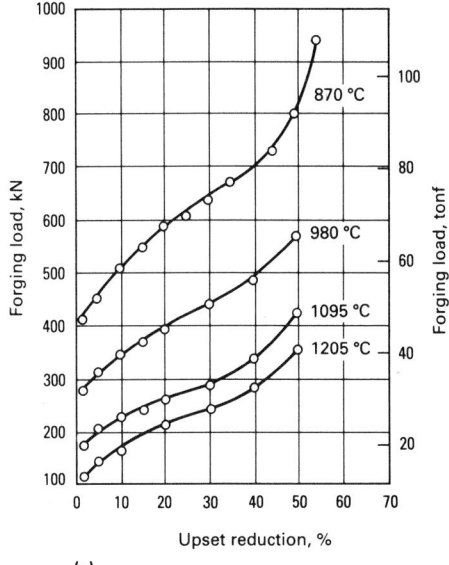

(a)

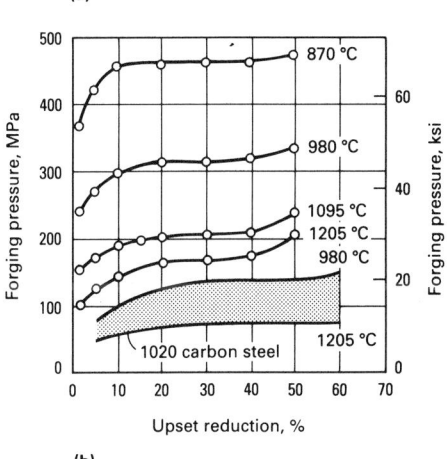

(b)

Fig. 8 Effect of upset reduction at four temperatures on forging load in the forging of A-286 (a), and the forging pressure for A-286 compared with that for 1020 steel (b). Source: Ref 2

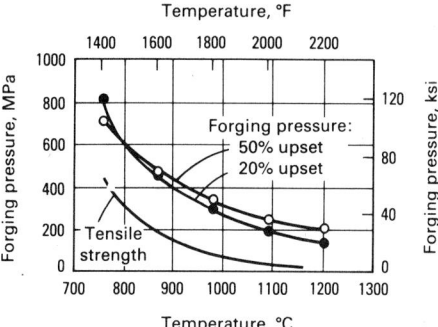

Fig. 9 Forging pressure vs. temperature for A-286. Also shown is the effect of increasing temperature on the tensile strength of the material. Upset strain rate: 0.7 s⁻¹. Source: Ref 1

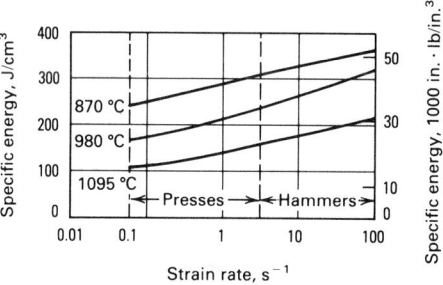

Fig. 10 Specific energy vs. strain rate in the press and hammer forging of A-286 at three temperatures. Source: Ref 1

the metal is difficult to deform at lower temperatures.

Sulfur or selenium can be added to type 410 to improve machinability. These elements can cause forging problems, particularly when they form surface stringers that open and form cracks. This can sometimes be overcome by adjusting the forging temperature or the procedure. With sulfur additions, it may be impossible to eliminate all cracking of this type. Therefore, selenium additions are preferred.

Ferritic Stainless Steels

The ferritic straight-chromium stainless steels exhibit virtually no increase in hardness upon quenching. They will work harden during forging; the degree of work hardening depends on the temperature and the amount of metal flow. Cooling from the forging temperature is not critical.

The ferritic stainless steels have a broad range of forgeability, which is restricted somewhat at higher temperatures because of grain growth and structural weakness but is closely restricted in finishing temperature only for type 405. Type 405 requires special consideration because of the grain-boundary weakness resulting from the development of a small amount of austenite. The other ferritic stainless steels are commonly finished at any temperature down to 705 °C (1300 °F). For type 446, the final 10% reduction should be made below 870 °C (1600 °F) to achieve grain refinement and room-temperature ductility. Annealing after forging is recommended for ferritic steels.

Precipitation-Hardening Stainless Steels

The semiaustenitic and martensitic PH stainless steels can be heat treated to high hardness through a combination of martensite transformation and precipitation. They are the most difficult to forge and will crack if temperature schedules are not accurately maintained. The forging range is narrow, and the steel must be reheated if the temperature falls below 980 °C (1800 °F). They have the least plasticity (greatest stiffness) at forging temperature of any of the classes and are subject to grain growth and δ-ferrite formation. Heavier equipment and a greater number of blows are required to achieve metal flow equivalent to that of the other types.

During trimming, the forgings must be kept hot enough to prevent the formation of flash-line cracks. To avoid these cracks, it is often necessary to reheat the forgings slightly between the finish-forging and trimming operations. Cooling, especially of the martensitic grades, must be controlled to avoid cracking.

Austenitic PH stainless steels are highly alloyed materials used for heat-resistant applications. The inclusion content of these alloys has a significant effect on their forgeability. Alloys such as A-286 (UNS S66286) containing titanium and aluminum can develop nitride and carbonitride segregation, which later appears as stringers in wrought bars and affects forgeability. This type of segregation is almost completely eliminated through the use of vacuum melting. Therefore, austenitic PH stainless steels can be forged into a greater variety of shapes with

greater reductions, approaching the forgeability of type 304 stainless steel.

Temperature has an important effect on forgeability. The optimal temperature range for forging A-286 and similar alloys is narrow. The forgeability of A-286, based on the forging load required for various upset reductions at four forging temperatures, is shown in Fig. 8(a). Figure 8(b) shows that, on the basis of forging pressure, A-286 is considerably more difficult to forge than 1020 steel, even though A-286 is among the most forgeable of the heat-resistant alloys. For example, as shown in Fig. 8(b), 1020 steel at 1205 °C (2200 °F) requires only about 69 MPa (10 ksi) for an upset reduction of 30%, but for the same reduction at the same temperature, A-286 requires approximately 172 MPa (25 ksi).

Forging pressures increase somewhat for greater upset reductions at normal forging temperatures. As shown in Fig. 9, the pressure for a 20% upset reduction of A-286 at 1095 °C (2000 °F) is about 193 MPa (28 ksi), but for an upset reduction of 50% the pressure increases to about 241 MPa (35 ksi). Figure 9 also shows that forging pressure is up to ten or twelve times greater than the tensile strength of the alloy at forging temperature.

Strain rates also influence forging pressures. Figure 10 shows that as strain rate increases, more energy is required in presses and hammers.

Duplex Stainless Steels

Because of their higher strength, duplex stainless steels are generally stiff when hot worked, relative to many other stainless grades. Rolling and forging equipment must have sufficient power to reduce the material while it is in the temperature range for optimum hot workability. The surface of finished forgings can be optimized by controlling the initial surface, material composition, phase balance, and hot-working temperature. Wrought structures generally produce a better surface after reforging than does cast material after the initial forging operation.

Forging Equipment

Stainless steels are generally forged with the same types of hammers, presses, upsetters, and rolling machines used to forge carbon and alloy steels. Descriptions of these machines are provided in Volume 14 of the *ASM Handbook*.

Hammers. Simple board-type gravity-drop hammers are not extensively used for the forging of stainless steel because of their low capacity and because greater control is obtained with other types of equipment. Power-drop hammers (steam or air) are widely used for open-die forgings as well as for all types of large and small closed-die forgings. The service life of the die is usually longer in hammers than in hydraulic presses; in a hammer, the hot workpiece is in contact with the dies (particularly the upper die) for a shorter length of time. Hammers cost less than presses of equivalent capacity and are generally more flexible than presses in the variety of functions they can fulfill.

Presses. Mechanical presses are used extensively for small forgings, less often for forgings weighing as much as 45 kg (100 lb) each, and seldom for forgings weighing more than 70 kg (150 lb). Mechanical presses cost more than hammers of equivalent capacity, but they require less operator skill and can produce forgings more rapidly than hammers.

Hydraulic presses can be used for all steps in the forging of stainless steel. However, they are more often used to complete intricate forgings after preforming in other types of equipment. Die life is usually shorter in a hydraulic press than in a hammer; in a press, the work metal contacts the dies for a longer period of time. However, there is less danger of local overheating of the metal in hydraulic presses because their action is slower than that of hammers.

Radial Forging Machines. Another tool that is increasing in use is the radial forging machine. This is a precision four-hammer forging machine that is capable of forging all grades of stainless steel into round, rectangular, square, or octagonal shapes. Different cross sections on the same piece are possible, including the forging of complicated step-down shafts.

The machine uses four axial symmetrical hammers, which are in opposing pairs and are electromechanically controlled by a preprogrammed processor to deliver 200 paired blows per minute to the work. Two hydraulically controlled manipulators, one in each side of the hammer box, rotate and position the workpiece during forging.

Each hammer delivers up to approximately 9000 kN (1000 tonf) of force per blow, depending on the size of the machine. As a result of the counterblow configuration, the workpiece receives enough energy so that isothermal reductions are possible, an advantage in the forging of grades with narrow hot-working ranges. The piece loses very little temperature during forging and sometimes actually increases in temperature; therefore, everything is finished in one heat. The feed and rotation motions of the chuck head are synchronized with the hammers to prevent twisting or stretching during forging.

In operation, the manipulator or chuck head on the entry side of the hammer box positions the workpiece between the four hammers and supports it until the length is increased so as to be grasped by the manipulator or chuck head at the exit side. Forging then continues in a back-and-forth mode until the desired finished cross section is

achieved. At the end of each forging pass, the trailing manipulator relinquishes its grip so that the end receives the same reduction as the rest of the workpiece. This results in uniformity in mechanical properties as well as dimensions. In general, experience with the radial forging machine indicates an oversize of 0.015 times the cold-finish dimension and typical tolerances for hot-forged products of approximately one-half the ASTM A 484 or one-fourth the DIN 7527 standards.

Dies

In most applications, dies designed for the forging of a given shape from carbon or alloy steel can be used to forge the same shape from stainless steel. However, because of the greater force used in forging stainless steel, more strength is required in the die. Therefore, the die cannot be resunk as many times for the forging of stainless steel, because it may break. When a die is initially designed for the forging of stainless steel, a thicker die block is ordinarily used in order to obtain a greater number of resinkings and therefore a longer total life. Die practice for the forging of stainless steel varies considerably among different plants, depending on whether forging is done in hammers or presses and on the number of forgings produced from other metals in proportion to the number forged from stainless steel.

Multiple-cavity dies for small forgings (less than about 10 kg, or 25 lb) are more commonly used in hammers and less commonly used in presses. If multiple-cavity dies are used, the cavities are usually separate inserts, because some cavities have longer service lives than others. With this practice, individual inserts can be changed as required. Larger forgings (more than about 10 kg, or 25 lb) are usually produced in single-cavity dies, regardless of whether a hammer or a press is used.

In forge plants in which carbon and alloy steels comprise the major portion of the metals forged, the usual practice is to use the same die

system (single-cavity vs. multiple-cavity) for stainless steel, accepting a shorter die life. This approach is generally more economical than using a separate die practice for a relatively small tonnage of forgings.

Practice is likely to be entirely different in shops in which most of the forgings produced are from stainless steel or some other difficult-to-forge metal, such as heat-resistant alloys. For example, in one plant in which mechanical presses are used almost exclusively, most of the dies are of the single-cavity design. Tolerances are always close, so practice is the same regardless of the quantity to be produced. A die is made with a finishing cavity, and after it is worn to the extent that it can no longer produce forgings to specified tolerances, the cavity is recut to become a semifinishing, or blocker, cavity. When it can no longer be used as a blocker die, its useful life is over because resinking would result in a thin die block.

Die Materials. In shops in which die practice is the same for stainless steel as for carbon and alloy steels, die materials are also the same. Compositions of tool and die materials are listed in Table 3. In shops in which special consideration is given to dies for stainless steel, small dies (for forgings weighing less than 9 kg, or 20 lb) are made solid from hot-work tool steel, such as H11, H12, or H13. For large dies, regardless of whether they are single- or multiple-impression, common practice is to make the body of the block from a conventional die-block low-alloy steel, such as 6G or 6F2. Inserts are of H11, H12, or H13 hot-work tool steel (or sometimes H26, where it has proved a better choice). In many specialty applications, nickel- and cobalt-base superalloys are fabricated for die inserts on conventional hot-work tool steel dies. Welded inlays of these alloys are also being used in critical areas for improved wear resistance and much higher hot strength.

Gripper dies and heading tools used for the hot upsetting of stainless steel are made from one of the hot-work tool steels. Small tools are machined from solid tool steel. Larger tools are made by in-

Table 3 Compositions of tool and die materials for hot forging

Designation	Nominal composition, %								
---	C	Mn	Si	Co	Cr	Mo	Ni	V	W
Chromium-base AISI hot-work tool steels									
H10	0.40	0.40	1.00	...	3.30	2.50	...	0.50	...
H11	0.35	0.30	1.00	...	5.00	1.50	...	0.40	...
H12	0.35	0.40	1.00	...	5.00	1.50	...	0.50	1.50
H13	0.38	0.30	1.00	...	5.25	1.50	...	1.00	...
H14	0.40	0.35	1.00	...	5.00	...	...	...	5.00
H19	0.40	0.30	0.30	4.25	4.25	0.40	...	2.10	4.10
Tunsten-base AISI hot-work tool steels									
H21	0.30	0.30	0.30	...	3.50	...	...	0.45	9.25
H22	0.35	0.30	0.30	...	2.00	...	...	0.40	11.00
H23	0.30	0.30	0.30	...	12.00	...	...	1.00	12.00
H24	0.45	0.30	0.30	...	3.0	...	...	0.50	15.00
H25	0.25	0.30	0.30	...	4.0	...	...	0.50	15.00
H26	0.50	0.30	0.30	...	4.0	...	...	1.00	18.00
Low-alloy proprietary steels									
ASM 6G	0.55	0.80	0.25	...	1.00	0.45	...	0.10	...
ASM 6F2	0.55	0.75	0.25	...	1.00	0.30	1.00	0.10	...
ASM 6F3	0.55	0.60	0.85	...	1.00	0.75	1.80	0.10	...

serting hot-work tool steels into bodies of a lower-alloy steel, such as 6G or 6F2.

Roll dies for roll forging are usually of the same material used for the roll forging of carbon or alloy steels. A typical die steel composition is Fe-0.75C-0.70Mn-0.35Si-0.90Cr-0.30Mo.

Die hardness depends mainly on the severity of the forging and on whether a hammer or a press is used. Die wear decreases rapidly as die hardness increases, but some wear resistance must always be sacrificed for the sake of toughness and to avoid breaking the dies.

Most solid dies (without inserts) made from such steels as 6G and 6F2 for use in a hammer are in the hardness range of 36.6 to 40.4 HRC. This range is suitable for forgings as severe as that of part 3 in Fig. 1. If severity is no greater than that of part 1 in Fig. 1, die hardness can be safely increased to the next level (41.8 to 45.7 HRC). If forging is done in a press, the dies can be safely operated at higher hardnesses for the same degree of forging severity. For example, dies for forgings of maximum severity would be 41.8 to 45.7 HRC and dies for minimum severity would be 47.2 to 50.3 HRC.

Inserts or solid dies made from hot-work tool steel are usually heat treated to 40 to 47 HRC for use in hammers. For forgings of maximum severity (part 3, Fig. 1), hardness near the low end of the range is used. For minimum severity (part 1, Fig. 1), die hardness will be near the high end of the range. Adjustment in die hardness for different degrees of forging severity is usually also needed for forging in presses, although a higher hardness range (usually 47 to 55 HRC) can be safely used.

The hardness of gripper-die inserts for upset forging is usually 44 to 48 HRC. For the heading tools, hardness is 48 to 52 HRC.

Roll-forging dies are usually heat treated to 50 to 55 HRC. Rolls for ring rolling, when made from hot-work tool steel, are usually operated in the hardness range of 40 to 50 HRC.

Die Life. Because of the differences in forgeability among stainless steels, die life will vary considerably, depending on the composition of the metal being forged and the composition and hardness of the die material. Other conditions being equal, the forging of types 309, 310, and 314 stainless steel and the PH alloys results in the shortest die life. The longest die life is obtained when forging lower-carbon ferritic and martensitic steels. Die life in forging type 304 stainless steel is usually intermediate. However, die life in forging any stainless steel is short compared to that obtained in forging the same shape from carbon or alloy steel.

Example 2: Die Life in the Upset Forging of Type 304, 4340, and 9310. The 100 mm (4 in.) upset shown in Fig. 11 was produced from three different metals in the same 150 mm (6 in.) upsetter and in the same gripper dies (H12 hot-work tool steel at 44 HRC). From the bar chart in Fig. 11, the effect of work metal composition on die life is obvious. Die life for upsetting type 304 stainless steel was less than one-fifth that for upsetting the low-carbon alloy steel (9310) and less than one-third that for upsetting 4340.

Example 3: Effect of Forging Severity on Die Life. The effect of the forging shape (severity) on die life for forging type 431 stainless steel is shown in Fig. 12. When forging to the relatively mild severity of shape A, the range of life for five dies was 6000 to 10,000 forgings, with an average of 8000. When forging severity was increased to that of shape B, the life of three dies ranged from approximately 700 to 2200 forgings, with an average of 1400.

Shapes A and B were both forged in the same hammer. Tool material and hardness were also the same for both shapes (6G die-block steel at 341 to 375 HB).

Heating for Forging

Recommended forging temperatures for most of the standard and heat-resistant stainless steels are listed in Table 1. The thermal conductivity of stainless steels is lower than that of carbon or low-alloy steels; therefore, stainless steels take longer to reach the forging temperature. However, they should not be soaked at the forging temperature, but should be forged as soon as possible after reaching it. The exact time required for heating stock of a given thickness to the established forging temperature depends on the type of furnace used. Time and stock thickness relationships for three types of furnaces are shown in Fig. 13.

The need to preheat forging stock will be dictated by the grade, size, and condition of the stock to be forged. Austenitic and ferritic grades, for example, are generally considered safe from thermal shock and can be charged directly into hot furnaces. Certain martensitic and PH grades should be preheated at temperatures in the range of 650 to 925 °C (1200 to 1700 °F), depending on section size and the condition of the material.

Section sizes larger than 150 by 150 mm (6 by 6 in.) require special consideration, because rapid heating of larger sections will result in differential expansion that could locally exceed the tensile strength of the interior of the section. The resulting internal crack, frequently termed *klink,* will often open transversely upon further reductions. Generally, the greater the ability of the stainless grade to be hardened to high hardness levels, the more susceptible it is to thermal shock.

The physical condition of the stainless steel must also be taken into consideration. Cast material (that is, ingot or continuous cast) will be more susceptible to thermal shock than semiwrought or wrought product.

Equipment. Gas-fired and electric furnaces are used with equal success for heating the stock. Gas-fired furnaces are more widely used because heating costs are usually lower. The gas employed should be essentially free from hydrogen sulfide and other sulfur-bearing contaminants. Oil-fired furnaces are widely used for heating the 400-series stainless steels and the 18-8 varieties, but because of the danger of contamination from sulfur in the oil, they are considered unsafe for heating the high-nickel grades. Trace amounts of vanadium present in the fuel oil can also cause surface problems because the resulting vanadium oxide will fuse with the high-chromium scale.

Although not absolutely necessary, heating of stainless steel is preferably done in a protective atmosphere. When gas heating is used, an acceptable protective atmosphere can usually be obtained by adjusting the fuel-to-air ratio. When the furnace is heated by electricity, the protective atmosphere (if used) must be separately generated. Induction heating is most often used to heat local portions of the stock for upsetting.

Temperature control within ±5 °C (±10 °F) is achieved by the use of various types of instruments. A recording instrument is preferred, because it enables the operator to observe the behavior of the furnace throughout the heating cycle.

It is recommended that the temperature of the pieces of forging stock be checked occasionally

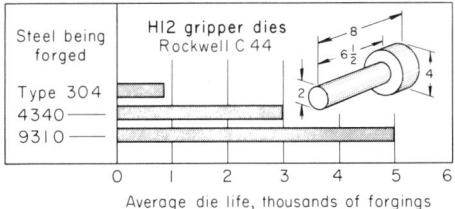

Fig. 11 Effect of steel being forged on the life of gripper dies in upsetting. Dimensions given in inches

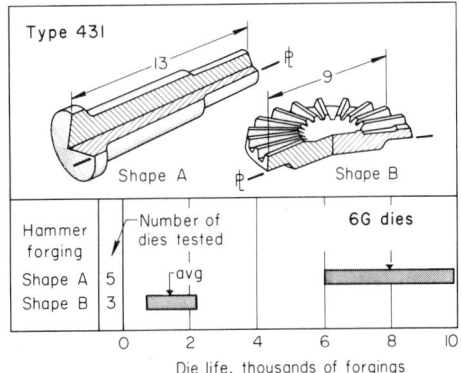

Fig. 12 Effect of severity of forging on die life. Dies: 341-375 HB. Dimensions given in inches

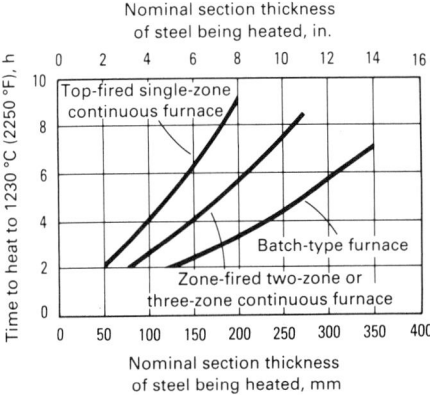

Fig. 13 Effect of section thickness on time for heating stainless steel in various types of furnaces. Source: Ref 5

with an optical or probe-type pyrometer as the pieces are removed from the furnace. This practice not only provides a check on the accuracy of the furnace controls but also ensures that the stock is reaching the furnace temperature.

Control of Cooling Rate. Cooling from the forging operations should also be considered in terms of grade and size. Austenitic grades are usually quenched from the forge. This is done to minimize the formation of intergranular chromium carbides and to facilitate cutting and machining after forging. Because martensitic grades are characterized by high hardenability, special precautions are taken in cooling them from forging temperatures. Common practice is to place hot forgings in insulating materials for slow cooling. For parts that have either heavy sections or large variation in section, it is often desirable to charge the forged parts into an annealing furnace immediately after forging.

In particular, the higher-carbon grades, such as 440A, 440B, and 440C, and the modified 420 types, such as UNS 41800 (ASTM A 565, Grade 615), must be carefully slow cooled after forging. These steels often require furnace-controlled interrupted cooling cycles to prevent cracks. A suitable cycle consists of air cooling the forgings to temperatures at which the martensite transformation is partially complete (between 150 and 250 °C, or 300 and 500 °F), then reheating the forgings in a furnace at a temperature of about 650 °C (1200 °F) before final cooling to room temperature. This procedure also prevents the formation of excessive grain-boundary carbides, which sometimes develop during continuous slow cooling.

The control cooling of 17-4 PH, 15-5 PH, and PH 13-8 Mo grades after forging must also be considered. These grades are austenitic upon cooling from forging or solution-treating temperatures until a temperature of approximately 120 to 150 °C (250 to 300 °F) is reached. At this temperature, transformation to martensite begins; this transformation is not complete until the piece has reached approximately 30 °C (90 °F) for 17-4 PH and 15-5 PH and 15 °C (60 °F) for PH 13-8 Mo. Cooling in this transformation range should be as uniform as possible throughout the cross section of the piece to prevent thermal cracking.

Upon completion of the forging of PH grades, sections less than 75 mm (3 in.) in thickness should be air cooled to between 30 and 15 °C (90 and 60 °F) before any further processing. Intricate forgings should first be equalized for a short period of time (30 min to 1 h, depending on size) in the temperature range of 1040 °C (1900 °F) to the forging temperature. The part can then be allowed to air cool to between 30 and 15 °C (90 and 60 °F). This equalization relieves forging stresses and improves temperature uniformity in the part. Nonuniformity in cooling may promote cracking. Forgings that are more than 75 mm (3 in.) in section, after equalizing, should be air cooled until dull red or black, covered immediately and completely on all sides with a light-gage metal cover (not galvanized sheet) or thin ceramic thermal sheeting, then allowed to cool undisturbed to between 30 and 15 °C (90 and 60 °F). Cooling should be done in areas that are free from drafts and away from furnaces where temperatures in the surrounding area are above 30 °C (90 °F). The covered, cooling steel should not be placed too near other large forged sections that have been cooled or are practically cooled, because this can interfere with the uniformity of the cooling.

Furnace cooling of 17-4 PH and 15-5 PH large or intricate sections may be desirable in cold weather because this extends the cooling time considerably. However, if necessary, the heated forgings should be air cooled to approximately 315 to 370 °C (600 to 700 °F), charged into a furnace, and equalized at that temperature. The furnace is then shut off, and the furnace and forgings are allowed to cool to room temperature.

Heating of Dies

Dies are always heated for the forging of stainless steel. Large dies are heated in ovens; small dies, by burners of various design.

There is no close agreement among forge shops on the maximum die temperature that should be maintained, although it is generally agreed that 150 °C (300 °F) should be the minimum temperature. A range of 150 to 200 °C (300 to 400 °F) is common. Dies are sometimes heated to 315 °C (600 °F). Die temperature is determined by means of temperature-sensitive crayons or surface pyrometers.

Die Lubrication

Dies should be lubricated before each blow. For forging in shallow impressions, a spray of colloidal graphite in kerosene or in low-viscosity mineral oil is usually adequate. Ordinarily, dies are sprayed manually, but in press forging, automatic sprays timed with the press stroke are sometimes used. For deeper cavities, however, it is often necessary to use a supplemental spray (usually manual) to reach the deep areas of the cavity or to swab the cavity with a conventional forging oil. Forging oils are usually mixtures of oil and graphite; the oil should be free of lead and sulfur. Forging oils are often purchased as greases and are then diluted with mineral oil to the desired viscosity. Any volatile lubricant should be used sparingly. With even a slight excess, vapor explosions are likely, and greater amounts can cause explosions that will eject the workpiece, possibly injuring personnel.

Glass is sometimes used as a lubricant or billet coating in press forging. The glass is applied by dipping the heated forging in molten glass or by sprinkling the forging with glass grit. Glass is an excellent lubricant, but its viscosity must be compatible with the forging temperature used. For optimal results, the viscosity of the glass should be maintained at 10 Pa · s (100 cP). Therefore, when different forging temperatures are used, a variety of glass compositions must be stocked. Another disadvantage of glass is that it will accumulate in deep cavities, solidify, and impair metal flow. Therefore, the use of glass is generally confined to shallow forgings that require maximum lateral flow.

Trimming

When production quantities justify the cost of tools, forgings are trimmed in dies. Hot trimming is preferred for all types of stainless steel, because less power is required and there is less danger of cracking than in cold trimming. The PH stainless steels must be hot trimmed to prevent flash-line cracks, which can penetrate the forging.

It is often practical to hot trim immediately after the forging operation, before the workpiece temperature falls below a red heat. Less often, forgings are reheated to 900 to 950 °C (1650 to 1750 °F) and then trimmed.

Tool Materials. Punches for the hot trimming of closed-die forgings are often made of 6G or 6F2 die block steel at 41.8 to 45.7 HRC, and blades are made of a high-alloy tool steel, such as D2, at 58 to 60 HRC. In some forge shops, both punches and blades for hot trimming are made of a carbon or low-alloy steel (usually with less than 0.30% C) and then hardfaced, generally with a cobalt-base alloy (a typical composition is Co-1.5C-30Cr-8W).

Upset forgings can be hot trimmed in a final pass in the upsetter or in a separate press. For trimming in the upsetter, H11 tool steel at 46 to 50 HRC has performed successfully on a variety of forgings with a normal flash thickness. For the trimming of heavy flash in the upsetter, H21 at 50 to 52 HRC is recommended. Tools for hot trimming in a separate press are also made of a hardfaced 0.30% C or low-alloy steel.

Cleaning

Stainless steels do not form as much scale as carbon or alloy steels, especially when a protective atmosphere is provided during heating. However, the scale that does form is tightly adherent, hard, and abrasive. It must be removed prior to machining or tool life will be severely impaired.

Mechanical or chemical methods, or a combination, can be used to remove scale. Abrasive blast cleaning is an efficient method and is applicable to forgings of various sizes and shapes in large or small quantities. When surfaces will not be machined or passivated, blasting must be done with only silica sand; the use of steel grit or shot will contaminate the surfaces and impair corrosion resistance.

Abrasive blast cleaning is usually followed by acid pickling. The forgings are then thoroughly washed in water.

Barrel finishing (tumbling) is sometimes used for descaling. Acid pickling is recommended after tumbling.

Wire brushing is sometimes used for removing scale from a few forgings. Brushes with stainless steel wire must be used unless the forgings will be machined or passivated.

Salt bath descaling followed by acid cleaning and brightening is an efficient method of removing scale. A typical procedure is detailed in Table 4. Additional information on scale removal is available in the article "Surface Engineering" in this Volume.

Table 4 Cycle for sodium hydride (reducing) descaling of annealed stainless steel forgings

Operation sequence	Bath composition	Bath temperature, °C (°F)	Treatment time, min
Descale	1.5 to 2.0% NaH	400-425 (750-800)	20
Quench	Water (circulated in tank)	Cold	1-3
Acid clean	10% H_2SO_4	65 (145)	20
Acid brighten	10% HNO_3-2% HF	65 (145)	30
Rinse	Water (high-pressure spray)	Ambient	2
Rinse	Water	80 (175)	1 - 2

Cold Heading

Cold heading is a cold forging process in which the force developed by one or more strokes (blows) of a heading tool is employed to upset, or displace, the metal in a portion of a wire or rod blank to form a section of different contour or, more commonly, of larger cross section than the original. The process is widely used to produce a variety of small and medium-size hardware items (e.g., bolts and rivets). However, the process is not limited to the cold deformation of the ends of a workpiece or to conventional upsetting. Metal displacement may be imposed at any point, or at several points, along the length of the workpiece and may incorporate extrusion in addition to upsetting. Advantages of the process over machining of the same parts from suitable bar stock include the minimal waste material, increased tensile strength from cold work, and controlled metal flow.

Although cold heading is most commonly performed on low-carbon steels having hardnesses of 75 to 87 HRB, some stainless steels, such as the austenitic types 302, 304, 305, 316, 321, and 384 and the ferritic and martensitic types 410, 430, and 431, can be cold headed. One of the most widely used cold-heading stainless steels is UNS S30430, which is identified by some cold-heading engineers as 302 HQ. It is similar in composi-

tion to type 304 except that it contains 3 to 4 % Cu, which results in a significant reduction in its cold-working characteristics. Work-hardening characteristics of various cold-heading stainless steels are compared in Fig. 14.

Because stainless steels work harden more rapidly than carbon steels, they are more difficult to cold head. More power is required, and cracking of the upset portion of the work metal is more likely than with carbon or low-alloy steels. These problems can be alleviated by preheating the work metal (see the section "Warm Heading" in this article).

Rating Formability

Metals and alloys are rated for cold heading on the basis of the length of stock, in terms of diameter, that can be successfully upset. Equipped with flat-end punches, the maximum length of unsupported cold-heading-quality stainless steel wire that can be successfully upset in one blow to form a good concentric head is from 2 to $2\frac{1}{2}$ times the original wire diameter. If additional blows are used, this length can be doubled. Figure 15 illustrates the problem of trying to head a wire of unsupported length exceeding that which has been recommended.

The maximum diameter that can be formed in this same wire in one blow is about $2\frac{1}{4}$ times the original wire diameter. Additional blows can upset the austenitic grades to maximum diameters ranging from 3 to $3\frac{1}{2}$ times that of the stock diameter, whereas the straight-chromium grades can be worked to the same extent as carbon steel.

Typical tolerances that can be expected during cold heading of stainless steels are (Ref 6):

Dimension, mm (in.)	Tolerance, mm (in.)
Diameter	
≤4.8 ($\frac{3}{16}$)	±0.025 (0.001)
>4.8-9.5 ($\frac{3}{16}$–$\frac{3}{8}$)	±0.038 (0.0015)
>9.5-14.3 ($\frac{3}{8}$–$\frac{9}{16}$)	±0.05 (0.002)
Length	
≤25 (1)	±0.013 (0.005)
25-75 (1-3)	±0.75 (0.030)
75-150 (3-6)	±1.0 (0.040)

Machines

Standard cold headers are classified according to whether the dies open and close to admit the work metal or are solid, and according to the number of strokes (blows) the machine imparts to the workpiece during each cycle. The die in a single-stroke

machine has one mating punch; in a double-stroke machine, two punches. The two punches usually reciprocate, so that each contacts the workpiece during a machine cycle. The straight-chromium grades, such as types 410 and 430, are often processed with single-stroke headers; austenitic grades require double-stroke headers.

Where additional strokes are required for more intricate contours, multistation or progressive headers are used. On such machines, parts are mechanically transferred from one die to the next, and all stations work simultaneously so that a part is finished and ejected at each stroke. These machines may have as many as six stations or dies.

Tools and Tool Materials

Tools used in cold heading consist principally of punches or hammers and dies. The dies can be made as one piece (solid dies) or as two pieces (open dies), as shown in Fig. 16.

Solid dies (known also as closed dies) consist of a cylinder of metal with a hole through the center (Fig. 16a). Solid dies may be made entirely from one material, or they may be made with the center portion surrounding the hole as an insert of a different material.

Open dies (also called two-piece dies) consist of two blocks with matching grooves in their faces (Fig. 16b). When the grooves in the blocks are put together, they match to form a die hole as in a solid die. The die blocks have as many as eight grooves on various faces, so that as one wears the block can be turned to make use of a new groove.

Tool Materials. The shock loads imposed on cold-heading tools must be considered in selecting tool materials. For optimum tool life it is essential that both punches and dies have hard surfaces (preferably HRC 60 or higher). However, with the exception of tools for cold heading of hard materials, the interior portions of the tools must be softer (HRC 40 to 50, and sometimes as low as HRC 35 for larger tools) or breakage is likely.

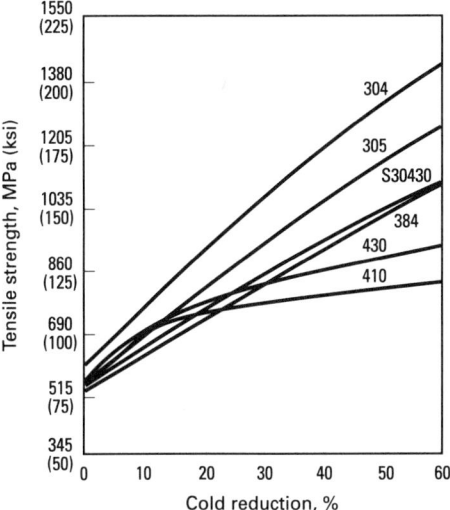

Fig. 14 Comparison of various stainless steels showing degree of work-hardening effect as a function of tensile strength increase and percentage of cold reduction. Source: Ref 6

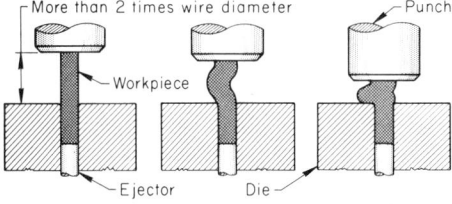

Fig. 15 Typical folding effect obtained with a flat-end punch when heading stainless steel having an unsupported length of more than about $2\frac{1}{4}$ diameters

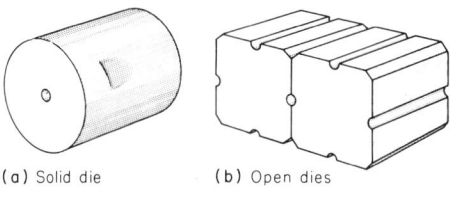

Fig. 16 Solid (one-piece) and open (two-piece) cold-heading dies

To meet these conditions, shallow-hardening tool steel such as W1 or W2 is used extensively for punches and open dies and for solid dies made without inserts. Inserts are commonly made from higher-alloy tool steels, such as D2 or M2, or from tungsten carbide having a relatively high percentage of cobalt (13 to 25%).

Lubrication

Although some of the more ductile metals can be successfully cold headed to moderate severity without a lubricant, most metals to be cold headed are lubricated to prevent galling of the work metal or the dies, sticking in the dies, and excessive die wear. Stainless steels are often electroplated with copper and then lubricated with oil or molybdenum disulfide. Oxalates are sometimes used instead of copper plating.

Warm Heading

In warm heading (a variation of the cold-heading process), the work metal is heated to a temperature high enough to increase its ductility. A rise in work-metal temperature usually results in a marked reduction in the energy required for heading. Temperatures for warm heading range from 175 to 540 °C (350 to 1000 °F), depending on the characteristics of the work metal.

Applications. Warm heading is occasionally used to produce an upset that would have required a larger machine if the upsetting had been done cold, but by far the most extensive use of warm heading is for the processing of difficult-to-head metals, such as austenitic stainless steels. Because they work harden rapidly, austenitic stainless steels are best headed at slow ram speeds.

The data shown in Fig. 17 suggest that the speed of the heading punch greatly affects the headability of these stainless steels. According to investigation, 80% of the loss in ductility caused by heading speed can be recovered if the metal is heated to between 175 and 290 °C (350 and 550 °F). The increase in headability with increasing temperature is indicated in Fig. 18.

Machines and Heating Devices. Warm-heading machines are essentially the same as cold-heading machines except that warm-heading machines are designed to withstand the elevated temperature of the work metal. Induction heating coils or resistance heating elements can be used as auxiliary heating equipment.

Induction heating is the method most commonly used to heat work material for warm heading, although direct resistance heating is also used in some applications. The main disadvantage of induction heating is the high initial cost of the power supply. Therefore, its use is generally restricted to continuous high production.

Direct resistance heating, on the other hand, has the advantages of simplicity of equipment, accuracy of control, safety (because voltage is low), and adaptability to heating of a continuous length of work metal. The usual setup for resistance heating employs a second feeder-roll stand similar to that already on the header. The second stand is positioned about 1.5 m (5 ft) behind the first, and the work stock (work metal) is fed through both sets of rolls. Leads from the electrical equipment are attached to the two sets of rolls, and the circuit is completed by the portion of the wire that passes between them. The wire (work metal) then becomes the resistance heater in the circuit.

Tools. Whether the same tools can be used for warm heading as for cold heading depends entirely on the temperature of the tools during operation. Although the tools usually operate at a temperature considerably lower than that of the work metal, it is important that the tool temperature be known. Tool temperature can be checked with sufficient accuracy by means of temperature-sensitive crayons. Under no circumstances should the tool be allowed to exceed the temperature at which it was tempered after hardening. This tempering temperature is usually 150 °C (300 °F) for carbon tool steel such as W1 or W2. Tools made from a high-alloy tool steel, such as D2, ordinarily should not be permitted to operate above 260 °C (500 °F).

When tool temperatures exceed those discussed above, the use of tools made from a hot-work tool steel, such as H12, is appropriate. However, the lower maximum hardness of such a steel somewhat limits its resistance to wear. A high-speed tool steel such as M2 will provide the high hardness and the resistance to tempering needed for long tool life.

Other Advantages of Warm Heading. As the heading temperature of a work-hardenable material increases, the resulting hardness decreases, as shown in Fig. 19. If a material is warm headed, the hardness will remain low enough to permit such secondary operations as thread rolling, trimming, drilling, and slotting.

In cold heading, the upset head of a work-hardening metal is very hard, a rolled thread is moderately hard, and the undeformed shoulder is relatively soft. These variations can be minimized by warm heading.

Hot Extrusion

Hot extrusion is the process of forcing a heated billet to flow through a shaped die opening. The temperature at which extrusion is performed depends on the material being extruded. Hot extrusion is used to produce long, straight metal products of constant cross section, such as bars, solid and hollow sections, tubes, wires, and strips, from materials that cannot be formed by cold extrusion. The three basic types of hot extrusion are nonlubricated, lubricated, and hydrostatic (Fig. 20).

In nonlubricated hot extrusion, the material flows by internal shear, and a dead-metal zone is formed in front of the extrusion die (Fig. 20a). Nonlubricated extrusion is not recommended for stainless steels. Lubricated extrusion, as the name implies, uses a suitable lubricant (glass for stainless steels) between the extruded billet and the die (Fig. 20b). In hydrostatic extrusion, a fluid film present between the billet and the die exerts pressure on the deforming billet (Fig. 20c). The hydrostatic extrusion process is primarily used when conventional lubrication is inadequate (e.g., in the extrusion of special alloys, composites, or clad materials). For all practical purposes, hydrostatic extrusion can be considered an extension of the lubricated hot extrusion process. More detailed information on hot and hydrostatic extrusion can be found in Volume 14 of the *ASM Handbook*.

General Description of Extrusion (Ref 7)

The most commonly used process for extruding stainless steel parts is direct extrusion (Fig. 21a), in which, during extrusion, the container is motionless and is integral with a die showing an axial aperture with the cross section corresponding to the outside contour of the desired product. A cylindrical ram designed for a sliding fit in the

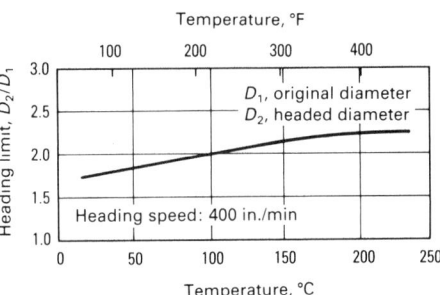

Fig. 18 Effect of work-metal temperature on heading limit of austenitic stainless steel

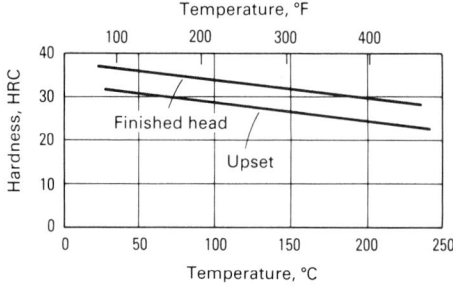

Fig. 19 Effect of heading temperature on the hardness of the upset portion and finished head of type 305 stainless steel flat-head machine screws

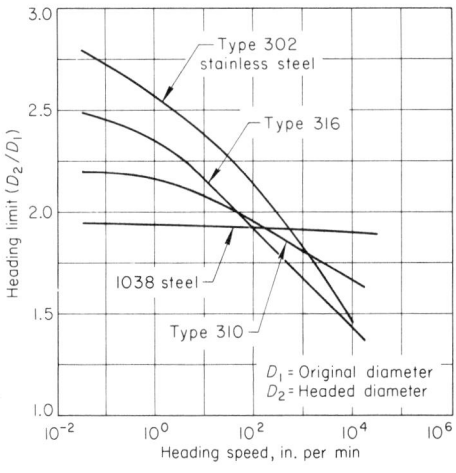

Fig. 17 Effect of heading speed on heading limits for three austenitic stainless steels and for 1038 steel

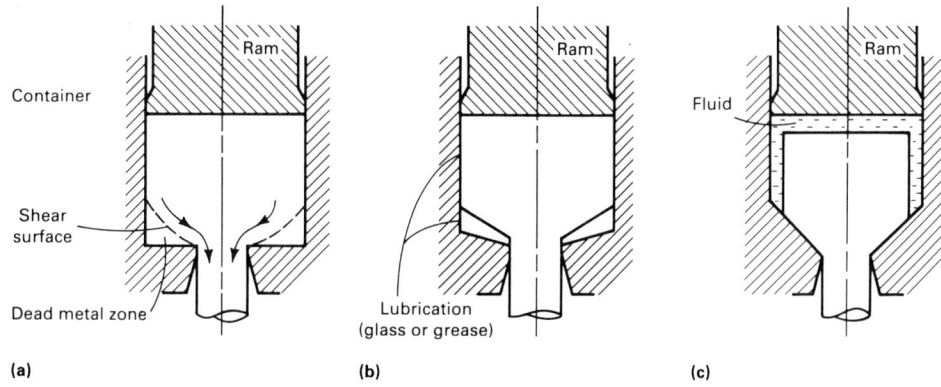

Fig. 20 Schematics of the nonlubricated (a), lubricated (b), and hydrostatic (c) hot extrusion processes

container is actuated by the hydraulic or mechanical force of the press, runs through the rear end of the container, and forces the metal of the billet to flow through the die aperture.

If a hollow product (e.g., a tube) is desired (Fig. 21b), the billet inserted into the container is axially hollow and a mandrel protruding from the front face of the ram runs through the billet hole up to the aperture of the die, which it partly closes. The cross-sectional contour of the mandrel is that which is desired for the inside hole of the extruded product so that a properly outlined ringlike aperture is available for the metal to flow through.

The ram is stopped before coming into contact with the die so that a nondeformed part of the billet, called the *discard,* remains in the container. The discard is then severed from the extruded product and evacuated (Fig. 21c).

Forces Involved. The force F' transmitted by the ram in order to cause the metal to flow out consists of two elements:

- The force F needed for the mere deformation of the metal
- The force $F' - F$ required to overcome the friction between the metal billet and the container wall and the mandrel

The latter corresponds to a waste of energy: at the beginning of the extrusion process its dissipation generates an overheating of the container and of the billet skin, irregular redundant work in the metal, and cracks on its surface. Progressively, as the friction is reduced, this force is dissipated less in the metal, but more in the hydraulic piping and valves of the extrusion press, which in turn are warmed. For this reason, this friction force has always been

kept as low as possible by lubricating between the lateral surfaces of the billet and the container.

Calculation of the Force F Needed for Elongating the Metal. Elongation of the metal is defined by the extrusion ratio δ, namely the ratio between the cross-sectional areas available to the metal in the container and in the die aperture, respectively. (Delta is also equal to the ratio between a given length of extruded product and the length of billet needed for producing it, provided that the billet fills the container.)

According to Ref 8, whenever d roughly exceeds 10:1, the force F is in proportion with the logarithm of the extrusion ratio and with the cross-sectional area A available to the metal in the container:

$$F = KA \ln \delta \qquad \text{(Eq 1)}$$

The extrusion factor K is expressed in the same unit system as pressure and depends on the composition of the billet alloy and on its temperature when being extruded. Steel extruders commonly call this factor the *resistance to deformation by extrusion.* Figure 22 shows its values as a function of temperature for various grades of stainless steels.

Lubrication

In the extrusion of steels and titanium alloys, the Sejournet process is the most commonly used for lubrication (Ref 9). In this process, the heated billet is rolled over a bed of ground glass or is sprinkled with glass powder to provide a layer of low-melting glass on the billet surface. Before the billet is inserted into the hot extrusion container, a

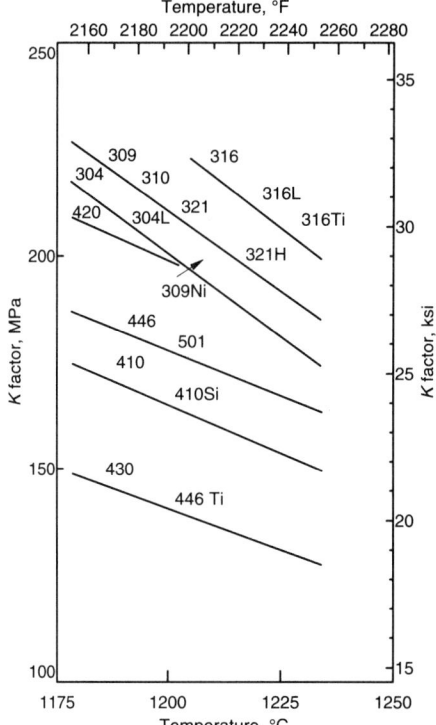

Fig. 22 K factor vs. temperature for various grades of steel

suitable lubricating system is positioned immediately ahead of the die.

It is common practice to use several types of glass for lubricating different alloys, each type of glass having a closely controlled composition and frit size to ensure optimum lubricating properties at the chosen extrusion temperature. For a stainless steel being extruded at 1150 to 1200 °C (2100 to 2200 °F), a soda-lime glass containing about 70% silica (SiO_2) is chosen for the extrusion-die interface and a high borax/low-silica glass is chosen for billet/liner lubrication (Ref 10). For extrusion at temperatures in excess of 1200 °C (2200 °F), borosilicate glasses typically containing 70% SiO_2 and 15% B_2O_3 are used at the die face.

Tooling

The tooling for hot extrusion consists of such components as containers, container liners, stems (rams), dummy blocks, mandrels, spider or bridge dies for producing hollow extrusions, and flat or

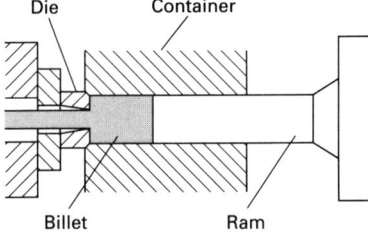

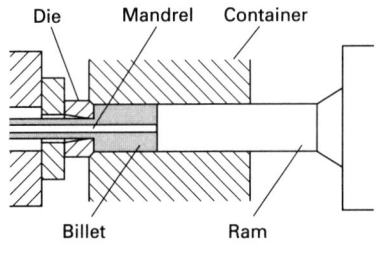

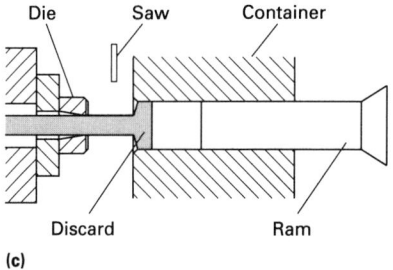

Fig. 21 Schematics showing the direct extrusion of a bar (a), a tube (b), and the completion of the extrusion process (c). Source: Ref 7

feeder plate dies. Flat-face and shaped dies are the two most common types (Fig. 23), and both are used for extrusion of stainless steels. Flat-face dies (also termed *square dies*) have one or more openings (apertures) that are similar in cross section to that of the desired extruded product. Dies for lubricated extrusion (also called *shaped, converging* or *streamlined dies*) often have a conical entry opening with a circular cross section that changes progressively to the final extruded shape required. Flat-face dies are easier and less expensive to design and manufacture than shaped dies. Table 5 lists commonly used tooling materials.

Processing Route

Ferrous extrusion, in contrast to nonferrous extrusion, is performed rapidly to minimize heat loss, maintain optimum lubrication conditions, maximize tool life, and minimize extrusion pressure. At the plant described in Ref 10, a 100 kg (220 lb) billet is typically extruded to a 6 to 7 m (20 to 23 ft) length of bar in less than 5 s, undergoing a reduction in area of typically 85 to 95%.

The key operations for the production of stainless steel extrusions are described below.

Billet Cutting. The incoming bar, which is supplied bright finished in approximately 6 m (20 ft) lengths is cut on band saws to a weight determined by the finished product length required. Billet weights of between 20 to 120 kg (45 to 265 lb) are commonly processed.

Billet Radiusing. The billet face that will be in contact with the die prior to extrusion is radiused to provide a lead-in to the die, which reduces peak pressure at the start of extrusion and improves the surface finish at the front of the extruded bar.

Billet Heating. Induction heaters, each rated at 500 kW, are used to raise the billet to the re-

quired extrusion temperatures. Heating times vary according to billet diameter, weight, and material type, but would typically be 7 min for a 90 kg (200 lb) billet of austenitic stainless steel.

Lubrication. A low-viscosity glass is used to lubricate between the billet and extrusion liner and a higher-viscosity glass is used to lubricate the extrusion itself. After extrusion the bar may be air cooled or, in the case of austenitic stainless products, water quenched to provide a fully solution-treated product. Water quenching has the added benefit of cracking the adherent lubricating glass film from the extruded section, thus promoting rapid descaling on subsequent acid pickling.

Straightening and Detwisting. When cool, the extruded sections are straightened and detwisted on a stretch-straightening bench in one operation, during which more of the glass coating scales off.

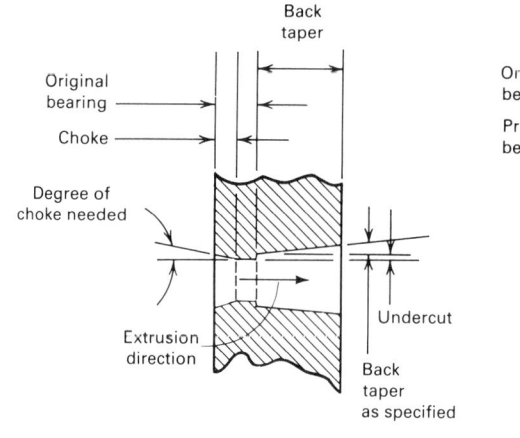 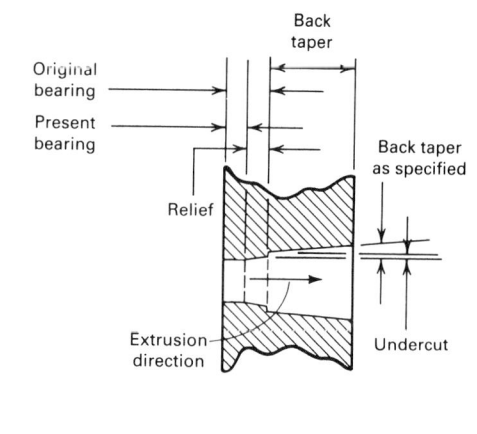

Fig. 23 Shaped die (a) and flat die (b) for hot extrusion

Table 5 Typical materials and hardnesses for tools used in hot extrusion of stainless steels

Tooling application	Tool material	Hardness, HRC
Dies, for both shapes and tubing	H13	44-48
	Cast H21 inserts	51-54
Dummy blocks, backers, bolsters, and die rings	H11, H12, H13	40-44
	H19, H21	40-42
	Inconel 718	...
Mandrels	H11, H13	46-50
Mandrel tips and inserts	H11, H12, H13	40-44
	H19, H21	45-50
Liners	H11, H12, H13	42-47
Rams	H11, H12, H13	40-44
Containers	H13	35-40

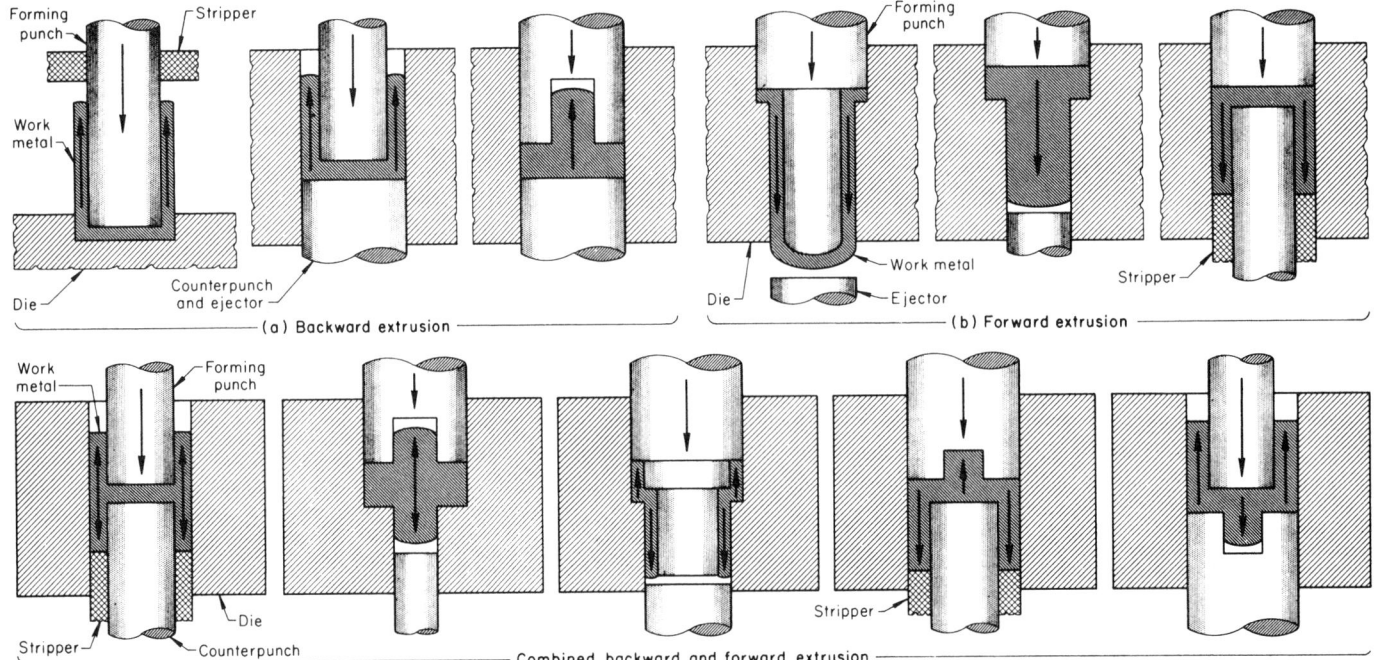

Fig. 24 Displacement of metal in cold extrusion: (a) backward, (b) forward, and (c) both backward and forward

Descaling. Residual glass and scale are removed by immersing austenitic stainless sections in a hot nitric/hydrofluoric acid descaling bath. The hydrofluoric acid is essential to remove the adherent glass lubricant. Martensitic stainless steels are shotblasted to remove heat-treatment scale and residual glass lubricant.

Inspection. Before shipping, a full-dimensional inspection is performed on each batch of extrusions to ensure that the profile conforms to drawing tolerances.

Cold Extrusion

Cold extrusion is so called because the slug or preform enters the die at room temperature or at a temperature appreciably below the recrystallization temperature. Any subsequent rise in temperature, which may amount to several hundred degrees Fahrenheit, is caused by the thermomechanical effects of plastic deformation and friction. Cold extrusion involves backward or forward, or combined backward-and-forward, displacement of metal by plastic flow under steady, though not uniform, pressure. Backward displacement from a closed die is in the direction opposite to punch travel, as shown in Fig. 24(a). Workpieces are often cup-shape and have wall thicknesses equal to the clearance between the punch and die. In forward extrusion, the work metal is forced in the direction of the punch travel, as shown in Fig. 24(b). Sometimes these two basic methods of extrusion are combined so that some of the work metal flows backward and some forward, as shown in Fig. 24(c).

Metals Cold Extruded. The same alloys and alloy characteristics described in the section "Cold Heading" are applicable to cold extrusion.

Production runs as small as 500 pieces are practical, depending on part size and the type of stainless steel used. The 400-series stainless steels, for instance, are as readily extrudable as carbon steel, whereas the austenitic 300-series grades, which work harden, require more force. Because of the higher pressures required for the 300-series types, die wear is higher.

About 45 kg (100 lb) is the maximum weight of a stainless steel part that can be cold extruded. The maximum diameter of a part that can be cold extruded in stainless steel is about 150 mm (6 in.); lengths of up to 2 m (80 in.) are possible. Warm extrusion (i.e., heating the slug slightly prior to extruding) can enhance the above-mentioned capabilities somewhat.

ACKNOWLEDGMENTS

The information in this article is largely taken from:

- T. Harris and E. Priebe, Forging of Stainless Steels, *Forming and Forging,* Vol 14, *ASM Handbook* (formerly 9th ed., *Metals Handbook*), ASM International, 1988, p 222-230
- S.K. Srivastava, *Forging of Heat-Resistant Alloys, Forming and Forging,* Vol 14, ASM Handbook (formerly 9th ed., Metals Handbook), ASM International, 1988, p 231-238
- Cold Heading, *Forming and Forging,* Vol 14, ASM Handbook (formerly 9th ed., Metals Handbook), ASM International, 1988, p 291-298
- Conventional Hot Extrusion, *Forming and Forging,* Vol 14, *ASM Handbook* (formerly 9th ed., *Metals Handbook*), ASM International, 1988, p 315-326

- Cold Extrusion, *Metals Handbook Desk Edition,* American Society for Metals, 1985, p 26-49 to 26-51

REFERENCES

1. A.M. Sabroff, F.W. Boulger, and H.J. Henning, *Forging Materials and Practices,* Reinhold, 1968
2. H.J. Henning, A.M. Sabroff, and F.W. Boulger, "A Study of Forging Variables," Report ML-TDR-64-95, U.S. Air Force, 1964
3. *Open Die Forging Manual,* 3rd ed., Forging Industry Association, 1982, p 106-107
4. *ASME Boiler and Pressure Vessel Code,* Section III, Division I, Figure NB-2433.1-1, American Society of Mechanical Engineers, 1986
5. *The Making, Shaping, and Treating of Steel,* 8th ed., United States Steel Corp., 1964, p 617
6. "Cold Forming Stainless Steel Bar and Wire," American Iron and Steel Institute, April 1976
7. J. Sejournet and H. Thannberger, The Extrusion of Stainless Steel Components, *Handbook of Stainless Steels,* D. Peckner and I.M. Bernstein, Ed., McGraw-Hill, 1977, p 23-1 to 23-15
8. E. Siebel and E. Fangmeier, Untersuchen über den Kraftdedarf beim Pressen und Lochen, *Mitt. Kaiser-Wilhem-Inst. Eisenforsch. Duesseldorf,* Vol 13, p 29, 1931 (Translated by André Collinet, Librairie Polytechnique Paris et Leige, 1936)
9. J. Sejournet and J. Delcroix, Glass Lubricant in the Extrusion of Steel, *Lubr. Eng.,* Vol 11, 1955, p 389-396
10. J. Middleton, Hot Extrusion of Special Sections in Stainless Steel, *Stainless Steels '87,* Institute of Metals, 1988, p 21-31

Heat Treating

HEAT TREATING of stainless steel produces changes in physical condition, mechanical properties, and residual stress level and restores maximum corrosion resistance when that property has been adversely affected by previous fabrication or heating. Frequently, satisfactory corrosion resistance and optimum mechanical properties are obtained in the same heat treatment.

Austenitic Stainless Steels

In furnace loading, the high thermal expansion of austenitic stainless steels (about 50% higher than that of mild carbon steel) should be considered. The spacing between parts should be adequate to accommodate this expansion. Stacking, when necessary, should be employed judiciously to avoid deformation of parts at elevated temperatures.

Susceptibility to Intergranular Attack

Austenitic stainless steels can be divided into five groups:

- *Conventional austenitics,* such as types 301, 302, 303, 304, 305, 308, 309, 310, 316, and 317
- *Stabilized compositions,* primarily types 321, 347, and 348
- *Low-carbon grades,* such as types 304L, 316L, and 317L
- *High-nitrogen grades,* such as AISI types 201, 202, 304N, 316N, and the Nitronic series of alloys
- *Highly alloyed austenitics,* such as 317LM, 317LX, JS700, JS777, 904L, AL-4X, 2RK65, Carpenter 20Cb-3, Sanicro 28, AL-6X, AL-6XN, and 254 SMO

The compositions of standard and nonstandard austenitic stainless steels are described in the articles "Metallurgy and Properties of Wrought Stainless Steels" and "Metallurgy and Properties of Cast Stainless Steels" in this Volume.

Conventional austenitics cannot be hardened by heat treatment, but will harden as a result of cold working. These steels are usually purchased in an annealed or cold-worked state. Following welding or thermal processing, a subsequent anneal may be required for optimum corrosion resistance, softness, and ductility. During annealing, chromium carbides, which markedly

Table 1 Recommended annealing temperatures for austenitic stainless steels

UNS No.	Designation	Temperature(a) °C	Temperature(a) °F	UNS No.	Designation	Temperature(a) °C	Temperature(a) °F
Conventional grades				**High-nitrogen grades**			
S30100	301	1010-1120	1850-2050	S20100	201	1010-1120	1850-2050
S30200	302	1010-1120	1850-2050	S20200	202	1010-1120	1850-2050
S30215	302B	1010-1120	1850-2050	S30451	304N	1010-1120	1850-2050
S30300	303	1010-1120	1850-2050	S31651	316N	1010-1120	1850-2050
S30323	303Se	1010-1120	1850-2050	S24100	Nitronic 32, 18Cr-2Ni-12Mn	1010-1065	1850-1950
S30400	304	1010-1120	1850-2050	S24000	Nitronic 33	1040-1095	1900-2000
S30500	305	1010-1120	1850-2050	S21904	Nitronic 40, 21Cr-6Ni-9Mn	980-1175	1800-2150
S30800	308	1010-1120	1850-2050	S20910	Nitronic 50, 22Cr-13Ni-5Mn	1065-1120	1950-2050
S30900	309	1040-1120	1900-2050	S21800	Nitronic 60	1040-1095	1900-2000
S30908	309S	1040-1120	1900-2050	S28200	18-18 Plus	1040-1095	1900-2000
30100	310	1040-1065	1900-1950	**Highly alloyed grades**			
S31008	310S	1040-1065	1900-1950	S31725	317LM	1120-1150	2050-2100
S31600	316	1040-1120	1900-2050	...	317LX	1120-1150	2050-2100
S31700	317	1065-1120	1950-2050	...	317L Plus	1120-1150	2050-2100
Stabilized grades				...	317LMO	1120-1150	2050-2100
S32100	321	955-1065	1750-1950	...	7L4	1120-1150	2050-2100
S34700	347	980-1065	1800-1950	...	JS700	1065-1150	1950-2100
S34800	348	980-1065	1800-1950	...	JS777	1065-1150	1950-2100
N08020	20Cb-3	925-955	1700-1750	N08904	904L	1075-1125	1965-2055
Low-carbon grades				...	AL-4X	1075-1125	1965-2055
S30403	304L	1010-1120	1850-2050	...	2RK65	1075-1125	1965-2055
S30453	304LN	1010-1120	1850-2050	N08028	Sanicro 28	...	...
S31603	316L	1040-1110	1900-2025	N08366	AL-6X	1205-1230	2200-2250
S31653	316LN	1040-1110	1900-2025	S31254	254SMO	1150-1205	2100-2200
S31703	317L	1040-1110	1900-2025				

(a) Temperatures given are for annealing a composite structure. Time at temperature and method of cooling depend on thickness. Light sections may be held at temperature for 3 to 5 min per 2.5 mm (0.10 in.) of thickness, followed by rapid air cooling. Thicker sections are water quenched. For many of these grades, a postweld heat treatment is not necessary. For proprietary alloys, alloy producers may be consulted for details. Although cooling from the annealing temperature must be rapid, it must also be consistent with limitations of distortion.

decrease resistance to intergranular corrosion, are dissolved. Annealing temperatures, which vary somewhat with the composition of the steel, are given in Table 1 for wrought alloys and in Table 2 for the corresponding cast alloys. Table 3 includes compositions and typical microstructures for selected austenitic corrosion-resistant cast steels listed in Table 2.

Because carbide precipitation can occur at temperatures between 425 and 900 °C (800 and 1600 °F), the annealing temperature should be safely above this limit. Moreover, because all carbides should be in solution before cooling begins, and because the chromium carbide dissolves slowly, the highest practical temperature consistent with limited grain growth should be selected. This temperature is in the vicinity of 1095 °C (2000 °F).

Cooling from the annealing temperature must be rapid, but it must also be consistent with distortion limitations. Whenever distortion considerations permit, water quenching is used, thus ensuring that dissolved carbides remain in solution. Because type 310 precipitates carbides more rapidly, this material invariably requires water quenching. Where distortion considerations rule out such a fast cooling rate, cooling in an air blast is used. With some thin-section parts, even this intermediate rate of cooling produces excessive distortion, and parts must be cooled in still air. If still air does not provide a cooling rate sufficient to prevent carbide precipitation, maximum corrosion resistance will not be obtained. A solution to this dilemma is the use of a stabilized grade or one of the low-carbon alloys.

Stabilized austenitic alloys (types 321, 347, 348, and Carpenter 20Cb-3) contain controlled amounts of titanium or niobium, which render the steel nearly immune to intergranular precipitation of chromium carbide and its adverse effects on corrosion resistance. Nevertheless, these alloys may require annealing to relieve stresses, to increase softness and ductility, or to provide additional stabilization.

To obtain maximum softness and ductility, the stabilized grades are annealed at the temperatures shown in Table 1. Unlike the unstabilized grades, these steels do not require water quenching or other acceleration of cooling from the annealing temperature to prevent subsequent intergranular corrosion. Air cooling is generally adequate.

When maximum corrosion resistance of the stabilized austenitic grades is required, it may be necessary to employ a heat treatment known as a *stabilizing anneal*. The treatment consists of holding at 845 to 900 °C (1550 to 1650 °F) for up to 5 h, depending on section thickness. It may be applied prior to, or in the course of, fabrication, and it may be followed by short-time stress relieving at 705 °C (1300 °F) without danger of harmful carbide precipitation (see the section "Stress Relieving of Austenitic Stainless Steels" in this article).

Carpenter 20Cb-3 stainless steel is unlike the conventional stabilized austenitics (types 321, 347, and 348) because of its higher alloy content and improved corrosion resistance. This alloy normally is stabilized and annealed at 925 to 955 °C (1700 to 1750 °F). For special applications, the alloy can be annealed at higher temperatures (up to 1150 °C, or 2100 °F), but this is permissible only if it will not be subject to welding or heating temperatures greater than 540 °C (1000 °F).

Certain restrictions on furnace atmosphere are mandatory. Furnace combustion must be carefully controlled to eliminate carburizing or excessively oxidizing conditions. Because the properties of the stabilized steels are based on their original carbon content, carbon absorption cannot be tolerated. Excessively oxidizing conditions cause the formation of a scale that is difficult to remove in subsequent descaling operations. Direct impingement of flame on the work must be prevented. The sulfur content of the furnace atmosphere, particularly in oil-fired furnaces, must be kept low; natural gas, not producer gas, should be used.

Low-carbon austenitics are intermediate in their tendency to precipitate chromium carbides

to the stabilized and unstabilized grades. Their carbon content (0.03% max) is low enough to reduce precipitation of intergranular carbides. This characteristic of limited sensitization is of particular value in welding, flame cutting, and other hot-working operations. These materials do not require the quenching treatment that unstabilized grades require to retain carbon in solid solution. Nevertheless, the low-carbon alloys are not satisfactory for long-time service in the sensitizing temperature range of 540 to 760 °C (1000 to 1400 °F), because they are not completely immune to the formation of carbides deleterious to corrosion resistance. Recommended annealing temperatures for the low-carbon alloys are given in Table 1.

The effects of sensitization and susceptibility to general corrosion vary among the low-carbon alloys, depending on their chemical composition. Because they contain molybdenum, types 316L and 317L are susceptible to σ-phase formation as a result of long-time exposure at 650 to 870 °C (1200 to 1600 °F). However, the corrosion resistance of these grades can be improved by employing a stabilizing treatment (ASTM A 262C), consisting of holding at 885 °C (1625 °F) for 2 h, prior to stress relieving at 675 °C (1250 °F). After receiving the stabilizing heat treatment, these alloys pass the copper-copper sulfate 16% sulfuric acid test (ASTM A 262, Practice E) for freedom from intergranular carbide precipitation.

Magnetic Permeability. The low-carbon alloys are frequently used in the production of articles requiring low magnetic permeability. These materials are nonmagnetic in the fully annealed condition, with permeabilities below 1.02 max at 0.02 T (200 G), but they may develop ferromagnetic qualities as a result of cold working during fabrication. Cold working may generate some low-carbon martensite, which is strongly magnetic. Fusion welding with a low-nickel filler rod is another possible cause of magnetism. Magnetism due to any of these causes can be eliminated by a full anneal to restore the alloy to its fully austenitic condition.

Table 2 Annealing of ferritic and austenitic stainless steel castings

| Type | Minimum temperature | | Quench(a) | Typical ultimate tensile strength(b) | |
	°C	°F		MPa	ksi
For full softness					
CB-30	790	1450	FC + A(c)	660	95
CC-50	790	1450	A	670	97
For maximum corrosion resistance					
CE-30	1095	2000	W, O, A	670	97
CF-3	1040	1900	W, O, A	530	77
CF-3M	1040	1900	W, O, A	530	77
CF8	1040	1900	W, O, A	530	77
CF-8C(d)	1040	1900	W, O, A	530	77
CF-8M	1040	1900	W, O, A	550	80
CF-12M(e)	1040	1900	W, O, A	550	80
CF-16F	1040	1900	W, O, A	530	77
CF-20	1040	1900	W, O, A	530	77
CH-20	1095	2000	W, O, A	610	88
CK-20	1095	2000	W, O, A	520	76
CN-7M	1120	2050	W, O, A	480	69

(a) FC, furnace cool; W, water; O, oil; A, air. (b) Approximate. (c) Furnace cool to 540 °C (1000 °F) and then air cool. (d) CF-8C may be reheated to 870 to 925 °C (1600 to 1700 °F) and then air cooled for precipitation of niobium carbides. (e) CF-12M should be quenched from a temperature above 1095 °C (2000 °F).

Table 3 Compositions and typical microstructures of Alloy Casting Institute (ACI) corrosion-resistant cast steels

ACI type	UNS No.	Wrought alloy type(a)	ASTM specifications	Most common end-use microstructure	Composition(b), %					
					C	Mn	Si	Cr	Ni	Others(c)
Chromium steels										
CA-15	J91150	410	A 743, A 217, A 487	Martensite	0.15	1.00	1.50	11.5-14.0	1.0	0.50 Mo(d)
CA-15M	J91151	...	A 743	Martensite	0.15	1.00	0.65	11.5-14.0	1.0	0.15-1.00 Mo
CA-40	J91153	420	A 743	Martensite	0.40	1.00	1.50	11.5-14.0	1.0	0.5 Mo(d)
CA-40F	...	...	A 743	Martensite	0.2-0.4	1.00	1.50	11.5-14.0	1.0	...
CB-30	J91803	431, 442	A 743	Ferrite and carbides	0.30	1.00	1.50	18.0-22.0	2.0	...
CC-50	J92615	446	A 743	Ferrite and carbides	0.30	1.00	1.50	26.0-30.0	4.0	...
Chromium-nickel steels										
CA-6N	J91650	...	A 743	Martensite	0.06	0.50	1.00	10.5-12.5	6.0-8.0	...
CA-6NM	J91540	...	A 743, A 487	Martensite	0.06	1.00	1.00	11.5-14.0	3.5-4.5	0.4-1.0 Mo
CA-28MWV	...	...	A 743	Martensite	0.20-0.28	0.50-1.00	1.00	11.0-12.5	0.50-1.00	0.9-1.25 Mo; 0.9-1.25 W; 0.2-0.3 V
CB-7Cu-1	J92180	...	A 747	Martensite, age hardenable	0.07	0.70	1.00	15.5-17.7	3.6-4.6	2.5-3.2 Cu; 0.20-0.35 Nb; 0.05 N max
CB-7Cu-2	J92110	...	A 747	Martensite, age hardenable	0.07	0.70	1.00	14.0-15.5	4.5-5.5	2.5-3.2 Cu; 0.20-0.35 Nb; 0.05 N max
CD-4MCu	J93370	...	A 351, A 743, A 744, A 890	Austenite in ferrite, age hardenable	0.04	1.00	1.00	25.0-26.5	4.75-6.0	1.75-2.25 Mo; 2.75-3.25 Cu
CE-30	J93423	312	A 743	Ferrite in austenite	0.30	1.50	2.00	26.0-30.0	8.0-11.0	...
CF-3(e)	J92700	304L	A 351, A 743, A 744	Ferrite in austenite	0.03	1.50	2.00	17.0-21.0	8.0-12.0	...
CF-3M(e)	J92800	316L	A 351, A 743, A 744	Ferrite in austenite	0.03	1.50	2.00	17.0-21.0	8.0-12.0	2.0-3.0 Mo
CF-3MN	...	...	A 743	Ferrite in austenite	0.03	1.50	1.50	17.0-21.0	9.0-13.0	2.0-3.0 Mo; 0.10-0.20 N
CF-8(e)	J92600	304	A 351, A 743, A 744	Ferrite in austenite	0.08	1.50	2.00	18.0-21.0	8.0-11.0	...
CF-8C	J92710	347	A 351, A 743, A 744	Ferrite in austenite	0.08	1.50	2.00	18.0-21.0	9.0-12.0	Nb(f)
CF-8M	J92900	316	A 351, A 743, A 744	Ferrite in austenite	0.08	1.50	2.00	18.0-21.0	9.0-12.0	2.0-3.0 Mo
CF-10	J93401	...	A 351	Ferrite in austenite	0.04-0.10	1.50	2.00	18.0-21.0	8.0-11.0	...
CF-10M	...	...	A 351	Ferrite in austenite	0.04-0.10	1.50	1.50	18.0-21.0	9.0-12.0	2.0-3.0 Mo
CF-10MC	J92971	...	A 351	Ferrite in austenite	0.10	1.50	1.50	15.0-18.0	13.0-16.0	1.75-2.25 Mo
CF-10SMnN	...	...	A 351, A 743	Ferrite in austenite	0.10	7.00-9.00	3.50-4.50	16.0-18.0	8.0-9.0	0.08-0.18 N
CF-12M	...	316	...	Ferrite in austenite or austenite	0.12	1.50	2.00	18.0-21.0	9.0-12.0	2.0-3.0 Mo
CF-16F	J92701	303	A 743	Austenite	0.16	1.50	2.00	18.0-21.0	9.0-12.0	1.50 Mo max; 0.20-0.35 Se
CF-20	J92602	302	A 743	Austenite	0.20	1.50	2.00	18.0-21.0	8.0-11.0	...
CG-6MMN	J93799	...	A 351, A 743	Ferrite in austenite	0.06	4.00-6.00	1.00	20.5-23.5	11.5-13.5	1.50-3.00 Mo; 0.10-0.30 Nb; 0.10-30 V; 0.20-0.40 N
CG-8M	J93000	317	A 351, A 743, A 744	Ferrite in austenite	0.08	1.50	1.50	18.0-21.0	9.0-13.0	3.0-4.0 Mo
CG-12	J93001	...	A 743	Ferrite in austenite	0.12	1.50	2.00	20.0-23.0	10.0-13.0	...
CH-8	J93400	...	A 351	Ferrite in austenite	0.08	1.50	1.50	22.0-26.0	12.0-15.0	...
CH-10	J93401	...	A 351	Ferrite in austenite	0.04-0.10	1.50	2.00	22.0-26.0	12.0-15.0	...
CH-20	J93402	309	A 351, A 743	Austenite	0.20	1.50	2.00	22.0-26.0	12.0-15.0	...
CK-3MCuN	...	...	A 351, A 743, A 744	Ferrite in austenite	0.025	1.20	1.00	19.5-20.5	17.5-19.5	6.0-7.0 V; 0.18-0.24 N; 0.50-1.00 Cu
CK-20	J94202	310	A 743	Austenite	0.20	2.00	2.00	23.0-27.0	19.0-22.0	...
Nickel-chromium steel										
CN-3M	...	...	A 743	Austenite	0.03	2.00	1.00	20.0-22.0	23.0-27.0	4.5-5.5 Mo
CN-7M	N08007	...	A 351, A 743, A 744	Austenite	0.07	1.50	1.50	19.0-22.0	27.5-30.5	2.0-3.0 Mo; 3.0-4.0 Cu
CN-7MS	J94650	...	A 743, A 744	Austenite	0.07	1.50	3.50(g)	18.0-20.0	22.0-25.0	2.5-3.0 Mo; 1.5-2.0 Cu
CT-15C	...	...	A 351	Austenite	0.05-0.15	0.15-1.50	0.50-1.50	19.0-21.0	31.0-34.0	0.5-1.5 V

(a) Type numbers of wrought alloys are listed only for nominal identification of corresponding wrought and cast grades. Composition ranges of cast alloys are not the same as for corresponding wrought alloys; cast alloy designations should be used for castings only. (b) Maximum unless a range is given. The balance of all compositions is iron. (c) Sulfur content is 0.04% in all grades except: CG-6MMN, 0.030% S (max); CF-10SMnN, 0.03% S (max); CT-15C, 0.03% S (max); CK-3MCuN, 0.010% S (max); CN-3M, 0.030% S (max); CA-6N, 0.020% S (max); CA-28MWV, 0.030% S (max); CA-40F, 0.20-0.40% S; CB-7Cu-1 and -2, 0.03% S (max). Phosphorus content is 0.04% (max) in all grades except: CF-16F, 0.17% P (max); CF-10SMnN, 0.060% P (max); CT-15C, 0.030% P (max); CK-3MCuN, 0.045% P (max); CN-3M, 0.030% P (max); CA-6N, 0.020% P (max); CB-7Cu-1 and -2, 0.035% P (max). (d) Molybdenum not intentionally added. (e) CF-3A, CF-3MA, and CF-8A have the same composition ranges as CF-3, CF-3M, and CF-8, respectively, but have balanced compositions so that ferrite contents are at levels that permit higher mechanical property specifications than those for related grades. They are covered by ASTM A 351. (f) Nb, 8 × %C min (1.0% max); or Nb + Ta × %C (1.1% max). (g) For CN-7MS, silicon ranges from 2.50 to 3.50%.

High-nitrogen austenitic stainless steels are heat treated in the same manner and are subject to the same problems (carbide precipitation and distortion) as conventional austenitics. They cannot be hardened by heat treatment but will harden by cold working. High-nitrogen austenitics are annealed to ensure maximum corrosion resistance, softness, and ductility. Rapid cooling is preferred. Annealing temperature ranges are listed in Table 1.

Highly alloyed austenitic stainless steels contain large amounts of molybdenum to provide very good resistance to chloride corrosion. They usually are produced with low carbon to avoid sensitization and may contain copper for in-

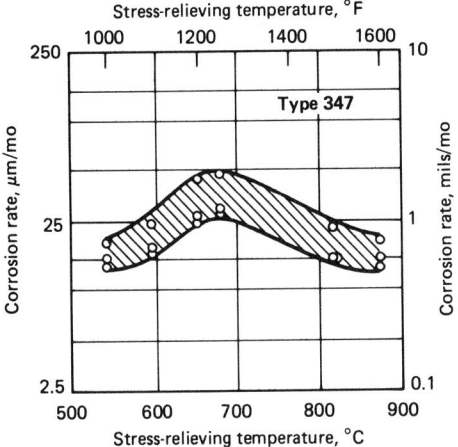

Fig. 1 Effect of stress relieving on corrosion rate of type 347 stainless steel in boiling 65% HNO₃. All stress-relief treatments lasted 2 h.

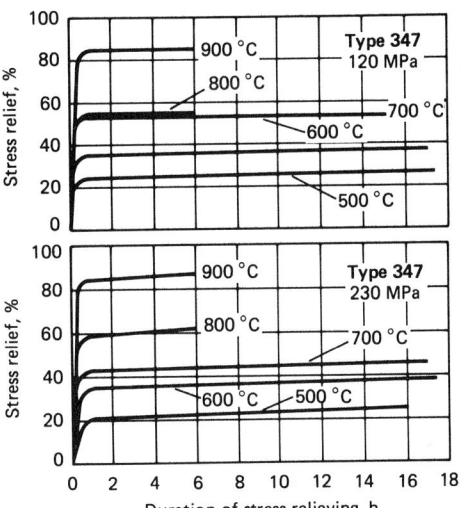

Fig. 2 Stress relief obtained in type 347 stainless steel, as a function of temperature, initial stress, and time at temperature

creased acid resistance. These alloys are austenitic in the mill-annealed condition but may form σ- or δ-ferrite phases under certain conditions of heat treatment or service. Such phases may be detrimental to corrosion resistance and mechanical properties. Annealing temperatures are confined to a narrow range to avoid formation of σ-phase at lower temperature or δ-ferrite at higher temperature. Rapid cooling following annealing is usually advisable, especially in heavy sections. Stress-relief treatments may be used below the annealing temperature range, but holding times should be kept at a minimum to avoid σ-phase and sensitization problems.

Magnetic Permeability. The more highly alloyed austenitic grades, along with the high-nitrogen grades such as 316N, the Nitronic family, and Carpenter 18-18 Plus, will not develop low-carbon martensite with cold work and therefore do not require a full anneal to reduce magnetic permeability. The permeability of these alloys will

remain below 1.02 even with significant amounts of cold work.

Bright Annealing of Austenitic Stainless Steels

All grades of austenitic stainless steel can be bright annealed in either pure hydrogen or dissociated ammonia, provided that the dew point of the atmosphere is less than −50 °C (−60 °F) and the workpieces, upon entering the furnace, are dry and scrupulously clean. The furnaces used in bright annealing must be clean, moisture-free, and tight if low dew points are to be maintained. If a low dew point is not maintained, a thin greenish oxide will form on the work. This oxide is very difficult to remove in subsequent descaling operations.

To maintain close control of dew point, atmosphere samples should be withdrawn from the furnace at frequent intervals and tested or continuously monitored, as in most commercial operations. Traces of oxygen in hydrogen gas can be removed before the gas enters the furnace by passing the gas through a catalytic tower that causes excess oxygen to combine with the hydrogen to form water vapor. The gas is then passed through activated alumina to remove moisture.

In using dissociated ammonia, it is important that maximum dissociation be obtained before the gas enters the furnace. The presence of any undissociated ammonia will result in objectionable nitriding action. Because the undissociated gas is entirely soluble in water, its removal can be easily accomplished. However, the remaining fully dissociated product must be processed through drying towers to restore the required low dew point.

Stress Relieving of Austenitic Stainless Steels

Austenitic stainless steels have good creep resistance; consequently, these steels must be heated to about 900 °C (1650 °F) to attain adequate stress relief. In some instances, heating to the annealing temperature may be desirable. Holding at a temperature lower than about 870 °C (1600 °F) results in only partial stress relief. The most effective stress-relieving results are achieved by slow cooling. Quenching or other rapid cooling, as is normal in the annealing of austenitic stainless steel, will usually reintroduce residual stresses. Stress relieving is only necessary when austenitic stainless parts are subjected to corrosive conditions conducive to stress corrosion or intergranular corrosion failures.

Selection of Treatment. Selection of an optimum stress-relieving treatment is difficult, because heat treatments that provide adequate stress relief can impair the corrosion resistance of stainless steel, and heat treatments that are not harmful to corrosion resistance may not provide adequate stress relief. To avoid specifying a heat treatment that might prove harmful, ASME Code neither re-

Table 4 Stress-relieving treatments for austenitic stainless steels

Application or desired characteristics	Extra-low-carbon grades, such as 304L and 316L	Stabilized grades, such as 318, 321, and 347	Unstabilized grades, such as 304 and 316
		Suggested thermal treatment(a)	
Severe stress corrosion	A, B	B, A	(b)
Moderate stress corrosion	A, B, C	B, A, C	C(b)
Mild stress corrosion	A, B, C, E, F	B, A, C, E, F	C, F
Remove peak stresses only	F	F	F
No stress corrosion	None required	None required	None required
Intergranular corrosion	A, C(c)	A, C, B(c)	C
Stress relief after severe forming	A, C	A, C	C
Relief between forming operations	A, B, C	B, A, C	C(d)
Structural soundness(e)	A, C, B	A, C, B	C
Dimensional stability	G	G	G

(a) Thermal treatments are listed in order of decreasing preference. A: Anneal at 1065 to 1120 °C (1950 to 2050 °F) and then slow cool. B: Stress relieve at 900 °C (1650 °F) and then slow cool. C: Anneal at 1065 to 1120 °C (1950 to 2050 °F) and then quench or cool rapidly. D: Stress relieve at 900 °C (1650 °F) and then quench or cool rapidly. E: Stress relieve at 480 to 650 °C (900 to 1200 °F) and then slow cool. F: Stress relieve at below 480 °C (900 °F) and then slow cool. G: Stress relieve at 205 to 480 °C (400 to 900 °F) and then slow cool (usual time, 4 h per inch of section). (b) To allow the optimum stress-relieving treatment, the use of stabilized or extra-low-carbon grades is recommended. (c) In most instances, no heat treatment is required, but where fabrication procedures may have sensitized the stainless steel the heat treatments noted may be employed. (d) Treatment A, B, or D also may be used, if followed by treatment C when forming is completed. (e) Where severe fabricating stresses coupled with high service loading may cause cracking. Also, after welding heavy sections

Table 5 Residual stresses in welded austenitic stainless steel before and after various treatments

Treatment Temperature			Residual stress	
°C	°F	Time, h	MPa	ksi
After welding 235 mm (9.25 in.) OD, 165 mm (6.5 in.) ID pipe				
As-welded			207-177	30.0-25.7
595	1100	16	138	20.0
595	1100	48	138	20.0
595	1100	72	159	23.0
650	1200	4	148-166	21.5-24.0
After welding 127 mm (5 in.) OD, 102 mm (4 in.) ID pipe				
As-welded			128-101	18.5-14.7
650	1200	4	94-105	13.7-15.3
650	1200	12	110	16.0
650	1200	36	108	15.6
900	1650	2	nil	nil
1010	1850	1	nil	nil

Table 6 Recommended annealing treatments for ferritic stainless steels

UNS No.	Designation	Treatment temperature	
		°C	°F
Conventional ferritic grades			
S40500	405	650-815	1200-1500
S40900	409	870-925	1600-1700
S43000	430	705-790	1300-1450
S43020	430F	705-790	1300-1450
S43400	434	705-790	1300-1450
S44600	446	760-830	1400-1525
S43035	439	870-925	1600-1700
Low-interstitial ferritic grades(a)			
...	18 SR	870-925	1600-1700
S44400	444	955-1010	1750-1850
S44626	E-Brite	760-955	1400-1750
S44660	Sea-Cure (SC-1)	1010-1065	1850-1950
...	AL 29-4C	1010-1065	1850-1950
S44800	AL 29-4-2	1010-1065	1850-1950
S44635	MONIT	1010-1065	1850-1950

(a) Postweld heat treating of the low-interstitial ferritic stainless steels is generally unnecessary and frequently undesirable. Any annealing of these grades should be followed by water quenching or very rapid cooling.

quires nor prohibits stress relief of austenitic stainless steel.

Metallurgical characteristics of austenitic stainless steels that may affect the selection of a stress-relieving treatment are discussed below:

- *Heating in the range from 480 to 815 °C (900 to 1500 °F):* Chromium carbides will precipitate in the grain boundaries of wholly austenitic unstabilized grades. In partially ferritic cast grades, the carbides will precipitate initially in the discontinuous ferrite pools rather than in a continuous grain-boundary network. After prolonged heating such as is necessary for heavy sections, however, grain-boundary carbide precipitation will occur. For cold-worked stainless, carbide precipitation may occur at temperatures as low as 425 °C (800 °F); for types 309 and 310, the upper limit for carbide precipitation may be as high as 900 °C (1650 °F). In this condition, the steel is susceptible to intergranular corrosion. By using stabilized or extra-low-carbon grades, these intergranular precipitates of chromium carbide can be avoided.
- *Heating in the range from 540 to 925 °C (1000 to 1700 °F):* The formation of hard, brittle σ-phase may result, which can decrease both corrosion resistance and ductility. During the times necessary for stress relief, σ-phase will not form in fully austenitic wrought, cast, or welded stainless. However, if the stainless is partly ferritic, the ferrite may transform to σ-phase during stress relief. This is generally not a problem in wrought stainless steels, because they are fully austenitic. However, some wrought grades, particularly types 309, 309Cb, 312, and 329, may contain some ferrite. Furthermore, the composition of most austenitic stainless welds and castings is intentionally adjusted so that ferrite is present as a deterrent to cracking. The niobium-containing cast grade

CF-8C normally contains 5 to 20% ferrite, which is more likely to transform to σ-phase than the niobium-free ferrite in the unstabilized CF-8 grade.

- *Slow cooling an unstabilized grade (other than an extra-low-carbon grade):* Through either of the above temperature ranges, slow cooling may allow sufficient time for these detrimental effects to take place.
- *Heating at 815 to 925 °C (1500 to 1700 °F):* The coalescence of chromium carbide precipitates or σ-phase will occur, resulting in a form less harmful to corrosion resistance or mechanical properties.
- *Heating at 955 to 1120 °C (1750 to 2050 °F):* This annealing treatment causes all grain-boundary chromium carbide precipitates to redissolve, transforms σ-phase back to ferrite, and fully softens the steel. Long heating times (>1 h) may even dissolve some of the ferrite present and further reduce the probability that σ-phase will reform upon slow cooling.
- *Stress relieving to improve notch toughness:* Unlike carbon and alloy steels, austenitic steels are not notch-sensitive. Consequently, stress relieving to improve notch toughness would be of no benefit. Notch-impact strength may actually be decreased if the steel is stress relieved at a temperature at which chromium carbide is precipitated or σ-phase is formed.

Although stabilized alloys do not require high-temperature annealing to avoid intergranular corrosion, the stress-relieving temperature exerts an influence on the general corrosion resistance of these alloys. Figure 1 shows the effect of stress relieving for 2 h at various temperatures on the corrosion rate of type 347 stainless steel in boiling 65% nitric acid. The corrosion resistance of type 347 is better when the material is treated at 815 to 870 °C (1500 to 1600 °F) than when treated at 650 to 705 °C (1200 to 1300 °F). The 650 to 705 °C (1200 to 1300 °F) stress relief may promote the formation of a small quantity of chromium carbides as a result of free carbon not previously tied up as niobium carbides.

Figure 2 shows how the percentage of stress relief increases with an increase in stress-relieving temperature for type 347 stainless steel. These data also demonstrate the relative unimportance of holding time.

General Recommendations. Selection of the proper stress-relieving treatment involves consideration of the specific material used, the fabrication procedures involved, and the design and operating conditions of the equipment. Stress relieving generally is not advisable unless the service environment is known or suspected to cause stress corrosion. If stress relieving seems warranted, due regard should be given to the metallurgical factors and their effect on the steel in the intended service. The use of stabilized or extra-low-carbon grades is an advantage in view of the greater latitude allowed in stress relieving.

Table 4 offers suggested stress-relieving treatments for various service applications and environments. Because of the varying degrees of stress relief that may be required, the number of

different grades of stainless in use, the many fabricating procedures that may be employed, and the multitude of service requirements, many alternative treatments are indicated in Table 4 to allow selection of the stress-relieving treatment best suited to particular circumstances.

Results Obtained by Various Treatments. Austenitic stainless steels have in many instances been stress relieved at temperatures normally used for carbon steels (540 to 650 °C, or 1000 to 1200 °F). Although at these temperatures virtually all residual stress is relieved in carbon steel, only 30 to 40% of the residual stress is relieved in austenitic stainless (Fig. 2). Because the treatment does not provide adequate stress relief, stainless stress relieved in this temperature range is often susceptible to stress corrosion. Table 5 shows the residual stresses remaining in solid austenitic stainless steel after they were stress relieved for various times at temperatures ranging from 595 to 1010 °C (1100 to 1850 °F).

Annealing and Water Quenching. Numerous instances have been reported in which satisfactory service was obtained for vessels and parts that were stress relieved by being annealed (at 1065 to 1120 °C, or 1950 to 2050 °F) and water quenched. However, it is unlikely that these products were subjected to service environments conducive to severe stress corrosion, such as chloride-containing environments, because a water quench will almost always reintroduce high residual stresses.

Intergranular Corrosion. In a number of instances, partially stress-relieved stainless steel parts have failed through intergranular corrosion. For example, partially stress-relieved (at 620 to 650 °C, or 1150 to 1200 °F) type 316 stainless steel hardware used in coastal steam stations failed due to intergranular attack in seawater over a span of less than 6 months. Another typical case of intergranular corrosion involved a type 304 stainless steel heat exchanger (partially stress relieved at 650 °C, or 1200 °F, for 2 h and furnace cooled) that failed within 7 days.

Prevention of Stress Corrosion by Stress Relieving. A number of instances have been recorded in which beneficial effects were derived from an adequate stress-relief treatment. For instance, heaters made of type 316L failed after a few weeks of service while in contact with acid organic chloride and ammonium chloride, but when stress relieved at 955 °C (1750 °F) were completely free of stress-corrosion cracking (SCC) after four years of service under the same conditions.

When two type 316L stainless steel vessels were used in 85% phosphoric acid service, the vessel not stress relieved underwent extensive stress corrosion, whereas the stress-relieved (540 °C, or 1000 °F) vessel was completely free of stress corrosion. Even though a stainless steel component may not be completely stress relieved, reducing the stress level may totally prevent stress corrosion.

Stress relief of unstabilized grades of stainless steel at 900 °C (1650 °F) will result in some intergranular carbide precipitation, but a small amount of intergranular attack often is preferable to failure within a few weeks by SCC. Moreover, the in-

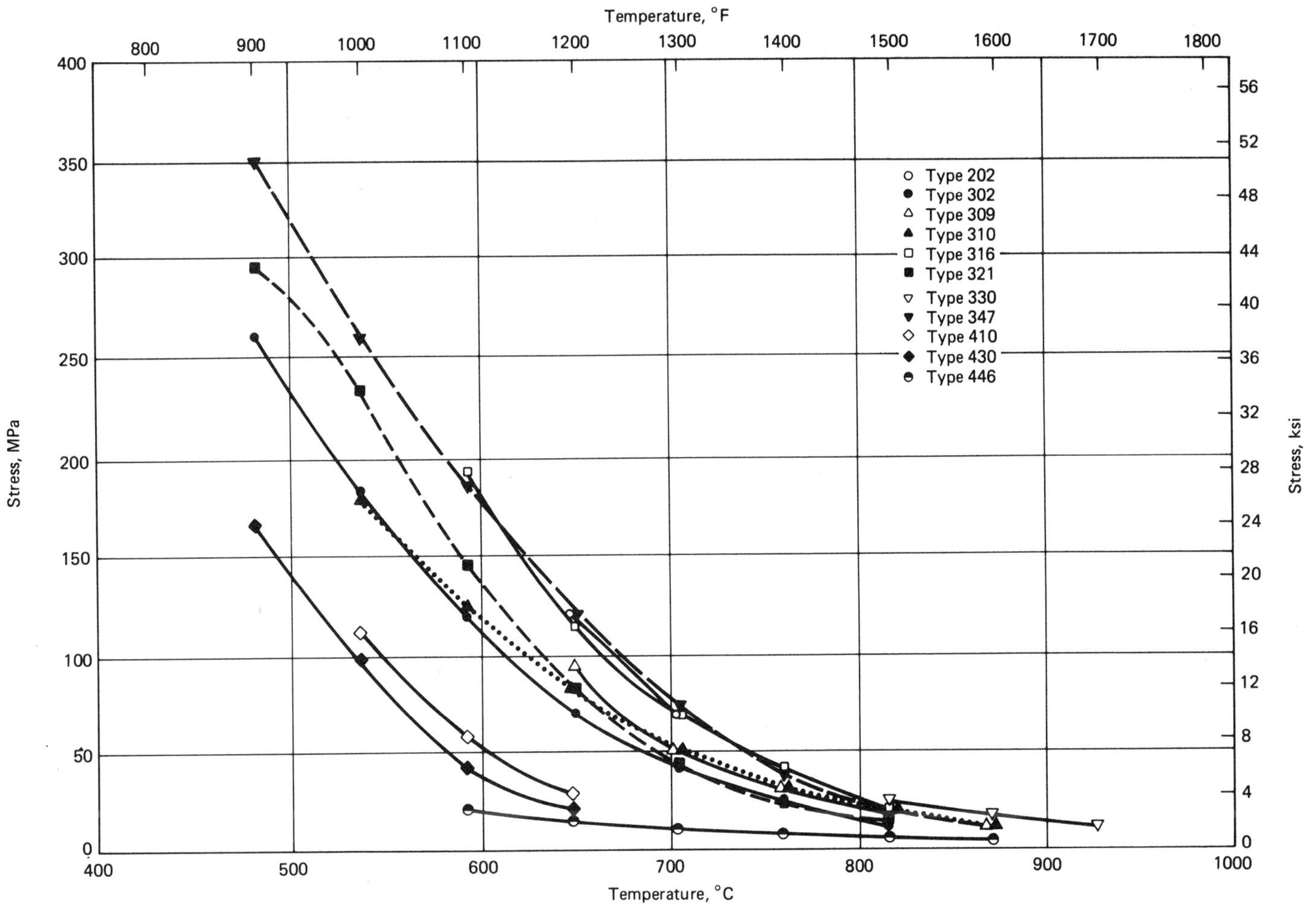

Temperature, °F

(Chart: 10,000 h stress-rupture strength vs Temperature)

Legend:
- ○ Type 202
- ● Type 302
- △ Type 309
- ▲ Type 310
- □ Type 316
- ■ Type 321
- ▽ Type 330
- ▼ Type 347
- ◇ Type 410
- ◆ Type 430
- ◕ Type 446

Fig. 3 10,000 h stress-rupture strength of wrought stainless steels. All samples were annealed, with the exception of type 410 (heat treated at 980 °C, or 1800 °F, for ½ h, oil quenched, tempered at 650 °C, or 1200 °F, for 2 h and then air cooled). Extrapolated data were used for all curves.

tergranular attack probably can be avoided by using an extra-low-carbon or stabilized grade of austenitic stainless steel.

Ferritic Stainless Steels

The ferritic stainless steels can be divided into two groups:

- Conventional ferritics, such as types 405, 409, 430, 434, 439, and 446
- Low-interstitial ferritics, such as types 444, E-Brite, Sea-Cure, AL 29-4C, and AL 29-4-2

The ferritic stainless steels are not normally hardened by quenching, but rather develop minimum hardness and maximum ductility, toughness, and corrosion resistance in the annealed-and-quenched condition. Therefore, the only heat treatment applied to the ferritics is annealing. This treatment relieves stresses developed during welding or cold working and provides a more homogeneous structure by dissolving transformation products formed during welding. Postweld heat treatment of the low-interstitial ferritic stainless steels is generally unnecessary and is frequently undesirable. Ta-

ble 6 summarizes current annealing practices for the ferritic grades.

Austenite-Martensite Embrittlement. When grades such as 430 and 434 are cooled rapidly from above 925 °C (1700 °F), they may become brittle from austenite's transforming to as much as 30% martensite. This may be corrected by a tempering treatment such as 650 to 790 °C (1200 to 1450 °F), which softens the alloy.

After such a treatment, some carbide formation can occur. After severe cold working, annealing at a temperature of less than 925 °C (1700 °F) is recommended to avoid further sensitization. Stabilized ferritics such as 439 or 444 avoid the austenite-martensite embrittlement concern by removing the strong austenite-forming elements (carbon plus nitrogen) from solution.

475 °C (885 °F) Embrittlement. A potentially harmful form of embrittlement common to the ferritic grades can develop from prolonged exposure to, or slow cooling within, the temperature range from about 370 to 540 °C (700 to 1000 °F), with the maximum rate of embrittlement occurring at about 475 °C (885 °F). The embrittlement is caused by precipitation of the α'-phase, and the effects of embrittlement increase rapidly with chromium content. Lower-chromium alloys such

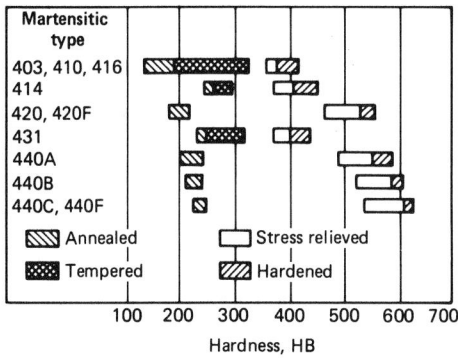

Fig. 4 Effect of heat treatments on the hardness of wrought martensitic stainless steels

as type 409 show little tendency to embrittle with 475 °C (885 °F) exposure. Certain heat treatments must be controlled to avoid embrittlement. The brittle condition can be eliminated by the treatments listed in Table 6, using temperatures clearly above the upper boundary of embrittlement, followed by rapid cooling to prevent a recurrence.

Intermetallic Phase Embrittlement. Intermetallic phases, such as σ, χ, and Laves, may form at elevated temperatures in ferritic stainless

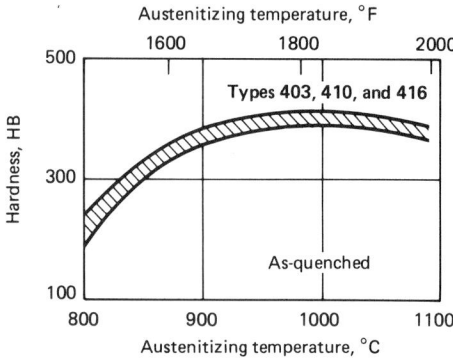

Fig. 5 Effect of austenitizing temperature on as-quenched hardness. Specimens were wrought martensitic stainless steels containing 0.15% max C.

Table 7 Recommended annealing temperatures for selected duplex stainless steels

UNS No.	Designation	Annealing temperature(a) °C (°F)
S32900	329	925-955 (1700-1750)
S32950	7 Mo Plus	995-1025 (1825-1875)
S31500	3RE60	975-1025 (1785-1875)
S31803	SAF 2205	1020-1100 (1870-2010)
S31260	DP-3	1065-1175 (1950-2150)
S32550	Ferralium 255	1065-1175 (1950-2150)

(a) Cooling from the annealing temperature must be rapid, but it also must be consistent with limitations of distortion.

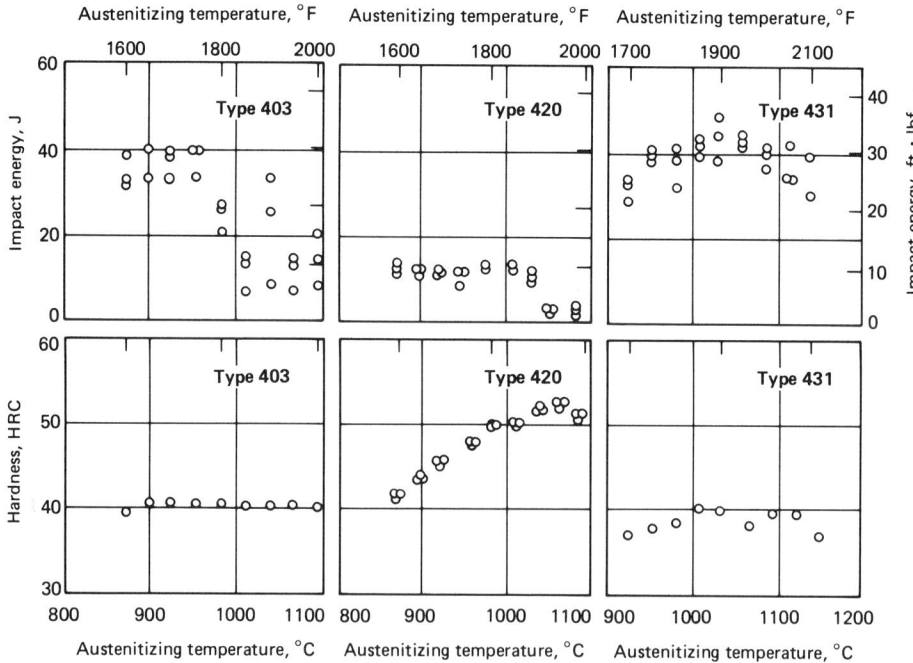

Fig. 6 Effect of variations in austenitizing temperature on hardness and impact strength of wrought martensitic stainless steels. Specimens were tempered at 480 °C (900 °F) for 4 h.

steels containing more than about 14% Cr and/or additional elements such as niobium or molybdenum. These intermetallic phases increase hardness (sometimes usefully) and decrease ductility, notch toughness, and corrosion resistance. The temperature range over which these phases form is approximately 595 to 1000 °C (1100 to 1830 °F). Generally, such phases are of most concern when affected parts are cooled to room temperature. At elevated temperatures, the phases do not appear to be a major problem from a ductility or toughness standpoint. In the case of Laves phase, such intermetallics can even improve high-temperature creep strength. Figure 3 compares stress-rupture properties of selected ferritic and austenitic stainless steels.

Intermetallic phase embrittlement is primarily a service problem involving long exposures at elevated temperatures. These phases can be dissolved by heating to above 1000 °C (1830 °F).

Duplex Stainless Steels

Duplex stainless steels consist of a mixed microstructure of austenite and ferrite. Some duplex stainless steels are rich in ferrite, others in austenite, and others are equally balanced. Compared with type 316, the annealed duplex alloys provide improved resistance to chloride SCC. Although the duplex grades are generally not as resistant to SCC as the low-interstitial ferritics, they are normally available

in heavier section thicknesses. Another useful characteristic of the duplex grades is that they typically have yield strengths more than twice those of conventional austenitic stainless steels. In thicker sections, the duplex alloys are more impact resistant than ferritic alloys.

Duplex stainless steels, such as SAF 2205, AF 22, DP 3, and Ferralium alloy 255, are alloyed with 0.15 to 0.20% N. This minimizes alloy element segregation between the ferrite and austenite, thereby improving as-welded corrosion resistance to a level greater than that of type 329 alloy. The nitrogen addition also increases the precipitation of austenite during casting and welding and prevents high ferrite content in rapidly cooled welds. Recommended annealing temperatures for duplex stainless steels are listed in Table 7.

Martensitic Stainless Steels

The heat treating of martensitic stainless steels is essentially the same as for plain-carbon or low-alloy steels, in that maximum strength and hardness depend chiefly on carbon content. The principal metallurgical difference is that the high alloy content of the stainless grades causes the transformation to be so sluggish, and the hardenability to be so high, that maximum hardness is produced by air cooling in the center of sections up to approximately 305 mm (12 in.) thick.

Surface hardness ranges for the various heat-treated conditions, from fully annealed to fully hardened, are given in Fig. 4. The martensitic stainless steels are more sensitive to heat treating variables than are carbon and low-alloy steels; rejection rates due to faults in heat treating are correspondingly high.

Prior Cleaning. To avoid contamination, all parts and heat treating fixtures must be cleaned thoroughly before being placed in the furnace. Proper cleaning is particularly important when the heat treatment is to be performed in a protective atmosphere. Grease, oil, and even location lines made using an ordinary lead pencil can cause carburization. Perspiration stains from fingerprints are a source of chloride contamination and may cause severe scaling in oxidizing atmospheres. Furthermore, a protective atmosphere cannot be effective unless it is permitted to make unobstructed contact with metal surfaces.

Preheating. Martensitic stainless steels normally are hardened by being heated to the austenitizing range of 925 to 1065 °C (1700 to 1950 °F) and then cooled in air or oil.

The thermal conductivity of stainless steels is characteristically lower than that of carbon and alloy steels. Accordingly, high thermal gradients and high stresses during rapid heating may cause warpage and cracking in some parts. To avoid these problems, preheating is usually recommended in the treatment of martensitic stainless steels. In annealing or hardening, the following parts should be preheated:

- Parts with heavy sections
- Parts with both thin and thick sections
- Parts with sharp corners and re-entrant angles
- Heavily ground parts
- Parts machined with heavy, deep cuts
- Parts that have been cold formed or straightened
- Previously hardened parts that are being re-heat-treated

Preheating is normally accomplished at 760 to 790 °C (1400 to 1450 °F), and heating need be continued only long enough to ensure that all portions of each part have reached the preheating temperature.

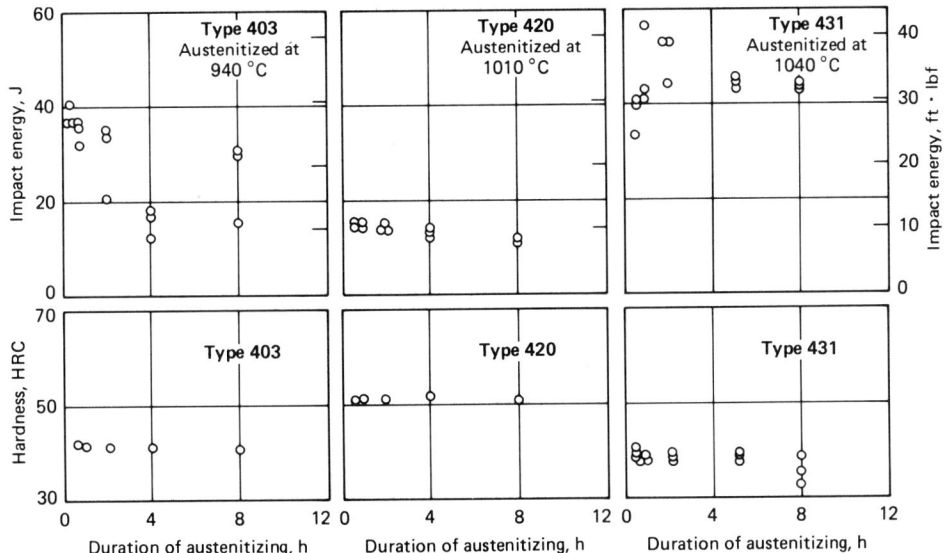

Fig. 7 Effect of variations in austenitizing time on hardness and impact strength of wrought martensitic stainless steels. Specimens were tempered at 480 °C (900 °F) for 4 h.

Large heavy parts are sometimes preheated at approximately 540 °C (1000 °F) prior to the higher-carbon types 431, 420, and 440.

Austenitizing temperatures, soaking times, and quenching media are summarized in Table 8. When maximum corrosion resistance and strength are desired, the steel should be austenitized at the high end of the temperature range. For alloys that are to be tempered above 565 °C (1050 °F), the low side of the austenitizing range is recommended because it enhances ductility and impact properties.

The effect of austenitizing temperature on the as-quenched hardness of three martensitic grades is shown in Fig. 5. Hardness increases with increasing austenitizing temperature to about 980

°C (1800 °F), then decreases because of austenite retention and (occasionally) the formation of δ-ferrite. Certain anomalies in these steels that should be considered before specifying a heat-treating procedure are exemplified in the opposing injurious effects of the high and low extremes of austenitizing temperature, depending on the subsequent tempering temperature.

The effect of variations in austenitizing temperature on the impact strength and room-temperature hardness of types 403, 420, and 431 is plotted in Fig. 6 to 8. Table 9 shows that the Izod impact properties of type 431 are caused by retained austenite.

Soaking times employed in the hardening of martensitic stainless steels represent a compro-

mise between achieving maximum solution of chromium-iron carbides for maximum strength and corrosion resistance and avoiding decarburization, excessive grain growth, retained austenite, brittleness, and quench cracking. For sections with a thickness of 13 mm (½ in.) or less, a soaking time of 30 to 60 min is sometimes recommended. For most parts, adding 30 min for each additional inch of thickness or fraction thereof has proved adequate. However, soaking times should be doubled if parts to be hardened have been fully annealed or isothermally annealed.

Quenching. Because of their high hardenability, martensitic stainless steels can be quenched in either oil or air. Some decrease in corrosion resistance and ductility, resulting from air quenching, may occur in these grades. These steels may precipitate carbides in grain-boundary areas if heavy sections are cooled slowly through the temperature range of about 870 to 540 °C (1600 to 1000 °F). Too slow a cooling rate in bright annealing these alloys may impair their corrosion resistance (see the section "Austenitic Stainless Steels" in this article). Although oil quenching is preferred, air cooling may be required for large or complex sections to prevent distortion or quench cracking. Martempering is particularly easy with these steels because of their high hardenability.

Retained Austenite. The higher-carbon martensitic grades, such as 440C, and the higher-nickel type 431 are likely to retain large amounts of untransformed austenite in the as-quenched structure, frequently as much as 30% by volume. Stress relieving at about 150 °C (300 °F) has little effect. Delayed transformation, particularly in type 440C, may occur as a result of temperature fluctuations in service, thus resulting in embrittlement and unacceptable dimensional changes.

Subzero Cooling. A portion of the austenite retained in quenching may be transformed by subzero cooling to about –75 °C (–100 °F) immediately after

Table 8 Procedures for hardening and tempering wrought martensitic stainless steels to specific strength and hardness levels

Type	Austenitizing(a) Temperature(b) °C	Austenitizing(a) Temperature(b) °F	Quenching medium(c)	Tempering temperature(d) °C min	Tempering temperature(d) °C max	Tempering temperature(d) °F min	Tempering temperature(d) °F max	Tensile strength MPa	Tensile strength ksi	Hardness, HRC
403, 410	925-101	1700-1850	Air or oil	565	605	1050	1125	760-965	110-140	25-31
				205	370	400	700	1105-1515	160-220	38-47
414	925-1050	1700-1925	Air or oil	595	650	1100	1200	760-965	110-140	25-31
				230	370	450	700	1105-1515	160-220	38-49
416, 416Se	925-1010	1700-1850	Oil	565	605	1050	1125	760-965	110-140	25-31
				230	370	450	700	1105-1515	160-220	35-45
420	980-1065	1800-1950	Air or oil(e)	205	370	400	700	1550-1930	225-280	48-56
431	980-1065	1800-1950	Air or oil(e)	565	605	1050	1125	860-1035	125-150	26-34
				230	370	450	700	1210-1515	175-220	40-47
440A	1010-1065	1850-1950	Air or oil(e)	150	370	300	700	...	...	49-57
440B	1010-1065	1850-1950	Air or oil(e)	150	370	300	700	...	...	53-59
440C, 440F	1010-1065	1850-1950	Air or oil(e)	...	160	...	325	...	...	60 min
				...	190	...	375	...	...	58 min
				...	230	...	450	...	...	57 min
				...	355	...	675	...	...	52-56

(a) Preheating to a temperature within the process annealing range (see Table 10) is recommended for thin-gage parts, heavy sections, previously hardened parts, parts with extreme variations in section or with sharp reentrant angles, and parts that have been straightened or heavily ground or machined, to avoid cracking and minimize distortion, particularly for types 420, 431, and 440A, B, C, and F. (b) Usual time at temperature ranges from 30 to 90 min. The low side of the austenitizing range is recommended for all types subsequently tempered to 25 to 31 HRC; generally, however, corrosion resistance is enhanced by quenching from the upper limit of the austenitizing range. (c) Where air or oil is indicated, oil quenching should be used for parts more than 6.4 mm (¼ in.) thick; martempering baths at 150 to 400 °C (300 to 750 °F) may be substituted for an oil quench. (d) Generally, the low end of the tempering range of 150 to 370 °C (300 to 700 °F) is recommended for maximum hardness, the middle for maximum toughness, and the high end for maximum yield strength. Tempering in the range of 370 to 565 °C (700 to 1050 °F) is not recommended because it results in low and erratic impact properties and poor resistance to corrosion and stress corrosion. (e) For minimum retained austenite and maximum dimensional stability, a subzero treatment –75 ± 10 °C (– 100 ± 20 °F) is recommended; this should incorporate continuous cooling from the austenitizing temperature to the cold transformation temperature.

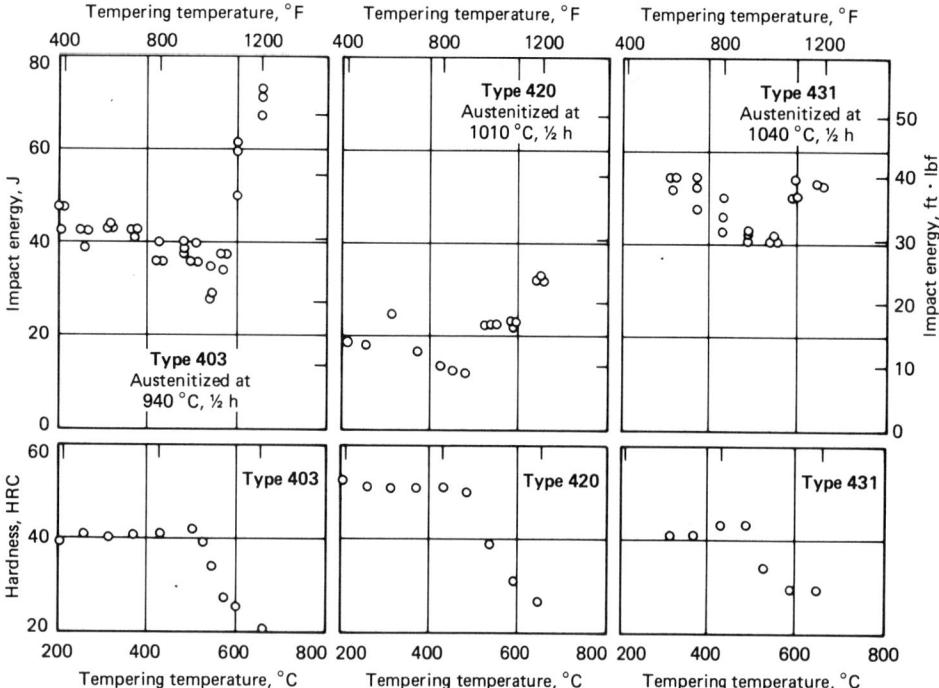

Fig. 8 Effect of variation in tempering temperature on hardness and impact strength of wrought martensitic stainless steels

Table 9 Izod impact energy of wrought martensitic stainless steels using selected heat treatments

Temperature				Izod impact energy	
Austenitizing		Tempering			
°C	°F	°C	°F	J	ft · lbf
980	1795	315	600	20.3-33.9	15.0-25.0
1065	1950	315	600	40.7-81.3	30.0-60.0
980	1795	595	1100	74.6-108.5	55.0-80.0
1065	1950	595	1100	61.0-74.6	45.0-55.0

Although the strength, elongation, and hardness curves shown in Fig. 9 to 14 appear to have the same general form as those of low-alloy steel, the increase in tensile strength and hardness between 400 and 510 °C (750 and 950 °F) may be associated with a serious decrease in notch toughness, whereas tempering on the high side of the temperature range generally coincides with a decrease in corrosion resistance. The tempering temperatures most frequently employed to achieve desired hardness and other mechanical properties are included in Table 8.

The Izod impact curves in Fig. 9 to 14 reveal a loss of impact strength when parts are tempered within the range of 370 to 650 °C (700 to 1200 °F). Tempering within this range also results in decreased corrosion resistance, particularly resistance to SCC (Fig. 15). Double tempering (cooling parts to room temperature after the first tempering treatment) also is beneficial for resistance to stress corrosion.

Annealing. Temperatures and resulting hardnesses for process (subcritical) annealing, full annealing, and isothermal annealing are given in Table 10.

Full annealing is an expensive and time-consuming treatment; it should be used only when required for subsequent severe forming. Types 414 and 431 do not respond to full or isothermal annealing procedures within a reasonable soaking period.

quenching. To obtain maximum transformation of retained austenite, double tempering may be necessary. Parts should be air cooled to room temperature between the tempering cycles.

Subzero cooling is frequently included in the hardening treatment of parts such as the slides and sleeves of slide valves, and bearings requiring maximum dimensional stability.

Reheating. For fully hardened steels, increasing degrees of recovery are achieved by:

• *Stress relieving* at 150 to 370 °C (300 to 700 °F) after hardening to reduce transformation

stresses without significantly affecting microconstituents or mechanical properties
• *Tempering* at intermediate temperatures to modify properties
• *Subcritical annealing* (variously called *process, mill,* or *low annealing*) in the upper portion of the ferritic range, just below the lower critical Ac₁ temperature, to achieve maximum softening without the complications of re-entering the γ or austenitic field. (At the Ac₁ temperature, austenite begins to form.)
• *Full annealing* for maximum softening by a return to the austenitic range, followed by slow cooling

Table 10 Annealing temperatures and procedures for wrought martensitic stainless steels

Type	Process (subcritical) annealing			Full annealing			Isothermal annealing(c)	
	Temperature(a)			Temperature(b)(c)			Procedure(d)	
	°C	°F	Hardness	°C	°F	Hardness	°C (°F)	Hardness
403, 410	650-760	1200-1400	86-92 HRB	830-885	1525-1625	75-85 HRB	Heat to 830-885 (1525-1625); hold 6 h at 705 (1300)	85 HRB
414	650-730	1200-1345	99 HRB-24 HRC	Not recommended			Not recommended	
416, 416Se	650-760	1200-1345	86-92 HRB	830-885	1525-1625	75-85 HRB	Heat to 830-885 (1525-1625); hold 2 h at 720 (1330)	85 HRB
420	675-760	1245-1400	94-97 HRB	830-885	1525-1625	86-95 HRB	Heat to 830-885 (1525-1625); hold 2 h at 705 (1300)	95 HRB
431	620-705	1150-1300	99 HRB-30 HRC	Not recommended			Not recommended	
440A	675-760	1245-1400	90 HRC-22 HRC	845-900	1555-1650	94-98 HRB	Heat to 845-900 (1555-1650); hold 4 h at 690	98 HRB
440B	675-760	1245-1400	98 HRB-23 HRC	845-900	1555-1650	95 HRB-20 HRC	Same as 440A	20 HRC
440C, 440F	675-760	1245-1400	98 HRB-23 HRC	845-900	1555-1650	98 HRB-25 HRC	Same as 440A	25 HRC

(a) Air cool from temperature; maximum softness is obtained by heating to temperature at high end of range. (b) Soak thoroughly at temperature within range indicated; furnace cool to 790 °C (1455 °F); continue cooling at 15 to 25 °C/h (27 to 45 °F/h) to 595 °C (1100 °F); air cool to room temperature. (c) Recommended for applications in which full advantage may be taken of the rapid cooling to the transformation temperature and from it to room temperature. (d) Preheating to a temperature within the process annealing range is recommended for thin-gage parts, heavy sections, previously hardened parts, parts with extreme variations in section or with sharp reentrant angles, and parts that have been straightened or heavily ground or machined to avoid cracking and minimize distortion, particularly for types 420 and 431, and 440A, B, C, and F.

Isothermal annealing is recommended where maximum softening is required and adequate facilities for controlled slow cooling are not available.

Subcritical annealing is recommended for all applications that do not require maximum softness.

Full annealing, isothermal annealing, and especially repeated process annealing promote the formation of coarse carbides that take longer to dissolve at austenitizing temperatures.

Salt Baths. Many stainless steel parts are heat treated in molten salt, with excellent results. The baths usually employed consist of barium chloride with 5 to 35% sodium or potassium chloride. Alkaline-earth and other metallic oxides build up in these baths through use, but these oxides are not harmful to low-carbon stainless steels. However, if these salt baths are also to be used for hardening other alloy steels, to avoid surface decarburization it is necessary to rectify the baths with graphite to remove the metallic oxides and with methyl chloride gas to convert the alkaline-earth oxides back to chlorides. A bath treated with methyl chloride will carburize low-carbon stainless steels unless it is aged for at least 24 h beforehand. To avoid this problem, stainless steel parts should be heat treated in a salt bath reserved exclusively for stainless steels.

Protective Atmospheres. Argon or helium, if used as a protective atmosphere, should be exceptionally dry (with a dew point below –50 °C, or –60 °F). Because these gases are expensive and cannot be generated, they are rarely used. Exothermic and endothermically generated gas can be used with excellent results. These require dewpoint or infrared control so as not to carburize or decarburize the stainless grade being heat treated. Endothermic gas containing approximately 40% H can embrittle martensitic stainless steels that are oil quenched.

An exothermic gas ratio of 6.5 or 7 to 1 is satisfactory for grades of stainless containing not more than 0.15% C. For endothermic atmospheres, dew points for specific steels and austenitizing temperatures are listed in Table 11.

Hydrogen embrittlement can become an important concern in the martensitic grades, generally increasing with hardness and carbon content. (It is variable and less acute in ferritic steels, and it is virtually unknown in the austenitic grades.) The embrittling hydrogen may be acquired as a result of the melting process, a heat-treating atmosphere, or chemical and electrochemical processes such as pickling and electroplating.

Most heat-treating atmospheres contain hydrogen in the form of moisture, hydrocarbons, or elemental hydrogen as an atmosphere or a dissociation product. The use of pure hydrogen or dissociated ammonia for bright annealing in one plant was associated with cracking of wire coils of types 431 and 440C, although other plants have reported no similar difficulty. Nevertheless, it is possible that some loss in ductility may result from the bright annealing of any of the martensitic stainless steels.

Less severe, the use of H_2 annealing gas with a titanium- or aluminum-bearing ferritic or martensitic grade, such as type 409, can lead to H_2 pickup and a resultant loss of bend ductility as-annealed.

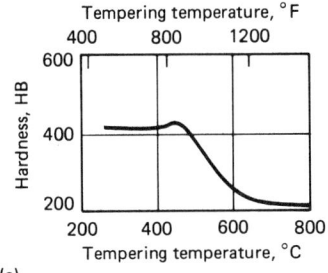

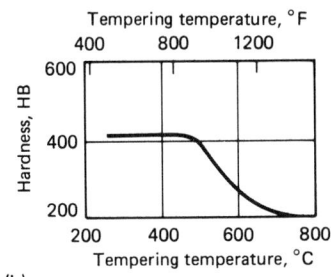

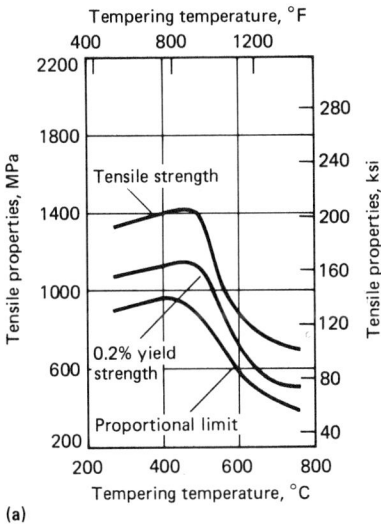

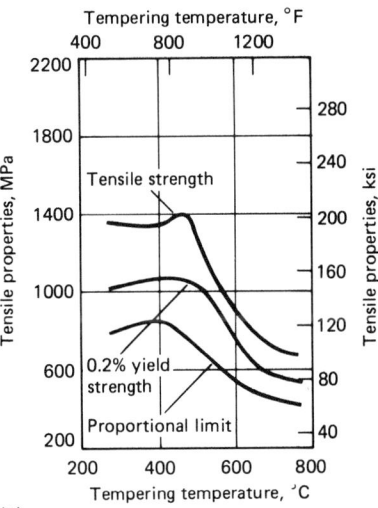

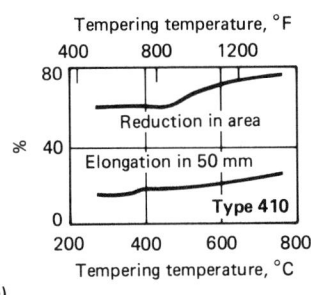

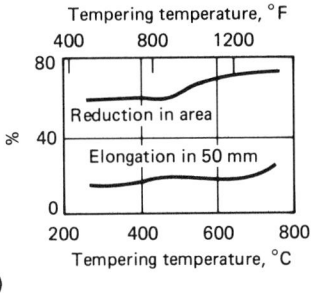

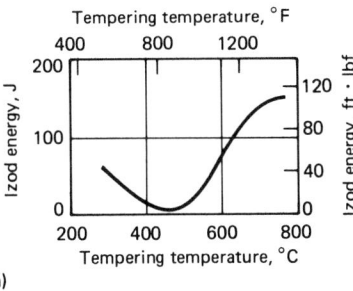

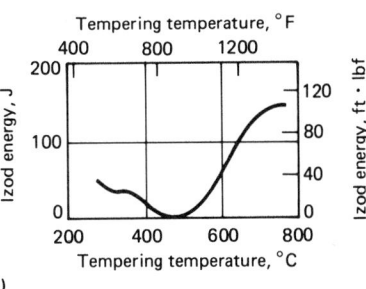

Fig. 9 Effect of austenitizing and tempering temperatures on mechanical properties of type 410 martensitic stainless steel. Austenitized 30 min; oil quenched to 65 to 95 °C (150 to 200 °F); double stress relieved at 175 °C (350 °F) for 15 min and water quenched; tempered 2 h. (a) Quenched from 925 °C (1700 °F). (b) Quenched from 1010 °C (1850 °F)

Table 11 Dew points of selected wrought martensitic stainless steels at various austenitizing temperatures

Alloy	Austenitizing temperature		Dew point	
	°C	°F	°C	°F
420	1010	1850	10-12	50-54
403, 410, 414, 416, 431	980	1795	16-18	61-64
440C	1040	1905	2-4	36-39

Low-temperature soaks of 175 to 230 °C (350 to 450 °F) in air will outgas embrittled ferritic alloys. Mill specifications outlining such baking procedures do exist.

Embrittlement has been found in oil-quenched types 403, 410, 414, and 431. Air quenching or the subsequent tempering of oil-quenched material releases the entrapped hydrogen, and ductility is restored. If a green oxide appears on the oil-quenched alloy, this must be removed prior to tempering or it will interfere with the release of entrapped hydrogen.

Additional information is available in the article "Embrittlement of Steels" in Volume 1 of the *ASM Handbook*.

Precipitation-Hardening Stainless Steels

In the heat treating of precipitation-hardening (PH) stainless steels, areas of primary interest include:

- Cleaning prior to heat treatment
- Furnace atmospheres
- Time-temperature cycles
- Effect of variations in cycles
- Scale removal after heat treatment

Prior Cleaning. All parts must be cleaned thoroughly prior to heat treating. Because the chemical composition of these steels is delicately balanced, failure to remove drawing lubricants, cutting oils, and grease can lead to surface carburization and improper response to heat treatment. As a secondary benefit, thorough cleaning promotes the formation of a uniform surface scale that is readily removable.

The recommended cleaning procedure comprises vapor degreasing or solvent cleaning, followed by mechanical scrubbing with a mild abrasive alkaline cleaner to remove insoluble soils. All traces of cleaners should be removed by thoroughly rinsing with warm water.

Wet or dry abrasive blasting may be substituted for the above procedure. Recommended grits and operating details for blasting are given in Table 12. After blasting, all traces of abrasive must be removed from the work by scrubbing thoroughly.

In some applications, cleaning prior to heat treating may be accomplished by closely controlled pickling in a 10% HNO_3-2% HF aqueous solution at 45 to 60 °C (110 to 140 °F). Time should be limited to 2 or 3 min. This method is not recommended for cleaning severely formed or previously heat-treated parts. Proprietary inhibited scale-removal preparations are available.

Furnaces fired with oil or natural gas are not entirely satisfactory for the heat treatment of PH steels unless the finished surfaces are to be subsequently machined. In such units, it is difficult to control combustion contaminants and to eliminate flame impingement on the parts being treated. Electric furnaces or gas-fired radiant-tube furnaces are generally used for heat treating PH stainless steels.

Furnace Atmospheres. Air is a satisfactory furnace atmosphere for austenite-conditioning and annealing operations. Controlled reducing atmospheres, such as dissociated ammonia or bright-annealing gas, introduce the potential hazard of nitriding or carburizing, either of which has a deleterious effect on mechanical properties.

Bright annealing can be done in hydrogen, argon, or helium atmospheres, provided that a dew point of −55 °C (−65 °F) or lower is maintained. The cooling rate from the annealing temperature must be approximately equal to that of cooling in still air. Austenite-conditioning treatments at tem-

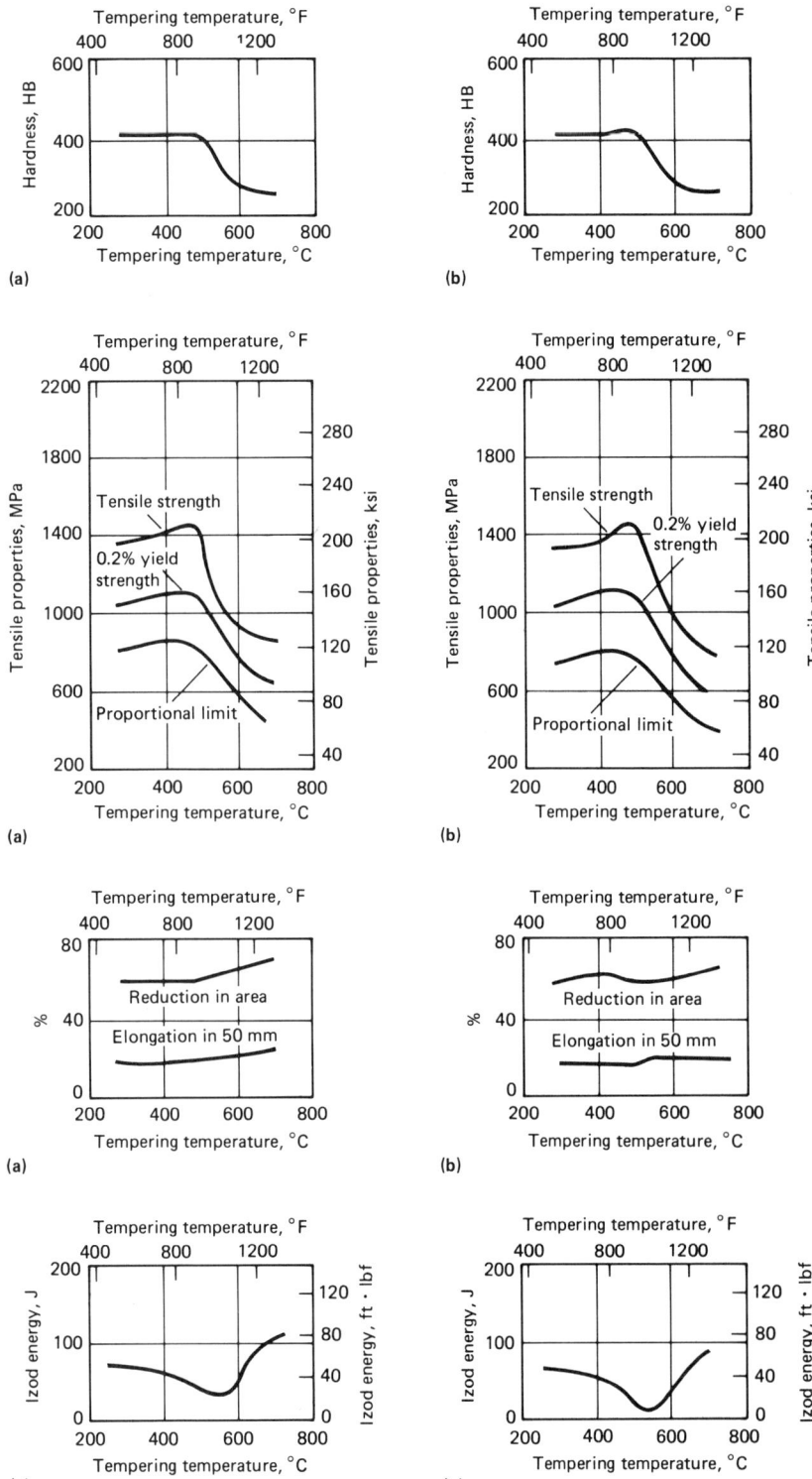

Fig. 10 Effect of austenitizing and tempering temperatures on typical mechanical properties of type 414 martensitic stainless steel. Austenitized 30 min; oil quenched to 65 to 95 °C (150 to 200 °F); double stress relieved at 175 °C (350 °F) for 15 min and water quenched; tempered 2 h. (a) Quenched from 925 °C (1700 °F). (b) Quenched from 1040 °C (1900 °F)

Table 12 Recommended conditions for abrasive blast cleaning of precipitation-hardening stainless steels prior to heat treatment

Abrasive		Nozzle			Air pressure		Cleaning speed	
Material	Grit No.	Size mm	in.	Angle, °	kPa	psi	mm^2/s	in.^{2}/min
Alumina (dry)	30	6.4	¼	45-60	170-655(a)	25-95(a)	130-215	12-20
Garnet or alumina (dry)	36	9.5	⅜	60	240	35	645	60
Wet blasting	220	6.4	¼	45-60	170-655(a)	25-95(a)	65-110	6-10

(a) Depending on metal thickness

peratures as high as 925 to 955 °C (1700 to 1750 °F) may also be performed in dry hydrogen, argon, or helium, maintaining the same low dew point. A scale-free surface will be obtained.

The lower austenite-conditioning temperatures, such as 760 °C (1400 °F), present difficulties in achieving scale-free surfaces in dry hydrogen, argon, or helium. An air atmosphere is generally used at these temperatures. For complete freedom from scale or discoloration at the lower temperatures, a vacuum furnace is required.

Final hardening of PH steels is performed at relatively low temperatures, and an air atmosphere is acceptable for these treatments.

Heat-Treating Procedures. Recommended procedures for full annealing, austenite conditioning, transformation cooling, and age tempering (precipitation hardening) are given in Table 13.

17-4 PH (UNS S17400) is a precipitation-hardening steel that has an essentially martensitic structure and limited formability when supplied in the solution-treated condition. Fabrication is followed by hardening in the range of 480 to 620 °C (900 to 1150 °F) (Table 13).

Care should be taken in using this alloy in the solution-treated condition because of its relatively low ductility. Hardening to any of the strength levels shown in Table 13 improves toughness.

17-7 PH (UNS S17700) is normally supplied in the solution-annealed condition (condition A), in which it is soft and formable. Heat treatment is accomplished through the use of the transformation-hardened (TH) or refrigeration-hardened (RH) procedures indicated in Table 13. The choice of heat-treatment method is usually dictated by the ease with which the particular sequence fits into the production techniques of the user. Parts that receive significant deformation should be heat treated to RH 950, or soft spots may result.

This alloy is also supplied in the cold-rolled condition (condition C). Here, transformation has been achieved by cold rolling, and heat treatment is reduced to a single step: 480 °C (900 °F) for 1 h. Although strength and stress-corrosion resistance are greatly increased by this treatment, ductility is reduced and formability is limited.

PH 15-7 Mo (UNS S15700) is a high-strength modification of 17-7 PH. It is supplied in the same condition as 17-7 PH and requires identical heat-treating procedures. Table 13 illustrates the strength levels obtainable with PH 15-7 Mo.

15-5 Ni alloys (UNS S15500) are normally supplied in the solution-treated condition. As with 17-4 PH, care should be used in applying the material in the solution-treated condition. The alloy can be hardened by heating to a temperature in the

range of 480 to 620 °C (900 to 1150 °F) for 1 to 4 h, depending on the temperature, and then air cooling. Table 13 illustrates typical strength levels versus hardening procedures.

13-8 Mo alloys (UNS S13800) are normally supplied in the solution-treated condition. They can be hardened to high strength levels by a single low-temperature treatment. Table 13 illustrates typical strength levels versus hardening procedures.

AM-350 and Pyromet 350 (UNS S35000) are normally purchased in the solution-treated condition; however, after severe forming or cold working, such material may require a second annealing treatment. The annealing temperature limits, indicated in Table 13, are critical. High temperatures reduce strength; lower temperatures adversely affect formability.

After annealing and conditioning at 930 °C (1710 °F), AM-350 is usually cooled at subzero temperatures, then aged at 455 °C (850 °F) for 3 h; this treatment produces maximum strength. Maximum toughness is achieved by aging in the range of 480 to 540 °C (900 to 1000 °F). The recommended temperature for subzero cooling must be carefully observed. Cooling to much lower temperatures, such as –195 °C (–320 °F), results in incomplete transformation, as does failure to hold at the recommended temperature for at least 3 h.

AM-355 and Pyromet 355 (UNS S35500) flat products are supplied in either the solution-treated or solution-treated and cold-rolled condition, whereas bar products are usually supplied in the equalized-and-overtempered condition for best machinability. Most castings are supplied in the as-cast condition.

Although, as indicated in Table 13, the homogenizing and austenite-conditioning treatments applied to castings differ from those applied to wrought materials (higher temperatures being used for castings in both treatments), subzero cooling is required for all forms to obtain maximum toughness and corrosion resistance. The full annealing treatment shown in Table 13 would normally be applicable only to flat products. The machinability treatment is required for obtaining good machining characteristics in this alloy.

Wrought materials should be aged at 455 °C (850 °F) for maximum ductility and toughness. The usual aging treatment for castings consists of holding at 455 °C (850 °F) for 2 h.

Custom 450 (UNS S45000) stainless steel is normally supplied in the solution-treated condition, requiring no further heat treatment for many applications. It is easily fabricated in the annealed condition. A single-step hardening treatment develops higher strength with good ductility and toughness.

The recommended minimum hardening temperature of 480 °C (900 °F) produces the optimum combination of strength, ductility, and toughness. Hardening at temperatures up to 620 °C (1150 °F) increases ductility and decreases strength (Table 13).

Custom 455 (UNS S45500) stainless steel is normally in the annealed condition, making it relatively soft and easily formable. A single-step hardening treatment develops exceptionally high yield strengths with good ductility and toughness. Hardening is accomplished by heating in the range of 480 to 565 °C (900 to 1050 °F) (Table 13).

Variations in Heat-Treating Cycles. One of the principal advantages of PH stainless steels is their versatility. Although certain heat treatments have been classified as standard, certain applications require deviations from these standards. The curves in Fig. 16 to 20 show how these deviations affect mechanical properties.

Scale Removal after Heat Treating. The amount and nature of scale vary with the cleanliness of the work being treated, the furnace atmosphere, and the temperature and duration of heat treatment. In the following discussion, it will be assumed that all heat-treating operations are performed in an air atmosphere. A variety of descaling methods may be employed; the choice depends on the type of steel and the facilities available.

Scale formed during homogenization or full annealing can be effectively removed using a 10% HNO_3-2% HF aqueous solution at 45 to 60 °C (110 to 140 °F). Exposure to the acid solution should be limited to a period of 3 min. Removal of loosened scale may be facilitated by the use of high-pressure water or steam. A uniform surface is evidence of a well-cleaned part. The use of molten salts to condition the scale is limited, because the temperature involved (about 450 °C, or 850 °F) can age harden any martensite in the microstructure.

Austenite-conditioning treatments produce a scale that is best removed by mechanical means. Wet grit-blasting processes are commonly used. Acids should be avoided, because they are a possible source of intergranular attack.

The final step in heat treating (precipitation hardening) produces a discoloration, or heat tint. Mechanical methods should be used to remove this oxide from 17-7 PH, PH 15-7 Mo, AM-350, and AM-355. The HNO_3-HF solution has been used on these steels, but extreme care is required to prevent intergranular attack. The acid solution may be used satisfactorily with 17-4 PH. To a lesser extent, electropolishing is sometimes used to remove the final heat tint. Proprietary cleaners are also available.

Table 13 Recommended heat-treating procedures for semiaustenitic precipitation-hardenable stainless steels

UNS S17400

Homogenization. 1175 ± 15 °C (2150 ± 25 °F) for 2 h + 30 min per 25 mm (1 in.).(a)

Austenite conditioning (solution treatment). 1040 ± 15 °C (1900 ± 25 °F) for 30 min + 30 min per 25 mm (1 in.).(a)

Transformation cooling. To below +30 °C (+90 °F)

Precipitation hardening. To obtain minimum tensile strengths shown, use the following treatments for wrought alloys(b):

MPa	ksi	°C	°F	h
1310	190	480 ± 5	(900 ± 10)	1
1170	170	495 ± 5	(925 ± 10)	4
1070	155	555 ± 5	(1030 ± 10)	4
1030	150	565 ± 5	(1050 ± 10)	4
1000	145	580 ± 5	(1075 ± 10)	4
930	135	620 ± 5	(1150 ± 10)	4

Comparable treatments for cast materials(b):

MPa	ksi	°C	°F	h
1240	180	480 ± 5	(900 ± 10)	4
1170	170	495 ± 5	(925 ± 10)	4
1035	150	540 ± 5	(1000 ± 10)	4
895	130	595 ± 5	(1100 ± 10)	4

UNS S17700

Solution annealing. 1065 ± 15 °C (1950 ± 25 °F) for 3 min + 1 min per 0.25 mm (0.01 in.); air cool

RH treatments

Austenite conditioning. 955 ± 15 °C (1750 ± 25 °F) for 10 min + 1 min per 0.25 mm (0.01 in.); air cool(c)

Transformation cooling. To below −70 °C (−90 °F) for 8 h

Precipitation hardening. To obtain minimum tensile strengths shown, the following treatments are recommended(b):

MPa	ksi	°C	°F	h
1450	210	510 ± 5	(950 ± 10)	1
1240	180	565 ± 5	(1050 ± 10)	1
1170	170	580 ± 5	(1075 ± 10)	1
1035	150	595 ± 5	(1100 ± 10)	1

TH Treatments

Austenite conditioning. 760 ± 15 °C (1400 ± 25 °F) for 1½ h; cool within 1 h to below 15 °C (60 °F) but above 0 °C (32 °F), and hold at least ½ h before precipitation hardening

Precipitation hardening. To obtain minimum tensile strengths shown, the following treatments are recommended(b):

MPa	ksi	°C	°F	h
1240	180	565 ± 5	(1050 ± 10)	1½
1170	170	580 ± 5	(1075 ± 10)	1½
1035	150	595 ± 5	(1100 ± 10)	1½

UNS S15700

Solution annealing. Same as for 17-7 PH

RH treatments

Austenite conditioning. Same as for 17-7 PH

Transformation cooling. Same as for 17-7 PH

Precipitation hardening. To obtain minimum tensile strengths shown, the following treatments are recommended(b):

MPa	ksi	°C	°F	h
1550	225	510 ± 5	(950 ± 10)	1
1310	190	565 ± 5	(1050 ± 10)	1

TH treatments

Austenite conditioning. 760 ± 15 °C (1400 ± 25 °F) for 1½ h; cool within 1 h to below 15 °C (60 °F) but above 0 °C (32 °F), and hold at least ½ h before precipitation hardening

Precipitation hardening. For minimum tensile strength of 1310 MPa (190 ksi)(b): 565 ± 5 °C (1050 ± 10 °F) for 1½ h

UNS S35000

Solution annealing. Wrought materials only: 1065 ± 15 °C (1950 ± 25 °F) for 3 min + 1 min per 0.25 mm (0.01 in.); air cool

Austenite conditioning. 930 ± 5 °C (1710 ± 10 °F) for 10 min + 1 min per 0.25 mm (0.01 in.); air cool(c)

Transformation cooling. To −75 ± 5 °C (−100 ± 10 °F) for 3 h (minimum)

Precipitation hardening. To obtain minimum tensile strengths shown, the following treatments are recommended(b):

MPa	ksi	°C	°F	h
1275	185	455 ± 5	(850 ± 10)	3
1170	170	510 ± 5	(950 ± 10)	3
1140	165	540 ± 5	(1000 ± 10)	3

UNS S35500

Homogenization. Castings only: 1095 ± 15 °C (2000 ± 25 °F) for 2 h; air cool (water quench sections over 50 mm, or 2 in.). Bar and forgings: 1050 ± 15 °C (1925 ± 25 °F) for 1 to 3 h; water quench. Cool all forms to below −70 °C (−90 °F) and hold 3 h minimum.

Solution annealing. 1025 ± 15 °C (1875 ± 25 °F) for 1 h per 25 mm (1 in.); water quench

Machinability treatment. 760 ± 15 °C (1400 ± 25 °F) for 3 h; air cool. Refrigerate to −70 °C (−90 °F) and hold for 3 h. Reheat to 565 ± 15 °C (1050 ± 25 °F) for 3 h.

For −70 °C (−90 °F) transformation:

Austenite conditioning. Castings: 980 ± 15 °C (1800 ± 25 °F) for 2 h; air cool (oil quench sections over 3 mm, or 0.125 in.). Wrought materials: 930 ± 15 °C (1710 ± 25 °F) for 15 min per in.; air cool (oil quench sections over 3 mm, or 0.125 in.)

Transformation cooling. To −75 ± 5 °C (−100 ± 10 °F) for 3 h

Precipitation hardening. To obtain minimum tensile strengths shown, use the following treatments for wrought alloys(b):

MPa	ksi	°C	°F	h
1310	190	455 ± 5	(850 ± 10)	3
1170	170	540 ± 5	(1000 ± 10)	3

For castings, to obtain minimum tensile strength of 1240 MPa (180 ksi)(b): 455 ± 5 °C (850 ± 10 °F) for 2 h

UNS S45000

Solution annealing. 1040 ± 15 °C (1900 ± 25 °F) for 1 h at heat(d), water quench

Precipitation hardening. Typical tensile strengths shown may be obtained by the following treatments:

MPa	ksi	°C	°F	h
1345	195	480 ± 5	(900 ± 10)	4, air cool
1170	170	540 ± 5	(1000 ± 10)	4, air cool
1105	160	565 ± 5	(1050 ± 10)	4, air cool
965	140	620 ± 5	(1150 ± 10)	4, air cool

UNS S45500

Solution annealing. 830 ± 15 °C (1525 ± 25 °F) for 1 h at heat(d), water quench

Precipitation hardening. Typical tensile strengths shown may be obtained by the following treatments:

MPa	ksi	°C	°F	h
1725	250	480 ± 5	(900 ± 10)	4, air cool
1620	235	510 ± 5	(950 ± 10)	4, air cool
1450	210	540 ± 5	(1000 ± 10)	4, air cool
1310	190	565 ± 5	(1050 ± 10)	4, air cool

UNS S15500

Solution annealing. 1040 ± 15 °C (1900 ± 25 °F) for 1 h(d), water quench

Precipitation hardening. Typical tensile strengths shown may be obtained by the following treatments:

MPa	ksi	°C	°F	h
1380	200	480 ± 5	(900 ± 10)	1, air cool
1170	170	550 ± 5	(1025 ± 10)	4, air cool
1000	145	620 ± 5	(1150 ± 10)	4, air cool

H1150M condition (after annealing). 760 ± 8 °C (1400 ± 15 °F) for 2 h, air cool + 620 ± 5 °C (1150 ± 10 °F) for 4 h, air cool

Typical tensile strength. 860 MPa (125 ksi)

UNS S13800

Solution annealing. 925 ± 8 °C (1700 ± 15 °F) for 1 h(d), air cool or oil quench

Precipitation hardening. Typical tensile strengths shown may be obtained by the following treatments:

MPa	ksi	°C	°F	h
1550	225	510 ± 5	(950 ± 10)	4, air cool
1310	190	565 ± 5	(1050 ± 10)	4, air cool
1000	145	620 ± 5	(1150 ± 10)	4, air cool

H1150M condition (after annealing). 760 ± 8 °C (1400 ± 15 °F) for 2 h, air cool + 620 ± 5 °C (1150 ± 10 °F) for 4 h, air cool

Typical tensile strength. 895 MPa (130 ksi)

(a) To prevent cracking and ensure uniform properties, cool as follows: 75 mm (3 in.) and less, oil quench or air cool; 75 to 150 mm (3 to 6 in.), air cool; 150 mm (6 in.) and over, air cool under cover. *All parts must be cooled to below 30 °C (90 °F) prior to the precipitation-hardening cycle.* (b) If hardness exceeds maximum specified, reheat treat at a slightly higher temperature for a minimum of 30 min. (c) Air cool to room temperature; *do not reheat before transformation cooling.* (d) Time at heat is dependent upon section size. Normally, a 1 h hold at temperature is suggested.

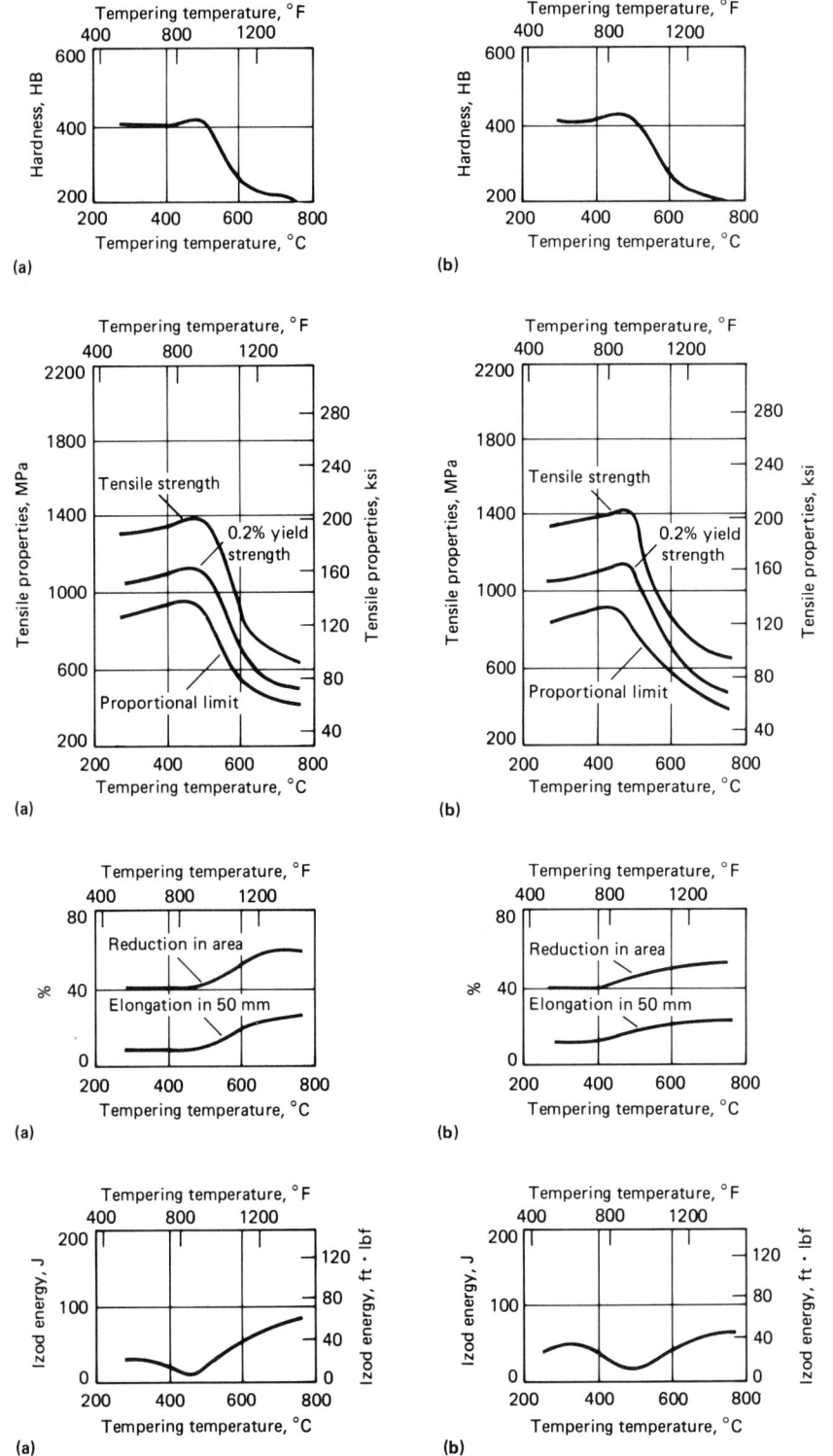

Fig. 11 Effect of austenitizing and tempering temperatures on typical mechanical properties of type 416 martensitic stainless steel. Austenitized 30 min; oil quenched to 65 to 95 °C (150 to 200 °F); double stress relieved at 175 °C (350 °F) for 15 min and water quenched; tempered 2 h. (a) Quenched from 925 °C (1700 °F). (b) Quenched from 980 °C (1800 °F)

Stainless Steel Castings

The heat treatment of stainless steel castings follows closely in purpose and procedure the thermal processing of comparable wrought materials. However, the differences in detail warrant separate consideration here.

Because they are not cold worked or cold formed, castings of the older, conventional martensitic grades CA-15 and CA40 (UNS J91150 and J91153) do not require subcritical annealing to remove the effects of cold working. However, in work-hardenable ferritic alloys, machining and grinding stresses are relieved at temperatures from about 260 to 540 °C (500 to 1000 °F). Casting stresses in the martensitic castings noted above should be relieved by subcritical annealing prior to further heat treatment. When these hardened martensitic castings are stress relieved, the stress-relieving temperature must be kept below the final tempering or aging temperature.

An improved cast martensitic alloy, CA-6NM (UNS J91540), possesses better casting behavior, improved weldability, and equals or exceeds all of the mechanical, corrosion, and cavitation resistance properties of CA-15. As a result, it has largely replaced the older alloy. Both CA-6NM and CA-15 castings are usually supplied in the normalized and tempered condition: normalized at 955 °C (1750 °F) min and tempered at 595 °C (1100 °F) min. When it is necessary or desirable to anneal CA-6NM castings, a temperature of 790 to 815 °C (1450 to 1500 °F) should be used. The alloy should be furnace cooled or otherwise slow cooled to 595 °C (1100 °F), after which it may be cooled in air. When stress relieving is required, CA-6NM may be heated to 620 °C (1150 °F) max and then slowly cooled to prevent martensite formation.

Homogenization

Alloy segregation and dendritic structures can occur in castings and may be particularly pronounced in heavy sections. Because castings are not subjected to the high-temperature mechanical reduction and soaking treatments entailed in the mill processing of wrought alloys, it is frequently necessary to homogenize some alloys at temperatures above 1095 °C (2000 °F) to promote uniformity of chemical composition and microstructure. Full annealing of martensitic castings results in recrystallization and maximum softness but is less effective than homogenization in eliminating segregation. Homogenization is a common procedure in the heat treatment of precipitation-hardening castings.

Ferritic and Austenitic Alloys

The ferritic, austenitic, and mixed ferritic-austenitic alloys are not hardenable by heat treatment. They can be heat treated to improve their corrosion resistance and machining characteristics. The ferritic alloys CB-30 and CC-50 (UNS J91803 and J92615, respectively) are annealed by being heated above 790 °C (1450 °F) to relieve stresses and reduce hardness (Table 2).

Solution Annealing. The austenitic alloys achieve maximum resistance to intergranular corrosion by the high-temperature heating and quenching procedure known as *solution annealing* (Table 2). As-cast structures, or castings exposed to temperatures in the range from 425 to 870 °C (800 to 1600 °F), may contain complex chromium carbides precipitated preferentially along grain boundaries in wholly austenitic alloys. This microstructure is susceptible to intergranular corrosion, especially in oxidizing solutions. (In partially ferritic alloys, carbides tend to precipitate in the discontinuous ferrite pools; thus, these alloys are less susceptible to intergranular attack.) The purpose of solution annealing is to ensure complete solution of carbides in the matrix and to retain these carbides in solid solution.

Solution-annealing procedures for all austenitic alloys are similar and consist of heating to a temperature of about 1095 °C (2000 °F), holding for a time sufficient to accomplish complete solution of carbides, and quenching at a rate fast enough to prevent reprecipitation of the carbides, particularly while cooling through the range from 870 to 540 °C (1600 to 1000 °F). Temperatures to which castings should be heated prior to quenching vary somewhat, depending on the alloy (Table 2).

Stabilizing Treatment. As shown in Table 2, a two-step heat-treating procedure may be applied to the niobium-containing CF-8C (UNS J92710) alloy. The first treatment consists of solution annealing. This is followed by a stabilizing treatment at 870 to 925 °C (1600 to 1700 °F), which precipitates niobium carbides, prevents formation of the damaging chromium carbides, and provides maximum resistance to intergranular attack.

Because of their low carbon contents, as-cast CF-3 and CF-3M (UNS J92700 and J92800, respectively) do not contain enough chromium carbides to cause selective intergranular attack, and hence they may be used in some corrodents in this condition. For maximum corrosion resistance, however, these grades require solution annealing.

Martensitic Alloys

Castings of the CA-6NM composition should be hardened by air cooling or oil quenching from a temperature of 1010 to 1065 °C (1850 to 1950 °F). The carbon content of this alloy is lower than that of CA-15, which, along with the addition of molybdenum and nickel, enables the alloy to harden completely without significant austenite retention when cooled as suggested.

The choice of cooling medium is determined primarily by the maximum section size. Section sizes greater than 125 mm (5 in.) will harden completely when cooled in air. CA-6NM is not prone to cracking during cooling from elevated temperatures. For this reason, no problem should arise during the air cooling or oil quenching of configurations that include both thick and thin sections.

A wide range of mechanical properties are available through the choice of tempering temperature. Castings of CA-6NM are normally supplied normalized and tempered at 595 to 620 °C (1100 to 1150 °F). Reaustenitizing occurs upon tempering above 620 °C (1150 °F), the amount of reaustenitization increasing with increasing temperature. Depending on the amount of this transformation, cooling from such tempering temperatures may adversely affect both ductility and toughness through the transformation to untempered martensite.

Even though the alloy is characterized by a decrease in impact strength when tempered in the range of 370 to 595 °C (700 to 1100 °F), the minimum reached is significantly higher than that of

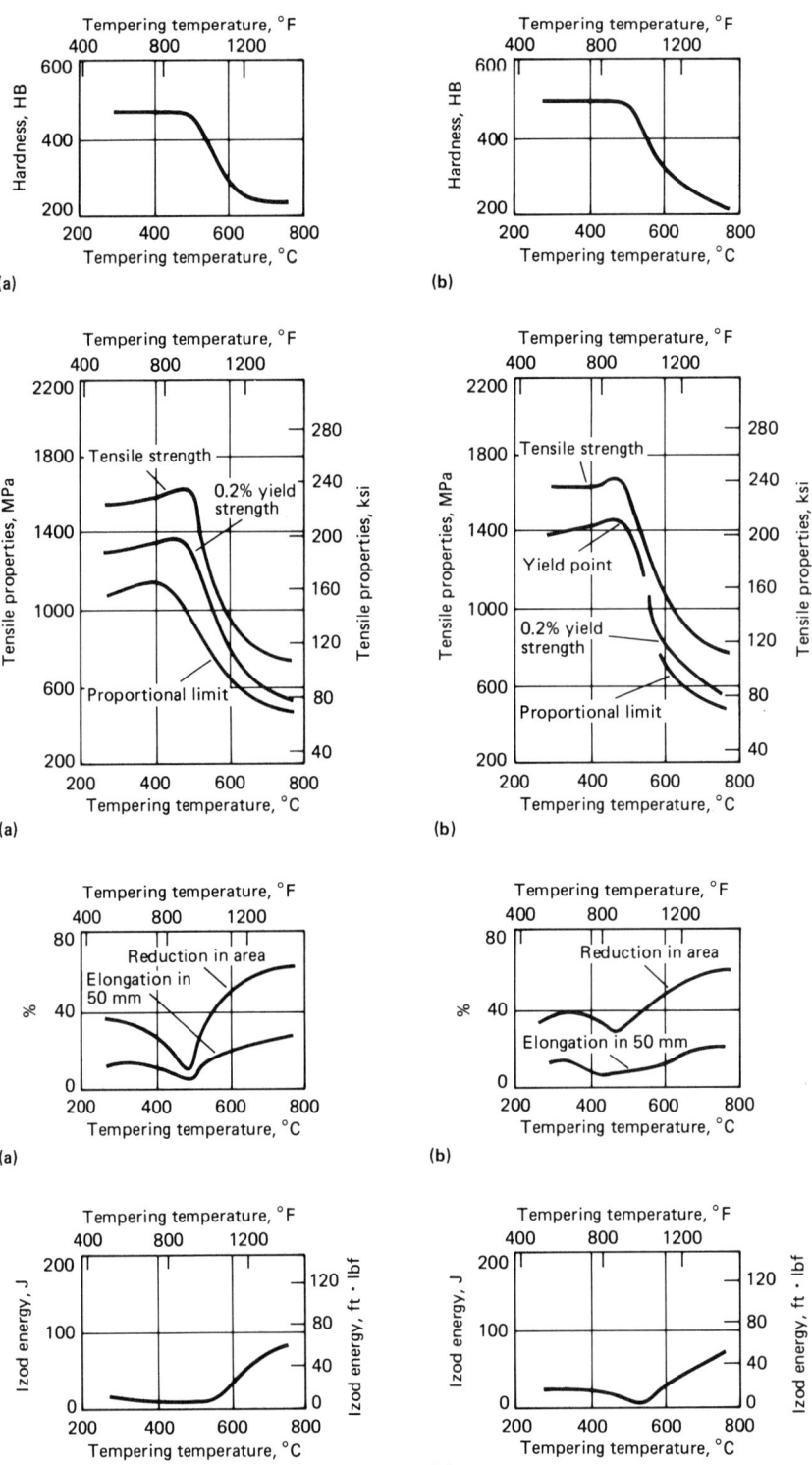

Fig. 12 Effect of austenitizing and tempering temperatures on typical mechanical properties of type 420 martensitic stainless steel. Austenitized 30 min; oil quenched to 65 to 95 °C (150 to 200 °F); double stress relieved at 175 °C (350 °F) for 15 min and water quenched; tempered 2 h. (a) Quenched from 925 °C (1700 °F). (b) Quenched from 1025 °C (1875 °F)

CA-15. This improvement in impact toughness results from the presence of molybdenum and nickel in the composition and from the lower carbon content. The best combination of strength with toughness is obtained when the alloy is tempered above 150 °C (950 °F).

Figure 21 shows the effect of tempering temperature on the hardness, strength, ductility, and toughness properties of CA-6NM. Strengths even higher than those considered typical can be obtained by tempering at lower temperatures without a significant loss of ductility or toughness.

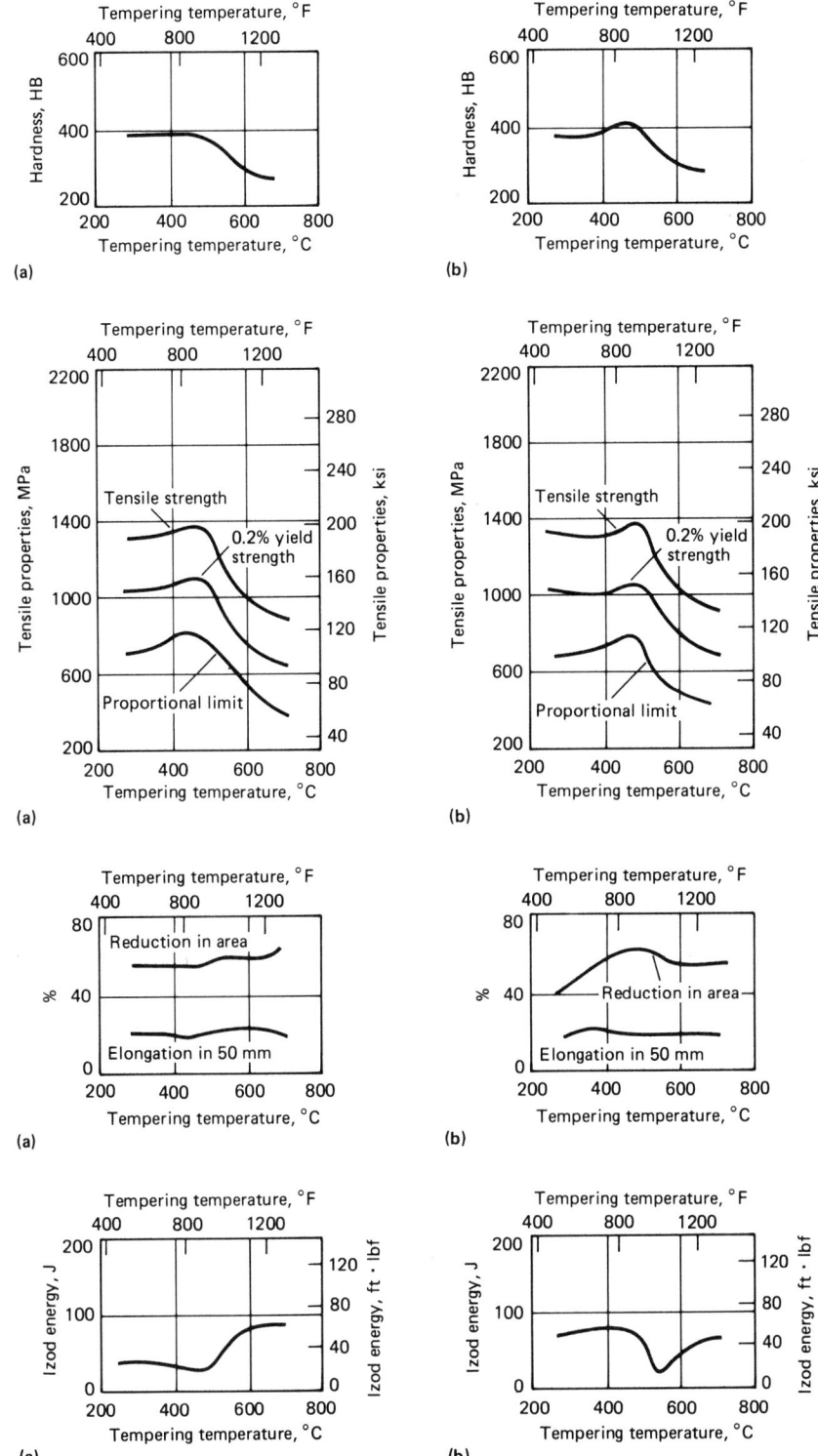

Fig. 13 Effect of austenitizing and tempering temperatures on typical mechanical properties of type 431 martensitic stainless steel. Austenitized 30 min; oil quenched to 65 to 95 °C (150 to 200 °F); double stress relieved at 175 °C (350 °F) for 15 min and water quenched; tempered 2 h. (a) Quenched from 925 °C (1700 °F). (b) Quenched from 1040 °C (1900 °F)

tlement in the annealed or annealed-and-cold-worked condition, even when exposed for long periods at 370 to 480 °C (700 to 900 °F). Data are not currently available on such steels in the quenched-and-tempered or normalized-and-tempered condition.

Another significant practical advantage of CA-6NM is its relative freedom from the rapid drop in hardness when tempered above about 510 °C (950 °F). Figure 22 shows clearly that a given increase in tempering temperature produces a much more gradual decrease in hardness as compared with CA-15. This makes heat treating much easier and less expensive and decreases the frequency of rejects and/or the necessity for re-heat treatment.

The hardening procedures for CA-15 castings are similar to those used for the comparable wrought alloy (type 410). Austenitizing consists of heating to 955 to 1010 °C (1750 to 1850 °F) and soaking for a minimum of 30 min; the high side of this temperature range is normally employed. Parts are then cooled in air or quenched in oil. To reduce the probability of cracking in the brittle, untempered martensitic condition, tempering should take place immediately after quenching.

Tempering is performed in two temperature ranges: up to 370 °C (700 °F) for maximum strength and corrosion resistance, and from 595 to 760 °C (1100 to 1400 °F) for improved ductility at lower strength levels. Tempering in the range of 370 to 595 °C (700 to 1100 °F) is normally avoided because of the resultant low impact strength. Figure 23 shows the nominal mechanical properties obtained in CA-15 castings as a function of tempering temperature. Additional data on mechanical properties are given in Table 14. These data are based on several heats of shell cast CA-15 alloy. The standard heat treating procedures for CA-15, CA-40, and CA-6NM are given in Table 15. In the hardened and tempered condition, CA-40 provides higher tensile strength and lower ductility than CA-15 tempered at the same temperature. Both alloys can be annealed by cooling slowly from the range of 845 to 900 °C (1550 to 1650 °F).

Additional information is available in the article "Metallurgy and Properties of Cast Stainless Steels" in this volume.

Precipitation-Hardening Alloys

Precipitation-hardenable castings should be subjected to a high-temperature homogenization treatment to reduce alloy segregation and to obtain more uniform response to subsequent heat treatment. Even investment castings that are cooled slowly from the pouring temperature exhibit more nearly uniform properties when they have been homogenized. Recommended hardening alloys 17-4 PH (UNS S17400) and AM-350 (UNS 35000) are included in Table 13.

17-4 PH Castings. When 17-4 PH (ASTM CB-7Cu-1 and CB-7Cu-2) is cast in plastic-bonded shell molds, the surface is carburized by decomposition of the binder. The added carbon prevents proper heat-treating response of the casting surface. Satisfactory response is obtained

The minor loss of toughness and ductility that does occur is associated with the lesser degree of tempering that takes place at the lower temperature and not with embrittlement, as might be the

situation with other 12% Cr steels that contain no molybdenum. The addition of molybdenum to 12% Cr steels makes them unusually stable thermally and normally not susceptible to embrit-

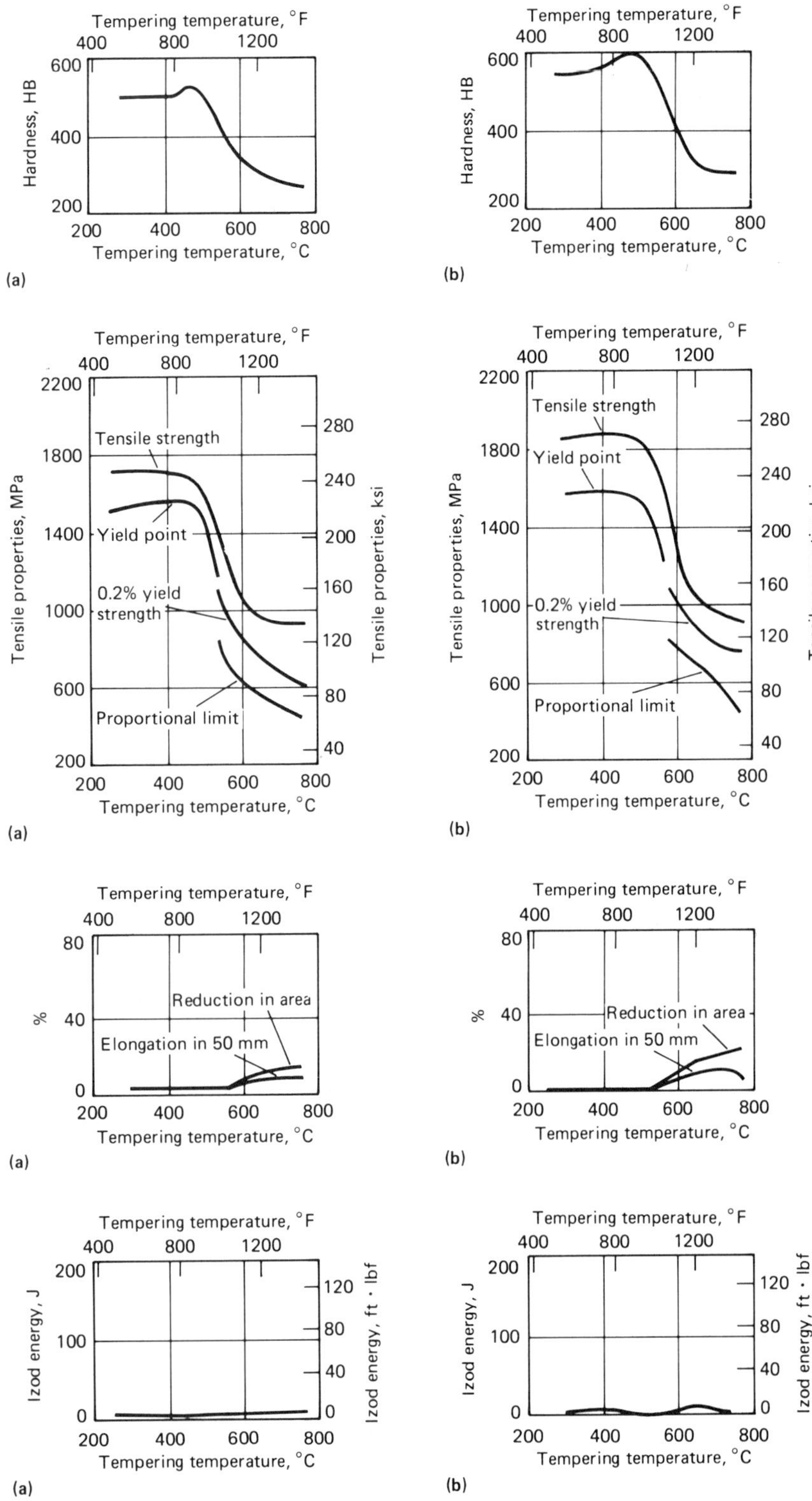

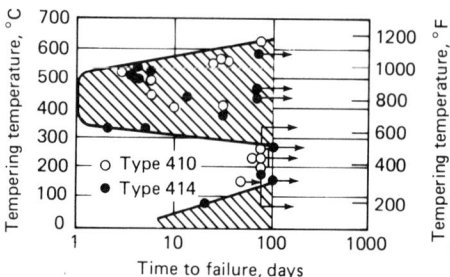

Fig. 15 Effect of tempering temperature on the stress-corrosion characteristics of two wrought martensitic stainless steels at high stress. Data apply to a stress level of 350 MPa (80 ksi) for tests in a salt fog cabinet.

Fig. 14 Effect of austenitizing and tempering temperatures on typical mechanical properties of type 440C martensitic stainless steel. Austenitized 1 h at 925 °C (1700 °F) and 2 h at 1040 °C (1900 °F); oil quenched to 65 to 95 °C (150 to 200 °F); double stress relieved at 175 °C (350 °F) for 15 min and water quenched; tempered 2 h. (a) Quenched from 925 °C (1700 °F). (b) Quenched from 1040 °C (1900 °F)

The tendency of 17-4 PH castings to overage is reduced by the addition of about 0.25% Nb + Ta to the alloy. The effect of time at aging temperature on the mechanical properties of niobium-free and niobium-containing 17-4 PH investment castings is shown in Table 17.

AM-350 and AM-355. Although investment castings made of these alloys do not necessarily require a homogenizing treatment, homogenization provides a more uniform response to subsequent heat treatment. Shell mold and sand castings made of AM-355 that were extremely brittle without homogenization regained ductility after homogenizing at 1095 °C (2000 °F) for 2 h minimum. Heat-treating procedures and the effects of tempering temperatures up to 650 °C (1200 °F) on the mechanical properties of AM-355 shell mold castings are given in Table 18.

When AM-355 castings are welded, maximum mechanical properties are obtained when the castings are fully heat treated after welding (Table 19). Heat treatments prior to welding have little effect on properties when a complete heat treatment follows welding.

Surface Hardening

In certain applications, surface hardening is performed to improve the resistance of stainless steel alloys to galling and wear through the formation of hard dispersions. The softer, tougher interior of the alloy remains unaffected, and thus provides impact resistance. The process encompasses a variety of techniques, including nitriding, carburizing, boriding, and flame hardening. The essential feature of all these techniques is that they modify the chemical composition of the alloy surface.

Gas Nitriding

Gas nitriding is a case-hardening process whereby nitrogen is introduced into the surface of an alloy by holding the metal at a suitable temperature in contact with a nitrogenous gas, usually ammonia. Quenching is not required for the production of a hard case. The nitriding temperature for all steels is between 495 and 565 °C (925 and 1050 °F).

Because of the absence of a quenching requirement, with attendant volume changes, and

when surface carbon is removed prior to the homogenization treatment.

In addition to homogenization, other heat treating procedures for 17-4 PH castings include solution annealing and precipitation hardening.

Details of these procedures are given in Table 13. The preferred temperature range for precipitation hardening is 480 to 595 °C (900 to 1100 °F). The mechanical properties obtained at different aging temperatures are given in Table 16.

Table 14 Effects of four methods of heat treatment on typical mechanical properties of cast CA-15

Specimens were taken from shell mold cast keel blocks; data indicate results obtained on four specimens treated by each method.

Heat treatment(a)	Ultimate tensile strength		Yield strength		Elongation in 50 mm (2 in.), %	Reduction in area, %
	MPa	ksi	MPa	ksi		
Treatment 1	1230	178	1005	146	9.0	13.0
Homogenize: 1 h at 1040 °C (1900 °F), AC	1250	181	970	141	12.5	28.0
Solution anneal: ½ h at 955 °C (1750 °F), OQ	1275	185	985	143	7.0	14.0
Temper: 3 h at 300 °C (575 °F), AC	1315	191	1020	148	8.0	12.5
Treatment 2	1260	183	1115	162	6.5	9.5
Anneal: 1 h at 900 °C (1650 °F), FC	1296	188	1130	164	5.5	16.0
Solution anneal: 1¼ h at 1010 °C (1850 °F), OQ	1340	194	1070	155	9.0	23.0
Temper: 3 h at 370 °C (700 °F), OQ	1380	200	1050	152	12.0	42.0
Treatment 3(b)	795	115	485	70	15.5	60.0
Anneal: 1 h at 900 °C (1650 °F), FC	810	117	630	91	16.5	37.0
Solution anneal: 1¼ h at 1010 °C (1850 °F), OQ	830	120	680	98	9.5	23.0
Temper: 2 h at 620 °C (1150 °F), AC	860	125	585	85	12.5	32.0
Treatment 4(c)	685	99	525	76	21.0	65.0
Anneal: 1 h at 900 °C (1650 °F), FC	710	103	545	79	20.5	56.0
Solution anneal: 1½ h at 995 °C (1825 °F), FAC	710	103	545	79	18.5	61.5
Temper: 2 h at 705 °C (1300 °F), AC	720	104	550	80	20.5	60.0

(a) Each treatment comprised three processes as listed. AC, air cool; OQ, oil quench; FC, furnace cool; FAC, forced-air cool. (b) AMS 5351-B. (c) MIL-S-16993

the comparatively low temperatures employed in this process, nitriding produces less distortion and deformation than either carburizing or conventional hardening. Some growth occurs as a result of nitriding, but volumetric changes are relatively small.

Although at suitable temperatures all steels are capable of forming iron nitrides in the presence of nascent (elemental) nitrogen, nitriding results are more favorable in those steels that contain one or more of the major nitride-forming alloying elements. Aluminum is the strongest nitride former, but chromium can approximate the results obtainable with aluminum if the chromium content is high enough.

Because of their chromium contents, all stainless steels can be nitrided to some degree. Although nitriding adversely affects corrosion resistance, it increases surface hardness and provides a lower coefficient of friction, thus improving abrasion resistance.

Austenitic and Ferritic Alloys. Austenitic stainless steels of the 300 series are the most difficult to nitride. Nevertheless, types 301, 302, 303, 304, 308, 309, 316, 321, and 347 have been successfully nitrided. These nonmagnetic alloys cannot be hardened by heat treating; consequently, core material remains relatively soft, and the nitrided surface is limited as to the loads it can support. This is equally true of the nonhardenable ferritic stainless steels. Alloys in this group that have been satisfactorily nitrided include types 430 and 446. With proper prior treatment, these alloys are somewhat easier to nitride than the 300 series alloys.

Hardenable Alloys. The hardenable martensitic alloys are capable of providing high core strength to support the nitrided case. Hardening, followed by tempering at a temperature that is at least 15 °C (25 °F) higher than the nitriding temperature, should precede the nitriding operation. Precipitation-hard-

ening alloys, such as 17-4 PH, 17-7 PH, and A-286, also have been successfully nitrided.

Prior Condition. Before being gas nitrided, 300-series steels and nonhardenable ferritic steels should be annealed and relieved of machining stresses. The normal annealing treatments generally employed to obtain maximum corrosion resistance are usually adequate. Microstructure should be as nearly uniform as possible. Observance of these prior conditions will prevent flaking or blistering of the nitrided case. Martensitic steels should be in the quenched-and-tempered condition.

A special pretreatment for type 410 stainless steel is hardening from a lower-than-normal temperature. This results in a very uniform nitrided case with reduced internal stresses. Cracking or spalling of the case is avoided; formation of brittle grain-boundary carbonitrides is suppressed. Austenitizing at 860 °C (1580 °F), followed by tempering at 595 °C (1100 °F), uniformly distributes carbides and provides low residual stress. Case growth is accommodated by a hardness of about 25 HRC.

Surface Preparation. The nitriding of stainless steels requires certain surface preparations that are not required for nitriding low-alloy steels. Primarily, the film of chromium oxide that protects stainless alloys from oxidation and corrosion must be removed. This can be accomplished by dry honing, wet blasting, pickling, chemical reduction in a reducing atmosphere, submersion in molten salts, or one of several proprietary processes. Surface treatment must precede placement of the parts in the nitriding furnace. If there is any doubt of the complete and uniform depassivation of the surface, further reduction of the oxide may be accomplished in the furnace by means of a reducing hydrogen atmosphere or halogen-based proprietary agents. Of course, the hydrogen must be dry (free of water and oxygen).

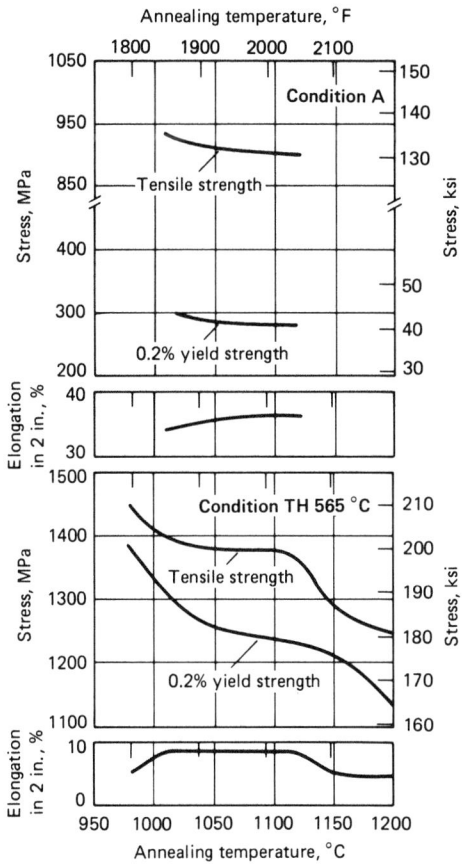

Fig. 16 Effect of variations in annealing temperature on typical mechanical properties of 17-7 PH sheet, strip, and plate

Before being nitrided, all stainless parts must be perfectly clean and free of embedded foreign particles. After depassivation, care should be exercised to

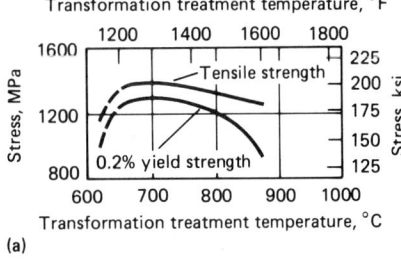

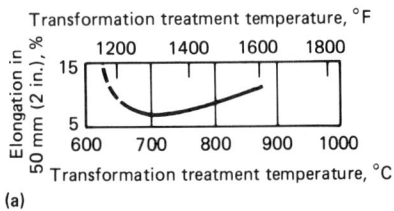

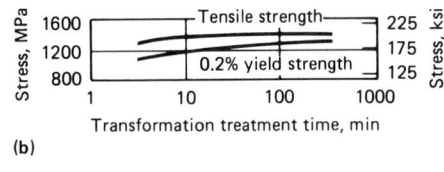

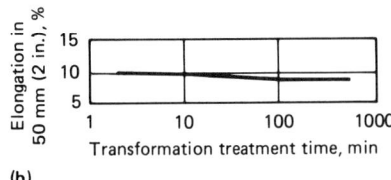

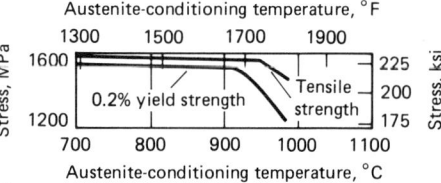

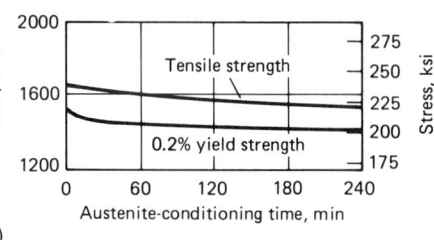

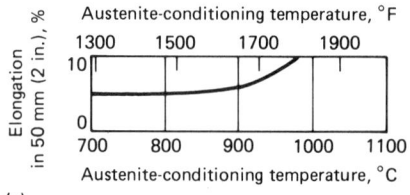

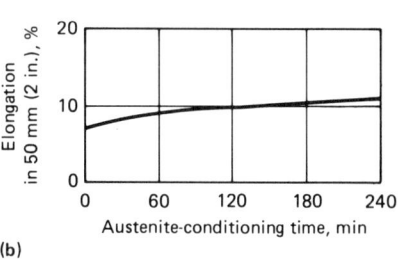

Fig. 17 Effect of variations in transformation treatment temperature and time on typical mechanical properties of 17-7 PH sheet, strip, and plate. (a) Heated for 90 min; cooled to 15 °C (60 °F); hardened at 565 °C (1050 °F). (b) Heated at 760 °C (1400 °F); hardened at 565 °C (1050 °F) for 90 min

Fig. 18 Effect of variations in austenite-conditioning temperature and time on typical mechanical properties of 17-7 PH sheet, strip, and plate. (a) Heated for 10 min; air cooled; liquid cooled to −75 °C (−100 °F) for 8 h; hardened at 510 °C (950 °F) for 1 h. (b) Heated at 955 °C (1750 °F); air cooled; liquid cooled to −75 °C (−100 °F) for 8 h; hardened at 510 °C (950 °F) for 1 h

avoid contaminating stainless surfaces with fingerprints. Sharp corners should be replaced with radii of not less than 1.6 mm (¹⁄₁₆ in.).

Nitriding Cycles. In general, stainless steels are nitrided in single-stage cycles at temperatures from about 495 to 595 °C (925 to 1100 °F) for periods ranging from 20 to 48 h, depending on the depth of case required. Dissociation rates for the single-stage cycle range from 20 to 35%; a two-stage cycle using 15 to 30% in the first phase and 35 to 45% in the second phase is also used. Thus, except for the prior depassivation of the metal surface, the nitriding of stainless steels is similar to the single-stage nitriding of low-alloy steels.

Nitriding Results. Hardness gradients are given in Fig. 24 for types 302, 321, 430, and 446. These data are based on a 48 h nitriding cycle at 525 °C (975 °F), preceded by suitable annealing treatments. A general comparison of the nitriding characteristics of 300- and 400-series steels is presented in Fig. 25; the comparison reflects the superior results that are obtained with 400-series steels, as well as the effects of nitriding temperature on case depth. Data are plotted for single-stage nitriding at temperatures of 525 and 550 °C (975 and 1025 °F). For steels of both series, greater case depths were obtained at the higher nitriding temperature.

Applications. Although nitriding increases the surface hardness and wear resistance of stainless steels, it decreases general corrosion resistance by combining surface chromium with nitrogen to form chromium nitride. Consequently, nitriding is not recommended for applications in which the corrosion resistance of stainless steel is of major importance. For example, a hot-air valve made of cast type 347 and used in the cabin-heating system of a jet airplane was nitrided to improve its resistance to wear by the abrading action of a sliding butterfly. When the valve remained in the closed position for an extended period, the corrosive effects of salt air froze the valve into position so that it could not be opened.

In contrast, a manufacturer of steam-turbine power-generating equipment has successfully used nitriding to increase the wear resistance of types 422 and 410 stainless steel valve stems and bushings that operate in a high-temperature steam atmosphere. Large quantities of these parts have operated for 20 years or more without difficulty. In a few instances, a light-blue oxide film formed on the valve stem diameter, causing it to "grow" and thus reduce the clearance between stem and bushing; the growth condition, however, was not accompanied by corrosive attack.

Table 15 Heat treatment of martensitic stainless steel castings

| Alloy | Annealing temperature(a) | | Hardening treatment | | | | Typical ultimate tensile strength(c) | |
| | °C | °F | Austenitizing temperature(b) | | Tempering temperature | | | |
			°C	°F	°C	°F	MPa	ksi
CA-15	845-900	1550-1650	...	...	...	...	550	80
	...	...	925-1010(d)	1700-1850(d)	370 max(e)	700 max(e)	1380	200
	...	...	925-1010(d)	1700-1850(d)	595-760	1100-1400	690-930	100-135
CA-40	845-900	1550-1650	...	...	...	...	620	90
	...	...	980-1010	1800-1850	315 max(e)	600 max(e)	1515	220
	...	...	980-1010	1800-1850	595	1100	1035	150
	...	...	980-1010	1800-1850	650	1200	965	140
	...	...	980-1010	1800-1850	760	1400	760	110
CA-6NM	790-815	1450-1500	...	...	...	...	550	80
	...	...	950-980	1750-1800	595-620	1100-1150	830	120

(a) Annealing for maximum softness; slow furnace cool from temperature. (b) Quench in oil or air. (c) Approximate. (d) Hold at temperature for a minimum of 30 min. (e) Tempering at 370 to 595 °C (700 to 1100 °F) is not recommended because low-impact ductility results.

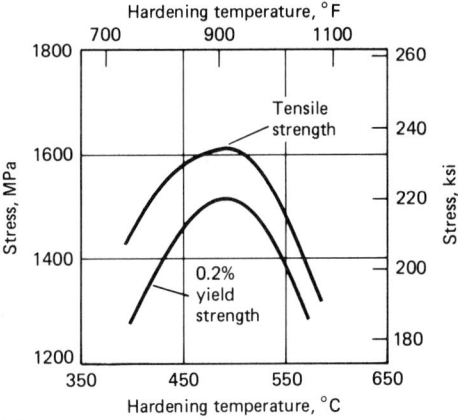

(a)

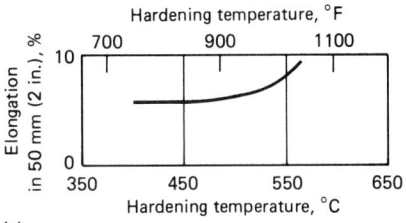

(a)

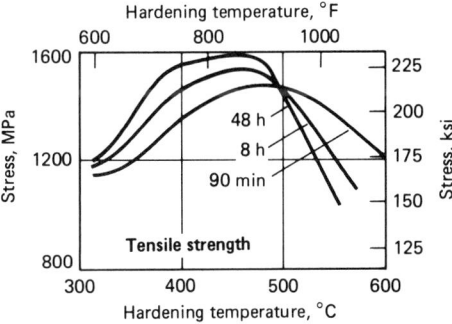

(b)

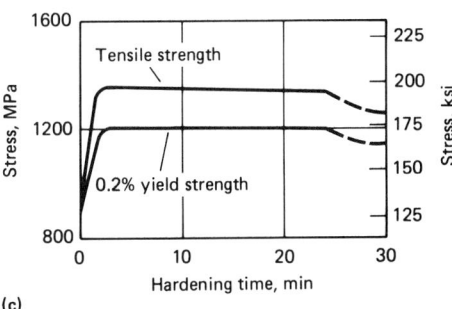

(c)

Fig. 19 Effect of variations in hardening temperature and time on typical mechanical properties of 17-7 PH sheet, strip, and plate. (a) Heated at 955 °C (1750 °F) for 10 min; air cooled; liquid cooled to –75 °C (–100 °F) for 8 h; hardened for 1 h. (b) Heated at 760 °C (1400 °F) for 90 min; air cooled to room temperature; water quenched to 15 °C (60 °F); hardened as indicated. Elongation data not available. (c) Heated at 760 °C (1400 °F) for 90 min; air cooled to room temperature; water quenched to 15 °C (60 °F); hardened at 565 °C (1050 °F). Elongation data not available

Nitrided stainless steel is also being used in the food-processing industry. In one application, nitrided type 321 was used to replace type 302 for a

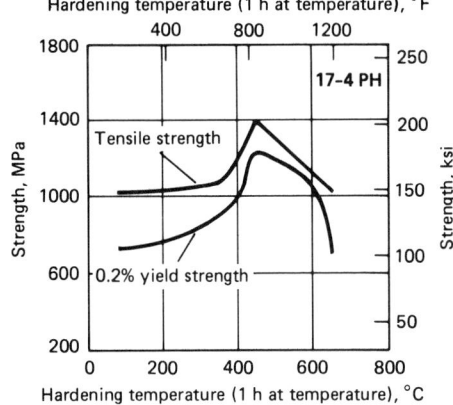

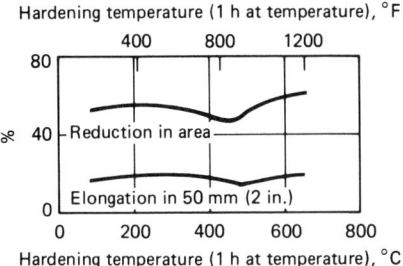

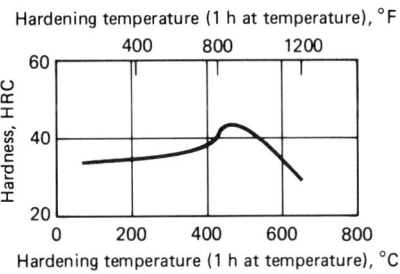

Fig. 20 Effect of hardening temperature on typical room-temperature properties of 17-4 PH that was solution treated at 1040 °C (1900 °F) for 30 min and air cooled. Data are average values for bars 25 to 89 mm (1 to 3 in.) in diameter from four heats.

motor shaft used in the aeration of orange juice. Because the unhardened 302 shaft wore at the rubber-sealed junction of the motor and the juice, leaks developed within three days. The nitrided 321 shaft ran for 27 days before wear at the seal resulted in leakage. In machinery used in the preparation of dog food, nitrided type 420 gears have replaced gears made of an unhardened stainless alloy and have exhibited a considerable increase in life.

Modern synthetic fibers, several of which are highly abrasive, have increased the wear of textile machinery. Mechanical parts in textile machines are subjected to high humidity, absence of lubrication, high-speed movements with repeated cycling, and the abrasive action of fibers traveling at high speeds. A shear blade made of hardened (62 to 64 HRC) 1095 steel experienced a normal life of about one million cuts (four weeks of service) in cutting synthetic fibers at the rate of 90 cuts/min. In contrast, a nitrided type 410 blade with 0.04 mm (0.0015 in.) case depth showed less wear after completion of five million cuts.

With nitrided stainless steels, the case almost always has lower corrosion resistance than the base material; nevertheless, the corrosion resistance of the case can be adequate for certain applications. For example, nitrided types 302 and 410 stainless steel resist attack from every conditioner and size in the textile industry but do not resist attack from the acetic acid used in dyeing liquors.

Nitrided stainless steel is not resistant to mineral acids and is subject to rapid corrosion when exposed to halogen compounds. However, a nitrided type 302 piston lasted for more than five years in a liquid-ammonia pump; it replaced a piston made of an unnitrided 300-series alloy that lasted approximately six months. Nitrided 17-4 PH impellers have performed satisfactorily and without corrosion in various types of hydraulic pumps.

Plasma (Ion) Nitriding and Liquid Nitriding

Plasma, or ion, nitriding is a method of surface hardening that uses glow discharge technology to introduce nascent nitrogen to the surface of a metal part for subsequent diffusion into the material. In a vacuum, high-voltage electrical energy is used to form a plasma, through which nitrogen ions are accelerated to impinge on the workpiece. This ion bombardment heats the workpiece, cleans the surface, and provides active nitrogen. Ion nitriding provides better control of case chemistry and uniformity and has other advantages, such as lower part distortion than conventional gas nitriding.

The diffusion zone of a nitrided case can best be described as the original core microstructure with some solid solution and precipitation strengthening. In iron-base materials, the nitrogen exists as single atoms in solid solution at lattice sites or interstitial positions until the limit of nitrogen solubility (0.4 wt% N) in iron is exceeded. This area of solid-solution strengthening is only slightly harder than the core. The depth of the diffusion zone depends on the nitrogen concentration gradient, time at a given temperature, and the chemistry of the workpiece.

As the nitrogen concentration increases toward the surface, very fine, coherent precipitates are formed when the solubility limit of nitrogen is exceeded. The precipitates can exist both in the grain boundaries and within the lattice structure of the grains themselves. These precipitates, in the form of nitrides, distort the lattice and pin crystal dislocations and thereby substantially increase the hardness of the material. Hardness profiles for various ion-nitrided materials are shown in Fig. 26.

For most ferrous alloys, the diffusion zone formed by nitriding cannot be seen in a metallograph because the coherent precipitates generally are not large enough to resolve. In stainless steels, however, the chromium level is high enough for extensive nitride formation, which can be seen in etched cross section (Fig. 27).

Ion nitriding has a strong advantage over competing processes in the case of stainless steels, particularly austenitic or 300-series materials. The chromium oxide passive layer on the surface represents a barrier to nitriding and must be re-

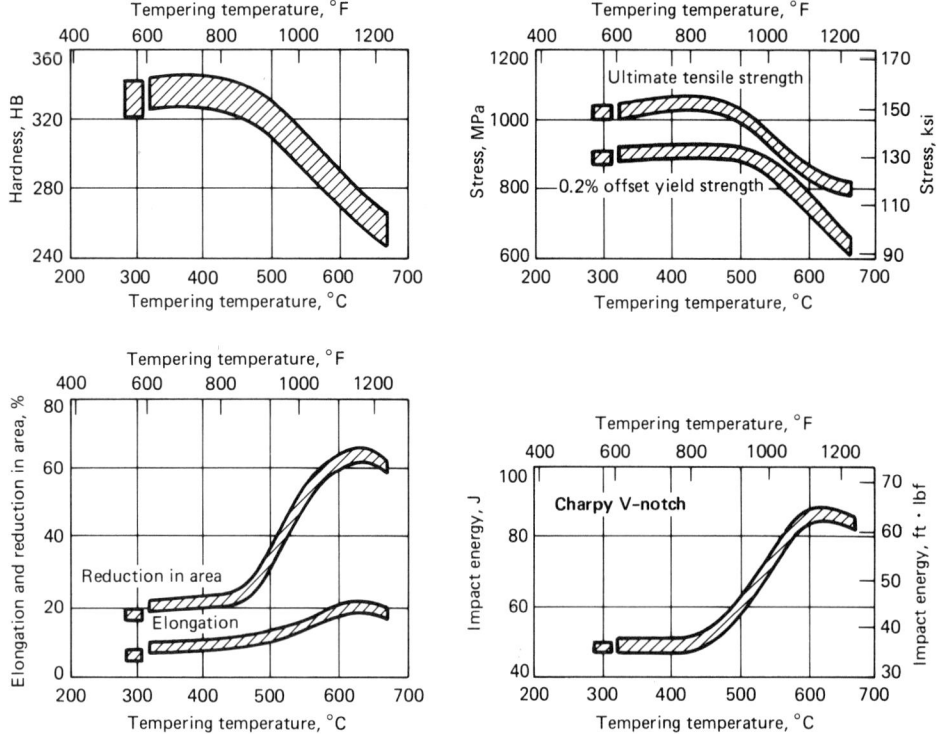

Fig. 21 Effect of tempering temperature on the mechanical properties of a CA-6NM standard keel block. Courtesy of ESCO Corp.

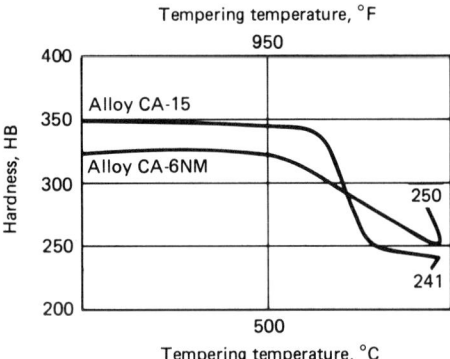

Fig. 22 Influence of tempering temperature on the hardness of CA-6NM and CA-15. Courtesy of ESCO Corp.

Table 16   Effect of temperature of 1 h aging treatment on typical properties of investment cast 17-4 PH stainless steels
Data obtained using cast test bars.

Aging temperature(a)		Ultimate tensile strength		Yield strength, 0.2%		Elongation in 50 mm (2 in.), %	Hardness, HRC
°C	°F	MPa	ksi	MPa	ksi		
Alloy with 0.15 to 0.40% Nb							
	As-cast	1055	153	770	112	3.5	...
480	900	1380	200	1055	153	15	44
510	950	1360	197	1082	157	13	42
540	1000	1130	164	970	141	14	39
565	1050	1125	163	1040	151	16	35
595	1100	1115	162	985	143	16	34
650	1200	1015	147	860	125	15	30
Alloy without niobium							
	As-cast	1115	162	985	143	2.7	38
480	900	1365	198	1145	166	12	43
510	950	1255	182	1110	161	13	42
540	1000	1280	186	1095	159	14	38
565	1050	980	142	910	132	16	35
595	1100	1080	157	840	122	16	34
650	1200	1055	153	895	130	12	32

(a) Before aging, specimens were homogenized (1½ at 1150 °C, or 2100 °F, air cool) and solution annealed (½ h at 1040 °C, or 1900 °F), oil quench): subzero transformation not employed. After 1 h at aging temperature, specimens were air cooled.

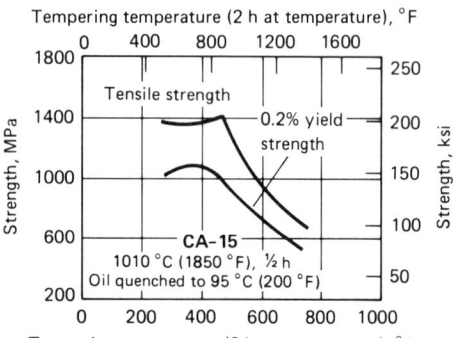

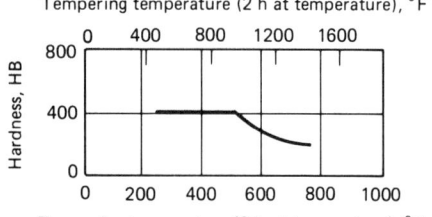

Fig. 23 Effect of tempering temperature on typical room-temperature mechanical properties of CA-15 castings

moved prior to processing. During gas nitriding of stainless steels, this passive layer is removed by wet blasting, pickling, or chemical reduction. With ion nitriding, however, this layer can be removed by sputtering in hydrogen in the vessel itself just before introduction of the process gas. With most materials, even the sputtering that oc-

curs naturally during the actual nitriding process is enough to yield good nitriding results.

Liquid nitriding is performed in a molten, nitrogen-bearing, fused-salt bath containing either cyanides or cyanates. Unlike liquid carburizing and cyaniding, which employ baths of similar composition, liquid nitriding is a subcritical (that

is, below the critical transformation temperature) case-hardening process. Thus, processing of finished parts is possible because dimensional stability can be maintained. Also, liquid nitriding adds more nitrogen and less carbon to ferrous materials than are obtained through higher-temperature diffusion treatments.

Cyanide-free liquid nitriding salt compositions have also been introduced. However, in the active bath, a small amount of cyanide, generally

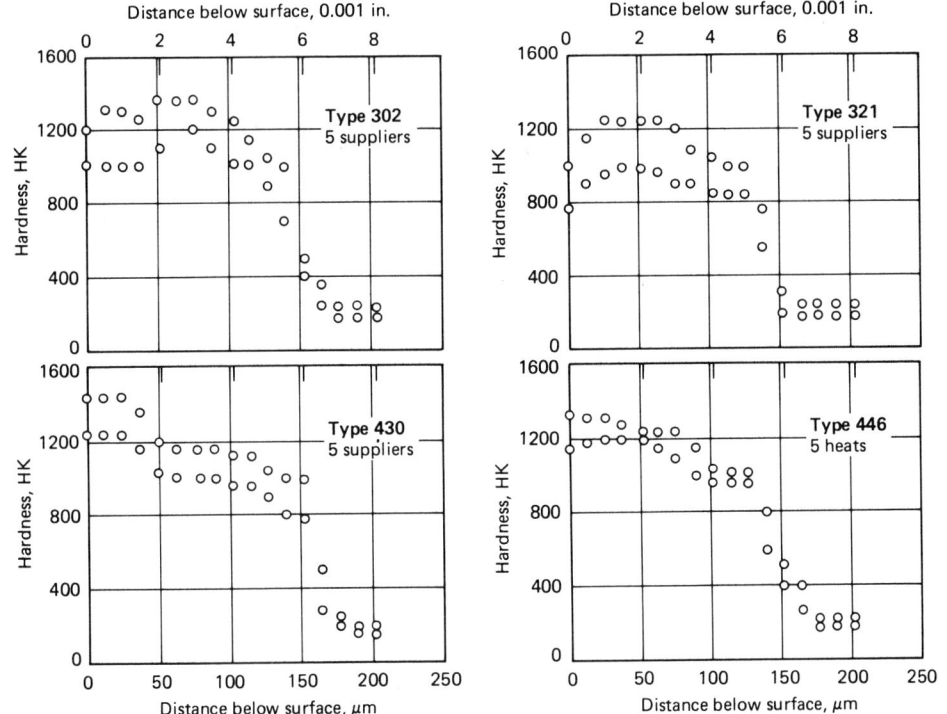

Fig. 24 Hardness range as a function of case depth for four stainless steels that were annealed prior to nitriding. Annealing temperature: types 302 and 321, 1065 °C (1950 °F); type 430, 980 °C (1800 °F); and type 446, 900 °C (1650 °F)

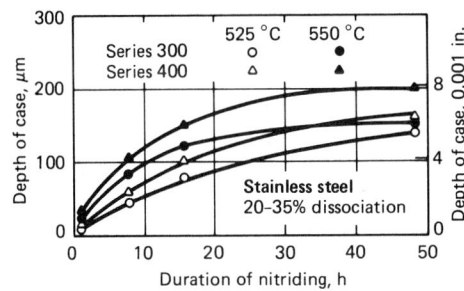

Fig. 25 Comparison of the nitriding characteristics of 300- and 400-series stainless steels, single-stage nitrided at 525 and 550 °C (975 and 1025 °F), respectively

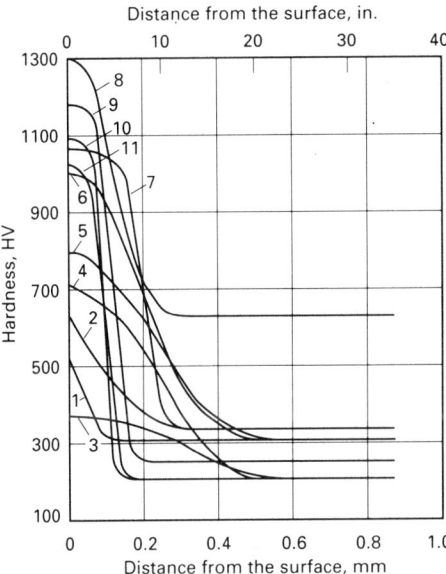

Fig. 26 Hardness profiles for various ion-nitrided materials. 1, gray cast iron; 2, ductile cast iron; 3, AISI 1040; 4, carburizing steel; 5, low-alloy steel; 6, nitriding steel; 7, 5% Cr hot-work steel; 8, cold-wored die steel; 9, ferritic stainless steel; 10, AISI 420 stainless steel; 11, 18-8 stainless steel

Table 17 Effect of aging time at 480 °C (900 °F) on typical properties of investment cast 17-4 PH stainless steels(a)

Aging time, h	Ultimate tensile strength		Yield strength		Elongation in 25 mm (1 in.), %	Hardness, HRC
	MPa	ksi	MPa	ksi		
Alloy with 0.15 to 0.40% Nb						
½	1385	201	1275	185	7	45
1	1380	200	1070	155	15	44
2	1340	194	1055	153	13	45
4	1295	188	1075	156	9	43
Alloy without niobium						
½	1385	201	1075	156	10	43
1	1365	198	1130	164	12	43
2	1395	202	1080	157	12	44
4	1180	171	980	142	16	38
8	1130	164	970	141	14	37

(a) Treatment prior to aging: 1½ h at 1150 °C (2100 °F), air cool; 1 h at 1040 °C (1900 °F), oil quench

Table 18 Effects of tempering temperature on typical properties of shell mold cast AM-355(a)

Condition	Ultimate tensile strength		Yield strength(b)		Elongation in 50 mm (2 in.), %	Reduction in area, %
	MPa	ksi	MPa	ksi		
Annealed	1290	187	485	70	6	3.5
Subzero transformed	1400	203	965	140	6	2.5
Tempered 3 h at °C (°F):						
480 (900)	1440	209	1170	170	20	9
540 (1000)	1325	192	1095	159	34	13
595 (1100)	1195	173	940	136	35	14
650 (1200)	1015	147	595	86	33	15

(a) Treatment prior to tempering: 1½ h at 1095 °C (2000 °F) and then furnace cool to 980 °C (1800 °F); soak at 980 °C (1800 °F) for 1½ h and then water quench; subzero cool at –85 °C (–120 °F) for 6 h. (b) 0.2% offset

up to 5%, is produced as part of the reaction. This is a relatively low concentration, and these compositions have gained widespread acceptance within the heat treating industry because they contribute substantially to the alleviation of a potential source of pollution.

The wear and gall resistance of stainless steels can be improved by aerated liquid nitriding, a proprietary process (U.S. Patent 3,022,204) in which measured amounts of air are pumped through the molten bath. Immersion in the molten salt at 570 °C (1060 °F) develops a physical compound zone in stainless steels that, depending on treatment time, varies between 0.005 and 0.025 mm (0.0002 and 0.001 in.). Although the hardness of this wear-resistant surface measures 70 to 72 HRC, the surface is tough and ductile (Ref 1).

Liquid nitriding treatments result in some loss in corrosion resistance, because the formation of nitrides and carbides depletes adjacent matrix areas. Corrosion data based on weight loss indicate that liq-

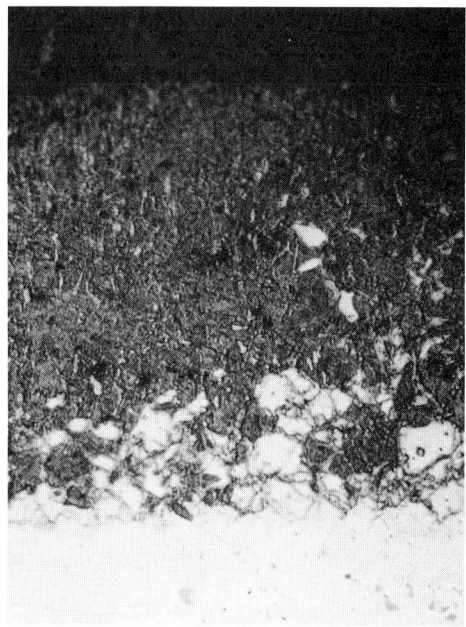

Fig. 27 Observable diffusion zone on the unetched (white) portion of an ion-nitrided 416 stainless steel. Nital etched. 500×

uid-nitrided stainless steels lose approximately 50% of their corrosion resistance. However, these materials remain substantially superior to untreated carbon and low-alloy steels (Ref 1).

Liquid nitriding is one of the few heat treatments that can produce a wear-resistant hard surface, improve fatigue properties, and retain to a significant extent the good corrosion resistance of stainless steels in a single operation. In addition, subsequent quenching is not required, allowing flexibility in design and final machining (Ref 1).

Carburizing, Boriding, and Flame Hardening

Carburizing is a case-hardening process in which carbon is dissolved in the surface layers of

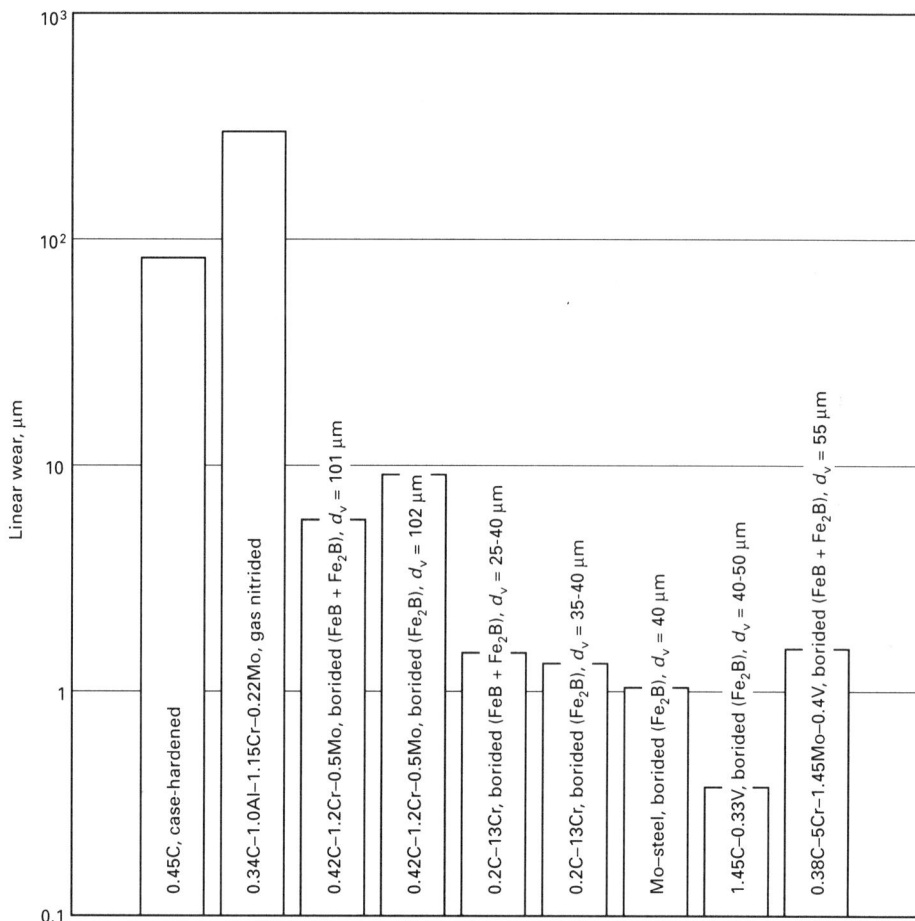

Fig. 28 Effect of steel composition (nominal values in wt%) on wear resistance under abrasive wear (d_v = thickness of the boride layer). Test conditions: DP-U grinding tester, SiC paper 220, testing time 6 min. Source: Ref 2, 3

a steel part at a temperature sufficient to render the material austenitic, followed by quenching and tempering to form a martensitic microstructure. The resulting gradient in carbon content below the surface of the part causes a gradient in hardness, producing a strong, wear-resistant surface layer. In gas carburizing, commercially the most important variant of carburizing, the source of

carbon is a carbon-rich furnace atmosphere produced either from gaseous hydrocarbons (e.g., methane, propane, or butane) or from vaporized hydrocarbon liquids.

Stainless steels can be carburized to improve surface hardness and resistance to galling. The availability of substantial amounts of chromium promotes the rapid formation of chromium car-

Table 19 Effect of heat treating and welding sequence on typical properties of AM-355 castings

Sequence(a)	Ultimate tensile strength		Yield strength, 0.2%		Elongation in 50 mm (2 in.), %
	MPa	ksi	MPa	ksi	
Heat treated after welding					
A	1450	210	1105	160	15
B	1380	200	1115	162	12
C	1415	205	1070	155	12
D	1415	205	1105	160	8
Not heat treated after welding					
E	1070	155	830	120	11

(a) Heat treating and welding procedures and sequences were as follows: A, 2 h at 1095 °C (2000 °F) and then air cool; 2 h at 1010 °C (1850 °F) and then water quench; 3 h at –75 °C (–100 °F); 3 h at 455 °C (850 °F) and then air cool; 3 h at 510 °C (950 °F) and then air cool; helium-shielded arc welding; repeat heat treatment. B, 2 h at 1095 °C (2000 °F) and then air cool; 2 h at 1010 °C (1850 °F) and then water quench; 3 h at –75 °C (–100 °F); 3 h at 455 °C (850 °F) and then air cool; 3 h at 510 °C (950 °F) and then air cool; 2 h at 1010 °C (1850 °F) and then water quench; helium-shielded arc welding, repeat heat treatment through 510 °C (950 °F) tempering. C, Helium-shielded arc welding; 2 h at 1095 °C (2000 °F) and then air cool; 2 h at 1010 °C (1850 °F) and then water quench; 3 h at –75 °C (–100 °F); 3 h at 455 °C (850 °F) and then air cool; 2 h at 1010 °C (1850 °F) and then water quench; helium-shielded arc welding; 2 h at 1095 °C (2000 °F) and then air cool; 2 h at 1010 °C (1850 °F) and then water quench; 3 h at –75 (–100 °F); 3 h at 455 °C (850 °F) and then air cool; 3 h at 510 °C (950 °F) and then air cool. E, 2 h at 1095 °C (2000 °F) and then air cool; 2 h at 1010 °C (1850 °F) and then water quench; 3 h at –75 °C (–100 °F); 3 h at 455 °C (850 °F) and then air cool; 3 h at 510 °C (950 °F) and then air cool; helium-shielded arc welding

bides at the surface, and surface hardness values of 700 to 750 HV have been measured. Precipitation-hardenable stainless steels can be gas carburized to improve resistance to galling. Treatment temperatures up to 1010 °C (1850 °F) may be required (Ref 1).

In austenitic grades, much of the chromium carbide formed migrates and is precipitated in the grain boundaries, promoting susceptibility to intergranular corrosion. Carbide distribution tends to be less segregated in the martensitic grades, but they are also subject to localized corrosion and particularly SCC (Ref 1).

Carburizing is not generally recommended for stainless steels because of the reduction in corrosion resistance brought on by chromium precipitation. Since the precipitated chromium tends to exist at the expense of adjacent areas, localized galvanic cells may develop. In the carburizing process, surface physical properties are obtained at the expense of surface chemical properties (Ref 1).

Because of these disadvantages, most of the carburizing of stainless steel is "accidental" and can be traced to surface contamination. Carbonaceous compounds such as charcoal, coke, oil, and grease can promote carburization under the proper conditions. Molten salt baths that contain cyanide to prevent decarburization may also become carburizing in contact with stainless steels (Ref 1).

Boriding, or boronizing, is a thermochemical surface hardening process that involves heating well-cleaned material in the range of 700 to 1000 °C (1300 to 1830 °F), preferably for 1 to 12 h, in contact with a boronaceous solid powder (boronizing compound), paste, liquid, or gaseous medium.

The resultant diffusion zone is known for its low coefficient of friction and high surface hardness, which may reach values of 1800 HV. Case depths of 0.05 mm (0.002 in.) can be achieved with 1 to 5 h treating times (Ref 1). Figure 28 shows the influence of steel composition on abrasive wear resistance. Boriding can considerably enhance the corrosion-erosion resistance of ferrous materials in nonoxidizing dilute acids (Fig. 29) and alkali media, and it is increasingly used to this advantage in many industrial applications (Ref 4).

Chromium considerably modifies the structure and properties of iron borides. As the chromium content of the base material increases, progressive improvements in the following effects are observed: formation of boron-rich reaction products, decrease in boride depth, and flattening or smoothening of the coating/substrate interface (Ref 6). A reduction of boride thickness has also been noticed in ternary Fe-12Cr-C steels with increasing carbon content (Ref 7).

Flame hardening is a heat-treating process in which a thin surface shell of a steel part is heated rapidly to a temperature above the critical point of the steel. After the grain structure of the shell has become austenitic (austenitized), the part is

quickly quenched, transforming the austenite directly to martensite while leaving the core of the part in its original state.

Flame hardening employs direct impingement of a high-temperature flame or high-velocity combustion product gases. The part is then cooled at a rate that will produce the desired levels of hardness and other properties. The high-temperature flame is obtained by combustion of a mixture of fuel gas with oxygen or air; flame heads are used for burning the mixture. Depths of hardening from about 0.8 to 6.4 mm (1/32 to 1/4 in.) or more can be obtained, depending on the fuels used, the design of the flame head, the duration of heating, the hardenability of the work material, and the quenching medium and method of quenching used.

Hardening by flame differs from true case hardening because the hardenability necessary to attain high levels of hardness is already contained in the steel, and hardening is obtained by localized heating. Although flame hardening is mainly used to develop high levels of hardness for wear resistance, the process also improves bending and torsional strength and fatigue life.

Flame hardening can be applied to martensitic stainless steels. The nature of flame hardening, however—especially the relatively high temperature gradients and higher-than-normal surface temperatures—may cause the retention of excessive amounts of austenite in many highly alloyed materials, with possible low hardness and transformation to untempered martensite in service, accompanied by brittleness. Typical hardnesses obtained for martensitic stainless steels by flame heating and quenching in air or oil are given in Table 20.

ACKNOWLEDGMENT

The information in this article is largely taken from:

- Heat Treating of Stainless Steels, *Heat Treating*, Vol 4, *ASM Handbook*, ASM International, 1991, p 769-792
- Gas Nitriding, *Heat Treating*, Vol 4, *ASM Handbook*, ASM International, 1991, p 401-402

REFERENCES

1. W.G. Wood, Surface Hardening of Stainless Steels, *Handbook of Stainless Steels*, D. Peckner and I.M. Bernstein, Ed., McGraw-Hill, 1977
2. R. Chatterjee-Fischer, Chapter 8, *Surface Modification Technologies*, T.S. Sudarshan, Ed., Marcel Dekker, 1989, p 567-609
3. K.H. Habig and R. Chatterjee-Fischer, *Tribol. Int.*, Vol 14 (No. 4), 1981, p 209-215
4. W.J.G. Fichtl, "Saving Energy and Money by Boronizing," presented at meeting of the Japan Heat Treating Association (Tokyo), 25 Nov 1988; "Boronizing and Its Practical Applications," presented at 33rd Harterei-Kolloquium (Wiesbaden), 5-7 Oct 1977; *Heat Treat. Met.*, 1983, p 79-80
5. W.J.G. Fichtl, *Härt.-Tech. Mitt.*, Vol 29 (No. 2), 1974, p 113-119
6. M. Carbucicchio and G. Sambogna, *Thin Solid Films*, Vol 126, 1985, p 299-305
7. P. Goeurist, R. Fillitt, F. Thevenol, J.H. Driver, and H. Bruyas, *Mater. Sci. Eng.*, Vol 55, 1982, p 9-19

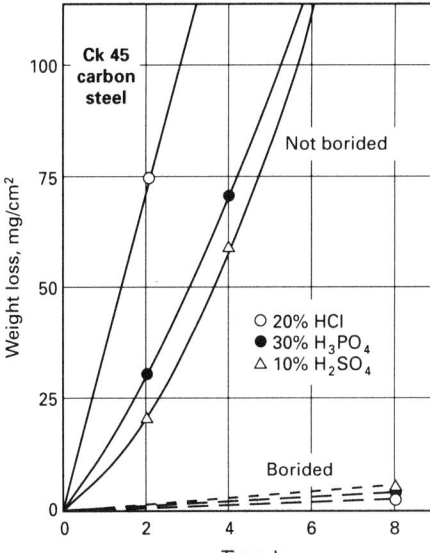

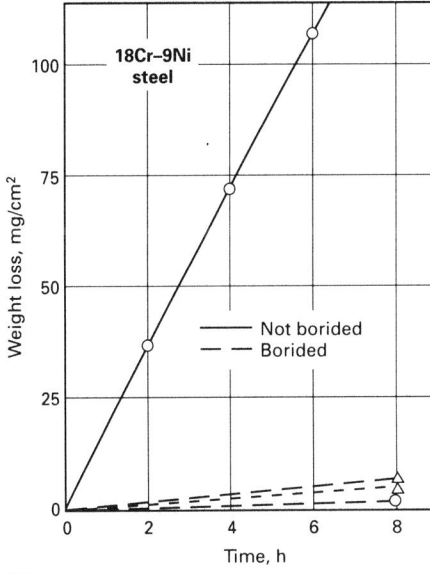

Fig. 29 Corroding effect of mineral acids on boronized and nonboronized (a) 0.45% C (Ck 45) steel and (b) 18Cr-9Ni (X10CrNiTi18 9) steel at 56 °C (130 °F). Source: Ref 4, 5

Machining

MACHINING methods for stainless steels, the stainless steels that are available, and how and why the stainless steels differ in machining performance are the topics addressed in this article. With regard to machining methods, emphasis is given to conventional techniques, such as turning, drilling, and sawing, because most stainless steels are machined using such techniques. However, special or nontraditional machining techniques are reviewed in the closing portion of the article. More details on each of the machining processes described below can be found in Volume 16 of the *ASM Handbook*.

General Material and Machining Characteristics

The common aspect of stainless steels is the presence of a minimum of about 11% Cr to provide the excellent corrosion and oxidation resistance that are the chief characteristics of the materials. However, stainless steels do not constitute a single, well-defined material, but instead comprise several families of alloys, each generally having its own characteristic microstructure, alloying elements, and range of properties. Compositional differences within each family can also produce a variety of alloys suited to a wide range of applications.

Because of the wide variety of stainless steels available, a simple characterization of their machinability can be somewhat misleading. As shown in later sections of this article, the machinability of stainless steels varies from low to very high, depending on the final choice of alloy.

In general, however, stainless steels are considered more difficult to machine than other metals, such as aluminum or low-carbon steels. Stainless steels have been characterized as gummy during cutting, showing a tendency to produce long, stringy chips that seize or form a built-up edge on the tool. This may result in reduced tool life and degraded surface finish. These general characteristics are due to the following properties, which are possessed by stainless steels to different extents (Ref 1, 2):

- High tensile strength (Fig. 1)
- Large spread between yield strength (YS) and ultimate tensile strength (UTS) (Fig. 1)
- High ductility and toughness
- High work-hardening rate (Fig. 1)
- Low thermal conductivity (Fig. 2)

Despite these properties, stainless steels can be machined under the appropriate conditions. In general, more power is required to machine stainless steels than carbon steels. Cutting speeds must often be lower, a positive feed must be maintained, and tooling and fixtures must be rigid. Chip breakers or curlers may be needed on the tools, and care must be taken to ensure good lubrication and cooling during cutting (Ref 4). These and other practices are discussed in more detail in the sections on individual conventional machining techniques in this article.

Classification of Stainless Steels

Stainless steels can be divided into five families. Four are based on the characteristic micro-

structure of the alloys in the family: ferritic, martensitic, austenitic, and duplex (austenitic plus ferritic). The fifth family, the precipitation-hardenable alloys, is based on the type of heat treatment used, rather than microstructure. Characteristics and properties of these five alloy families are described in Ref 5 and 6 and in the articles "General Introduction" and "Metallurgy and Properties of Wrought Stainless Steels" in this Volume.

From a machining standpoint, stainless steels can also be divided into the non-free-machining alloys and the free-machining alloys. Free-machining alloys form a limited group that includes some of the alloys of the five basic families. Non-free-machining and free-machining alloys may be available in versions having enhanced machining properties.

Free-machining alloys contain a free-machining additive such as sulfur to form inclusions that significantly improve overall machining characteristics. In some cases, other compositional changes can be made either within or outside the broad compositional ranges of the corresponding non-free-machining alloy. Such additional changes in composition may improve machining characteristics beyond those obtained by the simple addition of the free-machining additives.

The benefit of improved machining characteristics by the addition of sulfur or other free-machining additives is not obtained without changes in other properties. In particular, the following properties may be degraded by the addition of a free-machining agent:

- Corrosion resistance
- Transverse ductility and toughness
- Hot workability
- Cold formability
- Weldability

In some cases, variants of the basic free-machining alloy are available to provide an optimum combination of machinability with another property. However, the tradeoff among the various properties must still be considered when selecting an alloy; that is, the ease of machining must be balanced against the possible reduction in other important properties, such as corrosion resistance.

Table 1 lists some non-free-machining and free-machining alloys within the ferritic, martensitic, and austenitic families. Free-machining alloys are currently unavailable in the duplex or precipitation-hardenable families. Because duplex alloys are noted for excellent corrosion resistance but have somewhat limited hot workability, the addition of a free-machining agent, which would likely degrade both properties, would be

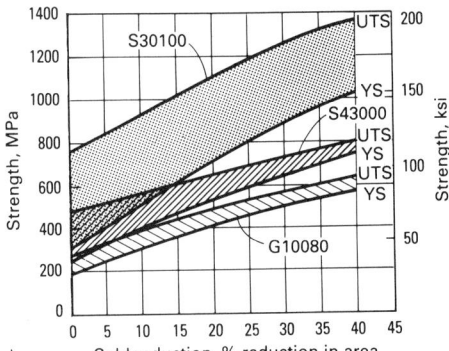

Fig. 1 Comparison of tensile strengths, spread between yield and ultimate tensile strengths, and work-hardening rate for S30100 austenitic stainless steel, S43000 ferritic stainless steel, and G10080 carbon steel

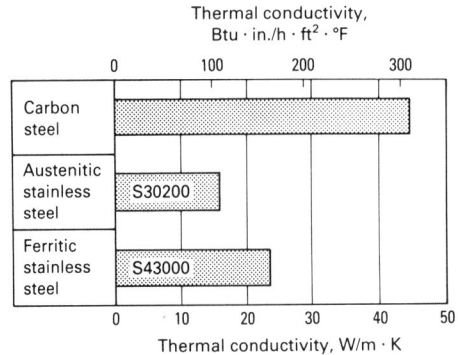

Fig. 2 Comparison of thermal conductivities for carbon steel, S30200 austenitic stainless steel, and S43000 ferritic stainless steel. Source: Ref 3

Table 1 Correspondence of non-free-machining and free-machining stainless steels

Non-free-machining alloys	Related free-machining alloys	
	Selenium-bearing	Sulfur-bearing
Ferritic		
S43000	S43023	S43020
S44400	...	S18200(a)
		S18235
Martensitic		
S41000	S41623	S41600
		S41610(b)
S42000	S42023	S42020
S44004	S44023	S44020
Austenitic		
...	...	S20300
S30200/S30400	S30323	S30300
		S30310(b)
		S30345(c)
		S30360(d)
S30430	...	S30330
		S30431(e)
S31600	...	S31620
S34700	S34723	S34720

(a) Does not contain titanium. (b) Contains high manganese. (c) Contains aluminum. (d) Contains lead. (e) Contains lower copper

undesirable. Similarly, precipitation-hardenable alloys are noted for good toughness at high strength levels, making it undesirable to add a free-machining agent, which would degrade toughness.

The best-known alloys in the three families represented, S43000 (ferritic), S41000 (martensitic), and S30400 (austenitic), have corresponding free-machining alloys (Table 1). In addition, the more corrosion-resistant molybdenum-bearing alloys S44400 and S31600 have free-machining versions in the ferritic and austenitic families, respectively, and the higher-carbon, higher-strength alloys S42000 and S44004 have free-machining versions in the martensitic family. Consequently, a variety of basic free-machining alloys are available to satisfy the two most important selection criteria for stainless steels, namely, corrosion resistance and mechanical properties (strength/hardness).

A variety of additional distinctions can be made among the other alloys listed in Table 1. Free-machining versions are available for S34700, a niobium-stabilized austenitic alloy, and for S30430, a copper-bearing alloy noted for a low work-hardening rate and excellent cold formability for an austenitic alloy. The free-machining versions of S30430 (S30330 and S30431) are intended to offer a good combination of cold formability and machinability. Another alloy that can offer this combination of properties is S30345. The selenium-bearing free-machining alloys are also noted for better cold formability than the sulfur-bearing alloys and can be used where machined surface finish is more important than tool life.

Alloy S20300, which lacks a corresponding non-free-machining version, is a high-manganese, high-copper alloy with excellent machinability for an austenitic alloy. It can be substituted for S30300, specifications permitting. Higher manganese is present in S41610 and S30310, aluminum in S30345, and lead in S30360. These compositional modifications are intended to improve machining performance.

Versions of S30300, S41600, and S43020 are also available to provide combinations of properties not obtainable with the standard alloys. The compositions of such versions still fall within the broad ranges of the standard alloy. For example, S30300 and S41600 are available in forging-quality versions, which are intended to provide a good combination of hot workability and machinability. Alloy S41600 is also available in a modified version intended to provide a higher quenched hardness level after bright hardening. Alloy S43020 is available in a modified version for optimum soft-magnetic properties.

Enhanced-Machining Alloys. The compositions and processing of alloys can also be modified within broad limits to provide an optimum level of machining performance. This approach has been taken with both non-free-machining and free-machining alloys, resulting in enhanced-machining alloys that meet the same specifications as the standard alloys. It should be noted that the enhanced-machining versions of the non-free-machining alloys provide machining performance superior to that of the corresponding standard alloys, but still do not provide the machinability of comparable free-machining alloys. However, other properties, such as corrosion resistance, ductility, toughness, weldability, and cold formability, will be superior to those of the corresponding free-machining alloy. Thus, the enhanced-machining versions of the non-free-machining alloys provide a means of obtaining improved machining performance without significant degradation of other properties.

There are many possibilities for tailoring enhanced-machining alloys, because the latitude in the composition and processing of stainless steel alloys is great enough to provide a variety of levels of machinability. As a result, some alloys are available in more than one enhanced-machining version. For example, S41600 is available in an enhanced-machining version that meets certain minimum hardness requirements and in a version that provides even higher machining performance but does not meet the same hardness requirements. Obviously, the level of machinability necessary and the compromises to be made in other properties depend on the needs of the user. Before specifying or purchasing an alloy, the producer should be consulted to determine the proper alloy or, more important, the proper version of the alloy.

Machinability

Machinability refers to several specific aspects of machining a material, and its definition must be precisely specified in a particular application. Some of the specific criteria for defining machinability include:

- Tool life or tool wear
- Machined surface finish
- Chip removal
- Cutting rate
- Productivity

The relative importance of these criteria varies, and the criteria may be interdependent in various ways.

Machinability also depends on many variables in the machining process. Because of this and the different criteria of machinability, the ranking or extrapolation of machinability must be viewed with caution. Some of the variables that may affect the evaluation of machinability are:

- Rigidity of tooling or fixtures
- Tool material and tool geometry
- Type of cutting fluid
- Type of machining operation

Generally, the harder the material, the more difficult it is to machine. However, machinability is more directly influenced by microstructure than by hardness. The machinability of many classes of alloys can be improved if the microstructure is a two-phase structure consisting of either a brittle or easily sheared second phase dispersed throughout a moderately ductile matrix. Stainless steels have a high alloy content that reduces machinability, but free-machining stainless steels are available that compare favorably with some free-machining carbon steels.

Machinability Additives

The most important machinability additives are those that form inclusions in the metal. Such additives include sulfur, selenium, tellurium, lead, bismuth, and certain oxides. The role of these inclusions in improving machining performance has been the basis of much study, and theories include lubrication, chip embrittlement, and stress-concentration effects as the mechanisms for improving machinability. Whatever the reason, free-machining inclusions increase tool life, allow higher cutting rates, and may also affect chip breakage/disposability and the machined surface finish.

Elements that modify the matrix of the metal or the size, distribution, and mechanical properties of the free-machining inclusions can also improve machinability beyond the level achieved with the free-machining additive alone, although these additional additives are of secondary importance. Compositional changes that modify the inclusions are discussed in the sections below that cover the appropriate inclusion. Modifications of the matrix are discussed in the section "Machinability of Alloy Families" in this article. An exception is phosphorus, which has traditionally been discussed with the inclusion-forming machinability additives.

Sulfur. The use of sulfur to improve the overall machining characteristics of stainless steels dates back to the early 1930s, when alloys similar to the current S41600 and S30300 which contain a minimum of 0.15% S, were developed (Ref 7, 8). Since then, sulfur has been the primary element used to provide free-machining characteristics in stainless steels. The amount of sulfur that can be added to a stainless steel is limited by the allow-

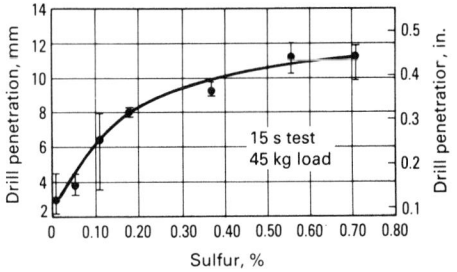

Fig. 3 Effect of sulfur content on machinability in a drill penetration test for an 18Cr-9Ni austenitic stainless steel

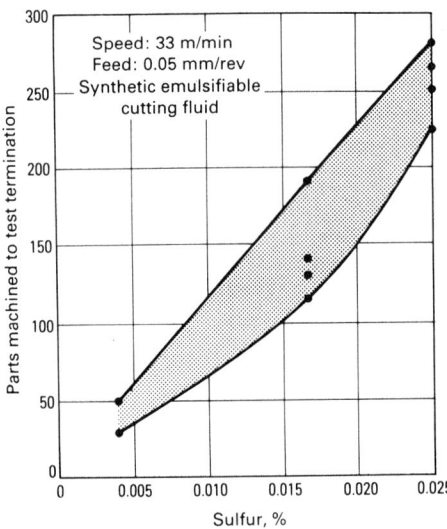

Fig. 4 Effect of low levels of sulfur on machinability in a screw machine test for S30400 austenitic stainless steel. Termination is defined as a 0.075 mm (0.003 in.) increase in the diameter of the part being cut.

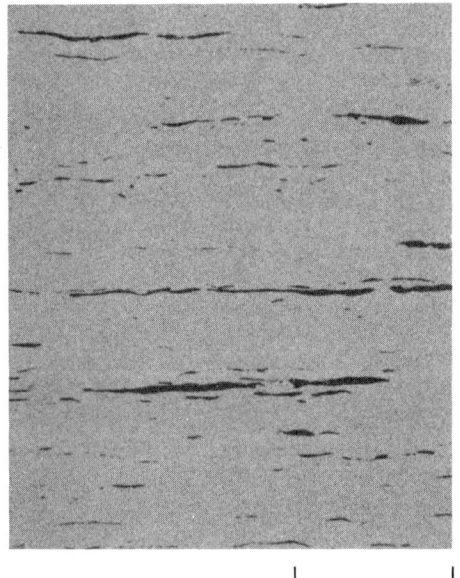

Fig. 5 Sulfide inclusions in S30300 austenitic stainless steel

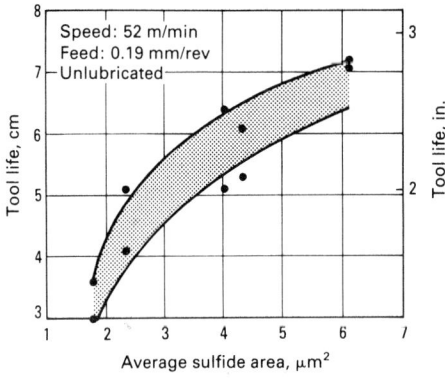

Fig. 6 Effect of sulfide size on machinability in a tool life test for S30300 austenitic stainless steel. Tool life is measured as the distance traveled along a 23.2 mm (0.915 in.) diam bar until tool failure.

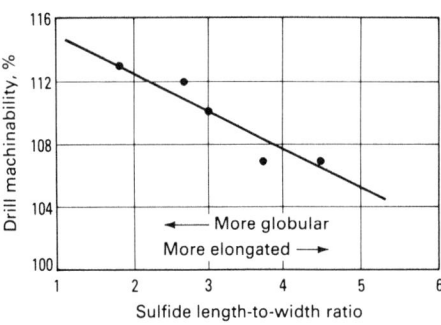

Fig. 7 Effect of sulfide shape on machinability in a drill test for S30300 austenitic stainless steel. Source: Ref 9

Fig. 8 Effect of sulfide size on machined surface finish for a free-machining austenitic stainless steel. Source: Ref 11

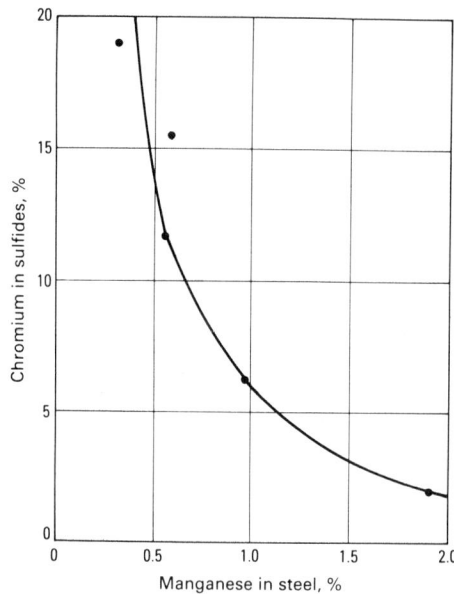

Fig. 9 Effect of manganese content in steel on chromium content in sulfides for a free-machining 13% Cr martensitic stainless steel. Source: Ref 14

able degradation of other properties, particularly hot and cold workability in the producer's mill.

Increases in sulfur continuously increase the ease of cutting, although generally at a decreasing rate (Fig. 3). Increasing sulfur also produces relatively large increases in tool life, even within the typical limit of sulfur content (0.030% maximum) allowed for non-free-machining alloys (Fig. 4). Close control of sulfur to the upper end of this range is at least part of the explanation for the enhanced-machining versions of the standard non-free-machining alloys (Ref 9, 10).

Sulfur is present in stainless steels in the form of discrete sulfide inclusions (Fig. 5). Sulfides that are larger and more globular provide a greater benefit to machining than smaller and elongated ones (Ref 9-11), as shown in Fig. 6 and 7. Although larger sulfides benefit tool life or ease of cutting, they can be detrimental to machined surface finish (Fig. 8). This is a case in which the definition of machinability is important.

Except at low levels of manganese, the sulfides in free-machining stainless steels are basically manganese sulfides containing chromium and iron. As the manganese level or manganese-to-sulfur ratio increases in a stainless steel, the composition of the sulfide will change (Ref 12-14), as shown in Fig. 9. Higher manganese or a higher manganese-to-sulfur ratio will further improve the machinability of free-machining ferritic, martensitic, and austenitic stainless steels (Ref 15-19), as shown in Fig. 10. The use of higher manganese to increase machinability also has an effect on corrosion resistance. Stainless steels containing manganese-rich sulfides can be less corrosion resistant than those containing sulfides with a higher chromium content (Ref 13-15). Whether any loss in corrosion resistance is significant depends on the specific environment. Free-machining austenitic alloys are not affected to the same extent as free-machining ferritic and martensitic alloys (Fig. 11).

Stainless steels specifically containing higher manganese levels for improved machinability include S20300 (5 to 6.50% Mn), S30310 (2.50 to 4.50% Mn), and S41610 (1.50 to 2.50% Mn). Other free-machining alloys, such as S30300, can be melted with manganese on the high end of the allowable range to improve machinability. On the other hand, manganese can also be intentionally limited in S30300 or S41600 to give these free-machining alloys improved corrosion resistance.

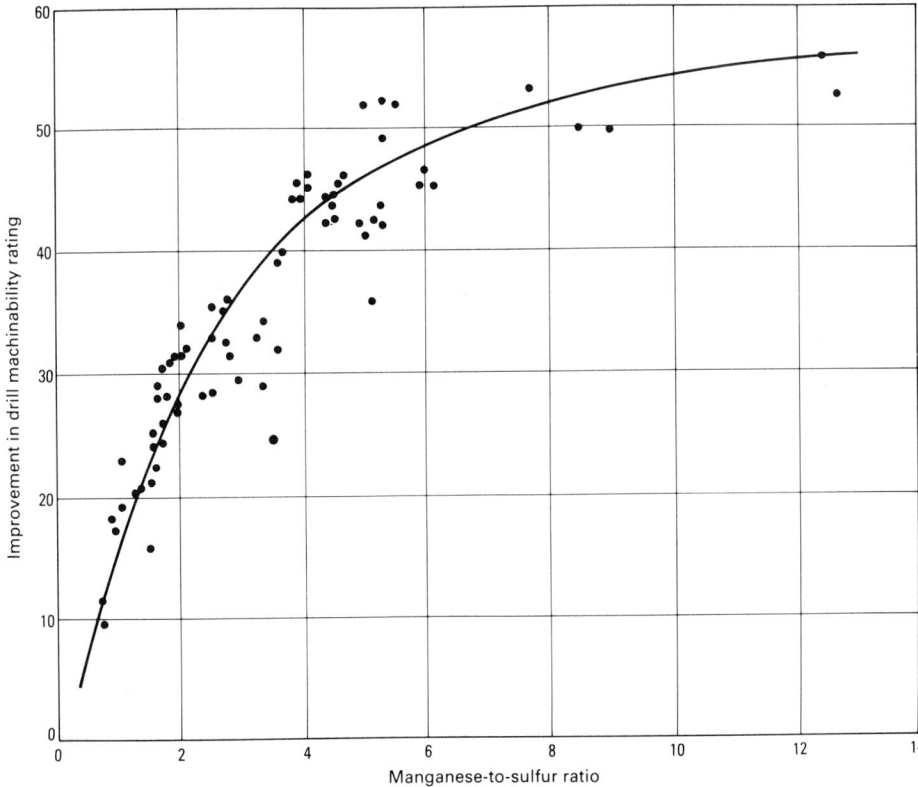

Fig. 10 Effect of manganese-to-sulfur ratio on machinability in a drill test for a free-machining martensitic stainless steel. Source: Ref 16

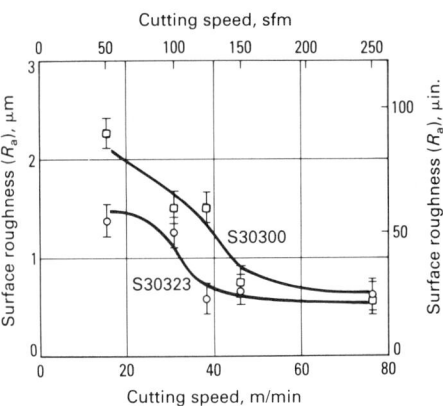

Fig. 13 Comparison of machined surface finish obtained for sulfur-bearing (S30300) and selenium-bearing (S30323) austenitic stainless steels in a plunge machining test. Source: Ref 2

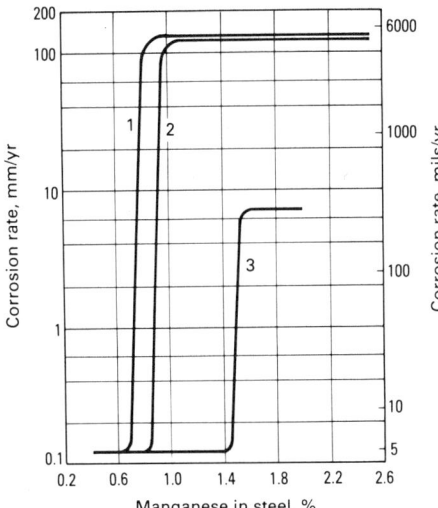

Fig. 11 Effect of manganese content on the corrosion of free-machining stainless steels in a 10% nitric acid solution at 24 °C (75 °F). 1, 13% Cr martensitic alloy; 2, 17% Cr ferritic alloy; 3, 18Cr-9Ni austenitic alloy. Source: Ref 14

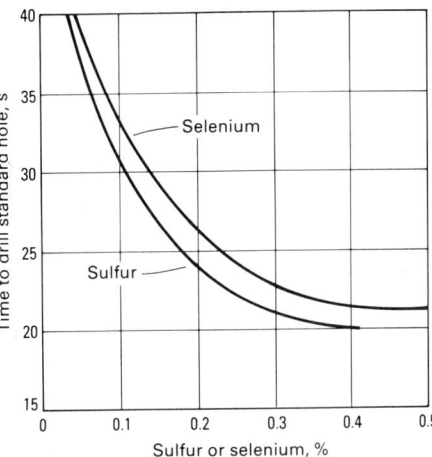

Fig. 12 Comparison of the effect of selenium and sulfur on machinability in a drill test for a 13.5% Cr martensitic stainless steel at 19 to 21 HRC. Source: Ref 24

Instead of limiting manganese to improve the corrosion resistance of a free-machining stainless steel, another approach has been to produce alternative sulfides, such as titanium sulfides (Ref 20-22). An example of this approach is S18235 which contains 0.15 to 0.35% S and 0.30 to 1.00% Ti.

Selenium is the next most commonly used free-machining agent in stainless steels, forming inclusions generally analogous to sulfides. Typically, selenium is less effective than an equivalent weight percent of sulfur in improving the overall machining characteristics of stainless steels (Ref 11, 17, 23-26), as shown in Fig. 12. However, there are reports to the contrary (Ref 2). Selenium-bearing alloys, which normally contain a minimum of 0.15% Se, can provide a better ma-

chined surface finish than sulfur-bearing alloys (Fig. 13). In addition to the possibility of a better machined surface finish, selenium-bearing stainless steels may offer improved cold formability and somewhat improved corrosion resistance compared to the corresponding sulfur-bearing alloys (Ref 11, 23-27). Selenium additions have also been used in sulfur-bearing alloys to promote sulfides that are larger and more globular and therefore more beneficial to machinability (Ref 28, 29).

Tellurium, like selenium, forms inclusions similar to sulfides. Tellurium has been shown to be more effective than sulfur in improving the machinability of an austenitic stainless steel (Fig. 14). Like selenium, tellurium can be used to promote sulfides that tend to retain their globular shape (Ref 28, 29), as shown in Fig. 15. The utility of tellurium is limited, primarily because of its adverse effect on hot workability. This is particularly true for austenitic alloys (Ref 11, 17, 26). However, tellurium has recently been used in a ferritic alloy in conjunction with sulfur and lead (Ref 25).

Lead and bismuth have low solubility in stainless steels, forming metallic inclusions that benefit machinability, particularly in austenitic stainless steels (Ref 17, 23-25, 30-34). Lead is more beneficial to the machinability of an austenitic stainless steel than other common free-machining additives (Fig. 14). The use of lead, with or without limited sulfur, also reportedly results in better machined surface finish, corrosion resistance, and cold formability than the use of higher sulfur alone (Ref 25, 30, 32). Somewhat similar benefits have been attributed to the use of bismuth (Ref 34).

Despite the benefits associated with the use of lead or bismuth, alloys containing these elements are commercially available only to a limited extent. Problems with the use of lead include toxicity, reduction in hot workability, and erratic machinability associated with the difficulty in obtaining a uniform dispersion in the steel (Ref 17, 23, 34). Boron additions have been used to alleviate the hot-workability problems (Ref 32). The use of bismuth involves similar problems, except for toxicity (Ref 33, 34).

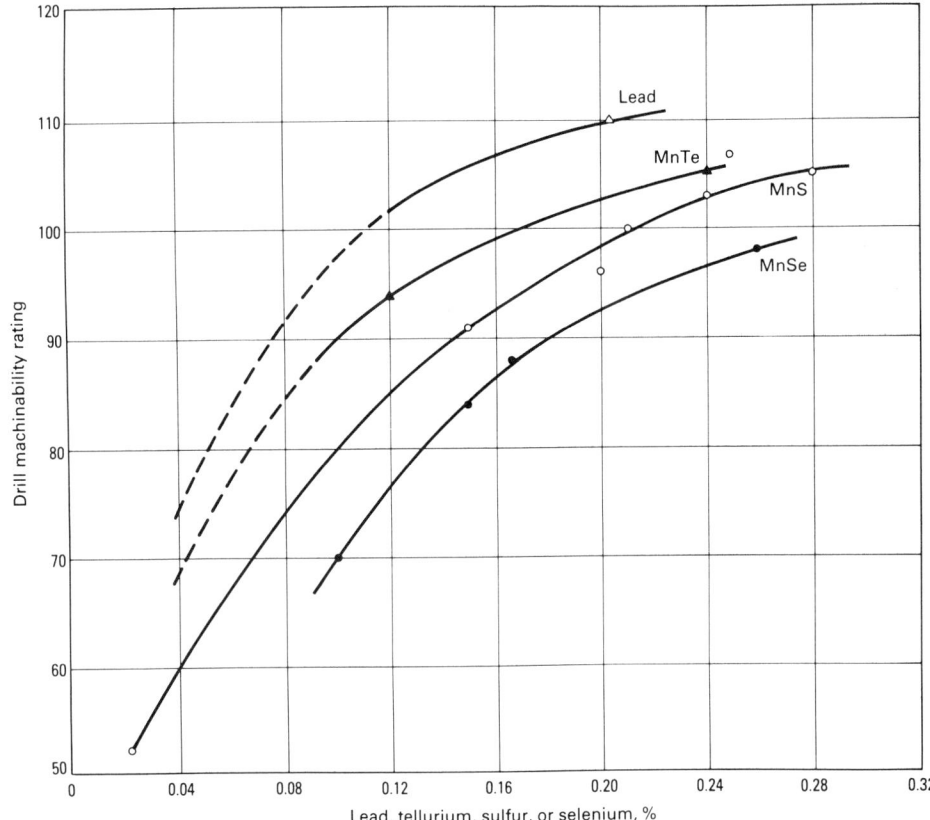

Fig. 14 Comparison of the effect of lead or tellurium (MnTe) with sulfur (MnS) and selenium (MnSe) on machinability in a drill test for an 18Cr-9Ni austenitic stainless steel. Source: Ref 17

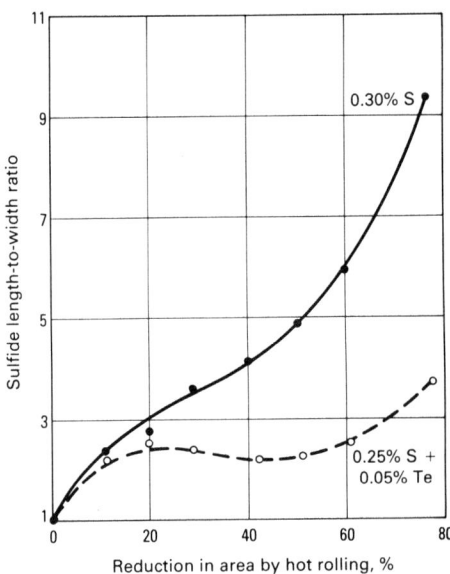

Fig. 15 Effect of tellurium on sulfide shape in a 13% Cr martensitic stainless steel that is reduced in area by various percentages by hot rolling at 1177 °C (2150 °F)

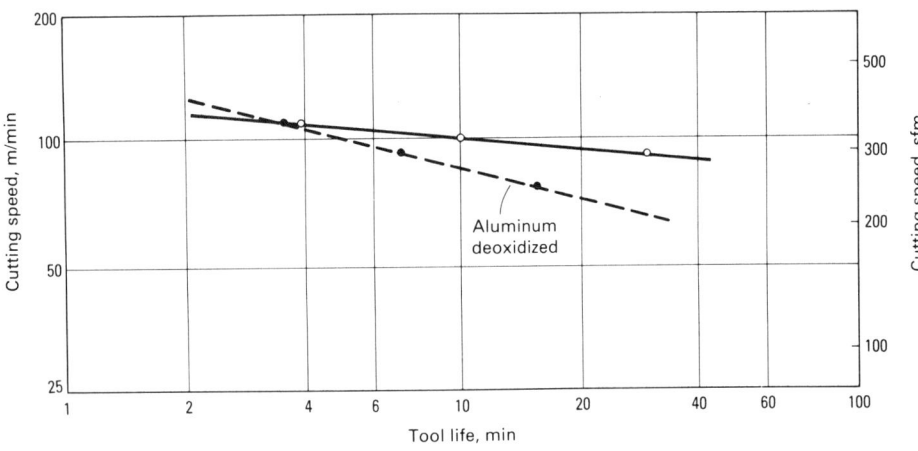

Fig. 16 Effect of aluminum oxide inclusions on the tool life of S43020. Source: Ref 15

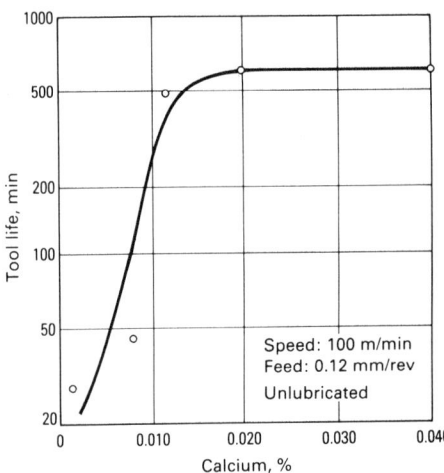

Fig. 17 Effect of calcium content on carbide tool life for an austenitic stainless steel. Source: Ref 37

Controlled Oxides. Stainless steels may contain oxides as a result of deoxidation or reoxidation. In some cases, such oxides may be deleterious to machinability. The deoxidation of standard air-melted stainless steels is generally accomplished with silicon. The deoxidation of machining grades with aluminum should be avoided because aluminum oxides are highly abrasive and degrade tool life (Ref 11, 15, 28, 29, 35), as shown in Fig. 16.

However, calcium deoxidation can form inclusions that are actually beneficial to machinability under certain conditions (Ref 35-37). This involves the formation of calcium-(aluminum)-silicates in the steel. Such inclusions will soften during high-speed machining with titanium carbide tools, forming a protective layer on the tool. The increase in carbide tool life with increasing calcium content is shown in Fig. 17. The composition of the inclusions (i.e., the proportions of CaO, SiO$_2$, and Al$_2$O$_3$) must be tightly controlled to obtain oxides that will properly soften in the cutting speed range used (Ref 36).

Phosphorus is added in conjunction with sulfur or selenium to enhance machinability, not by forming inclusions but by modifying the matrix properties of the alloy. The original purpose in adding phosphorus was to embrittle tough austenitic alloys (Ref 8). Phosphorus has only a small beneficial effect in an austenitic alloy and is detrimental above a certain level (Fig. 18).

Machinability of Alloy Families

Significant differences in machinability exist between different alloy systems and alloy families, including the various free-machining alloys. This section will discuss machinability both

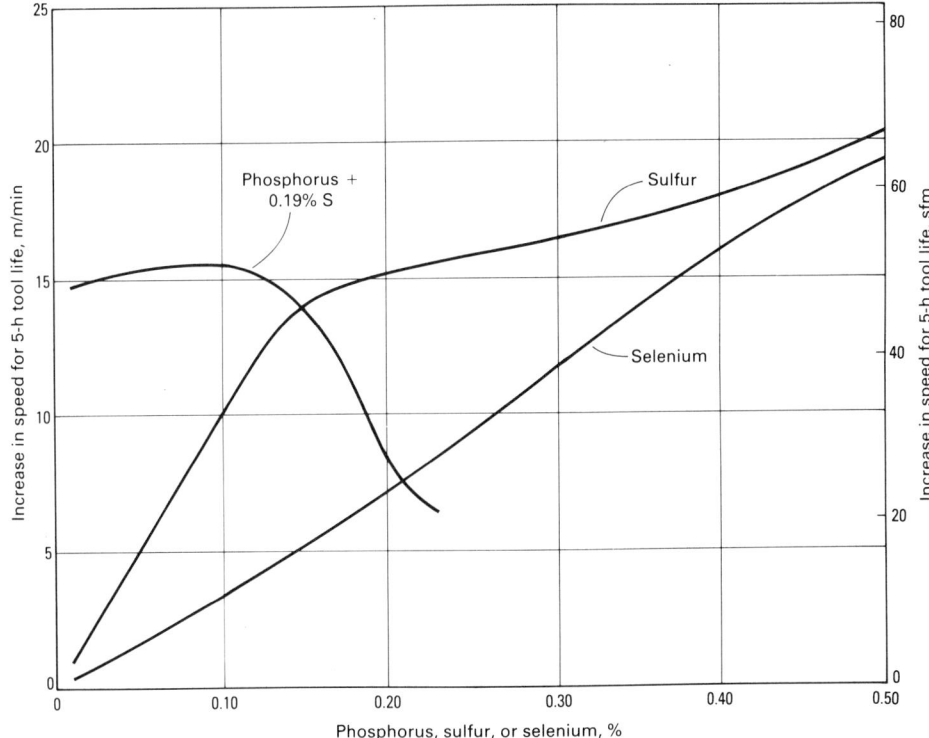

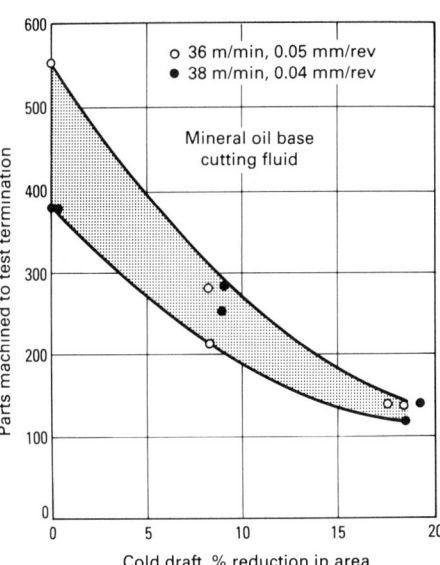

Fig. 19 Effect of percent cold draft on machinability in a screw machine test for an enhanced-machining version of S30400. Termination is defined as a 0.075 mm (0.003 in.) increase in the diameter of the part being cut.

Fig. 18 Effect of phosphorus on cutting speed (tool life) for a 0.19S-18Cr-8Ni austenitic stainless steel compared to a similar steel containing only sulfur or selenium. Source: Ref 23

within and among the five basic families of stainless steels.

Ferritic and Martensitic Alloys. Free-machining ferritic alloys (such as S43020) and annealed, low-carbon, free-machining martensitic alloys (such as S41600) are the easiest of the stainless steels to machine (Ref 2, 27, 38-40). In fact, their machinability ratings approach and in some cases are comparable to those of certain free-machining carbon steels (Ref 27, 38, 39). The non-free-machining lower-chromium ferritic alloys (S40500, S43000) and annealed, low-carbon, straight-chromium martensitic alloys (S40300, S41000) are also generally easier to machine than most other non-free-machining alloys (Ref 27, 38-40). The higher-chromium ferritic alloys, such as S44600, are considered by some to be somewhat more difficult to machine than the lower-chromium alloys because of gumminess and stringy chips (Ref 41, 42).

Other than the presence or lack of a free-machining additive, the machining characteristics of martensitic stainless steels are influenced by:

- Hardness level
- Carbon content
- Nickel content
- Phase balance (i.e., the percentage of free or δ-ferrite in the martensitic matrix)

Increasing the hardness level of a particular alloy results in a decrease in machinability as measured by various criteria (tool life, drillability, and so on) (Ref 2, 24, 40, 43). Within certain limits, however, surface finish can be improved by machining harder material (Ref 24, 40).

In the martensitic grades, machinability decreases as the carbon content increases from S41000 (0.15% max C) to S42000 (0.15% min C) to S44004 (0.95 to 1.20% C), or from S41600/S41623 (0.15% max C) to S42020/S42023 (0.15% min C) to S44020/S44023 (0.95 to 1.20% C). With higher carbon levels, there also tends to be a smaller difference in machinability between the corresponding free-machining and non-free-machining versions. These effects are primarily due to the increasing quantities of abrasive chromium carbides present as carbon level increases in this series of alloys. As a further detriment to machinability, annealed hardness level increases with increasing carbon level (Ref 24, 40-42).

Nickel content also influences machinability by increasing annealed hardness levels. Consequently, alloys such as S41400 and S43100 containing 1.25 to 2.50% Ni will be more difficult to machine than S41000 (no nickel) in the annealed condition (Ref 38, 39).

Changing the phase balance has been used to improve the machining characteristics of S41600. It has generally been found that increasing free or δ-ferrite content results in improved machinability, including tool life and surface finish (Ref 9, 24, 40, 43-45). The introduction of a higher ferrite content also results in decreasing hardness capability.

Austenitic Alloys. The difficulties in machining attributed to stainless steels in general are more specifically attributable to the austenitic stainless steels (Ref 27, 39-42, 45). Compared to ferritic and martensitic alloys, typical austenitic alloys have a higher work-hardening rate, a wider spread between yield and ultimate tensile strengths, and higher toughness and ductility. When machining austenitic stainless steels, particularly the non-free-machining alloys, several factors become more pronounced:

- Tools will run hotter with more tendency to form a large built-up edge.
- Chips will be stringier with a tendency to tangle, making their removal difficult.
- Chatter will be more likely if tool rigidity is inadequate or marginal.
- Cut surfaces will be work hardened and more difficult to machine if cutting is interrupted or if the feed rate is too low.

Because of these factors, the general precautions for machining stainless steels are particularly important for austenitic alloys.

Although there have been differing opinions (Ref 23), a moderate amount of cold work has been regarded as beneficial to the overall machining characteristics of austenitic stainless steels (Ref 40, 42). The cold working will reduce the ductility of the material, which results in cutting with a cleaner chip and less tendency for a builtup edge. This produces a better machined surface finish but with some loss of tool life due to the higher hardness level (Ref 40).

Automatic screw machine testing has shown that the effects of cold working and hardness are variable and may or may not be seen, depending on the type of alloy and machining conditions. In such testing, tool life has been reduced by an increasing level of cold work for both free-machining (S30300) and non-free-machining (S30400, S31600) austenitic stainless steels. This effect is shown in Fig. 19 for S30400. On the other hand, there have also been indications under different cutting conditions of an optimum level of tool life at an intermediate level of cold work (Fig. 20).

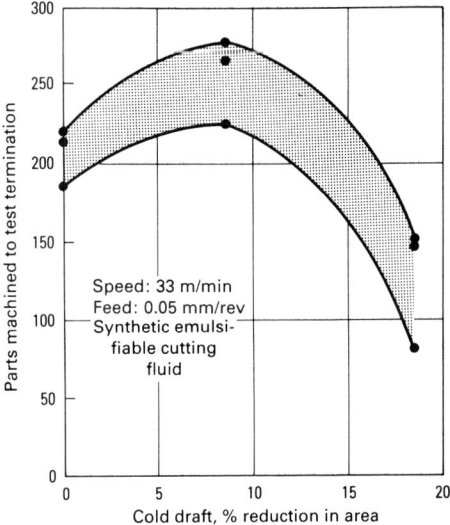

Fig. 20 Effect of percent cold draft on machinability in a screw machine test for an enhanced-machining version of S30400. Termination is defined as a 0.075 mm (0.003 in.) increase in the diameter of the part being cut.

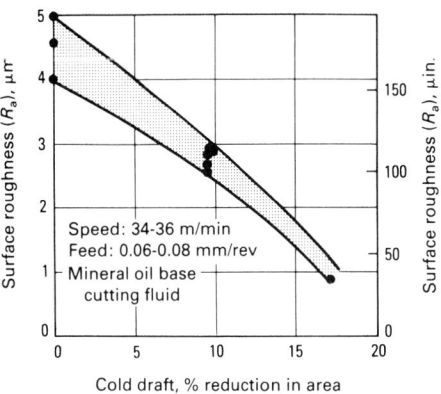

Fig. 21 Effect of percent cold draft on machined surface finish in a screw machine test for an enhanced-machining version of S31600

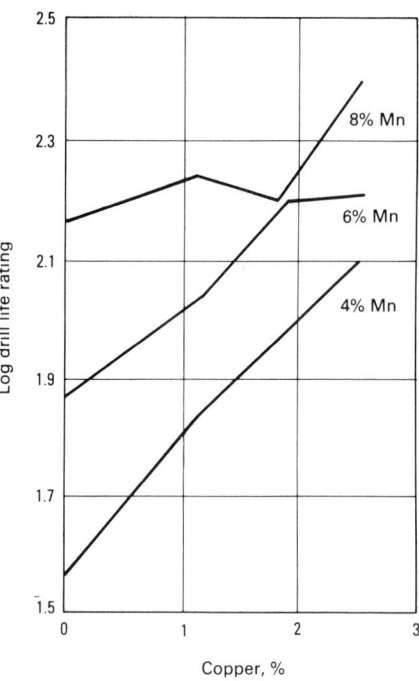

Fig. 22 Effect of copper and manganese contents on machinability in a drill test for a free-machining chromium-manganese-nickel austenitic stainless steel. Source: Ref 19

Machined surface finish can be improved by an increasing level of cold work for non-free-machining alloys (S30400, S31600). Figure 21 shows this effect for S31600. A decreasing tendency for tool chatter with increasing cold work has also been seen for these alloys. On the other hand, the use of cold-drawn bar does not consistently benefit the machined surface finish of a free-machining alloy (S30300).

Additions of manganese or copper can increase the machinability (Fig. 22) and decrease the high work-hardening rate of the lower-alloy austenitic stainless steels (Ref 19, 45-48). Austenitic free-machining alloys that have additions of manganese and/or copper include S20300 (5.00 to 6.50% Mn, 1.75 to 2.25% Cu), S30310 (2.50 to 4.50% Mn), S30330 (2.00% max Mn, 2.50 to 4.00% Cu), and S30431 (2.00% max Mn, 1.30 to 2.40% Cu). Although higher alloy content generally reduces the work-hardening rate, it may not necessarily benefit machinability. Highly alloyed austenitic stainless steels, such as S30900 (22 to 24% Cr, 12 to 15% Ni), S31000 (24 to 26% Cr, 19 to 22% Ni), and N08020 (19 to 21% Cr, 32 to 38% Ni), tend to be more difficult to machine (Ref 38, 39).

Carbon and nitrogen can affect the work-hardening rate and will increase the strength and hardness of austenitic stainless steels. Higher levels of either or both elements will decrease machinability (Fig. 23). Consequently, the high-nitrogen austenitic alloys, such as S20910 (0.20 to 0.40% N) and S28200 (0.40 to 0.60% N), are more difficult to machine than the standard lower-nitrogen austenitic alloys (Ref 38).

Strong carbide/nitride-forming elements, including titanium and niobium, are used in stainless steels such as S32100 and S34700 to prevent grain-boundary carbide, which can reduce intergranular corrosion resistance. However, the carbide/nitride inclusions are abrasive and will increase tool wear (Fig. 24).

Duplex Alloys. The machinability of duplex stainless steels is limited by their high annealed strength level. Figures 25 and 26 compare the machinability of a duplex alloy, S32950, with that of

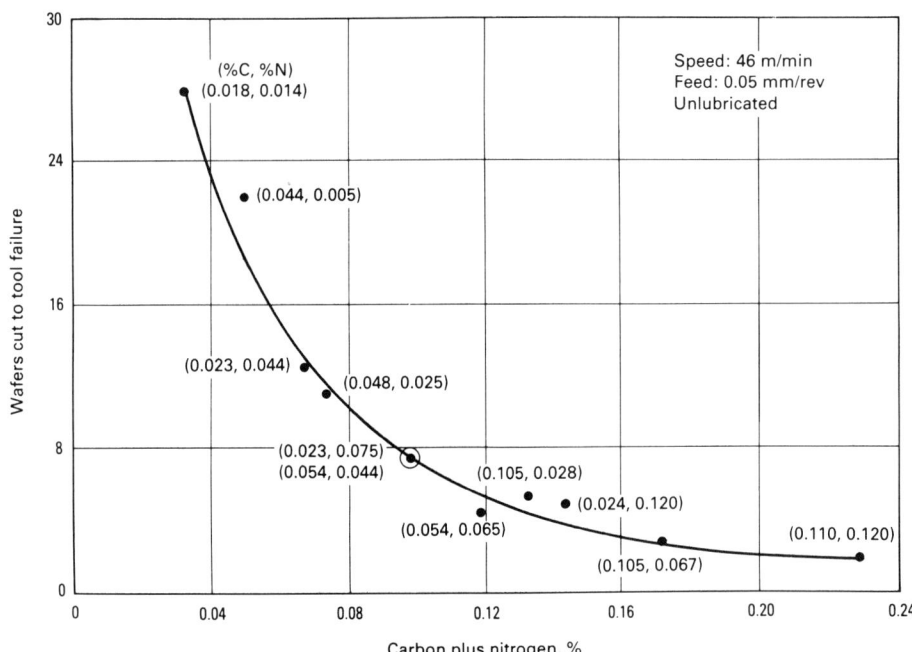

Fig. 23 Effect of carbon and nitrogen contents on machinability in a tool life test for a free-machining 18Cr-9Ni-3Mn austenitic stainless steel. Source: Ref 49

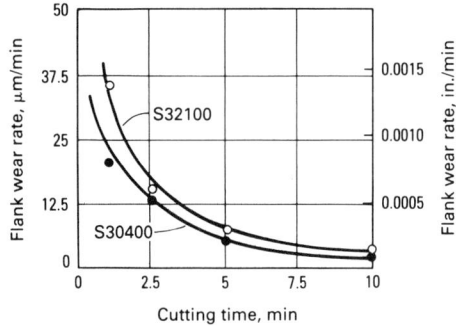

Fig. 24 Comparison of tool wear for austenitic stainless steels with (S32100) and without (S30400) titanium carbide inclusions. Source: Ref 50

Table 2 Relative machinability of S17400 in various heat-treated conditions

Condition	Typical hardness, HRC
Improved machinability (higher cutting speed)	
H1150M	27
H1150	33
H1075	36
A (solution treated)	34
H1025	38
H900	44
Improved surface finish	

Source: Ref 51

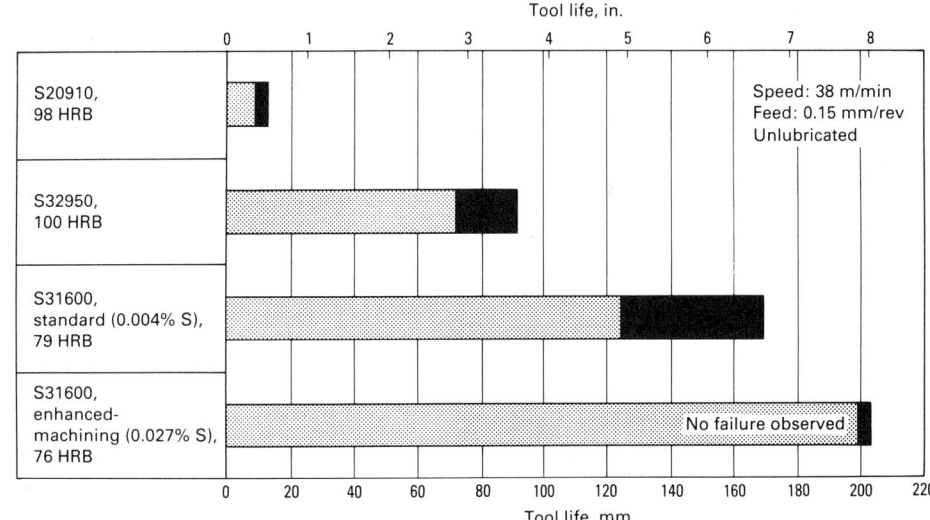

Fig. 25 Comparison of tool life for a duplex stainless steel (S32950), a high-nitrogen (0.20 to 0.40% N) austenitic stainless steel (S20910), and a standard and enhanced-machining austenitic stainless steel (S31600). Tool life is measured as the distance traveled along a 25 mm (1.0 in.) diam bar until tool failure. Shaded areas represent distance to failure.

a high-nitrogen austenitic alloy, S20910, and a conventional austenitic alloy, S31600, in standard (0.004% S) and enhanced-machining (0.027% S) versions. The duplex alloy (S32950) has a hardness level comparable to that of the high-nitrogen austenitic alloy (S20910) but provides better machinability. However, it does not machine as well as either the standard or the enhanced-machining S31600 alloys.

Other nitrogen-bearing duplex alloys are expected to machine similarly to S32950. No enhanced-machining versions of duplex alloys are available.

Precipitation-Hardenable Alloys. The machinability of precipitation-hardenable stainless steels depends on the type of alloy and its hardness level. Martensitic precipitation-hardenable stainless steels (S13800, S15500, S17400) are often machined in the solution-treated condition; therefore only a single aging treatment is required afterward to reach the desired strength level. In this condition, the relatively high hardness limits machinability. Most of these alloys machine comparably to, or somewhat worse than, a standard austenitic alloy such as S30400. Alloy

S17400 is available in enhanced-machining versions that allow machining at higher speeds with a significantly reduced tendency toward chatter.

Martensitic precipitation-hardenable stainless steels can also be machined in an aged condition so that heat treating can be avoided and closer tolerances maintained. The ease of cutting generally varies with the hardness or heat-treated condition (Table 2).

In the annealed, austenitic condition, semi-austenitic alloys (S17700, S35000, S35500) can be expected to machine with difficulty, somewhat worse than an alloy such as S30200, which has a high work-hardening rate. Alloys S35000 and S35500 can be supplied in an equalized and overtempered condition, which will provide the

best machinability. As with the martensitic precipitation-hardenable alloys, machining difficulties increase with the aged hardness level.

Austenitic precipitation-hardenable alloys, such as S66286, machine quite poorly, requiring slower cutting rates than even the highly alloyed austenitic stainless steels (Ref 38). Machining in an aged condition will require even slower speeds.

General Guidelines

The characteristics of stainless steels that have a large influence on machinability include relatively high tensile strength, high work-hardening rate, particularly for the austenitic alloys, and high ductility. These factors explain the tendency of the material to form a built-up edge on the tool during traditional machining operations. The chips removed during machining exert high pressures on the nose of the tool that, when combined with the high temperature at the chip-tool interface, cause pressure welding of portions of the chip to the tool. In addition, the low thermal conductivity of stainless steels contributes to a continuing heat buildup.

The difficulties involved in the traditional machining of stainless steels can be minimized by observing the following points:

- Because more power is generally required to machine stainless steels, equipment should be used only up to about 75% of the rating for carbon steels.
- To avoid chatter, tooling and fixtures must be as rigid as possible. Overhang or protrusion of either the workpiece or the tool must be minimized. This applies to turning tools, drills, reamers, etc.
- To avoid glazed, work-hardened surfaces, particularly with austenitic alloys, a positive feed must be maintained. In some cases, increasing the feed and reducing the speed may

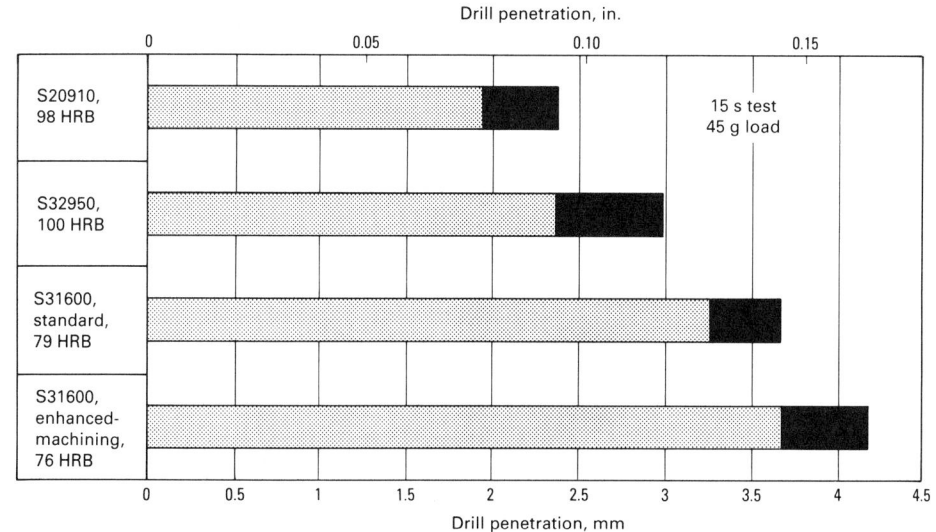

Fig. 26 Comparison of machinability in a drill penetration test for a duplex stainless steel (S32950), a high-nitrogen (0.20 to 0.40% N) austenitic stainless steel (S20910), and a standard and enhanced-machining austenitic stainless steel (S31600)

Table 3 Nominal turning parameters for wrought stainless steels—single point and box tools

Depending on actual machining conditions, optimum parameters may be higher or lower than those given.

										Carbide tools								
	Depth of cut(b)		High-speed steel tools(c)					Speed, brazed		Speed, indexable		Speed, coated		Feed		Tool		
			Speed		Feed		Tool											
UNS designation(a)	mm	in.	m/min	sfm	mm/rev	in./rev	material	m/min	sfm	m/min	sfm	m/min	sfm	mm/rev	in./rev	material		
Free-machining alloys																		
Ferritic alloys																		
S18235, S43020, S43023	3.8	0.150	50	165	0.38	0.015	M2/M3	155	510	175	575	229	750	0.38	0.015	C6, CC6/		
	0.75	0.030	56	185	0.18	0.007		175	575	198	650	259	850	0.18	0.007	C7, CC7		
S18200	3.8	0.150	53	175	0.38	0.015	M2/M3	160	525	183	600	236	775	0.38	0.015	C6, CC6/		
	0.75	0.030	61	200	0.18	0.007		183	600	206	675	267	875	0.18	0.007	C7, CC7		
Martensitic alloys																		
S41600, S41610, S41623	3.8	0.150	53	175	0.38	0.015	M2/M3	160	525	183	600	236	775	0.38	0.015	C6, CC6/		
	0.75	0.030	61	200	0.18	0.007		183	600	206	675	267	875	0.18	0.007	C7, CC7		
S42020, S42023	3.8	0.150	32	105	0.38	0.015	T15/M42	130	425	152	500	183	600	0.38	0.015	C6, CC6/		
	0.75	0.030	40	130	0.18	0.007		152	500	175	575	206	675	0.18	0.007	C7, CC7		
S44020, S44023	3.8	0.150	26	85	0.38	0.015	T15/M42	114	375	130	425	160	525	0.38	0.015	C6, CC6/		
	0.75	0.030	30	100	0.18	0.007		130	425	145	475	175	575	0.18	0.007	C7, CC7		
Austenitic alloys																		
S20300, S30300, S30310, S30360	3.8	0.150	34	110	0.38	0.015	M2/M3	130	425	145	475	175	575	0.38	0.015	C2, CC2/		
	0.75	0.030	40	130	0.18	0.007		152	500	168	550	213	700	0.18	0.007	C3, CC3		
S30323, S30330, S30345, S30431, S31620, S34720, S34723	3.8	0.150	27	90	0.38	0.015	T15/M42	107	350	122	400	160	525	0.38	0.015	C2, CC2/		
	0.75	0.030	32	105	0.18	0.007		122	400	137	450	183	600	0.18	0.007	C3, CC3		
Non-free-machining alloys																		
Ferritic alloys																		
S40500, S40900, S43000, S43400	3.8	0.150	30	100	0.38	0.015	M2/M3	122	400	137	450	183	600	0.38	0.015	C6, CC6/		
	0.75	0.030	38	125	0.18	0.007		152	500	168	550	229	750	0.18	0.007	C7, CC7		
S44200, S44300, S44400, S44600	3.8	0.150	27	90	0.38	0.015	T15/M42	107	350	122	400	168	550	0.38	0.015	C2, CC2/		
	0.75	0.030	34	110	0.18	0.007		137	450	152	500	213	700	0.18	0.007	C3, CC3		
Martensitic alloys																		
S40300, S41000	3.8	0.150	30	100	0.38	0.015	M2/M3	122	400	137	450	183	600	0.38	0.015	C6, CC6/		
	0.75	0.030	38	125	0.18	0.007		152	500	168	550	229	750	0.18	0.007	C7, CC7		
S41400, S42000, S42010, S43100	3.8	0.150	26	85	0.38	0.015	T15/M42	107	350	114	375	152	500	0.38	0.015	C6, CC6/		
	0.75	0.030	30	100	0.18	0.007		114	375	137	450	183	600	0.18	0.007	C7, CC7		
S44002, S44003, S44004	3.8	0.150	20	65	0.38	0.015	T15/M42	84	275	91	300	114	375	0.38	0.015	C6, CC6/		
	0.75	0.030	24	80	0.18	0.007		107	350	114	375	152	500	0.18	0.007	C7, CC7		
Austenitic alloys																		
S20100, S30100, S30200, S30400, S30403, S30430, S30500, S31600, S31603, S32100, S34700, S38400	3.8	0.150	26	85	0.38	0.015	T15/M42	99	325	107	350	137	450	0.38	0.015	C2, CC2/		
	0.75	0.030	30	100	0.18	0.007		107	350	122	400	160	525	0.18	0.007	C3, CC3		
S30900, S30908, S31000, S31008, S31700, S31703	3.8	0.150	23	75	0.38	0.015	T15/M42	91	300	99	325	130	425	0.38	0.015	C2, CC2/		
	0.75	0.030	27	90	0.18	0.007		99	325	114	375	152	500	0.18	0.007	C3, CC3		
S20910, S21904, S24100, S28200, S30452, N08020	3.8	0.150	17	55	0.38	0.015	T15/M42	53	175	61	200	76	250	0.38	0.015	C2, CC2/		
	0.75	0.030	21	70	0.18	0.007		61	200	76	250	91	300	0.18	0.007	C3, CC3		
Duplex alloys																		
S31803, S32550, S32900, S32950	3.8	0.150	23	75	0.38	0.015	T15/M42	91	300	99	325	130	425	0.38	0.015	C2, CC2/		
	0.75	0.030	27	90	0.18	0.007		99	325	114	375	152	500	0.18	0.007	C3, CC3		
Precipitation-hardenable alloys(a)																		
S15500, S17400, S17700, S45000	3.8	0.150	24	80	0.38	0.015	T15/M42	91	300	107	350	137	450	0.38	0.015	C6, CC6/		
	0.75	0.030	29	95	0.18	0.007		107	350	122	400	160	525	0.18	0.007	C7, CC7		
S13800, S35000, S35500, S45500	3.8	0.150	23	75	0.38	0.015	T15/M42	84	275	99	325	130	425	0.38	0.015	C6, CC6/		
	0.75	0.030	27	90	0.18	0.007		99	325	114	375	152	500	0.18	0.007	C7, CC7		
S66286	3.8	0.150	15	50	0.38	0.015	T15/M42	76	250	91	300	107	350	0.38	0.015	C6, CC6/		
	0.75	0.030	18	60	0.18	0.007		91	300	107	350	122	400	0.18	0.007	C7, CC7		

(a) All machining parameters given are for material in the annealed condition (140-270 HB) except the precipitation-hardenable grades, which are solution treated (150-325 HB) or equalized and overtempered for S35000 and S35500. For material heat treated or cold drawn to hardnesses higher than their normal annealed (or softest) level, best results are obtained by reducing speeds by approximately 10% to as much as 60% at the higher hardnesses. Premium high-speed steel or carbide tooling may also be required to cut high-hardness material. (b) The 0.75 mm (0.030 in.) depth of cut represents conditions for a finishing cut, while the 3.8 mm (0.150 in.) depth of cut represents conditions for a roughing cut. (c) Any premium high-speed steel (T15, M33, M41-47) can be used where the designated tool material is T15, M42. Source: Ref 38, 52

be necessary. Dwelling, interrupted cuts, or a succession of thin cuts should be avoided.

- Lower cutting speeds may be necessary, particularly for non-free-machining austenitic alloys, precipitation-hardenable stainless steels, or higher-hardness martensitic alloys. Excessive cutting speeds result in tool wear or tool failure and shutdown for tool regrinding or replacement. Slower speeds with longer tool life are often the answer to higher output and lower costs.

- Tools, both high-speed steel and carbides, must be kept sharp, with a fine finish to minimize friction with the chip. A sharp cutting edge produces the best surface finish and provides the longest tool life. To produce the best cutting edge on high-

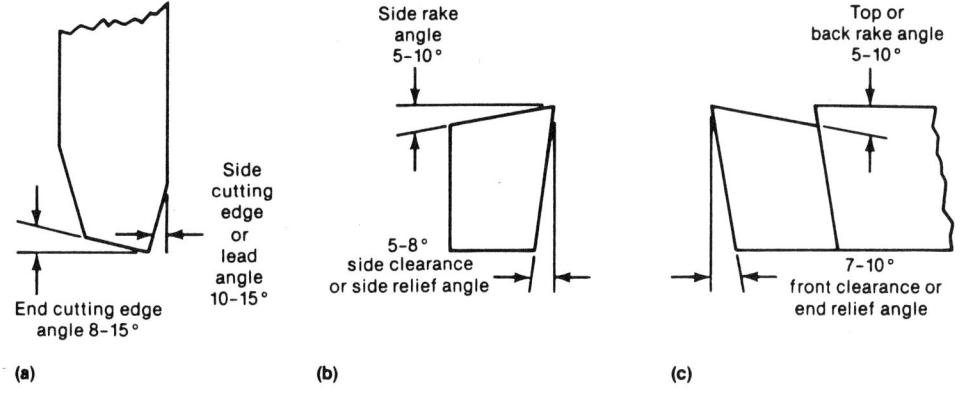

Fig. 27 Suggested geometries for single-point turning tools used on stainless steels. (a) Plan view. (b) End view. (c) Side view

speed steel tools, 60-grit roughing should be followed by 120- and 150-grit finishing. Honing produces an even finer finish.

- Cutting fluids must be selected or modified to provide proper lubrication and heat removal. Fluids must be carefully directed to the cutting area at a sufficient flow rate to prevent overheating.

Cutting Fluids

Machining stainless steel without a cutting fluid is usually restricted to low production quantities or to specific operating conditions in which use of cutting fluid is impractical, such as the machining of large workpieces or complex shapes. Complex shapes are sometimes machined dry to avoid entrapment of fluid that would impair subsequent processing or service.

The use of a cutting fluid is more desirable for machining stainless steels than for machining carbon or alloy steels, for two reasons. First, stainless steels are generally less machinable than carbon or alloy steels, and second, the lower heat conductivity of stainless steels increases the need for cooling.

Water-soluble oils (usually in proportions of 1 part oil to 12 to 20 parts water) and sulfochlorinated cutting oils (having a viscosity of 300 Saybolt Universal seconds [SUS] maximum at 38 °C, or 100 °F) are the cutting fluids most widely used in machining stainless steels.

Water-soluble oils are used for most single-point tool operations such as turning and boring. Soluble oils cost less than sulfochlorinated oils, are easy to supply to the cutting area in copious amounts, and function as an acceptable means of cooling and flushing away chips. Soluble oils are also successfully used for milling and for machining in turret lathes and bar and chucking machines when several operations take place consecutively or simultaneously.

Sulfochlorinated or other additive-type cutting oils are infrequently used for the turning, boring, or milling of stainless steels, although there are operating conditions for which sulfochlorinated oils have proved to be the best choice. Examples of such conditions are excessively hard work metal, the use of high-speed steel tools (because of interrupted cutting), and critical surface finish requirements.

Stainless steels are drilled with twist drills using soluble oil, although as the depth of the hole increases, the frequency of using sulfochlorinated or other additive oils increases. Soluble oil is typically used for the reaming of stainless steels. The gun drilling or other deep-hole drilling of stainless steels is generally done with sulfochlorinated or other additive-type oils. When additive oils are used, viscosity should be no higher than 300 SUS at 38 °C (100 °F) in order to permit the necessary flow.

For the broaching of stainless steels, best results are obtained with additive-type cutting oils. The same applies to tapping and to die threading. Soluble oil is used for sawing stainless steels.

Sulfochlorinated Oils. In the machining of stainless steels, a sulfochlorinated petroleum oil should be used that contains active sulfur and either approximately 8 to 10% fatty oil (viscosity will be approximately 200 SUS at 38 °C, or 100 °F) or no fatty-base oil (viscosity will be approximately 130 SUS at 38 °C, or 100 °F). The first oil is generally used for the non-free-machining types of stainless steels, while the second oil is usually preferred for the free-machining alloys.

Either of these oils, depending on the work being done, can be used straight or thinned with a blending oil, the best of which is paraffin oil. Normally, a 1:1 mixture of sulfurized oil with paraffin oil is used initially. If excessive tool wear occurs, more paraffin blending oil should be added. If the chips weld to the tool or if the tool burns, there may be too much paraffin blending oil in the mixture. In that case, an addition of more sulfurized oil is indicated.

The following are suggested starting points for mixtures of sulfurized oils and paraffin oil for various types of machining operations:

- When using high-speed, light-feed automatic screw machines, principally for turning, forming, and cutoff operations with the free-machining alloys, one part sulfurized oil to five parts paraffin oil is suggested.
- When using screw machines at normal or average speed or performing operations that include threading, tapping, drilling, and milling of the free-machining alloys, one part sulfurized oil to three parts paraffin oil is suggested.
- For coarse bolt threading, nut tapping, pipe threading, and broaching, one part sulfurized oil to two parts paraffin oil is suggested.
- In general, when machining the austenitic stainless steels (except the free-machining type), a mixture of one to one of the first oil type (8 to 10% fatty oil) and paraffin oil is suggested. Care must be exercised to ensure that the viscosity of the cutting fluid is sufficiently low to allow it to reach the point of cutting. Usually 120 SUS at 20 °C (70 °F) is satisfactory.
- A good criterion for starting new jobs is to remember that the more difficult the steel is to machine, the more sulfurized oil is needed. For the free-machining steels, the mixture can contain a larger percentage of paraffin-base oil.

Emulsifiable Fluids. Water-emulsifiable (water-soluble) cutting fluids are applicable to machining stainless steels, particularly in situations that require greater cooling capability. However, the water-based fluids are unsuitable in those cases in which the cutting fluid and machine lubrication oils have the potential of mixing. Many of the water-emulsifiable fluids will not withstand some of the more severe cutting operations. Nevertheless, water-based fluids are successfully used in many machining operations, as discussed earlier.

The cutting fluid should contain polar and extreme-pressure additives, and favorable results have been obtained with some of the synthetic emulsifying systems. Compared to the cutting oils, the water-emulsifiable fluids can result in better machined surface finishes, less heat-affected zone in the tool, and therefore less regrinding and increased productivity for some grades of stainless steel.

Turning

Turning operations on automatic screw machines and turret lathes involve so many variables that it is impossible to make specific recommendations that would apply to all conditions. Suggested tool angles, cutting speeds, and feeds are primarily starting points for each specific job. Table 3 lists reasonable speeds and feeds for single-point turning; Table 4, for cutoff and forming operations.

Single-Point Turning Tools. Grinding tools properly is particularly important in machining stainless steels. Figure 27 shows suggested starting geometries for high-speed steel single-point turning tools. Tools with a 5 to 10° positive top rake angle will generate less heat and cut more freely with a cleaner surface. It is also beneficial to select as large a tool as possible to provide a greater heat sink as well as a more rigid setup. To ensure adequate support for the cutting edge, the front clearance angle should be kept to a minimum, that is, 7 to 10°, as shown in Fig. 27. Austenitic stainless steels, because of their toughness and work-hardening characteristics, require tools ground with top rake angles on the high side of the 5 to 10° range to

Table 4 Nominal turning parameters for wrought stainless steels—cutoff and form tools

Depending on actual machining conditions, the optimum parameters may be higher or lower than those given.

UNS designation(a)	Speed m/min (sfm)	1.6 mm (1/16 in.)	3.2 mm (1/8 in.)	6.4 mm (1/4 in.)	13 mm (1/2 in.)	25 mm (1 in.)	38 mm (1 1/2 in.)	50 mm (2 in.)	Tool material(a)(b)(c)
				Feed, mm/rev (in./rev), for tool width of:					
Free-machining alloys									
Ferritic alloys									
S18235, S43020, S43023	46 (150)	0.038 (0.0015)	0.05 (0.002)	0.064 (0.0025)	0.064 (0.0025)	0.05 (0.002)	0.038 (0.0015)	0.025 (0.001)	M2, M3
	122 (400)	0.038 (0.0015)	0.05 (0.002)	0.064 (0.0025)	0.064 (0.0025)	0.05 (0.002)	0.038 (0.0015)	0.025 (0.001)	C6
S18200	50 (165)	0.038 (0.0015)	0.05 (0.002)	0.064 (0.0025)	0.064 (0.0025)	0.05 (0.002)	0.038 (0.0015)	0.025 (0.001)	M2, M3
	130 (425)	0.038 (0.0015)	0.05 (0.002)	0.064 (0.0025)	0.064 (0.0025)	0.05 (0.002)	0.038 (0.0015)	0.025 (0.001)	C6
Martensitic alloys									
S41600, S41610, S41623	46 (150)	0.05 (0.002)	0.064 (0.0025)	0.075 (0.003)	0.064 (0.0025)	0.05 (0.002)	0.038 (0.0015)	0.025 (0.001)	M2, M3
	122 (400)	0.05 (0.002)	0.064 (0.0025)	0.075 (0.003)	0.064 (0.0025)	0.05 (0.002)	0.038 (0.0015)	0.025 (0.001)	C6
S42020, S42023	30 (100)	0.038 (0.0015)	0.05 (0.002)	0.064 (0.0025)	0.05 (0.002)	0.038 (0.0015)	0.025 (0.001)	0.025 (0.001)	M2, M3
	99 (325)	0.038 (0.0015)	0.05 (0.002)	0.064 (0.0025)	0.05 (0.002)	0.038 (0.0015)	0.025 (0.001)	0.025 (0.001)	C6
S44020, S44023	23 (75)	0.025 (0.001)	0.038 (0.0015)	0.051 (0.002)	0.05 (0.002)	0.038 (0.0015)	0.025 (0.001)	0.025 (0.001)	M2, M3
	76 (250)	0.025 (0.001)	0.038 (0.0015)	0.051 (0.002)	0.05 (0.002)	0.038 (0.0015)	0.025 (0.001)	0.025 (0.001)	C6
Austenitic alloys									
S20300, S30300, S30310, S30360	30 (100)	0.038 (0.0015)	0.05 (0.002)	0.064 (0.0025)	0.05 (0.002)	0.038 (0.0015)	0.025 (0.001)	0.025 (0.001)	M2, M3
	99 (325)	0.038 (0.0015)	0.05 (0.002)	0.064 (0.0025)	0.05 (0.002)	0.038 (0.0015)	0.025 (0.001)	0.025 (0.001)	C6
S30323, S30330, S30345, S30431, S31620, S34720, S34723	24 (80)	0.038 (0.0015)	0.05 (0.002)	0.05 (0.002)	0.05 (0.002)	0.038 (0.0015)	0.025 (0.001)	0.025 (0.001)	M2, M3
	91 (300)	0.038 (0.0015)	0.05 (0.002)	0.05 (0.002)	0.05 (0.002)	0.038 (0.0015)	0.025 (0.001)	0.025 (0.001)	C2
Non-free-machining alloys									
Ferritic alloys									
S40500, S40900, S43000, S43400	27 (90)	0.025 (0.001)	0.038 (0.0015)	0.05 (0.002)	0.05 (0.002)	0.038 (0.0015)	0.038 (0.0015)	0.025 (0.001)	M2, M3
	99 (325)	0.025 (0.001)	0.038 (0.0015)	0.05 (0.002)	0.05 (0.002)	0.038 (0.0015)	0.038 (0.0015)	0.025 (0.001)	C6
S44200, S44300, S44400, S44600	24 (80)	0.025 (0.001)	0.038 (0.0015)	0.05 (0.002)	0.05 (0.002)	0.038 (0.0015)	0.038 (0.0015)	0.025 (0.001)	M2, M3
	91 (300)	0.025 (0.001)	0.038 (0.0015)	0.05 (0.002)	0.05 (0.002)	0.038 (0.0015)	0.038 (0.0015)	0.025 (0.001)	C6
Martensitic alloys									
S40300, S41000	27 (90)	0.038 (0.0015)	0.05 (0.002)	0.064 (0.0025)	0.05 (0.002)	0.05 (0.002)	0.038 (0.0015)	0.025 (0.001)	M2, M3
	99 (325)	0.038 (0.0015)	0.05 (0.002)	0.064 (0.0025)	0.05 (0.002)	0.05 (0.002)	0.038 (0.0015)	0.025 (0.001)	C6
S41400, S42000, S42010, S43100	23 (75)	0.025 (0.001)	0.038 (0.001)5	0.05 (0.002)	0.05 (0.002)	0.038 (0.0015)	0.038 (0.0015)	0.025 (0.001)	M2, M3
	84 (275)	0.025 (0.001)	0.038 (0.0015)	0.05 (0.002)	0.05 (0.002)	0.038 (0.0015)	0.038 (0.0015)	0.025 (0.001)	C6
S44002, S44003, S44004	15 (50)	0.025 (0.001)	0.038 (0.0015)	0.05 (0.002)	0.05 (0.002)	0.038 (0.0015)	0.038 (0.0015)	0.025 (0.001)	M2, M3
	61 (200)	0.025 (0.001)	0.038 (0.0015)	0.05 (0.002)	0.05 (0.002)	0.038 (0.0015)	0.038 (0.0015)	0.025 (0.001)	C6
Austenitic alloys									
S20100, S30100, S30200, S30400, S30403, S30430, S30500, S31600, S31603, S32100, S34700, S38400	23 (75)	0.038 (0.0015)	0.038 (0.0015)	0.05 (0.002)	0.05 (0.002)	0.038 (0.0015)	0.025 (0.001)	0.025 (0.001)	M2, M3
	84 (275)	0.038 (0.0015)	0.038 (0.0015)	0.05 (0.002)	0.05 (0.002)	0.038 (0.0015)	0.025 (0.001)	0.025 (0.001)	C2
S30900, S30908, S31000, S31008, S31700, S31703	21 (70)	0.038 (0.0015)	0.038 (0.0015)	0.05 (0.002)	0.05 (0.002)	0.038 (0.0015)	0.038 (0.0015)	0.025 (0.001)	M2, M3
	76 (250)	0.038 (0.0015)	0.038 (0.0015)	0.05 (0.002)	0.05 (0.002)	0.038 (0.0015)	0.038 (0.0015)	0.025 (0.001)	C2
S20910, S21904, S24100, S28200, S30452, N08020	12 (40)	0.025 (0.001)	0.038 (0.0015)	0.038 (0.0015)	0.038 (0.0015)	0.038 (0.0015)	0.025 (0.001)	0.025 (0.001)	M42, T15
	46 (150)	0.025 (0.001)	0.038 (0.0015)	0.038 (0.0015)	0.038 (0.0015)	0.038 (0.0015)	0.025 (0.001)	0.025 (0.001)	C2
Duplex alloys									
S31803, S32550, S32900, S32950	21 (70)	0.038 (0.0015)	0.038 (0.0015)	0.05 (0.002)	0.05 (0.002)	0.038 (0.0015)	0.038 (0.0015)	0.025 (0.001)	M2, M3
	76 (250)	0.038 (0.0015)	0.038 (0.0015)	0.05 (0.002)	0.05 (0.002)	0.038 (0.0015)	0.038 (0.0015)	0.025 (0.001)	C2
Precipitation-hardenable alloys(a)									
S15500, S17400, S17700, S45000	20 (65)	0.025 (0.001)	0.038 (0.0015)	0.05 (0.002)	0.038 (0.0015)	0.025 (0.001)	0.025 (0.001)	0.013 (0.0005)	M42, T15
	61 (200)	0.025 (0.001)	0.038 (0.0015)	0.05 (0.002)	0.038 (0.0015)	0.025 (0.001)	0.025 (0.001)	0.013 (0.0005)	C2
S13800, S35000, S35500, S45500	15 (50)	0.025 (0.001)	0.038 (0.0015)	0.05 (0.002)	0.038 (0.0015)	0.025 (0.001)	0.025 (0.001)	0.013 (0.0005)	M42, T15
	53 (175)	0.025 (0.001)	0.038 (0.0015)	0.05 (0.002)	0.038 (0.0015)	0.025 (0.001)	0.025 (0.001)	0.013 (0.0005)	C2
S66286	14 (45)	0.025 (0.001)	0.038 (0.0015)	0.05 (0.002)	0.038 (0.0015)	0.025 (0.001)	0.025 (0.001)	0.013 (0.0005)	M42, T15
	49 (160)	0.025 (0.001)	0.038 (0.0015)	0.05 (0.002)	0.038 (0.0015)	0.025 (0.001)	0.025 (0.001)	0.013 (0.0005)	C2

(a) All machining parameters given are for material in the annealed condition (140-270 HB) except the precipitation-hardenable grades, which are solution treated (150-325 HB) or equalized and overtempered for S35000 and S35500. For material heat treated or cold drawn to hardnesses higher than their normal annealed or softest level, best results are obtained by reducing speeds by approximately 10% to as much as 60% at the higher hardnesses. Premium high-speed steel or carbide tooling may also be required to cut high-hardness material. (b) Any premium high-speed steel (T15, M33, M41-47) can be used where the designated tool material is T15, M42. (c) Tool widths of 1.6-13 mm (1/16-1/2 in.) are for cutoff tools and 25-50 mm (1-2 in.) for form tools. Source: Ref 38, 52

control the chips, and they may require increased side clearance angles to prevent rubbing and localized work hardening.

The non-free-machining stainless steels tend to produce long, stringy chips that can be very troublesome. This difficulty can be alleviated by using chip curlers or chip breakers that, in addition to controlling long chips, reduce friction on the cutting edge of the tool. Chip breakers or curlers for the free-machining stainless steels do not need to be as deep as those for the non-free-machining alloys. Otherwise, the depth of cut and the feed rate usually govern the width and depth of the curler or breaker. Heavier chips require deeper curlers or breakers, but they must be ground without weakening the cutting edge. If a chip curler or breaker cannot be ground into the tool, it is advisable to have a steep top rake angle.

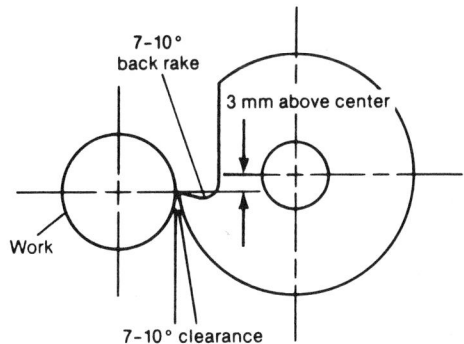

Fig. 28 Suggested geometries for circular cutoff tools used on stainless steels

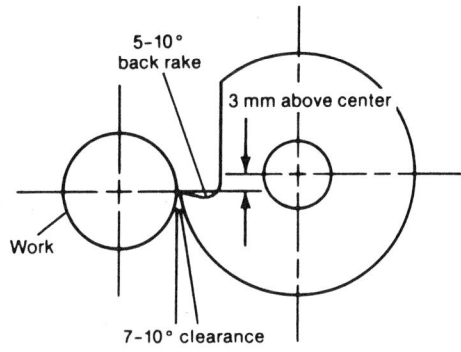

Fig. 29 Suggested geometries for circular form tools used on stainless steels

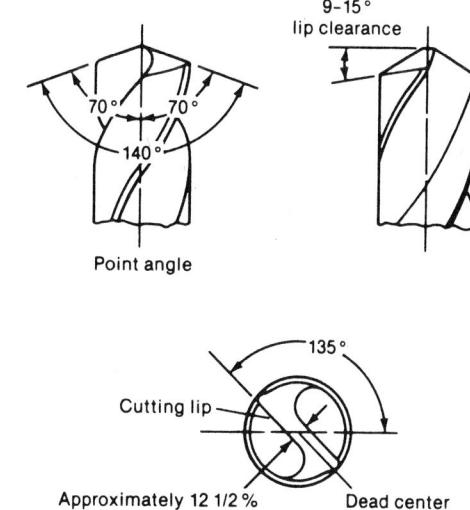

Fig. 30 Suggested geometries for drills used on stainless steels

Carbide tools can be used in single-point turning operations and will allow higher speeds than high-speed steel tools. However, carbide tooling requires even greater attention to the rigidity of the tooling and the workpiece, and interrupted cuts should be avoided.

Cutoff Tools. Either blade-type or circular cutoff tools are used for stainless steel applications. Blade-type tools usually have sufficient bevel for side clearance, that is, 3° minimum, but may need greater clearance for deep cuts. In addition, they should be ground to provide for top rake and front clearance. The front clearance angle is 7 to 10°. A similar angle is used for the top rake, or a radius or shallow concavity can be ground instead. The end cutting edge angle can range from less than 5 to 15°, with the angle decreasing for larger-diameter material.

Angles for circular cutoff tools are similar to those for blade-type tools, including a top rake angle of 7 to 10° (Fig. 28). Circular cutoff tools are more rigid than the blade-type and can withstand more shock. Therefore, they may be preferred for automatic screw machine operations in which they are fed into drilled or threaded holes. Because of their size, they also dissipate heat better.

Carbide-tip cutoff tools can be used. However, shock loading from interrupted cuts must be taken into consideration when selecting the carbide.

Form tools are usually dovetail or circular. The speeds and feeds for form tools are influenced by the width of the tool in relation to the diameter of the bar, the amount of overhang, and the contour or shape of the tool. Generally, the width of the form tool should not exceed $1\frac{1}{2}$ times the diameter of the workpiece; otherwise, chatter may be a problem.

Dovetail form tools should be designed with a front clearance angle of 7 to 10° and should be ground with a top rake angle of 5 to 10°. Angles for circular form tools are similar (Fig. 29). Higher rake angles within the 5 to 10° range can be used for roughing operations and lower rake angles for finishing. The design of the tool should incorporate sufficient side clearance or relief angles, typically 1 to 5° depending on the depth of cut, to prevent rubbing and localized heat buildup, particularly during rough forming. It may also be necessary to round corners. A finish form or shave tool may be necessary to obtain the final shape, especially for deep or intricate cuts.

Carbide-tip tooling can be used for forming operations. However, as with cutoff tools, shock loading from interrupted cuts must be taken into consideration.

A shaving tool can be used to obtain optimum machined surface finish or close tolerances on formed parts. Shaving tools remove metal with a tangential rather than a radial cut, with the workpiece supported by integral rollers. Usually a thin layer of metal (approximately 0.13 to 0.25 mm, or 0.005 to 0.010 in.) is removed at relatively high speeds. The tool must have a very smooth finish on the cutting edge because the finish of the tool will influence the finish of the part. A clearance angle of about 10° is normally needed.

Drilling

In any drilling operation, the following factors are important:

- Work must be kept clean and chips removed frequently because dirt and chips act as an abrasive to dull the drill.
- Drills must be correctly ground.
- Drills must be properly aligned and the work firmly supported.
- A stream of cutting fluid must be properly directed at the hole.
- Drills should be chucked for the shortest drilling length to avoid whipping or flexing, which may break drills or cause inaccurate work.
- Heavier feeds and lower speeds may be necessary to reduce or eliminate work hardening.

When working with stainless steels, particularly the austenitic alloys, it is advisable to use a sharp three-cornered punch rather than a prick punch to avoid work hardening the material at the mark. Drilling templates or guides may also be helpful in locating the mark.

To relieve chip packing and congestion, drills must occasionally be backed out. The general rule is to drill to a depth of three to four times the diameter of the drill for the first bite, one or two diameters for the second bite, and around one diameter for each of the subsequent bites. A groove ground parallel to the cutting edge in the flute for chip clearance will allow deeper holes to be drilled per bite, particularly with larger-size drills. The groove breaks up the chip for easier removal.

Drills should not be allowed to dwell during cutting, particularly with austenitic stainless steels. Allowing the drill to dwell or ride causes glazing on the bottom of the hole, which makes restarting difficult. Therefore, when relieving chip congestion, drills must be backed out quickly and reinserted at full speed to avoid glazing.

Drilling Parameters. Drill feed is an important factor in determining the rate of production. Because proper feed increases drill life and production between grinds, it should be carefully selected for each job. Table 5 lists feeds and speeds for drills of various sizes.

Small-Diameter Drills. Procedures used with large or normal-size drills will not always prove successful for small-diameter drills, that is, 1.8 mm (0.070 in.) and under. These very small drills are subject to deflection, both torsional and longitudinal, because of their length in relation to their diameter. In addition, the web on small drills is proportionally heavier than on large drills. This thicker web adds the strength needed for the required work pressure, but it decreases chip clearance. Therefore, the depth of each bite may have to be reduced. All small-diameter drilling is actually deep-hole drilling; therefore, careful resharpening, frequent and adequate chip removal, and feeds and speeds that are properly adjusted to the strength and load-carrying capacity of the drill are very important. Good small-hole drilling is dependent on feeds that produce chips instead of powder.

Grinding of Drills. It is especially important to grind drills correctly. Figure 30 shows suggested geometries for high-speed steel drills to be used with stainless steels. The point angle should be 140°, although a smaller angle can be used for easier-to-machine alloys. A larger angle produces a more easily removed chip when drilling hard or tough alloys.

Table 5 Nominal drilling parameters for wrought stainless steels
Depending on actual machining conditions, the optimum parameters may be higher or lower than those given.

UNS designation	Speed (a), m/min (sfm)	Feed, mm/rev (in./rev), at a nominal hole diameter of:							Tool material(a)
		1.6 mm (1/16 in.)	3.2 mm (1/8 in.)	6.4 mm (1/4 in.)	13 mm (1/2 in.)	25 mm (1 in.)	38 mm (1½ in.)	50 mm (2 in.)	
Free-machining alloys									
Ferritic alloys									
S18235, S43020, S43023	46 (150)	0.025 (0.001)	0.075 (0.003)	0.15 (0.006)	0.25 (0.010)	0.43 (0.017)	0.53 (0.021)	0.635 (0.025)	M1, M7, M10
S18200	49 (160)	0.025 (0.001)	0.075 (0.003)	0.15 (0.006)	0.25 (0.010)	0.43 (0.017)	0.53 (0.021)	0.635 (0.025)	M1, M7, M10
Martensitic alloys									
S41600, S41610, S41623	40 (130)	0.025 (0.001)	0.075 (0.003)	0.15 (0.006)	0.25 (0.010)	0.43 (0.017)	0.53 (0.021)	0.635 (0.025)	M1, M7, M10
S42020, S42023	26 (85)	0.025 (0.001)	0.075 (0.003)	0.15 (0.006)	0.25 (0.010)	0.43 (0.017)	0.53 (0.021)	0.635 (0.025)	M1, M7, M10
S44020, S44023	18 (60)	0.025 (0.001)	0.075 (0.003)	0.15 (0.006)	0.25 (0.010)	0.43 (0.017)	0.53 (0.021)	0.635 (0.025)	M1, M7, M10
Austenitic alloys									
S20300, S30300, S30310, S30360	30 (100)	0.025 (0.001)	0.075 (0.003)	0.15 (0.006)	0.25 (0.010)	0.43 (0.017)	0.53 (0.021)	0.635 (0.025)	M1, M7, M10
S30323, S30330, S30345, S30431, S31620, S34720, S34723	23 (75)	0.025 (0.001)	0.05 (0.002)	0.10 (0.004)	0.175 (0.007)	0.30 (0.012)	0.38 (0.015)	0.46 (0.018)	M1, M7, M10
Non-free-machining alloys									
Ferritic alloys									
S40500, S40900, S43000, S43400	18-21 (60-70)	0.025 (0.001)	0.05 (0.002)	0.10 (0.004)	0.175 (0.007)	0.30 (0.012)	0.38 (0.015)	0.46 (0.018)	M1, M7, M10
S44200, S44300, S44400, S44600	15-20 (50-65)	0.025 (0.001)	0.05 (0.002)	0.10 (0.004)	0.175 (0.007)	0.30 (0.012)	0.38 (0.015)	0.46 (0.018)	M1, M7, M10
Martensitic alloys									
S40300, S41000	18-21 (60-70)	0.025 (0.001)	0.075 (0.003)	0.15 (0.006)	0.25 (0.010)	0.41 (0.016)	0.53 (0.021)	0.635 (0.025)	M1, M7, M10
S41400, S42000, S42010, S43100	15-18 (50-60)	0.025 (0.001)	0.075 (0.003)	0.15 (0.006)	0.25 (0.010)	0.41 (0.016)	0.53 (0.021)	0.635 (0.025)	M1, M7, M10
S44002, S44003, S44004	12-15 (40-50)	0.025 (0.001)	0.075 (0.003)	0.15 (0.006)	0.25 (0.010)	0.41 (0.016)	0.53 (0.021)	0.635 (0.025)	M1, M7, M10
Austenitic alloys									
S20100, S30100, S30200, S30400, S30403, S30430, S30500, S31600, S31603, S32100, S34700, S38400	15-18 (50-60)	0.025 (0.001)	0.05 (0.002)	0.10 (0.004)	0.175 (0.007)	0.30 (0.012)	0.38 (0.015)	0.46 (0.018)	M1, M7, M10
S30900, S30908, S31000, S31008, S31700, S31703	12-15 (40-50)	0.025 (0.001)	0.05 (0.002)	0.10 (0.004)	0.175 (0.007)	0.30 (0.012)	0.38 (0.015)	0.46 (0.018)	M1, M7, M10
S20910, S21904, S24100, S28200, S30452, N08020	9-14 (30-45)	0.025 (0.001)	0.05 (0.002)	0.10 (0.004)	0.175 (0.007)	0.30 (0.012)	0.38 (0.015)	0.46 (0.018)	M42, T15(b)
Duplex alloys									
S31803, S32550, S32900, S32950	12-15 (40-50)	0.025 (0.001)	0.05 (0.002)	0.10 (0.004)	0.175 (0.007)	0.30 (0.012)	0.38 (0.015)	0.46 (0.018)	M1, M7, M10
Precipitation-hardenable alloys									
S15500, S17400, S17700, S45000	15-18 (50-60)	0.025 (0.001)	0.05 (0.002)	0.10 (0.004)	0.175 (0.007)	0.25 (0.010)	0.30 (0.012)	0.38 (0.015)	M42, T15(b)
S13800, S35000, S35500, S45500	12-15 (40-50)	0.025 (0.001)	0.05 (0.002)	0.10 (0.004)	0.175 (0.007)	0.25 (0.010)	0.30 (0.012)	0.38 (0.015)	M42, T15(b)
S66286	8-12 (25-40)	0.025 (0.001)	0.05 (0.002)	0.10 (0.004)	0.175 (0.007)	0.25 (0.010)	0.30 (0.012)	0.38 (0.015)	M42, T15(b)

(a) All speeds given are for material in the annealed condition (140-270 HB) except for the precipitation-hardenable grades, which are solution treated (150-325 HB) or equalized and overtempered for S35000 and S35500. For material heat treated or cold drawn to hardnesses higher than their normal annealed or softest level, best results are obtained by reducing speeds by approximately 25% to as much as 75% depending on hardness. Premium high-speed steel or carbide drills may also be necessary at the higher hardnesses. (b) Any premium high-speed steel (T15, M33, M41-47) can be used where the designated tool material is T15, M42. Source: Ref 38, 52

The lip clearance should be between 9 and 15°, and the two cutting edges must be equal in length and angle. The web thickness at the point should be about 12.5% of the drill diameter or less. A thinner web reduces feed pressure, heat generation, and glazing or work hardening of the bottom of the hole. Grinding fixtures should be used when regrinding drills. For best results in grinding high-speed steel drills, medium-grain, soft-grade dry wheels should be used. Blueing or burning is to be avoided, as is quenching. Quenching will often check or crack the drill if it has been overheated.

Special Drills. Drills should be chucked for the shortest drilling length. Some jobs, however, require exceptionally deep drilled holes where the depth of the hole is eight to ten times the diameter. In such cases, short chucking is impossible, and special drills known as crankshaft hole drills may be useful. These drills were originally designed for drilling oil holes in forged crankshafts and connecting rods, but they have found widespread use in drilling deep holes. They are made with a very heavy web and a higher spiral or helix angle to aid in chip removal. They usually have a notched-point-type of web thinning, which is done on a sharp-cornered hard grinding wheel.

A cotter pin drill should be used to drill small cross holes in the heads of bolts, screws, pins, and so on. Like a crankshaft hole drill, it is a more heavily constructed drill that withstands abnormal strains and has a faster or higher helix angle to aid in chip removal.

Tapping

Whenever possible, it is desirable to use free-machining grades for tapping, especially when blind holes are specified, to minimize the difficulty of removing and disposing of chips. The gummy, stringy chips resulting from the non-free-machining grades of stainless steel are a source of difficulty in tapping.

In tapping all grades of stainless steel, especially the non-free-machining grades:

- Use taps that are as large as permissible in diameter (high side of the tolerance).
- Keep the thread pitch as fine as possible, because the finer the pitch, the less metal removed per tooth.

- Keep the percentage of full thread as low as permissible (60 to 75% is a preferred range, but where the depth of the tapped hole exceeds twice the diameter of the tap, it is economical to use only 50% thread).
- Use a flood of cutting oil (under pressure of at least 35 kPa, or 5 psi, when tapping blind holes).

The difficulties encountered in tapping stainless steel are often a result of work-hardened surfaces caused by previous drilling or reaming operations. Thus, when tapping problems arise, an investigation of the drilling and reaming conditions is recommended. Chips must be cut in either drilling or reaming; consequently, when drills or reamers are permitted to burnish rather than cut, surfaces become work hardened. The degree of work hardening varies among the different grades of stainless steel; the austenitic grades are the most susceptible.

Tap Material and Design. High-speed steel taps are nearly always used for tapping stainless steel. Chip removal is important when tapping

tight-fitting, close-tolerance (class 3) threads, and the flutes should not be too shallow or the lands too wide.

Consideration must also be given to the number of flutes on the tap. With small holes, a tap with four flutes is more likely to produce chip congestion than one with fewer flutes. Therefore, general practice is to use a tap with fewer flutes as the size of the hole decreases. For cutting class 3 threads, taps should have two flutes for holes up to size No. 6 (5.2 mm, or 0.204 in., in diameter). Three-flute taps are satisfactory for holes between 5.2 and 13 mm (0.204 and ½ in.) in diameter. Three-flute taps reduce the possibility of cutting over size but provide less chip clearance than two-flute taps. Holes larger than 13 mm (½ in.) in diameter are tapped with four-flute taps.

Types. Heavy-duty spiral-point and heavy-duty spiral-flute taps are generally used for the tapping of stainless steel alloys (Fig. 31). Spiral-point taps push the chips ahead of the tap and should not be used for tapping blind holes unless

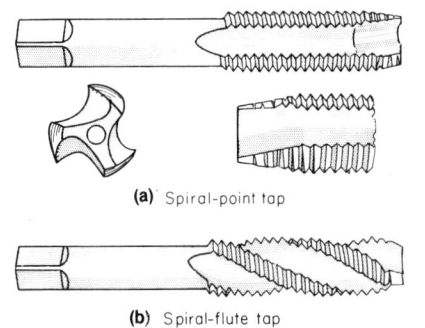

(a) Spiral-point tap

(b) Spiral-flute tap

Fig. 31 Two basic styles of solid taps used on stainless steels

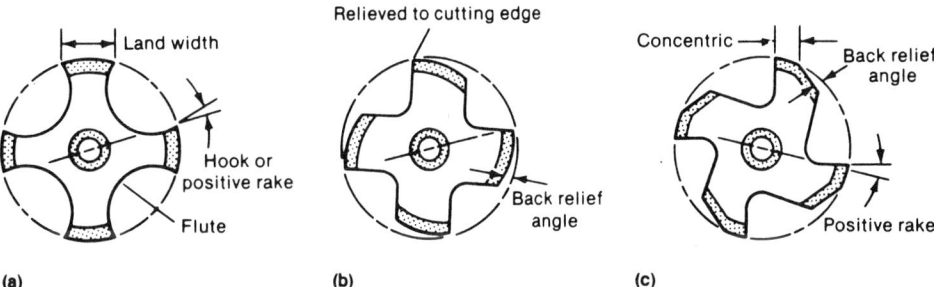

Fig. 32 Relief of lands on taps. (a) Lands concentric with hole. (b) Lands fully eccentric with hole, with full relief. (c) Lands partly concentric with hole, but with final relief

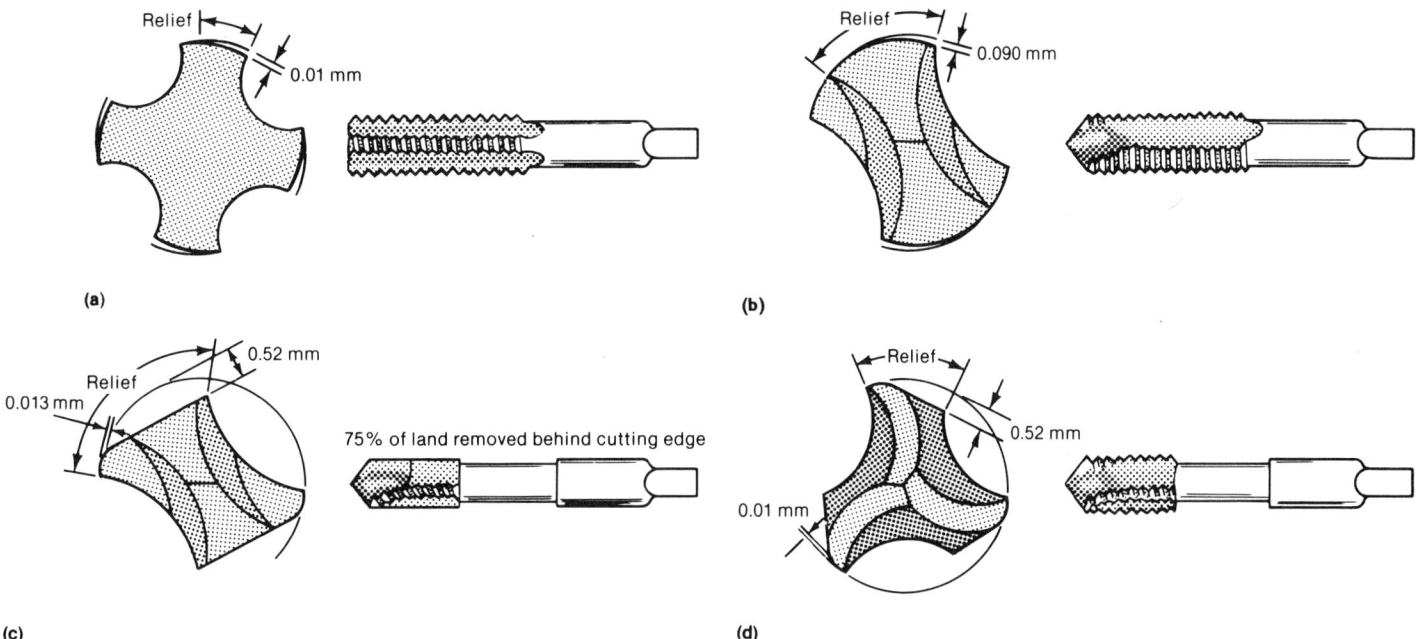

Fig. 33 Progressive modification of tap design for tapping ¼-32 threads in stainless steel valve bonnets. (a) Original design: four-flute plug top with conventional relief. Life: 2 holes. (b) Changed to two-flute tap with spiral point and 70% land relief. Life: 8 holes. (c) Two-flute tap improved by full relief and removal of all but 17 threads. Life: 264 holes. (d) Final design: three-flute tap with full relief. Life: 3000 holes. Tap shown in (a) underwent five revisions before final design (d), which produced a 1500-fold increase in tool life in tapping 6 mm (¼ in.) diam holes in valve bonnets of soft austenitic stainless steels (S30400, S31600, and N08330). Two intermediate redesigns are shown in (b) and (c). Taps of all designs were of M2 high-speed steel and had standard lead and hook angles.

Table 6 Nominal tapping parameters for wrought stainless steels
Depending on actual machining conditions, optimum parameters may be higher or lower than those given.

UNS designation	Speed(a), m/min (sfm), at a pitch (threads per 25 mm, or 1 in.) of:				Tool material(b)
	≤7	8-15	16-24	>24	
Free-machining alloys					
Ferritic alloys					
S43020, S18235, S43023	6 (20)	9 (30)	14 (45)	15 (50)	M1, M7, M10
S18200	6 (20)	9 (30)	14 (45)	15 (50)	M1, M7, M10
Martensitic alloys					
S41600, S41610, S41623	6 (20)	9 (30)	14 (45)	15 (50)	M1, M7, M10
S42020, S42023	5 (15)	8 (25)	11 (35)	12 (40)	M1, M7, M10
S44020, S44023	4 (12)	5.5 (18)	6.7 (22)	8 (25)	M1, M7, M10
Austenitic alloys					
S20300, S30300, S30310, S30360	5 (15)	8 (25)	11 (35)	12 (40)	M1, M7, M10
S30323, S30330, S30345, S30431, S31620, S34720, S34723	4 (12)	6 (20)	9 (30)	11 (35)	M1, M7, M10
Non-free-machining alloys					
Ferritic alloys					
S40500, S40900, S43000, S43400	5 (15)	8 (25)	11 (35)	12 (40)	M1, M7, M10
S44200, S44300, S44400, S44600	4 (12)	6 (20)	9 (30)	11 (35)	M1, M7, M10
Martensitic alloys					
S40300, S41000	5 (15)	8 (25)	11 (35)	12 (40)	M1, M7, M10
S41400, S42000, S42010, S43100	4 (12)	5.5 (18)	8 (25)	9 (30)	M1, M7, M10
S44002, S44003, S44004	3 (10)	4 (12)	5 (16)	6 (20)	Nitrided M1, M7, M10
Austenitic alloys					
S20100, S30100, S30200, S30400, S30403, S30430, S30500, S31600, S31603, S32100, S34700, S38400	4 (12)	5.5 (18)	6.7 (22)	8 (25)	M1, M7, M10
S30900, S30908, S31000, S31008, S31700, S31703	4 (12)	4.5 (15)	6 (20)	7 (23)	M1, M7, M10
S20910, S21904, S24100, S28200, S30452, N08020	3 (10)	4 (12)	5 (16)	6 (20)	Nitrided M1, M7, M10
Duplex alloys					
S31803, S32550, S32900, S32950	4 (12)	4.5 (15)	6 (20)	7 (23)	M1, M7, M10
Precipitation-hardenable alloys					
S15500, S17400, S17700, S45000	4 (12)	5.5 (18)	6.7 (22)	8 (25)	M1, M7, M10
S13800, S35000, S35500, S45500	3 (10)	4.5 (15)	6 (20)	6.7 (22)	M1, M7, M10
S66286	2 (8)	4 (12)	5.5 (18)	6 (20)	Nitrided M1, M7, M10

(a) All speeds given are for tapping 65-75% threads in shallow through holes. Speeds should be reduced when tapping blind holes, deep holes, or higher percentage of thread. All speeds are for material in the annealed condition (140-270 HB) except the precipitation-hardenable grades, which are solution treated (150-325 HB) or equalized and overtempered for S35000 and S35500. For material heat treated or cold drawn to hardnesses higher than the annealed or softest level, best results are obtained by reducing speeds by approximately 25% to as much as 60% depending on hardness. (b) Nitrided taps may be necessary for some grades at the higher hardness levels. Source: Ref 38, 52

there is sufficient untapped depth to accommodate the chips at the bottom of the hole. Spiral-flute taps pull the chips from the tapped hole and can be used for tapping either blind or through holes. Straight-flute taps are used for holes larger than 13 mm ($\frac{1}{2}$ in.) in diameter.

Tap Geometry. For austenitic alloys, a hook grind is best. The hook angle is commonly 15 to 20° for austenitic alloys with hardnesses from 135 to 275 HB. Occasionally, because of a combination of factors on certain work, the hook grind will not produce satisfactory results. In such cases, an interrupted-thread tap with an uneven number of flutes may be desirable because it requires 40 to 50% less power than regular taps (this may be important when the tapping machine lacks power).

For ferritic, martensitic, and precipitation-hardenable alloys, the common rake angles are 8 to 12° for alloys with a hardness of 135 to 275 HB and 0 to 5° for alloys with a hardness of 275 to 325 HB. Above 325 HB, 0° is the common rake angle for the martensitic and precipitation-hardenable alloys.

The problem of roughness on the back face of the thread can sometimes be overcome by grinding the heel of the lands so that the bearing area is reduced. This back relief prevents tearing of the threads when the tap is backed out. Roughness can also be caused by insufficient rake or hook angle.

Back relief (or relieving the thread) may either have the lands fully eccentric with the hole or may have the lands partly concentric with the hole (Fig. 32). Suggested back relief angles (Fig. 32) are 10° for austenitic alloys with hardnesses of 135 to 275 HB and 8° for ferritic, martensitic, and precipitation-hardenable alloys with hardnesses of 135 to 325 HB. Back relief is approximately 5° for deep holes and 6 to 8° for the martensitic and precipitation-hardenable alloys with hardnesses of 325 to 425 HB.

Example: Progressive Modification of Tap Design for Soft Austenitic Stainless. As the result of a series of modifications in tap design, the tool life of taps used to thread S30400 and S31600 austenitic stainless steels on a single-spindle automatic machine was extended from 2 to 3000 holes per tap. Before the final (and most satisfactory) tap design was developed, tap breakage had been caused by the jamming of chips in the lands of the tap and by the tapping of holes previously work hardened in a drilling operation. In addition, the generation of excessive heat during tapping had caused breakdown of the tap teeth at the cutting tips.

The two austenitic stainless grades tapped were in the annealed condition, with a hardness of 208 HB or less. The application consisted of drilling and tapping 6 mm ($\frac{1}{4}$ in.) diameter holes in a valve bonnet. Tap size was $\frac{1}{4}$-32. All parts were required to have a class 3 fit on 80% of the threads, and the threads had to be smooth and free of tear marks.

The final tap design was achieved in six steps. Taps of all six designs were made of grade M2 high-speed steel and received no special surface treatment. The original tap and three of the redesigns, including the final one, are illustrated in Fig. 33.

In the initial setup, a standard four-flute, conventionally relieved, ground plug tap (Fig. 33a) was used. With two machine speeds available, tapping was performed at 275 rev/min (~5.5 m/min, or 18 sfm), and the tap was withdrawn at a speed of 610 rev/min (~12 m/min, or 40 sfm). Thus, the ratio of withdrawal speed to threading speed was 2.2:1. For lubrication, a mineral-based oil containing fatty oils and active sulfur was used; its viscosity was similar to that of SAE 20 oil. Under these conditions, not more than two holes could be tapped before heavy chips became packed in the flutes of the tap, which resulted in tap breakage.

Because greater chip relief was obviously required, a two-flute tap (Fig. 33b) was tried. This tap, which provided a land that was larger and stronger in cross section, was ground to a spiral point that afforded a path for chip disposal. Tapping was performed with this two-flute tap at the same speeds and feeds and with the same cutting oil that had been used with the original four-flute taps. This tap resulted in more rubbing. Galling occurred during withdrawal of the tap at high speed, and chips jammed the flutes, restricting flow of the cutting fluid.

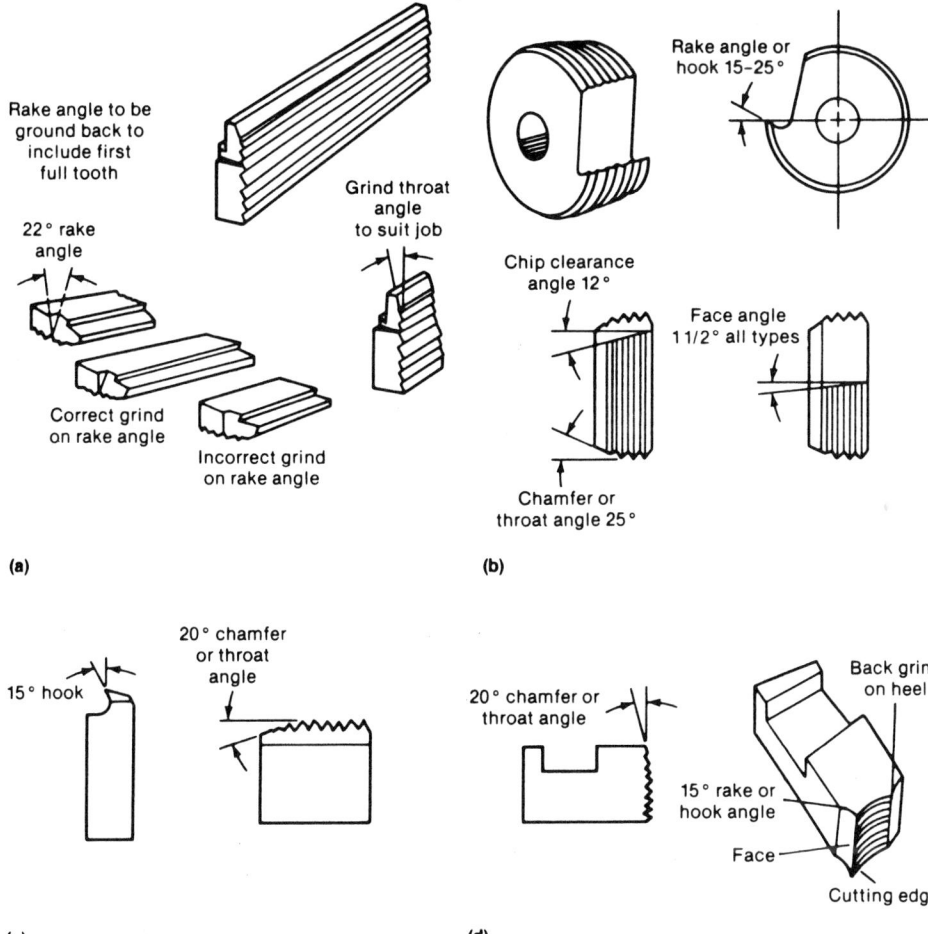

Fig. 34 Suggested geometries of thread chasers used for stainless steels. (a) Tangent-type chaser. (b) Circular-type chaser. (c) Insert-type chaser. (d) Radial-type chaser

The two-flute tap was modified to full relief, which allowed a greater flow of cutting oil around the cutting tips. This modification helped preserve cutting edges, reduced galling, and increased tap life to 22 holes.

Next, to increase the flow of cutting fluid to the tips, all threads to the rear of the 17th tooth (17 being the minimum number of teeth required for threading the part) were removed. Under those conditions, thread quality was improved, and tool life was extended to 85 holes per tap.

The two-flute tap was modified again by removing approximately 75% of the land behind the cutting edge to the depth of the root diameter at the trailing edge of the land (Fig. 33c). This decrease in cutting tool area permitted an increase in the flow of cutting fluid to the cutting edges and reduced the area of the thread drag that occurred when the tap was withdrawn from the hole at high speeds.

The three-flute tap, representing the final improvement in design, incorporated an increase in the number of cutting edges (from two to three), thus providing increased distribution of cutting fluid around each row of cutting edges. Except for its having three flutes (Fig. 33d), it retained the same design as that shown for the two-flute tap.

To reduce the amount of work-hardened metal developed as a result of drilling, drill size was changed from a No. 5 to a No. 6, and a 5.3 mm (0.2087 in.) drill was used to finish the hole before tapping. After producing 3000 holes, the new tap showed little sign of wear. Galling and metal flow at the tips of the stainless steel threads were virtually eliminated. The threads were smooth and were gaged satisfactorily with a class 3 thread gage.

Tapping Parameters and Cutting Fluid. Typical cutting speeds for tapping various stainless steels are listed in Table 6. Proper lubrication also plays an important role in tapping operations. Although the sulfurized oils have proved most successful, specific compositions or ratios of sulfurized oils to paraffin-based oils are required on certain jobs. After the best mixture has been determined, it is equally important that the flow of the cutting fluid to the taps and the work be considered. It is often desirable to use two streams of cutting fluid, one on each side of the tap. The flow should be started before the tap begins to cut and should not be shut off until after the cut is finished.

Die Threading

Thread chasers for self-opening die heads are made of high-speed steel. The standard commer-

cial chasers generally have a satisfactory life when they are kept sharp and correctly ground for the materials cut.

Figure 34 shows suggested geometries of the four main types of thread-cutting tools. The most frequently used chaser for close-tolerance threads is the tangent type (Fig. 34a). It is particularly adaptable for heavy-duty jobs, such as producing long, coarse threads. The tangent-type chaser maintains thread size better on heavy-duty work and provides good life between grinds. Whenever possible, a 20° throat angle should be used. However, where the threads do not run into a shoulder, a 15° throat is better.

The circular type (Fig. 34b) is considered to be the universal thread chaser because it is adaptable to all types of threads and will work equally well on tubing. This type of chaser should generally have a 25° throat angle.

The insert-type chaser (Fig. 34c) is widely used. It produces good threads on non-free-machining alloys at a low cost. A 20° throat angle is usually suitable for this type of chaser.

The radial-type chaser (Fig. 34d) will produce very smooth threads because it is ground to follow the shape or contour of the threaded piece. This type of chaser has been successfully used where extremely fine threads are required when form plunge tools are used with screw machines. Radial chasers typically have a 20° throat angle.

The throat angle or chamfer will vary slightly from the typical geometries given for each of the chasers, based on the type of thread being cut and the grade of stainless steel being machined. In general, it is advisable to use a $1\frac{1}{2}$- to 3-thread chamfer or lead on the throat. This will usually produce a smooth thread with a fine finish and will increase chaser life between grinds. The advantage of using a long throat angle is that each tooth makes a smaller cut and consequently produces cleaner threads. For example, in one case, a 45° throat angle produced a chip approximately 0.46 mm (0.018 in.) thick, while a 15° throat angle produced a chip only 0.17 mm (0.0065 in.) thick.

When threading close to a shoulder where a long throat angle cannot be used, it may be necessary to grind only a $\frac{1}{2}$- or 1-thread chamfer on the chaser. If this short throat angle produces a rough thread, a smooth finish can be obtained by running the chaser over the workpiece a second time, or the thread can be cut in two operations by first taking a rough cut and then finishing with a second cut.

Die-Threading Parameters and Cutting Fluid. Suggestions for cutting speeds are found in Table 7. Regardless of the type of chaser being used, speeds will vary somewhat with the type of thread being cut. Acme threads are usually cut at somewhat slower speeds. Where extremely fine threads are required, it might be desirable to decrease speeds to 1.5 to 4.5 m/min (5 to 15 sfm). In addition, when cutting fine threads, an advantage will be found in diluting heavy sulfurized oil with paraffin oil, generally one part sulfurized oil to five parts paraffin. The oil must be kept clean and free of chips, which could damage the threads.

Percentage of Thread. As with tapping, the percentage of thread being cut influences production rate and cost. Cutting threads with the maximum major diameter and/or minimum pitch diameter allowed for the class of thread involved means that more metal must be removed. This decreases tool life and does not necessarily produce a stronger thread. The blank should be turned to leave the minimum allowable stock.

Thread Rolling

Thread rolling can be done on automatic screw machines and turret lathes. However, the equipment must have sufficient power and rigidity for stainless steels. As discussed previously, stainless steels have high strength and work-hardening rates; therefore, substantial pressure is required to form the threads. These characteristics of stainless steels may also limit the amount of thread that can be formed, and care must be taken to avoid work hardening the surface prior to thread rolling. Despite these cautions, however, thread rolling offers certain advantages. The threads produced are stronger and tougher than cut threads and can be more accurate in size. Generally, the non-free-machining alloys will produce smoother and cleaner threads than the free-machining alloys.

Milling

High-speed steel cutters are used in milling stainless steels, although tooling with carbide inserts can also be used, particularly for alloys that are more difficult to machine. Generally, the smoothest finishes are obtained with helical or spiral cutters running at high speed, particularly for cuts over 19 mm (0.75 in.) wide. Helical cutters cut with a shearing action and thus cut more freely and with less chatter than straight-tooth cutters. Coarse-tooth or heavy-duty cutters work under less stress and permit higher speeds than fine-tooth or light-duty cutters. They also have more space between the teeth to aid in chip disposal.

For heavy, plain milling work, a heavy-duty cutter with a faster, 45° left-hand spiral is preferred. The higher angle allows more teeth to contact the work at the same time. This applies steady pressure on the arbor and spindle, thus reducing chatter. In wide, slab milling, such cutters are particularly necessary to produce smooth finishes and to avoid chatter.

Milling deep slots in stainless steel sometimes presents the problems of chatter, binding, and jamming of wide chips. These difficulties can be eliminated by using a staggered-tooth cutter. Its alternating teeth cut only half of the slot, thus taking a smaller bite and producing a shorter chip. For the end milling of stainless steels, the solid-shank end mill is preferred because of its high strength.

Grinding of Milling Cutters. Figure 35 shows the rake angle, land width, and primary and secondary clearance for high-speed steel cutters. The geometries shown provide sufficient strength and clearance. On cutters up to 100 mm (4 in.) in diameter, the maximum clearance shown in Fig. 35 should be used, remembering that small cutters require a greater clearance angle than large cutters. Sufficient clearance behind the cutting edge

of every tooth is necessary to avoid a rubbing or burnishing action. Excessive vibration may indicate that the cutter has insufficient clearance (rigidity of the tooling and fixtures should also be considered). Hogging-in generally indicates too much rake (or possibly too high a cutting speed).

Milling Parameters and Cutting Fluid. Table 8 lists speeds and feeds for end (peripheral) milling of stainless steels using either high-speed steel or carbide tooling. It may be necessary to vary feeds from the nominal values. If the feed is too light, the tool will burnish the work; if too heavy, tool life will be shortened.

Speeds and feeds also vary for heavy roughing cuts and lighter finishing cuts. For example, a roughing cut would be run with heavier feeds and slower speeds than those used for finishing cuts. Regardless of the type of cut, both work and tool should be flooded with a good sulfurized oil properly diluted with paraffin oil, or preferably a good emulsifiable fluid. Milling generates considerable heat, which must be carried off by the cutting fluid; otherwise, the work will distort and the tool edges will dull or chip rapidly.

Once a milling cut has been started, it should not be stopped unless absolutely necessary because the

Table 7 Nominal die-threading parameters for wrought stainless steels
Depending on actual machining conditions, optimum parameters may be higher or lower than those given.

UNS designation	Speed(a), m/min (sfm), at a pitch (threads per 25 mm, or 1 in.) of:				Tool material
	≤7	8-15	16-24	>24	
Free-machining alloys					
Ferritic alloys					
S18235, S43020, S43023	5-8 (15-25)	8-11 (25-35)	11-14 (35-45)	12-15 (40-50)	M1, M2, M7, M10
S18200	5-8 (15-25)	8-11 (25-35)	11-14 (35-45)	12-15 (40-50)	M1, M2, M7, M10
Martensitic alloys					
S41600, S41610, S41623	5-8 (15-25)	8-11 (25-35)	11-14 (35-45)	12-15 (40-50)	M1, M2, M7, M10
S42020, S42023	3-5 (10-15)	5-8 (15-25)	8-11 (25-35)	11-12 (35-40)	M1, M2, M7, M10
S44020, S44023	2-5 (8-15)	3-6 (10-20)	5-8 (15-25)	8-9 (25-30)	M1, M2, M7, M10
Austenitic alloys					
S20300, S30300, S30310, S30360	3-5 (10-15)	5-8 (15-25)	8-11 (25-35)	11-12 (35-40)	M1, M2, M7, M10
S30323, S30330, S30345, S30431, S31620, S34720, S34723	2-5 (8-15)	4-7 (12-22)	6-9 (20-30)	9-11 (30-35)	M1, M2, M7, M10
Non-free-machining alloys					
Ferritic alloys					
S40500, S40900, S43000, S43400	1.5-5 (5-15)	3-8 (10-25)	6-11 (20-35)	8-12 (25-40)	M1, M2, M7, M10
S44200, S44300, S44400, S44600	1.5-4 (5-12)	2-5 (8-15)	3-6 (10-20)	5-8 (15-25)	M1, M2, M7, M10
Martensitic alloys					
S40300, S41000	1.5-5 (5-15)	3-8 (10-25)	6-11 (20-35)	8-12 (25-40)	M1, M2, M7, M10
S41400, S42000, S42010, S43100	1.5-5 (5-15)	3-6 (10-20)	6-9 (20-30)	8-11 (25-35)	M1, M2, M7, M10
S44002, S44003, S44004	1.5-4 (5-12)	2-5 (8-15)	3-6 (10-20)	5-8 (15-25)	M1, M2, M7, M10
Austenitic alloys					
S20100, S30100, S30200, S30400, S30403, S30430, S30500, S31600, S31603, S32100, S34700, S38400	2-5 (8-15)	3-6 (10-20)	5-8 (15-25)	8-9 (25-30)	M1, M2, M7, M10
S30900, S30908, S31000, S31008, S31700, S31703	1.5-3 (5-10)	2-4 (8-13)	3-5 (10-15)	5-6 (15-20)	M1, M2, M7, M10
S20910, S21904, S24100, S28200, S30452, N08020	1-2 (4-8)	2-3 (6-10)	2-4 (8-12)	3-5 (10-15)	M1, M2, M7, M10
Duplex alloys					
S31803, S32550, S32900, S32950	1.5-3 (5-10)	2-4 (8-13)	3-5 (10-15)	5-6 (15-20)	M1, M2, M7, M10
Precipitation-hardenable alloys					
S15500, S17400, S17700, S45000	1.5-4 (5-12)	2-5 (8-15)	3-6 (10-20)	5-8 (15-25)	M1, M2, M7, M10
S13800, S35000, S35500, S45500	1.5-3 (5-10)	2-4 (8-13)	3-5 (10-15)	5-6 (15-20)	M1, M2, M7, M10
S66286	1-2 (4-8)	2-3 (6-10)	2-4 (8-12)	3-5 (10-15)	M1, M2, M7, M10

(a) All speeds are for material heat treated or cold drawn to low-to-intermediate hardness levels. All speeds should be reduced 20-30% for taper threads.
Source: Ref 38, 52

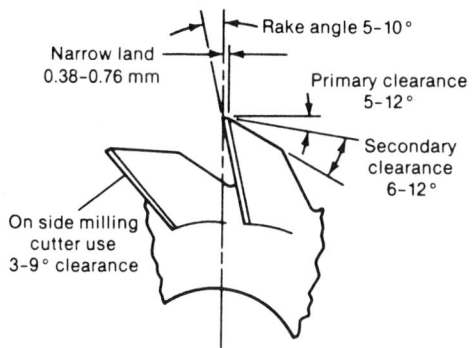

Fig. 35 Suggested geometries of milling cutters used for stainless steels

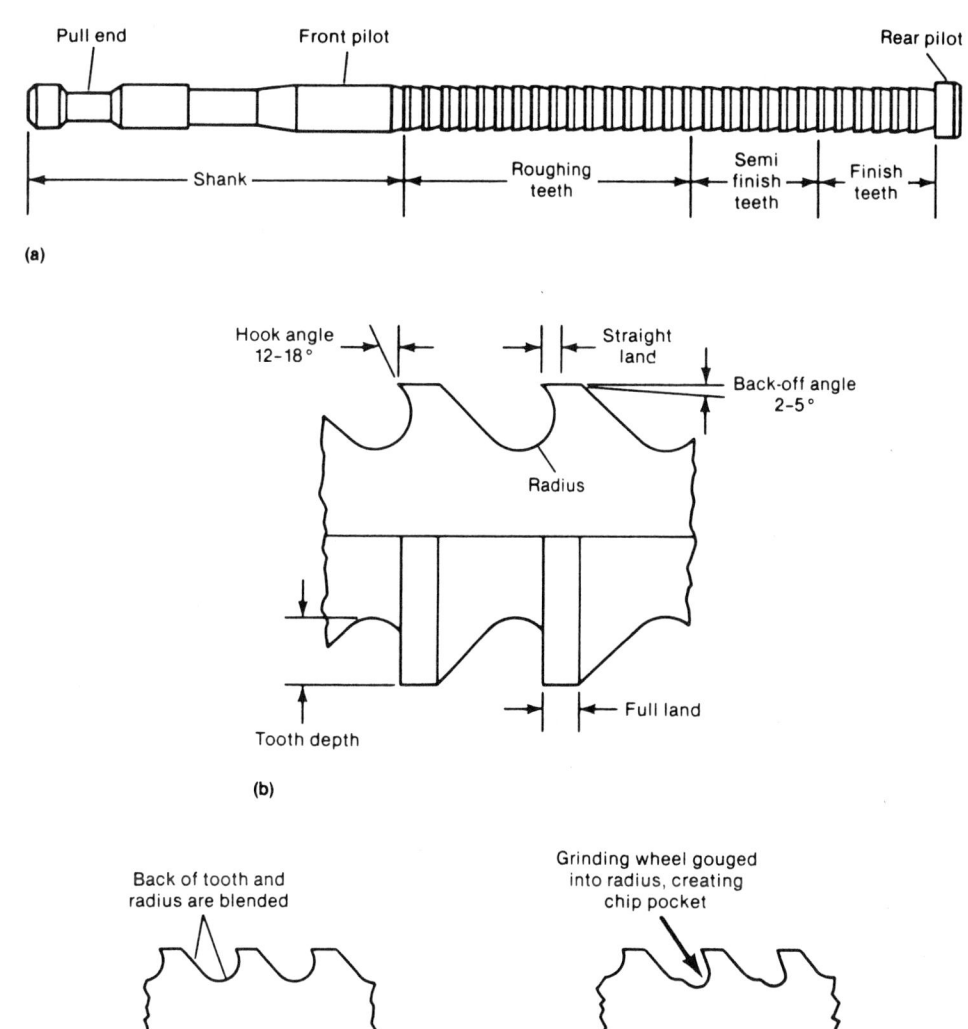

Fig. 36 Typical one-pass internal broaching tool (a), along with suggested geometries (b) and grinding techniques (c)

tool will undercut when starting again. When it becomes necessary to back out, the tool should be placed two or three turns behind the work before starting again. This eliminates the danger of backlash and guards against undercutting.

Broaching

Broaches for stainless alloys are made of high-speed steel. A broach is a simple tool to handle, because the broach manufacturer builds into it the necessary feed and depth of cut by steps from one tooth to another. Basically, a broach can provide a roughing cut, a semifinished cut, a final precision cut, or any combination of these operations (Fig. 36). Some broaches are made with burnishing buttons when a burnished finish is required. Because the form or shape of a broach tooth is unlimited, there is no limit to the shape or contour of broached surfaces.

In designing the radius for the broach, the manufacturer provides maximum tooth strength and a pocket for chips. Depending on the job, the broach manufacturer can also incorporate into the broach such items as side relief (flat broaches), undercut and clearance (spline broaches), and chip breakers (to handle wide chips).

When a broach becomes dull, it should be resharpened only on a broach grinder or returned to the manufacturer for regrinding. For internal broaches, the backoff angle should be held to a minimum, preferably 2° and not more than 5° (Fig. 36). Too much backoff angle will shorten broach life because of size reductions from resharpening.

Any nicks on the cutting edges of the broach will score the surface of the work. Therefore, careful handling is very important.

Broaching Parameters and Cutting Fluid. Table 9 lists nominal feeds and speeds for broaching various stainless steels. Sulfochlorinated oils diluted with paraffin oil, rather than water-soluble oils, are suggested.

When broaching hard (35 HRC) stainless steel, it is necessary to reduce the speed and to use a lubricant with very little thinning. Broaches have been used to cut stock harder than 35 HRC, but the cost is usually prohibitive because the broach dulls rapidly. Where higher hardnesses are required, pieces should first be broached and then heat treated. To remove any light scale and to cor-

rect possible distortion resulting from heat treating, a special broach known as a hard gear broach can be used on machines having sufficient power.

Reaming

The difficulties involved in reaming stainless steel are most often caused by previous operations, particularly with the non-free-machining austenitic alloys. For example, if the feed in drilling is too light, the hole wall can be severely work hardened and can resist cutting by the reamer. It is also important that ample material be left from the previous operation to allow the reamer to get below any work-hardened layer.

Reamer Design. Reamers of straight or spiral-flute design are used for both straight and tapered holes. Spiral-flute reamers are usually preferred because they are less susceptible to chatter, can better

dispose of chips from deep holes, and are capable of producing a better finish.

Recommended design for high-speed steel reamers for all grades of stainless steel at 135 to 425 HB is:

Margin (or land) width, mm (in.)	0.13-0.38 (0.005-0.015)
Chamfer angle, degrees	30-40
Chamfer length, mm (in.)	1.5 ($^1/_{16}$)
Chamfer relief angle, degrees	4-5
Radial rake angle, degrees	3-8
Helix angle, degrees	0-10
Primary relief angle, degrees	4-8

For carbide-tip reamers, margin (land) width should be 0.05 to 0.13 mm (0.002 to 0.005 in.) for reaming all free-machining stainless steels (135 to 425 HB) and non-free-machining martensitic grades up to 52 HRC. For reaming the non-free-machining ferritic and austenitic grades and the precipitation-hardening grades, the margin should be increased to

Table 8 Nominal end (peripheral) milling parameters for wrought stainless steels

Depending on actual machining conditions, optimum parameters may be higher or lower than those given. See Ref 52 for speeds and feeds in face, side, and hollow milling.

UNS designation	Speed(a)(b), m/min (sfm)	Feed, mm/tooth (in./tooth), at a cutter diameter of:				Tool material(a)
		6 mm (¼ in.)	13 mm (½ in.)	19 mm (¾ in.)	25-50 mm (1-2 in.)	
Free-machining alloys						
Ferritic alloys						
S18235, S43020, S43023	43 (140)	0.025 (0.001)	0.05 (0.002)	0.075 (0.003)	0.10 (0.004)	M2, M7
	122 (400)	0.025 (0.001)	0.05 (0.002)	0.13 (0.005)	0.175 (0.007)	C6
S18200	44 (145)	0.05 (0.002)	0.075 (0.003)	0.13 (0.005)	0.15 (0.006)	M2, M7
	125 (410)	0.05 (0.002)	0.075 (0.003)	0.13 (0.005)	0.175 (0.007)	C6
Martensitic alloys						
S41600, S41610, S41623	43 (140)	0.05 (0.002)	0.075 (0.003)	0.13 (0.005)	0.15 (0.006)	M2, M7
	122 (400)	0.05 (0.002)	0.075 (0.003)	0.13 (0.005)	0.175 (0.007)	C6
S42020, S42023	30 (100)	0.05 (0.002)	0.075 (0.003)	0.13 (0.005)	0.15 (0.006)	M2, M7
	91 (300)	0.025 (0.001)	0.075 (0.003)	0.13 (0.005)	0.175 (0.007)	C6
S44020, S44023	26 (85)	0.025 (0.001)	0.05 (0.002)	0.075 (0.003)	0.10 (0.004)	M2, M7
	76 (250)	0.025 (0.001)	0.075 (0.003)	0.13 (0.005)	0.175 (0.007)	C6
Austenitic alloys						
S20300, S30300, S30310, S30360	35 (115)	0.05 (0.002)	0.075 (0.003)	0.13 (0.005)	0.15 (0.006)	M2, M7
	107 (350)	0.025 (0.002)	0.075 (0.003)	0.13 (0.005)	0.15 (0.006)	C2
S30323, S30330, S30345, S30431, S31620, S34720, S34723	30 (100)	0.025 (0.001)	0.05 (0.002)	0.10 (0.004)	0.13 (0.005)	M2, M7
	91 (300)	0.025 (0.001)	0.05 (0.002)	0.10 (0.004)	0.13 (0.005)	C2
Non-free-machining alloys						
Ferritic alloys						
S40500, S40900, S43000, S43400	34 (110)	0.05 (0.002)	0.075 (0.003)	0.13 (0.005)	0.15 (0.006)	M2, M7
	107 (350)	0.05 (0.001)	0.05 (0.002)	0.10 (0.004)	0.15 (0.006)	C6
S44200, S44300, S44400, S44600	30 (100)	0.05 (0.002)	0.075 (0.003)	0.13 (0.005)	0.15 (0.006)	M2, M7
	91 (300)	0.025 (0.001)	0.05 (0.002)	0.10 (0.004)	0.15 (0.006)	C6
Martensitic alloys						
S40300, S41000	34 (110)	0.05 (0.002)	0.075 (0.003)	0.13 (0.005)	0.15 (0.006)	M2, M7
	107 (350)	0.025 (0.001)	0.05 (0.002)	0.10 (0.004)	0.15 (0.006)	C6
S41400, S42000, S42010, S43100	27 (90)	0.025 (0.001)	0.05 (0.002)	0.075 (0.003)	0.10 (0.004)	M2, M7
	82 (270)	0.025 (0.001)	0.05 (0.002)	0.10 (0.004)	0.15 (0.006)	C6
S44002, S44003, S44004	23 (75)	0.025 (0.001)	0.05 (0.002)	0.075 (0.003)	0.10 (0.004)	M2, M7
	69 (225)	0.025 (0.001)	0.05 (0.002)	0.10 (0.004)	0.15 (0.006)	C6
Austenitic alloys						
S20100, S30100, S30200, S30400, S30403, S30430, S30500, S31600, S31603, S32100, S34700, S38400	24 (80)	0.05 (0.002)	0.075 (0.003)	0.13 (0.005)	0.15 (0.006)	M2, M7
	82 (270)	0.025 (0.001)	0.05 (0.002)	0.075 (0.003)	0.13 (0.005)	C2
S30900, S30908, S31000, S31008, S31700, S31703	23 (75)	0.05 (0.002)	0.075 (0.003)	0.13 (0.005)	0.15 (0.006)	M2, M7
	79 (260)	0.025 (0.001)	0.05 (0.002)	0.075 (0.003)	0.13 (0.005)	C2
S20910, S21904, S24100, S28200, S30452, N08020	15 (50)	0.025 (0.001)	0.05 (0.002)	0.05 (0.002)	0.075 (0.003)	M2, M7
	49 (160)	0.025 (0.001)	0.05 (0.002)	0.075 (0.003)	0.10 (0.004)	C2
Duplex alloys						
S31803, S32550, S32900, S32950	23 (75)	0.05 (0.002)	0.075 (0.003)	0.13 (0.005)	0.15 (0.006)	M2, M7
	79 (260)	0.025 (0.001)	0.05 (0.002)	0.075 (0.003)	0.13 (0.005)	C2
Precipitation-hardenable alloys						
S15500, S17400, S17700, S45000	26 (85)	0.025 (0.001)	0.05 (0.002)	0.075 (0.003)	0.10 (0.004)	M2, M7
	84 (275)	0.025 (0.001)	0.05 (0.002)	0.10 (0.004)	0.15 (0.006)	C2
S13800, S35000, S35500, S45500	23 (75)	0.025 (0.001)	0.05 (0.002)	0.075 (0.003)	0.10 (0.004)	M2, M7
	82 (270)	0.025 (0.001)	0.05 (0.002)	0.10 (0.004)	0.15 (0.006)	C2
S66286	5 (50)	0.025 (0.001)	0.05 (0.002)	0.05 (0.002)	0.075 (0.003)	M2, M7
	53 (175)	0.025 (0.001)	0.05 (0.002)	0.075 (0.003)	0.10 (0.004)	C2

(a) All speeds given are for material in the annealed condition (140-270 HB) except for the precipitation-hardenable grades, which are solution treated (150-325 HB) or equalized and overtempered for S35000 and S35500. For material heat treated or cold drawn to hardnesses higher than their normal annealed or softest level, best results are obtained by reducing speeds approximately 15% to as much as 75% depending on hardness. Premium high-speed steel or carbide cutters may also be necessary at the higher hardnesses. (b) Depth of cut for all speeds and feeds given is 1.3 mm (0.050 in.). Source: Ref 38, 52

0.13 to 0.25 mm (0.005 to 0.010 in.). For reaming all grades, carbide-tip reamers should have the following geometry:

Chamfer (lead) angle, degrees	2
Chamfer length, mm (in.)	4.8 (³⁄₁₆)
Radial rake angle, degrees	7-10
Helix angle, degrees	5-8
Primary relief angle, degrees	7-15

Reaming Parameters and Cutting Fluid. Feeds and speeds for reaming stainless steels are listed in Table 10 for high-speed steel or carbide tooling and for roughing or finishing operations. When finish of the hole is not critical, the parameters for roughing can be used. Smooth finishes require significantly lower speeds. When both size and finish are important, a two-step operation should be used with both roughing and finishing cuts.

The cutting fluid must be given careful consideration to avoid overheating. In addition to providing good lubrication, the cutting fluid must be a coolant to carry away the heat that would otherwise burn the cutting edges of the reamer. The cutting fluid must also be kept clean. Reaming produces slivers and very fine chips, which can float in the cutting fluid and damage the surface finish of the work, especially if the machine is equipped with a recirculating system.

Sawing

High-speed steel blades are used for cutting wrought and cast stainless steels by band sawing and power hacksawing. Pitches for band saw blades are eight to ten teeth per 25 mm (1 in.) for cutting material up to 6 mm ($\frac{1}{4}$ in.) thick, six to eight teeth per 25 mm (1 in.) for thicknesses of 6 to 32 mm ($\frac{1}{4}$ to $1\frac{1}{4}$ in.), and three to six teeth per 25 mm (1 in.) for materials thicker than 38 mm ($1\frac{1}{2}$ in.).

Power hacksaw blades of ten teeth per 25 mm (1 in.) are recommended for material up to 20 mm ($\frac{3}{4}$ in.) thick. Coarser blades of six teeth per 25 mm (1 in.) are used for material from 20 to 50 mm ($\frac{3}{4}$ to 2 in.) thick; blades of four teeth per 25 mm (1 in.) are used for material 50 mm (2 in.) thick or more.

Feeds and speeds for sawing stainless steel are primarily influenced by the hardness of the material being cut. Table 11 lists some nominal feeds and speeds for the hacksawing of stainless steels. Table 12 lists speeds for the contour band sawing of stainless steels.

Grinding

Aluminum oxide wheels are most commonly used for stainless steels. Silicon carbide wheels can also be used, but at a reduced wheel life. Their use is therefore limited to special applications. Medium-density wheels of hardness grades H to L are generally selected for stainless steels, although harder wheels are used for thread grinding. Grit sizes commonly used are 46, 54, or 60; finer grits can be used to produce a finer finish. Vitrified bond wheels are normally used, although the stronger resinoid bond wheels are preferred for equipment operated at higher speeds. Grinding wheels used previously to grind another metallic material should not be used to grind a stainless steel, because particles of the other material may be embedded in the stainless steel, affecting its corrosion resistance.

Grinding Parameters and Cutting Fluid. For many grinding operations, typical wheel speeds are 1500 to 2000 m/min (5000 to 6500 sfm). For surface grinding, table speeds are 15 to 30 m/min (50 to 100 sfm), with a down feed of up to 0.050 mm/pass (0.002 in./pass) for roughing and 0.013 mm/pass (0.0005 in./pass) for finishing, and a cross feed of 1.3 to 13 mm/pass (0.050 to 0.500 in./pass). Thread grinding is done at higher speeds with harder wheels, as mentioned previously.

Because of the lower thermal conductivity of stainless steels, a good coolant is necessary when grinding them. Conventional water-soluble fluids generally provide lower grinding wheel life than heavy-duty sulfochlorinated soluble oils at a concentration of about 10%.

Nontraditional Machining Operations

Although most stainless steels are machined with conventional techniques, nontraditional techniques are used when machining alloys with extreme toughness or hardness or when machining intricate shapes. This section will briefly describe some of the nontraditional machining techniques that have been successfully applied to stainless steels. More detailed information on the processes and basic operating parameters can be found in the Section "Nontraditional Machining Processes" in Volume 16 of the *ASM Handbook*.

Abrasive jet machining is a process that removes material from a workpiece through the use of abrasive particles entrained in a high-velocity gas stream. The abrasive jet machining process removes material by the impingement of abrasive particles on the work surface. The process differs from conventional sandblasting in that abrasive jet machining has smaller-diameter abrasives (from 10 to 50 μm) and a more finely controlled delivery system. Abrasive jet machining is typically used to clean and deburr stainless steels.

Abrasive jet machining generates surfaces with a granular, matte texture. Surface finishes range from 0.15 to 1.5 μm (6 to 60 μin.), depending on grit size. Table 13 lists some surface finishes attained on annealed austenitic stainless steel. Tolerances of the abrasive jet machining process can range from ±0.13 to 0.05 mm (±0.005 to 0.002 in.).

Abrasive waterjet machining operates by the impingement of a high-velocity, abrasive-laden fluid jet against the workpiece, yet it produces no

Table 9　Nominal broaching parameters for wrought stainless steels

UNS designation	Speed(a) m/min	sfm	Chip load mm/tooth	in./tooth	Tool material(a)(b)
Free-machining alloys					
Ferritic alloys					
S18235, S43020, S43023	9	30	0.10	0.004	M2, M7
S18200	11	35	0.10	0.004	M2, M7
Martensitic alloys					
S41600, S41610, S41623	9	30	0.10	0.004	M2, M7
S42020, S42023	8	25	0.075	0.003	M2, M7
S44020, S44023	6	20	0.075	0.003	M2, M7
Austenitic alloys					
S20300, S30300, S30310, S30360	8	25	0.10	0.004	M2, M7
S30323, S30330, S30345, S30431, S31620, S34720, S34723	6	20	0.10	0.004	M2, M7
Non-free-machining alloys					
Ferritic alloys					
S40500, S40900, S43000, S43400	6	20	0.075	0.003	M2, M7
S44200, S44300, S44400, S44600	6	20	0.075	0.003	M2, M7
Martensitic alloys					
S40300, S41000	8	25	0.10	0.004	M2, M7
S41400, S42000, S42010, S43100	5	15	0.075	0.003	T15, M42
S44002, S44003, S44004	5	15	0.05	0.002	T15, M42
Austenitic alloys					
S20100, S30100, S30200, S30400, S30403, S30430, S30500, S31600, S31603, S32100, S34700, S38400	6	20	0.075	0.003	M2, M7
S30900, S30908, S31000, S31008, S31700, S31703	5	15	0.075	0.003	T15, M42
S20910, S21904, S24100, S28200, S30452, N08020	3	10	0.075	0.003	T15, M42
Duplex alloys					
S31803, S32550, S32900, S32950	5	15	0.075	0.003	T15, M42
Precipitation-hardenable alloys					
S15500, S17400, S17700, S45000	5	15	0.05	0.002	T15, M42
S13800, S35000, S35500, S45500	3	10	0.05	0.002	T15, M42
S66286	2	8	0.05	0.002	T15, M42

(a) All speeds are for material in the annealed condition (140-270 HB) except the precipitation-hardenable grades, which are solution treated (150-325 HB) or equalized and overtempered for S35000 and S35500. For material heat treated or cold drawn to hardnesses of 275-375 HB (325-375 for precipitation-hardenable grades) speed reductions of approximately 15-60% may be necessary for best results. Premium high-speed steel broaches may be necessary for higher-hardness material. (b) Any premium high-speed steel (T15, M33, M41-47) can be used where the designated tool material is T15, M42. Source: Ref 38, 52

334 / Fabrication and Finishing

Table 10 Nominal reaming parameters for wrought stainless steels

Depending on actual machining conditions, the optimum parameters may be higher or lower than those given.

UNS designation	Speed(a) m/min	sfm	Feed 6 mm (¼ in.)	13 mm (½ in.)	25 mm (1 in.)	50 mm (2 in.)	Tool material(a)(b)	
Free-machining alloys								
Ferritic alloys								
S18235, S43020, S43023	40	130	0.13 (0.005)	0.20 (0.008)	0.25 (0.010)	0.38 (0.015)	M7	Roughing
	46	150	0.20 (0.008)	0.30 (0.012)	0.41 (0.016)	0.61 (0.024)	C2	
	18	60	0.10 (0.004)	0.15 (0.006)	0.20 (0.008)	0.30 (0.012)	M7	Finishing
	21	70	0.15 (0.006)	0.20 (0.008)	0.25 (0.010)	0.30 (0.012)	C2	
S18200	40	130	0.18 (0.005)	0.20 (0.008)	0.25 (0.010)	0.38 (0.015)	M7	Roughing
	46	150	0.20 (0.008)	0.30 (0.012)	0.41 (0.016)	0.61 (0.024)	C2	
	18	60	0.10 (0.004)	0.15 (0.006)	0.20 (0.008)	0.30 (0.012)	M7	Finishing
	21	70	0.15 (0.006)	0.20 (0.008)	0.25 (0.010)	0.30 (0.012)	C2	
Martensitic alloys								
S41600, S41610, S41623	40	130	0.13 (0.005)	0.20 (0.008)	0.25 (0.010)	0.38 (0.015)	M7	Roughing
	46	150	0.20 (0.008)	0.30 (0.012)	0.41 (0.016)	0.61 (0.024)	C2	
	18	60	0.10 (0.004)	0.15 (0.006)	0.20 (0.008)	0.30 (0.012)	M7	Finishing
	21	70	0.15 (0.006)	0.20 (0.008)	0.25 (0.010)	0.30 (0.012)	C2	
S42020, S42023	30	100	0.13 (0.005)	0.20 (0.008)	0.25 (0.010)	0.38 (0.015)	M7	Roughing
	37	120	0.20 (0.008)	0.30 (0.012)	0.41 (0.016)	0.61 (0.024)	C2	
	15	50	0.10 (0.004)	0.15 (0.006)	0.20 (0.008)	0.30 (0.012)	M7	Finishing
	18	60	0.15 (0.006)	0.20 (0.008)	0.25 (0.010)	0.30 (0.012)	C2	
S44020, S44023	23	75	0.13 (0.005)	0.20 (0.008)	0.25 (0.010)	0.38 (0.015)	M7	Roughing
	27	90	0.20 (0.008)	0.30 (0.012)	0.41 (0.016)	0.61 (0.024)	C2	
	12	40	0.10 (0.004)	0.15 (0.006)	0.20 (0.008)	0.30 (0.012)	M7	Finishing
	15	50	0.15 (0.006)	0.20 (0.008)	0.25 (0.010)	0.30 (0.012)	C2	
Austenitic alloys								
S20300, S30300, S30310, S30360	27	90	0.15 (0.006)	0.23 (0.009)	0.28 (0.011)	0.46 (0.018)	M7	Roughing
	34	110	0.20 (0.008)	0.30 (0.012)	0.41 (0.016)	0.61 (0.024)	C2	
	15	50	0.10 (0.004)	0.15 (0.006)	0.20 (0.008)	0.25 (0.010)	M7	Finishing
	20	65	0.15 (0.006)	0.20 (0.008)	0.25 (0.010)	0.30 (0.012)	C2	
S30323, S30330, S30445, S30431, S31620, S34720, S34723	23	75	0.15 (0.006)	0.23 (0.009)	0.28 (0.011)	0.41 (0.018)	M7	Roughing
	30	100	0.20 (0.008)	0.30 (0.012)	0.41 (0.016)	0.61 (0.024)	C2	
	12	40	0.10 (0.004)	0.15 (0.006)	0.20 (0.008)	0.25 (0.010)	M7	Finishing
	17	55	0.15 (0.006)	0.20 (0.008)	0.25 (0.010)	0.30 (0.012)	C2	
Non-free-machining alloys								+
Ferritic alloys								
S40500, S40900, S43000, S43400	24	80	0.10 (0.004)	0.13 (0.005)	0.20 (0.008)	0.30 (0.012)	M7	Roughing
	29	95	0.20 (0.008)	0.30 (0.012)	0.41 (0.016)	0.61 (0.024)	C2	
	12	40	0.10 (0.004)	0.15 (0.006)	0.20 (0.008)	0.25 (0.010)	M7	Finishing
	18	60	0.15 (0.006)	0.20 (0.008)	0.25 (0.010)	0.30 (0.012)	C2	
S44200, S44300, S44400, S44600	23	75	0.10 (0.004)	0.13 (0.005)	0.20 (0.008)	0.30 (0.012)	M7	Roughing
	27	90	0.20 (0.008)	0.30 (0.012)	0.41 (0.016)	0.61 (0.024)	C2	
	11	35	0.10 (0.004)	0.15 (0.006)	0.20 (0.008)	0.25 (0.010)	M7	Finishing
	15	50	0.15 (0.006)	0.20 (0.008)	0.25 (0.010)	0.30 (0.012)	C2	
Martensitic alloys								
S40300, S41000	24	80	0.10 (0.004)	0.13 (0.005)	0.20 (0.008)	0.30 (0.012)	M7	Roughing
	29	95	0.20 (0.008)	0.30 (0.012)	0.41 (0.016)	0.61 (0.024)	C2	
	12	40	0.10 (0.004)	0.15 (0.006)	0.20 (0.008)	0.25 (0.010)	M7	Finishing
	18	60	0.15 (0.006)	0.20 (0.008)	0.25 (0.010)	0.30 (0.012)	C2	
S41400, S42000, S42010, S43100	20	65	0.10 (0.004)	0.13 (0.005)	0.20 (0.008)	0.30 (0.012)	M7	Roughing
	24	80	0.20 (0.008)	0.30 (0.012)	0.41 (0.016)	0.61 (0.024)	C2	
	11	35	0.10 (0.004)	0.15 (0.006)	0.20 (0.008)	0.25 (0.010)	M7	Finishing
	15	50	0.15 (0.006)	0.20 (0.008)	0.25 (0.010)	0.30 (0.012)	C2	
S44002, S44003, S44004	17	55	0.075 (0.003)	0.13 (0.005)	0.20 (0.008)	0.30 (0.012)	T15, M42	Roughing
	21	70	0.20 (0.008)	0.30 (0.012)	0.41 (0.016)	0.61 (0.024)	C2	
	11	35	0.075 (0.003)	0.10 (0.004)	0.15 (0.006)	0.20 (0.008)	T15, M42	Finishing
	15	50	0.10 (0.004)	0.15 (0.006)	0.20 (0.008)	0.25 (0.010)	C2	

(continued)

(a) All speeds given are for material in the annealed condition (140-270 HB) except for the precipitation-hardenable grades, which are solution treated (150-325 HB) or equalized and overtempered for S35000 and S35500. For material heat treated or cold drawn to hardnesses higher than their normal annealed or softest level, best results are obtained by reducing speeds by approximately 25% to as much as 75% depending on hardness. Premium high-speed steel or carbide tooling may also be necessary at the higher hardnesses. (b) Any premium high-speed steel (T15, M33, M41-47) can be used where the designated tool material is T15, M42. Source: Ref 38, 52

Table 10 (continued)

UNS designation	Speed(a) m/min	sfm	Feed, mm/rev (in./rev), at a reamer diameter of: 6 mm (1/4 in.)	13 mm (1/2 in.)	25 mm (1 in.)	50 mm (2 in.)	Tool material(a)(b)	
			Non-free-machining alloys (continued)					
Austenitic alloys								
S20100, S30100, S30200,	21	70	0.13 (0.005)	0.20 (0.008)	0.25 (0.010)	0.38 (0.015)	M7	Roughing
S30400, S30403, S30430,	26	85	0.20 (0.008)	0.30 (0.012)	0.41 (0.016)	0.61 (0.024)	C2	
S30500, S31600, S31603,	11	35	0.075 (0.003)	0.10 (0.004)	0.15 (0.006)	0.20 (0.008)	M7	Finishing
S32100, S34700, S38400	15	50	0.10 (0.004)	0.15 (0.006)	0.20 (0.008)	0.25 (0.010)	C2	
S30900, S30908, S31000,	21	70	0.13 (0.005)	0.20 (0.008)	0.25 (0.010)	0.38 (0.015)	T15, M42	Roughing
S31008, S31700, S31703	26	85	0.20 (0.008)	0.30 (0.012)	0.41 (0.016)	0.61 (0.024)	C2	
	11	35	0.075 (0.003)	0.10 (0.004)	0.15 (0.006)	0.20 (0.008)	T15, M42	Finishing
	15	50	0.10 (0.004)	0.15 (0.006)	0.20 (0.008)	0.25 (0.010)	C2	
S20910, S21904, S24100,	18	60	0.13 (0.005)	0.20 (0.008)	0.25 (0.010)	0.38 (0.015)	T15, M42	Roughing
S28200, S30452, N08020	23	75	0.20 (0.008)	0.30 (0.012)	0.41 (0.016)	0.61 (0.024)	C2	
	9	30	0.075 (0.003)	0.10 (0.004)	0.15 (0.006)	0.20 (0.008)	T15, M42	Finishing
	12	40	0.10 (0.004)	0.15 (0.006)	0.20 (0.008)	0.25 (0.010)	C2	
Duplex alloys								
S31803, S32550, S32900, S32950	21	70	0.13 (0.005)	0.20 (0.008)	0.25 (0.010)	0.38 (0.015)	T15, M42	Roughing
	26	85	0.20 (0.008)	0.30 (0.012)	0.41 (0.016)	0.61 (0.024)	C2	
	11	35	0.075 (0.003)	0.10 (0.004)	0.15 (0.006)	0.20 (0.008)	T15, M42	Finishing
	15	50	0.10 (0.004)	0.15 (0.006)	0.20 (0.008)	0.25 (0.010)	C2	
Precipitation-hardenable alloys								
S15500, S17400, S17700, S45000	18	60	0.13 (0.005)	0.20 (0.008)	0.25 (0.010)	0.38 (0.015)	T15, M42	Roughing
	23	75	0.20 (0.008)	0.30 (0.012)	0.41 (0.016)	0.61 (0.024)	C2	
	11	35	0.10 (0.004)	0.15 (0.006)	0.20 (0.008)	0.25 (0.010)	T15, M42	Finishing
	15	50	0.15 (0.006)	0.20 (0.008)	0.25 (0.010)	0.30 (0.012)	C2	
S13800, S35000, S35500, S45500	17	55	0.13 (0.005)	0.20 (0.008)	0.25 (0.010)	0.38 (0.015)	T15, M42	Roughing
	21	70	0.20 (0.008)	0.30 (0.012)	0.41 (0.016)	0.61 (0.024)	C2	
	9	30	0.10 (0.004)	0.15 (0.006)	0.20 (0.008)	0.25 (0.010)	T15, M42	Finishing
	14	45	0.15 (0.006)	0.20 (0.008)	0.25 (0.010)	0.30 (0.012)	C2	
S66286	15	50	0.13 (0.005)	0.20 (0.008)	0.25 (0.010)	0.38 (0.015)	T15, M42	Roughing
	20	65	0.20 (0.008)	0.30 (0.012)	0.41 (0.016)	0.61 (0.024)	C2	
	8	25	0.10 (0.004)	0.15 (0.006)	0.20 (0.008)	0.25 (0.010)	T15, M42	Finishing
	12	40	0.15 (0.006)	0.20 (0.008)	0.25 (0.010)	0.30 (0.012)	C2	

(a) All speeds given are for material in the annealed condition (140-270 HB) except for the precipitation-hardenable grades, which are solution treated (150-325 HB) or equalized and overtempered for S35000 and S35500. For material heat treated or cold drawn to hardnesses higher than their normal annealed or softest level, best results are obtained by reducing speeds by approximately 25% to as much as 75% depending on hardness. Premium high-speed steel or carbide tooling may also be necessary at the higher hardnesses. (b) Any premium high-speed steel (T15, M33, M41-47) can be used where the designated tool material is T15, M42. Source: Ref 38, 52

heat (and therefore no heat-affected zone) to degrade metals or other materials. The finished edge obtained by the process often eliminates the need for postmachining to improve surface finish.

A coherent fluid jet is formed by forcing high-pressure abrasive-laden water through a tiny sapphire orifice. The accelerated jet exiting the nozzle travels at more than twice the speed of sound and cuts as it passes through the workpiece. Cuts can be initiated at any point on the workpiece and can be made in any direction of contour, linear or tangential. The narrow kerf produced by the stream results in neither delamination nor thermal or nonthermal stresses along the cutting path. Table 14 lists some abrasive waterjet cutting rates for stainless steels.

Chemical milling, also referred to as *chem milling, chemical machining, chemical contouring,* and *chemietching,* is a method of processing structural metal parts by controlled chemical etching. The process either thins the parts in specific areas or removes metal from all surfaces. Areas from which metal is not to be removed are protected by special coatings termed *maskants* or *masks,* and parts are etched by immersion in a tank of etchant. The process is rarely electrically assisted. Most of the process applications are in the aerospace industry. Table 15 lists surface finishes obtainable with the chemical milling process.

Electrical discharge grinding is a process that removes metal by spark discharges between a rotating negative electrode grinding wheel and a positive workpiece immersed in a dielectric fluid. Each spark discharge melts or vaporizes a small amount of metal from the workpiece surface, producing a small crater at the discharge site. The grinding of stainless steel is illustrated in Table 16, which shows workpiece and wheel configurations for four parts and gives processing details.

Electrochemical machining is the controlled removal of metal by anodic dissolution in an electrolytic cell in which the workpiece is the anode and the tool is the cathode. The electrolyte is pumped through the cutting gap between the tool and the workpiece, while direct current is passed through the cell at a low voltage, to dissolve metal from the workpiece. Electrochemical machining is used for machining hard materials into complex shapes. The process is faster than electrical discharge machining and does not introduce metallurgical changes or distortion at the surface.

Electrostream and shaped tube electrolytic machining are modified electrochemical machining processes that are used for drilling small holes in corrosion-resistant metals. Both processes make use of charged acid electrolytes that are pumped onto the workpiece surface through small-diameter glass or titanium tubes.

Electron beam machining uses a focused beam of high-velocity electrons to remove material. In this process, a stream of electrons strikes an object and causes rapid melting and vaporization of the material. Electron beam machining is used in the high-precision drilling of fine holes or narrow slots in thin materials. Table 17 lists some electron beam drilling times of stainless steel.

Laser beam machining removes material by focusing a coherent beam of high-energy monochromatic light on the workpiece surface. Laser beam machining is also used to drill small-diameter holes. Unlike electron beam machining, laser beam machining does not require a vacuum.

Table 11 Nominal power hacksawing parameters for wrought stainless steels

Depending on actual machining conditions, optimum parameters may be higher or lower than those given.

UNS designation(a)	Pitch (teeth per 25 mm (1 in.) at a material thickness of:				Speed, strokes/min	Feed	
	<6 mm (¼ in.)	6-19 mm (¼–¾ in.)	19-50 mm (¾-2 in.)	>50 mm (2 in.)		mm/stroke	in./stroke
Free-machining alloys							
Ferritic alloys							
S18235, S43020, S43023	10	6	4	4	130	0.15	0.006
S18200	10	6	4	4	130	0.15	0.006
Martensitic alloys							
S41600, S41610, S41623	10	6	4	4	130	0.15	0.006
S42020, S42023	10	6	4	4	120	0.15	0.006
S44020, S44023	10	6	4	4	110	0.15	0.006
Austenitic alloys							
S20300, S30300, S30310, S30360	10	6	6	4	110	0.15	0.006
S30323, S30330, S30345, S30431, S31620, S34720, S34723	10	6	6	4	95	0.15	0.006
Non-free-machining alloys							
Ferritic alloys							
S40500, S40900, S43000, S43400	10	6	4	4	120	0.15	0.006
S44200, S44300, S44400, S44600	10	6	4	4	110	0.15	0.006
Martensitic alloys							
S40300, S41000	10	6	4	4	110	0.15	0.006
S41400, S42000, S42010, S43100	10	10	6	4	85	0.10	0.004
S44002, S44003, S44004	10	10	6	4	50	0.10	0.004
Austenitic alloys							
S20100, S30100, S30200, S30400, S30403, S30430, S30500, S31600, S31603, S32100, S34700, S38400	10	10	6	4	90	0.10	0.004
S30900, S30908, S31000, S31008, S31700, S31703	10	10	6	4	65	0.10	0.004
S20910, S21904, S24100, S28200, S30452, N08020	10	10	6	6	45	0.075	0.003
Duplex alloys							
S31803, S32550, S32900, S32950	10	10	6	4	65	0.10	0.004
Precipitation-hardenable alloys(a)							
S15500, S17400, S17700, S45000	10	10	6	4	60	0.10	0.004
S13800, S35000, S35500, S45500	10	10	6	4	60	0.10	0.004
S66286	10	10	6	4	45	0.075	0.003

(a) All machining parameters given are for material in the annealed condition (140-270 HB) except the precipitation-hardenable grades, which are solution treated (150-325 HB) or equalized and overtempered for S35000 or S35500. For material heat treated or cold drawn to hardnesses higher than the normal annealed or softest condition, speed reductions of approximately 10% to as much as 50% at the higher hardnesses are necessary for best results. Light-to-medium pressures are generally used (medium pressure at highest material thickness); heavy pressure can be used on the martensitic free-machining grades in the annealed condition at higher material thicknesses. Source: Ref 38, 52

Table 12 Speeds for the contour band sawing of stainless steels with M42 welded-edge high-speed steel saw bands

Data are based on the use of a suitable cutting fluid.

Steel being cut	Hardness, HB	Speed, m/min (sfm), for stock thickness of:		
		6.4-13 mm (¼-½ in.)(a)	25-75 mm (1-3 in.)(b)	150-300 mm (6-12 in.)(c)
201, 202, 302, 304	130-190	45 (150)	30 (100)	21 (70)
303, 303F	150-200	49 (160)	40 (130)	30 (100)
308(d), 309(d), 310(d), 330(d)	160-220	33 (110)	24 (80)	15 (50)
314(d), 316(d), 317(d)	160-220	29 (95)	18 (60)	12 (40)
321, 347	165-200	45 (150)	30 (100)	21 (70)
410, 420, 420F	140-185	53 (175)	33 (110)	26 (85)
416, 430F	155-195	70 (230)	49 (160)	24 (80)
430, 446	170-215	43 (140)	27 (90)	21 (70)
440 A(d), B(d), C(d)	160-190	33 (110)	27 (90)	15 (50)
440F, 443	175-215	43 (140)	35 (115)	18 (60)
17-7 PH(d), 17-4 PH(d)	150-360	33 (110)	21 (70)	15 (50)

(a) Regular tooth form; 10-pitch; minimum feed force, except average force for steels that are footnoted. (b) Regular tooth form; 6-pitch; average feed force, except maximum force for steels that are footnoted. (c) Hook tooth form; 3-pitch; maximum feed force. (d) Operating conditions for these stainless steels are slightly different from those for the others, as defined in footnotes (a) and (b). Source: Data are adapted from tables in "Fundamentals of Band Machining," Wilkie Brothers Foundation.

Table 13 Surface finishes for annealed S31600 stainless steel with different abrasive jet machining abrasives

Abrasive type	Grit size		Surface roughness(a)	
	µm	µin.	µm	µin.
Aluminum oxide	10	400	0.20-0.50	8-20
	25	1000	0.25-0.53	10-21
	50	2000	0.38-0.96	15-38
Silicon carbide	20	800	0.30-0.50	12-20
	50	2000	0.43-0.86	17-34
Glass bead	50	2000	0.30-0.96	12-38

(a) Initial surface was ground to 0.47 µm (18.5 µin.). Source: Metcut Research Associates

Plasma arc cutting employs an extremely high-temperature, high-velocity, constricted arc between an electrode contained within the torch and the workpiece to be cut. The arc is concentrated by a nozzle onto a small area of the workpiece. The metal is continuously melted by the intense heat of the arc and then removed by the jetlike gas stream issuing from the torch nozzle. The plasma arc process is used to perform straight cuts of tough materials at high speeds. Table 18 provides some typical cutting rates with plasma arc machining.

Table 14 Cutting rates for stainless steels in abrasive water jet machining

	Thickness		Cutting rate	
Alloy	mm	in.	mm/min	in./min
S15500(a)	3	0.13	230-380	9-15
S15500(a)	64	2.50	13-25	0.5-1
S31600(a)	75 (diam)	3 (diam)	13-50	0.5-2
S17400(b)	25	1	50	2

(a) 275-345 MPa (40-50 ksi) pressure with 60-mesh garnet. (b) 200 MPa (30 ksi) pressure with 60-mesh garnet. Source: Ref 53, 54

Table 15 Surface finishes normally obtained by chemical milling

			Surface finish, R_a	
Alloy	Form	Etchant type	μm	μin.
301, 304, 316, 321	Sheet	HNO_3	0.75-1.5	30-60
347	Sheet	HNO_3	0.75-1.5	30-60
410	Sheet	HNO_3	1.0-1.5	40-60
13-8, 15-7, 17-7	Sheet	HNO_3, HCl, HF	0.75-1.5	30-60
AM 350, AM 355	Sheet	HNO_3, HCl, HF	0.75-1.5	30-60

Table 16 Typical applications and conditions for the electrical discharge grinding of stainless steels using 300 mm (12 in.) diam wheels
Dimensions in figure are given in inches.

	Work				Operating conditions					Results				
Part No.	Type of stainless steel	Description of workpiece	Shape produced	Dimensions of shape produced	Speed, rev/min	Volts	Amp	Capacitance, μF	Pulse frequency, kHz	Grinding rate, $mm^3 \times 10^3$/h ($in.^3$/h)	Cutting time, min	Volume wear ratio	Overcut, mm (in.) per side	Finish, μm (μin.)
1	303	Rod, 13.5 mm (0.531 in.) diam × 31.0 mm ($1^7/_{32}$ in.) long	3 grooves	4.8 mm ($^3/_{16}$ in.) wide, 5.54 mm (0.218 in.) deep; full-radius bottom	20	70	10	6	32	7.7 (0.470)	6	3:1	0.043 (0.0017)	5.0 (200)
2	304	Strip, 2.64 × 101.6 × 165.1 mm (0.104 × 4.000 × 6.500 in.)	Rib	15.2 mm (0.600 in.) wide, 0.25 mm (0.010 in.) deep; central web 0.25 mm (0.010 in.) wide	20	70	0.5	0.5	32	1.0 (0.06)	44	3:1	0.025 (0.001)	1.5 (60)
3	304	Strip, 3.2 × 75 × 500 mm ($^1/_8$ × 3 × 20 in.)	2 grooves	71.1 mm (2.800 in.) wide, 0.51 mm (0.020 in.) deep	20	70	2	2	130	2.56 (0.156)	400	6:1	0.025 (0.001)	1.5 (60)
4	304	Hexagonal tubing, 57 mm ($2^1/_4$ in.) × 1.25 mm (0.050 in.) wall	Face, step-cut end	Step, 4.75 mm (0.187 in.) deep	34	80	8	2	32	...	30	...	0.025 (0.001)	3.2 (125)

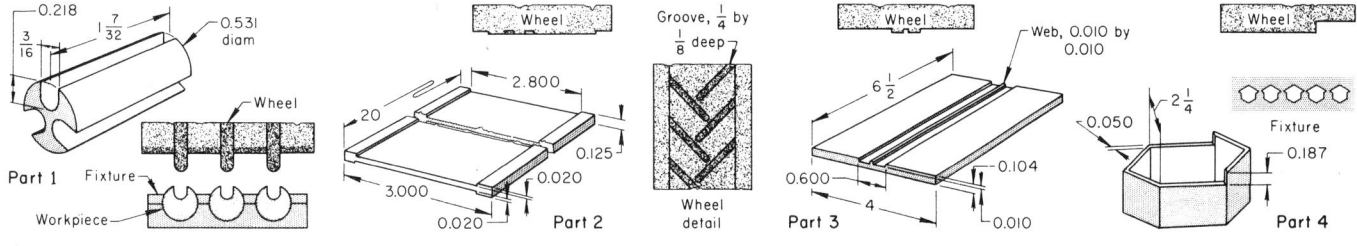

ACKNOWLEDGMENT

The information in this article is largely taken from:

- T. Kosa and R.P. Ney, Machining of Stainless Steels, *Machining*, Vol 16, *ASM Handbook* (formerly 9th ed., *Metals Handbook*), ASM International, 1989, p 681-707
- Nontraditional Machining Processes, *Machining*, Vol 16, *ASM Handbook* (formerly 9th ed., *Metals Handbook*), ASM International, 1989, p 509-594

Table 17 Parameters used to drill holes with electron beam machining

	Workpiece thickness		Hole diameter		Drilling time, s	Accelerating voltage, kV	Average beam current, μA	Pulse width, μs	Pulse frequency, Hz
Alloy	mm	in.	mm	in.					
Ferritic/martensitic	0.25	0.010	0.013	0.0005	<1	130	60	4	3000
Stainless steel	1.0	0.040	0.13	0.005	<1	140	100	80	50
Stainless steel	2.0	0.080	0.13	0.005	10	140	100	80	50
Stainless steel	2.5	0.100	0.13	0.005	10	140	100	80	50
Stainless steel	6.4	0.250	0.5-1.0	0.020-0.040	180	145	4000	2100	12.5

Source: Ref 55

REFERENCES

1. Machining and Abrasive Wheel Grinding of Carpenter Stainless Steels, *Carpenter Stainless Steels,* Selection, Alloy Data, Fabrication, Carpenter Technology Corp., 1987, p 240-241

2. V.A. Tipnis, Machining of Stainless Steels, *Wire,* Aug 1971, p 153-161

3. Metallurgy of Welding Stainless Steels, *Stainless Steels,* American Society for Metals, 1978, p 11-1 to 11-22

338 / Fabrication and Finishing

Table 18 Plasma arc cutting parameters for stainless steels

Thickness		Cutting speed		Power
mm	in.	mm/min	in./min	selection, A
6	0.25	1800	70	105
		2500	100	140
		3800	150	210
13	0.50	500	20	135
		1000	40	190
		1800	70	250
		2500	100	270
		3800	150	700
		5300	210	1000
25	1	250	10	175
		500	20	210
		760	30	270
		1000	40	350
		2000	80	540
		2800	110	1000
38	1.5	250	10	280
		500	20	420
		1000	40	620
		1800	70	1000
50	2	130	5	320
		250	10	420
		500	20	610
		1000	40	950
65	2.5	130	5	410
		250	10	550
		500	20	820
75	3	130	5	510
		250	10	675
		500	20	1020
90	3.5	130	5	550
		250	10	730
		500	20	1110
100	4	130	5	675
		250	10	900
115	4.5	130	5	900
130	5	75	3	1100
140	5.5	75	3	1100

Source: Ref 55

4. R.A. Lula, Fabrication of Stainless Steels—Machining, *Stainless Steels,* American Society for Metals, 1986, p 112-114
5. "Simplifying Stainless Steel Selection With Carpenter's Selectaloy Method," Carpenter Technology Corp., 1969
6. Corrosion Control, *Carpenter Stainless Steels, Selection, Alloy Data, Fabrication,* Carpenter Technology Corp., 1987, p 211-222
7. F.R. Palmer, Antifriction Corrosion-Resisting Steel, U.S. Patent 1,835,960, 1931
8. F.R. Palmer, Ferrous Alloy, U.S. Patent 1,961,777, 1934
9. F.M. Richmond, A Decade of Progress in Machinability, Finishing and Forming, *Met. Prog.,* Aug 1967, p 85-86
10. C.W. Kovach, Sulfide Inclusions and the Machinability of Steel, *Sulfide Inclusions in Steel,* American Society for Metals, 1975, p 459-479
11. C. Sparre, Stainless Free-Cutting Steel, *Wire,* April 1972, p 56-60
12. C.W. Kovach et al., The Sulfide Phases in Iron-Chromium Steels, *Trans. ASM,* Vol 61, 1968, p 575-581
13. A.J. Sedriks, Role of Sulfide Inclusions in Pitting and Crevice Corrosion of Stainless Steels, *Int. Met. Rev.,* Vol 28 (No. 5), 1983, p 295-307
14. M. Henthorne, Corrosion of Resulfurized Free-Machining Stainless Steels, *Corrosion,* Vol 26 (No. 12), Dec 1970, p 511-528
15. H.W. Garvin and R.M. Larrimore, Jr., Metallurgical Factors Affecting the Machining of a Free Machining Stainless Steel, *Mechanical Working of Steel II,* American Institute of Mining, Metallurgical, and Petroleum Engineers, 1965, p 133-150
16. C.W. Kovach and A. Moskowitz, Effects of Manganese and Sulfur on the Machinability of Martensitic Stainless Steels, *Trans. Met. Soc. AIME,* Vol 245, Oct 1969, p 2157-2164
17. C.W. Kovach and J.J. Eckenrod, Free Machining Austenitic Stainless Steels, *Proceedings of the 13th Mechanical Working and Steel Processing Conference,* American Institute of Mining, Metallurgical, and Petroleum Engineers, 1971, p 300-325
18. C.W. Kovach et al., Improved Free-Machining Ferritic Stainless Steel, British Patent 1,137,295, 1968
19. J.A. Ferree, Jr., Free Machining Austenitic Stainless Steel, U.S. Patent 3,888,659, 1975
20. R. Kiessling, Sulfide Inclusions: A Summary and Study of Sulfides in Resulfurized Ferritic ELI-Steels of the 18:2 Type, *Sulfide Inclusions in Steel,* American Society for Metals, 1975, p 104-122
21. R. Kiessling, Influence of Sulfide Composition on the Machinability and Corrosion Properties of a Resulfurized Ferritic 18:2 Steel, *Influence of Metallurgy on Machinability of Steels,* Proceedings of an International Symposium, American Society for Metals, 1977, p 253-261
22. H. Kiesheyer and H. Brandis, Titanium Alloyed Free-Machining Stainless Steels, *Bull. Cercle d'Études Metaux,* Vol 15 (No. 11), 1986
23. W.C. Clarke, Which Free-Machining Stainless?, *Metalwork. Prod.,* 27 May 1964, p 43-45
24. W.C. Clarke, Which Free-Machining Chromium Stainless?, *Metalwork. Prod.,* 9 Sept 1964, p 68-71
25. T. Fujiwara et al., Effects of Free-Machining Additives on Machinability of the 18Cr-2Mo Stainless Steel, *Influence of Metallurgy on Machinability of Steel: Proceedings of an International Symposium,* American Society for Metals, 1977, p 231-240
26. E. Herzog and J. Bellot, Influence of Tellurium and Selenium on the Properties of Some Steels, *Selenium and Tellurium in Iron and Steel,* Swedish Institute for Metal Research, 1969
27. "Free-Machining Stainless Steels," American Iron and Steel Institute, 1975
28. V.A. Tipnis, Stainless Steel Having Improved Machinability, U.S. Patent 3,846,186, 1974
29. V.A. Tipnis, Method of Making Stainless Steel Having Improved Machinability, U.S. Patent 3,933,480, 1976
30. N.L. McClymonds, Machinability of Leaded Stainless, *Met. Prog.,* Aug 1964, p 166, 168
31. N.L. McClymonds, Measuring Machinability, *Met. Prog.,* Aug 1967, p 183-184
32. K. Ono et al., Development of Leaded Free-Machining Austenitic Stainless Steel, *Denki Seiko (Electro. Furn. Steel),* Vol 54 (No. 4), Nov 1983, p 265-274
33. H. Pray et al., Addition of Bismuth for Producing Free-Machining Stainless Steels, *Proc. ASTM,* Vol 41, 1941, p 646-658
34. A. Kimura et al., Super STARCUT Stainless Steel 304BF with Bismuth, *Bull. Bismuth Inst.,* 1986, p 1-5
35. B. Heritier et al., Machinability of Stainless Steels: Evolution and Perspectives, *Bull. Cercle d'Études Metaux,* Vol 15 (No. 11), 1986
36. T. Kato et al., The Effect of Ca Oxide Inclusions on the Machinability of Heavy Duty Steels, *The Machinability of Engineering Materials,* American Society for Metals, 1983, p 323-337
37. T. Fujiwara and T. Ito, Calcium-Bearing Free-Machining Steels, *Bull. Jpn. Inst. Met.,* Vol 15 (No. 10), 1976, p 613-620 (BISI 17016)
38. "Guide to Machining Stainless Steels and Other Specialty Metals," Carpenter Technology Corp., 1985
39. D.M. Blott, Machining Wrought and Cast Stainless Steels, *Handbook of Stainless Steels,* McGraw-Hill, 1977, p 24-2 to 24-30
40. C.A. Divine, Jr., What to Consider in Choosing an Alloy, *Met. Prog.,* Feb 1968, p 19-23
41. L. Colombier and J. Hochmann, Manufacturing, Forming and Finishing Techniques—Machining, *Stainless and Heat Resisting Steels,* St. Martin's Press, 1968, p 508-514
42. Machining Operations, *Stainless Steel Fabrication,* Allegheny Ludlum Steel Corp., 1959, p 223-259
43. A. Moskowitz et al., Free-Machining Stainless Steels, U.S. Patent 3,401,035, 1968
44. C.W. Kovach and A. Moskowitz, How to Upgrade Free-Machining Properties, *Met. Prog.,* Aug 1967, p 173-180
45. J.R. Blank et al., Improved and More Consistent Steels for Machining, *Influence of Metallurgy on Machinability of Steel: Proceedings of an International Symposium,* American Society for Metals, 1977, p 397-419
46. W.C. Clarke, Jr., Free-Machining Stainless Steel and Method, U.S. Patent 2,697,035, 1954
47. J.J. Eckenrod and C.W. Kovach, Effects of Manganese on Austenitic Stainless Steels, *Met. Eng. Quart.,* Feb 1972, p 5-10
48. R.P. Ney, Sr., Free Machining, Cold Formable Austenitic Stainless Steel, U.S. Patent 4,444,588, 1984
49. J.J. Eckenrod et al., Low Carbon Plus Nitrogen, Free-Machining Austenitic Stainless Steel, U.S. Patent 4,613,367, 1986
50. P.K. Wright and A. Bagchi, Wear Mechanisms That Dominate Tool-Life in Machining, *J. Appl. Metalwork.,* Vol 1 (No. 4), 1981, p 15-23
51. "Carpenter Custom 630 (17Cr-4Ni)," Carpenter Technology Corp., 1971

52. *Machining Data Handbook,* Vol 1, Metcut Research Associates Inc., 1980
53. B.L. Schwartz, Principles and Applications of Water and Abrasive Jet Cutting, *High Productivity Machining: Materials and Processes,* American Society for Metals, 1985, p 291-298
54. A.L. Hitchcox, Vote of Confidence for Abrasive Waterjet Cutting, *Met. Prog.,* July 1986, p 33-42
55. *Machining Data Handbook,* Vol 2, Metcut Research Associates, Inc., 1980

SELECTED REFERENCES

- G.F. Benedict, *Nontraditional Manufacturing Processes,* Marcel Dekker, 1987
- D.M. Blott, How to Cut the Standard Grades, *Met. Prog.,* Feb 1968, p 337-343
- D. Daniels, AWJ Cutting: A New Tool for Metal Fabricators, *Met. Stamp.,* Sept 1986, p 3-6

- C.A. Divine, Jr., How to Machine the Stainless Steels, Carpenter Steel Company; originally published in *Mod. Mach. Shop,* 1968
- D. Elza and S. Burns, Lasers Take Their Place in Metalworking, *Mach. Tool Blue Book,* July 1985, p 34-38
- M. Field et al., The Surface Effects Produced in Nonconventional Metal Removal—Comparison with Conventional Machining Techniques, *Met. Eng. Quart.,* Aug 1966, p 32-45
- T.E. Gittens, Plasma Arc Cutting—Process Fundamentals, *Trans. AFS,* Vol 92, 1984, p 29-35
- S. Holden, The Plasma Cutting of Stainless Steel, *Stainless Steel Ind.,* Vol 13 (No. 74), July 1985, p 12-25
- B. Kellock, Have a Ball with a Cinderella Process!, *Mach. Prod. Eng.,* 19 May 1982, p 40-46

- "Machining the Austenitic Chromium-Nickel Stainless Steels," International Nickel Co., 1972
- N. McClymonds et al., Shop Practice, *Machining: Estimating Manual for Stainless Steels,* Joslyn Stainless Steels, 1963, p 79-122
- R.K. Mosavi, Comparing Laser and Waterjet Cutting, *Lasers Optronics,* Vol 6 (No. 7), July 1987, p 65-68
- *Nontraditional Machining,* Conference Proceedings, American Society for Metals, 1986
- V.K. Sarin, Ed., *High Productivity Machining: Materials and Processes,* Conference Proceedings, American Society for Metals, 1985, p 291-298
- R.J. Saunders, Laser Metalworking, *Met. Prog.,* July 1984, p 45-51
- W.F. Tutte, The Application of Laser Cutting to Stainless Steel, *Stainless Steel Ind.,* Vol 15 (No. 86), July 1987, p 9, 11

Welding

STAINLESS STEELS can be defined as alloys that contain at least approximately 11% Cr, no more than 1.5% C, and more iron than any other single element. There are five major families of stainless steels, based on microstructure and properties:

- Martensitic stainless steels
- Ferritic stainless steels
- Austenitic stainless steels
- Precipitation-hardening (PH) stainless steels
- Duplex ferritic-austenitic stainless steels

Each family has different weldability considerations because of the varied phase transformation behavior upon cooling from solidification to room temperature or below. Often, the optimal filler metal is not the one that most closely matches the base metal composition. The most successful procedures for one family often are markedly different from those that are appropriate for another family.

Stainless steel base metals and thus the welding filler metals used with them are almost invariably chosen on the basis of adequate corrosion resistance for the intended application. This usually means that the welding filler metal must at least match (and sometimes overmatch) the contents of the base metal in terms of specific alloying elements, such as chromium, nickel, and molybdenum.

After corrosion resistance has been considered, the avoidance of cracking becomes the unifying theme in filler metal selection and procedure development for the welding of stainless steels. Cracking can occur at temperatures that are just below the bulk solidus temperature of the alloy(s) being welded. This hot cracking, as it is called, can appear as large weld metal cracks, usually along the weld centerline. However, it can also appear as small, short cracks (microfissures) in the weld metal or in the heat-affected zone (HAZ) at the fusion line and, usually, perpendicular to it. Hot cracking in stainless steel welds is of most concern in austenitic weld metals, although it can occur in all types of stainless steel weldments.

Cracking can also occur at rather low temperatures, typically 150 °C (300 °F) or below, because of the interaction of high weld stresses, high-strength metal, and diffusible hydrogen. This cold cracking commonly occurs in martensitic weld metals, as well as HAZs, including those of PH stainless steels. Cold cracking can also occur in ferritic stainless steel weldments that have become embrittled by grain coarsening and/or second-phase particles.

In many instances of cold cracking, where the resulting weld has acceptable properties, the sub-stitution of a mostly austenitic filler metal (with appropriate corrosion resistance) for a martensitic or ferritic filler metal serves as a remedy. When hot cracking occurs in an austenitic weld metal, a common solution is to use a mostly austenitic filler metal that includes a small amount of ferrite. However, another approach to avoiding hot cracking may be necessary in situations that require low magnetic permeability, high toughness at cryogenic temperatures, resistance to media that selectively attack ferrite (such as urea), or postweld heat treatments (PWHTs) that embrittle ferrite, because their requirements may severely limit the amount of ferrite that is acceptable.

Welding engineers who are responsible for filler metal selection and procedure development for stainless steel welds often estimate the microstructure of the weld metal, taking the dilution effects into consideration. This task is best accomplished with a constitution diagram for the stainless steel weld metals. Several diagrams that have been developed over the years are described below in the section "Constitution Diagrams."

Following the discussion of constitution diagrams, applicable welding processes for stainless steels are outlined. Emphasis is placed on arc weld-ing processes and suggested procedures for successful welding of various joint types. This is followed by five major sections that describe the microstructural evolution of the weld mteal and the HAZ, susceptibility to defect formation during welding, mechanical and corrosion properties, filler metal selection, and weld process tolerence for the five families of wrought stainless steels. A final section describes special welding considerations for cast stainless steels.

For information on the chemical compositions, basic metallurgy, and properties of the base metals discussed in this article, the reader is referred to the articles "Metallurgy and Properties of Wrought Stainless Steels" and "Metallurgy and Properties of Cast Stainless Steels" in this Volume. Although some information on the corrosion problems of welded stainless steel structures is contained herein, more detailed information can be found in the article "Corrosion of Weldments" in this Volume.

Constitution Diagrams

The prediction of the microstructures and properties (such as hot cracking and corrosion resistance) for stainless steels has been the topic of

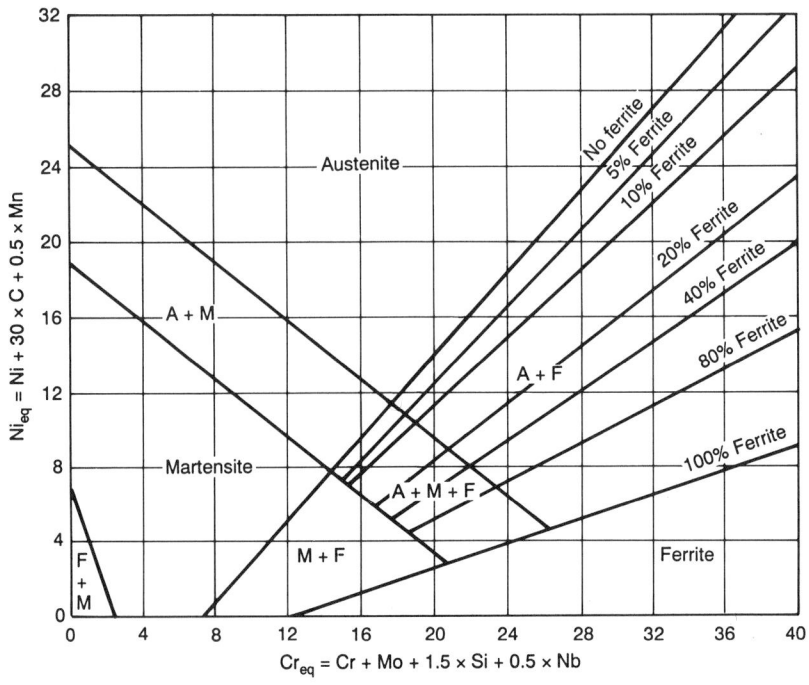

Fig. 1 Schaeffler constitution diagram for stainless steel weld metal

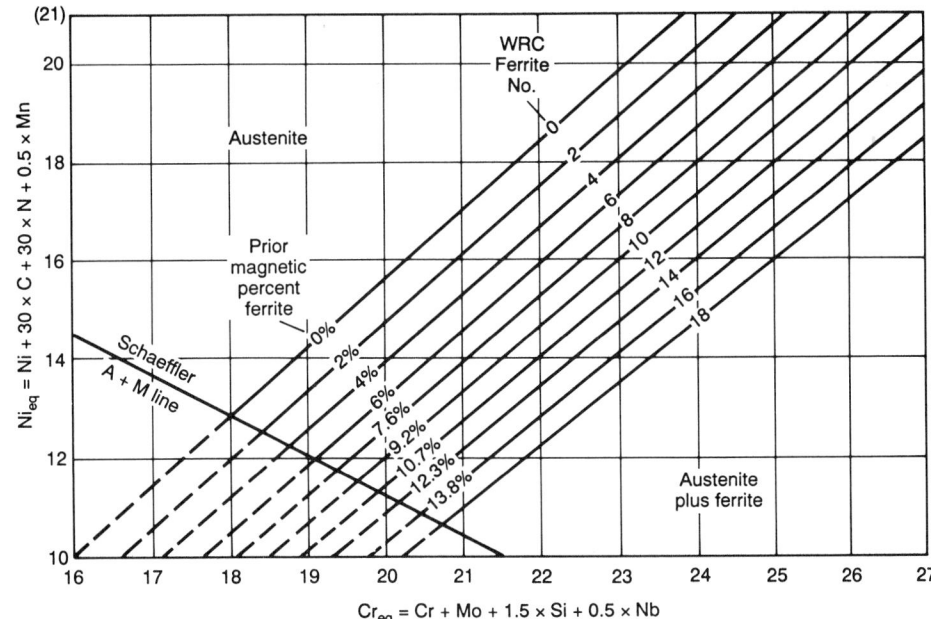

Fig. 2 DeLong constitution diagram for stainless steel weld metal. The Schaeffler austenite-martensite boundary is included for reference.

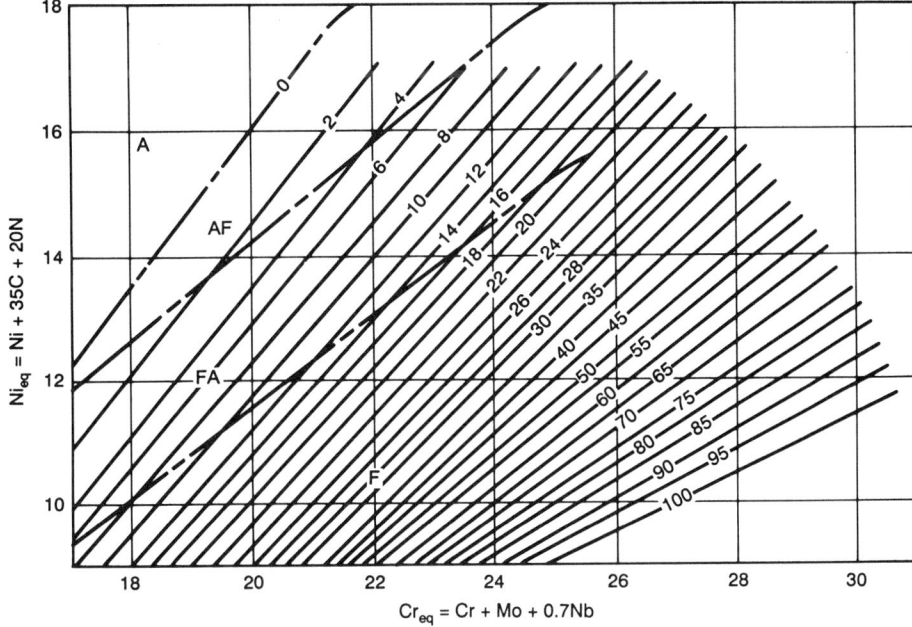

Fig. 3 WRC-1988 diagram, including solidification-mode boundaries

many studies. During the last two decades, four microstructure prediction diagrams have found the widest application. These include the Schaeffler diagram, the DeLong diagram, and the Welding Research Council (WRC) diagrams (WRC-1988 and WRC-1992). Each of these is described below.

Schaeffler Diagram. In 1949, Anton Schaeffler (Ref 1) published what has become known as the Schaeffler diagram (Fig. 1). This diagram proposed a relationship among alloy elements that promote the formation of ferrite (chromium-

equivalent, Cr_{eq}, elements) and elements that promote the formation of austenite and the suppression of ferrite (nickel-equivalent, Ni_{eq}, elements).

To use this diagram, both the chromium and nickel equivalents are first calculated from the composition of a given weld bead. Next, these equivalents are plotted as coordinates on the Schaeffler diagram. This allows an estimated weld metal microstructure to be determined from the boundaries given in the diagram.

Experience has shown that the Schaeffler diagram is reasonably accurate for conventional 300-

series stainless steel weld deposits from covered electrodes. However, it is of limited use when less conventional compositions are used and when a high level of nitrogen is present.

DeLong Diagram. W.T. DeLong recognized the effect of nitrogen in promoting austenite at the expense of ferrite. DeLong developed a new diagram (Ref 2) that covered a more restricted composition range and included the effect of nitrogen (Fig. 2). Specifically, a nickel equivalent of 30 × %N was added.

To use this diagram, the nickel and chromium equivalents are calculated from the weld metal analysis. If a nitrogen analysis of the weld metal is not available, then a value of 0.06% should be assumed for the gas-tungsten arc welding (GTAW) process, and covered electrodes and a value of 0.08% should be assumed for the gas-metal arc welding (GMAW) process. If the chemistry is accurate, then the diagram predicts the WRC Ferrite Number (FN) within æ3 in approximately 90% of the tests for the 308, 309, 316, and 317 alloy families.

In the DeLong diagram, the FNs for alloy 308, 308L, and 347 covered electrodes are similar to those in the Schaeffler diagram, but the 309, 316, and 317 alloy families have FNs that are about two to four times higher. Generally, the DeLong diagram correlates better with GTAW and GMAW weld metals than does the Schaeffler diagram, because it allows for nitrogen pickup.

In 1974, at about the time the DeLong diagram was being published, the measurement of ferrite in nominally austenitic stainless steel weld metals was standardized by the American National Standards Institute/American Welding Society (ANSI/AWS) A4.2 specification in terms of magnetically determined FNs, rather than the metallographically determined "percent ferrite" used by the Schaeffler diagram. The DeLong diagram became part of the "Boiler and Pressure Vessel Code" of the American Society of Mechanical Engineers.

WRC Diagrams. The DeLong diagram was subsequently discovered to seriously underestimate the ferrite content of weld metals with high manganese contents and overestimate the FN of highly alloyed weld metals, such as alloy 309. Consequently, the WRC both funded and collected data for the development of a new, more accurate diagram using computer mapping techniques (Ref 3, 4). A joint effort was conducted by the Colorado School of Mines and the U.S. National Institute of Standards and Technology. The product of this effort, known as the WRC-1988 diagram (Fig. 3), covers a broader range of compositions than does the DeLong diagram and removes the two errors noted above.

A modification of the WRC-1988 diagram, which allowed the Ni_{eq} to include a coefficient for copper, was first proposed by Lake in 1990 (Ref 5). This modification and an extension of the Cr_{eq} and Ni_{eq} axes were incorporated into the most recent constitution diagram, the WRC-1992 diagram (Ref 6) shown in Fig. 4. Its extended axes permit graphical estimation of the ferrite content of weld metal that comprises very different base metal(s) and filler metal, as could be done less precisely with the Schaeffler diagram.

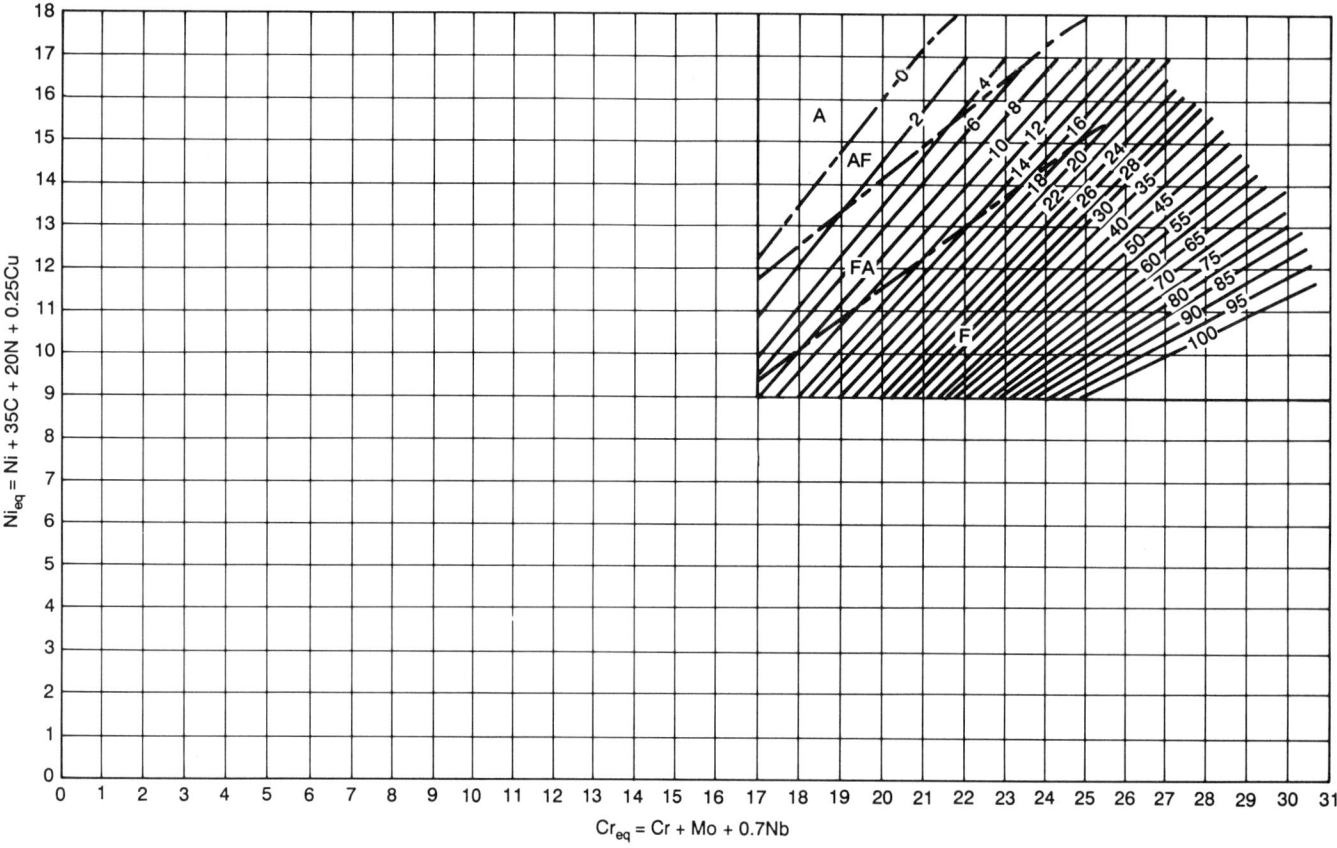

Fig. 4 WRC-1992 diagram with expanded scale for dilution calculations. Although extended axes allow a wide range of compositions to be located, the Ferrite Number (FN) prediction is only accurate for weld compositions that fall within the bounds of the iso-FN lines (0 to 100 FN). Limits of the Welding Research Council diagram were determined by the extent of the database, and extension of the lines could result in erroneous predictions. Source: Ref 6

Although the WRC-1992 diagram is more accurate in predicting ferrite content for many weld metals, the Schaeffler diagram still retains some utility because it can offer reasonably accurate predictions in terms of martensite in lean stainless steel compositions. This is because the WRC-1992 diagram does not include manganese. Manganese has been found to have no effect on the high-temperature transformation of ferrite to austenite during cooling. Therefore, it does not figure in the Nieq of the WRC-1992 diagram. However, it does have a significant effect on the low-temperature transformation of austenite to martensite during further cooling by tending to stabilize austenite at low temperatures. Without a manganese effect, it is not possible to put a boundary for the martensite phase in the WRC-1992 diagram.

If the weld deposit is austenitic, then an FN of around 4 or 5, minimum, typically suffices to prevent hot cracking. In addition, a deposit that is primarily austenitic will not cold crack. These two considerations will often influence filler metal selection and procedure development. In the following sections of this article, the WRC-1992 diagram and, occasionally, the Schaeffler diagram are used to illustrate the rationale behind many filler metal choices.

The ferrite that survives at room temperature after solidification is only a fraction of what existed during solidification. In terms of the utility

of constitution diagrams like the WRC-1992 diagram, it is currently thought (Ref 7) that finding ferrite at room temperature is only an indirect indication of the solidification mode. According to this theory, if the weld metal solidifies as ferrite first, with austenite appearing only in the latter stages of solidification, if at all, then the weld metal will be crack resistant. However, if the weld metal solidifies as austenite first, with ferrite only appearing in the latter stages of solidification, if at all, then the weld metal is at risk for cracking.

The dividing line between compositions that solidify as austenite first and compositions that solidify as ferrite first is approximated by the dashed line between the fields labeled "AF" (primary austenite solidification) and "FA" (primary ferrite solidification) in Fig. 3 and 4. This line is not parallel to the isoferrite lines. Rather, it is at a small angle to them, which means that more ferrite is needed at room temperature to represent evidence of primary ferrite solidification in higher-alloyed stainless steel weld metals than in lower-alloyed stainless steel weld metals.

Welding Process and Parameter Selection for Stainless Steels

Stainless steels of all types are weldable by virtually all welding processes. In part, process

selection is often dictated by available equipment. Perhaps the simplest and most universal welding process is manual shielded-metal arc welding (SMAW) with coated electrodes. It has been applied to material as thin as 1.2 mm (0.05 in.), and there is no upper limit on thickness. Other very commonly used processes for stainless steels are GTAW, GMAW, submerged arc welding (SAW), flux-cored arc welding (FCAW), and several forms of resistance welding. The plasma arc welding (PAW), laser-beam welding (LBW), and electron-beam welding (EBW) processes are also used.

Detailed discussion of all of the possible processes and parameters is beyond the scope of this article. However, the common arc welding processes are briefly discussed below, especially with regard to procedure and technique errors that can lead to loss of ferrite control with the common austenitic stainless steel weld metals that are designed to contain a small amount of ferrite (that is, solidify as primary ferrite) for protection from hot cracking.

Shielded-Metal Arc Welding. The ANSI/ AWS A5.4-92 specification provides for five different electrode coating types. If the alloy to be deposited were type 308, then the five coating types would be typified by the following five electrode classifications: E308-15, E308-16, E308-17, E308-25, and E308-26. Of these, E308-25 and E308-26 are typically very heavily coated electrodes, often made with mild steel or lower-al-

Table 1 Typical current ranges for stainless steel shielded-metal arc welding electrodes

Electrode diam		Current (DCEP), A		
mm	in.	For E3XX-15	For E3XX-16(a)	For E3XX-17(a)
1.6	1/16	20-40	20-40	...
2.0	5/64	30-50	30-50	35-55
2.4	3/32	30-70	40-70	40-80
3.2	1/8	45-95	60-100	75-110
4.0	5/32	75-130	90-140	95-150
4.8	3/16	95-165	120-185	130-200
6.4	1/4	150-225	200-300	...

(a) Current ranges are typically 10% higher when alternating current is used for E3XX-16 or E3XX-17 electrodes.

loyed core wire, with all or most of the alloying elements in the coating. For these two coating types (-25 and -26), the various commercial products are not sufficiently alike to permit a statement to be made about typical current ranges for the various sizes. The -25 coating type is recommended only for direct current, electrode positive (DCEP). The -26 coating type is recommended for alternating current, as well as DCEP. Both the -25 and -26 coating types are generally limited to welding in the flat and horizontal positions. The remaining three coating types are very well standardized in existing commercial products, although the -17 type has been classified separately from the -16 type only since the 1992 edition of the ANSI/AWS A5.4 specification.

The -15 coating type is recommended for welding on DCEP only. Its slag system, which generally consists of lime and fluorspar, permits the easiest out-of-position welding of all of the stainless steel electrode coating types, especially for fixed-position pipe welding. It tends to produce a convex weld surface profile, which provides the best cracking resistance when primary ferrite solidification is not achieved. It usually requires more welder skill to make attractive welds, but it also has the greatest resistance to porosity when the electrode is exposed to moisture or when the careless welder draws a long arc. Its arc is relatively harsh, and surface ripple is coarse. In general, it produces more spatter than the other coating types.

The -16 coating type is recommended for welding both DCEP and alternating current. Its slag system, which is very high in titanium dioxide, permits fairly easy out-of-position welding, but it is generally necessary to weave slightly for vertical-up welding, which is not necessary for the -15 coating type. It tends to produce a nearly flat surface profile. Some characteristics of the -16 coating are not quite as good as those of the -15 coating type, but are more than adequate for most

purposes: its weld metal cracking resistance when no ferrite is formed; its resistance to porosity, which is due to either moisture pickup or the drawing of a long arc; and its out-of-position weldability. Its weld surface appearance, spatter level, and slag removal are generally more attractive than those of the -15 coating type.

The -17 coating type is a modification of the -16 coating type, produced by substituting silica and silicates for some of the titanium dioxide, which welds both DCEP and alternating current.

Table 1 lists typical welding current ranges for the three more standardized electrode coating types. Welding voltage is determined by the arc length that the welder holds. Some -16 coated electrodes, and most -17 coated electrodes can be used by dragging the coating on the base metal surface, which maintains a short arc length. This length is generally desirable, because a longer arc length permits more air to enter the arc and the weld metal. Nitrogen from the air can be picked up by the weld metal and become an alloying element. This means that the careless welder who draws a long arc with an electrode designed to produce primary ferrite solidification can add enough nitrogen to change the solidification mode to primary austenite (refer to Fig. 3, which shows that nitrogen promotes austenite and suppresses ferrite). This can result in hot cracks in a weld metal, caused by electrodes designed to produce sufficient ferrite to avoid hot cracking. The -15 coating type is the least sensitive to this error, whereas the -17 coating type is generally the most sensitive.

Figure 5 provides the suggested procedures for SMAW of butt joints in stainless steel sheet

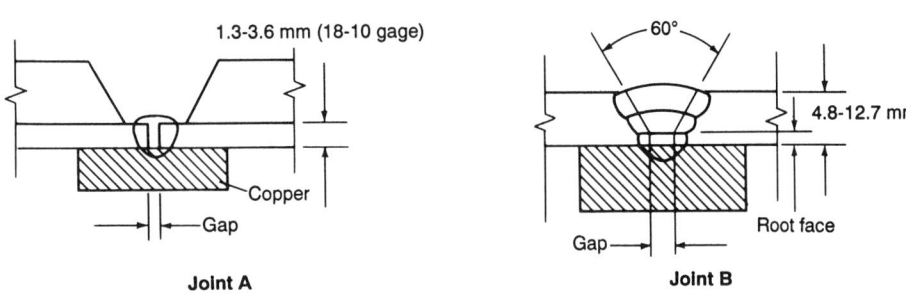

Plate thickness			Electrode diameter				Current (DCEP)(a), A		Arc speed				Amount of electrode required		Total time of weld		Gap		Root face	
			First pass		Additional passes				First pass		Additional passes									
mm	in.	Gage	mm	in.	mm	in.	First pass	Additional passes	mm/s	in./min	mm/s	in./min	kg/m	lb/ft	h/m	h/ft	mm	in.	mm	in.
Joint A																				
1.3	0.050	18	2.0	5/64	...	...	40(b)	...	5.9–6.8	14–16	...	...	0.030	0.020	0.0436	0.0133	0	0	0	0
2.0	0.078	14	2.4	3/32	...	...	60	...	4.9–5.3	11.5–12.5	...	...	0.057	0.038	0.0548	0.0167	0.8	1/32	0	0
3.6	0.140	10	3.2	1/8	...	...	85	...	3.6–4.0	8.5–9.5	...	...	0.119	0.080	0.0728	0.0222	0.8	1/32	0	0
Joint B																				
4.8	0.19	...	4.0	5/32	...	...	125	...	2.8–3.1	6.7–7.3	...	...	0.223	0.150	0.0938	0.0286	1.6	1/16	1.6	1/16
6.4	0.25	...	4.0	5/32	4.8(c)	3/16(c)	125	160(c)	2.4–2.7	5.7–6.3	3.2–3.6(c)	7.6–8.5(c)	0.506	0.340	0.1913	0.0583	2.4	3/32	1.6	1/16
9.5	0.38	...	4.0	5/32	4.8(d)	3/16(d)	125	160(d)	2.4–2.7	5.7–6.3	2.4–2.7(d)	5.7–6.3(d)	0.968	0.650	0.3281	0.100	2.4	3/32	1.6	1/16
12.7	0.50	...	4.0	5/32	4.8(e)	3/16(e)	125	160(e)	2.4–2.7	5.7–6.3	2.4–2.7(e)	5.7–6.3(e)	1.579	1.06	0.5479	0.167	2.4	3/32	1.6	1/16

(a) Alternating current can be used with 10% increase in current; E3XX-15 electrode can be used with 10% decrease in current. (b) Use DCEN. (c) Pass 2. (d) Passes 2 and 3. (e) Passes 2 through 5

Fig. 5 Suggested procedures for shielded-metal arc welding of butt joints in austenitic stainless steel from 1.3 mm (0.05 in., or 18 gage) to 12.7 mm (0.5 in.) in thickness in the flat position. E3XX-16 electrode. Source: Ref 8

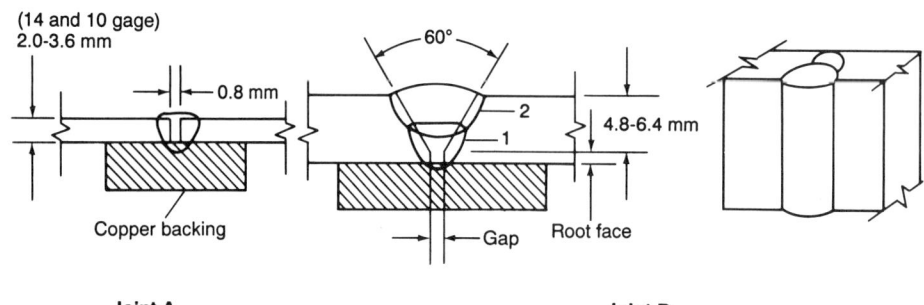

Fig. 6   Suggested procedures for shielded-metal arc welding of butt joints in austenitic stainless steel from 2.0 mm (0.08 in., or 14 gage) to 6.4 mm (0.25 in.) in thickness in the vertical and overhead positions. E3XX-15 electrode. Source: Ref 8

Plate thickness			Electrode diameter		Current (DCEP), A	Arc speed				Amount of electrode required		Total time of weld		Gap		Root face	
						First pass		Second pass									
mm	in.	Gage	mm	in.		mm/s	in./min	mm/s	in./min	kg/m	lb/ft	h/m	h/ft	mm	in.	mm	in.
Joint A																	
2.0(a)	0.078(a)	14	2.4	3/32	50	5.9–6.8	14–16	...	...	0.045	0.030	0.0436	0.0133	0	0	0	0
3.6	0.140	10	3.2	1/8	75	2.8–3.1	6.7–7.3	...	...	0.136	0.091	0.0938	0.0286	0	0	0	0
Joint B																	
4.8	3/16	...	4.0	5/32	110	2.2–2.5	5.2–5.8	...	...	0.238	0.160	0.1194	0.0364	1.6	1/16	1.6	1/16
6.4	1/4	...	4.0	5/32	110	2.2–2.5	5.2–5.8	1.8–2.0	4.3–4.7	0.551	0.370	0.2651	0.0808	2.4	3/32	1.6	1/16

(a) Conducted vertical down; all others vertical up

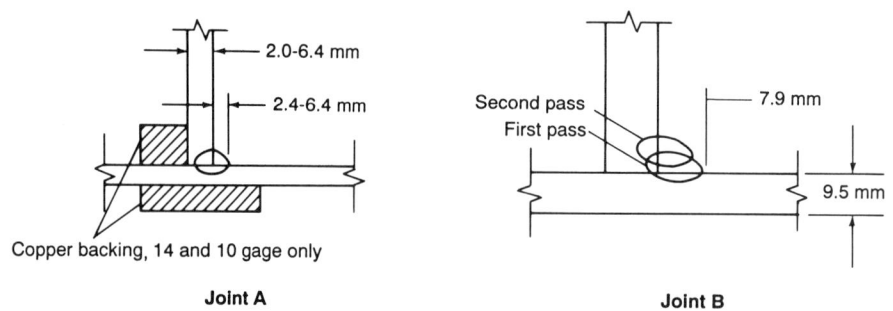

Fig. 7   Suggested procedures for shielded-metal arc welding of fillet joints in austenitic stainless steel from 2.0 mm (0.08 in., or 14 gage) to 9.5 mm (0.38 in.) in thickness in the flat or horizontal positions. E3XX-16 electrode. Source: Ref 8

Plate thickness			Weld size		Electrode diameter		Current (DCEP)(a), A	Arc speed				Amount of electrode required		Total time of weld	
								First pass		Second pass					
mm	in.	Gage	mm	in.	mm	in.		mm/s	in./min	mm/s	in./min	kg/m	lb/ft	h/m	h/ft
Joint A															
2.0	0.078	14	2.4	3/32	2.4	3/32	60	5.3–5.7	12.5–13.5	...	...	0.054	0.036	0.051	0.0154
3.6	0.140	10	3.2	1/8	3.2	1/8	85	5.3–5.7	12.5–13.5	...	...	0.083	0.056	0.051	0.0154
4.8	3/16	...	4.8	3/16	4.0	5/32	120	3.6–4.0	8.6–9.4	...	...	0.178	0.120	0.073	0.0222
6.4	1/4	...	6.4	1/4	4.8	3/16	160	2.6–2.9	6.2–6.8	...	...	0.328	0.220	0.101	0.0308
Joint B															
9.5	3/8	...	7.9	5/16	4.8	3/16	170	2.6–2.9	6.2–6.8	2.8–3.1	6.7–7.3	0.640	0.430	0.195	0.0594

Note: For vertical and overhead welding position, use same procedures as for vertical and overhead butt welds. (a) Alternating current can be used with a 10% increase in current; E3XX-15 electrode can be used with a 10% decrease in current.

and plate in the flat position. Figure 6 provides the suggested procedures for butt welds in the vertical and overhead positions. Figure 7 addresses fillet welds in the flat or horizontal positions. Figure 8 considers lap joints, and Fig. 9 considers corner joints. The information in these figures is meant only as a starting point in procedure development.

Although originally developed for austenitic stainless steels, the procedures are also reasonable starting points for other stainless steels within the guidelines given elsewhere in this article.

Submerged Arc Welding. The ANSI/AWS A5.9-92 specification classifies both solid and composite (metal-cored tubular or stranded)

wires that can be used for several welding processes, including SAW. Wires are classified only on the basis of their composition and whether they are solid or composite. For the ferrite-containing austenitic grades, the chromium content of a wire of a given alloy type is generally shifted to a higher level for the wires, compared with SMAW

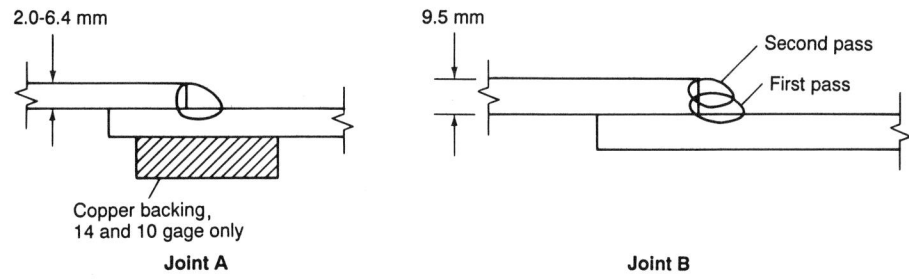

Plate thickness			Electrode diameter		Current (DCEP)(a), A	Arc speed				Amount of electrode required		Total time of weld	
						First pass		Second pass					
mm	in.	Gage	mm	in.		mm/s	in./min	mm/s	in./min	kg/m	lb/ft	h/m	h/ft
Joint A													
2.0	0.078	14	2.4	3/32	60	5.3–5.7	12.5–13.5	...	...	0.054	0.036	0.051	0.0154
3.6	0.140	10	3.2	1/8	90	5.3–5.7	12.5–13.5	...	...	0.083	0.056	0.051	0.0154
4.8	3/16	...	4.0	5/32	125	3.6–4.0	8.6–9.4	...	...	0.194	0.130	0.073	0.0222
6.4	1/4	...	4.8	3/16	170	2.6–2.9	6.2–6.8	...	...	0.357	0.240	0.101	0.0308
Joint B													
9.5	3/8	...	4.8	3/16	175	2.6–2.9	6.2–6.8	2.8–3.1	6.7–7.3	0.685	0.460	0.195	0.0594

(a) Alternating current can be used with a 10% increase in current; E3XX-15 electrode can be used with a 10% decrease in current.

Fig. 8 Suggested procedure for shielded-metal arc welding of lap joints in austenitic stainless steel from 2.0 mm (0.08 in., or 14 gage) to 9.5 mm (0.38 in.) in thickness in the horizontal

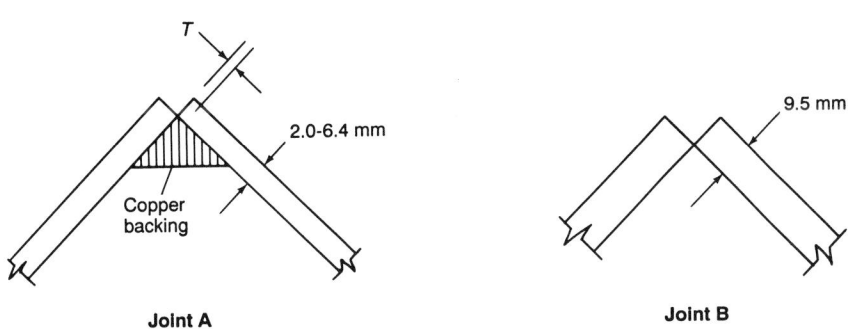

Plate thickness			Electrode diameter		Current (DCEP)(a), A		Arc speed				Amount of electrode required		Total time of weld		Thickness, T	
					First pass	Second pass	First pass		Second pass							
mm	in.	Gage	mm	in.			mm/s	in./min	mm/s	in./min	kg/m	lb/ft	h/m	h/ft	mm	in.
Joint A																
2.0	0.078	14	2.4	3/32	60	...	5.9–6.8	14–16	...	...	0.042	0.028	0.0436	0.0133	1.0	0.04
3.6	0.140	10	3.2	1/8	85	...	5.3–5.7	12.5–13.5	...	...	0.083	0.056	0.0505	0.0154	0.8	1/32
4.8	3/16	...	4.0	5/32	125	...	4.4–4.9	10.5–11.5	...	...	0.140	0.094	0.0597	0.0182	1.2	3/64
6.4	1/4	...	4.8	3/16	160	...	2.6–2.9	6.2–6.8	...	...	0.33	0.22	0.101	0.0308	1.6	1/16
Joint B																
9.5	3/8	...	4.8	3/16	160	175	2.6–2.9	6.2–6.8	2.4–2.7	5.7–6.3	0.67	0.45	0.210	0.0641	0	0

(a) Alternating current can be used with a 10% increase in current; E3XX-15 electrode can be used with a 10% decrease in current.

Fig. 9 Suggested procedure for shielded-metal arc welding of corner joints in austenitic stainless steel from 2.0 mm (0.08 in., or 14 gage) to 9.5 mm (0.38 in.) in thickness in the flat position. E3XX-16 electrode. Source: Ref 8

electrodes. For example, the chromium content for E308-XX electrodes ranges from 18.0 to 21.0%, but for ER308 wire, it is 19.5 to 22.0%. There is a good reason for this. The composition requirements for SMAW electrodes are for the all-weld metal deposit, that is, the finished weld, whereas the requirements for the wires are for the wire composition, the tool that is used to produce the finished weld. Some loss of chromium is to be

expected in transferring the metal across the arc in SAW, as well as in gas-shielded processes. In the SAW process, chromium recovery depends strongly on the specific flux chosen and on the choice of welding parameters.

The AWS filler metal specifications do not classify fluxes for SAW of stainless steels. However, practical experience indicates that there are essentially three groupings of SAW fluxes with

respect to chromium recovery. In SAW of carbon steels and low-alloy steels, it is common to describe fluxes as *neutral* or *active*, depending on whether the manganese and silicon contents of the deposited weld metal vary appreciably with changes in arc voltage or flux-to-wire ratio. However, a flux that is neutral with respect to manganese and silicon recovery may be very aggressive in removing chromium from the weld metal.

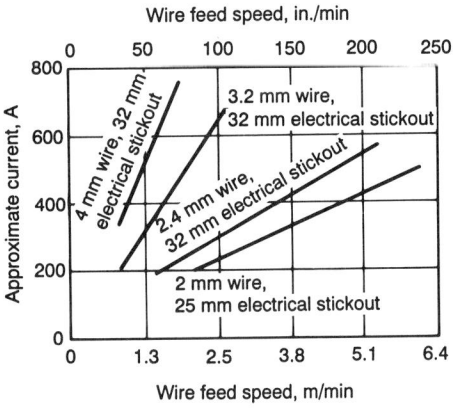

Fig. 10 Direct current electrode positive vs. wire-feed speed for submerged arc welding with E3XX

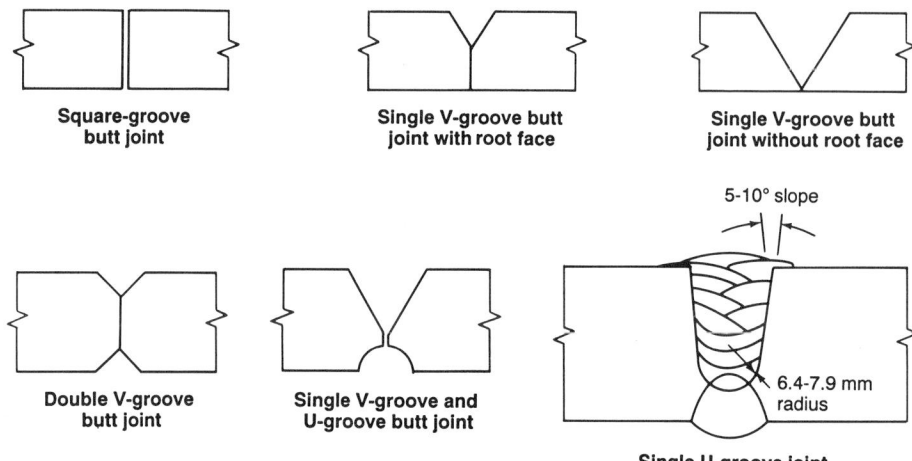

Fig. 11 Butt joint designs for submerged arc welding. Source: Ref 8

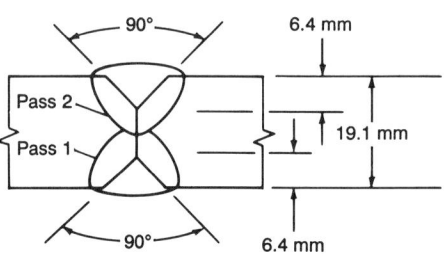

Fig. 12 Typical double-V weld in type 304 plate. Pass 1 was made at 700 A and 33 V, at 6.8 mm/s (16 in./min). Pass 2 was made at 950 A and 35 V, at 5.1 mm/s (12 in./min). Power, direct current, electrode positive; type 308 electrode, 4.8 mm (3/16 in.) diam; neutral flux. Source: Ref 8

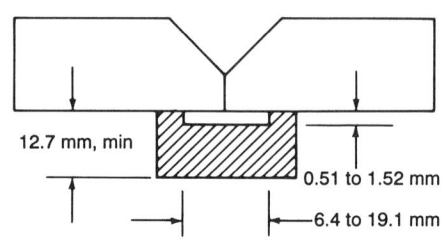

Fig. 13 Recommended groove dimensions for copper backing bars in the submerged arc welding of stainless steels. Source: Ref 8

Therefore, *neutral* and *active* descriptions from the ANSI/AWS A5.17 (mild steel submerged arc) or ANSI/AWS A5.23 (low-alloy submerged arc) specifications have no meaning with regard to stainless steel.

A somewhat quantitative grouping of fluxes for stainless steels relates all-weld metal chromium content to wire chromium content. A number of fluxes that are high in manganese silicate and the other oxides that are less stable than chromium oxide tend to deplete the chromium of the deposit on the order of 2%, or even more, in absolute terms. With such a flux, a wire of 21% Cr is likely to produce a deposit of only 19% Cr, which fits well with the higher chromium content of wires of ANSI/AWS A5.9, when compared with the electrodes of ANSI/AWS A5.4. With such fluxes, a higher arc voltage, or any other change that tends to increase the ratio of the flux melted to wire melted, will tend to reduce the chromium recovery further. These fluxes are sometimes referred to as *acid fluxes*.

A second group of fluxes for stainless steels are those composed primarily of oxides of calcium, magnesium, titanium, and aluminum, along with calcium fluoride. These compounds are more stable than chromium oxide. Fluxes of this group tend to produce only a small loss of chromium, typically of the order of 0.5 to 1.0%, in absolute terms, when compared with the wire compositions. With such fluxes, a higher voltage, or any other change that tends to increase the ratio of flux melted to wire melted, produces only a small increase in chromium loss. These fluxes are sometimes referred to as *basic fluxes*.

A third group of fluxes for stainless steels are those that include, in the individual flux particles, particles of chromium metal or alloy. The amount of this chromium is usually only slightly more than that needed to make up for the chromium that is lost to oxidation during welding. Therefore, a small chromium increase, typically of the order of 0.5 to 1%, is observed in the weld metal when compared with the wire. This chromium gain may increase with an increase in arc voltage or with any other welding parameter change that increases the ratio of flux melted to wire melted.

These fluxes are sometimes referred to as *chromium-compensating fluxes*.

Loss of chromium means not only loss of some corrosion resistance, but also loss of ferrite in nominally austenitic stainless steel weld metals that are intended to contain some ferrite. The use of an acid flux is likely to produce about 5 FN less than the FN value calculated from the wire composition using Fig. 3. The use of a basic flux is likely to produce almost the same FN as that calculated from the wire composition using Fig. 3. The use of a chromium-compensating flux is likely to produce as much as 5 FN, or more, greater than the FN value calculated from the wire composition using Fig. 3.

A further consideration in flux selection is carbon recovery with martensitic stainless steels. The acid fluxes tend to remove considerable carbon from high-carbon stainless steels, so that the ability to achieve a given hardness level is affected. The basic fluxes tend to recover nearly all of the wire carbon. The chromium-compensating fluxes can do either, depending on the specific oxide balance in a given flux. The use of either an acid flux or a chromium-compensating flux with a martensitic stainless steel wire like ER410 may produce ferrite stringers in what ought to be a fully martensitic deposit. As a result, the mechanical properties may be inferior.

Submerged arc welding permits much broader ranges of current for a given electrode size than does the SMAW process. Current is largely determined by wire-feed speed, although increased electrode extension ("stickout") will decrease current at a given wire-feed speed. Figure 10 presents typical wire-feed speed ranges for a variety of solid electrode sizes and the corresponding welding currents with austenitic filler metals. Other current ranges result when either composite or martensitic wires are used, because the electrical resistance of these wires differs from that of the austenitic wires. Nevertheless, Fig. 10 can provide a starting point. In general, as the wire-feed speed is increased, a corresponding voltage increase is appropriate for the best bead shape. Typically, 26 to 28 V produce the best results at the bottom end of the wire-feed speed range, and 32 to 36 V produce the best results at the top end of the wire-feed speed range.

Because there is no classification system for submerged arc fluxes for stainless steels, and because the broad range of chromium recovery that is possible depends on the specific flux chosen, either the advice or literature of the flux manufacturer should be obtained before using an unfamiliar flux.

Figures 11 and 12 provide joint preparations that have proved useful in submerged arc butt welding of stainless steel plate. Figure 13 provides copper backing information for one-side butt welding using the SAW process. Circumfer-

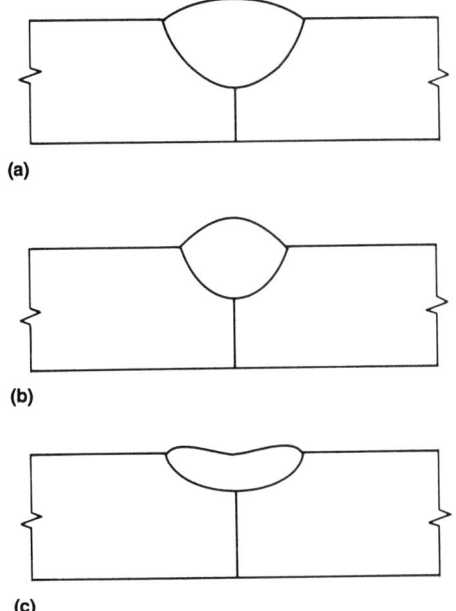

Fig. 14 Weld profiles. (a) Contour of a weld bead in the flat position with the work horizontal. (b) Welding slightly uphill. (c) Welding slightly downhill. Source: Ref 8

ential welding on tubular components is usually done by offsetting the welding head from top-dead-center, so that solidification occurs in the flat position, slightly uphill or slightly downhill. This affects the weld profile, as shown in Fig. 14.

Gas-Tungsten Arc Welding. The GTAW process is widely used for welding stainless steels, especially for full-penetration welds in thin-gage materials and root passes in thicker materials. For almost all GTAW of stainless steels, thoriated tungsten electrodes (ANSI/AWS A5.12 classification EWTh-2) are preferred, and welding utilizes argon gas shielding with direct current, electrode negative polarity. For heavy

sections, sometimes helium or argon-helium mixes can be used to achieve greater heat input or higher welding speeds.

Additions of hydrogen (of the order of 5%) to argon gas shielding have also been used, primarily for austenitic stainless steels, to provide higher heat input and a cleaner weld surface. Hydrogen additions are a possible source of embrittlement for all other types of stainless steels. Both manual and automatic procedures are suitable. In automatic welding, a voltage-controlled head can be used to maintain a constant arc length, and either cold-wire or hot-wire filler metal additions are used.

Many welds in tubing and light-gage material are made without filler metal additions, using square butt joints, lap joints, edge joints, corner joints, and the like. Then, the weld metal has nearly the same composition as the base metal. When welding austenitic stainless steels such as type 304 or 316, ferrite is usually desirable in the weld metal, but attempts to measure ferrite in the base metal before welding will generally detect no ferrite. This is not a cause for alarm, because the hot-working operations that were conducted to reduce the original stainless steel ingot to the final form generally cause all ferrite in the base metal to be transformed to austenite. Steelmakers generally prefer to adjust the composition of a stainless steel ingot to contain a small amount (typically 3 to 8 FN) of ferrite as-cast, because this improves resistance to the ingot's breaking up during the first reductions. Thus, their interest is similar to that of the welding engineer. Although no ferrite may be present after hot working, remelting during welding will return the original as-cast ferrite, which means that ferrite is usually found in the weld metal of autogenous joints in types 304, 316, and similar stainless steel alloys.

The potential for ferrite in an autogenous joint can be assessed from the base metal certified material test report (CMTR) using the WRC-1988 diagram. To be truly useful for this purpose, the CMTR should include nitrogen. If the CMTR indicates that

no ferrite is likely in the autogenous weld, then the addition of a filler metal that will provide ferrite ought to be considered, at least for base metals that normally can be expected to provide some ferrite in near-matching weld metal compositions.

Filler metals for the GTAW process are classified according to the ANSI/AWS A5.9 specification. Similar compositions in the form of consumable inserts, classified to the ANSI/AWS A5.30 specification, are also available for full-penetration root-pass welding. The consumable inserts provide a little surplus filler metal in order to attain an underside profile that is slightly convex. Consumable inserts can also be purchased with a variety of special shapes that assist in joint alignment, especially for welding pipe.

Pipe and tube welds are often made with a backing gas inside in order to prevent oxidation of the root surface. Although argon backing gas is the safest choice, it is more expensive than nitrogen, which has also been used. Small amounts of nitrogen from backing gas can be picked up in the weld metal, and cases are known where such nitrogen pickup was responsible for loss of ferrite and consequent hot cracking. Nevertheless, many successful welds have been made with nitrogen backing gas.

In GTAW of fully austenitic stainless steels, it is often advisable to add filler metal even when it does not appear to be needed. The proper addition of filler metal can be used to obtain a convex bead shape, which has better resistance to hot cracking than does the flat or slightly concave weld shape that often results when no filler metal is added. This can be of critical importance when welding fully austenitic stainless steels without cracking.

Successful GTAW of nominally austenitic stainless steels (the weld metals of which are designed to contain a little ferrite) can depend on the integrity of the gas shield. Drafts, low gas-flow rates, or excessively high gas-flow rates can cause air (which is about 80% nitrogen) to enter the arc. Nitrogen is then picked up by the weld metal, and

Table 2 Procedure range for gas-metal arc welding with ER3XXLSi electrodes by the short-circuit transfer mode

Characteristics	Wire feed speed		Approximate current, A	Arc voltage, V(a)	Deposition rate	
	m/min	in./min			kg/h	lb/h
For a 0.9 mm (0.035 in.) diam	3.0	120	55	19-20	0.9	2.0
electrode weighing 5.11 g/m (0.003 lb/ft),	3.8	150	75	19-20	1.2	2.5
using DCEP and a	4.6	180	85	19-20	1.4	3.0
13 mm (½ in.) electrical stickout,	5.2	205	95	19-20	1.6	3.4
with a shielding gas of 90He-7½Ar-2½CO$_2$	5.8	230	105	20-21	1.8	3.9
	6.9	275	110	20-21	2.1	4.6
	7.6	300	125	20-21	2.3	5.0
	8.3	325	130	20-21	2.5	5.4
	8.9	350	140	21-22	2.7	5.9
	9.5	375	150	21-22	2.9	6.3
	10.2	400	160	22-23	3.1	6.7
	10.8	425	170	22-23	3.3	7.1
For a 1.1 mm (0.045 in.) diam electrode	2.5	100	100	19-20	1.1	2.8
weighing 7.63 g/m (0.0045 lb/ft), 3.2	125	120	19-20	1.5	3.5	
using DCEP and a 13 mm (½ in.)	3.8	150	135	21	1.7	4.2
electrical stickout,	4.4	175	140	21	2.0	4.8
with a shielding gas of 90He-7½Ar-2½CO$_2$	5.6	220	170	22	2.6	6.1
	6.4	250	175	22-23	2.9	6.9
	7.0	275	185	22-23	3.2	7.6

(a) Arc voltages are measured from the wire feeder gun cable block to work.

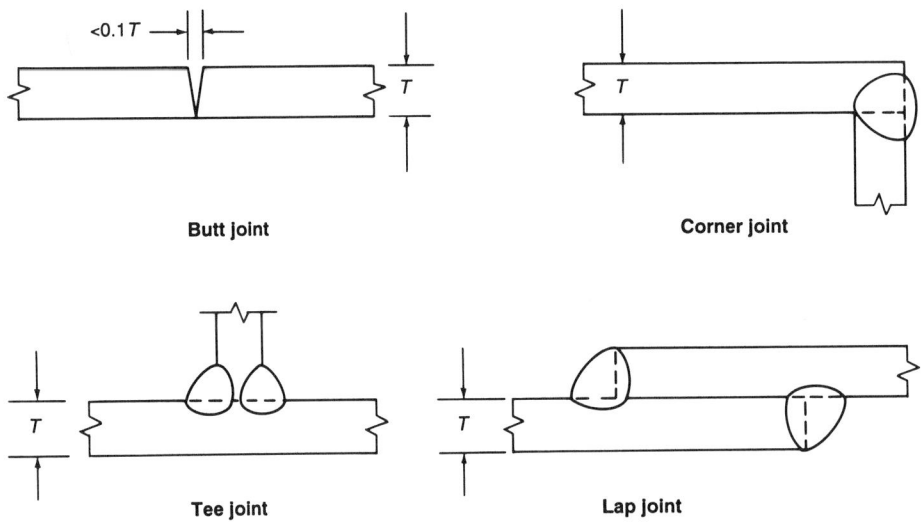

Fig. 15 Suggested procedures for gas-tungsten arc welding of butt, corner, tee, and lap joints in stainless steels. Source: Ref 8

Plate thickness, T		Current (DCEN)(a), A	Electrode diameter		Argon gas flow		Filler rod diameter		Arc speed		Total time of weld	
mm	in.		mm	in.	m³/h	ft³/h	mm	in.	mm/s	in./min	h/m	h/ft
Butt and corner joints												
1.6	1/16	80–100	1.6	1/16	0.3	10	1.6	1/16	5.1	12	0.0548	0.0167
2.4	3/32	100–120	1.6	1/16	0.3	10	1.6	1/16	5.1	12	0.0548	0.0167
3.2	1/8	120–140	1.6	1/16	0.3	10	2.4	3/32	5.1	12	0.0548	0.0167
4.8	3/16	200–250	2.4	3/32	0.4	15	3.2	1/8	4.2	10	0.0656	0.0200
6.4	1/4	200–350	3.2	1/8	0.56	20	3.2	1/8	3.4	8	0.0820	0.0250
12.7	1/2	225–375	3.2	1/8	0.7	25	3.2	1/8	3.4	8	0.0820	0.0250
Tee and lap joints												
1.6	1/16	90–110	1.6	1/16	0.3	10	1.6	1/16	4.2	10	0.0656	0.0200
2.4	3/32	110–130	1.6	1/16	0.3	10	1.6	1/16	4.2	10	0.0565	0.0200
3.2	1/8	130–150	1.6	1/16	0.3	10	2.4	3/32	4.2	10	0.0656	0.0200
4.8	3/16	225–275	2.4	3/32	0.4	15	3.2	1/8	3.4	8	0.0820	0.0250
6.4	1/4	225–350	3.2	1/8	0.56	20	3.2	1/8	3.4	8	0.0820	0.0250
12.7	1/2	225–375	3.2	1/8	0.7	25	3.2	1/8	3.4	8	0.0820	0.0250

(a) For vertical-up and overhead positions, decrease current 10 to 20%.

a weld, which ought to contain ferrite, can be rendered ferrite-free and sensitive to hot cracking. Proper gas-flow rates, typically 0.3 to 0.8 m³/h (10 to 30 ft³/h), and barriers that prevent moving air from reaching the arc area can be used to prevent nitrogen pickup. Special attention to the integrity of both shielding gas and backing gas can be especially important in the successful welding of third-generation ferritic stainless steels, which can be embrittled by traces of nitrogen that are picked up during welding.

Gas-tungsten arc welding can be done with a broad range of welding currents for most applications, with travel speed adjusted to make the proper size of weld for the current chosen. Each individual tungsten electrode size has a corresponding proper current range. These current ranges are not particular to stainless steels. Figure 15 provides some welding procedure information for beginning procedure development in GTAW of stainless steels.

Special attention should be given to the role of sulfur and other surface-active elements in controlling penetration in full-penetration gas-tungsten arc welds. It has been amply demonstrated that sulfur levels of the order of 0.005% and lower tend to produce penetration profiles with very low depth-to-width ratios, because of surface tension gradient effects. On the other hand, sulfur levels of 0.010% and higher seem to ensure a high depth-to-width ratio, which is desirable for full-penetration butt welds.

When searching for a small amount of filler metal for a GTAW application, especially in repair situations, it is not uncommon for the welder and/or engineer to be tempted to remove the coating from a covered electrode of nominally matching composition to a given base metal and to use the core wire for GTAW filler metal. This can be a very risky approach, because the coatings of many covered stainless steel electrodes provide alloy elements. The core wire may not be close to

the weld metal composition. For example, it is not uncommon to produce type 347 weld metal from a covered electrode whose core wire is type 308 and that has all of the niobium in the coating. It is also not uncommon to produce type 317L covered electrodes using type 316L core wire. Some stainless steel electrodes are made from mild steel core wire and have all of the alloy in the coating. Therefore, before attempting a gas-tungsten arc weld with the core wire from a covered electrode, those concerned should contact the electrode manufacturer to determine what core wire was used to make the electrode.

Gas-Metal Arc Welding. The GMAW process is used extensively for joining both thin and thick stainless steel base metals. Filler metals are classified to the ANSI/AWS A5.9 specification, as are filler metals for SAW or GTAW. For many applications with nominally austenitic filler metals that are intended to contain a little ferrite, high-silicon versions of the basic classifications are

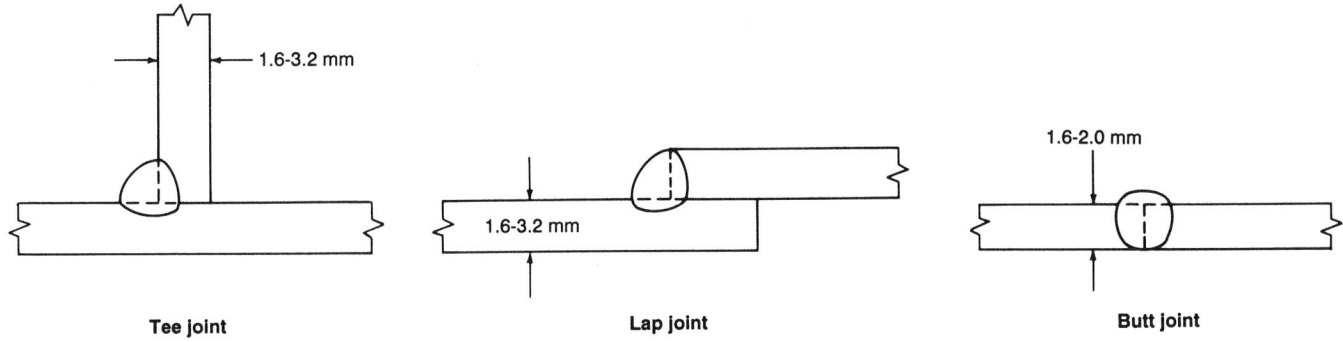

Tee joint   Lap joint   Butt joint

Plate thickness		Current (DCEP), A	Voltage, V(a)	Wire feed speed		Welding speed		Amount of electrode required		Total time of weld	
mm	in.			mm/s	in./min	mm/s	in./min	kg/m	lb/ft	h/m	h/ft
Tee and lap joints											
1.6	0.063	85	15	78	184	7.2–8.0	17–19	0.037	0.025	0.0364	0.0111
2.0	0.078	90	15	81	192	5.5–6.3	13–15	0.051	0.034	0.0469	0.0143
2.4	0.093	105	17	98	232	5.9–6.8	14–16	0.058	0.039	0.0436	0.0133
3.2	0.125	125	17	119	280	5.9–6.8	14–16	0.069	0.046	0.0436	0.0133
Butt joint											
1.6	0.063	85	15	78	184	8.0–8.9	19–21	0.034	0.023	0.0328	0.0100
2.0	0.078	90	15	81	192	4.9–5.3	11.5–12.5	0.058	0.039	0.0548	0.0167

(a) For Ar-25 CO_2 or Ar-2O; voltage is 6 to 7V higher for He-7$\frac{1}{2}$ Ar-2$\frac{1}{2}$ CO_2.

Fig. 16 Suggested procedures for gas-metal arc welding of tee, lap, and butt joints in 200- and 300-series stainless steels using the short-circuiting transfer mode. Shielding gas, argon plus 25% CO_2 or argon plus 2% O_2; gas flow, 0.4 to 0.6 m^3/h (15 to 20 ft^3/h); electrode, 0.8 mm (0.030 in.) diam. Source: Ref 8

Table 3 Procedure range for gas-metal arc welding with ER3XXLSi electrodes by axial spray transfer

Characteristics	Wire feed speed		Approximate current, A	Arc voltage, V(a)	Deposition rate	
	m/min	in./min			kg/h	lb/h
For a 0.9 mm (0.035 in.) diam electrode weighing 5.11 g/m (0.003 lb/ft), using DCEP and a 13 mm (½ in.) electrical stickout, with a shielding gas of 98Ar-2O$_2$	10.2	400	180	23	3.1	6.7
	10.8	425	190	24	3.3	7.1
	11.4	450	200	24	3.5	7.5
	12.1	475	210	25	3.7	8.0
For a 1.1 mm (0.045 in.) diam electrode weighing 7.63 g/m (0.0045 lb/ft), using DCEP and a 19 mm (¾ in.) electrical stickout, with a shielding gas of 98Ar-2O$_2$	6.1	240	195	24	2.8	6.6
	6.6	260	230	25	3.0	7.2
	7.6	300	240	25	3.5	8.3
	8.3	325	250	26	3.8	9.0
	9.1	360	260	26	4.2	10.0
For a 1.6 mm (1/16 in.) diam electrode weighing 16.14 g/m (0.01 lb/ft), using DCEP and a 19 mm (¾ in.) electrical stickout, with a shielding gas of 98Ar-2O$_2$	4.4	175	260	26	4.3	9.2
	5.1	200	310	29	4.9	10.5
	6.4	250	330	29	6.2	13.1
	7.0	275	360	31	6.8	14.4
	7.6	300	390	32	7.4	15.8

(a) Arc voltages are measured from the wire feeder gun cable block to work.

preferred for better wetting and bead shape. These high-silicon versions contain from 0.65 to 1.00% Si, versus 0.30 to 0.65% for the normal grades.

With thin materials, the short-circuiting transfer mode is primarily used, with 0.9 mm (0.035 in.) and 1.1 mm (0.045 in.) diameters being the most common. The preferred shielding gas is often a mixture of 90% He, 7.5% Ar, and 2.5% CO_2. Helium-rich gases provide higher voltage in short-circuiting transfer welding, resulting in better wetting and fewer problems with lack-of-fusion defects than occur with argon-rich gases.

However, argon-rich gas may be preferred for welding on very thin materials. Typical welding conditions for short-circuiting transfer welding are given in Table 2 and Fig. 16. Short-circuiting transfer is usable both in the flat position and out of position.

With thicker materials, the spray-transfer mode is most often used. In addition to the same two common diameters used in short-circuiting transfer, a 1.6 mm (1/16 in.) diameter is often used. The most common shielding gases are argon-rich mixtures, such as argon with from 1 to 5% oxygen, argon with a few percent of carbon dioxide, or argon with both oxygen and carbon dioxide added. Typical welding conditions for spray transfer are given in Table 3 and Fig. 17. Spray-transfer welding is limited to the flat and horizontal positions.

With special pulsing power sources, a spray-like transfer can be produced at a much lower average welding current, more like that of the short-circuiting transfer mode. Pulsed GMAW can permit out-of-position welding. So-called "synergic" power sources are claimed to auto-

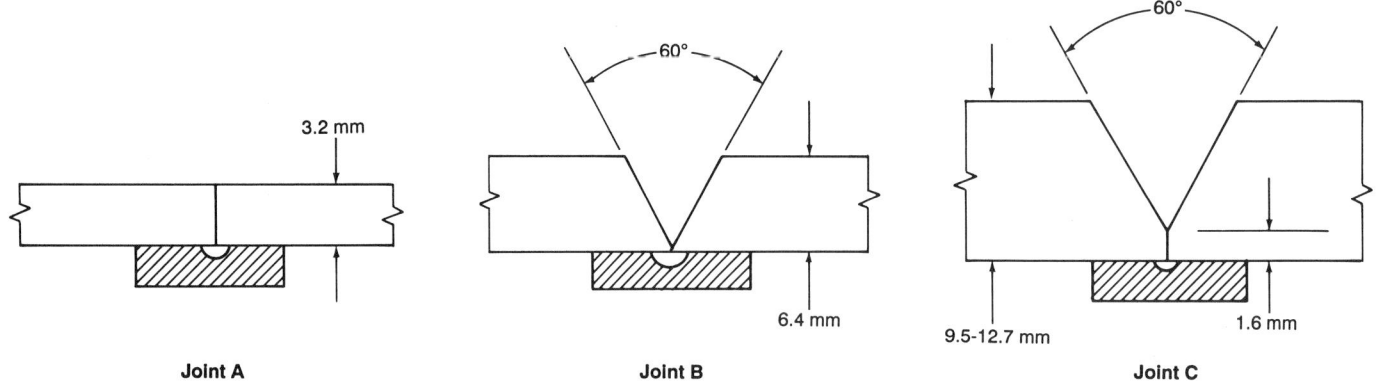

Fig. 17 Suggested procedures for gas-metal arc welding of butt joints in 200- and 300-series stainless steels using the spray-arc transfer mode. Shielding gas, argon plus 1% O_2; gas flow, 1 m³/h (35 ft³/h). Source: Ref 8

Plate thickness		Electrode diameter		Number of passes	Current (DCEP), A	Wire feed speed		Arc speed		Amount of electrode required		Total time of weld	
mm	in.	mm	in.			mm/s	in./min	mm/s	in./min	kg/m	lb/ft	h/m	h/ft
Joint A													
3.2	1/8	1.6	1/16	1	225	60	140	8.0–8.9	19–21	0.112	0.075	0.033	0.010
Joint B													
6.4	1/4	1.6	1/16	2	275	74	175	8.0–8.9	19–21	0.282	0.189	0.066	0.020
Joint C													
9.5	3/8	1.6	1/16	2	300	85	200	6.3–7.2	15–17	0.405	0.272	0.082	0.025
12.7	1/2	2.4	3/32	4	325	95	225	6.3–7.2	15–17	0.737	0.495	0.164	0.050

matically adjust pulse frequency to produce the transfer of a single drop with each pulse, despite variations in electrical stickout or wire-feed speed. The pulsed GMAW process is an area of rapid technological development at the present time.

All GMAW conducted with nominally austenitic filler metals that are intended to produce a little ferrite is sensitive to the integrity of the gas shielding, as is the GTAW process. Drafts and gas turbulence can permit air to enter the gas stream, resulting in nitrogen pickup and loss of ferrite. As with GTAW, proper gas-flow rates (0.8 to 1.1 m³/h, or 30 to 40 ft³/h) and the use of barriers to exclude drafts from the arc area are essential to shielding gas integrity.

Flux-Cored Arc Welding. The ANSI/AWS A5.22 specification provides for three different classifications of a given alloy type, based on recommended shielding. Using type 308L as an example, an electrode can be classified as E308LT-1 (carbon dioxide shielding), E308LT-2 (Ar-2O₂ shielding), or E308LT-3 (no gas shielding).

In practice, E308LT-1 (and other alloy wires designed for carbon dioxide gas shielding) are usually used in small diameters, that is, 1.6 mm (1/16 in.) and 1.1 mm (0.045 in.). Even 0.9 mm (0.035 in.) diameters are becoming available. Despite the use of carbon dioxide shielding gas, low-carbon-deposit compositions can be produced. Many of these wires, especially in 1.1 mm (0.045 in.) and smaller diameters, are welded in the vertical-up and overhead positions, as well as in the downhand position. Although the wires are classified with carbon dioxide gas shielding, in many cases they weld better in the vertical-up and over-

head positions with Ar-25CO₂ shielding. The small-diameter wires are generally made from austenitic stainless steel strip (often type 304L), which work hardens very much during reduction to its final diameter. Thus, these wires are mechanically rather hard and tolerate high feed-roll pressures. Equipment for feeding such wires can be the same as for GMAW solid wires.

It is doubtful that any flux-cored stainless steel wires exist that are correctly classified with Ar-2O₂. The scope of the ANSI/AWS A5.22 specification requires that a wire classified as flux cored must contain a minimum of 5% nonmetallics, by weight of the electrode. This much slag is not compatible with very high argon gas shielding. Certain metal-cored electrodes seem to be improperly classified as EXXXT-2, but they have almost no nonmetallic ingredients and are more properly classified as composite electrodes, according to the ANSI/AWS A5.9 specification.

In practice, E308LT-3 electrodes (and other stainless steel alloy compositions designed for welding without gas shielding) are commonly available in somewhat larger sizes than are the carbon dioxide classifications. The most popular size is still 2.4 mm (3/32 in.), although 2.0 mm (5/64 in.) and 1.6 mm (1/16 in.) sizes are also popular. These wires are generally usable only in the downhand and horizontal positions. In contrast to the carbon-dioxide-shielded wires, these wires generally produce rather shallow penetration. This feature can require somewhat higher welder skill levels to make sound x-ray-quality welds, because of the dangers of slag entrapment. Higher travel speed is usually necessary when this defect

is encountered. On the other hand, this shallow penetration is a major advantage for cladding operations, and these electrodes have been extensively used to achieve fully alloyed low-carbon overlays in a minimum number of layers.

The 2.4 mm (0.10 in.) electrodes, typified by E308LT-3, are generally made from thin, mild steel strip, with all alloying elements in the core. This makes for a mechanically soft wire that often requires special U-grooved gear drive rolls for the wire feeder. Such drive rolls can grip the wire positively all around its circumference and do not tend to flatten the wire, which results in the best feeding characteristics. Special drive-roll conversion kits are offered for feeding these and other very soft wires. Some 2.0 mm (0.08 in.) diameter wires are also very soft, and similar drive rolls may be necessary.

The flux-cored wires designed for use without gas shielding are virtually immune to any effects of drafts on weld metal ferrite content. They generally produce a fairly heavy fume plume, which means that fume-extracting welding guns or other local exhaust systems can be desirable. Because of their immunity to drafts, these wires lend themselves very well to local exhaust.

On the other hand, the wires designed for use without shielding gas are sensitive to nitrogen pickup that is due to excessive arc length, as are SMAW coated electrodes. A proper balance between wire-feed speed (current) and voltage will ensure proper ferrite control with such electrodes.

The wires designed for use with carbon dioxide (or Ar-25CO₂) are sensitive to loss of shielding gas caused by drafts or inappropriate gas-flow rates, although less so than solid wires in the GMAW process. Protection from drafts is necessary for ferrite control, and local exhaust must be used with care so as not to disturb the gas shield. Otherwise, nitrogen can be picked up by the weld and ferrite can be lost. These wires also appear to have a greater tendency to pick up moisture from humid air if they are carelessly stored for long periods of time. Moisture pickup is often evidenced by "worm track" porosity (surface porosity elongated parallel to the solidification direction). This can often be eliminated by increasing the electrical stickout to preheat the wire, but care must be used to avoid loss of gas shielding.

A simple technique is to recess the contact tip approximately 5 to 10 mm (0.2 to 0.4 in.) behind the end of the shielding gas cup, then weld with normal distance between the gas cup and the workpiece. In extreme cases of moisture pickup, the wire may require a bake at 260 to 315 °C (500 to 600 °F) to remove the moisture. In humid weather, it is best to return gas-shielded flux-cored stainless steel wires to their packaging, or to store them in a tight plastic bag or in a low-temperature oven (100 °C, or 212 °F), if the wire is not to be used overnight.

Welding Martensitic Stainless Steels

Martensitic stainless steels are essentially alloys of iron and chromium that possess a body-centered tetragonal structure in the heat-treated condition. The compositions of martensitic stainless steels are specifically formulated to render them amenable to a quench-and-temper heat treatment in order to produce high levels of strength and hardness. The response of martensitic stainless steels to the heat-treat process is essentially the same as that of plain carbon or low-alloy steels, where maximum strength and hardness primarily depend on carbon content. Although the chromium level of approximately 11 to 18 wt% in martensitic grades is the same as in some ferritic stainless steels, the higher carbon content of the martensitic grades results in a complete transformation from δ-ferrite to austenite at high temperatures (~980 °C, or 1800 °F), followed by a subsequent change to the hard martensite phase upon rapid cooling. The thermal cycle of heating and rapid cooling, which occurs within the confined HAZ during welding, is equivalent to a quenching cycle.

The high-carbon martensitic structure that is produced is extremely brittle in the untempered condition. Cracking can occur when the heated weldment and the surrounding martensitic HAZ are unable to contract to the same degree and at the same rate as the weld metal. Preheat and postweld cooling rates are important vehicles for controlling these shrinkage stresses and are further discussed later in this article. Because of their response to welding thermal cycles, martensitic stainless steels are considered to be the most difficult of the five stainless steel families to weld.

The extent to which HAZ hardening is present depends on the carbon content of the base metal. Higher carbon contents (>0.15%) will produce

greater hardness and, therefore, an increased susceptibility to cracking. Thus, types 440A, B, and C stainless steels are not usually considered for applications that require welding, and filler metals are not readily available in type 440 compositions.

In addition to the problems that result from localized stresses associated with the volume change upon martensitic transformation, the risk of cracking will increase when hydrogen from various sources is present in the weld metal. Therefore, the use of low-hydrogen consumables is mandatory. Hydrogen-induced cold cracking in martensitic stainless steel weldments is also discussed in more detail later in this article.

Weld Microstructure (Ref 10-12)

Detailed studies have been made on the transformation, tempering behavior, and resulting microstructures of martensitic stainless steel weldments. These studies were spurred by an interest in using 12Cr-1Mo-0.3V (HT9) martensitic stainless steel as a candidate material for the first wall/blanket of fusion-containment devices (Tokamaks) because of its improved resistance to swelling, low coefficient of thermal expansion (CTE), and high thermal conductivity relative to austenitic stainless steel.

During the welding of martensitic stainless steels, the fusion zone and that portion of the HAZ that is heated to a temperature higher than the austenitization temperature is transformed to a brittle, untempered martensite upon cooling to room temperature. Because the ductility, or fracture toughness, of the untempered martensite is inferior to that of the surrounding quenched-and-tempered microstructure, the material is unfit for service in the as-welded condition. Consequently, a PWHT must be employed to reduce the hardness and increase the toughness of the weld region. Recommended PWHT practices for martensitic stainless steels, including HT9, are described below in the section "Specific Welding Recommendations."

The as-welded properties of the weld fusion zone and its response to PWHT can often be controlled by the appropriate choice of weld filler metal. However, the properties of the HAZ can be controlled only by the judicious selection of the welding process and process parameters and by the use of a PWHT. As a result, the use of martensitic stainless steels depends, to a large extent, on the ability of the user to understand and control the properties of the weld HAZ.

An extensive review of the microstructure and properties of the HAZ in martensitic HT9 weldments is provided by Lippold (Ref 10-12). In his studies, a variety of autogenous bead-on-plate gas-tungsten arc welds were evaluated using both light optical microscopy and microhardness techniques. Prior to welding, the base metal plates were austenitized for 30 min at 1040 °C (1900 °F), followed by an air cool. Tempering was performed at 760 °C (1400 °F) for 1 h. The base metal microstructure consisted of a mixture of tempered lath martensite and alloy carbides, as shown in Fig. 18.

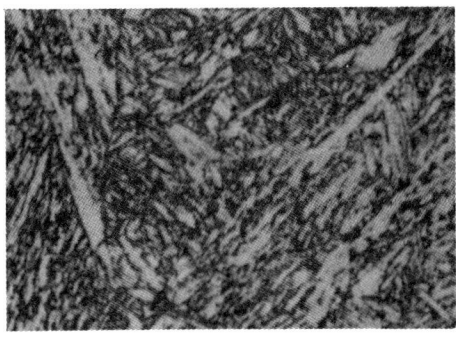

Fig. 18 Quenched-and-tempered base metal (HT9) microstructure, 22 to 25 HRC. Source: Ref 10

Table 4 Parameters for gas-tungsten arc welding of HT9 martensitic stainless steel

Voltage, V	12-16
Arc current, A	100-225
Travel speed, mm/s (in./min)	1.69 (4)
Electrode/work distance, mm (in.)	2.38 (0.094)
Electrode diameter, mm (in.)	3.18 (0.125)
Electrode material	W-2ThO$_2$
Shielding gas (argon), mm^3/s (ft^3/h)	365 (30)
Preheat	None

Source: Ref 10, 11

The welding parameters used in these studies are listed in Table 4. The welding current was varied in the range from 100 to 225 A in order to produce weld heat inputs ranging from 0.71 to 2.13 kJ/mm (18 to 54 kJ/in.). The plates were clamped in a copper fixture during welding in order to stimulate the structural restraint experienced by actual components during fabrication.

As shown in Fig. 19, the weld area consisted of the base metal (described above and shown in Fig. 18), the HAZ, and the fusion zone. Prior to tempering, the fusion zone microstructure comprised a mixture of untempered martensite and δ-ferrite, as shown in Fig. 20.

Four distinct regions were identified within the HAZ. These regions can be related to the phase fields on the iron-chromium-carbon equilibrium diagram shown in Fig. 21. The microstructures associated with these four regions are:

- *Region 1*, which is a two-phase region adjacent to the fusion line that consists of untempered martensite and ferrite. The ferrite forms along prior-austenite grain boundaries as this region is heated into the austenite-plus-ferrite phase field (designated "1" in Fig. 19 and 21).
- *Region 2*, which consists entirely of untempered martensite. As this portion of the HAZ is heated into the high-temperature regime of the austenite-phase field, alloy carbides from the original base metal microstructure completely dissolve, resulting in a carbide-free untempered martensite that exhibits a large prior austenite grain.

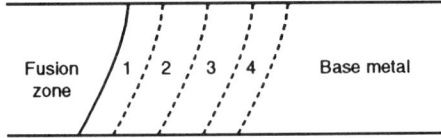

Four HAZ regions:

1 γ + ferrite ⟶ martensite + ferrite
2 Coarse-grained γ ⟶ martensite
3 Fine-grained γ ⟶ martensite
4 Overtempered base metal

Fig. 19 Four heat-affected zones observed in HT9 weldments. γ represents austenite. Source: Ref

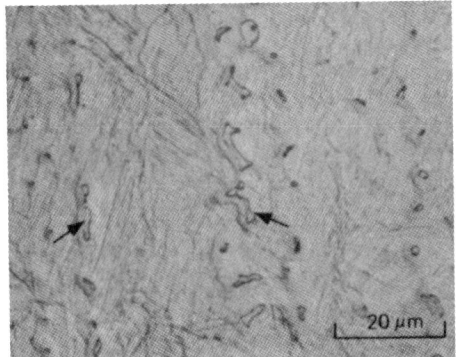

Fig. 20 As-welded gas-tungsten arc fusion-zone microstructure in HT9 weldments. Arrows indicate metastable δ-ferrite, which constitutes approximately 2 to 3 vol% of the structure. 1000×. Source: Ref 10

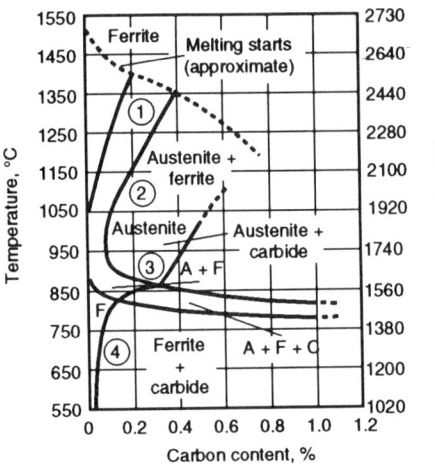

Fig. 21 Iron-chromium-carbon pseudobinary phase diagram for 12 wt% Cr steel. Circled numbers represent the four heat-affected zones shown in Fig. 19 and 22. Source: Adapted from Ref 13

- *Region 3*, which contains untempered martensite interspersed with undissolved alloy carbides. Because this region experiences a temperature excursion into the lower regime of the austenite-phase field, carbide dissolution is incomplete and the prior-austenite grain size is smaller relative to Region 2.
- *Region 4*, which consists of tempered martensite and overaged carbides. It appears to be vir-

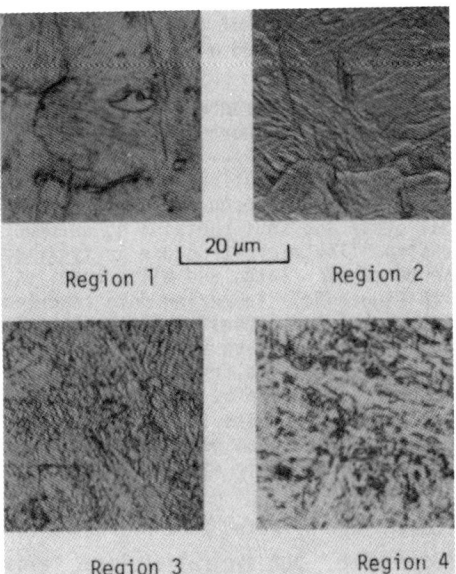

Fig. 22 Gas-tungsten arc welded heat-affected zone microstructures in HT9 weldments. Source: Ref 10

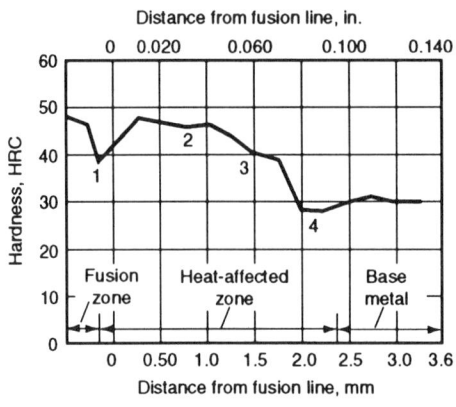

Fig. 23 Microhardness traverse across a gas-tungsten arc weld in HT9 stainless steel (no preheat or postheat treatment). Source: Ref 11

tually identical to the base metal microstructure.

Representative microstructures of these four regions are shown in Fig. 22.

The microstructures in the HAZ can also be differentiated by means of a microhardness traverse, as shown in Fig. 23. The drop in hardness in Region 1 results from the presence of the softer ferrite phase situated at prior-austenite grain boundaries within the untempered martensite matrix. The highest hardness in the HAZ occurs in the region where carbide dissolution is nearly complete. Because the hardness of the martensite is almost entirely a function of the carbon content of the prior austenite, Region 2 exhibits the peak HAZ hardness. Within Region 3, the carbon content of the austenite is less because of the incomplete dissolution of the carbides at lower austenitization temperatures. Therefore, the resultant microstructure, which consists of untem-

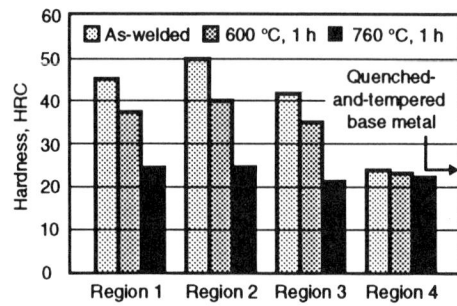

Fig. 24 Hardness as a function of postweld heat treatment temperature in the four heat-affected zones of HT9 weldments. Source: Ref 12

pered martensite and residual carbides, is softer than the adjacent untempered microstructure (Region 2). The hardness decrease in Region 4 results from overtempering the base metal microstructure at a temperature just below Ac_1 (the temperature at which austenite begins to form during heating), which is approximately 840 °C (1545 °F).

Figures 24 and 25 demonstrate the effect of PWHT on the hardness and toughness, respectively, of the four HAZ regions described above. As shown in these figures, a PWHT of 760 °C (1400 °F) for 1 h produced superior results.

Similar studies on HT9 have been carried out by Fenn and Jordan (Ref 14), with particular attention being given to δ-ferrite formation. Maintaining a δ-ferrite content that is as low as possible (<10 vol%) is important, because a homogeneous martensitic structure that is free of δ-ferrite islands results in a tougher weld. The investigations of these workers covered a variety of welding processes and a wide range of welding heat inputs and involved real and simulated HAZ material.

Weldability

Martensitic stainless steels can be welded in the annealed, hardened, and hardened-and-tempered conditions. Regardless of the prior condition of the steel, welding produces a hardened martensitic zone adjacent to the weld. In other words, the high-temperature HAZ will be in the as-quenched condition after welding, regardless of the prior condition of the material. In addition, the HAZ hardness is very much independent of the cooling rate over the temperature range experienced in common arc welding practices. This is evident from the isothermal transformation diagram shown in Fig. 26. Because such high hardness values render the material prone to cracking during fabrication, the selection of appropriate preheating levels and welding procedures is critical to the success of the welding process.

Hydrogen-Induced Cold Cracking. Weld-area cracking in martensitic stainless steels is primarily due to the presence of hydrogen in the hardened structure. Hydrogen-induced cold cracks form in welds when the weldment is at or near room temperature (typically, less than 150 °C, or 300 °F). Cracking may occur almost immediately or hours after cooling. In steel, cold cracks depend on the presence of a tensile stress, a sus-

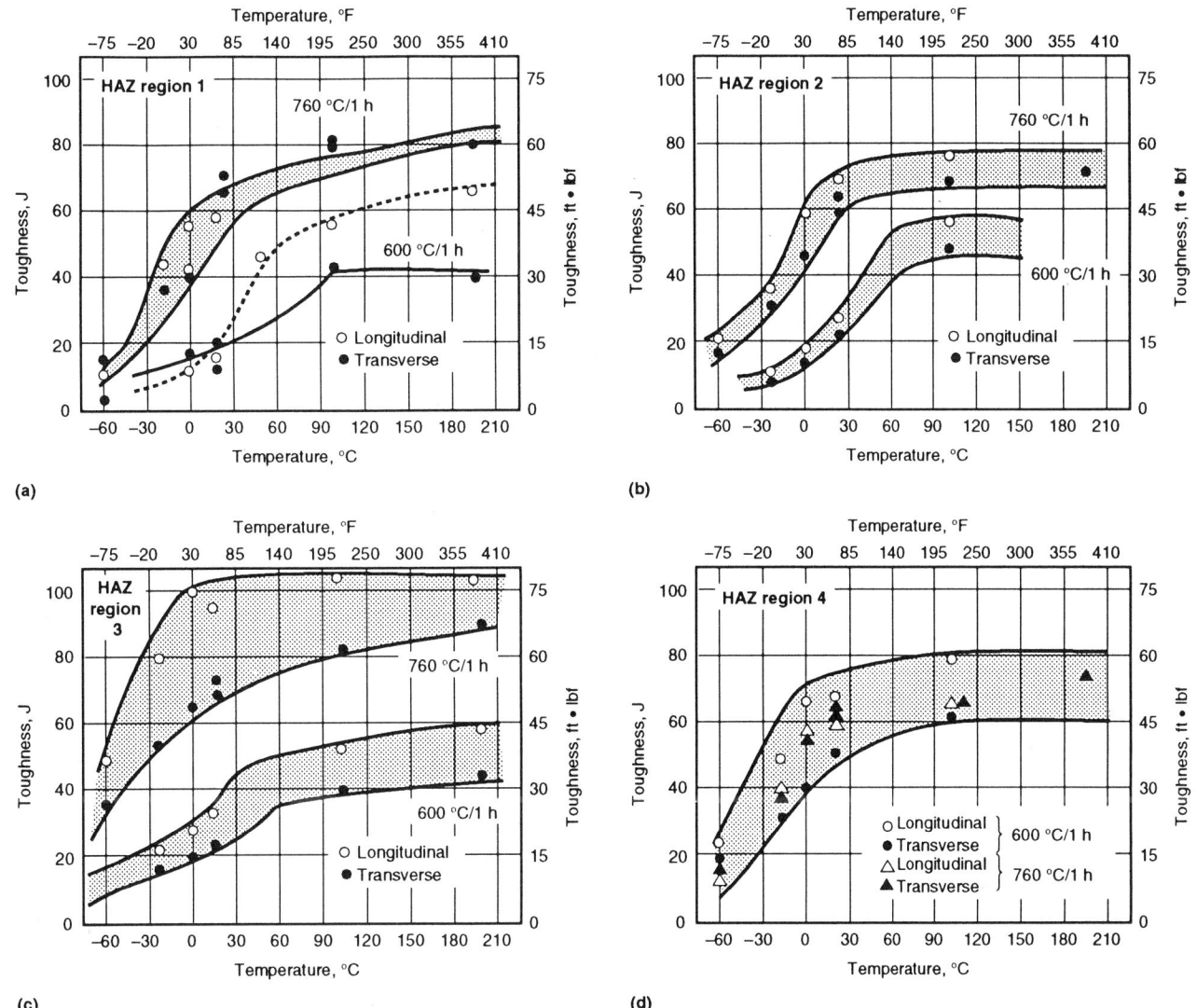

Fig. 25 Effect of orientation and postweld heat treatment on the toughness of HT9 weldments. (a) Region 1. (b) Region 2. (c) Region 3. (d) Region 4. See also Fig. 19 and 22. Source: Ref 12

ceptible microstructure, and sufficient hydrogen in the weld. Elimination of one or more of these factors greatly reduces crack susceptibility. The stress may arise from restraint by other components of a weldment or from the simple thermal stresses created by welding in a butt, groove, or T-joint.

The susceptibility of the microstructure to cold cracking relates to the solubility of hydrogen and the possibility of supersaturation. Austenite, in which hydrogen is highly soluble, is least susceptible to cold cracking, and martensite, in which the solubility is lower, is most susceptible, because the rapid cooling necessary for the austenite-to-martensite transformation traps the hydrogen in a state of supersaturation in the martensite. Because the solubility of hydrogen in body-centered cubic (bcc) martensite is low and diffusivity is high, austenitic filler metals are often selected to weld martensitic stainless steels. The discussion on filler metal selection later in this article provides more details.

The presence of hydrogen in a weld is generally due to moisture that is introduced in the shielding gas (or the electrode coating or flux), dissociated by the arc to form elemental hydrogen, and dissolved by the molten weld pool and by the adjacent region in the HAZ. In the supersaturated state, the hydrogen diffuses to regions of high stress, where it can initiate a crack. Continued diffusion of the hydrogen to the region of stress concentration at the crack tip extends the crack. This behavior means that hydrogen-induced cold cracking is time dependent—that is, time is needed for hydrogen diffusion—and the appearance of detectable cracks can be delayed until long after the weld has passed inspection. Additional information on the mechanisms of hydrogen cracking of weldments can be found in Ref 15 and 16.

For most commercial steels, the avoidance of hydrogen-induced cold cracking is based on the control of hydrogen. The sources of hydrogen (water, oils, greases, waxes, and rust that contains hydrogen or hydrates) should be eliminated. The hydrogen potential also can be minimized by using low-hydrogen, inert-gas welding processes, such as GTAW or GMAW, or by paying stringent attention to consumable drying and baking for flux-shielded welding processes, such as SMAW or FCAW. In addition, preheating must be applied to slow the rate of cooling. This allows more time for hydrogen to diffuse away from the weld area during cooling within the austenite range and, especially, following transformation to martensite.

Preheating is generally carried out in the temperature range from 200 to 300 °C (400 to 600 °F). In multipass welds, interpass temperatures must be maintained at the same level, and it is frequently beneficial to hold this temperature for some time after arc extinction to permit further hydrogen diffusion out of the joint. Postweld tempering is carried out to improve weld-area toughness. For higher-carbon steels (>0.2 wt% C), this process should be applied as soon as possible after welding to avoid the possibility of hydrogen-induced cracking from atmospheric corrosion. The weld must be cooled to a sufficiently low temperature to induce the austenite-to-martensite transformation (in principle, below the martensite

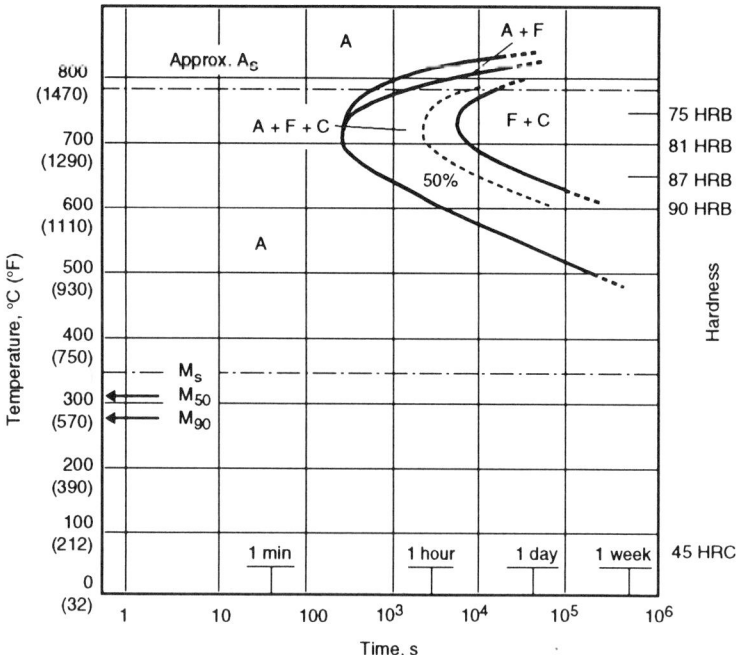

Fig. 26   Isothermal transformation diagram for type 410 stainless steel

completion point, M_f, as described below) prior to PWHT.

Material Composition and Selection of Preheat Temperature (Ref 17). The temperature at which austenite transforms to martensite upon cooling in martensitic stainless steels depends on material composition, particularly the carbon, manganese, nickel, chromium, and molybdenum contents. The martensite start temperature, M_s, for such steels can be calculated using the following equation developed by the Welding Institute (Ref 18):

$$M_s = 540 - (497 \times \%C + 6.3 \times \%Mn + 36.3 \times \%Ni + 10.8 \times \%Cr + 46.6 \times \%Mo) \,°C$$

(Eq 1)

It should be noted that all of the elements listed above lower the M_s temperature.

Using Eq 1 for a type 410 stainless steel, the M_s temperature is approximately 350 °C (660 °F). The temperature at which the transformation to martensite is complete, denoted by M_f, is approximately 100 °C (180 °F) below the M_s, that is, 256 °C (493 °F) for type 410. The preheat level should be below the M_f wherever possible, for example, 250 °C (480 °F) for type 410. However, if the M_f is less than about 150 °C (300 °F), as is the case with high-carbon (>0.2 wt% C) steels, it is not advisable to select a lower preheat level, because the embrittling effect of hydrogen can be significant at this temperature.

In most cases, the reason for choosing a preheat temperature below the M_f is to ensure that maximum transformation to martensite occurs. If this has not happened, then subsequent PWHT immediately after welding may be ineffective, for two reasons. First, the partially austenitic structure will retain hydrogen, which can lead to hy-

drogen cracking problems upon eventual cooling to room temperature, where untempered martensite with a high hydrogen concentration could form. Second, an isothermal transformation of the weld can take place during heat treatment, and the martensite that forms upon cooling to room temperature will be untempered and hard.

The major compositional factor influencing hydrogen-induced cold cracking is the material carbon content, because it determines the hardness of the transformed structure and its sensitivity to hydrogen embrittlement. Below levels of approximately 0.1 wt% C, and at least in thin sections (<5 mm, or 0.2 in.), it may be possible to weld without a preheat if hydrogen levels are low. For materials with high carbon levels (above 0.2 wt% C), both a preheat and a PWHT are essential. Such materials are particularly difficult to weld, because the M_f temperature may be well below 150 °C (300 °F). In such cases, alloys are frequently welded with a preheat of 250 °C (480 °F) but are allowed to cool to an intermediate temperature of approximately 150 °C (300 °F) prior to a hydrogen release treatment, a full PWHT, or both. For both low- and high-carbon martensitic stainless steels, the weld should not be allowed to cool to room temperature after welding before either a full PWHT or a hydrogen release treatment is conducted.

Conventional martensitic stainless steels containing 12 wt% Cr and 0.15 wt% C have been successfully welded for many years, but a number of developments have reduced the risk of hydrogen-induced cold cracking. In terms of composition, this is best achieved by lowering the carbon content, except that this also reduces the hardenability of the material. Consequently, alloys that contain nickel have been produced in order to attain higher hardenability. The most common of

these grades, particularly in Europe, is the 13Cr-4Ni-0.05C steels. Although the additional alloying reduces the M_s temperature, HAZ hydrogen-induced cold cracking resistance is substantially improved.

Heat Treatment

Preheating is one of the most effective means of avoiding weld cracking in martensitic stainless steels. The preheating temperature usually ranges from 200 to 300 °C (400 to 600 °F). As discussed previously, the material composition (particularly the carbon content) affects the preheat temperature. The use of the M_s equation (Eq 1) is helpful in determining an acceptable preheat temperature.

Another consideration that influences preheating requirements is material thickness. As described above, the restraint imposed by material thickness is also one of the factors controlling hydrogen-induced cold cracking in any welded joint. If the weld metal or HAZ has been embrittled by the presence of hydrogen, then the level of restraint in the joint may determine whether cracking occurs. The general rule for joint thickness is that the thicker the material, the greater the restraint; that is, the more material that is present, the greater the force opposing the dimensional changes in the weld area that is brought about through thermal and transformation stresses. In a repair weld situation that involves a groove, the restraint will be very high and a conservative approach is recommended. However, for a simple butt joint involving very thin material—for example, 3 mm (0.12 in.) or less—a preheat is generally considered unnecessary. This is particularly true with low-carbon (<0.10 wt% C) base metals. However, a preheating step is typically carried out.

Postweld Heat Treatment. The functions of a PWHT are to temper the martensite in the weld metal and HAZ, in order to reduce the hardness and increase the toughness, and to decrease residual stresses associated with welding. Postweld heat treatments used for martensitic stainless steels usually take one of two forms. The more common form involves tempering the weldment by heating it below the austenite start temperature, A_s (Fig. 26). This is generally carried out at temperatures ranging from 650 to 750 °C (1200 to 1400 °F). The weldment should be held at temperature for a minimum of 1 h per inch of weld thickness (Ref 17). Another form of PWHT involves heating the weldment above the austenite finish temperature, A_f, to austenitize the entire mass, and then cooling it to just above room temperature, followed by a second heat treatment at a temperature below the A_s, in order to temper the metal to the desired properties. The latter PWHT is used only when matching filler metals are used and maximum joint toughness must be achieved.

In addition, a low-temperature PWHT is sometimes carried out to facilitate the diffusion of hydrogen from the joint and decrease the likelihood of hydrogen-induced cold cracking (Ref 17). This type of PWHT is carried out at, or slightly above, the preheat temperature range of,

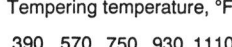

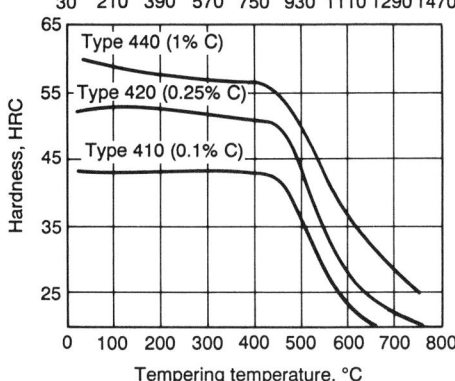

Fig. 27 Tempering response of martensitic stainless steels. Source: Ref 19

for example, 300 to 400 °C (550 to 750 °F). The 450 to 500 °C (840 to 930 °F) range should be avoided because it can compromise weld toughness.

Tempering at temperatures up to approximately 450 °C (840 °F) has little effect on the hardness of martensitic stainless steels, compared with the hardness of the same steel in the untempered condition. Tempering above 450 °C (840 °F) causes the hardness to fall rapidly with increasing tempering temperatures (Fig. 27), but at the same time, ductility increases. The tempering temperature upper limit is the A_s, which is about 800 °C (1470 °F) for the nickel-free alloys, such as types 410, 420, and 440. The addition of nickel to a martensitic alloy reduces the A_s appreciably.

Correlations of Heat Treatment and Carbon Content. Following are correlations of preheating and PWHT practice with the carbon contents and welding characteristics of martensitic stainless steels:

- *Carbon content below 0.10%:* Neither preheating nor PWHT is required except for very heavy sections; martensitic stainless steels with carbon contents this low are not standard.
- *Carbon content of 0.10 to 0.20%:* Preheat to 260 °C (500 °F); weld at this temperature; slow cool below 65 °C (150 °F); temper.
- *Carbon content of 0.20 to 0.50%:* Preheat to 260 °C (500 °F); weld at this temperature; slow cool below 65 °C (150 °F); austenitize and temper.
- *Carbon content greater than 0.50%:* Preheat to 260 °C (500 °F); weld with high heat input; anneal without letting the weldment cool below 260 °C (500 °F); austenitize and temper.

Filler Metal Selection

On the basis of hydrogen-cracking risk, the use of austenitic filler metals is preferable to the use of martensitic consumables of "matching" composition, because the solubility of hydrogen in a bcc structure (martensite) is low and diffusivity is high, as noted earlier. This contrasts with the situation in face-centered cubic (fcc) materials, such as austenite, where the solubility is high and

diffusivity is low. It follows that if a matching martensitic filler metal is employed, then the hydrogen introduced via the welding consumable (which occurs in every case, regardless of cleanliness) will diffuse into the adjacent HAZ, where it has the opportunity to embrittle the steel. However, if an austenitic filler metal is used, then the majority of hydrogen introduced through welding will remain in the austenitic weld metal, where its solubility is high. A high hydrogen concentration in the austenitic weld metal is unlikely to cause weld metal hydrogen-induced cracking, because the embrittling effect of hydrogen is considerably less in a predominantly austenitic weld structure than it is in a martensitic one.

Except for very small weldments or very-low-carbon base metals, martensitic stainless steels are not usually used in the as-welded condition. This is due to the very brittle weld area that normally results. This area includes the weld metal itself, if it has a matching or near-matching composition to that of the base metal, and the HAZ. However, repair situations can necessitate that the engineer work with these circumstances.

If a weldment of martensitic stainless steel must be used in the as-welded condition, then it is usually best to avoid both autogenous welds (no filler metal) and welds with matching filler metals. Small parts that are welded by LBW, EBW, or GTAW processes are an exception, because residual stresses can be very low and the welding processes generate almost no diffusible hydrogen.

If at all possible, an austenitic stainless filler metal, such as type 309 or 309L, or a duplex ferritic-austenitic stainless filler metal, such as type 312, should be chosen, depending on the base metal. The filler metal choice should provide for a small amount of ferrite in the weld metal, in order to avoid hot cracking. This can be anticipated by using the extended WRC-1992 diagram (Fig. 4). If the weld metal is austenite with a little ferrite, then the weld metal itself will have appreciable ductility, and only the HAZ will be at risk for cold cracking. This possibility can be minimized by using high preheat temperatures (200 °C, or 390 °F, minimum for type 410 base metal; 350 °C, or 660 °F, minimum for types 440A, 440B, and 440C base metals) and slow cooling after welding.

Example 1: Type 410 Base Metal (0.10C-12.5Cr-0.04N), Cr_{eq} = 12.5 and Ni_{eq} = 4.3, to be Welded with E309-16 Manual Electrode (0.05C-23.5Cr-13.0Ni-0.06N All-Weld-Metal Composition), Cr_{eq} = 23.5 and Ni_{eq} = 15.95. If the type 410 base metal is plotted in Fig. 28 (point A), along with the all-weld-metal composition of the E309-16 electrode (point B), then all possible mixtures of these two metals must lie along the line connecting these two points. If the root pass is diluted with 30% base metal (a typical result to expect), then the actual root pass composition will lie along the tie line, 30% of the distance from point B to point A. This composition is shown as point C in Fig. 28. It would correspond to slightly over 8 FN, which is quite safe in terms of the likelihood of hot cracking.

Furthermore, because the tie line is nearly parallel to the isoferrite lines in the diagram, major

changes in dilution would have practically no effect on weld metal ferrite content. Additional weld passes on top of the root pass would have compositions that are also along the tie line, but closer to the E309-16 all-weld-metal composition. Therefore, E309-16 would be a very good filler metal choice if a nonhardenable weld deposit is acceptable. By similar reasoning, type 309 (or 309L) would be an excellent choice for GMAW wire, FCAW wire, or SAW wire.

Example 2: Type 440A Base Metal (0.7C-17.0Cr-0.04N), Cr_{eq} = 17.0 and Ni_{eq} = 25.3, to be Welded with E309-16 Manual Electrode (0.05C-23.5Cr-13.0Ni-0.06N All-Weld-Metal Composition), Cr_{eq} = 23.5 and Ni_{eq} = 15.95. Because the type 440A base metal cannot be plotted on the WRC-1992 diagram, it is necessary to calculate the weld Cr_{eq} and Ni_{eq}. Assuming a 30% dilution, the weld Cr_{eq} = 0.7(E309-16 Cr_{eq}) + 0.3(440A Cr_{eq}) = 0.7(23.5) + 0.3(17.0) = 21.55, and the weld Ni_{eq} = 0.7(E309-16 Ni_{eq}) + 0.3(440A Ni_{eq}) = 0.7(15.95) + 0.3(25.3) = 18.8. Because the weld metal composition would clearly lie above and to the left of the 0 FN line in Fig. 4, there would be no ferrite in such a weld deposit. Therefore, E309-16 would not be a good choice for welding type 440A base metal.

Example 3: Type 440A Base Metal (0.7C-17.0Cr-0.04N), Cr_{eq} = 17.0 and Ni_{eq} = 25.3, to be Welded with E312-16 Manual Electrode (0.10C-29.0Cr-8.8Ni-0.06N), Cr_{eq} = 29.0 and Ni_{eq} = 13.3. Because the type 440A base metal cannot be plotted on the WRC-1992 diagram, it is necessary to calculate the weld Cr_{eq} and Ni_{eq}. Assuming a 30% dilution, the weld Cr_{eq} = 0.7(E312-16 Cr_{eq}) + 0.3(440A Cr_{eq}) = 0.7(29.0) + 0.3(17) = 25.4, and the weld Ni_{eq} = 0.7(E312-16 Ni_{eq}) + 0.3(440A Ni_{eq}) = 0.7(13.3) + 0.3(25.3) = 16.9. Plotting the weld Cr_{eq} and Ni_{eq} on the WRC-1992 diagram shows that this composition corresponds to about 12 FN. Therefore, E312-16 would be a good choice for welding type 440A base metal if a nonhardenable weld is acceptable.

However, unlike the situation in Example 1, the tie line from the E312-16 electrode all-weld-metal composition on the WRC-1992 diagram to the type 440A base metal composition is nearly perpendicular to the isoferrite lines. This means that large changes in dilution would have a strong effect on weld metal ferrite content. In particular, it can be calculated that an increase in dilution to just over 35% would put the weld composition into the primary austenite solidification mode and, therefore, at risk of hot cracking. Because higher dilution is normal in SAW and spray-transfer GMAW processes, the avoidance of these processes would be suggested by this example. However, the GMAW process using short-circuiting transfer with type 312 filler wire should be acceptable.

Although the welding filler metals of Examples 1 and 3 seem appropriate choices for avoiding hot cracking in joints in the martensitic stainless steels used in these examples, the weld metals would considerably undermatch the strengths of the base metals, unless the base metals were annealed. The base metals could easily have tensile strength values that exceed 1000 MPa (145 ksi), depending on their condition of heat

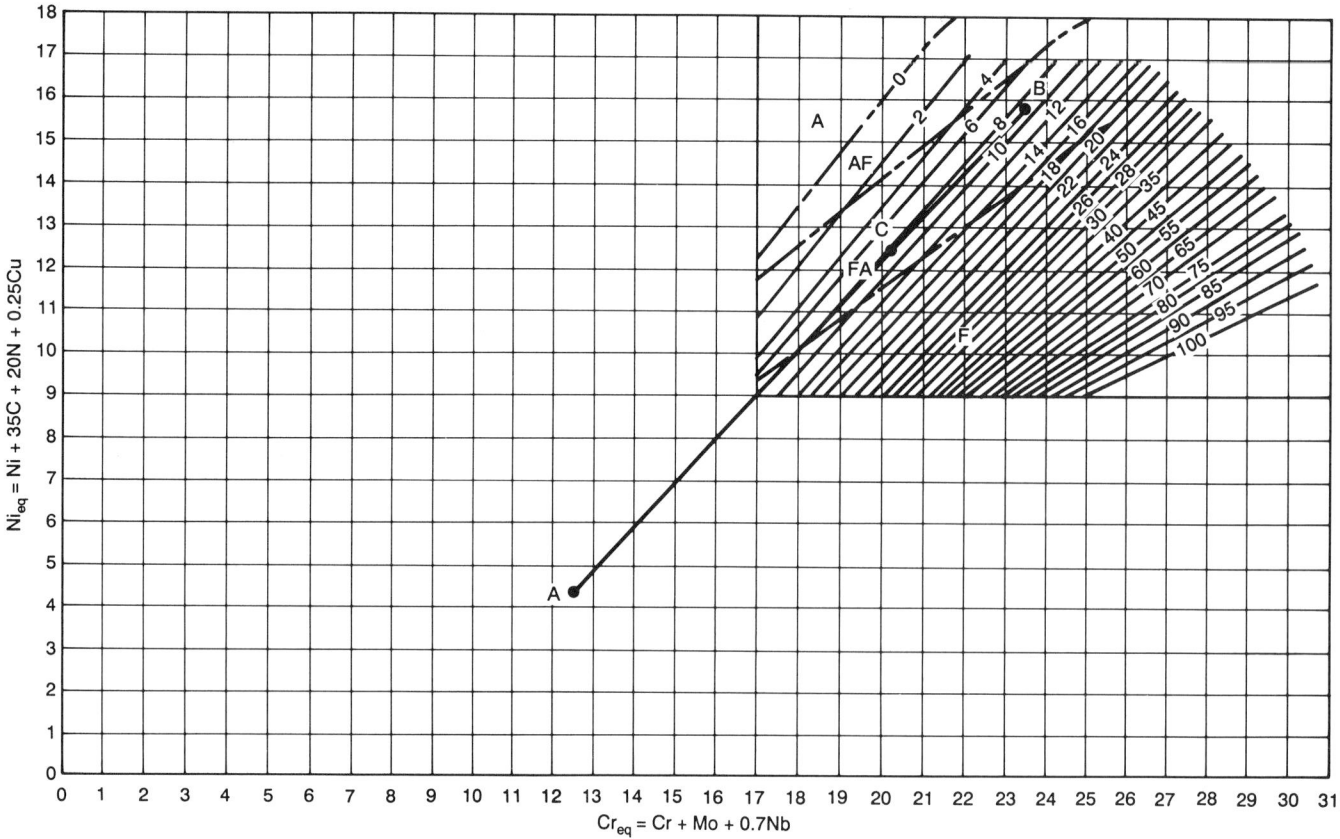

Fig. 28 Welding Research Council 1992 diagram with expanded scale for dilution calculations, in which ferrite is calculated for type 410 stainless steel welded with E309-16 (refer to Example 1)

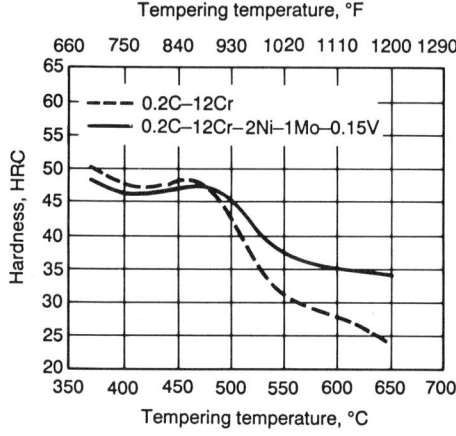

Fig. 29 Tempering response (2 h at temperature) of types 420 and modified 420 continuous caster roll overlay. Source: Ref 20

treatment before welding, whereas the weld metals are likely to have tensile strengths of the order of 550 to 600 MPa (80 to 90 ksi). Furthermore, the austenitic weld metals cannot be hardened by heat treatment. If higher-strength weld metal is essential, then a martensitic filler metal is necessary, which almost always requires a PWHT to obtain reasonable ductility in the weld metal.

Matching filler metals are used when the strength of the weld metal must be similar to that of the base metal or when maximum weld toughness is specified. The availability of matching filler metals is a problem for some martensitic stainless steels.

For covered electrodes, only E410-XX and E410NiMo-XX types are commercially significant, as indicated by the ANSI/AWS A5.4 classification. The same compositions are also the only entries in the flux-cored electrode standard, ANSI/AWS A5.22. These compositions, as well as the ER420 classification, are given as solid wires in the ANSI/AWS A5.9 standard. Therefore, Table 5, which designates matching filler metals along with selected base metals, has many voids in the filler metal listings. A few filler metal producers can produce special orders, such as tubular metal-cored electrodes, in compositions to match the other base metals. Otherwise, the fabricator may be forced to choose a filler metal that does not match the base metal.

One special case deserves mention. Literally thousands of tons of filler metal in the form of tubular wires have been deposited by submerged-arc overlay of type 420 and modified-composition weld metals on low-alloy steel rolls for continuous casters. In service, these rolls typically crack from thermal shock. After a period ranging from 6 months to 1 year, their surfaces are sufficiently damaged so that they must be removed from service. If cracking is not too deep, then the cracks can be machined off and the roll rewelded as before.

A very successful welding procedure has been to maintain preheat and interpass temperatures of at least 350 °C (660 °F) from the start to the finish of welding. Because this temperature is above the M_s of the weld metal, the weld metal remains as austenite during welding, which may last 1 day or longer. As many as three welding heads, each using 400 to 900 A, can be used on a roll that is about 2 m (6.5 ft) long, which helps to keep the roll hot. The welded roll is covered with insulating material and left to slowly cool to nearly room temperature. Then it is tempered, typically at temperatures of 450 °C (840 °F) or higher, to soften the overlay enough to make it machinable. Molybdenum, vanadium, and sometimes niobium can be added to the basic type 420 composition to modify the tempering response (as well as service performance). Figure 29 illustrates the change in tempering response that results from the alloy modifications.

Specific Welding Recommendations

This section provides specific arc welding procedural recommendations for the more commonly welded martensitic stainless steels. The free-machining grades (types 416, 416Se, 420F, 440F, and 440FSe) are not included, because these enhanced-machining alloys are not recommended for welding. Weld data related to the welding of martensitic stainless steels are avail-

Table 5 Properties and filler metals for nominally martensitic stainless steels

Designation	UNS No.	ASTM specification	Tensile strength		Yield strength		Elongation, %	Matching filler metals		
			MPa	ksi	MPa	ksi		A5.4	A5.9(a)	A5.22
XM-32	K64152	A 565	1000	145	790	115	15	...	...	...
403	S40300	A 479	480	70	275	40	20	E410-XX	ER410	E410T-X
410	S41000	A 240	450	65	205	30	20	E410-XX	ER410	E410T-X
410S	S41008	A 240	415	60	205	30	22	E410-XX	ER410	E410T-X
XM-30	S41040	A 479	480	70	275	40	13	...	...	...
...	S41041	A565	790	115	520	75	15	...	...	...
...	S41050	A 240	415	60	205	30	22	...	...	...
414	S41400	A 479	790	115	620	90	15	...	...	...
410NiMo	S41500	A 240	790	115	620	90	15	E410NiMo-XX	ER410NiMo	E410NiMoT-X
416	S41600	A 473	480	70	275	40	20	NCW	NCW	NCW
XM-6	S41610	A 582	NS	NS	NS	NS	NS	NCW	NCW	NCW
416Se	S41623	A 473	480	70	275	40	20	NCW	NCW	NCW
615	S41800	A 565	970	140	760	110	115	...	...	...
420	S42000	A 276	NS	NS	NS	NS	NS	...	ER420	...
...	S42010	A 276	NS	NS	NS	NS	NS	...	...	...
420F	S42020	A 565	NS	NS	NS	NS	NS	NCW	NCW	NCW
420FSe	S42023	A 565	NS	NS	NS	NS	NS	NCW	NCW	NCW
616	S42200	A 565	970	140	760	110	13	...	...	...
619	S42300	A 565	970	140	760	110	8	...	...	...
431	S43100	A 479	790	115	620	90	15	...	...	...
440A	S44002	A 276	NS	NS	NS	NS	NS	...	...	...
440B	S44003	A 276	NS	NS	NS	NS	NS	...	...	...
440C	S44004	A 276	NS	NS	NS	NS	NS	...	...	...
440F	S44020	A 582	NS	NS	NS	NS	NS	NCW	NCW	NCW
440FSe	S44023	A 582	NS	NS	NS	NS	NS	NCW	NCW	NCW
CA-15	...	A 743	620	90	450	65	18	E410-XX	ER4109	E410T-X
CA-15M	...	A 743	620	90	450	65	18	...	...	...
CA-40	...	A 473	690	100	480	70	15	...	ER420	...
CA-40F	...	A 743	690	100	480	70	12	NCW	NCW	NCW
CA6N	...	A 743	970	140	930	135	15	...	...	...
CA-6NM	...	A 743	760	110	550	80	15	E410NiMo-XX	ER410NiMo	E410NiMoT-X
CA-28MWV	...	A 743	970	140	760	110	10	...	...	...

NS, not specified; NCW, not considered weldable. (a) Metal-cored electrodes, indicated by a "C" in place of the "R" in the classification, are also included.

Table 6 Parameters for gas-metal arc welding of type 403 martensitic stainless steel

	Electrode	
	ER410NiMo	ER410
Voltage, V	30.5	28.0
Arc current, A	460	420
Travel speed, mm/s (in./min)	3.8 (9)	5.0 (12)
Electrode diameter, mm (in.)	2.38 ($^3/_{32}$)	2.38 ($^3/_{32}$)
Shielding gas (argon), mm^3/s (ft^3/h)	600 (50)	600 (50)
Preheat, °C (°F)	None	200 to 250 (400 to 450)

Source: Ref 21

able from both alloy producers and manufacturers of welding equipment and consumables. For example, some of the data listed below were obtained from Carpenter Technology Corporation and from Sandvik. Such companies should be consulted prior to welding martensitic stainless steels.

Type 403 can be satisfactorily welded using AWS E/ER309 austenitic filler metal. If a martensitic consumable must be used, then either AWS E/ER410 or 410NiMo is acceptable. Parts should be preheated to at least 200 to 250 °C (400 to 450 °F) before welding to prevent cracking. Following welding, a PWHT of 650 to 750 °C (1200 to 1400 °F) should be conducted.

Because of the considerable cracking that can occur when welding thick sections (greater than 25 mm, or 1 in.) of type 403, a program designed to select the optimal filler metal to produce crack-free welds was conducted by Westinghouse Elec-

tric Corporation (Ref 21). This study compared the mechanical properties of AWS ER410 and 410NiMo gas-metal arc welds in 25 mm (1 in.) thick type 403 stainless steel (normalized and tempered to 585 MPa, or 85 ksi; 0.2% yield strength). Table 6 lists the welding parameters that were used in this study.

Weldments were tested using U-bend, tensile, stress-rupture, and Charpy V-notch tests. Results indicated that AWS ER410NiMo weldments exhibited superior tensile and impact properties (Fig. 30 and 31) but had lower stress-rupture values (Fig. 32).

Type 410. The following recommendations for the arc welding of type 410 stainless steel are taken from Ref 17:

• Preheat to 250 °C (480 °F) and maintain this temperature during welding. Use an austenitic consumable such as AWS E/ER308 or 309. If a

stronger weld is desired, AWS E/ER410 should be used.
• After welding, allow the joint to cool to the preheat temperature, that is, 250 °C (480 °F).
• Before allowing the joint to cool to room temperature, conduct a tempering operation at 720 °C (1330 °F) and allow approximately 1 h per inch of thickness, with a minimum of 1 h.
• Cool to room temperature.

Type 414 can be welded using a filler metal of similar composition (AWS E/ER410 or 410NiMo) or an austenitic consumable (AWS E/ER309). Cracking is best prevented by preheating the part to at least 200 °C (400 °F) and maintaining that as a minimum interpass temperature. In addition, a PWHT that is in the range from 650 to 700 °C (1200 to 1300 °F) should be conducted.

Type 420. Satisfactory welds have been obtained in type 420 by preheating to a minimum of 200 °C (400 °F) before welding, followed by a PWHT of 675 to 750 °C (1250 to 1400 °F). If a filler metal is required, then AWS ER420 should be considered when the mechanical properties of the weld are important. If the mechanical properties of the weld do not have to match those of the base metal, then AWS E/ER309 should be considered.

HT9 (12Cr-1Mo-0.3V) martensitic stainless steel can be welded using SMAW, GTAW, or GMAW. The joint should be preheated to a temperature between 200 and 400 °C (400 and 600 °F). In the case of multipass welds, an interpass temperature of 250 °C (480 °F) is specified to prevent the transformation to untempered martensite

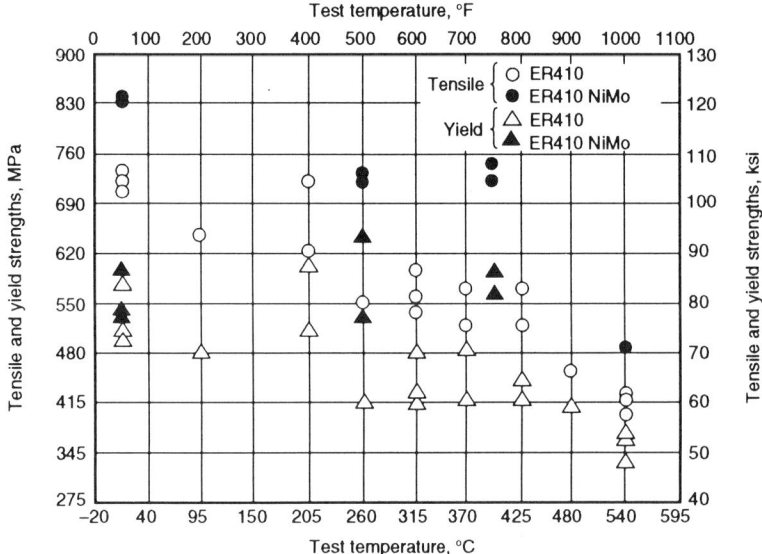

Fig. 30 Strength vs. test temperature for two martensitic stainless steel filler metals. Source: Ref 21

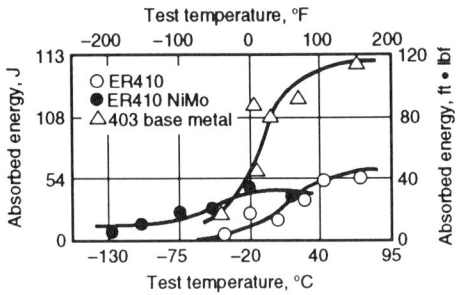

Fig. 31 Charpy V-notch values vs. test temperature for two martensitic stainless steel filler metals. Source: Ref 21

that occurs upon cooling to room temperature. Finally, a PWHT in the temperature range from 740 to 780 °C (1365 to 1470 °F), for a period ranging from 30 min to 2 h, is required immediately following welding. If a filler metal is used, then consumables of matching composition should be selected.

Type 431 can be welded satisfactorily with most of the arc welding processes. If a filler metal is required, then one of a similar composition, such as AWS E/ER410, should be considered. An austenitic filler metal, such as AWS E/ER310, can also be used if the mechanical properties of the weld and the response to heat treatment are not required to be similar to those of the base metal. To prevent cracking of the weldment, it is necessary to preheat the base metal to a temperature between 200 and 300 °C (400 and 600 °F) and maintain a minimum interpass temperature of 200 °C (400 °F). After welding, the weldment should receive a PWHT at 650 °C (1200 °F).

Types 440A, B, and C. Because of their high carbon contents (0.6 to 1.2 wt% C), these alloys are not generally considered to be weldable. However, successful welds using austenitic filler metals (AWS E312) have been made in type 440A stainless steel, which has the lowest carbon content

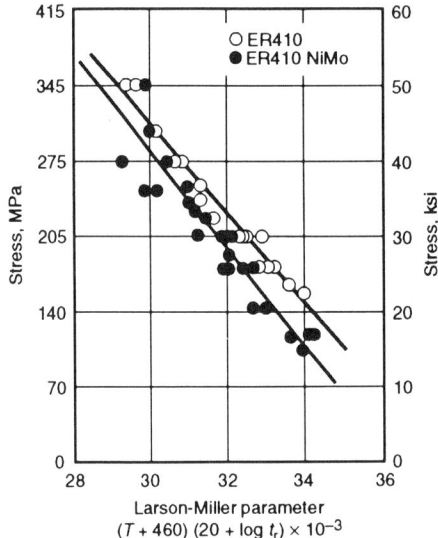

Fig. 32 Rupture stress as a function of the Larson-Miller parameter for two martensitic stainless steel filler metals. Source: Ref 21

of this group (0.60 to 0.75 wt% C). A case history outlining the proper GMAW of type 440A stainless steel is given in Example 3 of this article.

Non-Arc Welding Processes

Although arc welding processes (particularly GMAW, GTAW, and SMAW) are commonly used to join martensitic stainless steels, a variety of other joining methods also can be employed, such as laser- and electron-beam welding, resistance welding, flash welding, and friction welding. However, regardless of the method selected, a hard (untempered) weld microstructure results from the welding process, and the same PWHTs as those discussed above must be carried out.

Laser-Beam Welding. Although the lower heat input that is typical of laser welds results in faster cooling rates and steeper temperature gradients in the weld HAZ, the problems of high hardness and low toughness in the weld area persist. Lippold (Ref 10) has studied the microstructure of laser-beam welded martensitic stainless steels. The microstructure along the fusion boundary consists almost entirely of untempered martensite. The HAZ consists of two distinct microstructural regions. The first region immediately adjacent to the fusion line consists entirely of untempered martensite and extends less than 0.25 mm (0.01 in.) from the fusion line. The microstructure that is more remote from the fusion line consists of untempered martensite and carbides. The as-welded hardnesses of both the fusion zone and HAZ range from 52 to 56 HRC. As a result, a postweld tempering treatment is necessary. Lippold has shown that the tempering response of martensitic stainless steel laser welds is similar to that of arc-welded specimens. As shown in Fig. 33, tempering for 1 h at 800 °C (1470 °F) reduced the as-welded hardness of laser welds.

Lippold has also studied the effects of welding parameters on the quality of laser welds in HT9 martensitic steels (Ref 22). Laser welds were made in 6.35 mm (0.25 in.) thick HT9 plate using a variety of travel speed/focal length combinations at a constant power level of 6 kW. Welds made using low travel speed (1.27 mm/s, or 30 in./min), high heat input (0.47 kJ/mm, or 12 kJ/in.), and sharp focus were sound. Welds performed at sharp focus with travel speeds ranging from 1.69 to 4.23 mm/s (40 to 100 in./min) and heat inputs decreasing from 0.35 to 0.14 kJ/mm (12 to 3.6 kJ/in.) exhibited scattered porosity and occasional centerline cracking that occurred during the final stages of solidification. Defocusing the laser beam relative to the plate resulted in welds containing severe porosity and centerline cracks. Microstructural and microhardness evaluation of the welds indicated that the region of highest hardness occurred in the HAZ immediately adjacent to the fusion line.

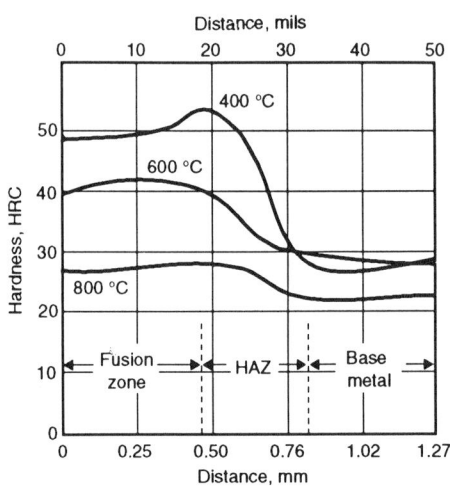

Fig. 33 Tempering behavior of HT9 laser-beam welds. Source: Ref 10

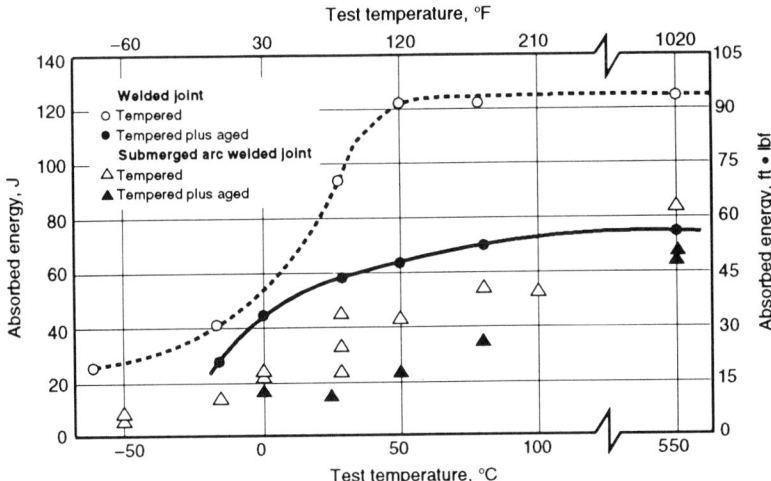

Fig. 34 Charpy V-notch data for weld joints of electron-beam welded alloy Fe-0.2C-12Cr-1Mo plates, compared with impact data for a submerged arc welded joint using a filler metal similar to Fe-0.2C-12Cr-1Mo. Conditions: tempered at 740 °C (1365 °F) and tempered plus aged at 550 °C (1020 °F) for 5000 h. Specimen orientation: transverse to weld. Source: Ref 24

Laser-beam welds can be autogenous, or filler metals can be used. Martensitic stainless steels can be joined to each other or to dissimilar materials. For example, successful welds have been made between type 403 stainless steel and Inconel 600 using AWS A5.14 class ENiCr-3 (Ni-20Cr-2.5Mn-2.25Nb) filler wire (Ref 23).

Electron-beam welding has been successfully conducted on modified 12 wt% Cr steels used for high-pressure, high-temperature components in power plants and in the chemical industry. In one study, electron-beam welds were made to join 21 mm (0.83 in.) thick Fe-12Cr-1Mo plates (Ref 24). After tempering at 740 °C (1365 °F) for 2 h, the welds were investigated by Charpy V-notch and tensile tests at temperatures up to 550 °C (1020 °F). Impact properties of the EBW joint were superior to those of SAW joints in the same

alloy (Fig. 34) and exceeded those of the base metal. As is the case with laser-beam welds, the HAZ of the electron-beam welds consisted of untempered martensite. A microhardness traverse across the weld revealed that the hardness in the fusion zone and HAZ region ranged from 300 to nearly 600 HV (30 to 55 HRC) (Fig. 35). Tempering subsequently lowered the hardness to below 300 HV.

Friction welding can be used to join martensitic stainless steels to themselves, as well as to other steels. As is the case with other welding processes, changes in hardness at and near the weld interface can be expected. Figure 36 shows changes in hardness of a welded joint made of JIS S45C (0.45 wt% C) carbon steel and type 440C stainless steel.

Resistance Welding. Martensitic stainless steels can be spot welded in the annealed, hardened, or quenched-and-tempered conditions. Regardless of the initial base metal hardness and the welding schedule, the HAZ adjacent to the weld nugget quenches to martensite. The hardness of the weld nugget and HAZ primarily depends on the carbon content of the steel, although it can be controlled somewhat with preheat, postheat, and tempering during the spot-welding cycle. The likelihood of cracking in the HAZ increases with the carbon content of the steel.

Flash Welding. As is the case with resistance spot welding, a hard HAZ is formed during the flash welding of martensitic stainless steels. This hard HAZ can be softened somewhat by a tempering cycle in the welding machine. A PWHT will

Table 7   Nominal chemical composition of representative Group I standard-grade 400-series ferritic stainless steels

UNS No.	Type	Composition(a), wt%			
		C	Cr	Mo	Other
S42900	429	0.12	14.0-16.0	...	...
S43000	430	0.12	16.0-18.0	...	...
S43020	430F	0.12	16.0-18.0	0.6	0.06 P; 0.15 min S
S43023	430FSe	0.12	16.0-18.0	...	0.15 min Se
S43400	434	0.12	16.0-18.0	0.75-1.25	...
S43600	436	0.12	16.0-18.0	0.75-1.25	Nb + Ta = 5 × %C min
S44200	442	0.20	18.0-23.0	...	...
S44600	446	0.20	23.0-27.0	...	...

(a) Single values are maximum unless otherwise indicated.

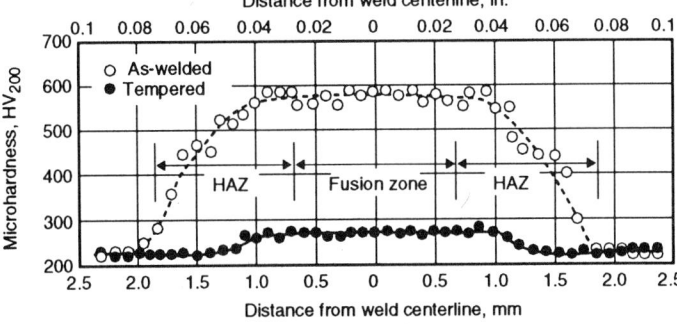

Fig. 35 Microhardness traverse across the weld in transverse cross sections of electron-beam welded alloy Fe-0.2C-12Cr-1Mo plate at the center of plate thickness; as-welded and conditioned and tempered for 2 h at 740 °C (1365 °F). Source: Ref 24

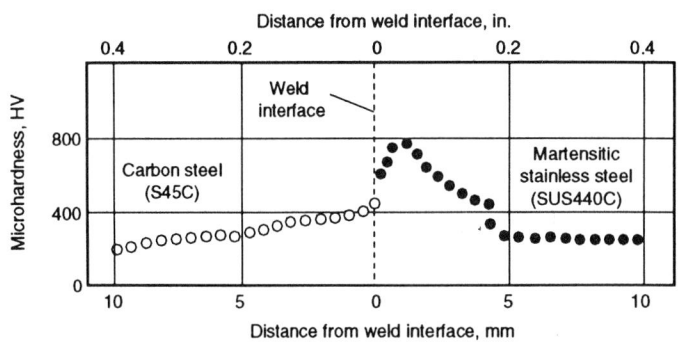

Fig. 36 Changes in hardness at and near a friction weld interface. Source: Ref 25

Table 8 Chemical compositions of Group II ferritic stainless steels

| UNS No. | Alloy designation | Composition(a), wt% | | | | |
		C	Cr	Mo	Ni	Other
S40500	405	0.08	11.5-14.5	...	...	0.10-0.30 Al
S40900	409	0.08	10.5-11.75	...	0.5	Ti = 6 × C min to 0.75 max
...	409Cb	0.02(b)	12.5(b)	...	0.2(b)	0.4 Nb(b)
S44100	441	0.02(b)	18.0(b)	...	0.3(b)	0.7 Nb(b), 0.3 Ti(b)
...	AL433	0.02(b)	19.0(b)	...	0.3(b)	0.4 Nb(b), 0.5 Si(b), 0.4 Cu(b)
...	AL446	0.01(b)	11.5(b)	...	0.2(b)	0.2 Nb(b), 0.1 Ti(b)
...	AL468	0.01(b)	18.2(b)	...	0.2(b)	0.2 Nb(b), 0.1 Ti(b)
...	YUS436S	0.01(b)	17.4(b)	1.2(b)	...	0.2 Ti(b)
S43035	439	0.07	17.00-19.00	...	0.5	Ti = 0.20 + 4 (C + N) min to 1.0 max
...	12SR	0.2	12.0	...	...	1.2 Al; 0.3 Ti
...	18SR	0.04	18.0	...	...	2.0 Al; 0.4 Ti
K41970	406	0.06	12.0-14.0	...	0.5	2.75-4.25 Al; 0.6 Ti

(a) Single values are maximum unless otherwise indicated. (b) Typical value

Table 9 Nominal chemical compositions of Group III ultrahigh-purity ferritic stainless steels

| UNS No. | Alloy designation | Composition(a), wt% | | | | | | |
		C	N	Cr	Mo	Ni	Nb	Other
S44726	E-Brite 26-1 (XM-27)	0.010	0.015	25-27	0.75-1.5	0.30	0.05-0.20	0.4 Mn
S44800	AL 29-4-2	0.010	0.020	28-30	3.5-4.2	2.0-2.5	...	...
S44700	AL 29-4	0.010	0.020	28-30	3.5-4.2	0.15	...	0.3 Mn
...	SHOMAC 30-2	0.003(b)	0.007(b)	30(b)	2(b)	0.2(b)	...	0.3 Mn
S44400	YUS 190L	0.004(b)	0.0085(b)	18(b)	2(b)	0.4(b)	...	...

(a) Single values are maximum unless otherwise stated. (b) Typical value

produce welds with properties approximately equal to those of the base metal.

Welding Ferritic Stainless Steels

Ferritic stainless steels constitute approximately one-half of the SAE/AISI-type 400-series stainless steels. These steels contain from 10.5 to 30% Cr along with other alloying elements, notably molybdenum. Ferritic stainless steels are noted for their excellent stress-corrosion cracking (SCC) resistance and good resistance to pitting and crevice corrosion in chloride environments.

Classification of Ferritic Stainless Steels

The ferritic stainless steels can be classified as Group I alloys, which are the standard ferritic stainless steels, Group II alloys, which are modified versions of the standard alloys, and Group III alloys, which contain very low interstitial element (carbon, nitrogen, and oxygen) contents or stabilizing elements for improved corrosion resistance and ductility in the as-welded condition.

Group I Alloys. Ferritic stainless steels of the 400-series Group I variety have been available for many years and are used primarily for their resistance to corrosion and scaling at elevated temperatures. Table 7 lists the chemical compositions of standard-grade Group I ferritic stainless steels. While these alloys have useful properties in the wrought condition, welding is known to reduce toughness, ductility, and corrosion resistance because of grain coarsening and formation of martensite. Welding these commercial grades usually requires preheat and PWHT. For these

reasons, the application of the 400-series Group I ferritic stainless steels is not as extensive as it might otherwise be, compared with the 300-series austenitic stainless steels, which enjoy ease of weldability.

Group II Alloys. To overcome some of the difficulties and to improve weldability, several of the standard-grade ferritics have been modified. These Group II ferritic stainless steels, which contain lower levels of chromium and carbon, along with additions of ferrite stabilizers, are listed in Table 8. Applications of these alloys involve exposure to high temperatures, such as for quenching racks and annealing boxes, and also for tanks for agricultural sprays, transformer cases, and automotive applications.

For example, type 405, containing nominally 12% Cr, is made with lower carbon and a small aluminum addition of 0.20% to restrict the formation of austenite at high temperatures so that hardening is reduced during welding. For maximum ductility and corrosion resistance, however, postweld annealing is necessary. Recommendations for welding include either a type 430 or 309 filler metal, the latter being used when increased weld ductility is desired.

Type 409 is one of the most widely used ferritic stainless steels. This alloy, which has a titanium addition, is used extensively in automotive exhaust systems and is often welded using the resistance welding processes.

Group III Alloys. In the late 1960s and early 1970s, researchers recognized that highly alloyed (higher chromium and molybdenum contents) ferritic stainless steels possessed a desirable combination of resistance to general corrosion, pitting, and SCC. These properties made them attractive alternatives to the 300-series austenitic

stainless steels, which are commonly plagued by failure as a result of chloride SCC. It was reasoned that by controlling the interstitial element content (carbon, nitrogen, and oxygen) of these new ferritic alloys, either by ultrahigh-purity processing methods or by stabilization, the formation of martensite could be eliminated, as well as the need for preheat and PWHT, so that welds would be corrosion resistant, tough, and ductile in the as-welded condition. To achieve these results, electron-beam vacuum refining, vacuum and argon-oxygen decarburization (AOD), and vacuum induction melting processes were used. From this beginning, two basic ferritic stainless alloy systems evolved.

Ultrahigh-Purity Group III Alloys. Ferritic alloys that have an interstitial element (C + N) content of less than 150 ppm are termed *ultrahigh purity.* Examples of these alloys, shown in Table 9, are available commercially. These alloys are produced by either electron-beam vacuum refining, vacuum induction melting, or vacuum oxygen decarburization. Plate is available up to 13 mm ($\frac{1}{2}$ in.) in thickness. Purity is especially important with the higher-chromium alloys because of the effect on ductility, toughness, and weldability. Although not mentioned in the chemistry specification for these alloys, oxygen and hydrogen are particularly harmful, and their levels must also be carefully restricted. A modest amount of niobium is added to some of these alloys to preserve corrosion resistance in the welded condition.

Intermediate-Purity Group III Alloys. When the interstitial element (C + N) content exceeds 150 ppm (but is less than 800 ppm), ferritic alloys are considered to be of intermediate purity. Alloys listed in Table 10 are available commercially and

Table 10 Nominal chemical compositions of Group III intermediate-purity ferritic stainless steels

UNS No.	Alloy designation	Composition(a), wt%					
		C	N	Cr	Mo	Ni	Ti
S44626	26-1 Ti	0.02(b)	0.025(b)	26(b)	1(b)	0.25(b)	0.5(b)
S44400	AISI 444	0.02(b)	0.02(b)	18(b)	2(b)	0.4(b)	0.5(b)
S44660	Sea-Cure	0.025	0.035	25-27	2.5-3.5	1.5-3.5	[0.20 + 4 (C + N)] ≤ (Nb + Ti) ≤ 0.80
S44635	Nu Monit	0.025	0.035	24.5-26	3.5-4.5	3.5-4.5	[0.20 + 4 (C + N)] ≤ (Nb + Ti) ≤ 0.80
S44735	AL 29-4C	0.030	0.045	28-30	3.6-4.2	1.0	6 (C + N) ≤ (Nb + Ti) ≤ 1.0

(a) Single values are maximum values unless otherwise stated. (b) Typical value

are produced typically by the AOD process. Because these steels have higher carbon and nitrogen contents, their ductility and toughness are inferior to those of the ultrahigh-purity alloys. For this reason, metal thickness is limited to a maximum of approximately 3 mm ($\frac{1}{8}$ in.) where toughness is adequate.

In order to maintain acceptable corrosion resistance in these alloys in the as-welded condition, titanium and/or niobium are added to tie up the carbon and nitrogen that otherwise would combine with the chromium to form chromium carbides and nitrides, which can lead to preferential intergranular attack in many environments. This form of attack is most readily observed in the HAZ. Although niobium and titanium are both stabilizers, they are not equivalent. Autogenous welds in titanium-containing alloys typically exhibit an equiaxed grain region near the weld centerline. Alloys stabilized only with niobium typically show a columnar weld structure with a sharply defined centerline and a propensity for weld cracking. To avoid this, one must keep the carbon content below 0.01%, keep the niobium content below 0.1%, and add titanium in amounts greater than 0.1%.

Although it has been claimed that the ultrahigh-purity alloys are costly to produce, many users have found that the cost differential of similar alloys produced by the AOD melting practice is not economical enough to warrant purchase of these alloys in preference to similar alloys of ultrahigh purity, especially considering the inferior ductility and toughness of welded AOD-refined materials.

Metallurgical Characteristics

All of the ferritic stainless steels ideally possess the bcc crystal structure known as ferrite at all temperatures below their melting temperatures (Fig. 37). Many of these alloys are subject to the precipitation of undesirable intermetallic phases when exposed to certain temperature ranges. The higher-chromium alloys can be embrittled by precipitation of the tetragonal σ-phase, which is based on the compound FeCr. Sigma phase has a lower temperature limit of formation (about 440 °C, or 825 °F). The σ solvus for the E-Brite alloy (see Table 9) is relatively low, probably less than 675 °C (1250 °F), and σ formation at low temperatures is sluggish. As a result, σ precipitation is rarely an issue for the E-Brite alloy during welding.

The presence of increased chromium and molybdenum contents in other ultrahigh-purity ferritic stainless steels raises their σ solvus

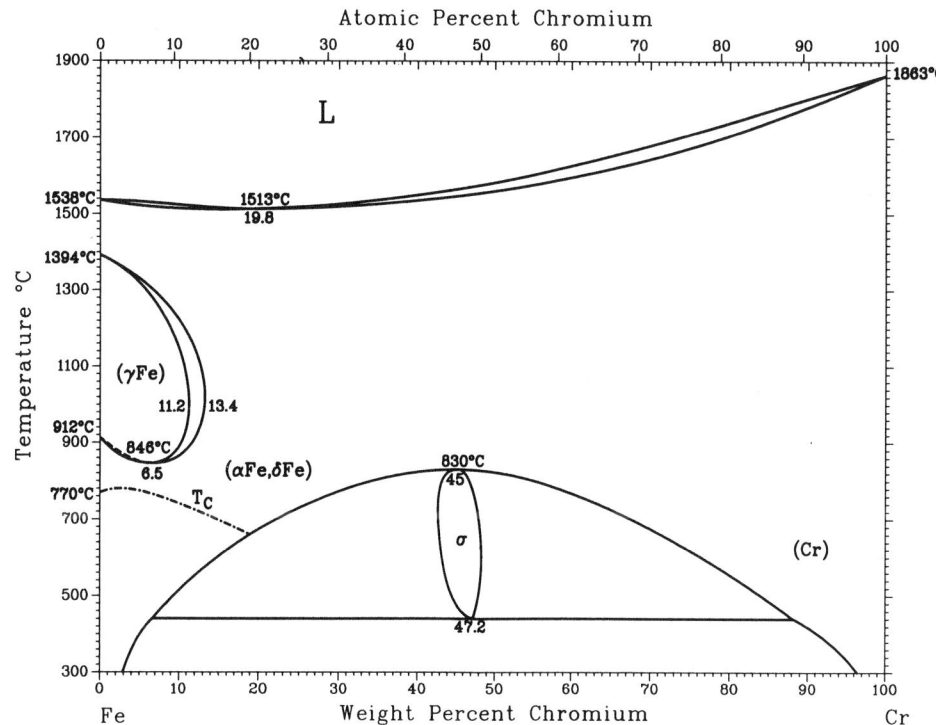

Fig. 37   Iron-chromium phase diagram. Source: ASM International/U.S. National Institute of Standards and Technology phase diagram project

temperatures to approximately 1000 °C (1830 °F). Molybdenum also promotes formation of the complex cubic χ-phase, which has a nominal composition of $Fe_{36}Cr_{12}Mo_{10}$. Sigma- and χ-phases are also stabilized by titanium. In the alloys other than E-Brite, these intermetallic phases form most rapidly at about 850 °C (1560 °F); consequently, these alloys must be cooled rapidly after annealing. Service exposure of welded ferritic alloys containing high levels of chromium and molybdenum should avoid these temperature ranges.

All of the ferritic stainless steels with chromium contents higher than 12% are also subject to embrittlement when exposed in the 370 to 550 °C (700 to 1200 °F) range. This embrittlement is most rapid at about 475 °C (885 °F) and is usually called *885 °F (475 °C) embrittlement*. The rate of 475 °C (885 °F) embrittlement increases with increasing chromium plus molybdenum contents. It is generally agreed that the severe embrittlement that occurs upon long-term exposure at these temperatures is due to the decomposition of the iron-

chromium ferrite phase into a mixture of iron-rich α and chromium-rich α′ phases. This embrittlement is thus often called α′ *embrittlement*. Additional reactions such as chromium carbide and nitride precipitation may play a significant role in the more rapid, early stages of 475 °C (885 °F) embrittlement. Short-term heat treatments at 620 to 650 °C (1120 to 1210 °F) can often alleviate 475 °C (885 °F) embrittlement, and such embrittlement can always be cured by a full-anneal heat treatment followed by rapid cooling.

The ferritic stainless steels have higher yield strengths and lower ductilities than austenitic stainless steels. Like carbon steels, and unlike austenitic stainless steels, the ferritic stainless alloys exhibit a transition from ductile-to-brittle behavior (Fig. 38) as the temperature is reduced, especially in notched impact tests. The ductile to brittle transition temperature (DBTT) for the ultrahigh-purity ferritic stainless steels is lower than that for type 430 and similar standard ferritic stainless steels. It is typically well below room temperature. The DBTT for the intermediate-pu-

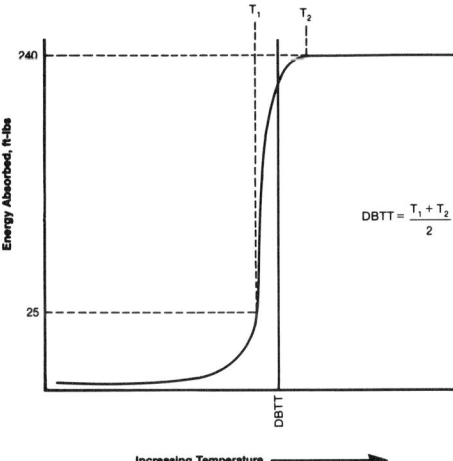

Fig. 38 Schematic of ductile-to-brittle impact toughness behavior in ferritic stainless steels

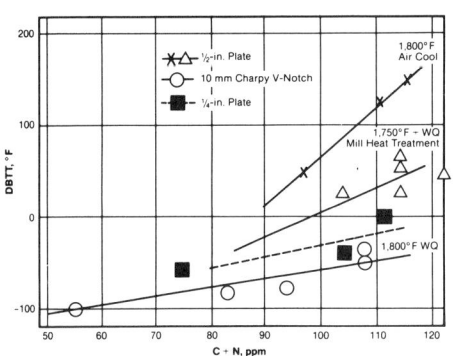

Fig. 39 Ductile-to-brittle transition temperature as a function of (C + N) content and thermal treatment. WC, water cooled

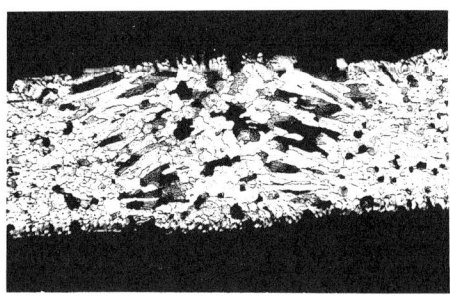

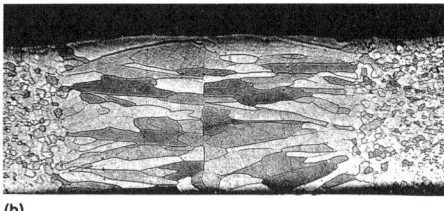

(b)

Fig. 40 Photomicrograph showing cross sections of welds in 1.4 mm (0.06 in.) sheet. (a) 18Cr-2Mo-Ti steel. (b) 18Cr-2Mo-Nb steel. Etchant used was X20 (hydrochloric/nitric/glycerol solution). Source: Ref 35, 36

rity stabilized ferritic stainless steels is similar to that for type 430 stainless steel. Since the DBTT decreases as metal thickness decreases, the stabilized alloys are available commercially only as sheet, strip, and light-wall tubing. The high-purity grades, because of their superior toughness, are available in thicker gages up to at least 6 mm ($^1/_4$ in.) plate. Nickel additions lower the DBTT and somewhat increase the thicknesses compatible with high toughness; nonetheless, with or without nickel, the ferritic stainless steels are not suitable for heavy-section applications.

In addition to the significant influence of section size (that is, thickness or mass) on the impact toughness of ferritic stainless steels, these alloys are cooling-rate sensitive. This effect is illustrated in Fig. 39. Depending on the cooling rate, precipitates of carbides and nitrides will tend to align along the grain boundaries or be randomly distributed in the matrix. Thus, grain size is an important factor relative to ductility and toughness. The finer the grain size, the higher the impact energy, just as in carbon or low-alloy steels.

Hunter and Eagar (Ref 26) investigated the mechanism of ductility loss in type 444 ferritic stainless steel (UNS S44400) welds stabilized with niobium and, in particular, titanium. It was found that stabilizing TiN or Nb(C,N) precipitates are dissolved during the autogenous GTAW process, resulting in a finer distribution of precipitates in the weld metal during solidification than in the base metal. The fracture appearance transition temperature (FATT) was studied using an Olsen cup test and was found to increase by almost 200 °C (360 °F), leading to decreased room-temperature ductility. Such an increase in FATT was not explainable solely in terms of grain growth. It was proposed that these finer precipitates were likely to contain chromium as well as titanium and niobium. The combination of chromium with the nitrogen releases more free titanium, which may have an embrittling effect.

Earlier, Pollard (Ref 27) studied the ductility of ferritic stainless steel weld metal in the 26 to 35% Cr range. He concluded that the most practi-

cal methods for maximizing the ductility of welds in ferritic stainless steels in gage thicknesses of at least 6 mm ($^1/_4$ in.) are:

- Keep the level of both substitutional and interstitial alloying elements as low as possible.
- Make additions of strong carbonitride-forming elements (logically as low as possible).

Weldability

The term *weldability* is defined here as meaning the ease with which sound welds can be made and the suitability of these welds to perform satisfactorily in service. It is necessary, therefore, that weldability include both the mechanical aspects, such as strength, ductility, and Charpy V-notch impact toughness, and the corrosion aspects, such as resistance to intergranular attack, SCC, and general overall corrosion.

The relative performance and weldability of ferritic alloys can best be determined by comparing the impact fracture behavior of these steels. Furthermore, impact testing of the HAZ as well as the weld should be included when qualifying both the welding procedure specification(s) and the welder for these materials. In addition to the Charpy V-notch impact energy (which includes examination of the DBTT), the lateral expansion and percent shear fracture of Charpy V-notch specimens also should be a part of a thorough analysis of weldability.

Over the years, two schools of thought have existed on how to weld the Group III ferritic stainless steels. One school recommends welding these alloys as one would the austenitics (this is not acceptable), and the other endorses using extra care and special techniques somewhat like those used to weld titanium. Extra care and special techniques are mandatory for Group III alloys. While the Group I alloys also require care, the welding of the Group II alloys is rather routine.

During the early to mid-1970s, a reluctance developed on the part of many users and fabricators to follow recommended procedures. As a result, many welds were produced that had inferior corrosion resistance, ductility, and impact toughness. Because of these problems, the weldability of the new ferritics was explored by many (Ref 28-34).

The unique as-welded properties of the Group III ferritics have been made possible by obtaining either very low levels of impurities, including carbon, nitrogen, and oxygen (ultrahigh-purity Grade III alloys) or a careful balance of niobium and/or titanium to match the carbon, nitrogen, and oxygen contents (intermediate-purity Group III alloys). For these reasons, every precaution must be taken and welding procedures must be selected that optimize gas shielding and cleanliness to avoid pickup of carbon, nitrogen, oxygen, and hydrogen.

Autogenous welds in ferritic stainless steels exhibit relatively simple microstructures. The grain size gradually increases from the edge of the HAZ to the fusion boundary. In unstabilized or niobium-stabilized welds, columnar grains extend from the fusion boundary to meet at a well-defined centerline (Fig. 40). In titanium-stabilized or dual-stabilized (niobium and titanium) welds, there is typically a transition from columnar grains near the fusion boundary to equiaxed grains near the weld centerline. The former structure shows a greater tendency for hot cracking.

With lower-chromium or high-carbon-content ferritic stainless alloys, such as types 409, 430, 434, 442, and 446, martensite formation during welding can occur, as illustrated in Fig. 41. In the as-welded condition, the DBTT will easily be above room temperature, with increased susceptibility to weld cracking during and after cooling from the molten state. Caution is advised when making welds under high restraint or in heavier section sizes. Preheat can be used under these conditions to slow the cooling rate and minimize stresses that can lead to cracking.

A further word of caution regarding selection of preheat and welding parameters: whereas higher heat inputs and preheats can reduce weld cracking in some ferritic stainless steels, grain growth in the weld HAZ can occur. Figure 42 shows grain growth in an ultrahigh-purity Fe-

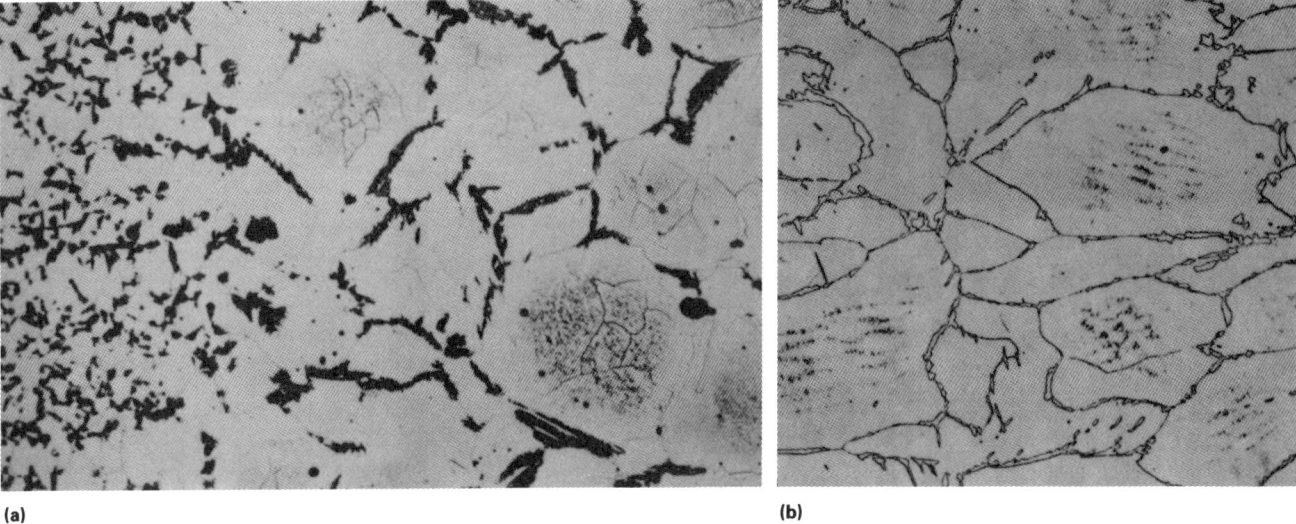

Fig. 41 Grain-boundary martensite formation in a type 430 ferritic stainless steel gas-tungsten arc weld. (a) Fusion zone. 100×. (b) Heat-affected zone. 150×. Source: Ref 37

28Cr-2Mo alloy in the base metal and HAZ. Excessive grain growth can produce losses in fracture toughness, ductility, and corrosion resistance.

Under some conditions, annealing after welding can be performed to eliminate martensite; however, the ferrite grains that have coarsened may grow even more. Annealing after welding generally is costly, can cause distortion, and usually is not practical in the field. Annealing of tubular products at the steel mill is the exception and is performed as standard procedure. This tube annealing is performed at high rates and is followed by quenching.

Regardless of the welding process used, joint preparation and thorough solvent degreasing (using a solvent that does not leave a residue) on both sides of the joint (inside and outside) are of paramount importance.

Welding Processes

Gas-Tungsten Arc Welding. When welding with the GTAW process, DCEN (or straight polarity) should be used. A tungsten-2% thoria electrode (AWS classification EWTh-2) with a tapered tip is recommended. Oxidation of the electrode tip or filler metal pickup is not acceptable because of the resulting reduction in arc stability. When this occurs, welding must be stopped and the electrode redressed. To optimize weld quality, a gas lens collet body and the largest-size ceramic nozzle should be used. With higher-speed automatic processes, a trailing gas shield is recommended to prevent excessive oxidation of the weld bead.

Argon, helium, or mixtures of the two can be used for shielding. Only high-purity gas should be used. Standard welding-grade gas may not be adequate because of cylinder contamination, and standard-grade cylinders are not certified as to purity level. On full-penetration welds or when welding thinner gages where oxidation of the backside can occur, back gas shielding with a high-quality gas is mandatory. When welding the

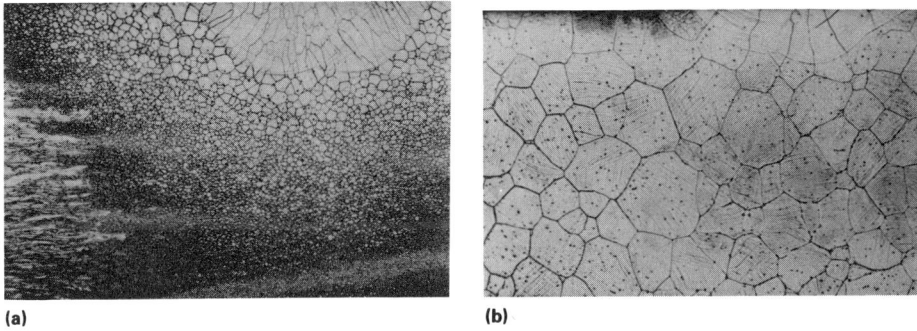

Fig. 42 Cross sections of partial-penetration gas-tungsten arc welds in high-purity Fe-28Cr-5Mo ferritic stainless steel. (a) Weld in warm-rolled sheet. (b) Weld in sheet that was preweld annealed at 1040 °C (1900 °F) for 60 min. Etched in 40% nitric acid electroetch. 11×

austenitic grades of stainless alloys, it is common to use nitrogen backing gas (usually to reduce costs or to enhance corrosion performance with these alloys). *Nitrogen backing gas must never be used when welding ferritics* because nitrogen pickup will cause severe embrittlement (loss of toughness and ductility) and loss of corrosion resistance. Inert backing gas should be used for at least two layers of deposited weld metal (3 mm, or 1/8 in., minimum).

Another common technique that is used when welding austenitics is to butt two pieces of metal together and weld from one side, then back grind the backside to sound metal and complete the joint. *This procedure must never be attempted when welding ferritics,* because all of the contaminated metal may not be completely removed. The result will be a defective, crack-sensitive ferritic weld.

To enhance weld quality and performance, especially for the Group III alloys, the following procedures are recommended:

- Thoroughly degrease the weld joint and adjacent surfaces back at least 50 mm (2 in.) on both sides of each joint member. This must also include the weld filler wire.

- Welding should only be performed with clean gloves. Dirty, sweaty, or damp welding gloves must never be used.
- Keep the welding torch at right angles to the work surface within 15° of vertical to prevent air aspiration into the inert gas shield.
- Gas lens screens that become contaminated with a drop or more of weld spatter must be changed immediately, because the disruption of gas flow from the torch nozzle causes air aspiration into the molten weld pool. Removal of contaminated weld metal is advised. Usually, the lens must be changed.
- Weaving the electrode is not permitted, except for a small amount to allow good sidewall fusion and tie-in. It should be noted that excessive weaving causes contamination of the weld pool, with a subsequent loss in fracture toughness, ductility, and corrosion resistance.
- When welding, keep the tip of the filler wire within the shielding gas envelope—another reason to use a gas lens and as large a gas cup as possible. If the filler wire tip becomes contaminated, either because it touched the tungsten electrode or because it was withdrawn from the inert gas envelope, welding must stop, the tip of

the contaminated wire must be cut back to sound metal, and the contaminated weld must be ground out and repaired.

- All hose connections must be of good quality and be tight to prevent air ingestion. Check all water seals in the torch. Air drafts in the welding area are to be avoided to prevent loss of the inert gas shield. Verify the integrity of the gas system with a weld button test. This is done by striking an arc on a test piece of E-Brite plate or other high-purity ferritic, establishing a small circular pool of molten metal approximately 13 mm ($\frac{1}{2}$ in.) in diameter, extinguishing the arc, and postpurging at least 6 s or more. The weld button must be bright and shiny and free of any heat tint. If not, the source of contamination must be found and corrected.
- Prepurge the torch before welding to remove air and/or moisture that has infiltrated the system. Postpurge all weld stops to prevent contamination. The postpurge time should be sufficient such that the weld stop is bright and shiny and free of any oxide heat tint or discoloration.
- A remote control should be used to allow gradual increase and decrease of current when initiating or extinguishing the arc.
- Avoid overheating and embrittling the weld by minimizing heat input and, in multipass welds, by keeping the interpass temperature below 95 °C (200 °F).
- When high-speed automatic welding is performed, a trailing gas shield is recommended.

Gas-Metal Arc Welding. With the GMAW process, DCEP (or reverse polarity) is used. The following methods of metal transfer across the welding arc are possible with GMAW:

- *Spray transfer* is characterized by high heat input and a fluid weld pool. Excessive grain growth is likely in the weld and HAZ. Spray transfer is not usually recommended when welding ferritic stainless steels, although some stabilized grades appear to be less sensitive to heat input. Heat input can be reduced with the pulsed GMAW process, thus allowing out-of-position welding.
- *Globular transfer* is characterized by lower heat input but is not normally used because of excessive spatter. Spatter can be minimized by proper choice of high-purity shielding gas and proper choice of power supply (for example, rapid arc power supplies that feature capacitive discharge electronics).
- *Short-circuiting transfer* features the lowest heat input of all the GMAW processes. However, lack-of-fusion defects are common with short-circuiting transfer if proper techniques are not followed.

Although grain growth can be controlled to some degree with higher weld travel speeds, lower interpass temperatures, and heat sinks, care must be taken to avoid weld defects such as lack of fusion and insufficient penetration. In some situations, the use of an austenitic filler metal can overcome the problem of weld grain growth because of the formation of a two-phase grain struc-

ture. However, the HAZ grain growth must not be forgotten when using one of these filler metals.

When welding ferritic and austenitic stainless steels with the GMAW process using one of the standard power supplies, pure argon shielding gas is usually not used because of arc instability, which causes air to be aspirated into the arc. As a result, the weld pool becomes enriched in nitrogen and oxygen. In the DCEP mode, the arc wanders, seeking spots that are emissive in character, usually oxides. This erratic arc behavior causes a disruption of the laminar flow of the inert gas, resulting in aspiration of air into the gas envelope.

One way to solve the arc wander problem has been to add an oxidizing element to the inert gas. Argon with 2% oxygen or with 2% carbon dioxide, typically used to weld plain carbon steel, low-alloy steel, and austenitic stainless steel, has been recommended for ferritic stainless steels as well. While this seems to be satisfactory for the stabilized ferritics in Group II, where the bulk of the applications are for automobile exhaust systems (type 409), these active, oxidizing shielding gases should *never* be used for the Group III higher-purity ferritics, stabilized or not, because of the dramatic degrading effect on toughness and ductility.

Still other investigators have shown that the arc wander problem associated with the GMAW process can be resolved by using an argon-helium mix, typically 75Ar-25He, and by ensuring that the inert gas is purified and free of contaminants such as air, moisture, and hydrocarbons. To further enhance operability and weld quality, a device covered in a U.S. patent (Ref 38) enables air and moisture to be excluded from entering the welding arc. By taking the high-purity inert gas system approach, rather than using a gas mixture containing reactive gases such as oxygen and carbon dioxide, critical reactive alloying elements such as titanium, niobium, aluminum, and chromium are not removed by oxidation. In this way, arc wander is virtually eliminated and wetting action is enhanced. Using this new technology, stable GMAW has been attained with pure argon. This patent also has possible application in any welding process that uses a wire-feed system.

Flux-cored arc welding functions in essentially the same manner as GMAW, except that instead of being solid, the filler wire is fabricated from a carbon steel, stainless steel, or nickel sheath that surrounds a core of alloying additions formulated to the desired weld deposit chemistry. Some FCAW consumables contain active fluxing ingredients, whereas others do not. In some instances, suppliers recommend the use of a supplementary gas shield, and sometimes the consumable is self-shielding. It is important to know the operating characteristics of the wire and when to use supplementary shielding gas, which usually gives better results. The advantages of using shielding gas purification as discussed for GMAW may apply here as well.

The FCAW process is not recommended for the Group III ferritic stainless steels because of the difficulty of maintaining alloy purity and because of the pickup of carbon, nitrogen, and oxygen. Flux-cored arc weld deposits are never as clean as those produced by solid-wire inert gas

welding processes. For less critical applications, or where an austenitic filler metal can usually be used, FCAW may be possible.

Because FCAW operates in the spray arc mode, higher heat inputs will result, making grain growth a potential problem. Although higher travel speeds can be employed with lower interpass temperature and heat sinks, care must be used to avoid lack-of-fusion defects.

Shielded Metal Arc Welding. In the SMAW process, DCEP is typically used. Shielded metal arc weld deposits made with covered electrodes are never as tough as welds made with an inert gas shielded process. For this reason, covered electrodes with matching composition are not available for the Group III ferritic stainless steels. Basically, the problem is one of purity, because carbon, nitrogen, and oxygen are difficult to suppress without seriously hampering welding electrode operability.

Where covered electrodes are available, proper storage is essential to avoid any pickup of moisture. Improper storage of SMAW consumables resulting in moisture pickup usually leads to weld porosity and, in some cases, hydrogen cracking.

For some ferritic stainless steels that must be used in the as-welded condition, and where postweld annealing is not practical or cost-effective, a dissimilar welding electrode can be used. The choice varies from the high-chromium austenitic grades such as type E310 or E310 ELC (which are fully austenitic) to a high-nickel alloy such as an ENiCrFe-2. Type E309 coated electrode (welds contain ferrite for resistance to hot cracking) and its low-carbon and higher-silicon variations have been used to advantage.

High-alloy austenitic weld metals do not flow as readily as the ferritic stainless steels. High-nickel alloy weld metal is particularly sluggish, with shallow penetration. This behavior requires that the welder use arc force and electrode manipulation to physically move the molten weld pool against the sides of the joint. Ferritic stainless steels have significantly higher melting temperatures than do the austenitic stainless steels or corrosion-resistant nickel-base alloys. When using austenitic filler metals to join ferritic stainless steel base metals, care must be exercised to ensure that sufficient heat has been applied to fuse the ferritic stainless steel base metal. Failure to follow these recommendations usually results in lack-of-fusion defects.

Depending on weld bead profile, slag entrapment can be a problem with some covered electrodes. If the slag does not chip out readily, grinding will be necessary. Trying to float out residual slag with successive molten weld passes is rarely successful. The net result is slag entrapment, which is readily apparent upon radiographic inspection. It should be remembered that grinding, if excessive, can result in more heat input via additional weld passes and ultimately cause grain growth. The net result could be a loss in HAZ toughness and ductility.

When welding ferritic stainless steels with the SMAW process, the following techniques are recommended:

- As with all other welding processes, weld joint surfaces should be carefully cleaned with solvent (both sides of each joint member) to remove any contaminant (e.g., oil, grease, or dirt) that could degrade weld properties and corrosion resistance.
- The arc should be struck in the bevel of the weld joint, rather than on the adjacent base metal.
- A short arc should be maintained to avoid the formation of porosity and to minimize oxidation effects and pickup of oxygen and nitrogen.
- Excessive inclination of the electrode should be avoided (a maximum incline of 20° from the vertical is generally satisfactory).
- A slight weave for tie-in and fusion is allowed, provided that it is not wider than three times the diameter of the electrode core wire.
- Crater cracks at weld stops must be ground out to sound metal before proceeding. Dye-penetrant inspection is the best way to ensure that all cracked material has been removed.

Plasma arc welding of ferritic stainless steels is very similar to GTAW, and the same precautions and recommendations apply. Concern has been voiced about the use of hydrogen gas with PAW because of the possibility of weld metal cracking caused by the interaction of hydrogen in the weld metal and in high-stress conditions. Gastungsten arc welding experience with type 409 indicates that hydrogen additions will cause embrittlement immediately after welding; however, most of the hydrogen diffuses out of the weld metal within 48 h and ductility is restored. The situation is more critical with higher-chromium alloys.

An advantage of the PAW process is that the unique high-intensity arc produces a weld bead characterized by deep penetration and a HAZ narrower than that produced by the GTAW process. The net result is that less HAZ grain growth is possible with PAW than with GTAW.

Resistance Welding. Spot welding, seam welding, and flash welding processes can be used provided that the loss in toughness can be tolerated. Seam welding has been used to fabricate panel coil-type heat exchanger surfaces. Whenever possible, argon inert gas should be used to protect the weld joint or seam (backside included) to minimize oxidation and the pickup of nitrogen. Titanium-stabilized alloys appear to be more resistant to the effects of nitrogen pickup due to poor shielding than are the high-purity alloys. This is apparently due to the formation of a protective TiN film that covers the weld pool.

Other Welding Processes. Ferritic stainless steels can be readily welded using the EBW process with hard vacuum. Friction welding and LBW are also possible. Where practical, the molten zone should be protected with an inert gas shield.

Submerged arc welding can be used to join some of the ferritic stainless grades; however, the high heat input associated with the process becomes troublesome because of undesirable grain growth in the weld HAZ. Choice of fluxes and control of residues become critical. Dilution can exceed 50%. Submerged arc welding is not suitable for the Group III alloys and generally is also not suitable for most of the other alloys.

Filler Metal Selection

Welds in ferritic stainless steel base metals can be produced several ways: (1) autogenously (that is, without the addition of filler metal), (2) with a matching filler metal composition, (3) with an austenitic stainless steel filler metal, or (4) using a high-nickel filler alloy. Table 11 lists some base metal/filler metal combinations for several ferritic stainless steels.

Before selecting a filler metal, consideration must be given not only to mechanical property requirements, especially weld ductility and toughness (including the weld HAZ), but also to the level of corrosion resistance required for the application. Autogenous welding may be considered for some of the high-purity Group III alloys, such as E-Brite 26-1. The mill-annealed product will have good mechanical properties and corrosion resistance, but if the interstitial levels of carbon, oxygen, and nitrogen are on the high side of the specification limits, the autogenous weld will exhibit not only poor ductility and toughness, but also poor corrosion resistance. To avoid this type of problem, material should be purchased with interstitial element levels on the low side of the specification range.

Filler metals of matching composition for the more common grades of Groups I and II ferritic stainless steels, such as types 409 and 430, are available as solid wire, metal-cored, or flux-cored wire (both gas-shielded and self-shielded), covered electrodes, and bare rod. Because of the reactivity of titanium and aluminum and poor transfer of these elements across the arc, the availability of consumables containing these elements is usually limited to bare wire or rod.

When nonstandard grade ferritic filler metals are not available, or because poor wire-drawing characteristics make production prohibitive, metal-cored or flux-cored filler metals offer a solution. Weld metal properties should be qualified before purchase.

Filler metals for the Group III alloys are available as matching composition in bare wire or rod form. Because Group III weldments are frequently used in the as-welded condition, it is strongly recommended that these filler metals be purchased having interstitials at the very low end of the alloy specification. For best ductility, toughness, and corrosion performance, the interstitial element (C + N + O) content should not exceed 120 ppm for the ultrahigh-purity grades (such as E-Brite 26-1, 29-4, and 29-4-2).

Because the Group III ferritics of intermediate purity rely on stabilization with titanium or titanium and niobium, welds have such poor toughness that welding with these filler metals is limited to very thin section sizes, such as thin-wall pipe, tubing, or sheet. When better toughness is required of stabilized grades with a ferritic consumable, welding should be performed with an ultrahigh-purity filler metal containing very low levels of (C + N + O). It should be noted that ultrahigh-purity welding consumables require careful handling and processing to keep interstitials at these very low levels. Keeping them clean at the job site is also mandatory.

Austenitic stainless steel filler metals are often used to join ferritic stainless steels to overcome poor weld ductility and toughness deficiencies; they do not display a DBTT as do ferritics. Although weld metal grain growth is usually not a problem (because a two-phase mixture of austenite and ferrite forms), grain growth in the weld HAZ of the ferritic base metal must not be overlooked. Sometimes the application of an austenitic filler can be a problem because of the rather large discrepancy in thermal expansion between the two alloys. In this regard, problems can range from (1) cracking due to thermal stress, (2) sensitization and loss of corrosion resistance if the austenitic filler metal is not a low-carbon grade or stabilized with titanium or niobium (corrosion can also result because of the heat from multipass welds or some subsequent thermal treatment after welding), or (3) stress relief that may not be fully effective because of the thermal expansion differences.

Table 11 Typical ferritic base metal/filler metal combinations

Base metal	Covered electrode, bare rod, or filler wire	Application
405	405 Nb	As-welded
	430	Annealed
	308(L), 309(L), 310(ELC)	As-welded
409	430	Annealed
	308(L), 409, 409Nb, 309LSi	As-welded
429	208(L), 309(L), 310(ELC)	As-welded
430	430	Annealed
	308(L), 309(L), 310(ELC)	Annealed or as-welded
439	430, 430Ti	Annealed or as-welded
442	442	Annealed
	308(L), 309(L), 310(ELC)	As-welded
446	446	Annealed
	308(L), 309(L), 310(ELC)	As-welded
E-Brite 26-1	ER26-1	As-welded
	Inconel 112, Hasteloy C-276, or Hasteloy C-22	As-welded
AL 29-4C	AL 29-4-2	As-welded
AL 29-4	AL 29-4-2	As-welded
AL-29-4-2	AL 29-4-2	As-welded

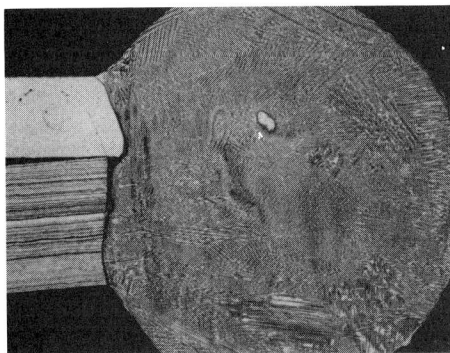

Fig. 43 Weld joining UNS S43735 superferritic stainless steel (top) to N08367 superaustenitic alloy (bottom) using N06625 nickel alloy filler metal. Note the difference between the meltback of superferritic and superaustenitic materials and the island of unmelted superferritic stainless steel near the center of the weld deposit. Both conditions indicate the high melting temperature of superferritic stainless steels relative to that of austenitic stainless steels or nickel alloys. Etched with mixed nitric/hydrochloric/acetic acid solution. 14×

High-nickel alloy filler metals have also been used successfully to join ferritics, especially the Group III alloys to themselves as well as to carbon steel, 300-series stainless steels, duplex stainless steels, superaustenitic stainless steels, and nickel-base alloys. Examples of nickel-base filler metals that have been used successfully are ENiCrFe-2, ENiCrMo-3, ERNiCrMo-1, and ERNiCrMo-3. In addition to their outstanding corrosion resistance, these high-nickel filler metals have CTEs that are similar to those of the ferritics they are joining. Although they have worked well with E-Brite alloy, attempts to use them with the 3 to 4% Mo grades of ultrahigh-purity ferritics have occasionally been less successful. Formation of brittle intermetallic compounds at the fusion boundary has been encountered in some cases, but good welds can be produced (Fig. 43). Sound welds have been produced using duplex stainless steel filler metal, but corrosion resistance of such joints may not be adequate in some applications.

Undoubtedly, the greatest quantity of ferritic stainless steel welded at the present time is type 409, which is used for automobile exhaust system components. The welds are virtually all single-pass fillet or lap welds. The most common filler metal is a matching composition supplied as a 1.1 mm (0.045 in.) diameter metal-cored wire (ANSI/AWS A5.9-92 classification EC409 or EC409Cb), which is used for GMAW with argon-oxygen gas mixtures, such as the popular 98Ar-2O₂ mixture. This filler metal is often used in robotic welding at high travel speeds and in the vertical-down position on rotating pieces that are 18 gage or less in thickness. Welding is done in a short-circuiting transfer mode, or nearly so.

Example 4. An alternative procedure for welding type 409 base metal in automotive exhaust applications is to use 0.9 mm (0.035 in.) diameter solid austenitic stainless wire, in the short-circuiting transfer mode, with an argon-oxygen gas mixture. Because of the thin gage of the base metal, dilution of the order of 40% can be anticipated. Because the filler metal ER308LSi

would exceed the corrosion resistance of the type 409 base metal, it could be considered. If the type 409 composition were 0.04C-0.5Mn-0.4Si-11.0Cr-0.5Ti (WRC-1988 $Cr_{eq} = 11.0$ and $Ni_{eq} = 1.4$; FN, off the diagram), and if the ER308LSi composition were 0.02C-1.5Mn-0.8Si-19.7Cr-10.2Ni-0.2Mo-0.04N (WRC-1988 $Cr_{eq} = 19.9$ and $Ni_{eq} = 11.7$; FN = 9.7), then the 40% dilution weld metal would have $Cr_{eq} = 16.34$, $Ni_{eq} = 7.58$, and FN would be off the diagram. Recalculating the chromium and nickel equivalents according to Schaeffler (Fig. 1), the weld metal would be deeply into the (A + M + F) field; that is, of the order of 50% martensite could be expected in the weld metal. This could be a problem for cracking or forming after welding. Therefore, ER308LSi may not be a good choice for welding type 409 base metal.

Example 5. Assume that ER309LSi is substituted for the ER308LSi of Example 4. If the ER309LSi composition were 0.02C-1.5Mn-0.8Si-23.5Cr-13.5Ni-0.2Mo-0.04N (WRC-1988 $Cr_{eq} = 23.7$ and $Ni_{eq} = 15.0$; FN = 12.8), then the 40% dilution weld metal would have $Cr_{eq} = 18.6$, $Ni_{eq} = 9.56$, and FN = 12.6. Recalculating the chromium and nickel equivalents according to Schaeffler (Fig. 1) puts the weld metal just at the upper edge of the (A + M + F) field; that is, a trace of martensite, at most, would be present in the weld metal. Furthermore, because the calculated weld metal FN is almost exactly the same as the calculated wire FN, the tie line from the wire composition to the base metal composition must be nearly parallel to the isoferrite lines in the WRC-1988 diagram. This means that the weld metal FN will be immune to changes in dilution, although excess dilution should be avoided because it would lead to more martensite. Thus, the ER309LSi filler metal would be a good choice for welding type 409 base metal.

Welding Procedures and Weld Properties

Effect of Shielding Gas Purity on Weld Toughness. The primary reasons for using shielding and backing gas are to protect the molten filler wire tip, the nonconsumable electrode (when used), the weld pool, and the solidified weld bead from atmospheric contamination. Researchers have shown that gas contaminants can cause cracking, varying degrees of weld bead oxidation, arc instability, and degradation of mechanical and corrosion properties. A particular gas or gas mixture might be used because of its availability or for enhanced arc stability, a particular mode of weld metal transfer, enhanced penetration or bead profile, or easier arc ignition.

There is no question that quality welds require quality shielding. It is essential that clean gas be maintained and delivered to the point of use. From a practical standpoint, factors that have been identified as relating to "bad gas" and welding problems include:

- Contaminated gas cylinders (by moisture/air)
- Contaminated and/or leaking gas manifold systems

- Damaged, defective, or loose shielding/backing gas line fittings
- Intrusion of contaminants when mixing gases

Achieving gas quality at the point of use can be difficult. Welding problems can occur with a single cylinder of gas or a series of cylinders. A manifold system can be particularly difficult to deal with because of its long length and numerous welding stations. As a result of poor gas quality, defects are produced that require repair, job completion can be delayed, and job quality can be compromised. The solution is a portable, cost-effective system that will remove contaminants from the shielding gas and backing gas, not only when working in the shop, but also in the field.

Because ferritic stainless steels are sensitive to interstitial element contaminants, it is important that these elements be removed so as not to degrade properties such as ductility, toughness, and corrosion resistance. Impurities commonly found in gas cylinder or manifold systems are moisture, oxygen, hydrocarbons (such as oils from compressors), and carbon dioxide (when not intentionally added). Moisture in CO_2 gas is also a common problem.

There are systems on the market that can eliminate gas contaminants to levels below 1 ppm, but they must rely on multicomponent, energy-intensive gettering. These systems are heavy, flow rates are usually restrictive, and lack of portability is a problem. Another system relies on a resin that is a single rechargeable compound, can effectively remove a variety of impurities to less than 10 ppb, operates at room temperature, and is light and portable. The effects of using such a system on the impact properties of 6 mm (¼ in.) thick E-Brite 26-1 alloy plate are shown in Fig. 44.

Hydrogen Embrittlement. Like other ferritic materials, the ferritic stainless steels are susceptible to hydrogen embrittlement. For this reason, the use of hydrogen-containing shielding gas should be avoided. Hydrogen can also be created from water, water vapor, or oils, and these should be rigorously excluded from the weld region. The presence of hydrogen in the weld can lead to cracking of the weld bead shortly after welding. It can also reduce ductility in uncracked welds. Hydrogen is often spontaneously outgassed from these alloys at room temperature and is readily lost during low-temperature (90 to 200 °C, or 200 to 400 °F) heat treatments. Hydrogen outgassing at room temperature, if it will occur, requires a few days to a few weeks. Surface films of oxides and/or nitrides can inhibit hydrogen outgassing, and it may be necessary to remove such films to facilitate hydrogen outgassing and restoration of ductility. Sensitivity to hydrogen is a function of alloy composition, microstructure, and strength. In general, the stabilized, high-chromium-plus-molybdenum materials, such as AL 29-4C alloy, are more sensitive than the high-purity, lower-chromium-plus-molybdenum materials, such as the E-Brite alloy.

Preheating. One of the main reasons for preheating is to reduce the temperature gradient between the weld area and the unaffected base metal. Any austenite that forms in nominally fer-

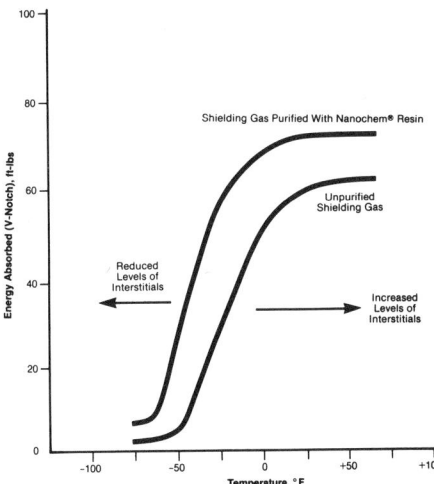

Fig. 44 Charpy V-notch impact test results from gas-tungsten arc welded E-Brite 26-1 plate. Weld conditions: plate thickness, 6 mm (¼ in.); shielding/backing gas, argon; shielding/backing gas impurity levels, H_2O 40 ppm and O_{20} ppm; shielding gas flow rate, 28 L/min (60 ft³/h); voltage, 14 V; current (direct current, electrode negative), 150 A; travel speed, 1.5 to 2.5 mm/s (3.5 to 6 in./min). Nanochem is a registered trademark of Hercules Inc. Source: Ref 39

ritic stainless steels will air harden to martensite even in heavy (>300 mm, or 12 in., diameter) sections. Preheating light-gage sheet will not prevent the formation of martensite. It is also unlikely that enough preheat could be applied to produce any significant post-transformation tempering. Hydrogen may be a factor in situations involving high stress and restraint. When additional preheat time is allowed, the hydrogen can diffuse out safely. Ferritic stainless steels that would benefit from preheat would be the Group I types (430, 434, 442, and 446).

When required, a preheat in the range of 150 to 230 °C (300 to 450 °F) is usually sufficient. Section sizes of 6 mm (¼ in.) or smaller generally do not need preheat, but such parameters as joint design, restraint, welding process, cooling rate, and dissimilar metal combinations (different CTEs), and base metal composition should be reviewed before making a final decision.

Preheat should not be used on the Group III alloys, especially the ultrahigh-purity steels. These alloys do not form martensite when welded, so no preheat is necessary. Furthermore, because these alloys have such low levels of impurities, excessive grain growth would occur compared with the Group I and Group II alloys.

Postweld annealing is normally performed on the Group I ferritic stainless steels. The purpose is to transform any martensite that may have formed during welding into a wholly ferritic structure (usually containing some spheroidized carbides) or to remove effects of high-temperature embrittlement and improve corrosion resistance. Annealing under these conditions does not refine coarsened ferrite grains; some form of metalworking is needed to achieve recrystallization and grain refinement.

When postweld annealing is required, the recommended temperature range is 790 to 850 °C

(1450 to 1550 °F). At these temperatures consideration must be given to oxidation of the metal surface and distortion effects. Fixturing to prevent metal deformation may be required. Sigma and χ formation is typically not a problem with the Group I alloys.

Cooling from the annealing temperature must be done carefully. Furnace cooling to 600 °C (1100 °F) is usually specified to minimize distortion from handling. Rapid cooling through the temperature range of 565 to 400 °C (1050 to 750 °F) is necessary to avoid 475 °C (885 °F) embrittlement. Depending on section thickness, forced-air cooling or water-spray quenching is usually performed.

Group III ferritic stainless steels (ultralow interstitials and the stabilized grades), particularly the high-chromium high-molybdenum alloys, are typically not annealed after welding because of the danger of precipitation of σ and χ phases in the temperature range of 550 to 900 °C (1020 to 1650 °F) unless the anneal is followed by a rapid quench. However, postweld annealing of welded tubes is common.

Corrosion Resistance. Investigators have determined that the loss of corrosion resistance of ferritic stainless steels after welding is caused by chromium depletion upon cooling from exposure to temperatures of 925 °C (1700 °F) (Ref 40-45). Sensitization due to chromium depletion occurs by holding or cooling through the temperature range of 425 to 700 °C (800 to 1300 °F). In the temperature range from 700 to 925 °C (1300 to 1700 °F), rapid diffusion of chromium in ferrite occurs, replenishing the chromium-depleted zones. For this reason, weldments that are annealed at 790 to 850 °C (1450 to 1550 °F) show good intergranular corrosion resistance despite the presence of intergranular precipitates of chromium-rich carbides and nitrides. Below 700 °C (1300 °F), little chromium diffusion occurs and corrosion resistance is not completely restored.

Conventional (Group I) 400-series ferritic stainless steels, such as types 430, 343, and 446, are susceptible to intergranular corrosion and to embrittlement in the as-welded condition. Corrosion in the weld area generally encompasses both the weld metal and weld HAZ. Early attempts to avoid some of these problems involved the use of austenitic stainless steel filler metals; however, failure by corrosion of the HAZ usually occurred even when exposure was to rather mild media for relatively short periods of time.

To overcome some of these earlier difficulties and to improve weldability, several of the standard grade ferritic stainless steels were modified. For example, type 405, containing nominally 12% Cr, is made with lower carbon and a small aluminum addition of 0.20% to restrict the formation of austenite at high temperatures so that hardening is reduced during welding. For maximum ductility and corrosion resistance, however, postweld annealing is necessary. Recommendations for welding include either a type 430 or 309 filler metal, the latter being used when increased weld ductility is desired.

As mentioned earlier in this article, researchers recognized that the high-chromium,

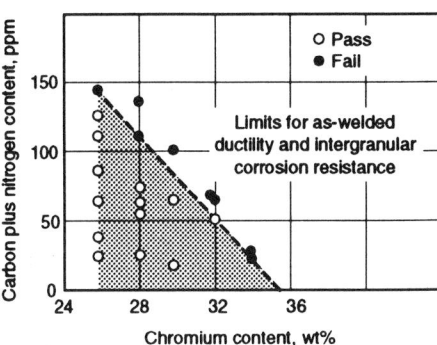

Fig. 45 Effect of interstitial levels and chromium content on as-welded ductility and intergranular corrosion resistance. Source: Ref 46

high-molybdenum ferritic stainless steels possess a desirable combination of good mechanical properties and resistance to corrosion. These properties make them attractive alternatives to the austenitic stainless steels, which often fail due to chloride SCC.

Reducing the total interstitial element levels in ferritic stainless steels improves weldability and corrosion resistance. Figure 45 shows the relationship of chromium content and (C + N) content on the combined properties of as-welded corrosion resistance and ductility. Table 12 lists this relationship separately for each property. As chromium content increases, the amount of (C + N) that can be tolerated for intergranular corrosion resistance increases. Conversely, for as-welded ductility, the amount of tolerable (C + N) is drastically reduced. Thus, at low chromium levels, as-welded corrosion resistance is the controlling factor; at high chromium levels, as-welded ductility is the factor that limits the use of high-chromium stainless steels.

To improve the corrosion resistance of ferritic stainless steels, two practical methods have been applied:

- *Lower interstitial levels:* Because the solubility of interstitial elements is low in ferrite, new melting and refining practices have been used to produce ultrahigh-purity ferritic (Group III) stainless alloys like those shown in Table 9.

Table 12 Limits of interstitial element (C + N) content for acceptable as-welded intergranular corrosion resistance and as-welded ductility
Sample thickness: 2.5 mm (0.1 in.)

Chromium content, wt%	Intergranular corrosion resistance(a), ppm (C + N)	Ductility(b), ppm (C + N)
19	60-80	>700
26	100-130	200-500
30	130-200	80-100
35	<250	<20

(a) Intergranular corrosion resistance in boiling 50% ferric sulfate-50% sulfuric acid solution. (b) No cracking as determined by slow bending around a 5 mm (0.2 in.) mandrel

With these low levels of carbon and nitrogen, chromium carbide and nitride precipitation cannot occur to a harmful degree; thus, as-welded ductility and corrosion resistance are maintained.

- *Stabilization of carbon and nitrogen:* This is achieved by the addition of carbide- and nitride-forming elements that are more stable than chromium carbides and chromium nitrides. Titanium and/or niobium are used to tie up the carbon and nitrogen in the matrix. Stabilization has proved effective in preventing sensitization of ferritic alloys such as 18Cr-2Mo and 26Cr-1Mo, as well as the higher chromium-molybdenum grades. Investigators have shown, however, that if excessive amounts of stabilizer are used beyond what is required for corrosion resistance, ductility and room-temperature impact properties are degraded (Ref 29, 47-49).

Corrosion resistance can also be improved by following proper welding procedures and recommendations. As described previously, preheating (except to remove moisture) or PWHT should not be performed. Postweld heat treatment is used only with the conventional ferritic stainless alloys.

Weld toughness is an important property of great interest to the design engineer as well as to the end user because of the influence of weld defects or notches on the performance of a material, such as in a piping system or pressure vessel, especially under high-strain-rate conditions. Because ferritic stainless steels undergo a transition from ductile to brittle behavior as the temperature decreases (Fig. 38), researchers have been able to show rather good correlation between the DBTT and weldability. The common method used to measure DBTT is the Charpy V-notch test.

Section size and thickness have a significant effect on the impact toughness of ferritic stainless steels (and all ferritic alloys). The effect of section size on DBTT is shown in Fig. 46. The thinner the material, the lower the DBTT.

The cooling rate from peak welding temperatures is very important because toughness appears to be strongly related to the precipitation and morphology of carbides and nitrides. Even in ultrahigh-purity E-Brite 26-1, chromium nitrides have been observed. Depending on cooling rate, these precipitates will align along the grain boundaries or intragranularly within the matrix. For this reason, grain size is important. The finer the grain size, the more uniform the properties and the tougher the material.

Figure 47 illustrates the effect of carbon, nitrogen, and stabilizing elements on 26Cr-1Mo alloys. As shown in Fig. 47, low interstitial levels correspond to lower DBTT values. It has been observed that notch brittleness is the result of the total interstitial element content (C + N), rather than the absolute value of each. Reducing the total interstitial element levels in ferritic stainless steels improves weldability and notch toughness. Another comparison is shown in Fig. 48. Here, the higher the purity of a 26Cr-1Mo alloy, the better the notch toughness and the lower the DBTT

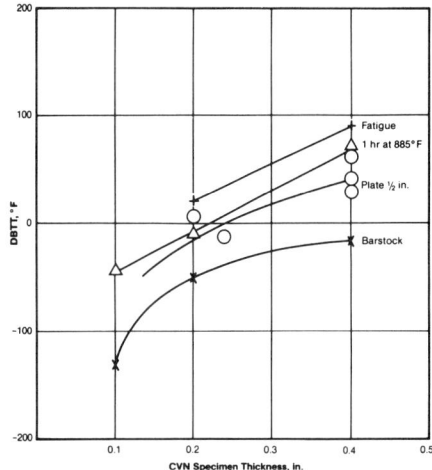

Fig. 46 Impact properties as a function of section thickness for XM-27 ferritic stainless steel. Source: Ref 50

when compared to a 26Cr-1Mo alloy stabilized with titanium. Although the titanium-stabilized alloy was 3 mm ($^1/_8$ in.) thick compared to the 6 mm ($^1/_4$ in.) thick E-Brite plate, the ultrahigh-purity alloy had decidedly superior notch toughness (DBTT = –40 °C, or –40 °F, for E-Brite vs. DBTT = 80 °C, or 175 °F, for 26-1 with titanium).

If the alloy thickness is reduced below 3 mm ($^1/_8$ in.), the stabilized grades start to display somewhat improved toughness. Because of the difficulty of measuring Charpy V-notch impact toughness in such thin gages, weld ductility as measured by a bend test (see Table 12) or bend angle has been determined to be an acceptable method of measuring weldability. Under these conditions, stabilized ferritic stainless steels have excellent as-welded ductility when stabilizers are present in the minimum amounts necessary for stabilization, but the room-temperature impact properties suffer. When excessive stabilizing element(s) are present, weld ductility decreases as excess stabilizer content increases. If welding techniques are poor and shielding gas is contaminated, the amounts of stabilizer added to prevent sensitization and embrittlement may be insufficient to combine with all of the carbon and nitrogen. Oxygen pickup can also be detrimental. The result is loss of ductility, toughness, and corrosion resistance. Shielding gas purity must not be overlooked.

Dissimilar austenitic filler metals can be used to overcome the difficulties of higher-than-desired weld metal DBTT. Typical Charpy V-notch toughness data are shown in Fig. 49.

Hot Cracking. Weld and HAZ hot cracking in the ferritic stainless steels is not as common a problem as with austenitic stainless steels. This is a result of the lower CTE of the ferritic stainless steels, as well as the greater solubility of sulfur and phosphorus in ferrite. However, excessive amounts of stabilizing elements have been shown to cause hot cracking as well as reduced ductility. Figure 50 shows hot cracks in the top surfaces of autogenous gas-tungsten arc welds in two type 444 ferritic stainless steel subscale varestraint test specimens. The stabilized alloys were found to be more

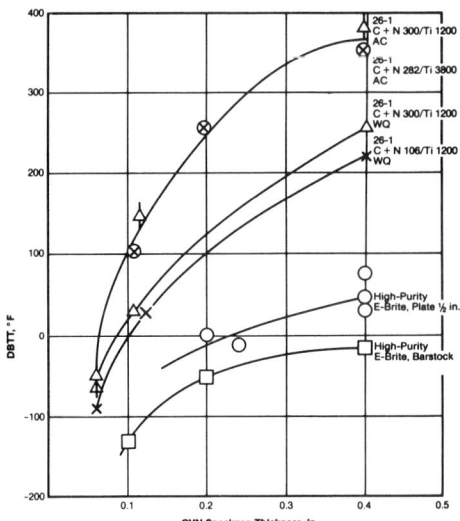

Fig. 47 Effect of alloy purity (interstitial element content) and stabilizer content (values given in parts per million) on the ductile-to-brittle transition temperature of ferritic stainless steels. AC, air cooled; WQ, water quenched. Source: Ref 50

susceptible to hot cracking than an alloy of similar composition with ultralow levels of impurities.

The alloy that contained 0.40% Nb as a stabilizing element cracked more severely than the alloy that contained 0.333% Ti, but the worst cracking occurred in an alloy that contained both niobium (0.394%) and titanium (0.171%). The high-purity alloy that contained a total (C + N) content of 47 ppm (and no stabilizing elements) produced no hot cracks when tested under the same conditions. Although sulfur and phosphorus can also cause hot cracking in the ferritic stainless steels, the excess levels of niobium and titanium (above that necessary to tie up the carbon and nitrogen) are a more common cause of hot cracking. Thus, the stabilizing elements must be kept to the minimum practical levels to avoid hot cracking and reduced ductility.

Along with hot cracking, which is not often a problem for ferritic stainless steel welds, autogenous welds in alloys stabilized only with niobium often suffer from low ductility and poor toughness. In highly restrained situations, cracks may propagate in the weld along its length. For this reason, ferritic stainless steels of high or intermediate interstitial content stabilized only with niobium are rarely welded. (Titanium-free, stabilized ferritic stainless steels do, however, provide better brazeability and may be selected for brazed rather than welded applications.) Reduction of total interstitial element content to below approximately 0.02% largely eliminates this problem. Thus, the Group III ultrahigh-purity alloys that contain niobium additions can be welded without fear of cracking. Addition of approximately 0.05% Ti or greater causes equiaxed grains to form near the weld centerline and yields improved weld properties. Thus, dual stabilized, intermediate-purity Group III ferritic stainless steels are used to provide toughness in both the base metal and the weld regions.

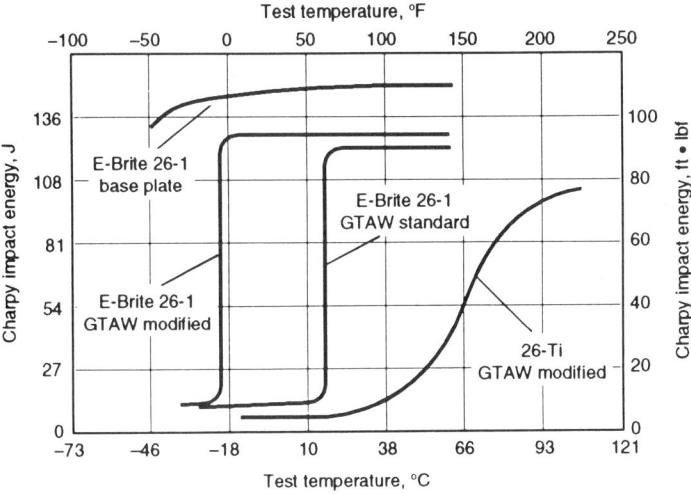

Fig. 48 Notch toughness of a gas-tungsten arc welded high-purity ferritic stainless steel (6 mm, or ¼ in., thick E-Brite 26-1 plate) vs. that of a titanium-stabilized alloy (3 mm, or ⅛ in., thick 26-1 Ti plate). Source: Ref 32

Fig. 49 Charpy V-notch toughness of shielded metal arc welds made in 6 mm (¼ in.) thick E-Brite 26-1 plate with different filler metals. Source: Ref 31

Welding Austenitic Stainless Steels

Austenitic stainless steels exhibit a single-phase, fcc structure that is maintained over a wide range of temperatures. This structure results from a balance of alloying additions that stabilize the austenite phase from elevated to cryogenic temperatures. Because these alloys are predominantly single phase, they can only be strengthened by solid-solution alloying or by work hardening. The exceptions are the precipitation-strengthened austenitic stainless steels.

The austenitic stainless steels were developed for use in both mild and severe corrosive conditions. They are also used at temperatures that range from cryogenic temperatures, where they exhibit high toughness, to elevated temperatures of nearly 600 °C (1110 °F), where they exhibit good oxidation resistance. Because the austenitic materials are nonmagnetic, they are sometimes used in applications where magnetic materials are not acceptable.

The most common types of austenitic stainless steels are the UNS S20000 and S30000 alloys (AISI 200 and 300 series). Within these two grades, the alloying additions, which are chosen to provide the desired properties at reasonable cost, can be considerably different. Furthermore, alloying additions and specific alloy composition can have a major effect on weldability and the as-welded microstructure. The 300-series alloys typically contain from 8 to 20% Ni and from 16 to 25% Cr. Minor alloying additions are approximately 1% Si (maximum), which is used as a deoxidizer; 0.02 to 0.08% C, which is used as an austenite stabilizer; and approximately 1.5% Mn, which is used both as an austenite stabilizer and as a sulfur and silicon compound former.

Depending on alloy composition, the austenitic stainless steels may solidify with a microstructure containing some retained ferrite at room temperature as a result of welding. Weld cracking, of which the most common form is solidification cracking, can be another consequence of welding.

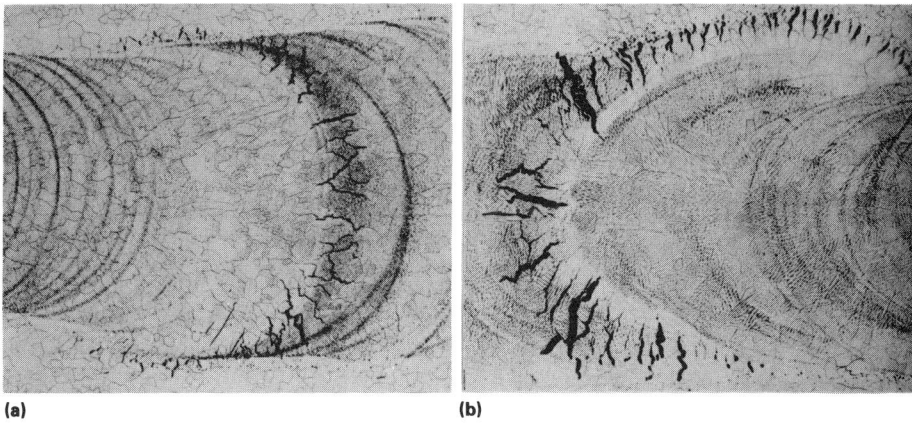

Fig. 50 Top surfaces of subscale varestraint test gas-tungsten arc welds in type 444 stainless steel. (a) Titanium-stabilized (0.333% Ti) type 444 alloy. (b) Niobium-stabilized (0.401% Nb) type 444 alloy. Source: Ref 51

Cracks can occur in various regions of the weld with different orientations, such as centerline cracks, transverse cracks, and microcracks in the underlying weld metal or adjacent HAZ. These cracks are primarily due to low-melting liquid phases, which allow boundaries to separate under the thermal and shrinkage stresses resulting from weld solidification and cooling. Other possible metallurgical consequences of welding are:

- The precipitation of intergranular, chromium-rich $M_{23}C_6$ chromium carbides in the weld HAZ, which can leave these regions sensitive to corrosion
- The transformation of weld ferrite to σ-phase during elevated-temperature service, which can reduce ductility and toughness

These phenomena can be either minimized or eliminated through alloy selection, process optimization, or PWHT. With an understanding of the evolution of the weld microstructure and the ability to control it, one can produce welds to meet a wide variety of service requirements.

General Welding Characteristics

The austenitic stainless steels are generally considered the most weldable of the stainless steels. Because of their physical properties, their welding behavior may be considerably different from those of the ferritic, martensitic, and duplex stainless steels. For example, the thermal conductivity of typical austenitic alloys is only approximately half that of the ferritic steels. Therefore, the weld heat input that is required to achieve the same penetration is considerably reduced. In contrast, the CTE of austenite is 30 to 40% greater than that of ferrite, which can result in increases in both distortion and residual stress because of welding. The molten weld pool of the austenitic stainless steels also tends to be more viscous, or sluggish, than ferritic and martensitic grades. This impedes the metal flow and wettability of welds in these materials, which may promote lack-of-fusion defects.

A major concern when welding the austenitic stainless steels is susceptibility to solidification

Table 13 Chromium- and nickel-equivalency relationships for austenitic stainless steels

Author	Year	Chromium equivalent, wt%	Nickel equivalent, wt%
Schaeffler	1949	$Cr + Mo + 1.5Si + 0.5Nb$	$Ni + 0.5Mn + 30C$
DeLong et al.	1956	$Cr + Mo + 1.5Si + 0.5Nb$	$Ni + 0.5Mn + 30C + 30N$
Hull	1973	$Cr + 1.21Mo + 0.48Si + 0.14Nb + 2.27V + 0.72W + 2.20Ti + 0.21Ta + 2.48Al$	$Ni + (0.11Mn - 0.0086Mn^2) + 24.5C + 14.2N + 0.41Co + 0.44Cu$
Hammar and Svennson	1979	$Cr + 1.37Mo + 1.5Si + 2Nb + 3Ti$	$Ni + 0.31Mn + 22C + 14.2N + Cu$
Siewert et al.	1992	$Cr + Mo + 0.7Nb$	$Ni + 35C + 20N + 0.25Cu$

and liquation cracking. As discussed below, these materials can be very resistant to these forms of high-temperature cracking if the material is compositionally balanced such that the solidification behavior and microstructure are controlled to ensure that the weld metal contains more than 3 vol% ferrite.

In cases where fully austenitic welds are required, such as when the weld must be nonmagnetic or when it is placed in corrosive environments that selectively attack the ferrite phase, the welds will solidify as austenite and the propensity for weld cracking will increase. In some alloys, such as type 310 and the superaustenitic grades, all the allowable compositions within the specification range solidify as austenite when welded. To minimize cracking in these welds, it is generally advisable to weld with low heat input and under low-constraint conditions.

Welds that are made at slower speeds and produce elliptical rather than teardrop-shaped pools are also generally less susceptible to cracking. This effect is particularly pronounced when welding thin sheet, as in the production of thin-wall tubing. Residual elements, which form low-melting liquid phases that promote cracking, should be kept to a minimum. These elements include phosphorus, sulfur, boron, selenium, niobium, silicon, and titanium. Small additions of oxygen and nitrogen are somewhat beneficial and are thought to affect the wetting characteristics of the liquid phases. However, high concentrations of these elements may promote porosity. Manganese also can reduce cracking susceptibility, primarily by tying up sulfur and silicon that would otherwise be available to form low-melting phases.

Microstructural Development

Although austenitic stainless steels are predominantly austenitic, they often contain small amounts of bcc ferrite, particularly in the weld metal. This ferrite is often described as δ-ferrite, because it forms at elevated temperatures and is distinguished from α-ferrite, which is the low-temperature form in iron-base alloys. In this section, the term *ferrite* refers to high-temperature δ-ferrite, unless noted otherwise. These alloys also may contain martensite, although the presence of this phase is unusual and limited to special composition and temperature ranges, forming only as a result of plastic deformation.

The solidification behavior and microstructural development of the weld metal of these alloys are quite complex and, until recently, were not well understood. In this class of alloys, weldability and subsequent weld performance are often directly related to weld microstructure. Thus, when welding these alloys, a general understanding of the welding metallurgy can be very beneficial in optimizing weld performance. Because chemical composition has the greatest influence on weld microstructure, a number of empirical relationships and constitution diagrams have been developed to predict microstructure based on actual or approximated composition. In all cases, the concepts of Cr_{eq} and Ni_{eq} have been used to normalize the effect of various alloying additions on the ferrite-forming and austenite-forming potencies, respectively. Considerable disagreement still exists regarding these equivalency relationships (Table 13) for austenitic stainless steels.

The following sections summarize the important aspects of solidification behavior and microstructural evolution that dictate weld metal ferrite content and morphology. An understanding of microstructural evolution and its ramifications in austenitic stainless steel welds is crucial, because it will dictate base metal and filler metal selection, as well as welding conditions.

Solidification Behavior

In austenitic stainless steels, the primary phase of solidification may be either austenite or ferrite. This is dictated predominantly by composition. It has been well documented (Ref 52-54) that welds that solidify as primary austenite are inherently more susceptible to weld solidification cracking than welds that solidify as primary ferrite. Thus, control of weld solidification behavior is critical to ensuring crack-free welds.

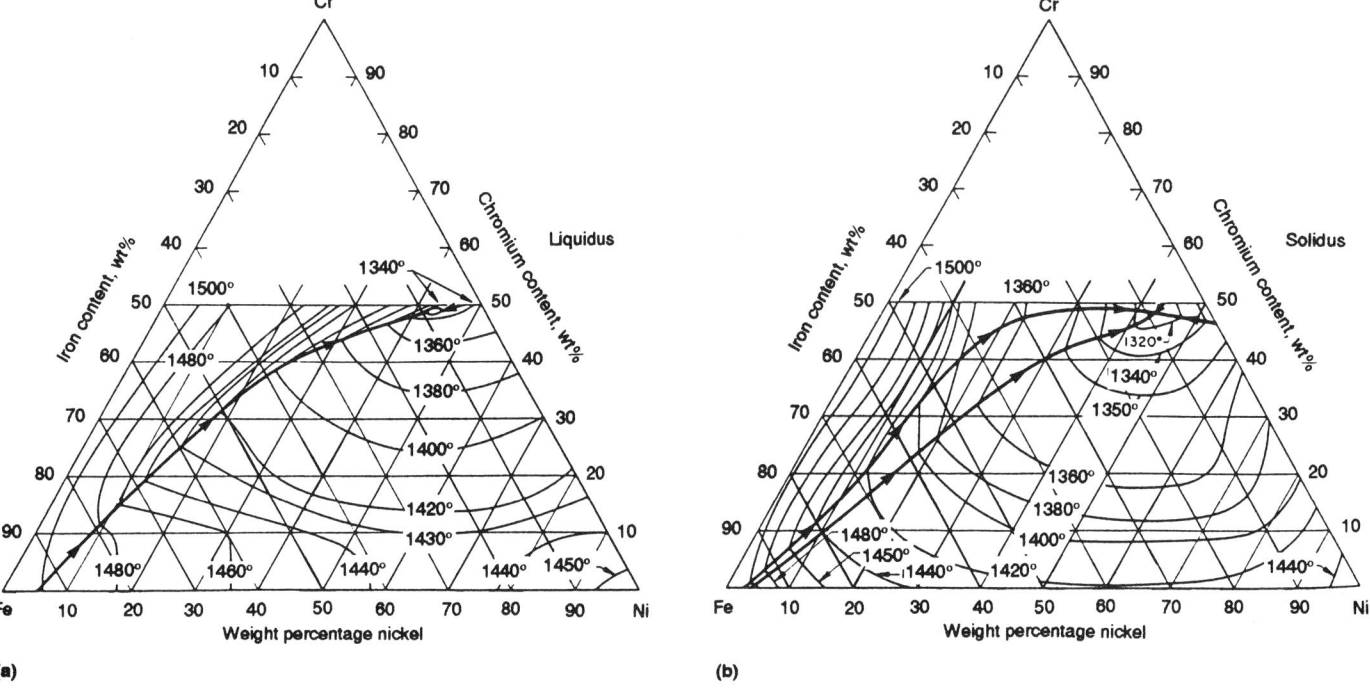

(a)   **(b)**

Fig. 51   Projections of (a) liquidus and (b) solidus surfaces, as isothermal contours on iron-nickel-chromium ternary diagram. Temperatures shown are in °F. Source: Ref 55

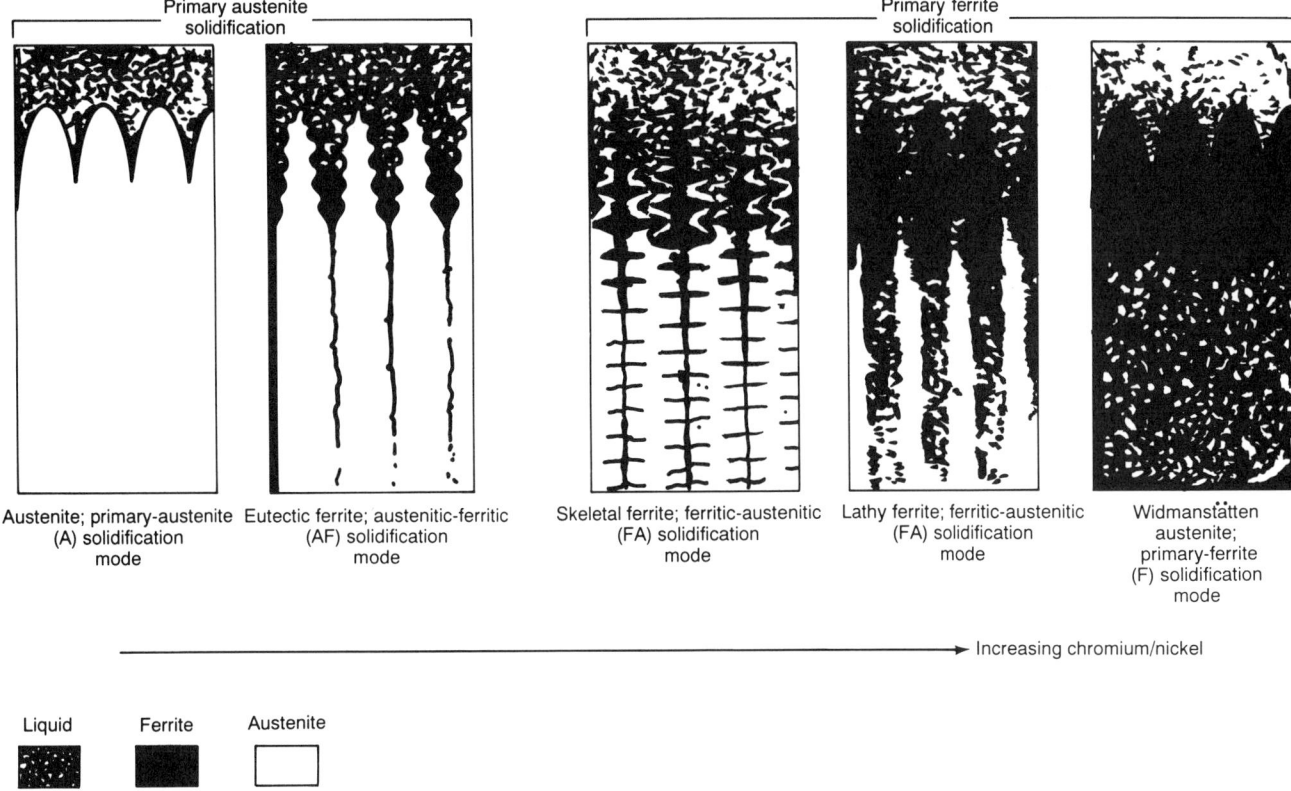

Fig. 52 Schematics showing solidification and solid-state transformation behavior of welds with increasing Cr_{eq}/Ni_{eq} ratios. Source: Ref 57

The iron-nickel-chromium ternary diagram assembled by Speich (Ref 55) can be used to discuss, in general terms, the solidification process. Figure 51 shows both liquidus and solidus surfaces. A eutectic trough extends to the ternary eutectic composition of roughly 49Cr-43Ni-8Fe. A peritectic trough at Fe-4Ni extends into the diagram to about 75% Fe, at which location the liquidus crosses the nickel-rich solidus, changing from peritectic to eutectic behavior.

In Fig. 51, it can be seen that for approximately 60 to 70% Fe, which is the iron content of many of the austenitic stainless steels, the liquidus lies along the chromium-nickel ratio of approximately 1.5. Compositions on the nickel-rich side of the liquidus will solidify as primary austenite, sometimes referred to as A-type solidification. Depending on composition, it may solidify with a small fraction of eutectic ferrite (AF-type solidification). Alloys on the chromium-rich side of the liquidus will solidify as primary ferrite with the peritectic or eutectic solidification of austenite (FA-type solidification). However, the solidification boundary between ferrite and austenite can be shifted because of the nonequilibrium solidification conditions of welding. For compositions that are farther from the peritectic/eutectic liquidus, the welds solidify completely as ferrite at higher chromium-nickel ratios (F-type solidification). The chromium-nickel ratio for single-phase ferrite solidification is often reported to range from 1.9 to 2.0.

A number of diagrams can be used to predict the primary phase of solidification based on the weld metal composition. The WRC-1992 diagram (Fig. 4) can be used to predict solidification behavior, in addition to ferrite content. Note that this diagram contains four solidification regimes, designated as A, AF, FA, and F. The austenite-ferrite microstructural morphologies associated with these regimes are described below.

Solid-State Transformations and Ferrite Morphologies

The final weld microstructure is controlled by both the solidification behavior and the subsequent solid-state transformations. A number of schematics have been published (Ref 56-59). The one by Brooks et al. (Ref 57), shown in Fig. 52, depicts some of the general characteristics of microstructural development. However, a much wider variety of microstructures exists in actual welds. The vertical sections of the iron-nickel-chromium ternary diagram for 70 and 60% Fe (Fig. 53) are useful in discussing the solid-state transformations. As indicated by these diagrams, during the cooling of primary austenite welds (AF-type), some of the eutectic ferrite may transform to austenite. The primary ferrite-solidified welds that exhibit peritectic/eutectic behavior during the final stages of solidification (FA-type) typically solidify with a large fraction of ferrite (Fig. 52). During cooling through the $(\delta + \gamma)$ two-phase field, much of the ferrite transforms to austenite, with chromium partitioning to the ferrite and nickel partitioning to the austenite, leaving ferrite only within the very cores of the original dendrites. When only several percent of the original ferrite is retained—which is often referred to as skeletal, or vermicular, ferrite—it may be difficult to distinguish between it and the eutectic ferrite that results from primary austenite solidification (Fig. 52), unless good metallographic techniques are used. However, the location of the ferrite is different. It resides within the core of the dendrites, in the case of FA-type solidification, rather than at the dendrite boundaries, in the case of AF-type solidification.

At higher chromium-nickel ratios, other ferrite morphologies are often observed, such as the lathy structure shown in Fig. 52. It is generally reported that the skeletal and lathy ferrite morphologies are indicative of primary ferrite with the secondary solidification of austenite, but these ferrite morphologies can also exist in welds that solidify as single-phase ferrite. At higher chromium-nickel ratios, a Widmanstätten austenite structure can also form in welds that solidify as single-phase ferrite. It should be noted that the solidification and transformation behavior shown in Fig. 52 is dependent not only on composition, but also on cooling rate. Extremely high solidification and cooling rates, such as those encountered during EBW or LBW, may significantly alter the microstructure relative to that predicted using the WRC-1992 diagram. This behavior is described below in the section "Solidification Behavior and Microstructure of High-Energy-Density Welds."

Micrographs of the three-dimensional structure of several weld ferrite morphologies compiled by David (Ref 61) are shown in Fig. 54.

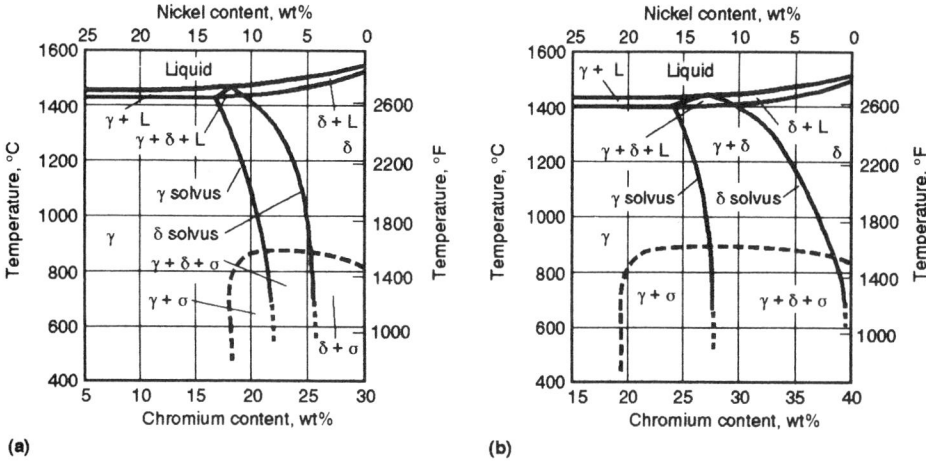

Fig. 53 Vertical sections of iron-nickel-chromium ternary diagram, at constant iron content. (a) 70% Fe. (b) 60% Fe. Source: Ref 60

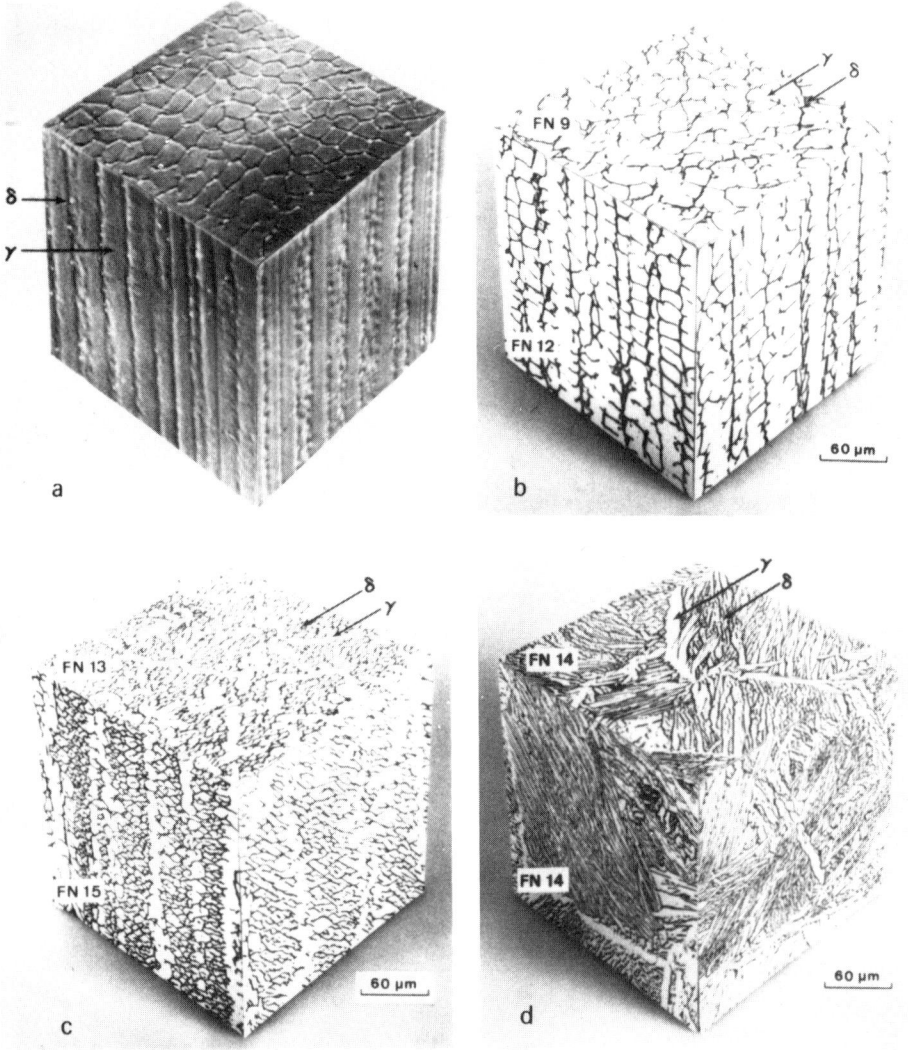

Fig. 54 Three-dimensional views of typical austenitic stainless steel weld morphologies; solidification direction, vertical. In each photograph, ferrite is the darker phase. (a) Cellular primary austenite solidification structure with intercellular eutectic ferrite in type 310. (b) Skeletal ferrite, 9-12 FN, in type 308. (c) Lathy or lacy ferrite, 13-15 FN, in type 308 multipass weld. (d) Acicular or Widmanstätten austenite, 14 FN, in upper portion of type 308 weld. Welds in (b) to (d) solidified as primary ferrite. Source: Ref 61

Small amounts of ferrite along solidification cell boundaries of a primary austenite structure are shown in Fig. 54(a). This very cellular-appearing solidification structure is characteristic of welds that solidify as austenite and results primarily from the microsegregation of chromium and, to a lesser extent, nickel along the solidification cell boundaries. Depending on alloy composition and welding conditions, final solidification may occur as a eutectic of ferrite and austenite. Figures 54(b) and (c) show ferrite along cell cores of primary ferrite structures, whereas Fig. 54(d) shows acicular ferrite or Widmanstätten austenite in a structure that solidified completely as ferrite. Additional details on solidification behavior and microstructural development are provided in Ref 57 and 62.

Alloying Effects on Solidification Behavior, Weld Microstructure, and Cracking Susceptibility. The relationship between solidification behavior and a composition factor, in terms of Cr_{eq}/Ni_{eq}, was established by Suutala and Moisio (Ref 63) using coefficients of: $Ni_{eq} = Ni + 0.3Mn + 22C + 14.2N + Cu$; and $Cr_{eq} = Cr + 1.37Mo + 1.5Si + 2Nb + 3Ti$ (see Table 13). A diagram (Fig. 55) was developed that delineates the four solidification types—A, AF, FA, and F—as described previously. Using their data, the demarcation between single-phase austenite solidification (A) and austenite solidification with the eutectic solidification of ferrite (FA) occurs at a Cr_{eq}/Ni_{eq} ratio of approximately 1.35. The transition to solidification as primary ferrite with the eutectic/peritectic solidification of austenite (FA) occurs at a Cr_{eq}/Ni_{eq} of approximately 1.5. This value has been found to be valid for most conventional 300-series alloys welded under normal arc welding conditions. This ratio increases with increasing solidification velocity. At the lower bounds of primary ferrite, some regions may solidify as ferrite and others as austenite. In this case, the region where primary austenite is most commonly located is along the weld centerline, where the solidification velocity is maximum. This transition between primary austenite and primary ferrite is especially important because of the strong relationship between solidification behavior and solidification-cracking susceptibility.

As indicated in Fig. 55, above a Cr_{eq}/Ni_{eq} ratio of approximately 1.95, solidification occurs as single-phase ferrite. However, other studies (Ref 59) indicate that single-phase ferrite solidification occurs at considerably lower Cr_{eq}/Ni_{eq} ratios and that the ratio of approximately 1.95 may more closely correlate to microstructures containing Widmanstätten austenite.

The Cr_{eq}/Ni_{eq} ratios defined above are valid only when using the Suutala and Moisio (Ref 63) equivalency relationships. Corresponding ratios for delineating the solidification behavior by using the WRC-1992 equivalencies are somewhat different. However, discrepancies between the two diagrams exist, as is apparent for lean alloys or pure iron-nickel-chromium ternaries. For example, the transition from primary austenite to primary ferrite is reported to occur at a Cr_{eq}/Ni_{eq} ratio of 1.5 by Suutala and Moisio (Ref 63), versus 1.4 in the WRC diagram.

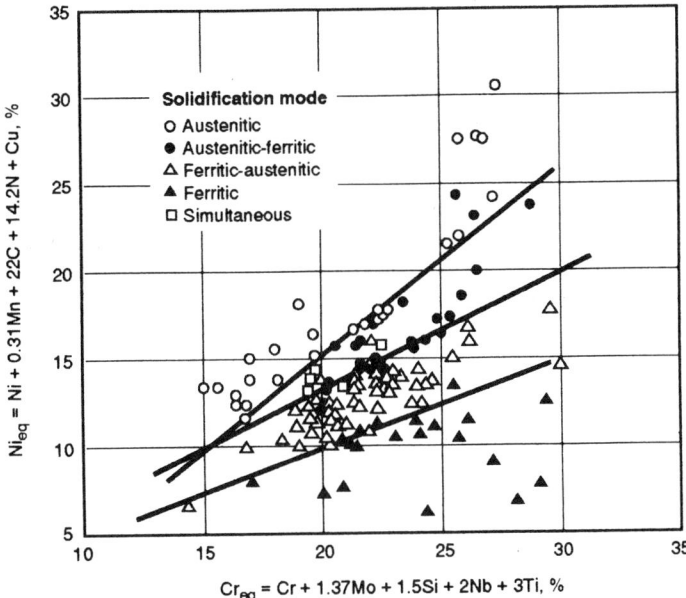

Fig. 55 Solidification mode (experimental) for variety of compositions, compared on basis of Cr_{eq}/Ni_{eq} ratio. Source: Ref 63

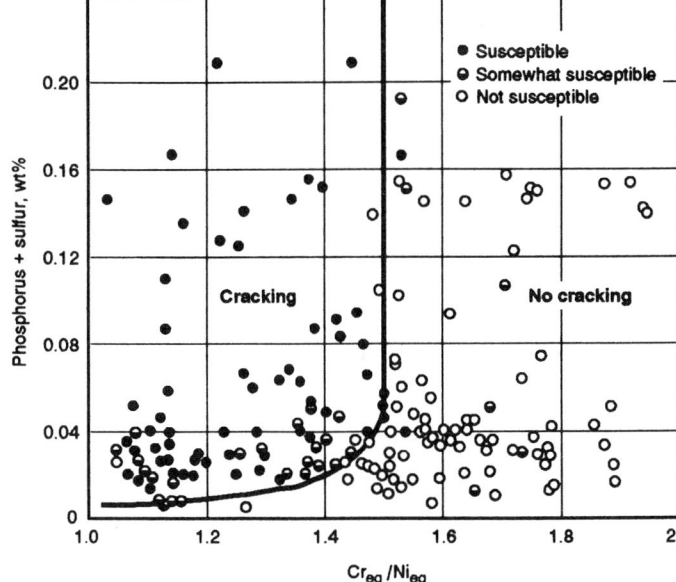

Fig. 56 Relationship between solidification cracking susceptibility and Cr_{eq}/Ni_{eq} ratio. Boundary between cracking and no cracking at Cr_{eq}/Ni_{eq} = 1.5 corresponds to change in solidification mode from primary austenite below 1.5 to primary ferrite above 1.5. Source: Ref 64

Takalo, Suutala, and Moisio (Ref 64) also described the solidification-cracking susceptibility of austenitic stainless steels by plotting their Cr_{eq}/Ni_{eq} ratios versus impurity content in terms of sulfur plus phosphorus. Their results are shown in Fig. 56. A dramatic transition in cracking susceptibility occurs at a value of approximately 1.5. This transition represents the shift in solidification behavior from primary austenite to primary ferrite, as described above, and reinforces the importance of controlling solidification behavior in order to avoid weld solidification cracking.

As noted previously, Schaeffler (Ref 1) developed one of the first diagrams for predicting weld microstructures. This diagram (Fig. 1) is especially useful for predicting microstructures between dissimilar alloys using a tie line between the two alloy compositions and the appropriate alloy dilution. The diagram was developed using the SMAW process, where the nominal nitrogen level was about 0.06 wt% and, as such, was not shown as an alloying addition. This diagram described the behavior of most of the alloys in use at the time and is relatively accurate for most 300-series alloys when using conventional welding processes.

The WRC-1992 diagram (Fig. 4), developed primarily with data from welds made by SMAW, is the most accurate diagram and is preferred in terms of the composition ranges for which it was established. In this diagram, the alloying elements have been limited to nickel, carbon, nitrogen, and copper in the Ni_{eq} and to chromium, molybdenum, and niobium in the Cr_{eq}. However, the diagram is applicable for manganese contents up to 10%, molybdenum contents up to 3%, nitrogen contents up to 0.2%, and silicon contents up to 1%.

When the WRC-1992 diagram is used for alloy systems containing significant amounts of alloying elements that have not been included in the diagram, predictions may be inaccurate. As discussed above, boundaries between the different solidification modes are also included on the diagram, although some disagreement exists with the boundaries established by other investigators. However, the most important boundary by far is the one separating primary ferrite from primary austenite solidification, in which some discrepancy still exists. The diagram does predict that the maximum amount of eutectic ferrite will not exceed a few percent, which is consistent with practical observations.

When using these diagrams to predict weld behavior, one must be aware that uncertainties in compositional analysis, as well as welding process and parameters, can affect predicted solidification behavior and ferrite content. One common occurrence in the welding of stainless steels is the possibility of nitrogen adsorption during welding when inadequate shielding is used. It is not uncommon that nitrogen levels of approximately 0.02% in the base material can be increased to values as high as 0.1%. This will significantly decrease ferrite content and may also result in a change in solidification mode from primary ferrite to primary austenite, which can have a drastic effect on weld solidification-cracking susceptibility. Thus, the nitrogen content of the deposited weld material must be used in making the prediction. However, with the use of the diagrams, magnetic measurements of FN, and an understanding of weld microstructural evolution, one can reasonably predict the nature of the weld microstructure.

Measurement of Weld Metal Ferrite

As described previously, weld metal ferrite content significantly influences both the weldability and service performance of austenitic stainless steels. Weld metal ferrite content can either be predicted using constitution diagrams, such as the WRC-1992 diagram (Fig. 4), or measured using instruments that take advantage of the ferromagnetic characteristics of the ferrite phase.

The term *Ferrite Number* has been adopted as a relative measure for quantifying ferrite content using standardized magnetic techniques (Ref 65). The FN approach was developed in order to reduce the large variation in ferrite levels determined for a given specimen when measured using different techniques by different laboratories. Ferrite Number approximates the "volume percent ferrite" at levels below 8 FN. Above this level, deviation occurs, where the FN value exceeds the actual volume percent ferrite. For example, a weld metal with 16 FN contains approximately 13.8 vol%.

A number of instruments are commercially available for determining the ferrite content of welds, including the Magne gage, Severn gage, and ferrite scope. The Severn gage and ferrite scope are particularly applicable for use in the field or on the production floor. The ferrite scope is also useful in measuring ferrite on welds of small cross section, as is often the case with electron-beam welds. Calibration procedures for magnetic measurement techniques are recommended in AWS A4.2 (Ref 65). These procedures use either the thickness standards of the U.S. National Institute of Standards and Technology or actual weld metal standards that include certified levels of weld metal ferrite.

It is important to understand that it is impossible to accurately determine the absolute ferrite content of austenitic stainless steel weld metals. Even on undiluted weld pads, ferrite variations from pad to pad must be expected because of slight changes in welding and measuring variables. On a large group of pads made from one heat or lot, using a standard pad welding and preparation procedure, two sigma values indicate that 95% of the tests are expected to be within a range of approximately ±2.2 FN at about 8 FN. If different pad welding and preparation procedures are used, then these variations will increase. Variations are also introduced based on the composition of the ferrite. The magnetic attraction of the ferrite may vary significantly with chemical composition. Thus, for the same volume percent ferrite, the FN determined by magnetic instruments may vary for weld pads made using different filler materials.

Even larger variations in ferrite content may be encountered if the welding technique allows excessive nitrogen pickup, in which case the ferrite can be much lower than otherwise expected. A nitrogen pickup of 0.10% typically will decrease the FN by about 8.

Austenitic stainless steel base materials are intentionally balanced compositionally to produce inherently lower ferrite content than matching weld metals. This is done, in part, to facilitate the hot workability of the material during forging, extrusion, and rolling operations. For this reason, special attention is required when making autogenous welds if primary ferrite solidification is desired to prevent solidification cracking. In general, weld metal diluted with base metal will also be somewhat lower in ferrite than the undiluted weld metal. For example, this effect is commonly observed when welding type 304 or 304L base metals with ER308 or ER309 filler materials.

The agreement between the predicted and measured weld metal ferrite content is also strongly dependent on the accuracy of the chemical analysis. Variations in the results of the chemical analyses encountered from laboratory to laboratory can significantly affect the predicted ferrite level, particularly if these variations occur in the detection of carbon and nitrogen. It is not uncommon for predicted and measured ferrite levels to differ by as much as 4 to 8 FN.

Nitrogen-Strengthened Stainless Steels. The addition of nitrogen to austenitic stainless steels significantly improves the strength and pitting resistance of the alloy and may also improve cryogenic toughness. These alloys may contain relatively high levels of manganese, because manganese increases the solubility of nitrogen in the austenite matrix, in addition to substituting for nickel as an austenite stabilizer.

In general, the weldability of these alloys is similar to the 300-series materials. The presence of ferrite in the as-deposited weld microstructure reduces weld-cracking susceptibility for the same reasons described previously. The prediction of weld metal ferrite content in these alloys has historically been problematic, because the DeLong diagram (Fig. 2) did not adequately account for large concentrations of nitrogen and manganese. Both Espy (Ref 66) and Hull (Ref 67) developed equivalency relationships and predictive diagrams that better cope with high levels of nitrogen. The Espy diagram represented a modification of the DeLong diagram and accounted for higher nitrogen and manganese lev-

els. Hull developed equivalencies (see Table 13) to predict ferrite levels in high-nitrogen, high-manganese stainless steels. The Ni_{eq} of 14.2 developed by Hull for nitrogen is significantly lower than the value of 20.0 used in the WRC-1992 diagram. However, the omission of manganese from the diagram is in agreement with the small Ni_{eq} assigned by Hull. Limited data suggest that the Hull and WRC-1992 diagrams are in fair agreement when predicting weld ferrite contents in these alloys with nitrogen contents as high as approximately 0.25%. At the higher nitrogen contents, one may expect that the WRC-1992 diagram will predict higher ferrite contents than the Hull diagram. From Table 13 it can be seen that Hammer and Svennson (Ref 68) used the same nickel equivalent developed by Hull.

Because of the high nitrogen contents of these steels, weld porosity may sometimes be encountered. The critical level of nitrogen, in terms of porosity problems, is lower for electron-beam welds made in vacuum (approximately 0.25%) than it is for welds made by GTAW, where porosity problems are usually not encountered at nitrogen levels of less than approximately 0.35%.

Solidification Behavior and Microstructure of High-Energy-Density Welds

Differences exist between the solidification behavior and microstructures of high energy-density welds and more conventional welds, such as those produced by SMAW and GTAW. These differences have been attributed to the rapid solidification velocities and cooling rates of the high-energy-density welds and, if not recognized, can have a drastic effect on weld quality and performance.

One characteristic of the high cooling rates during high-energy-density welding is a fine solidification cell size. However, changes in solidification behavior and solid-state transformation, compared with the behavior and transformation observed in gas-tungsten arc welds of the same alloy composition, can also occur. One of the most important effects of the rapid solidification rates of high-energy-density welds is a shift in solidification transition from primary austenite to primary ferrite to higher Cr_{eq}/Ni_{eq} ratios than those encountered in conventional arc welds. A change in solidification mode from primary ferrite to primary austenite, which resulted in centerline cracking of an electron-beam weld in type 304L, is shown in Fig. 57. It must be recognized that similar changes in solidification mode from primary ferrite to primary austenite can occur along the centerline of welds made with the more conventional welding processes, such as GTAW. This is especially common at higher welding speeds in materials with Cr_{eq}/Ni_{eq} ratios (Suutala and Moisio equivalents) slightly above 1.5.

Several microstructures can also exist in high-energy-density welds that have not been reported in welds of more moderate cooling rates. Basically, these microstructures consist of a single phase of either ferrite or austenite. An example of the single-phase austenite structure is shown on the right side of Fig. 58(a), where a carbon diox-

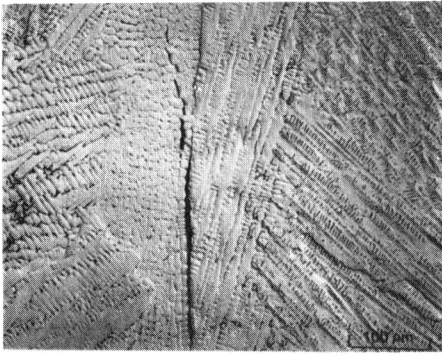

100 μm

Fig. 57 Solidification crack in electron-beam weld along weld center in region where solidification occurred as primary austenite as a result of higher solidification and cooling rates

ide laser-beam weld was made over a gas-tungsten arc weld in an alloy of 23Cr-12Ni-balance Fe with a Cr_{eq}/Ni_{eq} ratio of 1.9 (Ref 69). These welds solidify as single-phase ferrite, but they subsequently transform to approximately 100% austenite during cooling via a massive transformation. The gas-tungsten arc weld of this composition, shown at the left in Fig. 58(a), exhibits a typical two-phase microstructure with a FN of approximately 21.

Characteristics of the massively transformed austenitic structure include fairly small-faceted-appearing grain boundaries and little or no evidence of the cellular solidification that would result from microsegregation. This apparent lack of microsegregation may be due to the higher solute diffusivities in ferrite, as compared with austenite, which results in homogenization occurring during solidification and cooling and/or by reduced alloy partitioning occurring at the rapid solidification velocities (Ref 69, 70).

At high Cr_{eq}/Ni_{eq} ratios, high-energy-density welds can solidify completely as ferrite. However, because of suppression of the solid-state transformation of ferrite to austenite during the rapid cooling, a large fraction of the ferrite is retained at room temperature. This behavior has been reported in laser-beam welds of type 312. Microsegregation is also minimal in these welds, and the grain-boundary region sometimes exhibits Widmanstätten austenites rather than the faceted grain structure of the massively transformed austenite. An example of this microstructure is shown in Fig. 58(b). In some applications, such as the containment of high-pressure hydrogen, for which the austenitics are highly suited, a weld completely of ferrite would be unacceptable. With the massively transformed ferrite and the retention of ferrite at high Cr_{eq}/Ni_{eq} ratios, the composition range in which two-phase $(\delta + \gamma)$ microstructures exist in the high-energy-density welds is greatly reduced.

The shift from primary ferrite to primary austenite solidification at high solidification rates often leads to problems with weld cracking, as shown in the electron-beam weld in Fig. 57. Alloy selection based on solidification behavior pre-

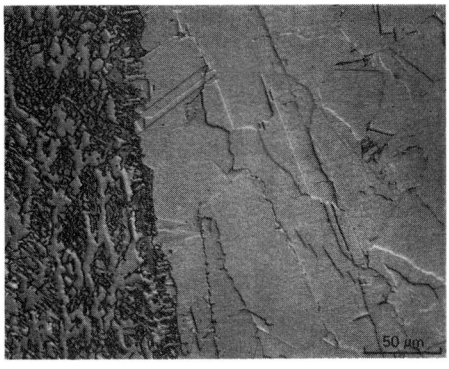

(a)

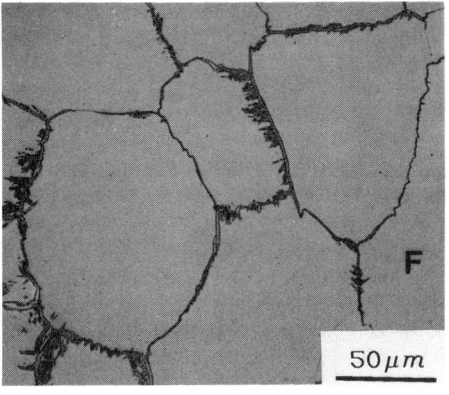

(b)

Fig. 58 Microstructures of laser-beam welded austenitic stainless steels. (a) Gas-tungsten arc weld shown on left, with CO_2 laser-beam weld shown on right, in alloy of Cr_{eq}/Ni_{eq} = 1.8. Laser-beam weld on right is single-phase austenite formed as a product of massive transformation. (b) Ferritic structure formed in laser-beam weld of Cr_{eq}/Ni_{eq} = 2.0. Source: Ref 69, 70

Fig. 59 Pulsed Nd:YAG laser-beam weld exhibiting severe solidification cracking as a consequence of primary austenite solidification, Cr_{eq}/Ni_{eq} = 1.6. Source: Ref 71

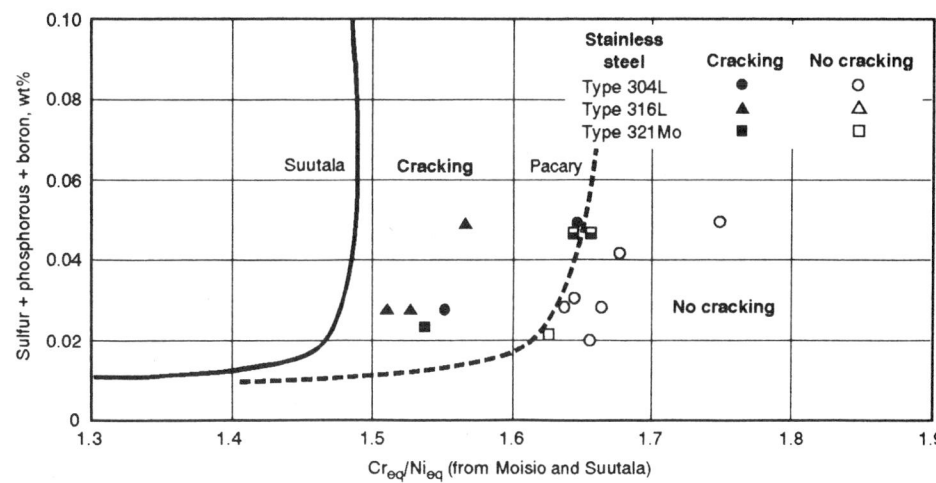

Fig. 60 Diagram for predicting weld solidification cracking susceptibility of pulsed laser welds in austenitic stainless steels. Note that Welding Research Council equivalents are used. Source: Ref 71

dicted by the WRC-1992 diagram or that of Suutala and Moisio (Ref 63) may not be valid.

For example, a pulsed Nd:YAG laser-beam weld in a 316L alloy with a Cr_{eq}/Ni_{eq} (Suutala and Moisio equivalents) of approximately 1.6 is shown in Fig. 59. Solidification of this weld has occurred as primary austenite, with resultant solidification cracking. Reference to the Suutala and WRC-1992 diagrams indicates that solidification would occur as primary ferrite with conventional gas-tungsten arc welds and that the weld should contain approximately 6 FN.

A modified Suutala diagram developed by Pacary et al. (Ref 71) (Fig. 60) shows the shift in solidification mode and associated cracking behavior of pulsed laser-beam welds. The critical cracking/no cracking demarcation shifts from the Cr_{eq}/Ni_{eq} ratio of approximately 1.48 (Suutala and Moisio equivalents) for conventional arc welding to approximately 1.7 for the pulsed laser-beam welds.

Katayama and Matsunawa (Ref 58) established the change in solidification using Schaeffler equivalents to also occur at the value of 1.7. These values are dependent on the welding process (for example, electron-beam welds and pulsed-Nd:YAG and carbon dioxide laser-beam welds), as well as on weld parameters (Ref 70). Because the pulsed-YAG technique produces the most rapid solidification interface velocities and cooling rates, the transition for this process should occur at the highest ratio. Thus, the selection of alloy compositions above the Cr_{eq}/Ni_{eq} ratio of approximately 1.7 (Suutala and Moisio equivalents) ensures solidification as primary ferrite and significantly reduces the risk of cracking, although higher accompanying ferrite content in the base material must also be expected.

Weld Defect Formation

Solidification cracking, which results from the formation of low-melting liquid films along grain boundaries during the last stages of solidification, is probably of greater concern to the weld-

ing engineer than is any other metallurgical defect in austenitic stainless steel welds. As discussed above, welds that solidify as primary austenite may be very susceptible to solidification cracking. This susceptibility is increased by elements that promote the formation of liquid phases. These elements include phosphorus and sulfur, which are often present as impurities, and silicon, niobium, titanium, and boron, which are sometimes present as minor alloying additions. In these welds, high manganese levels may be beneficial in reducing cracking, for example, by tying up sulfur and silicon. Several percent of eutectic ferrite may be somewhat beneficial in counteracting the detrimental effect of phosphorus and sulfur. However, because the amount of eutectic ferrite is alloy dependent and seldom exceeds several percent (see Fig. 4), it is not a practical solution for improving cracking resistance.

Cracking susceptibility is drastically reduced in welds that solidify as primary ferrite with the peritectic/eutectic solidification of austenite (FA-type), even at high levels of phosphorus and sulfur, as shown in Fig. 56. Welding electrodes such as 308L are specifically designed to produce a desired range of ferrite and thus promote this solidification mode. In applications where no such filler metal is used and cracking is a concern, it may be necessary to limit composition ranges or to select heats of material that solidify in this mode. However, at the higher Cr_{eq}/Ni_{eq} ratios, where welds solidify completely as ferrite, and when the transformation of ferrite to austenite occurs at lower temperatures, cracking susceptibility again increases, although not to the extent of welds solidifying as austenite. The solidification-cracking behavior can thus be directly related to the structures shown in Fig. 52 and 54. The welds that solidify as ferrite and exhibit skeletal and lathy morphologies are very resistant to cracking, whereas cracking increases in welds that exhibit microstructures of Widmanstätten austenite.

Many rationales have been proposed to explain the cracking behavior of the austenitic stainless steel welds. The two that seem to be most consistent in explaining this behavior are related to the n⊶ire of the weld microstructure during solidification and the early stages of cooling.

During single-phase solidification, the fairly planar ferrite/ferrite or austenite/austenite grain boundaries that form are easily wet by low-melting liquids, often involving eutectics with phosphides and sulfides. If sufficient stresses and strains are developed before these liquids are solidified, then solidification cracks can easily form and propagate. However, when solidification occurs as primary ferrite with the secondary solidification of austenite (FA-type), or if austenite is nucleated at the grain boundaries near the solidus temperature of welds solidifying completely as ferrite (F-type), then very irregular grain-boundary structures are formed. These ferrite/austenite boundaries that become potential crack paths are of lower energy than the grain boundaries of either of the single-phase structures. The resulting tortuous crack paths and/or the low-energy boundary configurations not readily wetted by the low-melting liquids are very resistant to the nucleation and propagation of cracks.

Thus, it can be seen that understanding and being able to identify solidification behavior is important in preventing solidification-cracking problems. Because increased solidification velocities and cooling rates shift the transition between primary austenite and primary ferrite to higher Cr_{eq}/Ni_{eq} ratios, this effect on weld cracking must be considered, as discussed in the section on high-energy-density welds in this article.

Heat-affected zone liquation cracking is occasionally observed in austenitic stainless steels, particularly in the stabilized grades (containing titanium and/or niobium). This cracking occurs as a result of the constitutional liquation of carbides, such as niobium carbide, in type 347 alloy, resulting in grain-boundary liquation. Heat-affected zone cracking can also occur in other alloy types as a result of impurity segregation along HAZ grain boundaries. This form of cracking is always intergranular and is located immediately adjacent to the weld fusion boundary. Occasionally, cracking is continuous across the fusion boundary into the weld metal.

Analogous to weld solidification cracking, alloys with a ferrite potential (predicted FN) above approximately 2 to 3 FN are generally resistant to HAZ liquation cracking. This results from the formation of ferrite along HAZ grain boundaries. Heat-affected zone cracking that is due to grain-boundary liquation also can be limited by minimizing heat input. Lower weld heat inputs result in steeper HAZ thermal gradients, thereby limiting the spatial extent over which cracking is possible.

Weld metal liquation cracking is defined as HAZ cracking that occurs in weld metal. By definition, this form of cracking is associated with multipass welds. The cracking that occurs is sometimes referred to as "microfissuring," or underbead cracking, because the cracks are typically small and located adjacent to the interpass fusion boundary in the previously deposited weld metal. These defects are almost always associated with fully austenitic weld metal and are located along solidification grain boundaries or migrated grain boundaries.

Analogous to weld solidification cracking, weld metal liquation cracking can generally be avoided by reducing the impurity levels in fully austenitic microstructures or by selecting filler metals that produce weld deposits containing more than approximately 3 FN.

Copper contamination cracking adjacent to austenitic stainless steel welds can also occur as a result of contact with copper or copper-bearing alloys, such as brass. This type of cracking is a form of liquid-metal embrittlement, whereby molten copper embrittles austenitic grain boundaries. Because copper melts at 1083 °C (1981 °F), this type of cracking caused by pure copper is only observed in regions of the weld (typically, the HAZ) that are heated near or above this temperature. Cracking is always intergranular, and traces of copper or copper-rich material usually can be observed along the grain boundary.

This contamination can often be traced to copper weld fixturing, contact tips, or fabrication tools. The use of alternate fixturing, often incorporating chromium plating, and the prevention of copper abrasion normally eliminate the problem.

Ductility dip cracking occurs in the solid state and is typically associated with the HAZ or weld metal in highly constrained welds or thick sections. Such cracking occurs as a result of strain-induced grain-boundary precipitation, which limits mid-temperature ductility, but it is much more common in precipitation-strengthened nickel-base alloys. However, this type of cracking has been observed in type 347 alloy, resulting from strain-induced precipitation of niobium carbides.

Weld porosity can result either from alloying additions (especially in the high-nitrogen alloys) or from contamination. In the Nitronic alloys, for example, nitrogen levels near the upper limit of 0.4% can result in porosity in gas-tungsten arc weld deposits, whereas lower levels (above approximately 0.25%) can result in excessive porosity in electron-beam welds. Porosity can also occur as a result of surface contamination, such as by oil and greases or undetected leaks in water-cooled welding torches or weld fixtures. Thus, surfaces should be thoroughly cleaned prior to welding. If wire brushing is used, then the brushes should be made of stainless steel and dedicated to stainless usage, rather than made of steel, which can result in iron deposition and in-service corrosion.

Sigma-Phase Embrittlement

Sigma is a hard, brittle phase that can form in stainless steels when they are held in the temperature range from approximately 600 to 800 °C (1110 to 1470 °F). The σ-phase compositional range shown in the vertical sections of Fig. 53 reveals that σ can form over a wide range of compositions. The tendency for σ-phase formation increases with increasing amounts of chromium, molybdenum, and silicon and is reduced somewhat by nitrogen, nickel, and carbon. As a consequence of alloy partitioning during both solidification and the solid-state transformation of ferrite to austenite, ferrite is enriched in the alloying elements, which promotes the σ-phase, and is depleted in the elements that retard its formation. Thus, ferrite in austenitic stainless welds is especially susceptible to σ-phase formation. The σ-phase has been observed to nucleate preferentially at the ferrite-austenite interface in weld metal.

The transformation kinetics of ferrite to σ has been studied by Vitek and David (Ref 72) in type 308 gas-tungsten arc welds (Fig. 61). They found that σ started to form after approximately 15 h at 725 °C (1335 °F) and that all the ferrite had transformed to σ and $M_{23}C_6$ after approximately 3000 h.

The notorious effect of σ-phase is a decrease in ductility and toughness. When materials are to be used in elevated-temperature service, the effects of σ formation must be considered. The σ-phase can be minimized by using filler materials that produce fully austenitic structures. However, even in these compositions, σ-phase formation can still occur, initiating in chromium-enriched interdendritic boundaries.

In cases where solidification cracking is a concern, some ferrite in the weld deposit is required. Weld metal ferrite content should be controlled in the range from 3 to 8 FN to prevent the formation of a continuous network of ferrite. Because the chromium content of σ is nearly double that of the weld ferrite, the potential maximum level of the σ-phase is always less than that of the original weld metal ferrite.

Corrosion Behavior

Austenitic stainless steel weldments are often subject to corrosive attack. The nature of this attack is a function of weld thermal history, service temperature and environment, and stress level (both residual and applied). Four general types of corrosive attack have been reported:

- Intergranular attack
- Stress-corrosion cracking
- Pitting and crevice corrosion
- Microbiologically influenced corrosion

Each phenomenon and its effect on service integrity is discussed below.

Carbide Precipitation and Intergranular Corrosion. Austenitic stainless steel weldments have often been subject to intergranular attack. This behavior is particularly prevalent in chloride-bearing aqueous environments, and it is usually typified by accelerated attack in the HAZ. The basis for this attack is related to a phenomenon known as sensitization, whereby exposure or slow cooling in the temperature range from 400 to 850 °C (750 to 1550 °F) promotes the formation of chromium-rich carbides ($M_{23}C_6$) along the austenite grain boundaries. This temperature range is commonly described as the "sensitization" temperature range, because exposure within it makes austenitic stainless steels particularly sensitive to intergranular attack. An example of intergranular corrosion in the HAZ of a weld in type 316L NaOH reactor vessel is shown in Fig. 62.

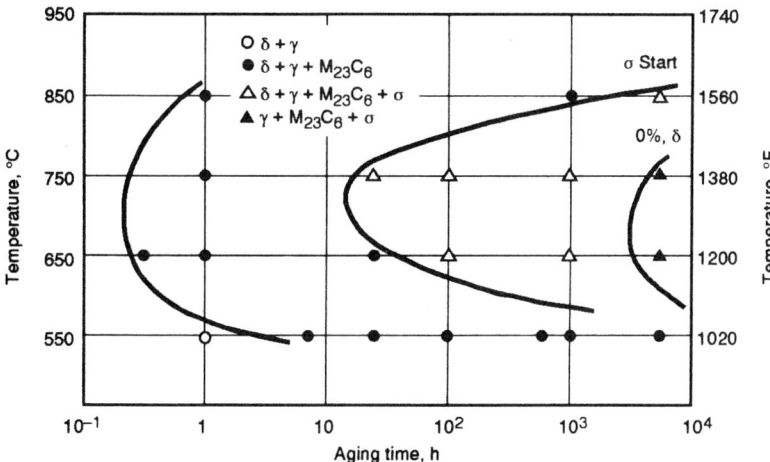

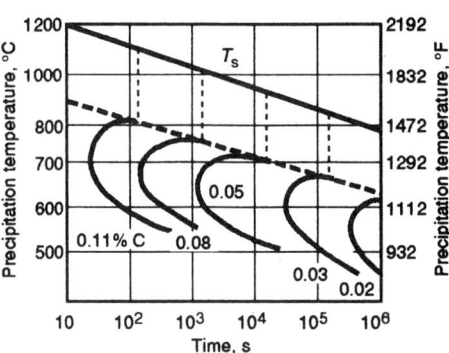

Fig. 63   Time-temperature-precipitation curves for an 18Cr-9Ni alloy with various carbon contents.
Source: Ref 73

Fig. 61   Time-temperature-transformation diagram for welded and aged type 308L alloy gas-tungsten arc welds.
Source: Ref 72

Fig. 62   Caustic stress-corrosion cracking in the heat-affected zone of a type 316L stainless steel NaOH reactor vessel. Cracks are branching and intergranular.

peratures, ranging from the melting point to the ambient base metal temperature, depending on the distance from the weld fusion boundary. Because heating and cooling in the weld HAZ are relatively rapid, regions of the HAZ that are heated to peak temperatures below about 650 °C (1200 °F) are immune to sensitization.

In addition, the HAZ region immediately adjacent to the fusion boundary is also resistant to sensitization, because carbon solubility is high at the peak temperatures achieved and cooling through the sensitization range is generally rapid enough to suppress carbide precipitation. This leaves a narrow region in the HAZ, somewhat removed from the fusion boundary, that will be heated into the sensitization temperature range. If the time within this temperature range is sufficient, then intergranular carbides will nucleate along austenite grain boundaries.

For a given thermal history, the level of precipitation and the associated degree of sensitization are approximately proportional to the carbon content of the austenitic stainless steel. Conventional austenitic stainless steels can retain a maximum of about 0.02 wt% C in solid solution over their service temperature range (up to 600 °C, or 1110 °F). Thus, as carbon content increases above this level, the driving force for carbide precipitation increases.

This can be illustrated by the time-temperature-precipitation curves shown in Fig. 63 for an 18Cr-9Ni alloy. Because of this, low-carbon grades of stainless steel (the so-called L-grades) are preferred for corrosive service where weldments must be used in the as-welded condition. The use of "stabilized" alloys, such as types 321 and 347, which contain additions of titanium and niobium, respectively, are also effective in reducing susceptibility to intergranular attack. Both titanium and niobium form stable carbides in the base metal that resist dissolution in the weld HAZ and/or at service temperatures in the sensitization range.

A phenomenon known as "knifeline" attack has been observed in the stabilized grades. However, its occurrence is associated with localized HAZ attack adjacent to the weld fusion boundary (Ref 74). Where temperatures exceed 1300 °C (2370 °F), niobium carbide and titanium carbide precipitates may dissolve and, upon reheating

Mechanistically, localized attack occurs immediately adjacent to the grain boundary because of precipitation of the chromium-rich carbides in the boundary. Carbide formation depletes the adjacent matrix in chromium to a level generally estimated to be less than 12 wt% Cr. The severity of attack depends on the corrosive media, the time and temperature of exposure, and the composition and metallurgical condition of the steel.

Unfortunately, sensitization can be a byproduct of the fusion welding process. During welding, the weld HAZ experiences peak tem-

into the sensitization temperature range, chromium carbide ($M_{23}C_6$-type) precipitation occurs preferentially to the reformation of either niobium carbide or titanium carbide. Subsequent exposure to a corrosive medium may result in intergranular attack that is extremely localized. In severe cases, it may often appear as if the weld has been cut out by a knife.

Weld metals containing even small amounts of δ-ferrite are not generally susceptible to such severe sensitization as wrought material of similar composition. In ferrite-containing weld metal, carbide precipitation occurs more uniformly throughout the structure at the austenite-ferrite interphase boundaries. Because the ferrite phase has a relatively high chromium content (of the order of 25 wt% in an 18Cr-8Ni alloy), chromium depletion caused by carbide formation is not so significant. Consequently, weld metal is not generally susceptible to intergranular corrosion. However, fully austenitic weld metals may be susceptible to intergranular attack when exposed to severely corrosive environments.

In general, it is possible to either minimize or eliminate intergranular attack in austenitic stainless steel weldments by using one or more of these methods:

- Use a low-carbon-content alloy, such as L-grade alloys with carbon contents on the order of 0.03 wt%.
- Use alloys that are stabilized by additions of niobium and titanium (such as types 347 and 321).
- Anneal the material prior to welding to remove any prior cold work (cold work accelerates carbide precipitation).
- Use low weld heat inputs and low interpass temperatures to increase weld cooling rates, thereby minimizing the time in the sensitization temperature range.
- In pipe welding, water cool the inside diameter after the root pass, which will eliminate sensitization of the inside diameter caused by subsequent passes.
- Solution heat treat after welding. Heating the structure into the temperature range from 900 to 1100 °C (1650 to 2010 °F) dissolves any carbides that may have formed along grain boundaries in the HAZ. (For large structures, this approach is usually impractical.)

The intergranular attack of the weld HAZ has also been observed at service temperatures well below the classic sensitization temperature range. This behavior, often called low-temperature sensitization (LTS), typically occurs after years of service exposure at temperatures below 400 °C (750 °F), even in low-carbon grades. Mechanistically, it is proposed (Ref 75) that carbide embryos form along grain boundaries in the weld HAZ and then grow to form chromium-rich carbides in service. Corrosive attack occurs via the chromium-depletion mechanism described previously. In order to combat LTS, either stabilized alloys or alloys containing higher nitrogen contents (such as type 316LN) are substituted for conventional or L-grade materials.

The stress-corrosion cracking of austenitic stainless steels may occur when an alloy is subjected simultaneously to a tensile stress and a specific corrosive medium. The important variables affecting SCC are temperature, environment, material composition, stress level, and microstructure. Crack propagation may be either transgranular or intergranular, depending on the interaction of these variables. Intergranular SCC can occur even though the alloy is insensitive to intergranular corrosion. The presence of residual tensile stresses in the HAZ may accelerate corrosion attack and cracking, particularly along sensitized grain boundaries.

Transgranular SCC is also observed in austenitic stainless steels. This form of cracking is usually indigenous to chloride environments (seawater), but it may also occur in caustic media. The ions of the halogen family (fluorine, chlorine, bromine, and iodine) are largely responsible for promoting transgranular SCC. Of the halides, the chloride ion causes the greatest number of failures. Figure 64 shows an example of transgranular SCC in type 316 stainless steel. Note that cracking has initiated at the toe of the weld, probably because of the high residual stress level at that location.

Methods for controlling SCC include:

- A stress-relieving or annealing heat treatment to reduce weld residual stresses
- Substitution of more resistant high-nickel alloys, high-chromium ferritic stainless steels, or duplex stainless steels, the latter of which have been designed specifically to minimize SCC
- Reduction of chloride and oxygen contents from the environment, because these two elements, in combination, are responsible for most SCC failures in austenitic stainless steels

Pitting, Crevice Corrosion, and Microbiologically Influenced Corrosion. Localized attack in the weld metal or HAZ may occur in the form of pitting or crevice corrosion, particularly in aqueous, chlorine-bearing environments.

Microbiologically influenced corrosion (MIC) often occurs preferentially in the weld metal of austenitic stainless steels. This curious form of attack is restricted to aqueous environments containing microbes that attach to the surface of

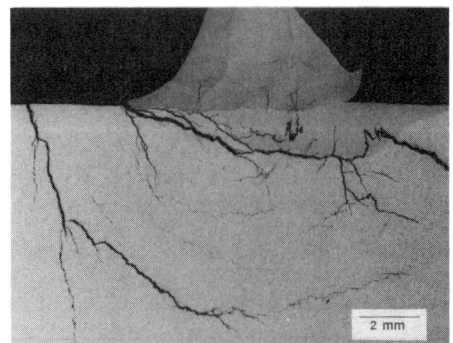

Fig. 64 Transgranular stress-corrosion cracking that has initiated near the toe of a weld in type 316L alloy

the weld. In pipe welds, pitting from MIC often initiates at the weld fusion line and proceeds into the weld metal. Sensitized HAZs also are common regions of attack, although the most preferred site of attack seems to be the weld metal. Attack is a strong function of pitting resistance of the material and is thus more common in type 304 alloy than in type 316.

Surface condition appears to have a large effect on MIC. Machining and grinding conducted on the inside of piping are thought to increase susceptibility to MIC by introducing rough surfaces for easy attachment by microbes and residual stresses, as well as localized metallurgical changes and corrosion pitting.

Superaustenitic Stainless Steels

The superaustenitic stainless steels represent a special class of austenitic stainless steels that contain high levels of nickel, molybdenum, and, in some cases, nitrogen. Typical composition ranges for superaustenitics are:

Element	Content, wt%
Chromium	20-26
Nickel	18-26
Molybdenum	5-7
Copper	0.5-4.0
Nitrogen	0.10-0.25
Carbon	0.020-0.035 (max)
Iron	bal

These alloys are designed for severely corrosive environments. They provide improved resistance to SCC, pitting, and crevice corrosion, relative to the standard 300 series of austenitic alloys. Higher nickel contents improve chloride SCC resistance, whereas molybdenum and nitrogen provide improved pitting and crevice corrosion resistance. In general, these alloys are compositionally balanced to ensure fully austenitic microstructures.

The weldability of most of these alloys is similar to that of fully austenitic grades of conventional stainless steel. Because these welds solidify as austenite and exhibit fully austenitic (no ferrite) microstructures, solidification cracking may be a problem in highly restrained joints. Typically, these alloys contain extremely low impurity levels, thus minimizing the likelihood of cracking.

The segregation of molybdenum in 6% Mo alloys during weld solidification has been reported to reduce corrosion resistance (Ref 76), particularly in severe pitting environments. The cell or dendrite cores in these alloys may exhibit molybdenum contents as low as 4.2 wt%, resulting in localized pitting attack at these sites. As a result, autogenous welding or the use of matching filler materials is normally avoided when severe service environments are anticipated. The use of molybdenum-containing nickel-base filler materials, such as alloy 625 (AWS ERNiCrMo-3), alloy C-276 (AWS ERNiCrMo-4), or alloy C-22 (AWS ERNiCrMo-10), is often recommended in order to avoid pitting. Precautions must be taken to prevent the formation of an unmixed zone adjacent to these overalloyed weld metals, because this re-

Table 14 Properties and filler metals for nominally austenitic stainless steels

Designation	UNS No.	ASTM specification	Comments	Tensile strength MPa	ksi	Yield strength MPa	ksi	Elongation, %	Matching filler metals A5.4	A5.9(a)	A5.22
...	S01815	A 167	...	540	78	240	35	40	...	...	...
201	S20100	A 240	201-1, both specifications	655	95	260	38	40	E240-XX	ER240	...
201	S20100	A 666	201-2, both specifications	655	95	310	45	40	E240-XX	ER240	...
...	S20161	A 479	...	860	125	345	50	40	E240-XX	ER240	...
202	S20200	A 240	...	620	90	260	38	40	E240-XX	ER240	...
202	S20200	A 666	...	620	90	260	38	40	E240-XX	ER240	...
XM-1	S20300	A 582	...	NS	NS	NS	NS	NCW	NCW	NCW	...
205	S20500	A 666	...	790	115	450	65	40	E240-XX	ER240	...
XM-19	S20910	A 240	Nitronic 50	690	100	380	55	35	E209-XX	ER209	...
XM-31	S21400	A 240	Sheet higher strength	720	105	380	55	40	E240-XX	ER240	...
XM-14	S21460	A 666	...	720	105	380	55	40	E240-XX	ER240	...
XM-17	S21600	A 240	Sheet higher strength	620	90	345	50	40	E209-XX	ER209	...
XM-18	S21603	A 240	Sheet higher strength	620	90	345	50	40	E209-XX	ER209	...
...	S21800	A 240	Nitronic 60	655	95	345	50	35	E240-XX	ER218	...
XM-10	S21900	A 276	Nitronic 40	620	90	345	50	45	E219-XX	ER219	...
XM-11	S21904	A 666	Sheet higher strength	620	90	345	50	45	E219-XX	ER219	...
XM-29	S24000	A 240	Nitronic 33	690	100	380	55	40	E240-XX	ER240	...
XM-28	S24100	A 276	Nitronic 32	690	100	380	55	30	...	...	...
...	S28200	A 276	...	760	110	415	60	35	...	...	...
301	S30100	A 666	Lower strength in A 167	620	90	205	30	40	...	...	...
302	S30200	A 240	...	515	75	205	30	40	E308-XX	ER308	E308T-X
302	S30200	A 666	...	515	75	205	30	40	E308-XX	ER308	E308T-X
302B	S30215	A 167	...	515	75	205	30	40	...	...	...
303	S30300	A 473	...	515	75	205	30	40	NCW	NCW	NCW
XM-5	S30310	A 582	...	NS	NS	NS	NS	NS	NCW	NCW	NCW
303Se	S30323	A 473	...	515	75	205	30	40	NCW	NCW	NCW
XM-2	S30345	A 582	...	NS	NS	NS	NS	NS	NCW	NCW	NCW
XM-3	S30360	A 582	...	NS	NS	NS	NS	NS	NCW	NCW	NCW
304	S30400	A 240, A 666	...	515	75	205	30	40	E308-XX	ER308	E308T-X
TP304	...	A 376	...	515	75	205	30	35	E308-XX	ER308	E308T-X
304L	S30403	A 240, A 666	...	480	70	170	25	40	E308L-XX	ER308L	E308LT-X
304H	S30409	A 240	...	515	75	205	30	40	E308H-XX	ER308H	E308T-X
TP304H	...	A 376	...	515	75	205	30	35	E308H-XX	ER308H	E308-X
...	S30415	A 240	...	600	87	290	42	40	...	...	...
XM-7	S30430	A 276	...	480	70	170	25	40	...	...	...
304N	S30451	A 240	...	550	80	240	35	30	...	...	...
304N	...	A 376	...	550	80	240	35	35	...	...	...
XM-21	S30452	A 240	Sheet higher strength	585	85	275	40	30	...	...	...
304LN	S30453	A 240	...	515	75	205	30	40	...	...	...
304LN	S30453	A 666	...	550	80	240	35	40	...	...	...
TP304LN	...	A 376	...	515	75	205	30	35	...	...	...
...	S30454	A 276	...	620	90	245	50	30	...	...	...
305	S30500	A 240	Lower strength in A 167	515	75	205	30	40	E308-XX	ER308	E308T-X
306	S30600	A 240	...	540	78	240	35	40	...	...	...
RA85H	S30615	A 240	...	620	90	275	40	35	...	...	...
308	S30800	A 167	...	515	75	205	30	40	E308-XX	ER308	E308T-X
...	S30815	A 167, A 240	...	600	87	310	45	40	...	...	...
309	S30900	A 167	...	515	75	205	30	40	E309-XX	ER309	E309T-X
309S	S30908	A 240	...	515	75	205	30	40	E309-XX	ER309	E309T-X
309H	S30909	A 240	...	515	75	205	30	40	E309-XX	ER309	E309T-X
309Cb	S30940	A 240	...	515	75	205	30	40	E309Cb-XX	...	...
309HCb	S30949	A 240	...	515	75	205	30	40	E309Cb-XX	...	...
310	S31000	A 240	...	515	75	205	30	40	E310-XX	ER310	E310T-X
310S	S31008	A 240	...	515	75	205	30	40	E310-XX	ER310	E310T-X
310H	S31009	A 240	...	515	75	205	30	40	E310-XX	ER310	E310T-X
310Cb	S31040	A 240	...	515	75	205	30	40	E310Cb-XX	...	...
310HCb	S31049	A 240	...	515	75	205	30	40	E310Cb-XX	...	...
310MoLN	S31050	A 240	...	550	80	240	35	30	...	...	...
254SMo	S31254	A 240	...	650	94	305	44	35	...	...	...
314	S31400	A 276	...	515	75	205	30	40	...	...	...
316	S31600	A 240	...	515	75	205	30	40	E316-XX	ER316	E316T-X
316	S31600	A 666	...	515	75	205	30	40	E316-XX	ER316	D316T-X
TP316	...	A 376	...	515	75	205	30	35	E316-XX	ER316	E316T-X
316L	S31603	A 240	...	480	70	170	25	40	E316L-XX	ER316L	E316LT-X
316L	S31603	A 666	...	480	70	170	25	40	E316L-XX	ER316L	E316LT-X
316H	S31609	A 240	...	515	75	205	30	40	E316H-XX	ER316H	E316T-X
TP316H	...	A 376	...	515	75	205	30	35	E316H-XX	ER316H	E316T-X
316Ti	S31635	A 240	...	515	75	205	30	40	E318-XX	ER318	...
316Cb	S31640	A 240	...	515	75	205	30	40	E318-XX	ER318	...
316N	S31651	A 240	...	550	80	240	35	35	...	...	...
316N	S31651	A 666	...	550	80	240	35	40	...	...	...
316N	...	A 376	...	550	80	240	35	35	...	...	...
316LN	S31653	A 240	...	515	75	205	30	40	...	...	...

(Continued)

NS, not specified; NCW, not considered weldable. (a) Electrodes with higher silicon (0.65-1.00%), indicated by "Si" added at the end of the classification were included. Metal-cored electrodes, included by a "C" in place of the "R" in the classification, are also included.

Table 14   Properties and filler metals for nominally austenitic stainless steels (continued)

Designation	UNS No.	ASTM specification	Comments	Tensile strength MPa	ksi	Yield strength MPa	ksi	Elongation, %	Matching filler metals A5.4	A5.9(a)	A5.22
TP316LN	...	A 376	...	515	75	205	30	35	...	...	...
...	S31654	A 276	...	620	90	345	50	30	...	...	...
317	S31700	A 240	...	515	75	205	30	35	E317-XX	ER317	E317LT-X
317L	S31703	A 240	...	515	75	205	30	40	E317L-XX	ER317L	E317LT-X
317LM	S31725	A 240	...	515	75	205	30	40	...	...	...
317LM	S31725	A 376	...	515	75	205	30	35	...	...	...
E17LMN	S31726	A 240	...	550	80	240	35	40	...	...	...
317LMN	S31726	A 376	...	550	80	240	35	35	...	...	...
317LN	S31753	A 240	...	550	80	240	35	40	...	...	...
321	S32100	A 240	...	515	75	205	30	40	E347-XX	ER321	E347T-X
TP321	...	A 376	...	515	75	205	30	35	E347-XX	ER321	E347T-X
321H	S32109	A 240	...	515	75	205	30	40	E347-XX	ER321	E347T-X
TP321H	...	A 376	...	515	75	205	30	35	E347-XX	ER321	E347T-X
...	S32615	A 240	...	550	80	220	32	25	...	...	...
347	S34700	A 240	...	515	75	205	30	40	E347-XX	ER347	E347T-X
TP347	...	A 376	...	515	75	205	30	35	E347-XX	ER347	E347T-X
347H	S34709	A 240	...	515	75	205	30	40	E347-XX	ER347	E347T-X
TP347H	...	A 376	...	515	75	205	30	35	E347-XX	ER347	E347T-X
348	S34800	A 240	...	515	75	205	30	40	E347-XX	ER347	E347T-X
TP348	...	A 376	...	515	75	205	30	35	E347-XX	ER347	E347T-X
348H	S34809	A 240	...	515	75	205	30	40	E347-XX	ER347	E347T-X
16-8-2H	...	A 376	...	515	75	205	30	35	E16-8-2-XX	ER16-8-2	...
XM-15	S38100	A 240	...	515	75	205	30	40	...	...	...
320	N08020	B 463	...	550	80	240	35	30	E320-XX	ER320	...
Sanicro 28	N08028	B 709	...	505	73	215	31	40	E383-XX	ER383	...
330	N08330	B 536	...	480	70	205	30	30	E330-XX	ER330	...
AL-6XN	N08367	B 688	...	690	100	310	45	30	...	...	...
904L	N08904	B 625	...	490	71	215	31	35	E385-XX	ER385	...
25-6Mo	N08925	B 625	...	600	87	295	43	40	...	...	...
CF-8	...	A 743	...	480	70	205	30	35	E308-XX	ER308	E308T-X
CG-12	...	A 743	...	480	70	195	28	35	E309-XX	ER309	E309T-X
CF-20	...	A 743	...	480	70	205	30	30	E308-XX	ER308	E308T-X
CF-8M	...	A 743, A 744	...	480	70	205	30	30	E316-XX	ER316	E316T-X
CF-8C	...	A 743, A 744	...	480	70	205	30	30	E347-XX	ER321	E347T-X
CF-16F	...	A 743	...	480	70	205	30	25	...	...	...
CH-20	...	A 743	...	480	70	205	30	30	E309-XX	ER309	E309T-X
CK-20	...	A 743	...	450	65	195	28	30	E310-XX	ER310	E310T-X
CE-30	...	A 743	...	550	80	275	40	10	...	...	...
CF-3	...	A 743, A 744	...	480	70	205	30	35	E308L-XX	ER308L	E308LT-X
CF10SMnN	...	A 743	...	585	85	290	42	30	...	...	...
CF-3M	...	A 743, A 744	...	480	70	205	30	30	E316L-XX	ER316L	E316LT-X
CF-3MN	...	A 743	...	515	75	255	37	35	...	...	...
CGMMN	...	A 743	...	585	85	290	42	30	...	...	...
CG-8M	...	A 743, A 744	...	515	75	240	35	25	E317-XX	ER317	E317LT-X
CN-3M	...	A 743	...	435	63	170	25	30	E385-XX	...	...
CM-7M	...	A 743, A 744	...	425	62	170	25	35	E320-XX	ER320	...
CM-7MS	...	A 743, A 744	...	480	70	205	30	35	...	...	...
CK-3MCuN	...	A 743, A 744	...	550	80	260	38	35	...	...	...

NS, not specified; NCW, not considered weldable. (a) Electrodes with higher silicon (0.65-1.00%), indicated by "Si" added at the end of the classification were included. Metal-cored electrodes, included by a "C" in place of the "R" in the classification, are also included.

gion may have the same susceptibility to corrosive attack as autogenous weld metal. More detail is provided in the next section.

Filler Metal Selection

Most weldments in nominally austenitic stainless steel base metals are put into service in the as-welded condition. In contrast to the situations with martensitic and ferritic stainless steel base metals, many of the nominally austenitic stainless steel base metals have matching, or near-matching, welding filler metals (see Table 14). In many cases, a nearly matching filler metal is a good choice.

Filler metal selection and welding procedure development for austenitic stainless steel base metals primarily depend on whether ferrite is possible and acceptable in the weld metal. In general,

if ferrite is both possible and acceptable, then suitable choices of filler metals and procedures are many. If the weld metal solidifies as primary ferrite, then the range of acceptable welding procedures can be as broad as it would be for ordinary mild steel. However, if ferrite in the weld metal is neither possible nor acceptable, then the filler metal and procedure choices are much more restricted because of hot-cracking considerations.

Most filler metal compositions are available in a variety of forms. When the presence of ferrite is possible, some filler metal manufacturers will tailor it to meet specific needs, at least in filler metals that are composites (for SMAW, FCAW, and metal-cored wires for GMAW or SAW processes). For example, in type 308 or 308L filler metals, which are typically selected for joining base metal types 302, 304, 304L, or 305, the filler metal can

be designed for zero ferrite, more than 20 FN, or any FN value between these extremes and still be within the composition limits for the classification in the relevant AWS filler metal specification.

In solid wires of type 308 or 308L, which are used for GMAW, GTAW, and SAW processes, the potential ferrite content of all-weld metal is often designed by the steel producer to provide maximum yield from the heat of steel. Stainless steel producers have generally found that the yield from a heat of steel, which will be reduced to "green rod" for supply to a filler metal producer, is maximized when the ferrite content ranges from 3 to 8 FN, based on the WRC-1988 diagram. Weld rod demand is usually for a minimum of 8 FN. Poor yields make the production of metal with more than 10 FN uneconomical and thus limit its availability. A lack of demand limits production and, therefore, the availability of green rod with less than 8 FN. Consequently, most solid-wire compositions are designed to achieve approximately 8 to 10 FN. Solid wires with compositions that are much beyond this range (as in austenitic grades that generally contain some ferrite) usually require special-order heat quantities (of 18 Mg, or 40,000 lb), dictate long lead times, and command premium prices.

With composite filler metals, the manufacturer can adjust both composition and ferrite content via alloying in either the electrode coating of SMAW electrodes or the core of flux-cored and metal-cored wires. Tailoring composition and ferrite for special applications is much more easily accomplished than it is for solid wires. For most off-the-shelf composite filler metals, the filler metal manufacturer has a target all-weld metal FN in mind when designing the filler metal. For a given alloy type, such as 308L, the target FN is likely to depend on the economics of filler metal design, the appropriate FN for the specific type of filler metal to avoid hot cracking, and market requirements.

For example, the ANSI/AWS A5.4 classification system recognizes three all-position coating types. In general, E308L-15 electrodes provide better hot-cracking resistance at low or no levels of ferrite than do E308L-16 electrodes, which, in turn, provide better hot-cracking resistance than do E308L-17 electrodes when little or no ferrite is present in the deposit. This difference in cracking resistance without ferrite primarily stems from bead shape. The E308L-15 electrodes tend to produce a convex bead shape. Convexity provides something of a riser, as in a casting, which tends to resist hot cracking. The E308L-16 electrodes tend to produce a nearly flat profile, which provides little or no riser. The E308L-17 electrodes tend to produce a concave profile (as well as a high-silicon deposit), which makes this the least crack-resistant coating type when there is little or no ferrite in the deposit. Furthermore, the sensitivity to nitrogen pickup with a long arc (and the consequent loss of ferrite) is least with E308L-15 and greatest with E308L-17 electrodes.

As a result, filler metal manufacturers generally aim their off-the-shelf E308L-15 electrodes toward a lower FN than they do their E308L-16 electrodes, which, in turn, are aimed toward lower FN values than are their E308L-17 electrodes. Of course, the same tendencies apply to other alloy compositions with the same coating types, which can be generalized as EXXX-15, EXXX-16, or EXXX-17, where XXX stands for 308, 308L, 309, 309L, 316, 316L, and so on.

Until 1992, the EXXX-17 coating type was not recognized by the ANSI/AWS A5.4 specification as being a distinct type, although the electrodes have been available for many years. Because electrodes that are properly classified as EXXX-17 generally weld satisfactorily on both direct current and alternating current, they had to be classified as EXXX-16 electrodes until the publication of ANSI/AWS A5.4-92 introduced the EXXX-17 classifications. Using these electrodes and meeting the vertical-up fillet weld size and convexity requirements of the EXXX-16 classifications were difficult to achieve, at best.

Although the EXXX-17 classifications have relaxed vertical-up fillet size and convexity requirements, some electrode manufacturers have been reluctant to change the classification of certain brand names (originally classified as EXXX-16) in order to more correctly reflect the true vertical-up capabilities of the electrodes. The knowledgeable fabricator can detect an electrode that is classified by its manufacturer as EXXX-16, when it properly ought to be classified as EXXX-17, either by attempting to meet the vertical-up fillet requirements of the EXXX-16 classification or by examining the all-weld metal composition that the electrode produces. The EXXX-17 electrodes all produce deposits of low manganese and high silicon. In general, a nominally austenitic electrode that has an all-weld-metal silicon content nearly as high as, or higher than, its manganese content (that is, silicon content approaches the 0.9% maximum of the specification) is in all probability properly classified as an EXXX-17 electrode.

Flux-cored and metal-cored electrodes do not have the clear distinctions that exist among the three main coating types. In general, both off-the-shelf flux-cored and metal-cored electrodes tend to have higher ferrite numbers, more like those of EXXX-17 electrodes, because the higher heat input that normally accompanies the use of these products tends to make the weld metal less crack resistant when little or no ferrite is present.

If a fully austenitic stainless steel as-welded deposit, or one with almost no ferrite, is necessary, and solidification as primary austenite or fully austenitic solidification is expected, then the choices of both filler metals and procedures are more restricted. When designing filler metals with low or no ferrite, the producer tries to obtain raw materials with minimal sulfur and phosphorus contents. Generally, high-silicon compositions are avoided because of their hot-cracking tendencies. Concave beads and high heat input are best avoided in procedure development. As a result, little or no filler metals are even offered commercially as EXXX-17 SMAW electrodes without ferrite. Submerged arc joining with fully austenitic filler metals is usually avoided because of cracking problems, although submerged arc cladding is more successful. The GMAW process is often restricted to a short-circuiting transfer mode.

A general rule to follow in procedure development for fully austenitic weld metals, in order to avoid or minimize cracking problems, is to "weld ugly." In particular, this means that if cracking is encountered, then welding procedures that produce markedly convex beads can overcome it. For compositions that are very crack sensitive, it may be necessary to make individual weld beads that are so convex that part of the weld bead must be ground away before the next bead is deposited. For the most crack-sensitive steels, such as type 320, crack-free welding with matching filler metal may be possible only with either small-diameter (1.6 to 2.4 mm, or 0.06 to 0.10 in.) E320-15 electrodes that are welded on the low side of the recommended current range or small-diameter (≤0.9 mm, or 0.04 in.) GMAW wire in the short-circuiting transfer mode.

Niobium, phosphorus, and sulfur in such alloys generally tend to make hot-cracking problems more severe. As a result, for type 320 stainless steel, both SMAW electrodes (E320LR-15) and GMAW wires (ER320LR) are available with reduced residual elements, as well as low carbon, so that niobium can be minimized without loss of the stabilization of carbides.

Additional welding procedure approaches to eliminating hot cracking with weld metals that solidify either fully austenitic or as primary austenite include those that reduce heat buildup in the steel. Low welding heat input and low preheat and interpass temperatures are all beneficial.

Weld puddle shape has a strong influence on hot-cracking tendencies. Narrow, deep puddles crack more readily than wide, shallow puddles. In particular, it is helpful to adjust welding conditions to obtain a weld pool that is elliptical in surface shape and to avoid teardrop-shape weld pools, the sharp tail of which tends to promote hot cracking. Low current and slow travel speed favor an elliptical pool shape. Copper chill blocks also can help to extract heat and speed cooling.

With fully austenitic or primary austenite solidification, it is essential to backfill weld craters to avoid crater cracks, which are a form of localized hot cracking. This means stopping the travel of the arc while continuing to add filler metal (with a down-sloping current, if possible) before breaking the arc, so that the crater becomes convex, rather than concave.

It was noted earlier that the usual choice for a filler metal composition for austenitic stainless steel matches or nearly matches that of the base metal. However, one situation generally requires an exception. This situation occurs when a high-molybdenum base metal is chosen for pitting or crevice corrosion resistance in a chloride-containing aqueous solution. Although the high molybdenum content of the weld metal provides resistance to localized corrosion, it invariably has segregation of molybdenum on a microscopic scale. The center of each dendrite is leaner in molybdenum than are the interdendritic spaces. The center of a dendrite then becomes a preferential site for localized corrosion.

It has been found that this preferential localized corrosion in the weld metal can be overcome by using a filler metal that is higher in molybdenum than is the base metal. Thus, a 3% Mo base metal (such as type 317L) requires a filler metal of at least 4% Mo. A 4% Mo base metal (such as type 904L) requires a filler metal of at least 6% Mo. A 6% Mo base metal requires a filler metal of at least 8% Mo. However, stainless steel weld metal that contains more than 5% Mo often has poor mechanical properties. Therefore, a nickel-base alloy of at least 8% Mo is usually chosen for filler metal when joining stainless steel with molybdenum contents of 4% and higher. The most common filler metals selected are the ENiCrMo-3 or ERNiCrMo-10 bare-wire classifications in the ANSI/AWS A5.14 specification.

Mechanical Properties

Austenitic stainless steels exhibit moderate strength and excellent toughness and ductility.

Table 15 Compositions for the four welds (A through D) included in Fig. 65

Weld	Composition, %								Process
	Fe	Cr	Ni	Mn	N	C	S	P	
A	bal	13	5	22	0.21	0.04	0.004	0.013	EBW
B	bal	20	25	1.6	0.16	0.01	0.001	0.010	GMAW
C	bal	18.1	20.4	5.4	0.16	0.03	0.007	0.006	GMAW
D	1	20	bal	3	...	0.02	...	...	GTAW

Because of these properties, austenitic filler materials are often used in dissimilar combinations with carbon steels and ferritic and martensitic stainless steels. The weld properties of austenitic stainless steels are essentially similar to those of the annealed base material. Typical base metal properties for austenitic stainless steels are listed in Table 14.

Weld geometry and alloy composition also affect weld properties. Most weld tensile properties are determined using specimens transverse to the weld direction. Because failure often occurs outside the weld metal, only minimum tensile strength values can be determined and no weld metal ductility data are generated. Impact toughness data are much more accurate, because a notch can be placed in the weld metal. Heat-affected zone mechanical property data are essentially nonexistent. Because the HAZ undergoes high temperatures during welding where carbide dissolution and grain growth can occur, it would be expected that this region may exhibit slightly lower strength than the annealed base metal.

In welds containing ferrite, the ferrite provides second-phase strengthening with a concomitant decrease in ductility. Thus, for an autogenous weld, the actual properties may vary somewhat from heat to heat in the same manner as the ferrite content. Typically, the tensile strength of welds is fractionally higher than the annealed wrought properties of similar compositions. However, the elongation and impact properties are reduced of the order of 30%. In multipass welds of thicker sections, warm working that results from the large strains encountered during cooling of subsequent passes can also result in significant increases in yield strengths and variations in strength from the top to the bottom of the weld deposit.

Nitrogen is a strong solid-solution strengthener, and thus its increase or decrease in the welding process may also affect weld properties. In wrought materials, each addition of approximately 0.01% N results in an approximate increase of 5.5 to 7 MPa (0.8 to 1 ksi) in yield strength. Thus, from a conservative standpoint, weld strength is often considered to be the same as that of the annealed base material.

Weld properties may be significantly influenced by service temperature. At elevated temperatures, carbide, nitride, and intermetallic formation may reduce mechanical and corrosion properties. At cryogenic temperatures, the strain-induced martensite transformation from austenite can result in reduced toughness and ductility relative to those properties in the homogeneous single-phase base material. In cases where filler metal is added, ASTM specifications provide minimum requirements.

Figure 65 shows data for yield strength and fracture toughness for several alloys (including stainless steels) that have been used in cryogenic applications. Compositions of the four welds included in Fig. 65 are listed in Table 15. At a temperature of 4 K, considerable data exist for type 316L stainless steel. Therefore, Fig. 65 includes a trend band for yield strength versus toughness (Ref 77). This alloy has a good balance of strength and toughness and has found application as the structural case for large superconducting magnets. As its strength increases (through additions of nitrogen), its toughness decreases.

Although the trend line for the matching-composition electrodes is not included in Fig. 65, it extends over the same strength range, although at only 50 to 70% of the toughness of the base metal (Ref 78). This lower toughness for welding electrodes of matching composition has driven the search for electrodes of different compositions that can match the properties of these base metals. Two fully austenitic stainless steel weld compositions (shown as A and B in Fig. 65 and Table 15) have been proposed for joining type 316LN (Ref 79-81).

In Fig. 66, Charpy V-notch absorbed-energy data at 77 K are plotted versus the yield strength for a number of weld metals. Because many structural designs specify a minimum of 30 or 40 J (22 or 30 ft · lb), numerous weld compositions can be considered at this temperature, including compositions that match that of the base plate.

In the lower right quadrant of Fig. 66 is a data point for a matching-composition weld for the Fe-21Cr-6Ni-9Mn steel (Ref 82). The low absorbed energy indicates that the nickel-base undermatch-ing weld compositions should be considered for applications with this composition at 77 K (Ref 83).

For the 300-series stainless steels, there are two trend bands. The lower band is for welds produced by the SMAW process, whereas the upper is for welds produced by the GTAW process. The difference is attributed to weld inclusions (Ref 84, 85). Above the GTAW trend band is one of the four special weld compositions identified in Table 15 (see composition B). This higher absorbed-energy level is comparable to the level that type 316LN plate would develop at this temperature. Additional information on mechanical properties at cryogenic temperatures can be found in the article "Low-Temperature Properties" in this Volume and in the article "Welding for Cryogenic Service" in Volume 6 of the *ASM Handbook*.

Weld penetration characteristics of austenitic stainless steels are generally poor, relative to ferritic and martensitic grades, because of the low thermal conductivity of the austenite. In addition, large heat-to-heat variations in weld penetration can occur when welding austenitic stainless, especially in autogenous welds or the root pass of multiple-pass gas-tungsten arc welds. These penetration variations have been attributed primarily to minor elements affecting the surface-tension-driven fluid flow within the weld pool (known as the Marongoni effect) (Ref 86).

The elements that influence penetration tend to be surface active and include sulfur, selenium, and oxygen. When present in sufficient quantity, these elements tend to increase weld penetration. However, other elements can have synergistic effects. Aluminum combined with oxygen can mitigate the effect of oxygen. Thus, high levels of

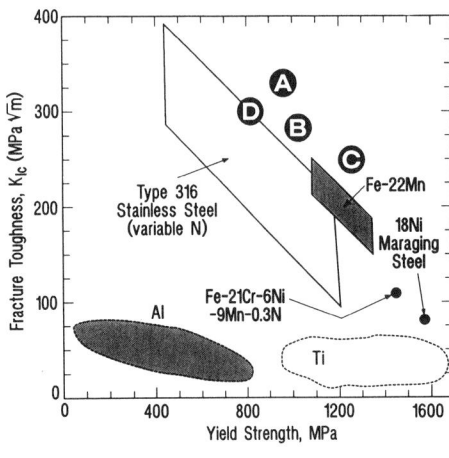

Fig. 65 Yield strength vs. fracture toughness for various base metal alloys and selected welds at 4 K. See Table 15 for chemical compositions of the four welds denoted A, B, C, and D.

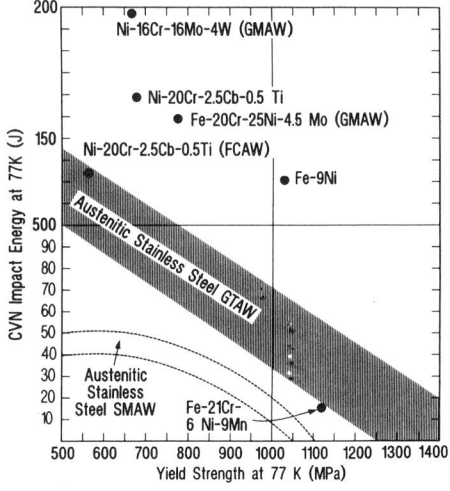

Fig. 66 Charpy V-notch absorbed energy vs. strength for various weld metals at 77 K

Table 16 Effect of stress-relief treatments on austenitic stainless steels

Stainless steel	Condition(a)	Stress-relief heat treatment(b)			
		200-400 °C (392-752 °F), ~40% peak	550-650 °C (1022-1202 °F), ~35%	850-900 °C (1562-1652 °F), ~85%	950-1050 °C (1742-1922 °F), ~95%
Type 304	SHT, SA(c)	NME	IGP	IGP	IGP(d)
	Weldments(c)	NME	IGP and SIP	IGP and SIP	IGP(d) and SIP(e)
Type 321	SHT, SA	NME	NME	NME	NME
	Weldments		SIP	SIP	SIP(e)
Type 304L	SHT, SA, and weldments	NME	NME	NME	NME
Type 316	SHT, SA(c), and weldments(c)	NME	IGP	IGP	IGP(d)
Type 316 + Ti	SHT, SA, and weldments	NME	NME	NME	NME
Type 316L	SHT, SA, and weldments	NME	NME	NME	NME

(a) SHT, solution heat treatment, rapidly cooled from ~1050 °C (1922 °F); SA, solution annealed, slowly cooled from ~1050 °C (1922 °F). (b) IGP, intergranular precipitation of chromium carbide (sensitization); NME, no metallurgical effect; SIP, strain-induced precipitation of carbides, in weldments over 19 mm (0.75 in.). (c) Likely to be sensitized prior to stress relief, unless of small section size and/or low carbon content. (d) During cooling (assumed always to be slow). (e) During heating

aluminum can decrease penetration. For example, heats of type 304L alloy with low sulfur contents (0.001 to 0.003 wt%) may have a weld depth-to-width ratio of only 0.25, whereas the same material, but with a sulfur content of 0.01 wt%, welded under identical conditions, will exhibit a depth-to-width ratio of greater than 0.5. Increased surface-oxygen content that results from wire brushing may also produce increased depth-to-width ratios in materials that otherwise have low penetration characteristics. However, this method is not often practiced because of problems with reproducibility.

In autogenous welds, penetration control is best achieved by the proper selection of base materials. The addition of hydrogen and helium to argon shielding gas may help to compensate for poor penetration. For example, 98Ar-2H$_2$ and Ar-5H$_2$ are commonly used in the manufacture of welded tubing to increase penetration at high travel speeds. Trimixes of argon, helium, and hydrogen may also be used to increase weld penetration.

Weld Thermal Treatments

Preheat and Interpass Heat Treatments. Because the austenitic stainless steels do not experience a martensitic transformation upon cooling, there is generally no benefit derived from the use of preheat or interpass temperature control during multipass welding. In fact, these thermal treatments may actually increase the degree of sensitization by reducing cooling rates and allowing more time for carbide precipitation. Preheat and interpass heating can also increase distortion and cracking susceptibility.

Postweld heat treatment is often required to relieve residual stresses in austenitic stainless steel weldments, particularly in thick sections. Because the CTE value and the elevated-temperature yield and creep strengths of austenitic materials are significantly greater than for ferritic materials, the magnitude of residual stresses is generally larger. Although the effect of residual stresses from welding is typically not as severe as when less ductile materials are used, they may still affect mechanical properties and corrosion behavior. Postweld heat treatment is particularly critical when machining must be performed after welding, because significant distortion may occur.

Perhaps of greatest concern, however, is the influence of residual stress on SCC resistance. As described in the section "Corrosion Behavior" in this article, high levels of residual stress associated with the weld may severely reduce SCC resistance in chlorine-bearing and caustic environments.

Stress relieving can be performed over a wide range of temperatures, depending on the amount of stress relaxation required. Time at temperature ranges from about 1 h per inch of section thickness at temperatures above 650 °C (1200 °F) to 4 h per inch of thickness at temperatures below 650 °C (1200 °F). Because of the high CTE value and low thermal conductivity of austenitic stainless steels, cooling from the stress-relieving temperature must be slow. Because the stress-relieving temperature range overlaps the sensitization temperature range, the stress-relieving temperature must be compatible with the extent of acceptable carbide precipitation and with the required amount of corrosion resistance. Nonstabilized stainless steels cannot be stress relieved in the sensitizing range without sacrificing corrosion resistance. Extra-low-carbon grades are affected much less, because sensitization is more sluggish. Stabilized grades exhibit minimal chromium carbide precipitation tendencies.

Higher stress-relief temperatures can be used for fully austenitic weld metals. For weld metals that contain ferrite, stress-relief temperatures above 650 °C (1200 °F) may result in weld embrittlement via σ formation.

For austenitic stainless steels, the estimated percentages of residual stresses relieved at various temperatures at the times previously noted are 85% stress relief at 845 to 900 °C (1550 to 1650 °F) and 35% stress relief at 540 to 650 °C (1000 to 1200 °F). The data compiled by Cole and Jones (Ref 87) in Table 16 show specific time-temperature combinations that represent a compromise between the degree of stress relieving and carbide precipitation, which can lead to reduced corrosion resistance and ductility.

Welding Duplex Stainless Steels

Duplex stainless steels are two-phase alloys based on the iron-chromium-nickel system. These materials typically comprise approximately equal proportions of the bcc ferrite and fcc austenite phases in their microstructure and are characterized by their low carbon content (<0.03 wt%) and additions of molybdenum, nitrogen, tungsten, and copper. Typical chromium and nickel contents are 20 to 30% and 5 to 10%, respectively.

The current commercial duplex stainless steels can be loosely divided into four generic types. Listed in order of increasing corrosion resistance, these alloy groups are:

• Fe-23Cr-4Ni-0.1N
• Fe-22Cr-5.5Ni-3Mo-0.15N
• Fe-25Cr-5Ni-2.5Mo-0.17N-Cu
• Fe-25Cr-7Ni-3.5Mo-0.25N-W-Cu

As with 18-8 austenitic stainless steels, duplex stainless steels are also frequently referred to by their chromium and nickel contents to describe the alloy class. The alloys listed above are then described as 2304, 2205, 2505, and 2507, respectively. The last alloy class is also frequently termed "super" duplex stainless steel.

The duplex stainless steel alloying additions are either austenite or ferrite formers. As the names suggest, certain elements will favor a higher proportion of austenite and others will favor ferrite. This is achieved by extending the temperature range over which the phase is stable. Among the major alloying elements in duplex stainless steels, chromium and molybdenum are ferrite formers, whereas nickel, carbon, nitrogen, and copper are austenite formers. The balance of austenite and ferrite formers will dictate the base material microstructure. Constitution diagrams, such as the WRC-1992 diagram (Fig. 4), can be used for estimating the weld metal ferrite content in welds and developing appropriate base material compositions.

The performance of duplex stainless steels can be significantly affected by welding. Due to the importance of maintaining a balanced microstructure and avoiding the formation of undesirable metallurgical phases, the welding parameters and filler metals employed must be accurately specified and closely monitored. The balanced microstructure of the base material (that is, equal proportions of austenite and ferrite) will be affected by the welding thermal cycle. If the balance is significantly altered and the two phases are no longer in similar proportions, the loss of material properties can be acute.

Because the steels derive properties from both austenitic and ferritic portions of the structure, many of the single-phase base material characteristics are also evident in duplex materials. Austenitic stainless steels have excellent weldability and low-temperature toughness, whereas their chloride SCC resistance and strength are comparatively poor. Ferritic stainless steels have high resistance to chloride SCC but have poor toughness, especially in the welded condition. A duplex microstructure with high ferrite content can therefore have poor low-temperature notch toughness, whereas a structure with high austenite content can possess low strength and reduced resistance to chloride SCC.

The high alloy content of duplex stainless steels also renders them susceptible to formation of intermetallic phases from extended exposure to high temperatures. Extensive intermetallic precipitation may lead to a loss of corrosion resistance and sometimes to a loss of toughness.

Microstructural Development

By assuming that a duplex stainless steel contains 68% Fe and 32% alloying elements (comprising nickel and chromium, but representing austenite and ferrite formers, respectively), the 68% Fe pseudobinary phase diagram can be used to explain the microstructural transformations that occur during heating and cooling (Fig. 67).

Composition. With approximately 30% Cr and 2% Ni (composition indicated by line A in Fig. 67), the steel will solidify completely to ferrite and remain ferritic down to room temperature. As the chromium content decreases and the nickel content increases, an alloy containing 28% Cr and 4% Ni, indicated by line B, will solidify as ferrite, remain fully ferritic until about 1200 to 1300 °C (2190 to 2370 °F), and then enter the dual-phase field (denoted by α + γ). A two-phase microstructure will be developed and maintained down to room temperature. Because the composition of alloy B lies to the far left of the dual-phase field, a microstructure rich in ferrite would be anticipated.

Current commercial duplex stainless steels with 25% Cr are more likely to contain about 7% Ni, indicated by line C, which upon cooling enters the dual-phase field at a much higher temperature, thereby allowing more time for the diffusion-driven solid-state transformation from ferrite to austenite. An alloy with composition C will solidify as ferrite and be fully ferritic for a narrow temperature range prior to entering the dual-phase field. It should be noted that alloys A, B, and C will solidify primarily as ferrite and will have ferritic matrices.

Heat Treatment. The sequence of phase transformation in duplex stainless steels upon cooling is (Fig. 67):

Liquid → liquid + ferrite →
ferrite → ferrite + austenite   (Eq 2)

The solid-state transformation from ferrite to austenite is considered to be diffusional and there-

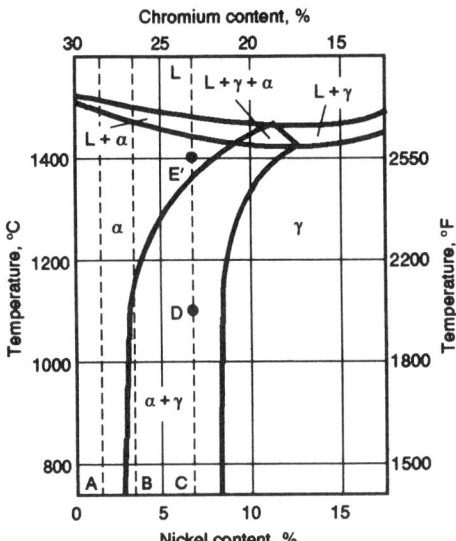

Fig. 67 Pseudobinary diagram at constant iron section (68 wt% Fe) of the Fe-Cr-Ni ternary system. See text for definition of lines A, B, and C and points D and E. Source: Ref 88

fore affected by time and temperature. Very rapid cooling from a temperature at which the steel is fully ferritic will result in suppression of the ferrite-to-austenite transformation and retention of a predominantly ferritic structure. The temperature range over which the transformation from ferrite to austenite occurs is highly dependent upon composition and grade (Fig. 67) but is typically from 1200 to 800 °C (2190 to 1470 °F). For this reason, a ΔT_{12-8} cooling rate term has been used when characterizing a duplex stainless steel thermal cycle (Ref 89, 90). A longer ΔT_{12-8} will result in more transformation from ferrite to austenite. In a weld of given thickness, longer ΔT_{12-8} values can be achieved by a higher heat input weld. The ΔT_{12-8} term has been employed in an effort to identify critical cooling rates necessary to develop acceptable austenite content in weld HAZs to achieve the desired mechanical and corrosion resistance properties. The critical ΔT_{12-8} for phase transformation is independent of material thickness, unlike heat input, but is highly dependent on alloy composition.

Low-temperature thermal cycles will not affect the austenite/ferrite balance, but they will control the extent of intermetallic phase precipitation. These steels should undergo rapid cooling (i.e., water quenching) through the precipitation temperature range to develop optimum properties. For welds, water quenching is usually not necessary or practical, but some means of forced cooling may be beneficial for productivity and quality reasons, particularly for multipass welds in the high-alloy grades.

To produce the necessary base material microstructure, an isothermal heat treatment is carried out at a temperature at which the steel is dual phase: approximately 1050 to 1100 °C (1920 to 2010 °F), or point D in Fig. 67 (Ref 91). To avoid the formation of intermetallic phases during cooling, water quenching from the soaking temperature is necessary.

Morphology. Wrought duplex stainless steel base material microstructures have a pronounced orientation of austenite islands in the ferritic matrix, parallel and transverse to the rolling direction, as a result of the hot and cold working following casting. The cast microstructure is very different and more similar to that observed in weld metal and the HAZ. Wrought and cast duplex structures are compared in the article "Metallurgy and Properties of Wrought Stainless Steels" in this Volume.

During the weld thermal cycle, the HAZ adjacent to the fusion line will become fully ferritic at temperatures above the austenite-to-ferrite transition temperature (point E in Fig. 67). Grain growth will occur and, regardless of the extent of austenite transformation that occurs during subsequent cooling, the coarse prior-ferrite grain boundaries will still be apparent (Fig. 68). Very rapid cooling from the fully ferritic phase field will retard austenite reformation in the HAZ and result in a predominantly ferritic structure, also shown in Fig. 68. When cooled more slowly, the austenite will form initially on the ferrite grain boundaries and then within the ferrite grains along preferred crystallographic planes in a manner similar to that of the cast material.

The HAZ in Fig. 68 is relatively wide and has a high ferrite content. Such a structure may lead to poor low-temperature notch toughness and reduced corrosion resistance. Nitrogen levels in the base steel are being steadily increased to improve weldability and to avoid the formation of structures similar to that shown in Fig. 68; some duplex stainless steels contain as much as 0.35 wt% N. A higher nitrogen level will increase the temperature at which ferrite begins to transform to austenite on cooling. This reduces the width of the transformed HAZ by limiting to a narrow temperature range the extent of the fully ferritic phase field. It also encourages more austenite reformation by starting the transformation at a much higher temperature. The recent grades of duplex stainless steels, which typically have a minimum of 0.20 wt% N, develop a very narrow HAZ in which the transformed region is often difficult to distinguish.

The sequence of transformation reactions in the weld metal is the same as for the HAZ, but due to the solidification pattern, the macroappearance is different and columnar grains are more typical (top left of Fig. 68). Duplex weld metal grain growth is epitaxial, with the large prior-ferrite grains in the HAZ dictating weld metal grain size and orientation. Austenite again forms preferentially on the grain boundaries, and intragranular austenite forms along preferred crystallographic planes as the weld metal continues to cool (Fig. 69).

Precipitates are often difficult to observe and require precise etching techniques and experience with the type of microstructure. Due to its highly detrimental effect on corrosion resistance and toughness and relative ease of formation, the most commonly investigated precipitate in duplex stainless steels is σ-phase, an Fe(Cr,Mo) intermetallic. Sigma will initially precipitate at phase boundaries in the ferrite phase and will then grow into the ferrite phase, which is richer in chromium and molybdenum. Only a small amount of a pre-

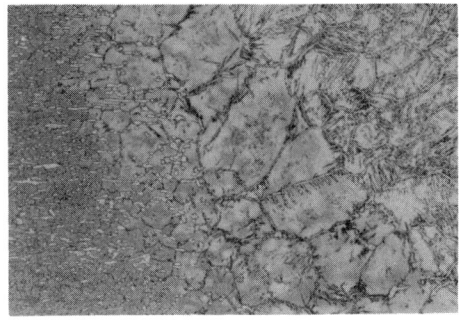

Fig. 68 Photomicrograph of an Fe-22Cr-5.5Ni-3Mo-0.15N duplex stainless steel weld area showing elongated parent plate morphology, a coarse-grain heat-affected zone high in ferrite, and columnar weld metal grains. Specimen electrolytically etched in 40% NaOH. 30×. Courtesy of The Welding Institute

cipitation is required to reduce mechanical and corrosion properties.

Welding and Weldability

Duplex stainless steel weldability is generally good, although the duplex steels are not as forgiving as austenitic stainless steels or as prone to degradation of properties as fully ferritic stainless steels. The current commercial grades are low in carbon (less than 0.03 wt%), thereby essentially eliminating the risk of sensitization and intergranular corrosion from carbide precipitation. The base material and filler metals also have low sulfur and phosphorus levels (less than 0.03 wt%), which in combination with the ferritic solidification reduce the likelihood of solidification cracking (hot cracking). Hydrogen cracking (cold cracking) resistance is also good due to the high hydrogen solubility in the austenite and the high percentage of austenite in the matrix. Nevertheless, solidification cracking and hydrogen cracking can occur in duplex alloys, and some precautions are necessary.

Preheat is generally not recommended for duplex stainless steels, but it may sometimes be specified in low-nitrogen grades, because thick sections and low-heat-input welding processes may, in combination, develop highly ferritic HAZs. For the more highly alloyed duplex stainless steels, a preheat can be highly detrimental and reduce corrosion resistance and mechanical properties.

Postweld heat treatment is not commonly used except in autogenous welds or welds with a filler metal composition that exactly matches that of the base steel. Although not always necessary, particularly if a nickel-enriched filler metal is used, it is common to subject duplex stainless steel welded pipe to PWHT after longitudinal seam welding—largely for the purpose of restoring the correct phase balance and redissolving unwanted precipitates. Postweld heat treatment temperatures of about 1050 to 1100 °C (1920 to 2010 °F) are used, depending on grade, followed by the same heat treatment applied to the base material during solution annealing—usually water quenching. The heat treatments commonly used

for structural steels (for example, 550 to 600 °C, or 1020 to 1110 °F) are totally inappropriate for duplex alloys and should never be considered.

Interpass Temperature Control. The need for interpass temperature control depends on alloy grade and composition. The more highly alloyed grades should have tighter interpass control. For the Fe-22Cr-5.5Ni-3Mo-0.15N steels, interpass temperatures of 150 to 200 °C (300 to 390 °F) are typical, whereas for the Fe-25Cr-7Ni-3.5Mo-0.25N-(Cu-W) steels, temperatures as low as 70 °C (160 °F) have been recommended (Ref 92).

Welding practices employed for austenitic stainless steels (for example, cleanliness, use of a backing gas, avoidance of contamination with carbon steel, and so on) should also be adopted for duplex stainless steels. The backing gas most commonly used is pure argon. However, the use of a backing gas without nitrogen can lead to nitrogen loss from the molten weld nugget, with probable loss in corrosion performance and toughness. Because of this, argon/nitrogen mixed gases for shielding and backing have been explored (Ref 93), and generally the corrosion resistance of welds produced with these gases has been superior to that of welds made with nitrogen-free gases. Pure nitrogen may also be used as a backing gas, but a concern exists that too much nitrogen may be picked up, thereby significantly affecting the phase balance locally by promoting the formation of austenite.

Open root gaps are commonly used in manual duplex stainless steel welding to limit the extent of dilution from the base material, because extensive base metal dilution will negate the effect of the nickel overalloying in the filler metal. To control the problems of too little austenite and intermetallic phase formation, associated with too-low and too-high heat inputs, respectively, duplex stainless steel welding procedures typically specify a "window" of allowable heat inputs. For the highly alloyed and heat-sensitive super duplex stainless steels, stringer beads are commonly specified, particularly in the hot pass (that is, the weld pass immediately following the root) and in some cases in split hot passes (that is, two hot passes side by side). The technique of using a low-heat-input hot pass has led to the use of the term "cold" pass (Ref 92).

Welding procedure qualification generally follows the mechanical property test requirements of a major code, for example, ASME Section IX (Ref 94) or API 1104 (Ref 95). There are also several tests (specifically phase balance assessment, microstructural examination, and a pitting corrosion test) used for duplex stainless steel weldment evaluation that are not typically employed for other stainless steels.

Phase Balance Assessment. The phase balance test measures the amount of austenite and ferrite present in the microstructure and is similar to tests used to measure ferrite in austenite and weld metals. However, the testing requirements are usually more exhaustive for duplex alloys and typically call for assessment of the ferrite content in the HAZ and weld metal and possibly at several through-thickness locations (Ref 96).

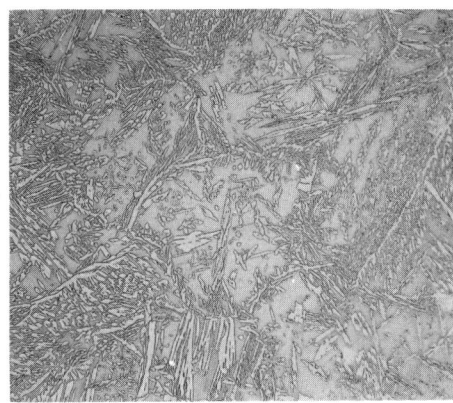

Fig. 69 Photomicrograph of duplex stainless steel weld metal with austenite laths (white) at prior-ferrite grain boundaries and along preferred crystallographic planes in a ferritic matrix. Sample electrolytically etched in 40% NaOH. 100×. Courtesy of The Welding Institute

The amount of ferrite in a duplex structure can be specified and measured in two ways. Percentage ferrite is measured by manual point counting or image analysis. These methods measure the area fraction of ferrite and austenite exposed on the surface of a sample under examination. The values are reported as a volume fraction, thereby linking the surface area measurement on one plane to the overall volume fraction in the sample. Percentage ferrite requirements are typically 35 to 65% and are applied to weld metal and the HAZ.

The alternative method uses the ferromagnetic properties of the ferrite to measure its proportion in the matrix. The FN system used for austenitic stainless steel weld metals (where the ferrite content is measured by attraction of a spring-loaded magnet) was not originally developed for high ferrite levels, such as those in duplex alloys, and was only calibrated to about 28 FN (Ref 97). Furthermore, the variations in iron content between the various duplex grades affected the magnetic attraction for a given phase balance (Ref 98). Because no reliable magnetic attraction system had been fully developed and proven at the time duplex alloys were seeing widespread industrial application, most specifications required ferrite percentage measurements. However, changes to the FN measuring system have now been made so that all ferrite levels in duplex alloys can be recorded, and the system has proved more reliable. To achieve the extended range, counterweights were added to the spring-loaded magnet (Ref 98). Specification requirements for weld metals are typically 50 to 90 FN. A rule-of-thumb conversion from FN to percentage is:

$$0.70(FN) = \% \text{ ferrite} \qquad (Eq\ 3)$$

Measurement of ferrite content in duplex stainless steels, however, is seldom currently performed with a magnetic measuring technique and is more commonly referred to in terms of percentage.

There are also some limitations to the application of the FN measuring system in certain regions of the weld. The measurement tool applies

Table 17 Typical compositions of selected commercial nickel-overalloyed welding consumables and AWS specifications for Fe-22Cr-5.5Ni-3Mo-0.15N duplex stainless steel

Manufacturer	Trade name	Composition, %				
		C	Cr	Ni	Mo	N
Covered electrodes						
Metrode	Supermet 2205	0.02	25	9.5	3.5	0.17
Sandvik	22.9.3.L	0.03	22	9.5	3.0	0.15
Avesta	2205-PW	0.025	22	9.5	3.0	0.13
Lincoln Norweld	Arosta 4462	0.025	22.0	9.0	3.0	0.14
Thyssen	Thermanit 22/09	<0.04	22.5	9.0	3.0	...
AWS A5.4	E2209	0.04(a)	21.0-24.0	8.0-10.0	2.5-4.0	0.08-0.20
Bare wire						
Sandvik	22.8.3.L	<0.02	22.5	8.0	3.0	0.14
Metrode	ER329N	0.015	22.3	8.3	3.0	0.15
Thyssen	22/09/SG	<0.025	23.0	9.0	3.0	...
Lincoln Norweld	LNT/LNM 4462	0.015	22.5	8.5	3.0	0.15
AWS A5.9(b)	ER 2209	0.04(a)	21.0-24.0	8.0-10.0	2.5-4.0	0.08-0.20

(a) Maximum. (b) Pending

well to large areas of finely dispersed ferrite, such as in the weld metal, but it cannot accurately measure small areas that may have locally high ferrite levels (for example, the weld HAZ). It also may provide inaccurate readings in base material measurements due to the effect of magnet deflection toward the relatively coarse base material ferritic matrix.

Microstructural Examination. Optical microstructural examination is included to determine whether extensive phase precipitation has occurred (for example, σ-phase, carbides, nitrides, and so on), and specifications frequently call for the absence of any deleterious phases. However, the interpretation of duplex stainless steel microstructures is so difficult that one cannot make a definitive assessment, especially without experience in studying similar structures. Detecting small proportions of precipitates by optical means is also relatively difficult.

The pitting corrosion test most commonly used for qualifying duplex stainless steels is a modification of the ASTM G 48 Practice A ferric chloride test (Ref 99). Other tests are available (for example, potentiostatic critical pitting temperature tests in 3 or 15% NaCl, and others involving the use of CO_2), but the ASTM G 48 test has been shown to detect material with substandard properties and is preferred to most other common test techniques. The test solution is not representative of most service conditions in that it is highly acidic and oxidizing and has a high chloride concentration, but the test is relatively easy to perform and can distinguish between good and bad welds.

As used on duplex stainless steels, the test involves the immersion of a welded coupon into a 10% $FeCl_3 \cdot 6H_2O$ solution for between 24 and 72 h at a temperature from 15 to 70 °C (60 to 160 °F), depending on material grade and specification requirements. Test assessment can be based on direct weight loss, visual observation of pitting, weight loss per unit of exposed area, or corrosion rate. The procedure as laid out by ASTM was not designed for duplex stainless steel weldment testing, and although it has been adapted in a number

of ways, its interpretation still presents difficulties (Ref 100).

Filler Metal Requirements. For most duplex stainless steel grades there are two types of filler metals:

- Filler metals with matching compositions
- Filler metals that are slightly overalloyed, principally with respect to nickel

The matching filler metal is used where a PWHT is performed, whereas welds made with filler metal enriched with nickel are used in the as-welded condition. The weld metal microstructure from a composition exactly matching that of the parent steel will contain a high ferrite content. The increase in nickel is made to improve the as-welded phase balance and increase austenite content. The ferrite content of a weld made with a nickel-enriched consumable would decrease significantly if subjected to PWHT. It may suffer from slightly reduced weld metal strength and could also be more susceptible to σ-phase formation during heat treatment.

The nickel level in the enriched weld metal will be approximately 2.5 to 3.5% greater than in the base material (for example, for the Fe-22Cr-5.5Ni-3Mo-0.15N duplex stainless steel base material containing 5.5% Ni, the filler metal will comprise 8.0 to 9.0% Ni, depending on consumable manufacturer and form). Nominal filler metal compositions for the Fe-22Cr-5.5Ni-3Mo-0.15N grade of duplex stainless steels, proprietary names, and AWS classifications, where appropriate, are reported in Table 17.

The higher-alloy filler metals are sometimes used for welding a less alloyed base material (for example, a duplex stainless steel filler metal with 25% Cr could be used for the root run in an Fe-22Cr-5.5Ni-3Mo-0.15N base metal). This is usually done to improve root weld metal corrosion resistance and thereby pass the qualification test requirements. In most cases, this does not lead to loss of mechanical properties; indeed, the more highly alloyed filler metal in the case above is likely to have greater strength.

To avoid all the requirements for weld metal phase balance and microstructural control neces-

sary with duplex filler metals, nickel-base consumables (for example, AWS A 5.14 ERNi-CrMo-3) have been used. The yield strengths, however, are slightly below those of the more highly alloyed grades, and the lack of nitrogen and the presence of niobium in the filler metal may contribute to unfavorable metallurgical reactions and the formation of intermetallic precipitates and areas of high ferrite content in the HAZ.

Cracking Behavior. Duplex stainless steels can suffer from weld metal hydrogen cracking and solidification cracking, but HAZ cracking has not been reported in practice and is considered highly unlikely to develop. Hydrogen cracking from welding and in-service hydrogen pickup has been observed (Ref 101). The duplex microstructure provides a combination of a ferritic matrix, where hydrogen diffusion can be fairly rapid, with intergranular and intragranular austenite, where the hydrogen diffusion is significantly slower, thereby acting as a barrier to hydrogen diffusion. The net effect appears to be that hydrogen can be "trapped" within ferrite grains by the surrounding austenite, particularly where it decorates the prior-ferrite grain boundaries. Due to these characteristics, low-temperature hydrogen-release treatments are not effective, and the hydrogen is likely to remain in the structure for a long period. Whether cracking actually develops will depend on a number of factors, including the total amount of trapped hydrogen, the applied strain, and the amount of ferrite and austenite in the structure. Weld metal hydrogen content from covered electrodes can be relatively high, and levels up to 25 ppm have been reported (Ref 102).

The problem of weld metal hydrogen cracking in practice must not be overstated. The reported incidences of hydrogen cracking in duplex stainless steels have been restricted to cases in which the alloy was heavily cold worked or weld metals experienced high levels of restraint or possessed very high ferrite contents in combination with very high hydrogen levels, as a result of poor control of covered electrodes or the use of hydrogen-containing shielding gas. Indeed, other studies have shown how resistant duplex stainless steel

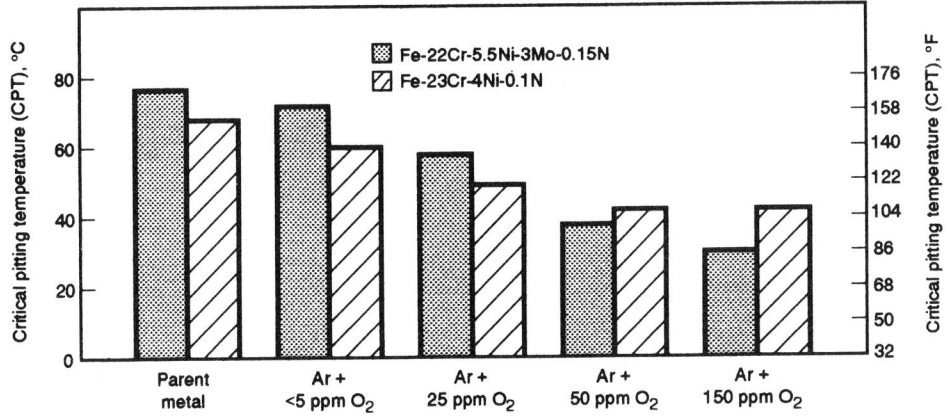

Fig. 70 Plot of pitting temperature vs. oxygen content of backing gas for Fe-22Cr-5.5Ni-3Mo-0.15N and Fe-23Cr-4Ni-0.1N duplex stainless steels tested in 3% NaCl and 0.1% NaCl solutions, respectively, both at an anodic potential of +300 mV. Source: Ref 109

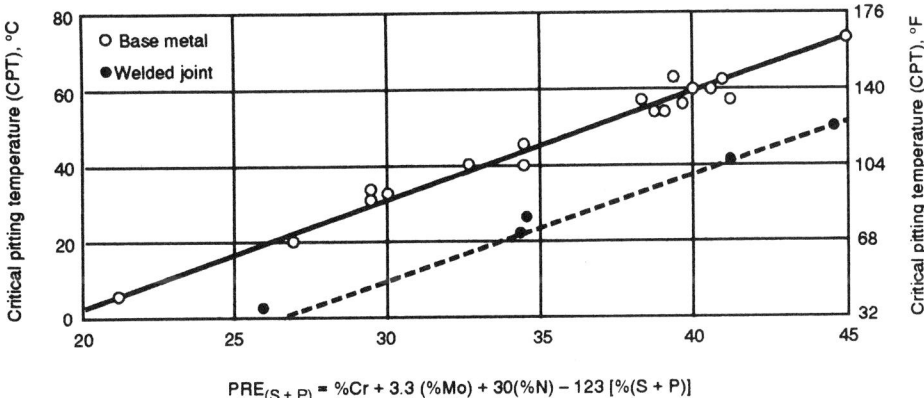

$$PRE_{(S + P)} = \%Cr + 3.3\,(\%Mo) + 30(\%N) - 123\,[\%(S + P)]$$

Fig. 71 Pitting corrosion resistance of base metal relative to weld metal placed in 6 wt% FeCl$_3$ solution for 24 h per ASTM G 48 (method A). Source: Ref 110

weld metals are to hydrogen cracking, even with consumables intentionally humidified (Ref 103), and that hydrogen-containing backing gases can be employed without producing cracking (Ref 104). There is no doubt an effect of hydrogen on the ductility of duplex stainless steels, and to avoid fabrication-related cracking problems, high-hydrogen-potential welding processes, such as SMAW, should be controlled by careful storage and use of electrodes, and by ensuring that the weld metal phase balance is within acceptable limits.

Solidification cracking in duplex stainless steels has not been reported as a commercial problem, but it has been witnessed in laboratory-made high-heat-input submerged arc welds (Ref 105). Cracking occurs at the solidification grain boundaries and has the appearance of running through the austenite phase. This is due to the subsequent solid-state transformation that occurs, in which the austenite forms predominantly on the prior-ferrite grain boundaries. The solidification cracking susceptibility is not great, however, and weldability cracking tests have shown that the performance of duplex stainless steels is similar to that of austenitic stainless materials with approximately 3 to 5 FN (Ref 106). Resistance to HAZ liquation cracking is also reportedly similar

to type 304 stainless steel (Ref 107) and unlikely to develop in practical welding situations.

Loss of Properties. The weld is usually the part of a system with reduced corrosion resistance and low-temperature toughness, and thus in many cases it is the limiting factor in material application. Welding primarily affects pitting corrosion, stress corrosion, and Charpy toughness.

Pitting corrosion resistance can be affected by many features of the welding operation, including:

- Localized segregation of alloying elements to the different constituent phases in the microstructure, producing areas lean in molybdenum and chromium
- Incorrect ferrite/austenite phase balance
- Formation of nitrides or intermetallic phases
- Loss of nitrogen from the root pass
- Presence of an oxidized surface on the underside of the root bead

The extent to which the reduction occurs depends on which of these factors are active and to what degree. Partitioning of alloying elements between the austenite and ferrite occurs in the weld metal, with chromium, molybdenum, and silicon partitioning to the ferrite, and carbon, nickel, and nitrogen to the austenite. The effect is not so apparent in as-de-

posited weld metals, but it becomes more significant as a result of reheating a previously deposited weld pass. The effect is also exacerbated by higher welding heat inputs.

Weld metal and HAZ microstructures with very high ferrite contents are also less resistant to pitting attack than are balanced structures. This is largely because predominantly ferritic structures are more prone to chromium nitride precipitation, which locally denudes the chromium concentration and lowers resistance to pitting attack.

Nitrogen loss in the root pass may reduce weld metal corrosion resistance. Up to 20% loss of nitrogen has been reported for gas-tungsten arc welds (Ref 108), and nitrogen-bearing backing gases have been explored and used in limited applications (Ref 93).

Cleanliness of the root-side purge gas may also affect pitting resistance. Figure 70 shows the effect of reducing oxygen content in an otherwise pure argon purge gas and its beneficial effect on pitting resistance. Also shown is the apparent benefit of using a reducing gas (NH$_{10}$), which would significantly reduce the tendency for oxide formation and leave the underbead appearance very shiny (Ref 109).

The net effect on pitting corrosion resistance may be observed by applying the ASTM G 48 pitting corrosion test to welds and base material with the same pitting resistance equivalent value, then assessing the reduction in critical pitting temperature (that is, the temperature at which pitting in the ferric chloride solution is first observed). The difference is approximately 20 °C (35 °F), as reported in Fig. 71, thereby quantifying the effect of reduced weld metal properties. Figure 71 also shows that the use of a super duplex stainless steel filler metal with a PRE value of about 40 on a Fe-22Cr-5.5Ni-3Mo-0.15N parent steel (which typically has a PRE value of about 33 to 35) will improve the weld metal pitting corrosion resistance, as assessed by the ASTM G 48 test, to approximately match that of the base material.

Resistance to chloride SCC does not appear to be affected significantly by welding per se. Nevertheless, welds are likely regions of attack for chloride SCC due to the presence of high stresses and the structural inhomogeneity present at the weld. If localized pitting is a necessary precursor for chloride SCC, the effects described above will also ultimately affect chloride SCC resistance.

There are three main causes of poor weld metal toughness:

- Very high ferrite content
- Presence of intermetallic phases or nitrides
- High weld metal oxygen concentration

Predominantly ferritic microstructures with a coarse grain size, as may be developed in a weld HAZ, have poor low-temperature notch toughness. Their performance is similar to that of ferritic stainless steels, and they may undergo low-energy cleavage fracture. The Fe-25Cr-5Ni-2.5Mo-0.17N-Cu and super duplex stainless steels are more susceptible to embrittlement through intermetallic phase precipitation, due to their increased kinetics of formation, and heat input and interpass temperature control are advised. Welding processes that produce high weld

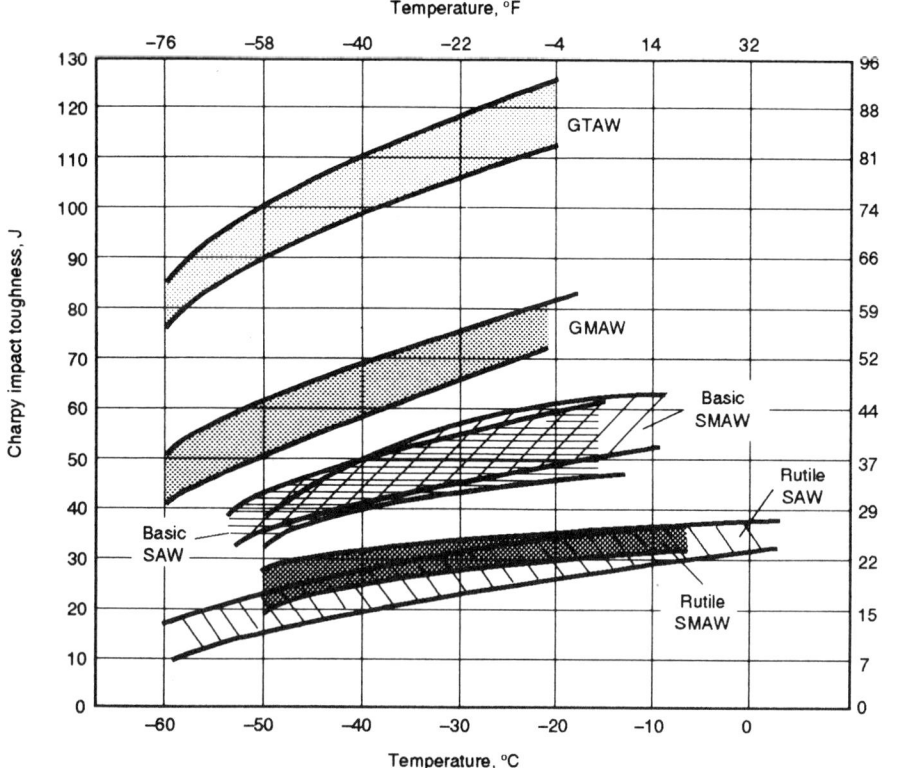

Fig. 72 Plot of Charpy V-notch toughness vs. temperature as a function of welding process for UNS S32760 alloy. The terms *basic* and *rutile* refer to lime-based and titania-based electrode coatings used with submerged arc welding and shielded-metal arc welding. Source: Ref 111

to establish whether solid-state welding processes offer significant advantages over fusion processes. The lack of a fused zone is potentially attractive to the welding of alloys that are prone to localized segregation effects.

Welding Precipitation-Hardening Stainless Steels

The PH stainless steels can be divided into three groups, based on microstructure and precipitation behavior. Martensitic PH stainless steels are solutionized at a high temperature and transform to low-carbon martensite during cooling to room temperature. Then they are further hardened by aging at an intermediate temperature to precipitate a second phase, which can be an intermetallic compound or a single component, such as copper. Both martensite and the precipitates harden the steel. Martensitic PH grades include:

Alloy	Type	UNS No.
PH13-8 Mo	XM-13	S13800
15-5PH	XM-12	S15500
17-4PH	630	S17400
Custom 450	XM-25	S45000
Custom 455	XM-16	S45500

Semiaustenitic PH stainless steels can be cooled from their solutionizing temperature to room temperature without martensite formation, remaining rather soft austenite as they cool. Then they are aged at an intermediate temperature, which causes carbides or an intermetallic compound to precipitate. This precipitation removes alloying elements and possibly carbon from the solid solution, which destabilizes the austenite and allows it to transform to martensite upon cooling from the aging temperature. Again, both martensite and the precipitates harden the steel. Semiaustenitic PH grades include:

Alloy	Type	UNS No.
PH15-7 Mo	632	S15700
17-7PH	631	S17700
AM-350	633	S35000
AM-355	634	S35500

Austenitic PH stainless steels contain enough alloys to be stable austenite upon cooling from their solutionizing temperature to room temperature. They are still stable austenite upon cooling from their aging temperature after intermetallic compounds are precipitated. In the case of austenitic PH stainless steels, only the precipitate hardens the alloy. As a result, the austenitic PH stainless steels cannot achieve tensile strengths as high as can be achieved with the martensitic or semiaustenitic grades. Austenitic PH grades include:

Alloy	Type	UNS No.
A-286	660	S66286
JBK-75(a)	...	...
(a) Modified version of A-286		

metal oxygen contents also produce welds with lower toughness, mainly due to the size and distribution of nonmetallic inclusions. Gas-shielded processes have the least oxygen potential and generally exhibit superior Charpy toughness properties (Fig. 72).

Applicable Welding Processes

Fusion Welding. Nearly all of the arc welding processes that are employed for other stainless steels can be used with duplex alloys, except where the process characteristic is to weld autogenously, such as EBW and LBW. In such circumstances a PWHT is nearly always necessary to restore the correct phase balance to the weld metal and to remove any undesirable precipitates. There are few reported differences in corrosion resistance between welding processes, but the nonmetallic inclusion distribution would be anticipated to have an effect. In most instances of pipe welding, where access is from one side only, GTAW is almost exclusively employed for the root pass. This provides a controllable, high-quality root bead that dictates the final corrosion performance of the weld. The inert gas on the backside of the weld can also be more closely controlled with this process. Aside from this preference, process selection will probably be dictated more by the availability of consumable form and economic and logistic considerations than by desired properties for the particular welding process.

Welds in duplex stainless steels have been made by all the major fusion welding processes and have performed satisfactorily. However, in a very few cases, the final application may necessitate the stipulation of a particular welding process. Where exceptional low-temperature toughness is required, gas-shielded processes may be specified because they produce higher weld metal toughness properties than flux-shielded processes (Fig. 72). Some consumable forms have not yet been fully developed for all grades of duplex stainless steels. Nevertheless, GTAW, SMAW, SAW, FCAW, and GMAW are commonly used with success for most alloy classes.

Solid-State Welding Processes. Few studies have been made of the solid-state welding characteristics of duplex stainless steels. Explosive welding has been applied to overlaying of tube sheets and similar items (Ref 104). Corrosion and mechanical properties are presumed to be similar to those of the parent material. Friction welding of duplex stainless steels has shown that the corrosion resistance of a friction weld zone can be significantly better than that of a corresponding arc weld in the same material (Ref 108). This is attributed to the absence of fusion and the related effects that can result (i.e., segregation and nitrogen loss). The bond line will, however, experience high temperatures, and some degree of transformation of the austenite to ferrite would be anticipated. Very rapid cooling will then probably suppress reformation of austenite, and a structure high in ferrite could result. There is ongoing effort

Some of the PH stainless steels (some martensitic and semiaustenitic grades) can solidify as primary ferrite and have very good resistance to hot cracking. Because martensite is also ferromagnetic, a magnetic FN loses meaning in terms of ensuring freedom from hot cracking. In the highly alloyed austenitic PH stainless steels, no ferrite is possible, and it is difficult to weld these without hot cracking.

The problems likely to be encountered in the welding of PH steels are different for each group, but they are similar for different steels within a group. Therefore, the weldability of the steels within each group can be best understood by first considering the welding of a typical steel from that group, which is invariably also the steel for which the most welding data are available. The weldability of other steels within the same group can then be understood by comparison with the "typical" steel.

Microstructural Evolution of Martensitic PH Stainless Steels

There have been no systematic studies of the solidification of welds in PH stainless steels, but the mechanisms involved are the same as for the standard austenitic stainless steels. The primary solidification mode can be predicted for a specific composition by using equations that were originally developed by Suutala (Ref 112) and have since been modified by the addition of an aluminum term and higher values for the carbon and nitrogen equivalents. These equations are (Ref 113):

$$Cr_{eq} = \%Cr + 1.4(\%Mo) + 1.5(\%Si) + 2(\%Nb) + 2.5(\%Al) + 3(\%Ti) \quad \text{(Eq 4)}$$

$$Ni_{eq} = \%Ni + 0.3(\%Mn) + 35(\%C) + 20(\%N) + \%Cu \quad \text{(Eq 5)}$$

Calculated values of the Cr_{eq}/Ni_{eq} ratios for typical PH steels are given in Table 18. According to Suutala (Ref 112), a Cr_{eq}/Ni_{eq} greater than 1.55 is required for primary ferrite solidification. Therefore, the calculated values for the Cr_{eq}/Ni_{eq} ratio indicate that all of the martensitic PH stainless steels except Custom 455 solidify as primary δ-ferrite. Upon cooling, nearly all of this ferrite first undergoes a transformation to austenite, which subsequently transforms to martensite at temperatures close to ambient. Custom 455 solidifies as primary austenite, which transforms to martensite upon cooling to ambient temperature. Although the as-welded fusion-zone microstructures of welds in martensitic PH steels made without filler metal or with a matching filler metal are predominantly martensitic, they may also contain a few percent of δ-ferrite in the untempered martensitic matrix (Fig. 73a). The morphology of this δ-ferrite is summarized in Table 18.

The δ-ferrite in welds made with moderate to high heat inputs may be intercellular or vermicular. Intercellular ferrite is formed as part of a divorced δ-γ eutectic, which is a result of segregation during the last stages of primary austenite solidification, whereas vermicular ferrite constitutes the untransformed cores of the primary ferrite dendrites. Very high cooling rates, such as may be experienced by welds made at high speeds in sheet material, suppress the transformation of δ-ferrite to austenite and promote the formation of acicular austenitic-ferritic structures, the austenite content of which subsequently transforms to martensite.

In the as-welded condition, the HAZs of welds in martensitic PH steels are distinguishable from the base metal by grain growth and an increased amount of ferrite in the high-temperature region close to the fusion line. Postweld solution treatments reduce the residual δ-ferrite content and refine the prior-austenite grain size of both the fusion zone and the HAZ. Likewise, aging simultaneously tempers the martensite and precipitates the age-hardening particles in the fusion zone, HAZ, and base metal. However, these particles are too small to observe by optical microscopy. Aging may also re-form up to 10% austenite at temperatures of 540 to 620 °C (1000 to 1150 °F), the amount increasing with aging temperature.

17-4PH Stainless Steel

Weldability. 17-4PH stainless steel is typical of the martensitic PH stainless steels. Its weldability is superior to that of the standard austenitic stainless steels because, due to its low carbon content, it does not require preheat to prevent cracking in thicknesses up to 100 mm (4.0 in.). The welding conditions used for arc welding 17-4PH stainless steel are essentially the same as those used for joining the standard austenitic stainless steels. However, neither welds nor base metals have the high ductility of the austenitic stainless steels, so care must be taken to avoid the presence of stress raisers. One common form of stress raiser is the built-in notch at the root of a partial-penetration weld. If design requirements dictate partial-penetration welds, the initiation of cracks at the root of the weld can be avoided by making the root pass with a ductile, low-strength filler metal such as type 308L, and then completing the balance of the weld with a matching high-strength heat-treatable filler metal.

Arc Welding. Gas-tungsten arc, gas-metal arc, and shielded metal arc welding processes have all been used extensively for joining 17-4PH stainless steel. Typical mechanical properties of arc welds in 17-4PH are presented in Table 19. The choice of welding process has little effect on the strength of welds after PWHT, but it does affect the weld metal cleanliness and resultant ductility and toughness. Gas-tungsten arc welds have the highest quality, and shielded metal arc welds have the lowest quality. However, shielded metal arc welds are generally satisfactory for all but the most critical applications.

Base Metal Condition for Welding. Depending on the thickness and level of restraint, 17-4PH stainless steel can be welded in the annealed (A) or overaged (H1100 or H1150) conditions. The welding of material in conditions H900 through H1075 is generally not recommended. Material up to 25 mm (1.0 in.) thick can usually be welded in condition A provided that the weld is not very heavily restrained. Highly restrained welds or welds in heavier sections are best welded in conditions H1100 or H1150.

Filler Metals. Type 630 covered electrodes and filler wires, which deposit weld metal that closely matches 17-4PH base metal in composition and heat treatment response, are used when high-strength welds are required. Austenitic filler metals, such as type 308L, can be used for joining 17-4PH when high strength is not required in the joint. Welds made with austenitic filler metals are less susceptible to hydrogen embrittlement than those made with martensitic filler metals and may be used in the as-welded condition.

Postweld Heat Treatment. In the as-welded condition, the weld metal and the high-temperature regions of the HAZs of welds in 17-4PH stainless steel have structures consisting primar-

Table 18 Effect of composition on the primary solidification mode and final as-welded microstructure of welds in precipitation-hardening steels

Alloy	Cr_{eq}/Ni_{eq}(a)	Observed weld-metal δ-ferrite, %	Predicted primary solidification mode(b)	Final as-welded microstructure
Austenitic types				
JBK-75	0.77	0	A	100% austenite
A-286	0.88	0	A	100% austenite
Martensitic types				
Custom 455	1.33	~0	A	~100% martensite
15-5PH	1.60	0-5	F	Martensite + intercellular or vermicular δ-ferrite
17-4PH	1.74	3-8	F	Martensite + vermicular δ-ferrite or acicular structure
Custom 450	1.82	0-5	F	Martensite + vermicular δ-ferrite or acicular structure
PH13-8 Mo	1.98	0	F	100% martensite
Semiaustenitic types				
AM-355	1.77	~5	F	Austenite + vermicular δ-ferrite or acicular structure
17-7PH	1.92	~25	F	Widmanstätten austenite in ferritic matrix
PH15-7 Mo	2.01	25-40	F	Widmanstätten austenite in ferritic matrix
AM-350	2.22	>15	F	Widmanstätten austenite in ferritic matrix

(a) $Cr_{eq} = \%Cr + 1.4(\%Mo) + 1.5(\%Si) + 2(\%Nb) + 2.5(\%Al) + 3(\%Ti)$; $Ni_{eq} = \%Ni + 0.3(\%Mn) + 35(\%C) + 20(\%N) + \%Cu$. Values are for typical compositions. (b) A, austenitic; F, delta ferritic

Table 19 Mechanical properties of 17-4PH arc welds

Thickness		Postweld heat treatment(b)	Tensile strength		0.2% yield strength		Elongation, %			Reduction in area, %	Failure location(c)	Izod impact energy(d)	
mm	in.		MPa	ksi	MPa	ksi	in 13 mm (0.5 in.)	in 25 mm (1 in.)	in 50 mm (2 in.)			J	ft·lbf
GTA welds(a)													
1.3	0.050	Aged 480 °C (900 °F), 1 h	1340	194	1295	188	7	...	3.0	...	FL	...	...
1.3	0.050	Aged 540 °C (1000 °F), 4 h	1235	179	1170	170	...	...	5.0	...	BM	...	...
1.3	0.050	Aged 595 °C (1100 °F), 4 h	1140	165	1105	160	14	...	5.5	...	FL	...	...
2.3	0.090	Aged 480 °C (900 °F), 1 h	1395	202	1290	187	16	...	5.0	...	FL	...	...
2.3	0.090	Aged 540 °C (1000 °F), 4 h	1240	180	1160	168	17	...	7.0	...	WM	...	...
2.3	0.090	Aged 595 °C (1100 °F), 4 h	1125	163	1060	154	...	...	9.0	...	BM	...	...
4.8	0.188	ST + aged 480 °C (900 °F), 1 h	1370	199	1260	183	...	17.0	9.0	35	WM	...	...
4.8	0.188	ST + aged 510 °C (950 °F), 1 h	1345	195	1255	182	...	18.0	9.0	42	WM	...	...
4.8	0.188	ST + aged 550 °C (1025 °F), 1 h	1215	176	1145	166	...	17.0	9.2	45	WM	...	...
GMA welds(a)													
4.8	0.188	ST + aged 480 °C (900 °F), 1 h	1400	203	1250	181	...	14.0	7.0	...	WM	...	...
4.8	0.188	ST + aged 510 °C (950 °F), 1 h	1275	185	1200	174	...	14.0	7.5	...	WM	...	...
4.8	0.188	ST + aged 550 °C (1025 °F), 1 h	1195	173	1125	163	...	15.0	7.5	...	WM	...	...
25	1.00	ST + aged 480 °C (900 °F), 1 h	1305	189	1150	167	...	...	7.3	21	WM	15	11
SMA welds(a)													
4.8	0.188	ST + aged 480 °C (900 °F), 1 h	1380	200	1275	185	...	13.0	6.5	29	...	...	...
4.8	0.188	ST + aged 510 °C (950 °F), 1 h	1280	186	1205	175	...	12.0	6.0	30	...	...	...
4.8	0.188	ST + aged 550 °C (1025 °F), 1 h	1195	173	1115	162	...	12.0	6.0	32	...	...	...
9.5	0.375	Aged 480 °C (900 °F), 1 h	1225	178	1060	154	...	10.0	...	32	BM	...	...
9.5	0.375	ST + aged 480 °C (900 °F), 1 h	1290	187	1185	172	...	11.0	...	48	WM	...	...
9.5	0.375	Aged 540 °C (1000 °F), 1 h	1105	160	940	136	...	11.0	...	29	WM	...	...
9.5	0.375	ST + aged 540 °C (1000 °F), 1 h	1170	170	1110	161	...	12.0	...	48	WM	...	...
9.5	0.375	Aged 595 °C (1100 °F), 1 h	1095	159	770	112	...	13.5	...	50	BM	...	...
9.5	0.375	ST + aged 595 °C (1100 °F), 1 h	1090	158	925	134	...	12.0	...	54	WM	...	...
25	1.00	Aged 480 °C (900 °F), 1 h	1090	158	815	118	...	...	8.0	21	WM	38	28
25	1.00	ST + aged 480 °C (900 °F), 1 h	1280	186	1125	163	...	...	9.5	36	WM	8	6
25	1.00	Aged 540 °C (1000 °F), 1 h	1070	155	745	108	...	...	9.5	27	WM	46	34
25	1.00	ST + aged 540 °C (1000 °F), 1 h	1150	167	1005	146	...	...	9.5	39	WM	23	17
25	1.00	Aged 595 °C (1100 °F), 1h	1090	158	765	111	...	...	7.5	18	WM	12	9
25	1.00	ST + aged 595 °C (1100 °F), 1 h	1090	158	890	129	...	...	11.0	38	WM	30	22

(a) All welds made in condition A with a 17-4PH coated electrode or filler wire. (b) ST = solution treated at 1035 °C (1900 °F) for 30 min; air cooled to 15 °C (60 °F) and held for 1 h. (c) WM, weld metal; FL, fusion line; BM, base metal. (d) Notch in transverse face of weld metal. Source: Ref 114

ily of untempered martensite plus a small amount of ferrite (Fig. 73a). Weldments exhibit an aging peak in the HAZ and a weld metal hardness that is only slightly less than that of the base metal in condition A (Fig. 74a). Weldments in 17-4PH stainless steel are not usually put into service in the as-welded condition except for repair welds where PWHT is impractical. In order to obtain weld properties approximating those of the base metal, PWHT is necessary. For single-pass welds made with the base metal in condition A, a simple aging treatment of 1 to 4 h at 480 to 620 °C (900 to 1150 °F) is usually sufficient. It simultaneously hardens the weld metal, HAZ, and base metal and lowers the residual stresses associated with the weld. Because only slight overaging occurs in the portion of the HAZ that is heated into the aging temperature range during welding (Fig. 74a), joint efficiencies of 97 to 100% are obtained (Ref 114).

In multipass welds, the repeated heating from the deposition of successive beads may leave a variation in structure from bead to bead that will result in nonuniform response to the aging treatment. Consequently, in the aged condition, weld yield and ultimate tensile strengths are only about 65% and 80 to 90%, respectively, of the base metal values (Ref 114). Solution treating the weld before hardening reduces the weld metal and HAZ ferrite contents and improves weld metal uniformity and response to heat treatment. As a result, weld strength increases to 80 to 90% and 90

to 95%, respectively, of the base metal yield and ultimate tensile strengths. For welds made with the base metal in the overaged condition, solution treatment is required if it is desired to heat treat the weldment to a higher strength level. In general, if the weld deposit is less than 13 mm (0.5 in.) in thickness, fairly good tensile properties can be obtained even if the solution treatment is omitted prior to aging. However, the toughness of the weld metal decreases with aging temperature above 540 °C (1000 °F), probably due to an unfavorable carbide morphology. Therefore, if weld deposits are 13 mm (0.5 in.) or greater in thickness and a postweld solution treatment is not feasible, an age-hardening temperature of 550 °C (1025 °F) or lower is suggested (Ref 114).

Electron-beam welding is used for joining 17-4PH stainless steel when precision welds with maximum strength and minimum distortion are required. Welding parameters are similar to those used for welding the standard austenitic stainless steels, and the same considerations as in arc welding apply to the choice of base metal condition for welding.

The most important characteristic of an electron-beam weld is the total heat input, which is only about 20% of that of a comparable arc weld (Ref 115). As a result, the HAZ is much narrower (Fig. 74b) and the weld metal is finer grained and has a lower ferrite content. Furthermore, because an electron-beam weld is usually a single-pass weld, the weld metal structure does not exhibit the inhomo-

geneities of a multipass arc weld. Consequently, the mechanical properties of electron-beam welds are generally superior to those of arc welds, particularly in regard to fracture toughness (Ref 116).

Typical mechanical properties of electron-beam welds in 17-4PH are presented in Table 20. Postweld aging alone results in joint efficiency of 95 to 100% and in total elongation values only slightly lower than those of the base metal; however, the toughness of welds in the H900 condition is low. Re-solution treating before aging has little effect on weld strength but markedly increases the toughness of welds aged at 480 °C (900 °F). However, it produces only a small increase in toughness for welds aged at higher temperatures.

15-5PH Stainless Steel

15-5PH stainless steel differs from 17-4PH in that its composition is balanced so that its structure is ferrite-free and material for bar and forging billets is vacuum arc remelted. As a result, the transverse ductility and toughness of 15-5PH stainless steel are superior to those of 17-4PH. However, its weldability is essentially the same as that of 17-4PH, and the same welding processes and procedures are used. A matching 15-5PH filler wire (AMS 5826) is available for critical applications, but it is most often welded with type 630 (17-4PH) covered electrodes or filler wire. Postweld heat treatment and weld mechanical properties are essentially identical to those for 17-4PH.

Autogenous welds in 15-5PH stainless steel contain less δ-ferrite than those in 17-4PH. Sufficient δ-ferrite is normally formed to prevent weld solidification cracking in gas-tungsten arc welds. However, the rapid cooling rates that are characteristic of EBW and LBW can produce welds with little or no δ-ferrite, which are susceptible to weld solidification cracking if welded with excessively high welding speeds. The strengths of defect-free electron-beam welds in 15-5PH are similar to those in 17-4PH, but the fracture toughness is higher (Table 20).

PH13-8 Mo Stainless Steel

PH13-8 Mo stainless steel is vacuum induction melted plus vacuum arc remelted. It is ferrite-free and is used where high fracture toughness is required in heavy sections. Its weldability is similar to that of 17-4PH stainless steel, and the same procedures are used. It can be welded with the same processes, although covered electrodes for SMAW are not available. Gas-tungsten arc and gas-metal arc welds can be made using a matching filler wire (AMS 5840). Although the final weld metal microstructure is ferrite-free (Fig. 73b), PH13-8 Mo has excellent resistance to weld solidification cracking because it solidifies as δ-ferrite and has low sulfur and phosphorus contents. After postweld solution treating and aging, the yield strengths and Charpy V-notch impact energies of multipass gas-tungsten arc welds in PH13-8 Mo stainless steel are 96 to 100% and 50 to 100%, respectively, of the base metal values (Fig. 75a), the difference between weld metal and base metal properties being greatest for aging temperatures above 540 °C (1000 °F). In heavy sections, PH13-8 Mo stainless steel is often joined by EBW. After PWHT, electron-beam welds have joint efficiencies of virtually 100%, and their fracture toughness is approximately the same as that of the base metal (Ref 118).

Custom 450 Stainless Steel

The composition of Custom 450 stainless steel is balanced so that base metal, HAZ, and weld metal are essentially fully martensitic. In most respects, its weldability is similar to that of 17-4PH, and it can be joined using the same welding processes and procedures. A matching filler wire (AMS 5763) is usually used for GTAW and GMAW of Custom 450 and is essential if the weldment is to be used without PWHT. A type 630 (17-4PH) filler wire or coated electrode can be used for joining Custom 450 if the weldment is postweld aged or solution treated and aged.

Custom 450 stainless steel is often used in condition A when only moderate strength is required. Material welded in this condition has acceptable weld properties in the as-welded condition, but Charpy V-notch impact energy is substantially increased by a postweld solution anneal at 1040 °C (1900 °F) (Ref 120). Higher strength levels are obtained by postweld aging or solution treating and aging. After postweld solu-

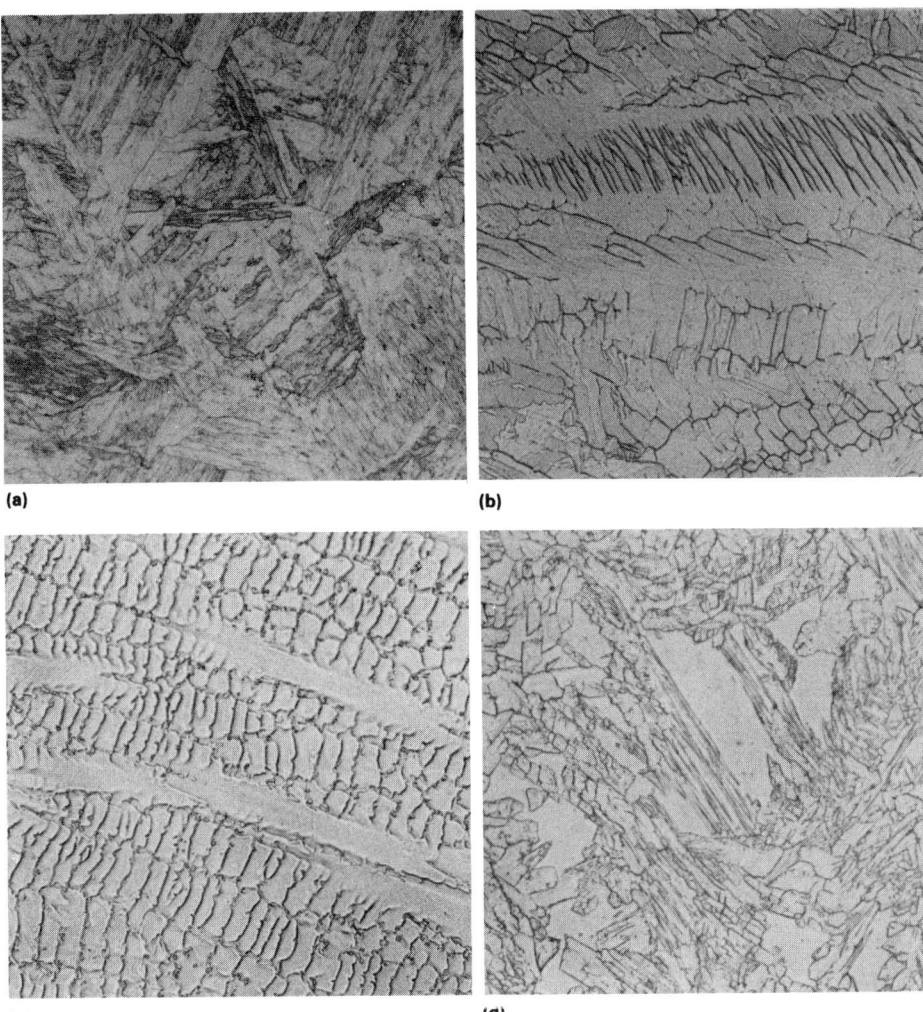

Fig. 73 Microstructures of autogenous gas-tungsten arc weld metal in the as-welded condition. (a) 17-4PH, δ-ferrite in a matrix of untempered martensite. Etchant: Fry's reagent. 440×. (b) PH13-8 Mo, untempered martensite. Etchant: Vilella's reagent. 440×. (c) 17-7PH, austenite plus about 20% δ-ferrite. Etchant: electrolytic nitric acid/acetic acid followed by electrolytic oxalic acid. 440×. (d) A-286, fully austenitic structure. Etchant: 90 mL hydrochloric acid, 5 mL nitric acid, 5 mL sulfuric acid, 1 mL hydrofluoric acid. 440×

tion treating and aging, the yield strengths of multipass gas-tungsten arc welds in Custom 450 are 98 to 100% of the base metal values. Weld metal Charpy V-notch impact energy increases with aging temperature from about 50% of the base metal value for welds aged at 480 °C (900 °F) to 100% for welds aged at 565 °C (1050 °F), as shown in Fig. 75(b).

Custom 455 Stainless Steel

Custom 455 stainless steel is vacuum induction melted plus vacuum arc remelted and is completely martensitic. It is joined primarily by GTAW, and a Custom 455 filler metal is available for multipass welds. Procedures are similar to those used for 17-4PH, but a lower postweld solution treatment temperature (815 to 845 °C, or 1500 to 1550 °F) is used. In small sections, joint efficiencies of 80% are obtained by postweld aging only and 100% by solution treating and aging the weldment. In large sections, joint efficiencies in excess of 85% are possible.

Microstructural Evolution of Semiaustenitic PH Stainless Steels

The semiaustenitic PH steels have a primary δ-ferritic solidification mode and, on cooling, the δ-ferrite partially transforms to austenite by a Widmanstätten reaction. This austenite is stable down to ambient temperature, so the as-welded structure of the fusion zone consists of austenite in a ferrite matrix (Fig. 73c). With the exception of AM-355, the percentage of retained ferrite in semiaustenitic PH welds is substantially higher than for welds in martensitic PH steels.

Postweld conditioning treatments destabilize the austenite so that it transforms to martensite at ambient or subzero temperatures. Subsequent aging simultaneously tempers the martensite and precipitates the strengthening particles, which are not visible by optical microscopy. The final fusion zone microstructure, therefore, consists of areas of retained ferrite in a tempered martensitic matrix. If a low conditioning temperature is used, carbide particles may also be observed at the ferrite-martensite interfaces.

In the as-welded and, to a lesser degree, the PWHT conditions, the HAZ is distinguishable from the base metal by an increase in grain size and ferrite content in the high-temperature region close to the fusion line.

17-7PH and PH15-7 Mo Stainless Steels

Weldability. 17-7PH and PH15-7 Mo stainless steels are typical of the semiaustenitic PH steels. As-deposited welds made without filler metal have weld metal and HAZ structures that are predominantly austenitic (Fig. 73c). This ductile structure is not susceptible to cold cracking, so 17-7PH and PH15-7 Mo are readily welded in any condition without preheat and without the need for critical control of interpass temperature or cooling rate. However, autogenous 17-7PH weld metal is not fully austenitic, but rather contains about 25% δ-ferrite versus 10 to 15% in the base metal. Likewise, autogenous PH15-7 Mo weld metal may contain up to 40% δ-ferrite versus 15% in the base metal. The δ-ferrite content of the weld metal is determined primarily by composition, but high values are also promoted to a lesser degree by thicker weld beads, higher welding currents, and higher welding speeds. A large volume fraction of δ-ferrite can make the weld metal susceptible to hot cracking and reduce the ductility of the weld metal in the heat-treated condition. If necessary, the δ-ferrite content of the weld metal can be reduced by the addition of an appropriate filler metal.

Filler Metals. Filler wires are available for 17-7PH (AMS 5824) and PH15-7 Mo (AMS 5812) stainless steels. The compositions of these wires have been adjusted so as to produce deposits with lower δ-ferrite contents than would be produced by the base metal compositions, while still responding correctly to the age-hardening treatment.

Covered electrodes are not available for 17-7PH and PH15-7 Mo stainless steels because excessive oxidation of aluminum would occur in the arc. However, type 630 (17-4PH) covered electrodes have been used successfully for joining 17-7PH. To obtain adequate heat treat response with this filler metal, welding conditions that produce high dilution and a compromise PWHT practice are required. A heat treatment of 870 °C (1600 °F) for 90 min is used to simultaneously solution treat the type 630 weld metal and condition the 17-7PH base metal (Ref 121). The weld is then refrigerated at –75 °C (–100 °F) for 1 h, depending on the properties required.

Standard iron-chromium-nickel filler metals, such as types 308, 308L, 309, and 347, can also be used for joining 17-7PH and PH15-7 Mo, but the weld metal will not respond to heat treatment in the same manner as the base metal. Response to heat treatment will depend on the ratio of austenite to ferrite-forming elements in the filler metal and the amount of dilution by the base metal. In most instances, weld strength will be much lower than that obtained with a matching filler metal, but ductility and toughness will be higher.

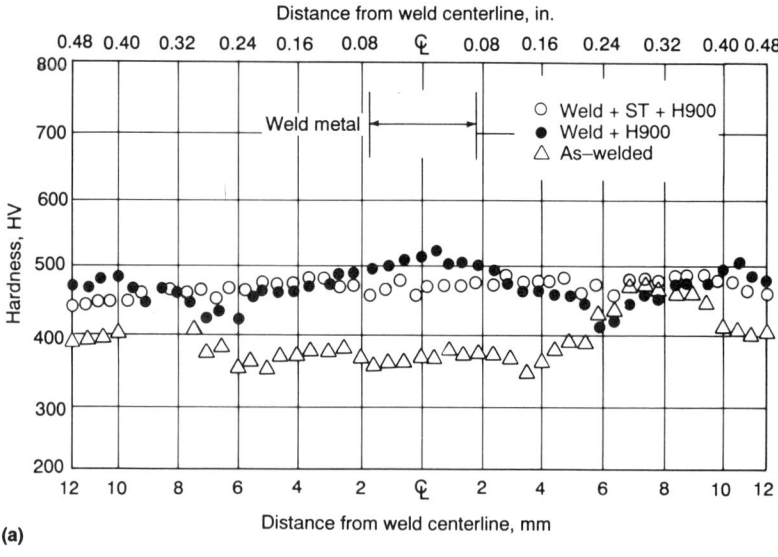

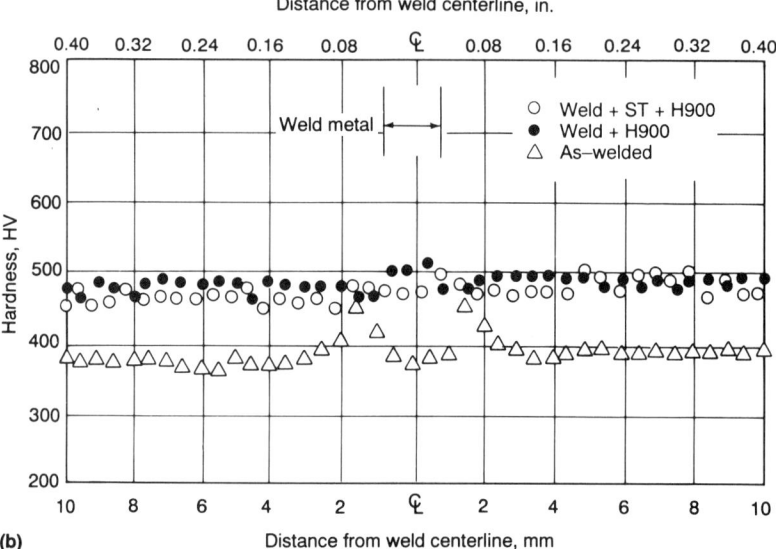

Fig. 74 Microhardness profiles of as-welded and postweld heat treated welds in 17-4PH made with (a) plasma arc welding and (b) electron-beam welding. Source: Ref 115

Gas-Tungsten Arc Welding. Because 17-7PH and PH15-7 Mo stainless steels are used primarily as sheet and strip, they are most frequently joined by GTAW. Preheating and postheating are not required to prevent cracking, but the selection of welding conditions requires more care than for the standard austenitic stainless steels. Helium gas is preferred over argon for shielding the arc, because helium minimizes the formation of a continuous aluminum oxide film on the surface of the weld pool (Ref 122). Particular care should be taken to provide efficient shielding of the weld pool in order to minimize loss of aluminum. Inert gas shielding should also be used on the underside of full-penetration welds to protect the weld root. Welding speeds typically are of the order of 5 mm/s (12 in./min) (Ref 121). Higher welding speeds can cause porosity at the fusion line. Welding currents and weld-pass sequence should be selected to minimize the weld cross-sectional area.

Gas-metal arc welding is used for joining 17-7PH and PH15-7 Mo in heavy sheet and plate

thicknesses. A mixture of 75He-25Ar is the most widely used shielding gas. Welding conditions are otherwise similar to those used for the standard austenitic stainless steels.

Postweld Heat Treatment. As-deposited welds in 17-7PH and PH15-7 Mo steels have a structure of austenite plus ferrite that is of much lower strength than the hardened base metal. A PWHT is thus essential if a weld strength similar to the base metal strength is required. The effects of PWHT on the tensile properties of gas-tungsten arc welds in 17-7PH and PH15-7 Mo steels are presented in Table 21; corresponding welding conditions are given in Table 22. The joint efficiencies of welds postweld hardened to the RH950 or TH1050 conditions without reannealing are 100% with weld reinforcement and 95 to 98% without it. Postweld reannealing before hardening has negligible effect on weld strength but increases weld ductility.

Resistance Welding. Spot and seam welding have been used extensively for joining 17-7PH

Table 20 Mechanical properties of electron-beam welds in martensitic precipitation-hardening steels

| Thickness | | Preweld | | Tensile strength | | 0.2% yield strength | | Elongation in 50 mm | Failure | CVN impact energy | | Fracture toughness | | |
mm	in.	condition	Postweld heat treatment(a)	MPa	ksi	MPa	ksi	(2 in.), %	location(b)	J	ft · lbf	MPa√m	ksi√in.	Ref
17-4 PH														
3.2	0.125	A	Aged 480 °C (900 °F), 1 h	1435	208	1365	198	11.0	BM	2.4	1.8	...	...	115
3.2	0.125	A	ST + aged 480 °C (900 °F), 1 h	1400	203	1270	184	12.2	BM	14.0	10.3	...	...	115
3.2	0.125	A	Aged 550 °C (1025 °F), 4 h	1165	169	1125	163	12.0	BM	15.6	11.5	...	...	115
3.2	0.125	A	ST + aged 550 °C (1025 °F), 4 h	1140	165	1090	158	12.0	BM	18.3	13.5	...	...	115
3.2	0.125	A	Aged 620 °C (1150 °F), 4 h	1025	149	985	143	15.4	BM	17.6	13.0	...	...	115
3.2	0.125	A	ST + aged 620 °C (1150 °F), 4 h	1020	148	985	143	14.6	BM	19.4	14.3	...	...	115
3.2	0.125	A	Aged 760 °C (1400 °F), 2 h + 620 °C (1150 °F), 4 h	965	140	745	108	16.4	BM	20.6	15.2	...	...	115
9.5	0.375	A	Aged 480 °C (900 °F), 1 h	1315	191	1235	179	12.6(c)	...	...	...	...	...	117
(e)	(e)	H1150	None	885	128	705	102	11(d) to 22	WM/BM	...	...	...	...	116
(e)	(e)	H1150	ST + aged 595 °C (1100 °F), 4 h	1055	153	...	...	...	...	...	...	$K_q = 187$	$K_q = 170$	116
15-5PH														
(e)	(e)	1150	ST + aged 565 °C (1050 °F), 4 h	...	...	1125	163	...	...	...	...	$K_q = 194$	$K_q = 176$	116
(e)	(e)	1150	ST + aged 595 °C (1100 °F), 4 h	...	...	1020	148	...	...	...	...	$K_{Ic} = 262$	$K_{Ic} = 238$	116
PH13-8 Mo														
(e)	(e)	H1150M	ST + aged 540 °C (1000 °F), 4 h	...	...	1415	205	...	...	...	...	$K_{Ic} = 110$	$K_{Ic} = 100$	118

(a) ST = solution treated: 17-4PH and 15-5PH at 1035 °C (1900 °F), PH13-8 Mo at 925 °C (1700 °F) for 30 min; air cool. (b) WM, weld metal; BM, base metal. (c) In 25 mm (1 in.). (d) Low value is for failure in the weld metal. (e) Exact value not reported—in range of 23 to 60 mm (0.90 to 2.37 in.)

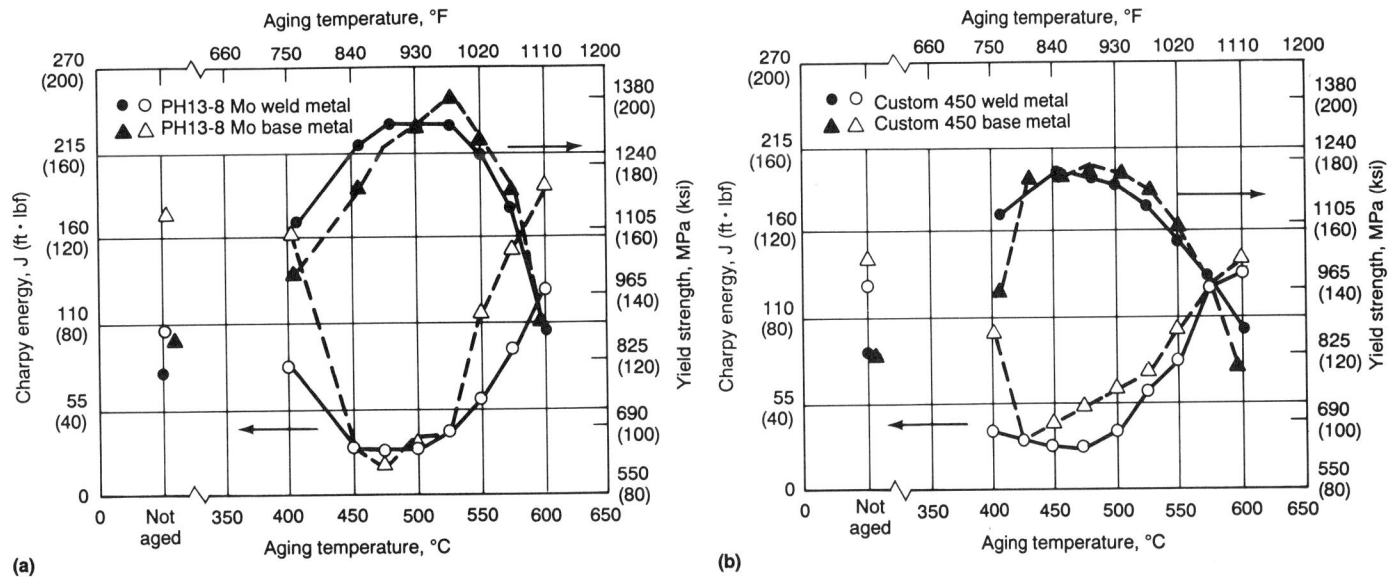

Fig. 75 Effect of aging temperature on the yield strength and Charpy V-notch impact energy of (a) PH13-8 Mo and (b) Custom 450 base metal and weld metal. Gas-tungsten arc welds made in 13 mm (0.50 in.) thick plate (condition A) with matching filler metals. Closed symbols represent yield strength values; open symbols represent impact values. Source: Ref 119

and PH15-7 Mo steels. For good results, particular attention should be given to the surface cleanliness of the steel. Surfaces to be joined should be free of oil, grease, dirt, and heat-treating scale. Welding schedules should use longer weld times, lower weld currents, and electrode forces 10 to 20% higher than those normally used for the standard austenitic stainless steels (Ref 123).

The best mechanical properties are obtained by welding just before or after final hardening. This practice produces weld nuggets with a tough austenitic microstructure. The tensile strength normal to the weld interface is a maximum for this condition, and the shear strength is not significantly lower than for nuggets in the hardened condition (Ref 121).

Sound flash butt welds can be produced in 17-7PH and PH15-7 Mo stainless steels, but ductility may be low as a result of ferrite stringers in the base metal being bent parallel to the weld interface.

AM-350 and AM-355 Stainless Steels

Weldability. AM-350 and AM-355 differ from 17-7PH and PH15-7 Mo stainless steels in that they do not contain aluminum. Martensitic transformation provides their major strengthening mechanism, with an additional but smaller contribution from the precipitation of Cr_2N or an isostructurally similar phase during tempering. The absence of any reactive elements makes the

weldability of AM-350 and AM-355 as good as that of the standard austenitic stainless steels and superior to that of 17-7PH.

Although these steels are most often joined by GTAW and GMAW, they can be joined by any of the processes used for the standard austenitic stainless steels, including SAW, EBW, LBW, and resistance welding. Like 17-7PH and PH15-7 Mo, these steels may be welded in the annealed or hardened conditions, and neither preheat nor special precautions with regard to interpass temperature or cooling rate are necessary. However, PWHT must be used if maximum weld strength is required.

Annealed AM-350 base metal contains 10 to 15% δ-ferrite, and welding produces even higher

Table 21 Tensile properties of gas-tungsten arc welds in 1.6 mm (0.062 in.) thick 17-7PH and PH15-7 Mo steels
See also Table 22.

Alloy	Preweld condition(a)	Postweld heat treatment(a)	Reinforcement	Tensile strength		0.2% yield strength		Elongation, %		Failure location(b)
				MPa	ksi	MPa	ksi	in 13 mm (0.5 in.)	in 50 mm (2 in.)	
Hardened and tested as-welded										
PH15-7 Mo	TH1050	None	Off	840	122	605	88	25.0	7.0	WM
PH15-7 Mo	R950	None	Off	795	115	600	87	22.0	6.0	WM
Welded and hardened										
17-7PH	A	TH1050	On	1415	205	1345	195	6.0	1.5	BM
17-7PH	A	RH950	On	1515	220	1415	205	6.0	2.0	BM
PH15-7 Mo	A	TH1050	On	1450	210	1415	205	...	5.0	BM
PH15-7 Mo	A	TH1050	Off	1415	205	1345	195	8.0	2.0	WM
PH15-7 Mo	A	RH950	On	1655	240	1550	225	...	5.0	BM
PH15-7 Mo	A	RH950	Off	1585	230	1480	215	5.0	2.0	WM
Welded, reannealed, and hardened										
17-7PH	A	A + TH1050	On	1435	208	1345	195	8.0	2.5	BM
PH15-7 Mo	A	A + TH1050	On	1450	210	1415	205	...	5.0	BM
PH15-7 Mo	A	A + TH1050	Off	1380	200	1345	195	10.0	2.5	WM
PH15-7 Mo	A	A + RH950	On	1620	235	1480	215	...	4.0	BM
PH15-7 Mo	A	A + RH950	Off	1585	230	1450	210	7.0	2.0	WM
PH15-7 Mo	A	R + A + RH950	Off	1660	241	1505	218	9.0	3.5	WM

(a) Preweld and postweld heat treating conditions. A (condition A): anneal at 1065 °C (1950 °F) for 10 min, air cool. R (refrigeration treatment for transformation): –75 °C (–100 °F) for 8 h. TH1050: 760 °C (1400 °F) for 90 min, air cool + 565 °C (1050 °F) for 90 min, air cool. RH950: 955 °C (1750 °F) for 10 min; air cool + –75 °C (–100 °F) for 8 h + 510 °C (950 °F) for 60 min; air cool. (b) WM, weld metal; BM, base metal

Table 22 Welding conditions for gas-tungsten arc welds described in Table 21

Welding condition	Alloy	
	17-7PH	PH15-7 Mo
Thickness, mm (in.)	1.59 (0.0625)	1.57 (0.062)
Shielding gas	Helium	Helium
Gas flow rate, L/min (ft³/h)	28 (60)	24 (50)
Welding speed, mm/s (in./min)	6.3 (15)	5.1 (12)
Current	As required for full penetration in a single pass	As required for full penetration in a single pass
Filler wire	1.6 mm (0.062 in.) diam W17-7PH	1.6 mm (0.062 in.) diam WPH15-7Mo
Wire feed rate, mm/s (in./min)	12 (28)	1 to 1

levels in autogenous weld metal and the high-temperature portion of the HAZ. In the subzero cooled and tempered (SCT) condition, the final structure consists of islands of ferrite surrounded by carbides in a tempered martensitic matrix. In contrast, the composition of AM-355 is balanced so that the base metal contains less than 5% d-ferrite in condition H (solution treated at 1065 °C, or 1950 °F) and 0% ferrite in the equalized plus overaged and tempered condition, and welding does not increase the ferrite content to any significant extent.

Filler Metals. An AM-355 filler wire (AMS 5780) with a composition identical to that of the base metal is available for joining AM-355. Likewise, a matching AM-350 filler wire (AMS 4774) is available for welding AM-350, but the AM-355 filler wire is usually preferred for this material because it gives slightly higher weld strengths after PWHT. The AM-355 filler wire can also be used with a proprietary flux for SAW. AM-355 covered electrodes have been developed for SMAW but may not be readily available.

Postweld Heat Treatment. Joint efficiencies of 90 to 100% can be obtained by PWHT of AM-350 and AM-355 welds. The PWHT for welds in AM-350 consists of annealing at 930 °C (1710 °F) (condition L) and cooling rapidly to room temperature, followed by subzero cooling to –75

°C (–100 °F) and tempering at 455 or 540 °C (850 or 1000 °F) (condition SCT).

Unlike AM-350, AM-355 must have a suitably prepared microstructure prior to the condition L treatment in order to minimize intergranular precipitation during this treatment. The required microstructure is produced by a prior heat treatment that involves carbide solution annealing for 1 to 3 h at 1040 °C (1900 °F), cooling rapidly enough to room temperature to avoid intergranular carbide precipitation in the temperature range 870 to 650 °C (1600 to 1200 °F), and subzero cooling to –75 °C (–100 °F). The subzero cooling causes a partial transformation to martensite, and during subsequent heat treatments in the carbide precipitation range, carbides precipitate in the former martensitic areas in preference to the grain boundaries. After this treatment, AM-355 weldments are annealed at 915 to 970 °C (1675 to 1775 °F), subzero cooled to –75 °C (–100 °F), and tempered at 455 or 540 °C (850 or 1000 °F) (condition SCT).

Resistance Welding. AM-350 and AM-355 can be spot welded either before or after the hardening treatment using conditions similar to those for standard austenitic stainless steels. Postweld heat treatments (for example, condition SCT) produce a moderate increase in tensile shear strength but also a corresponding decrease in

cross-tension strength. Consequently, the best combination of tensile shear and cross-tension strength is obtained by welding in the hardened condition and not by PWHT.

Welding A-286 Austenitic PH Stainless Steel

Weldability. A-286 stainless steel is highly alloyed, and because welds solidify entirely as austenite (Fig. 73d), they are susceptible to hot cracking in both the fusion zone and HAZ. Solidification cracking in the fusion zone results from the formation of a low-melting-point Laves-phase eutectic at the grain boundaries, which is produced by the segregation of titanium and other solutes during the last stages of solidification. This phase is enriched in titanium, nickel, silicon, and molybdenum and depleted in iron and chromium.

The same phase is also responsible for HAZ cracking. However, in the HAZ, the Laves-phase eutectic is formed by the constitutional liquation of (Ti,Mo)(C,N) inclusions. Constitutional liquation is a result of the rapid, nonequilibrium heating conditions typical of arc welding, which cause the carbonitrides to decompose more rapidly than their constituent elements can diffuse into the matrix. The result is the formation of solute-rich zones of eutectic composition (and hence low melting point) around the decomposing carbonitrides. This liquid then wets the grain boundaries, and the grains are pulled apart by shrinkage stresses as the weld cools. Of the residual elements normally present in A-286, silicon and boron have been found to have the greatest effect on hot cracking in both the fusion zone and HAZ.

The ease with which crack-free arc welds can be produced in A-286 depends on the grade of material, weld section thickness, amount of restraint, welding process and procedure used, and choice

Table 23 Tensile properties of welds in austenitic precipitation-hardening steels

Thickness mm	in.	Filler metal	Preweld condition(a)	Specimen(b)	Postweld heat treatment	Tensile strength MPa	ksi	0.2% yield strength MPa	ksi	Elongation, % in 25 mm (1 in.)	in 50 mm (2 in.)	Reduction in area, %	Comments	Ref
A-286 GTA Welds														
3.0	0.118	None	ST	BM	Aged 725 °C (1335 °F), 48 h	952	138	710	103	16	...	29	...	45
3.0	0.118	None	ST	W	Aged 725 °C (1335 °F), 48 h	850	123	659	96	8	...	35	No cracking	45
3.0	0.118	None	ST	BM	Aged 725 °C (1335 °F), 4 h + 650 °C (1200 °F), 5 h + 725 °C (1335 °F), 44 h	1020	148	777	113	20	...	28	...	45
3.0	0.118	None	ST	W	Aged 725 °C (1335 °F), 4 h + 650 °C (1200 °F), 5 h + 725 °C (1335 °F), 44 h	952	138	769	112	...	...	45	No cracking	45
35	1.38	A-286	ST	BM	ST 980 °C (1795 °F), 2 h + aged 725 °C (1335 °F), 16 h	1069	155	708	103	30	...	43	...	46
35	1.38	A-286	ST	W	None	724	105	611	89	15	...	34	...	46
35	1.38	A-286	ST	W	ST 980 °C (1795 °F), 2 h + aged 725 °C (1335 °F), 16 h	1033	150	665	96	31	...	48	Scattered microfissures in weld metal	46
A-286 EB Welds														
3.2	0.125	None	ST	BM	Aged 730 °C (1350 °F), 16 h	1047	152	793	115	...	23.0	...	...	47
3.2	0.125	None	ST	W	Aged 730 °C (1350 °F), 16 h	919	133	775	112	...	5.6	...	Microfissures in HAZ	47
3.2	0.125	None	ST + Aged	W	Reaged 730 °C (1350 °F), 16 h	889	130	...	...	...	9.4	...	Microfissures in HAZ	47
JBK-75 GTA Welds														
3.2	0.125	None	ST	BM	Aged 725 °C (1335 °F), 24 h	1130(c)	164(c)	...	...	...	...	...	...	52
3.2	0.125	None	ST	W	Aged 725 °C (1335 °F), 24 h	800(c)	116(c)	...	...	...	...	...	No cracking	52
3.2	0.125	None	ST	BM	Aged 725 °C (1335 °F), 24 h + 650 °C (1200 °F), 24 h	1215	176	965	140	17	...	41	...	52
3.2	0.125	None	ST	W	Aged 725 °C (1335 °F), 24 h + 650 °C (1200 °F), 24 h	945	137	841	122	4	...	26	No cracking	52
3.2	0.125	None	ST	BM	ST 950 °C (1740 °F) 24 h + 725 °C (1335 °F), 24 h	980(c)	142(c)	...	...	...	...	...	...	52
3.2	0.125	None	ST	W	ST 950 °C (1335 °F), 24 h + 650 °C (1200 °F), 24 h	980(c)	142(c)	...	...	...	...	...	No cracking	52

(a) ST = solution treated. (b) Transverse tensile specimens: BM, base metal; W, weldment. (c) Estimated from hardness

of filler metal. Both regular and welding grades of A-286 are produced. The welding grades (AMS 5858 and AMS 5895) have lower limits on manganese, silicon, sulfur, and phosphorus than the regular grades and exhibit greater resistance to hot cracking. Whenever possible, they should be specified in preference to the regular grades for applications that involve welding. Although A-286 is classified as a difficult-to-weld material, it can be joined successfully by GTAW, EBW, and resistance welding if the correct procedures are used.

Gas-Tungsten Arc Welding. When gas-tungsten arc welding A-286, the best results are obtained with the base metal in the solution-treated condition, low heat inputs, and minimum restraint. Autogenous crack-free gas-tungsten arc welds can be produced in thin sheet, but welds in thick sheet and plate require filler metal. A stringer-bead technique should be used for multipass welds in heavy sections.

The choice of filler metal depends on the application. The regular A-286 filler wires (AMS 5804) have lower limits on sulfur and phosphorus contents but are otherwise similar in composition to the base metal. Deposits made with these wires are the most prone to hot cracking, so they have been used primarily for single-pass welds. Premium quality A-286 filler wires (AMS 5805) with lower carbon, manganese, silicon, phosphorus, and boron contents and limits on oxygen, nitrogen, and hydrogen levels are also available. These wires are produced from vacuum-induction-melted material by wire rolling instead of drawing. They produce high-purity deposits that are less susceptible to hot cracking than those made using the regular filler wires and are used for critical applications such as jet engine repairs.

Dissimilar-metal filler wires are the usual choice for multipass welds if a matching filler metal is not essential, because they exhibit greater resistance to hot cracking than A-286 weld metal. Hastelloy W has been used extensively for joining A-286. It has excellent resistance to hot cracking, but its stress-rupture strength is substantially lower than that of A-286 weld metal and it is not suitable for many high-temperature environments. Type 310 filler metal has been used for joining A-286 plate. It has very good corrosion resistance in many media but is nonhardening. AMS 5675 (AWS A5.14 Class ERNiCrFe-6) filler metal is significantly less crack sensitive than A-286 and is age hardenable, but it does not quite match the strength of A-286.

Postweld Heat Treatment. Typical tensile properties of welds in A-286 are presented in Table 23. A-286 weld metal does not age harden as rapidly or to the same extent as the base metal. A PWHT of 725 °C (1335 °F) for 48 h is required to increase the yield and ultimate tensile strengths to 93% and 89%, respectively, of the base metal values (Ref 124). However, aging is much more rapid if the weld is first solution treated. For example, solution treating at 1080 °C (1975 °F) for 2 h and aging at 725 °C (1335 °F) for 16 h increases the yield and ultimate tensile strengths to 94% and 97%, respectively, of the base metal values. If a high-temperature solution treatment is not feasible, weld strength can be increased by using a low-temperature multistep heat treatment consisting of 4 h at 725 °C (1335 °F) plus 5 h at 650 °C (1202 °F) plus 44 h at 725 °C (1335 °F) (Ref 124). This heat treatment raises the yield and ultimate tensile strengths to 99% and 93%, respectively, of the base metal values.

Electron-Beam Welding. Although EBW is a low-heat input process compared to arc welding, its use does not guarantee freedom from hot cracking. However, crack-free electron-beam welds can be made in A-286 if heat input, welding speed, and restraint are low. A-286 can be electron-beam welded in both the solution-treated and hardened conditions. Resistance to hot cracking is greater in the solution-treated condition.

Electron-beam welds in A-286 are usually made without filler metal. In the as-welded condition, weld strength is about the same as for gas-tungsten arc welds in the same condition, but postweld aging is more effective in increasing weld strength than for gas-tungsten arc welds in A-286. For example, electron-beam welds made in 3.2 mm (0.128 in.) thick A-286 in the solution-treated condition have yield and ultimate tensile strengths of 98% and 88%, respectively, of the base metal values after aging at 720 °C (1330 °F) for 16 h (Ref 125).

Resistance Welding. A-286 stainless steel can be joined by resistance spot and seam welding in both the soft and hardened conditions, but the welds, as with those made by other fusion welding processes, are susceptible to hot cracking. However, some hot cracking can be tolerated in spot and seam welds, because cracking of up to 5 vol% of the weld nugget has little effect on static or cyclic weld strength if it is concentrated at the center of the weld nugget (Ref 126). Hot cracking can be reduced or eliminated by using electrode forces significantly higher than those used for the standard austenitic stainless steels. Welding conditions that slow down the cooling rate (for example, downsloping the weld current) have also been recommended as a means of eliminating cracking (Ref 126). Limited data suggest that longer weld times and lower weld currents than those used for standard austenitic stainless steels may also be beneficial.

Spot welds made in hardened material without PWHT have the best combination of shear and cross-tension strengths. For problems of hot cracking in seam welds in A-286, limited data indicate that the best results are obtained with a lower wheel speed, lower weld current, and longer on-plus-off time than are generally used for the standard austenitic stainless steels. Increased electrode force and continuous (rather than interrupted) weld current may also be used to prevent cracking (Ref 127).

Little information is available on conditions for flash butt welding of A-286, because these conditions vary from machine to machine and from application to application. However, A-286 is routinely joined by flash butt welding with excellent results. After postweld aging at 720 °C (1325 °F), weld properties are virtually equal to those of the base metal (Ref 128).

Welding JBK-75 Austenitic PH Stainless Steel

JBK-75 is a modification of A-286 with the low carbon, manganese, silicon, and boron contents of welding-grade A-286 plus a higher nickel content. The beneficial effect of the higher nickel content is explained by the concept of shrinkage brittleness (Ref 129). According to this concept, during the last stages of solidification, a minimum amount of eutectic liquid is required to fill all the dendritic fissures formed by the eutectic films. If a critical, subminimum amount of eutectic forms, severe cracking occurs. On the other hand, if only a very small amount of eutectic forms, no cracking occurs because enough solid boundaries are present to withstand the shrinkage stresses. Therefore, the beneficial effect of the high nickel content of JBK-75 is due to its increasing the amount of eutectic formed so that any microfissures that nucleate are self-healing. Consequently, JBK-75 has greater resistance to hot cracking than A-286 and can be gas-tungsten arc welded in heavier sections without cracking.

Mechanical properties of gas-tungsten arc welds in JBK-75 are presented in Table 23. Hardness measurements indicate that the weld ultimate tensile strength is only about 70% of the base metal value after postweld aging at 725 °C (1335 °F) for 24 h (Ref 130). Higher weld metal and base metal strengths and a joint efficiency, based on the ultimate tensile strength, of about 78% are ob-

tained by a double aging treatment consisting of 24 h at 72.5 °C (1335 °F) plus 24 h at 650 °C (1200 °F). Homogenizing at 950 °C (1740 °F) before aging also increases weld metal strength but simultaneously reduces the strength of the base metal. For example, a heat treatment consisting of 950 °C (1740 °F) for 24 h plus 725 °C (1335 °F) for 24 h produces a hardness of 30 HRC, which is equivalent to an ultimate tensile strength of about 965 MPa (140 ksi) in both the weld and base metal.

Welding Cast Stainless Steels

The development of casting technology has been driven by two distinct engineering perspectives. The first involves the potential economy of cast hardware relative to totally machined wrought parts. Complex, near-net shapes can be produced by a variety of casting processes, including sand casting, investment casting, and centrifugal casting (used almost exclusively for making tubular products). Casting also can be an extremely effective way of producing very large parts.

The second perspective is associated with metallurgical realities. Many alloys have been developed for which there are no true wrought counterparts. The chemical composition and microstructure of these alloys are such that deformation processing of large ingots into wrought product forms would be problematic. In addition, the very nature of the cast microstructure, which in general is composed of large grains, can provide benefits in high-temperature creep applications.

Unlike the case of wrought alloy designators, cast stainless steels are not grouped according to microstructural types, but by the intended service environment. The general classification of stainless steel castings places these alloys in one of two categories: corrosion-resistant alloys and heat-resistant alloys. The corrosion-resistant alloys have been designed primarily for service environments involving aqueous or liquid-vapor corrosives at temperatures of generally less than 315 °C (600 °F). Use at extended temperatures up to 650 °C (1200 °F) in selected environments may also be considered.

The heat-resistant alloys have been designed for use in service environments exceeding 650 °C (1200 °F) where aqueous corrosives do not exist. At these elevated temperatures, oxidation, sulfidation, and carburization/decarburization are the environmental effects of consequence. High-temperature mechanical strength, creep and stress-rupture resistance, and microstructural stability are the engineering requirements for these alloys. The high-temperature alloys are most readily distinguished from the corrosion-resistant alloys on the basis of carbon content (although other alloying elements may also vary considerably in response to service needs), with the high-temperature alloys containing 0.20 to 0.70 wt% C and the corrosion-resistant alloys generally containing less than 0.20 wt% C. Detailed information on the compositions, microstructures, properties, and applications of cast stainless steels can be found in the articles "Metallurgy and Properties of Cast Stainless Steels" and "Corrosion of Cast Stainless Steels" in this Volume.

Welding and Weldability of Cast Stainless Steels

Welding and Welding Processes. In general terms, there are two situations in which welding of stainless steel castings is required. One of these occurs before the casting ever leaves the foundry. Casting defects, such as hot tears, shrinkage cavities, and cold shuts, are often observed in stainless steel castings. Certain specifications preclude the acceptance of these castings for service use without repair. Fusion welding is an appropriate method for repair of these casting defects. The defects, identified through one of several possible procedures (for example, dye penetrant, radiography, or ultrasonic inspection), are removed by machining or grinding, leaving a clean joint surface onto which weld filler metal is added to produce a sound final product. For small, near-surface defects, autogenous welds (that is, no filler metal added) may be sufficient to eliminate the defects. A special case of repair welding is known by the term "upgrading." An "upgraded" casting is one that has been selectively welded in order to achieve a higher level of product specification acceptance.

The second situation requiring welding involves joining of the casting to other hardware, cast or wrought, as part of an engineering design. In this circumstance, the design rules for welding are similar to those for wrought alloys. Any of the fusion welding processes can be successfully employed in the welding of castings. Most common are the arc welding processes, especially autogenous and filler-metal-added GTAW, SMAW, and GMAW. Fabrication involving the use of extremely large castings may employ electroslag welding as the only reasonable economic choice. Other processes, such as EBW, LBW, and PAW, are also appropriate choices in many instances. A wide range of filler metals exist for joining of the various casting alloys. The choice depends on the specifics of the situation and on whether the weld will be to a similar or dissimilar alloy. The use of matching filler metal is generally suggested when welding like alloys. Where a matching consumable is not available, common choices are 308L and 316L for the low-nickel-content corrosion-resistant austenitic alloys. For the higher-nickel-content corrosion-resistant and heat-resistant alloys, appropriate choices may be consumables (bare electrodes for GTAW and GMAW) such as 20Cb-3 (AWS ER320/ER320LR) and nickel alloys such as C-276 (AWS ERNiCrMo-4), Alloy 625 (ERNiCrMo-3), and Inconel alloys 82 (AWS ERNiCr-3), 92 (AWS ERNiCrFe-6), and 182 (AWS ERNiCrFe-3).

Metallurgical Considerations. Castings are metallurgically more complex than wrought alloys. Segregation during dendritic solidification can lead to local variations in both chemical composition and microstructure. The vast majority of the heat-resistant alloys will terminate solidification with the formation of a eutectic-like carbide constituent that remains upon cooling of the casting to room temperature. This microstructural constituent helps to augment the creep resistance

Table 24 Compositions of alloys in CF-8M weldability study

Heat No.	Composition, wt%(a)									Ferrite, vol%
	C	Mn	Si	Cr	Ni	Mo	S	P	N	
1	0.08	0.60	1.05	18.32	13.20	2.26	0.016	0.035	0.041	0.17
2	0.06	0.44	1.08	21.10	9.55	2.52	0.008	0.021	0.048	22.8
3	0.05	0.26	0.83	17.65	12.03	2.05	0.017	0.021	0.06	1.48
4	0.06	1.17	0.60	18.18	12.08	2.48	0.016	0.027	0.05	4.16
5	0.07	0.57	0.99	18.21	9.57	2.39	0.019	0.024	0.06	7.60
6	0.04	0.21	0.38	19.55	15.38	2.88	0.025	0.036	0.04	2.00
7	0.10	0.30	0.69	21.31	10.62	2.34	0.032	0.046	0.05	14.24

(a) The balance is iron. Source: Ref 134

of this group of alloys. Subsequent heat treatment of these alloys is not common.

Many of the lower-nickel-content corrosion-resistant alloys (for example, CF-3, CF-8M, and CB-7Cu) have a duplex microstructure consisting of ferrite islands in a matrix of either austenite or martensite. Postcasting solution heat treatments used to prepare corrosion-resistant alloys for service are insufficient to homogenize the microstructure. The inhomogeneous microstructure of both groups of alloys will tend to promote relatively wide areas of partial melting adjacent to the fusion zone when compared with similar wrought alloys.

Martensitic Stainless Steel Castings. Special considerations exist for the welding of martensitic stainless steel castings (CA-6NM, CA-5, CA-40, CB-7Cu-1, and CB-7Cu-2). Quench cracking and a marked reduction in mechanical properties (especially ductility and impact toughness) may result from the welding of these alloys. Corrosion resistance may also be detrimentally affected by the thermal cycle that the material undergoes in the fusion zone and HAZ of welds.

Suggested welding practice often calls for the reheating and postheating of most of the martensitic alloys. Alloys CA-15 and CA-40 require reheating temperatures in the range of 200 to 315 °C (390 to 600 °F) and a PWHT temperature range of 610 to 760 °C (1130 to 1400 °F). Alloy CA-6NM requires a preheat temperature range of 100 to 150 °C (210 to 300 °F) and a PWHT temperature range of 590 to 620 °C (1095 to 1150 °F). The higher preheating temperatures should be used when welding thicker sections and higher carbon compositions of these alloys.

The PWHT for these alloys is a tempering operation intended to restore ductility and toughness at the expense of strength and hardness. Because of the broad range of potential tempering temperatures, a wide range of PWHT properties are possible.

Alloy CB-7Cu (1 and 2) has no suggested preheat temperature, but a range (480 to 590 °C, or 895 to 1095 °F) of PWHT temperatures is recommended. In the case of this alloy, the PWHT is an aging operation. In order to recover properties in the welded product, a full solution anneal (1040 °C, or 1095 °F, oil quench), followed by aging, is required. Direct aging without solution annealing will not fully restore preweld properties. The higher aging temperatures result in the lowest strength but also provide the highest ductility and toughness.

Welding Defects. The two most serious problems encountered in the welding of stainless steel castings, either during the repair of casting defects or for subsequent attachment to other structures, are solidification hot cracking and HAZ hot cracking. Figure 76 shows a prototypical hot crack extending both into the fusion zone and the HAZ of a casting alloy. Both of these phenomena involve separation of grain boundaries due to the presence of a wetting liquid phase and sufficient mechanical imposition.

Studies (Ref 131-135) have indicated that wholly austenitic stainless steel casting alloys are more susceptible to the formation of these types of defects than are duplex ferrite-plus-austenite alloys. In particular, Cieslak and Savage (Ref 133, 134) and Cadden (Ref 135) have shown that CF-8M alloys (being prototypical of a wide range of low-nickel corrosion-resistant casting alloys) having welds that solidify with ferrite as the primary solidification phase are much more resistant to hot cracking than are alloys that solidify with austenite as the primary solidification phase.

Table 24 lists the chemical compositions and ferrite content of a series of CF-8M castings used in a study of weldability (Ref 134). Figure 77 shows the fusion-zone hot-cracking susceptibility of these alloys determined using the varestraint test at $^1/_2$% applied strain. The alloys that solidified as primary austenite (γ) were more susceptible to cracking than those that solidified as primary ferrite (δ). With the exception of heat number 7, the primary ferrite alloys did not experience any cracking under this set of experimental conditions. The high levels of sulfur (0.032 wt%) and phosphorus (0.046 wt%) were identified as being responsible for the greater cracking sensitivity in heat number 7. This particular observation was important for establishing that ferrite content alone was not a sufficient criterion to preclude the possibility of hot cracking in duplex alloys.

In the same investigation, the hot-cracking sensitivity of the heat-resistant alloy HK-40 was also examined. This alloy solidifies as primary austenite and terminates solidification with a eutectic-like Cr_7C_3 carbide constituent. This is prototypical solidification behavior of a wide range of heat-resistant stainless steel casting alloys. It was found that cracking was exacerbated by low carbon content (0.38 wt%) and by high levels of combined sulfur and phosphorus (>0.026 wt%). Silicon addition also had a detrimental effect on cracking susceptibility when carbon content was low or when sulfur or phosphorus contents were

high. It was observed that hot cracks could be "healed" by the carbide eutectic-like constituent, suggesting that higher carbon contents in alloys of this type could be helpful in minimizing this type of defect. Similar results have been found for 16Cr-35Ni (HT type) (Ref 136) and high-carbon-content alloys such as 25Cr-20Ni (the cast equivalent of wrought type 310 containing up to 0.2 wt% C) (Ref 137).

A study of the weldability of alloy CN-7M identified sulfur, phosphorus, and silicon as being detrimental to the hot-cracking resistance of this high-nickel-content (29 wt% Ni) corrosion-resistant alloy (Ref 138). Specifically, silicon was found to promote the formation of an M_6C carbide eutectic-like constituent associated with intergranular hot-cracked regions. For a discussion of the hot-cracking susceptibility of a wide range of corrosion-resistant and heat-resistant casting alloys, along with microstructural analysis of the cracking behavior, a review of the work of Cadden (Ref 135) is suggested.

In many studies examining both the fusion zone and HAZ hot-cracking behavior of stainless steel casting alloys, the presence of sulfur and phosphorus has universally been identified with increased cracking susceptibility. To a somewhat lesser extent, so have silicon and niobium. Carbon can also be detrimental, although not all studies have reached the same conclusion. It can be said that if there is sufficient carbon present to result in the formation of terminal-stage, eutectic-like constituents, then the hot-cracking susceptibility will

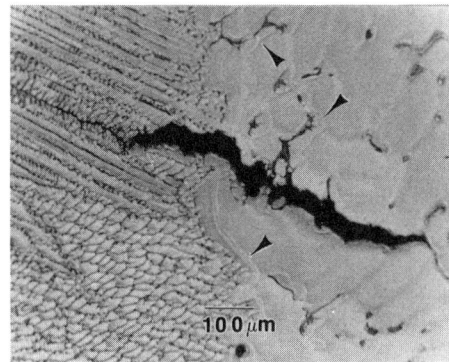

Fig. 76 Optical micrograph of the fusion-line region in a cast corrosion-resistant austenitic stainless steel. Note the hot crack extending both into the fusion zone (left) and back into the partially melted region of the heat-affected zone. Arrows indicate regions of partial melting.

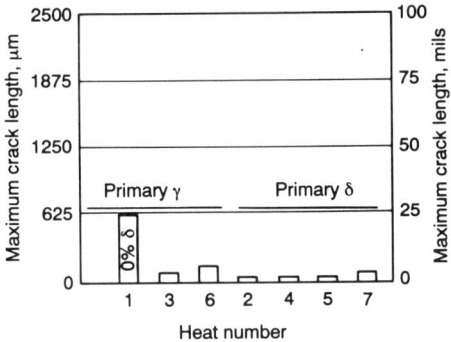

Fig. 77 Varestraint test results on several heats of CF-8M corrosion-resistant alloy. Tests were run at ½% augmented strain using an energy input of approximately 2.7 kJ/mm (69 kJ/in.). See Table 24 for heat number chemical compositions.

increase up to the point where the level of carbon promotes eutectic healing. Eutectic healing may eliminate the hot-cracking problem, but the reduction in ductility with increasing carbon content can limit the utility of the weld joint for an engineering application (Ref 136).

Each of these elements appears to increase cracking susceptibility in two possible ways. The first is by promoting the formation of low-melting-point constituents, and the second is by acting as a surfactant that promotes wetting of solidifying grain boundaries. Either phenomenon will promote an increased tendency toward fusion-zone or HAZ hot cracking.

A specific concern in the welding of corrosion-resistant stainless steel castings is the production of a sensitized microstructure. Sensitization occurs in stainless steel alloys when chromium-rich phases—$M_{23}C_6$ carbides, σ-phase, χ-phase, and Laves phase—precipitate during exposure to temperatures between 400 and 900 °C (750 and 1650 °F). The precipitation of these constituents can result in a local depletion of chromium (and also molybdenum), lowering the corrosion resistance to a point where corrosion-induced failure of the casting can result. Primary among the phases of concern is the $M_{23}C_6$ carbide (with M being primarily chromium). Precipitation of carbides at grain boundaries can occur during the fusion welding cycle at sites in both the HAZ and the fusion zone. Because the kinetics of precipitation are proportional to the carbon concentration, low-carbon grades (such as CF-3 or CF-3M) have been developed that can experience welding without producing a sensitized microstructure.

A final metallurgical consideration involves the welding of castings that have seen extended service at relatively high temperatures. For a variety of reasons, castings may have to be rewelded sometime during their service lifetime. This can pose a difficult problem if the temperature environment has modified the alloy microstructure so that additional constituents are present that adversely affect alloy ductility. It is always preferable to heat treat the casting to remove these unwanted microstructural features. This process may require solutionizing at temperatures above 1000 °C (1830 °F) and may be impractical for large castings. If solution heat treatment is not an option, then special care must be taken to ensure that the new weld joint design will have the lowest possible level of inherent restraint.

Weld Parameters. From an understanding of the metallurgical behavior of stainless steel casting alloys given above, general rules for fusion welding can be inferred. Low-heat-input processes are almost universally suggested. For alloys that are far from homogeneous, a high-heat-input process would produce flatter thermal gradients outside the fusion zone, creating a wider zone of partial melting and a greater microstructural sensitivity to HAZ hot cracking. The greater total shrinkage strain associated with the solidification of a large (high-energy-input) weld can create a restraint situation more likely to result in fusion-zone solidification cracking. The flatter thermal gradients of higher-energy-input welds reduce the cooling rates through the carbide precipitation temperature range, resulting in a higher likelihood of a sensitized structure in the corrosion-resistant alloys.

For the same reasons, low interpass temperatures are generally employed in the welding of these alloys. Interpass temperatures below 200 °C (400 °F) are common. For critical applications (especially among corrosion-resistant alloys), interpass temperatures of less than 150 °C (300 °F) are often specified. Spraying castings with water between passes is not uncommon for the austenitic corrosion-resistant alloys.

Preheating of castings prior to welding is almost never required and is generally not suggested, at least for the corrosion-resistant alloys, because the sensitization impact of such processing is similar to the use of high-energy-input welding parameters. In the case of heat-resistant alloy castings, preheating can be used to reduce the magnitude of thermal shrinkage strains, but again this benefit comes at the expense of a wider zone of partial melting. There is no known formula for preheating temperature and welding parameters for a given alloy that can ensure the preclusion of welding defects. Because of this technological limitation, the use of preheating prior to welding of these alloys is questionable.

Postweld solutionizing of corrosion-resistant alloys is always recommended. For the heat-treatable alloys (for example, CB-7Cu), a complete solutionizing and aging heat treatment is recommended to re-establish baseline properties. Where PWHT is not possible, it is even more important to weld using low-heat-input parameters.

Where direct fusion welding is not appropriate, as in the case of an extremely hot-crack-sensitive casting, other approaches might prove useful. One option is to "butter" the area of the crack-sensitive casting to be joined, using a consumable of a less crack-sensitive material. This "buttering" involves surfacing the casting locally with a consumable before fabricating the actual weld joint. With no joint present during the buttering operation, the restraint on the solidifying surface pass and the underlying HAZ of the casting can be quite small, and defects (fusion-zone and HAZ hot cracks) may be avoided. This surfaced area can be built up slowly to a thickness where it can then be prepared as a joint for a subsequent welded attachment. As another option, an insert of a less hot-crack-sensitive alloy can be inertia or friction welded onto the mating surface of the hot-crack-sensitive casting. This insert can then be prepared for subsequent fusion welding to the required structure. These options are contingent on the availability of consumable materials that are acceptable in the service environment.

ACKNOWLEDGMENTS

The information in this article is largely taken from:

- D.J. Kotecki, Welding of Stainless Steels, *Welding, Brazing, and Soldering*, Vol 6, *ASM Handbook*, ASM International, 1993, p 677-707
- J.R. Davis, Selection of Wrought Martensitic Stainless Steels, *Welding, Brazing, and Soldering*, Vol 6, *ASM Handbook*, ASM International, 1993, p 432-442
- K.F. Krysiak et al., Selection of Wrought Ferritic Stainless Steels, *Welding, Brazing, and Soldering*, Vol 6, *ASM Handbook*, ASM International, 1993, p 443-455
- J.A. Brooks and J.C. Lippold, Selection of Wrought Austenitic Stainless Steels, *Welding, Brazing, and Soldering*, Vol 6, *ASM Handbook*, ASM International, 1993, p 456-470
- D.N. Noble, Selection of Wrought Duplex Stainless Steels, *Welding, Brazing, and Soldering*, Vol 6, *ASM Handbook*, ASM International, 1993, p 471-481
- B. Pollard, Selection of Wrought Precipitation-Hardening Stainless Steels, *Welding, Brazing, and Soldering*, Vol 6, *ASM Handbook*, ASM International, 1993, p 482-494
- M.J. Cieslak, Selection of Cast Stainless Steels, *Welding, Brazing, and Soldering*, Vol 6, *ASM Handbook*, ASM International, 1993, p 495-499

REFERENCES

1. A.L. Schaeffler, Constitution Diagram for Stainless Steel Weld Metal, *Met. Prog.*, Vol 56 (No. 11), 1949, p 680-680B
2. W.T. DeLong, Ferrite in Austenitic Stainless Steel Weld Metal, *Weld. J.*, Vol 53 (No. 7), 1974, p 273s-286s
3. T.A. Siewert, C.N. McCowan, and D.L. Olson, Ferrite Number Prediction to 100 FN in Stainless Steel Weld Metal, *Weld. J.*, Vol 67 (No. 12), 1988, p 289s-298s
4. C.N. McCowan, T.A. Siewert, and D.L. Olson, "Stainless Steel Weld Metal: Prediction of Ferrite Content," WRC Bulletin 342, Welding Research Council, 1989
5. F.B. Lake, "Effect of Cu on Stainless Steel Weld Metal Ferrite Content," paper presented at 1990 American Welding Society Annual Meeting
6. D.J. Kotecki and T.A. Siewert, WRC-1992 Constitution Diagram for Stainless Steel Weld Metals: A Modification of the WRC-1988 Diagram, *Weld. J.*, Vol 71 (No. 5), 1992, p 171s-178s

7. J.C. Lippold and W.F. Savage, Solidification of Austenitic Stainless Steel Weldments: Part III-The Effect of Solidification Behavior on Hot Cracking Susceptibility, *Weld. J.*, Vol 61 (No. 12), 1982, p 388s-396s

8. J.M. Gerken and D.J. Kotecki, "Stainless Steels," Publication No. M250, Lincoln Electric Co., 1990

9. Engineering Report PROD/ES533, Lincoln Electric Co., 1992

10. J.C. Lippold, Transformation and Tempering Behavior of 12Cr-1Mo-0.3V Martensitic Stainless Steel Weldments, *J. Nucl. Mater.*, Vol 103 and 104, 1981, p 1127-1132

11. J.C. Lippold, "Microstructural Characterization of Autogenous GTA Welds in a 12Cr-1Mo-0.3V Steel," SAND80-8236, Sandia National Laboratories, Oct 1980

12. J.C. Lippold, The Effect of Postweld Heat Treatment on the Microstructure and Properties of the Heat-Affected Zone in 12Cr-1Mo-0.3V (HT9) Weldments, *Proc. Topical Conf. on Ferritic Alloys for Use in Nuclear Energy Technologies*, TMS, 1984, p 497-506

13. J.Z. Briggs and T.D. Parker, *The Super 12% Cr Steels*, Climax Molybdenum Co., 1965

14. R. Fenn and M.F. Jordan, Microstructure of Weld Heat-Affected Zone in 12Cr-1Mo Steel, *Met. Technol.*, Vol 9 (No. 8), 1982, p 327-337

15. J.M. Devletian and W.E. Wood, Principles of Joining Metallurgy, *Metals Handbook*, 9th ed., Vol 6, American Society for Metals, 1983, p 21-49

16. R.D. Stout et al., *Weldability of Steels*, 3rd ed., Welding Research Council, 1978

17. D.N. Noble, "Review of Practices for Welding Type 410 Stainless Steel," Edison Welding Institute

18. T.G. Gooch, Welding Martensitic Stainless Steels, *Weld. Inst. Res. Bull.*, Vol 18, Dec 1977

19. "Carpenter Stainless Steels—Working Data," Carpenter Technology Corp., 1983

20. Engineering Report ES-489, Lincoln Electric Co., 1991

21. R.E. Clark and L.E. Wagner, Comparison of ER410 and ER410NiMo Gas Metal Arc Weld Metal, *Cast Metals for Structural and Pressure Containment Applications*, American Society of Mechanical Engineers, 1979, p 153-169

22. J.C. Lippold, Analysis of Welds in HT9, *Alloy Development for Irradiation Performance*, DOE/ER 0045-4, U.S. Department of Energy, 1981, p 126-139

23. G.J. Bruck, Dilution Control in Horizontal Laser Beam Welding of Dissimilar Metals, *The Changing Frontiers of Laser Materials Processing*, IFS Publications, 1987, p 149-159

24. K. Kussmaul et al., Mechanical Properties and Structure of Electron Beam Welds in Alloy Fe-0.2%C-12%Cr-1%Mo, *Weld. J.*, Vol 63 (No. 9), Sept 1984, p 267s-272s

25. A. Ishibashi et al., Studies on Friction Welding of Carbon and Alloy Steels (3rd Report: Adequate Welding Conditions for High Alloy Steels and Distributions of Alloy Elements Near Weld Interface), Paper No. 216, *Bull.*

Jpn. Soc. Mech. Eng., Vol 26, June 1983, p 1080-1087

26. G.B. Hunter and T.W. Eagar, Ductility of Stabilized Ferritic Stainless Steel Welds, *Met Trans. A*, Vol 11A (No. 2), Feb. 1980, p213-218

27. B. Pollard, Ductility of Ferritic Stainless Weld Metal, *Weld. J.*, Apr 1972, p 222s-230s

28. K.E. Dorschu, Weldability of a New Ferritic Stainless Steel, *Weld. J.*, Sept 1971

29. R.N. Wright, "The Toughness of Ferritic Stainless Steels," Materials Engineering Dept., Rensselaer Polytechnic Institute, 1979

30. D.H. Kah and D.W. Dickinson, Weldability of Ferritic Stainless Steel, *Weld. J.*, Aug 1981, p 135s-142s

31. K.F. Krysiak, Weldability of the New Generation of Ferritic Stainless Steels—Part I, Paper 92, presented at the National Association of Corrosion Engineers Conference (Toronto), 14-18 April 1975

32. K.F. Krysiak, Weldability of the New Generation of Ferritic Stainless Steels—Update, *Symposium on Ferritic Stainless Steels* (San Francisco), 23-24 May 1979

33. R. Lowrie, Welding E-Brite 26-1 to Other Alloys, *Weld. J.*, Nov 1973, p 500s-506s

34. Y. Okazaki, R. Todoroki, T. Sakamoto, and T. Zaizen, On the Properties of High-Purity 19 Cr-2 Mo Ferritic Stainless Steel Welds, Paper 118, presented at the National Association of Corrosion Engineers Conference (Toronto), 6-10 April 1981

35. J.M. Sawhill, Jr. and A.P. Bond, Ductility and Toughness of Stainless Steel Welds, *Weld. J.*, Vol 55 (No. 10), 1976, p 33s-41s

36. J.F. Grubb and S.D. Washko, The Effect of Niobium and Titanium Dual Stabilization on the Weldability of 11% Chromium Ferritic Stainless Steels, *Proc. Int. Conf. Stainless Steels* (Chiba, Japan), 10-13 June 1991, Iron and Steel Institute of Japan, p 1062-1068

37. J.F. Grubb, Ph.D. thesis, Rensselaer Polytechnic Institute, May 1982

38. U.S. Patent 5,081,334, "Improved Gas Shielding," 14 Jan 1992

39. K.F. Krysiak, Weldability of Ferritic Stainless Steels—An Overview, *Weld. J.*, April 1986

40. J.J. Demo, *Corrosion*, Vol 27 (No. 3), 1971, p 531

41. R.H. Hodges, *Corrosion*, Vol 27 (No. 3), 1971, p 119

42. R.H. Hodges, *Corrosion*, Vol 27 (No. 3), 1971, p 164

43. E. Baerlecken, W.A. Fischer, and K. Lorenz, Untersuchungen über das Umwandlungsverhalten, die Kerbschlagzhigkeit und die Neigung zur interkristallinen Korrosion von Eisen-Chrom-Legierungen mit Chromgehalten bis 30% [Inquiry into the Transformation, Notched Impact Toughness, and the Susceptibility toward Intercrystalline Corrosion of Iron-Chromium Alloys with Chromium Contents up to 30%], *Stahl Eisen*, Vol 81 (No. 12), June 1961, p 768-778

44. G. Herbsleb and W. Schewenk, *Werkst. Korros.*, Vol 19, 1968, p 103

45. J.J. Demo and A.P. Bond, Intergranular Corrosion and Embrittlement of Ferritic Stainless Steels, Vol 31 (No. 1), Jan 1975, p 21-22

46. J.J. Demo, *Metall. Trans.*, Vol 5 (No. 11), Nov 1974, p 2253

47. M. Semchyshen, A.P. Bond, and J.H. Dundas, *Proc. Symp. Toward Improving Ductility and Toughness* (Kyoto, Japan), 1971, p 239

48. B. Pollard, *Met. Technol.*, Vol 1, Part 1, Jan 1974, p 31

49. J. Hochmann, "The Influence of Vacuum Fusion on the Properties of 25% Cr Ferritic Steels," Ph.D. thesis, Paris, 1950

50. W.A. Matejka and R.J. Knoth, E-Brite 26-1, The High-Purity Approach to High Chromium Ferritic Stainless Steels, *ASTM Symposium* (Bal Harbour, FL), ASTM, 6 Dec 1973

51. R.D. Campbell, Ferritic Stainless Steel Welding Metallurgy, *Key Engineering Materials*, Vol 69 and 70, Trans Tech Publications, Switzerland, 1992, p 167-216

52. H. Thier, *DVS-Ber.*, Vol 41, 1976, p 100-104

53. I. Matsumoto, K. Tamaki, and M. Matsuma, *J. Jpn. Weld. Soc.*, Vol 41 (No. 11), 1972, p 1306-1314

54. J.C. Lippold and W.F. Savage, *Weld. J.*, Vol 61, 1982, p 388s-396s

55. G.R. Speich, *Metals Handbook*, 8th ed., Vol 8, American Society for Metals, 1973, p 424

56. N. Suutala, T. Takalo, and T. Moisio, *Metall. Trans. A*, Vol 10A, 1979, p 512-514

57. J.A. Brooks, J.C. Williams, and A.W. Thompson, in *Trends in Welding Research*, S.A. David, Ed., American Society for Metals, 1982, p 331-355

58. S. Katayama and A. Matsunawa, *Proc. Int. Conf. on Advanced Laser Electro-Optics (ICALEO)* (San Francisco), 1985

59. J.A. Brooks, N.C.Y. Yang, and J.S. Krafcik, On the Origin of Ferrite Morphologies of Primary Ferrite Solidified Stainless Steel Welds, *Trends in Welding Research*, ASM International, 1993

60. J.W. Pugh and J.D. Nisbet, *Trans. TMS-AIME*, Vol 188, 1950, p 268-276

61. S.A. David, *Weld. J.*, Vol 60, 1981, p 63-s to 71-s

62. J.A. Brooks and A.W. Thompson, *Int. Mater. Rev.*, Vol 36 (No. 1), 1991, p 16-44

63. N. Suutala and T. Moisio, The Use of Chromium and Nickel Equivalents in Considering Solidification Phenomena in Austenitic Stainless Steels, *Solidification Technology in the Foundry and Casthouse*, The Metals Society preprint, 1980

64. T. Takalo, N. Suutala, and T. Moisio, *Metall. Trans. A*, Vol 10A, 1979, p 1173-1181

65. "Standard Procedures for Calibrating Magnetic Instruments to Measure the Delta Ferrite Content of Austenitic and Duplex Austenitic-Ferritic Steel Weld Metal," AWS 4.2-91, American Welding Society, 1991

66. R.H. Espy, *Weld. J.*, Vol 61, 1982, p 149-s to156-s

67. F.C. Hull, *Weld. J.*, Vol 46, 1967, p 399-s to 409-s

68. O. Hammer and U. Svennson, *Solidification and Casting of Metals*, The Metals Society, 1979, p 401-410

69. J.A. Brooks, M.I. Baskes, and F.A. Greulich, *Metall. Trans. A*, Vol 22A, 1991, p 915-925

70. J.W. Elmer, S.M. Allen, and T.W. Eagar, *Metall. Trans. A*, Vol 20A, 1989, p 2117-2131

71. G. Pacary, M. Moline, and J.C. Lippold, EWI Research Brief B9008, Edison Welding Institute, 1990

72. J.M. Vitek and S.A. David, *Weld. J.*, Vol 63, 1984, p 246s-253s

73. V. Cihal, *Prot. Met.* (Russia), Vol 4 (No. 6), 1968, p 653

74. C.J. Novak, Sensitization, *Handbook of Stainless Steels*, D. Peckner and I.M. Bernstein, Ed., McGraw-Hill, 1977, p 4-35 to 4-53

75. M.C. Juhas and B.E. Wilde, *Corrosion*, Vol 46, 1990, p 812-822

76. T.G. Gooch, Paper 296, *Proc. Corrosion '92* (Nashville), National Association of Corrosion Engineers, 1992

77. N.J. Simon and R.P. Reed, Strength and Toughness of AISI 304 and 316 at 4 K, "Materials Studies for Magnetic Fusion Energy Applications at Low Temperatures—X," NBSIR 86-3050, National Bureau of Standards, 1986

78. R.L. Tobler, T.A. Siewert, and H.I. McHenry, Strength-Toughness Relationship of Austenitic Stainless Steel Welds at 4 K, *Cryogenics*, Vol 26, 1986

79. C.N. McCowan, T.A. Siewert, and R.L. Tobler, Tensile and Fracture Properties of an Fe-18Cr-20Ni-5Mn-0.16N Fully Austenitic Weld Metal at 4 K, *J. Eng. Mater. Technol.*, Vol 108, 1986

80. T.A. Siewert and C.N. McCowan, The Fracture Toughness of 25Cr-22Ni-4Mn-2Mo Stainless Steel Welds at 4 K, "Materials Studies for Magnetic Fusion Energy Applications at Low Temperatures—XII," NISTIR 3931, National Institute of Standards and Technology, 1990

81. A.O. Kluken, C.N. McCowan, and T.A. Siewert, Effect of Inclusion Volume Fraction and Size Distribution on the Cryogenic Toughness of Austenitic Stainless Steel Weld Metals, submitted for publication in *Microstructural Science*, Vol 19, ASM International/International Metallographic Society, 1993

82. R.H. Espy, Weldability of 21-6-9 Stainless Steel (Armco Nitronic Stainless Steel), "Materials Studies for Magnetic Fusion Energy Applications at Low Temperatures—I," NBSIR 78-884, National Institute of Standards and Technology, 1978

83. D.J. Alexander and G.M. Goodwin, Thick-Section Weldments in 21-6-9 and 316LN Stainless Steel for Fusion Energy Applications, submitted to *J. Nucl. Mater.*, 1992

84. C.N. McCowan and T.A. Siewert, Fracture Toughness of 316L Stainless Steel Welds with Varying Inclusion Contents at 4 K, *Adv. Cryogenic Eng. (Mater.)*, Vol 34, 1989

85. H. Kim, B.W. Oh, J.G. Youn, G.-W. Bahng, and H.-M. Lee, Effect of Oxygen Content on Cryogenic Toughness of Austenitic Stainless Steel Weld Metal, *Adv. Cryogenic Eng. (Mater.)*, Vol 34, 1989

86. C.R. Heiple and J.R. Roper, *Weld. J.*, Vol 61, 1982, p 97s

87. C.L. Cole and J.D. Jones, Publication 117, Iron and Steel Institute, 1969, p 74

88. R.J. Brigham and E.W. Tozer, Effect of Alloying Additions on the Pitting Resistance of 18% Cr Austenitic Stainless Steel, *Corrosion*, Vol 30 (No. 5), May 1974, p 161-166

89. H. Hoffmeister and R. Mundt, *Arch. Eisenhutt.*, Vol 52 (No. 4), p 159-164

90. D.N. Noble and T.G. Gooch, The Effects of Heat Input and Chemical Composition on Microstructure in Arc Welded UNS S31803 Type Duplex Stainless Steels, *ASM Materials Week '87*, ASM International, Oct 1987

91. "Sandvik SAF 2507—A High Performance Duplex Stainless Steel," Sandvik Steel Trade Literature, Pamphlet S-1875-ENG, Sept 1987

92. A.W. Stephenson, P.C. Gough, and J.C.M. Farrar, "The Weldability of Super Duplex Alloys—Welding Consumables and Procedure Development for Zeron 100," *Proc. Int. Inst. Welding Annual Assembly Conf.*, July 1991

93. O. Jonsson, M. Liljas, and P. Stenvall, The Role of Nitrogen in Longitudinal Welding of Tubing in Duplex Stainless Steels, *Duplex Stainless Steels Conf. Proc.*, American Society for Metals, 1983, p 461-468

94. "Welding and Brazing Qualifications," 1989 Boiler and Pressure Vessel Code, Section IX, American Society of Mechanical Engineers

95. "Welding of Pipelines and Related Facilities," Standard 1104, American Petroleum Institute

96. "Specification for CRA Linepipe," Standard 5LC, American Petroleum Institute

97. "Standard Procedures for Calibrating Magnetic Instruments to Measure the Delta Ferrite Content of Austenitic Stainless Steel Weld Metals," AWS A4.2-74, American Welding Society

98. D.J. Kotecki, Extension of the WRC Ferrite Number System, *Weld. J.*, Nov 1982, p 352s-361s

99. "Testing for Pitting and Crevice Corrosion Resistance of Stainless Steels and Related Alloys by the Use of Ferric Chloride Solution," Standard G 48, Practice A, ASTM

100. R.A. Corbett, Problems in Utilizing ASTM G 48 to Evaluate High Alloy Stainless Steels, Paper 298, *Corrosion '92*, National Association of Corrosion Engineers, 1992

101. P. Sentance, The Brae Field, *Stainl. Steel Eur.*, Vol 4 (No. 20), Sept 1992, p 38-41

102. C.D. Lundin, K. Kikuchi, and K.K. Kahn, Phase I Report, "Measurement of Diffusible Hydrogen Content and Hydrogen Effects on the Cracking Potential of Duplex Stainless Steel Weldments," Welding Research Council, March 1991

103. R.A. Walker and T.G. Gooch, Hydrogen Cracking of Welds in Duplex Stainless Steel, *Corrosion*, Vol 47 (No. 8), Sept 1991, p 1053-1063

104. B. Larsson and B. Lundqvist, "Fabricating Ferritic-Austenitic Stainless Steels," Sandvik Steel Trade Literature, Pamphlet S-51-33-ENG, Oct 1987

105. J. Honeycombe and T.G. Gooch, *Weld. J.*, Vol 56 (No. 11), Nov 1977, p 339s-353s

106. I. Varol, W.A. Baeslack, and J.C. Lippold, *Metallography*, Vol 23 (No. 1), 1989

107. J.C. Lippold, W.A. Baeslack, and I. Varol, Welding of Duplex Stainless Steels, *Weld. J.*, in press

108. T.G. Gooch, Corrosion Resistance of Welds in Duplex Stainless Steels, *Duplex Stainless Steels Conf. Proc.*, American Society for Metals, 1983, p 325-346

109. L. Odegard and S.-A. Fager, The Root Side Pitting Corrosion Resistance of Stainless Steel Welds, *Sandvik Steel Weld. Rep.*, No. 1, 1990

110. R. Dolling, V. Neubert, and P. Knoll, The Corrosion Behaviour of Super Duplex Steel Cast Alloys with a PREN >41, *Duplex Stainless Steels Conf. Proc.*, Vol 2, Les Editions de Physique, Les Ulis Cedex, Oct 1991, p 1341-1351

111. P.C. Gough and J.C.M. Farrar, Factors Affecting Weld Root Run Corrosion Performance in Duplex and Super Duplex Pipework, *ASM Materials Week '87*, ASM International, Oct 1987, p 1009-1025

112. N. Suutala, Effect of Solidification Conditions on the Solidification Mode in Stainless Steels, *Metall. Trans. A*, Vol 14A, Feb 1983, p 191-197

113. B. Pollard, unpublished work

114. "Armco Fabricating Data," Bulletin SF-2, Armco, Inc., Feb 1966

115. C. Chen and J.S. Yeh, Electron Beam and Plasma Arc Welding of 17-4PH Stainless Steel, *Proc. Conf. Power Beam Processing: Electron, Laser, Plasma Arc* (San Diego), ASM International, 1988, p 45-54

116. A.J. Turner, Electron Beam Welding Thick Section Precipitation-Hardening Steel, *Weld. J.*, Vol 60, Jan 1981, p 18-26

117. M.U. Islam, G. Campbell, and R. Hsu, Fatigue and Tensile Properties of EB Welded 17-4PH Steel, *Weld. J.*, Vol 68, Sept 1989, p 45-50

118. A.J. Turner, Electron Beam Welding of High Volume Aircraft Components, *Proc. Conf. Fundamental and Practical Approaches to the Reliability of Welded Structures* (Osaka, Japan), Vol 1, Japan Welding Society, 1982, p 139-144

119. W.R. Cieslak, J.A. Brooks, and W.M. Garrison, Jr., The Weldability, Microstructure and Properties of Precipitation Strengthened Martensitic Stainless Steels, *Proc. Conf. Advances in Welding Science and Technology* (Gatlinburg, TN), ASM International, 1986

120. "Welding Carpenter Custom 450 Multiple Strength Stainless Steel," Product Data Bulletin, Carpenter Technology Corp., Jan 1973

121. "Armco Fabricating Data," Bulletin SF-5, Armco, Inc., Dec 1967

122. G.E. Linnert, Welding Precipitation-Hardening Stainless Steels, *Weld. J.*, Vol 36, Jan 1957, p 9-27

123. F.J. Hawkins, Welding of Age-Hardenable Stainless Steels, *Weld. Res. Counc. Bull.*, No. 103, Feb 1965

124. L.T. Summers, "Effect of Chemical Segregation on the Microstructure and Properties of A-286 Weldments," Ph.D. dissertation, University of California, Berkeley, 1984

125. R.E. Roth and N.F. Bratkovich, Characteristics and Strength Data of Electron Beam

Welds in Four Representative Materials, *Weld. J.*, Vol 41, May 1962, p 229s-240s

126. I.F. Squires, Determination of Resistance Spot Welding Conditions for Some Heat-Resisting Stainless Steels, *Br. Weld. J.*, Vol 9, March 1962, p 149-157

127. P.M. Knowlson, Determination of Resistance Seam Welding Conditions for Some Heat Resisting Steels, *Br. Weld. J.*, Vol 9, 1962, p 436-445

128. J.J. Vagi, R.M. Evans, and D.C. Martin, "Welding Precipitation-Hardening Stainless Steels," NASA Tech. Memo. X-53582, 28 Feb 1967

129. B.I. Medovar, On the Nature of Weld Hot Cracking, translated from *Avtom. Svarka*, Vol 7 (No. 4), 1954, p 12-28

130. M.J. Strum, L.T. Summers, and J.W. Morris, Jr., The Aging Response of a Welded Iron-Based Superalloy, *Weld. J.*, Vol 62, Sept 1983, p 235s-242s

131. H.S. Avery, Cast Heat-Resistant Alloys for High-Temperature Service, *Weld. Res. Counc. Bull.*, No. 143, Aug 1969

132. "The Welding of Cast Austenitic Steels," Welding Institute Report Series, The Welding Institute, Sept 1970, Phases 1-4

133. M.J. Cieslak and W.F. Savage, *Weld. J.*, May 1980, p 136-s to 146-s

134. M.J. Cieslak and W.F. Savage, "Weldability and Solidification Phenomena of Cast High Alloy Heat Resistant Alloy HK-40 and Corrosion Resistant 19Cr-9Ni-2.5Mo Steels," Report A-69, Steel Founders' Society of America, 1980

135. C.H. Cadden, "Weldability of High Alloy Castings," M.S. thesis, Rensselaer Polytechnic Institute, May 1981

136. D. Rozet, H.C. Campbell, and R.D. Thomas, *Weld. J.*, Oct 1949, p 481-s to 491-s

137. Y. Arata, F. Matsuda, and S. Katayama, *Trans. JWRI*, June 1977, p 105-116

138. M.J. Cieslak and W.F. Savage, *Weld. J.*, May 1985, p 119-s to 126-s

Brazing, Soldering, and Adhesive Bonding

STAINLESS STEELS can be joined by a wide variety of processes including welding, brazing, soldering, adhesive bonding, and mechanical fastening. Brazing, by definition, employs filler metal having a liquidus above 450 °C (840 °F) and below the solidus of the base metal. Brazing is distinguished from soldering by the melting point of the filler metal: solders melt below 450 °C (840 °F). Brazing differs from welding in that no substantial amount of the base metal is melted during brazing. Thus the temperatures for brazing stainless steel are intermediate between those for welding and soldering. Also, brazed stainless steel assemblies generally are between welded and soldered assemblies in terms of strength and resistance to corrosion.

Adhesive bonding is a materials joining process in which an adhesive (usually a thermosetting or thermoplastic resin) is placed between faying surfaces and solidifies to produce an adhesive bond. In terms of production cost, ability to accommodate manufacturing tolerances and component complexity, facility and tooling requirements, reliability, and repairability, adhesive bonding is very competitive when compared to other joining methods.

Brazing

Stainless steels as a group are not difficult to braze, but those alloys that also contain titanium or aluminum require additional precautions to prevent alloy oxidation during the brazing cycle. Excellent results can be obtained when standard wrought stainless steels are brazed.

The brazeability and weldability of these steels do vary with composition. The quality of brazed joints depends on the selection of the brazing process, process temperature, filler metal, and the type of protective atmosphere or flux that is used. These choices must be compatible with the intended performance of the brazed item.

Applicability

Brazing is often used to join stainless steels to a variety of dissimilar metals, such as carbon steels, low-alloy steels, and copper alloys, in combinations that would not otherwise weld satisfactorily. This capability is a principal advantage of the brazing process.

A wide variety of brazing filler-metal compositions are available to achieve compatibility, strength, corrosion resistance, and other desirable properties when joining dissimilar metals. When

the appropriate heating techniques are employed, brazing provides a means to obtain strong, corrosion-resistant, leak-tight joints in small or thin-wall components with minimal buckling or warpage. Brazing can also produce joints in delicate assemblies and in very thin-gage metals that would be difficult or impossible to obtain if conventional welding techniques were used. Brazing is also suitable for the mass production of small- and medium-sized assemblies on various types of continuous furnace equipment. Finally, brazing enables the production of joints in inaccessible locations by the preplacement of filler metal and the subsequent heating of the workpiece. Often, such joints cannot be made by other joining processes.

Brazeability

As a class, stainless steels are no more difficult to braze than carbon and low-alloy steels. The high quantities of chromium that are present in stainless steels cause the chromium oxide films that are found on the surfaces of all stainless steels, as well as the films of titanium oxide that form on the surfaces of titanium-stabilized stainless steels, such as type 321. If these oxides, which are both refractory and strongly adherent, are inadequately removed, they will prevent the molten filler metal from wetting the base metal, and thus will prevent a capillary joint from being formed between the metals being joined.

The formation of chromium oxide is accelerated when stainless steels are heated in air. Although the oxide may have been removed from the surface by chemical cleaning at room temperature, a new oxide layer that seriously interferes with wetting will rapidly form when the steel is heated in air to the brazing temperature. The adverse effect of oxides on wetting can be alleviated by:

- Chemically cleaning the surface oxide from the steel at room temperature, quickly followed by heating to the brazing temperature in a chemically inert gaseous atmosphere, such as argon
- Heating the steel directly to the brazing temperature in a strongly reducing atmosphere, such as hydrogen, after a less-intense cleaning, which chemically reduces the oxide and thereby promotes wetting action
- Coating the area at the joint with a chemically active flux that dissolves the oxide during heating to the brazing temperature
- Heating in a vacuum (after cleaning), which reduces many oxides, such as chromium oxide, and prevents the gross formation of other oxides

- Degreasing alone, if the proper flux or controlled atmosphere is used, prior to brazing stainless steels with clean surfaces, that is, without black or green oxide coatings
- Selecting lower-melting-point brazing filler metals to reduce oxidation potential

Inclusions and Surface Contaminants. When brazing stainless steel, base-metal inclusions and surface contaminants are even more deleterious than they are when brazing carbon steel. Base-metal inclusions, such as oxides, sulfides, and nitrides, interfere with the flow of filler metal. Flow is also impeded by surface contaminants, which may include lubricants, such as oil, graphite, and molybdenum disulfide, that are applied during machining, forming, and grinding. Other contaminants are the aluminum oxide particles that are produced either by grit blasting or by grinding with aluminum oxide wheels or belts.

Some filler-metal powders that are used in paste form with stainless steel contain organic binders. Acrylics and other plastics are often used for this purpose. Although some powders form a soot residue, it usually does not interfere with filler metal flow.

The brazing characteristics of stainless steel can also be seriously impaired by unsuitable fixturing materials, such as graphite, or by a protective atmosphere that contains nitrogen. Carbon in graphite fixtures unites with hydrogen to form methane (CH_4), which carburizes stainless steel and impairs its corrosion resistance. Dissociated ammonia will result in nitriding of the stainless steel, unless the ammonia is sufficiently dry and completely (100%) dissociated. Both carburizing and nitriding interfere with brazing quality.

Brazing Processes. Stainless steels can be brazed by all conventional brazing processes, including furnace, torch, induction, resistance, and salt-bath dip brazing. Furnace brazing is most widely used, because applications generally require brazing in protective atmospheres, including a vacuum. Most of the applications described in this article use furnace brazing. Detailed information on brazing processes can be found in Volume 6 of the *ASM Handbook*.

Brazing Filler Metal

Most stainless steels can be brazed with any one of several different filler-metal families, including silver, nickel, copper, and gold. In most applications, filler metals are selected on the basis of their mechanical properties, corrosion resistance, service temperature, and compatibility with the base metal. This selection leads to the required brazing temperature, based on service use or manufacturing sequence, and to the required heating method. Table 1 lists the composition requirements of the filler metals that are most commonly used to braze stainless steels. A complete list of brazing filler metals can be found in ANSI/AWS A5.8, which specifies filler metals for the brazing and braze welding processes.

Silver brazing filler metals, specifically the BAg group, are the most widely used type of filler metal in the brazing of stainless steels. The BAg-3 filler metal, which contains 3% Ni, is probably selected most frequently, although several other filler metals also can be used successfully. Silver brazing filler metals, especially those that contain zinc and cadmium, are primarily used in torch brazing where flux is applied, and they should not be considered for furnace brazing.

Joints brazed with silver-base filler metals cannot be used for high-temperature service applications. The recommended maximum service temperature is 370 °C (700 °F) (BAg-3). The recommended joint fitting allowances for silver brazing are relatively loose, that is, the diametral clearance is generally from 0.05 to 0.10 mm (0.002 to 0.004 in.).

Of the silver brazing filler metals shown in Table 1, all except BAg-19 and, possibly, BAg-13,

Table 1 Typical compositions and properties of standard brazing filler metals for brazing stainless steel

Brazing filler metal	Composition(a), %								Other elements total	Solidus temperature		Liquidus temperature		Brazing temperature range	
	Ag	Cu	Zn	Cd	Ni	Sn	Li	Mn		°C	°F	°C	°F	°C	°F
Silver															
BAg-1	44.0-46.0	14.0-16.0	14.0-18.0	23.0-25.0	...	...	...	...	0.15	610	1125	620	1145	620-760	1145-1400
BAg-1a	49.0-51.0	14.5-16.5	14.5-18.5	17.0-19.0	...	...	...	...	0.15	630	1160	635	1175	635-760	1175-1400
BAg-2	34.0-36.0	25.0-27.0	19.0-23.0	17.0-19.0	...	...	...	...	0.15	610	1125	700	1295	700-845	1295-1550
BAg-2a	29.0-31.0	26.0-28.0	21.0-25.0	19.0-21.0	...	...	...	...	0.15	610	1125	710	1310	710-845	1310-1550
BAg-3	49.0-51.0	14.5-16.5	13.5-17.5	15.0-17.0	2.5-3.5	...	...	...	0.15	630	1170	690	1270	690-815	1270-1500
BAg-4	39.0-41.0	29.0-31.0	26.0-30.0	...	1.5-2.5	...	...	...	0.15	670	1240	780	1435	780-900	1435-1650
BAg-5	44.0-46.0	29.0-31.0	23.0-27.0	...	...	...	...	...	0.15	680	1250	745	1370	745-845	1370-1550
BAg-6	49.0-51.0	33.0-35.0	14.0-18.0	...	...	...	...	...	0.15	690	1270	775	1425	775-870	1425-1600
BAg-7	55.0-57.0	21.0-23.0	15.0-19.0	...	...	4.5-5.5	...	...	0.15	620	1145	650	1205	650-760	1205-1400
BAg-8	71.0-73.0	bal	...	...	...	...	...	...	0.15	780	1435	780	1435	780-900	1435-1650
BAg-8a	71.0-73.0	bal	...	...	...	...	0.25-0.50	...	0.15	770	1410	765	1410	765-870	1410-1600
BAg-9	64.0-66.0	19.0-21.0	13.0-17.0	...	...	...	...	...	0.15	670	1240	720	1325	720-845	1325-1550
BAg-10	69.0-71.0	19.0-21.0	8.0-12.0	...	...	...	...	...	0.15	690	1275	740	1360	740-845	1360-1550
BAg-13	53.0-55.0	bal	4.0-6.0	...	0.5-1.5	...	...	...	0.15	720	1325	860	1575	860-970	1575-1775
BAg-13a	55.0-57.0	bal	...	...	1.5-2.5	...	...	...	0.15	770	1420	895	1640	870-980	1600-1800
BAg-18	59.0-61.0	bal	...	...	...	9.5-10.5	...	...	0.15	600	1115	720	1325	720-845	1325-1550
BAg-19	92.0-93.0	bal	...	...	...	...	0.15-0.30	...	0.15	760	1400	890	1635	875-980	1610-1800
BAg-20	29.0-31.0	37.0-39.0	30.0-34.0	...	...	...	...	...	0.15	680	1250	765	1410	765-870	1410-1600
BAg-21	62.0-64.0	27.5-29.5	...	...	2.0-3.0	5.0-7.0	...	...	0.15	690	1275	800	1475	800-900	1475-1650
BAg-22	48.0-50.0	15.0-17.0	21.0-25.0	...	4.0-5.0	...	...	7.0-8.0	0.15	680	1260	700	1290	700-830	1290-1525
BAg-23	84.0-86.0	...	...	...	...	...	...	Remainder	0.15	960	1760	970	1780	970-1040	1780-1900
BAg-24	49.0-51.0	19.0-21.0	26.0-30.0	...	1.5-2.5	...	...	...	0.15	660	1220	705	1305	710-843	1305-1550
BAg-25	19.0-21.0	39.0-41.0	33.0-37.0	...	...	...	4.5-5.5	...	0.15	740	1360	790	1455	790-846	1455-1555
BAg-26	24.0-26.0	37.0-39.0	31.0-35.0	...	1.5-2.5	...	1.5-2.5	...	0.15	710	1305	800	1475	800-870	1475-1600
BAg-27	24.0-26.0	34.0-36.0	24.5-28.5	12.5-14.5	...	...	...	...	0.15	610	1125	745	1375	745-860	1375-1575
BAg-28	39.0-41.0	29.0-31.0	26.0-30.0	...	...	1.5-2.5	...	...	0.15	650	1200	710	1310	710-845	1310-1550
BAg-33	24.0-26.0	29.0-31.0	26.5-28.5	16.5-18.5	...	...	...	...	0.15	610	1125	680	1260	680-760	1260-1400
BAg-34	37.0-39.0	31.0-33.0	26.0-30.0	...	...	1.5-2.5	...	...	0.15	650	1200	720	1330	720-845	1330-1550

Brazing filler metal	Composition(a), %				Other elements total	Solidus temperature		Liquidus temperature		Brazing temperature range	
	Cu	P	Pb	Al		°C	°F	°C	°F	°C	°F
Copper											
BCu-1	99.90(b)	0.075	0.02	0.01	0.10	1080	1981	1080	1981	1095-1150	2000-2100
BCu-1a	99.0(b)	...	...	...	0.30	1080	1981	1080	1981	1095-1150	2000-2100
BCu-2	86.5(b)	...	...	...	0.50	1080	1981	1080	1981	1095-1150	2000-2100 (continued)

Brazing filler metal	Composition(a), %														Other elements total	Solidus temperature		Liquidus temperature		Brazing temperature range	
	Cr	B	Si	Fe	C	P	S	Al	Ti	Mn	Cu	Zr	Ni		°C	°F	°C	°F	°C	°F
Nickel(c)																				
BNi-1	13.0-15.0	2.75-3.50	4.0-5.0	4.0-5.0	0.6-0.9	0.02	0.02	0.05	0.05	...	...	0.05	bal	0.50	975	1790	1035	1900	1065-1205	1950-2200
BNi-1a	13.0-15.0	2.75-3.50	4.0-5.0	4.0-5.0	0.06	0.02	0.02	0.05	0.05	...	...	0.05	bal	0.50	975	1790	1075	1970	1075-1205	1970-2200
BNi-2	6.0-8.0	2.75-3.50	4.0-5.0	2.5-3.5	0.06	0.02	0.02	0.05	0.05	...	...	0.05	bal	0.50	990	1780	1000	1830	1010-1175	1850-2150
BNi-3	...	2.75-3.50	4.0-5.0	0.5	0.06	0.02	0.02	0.05	0.05	...	...	0.05	bal	0.50	980	1800	1035	1900	1010-1175	1850-2150
BNi-4	...	1.5-2.2	3.0-4.0	1.5	0.06	0.02	0.02	0.05	0.05	...	...	0.05	bal	0.50	980	1800	1065	1950	1010-1175	1850-2150
BNi-5	18.5-19.5	0.03	9.75-10.50	...	0.10	0.02	0.02	0.05	0.05	...	...	0.05	bal	0.50	1080	1975	1135	2075	1150-1205	2100-2200
BNi-6	...	...	...	...	0.10	10.0-12.0	0.02	0.05	0.05	...	...	0.05	bal	0.50	880	1610	875	1610	925-1095	1700-2000
BNi-7	13.0-15.0	0.01	0.10	0.2	0.08	9.7-10.5	0.02	0.05	0.05	0.04	...	0.05	bal	0.50	890	1630	890	1630	925-1095	1700-2000
BNi-8	...	...	6.0-8.0	...	0.10	0.02	0.02	0.05	0.05	21.5-24.5	4.0-5.0	0.05	bal	0.50	980	1800	1010	1850	1010-1095	1850-2000
BNi-9	13.5-16.5	3.25-4.0	...	1.5	0.06	0.02	0.02	0.05	0.05	...	...	0.05	bal	0.50	1055	1930	1055	1930	1065-1205	1950-2200 (continued)

Table 1 (continued)

Brazing filler metal	Composition(a), %				Other elements total	Solidus temperature		Liquidus temperature		Brazing temperature range	
	Au	Cu	Pd	Ni		°C	°F	°C	°F	°C	°F
Precious metals											
BAu-1	37.0-38.0	Remainder	...	...	0.15	990	1815	1015	1860	1015-1095	1860-2000
BAu-2	79.5-80.5	Remainder	...	...	0.15	890	1635	890	1635	890-1010	1635-1850
BAu-3	34.5-35.5	Remainder	...	2.5-3.5	0.15	975	1785	1030	1885	1030-1090	1885-1995
BAu-4	81.5-82.5	Remainder	...	Remainder	0.15	950	1740	950	1740	950-1005	1740-1840
BAu-5	29.5-30.5	...	33.5-34.5	35.5-36.5	0.15	1135	2075	1165	2130	1165-1230	2130-2250
BAu-6	69.5-70.5	...	7.5-8.5	21.5-22.5	0.15	1010	1845	1045	1915	1045-1120	1915-2050

Brazing filler metal	Composition(a), %													Other elements total	Solidus temperature		Liquidus temperature		Brazing temperature range	
	Cr	B	Si	Fe	C	P	S	Al	Ti	Mn	Cu	Zr	Ni		°C	°F	°C	°F	°C	°F
Cobalt																				
BCo-1	18.0-20.0	16.0-18.0	7.5-8.5	3.5-4.5	1.0	0.7-0.9	0.35-0.45	0.02	0.02	0.05	0.05	0.05	Remainder	0.50	1120	2050	1150	2100	1150-1230	2100-2250

(a) Single values are maximum percentages, unles otherwise indicated. (b) Minimum. (c) All BNi alloys have a limit of 0.10 Co and 0.005 Se. Source: AWS A5.8-81, "Specification for Brazing Filler Metals"

are used at brazing temperatures that fall within the effective range of sensitizing temperatures (540 to 870 °C, or 1000 to 1600 °F) for austenitic stainless steels. Chromium carbide precipitation occurs in the sensitizing temperature range, which impairs the corrosion resistance of the base metal. Carbide precipitation, however, depends on time as well as temperature, and exposure to the sensitizing temperature range for only a few minutes is unlikely to result in a significant amount of precipitate. Nevertheless, the lower melting temperatures of the silver brazing filler metals prohibit the resolution treatment of the base metal after brazing. If corrosion resistance in service is sufficiently critical, an extra-low-carbon, titanium- stabilized or niobium-tantalum-stabilized type should be selected instead of a nonstabilized type of austenitic stainless steel.

Ferritic and martensitic stainless steels that contain little or no nickel are susceptible to interface corrosion in plain water or moist atmospheres, when they are brazed with nickel-free silver brazing filler metals, using a liquid or paste flux. Filler metal that contains nickel helps to prevent interface corrosion. However, for complete protection, special silver brazing filler metals that contain nickel and tin (for example, BAg-21) could be used, and brazing should be done in a protective atmosphere without flux.

Most silver brazing filler metals contain appreciable amounts of copper and zinc, either singly or in combination. Overheating or heating for an excessive period of time may result in extensive penetration of grain boundaries by copper and zinc, thereby embrittling the brazed joint.

Cadmium, which is added to some silver brazing filler metals to lower the melting temperature and improve wetting, also penetrates grain boundaries. The effect is accelerated when parts are brazed under tensile stress. Cadmium-containing fumes are extremely toxic, and operators must take every precaution to avoid inhaling

them. Many new alloys that have brazing and functional characteristics similar to those of the cadmium-bearing alloys, but without their environmental and safety concerns, are being introduced to the market. Filler metals that contain cadmium and/or zinc should not be used in a protective atmosphere, including vacuum, because cadmium gases off readily. Because the loss of zinc or cadmium raises the melting point of the filler metal, brazeability is adversely affected.

Virtually all of the silver brazing filler metals are suitable for brazements that are used in fabricating vacuum chambers and pumps, where pressures as low as 1.3×10^{-3} Pa (10^{-5} torr) are encountered. However, for high-vacuum work (pressures of less than 1.3×10^{-4} Pa, or 10^{-6} torr), the filler metal must not contain cadmium or zinc. Vaporization of these metals interferes with the production of the vacuum and can contaminate the vacuum chamber and pumps. Selection of a suitable silver brazing filler metal for service in vacuum at a pressure below 1.3×10^{-3} Pa (10^{-5} torr) is considered in Example 1.

Nickel brazing filler metals are the next most frequently used filler metals for stainless steels. The BNi group of nickel brazing filler metals provides joints that have excellent corrosion resistance and high-temperature strength. These filler metals are typically supplied in the form of powders mixed with a binder. A limited number of filler metals are also available as sintered rods, preforms, and foils. However, these filler metals may alloy with stainless steel, forming intermetallic phases with two undesirable characteristics. First, the phases are considerably less ductile than either the base metal or the filler metal, even at elevated temperatures, and are therefore a potential source of rupture. Second, the alloys formed with stainless steel are higher-melting-point alloys that are likely to freeze at brazing temperatures, thus blocking further flow into the joint during brazing. To achieve flow in deep joints, diametral clearances as large as 0.10 to 0.20 mm (0.004 to

0.008 in.) are necessary. Knurling of male members sometimes helps in the centering of loosely fitting components. With such large clearances, joints that are brazed with nickel brazing filler metals do not develop their greatest strength. The brazed joint is much stronger with a clearance of 0.025 to 0.076 mm (0.001 to 0.003 in.).

Because of the relatively high brazing temperatures required for the nickel brazing filler metals, their use is generally limited to furnace brazing in a controlled atmosphere (including vacuum), although there are occasional exceptions, as will be seen when Fig. 16 is discussed. Torch brazing with BNi brazing filler metals is used to braze small parts and small quantities.

Copper Brazing Filler Metals. The high brazing temperature and the need for a protective atmosphere generally limit the use of copper filler metals to furnace applications. The BCu brazing filler metals (which are practically pure copper) melt at approximately 1080 °C (1980 °F) and flow freely at 1120 °C (2050 °F).

Copper is not recommended for exposure to certain corrosive substances, such as the sulfur in jet fuel and in sulfur-bearing atmospheres. Furthermore, copper brazing filler metals exhibit poor oxidation resistance at elevated temperatures and should not be exposed to service temperatures higher than 430 °C (800 °F). When copper brazing filler metal is used, the recommended diametral allowance on joint fit ranges from a 0.10 mm (0.004 in.) clearance to a 0.05 mm (0.002 in.) interference.

Copper-Clad Brazing Materials. Many engine oil coolers and heat exchanger assemblies are currently made from stainless steel and use copper as the brazing filler metal. This base metal and filler metal combination is also available as a clad brazing material, where a copper brazing filler metal is clad to a stainless steel base material. These copper-clad brazing materials are produced as strips with the copper brazing filler metal on either one or both sides. Although the 300 and 400 series of stainless steels have been the most widely used base metal materials, low-carbon steels are being used in applications with less-strict corrosion-resistance and strength requirements. Table 2 lists the typical clad brazing strip products that are used in the fabrication of compact heat exchangers for the automotive, trucking, and aircraft industries.

Precautions that must be exercised during the brazing cycle, when using clad brazing materials, are identical to those that must be used when brazing the monolithic metals. For example, low-carbon versions of the 300 series of stainless steels are recommended to reduce the potential for sensitization during cooling from the brazing temperature. An excessively slow cooling rate should be avoided, because it can result in carbide precipitation in the grain boundaries of the stainless steel base material.

For a similar reason, a stabilized grade of 400 stainless steel is recommended to avoid the embrittlement phenomenon that also can result from improper cooling down from the brazing temperature. Typically, low levels of titanium, niobium, or a combination of the two, provide sufficient protection against embrittlement by minimizing the migration of carbon and any dissolved gases, without seriously reducing the wettability of the stainless steel. The niobium grades should be preferred because they are easy to braze, when compared to titanium-stabilized grades.

The copper brazing filler metal that is typically used in these applications conforms to the American Welding Society (AWS) filler-metal specification AWS A5.B, Class BCu-1. Past processing experience has shown that this type of filler metal performs very well in brazed heat exchangers that utilize both 300 and 400 series stainless steels as base materials.

One design benefit of using clad brazing materials is a reduction of the clearance between the parts, because no allowance needs to be made for the insertion of thick shims, wires, or preforms.

Another benefit is that less copper brazing filler metal can be used, because the concerns associated with the handling of shim material have been eliminated. The thinner copper coating thickness, which typically ranges from 0.025 to 0.075 mm (0.001 to 0.003 in.), results in less shrinkage during brazing and is less likely to cause large brazing fillets. Consequently, the possibility that excess brazing filler metal will clog

small passageways is greatly reduced. The typical joint shown in Fig. 1 illustrates the small-geometry passages that can be achieved and the capillary action of the brazing filler metal as it forms the fillets at the joints.

Yet another benefit of using clad metals is that once the parts are assembled and fixtured, the brazing filler metal will not shift, move, or fall out as a result of the movement of fixtured assemblies prior to or during the brazing cycle. Additional information on clad brazing materials can be found in the article "Stainless Steel Cladding and Weld Overlays" in this Volume.

Gold brazing filler metals (the BAu group) are sometimes used for the brazing of stainless steel, although their high cost restricts their use to specialized applications such as the fabrication of aerospace equipment (Example 4). When gold brazing filler metal is used, there is minimal alloying with the stainless steel base metal. As a result, joints exhibit good ductility, strength, and corrosion resistance. When maximum corrosion resistance is needed, BAu-4 should be used.

Cobalt brazing filler metals (the BCo-1 group) are very rarely used for the brazing of stainless steels. However, this type of filler metal is included in Table 1, and it is available for that purpose.

Filler Metal Wettability

Wetting is the ability of the molten brazing filler metal to adhere to the surface of a metal in the solid state and, when cooled below its solidus temperature, to make a strong bond with that metal. Wetting is a function not only of the nature of the brazing filler metal, but of the degree of interaction between materials to be joined. Good wetting and spreading of the liquid filler metal on the base metal are necessary in brazing, because the mechanics of the process demand that the filler metal be brought smoothly, rapidly, and continuously to the joint opening. If the conditions within the capillary space of the joint do not promote good wetting, then the filler metal will not be drawn into the space by capillary attraction.

Keller et al. (Ref 1) undertook an extensive study of the wettability of commercial braze filler metals (Table 3) on type 304 stainless steel, the most common of the austenitic stainless steels; type 316 stainless, which is often substituted for type 304 when increased corrosion resistance is desired; and 21-6-9 (UNS S21904), a low-carbon, high-manganese stainless steel that is an attractive alternative to

types 304 or 316 for certain applications. Because the 21-6-9 steel (Fe-0.04C-21Cr-6Ni-9Mn) has a very stable austenitic structure, it is attractive for cryogenic applications (see the article "Low-Temperature Properties" in this Volume).

Because high wettability means that the thermocapillary attraction that fills the braze joint is strong, wettability is an important component of braze performance. The wettability index (WI) developed by Feduska (Ref 2) is used as the measure of wettability. The WI is defined as the area covered by the braze metal filler times the cosine of the contact angle between the braze and the base metal. Therefore, the higher the WI, the better the braze filler metal wets the base metal. It should be emphasized that the WI, as defined, is a relative measure and depends on the volume of filler metal used.

The WIs for each braze filler metal at each temperature on type 316 stainless steel, type 304L stainless steel, and 21-6-9 stainless steel are provided in Table 4. Wetting indices greater than 0.05 are indicative of good performance during brazing, whereas WI values greater than 0.10 are indicative of excellent performance during brazing (Ref 2).

A comparison of the WI of the braze filler metals on the three stainless steels revealed these trends:

- Filler metals generally wet type 316 stainless steel better than type 304 stainless steel and generally wet type 316 stainless better than 21-6-9 stainless.

400 μm

Fig. 1 Photomicrograph of a passageway in a stainless steel heat exchanger fabricated using copper-clad stainless steel clad brazing material

Table 2 Typical clad brazing strip products

Material	Clad layer ratios	Thickness		Temper	Tensile strength		0.2% yield strength		Elongation, %
		mm	in.		MPa	ksi	MPa	ksi	
C12200 copper clad to 409 stainless steel	10/80/10 5/80/15	0.51-0.76	0.020-0.030	Annealed	400	58	230	33	37
C12200 copper clad to 304L stainless steel	13.5/86.5 10/80/10	0.51-0.30	0.020-0.012	Annealed Annealed	635 620	92 90	290 275	42 40	56 55
C12200 copper clad to 1008 steel	10/80/10	0.38	0.015	No. 4 temper	380	55	290	42	35
C52400 phosphor bronze clad to C10200 copper	10/80/10	0.51	0.020	Annealed	275	40	97	14	48

Table 3 Composition of selected filler metals used for wettability indices study
See Table 4 for results.

Filler metal	Composition	Liquidus		Solidus	
		°C	°F	°C	°F
Silver	99.99Ag	961	1762	961	1762
Cusil	72Ag-28Cu	780	1436	780	1436
Palcusil 5	68Ag-27Cu-5Pd	810	1490	807	1485
Palcusil 10	58Ag-32Cu-10Pd	852	1566	824	1515
Palcusil 15	65Ag-20Cu-15Pd	900	1650	850	1560
Palcusil 25	54Ag-21Cu-25Pd	950	1740	900	1650
Gapasil 9	82Ag-9Ga-9Pd	880	1615	845	1555
Nicusil 3	71.5Ag-28.1Cu-0.75Ni	795	1465	780	1435
Nicusil 8	56Ag-42Cu-2Ni	893	1639	771	1420
T-50	62.5Ag-32.5Cu-5Ni	866	1591	780	1435
T-51	75Ag-24.5Cu-0.5Ni	802	1476	780	1435
T-52	77Ag-21Cu-2Ni	830	1525	780	1435
Cusiltin 5	68Ag-27Cu-5Sn	760	1400	743	1369
Cusiltin 10	60Ag-30Cu-10Sn	718	1324	602	1116
Braze 630	63Ag-28Cu-6Sn-3Ni	800	1472	690	1275
Braze 580	57Ag-33Cu-7Sn-3Mn	730	1345	605	1120
Braze 655	65Ag-28Cu-5Mn-2Ni	850	1560	750	1380
Silcoro 60	60Au-20Ag-20Cu	845	1550	835	1535
Nioro	82Au-18Ni	950	1740	950	1740
Palnioro 7	70Au-22Ni-8Pd	1037	1899	1005	1840
Incuro 60	60Au-37Cu-3In	900	1650	860	1580
Silcoro 75	75Au-20Cu-5Ag	895	1645	885	1625
Nicoro 80	81.5Au-16.5Cu-2Ni	925	1695	910	1670
Palcusil 20	52Au-28Cu-20Pd	925	1695	875	1605
Gold	99.99Au	1064	1947	1064	1947
Palniro 4	30Au-36Ni-34Pd	1169	2136	1135	2075
Palniro 1	50Au-25Ni-25Pd	1121	2050	1102	2016
Ticusil	68.8Ag-26.7Cu-4.5Ti	850	1560	830	1525
Palnicusil	48Ag-18.9Cu-10Ni-22.5Pd	1179	2154	910	1670
Palco	65Pd-35Co	1235	2255	1230	2245
Incusil 15	62Ag-24Cu-15In	705	1300	630	1165
Incusil 10	63Ag-27Cu-10In	730	1345	685	1265
BAg-8a	71.8Ag-28Cu-0.2Li	760	1400	760	1400
BAg-19	92.5Ag-7.3Cu-0.2Li	890	1635	760	1400
Braze 071	85Cu-7Ag-8Sn	986	1807	665	1230
Braze 852	85Ag-15Mn	970	1780	960	1760
Nioroni	73.8Au-26.2Ni	1010	1850	980	1795
Nicuman 23	67.5Cu-23.5Mn-9Ni	955	1750	925	1695
Palsil 10	90Ag-10Pd	1065	1950	1002	1836
Palni	60Pd-40Ni	1238	2260	1238	2260

- The degree of wetting of most braze filler metals on 21-6-9 stainless was equal to or better than it was on type 304 stainless (Ref 3).
- The improved wettability of braze filler metals on type 316 stainless is believed to be due to the presence of molybdenum in the surface oxide, whereas the enhanced wetting on 21-6-9 stainless versus type 304 stainless is believed to be due to the higher manganese content of the surface oxide.

Essentially, the successful joining of components by the brazing process depends on the selected brazing filler metal having a melting point above 450 °C (840 °F) and wetting the base metal without melting it. Furthermore, the joint must be designed to ensure that the mating surfaces of the components are parallel and close enough together to cause capillary attraction.

Fluxes

Flux usually is not required for furnace brazing in strongly reducing or inert atmospheres. However, in some furnace brazing applications, flux is necessary. It is always required for torch brazing and is usually required for induction and resistance brazing, unless atmospheric protection is provided.

Any of the AWS types of FB3-A through FB3-J fluxes are suitable for all stainless steel brazing applications where flux is needed. The ANSI/AWS 5.31 specification for fluxes used in brazing and braze welding processes provides more details. There are basically three groups of these fluxes, based on their activity range, and they are further classified by their form (powder, paste, slurry, or liquid). The FB3-A, -F, and -G types of flux contain borates and fluorides and have an effective temperature range from 570 to 870 °C (1050 to 1600 °F). These fluxes are suitable for use with silver brazing filler metals.

Type FB3-C flux contains the same ingredients as type FB3-A, except for the addition of boron, and it has a higher effective temperature range from 570 to 930 °C (1050 to 1700 °F). This flux has an extended heating time capability.

The FB3-D, -I, and -J types of flux also contain borates and fluorides, such that their activity ranges from 760 to 1200 °C (1400 to 2200 °F). These fluxes are often selected for use with silver brazing filler metals if the brazing temperature is above 730 °C

(1350 °F). They are well suited for use with copper, nickel, and gold brazing filler metals.

Torch Brazing

For stainless steel, the fundamentals of torch brazing, as well as the advantages and limitations, are basically the same as for carbon steels. However, because of the metallurgical characteristics of stainless steel and its requirements for corrosion resistance, the best results are obtained when special consideration is given to the type of flame at the torch and to the filler-metal composition.

Flame Adjustment. To aid in reducing the oxide that is already present, and to prevent further oxidation of the workpiece surfaces, a flame that ranges from neutral to slightly reducing should be used when torch brazing stainless steel to itself. A reducing flame is also satisfactory for brazing stainless steel to nickel alloys or carbon steels. Although a slightly oxidizing flame is typically best for brazing oxide-containing (tough pitch) copper, a slightly reducing flame is usually best when brazing stainless steel to copper. Use of a reducing flame to braze copper is not recommended because this type of flame will remove oxygen from the copper and can also cause hydrogen embrittlement.

Filler Metals. The silver brazing filler metals that flow at relatively low temperatures are used almost exclusively for the torch brazing of stainless steels. BAg-3 is most often used, because it flows well in the temperature range from 700 to 760 °C (1300 to 1400 °F) and provides joints that have greater resistance to corrosion than those brazed with filler metals such as BAg-1 or BAg-1a (although these filler metals are also used). The use of brazing filler metals that require temperatures higher than approximately 760 °C (1400 °F) results in excessive oxidation, thus making it difficult to obtain adequate wetting of the brazed joint. In special applications, higher-melting-point filler metals must be used (Example 1).

Flux. Type FB3-A flux is most widely used for the torch brazing of stainless steel because it has a working range from 560 to 870 °C (1050 to 1600 °F) and is well suited for use with the lower-melting-point silver brazing filler metals. However, in some applications, other types of FB3 fluxes are preferred.

Example 1. Torch Brazing of Parts for High-Vacuum Service. The sleeve and tube assembly shown in Fig. 2 is typical of brazements used in vacuum systems. The tubes and the sleeve are type 304L austenitic stainless steel. The BAg-18 (60Ag-10Sn-30Cu) brazing filler metal, which has proved satisfactory for the brazing of assemblies used in high-vacuum service, was used with type FB3-B flux. This silver brazing filler metal does not contain zinc or cadmium. It should be noted that vacuum grades of the silver brazing filler metals, such as BVAg-18, are available, and that they limit the amount of impurities that can be detrimental to components of the vacuum tube industry. Again, ANSI/AWS A5.8 should be consulted for further details.

Brazing was conducted with a manually manipulated oxyacetylene torch and a strong reducing flame. The assembly shown in Fig. 2 could have been brazed in a furnace or by induction, but production was small and did not justify the investment for such equipment.

Example 2. Torch Brazing of Stainless Steel to Nickel. The brazed assembly shown in Fig. 3, which consists of a type 304 stainless steel tube and a pure nickel tube, was resistance heated in service. Requirements for this assembly were:

- Transmission of electricity without developing hot spots
- Straightness and smoothness, because the assembly had to slide into a larger assembly
- Joining at minimum temperature, because numerous small insulated wires were in the assembly at the time of joining and were sub-

ject to damage if the joining temperature was too high

Torch brazing with silver brazing filler metal proved to be a desirable way to make the joint, because of the relatively low brazing temperature, high electrical conductivity of the joint, minimal distortion, ease of removing excess filler metal, and ease of radiographic inspection.

The joint design (Fig. 3) allowed the preplacement of the brazing filler metal (BAg-1a) in a 3.2 mm (0.126 in.) wide groove that was machined into the shoulder of the nickel tube. The filler metal was then melted with a torch, and both filler metal and shoulder were machined to match the inside diameter of the stainless tube (zero-clearance fit).

Several heating methods were tried in an attempt to braze the nickel tube to the stainless steel tube, including induction heating in an inert gas and multiple-torch heating. However, the use of a single oxyacetylene torch operated by a skilled technician proved to be the most successful method. The sequence of operations for single-torch brazing was:

- Components were cleaned with acetone.
- Flux paste was placed on the nickel tube in the area to be brazed.
- The two tubes were assembled in a fixture with a 0.13 mm (0.005 in.) gap that showed surface (detail A in Fig. 3).
- The assembly was heated with a torch until the filler metal flowed to the outside surface (flow

Table 4 Wettability indices of braze filler metals on selected stainless steel base metals

See Table 3 for filler metal nominal compositions.

Filler metal	Test temperature °C	°F	Type 316	21-6-9	Type 304
Silver	975	1785	...	...	...
	1000	1830	0.008	...	0.015
	1050	1920	0.041	...	0.023
	1100	2010	0.053	...	0.020
	1150	2100	...	...	...
Cusil	800	1470	...	0.013	...
	850	1560	...	0.007	...
	900	1650	0.022	0.016	0.003
	925	1695	0.032	...	...
	950	1740	0.037	...	...
Palcusil 5	800	1470	0.027	...	...
	850	1560	...	0.014	...
	900	1650	0.047	0.020	0.011
	950	1740	0.080	0.061	0.035
Palcusil 10	850	1560	0.035	0.020	0.015
	900	1650	0.057	0.050	0.025
	950	1740	0.107	0.101	0.062
Palcusil 15	900	1650	0.107	0.092	0.068
	950	1740	0.152	0.170	0.119
	1000	1830	0.754	0.263	0.212
Palcusil 25	950	1740	0.104	0.107	0.096
	975	1785	0.225	...	...
	1000	1830	...	0.283	0.226
Gapasil 9	900	1650	0.023	...	...
	950	1740	0.068	...	...
	1000	1830	0.269	...	...
Nicusil 3	800	1470	0.006	0.000	0.012
	850	1560	0.027	0.017	0.008
	900	1650	0.041	0.039	0.021
	925	1695	0.051	...	...
	950	1740	0.064	...	...
Nicusil 8	850	1560	0.024	...	...
	900	1650	0.052	...	0.033
	950	1740	0.085	...	0.064
	1000	1830	...	...	0.229
T-50	850	1560	0.024	...	...
	900	1650	0.038	...	0.026
	950	1740	0.062	...	0.057
	1000	1830	...	...	...
T-51	800	1470	0.007	...	...
	850	1560	0.029	...	...
	900	1650	0.039	...	...
	950	1740	...	...	0.029
	1000	1830	...	...	0.082
T-52	850	1560	0.027	...	0.001
	900	1650	0.045	...	0.014
	950	1740	0.063	...	0.045
	1000	1830	...	...	0.090
Cusiltin 5	850	1560	0.015	...	0.000
	875	1605	0.043	...	...
	900	1650	0.047	...	0.013
	950	1740	...	...	0.033

Filler metal	Test temperature °C	°F	Type 316	21-6-9	Type 304
	1000	1830	...	...	...
Cusiltin 10	750	1380	...	0.025	0.000
	800	1470	...	0.017	0.023
	825	1515	0.021	...	...
	850	1560	0.034	0.051	0.050
	875	1605	0.043	...	...
Braze 630	800	1470	0.014	0.037	0.023
	850	1560	0.046	0.065	0.024
	900	1650	0.064	...	...
Braze 580	750	1380	0.020	0.060	0.060
	800	1470	0.051	0.056	0.089
	850	1560	0.073	0.120	0.102
	875	1605	0.078	...	...
Braze 655	825	1515	0.080	...	...
	850	1560	0.110	0.037	0.074
	875	1605	0.116	...	...
	900	1650	...	0.137	0.124
Silcoro 60	850	1560	...	0.005	0.004
	900	1650	0.039	0.007	0.011
	925	1695	0.051	...	...
	950	1740	0.073	0.025	0.016
	1000	1830	...	0.055	0.037
Nioro	950	1740	...	0.000	0.000
	975	1785	0.049	...	...
	1000	1830	0.061	0.060	0.065
Palniro 7	1025	1875	...	...	...
	1050	1920	0.053	...	...
	1075	1965	0.073	...	...
Incuro 60	900	1650	0.010	...	...
	950	1740	0.025	...	...
	1000	1830	0.091	...	...
Silcoro 75	900	1650	0.006	...	...
	950	1740	0.057	...	...
	1000	1830	0.170	...	...
Nicoro 80	950	1740	0.041	0.019	0.016
	1000	1830	0.163	0.126	0.070
	1050	1920	0.413	0.190	0.084
Palcusil 20	875	1610	0.061	...	...
	900	1650	0.110	...	...
	925	1695	0.122	...	...
Gold	1070	1960	...	...	0.088
	1075	1965	0.087	...	...
	1100	2010	0.358	...	0.238
	1150	2100	...	...	0.355
Palniro 4	1175	2145	0.036	...	...
	1200	2190	0.061	...	...
	1225	2235	0.078	...	...
Palniro 1	1125	2055	0.041	...	...
	1150	2100	0.063	...	...
	1175	2145	0.075	...	...
Ticusil	875	1605	0.032	...	...
	900	1650	0.057	...	...

Filler metal	Test temperature °C	°F	Type 316	21-6-9	Type 304
	950	1740	0.083	...	...
Palnicusil	950	1740	0.025	...	0.038
	975	1785	0.213	...	...
	1000	1830	...	...	...
	1025	1875	0.362	...	...
	1050	1920	...	...	...
	1075	1965	0.336	...	...
	1100	2010	...	...	...
Palco	1250	2280	0.000	...	...
	1275	2325	0.073	...	...
	1300	2370	0.159	...	...
Incusil 15	750	1380	...	...	...
	800	1470	...	...	...
	850	1560	...	...	...
Incusil 10	750	1380	...	...	...
	800	1470	...	...	...
	850	1560	0.008	...	...
BAg-8a	800	1470	0.005	...	...
	850	1560	0.008	...	...
	900	1650	0.032	...	...
	950	1740	0.045	...	...
BAg-19	950	1740	0.016	...	...
	1000	1830	0.016	...	...
	1050	1920	0.034	...	...
Braze 071	1000	1830	0.066	0.106	0.101
	1050	1920	...	0.125	0.101
Braze 852	1000	1830	0.039	0.037	0.038
	1050	1920	0.029	0.038	0.042
	1100	2010	0.043	0.037	0.020
Nioroni	1000	1830	0.068	...	...
	1025	1875	0.070	...	...
	1100	2010	0.116	...	...
Nicuman 23	950	1740	0.026	...	...
	975	1785	0.099	...	...
	1000	1830	0.091	...	...
	1025	1875	0.091	...	...
Palsil 10	1050	1920	0.113	...	...
	1075	1965	0.113	...	...
	1100	2010	0.126	...	...
Palni	1225	2235	...	...	...
	1250	2280	0.068	...	...
	1275	2325	0.078	...	...
	1300	2370	0.107	...	...
Palmansil 5	950	1740	...	...	0.057
	1000	1830	...	...	...
	1050	1920	...	...	...
	1100	2010	...	...	...

temperature of 640 °C, or 1175 °F, for BAg-1a).

- Excess flux that flowed to the surface was removed manually.

It was possible to inspect the entire joint by making two radiographs. Only scattered porosity was detected in a routine radiographic inspection of the brazed joints.

Furnace Brazing

Almost all furnace brazing of stainless steel is done in a protective atmosphere (including vacuum). One exception is the application described in Example 11, in which air was the furnace atmosphere. In this case, a liquid flux was used and the time at brazing temperature was short, which helped to prevent excessive oxidation.

The protective atmospheres most often used in furnace brazing of stainless steel are dry hydrogen and dissociated ammonia. These atmospheres are effective in reducing oxides, protecting the base metal, and promoting the flow of brazing filler metal. The low-cost exothermic atmospheres that are widely used in furnace brazing of low-carbon steel are not suitable for stainless steel. An inert gas, such as argon, or a vacuum environment, can be used to satisfy special requirements and to provide protection in applications for which hydrogen or hydrogen-bearing gases are unsatisfactory.

Selection of the furnace atmosphere depends on the degree of protection that must be given to the base metal or metals, the flow characteristics of the brazing filler metal, the brazing temperature, and cost. Special requirements that arise from the brazing of dissimilar metals are often a major factor in atmosphere selection. The availability of equipment can also be an important consideration.

Furnace Brazing in Dry Hydrogen. A dry hydrogen atmosphere is preferred for many stainless steel brazing applications. Hydrogen, which is the most strongly reducing protective atmosphere, reduces chromium oxide and promotes excellent wetting by many filler metals without the need for flux. The principal disadvantages of hydrogen are its cost, its difficulty in drying sufficiently, the need for special furnace equipment, and the potential danger involved in improper storage and handling. The following examples describe applications in which a specific type of stainless steel was joined to either the same or another type of stainless steel.

Example 3. Selection of BAg-13 Silver Brazing Filler Metal for Brazing at 930 °C (1700 °F). The type 347 stainless steel retainer assembly shown in Fig. 4 was furnace brazed in dry hydrogen, using BAg-13 silver brazing filler metal, which was selected in preference to lower-melting-point silver brazing filler metals because the upper limit of its brazing temperature range (860 to 970 °C, or 1575 to 1775 °F) permitted brazing at 930 °C (1700 °F). At furnace temperatures above 980 °C (1800 °F), dry hydrogen is strongly reducing, and the use of a brazing flux is not required for satisfactory wetting action. Thus, by judicious selection of the brazing filler metal

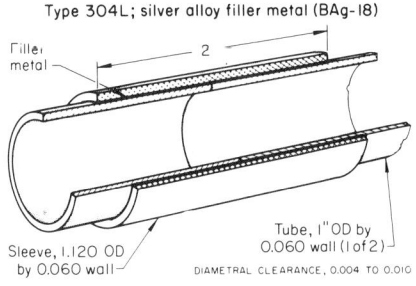

Fig. 2 Assembly that was torch brazed with a silver brazing filler metal for use in a high-vacuum-atmosphere system. Dimensions given in inches

and the furnace atmosphere, the extra cost of applying the flux and of removing flux residue after brazing was avoided.

The components were vapor degreased, assembled (keeping their outside diameters concentric), and spot welded (to make them self-jigging) at four locations 90° apart (Fig. 4). A ring of brazing filler metal wire in a 1 mm (0.040 in.) diameter was preplaced at the joint, and assemblies were loaded two-across on the mesh belt of a conveyor-type furnace. The heating chamber of the furnace was elevated from the entrance and discharge level to conserve the lighter-than-air hydrogen and to prevent oxygen in the atmosphere from mixing with the hydrogen, which could either raise the dew point or cause an explosion.

Quality standards for brazed assemblies, which were checked by 100% visual inspection, required that the joint exhibit full braze penetration (360° fillets on both sides of the joint) and be pressure-tight.

Example 4. Use of a Gold Brazing Filler Metal for Brazing in an Aerospace Heat Exchanger. In the fabrication of a high-reliability heat exchanger for manned space flights, 2552 fins of 0.10 mm (0.004 in.) thick type 347 stainless steel were brazed to 0.64 mm (0.025 in.) thick type 347 stainless steel side panels, as shown in Fig. 5. The 5104 fin-to-panel joints had to be strong and corrosion resistant.

Silver and copper brazing filler metals could not be used because of their incompatibility with sulfur-bearing rocket fuel. The BNi series of nickel brazing filler metals had the necessary compatibility but made nonductile joints that were unreliable under tension peel stress. Therefore, gold brazing filler metals were used. The necessary brazing characteristics for the fin-to-panel joints were present in BAu-4 (nominal composition, 82Au-18Ni). The strength and ductility of the resulting brazed joints justified the high cost of this particular brazing filler metal.

The fins and side panels were cleaned by vapor degreasing. The side panels were then pickled, rinsed in clean water, and dried. The brazing filler metal was deposited on the panels in the form of a powder suspended in an organic binder. Multiple lap joints were made between the flat-crown-hairpin ends of the fins and the flat side panels. The assembly was placed in a fixture (Fig. 5), and then the entire assembly and fixture were placed in the retort of a bell-type furnace and sealed. The sealed

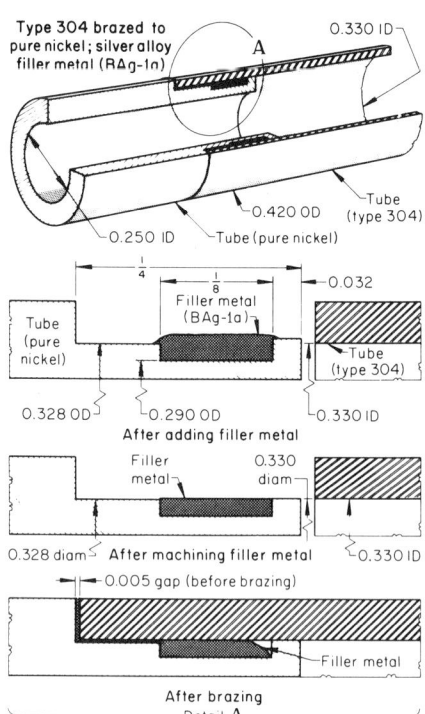

Fig. 3 Torch-brazed assembly of a stainless steel tube and a pure nickel tube. Dimensions given in inches

retort was purged with a volume of hydrogen that was equivalent to five times that of the retort. The retort was then heated to a brazing temperature of 1020 °C (1860 °F) and held for 7 to 10 min. The joint gaps at brazing temperature ranged from 0.000 to 0.254 mm (0.010 in.). After brazing, the retort was purged with argon while being cooled to 150 °C (300 °F) and was not opened until after purging and cooling.

The joints brazed by this procedure were the final brazed joints in the assembly. In a prior brazing operation, tubes had been joined to the fins (Fig. 5) by brazing at 1080 °C (1970 °F) using a higher-melting-point gold brazing filler metal of 70Au-22Ni-8Pd.

The completed assemblies were visually inspected and pressure tested at pressures that far exceeded those of the intended service environment: 1.86 MPa (270 psi) on the outside of the tubes and 11.8 MPa (1710 psi) on the inside. Acceptance pressure test values were 3.7 MPa (540 psi) on the outside and 15.7 MPa (2275 psi) on the inside of the tubes. Selected brazed assemblies were tested to bursting. These assemblies were required to withstand at least three times the service pressures before bursting. The assemblies that were brazed with gold brazing filler metals passed all tests and had three times the bursting strength of the assemblies brazed with undiffused nickel brazing filler metal.

Example 5. Combination Brazing and Solution Heat Treatment of an Assembly of Three Types of Stainless Steel. Three different stainless steels were selected to make the cover for a hermetically sealed switch. The switching action had to be transmitted through the cover without breaking the seal. This was accomplished

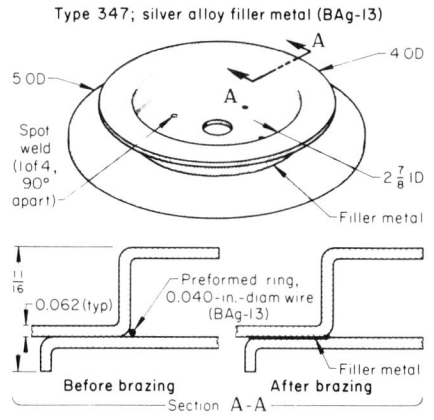

Type 347; silver alloy filler metal (BAg-13)

Furnace brazing in dry hydrogen

Furnace	Continuous conveyor(a)
Fixtures	None
Furnace temperature, °C (°F)	980 ± 5 (1800 ± 10)
Brazing temperature, °C (°F)	925 ± 5 (1700 ± 10)
Hydrogen dew points, °C (°F)	−75 (−100)(b); −60 (−70)(c)
Hydrogen flow rate, m³/h (ft³/h)	11 (400)
Filler metal(d)	BAg-13
Joint position during brazing	Horizontal
Conveyor travel speed, m/h (ft/h)	9 (30)
Time at brazing temperature, min(e)	5
Production rate, assemblies/h	120

(a) Electricity heated (60 kW), constructed with heating chamber higher than entrance and discharge ends. (b) Incoming. (c) Exhaust. (d) In form of 1 mm (0.040 in.) diameter wire-ring preforms. (e) Cooled in hydrogen atmosphere to room temperature

Fig. 4 Retainer assembly furnace brazed with BAg-13 filler metal. Dimensions given in inches

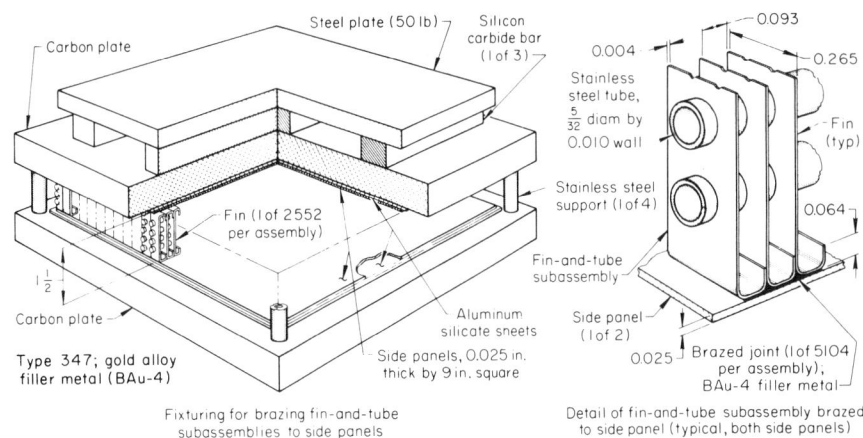

Type 347; gold alloy filler metal (BAu-4)

Fixturing for brazing fin-and-tube subassemblies to side panels

Detail of fin-and-tube subassembly brazed to side panel (typical, both side panels)

Furnace brazing in dry hydrogen

Furnace	Bell(a)
Fixtures	(See illustration)
Brazing temperature, °C (°F)	1015 (1860)
Hydrogen dew point (max), °C (°F)	−60 (−80)(b)
Purging(c)	5
Filler metal(d)	BAu-4
Number of assemblies per load	1

Processing time per assembly

Clean components, min	45
Preplace filler metal, h	1.25
Assemble components in fixture, h	4
Time at brazing temperature, min	7–10
Total time in furnace(e), h	4
Inspect, h	1
Pressure test, h	40

(a) Electrically heated, with 36 in. diam retort with water-cooled rubber seals. (b) Hydrogen was purchased as cylinder hydrogen, then passed through an electrolytic drier. (c) Number of volume changes in retort. (d) 200-mesh powder suspended in an organic binder. (e) Including cooling to 150 °C (300 °F) in retort, which was purged with argon before being opened

Fig. 5 Heat-exchanger assembly in brazing fixture and detail of joints brazed with gold brazing filler metal. Dimensions given in inches

by providing a diaphragm through which a shoulder pin was inserted, as shown in Fig. 6. The switch was actuated by depressing the pin, which in turn deflected the diaphragm. The pin (type 303), the diaphragm (PH 15-7 Mo), and the cover (type 305) were assembled as shown in Fig. 6, and then brazed using a silver-base filler metal in a furnace with dry hydrogen.

Silver brazing filler metal BAg-19 was chosen because it flowed at a temperature that coincided with the solution heat-treating temperature for the PH 15-7 Mo diaphragm (950 °C, or 1750 °F). A holding fixture was needed to keep the PH 15-7 Mo diaphragm in position during the brazing cycle. To avoid carburizing the diaphragm, the material selected for the fixture was stainless steel, rather than graphite. The furnace was a batch-type tube furnace with a 120 mm (5 in.) diameter high-heat zone that was 460 mm (18 in.) long. The moisture content of the hydrogen atmosphere was carefully controlled, because the lithium-containing filler metal flowed too freely when the atmosphere was too dry, and it did not seal the joints.

After being cleaned, the components were assembled with two preform rings of BAg-19 wire. Tweezers were used to avoid contaminating the cleaned surfaces. Each assembly was held in a stainless steel fixture, which in turn was placed on a stainless steel furnace sled. The sled was pushed into the high-heat zone of the furnace and held at

950 °C (1750 °F) for 10 min, before being pulled into an intermediate cooling zone at 540 °C (1000 °F) and held for 5 min. Finally, it was pulled to the water-cooled zone, where it cooled to room temperature. The brazing of the two joints and the solution treating of the PH 15-7 Mo diaphragm were accomplished simultaneously at the brazing temperature of 950 °C (1750 °F). To complete the heat-treating process, the assembly was cooled to −70 °C (−100 °F), held for 8 h, and then aged at 510 °C (950 °F) for 1 h.

A 25 mm (1 in.) square piece of PH 15-7 Mo was processed with each batch of cover assemblies and used as a hardness test specimen to verify that the diaphragms had been correctly heat treated. Brazed assemblies were inspected by the brazing operator. The joints were required to be fully sealed and to not have any voids. The pins were required to be perpendicular within 4°. Perpendicularity was measured on a comparator. Randomly selected samples were given a push-out test, in which joints had to withstand a push of 60 N (14 lbf). All assemblies were given 100% visual inspection at high magnification.

Example 6. Simultaneous Brazing of a Heat-Exchanger Assembly. An air-to-air heat-exchanger assembly, shown in Fig. 7, consisted of 185 thin-wall (0.20 mm, or 0.008 in.) tubes and two 1.6 mm (1/16 in.) thick headers. All components were made of type 347 stainless steel. The tubes were assembled with the headers by flaring the tube ends to lock them in place and provide metal-to-metal contact for the brazing filler metal. All 370 joints were brazed during a single pass through a continuous conveyor-type electric furnace.

Although a nickel brazing filler metal was preferred for this high-temperature application be-

cause of the resistance to heat and corrosion that it provides, the selection of a specific nickel brazing filler metal presented a problem. Higher-melting-point, boron-containing nickel brazing filler metals, such as BNi-1 and BNi-3, will react with the base metal, partially dissolve, and therefore are likely to erode thin materials. Fortunately, the extent of erosion can be modified by controlling the brazing temperature and time, as well as the amount of filler metal.

Although there are nickel brazing filler metals that contain silicon in place of boron, they generally require much higher brazing temperatures, which can result in grain coarsening in the base metal. Therefore, after numerous tests, BNi-3 filler metal was selected on the basis of its brazing temperature and excellent fluidity. The problem of applying the correct amount of filler metal to avoid erosion was solved by preparing a slurry from an accurately controlled mixture of filler-metal powder, acrylic-resin binder, and xylene thinner.

Before the filler metal was applied, the heat-exchanger assembly was cleaned ultrasonically in acetone and carefully weighed to determine the proportionate weight of filler metal that would be required. Half of the total amount of filler metal was then applied to one end of the assembly by spraying. The assembly was reweighed, and the remaining filler metal was applied to the opposite end. At all stages of processing, the assembly was handled by operators wearing clean, lint-free cotton gloves.

The assembly was placed on a holding fixture made of stainless steel sheet, on which a stop-off compound had been applied to prevent the assembly from brazing to the fixture if the brazing filler metal flowed excessively. Assemblies were placed 300 mm (12 in.) apart on the conveyor, as they traveled through the furnace at 9 m/h (30 ft/h) under the protection of dry hydrogen.

After brazing, each side was subjected to 100% visual inspection to detect the presence of fillets, and the assemblies were pressure tested in accordance with customer requirements. Because of the thin-wall (0.20 mm, or 0.008 in.) tubing, this assembly was brazed more consistently and at a lower cost than could have been achieved by other joining processes.

Example 7. Combined Brazing and Hardening of a Shaft Assembly. The shaft assembly shown in Fig. 8 consists of three bars or screw machine products (a shaft, a drive pin, and a guide pin) and two stampings (upper and lower mounting plates), all made from type 410 stainless steel and furnace brazed together using four joints. By brazing with copper filler metal at 1120 °C (2050 °F), it was possible to austenitize and harden the assembly to the required minimum hardness value of 40 HRC during the brazing and cooling operations, thereby avoiding separate hardening operations after brazing.

Because the joints were all relatively short, an interference fit of 0.000 to 0.025 mm (0.001 in.) was satisfactory. Typically, a clearance fit between mating parts is required with longer joints in stainless steel. The automatic staking of components was used to make the assembly self-fixturing.

As shown in Fig. 8, a full ring of 0.50 mm (0.020 in.) diameter BCu-1 copper wire was preplaced around the 13 mm (½ in.) diameter shaft to braze the shaft to the upper and lower mounting plates. A small amount of BCu-2 copper paste was

applied at one end of the drive pin to braze it to the two mounting plates. Because of the separation between the two plates on the guide-pin side, a small amount of BCu-2 copper paste was manually applied on each end of the guide pin. The assemblies were placed in brazing trays, with the shaft in a vertical position, and they were supported in this position by ceramic spacers.

The brazing trays were then placed on the mesh belt of a continuous-type conveyor furnace containing a dry hydrogen atmosphere. They were transported up an incline to the horizontal preheat and high-heat chambers at a speed of 6 m/h (20 ft/h). Because the assemblies were small, they became heated to the brazing temperature in about 2 min. After 8 min at the brazing temperature, the assemblies were conveyed into water-jacketed cooling chambers, where they cooled rapidly in the hydrogen atmosphere to room temperature. Brazed assemblies that were bright and oxidation-free emerged from the exit end of the furnace.

The brazed assemblies were 100% visually inspected for complete joint coverage. Hardness tests on a sampling basis were used to determine whether the assemblies had responded properly to hardening. Tempering to the desired final hardness followed the simultaneous brazing and hardening operation.

Example 8. Medical Device Brazed, Rather Than Welded, in Hydrogen. Because of the need for strong, corrosion-resistant, and leak-proof joints in a stainless steel blood-cell washer (Fig. 9), the process that was selected was hydrogen furnace brazing with BNi-7 brazing filler metal. The devices are used to expedite and standardize cell-washing procedures in blood banks

and hematology laboratories. Therefore, neither voids nor cracks could be tolerated, because the possibility of breeding bacteria in the devices had to be avoided.

Brazing, rather than welding, was chosen to join the manifold and the delicate tube parts of the washer, a rake-like component with twelve prong-like cannulas tubes that extend approximately 150 mm (6 in.) from a cylindrical manifold.

The manifold assembly was brazed using BNi-7 nickel brazing filler metal in a hydrogen atmosphere at 1040 °C (1900 °F). After assembling the tubes to the manifold, the brazing filler metal was applied to the joints and the assembly was placed in the furnace. Components were wired to stainless steel fixtures to maintain uniform tube spacing.

The brazing permitted the filler metal to flow completely around the thin-wall tubes, which was not possible with welding, leaving smooth fillets without voids that could trap harmful bacterial particles. Additional advantages of brazing were that it minimized the amount of assembly distortion, eliminated flux hazards, simplified inspection procedures, and prevented oxidation.

Furnace Brazing in Dissociated Ammonia. When ammonia is free of moisture and is 100% dissociated, it becomes a suitable atmosphere for the brazing of stainless steel using selected brazing filler metals without requiring a flux. Although dissociated ammonia is strongly reducing, it is less so than pure, dry hydrogen. Consequently, it will promote wetting action by reduc-

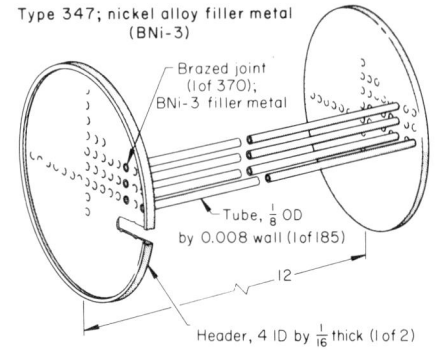

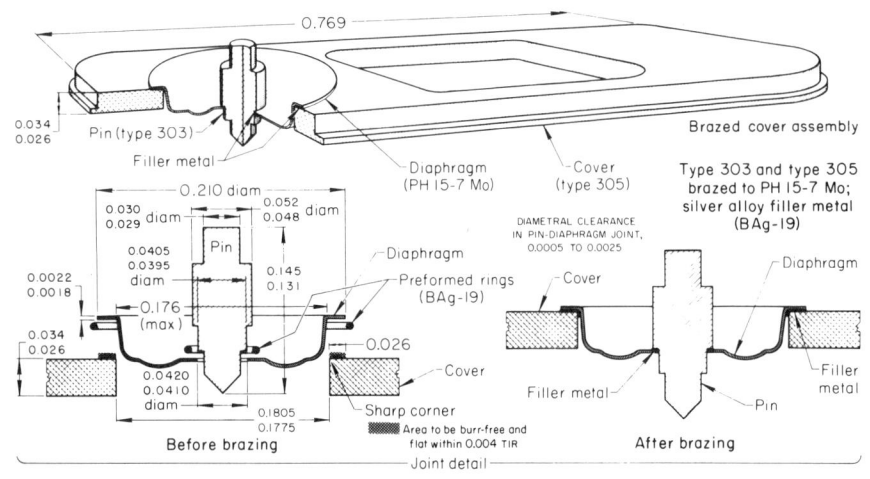

Furnace brazing in dry hydrogen

Furnace(a)	Continuous conveyor
Fixture material(b)	Type 347 stainless steel
Furnace temperature, °C (°F)	1120 ± 5 (2050 ± 10)
Brazing temperature, °C (°F)	1065 ± 5 (1950 ± 10)
Hydrogen dew points, °C (°F)	−75 (−100)(c);
	−60 (−70)(d)
Hydrogen flow rate, m³/h (ft³/h)	17 (600)
Filler metal(e)	BNi-3 powder
Conveyor travel speed, m³/h (ft³/h)	9 (30)
Time at brazing temperature, min	5
Cooling	In hydrogen atmosphere
Assembly production rate/h	15

(a) Electrically heated (60 kW), constructed with heating chamber higher than entrance and discharge ends. (b) Holding fixture fabricated from 3.2 mm (⅛ in.) thick sheet. (c) Incoming. (d) Exhaust. (e) Mixed to a slurry with acrylic resin and xylene thinner; powder-to-vehicle ratio, 70/30

Furnace brazing in dry hydrogen

Furnace(a)	Batch-type tube	Time at brazing temperature, min	10
Fixture material(b)	Stainless steel	Time in first cooling zone(d), min	5
Brazing temperature, °C (°F)	955 ± 8 (1750 ± 15)	Time in final cooling zone(d), min	5
Filler metal(c)	BAg-19	Assemblies produced in 8 h	1000

(a) Three-zone furnace with a high-heat zone 125 mm (5 in.) in diameter by 460 mm (18 in.) long. (b) Fixture located and held components of assembly together and was placed on a stainless steel sled for transport through the furnace. (c) Preformed wire rings. (d) At 540 °C (1000 °F). (e) Water-cooled zone, in which assembly was cooled to room temperature. To complete heat treatment of the PH 15-7 Mo diaphragm, assembly was cooled to −75 °C (−100 °F) and held for 8 h, then aged at 510 °C (950 °F) for 1 h.

Fig. 6 Three-steel switch-cover assembly that used brazing temperature as part of solution heat treatment. Dimensions in figure given in inches

Fig. 7 Heat-exchanger assembly with tube-to-header joints brazed in one pass through a furnace. Dimensions given in inches

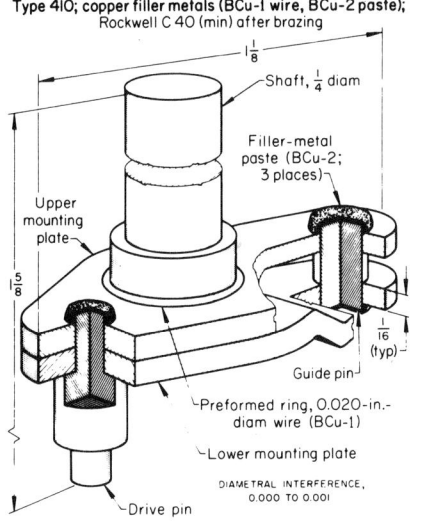

Type 410; copper filler metals (BCu-1 wire, BCu-2 paste); Rockwell C 40 (min) after brazing

Furnace brazing in dry hydrogen

Furnace(a)	Continuous conveyor
Fixtures(b)	None
Furnace temperature, °C (°F)	1175 ± 5 (2150 ± 10)
Brazing temperature, °C (°F)	1120 ± 5 (2050 ± 10)
Hydrogen dew points, °C (°F)	−75 (−100)(c); −60 (−75)(d)
Hydrogen flow rate, m³/h (ft³/h)	11 (400)
Filler metal(e)	BCu-1 wire, BCu-2 paste
Conveyor travel speed, m/h (ft/h)	6 (20)
Time at brazing temperature (f), min	8
Cooling	In hydrogen atmosphere
Assembly production rate/h	800

(a) Electrically heated (60 kW), constructed with heating chamber higher than entrance and discharge ends. (b) Components were staked, for self-fixturing. Assemblies, supported by ceramic spacers to keep shaft end up, were brazed on trays. (c) Incoming. (d) Exhaust. (e) Wire was a 0.51 mm (0.020 in.) diameter preformed ring; paste was applied at one end of drive pin, both ends of guide pin. (f) Assemblies were in high heat zone for about 10 min.

Fig. 8 Four-joint shaft assembly that was simultaneously furnace brazed and heated for hardening. Dimensions given in inches

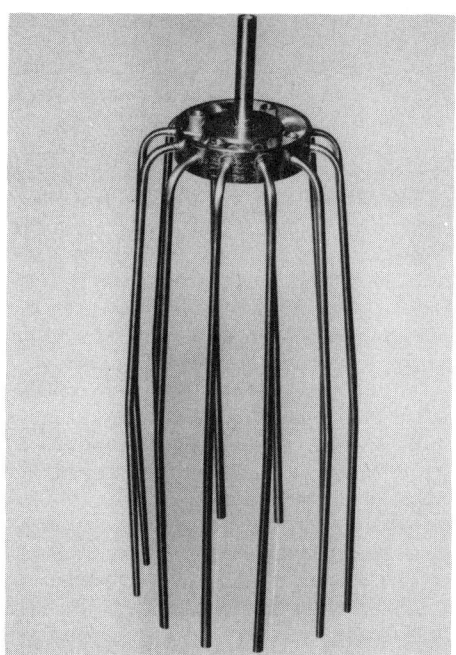

Fig. 9 Manifold and cannulas tube assembly of a blood-cell washer that was hydrogen furnace brazed with BNi-7 brazing filler metal at 1040 °C (1900 °F). Courtesy of Wall Colmonoy Corp.

ing chromium oxide on the surface of stainless steel, but it may not be sufficiently reducing to promote the flow of some brazing filler metals, such as copper oxide powders. Because of its high (75%) hydrogen content, dissociated ammonia forms explosive mixtures with air and must be handled with the same precautions as those required for the handling of hydrogen.

A dissociated-ammonia atmosphere is prepared by heating anhydrous liquid ammonia in the presence of an iron or nickel catalyst. The decomposition of ammonia to form hydrogen and nitrogen begins at 315 °C (600 °F), and the rate of decomposition increases with temperature. Unless the atmosphere used in brazing stainless steel is completely decomposed, that is, 100% dissociated, even minute amounts of raw ammonia (NH₃) in the atmosphere will cause the nitriding of stainless steel, especially steels containing little or no nickel. In addition, because of the solubility of ammonia in water, the atmosphere that comes from the dissociator must be extremely dry (preferably having a dew point of −60 °C, or −80 °F, or lower). To ensure a very low dew point, the atmosphere that comes from the dissociator is com-

monly processed by being passed through a molecular-sieve dryer. To avoid the oxidation of base metal and brazing filler metal, the atmosphere must be kept pure and dry while it is inside the furnace. In the following examples of production practices, dissociated ammonia was used successfully in the furnace brazing of austenitic and precipitation-hardening (PH) stainless steels.

Example 9. Brazing in Dissociated Ammonia without Flux. The pressure gage subassembly shown in Fig. 10 comprises five diaphragms of 17-7 PH stainless steel, a deep-drawn cup and a top fitting of type 304 stainless steel, and a connector of copper alloy C14500 (tellurium-bearing copper). Originally, these subassemblies were furnace brazed with a silver brazing filler metal that required a flux. Because applying flux and assembling the fluxed components with gloved hands was time consuming, the decision was made to change to fluxless brazing in an atmosphere of dissociated ammonia. Although this necessitated using a more-expensive brazing filler metal (BAg-19), the higher cost was offset by the greater productivity of each operator. In addition, subassemblies brazed with BAg-19 in dissociated ammonia exhibited fewer leaks and had improved corrosion resistance and a better appearance than those brazed with the original filler metal and a flux.

Prior to brazing, the deep-drawn type 304 cups were fully annealed at 1090 °C (2000 °F). Annealing served to avoid the erosive penetration of brazing filler metal in zones of high residual stress. All components were chemically cleaned and then assembled by hand, along with seven preplaced rings of brazing filler metal. The assemblies were placed on holding fixtures, which were loaded on the belt of a conveyor furnace heated to 980 °C (1800 °F). The cooling chamber of the furnace was cooled to below 15 °C (60 °F)

to ensure rapid cooling of the 17-7 PH diaphragms from the solution-treating temperature, thereby combining solution treating with the brazing operation.

After brazing, the assemblies were cooled to −40 °C (−40 °F), dried, and then heated to 510 °C (950 °F) in dry, dissociated ammonia to harden the diaphragms to 44 to 48 HRC. Brazed assemblies were pressure tested in a bellows halogen leak detector by applying freon at 520 kPa (75 psi) and then adding compressed air to bring the total pressure up to 2.1 MPa (300 psi). Leakage of freon in the gas-air mixture would have been detected by the halogen leak detector. The requirement was for no leakage at the most sensitive setting of the leak detector.

The rejection rate for leakage, based on the 750,000 bellows that were produced, dropped from 2.8%, with the original silver brazing filler metal, to 1.0%, with the BAg-19 brazing filler metal. Field corrosion returns dropped 96%. By eliminating the stains caused by flux, it was no longer necessary to paint the assemblies.

Furnace Brazing in Argon. Argon is occasionally used as a furnace atmosphere when brazing stainless steels to other stainless steels or to reactive metals such as titanium (Example 10). Argon has the advantage of being chemically inert in relation to all metals. Therefore, it is a useful protective atmosphere for metals that can combine with or absorb reactive atmospheres such as hydrogen. Because an argon atmosphere has the disadvantage of being unable to reduce oxides, the surfaces of stainless steel components must be exceptionally clean and oxide-free when brazed in argon.

Example 10. Brazing in an Argon Atmosphere. A manufacturer of jet engines designed a gear-reduction box of commercially pure titanium. This complicated fabrication was made from assemblies of stampings and machined forgings, most of which were joined by gas-tungsten arc welding (GTAW) in argon-filled welding chambers. However, brazing was more appropriate for the joining of some assemblies.

A typical assembly that was furnace brazed in argon is shown in Fig. 11. This assembly consisted of a machined forging of commercially pure titanium (per Aerospace Material Specification 4921) and a length of seamless type 347 stainless steel tubing that was flared or expanded for a distance of approximately 8 mm (5/16 in.) to accept the titanium forging.

The outside diameter of the titanium forging was held to 12.70 mm (0.500 in.), +0.000 and −0.025 mm (−0.001 in.). The inside diameter of the stainless steel tube was held to 12.73 mm (0.501 in.), +0.025 mm (+0.001 in.) and −0.000 mm or in. This allowed for a diametral clearance of 0.025 to 0.076 (0.001 to 0.003 in.) between components at room temperature. From 0 to 900 °C (32 to 1650 °F), the mean coefficient of thermal expansion (CTE) of commercially pure titanium is 10.3⁻⁶/K. From 0 to 870 °C (32 to 1600 °F), the mean CTE of type 347 stainless steel is 20 × 10⁻⁶/K. Calculation of the expansion that would occur when both components were heated to 900 °C (1650 °F) indicated a 0.102 mm (0.004 in.) diametral clearance between the titanium and the stainless steel. Adding the diametral clearance at room temperature (0.025 to 0.076 mm, or 0.001 to 0.003 in.) to the 0.102 mm (0.004 in.) clearance gave a total diametral clearance at brazing temperature of 0.127 to 0.178 mm (0.005 to 0.007 in.), which is within a range that will result in a successful joint.

The selected brazing filler metal was the BAg-19 silver alloy, because it has high fluidity in an argon atmosphere and a brazing temperature that is lower than that of pure silver. Most alloy elements in silver brazing filler metals form brittle intermetallic compounds with titanium, which result in unreliable joints. With the exception of a minute amount of lithium, the only alloying element contained in BAg-19 is 7.5% Cu. By limiting the time at brazing temperature, sound ductile joints were made, and the formation of the titanium copper intermetallic phase was minimized.

Prior to assembly, the titanium forging was degreased and cleaned in a solution that contained 40% nitric acid plus 2% hydrofluoric acid. The stainless steel tubing and the brazing filler metal (preformed rings of 0.102 mm, or 0.004 in., diameter BAg-19 wire) were cleaned by washing in acetone. Operators wore clean, lint-free, white cotton gloves for all subsequent handling of the components during assembly, and kept them on until after brazing was completed.

The titanium forging was inserted into the expanded end of the stainless steel tube until it was completely seated. A brazing filler metal ring was placed around the outside diameter of the titanium tube at the joint intersection. The assembly was placed upright (forging down) in a titanium sheet-metal-holding fixture and was loaded into an Inconel retort. The retort was designed for

displacement purging with an inlet and exit manifold for the argon atmosphere. After loading, the retort cover was seal welded to its base, using the GTAW process.

The retort was purged for 30 min with pure, dry argon at 4.2 m³/h (150 ft³/h) and then placed in a gas-fired pit-type furnace. The retort was heated to 315 °C (600 °F), and it was held at that temperature for an additional 30 min, or until the dew point of the exiting argon was −60 °C (−70 °F), as recorded on an electrolytic water analyzer. The furnace temperature was then raised until the assembly temperature reached 900 °C (1650 °F), as indicated by a Chromel-Alumel thermocouple attached to the titanium holding fixture within the retort. As soon as this temperature was reached, the retort was removed from the furnace and fan-cooled to room temperature.

The retort cover was opened by grinding away the seal weld, and the assemblies were removed. The titanium and stainless steel components emerged bright and clean, with evidence of excellent brazing filler metal flow. Radiographic inspection showed over 95% joint coverage. All joints were visually inspected on both sides.

Furnace Brazing in an Air Atmosphere. The principal advantages of furnace brazing are high production rates and a means for using controlled protective atmospheres at controlled dew points, which often precludes the use of a flux to obtain satisfactory wetting action. In most furnace-brazing applications, both of these advantages are exploited. Occasionally, however, furnace brazing is selected solely on the basis of production rate, and brazing is performed without a protective atmosphere, but with a suitable flux.

Under these conditions, the lower-melting-point brazing filler metals are generally selected, as in the following application.

Example 11. Substitution of Furnace Brazing in Air Atmosphere for Torch Brazing. The gas-valve bobbin assembly shown in Fig. 12 was satisfactorily brazed by both the torch and furnace brazing processes. The choice of process primarily depended on the required production rate. Cost data proved that furnace brazing increased the production rate per hour, reduced the direct labor rate per hour, and reduced the direct labor cost per assembly.

As Fig. 12 shows, the bobbin assembly consisted of four parts: a screw made of type 446 stainless steel, a base made of type 303 stainless steel, a tube made of a copper alloy closely related to nickel silver (74Cu-22Ni-4Zn), and a plug made of copper alloy C18700 (99Cu-1Pb), which held the screw in place and blocked gas passage through the tube.

All components were thoroughly vapor degreased before brazing. They were assembled with two preformed rings of 0.787 mm (0.031 in.) diameter BAg-3 brazing filler metal wire. The diametral clearance on the joints was 0.076 to 0.127 mm (0.003 to 0.005 in.). One preform, with a 9.5 mm (0.374 in.) internal diameter, was placed over the neck of the plug. The other, with a 12.7 mm (0.5 in.) internal diameter, was placed over the tube adjacent to the base joint. The joint areas were coated with type FB3-A brazing flux, and the assemblies were brazed in a continuous-belt conveyor furnace. Brazing filler metal BAg-3 was chosen, in preference to BAg-1 or BAg-1a, in order to avoid the risk of interface corrosion.

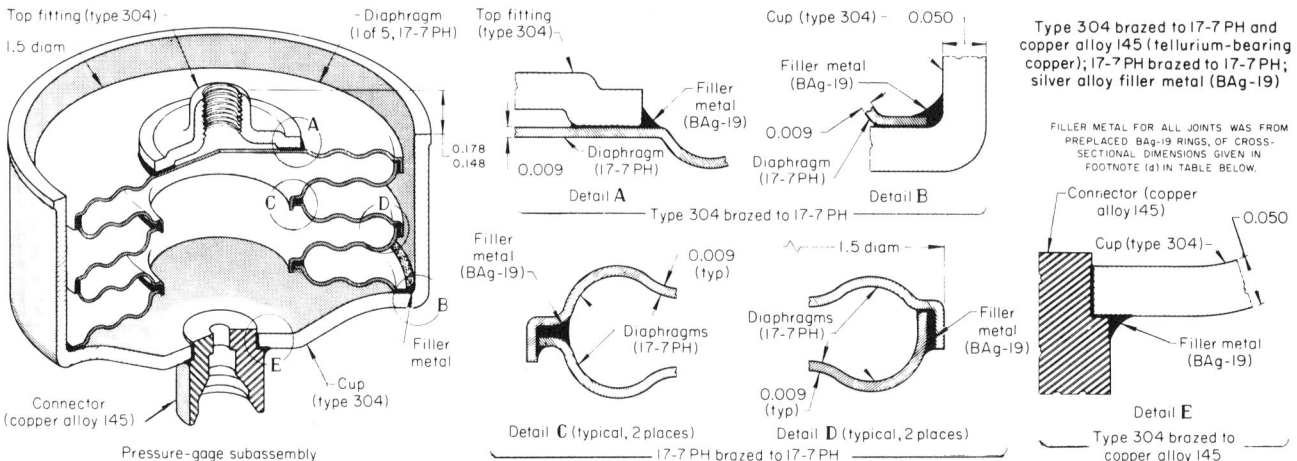

Furnace brazing in dissociated ammonia			
Furnace(a)	Chain-belt conveyor	Flux(e)	None
Furnace temperature(b), °C (°F)	980 (1800)	Furnace belt speed, mm/min (in./min)	255 (10)
Dissociated-ammonia dew point(c), °C (°F)	−60 (−80)	Heating time, min	5
Filler metal(d)	BAg-19	Cooling-chamber temperature(f), °C (°F)	15 (60)
		Precipitation-hardening temperature(g), °C (°F)	510 (950)

(a) Electrically heated, with elevated high-heat zone. (b) For brazing the subassembly and simultaneously solution heat treating the 17-7 PH diaphragms. (c) Achieved by running the dissociated ammonia through a molecular-sieve dryer after cracking. (d) Cross-sectional dimensions (and product forms) of preplaced rings were: for joint between diaphragm and top fitting (detail A), 1.3 mm (0.050 in.) wide by 0.10 to 0.13 mm (0.004 to 0.005 in.) thick stamping; for outside joints between diaphragm segments (detail D) and joint between diaphragm and cup (detail B), thick (ribbon); for inside joints between diaphragm segments (detail C), 0.76 mm (0.030 in.) wide by 0.13 mm (0.005 in.) thick (ribbon); and for joint between cup and connector (detail E), 1.52 by 0.254 mm (0.060 by 0.010 in.) (wire). (e) Use of BAg-19 eliminated the need for flux, which had been required with the silver filler metal originally used. (f) To cool rapidly from 980 °C (1800 °F) and ensure solution treatment of the 17-7 PH diaphragms. (g) In dry dissociated ammonia, after subassembly had been cooled to −40 °C (−40 °F) and dried. The 17-7 PH diaphragms were hardened to 44 to 48 HRC.

Fig. 10   Pressure-gage subassembly that combined furnace brazing with solution heat treatment. Dimensions given in inches

Furnace Brazing in a Vacuum Atmosphere. The majority of vacuum brazing is performed in two types of equipment utilizing either hot- or cold-walled furnaces. The hot-walled structure utilizes a retort that is evacuated and placed into a furnace, which provides the heat source. The retort can be single-pumped, providing a vacuum to temperatures up to 980 °C (1800 °F), or double-pumped for temperatures above 980 °C (1800 °F) to prevent the retort from collapsing. Limitations of the hot-walled furnace (retort) include longer cycle times, because the retort is heated externally; a 1200 °C (2200 °F) temperature limit; and slower cooling rates. Some advantages of hot-walled furnaces are lower initial capital expenditures, reduced contamination from the retort, and easy upkeep and maintenance.

The cold-walled vacuum furnace is typically designed with a water-cooled outer jacket that is protected by radiation shielding adjacent to the inner wall. The heating elements are exposed directly to the workload. A braze cycle may have temperatures that exceed 2200 °C (4000 °F), depending on the heating element material and the load-support structure. Heating and cooling rates for cold-walled vacuum furnaces are substantially less than they are for the hot-walled vacuum retort. Higher braze temperatures, in excess of 1260 °C (2300 °F), are obtainable in vacuum furnaces and are frequently employed.

Effect of Filler-Metal Composition. Vacuum brazing of many structural configurations made of austenitic stainless steels offers excellent heat and corrosion resistance for high-temperature service applications. Brazing filler metals, such as gold, gold-palladium, and nickel, offer greater high-temperature strength and oxidation resistance. Problems can occur when brazing the 300 series of stainless steels because of the carbide precipitation and loss of corrosion resistance that result when brazing in the temperature range from 480 to 815 °C (900 to 1500 °F). Brazing at temperatures in excess of 815 °C (1500 °F), using brazing filler metals with melting points that are higher than this temperature, followed by rapid cooling, will reduce carbide precipitation and improve corrosion properties.

Occasionally, wetting does not occur with a particular lot of stainless steel. Generally, alloying elements such as titanium and aluminum contribute to poor wettability.

Martensitic stainless steels, such as the 400 series, can be brazed successfully in vacuum. The use of a suitable brazing filler metal can result in austenitizing and brazing at the same time, followed by rapid cooling to harden the stainless steel.

Care must be exercised when selecting brazing filler metals for use in vacuum. Silver brazing filler metals, such as BAg-1, BAg-1a, and BAg-3, contain alloying elements of zinc and cadmium, which have very high vapor pressures. These elements vaporize if the furnace pressure is too low or the brazing temperature is excessive, or if a combination of these conditions exists. Copper and silver also vaporize under low-pressure conditions at higher brazing temperatures. Therefore, if brazing alloys containing copper or silver are to be used in vacuum, the furnace chamber must be

backfilled with an appropriate atmosphere to 40 to 65 Pa (0.3 to 0.5 torr) until melting occurs to prevent the loss of these elements. Caution must be exercised with the furnace exit gases because these gases are extremely toxic. Two materials that should never be put in a vacuum furnace under any condition are zinc and cadmium. It is recommended that specific alloys (for example, BAg-8 or BAg-13a) or other alloys free of zinc or cadmium be used when brazing in a vacuum furnace. A partial pressure may still be required for many of the alloys to prevent the vaporization of the silver.

Example 12. Vacuum Brazing to Improve Beverage Can Filling Nozzle. Because of a continuous problem in obtaining uniform and void-free fillets when using silver brazing filler metals and induction brazing methods, a switch was made to vacuum furnace brazing using a nickel brazing filler metal. The beverage filling nozzle shown in Fig. 13 is an assembly consisting of 16 short tubes brazed to a cast body section that connects to the supply piping. The tubes are pressed into the holes that are drilled at angles through the body, and then brazed to form a tight joint. Both the body and tubes are made from type 304 stainless steel.

The nozzles require a smooth surface that will not harbor bacteria. This means that the brazed joints must have uniform, smooth fillets and full-length, void-free filler metal penetration. In addition, the entire assembly must be resistant to chemical attack by the beverages being handled, by steam, or by cleaning compounds.

The prior method of brazing using silver-base filler metals was not very successful in obtaining void-free joints or consistent results. In addition, many of the beverages being handled did attack the silver brazing filler metal, causing corrosion and discoloration in the joint area. The nickel brazing filler metal selected for this application was BNi-9 (81.5Ni-15Cr-3.5B), because of its excellent capillary flow characteristics, low base-metal erosion, and self-fluxing properties. In addition, the alloy would be unaffected by subsequent processing operations, which include passivation and electropolishing.

The stainless parts were degreased and a small bead of the nickel brazing filler metal was placed around each tube. The brazing was done in a vacuum furnace at 1135 °C (2075 °F), where the part was heated and cooled at a controlled rate to ensure thermal stability. Careful control of the brazing cycle is the key element in obtaining the uniform fillets and void-free joints required for the nozzles.

Example 13. Cryogenic Valve Nickel Brazed in Vacuum. Cryogenic valves that are used to handle liquid nitrogen and liquid hydrogen require construction that provides high strength and impact resistance at extremely low temperatures, as well as light weight and good corrosion resistance (Fig. 14). Valves that are part of the propellant loading systems for ballistic missiles were used at temperatures of –250 °C (–425 °F), and at pressures of nearly 41.4 MPa (6 ksi). The body, flanges, seat, and

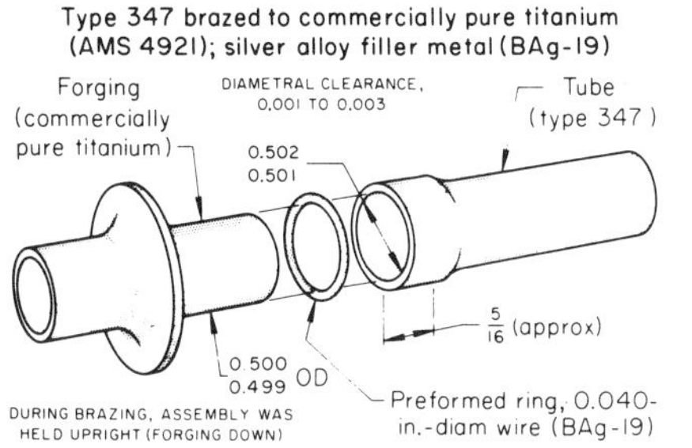

Type 347 brazed to commercially pure titanium (AMS 4921); silver alloy filler metal (BAg-19)

Furnace brazing in argon

Furnace(a)	Pit
Retort(b)	Inconel
Fixture material(c)	Titanium sheet
Furnace temperature, °C (°F)	925 ± 5 (1700 ± 10)
Brazing temperature, °C (°F)	900 ± 5 (1650 ± 10)
Argon dew points, °C (°F)	−65 (−85)(d); −60 (−70)(e)
Argon flow rate (purging to cooling), m³/h (ft³/h)	4 (150)
Filler metal(f)	BAg-19
Time at brazing temperature, min	<1
Cooling	In argon, to room temperature
Assembly production lot per cycle	1–20

(a) Gas fired, 1.8 m (72 in.) diameter, 1.8 m (72 in.) deep. (b) 610 mm (24 in.) diameter and length. (c) Holding fixture, to keep assembly upright (forging down) during brazing. (d) Incoming. (e) Exhaust. (f) 1 mm (0.040 in.) diameter wire

Fig. 11 Stainless steel and titanium assembly that was furnace brazed in an argon atmosphere. Dimensions given in inches

---

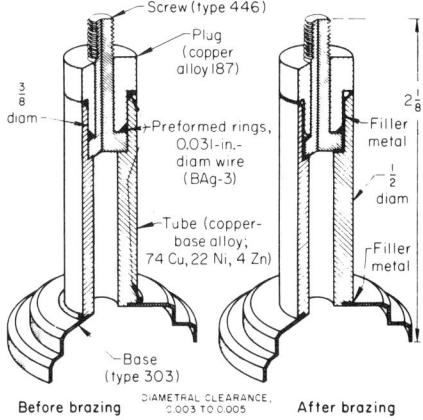

Types 446 and 303, and copper alloy 187 brazed to copper-base alloy (74 Cu, 22 Ni, 4 Zn); type 446 brazed to copper alloy 187 (99Cu,1Pb); silver alloy filler metal (BAg-3)

Furnace brazing in air atmosphere

Furnace(a)	Continuous belt
Furnace temperature, °C (°F)	745–790 (1370–1450)
Filler metal(b)	BAg-3
Flux	AMS 3410D (AWS type 3A)
Time at brazing temperature, min	1 (max)
Assembly production rate/h	140

(a) Air atmosphere. (b) Preformed rings, preplaced as shown in illustration, 0.8 mm (0.031 in.) diameter

Fig. 12 Stainless steel and copper gas-valve bobbin that was furnace brazed in an air atmosphere. Dimensions given in inches

bonnet were brazed with BNi-2 brazing filler metal in a vacuum furnace.

The valve seat and disc were cast from 17-7 or 17-4 PH steel or from cobalt-base Stellite. They were brazed in place at the same time the assembly was brazed. Brazing replaced the welding of the seat, which in this case had trouble in terms of weld deposit cracking. All parts, except the valve seat, were finish-machined before brazing. By eliminating the need for machining after brazing, costs were reduced enough to pay for the brazing operation.

Induction Brazing

The behavior of stainless steels, in terms of heating via electrical induction, depends on the metallurgical and physical properties of the particular material. This behavior can be considerably different from that of carbon and low-alloy steels, as well as from that of the more widely used nonferrous metals. In addition, the response of the steel to induction heating varies considerably, depending on whether a stainless steel is magnetic or nonmagnetic at room temperature. Differences in specific heat and electrical conductivity markedly affect the response to heating by induction.

Ferritic and martensitic (400 series) stainless steels are ferromagnetic at all temperatures, up to the Curie temperature. Thus, given the same power input, these steels generally heat faster than austenitic stainless steels, which are nonmagnetic in the annealed condition. Although cold working may induce slight magnetism in the austenitic chromium steels, the 400 series of stainless steels are strongly magnetic. The rate of heating to the temperature at which the filler metal flows usually affects induction-coil design and coupling. It may also influence the selection of power output frequency and other processing variables.

Stainless steels can be induction brazed in an air atmosphere, using a suitable flux. However, for critical applications, induction brazing is sometimes done in a protective or a vacuum atmosphere (refer to Example 14). In other applications, an inert gas, such as argon, can be used as a protective atmosphere to either minimize or prevent oxidation.

Example 14. Brazing a Tube to an End Blank. The assembly shown in Fig. 15, which is part of a solenoid, consisted of a type 321 stainless steel brazed to a type 416 end blank. The former material is a nonmagnetic austenitic steel, whereas the latter is martensitic and ferromagnetic. Consequently, although both metals were easily brazed, the achievement of a proper joint clearance between the two components was complicated by the marked differences in the CTEs of the two steels. Thus, calculations were needed to determine the room-temperature clearance required to provide a suitable clearance at the brazing temperature.

Because the assembly was not intended for high-temperature service, the selection of the low-melting-point silver brazing filler metal (BAg-1) and a relatively low brazing temperature of 650 °C (1200 °F) were used to minimize heating and oxidation of the stainless steel components.

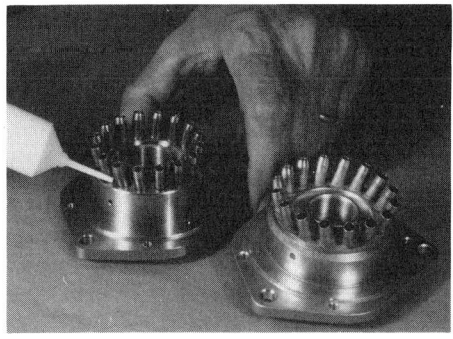

Fig. 13 Stainless steel type 304 beverage can filling nozzle. Tubes are vacuum brazed with a nickel brazing filler metal at 1120 °C (2050 °F). Left, location where paste alloy is placed around tube. Right, completed nozzle, showing smooth, void-free fillets. Courtesy of Wall Colmonoy Corp.

Fig. 14 Cryogenic valve that was vacuum brazed with BNi-2 brazing filler metal. All joints on the body, flanges, seat, and bonnets were brazed simultaneously. Courtesy of Wall Colmonoy Corp.

For brazing that is conducted at this temperature, calculations based on CTE values showed that the following dimensions and tolerances in the joining area would be satisfactory: for the tube diameter, 12.4 mm (0.494 in.) +0.000, –0.025 mm (–0.001 in); and for the inside diameter of the end blank, 12.7 mm (0.500 in.) +0.000, –0.025 mm (–0.001 in.). Thus, the diametral clearance at room temperature ranged from 0.127 to 0.178 mm (0.005 to 0.007 in.).

The shape of the assembly and the low melting point and brazing temperatures favored brazing by induction. The end blank was in the hardened and tempered condition prior to brazing, and the short induction heating cycle (10 s) did not reduce the hardness to less than the required minimum.

Prior to brazing, the components were vapor degreased. The end of the tube was dipped in flux and inserted in the end blank. A preformed ring of filler-metal wire was slipped over the tube and positioned at the top of the joint. Then, the end blank was placed on a holding fixture, positioned in a single-turn inductor (Fig. 15), and heated for 10 s.

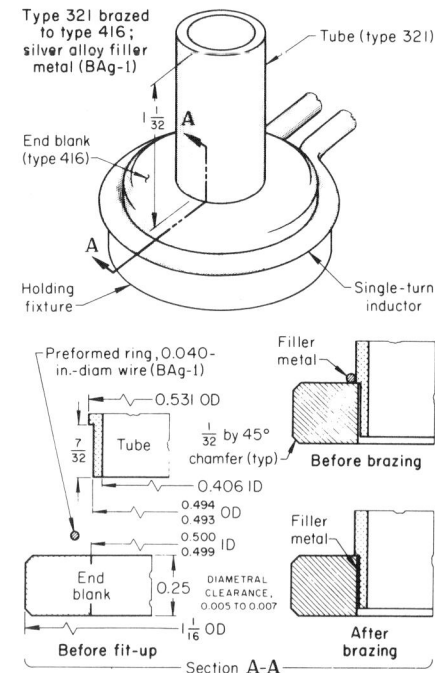

Induction brazing

Power supply(a), kW; kHz	20; 450
Inductor	Single-turn, copper tube
Brazing temperature, °C (°F)	650 (1200)
Filler metal(b)	BAg-1
Flux	AWS type FB3A
Time at brazing temperature, s	10
Cooling time in fixture, s	10
Assembly production rate/h	140

(a) Vacuum tube. (b) Wire form in 1 mm (0.040 in.) diameter

Fig. 15 Induction-brazed assembly. Dimensions given in inches

After brazing, the assembly was cooled in air for 10 s before being removed from the holding fixture. The assembly was then washed in hot water to remove the flux residue.

Example 15. Induction Brazing in a Vacuum Atmosphere. A distinctive advantage of induction brazing, as applied to stainless steel, is its suitability for simple setups that permit brazing in vacuum. Closed, nonmetallic containers with reasonably good strength and dielectric properties can provide an enclosure for the assembly to be brazed and can be evacuated prior to brazing. Because the inductor can be placed outside the container, it can heat the assembly efficiently without being part of the vacuum system.

Stainless steel collar-and-tube assemblies (Fig. 16) were brazed in a simple setup that combined induction heating and the protection afforded by heating in vacuum. The vacuum container consisted of a high-silica, low-expansion glass tube with copper end fittings connected to a vacuum system. The collar-and-tube components, with preformed BNi-7 filler-metal rings pressed into place on the shoulder of each collar, were positioned and held inside the glass tube by means of a simple holding fixture. The tube was sealed and evacuated with a multiple-turn inductor, outside the tube, in position to heat one of the collars. When the vacuum reached 0.133 Pa (10^{-3} torr), heating was started. The collar was heated slowly to 970 °C (1775 °F). After 4 min, the power was shut off. The tube was then repositioned to bring the second collar into the field of the inductor, and the heating sequence was repeated.

When the second collar had cooled to the point at which no glow was visible in normal light, the tube was backfilled for 5 min with argon. Brazed joints were inspected visually and metallographically. They were found to be sound and acceptable in all respects. The induction heating source was an 8 kVA spark-gap converter with an operating frequency of 175 to 200 kHz. The water-cooled external inductor coil was made of 6.4 mm ($\frac{1}{4}$ in.) diameter copper tubing. The production rate was 22 assemblies per day.

Dip Brazing in a Salt Bath

The brazing of stainless steel by immersing either all or a portion of the assembly in molten salt offers essentially the same advantages and limitations that would apply to the brazing of similar assemblies made of carbon steel.

Example 16. Change from Torch or Induction Brazing to Dip Brazing. The television wave-guide assembly shown in Fig. 17 consisted of a type 304 stainless steel flange brazed to a tube of copper alloy C23000 (red brass, 85Cu-15Zn). Satisfactory end use depended on minimal distortion. When the assembly was brazed by torch or induction brazing, the rejection rate sometimes reached 70%, because of distortion caused by uneven heating. When dip brazing was adopted, the rejection rate dropped to nearly zero.

Prior to brazing, the stainless steel flange was degreased and pickled, and the brass tube was degreased and bright dipped. Then, the flange was placed on the tube, the tube end was flared outward slightly, a preform of the BAg-3 filler metal was placed over the tube adjacent to the flange, and FB3-A (AMS 3410D) flux was applied to the joint. The assembly was suspended flange-down over an electrically heated salt bath to preheat the flange and dry the flux. Next, the assembly was lowered slowly into the molten bath, which was maintained at 730 °C (1350 °F) for a distance of approximately 25 mm (1 in.) above the flange. After being held in the bath for 0.5 min, the assembly was removed and air cooled. The flux residue was removed by rinsing the assembly in 60 °C (140 °F) water. The production rate was 30 assemblies per hour.

High-Energy-Beam Brazing

High-energy-beam brazing techniques, such as those based on electron or laser beams, have been used to a limited extent. Both electron- and laser-beam brazing are performed in a manner similar to electron- and laser-beam welding, except that the beam is defocused to provide a larger beam and to reduce the power density to prevent the base metal from melting. Generally, the speed at which the beam is swept is increased so that a

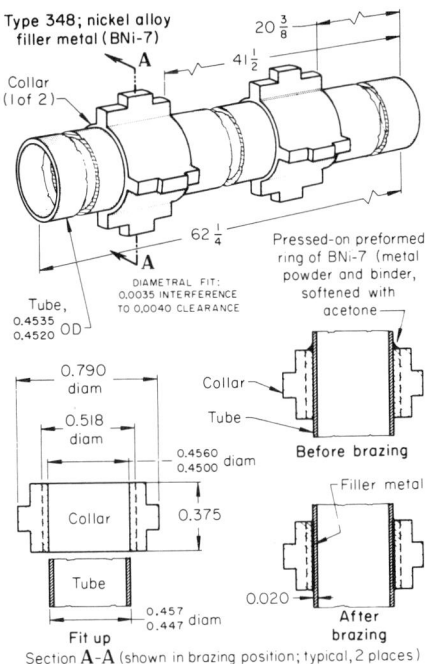

Fig. 16 Collar and tube assembly that was induction brazed in vacuum. Dimensions given in inches

larger area of the part is heated and more uniform heating of the part occurs.

In electron-beam brazing, the high vacuum used in the work chamber (0.0133 to 0.00133 Pa, or 10^{-4} to 10^{-5} torr) permits the adequate flow of brazing filler metal on properly cleaned joints without the use of a reducing atmosphere or flux. Thus, flux entrapment does not occur, and the work does not require cleaning after brazing. The high-vacuum atmosphere and the absence of flux provide a brazing environment that avoids the problems associated with prepared atmospheres, which are encountered when brazing some stainless steels, as well as the more-reactive metals (such as titanium).

In laser-beam brazing, the parts are normally protected with a shielding gas to prevent the occurrence of oxidation. If necessary, the beam spot diameter can be enlarged substantially, depending on the type of equipment, while providing an adequate amount of heat input for brazing. A work movement technique can be used if an area substantially larger than the beam spot size is to be heated, and the work can be rotated or indexed under the beam for uniform heating (Example 18). In high-energy brazing, the brazing temperatures are quickly attained, and heat can be localized to minimize grain growth, the softening of cold-worked metal, and, in austenitic stainless steels, the sensitizing of the material by carbide precipitation.

Applications. Electron-beam brazing is a convenient method for brazing small assemblies, such as instrument packages. It combines the versatility and close controllability of electron-beam heating with the advantages of vacuum brazing. Packaged devices can be encapsulated with an internal vacuum without damaging the basic package.

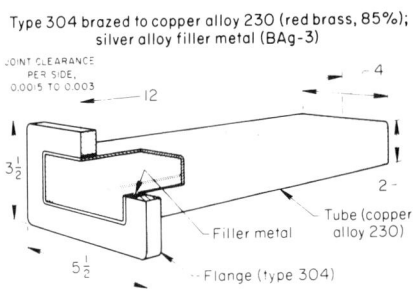

Fig. 17 Television wave-guide assembly joined by salt-bath dip brazing. Dimensions given in inches

Tube-to-header joints in small heat-transfer equipment made of heat-resistant alloys and refractory metals are sometimes brazed using an electron beam. In one technique, the tube-to-header joint is electron-beam welded on the top side of the header. The heat of the beam causes the brazing filler metal that is preplaced on the reverse side of the header at the joint to melt and flow. Small-diameter, thin-wall stainless steel tubes are readily joined by electron-beam brazing, as described below in Example 17.

Laser-beam brazing applications are difficult, if not impossible, to achieve by ordinary brazing methods. Application examples include:

- Miniature thin-wall precision parts that require minimal heat input during joining operations to maintain dimensional tolerances
- Thin base metals, 0.1 mm (0.004 in.) and less, that tend to become eroded and sometimes perforated during brazing operations using filler metals or fluxes
- Joints on assemblies containing heat-sensitive materials or parts that cannot be removed during joining operations
- Brazed joints near glass-to-metal seals, adhesively bonded joints, or other thermally sensitive connections
- Connections inside evacuated or pressurized vessels or containers (e.g., within sealed glass vacuum tubes)

Example 17. Use of Defocused Beam for the Electron-Beam Brazing of Small Tubes. Capillary and other small-diameter tubes used in instrument packages required that leak-tight joints be made without overheating the other portions of the assembly. The avoidance of flux was also necessary, because entrapped flux would be either difficult or impossible to remove. These conditions were satisfied by electron-beam brazing.

Figure 18 shows a typical joint in type 304 tubing with a 2.55 mm (0.100 in.) outside diameter and a 0.254 mm (0.010 in.) thick wall that was brazed by the electron-beam process. The joint design was based on the use of a 19 mm ($\frac{3}{4}$ in.) long socket coupling that was counterbored with a diametral clearance of 0.076 to 0.127 mm (0.003 to 0.005 in.) over the tube diameter and to a depth of 6.4 mm ($\frac{1}{4}$ in.). The average joint clearance (per side) was therefore 0.050 mm (0.002

in.). Tubes and socket couplings were deburred and solvent cleaned. They were then assembled with two wire-ring preforms of BCu-1 brazing filler metal, as shown in Fig. 18. The tubes were held in position with a small clamping fixture, and the assembly was mounted in a fixed position on a table in the vacuum chamber.

After pumpdown, the joint was brought to the brazing temperature by moving the table back and forth under the defocused electron beam, which caused the heat of the 4.76 mm ($^3/_{16}$ in.) diameter beam spot to be applied primarily to the central portion of the coupling. After being heated by conduction at a relatively low beam power, the brazing filler metal melted and flowed through the joint in approximately 30 s.

About ten assemblies were brazed, at a rate of one per pumpdown, using the machine settings and other brazing conditions specified in Fig. 18. Sensitizing the austenitic stainless steel was not a problem in this application, because the service environment was not significantly corrosive. The relatively short-time brazing cycle minimized grain growth and the dilution of the thin-wall tubing with copper brazing filler metal.

Example 18. Laser Brazing Capillary Tubing to a Pressure Sensor Fitting. A miniature pressure sensor assembly required a strong, pressure-tight (several thousand pounds per square inch) joint between 70Cu-30Ni capillary tubing, with an outside diameter of 0.178 mm (0.007 in.) and a wall thickness of 0.05 mm (0.002 in.), and a

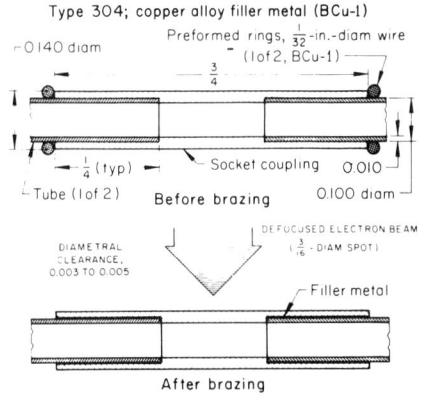

Type 304; copper alloy filler metal (BCu-1)

Electron-beam brazing

Joint type	Cylindrical sleeve
Filler metal(a)	BCu-1
Machine capacity, kW	3
Gun type	Fixed diode
Vacuum chamber diameter, mm (in.)	610 (24)
Maximum vacuum, Pa (torr)	0.00133 (1×10^{-5})
Fixture	Holding jig
Pumpdown time, min	30
Brazing power, kV; mA	18; 20–30
Beam spot size diameter, mm (in.)	4.76 ($^3/_{16}$)
Brazing vacuum, Pa (torr)	0.00133 (1×10^{-5})
Brazing time, s	30

(a) Wire form in 0.03 mm ($^1/_{32}$ in.) diameter

Fig. 18 Joint between two capillary tubes of an instrument package, made by electron-beam brazing using a low-power defocused beam in a high-vacuum atmosphere. Dimensions given in inches

type 316 stainless steel fitting having a wall thickness of 0.127 mm (0.005 in.). Previous attempts by conventional brazing techniques invariably caused flow of the brazing alloy into the 0.076 mm (0.003 in.) diameter bore of the capillary tubing, closing it. Attempts to fusion weld the copper-nickel to stainless steel were similarly unsuccessful. The parts were successfully laser brazed using the procedure described below:

- *Laser characteristics:* Neodymium YAG 50-W pulsed laser; 100 mm (4 in.) focal length lens; TEM_{01} mode; pulse interval, 3 s; laser pulse energy, 0.87 J; measured beam spot diameter at workpiece, 0.9 mm (0.036 in.); total pulse width, 6 ms; effective pulse width, 5.1 ms; peak pulse power, 0.2 kW (energy density = 1.4 × 10^2 J/cm^2; power density = 2.7×10^4 W/cm^2
- *Flux:* Standard fluoride-based silver brazing flux mixed with powdered brazing filler metal in a flux-to-filler-metal proportion of 1-to-20 by volume
- *Filler metal:* Prealloyed powdered -325 mesh BAg-1 filler and flux mixture (water added to make paste consistency) was preplaced in joint region and a controlled volume provided in the joint by drawing a 1 mm (0.04 in.) diameter metering rod through the mixture, allowing the surface of the rod to run along the sides of the joint members. The resulting meniscus-shaped volume of the flux and filler mixture was dried thoroughly under an infrared heat lamp before brazing.
- *Shielding gas:* The entire joint region was blanketed with pure argon using a shaped porous bronze gas-distribution shielding fixture with a hole to allow access for the laser beam.
- *Laser/joint configuration:* The length of capillary tubing was first assembled to the stainless steel fitting by inserting the end of the tubing into a hole drilled through the fitting. This positioned the tubing in the desired location and retained it in alignment during brazing. As shown in Fig. 19, the entire joint assembly was rotated incrementally with each laser pulse, allowing about an 80% overlap of each previously brazed spot. The laser head was fixed above the rotation fixture holding the part. A series of tacks equally spaced around the periphery of the joint were made first, followed by a full rotation of the joint for the brazing cycle.

Soldering

As defined in the introduction to this article, soldering involves temperatures below 450 °C (840 °F). Although all of the stainless steels can be joined by soldering when the proper techniques are used, these materials are not generally soldered because they are used in applications which involve high strength and/or corrosion/heat resistance. Nevertheless, soldered stainless steel joints still find applications in architecture, food processing, and plumbing. As with brazing, chromium oxide films must be adequately removed to enhance solderability. Types of soldering processes used to join stainless steels include iron soldering

(the soldering iron or bit), torch soldering, furnace and infrared soldering, dip soldering, resistance soldering, induction soldering, and laser soldering. Each of these processes are described in Volume 6 of the *ASM Handbook*.

Precleaning and Surface Preparation

Oil, film, grease, tarnish, paint, pencil markings, cutting lubricants, and general atmospheric dirt interfere with the soldering process. A clean surface is imperative to ensure a sound and uniform quality soldered joint. Fluxing alone cannot substitute for adequate precleaning. Therefore, a variety of techniques are used to clean and prepare the surface of metal to be soldered. The importance of cleanliness and surface preparation cannot be overemphasized. These steps help ensure sound soldered joints, as well as a rapid production rate. Precleaning can also greatly reduce repair work due to defective soldered joints. The most common cleaning methods for stainless steels are degreasing, acid cleaning, and mechanical abrasion.

Degreasing. Either solvent or alkaline degreasing prior to soldering is recommended for cleaning oily or greasy surfaces. It should be noted that the list of frequently used organic solvents has changed, because the use of chlorofluorocarbon-base materials has been restricted by environmental laws and codes. Substitute materials include acetone, isopropyl alcohol, terpenes, alkaline detergent solutions (for example, 1 to 3% trisodium phosphate with surfactants), and newer semiaqueous compounds. Of the solvent degreasing methods, the vapor condensation of halogenated hydrocarbon-type solvents probably leaves the least residual film on the surface. The cold articles to be degreased are suspended above the boiling solvent, causing the vapor to condense on the articles and drain back into the boiling liquid. Only clean, freshly distilled solvent contacts the material to be cleaned, so there is no recontamination to hinder the degreasing. It is critical that toxicity to workers and the potential fire hazard generated by fumes or aerosols be adequately assessed when vapor degreasing is carried out.

The least satisfactory method of degreasing is to rub the articles with a cloth saturated with solvent. In the absence of vapor degreasing apparatus, immersion in liquid solvents or in detergent solutions is often a suitable procedure. The efficiency of this method of cleaning can be considerably enhanced by incorporating ultrasonic cleaning. This method employs vibrational waves which, through cavitation, promote removal of soils, grit, or grease.

Alkali detergents are also used for degreasing. In general, a 1 to 3% solution of trisodium phosphate and a wetting agent is satisfactory. All cleaning solutions must be thoroughly washed from base-metal surfaces by steam or water before soldering. Whenever water is used, soft water is preferable, as residues from hard water may interfere with the soldering. These cleaning methods are especially designed for substantial volume and should be used according to proper safety precautions and suitability for the application.

Acid Cleaning. The removal of heavy oxide layers from stainless steel surfaces is performed by acid cleaning, or pickling, when the chemical action of the flux is incapable of removing the oxide layer during the soldering process. Prior to acid cleaning, the surface must be completely cleaned of organic contaminants, to ensure the effectiveness of the cleaning process. Water-base solutions typically do not penetrate organic films. Surface layers other than oxides, such as sulfides, hydrides, or chlorides, may require specialized cleaning solutions. For increasingly thicker layers, whether an oxide film or another type of surface contaminant, longer cleaning periods or more aggressive chemicals are required for the removal process. However, either approach increases the chance of damage to the substrate.

General solutions used to clean metal surfaces consist of hydrochloric, sulfuric, orthophosphoric, nitric, and hydrofluoric acids used either singly or mixed. Specific solutions used for cleaning stainless steels include:

- H_3PO_4 (100%):9H_2O to 2H_3PO_4 (100%): 3H_2O
- 2H_2SO_4 (77%):HCl (25%):8H_2O
- 2HNO_3 (70%):3HF:5H_2O

Inhibitors are typically added to commercially available acid solutions to prevent pitting. Distilled or deionized water should be used in solutions to prevent unwanted deposits and residual films after cleaning. Electropolishing processes can also be used to remove metal-oxide layers.

Whether a chemical etch or an electropolishing procedure is used, the corrosive solutions must be thoroughly rinsed from the surfaces to prevent staining or latent corrosion. These artifacts may also deteriorate solderability in follow-up processing steps. Rinses with distilled water, followed by an alcohol rinse to remove the water, is a typical sequence. Workpieces should not be dried with unfiltered or undried "house" compressed air, because oil and water droplets from the air line will quickly contaminate the surface. Once cleaned, the surface should be soldered as soon as possible to limit reoxidation, or measures should be taken to protect surfaces from further contamination.

Mechanical abrasion can be used to remove excessively thick oxide films. Techniques include using sandpaper, steel wool, or metal files, or blasting with particulates. However, solderability can be quickly degraded by abrasive media that become embedded in the substrate surface and are not readily wetted by the molten solder. Procedures that use abrasive particles (blasting or sandpaper) or steel wool should be followed by a chemical etching treatment to remove the layer of surface material containing the foreign particles. Metal files are used to prepare the surfaces of larger, more-rugged substrates, such as pipes and fittings, and they should be cleaned of contaminant materials prior to use.

Coatings. Difficult-to-solder materials like stainless steels may lose their solderability too quickly after precleaning and become unprocessible. In these instances, coatings can be applied to protect the base metal prior to final assembly. Methods of application include electroplating,

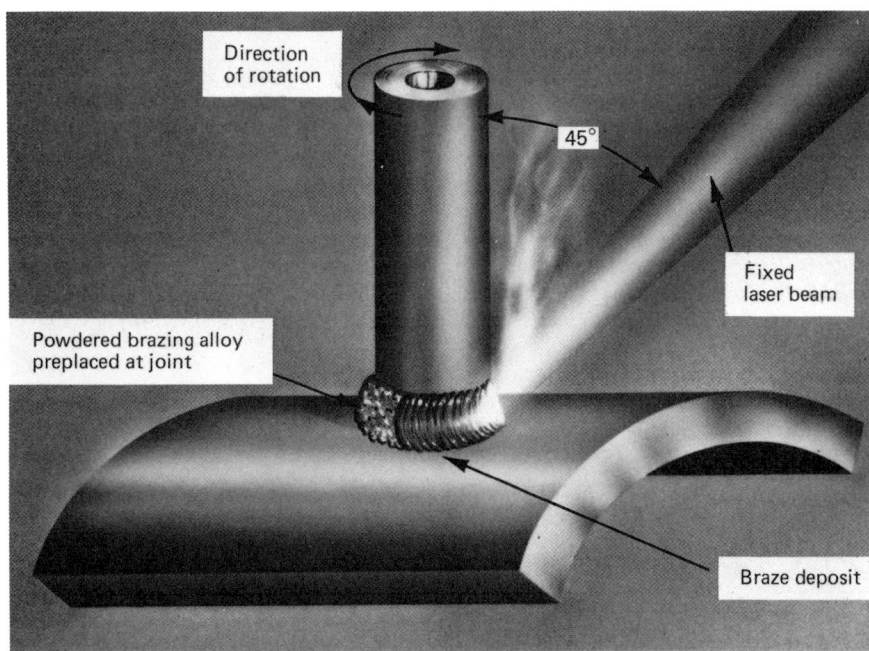

Fig. 19 Laser brazing of capillary tubing to pressure sensor fitting

electroless plating, evaporation, chemical vapor deposition, or dipping in a molten metal bath. Table 5 identifies 100Sn and tin-lead solder coatings that are used to protect base-metal solderability. These protective coatings can be electroplated on the surface or they can be applied by dipping the substrate into a hot solder or tin bath. Substrates with electroplated films can be heated above the melting temperature of the coating to "fuse" it, which provides an improved seal against air and contaminants, similar to the protection obtained with hot-dipped tin or solder coatings. Electroless tin processes, including "immersion" platings, are also used.

Solderability can also be improved by electroplating a "solderable" layer of nickel onto the stainless steel substrate. These films must be adequately thick (1.5 to 4 μm) to avoid being consumed by the metallurgical reaction with the solder, and they must exhibit adequate adhesion to the base material. A gold "protective" layer 1.3 to 2.5 μm thick can also be deposited onto the solderable nickel coating in order to prevent excessive oxidation or contamination. This protective layer is then consumed by the solder.

Gold plating layers should be removed by hot-solder dipping twice in a bath of molten solder if the calculated gold content of the solder joint will exceed 3 to 4 wt%, in order to prevent solder-joint embrittlement by gold-tin intermetallic formation. Electroplated gold layers should be pure gold, preferably type III, 99.9% pure, and grade A, according to MIL-G-45204C. Gold coatings alloyed with cobalt, nickel, or both (termed "hard gold"), which are used for wear resistance, are difficult to solder, because of oxidation of the cobalt or nickel component. Only matte finishes should be specified for soldering applications. "Bright" platings require organic additives in the

bath, which then become entrapped in the gold coating and subsequently volatize during soldering. This creates voids in the joints and poor wetting properties.

Surface Finish. Unpolished pickled finishes No. 1 and No. 2 or polished surfaces No. 3, No. 4, or No. 6 are preferred to the brightly polished surfaces No. 7 and No. 8. If highly polished surfaces are to be soldered, they should be roughened first with emery cloth or by any other suitable means, as solder will adhere more readily to a slightly roughened surface. Surface finishes for stainless steels are described in detail in the article "Surface Engineering" in this Volume.

Solders and Fluxes

Solders. Principal soldering alloys used to join stainless steels are the tin-lead alloys. Pure tin, tin-antimony, and tin-silver solders are used for food handling and other applications where lead would be hazardous. Tables 6 and 7 list properties and applications, respectively, of applicable solder alloys. More detailed information on solder alloys can be found in the article "General Soldering" in Volume 6 of the *ASM Handbook*.

Fluxes. The major role of the flux is the removal of thin tarnish layers during the initial stages of the soldering process, thereby permitting the molten solder to react with the substrate and to spread. The flux has two additional functions. One is that it lowers the surface tension of the solder, allowing it to more readily fill gaps and holes by capillary action. The other function is that the flux coating protects the metal surface from reoxidation during the heating steps just prior to soldering.

Fluxes contain three principal ingredients: an active chemical compound, such as halide, for oxide removal; wetting agents to improve surface cover-

Table 5 Tin and solder coatings to preserve base-metal solderability

Coating	Thickness μm	Thickness μin.	Comments
Electroplated 100Sn	7.6-13	300-500	Concern for whisker growth with moisture and residual stresses; recommended fusing
Electroplated 100Sn, fused	2.5-13	100-500	Melting point of tin, 232 °C (450 °F)
Electroplated Sn-Pb	7.6-23	300-900	Available compositions: 63Sn-37Pb, 95Pb-5Sn, etc.; plating composition may deviate from nominal values
Electroplated Sn-Pb, fused	2.5-13	100-500	Melting points: 63Sn-37Pb, 183 °C (361 °F); 95Pb-5Sn, 314 °C (597 °F)
Hot-dipped 100Sn or Sn-Pb (63Sn-37Pb)	>5.1	>200	Uniform coverage required
Electroless ("immersion") 100Sn	~1.5	~60	Protection sensitive to deposition process details; qualification tests recommended

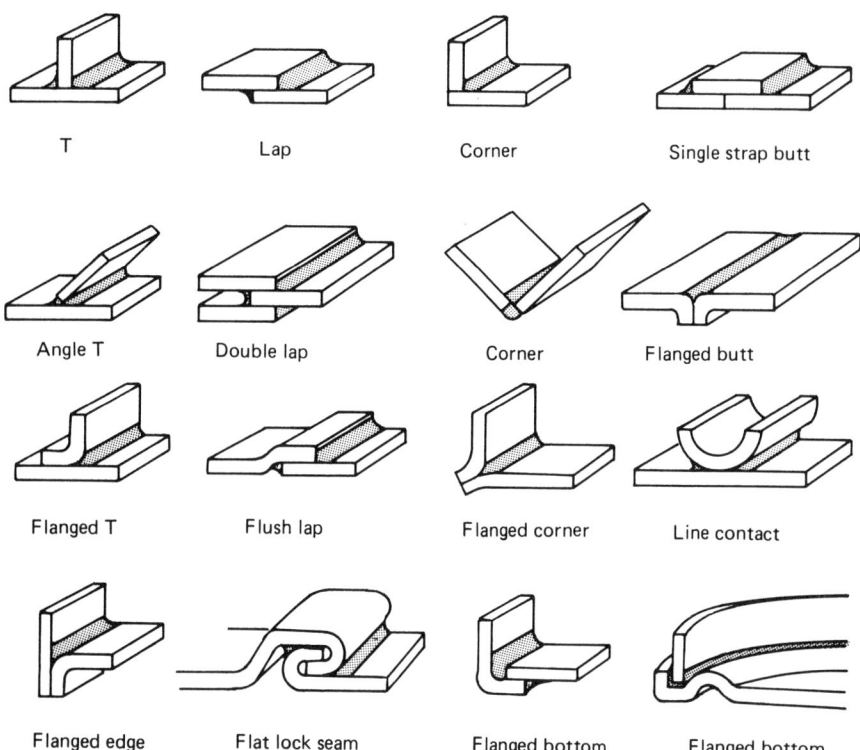

Fig. 20 Common structural solder joints

T   Lap   Corner   Single strap butt

Angle T   Double lap   Corner   Flanged butt

Flanged T   Flush lap   Flanged corner   Line contact

Flanged edge   Flat lock seam   Flanged bottom   Flanged bottom

age; and a vehicle to dilute and mix the cleaning compound and wetting agents together. The vehicle, which is removed by evaporation during the soldering process, is typically water, isopropyl alcohol, glycerin, glycol (for liquid fluxes), or petroleum jelly (for flux pastes or creams). Fluxes are characterized by their cleaning agent and are assigned to one of these categories of increasing activity: rosin-base fluxes, organic-acid fluxes (also called "intermediate" or "water-soluble" fluxes), and inorganic-acid fluxes.

The inorganic-acid fluxes, which are used for soldering stainless steels, are broken down into two categories:

- Pure acids, such as hydrochloric, hydrofluoric, or phosphoric acids, which have surfactants added to enhance coverage
- Inorganic salt mixtures or solutions, which may also contain surfactants

Proper flux selection is based on the salt mixture having a melting temperature that is less than that of the solder. The molten salt reduces the surface oxides and coats the base metal to prevent reoxidation during the soldering process. Flux activity is further increased by dissolving the flux in a water vehicle. The salts break down to release Cl⁻ ions, which combine with water to form a hydrochloric acid (HCl) "activator." The fluxes, particularly the water solutions, may contain surfactants to assist the complete coverage of the joint area. A paste form of the flux uses petroleum jelly as the vehicle. Typical inorganic flux solutions for stainless steels include:

1. Zinc chloride, mL (oz)	2510 (85)
Ammonium chloride, mL (oz)	190 (6.5)
Stannous chloride, mL (oz)	270 (9)
Hydrochloric acid, mL (oz)	60 (2)
Wetting agent (optional), wt%	0.1
Water	(a)
2. Zinc chloride, mL (oz)	1420 (48)
Ammonium chloride, mL (oz)	150 (5)
Hydrochloric acid, mL (oz)	90 (3)
Wetting agent (optional), wt%	0.1
Water	(a)

(a) To make 3.8 mL (1 gal)

Due to the corrosive nature of these fluxes, the flux residues and the fluxes themselves must be thoroughly removed after processing. Residues are removed by hot water rinses and follow-up polar-solvent rinses.

Joint Types

Any of the usual types of solder joints can be used to join stainless steels. Figure 20 illustrates the various types of structural solder joints. The joint should be designed in such a way that the solder is not required to contribute to the structural strength of the assembly. The stainless steels have tensile strengths ranging from about 500 to 2000 MPa (70 to 290 ksi). When these strengths are compared to 13 to 48 MPa (2000 to 7000 psi) for solders, it can easily be seen why the joint should not be depended upon for strength. When strength is required, the parts should be riveted or a lock seam joint should be

Table 6 Properties of solders used to join stainless steels

Alloy	Tensile strength MPa	Tensile strength ksi	Shear strength MPa	Shear strength ksi	Density, g/cm³	Melting range Solidus °C	Solidus °F	Liquidus °C	Liquidus °F
50Sn-50Pb	41.4	6.0	35.8	5.2	8.89	183	361	216	421
60Sn-40Pb	52.5	7.6	38.6	5.6	8.53	183	361	190	374
100% Sn	11.7	1.7	12.4	1.8	7.28	232	450	232	450
95Sn-5Sb	40.7	5.9	41.4	6.0	7.20	233	451	240	464
96Sn-4Ag	(a)	(a)	(a)	(a)	7.36	221	430	221	430

(a) The short-term bulk solder strength of tin-silver solder is similar to that of tin-antimony solder. Source: Nickel Development Institute

used. A good seal can best be obtained if the joint areas are precoated before assembly.

In the event the parts are to be used in highly corrosive environments or at elevated temperatures, the joint must be located in such a manner that it will not be subject to corrosion or high temperature. If this cannot be done, welding or brazing should be considered in lieu of soldering.

Adhesive Bonding

Although adhesive bonding of metals is usually associated with the use of light metals (aluminum and titanium and their alloys) in aerospace or aircraft structures, stainless steels can also be joined by this method. Adhesive bonding of stainless steels has the following inherent characteristics that make it useful:

- The joint is almost invisible, enhancing product appearance.
- Loading of the joint is evenly distributed.
- The adhesive acts to seal out the environment.
- The adhesive can aid in reducing some of the galvanic corrosion that ordinarily occurs when dissimilar metals are joined and subsequently exposed to an electrolyte.
- It provides intimate joining of metals and nonmetals that previously could be attached only by mechanical methods.
- An intimate joint can be made between similar or different metals of markedly different thickness.
- Intimate joining of stainless steel sheet to thin nonmetallic films is possible.
- Adhesive-bonded structures are superior in their resistance to sonic vibrations (sonic life, 10 to 1) compared to other standard construction.
- Fatigue characteristics of bonded joints (particularly in aircraft) are superior to those of joints made by other methods.
- Conventional structures that would be difficult to machine can often be fabricated more easily as laminate structures.
- Adhesives often permit extensive design simplification.

Functions of Adhesive-Bonded Joints

Mechanical Fastening. The major function of adhesives is for mechanical fastening. Because an adhesive can transmit loads from one member of a joint to another, it allows a more uniform stress distribution than is obtained using a mechanical fastener. Thus, adhesives often permit the fabrication of structures that are mechanically equivalent or superior to conventional assemblies and, furthermore, have cost and weight benefits. For example, adhesives can join thin metal sections to thick sections so that the full strength of the thin section is used. (Conventional mechanical fastening or spot welding produces a structure whose strength is limited to that of the areas of the thin section that contact the fasteners or the welds.)

Sealing and Insulating. Because the adhesive in a properly prepared joint provides full con-

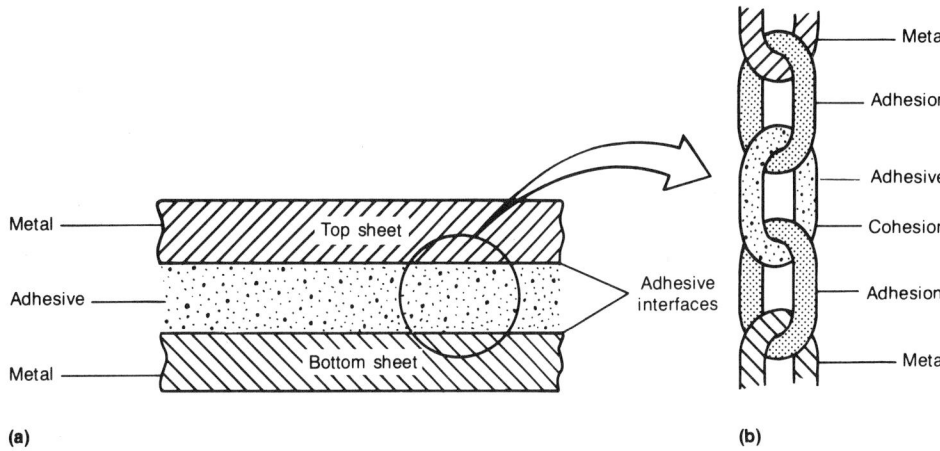

Fig. 21 Schematic of a metal-to-metal adhesive-bonded joint. (a) Adhesive sandwiched between two metal sheets. (b) Analogy of adhesive-bonded joint components to individual links in a chain

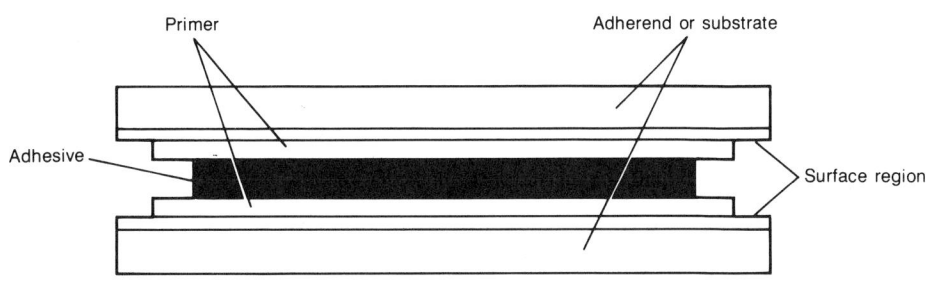

Fig. 22 Idealized adhesively bonded assembly

Table 7 Characteristics of solder alloys used to join stainless steels

Alloy	Color match to stainless steel	Use	Comments
50Sn-50Pb	Poor	Duct work, roofing, and sheet metal assemblies where appearance and special joint properties are not important	Satisfactory general-purpose solder. Not for color matching
60Sn-40Pb	Fair	Signs, ornamental trim, and flashing where appearance is more important. Used for tinning	Best all-around tin-lead solder. May discolor with time. Has better wetting and flowing characteristics than 50Sn-50Pb
Pure tin	Good	Distilled water equipment or special chemical use where lead cannot be tolerated	Low joint strength (see Table 6). Good corrosion resistance. Nontoxic. Good color match
95Sn-5Sb	Good	Food handling equipment where lead must be avoided. Refrigeration equipment to −70 °C (−95 °F)	Wide service-temperature range. Good solder for food contact applications. Good nonstaining properties. Better joint strength. Higher cost
96Sn-4Ag	Very good	Food handling equipment and fine ornamental work requiring higher strength	Best color match and blending properties. Good joint strength and corrosion resistance. Highest cost

Source: Nickel Development Institute

tact with mating surfaces, it forms a barrier so fluids do not attack or soften it. An adhesive may also function as an electrical and/or thermal insulator in a joint.

Resisting Corrosion and Vibration. Adhesives can also prevent electrochemical corrosion in joints between dissimilar metals. They may also act as vibration dampers. The mechanical damping characteristics of an adhesive can be changed by formulation. However, changing such a property in an adhesive generally changes other properties of the joint, such as tensile or shear strength, elongation, or resistance to peel or cleavage.

Fig. 23 Comparative water-break test results showing that water forms a thin, continuous coating and wets the entire area of a properly prepared surface (left), whereas it collects in discrete beads and is repelled by an unprepared or improperly prepared surface (right)

Resisting Fatigue. A property somewhat related to the ability to damp vibration is resistance to fatigue. A properly selected adhesive can generally withstand repeated strains induced by cyclic loading without the propagation of failure-producing cracks.

Smoothing Contours. Adhesives usually do not change the contours of the parts they join. Unlike screws, rivets, or bolts, adhesives give little or no visible external evidence of their presence.

Characteristics of an Adhesive Joint

An adhesive-bonded joint is analogous to a chain consisting of a number of individual links (Fig. 21), the weakest of which finally determines the strength of the chain. As shown in Fig. 22, the chain consists of:

- *Metal adherend:* a body held to another body by an adhesive
- *Substrate:* a material upon the surface of which an adhesive-containing substance is spread for any purpose, such as bonding or coating (broader term than *adherend*)
- *Primer:* a coating applied to a surface, prior to the application of an adhesive, to improve the performance of the bond
- *Adhesive:* a substance capable of holding materials together by surface attachment

Surface preparation of the adherends is necessary prior to the application of an adhesive. The treatment may range from a simple solvent wipe that is completed in seconds to a multistage cleaning and chemical treatment requiring 30 min or more.

The purpose of prebond treatments is to remove existing adventitious surface layers from the parts to be joined and to replace them with sound surface layers known to be suitable for the application. If a layer of grease or oil on an adherend is not removed, or if it is not absorbed and dispersed by the adhesive, it will affect the performance of the joint. Similarly, a thick or weak oxide layer on a metal adherend lowers joint strength and durability. It may be desirable to treat the surface, replacing an existing layer with a thinner and/or stronger oxide layer and/or one with different microroughness characteristics, as described in the following section.

Surface Preparation (Ref 4)

To correctly prepare the surface to be joined, all grease, oil, and foreign particles should be removed. With most high-performance adhesives this step is critical, because for good wetting the adherend should have a higher surface tension than the adhesive. Even a thumbprint on an otherwise clean surface can prevent the adhesive from spontaneously wetting and spreading.

Organic contaminants are removed by degreasing, while loose deposits are dislodged by mechanical methods (wire brushing, rubbing

Table 8 Surface treatments for adhesive bonding of stainless steels

Cleaning	Abrasion or chemical treatment		Method
Degrease by washing in trichloroethane (see ASTM D 2651 for alternative procedures).	Remove surface deposits with nonmetallic agent—alumina grit paper.		
	(A) General purpose treatment:		(A)
	Bath 1:		
	Sodium metasilicate	2.5 pbw	Immerse in Bath 1 for 10 min at 160-180 °F (71-82 °C).
	Tetrasodium pyrophosphate	1.1 pbw	Rinse thoroughly in running tapwater, then in cold DI water.
	Sodium hydroxide	1.1 pbw	Oven dry at 200 °F (93 °C) for 10 min.
	Nacconol NR (Allied Chemical Corp.)	0.3 pbw	Bond as soon as possible.
	DI water	95 pbw	
	(B) For high-temperature use, further treat the metal:		(B)
	Bath 2:		
	Oxalic acid	1 pbw	Immerse metal for 10 min in Bath 2 at 185-195 °F (85-90 °C).
	Conc. H_2SO_4 (s.g. 1.86)	1 pbw	Under cold running water, scrub away any black residue with clean, stiff bristle brush.
	DI water	8 pbw	Rinse in DI water.
	Dissolve oxalic acid before stirring in the H_2SO_4.		Dry in oven at 200 °F (93 °C) for 10-15 min.
	(C) For resistance to high peel stresses, further treat metal from (A). [Do not combine (B) and (C) treatments.]		(C)
	Bath 3:		
	$Na_2Cr_2O_7 \cdot 2H_2O$	3.5 pbw	Immerse in Bath 3 at 140-160 °F (60-71 °C) for 15 min.
	DI water	3.5 pbw	Scrub under cold running water with stiff bristle brush.
	Conc. H_2SO_4 (s.g. 1.86)	200 pbw	Rinse in DI water. Dry in oven at 200 °F (93 °C) for 10-15 min.

Notes: pbw = parts by weight; s.g. = specific gravity; DI = distilled or deionized. Source: Ref 4

Table 9 Tensile lap-shear strengths of high-temperature thermosetting adhesives bonded to stainless steel

Adhesive	Tensile lap-shear strength									
	At 25 °C (75 °F)		At 65 °C (150 °F)		At 120 °C (250 °F)		At 175 °C (350 °F)		At 205 °C (400 °F)	
	MPa	ksi	MPa	ksi	MPa	ksi	MPa	ksi	MPa	ksi
Nitrile phenolic	34.5	5.0	31.0	4.5	24.8	3.6	13.1	1.9		0
Polybenzimidazole	20.7	3.0	19.7	2.85	19.0	2.75	17.9	2.6	16.5	2.4
Epoxy phenolic	19.7	2.85	18.3	2.65	15.9	2.3	13.8	2.0	12.1	1.75
Polyimide	17.9	2.6	16.2	2.35	14.5	2.1	12.0	1.75	10.3	1.5
Epoxy	15.9	2.3	12.8	1.85	9.7	1.4	6.2	0.9	1.0	0.15

Source: Ref 6

Table 10 Tensile lap-shear strengths of glass-phenolic laminate bonded to type 301 stainless steel with nitrile phenolic adhesive

Number of days	Exposure to humidity(a)					
	At 25 °C (75 °F)		At 120 °C (250 °F)		At –55 °C (–70 °F)	
	MPa	psi	MPa	psi	MPa	psi
0	23.8	3450	10.0	1450	23.1	3350
10	21.7	3150	5.9	850	22.1	3200
20	20.0	2900	4.1	600	20.1	2920
30	19.3	2800	4.0	580	19.7	2850
50	18.5	2680	3.1	450	19.3	2800
70	18.3	2650	2.6	380	19.2	2780
90	17.9	2600	2.1	300	18.6	2700

(a) Per MIL-E-5272. Source: Ref 6

with steel wool, grit blasting, etc.) or washing with acids, alkali solutions, or other such chemicals. Stainless steels are best cleaned by vapor degreasing with trichloroethane, followed by sandblasting or, preferably, by chemical etching. Chemical treatments may be confined to the bonding areas, but degreasing should be done to the entire assembly. A cleaned assembly should be bonded as soon after the cleaning operation as possible, or an adhesive primer should be applied. However, if storage is necessary, special precautions should be taken so that the assembly does not become contaminated. All parts should be tightly wrapped or placed in airtight and oil-free containers. Etched surfaces must never be touched with bare hands, because even wiping the surface with a clean cloth can affect the bond. Handlers should wear clean cotton gloves and use clean tools.

Water is often used to test a metal surface for cleanness. A small portion is placed on the surface. If the water distributes evenly, then the stainless should wet well with an adhesive. But if it beads or crawls, then the surface should be cleaned again and the test repeated. Figure 23 shows the results of a water-break test for determining the adequacy of surface preparation.

Bonding should be performed in a room separate from other manufacturing operations. When bonding is done in the same area as plastic or rubber molding, a physical barrier should be erected between the two operations to prevent airborne mold lubricants from depositing on the metal. Similar hazards are presented by spray painting, electroplating, etching, and machining with coolants. Storage and assembly areas should be en-

closed, and air to these areas filtered and under slight pressure.

Degreasing. To degrease stainless steel surfaces with a degreasing unit, the metal should be suspended in a stabilized trichloroethane vapor bath for about 30 seconds. The bath should be checked frequently for accumulated contaminants. If a degreasing unit is not available, the surface should be cleaned with a white cotton rag or pieces of absorbent cotton dampened in trichloroethane. Rags should be changed frequently and the surface should be allowed to stand several minutes while the chemical evaporates. Although nonflammable, trichloroethane is toxic in both liquid and vapor forms, and the working area should be well ventilated. Gloves should be worn when handling this solvent, and smoking should not be allowed.

Surface Abrasion. Smooth stainless steel surfaces can be improved for bonding by roughening with abrasives such as medium grit emery paper. Abrasion should always be followed by degreasing to remove contaminants and loose particles.

Blasting with a fine grit is the best method for removing surface deposits (oxide films, tarnish, rust, mill scale, and other contaminants) from stainless steels. This method should be used only on structures thick enough to resist distortion. With thinner materials, contaminants should be removed by vapor honing. This method is similar to grit blasting but uses high-velocity water or steam instead of air. If neither method is appropriate, abrasive disks, belts, cloth, medium-grit emery paper, or wire brushes can be used.

Chemical Treatment (Ref 5). Although there is considerable evidence that chemical surface treatments improve the substrate bondability

of stainless steels by producing highly adherent oxides, there is no general agreement on which treatment is the best. One etchant commonly used with stainless steels is an HNO_3-HF mixture; another is chromic acid. Various solutions based on sulfuric acid have also been beneficial, and several researchers have investigated a wide variety of solutions based on acids with dichromates added, with and without anodization. The treatment judged to be the best by one researcher did not receive the same ranking from another. All of the treatments use a highly concentrated, very active solution that attacks grain boundaries and the chromium-poor regions around chromium carbide particles. Table 8 lists recommended surface treatment procedures for stainless steels.

Adhesives

Adhesive selection for bonding stainless steels involves the use of thermosetting resins. These adhesive types undergo chemical changes during the polymerization process that will not allow them to revert back to a liquid when subjected to elevated temperatures (they char) and in many cases render them incapable of being dissolved by solvents and most acids. However, they may be degraded to a serious substandard condition by long-term subjection to these chemical agents or heat. The thermosetting systems are usually much stronger than thermoplastics, especially at elevated temperatures. Table 9 compares tensile lap-shear strengths of various high-temperature thermosetting resins. The effects of temperature and humidity on a nitrile phenolic adhesive used to bond type 301 stainless steel to a glass-phenolic laminate are shown in Table 10.

Although anaerobic adhesives are not classified within the thermoset adhesive family, they are widely used to fasten male/female fitted joints and flat bonded surfaces. Bonding with anaerobics requires the use of primers. More detailed information on anaerobic and thermosetting adhesives can be found in *Volume 3 of the Engineered Materials Handbook* published by ASM International.

ACKNOWLEDGMENTS

The information in this article is largely taken from:

• M.J. Lucas, Jr., Brazing of Stainless Steels, *Welding, Brazing and Soldering,* Vol 6, *ASM*

Handbook, ASM International, 1993, p 911-923
- M.M. Schwartz, Fundamentals of Brazing, *Welding, Brazing and Soldering,* Vol 6, *ASM Handbook,* ASM International, 1993, p 114-125
- M. Karovolis, S. Jha, J. Forster, and K. Meekins, Application of Clad Brazing Materials, *Welding, Brazing and Soldering,* Vol 6, *ASM Handbook,* ASM International, 1993, p 961-963
- C.E. Witherell, Laser Brazing, Vol 6, 9th ed., *Metals Handbook,* American Society for Metals, 1983, p 1064-1066
- R.E. Beal et al., Soldering, Vol 6, 9th ed., *Metals Handbook,* American Society for Metals, 1983, p 1069-1101
- P.T. Vianco, General Soldering, *Welding, Brazing, and Soldering,* Vol 6, *ASM Handbook,* ASM International, 1993, p 964-984

REFERENCES

1. D.L. Keller, et al., Wettability of Brazing Filler Metals, *Weld. J.,* Vol 69 (No. 10), 1990, p 31-34
2. W. Feduska, High-Temperature Brazing Alloy-Base Metal Wetting Reactions, *Weld. J.,* Vol 38 (No. 3), 1959, p 1225-1305
3. W.S. Bennett, et al., Vacuum Brazing Studies on High-Manganese Stainless Steels, *Weld. J.,* Vol 53, 1974, p 510s-516s
4. C.L. Mahoney, Surface Preparation for Adhesive Bonding, *Handbook of Adhesives,* 3rd ed., I. Skeist, Ed., Van Nostrand Reinhold, 1990, p 74-93
5. H.M. Clearfield, D.K. McNamara, and G.D. Davis, Surface Preparation of Metals, *Adhesives and Sealants, Vol 3, Engineered Materials Handbook,* ASM International, 1990, p 259-275
6. C.V. Cagle, Bonding of Steels, *Handbook of Adhesive Bonding,* McGraw-Hill Book Co., 1973, p 14-1 to 14-15

Surface Engineering

ALTHOUGH STAINLESS STEEL is naturally passivated by exposure to air and other oxidizers, additional surface treatments often are needed to prevent corrosion. Passivation, pickling, electropolishing, and, in some cases, mechanical cleaning are important surface treatments for the successful performance of stainless steel used for piping, pressure vessels, tanks, and machined parts in a wide variety of applications, including pulp mills, nuclear power plants, hospital sterilization systems, food processing equipment, biotechnology processing plants, breweries, electronic-chip washing facilities, swimming pool hardware, water treatment plants, and chemical process plants.

Determining which treatment should be used for specific applications is sometimes confusing. A good place to start is with ASTM A 380 (Ref 1), which is an excellent resource document for the cleaning and descaling of stainless steel parts, equipment, and systems, although it does not cover electropolishing.

Mill Finishes (Ref 2)

The standard industry designations for stainless steel finishes are classified by mill form. There are separate finish (or condition) designations for sheet, strip, plate, bar, rod, wire, and tubing. Table 1 classifies the various stainless steel product forms. More detailed information can be found in the article "Metallurgy and Properties of Wrought Stainless Steels" in this Volume.

Stainless Steel Sheet Finishes

Stainless steel sheets are produced on continuous mills or hand mills. The steel is usually cast in ingot form and rolled on a slabbing or blooming mill to slabs or sheet bars. Alternatively, the steel may be cast directly in slab form ready for finish hot rolling.

Sheets produced on continuous mills from slabs are rolled into coils and processed by annealing, descaling, and cold reducing to specified thickness, then by further annealing and descaling. Coils or lengths cut from coils may then be subjected to light cold rolling for finish on dull or bright rolls.

Sheet finishes (Table 2) are designated by a system of numbers: No. 1, 2D, and 2B for rolled (unpolished) finishes; and No. 3, 4, 6, 7, and 8 for polished finishes.

No. 1 is a very dull finish produced by first hot rolling the steel on hand sheet mills to the specified thickness and then annealing and descaling. It is used in industrial applications for resistance to heat or corrosion, where a smooth finish is not of particular importance.

No. 2D is a dull finish produced on either hand sheet mills or continuous mills by cold rolling to the specified thickness and then annealing and descaling. The dull finish may result from the descaling operation or may be developed by a final light cold-roll pass on dull rolls. This finish favors surface retention of lubricants in deep-drawing operations. It generally is used in forming deep-drawn articles that may be polished after fabrication.

No. 2B is a bright, cold-rolled finish commonly produced in the same way as No. 2D, except that the annealed and descaled sheet receives a final light cold-roll pass on polished rolls. It is a general-purpose finish used for all but exceptionally difficult deep-drawing applications. This finish is more readily polished than No. 1 or 2D.

No. 3 is an intermediate polished finish for use where a semifinished polished surface is required and a further finishing operation follows fabrication. For sheets or articles that will not be subject to additional finishing or polishing, No. 4 finish is recommended.

No. 4 is a general-purpose polished finish widely used for architectural panels and trim and for dairy, restaurant, and kitchen equipment. Following initial grinding with coarser abrasives, sheets are finally finished with lubricated 120- to 150-mesh abrasive belts.

No. 6 is a dull satin finish having lower reflectivity than No. 4. It is produced by tampico brushing No. 4 finished sheets in a medium of abrasive and oil and is used for architectural applications and ornamentation where a high luster is undesirable. It also is used to contrast with brighter finishes.

No. 7 is a finish with a high degree of reflectivity, produced by buffing a finely ground surface without removing the grit lines. It is used chiefly for architectural and ornamental purposes.

No. 8 is the most reflective finish and is obtained by polishing with successively finer abrasives and buffing extensively with very fine buffing rouges. The surface is essentially free of grit lines from preliminary grinding operations.

Table 1 Classification of stainless steel product forms

Item	Description	Thickness mm	Thickness in.	Width mm	Width in.	Diameter or size mm	Diameter or size in.
Sheet	Coils and cut lengths						
	Mill finishes No. 1, 2D, and 2B	<5	<$^3/_{16}$	≥610	≥24	...	...
	Polished finishes No. 3, 4, 6, 7, and 8	<5	<$^3/_{16}$	All widths		...	...
Strip	Cold-finished coils or cut lengths	<5	<$^3/_{16}$	<610	<24	...	...
Plate	Flat rolled or forged	≥5	≥$^3/_{16}$	>25	>10	...	...
Bar	Hot-finished rounds, squares, octagons, and hexagons	...	...	...	...	≥6	≥$^1/_4$
	Hot-finished flats	≥3	≥$^1/_8$	6-25	$^1/_4$-10	...	...
	Cold-finished rounds, squares, octagons, and hexagons	...	...	...	...	>13	>$^1/_2$
	Cold-finished flats	...	....	≥9.5	≥$^3/_8$	...	...
Wire	Cold-finished only						
	Round, square, octagon, hexagon, flat wire	0.25 to <5	0.010 to <$^3/_{16}$	1.6 to <9.5	$^1/_{16}$ to <$^3/_8$	≤13	≤$^1/_2$
Pipe and tubing	Several different classifications, with differing specifications, are available. For information on standard sizes, consult Committee of Stainless Steel Producers, AISI.						
Extrusions	No standard shapes, but of potentially wide interest. Currently limited in size to approximately 165 mm (6$^1/_2$ in.) diam circle, or structurals to 125 mm (5 in.) diam.						

Source: Ref 2

Table 2 Standard mechanical sheet finishes

Finish	Description
Unpolished or rolled finishes	
No. 1	A rough, dull surface that results from hot rolling to the specified thickness followed by annealing and descaling
No. 2D	A dull finish that results from cold rolling followed by annealing and descaling, and may perhaps get a final light roll pass through unpolished rolls. A 2D finish is used where appearance is of no concern.
No. 2B	A bright, cold-rolled finish resulting in the same manner as No. 2D finish, except that the annealed and descaled sheet receives a final light roll pass through polished rolls. This is the general-purpose cold-rolled finish that can be used as is, or as a preliminary step to polishing.
Polished finishes	
No. 3	An intermediate polished surface obtained by finishing with a 100-grit abrasive. Generally used where a semifinished polished surface is required. A No. 3 finish usually receives additional polishing during fabrication.
No. 4	A polished surface obtained by finishing with a 120 to 150-mesh abrasive, following initial grinding with coarser abrasives. This is a general-purpose bright finish with a visible "grain" that prevents mirror reflection.
No. 6	A dull satin finish having lower reflectivity than No. 4 finish. It is produced by tampico brushing the No. 4 finish in a medium of abrasive and oil. It is used for architectural applications and ornamentation where a high luster is undesirable, and to contrast with brighter finishes.
No. 7	A highly reflective finish that is obtained by buffing finely ground surfaces but not to the extent of completely removing the grit lines. It is used chiefly for architectural and ornamental purposes.
No. 8	The most reflective surface, obtained by polishing with successively finer abrasives and buffing extensively until all grit lines from preliminary grinding operations are removed. It is used for applications such as mirrors and reflectors.

Source: Ref 2

Table 3 Mill finishes available on stainless steel sheet and strip

See text for explanation of numerical designations of finishes.

Type	Sheet		Strip
	Unpolished	Polished	
Austenitic steels(a)			
201	2D, 2B	(b)	1, 2
202	2D, 2B	3, 4	1, 2
301	2D, 2B	(b)	1, 2
302	2D, 2B	3, 4, 6, 7	1, 2
302B	2D	(b)	...
304	2D, 2B	3, 4, 6, 7	1, 2
304L	2D, 2B	4	1, 2
305	2D, 2B	(b)	1, 2
309, 309S	2D	(b)	1, 2
310	2D	(b)	1, 2
316	2D, 2B	4	1, 2
316L	2D, 2B	(b)	1, 2
321	2D, 2B	(b)	1, 2
347	2D, 2B	(b)	1, 2
348	2D, 2B	(b)	1, 2
Martensitic steels			
403	2D, 2B	(b)	1, 2
410	2D, 2B	(b)	1, 2
420	(c)	(c)	1, 2
440A, B, and C	(c)	(c)	(d)
Ferritic steels(a)			
430	2D, 2B	3, 4	1, 2
446	2D, 2B	(b)	1, 2

(a) All grades listed, in both sheet and strip form, are regularly available in the smooth rolled and bright annealed condition. (b) Usually not polished. (c) Not available in sheet form. (d) Material available in strip form on special order only; finish negotiated with supplier

This finish is most widely used for press plates and for small mirrors and reflectors. Sheets can be produced with one or both sides polished. When sheet is polished on one side only, the other side may be rough ground in order to obtain the necessary flatness. The relationship between abrasive grit numbers and surface roughness in terms of micrometers is sometimes a basis for specification. The values are approximately as follows:

Abrasive grit No.	Surface roughness	
	μm	μin.
500	0.10 to 0.25	4 to 10
320	0.15 to 0.38	6 to 15
240	0.20 to 0.51	8 to 20
180	0.64 max	25 max
120	1.14 max	45 max
60	3.56 max	140 max

Stainless Steel Strip Finishes

Hot-rolled stainless steel strip is a semifinished product obtained from the hot rolling of slabs or billets and produced for conversion by cold rolling. Cold-rolled stainless steel strip is manufactured from hot-rolled, annealed, and pickled strip by cold rolling on polished rolls. Depending on the thickness desired, the cold rolling requires various numbers of passes through the mill to effect the necessary reduction and to secure the desired surface characteristics and mechanical properties. Only three rolled (unpolished) finishes (No. 1, No. 2, and bright annealed) and one polished finish (mill buffed) are commonly supplied on stainless steel strip.

No. 1 finish is produced by cold rolling, annealing, and pickling. Appearance varies from dull gray matte to fairly reflective, depending largely on stainless steel type. This finish is used for severely drawn or formed parts, as well as for applications where the brighter No. 2 finish is not required, such as parts to be used at high temperatures. No. 1 finish for strip approximates No. 2D finish for sheet in corresponding chromium-nickel or chromium-nickel-manganese types.

No. 2 finish is produced by the same treatment used for No. 1 finish, followed by a final light cold-rolling pass, which generally is done using highly polished rolls. This final pass produces a smoother and more reflective surface, the appearance of which varies with stainless steel type. No. 2 finish for strip is a general-purpose finish widely used for household appliances, automotive trim, tableware, and utensils. No. 2 finish for strip approximates No. 2B finish for sheet in corresponding chromium-nickel or chromium-nickel-manganese stainless steels.

Bright annealed finish is a bright, cold-rolled, highly reflective finish retained by final annealing in a controlled-atmosphere furnace. The purpose of atmosphere control is to prevent scaling or oxidation during annealing. The atmosphere usually consists of either dry hydrogen or dissociated ammonia. Bright annealed strip is used most extensively for automotive trim.

Mill-buffed finish is a highly reflective finish obtained by subjecting either No. 2 or bright annealed coiled strip to a continuous buffing pass. The purpose of mill buffing is to provide a finish uniform in color and reflectivity. It also can provide a surface receptive to chromium plating. This type of finish is used chiefly for automotive trim, household trim, tableware, utensils, fire extinguishers, and plumbing fixtures.

Grade Limitations. Not all of the standard compositions of stainless steel strip are available in each of the standard mill finishes. Surface finishes of these products depend on end use rather than any restriction imposed by the supplier. Table 3 lists the finishes most often applied to sheet and strip of a number of standard grades of austenitic, martensitic, and ferritic steels.

Stainless Steel Plate Finishes

Stainless steel plates usually are produced by hot rolling from slabs that have been directly cast or rolled from ingots; some plates may be produced by direct rolling from the ingot.

Plates are generally produced in the annealed condition and are either blast cleaned or pickled. When blast cleaned, the plates are subjected to further cleaning in appropriate acids to remove possible iron contamination. Stainless steel plate can be produced in the conditions and surface finishes shown in Table 4.

Table 4 indicates that polished finishes similar to those for sheet are available for plate. Technically speaking, there is no No. 4 finish for plate, nor is there a No. 8 finish. However, arrangements can be made either with a mill or an independent polisher to grind and polish plate in the same manner as sheet. This work should be specified on the basis of submitted samples.

Table 4 Conditions and surface finishes for stainless steel plate

Condition and finish	Description and remarks
Hot rolled	Scale not removed; not heat treated; plate not recommended for final use in this condition.(a)
Hot or cold rolled, annealed or heat treated	Scale not removed; use of plate in this condition generally confined to heat-resisting applications; scale impairs corrosion resistance.(a)
Hot or cold rolled, annealed or heat treated, blast cleaned or pickled	Condition and finish commonly preferred for corrosion-resisting and most heat-resisting applications
Hot or cold rolled, annealed, descaled, and temper passed	Smoother finish for specialized applications
Hot rolled, annealed, descaled, cold rolled, annealed, descaled, optionally temper passed	Smooth finish with greater freedom from surface imperfections than any of the above
Hot or cold rolled, annealed or heat treated, surface cleaned and polished	Polished finishes similar to the polished finishes on sheet

(a) Surface inspection is not practicable for plate that has not been pickled or otherwise descaled. Source: Ref 2

Table 5 Conditions and surface finishes for stainless steel bar

Condition	Surface finish
Hot worked only	Scale not removed (except for spot conditioning) Rough turned(a)(b) Blast cleaned
Annealed or otherwise heat treated	Scale not removed (except for spot conditioning) Rough turned(a) Pickled or blast cleaned and pickled Cold drawn or cold rolled Centerless ground(a) Polished(a)
Annealed and cold worked to high tensile strength(c)	Cold drawn or cold rolled Centerless ground(a) Polished(a)

(a) Applicable to round bar only. (b) Bar of 400-series stainless steels that are highly hardenable, such as types 414, 420, 420F, 431, 440A, 440B, and 440C, are annealed before rough turning. Other hardenable types, such as types 403, 410, 416, and 416Se, also may require annealing, depending on composition and size. (c) Produced only in mill orders; made predominantly in types 301, 302, 303Se, 304, 304N, 316, and 316N. Source: Ref 2

Plate commonly is conditioned by localized grinding to remove surface imperfections on either or both surfaces; ground areas are well flared and the thickness is not reduced below the allowable tolerance in any of these areas.

Stainless Steel Bar Finishes

Hot-finished bars are commonly produced by hot rolling, forging, or pressing ingots to intermediate-size blooms or billets, which are subsequently hot rolled, forged, or extruded to final dimensions. (In some mills, the process starts with continuous-cast sections.) The selection of rolling, forging, or extruding as the finishing method depends on several factors, including the composition of the steel and the final size. It is common practice to process bars in straight lengths, although smaller bars produced by rolling may be coiled.

Following hot rolling or forging, hot-finished bars may be subjected to various operations, including annealing or other heat treating; cleaning by pickling, blast cleaning, or other methods of descaling; rough turning; and machine straightening. When only improved surface is required, as for bars intended for forging, bars can be turned or ground.

Cold-finished bars are produced from hot-finished bars by additional operations to give close tolerance, improved surface finish, or specific mechanical properties.

Stainless steel bar is produced in the conditions and surface finishes given in Table 5. It is important that both condition and finish be specified, because each finish is applicable only to certain conditions.

The finish on stainless steel bar is generally the result of processes used to size the bar or to improve the surface and usually not for the purpose of achieving a certain surface appearance. Turning, for instance, improves the surface by removing undesirable defects. It is difficult, if not impossible, to obtain a hot-rolled surface that the customer can use without removal of a portion of the "skin." Turning is accomplished by passing the bar through a turning machine or lathe, using one or more passes, depending on the amount of material to be removed.

Sometimes the final surface or dimension of round bar can be achieved only by centerless grinding. Centerless grinding differs from turning in that a grinding wheel is used for metal removal instead of a cutting tool, and more accurate dimensions and better surface finish are obtained. The centerless grinding machine is constructed so that the bar is supported under the greater portion of its length as well as under the grinding wheel, other than at the ends.

In some cases, a highly polished bar is desired rather than the standard centerless ground finish. In this case, centerless ground bars are passed through a polishing or lapping machine that imparts a higher degree of polish. Flat or shaped bars cannot be centerless ground, so any finish requirements are achieved by methods similar to those used for strip.

Stainless Steel Wire Finishes

Stainless steel wire is derived by cold finishing a coiled hot-rolled and annealed rod to obtain the desired size with dimensional accuracy, improved surface, and specific mechanical properties. Wire is produced in a number of tempers and finishes. The finishes on wire are usually applied to meet the requirements of further processing, such as drawing, forming into parts, or coiling into springs.

Oil- or grease-drawn finish is a special bright finish for wire intended for uses such as racks and handles, where the finish supplied is to be the final finish of the end product. In producing this finish, lower drawing speeds are necessary and additional care in processing is needed to provide a surface with few scratches and with only a very light residue of lubricant.

Diamond-drawn finish is a very bright finish generally limited to wet-drawn stainless steel wire in fine sizes. Drafting speeds are necessarily reduced to obtain the desired brightness.

Copper-coated wire is supplied when a special finish is required for lubrication in an operation such as spring coiling or cold heading. Generally, copper-coated wire is drawn after the coating, the amount depending on the desired cold-worked temper of the wire.

Tinned wire is coated by passing single strands through a bath of molten tin. Tinned wire is used in soldering applications. The temper of the finished wire is controlled by processing prior to tinning.

Lead-coated wire is coated by passing single strands through, or immersing bundles of wire in, a bath of molten lead. The wire is then drawn to final size, with the lead forming a thin coating over the entire surface. This coating is useful on wire for coil springs, where it serves as a lubricant during coiling operations.

Stainless Steel Tubing and Pipe Finishes

Hot-finished tubular products produced by the seamless processes have a surface finish comparable to hot-rolled bars. Welded tubular products produced from hot-rolled sheets, strip, or plate retain the general surface finish of those flat-rolled products. Thin-wall tubular products, because of greater reduction during the rolling operation and the lower finishing temperatures, may have a smoother surface than those with heavy walls.

Stainless steel tubular products are cold worked to improve dimensional limits, control the weld bead on the inside (in the case of welded tubing), or condition the weld for grain refinement during the annealing operation. Cold finishing may include cold drawing, tube reducing, or swaging. Tubes may also be rough turned (machined) or honed, such as for hydraulic cylinders.

Tubular products may be polished, but instead of "typical" finish designations, the polished finishes for tubing are usually indicated by the grit size, such as 80-, 120-, 180-, or 320-grit. Note that for the exterior surface of round tubing, grit lines are longitudinal.

Tubing may be specified polished on the outside, the inside, or both surfaces. Welded and cold-finished seamless tubing is suitable for grinding or polishing and is produced in sizes up to 168 mm ($6\frac{5}{8}$ in.) outer diameter with polished outside surfaces. It is not practical to polish interior surfaces of tubes with an inner diameter of less than 19 mm ($\frac{3}{4}$ in.).

Preservation of Mill Finishes

When a finished part is made, the original mill finish may be retained with little or no modification, depending on fabrication requirements. If this finish is satisfactory, no additional finishing operations are necessary. Therefore, every effort should be made to preserve the mill finish while the steel is in storage or being processed. The following preventive measures will serve to minimize additional cleaning and polishing:

- Steel should be kept in original containers or wrappers until fabrication actually begins.
- Steel should be stored indoors, on clean racks, shelves, or platforms, and should be covered wherever possible.
- Storage areas should be kept free of shop dirt, pickling or plating fumes, particles of scale from steel fabrication, and other contaminants.
- Storage areas should not be located beneath line shafting from which lubricating oils and grease may fall.
- Fabricating equipment should be cleaned of all residues before being used for a new operation on stainless steel.
- Steel should be handled with clean gloves or cloths, to avoid fingerprints.
- Only marking materials that leave no permanent blemishes on work should be used.
- Whenever feasible, paper or other protective covering should be placed on all surfaces between processes.

- Chips should not be removed by compressed air, which may contain oil or other contaminants.

Abrasive Blast Cleaning

Aspects of abrasive blast cleaning that apply particularly or exclusively to stainless steel include sandblasting, shot blasting, and wet blasting. For more complete information, see the article "Abrasive Blast Cleaning" in Volume 5 of the *ASM Handbook*.

Sandblasting is effective for rapidly removing heavy or tightly adhering scale before acid pickling. Applied to stainless steel, it is not a complete cleaning procedure. Types of work for which it is frequently used include heavily scaled plate sections, forgings and castings, and parts made of straight chromium steel that have developed a tightly adhering scale during annealing. It is fast and economical when used in conjunction with a final pickling treatment.

Only clean silica sand should be used. If the sand is iron-bearing or becomes contaminated with scale, minute particles of these contaminants can become embedded in the metal. The only sure way to remove such contaminants and to produce a thoroughly clean, rust-free surface is to follow the blasting with an acid pickling treatment.

Sandblasting should not be used on materials that are too light to stand the blast pressure, because distortion results from the local stretching caused by impingement of the sand. The blast should be kept moving to avoid excessive cutting at localized points.

Shot Blasting. The use of carbon steel shot, steel wire, or iron grit as blasting media is not recommended, because they may cause particles of iron to become embedded and seriously detract from the corrosion resistance of stainless steel surfaces. Unless these contaminants are completely removed by acid pickling, they can rust and begin pitting.

The use of stainless steel shot or grit reduces the danger of rusting, but it cannot eliminate the possibility of residual oxide scale. Final pickling is mandatory for maximum corrosion resistance of surfaces so treated.

Stainless steels, and particularly those of the 300 series, work harden when they are subjected to cold working. Therefore, if work hardening of the surface is undesirable for a particular application, shot blasting should not be used.

Wet blasting is adaptable for use with stainless steel. Various abrasives conveyed in liquid carriers are discharged at the work by compressed air. A variety of finishes can be obtained through selection of abrasives and adjustment of pressures. Finishes that are much smoother than those resulting from blasting with dry sand and that are similar in appearance to a No. 6 (tampico-brushed) finish may be obtained by wet blasting. As in sandblasting, a final pickling treatment and water washing are required.

Acid Descaling (Pickling)

Acid descaling, or pickling, is the removal of heavy, tightly adherent oxide films resulting from hot-forming operations, thermal treatments (such as annealing or hardening), or welding (Ref 3). Because most stainless steel products received from the producing mill have been pickled, descaling is required only as a result of subsequent manufacturing operations.

In evaluating the different methods for removing scale, it should be kept in mind that scale on stainless steel is far more complex than scale formed on plain mild steel. The scale on stainless steel consists of oxides of chromium, nickel, and/or other alloying elements, in addition to iron, and the ease of removal depends on base metal composition and the thermal treatment to which it is exposed. The problem may be further complicated by the presence of lubricants. Lubricants and other contamination should be removed before thermal treatment.

When the metal is exposed to hot gases containing oxygen, a heavy scale is formed. A heavy scale, because it is readily exposed to the oxygen only near the surface, may be oxygen rich at the surface and metal rich near the base metal. Most oxygen-rich scale is readily soluble in common pickling acids, but the metal-rich scale may require acids aggressive to the base metal itself. For this reason, pickling is sometimes preceded by a

Table 6 Acid descaling (pickling) of stainless steel

Alloy(a)	Condition(b)	Code	Solution, vol%(c)	Temperature °C	Temperature °F	Time, min(d)
200-, 300-, and 400-series, precipitation-hardening, and maraging alloys (except free-machining alloys)	Fully annealed only	A	H_2SO_4 (8-11%)(e) Follow by treatment D or F, Annex A2 (ASTM A 380) as appropriate.	66-82	150-180	5-45 max
200- and 300-series alloys; 400-series alloys containing 16% Cr or more; precipitation-hardening alloys (except free-machining alloys)	Fully annealed only	B	HNO_3 (15-25%) plus HF (1-8%)(f)(g)	21-60 max	70-140 max	5-30
All free-machining alloys and 400-series alloys containing less than 16% Cr	Fully annealed only	C	HNO_3 (10-15%) plus HF ($\frac{1}{2}$-$1\frac{1}{2}$%)(f)(g)	20 (up to 60 with caution)	70 (up to 140 with caution)	5-30

(a) This table is also applicable to the cast grades equivalent to the families of wrought materials listed. (b) Other heat treatments may be acceptable if proven by experience. See sections 5.2.1, A2.4, and A2.5 of ASTM A 380 for further information. (c) Solution prepared from reagents of following weight percent: H_2SO_4, 98; HNO_3, 67; HF, 70. (d) Minimum contact times necessary to obtain the desired surface should be used in order to prevent overpickling. Tests should be made to establish correct procedures for specific applications. (e) Tight scale may be removed by a dip in this solution for a few minutes followed by water rinse and HNO_3-HF. (f) For reasons of convenience and handling safety, commercial formulations containing fluoride salts may be found useful in place of HF for preparing HNO_3-HF solutions. (g) After pickling and water rinsing, an aqueous caustic permanganate solution containing 10 wt% NaOH and 4 wt% $KMnO_4$, 71 to 82 °C (160 to 180 °F), 5 to 60 min, may be used as a final dip for removal of smut, followed by thorough water rinsing and drying. Source: Ref 1

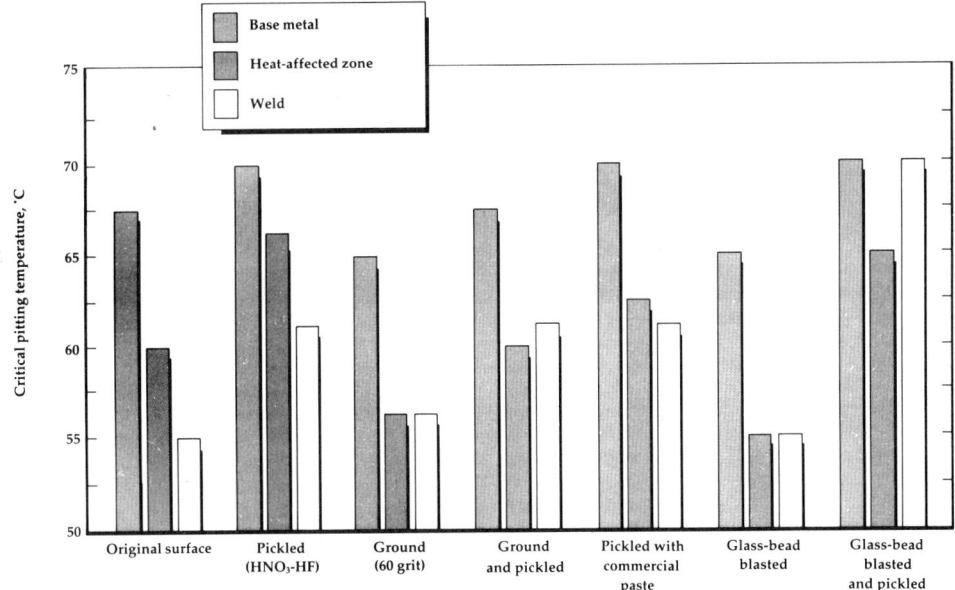

Fig. 1   Pickling of stainless steel increases the critical pitting temperature in FeCl₃ in the base metal, heat-affected zone, and weld areas. Mechanical cleaning treatments that are performed without a subsequent pickling treatment decrease the critical pitting temperature.

roller or nylon brush. Paste must be washed off within 15 to 30 min of application, or corrosion will initiate. Personnel need protective clothing and training in safe handling procedures.

Although postfabrication pickling improves the performance of stainless steels in a variety of applications, until recently there has been very little research data to support field experience. Quantitative data on the increase in critical pitting temperature in ferric chloride ($FeCl_3$) (ASTM G 48) show that pickling provides a 2.5 to 10 °C (4.5 to 18 °F) improvement in performance (Fig. 1). Although not large, the improvements in lightly ground surfaces and glass-bead-blasted surfaces are uniformly positive, indicating that pickling provides benefits beyond those obtained with the best controlled mechanical treatments.

Salt Bath Descaling

The removal of oxide scale can be accelerated by using baths of molten sodium hydroxide to which certain reagents are added. These baths can be used with virtually all grades of stainless steel. Salt bath descaling has several advantages:

- It acts only on the scale and does not result in metal loss or etching.
- It does not preferentially attack areas in which intergranular carbides are present.
- It is particularly useful in descaling the straight chromium grades without the preliminary sandblasting that is frequently required before acid descaling.

Use of molten salts is not recommended for those stainless steels that precipitation harden at the operating temperature of the bath. Procedures and equipment for descaling in molten salt are described in the article "Molten Salt Bath Cleaning" in Volume 5 of the *ASM Handbook*.

Sequence of Cleaning Methods

Usually, more than one method of cleaning is used to remove scale from stainless steel. For instance, in mill processing sheet, salt bath descal-

preconditioning step, such as an alkaline salt bath, or scale removal by mechanical means, such as shot blasting.

The final step, however, involves elimination of scale and other surface defects through removal of the normal, protective oxide layer and 25 to 40 μm (0.001 to 0.0015 in.) of the substrate metal by pickling the surface in a nitric-hydrofluoric acid (HNO_3-HF) bath. The protective film then reforms in air over the freshly cleaned surface. This oxide film is uniform and leaves the stainless surface in its normal passive condition.

Although pickling is not strictly a passivating treatment, it provides many of the same benefits. Pickling is most useful for localized cleaning of welded areas, but it also can be used to improve the corrosion resistance of mechanically cleaned surfaces.

Disposal of pickle liquor is a growing problem. It tends to limit pickling by immersion to those fabricator and chemical cleaning contractors that have pickle tanks and approved arrangements for disposal.

Pickling at the steel mill removes the oxide scale that forms during annealing. Mill pickling also removes manganese sulfides or other inclusions in the surface and removes surface layers that may have been depleted of chromium during annealing.

ASTM A 380 (Ref 1) lists three pickling solutions for stainless steel (Table 6). Fabricated austenitic stainless steels can be pickled by immersion in a standard 10% HNO_3, 2% HF bath at 50 °C (120 °F). For localized pickling or if the fabricated component is too large to be immersed, commercial HNO_3-HF pickle pastes can be just as effective. Pickle paste can be applied with a paint

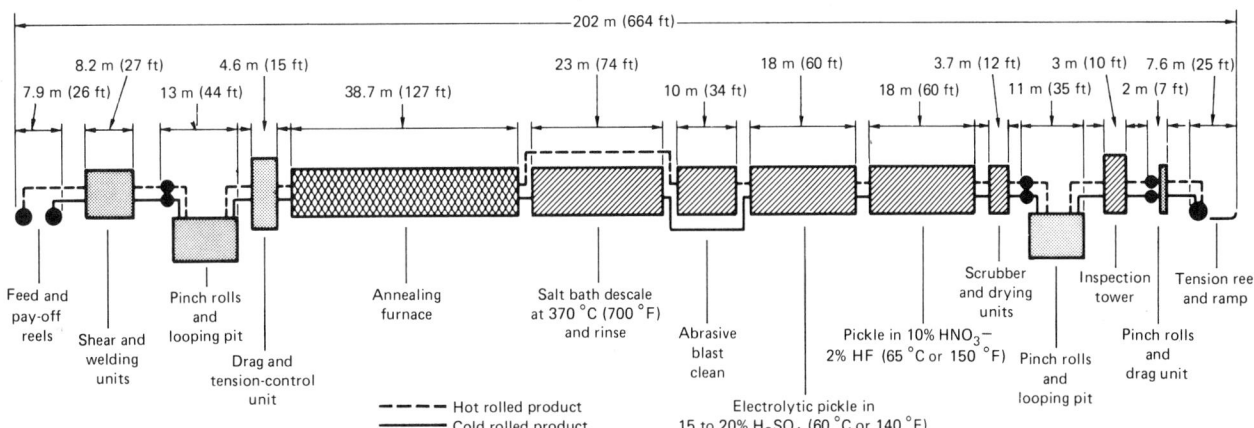

Fig. 2   Sequence of annealing and scale-removing operations in mill processing of stainless steel sheet

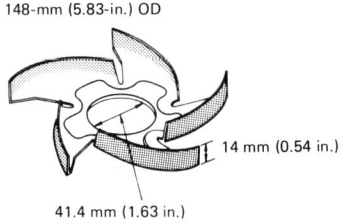

148-mm (5.83-in.) OD

14 mm (0.54 in.)

41.4 mm (1.63 in.)

Fig. 3   Impeller polished to No. 2B finish by fixtured tumbling. The impeller (type 316 sheet) is used in milk-processing equipment.

ing and acid pickling often are used for a cold-rolled product and abrasive blast cleaning and acid pickling for a hot-rolled product.

In a continuous annealing and pickling line, multistep cleaning usually occurs twice in producing stainless steel sheet. The sequence of operations is: hot roll, anneal, descale, pickle, cold reduce 30 to 50%, anneal, descale, and pickle. As shown in Fig. 2, salt descaling is used for cold-rolled sheet, whereas the salt is bypassed and abrasive blast cleaning is used when a hot-rolled product is being cleaned. Salt also can be eliminated on low-chromium cold-rolled sheet.

Cold-rolled sheet is left in the salt bath 10 to 15 min. Oxides are not removed from the surface. The rack of hot sheet is transferred to a water bath, and the violent reaction that results upon immersion blasts much of the scale from the steel. The surface is essentially free of scale, but quite dull and dirty. To remove the last remnants of oxide, the rack is transferred to a 10 to 15% sulfuric acid (H_2SO_4) solution at 70 °C (160 °F) for 3 to 5 min. After removal from the H_2SO_4 tank, the rack of sheet steel is rinsed and then immersed for 1 to 2 min in HNO_3-HF (8 to 10% HNO_3, 1 to 2% HF) at 60 °C (140 °F). This removes all smut and residue and produces a white finish. The sheet is finally rinsed, removed from the rack, scrubbed, and dried with an air blast.

Mass (Barrel) Finishing

Mass (barrel) finishing provides a combined tumbling and abrasive action that can be advantageously used for surface treating stainless steel parts. It is adaptable to removal of burrs, scale, and residual flux, and it also can be used for light surface treatment, such as cleaning, burnishing, or coloring. For more information, see the article "Mass Finishing" in Volume 5 of the *ASM Handbook*.

Post-Treatments. Once a mass finishing treatment is completed, stainless steel parts are rinsed thoroughly in water and dipped in a 20 vol% solution of HNO_3 at 50 °C (120 °F) for 10 to 15 min. This is followed by another water rinse. If any oxide scale remains on the work after mass finishing, it must be removed by acid pickling.

Mass Finishing Processes

The following examples describe mass finishing procedures that are applied to stainless steel production parts.

Eggcups. Because of its shape, a stainless steel eggcup cannot be finished economically by polishing and buffing. Mass finishing is much less expensive and provides a commercially acceptable finish.

In one plant, eggcups are tumbled in a horizontal, two-compartment barrel that has a steel shell and is completely lined with hardwood. All interior walls, partitions, and trapdoors are covered with hardwood to prevent contact between the stainless cups and the steel shell.

After preliminary washing of the eggcups, granite chips (size 4 or 5) are placed in the barrel with them; the ratio of cups to chips is maintained at 1 to 1. The barrel is then completely filled with warm water and a compound containing lye and a detergent. For a normal finish, the tumbling cycle is continued for 2 h. If at the end of this cycle a still brighter finish is desired, the following procedure is used:

1. Drain water and compound from barrel.
2. Refill barrel with clear water.
3. Tumble load for several minutes.
4. Drain liquid from barrel.
5. Add water and compound as for initial tumbling cycle.
6. Tumble load for a time depending on the degree of brightness desired.

Impellers. Used in milk-processing equipment, the small impeller shown in Fig. 3 is made of type 316 sheet and requires a 2B finish. This finish is obtained by fixture tumbling in two stages.

First, the parts and holding fixture are secured to the finishing barrel, and a mixture of fused alumina media of various sizes to accommodate large and small radii is added until the barrel is about 70% full. A slightly alkaline, coarse abrasive compound, which serves to increase cutting action, is also added. Water level is about 25 mm (1 in.) above the tumbling mixture. The barrel is rotated clockwise for 2 h and then counterclockwise for 2 h to ensure positive action of the mixture on all surfaces. The 4 h cycle removes sharp edges and small nicks and scratches, and it provides a dull satin finish.

To obtain the required 2B finish, the barrel is thoroughly flushed with water until all abrasives and dirt have been removed. A completely soluble nonabrasive (burnishing) compound is then added to serve as a lubricant and to color the parts, and the water level is increased to 75 mm (3 in.) above the mixture to aid dirt suspension. The same 4 h, two-direction tumbling cycle is then repeated.

Heat-exchanger plates, press formed of 1.27 mm (0.050 in.) thick type 316 stainless steel sheet, are fixture tumbled to restore original mill finish and color. Twenty-six of these plates (230 mm, or 9 in., wide; 800 mm, or 31½ in., long) are held in the fixture, which is designed to retain them on edge and at right angles to the axis of the barrel. Fixture and parts are loaded into the barrel together with 225 kg (500 lb) of No. 6 bonded chips, which fill the barrel to 65% of its capacity. Then a low-pH descaling compound is added to remove oxidation and discoloration, and, finally, water is added to 25 mm (1 in.) above the chip level.

The barrel rotates, at 15 rev/min, for ½ h clockwise and ½ h counterclockwise. Following this cycle, the barrel is flushed with water to remove all residue and is recharged with a nonabrasive burnishing compound that produces a high color and luster. The water level is increased to 75 mm (3 in.) above the chip level to allow for heavy suds and to improve dirt suspension. The same rotation cycle is then repeated, except that running time is increased to 2 h. After burnishing, the parts and fixture are removed from the barrel and flushed with hot water.

Finishing Methods

This section deals with the finishing of stainless steels as practiced by the fabricator or manufacturer: grinding (used here to mean metal removal for the purpose of altering surface finish, not to achieve close dimensional tolerances), polishing, and buffing. Table 7 summarizes the sequence of operations for the grinding, polishing, and buffing of stainless steels.

Before discussing each of these processes, it is useful to review the inherent characteristics of stainless steels that set these materials apart from other metals, and to emphasize the ever-present need to avoid any practices that may result in a loss in corrosion resistance or a reduction in mechanical property values. For example, stainless steels, as a group, are characterized by:

- *High tensile strength* determines the power necessary for efficient metal removal in grinding and polishing.
- *High surface hardness* governs the selection of abrasive materials and their cutting behavior.
- *Low heat conductivity* requires attention to precautionary measures that will prevent rapid or excessive rise in temperature, which can cause heat tint discoloration and, possibly, a reduction in corrosion resistance.
- *Rapid work hardening* necessitates proper grinding techniques, especially of austenitic grades in which residual stresses at the metal surface may affect in-service corrosion resistance.
- *The need for cleanliness* requires that attention be given to grinding and polishing media to keep them clean and free of iron particles, which can be picked up if used with carbon or alloy steel products.

Grinding

Grinding is used for preliminary surface conditioning before polishing and as a means of removing excess metal from weld beads and flash from forgings and castings. It also is used for dressing gas-cut welding edges. These operations usually require coarse or rough grinding. However, as the refinement of the surface increases with the use of finer abrasives, grinding begins to approach polishing; the dividing line between fine grinding and polishing is seldom clear cut.

Solid wheels are used for coarse grinding and include the vitreous and rubber-bonded or plastic-bonded types. They should be free cutting to avoid loading and glazing. Abrasives frequently

Table 7 Sequence of grinding, polishing, and buffing operations

Operation	Stage	Wheels	Grit size	Abrasive	Method	Purpose
Grinding	Rough	Solid wheels; rubber or bakelite bonded, soft body	20-30	Manufactured types, such as Al$_2$O$_3$ or SiC	Dry	For rough work on castings, forgings, and weld beads that may require it. Castings are usually sandblasted initially.
Grinding	Finish	Same as above; or setup disk wheels or abrasive belts	36-80	Manufactured types, such as Al$_2$O$_3$ or SiC	Dry	For subsequent operations on the above and also preliminary to polishing operations on hot-rolled plate. May also be employed for touchup work (removing deep scratches and tool marks prior to polishing).
Polishing	Rough	Setup disk canvas compress wheels or abrasive belts	80-100	Manufactured types, such as Al$_2$O$_3$ or SiC	Grease stick	To produce a rough polished finish and to remove imperfections left by hand wheel grinding. Also use as a preparatory operation for a final polish corresponding to standard No. 4 mill finish. This is the usual starting on cold-rolled sheet.
Polishing	No. 4 finish	Setup disk canvas compress wheels or abrasive belts	120-150	Manufactured types, such as Al$_2$O$_3$ or SiC	Grease stick	To provide a finish similar to standard No. 4 mill finish. Variations in fineness of finish should be expected with variations in condition of grit, as between a new or worn belt.
Polishing	No. 6 finish (tampico)	Tampico brush type	Start with No. 4 finish	…	Pumice pastes made up on the job, or commercially available manufactured compositions	To provide a finish corresponding to standard No. 6 mill finish.
Polishing	Pre-No. 7 finish	Made-up cloth wheels or abrasive belts	180	Manufactured types	Grease stick	To provide a finish preparatory to buffing for standard No. 7 finish. May be used as final finish on drawn parts and architectural trim.
Polishing	Pre-No. 8 finish	Made-up cloth wheels or abrasive belts	240 to flour	Manufactured types or Turkish emery	Grease stick	To provide a final polished finish preliminary to a mirror finish.
Polishing	Satin finishing	Full disk buffs, loose or concentric sewed		Greaseless compounds applied to the wheel as required. These are available in many grit sizes.	…	A method of producing satin finishes. Fineness of finish varies with composition employed.
Buffing	Cutting	Bias-type, sewed piece, or full disk buffs		Use stainless steel cutting compound on buff.	…	Apply as needed to remove any residual polishing lines or other imperfections prior to color buffing for high-luster finishes such as No. 7. May be applied directly to bright cold-rolled strip.
Buffing	Coloring	Full disk or bias-type buff		Use stainless steel coloring compound.	…	For final coloring to bright lusters such as No. 7 and mirror. High speeds for brightness (approximately 50 m/s, or 10,000 sfm). Lower speeds for satinlike finish (approximately 20 to 30 m/s, or 3500 to 6000 sfm).

Source: Ref 2

used are aluminum oxide (Al$_2$O$_3$) and silicon carbide (SiC) in grit sizes ranging from 20 to 36 (for initial or coarse cutting) to 60 (for subsequent finishing work).

Surface speeds for solid wheels usually range between 25.5 and 30.6 m/s (5000 and 6000 sfm). For safety, wheels should never be operated above their maximum permissible speed. For maximum cutting efficiency, they should not be run at less than recommended speeds.

Wheel Operation. Grinding wheels should never be forced; forcing causes excessive wheel breakdown and localized high temperature in the workpiece. In addition, the wheel should not be allowed to ride on the workpiece with insufficient pressure, because this causes rapid glazing of the wheel.

The elimination of heat buildup in localized zones is of major importance with stainless steel. The low thermal conductivity of stainless steel contributes to increased thermal distortion. This applies particularly to the chromium-nickel grades, of which the coefficients of thermal expansion are relatively high. Holding the metal at low temperature avoids heat tinting, which becomes evident at 230 to 260 °C (445 to 500 °F) and above. Marked increases in metal temperature can reduce the hardness of heat-treated grades and precipitate carbides in the unstabilized chromium-nickel grades, which are susceptible to intergranular corrosion.

Rough surfaces on weldments, castings, and forgings are cut down to the general finish contour with a solid wheel of either Al$_2$O$_3$ or SiC of grit size from 20 to 40 and with a bond loose enough to allow the wheel to remain open and free cutting without excessive wheel wear. Again, it is important to prevent local overheating, which can cause either mechanical or metallurgical damage, and to avoid excessive metal removal, allowing sufficient material for further finishing. Surface contamination is not important at this stage of finishing.

The next roughing operation, which in many applications may replace the solid-wheel operation, requires the use of a portable disk grinder, powered by air or electricity, using abrasive disks coated with Al$_2$O$_3$ ranging in grit size from 80 to 120. Localized overheating may be prevented by applying a small stream of water or water-soaked rags to the side not being ground.

Weld Beads. Excess metal in weld beads ordinarily is removed by grinding, although an initial cut may be made with a cold chisel when the size of the bead warrants it. Grinding procedures and precautions conform to those previously described, except that the width of weld beads precludes right-angle cutting with successive grit sizes. Usually, a raised bead will take a fairly coarse grit at the outset. Canting of wheels must be avoided; otherwise, grooves may be cut parallel to the bead and undesirable thinness will result. Limiting stops attached to portable grinders may be installed to prevent canting and excessive metal removal.

Table 8   Grit sizes and belt speeds for abrasive belt roughing and polishing

Product	Roughing				Rough polishing			Polishing			Polishing aid(a)
	Obstruction or roughness removed	Grit size, mesh	Belt speed m/s	Belt speed sfm	Grit size mesh	Belt speed m/s	Belt speed sfm	Grit size for successive stages, mesh	Belt speed m/s	Belt speed sfm	
Billets, alloy or stainless steel	...	...	...	...	50	17.9	3500	...	...	...	G
Cutlery, stainless steel											
Blades—tapering	...	50	28	5500	80	28	5500	180	28	5500	G
Forks or knives	...	...	...	...	80	26.5	5200	1500	26.5	5200	G
Spoons	...	...	...	...	...	...	...	150, 220	26.5	5200	G
Hypodermic needles, stainless steel	...	...	...	...	...	...	...	320(b), 400(b)	23.5	4600	WSO
Jet blades, stainless steel											
Airfoil	...	...	...	...	50	28	5500	120	28	5500	O
Longitudinal	...	...	...	...	...	...	...	80, 100, 120, 150, 180	(c)	(c)	O
Stainless steel											
Coil (series 300)	Pits	60	17.3	3400	80	17.3	3400	120, 150	17.3	3400	O
Pots and pans	Wrinkles	80	25.5	5000	...	...	...	220, 320(b)	25.5	5000	G
Press plates	Scratches	80	20.4	4000	100	20.4	4000	120, 150, 180, 240, 320	20.4	4000	G
Sheets, No. 3 finish	...	...	...	...	80	20.4	4000	100	20.4	4000	G
Sheets, No. 4 finish	Inclusions	100	20.4	4000	120	20.4	4000	150(b)	20.4	4000	G
Sheets, No. 7 finish	Inclusions	100	20.4	4000	150	20.4	4000	180(b), 240(b), 280(b)	20.4	4000	G
Tubes	...	...	...	...	150	17.9	3500	220, 280, 320	23	4500	O
Turbine nozzles and buckets	...	...	...	...	80	25.5	5000	120	23	4500	G

Note: Table refers to abrasive belts coated with Al_2O_3, unless grit size is footnoted to indicate otherwise. (a) G, grease; O, oil; WSO, water-soluble oil. (b) Silicon carbide. (c) Fixture abrasive, reciprocating. Source: Ref 2

When grinding is to be followed by polishing, as for weld joints on polished sheet, the grinding operation must terminate sufficiently above the level of the base metal to allow enough metal for final polishing to finish flush, without a ridge or groove. Limiting stops on grinding machines are helpful.

For economic reasons, grinding of weld joints in cold-rolled or polished sheet should be held to a minimum by using welding procedures that avoid high beads of excess metal. The grinding step can often be eliminated, allowing the workpiece to go directly into the polishing operations where finer abrasives are used.

Metal adjacent to beads that are being ground should be protected from flying bits of metal cuttings by shields of material such as paper. Wet rags may be laid on the workpiece to absorb heat and reduce thermal distortion, particularly on thin-gage material.

Progressive Grinding. To remedy an existing surface condition, such as removing scale patterns or indentations from hoisting clamps on an annealed plate, a series of wheels of decreasing grit size is often needed. The initial grit size is selected on the basis of which coarseness is needed to remove the major portion of the unwanted condition. After the workpiece has been partly dressed down, the operation is completed by using a graduated series of successively finer wheels until the desired final finish is attained. The use of a relatively soft plastic wheel impregnated with fine, sharp grit makes it possible to reduce the number of finishing operations because of the combination of free cutting and wheel resilience for ease in blending.

The direction of wheel traverse across the work is changed by 90° with each change in grit size to remove residual grinding lines. As each change is made, workpiece surfaces should be brushed thoroughly to remove any particles of the preceding abrasive or of metal cuttings that mar the performance of the finer grit to follow. The progression from coarse to fine grit size may be made in steps of 20- to 40-mesh.

When using a flat disk grinder, with which cutting is performed against the face (instead of the rim) of the wheel, a rotary or circular traversing motion is most frequently used. This eliminates the need for reversing the direction of grinding with each change of grit size.

Belt Grinding. Belts carrying abrasives of various grit sizes are widely used for grinding and polishing stainless steel surfaces. Although many complex shapes can be belt ground, a simple projection may make belt grinding impossible (e.g., the studs welded to a cookware pot or pan to which the handle is affixed). In this application, the finishing operations, from grinding to color buffing, must be completed before the studs are welded in place. Grit sizes and belt speeds for abrasive grit roughing and polishing are given in Table 8.

Mechanized Belt Grinding. In mechanized belt grinding, longer belts provide a longer belt life and dissipate heat more effectively. Thus, longer belts frequently are operated without a coolant, eliminating a postgrinding cleaning operation.

In belt grinding of rectangular stainless steel sinks, for example, it was necessary to use short belts to reach all internal surfaces. Each sink was ground in a machine with four grinding heads indexing about the main column of the machine while the sink was held in a cradle that rotated in a horizontal plane. A narrow belt ground the radii between the bottom and the side walls of the sink. Wider belts were used to grind the side walls; these belts were comparatively short and required the use of a coolant. Belt abrasives varied in grit size from 80- to 220-mesh, depending on the desired finish.

On a typical grinding machine using a 2200 mm (86 in.) wide abrasive belt and powered by a 250 hp alternating current motor, a positive hydraulic reciprocating drive permits instantaneous variations in table speed; belt speed is fixed at 25.5 m/s (5000 sfm). The 2200 mm (86 in.) belt travels over a conventional vertical-head assembly consisting of a dynamically balanced upper idler roll of steel and a rubber-covered serrated lower contact roll. A pneumatic belt-centering device ensures positive tracking of the abrasive belt and is adjustable to compensate for belts of different widths. Incorporated into the entire worktable is a 2200 mm (86 in.) wide vacuum chuck 4.9 m (16 ft) long. To produce single or compound tapers, a worktable can be tilted to any angle, for either right-hand or left-hand tapered sheets.

Example 1: Mechanized Belt Grinding of Type 302 Stainless Steel. Type 302 sand-cast heat-treating fixtures, each 1500 mm (60 in.) long, 810 mm (32 in.) wide, and 200 mm (8 in.) thick and weighing 270 kg (600 lb), were tested to determine whether fixtures of this type and weight could be refinished by coated abrasive methods. The specified finish for the working surfaces of the fixtures was 2.5 μm (100 μin.). With belt speed at 25.5 m/s (5000 sfm) and table speed at 0.03 to 0.04 m/s (6 to 8 sfm), the fixtures were rough ground and finish ground, using waterproof cloth belts coated with Al_2O_3 abrasive. Grit size was 36 mesh for rough grinding, 60 mesh for finish grinding. Coolant was water-soluble oil.

To attain the specified 2.5 μm (100 μin.) surface, approximately 1.3 mm (0.050 in.) of material was removed from each side of each fixture during rough grinding, and 0.25 mm (0.010 in.) was removed in finish grinding. The rough grinding cycle required about 2½ h for each side and finish grinding about ½ h. Planing, previously used for refinishing these fixtures, had required 4 h for each side.

Example 2: Mechanized Belt Grinding of Type 347 Stainless Steel. Type 347 sheet was tested to determine whether a desired scratch pattern and a 0.8 μm (30 μin.) finish could be obtained using this equipment. Each sheet was 1800 by 910 by 0.9 mm (72 by 36 by 0.035 in.). Because of thinness, using the vacuum-chuck worktable to hold the sheet down during grinding would have been impractical. A tension fixture was devised especially for this purpose.

Grinding was done at a belt speed of 25.5 m/s (5000 sfm) and at table speeds of 0.04 and 0.05 m/s (8 and 10 sfm). Belts used were waterproof cloth coated with Al_2O_3 abrasive (120 mesh for roughing, 150 mesh for finishing). A water-soluble oil coolant was used.

The material removed, from one side only, was approximately 0.05 mm (0.002 in.) in rough grinding and 0.025 mm (0.001 in.) in finish grinding. Rough grinding and finish grinding cycles each required 20 min. The desired scratch pattern and the 0.75 μm (30 μin.) surface finish were obtained on the sheet.

Example 3: Mechanized Belt Grinding of Type 310 Stainless Steel. Type 310 surface plates (nonmagnetic) were tested to determine whether the required finish of 0.5 μm (20 μin.) could be obtained and also to compare the time required for abrasive belt grinding with that for resurfacing these plates with a surface grinding operation. Approximately 25 plates, most ranging in size from 760 by 150 by 32 mm to 460 by 760 by 25 mm (30 by 6 by 1¼ in. to 18 by 30 by 1 in.), were ground; the largest plate processed was 3 m (10 ft) long and 460 mm (18 in.) wide.

Grinding was performed using waterproof cloth Al_2O_3 abrasive belts of 36-mesh grit size for roughing, 60-mesh for finishing. Coolant was water-soluble oil. Belt speed was 25.5 m/s (5000 sfm); table speed was 0.025 to 0.03 m/s (5 to 6 sfm). In rough grinding, 0.3 to 0.4 mm (0.012 to 0.016 in.) of material was removed, which included removal of hard scale on the top surface of each plate. In finish grinding, 0.15 to 0.2 mm (0.006 to 0.008 in.) was removed.

The required surface finish of 0.1 μm (20 μin.) was attained. Total grinding time for the largest plate was 2½ h; this compared with 6 h required for resurfacing these plates on a large surface grinder.

Belt life is influenced primarily by belt speed, type of material being ground and its hardness, pressure of the belt against the work, type of contact roll, type of lubricant (if a lubricant is required), and uniformity of the finish desired. In belt grinding of stainless steel, the recommended belt speed is approximately 20.4 m/s (4000 sfm).

With the exception of the precipitation-hardening stainless steels, the hardness of the steel has a greater effect on the life of a grinding belt than its composition. Hardness also affects surface finish, and a high-quality finish is easier to obtain on a harder stainless than on one that is softer. With precipitation-hardening alloys, best grinding results are obtained with a waterproof cloth abrasive belt and a water-soluble oil lubricant.

Pressure of the workpiece against the abrasive belt is probably the most important factor affecting belt life. Excessive pressure on a new belt causes glazing of the abrasive and greatly reduces cutting action. Therefore, new belts should be subjected to very light pressures during the break-in period and until the belt is capable of maintaining a uniform cutting action. A light belt pressure is preferred, and increased stock removal should be obtained by changing to a coarser belt.

The contact roll that backs up the abrasive belt is another important factor; a properly serrated contact roll may increase belt life by as much as 60%. The angle of the serration affects both belt life and finish. To obtain fine finishes, contact rolls serrated at an angle of 75° to the axis of the spindle should be used. Rough finishing requires a 30° angle. For general work, contact rolls may be made with a 45° serration, using a 9.5 mm (⅜ in.) groove and 9.5 mm (⅜ in.) land. Hardness of the contact roll should range between 50 to 65 on the Shore scleroscope A-scale.

When lubricants are used, they should maintain free-cutting (nonloading) edges, add color to the finished product, maintain a cool cutting surface, and be easy to apply. Lubricants may be in the form of grease sticks, waxes, or cutting oils. Cutting oils generally are more effective when they are diluted as much as 4 to 1 with kerosene.

Safety. Metal fines collected in a container near machines during the belt grinding of stainless steel should be removed regularly, because the fines, together with polishing compounds or oils that are collected with them, constitute a potential fire hazard. Fires in the duct system can be extremely serious because of the high air flow in the ducts. Fire-extinguishing equipment should be close to any machines using abrasive belts.

When wide abrasive belts are used, equipment with automatic tracking to center the belt in relation to the work is advantageous. All abrasive belt machinery should be equipped with motors that are totally enclosed.

Safety training for operators should begin with thorough instruction in the proper use of equipment, because most severe injuries result from improper use. The most common injuries are burns, cuts, and eye injuries. Serious accidents may arise from the snagging of parts because of improper loading, improper use of lubricating devices, and careless placement of hands and arms while the machine is in operation.

Polishing

Polishing operations use abrasives that are mounted on prepared shaped wheels or on belts that provide a resilient backing. The stainless steel to be polished may be in either a smooth rolled or a previously ground condition. For the smooth-rolled condition, the starting grit size should be selected in the range of 150 to 220. For the ground condition, the initial grit should be coarse enough to remove or smooth out any residual cutting lines or other surface imperfections left from grinding. In either instance, the treatment with the initial grit should be continued until a clean, uniform, blemish-free surface texture is obtained. The initial grit size to use on a preground surface may be set at about 20 numbers finer than the last grit used in grinding and may be changed, if necessary, after inspection. A tallow lubricant may be used to reduce the sharpness of cutting. With broad-belt grinding of stainless steel sheet, the use of a lubricant or coolant is mandatory.

After completion of the initial stage of polishing, wheels or belts are changed to provide finer grits. The step-up in fineness is usually by 30 to 40

numbers. Each succeeding treatment is continued until all residual marks of the preceding cut are removed. Grease in stick form is applied to wheels carrying abrasives of 150 mesh and finer. Aluminum oxide buffing compounds and powdered pumice are preferred for use with abrasives of 200 mesh and finer grit size.

Polishing speeds are generally somewhat higher than those used in grinding. A typical speed for a coated-wheel operation is 38.3 m/s (7500 sfm).

The same precautions that must be observed in the grinding of stainless steel are equally applicable to polishing:

- Avoidance of iron or other contamination
- Care of wheels and belts when not in use
- Restriction of the use of wheels and belts to stainless steel only
- Avoidance of excessive pressure while polishing
- Operation at proper speeds
- Avoidance of localized heat buildup because of dwelling at one spot
- Removal of loose cuttings and bits of abrasive from work surfaces before changing from one grit size to another

Buffing

Buffed finishes are produced on stainless steel surfaces by using equipment, materials, and techniques that are similar to those used on other materials (see the article "Finishing Processes Using Multipoint or Random Cutting Edges" in Volume 5 of the *ASM Handbook*). However, the skill needed for producing the high lusters obtainable on stainless steel is gained only through actual experience. Buffed finishes are not recommended for the stabilized grades of stainless steel, such as types 321 and 347, because these materials contain fine, hard particles of titanium or columbium compound that show up as pits on bright finishes.

The first step in applying a buffed finish of desired luster and color is to provide a smooth surface, free of scratches and any other defects. For this reason, buffing is generally performed in two stages: hard buffing (cutting down) and color buffing.

Hard buffing follows polishing, which generally ends with the use of abrasives of 200- to 250-mesh grit size. The fine scratches left by polishing are cut down with a buff that carries no previously glued-on abrasive. Instead, such abrasive as is needed is applied intermittently to the buffing wheel as it rotates, either by rubbing a cutting compound in bar or stick form against it or by spraying it with a liquid compound. These cutting compounds contain very fine artificial abrasives, such as Al_2O_3, of about 300-mesh grit size and a stiff grease or other material that acts as a binder. They adhere to the wheel by impregnating the cloth disks. Hard buffing may be conducted at from 33.2 m/s (6500 sfm) up to a maximum of 51 m/s (10,000 sfm).

Color buffing is performed in the same manner as hard buffing, except that a coloring compound is substituted for the cutting compound and speeds are held below 35.7 m/s (7000 sfm). Various compounds (rouges and other extremely fine abrasives) for use on stainless steel are available commercially, both in bar form for hand application and in liquid form for automatic application. The use of any material that may contribute to loss of corrosion resistance by stainless steel surfaces should be avoided.

Direct color buffing, without previous polishing or hard buffing, may be satisfactory for certain applications, such as:

- A color-buffing wheel may be applied directly on type 430 that has been given a finishing pass on a polished mill roll after final pickling.
- Small articles blanked from bright-finished straight-chromium steel strip and then tumbled for burr removal may have a satisfactory appearance if run under a color buff for brightening.
- Smooth, defect-free surfaces that have been electrolytically polished provide a good base for color buffing. By masking before buffing, contrasting surface effects can be obtained as a result of the difference in reflectivity obtainable by electrolytic polishing and by color buffing.

However, color buffing does not remove scratches or other surface defects, because cloth wheels without coarse abrasives, which are used for color buffing, do not remove surface imperfections. Therefore, the continued presence of such imperfections on finished products must be expected.

Effect of Polishing and Buffing on Corrosion Resistance. In addition to altering the appearance of stainless steels, polishing and buffing may have a considerable effect on the corrosion resistance of these materials. For example, a steel with a No. 2B finish as received from the mill has excellent corrosion resistance. This can be adversely affected by polishing with coarse abrasive, but it can be fully restored by polishing to a No. 4 finish or higher. Polishing to a No. 7 or 8 finish, by removing very fine pits and other surface defects, improves corrosion resistance over that afforded by the original No. 2B finish.

Tanks for storing raw milk provide a commercial example of the importance of a polished finish to sanitary and corrosion-resistance properties. According to the sanitary codes, these tanks must be made of 300-series stainless steel, and all surfaces that come in contact with the milk must be polished to a pit-free No. 4 finish or better. The high finish not only promotes sanitary properties but also provides improved resistance to corrosion by the chlorine-bearing chemical used in scouring the tanks after each use.

Several polishing and buffing compounds contain iron and iron compounds, which can be highly deleterious to the corrosion resistance of stainless steel. The amount of iron in these compounds that can be tolerated is extremely small (for maximum protection, less than 0.01% Fe). If more than one polishing operation is involved, slightly more iron can be tolerated in the early stages of polishing, but the final stage should be virtually iron free. Magnetic oxides of iron are as damaging as iron powder; the oxides generally occur in Turkish emery as well as in several synthetic abrasives. Their presence is most accurately determined by chemical analysis.

Cleaning and Passivation after Buffing. Cleaning is always required after a final buffing operation in which a surface finish of No. 4 or finer is achieved. The workpiece is vapor degreased or is cleaned with whiting (precipitated calcium carbonate), powdered chalk, or dehydrated lime, which is applied with a soft flannel cloth. This picks up the grease or lubricant from a color-buffing operation. The workpiece must then be protected from damage in handling.

Passivation is not required after buffing or fine polishing if the surface obtained is chemically clean and free of oil, grease, or adhesives used in the polishing media. A clean surface passivates itself naturally when it is exposed to air. However, if foreign metal, such as iron, has been picked up in the buffing operation, it must be removed by pickling or passivation.

Matching Mill Finishes

In the fabrication of No. 4 polished sheet, it frequently is necessary to refinish weld zones to blend them with the original finish. Although it is virtually impossible to match a machine-polished surface except by duplicating the original polishing, a close blending may be obtained by skillful use of manual methods.

If the original machine-polished lines are parallel with the line of the weld, the bead can be dressed down by grinding with a hard or soft wheel and then be finished by polishing with, progressively, No. 80 and No. 120 (and possibly No. 150) grit on a setup wheel driven by a portable machine. The traversing of this wheel should be kept in line with the run of the bead so that its cut lines are kept parallel with those of the original machine-polished surface.

To avoid residual ridges or grooves, the metal of the joint should be brought flush with that of the basis metal. For a given starting grit size, the depth of the scratches produced depends on the amount of use it has received; thus, samples should be run before starting on finish work.

If the machine-polished lines are not parallel with the line of the weld, final manual polishing should be done in the direction of the machine polishing. If the original polish lines on the two sides of a joint are not parallel with each other (e.g., if they are parallel with the bead on one side and perpendicular to the bead on the other), the best procedure is to run the polishing cut lines along (not across) the bead. The girth weld between a tank shell and head exemplifies this problem. The cut lines of the shell extend around the unit and lie parallel with the girth joint, whereas the cut lines on the head are perpendicular, parallel, and at an angle around the periphery. Swinging such an assembly on the faceplate of a large lathe would permit repolishing the head and dressing the weld joint on the same setup, thus rendering parallel all of the cut lines on the head, joint, and shell. For this application, abrasive paper (or pieces cut from a belt) may be backed up with a block of wood or some softer material and guided by hand along the line of the weld joint.

Electrocleaning and Electropolishing

Electrocleaning, an electropolishing technique, is a useful alternative to pickling treatments. Although electrocleaning is not covered under ASTM A 380, it is widely used to remove imperfections from the surface of stainless steel after fabrication. It removes embedded iron particles and similar film defects, as does pickling. Unlike pickling, electrocleaning does not roughen the surface, but rather makes it smoother. A 12 V direct current power source with variable current capability is connected to the stainless steel, making it the anode. A copper cathode and an electrolyte, usually phosphoric acid (H_3PO_4), are then used to corrode away the protective film and several layers of the surface in a controlled manner by varying the current and dwell time.

Electrocleaning can be performed in most plating shops by immersion. Localized electrocleaning with field kits is widely practiced to remove heat tint and weld-related defects from the heat-affected zone (Fig. 4).

Electropolishing is the same process as electrocleaning but is generally performed for a longer time. Electropolishing is used primarily to produce a very smooth, bright, easily cleaned surface with maximum corrosion resistance. It removes the surface layer of a metal by anodic treatment in an acid bath. Conditions for electropolishing of stainless steels in acid electrolytes are given in Table 9. More detailed information can be found in the article "Electropolishing" in Volume 5 of the *9th Edition of Metals Handbook*.

Electropolishing is applicable to all stainless steel grades, hot or cold finished, cast or wrought. The amount of metal removed is subject to close control, depending on the desired result. The resulting surfaces have a bright, passive finish. The process is most frequently applied to cold-finished surfaces, because they yield a smoother finish than can conventionally be obtained on hot-finished surfaces. As in electroplating, the results depend on the contour and shape of the part. The end-grain surfaces of the free-machining stainless grades, such as types 303 and 416, will appear frosty after electropolishing because of removal of the sulfide inclusions.

Electropolishing can be used as a preliminary brightening operation before final buffing, particularly on drawn parts with burrs, sharp radii, or

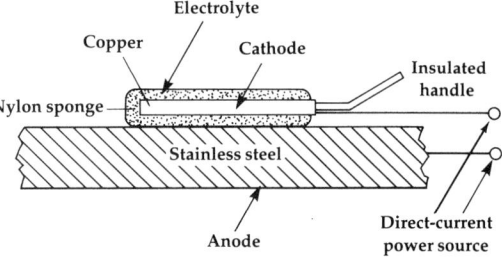

Fig. 4 Simple tool for localized electrocleaning of heat tint from the surface of stainless steel

Table 9 Conditions for electropolishing in acid electrolytes

Type of metal (and product)	Purpose of treatment	Bath volume		Installed power		Current density		Polishing cycle, min	Daily production			Oper-ators
									No. of parts	Area		
		L	gal	A	V	A/dm^2	A/ft^2			m^2	ft^2	
Sulfuric-phosphoric acid electrolytes												
Monel (fishline guides)	Smooth	750	200	500	12	…	…	5-8	2000	1.5-2.5	15-25	2
302 and 430 stainless (job-shop work)	Bright finish	1150	300	1500	15	30	300	3-8	3500	25	250	2
302 and 202 stainless (plumbing-ware)	Bright finish	1150	300	1500	12	30	300	3-4	1000-2000	…	…	1
303 stainless (food-processing equipment)	Bright finish	2650	700	2500	18	20	200	4-10	400-500	190-370	2000-4000	2
Series 300 and 400 stainless (job-shop work)	Various	2250	600	3000	18	…	…	10(avg)	25-400	5-45	50-500	2
304 stainless	Brighten; deburr	1300	350	2000	12	30	300	4	3000	55-75	600-800	1
Stainless steel (aircraft compo-nents)	…	2650	700	3000	18	25-30	250-300	5	200	30	300	1
430 stainless	Bright finish	1500	400	1500	14	…	…	1-2	7000	75	800	1
430 stainless (trim items)	Brighten; deburr	1500	400	750	18	…	…	3	12 000	230	2500	1
430 stainless (automotive trim)	Bright finish	3800	1000	3000	18	30	300	4	250/h	…	…	1
430 stainless (automotive rain shields)	Bright finish	3800	1000	3000	18	25	250	5	450/h	…	…	1
Stainless and carbon steels (job-shop work)	Brighten; deburr	1500	400	1500	12	25-40	250-400	Varies	Varies	…	…	1
4140 steel	Prepare for chromium plate	3200	850	4000	12	15	150	10	7000-10 000	45-75	500-800	3
Phosphoric-chromic acid electrolytes												
Brass (lighting fixtures)	Final finish(a)	1500	400	1500	18	30-40	300-400	8-15	100-1500	9 or 10	100	1
Brass and copper (electronics contactors)(b)	Smooth	50	10	100	12	…	…	5	100	0.2	2	1(c)
Low-carbon steel, Nitralloy, 440 (paper knives)(d)	Smooth; sharpen	5700	1500	4000	18	…	…	8	75-80	…	…	1
Steel (aircraft instrument and con-trol parts)	…	1700	450	2000	18	…	…	2-4	50	0.5-0.7	5-8	2
Sulfuric-phosphoric-chromic acid electrolytes												
Aluminum	Prepare for anodizing	1900	500	300	18	…	…	3-4	5000-6000	35	400	1
Aluminum (nameplates)	Prepare for anodizing	2250	600	1500	18	10	100	6-12	4000	9 or 10	100	2
Aluminum (eyeglass frames)	Prepare for anodizing	1150	300	1000	24	10	100	6-12	9000	12	130	2
302 stainless (surgical instru-ments)	Smooth; polish	3600	950	3000	18	30	300	5	5000	…	…	1
Carbon steel	Smooth; deburr	1500	400	…	…	30	300	2	5000	90	1000	1
4130 steel (tools)	Bright finish	950	250	1500	9	17.5	175	4	2000-5000	…	…	2

(a) Some hand coloring after electropolishing. (b) Also electropolished in phosphoric acid bath. (c) Part time. (d) Knives made from all three metals

recessed areas, and it serves to reduce the amount of buffing required. Electropolishing is applied to decorative automotive parts and accessories, conveyor systems for food-handling equipment, animal cages, and pharmacy equipment. It provides an economical finish on many parts that are difficult or impossible to finish by conventional polishing, such as items made from wire.

In contrast to mechanical finishing methods, electropolishing may make inclusions in the material more visible. Some types of inclusions are dissolved out, whereas others remain in relief. Electropolishing has been used as a surface-inspection technique to reveal residual foreign material, such as embedded scale and particles of iron, carbide precipitation, and weld defects. The surface obtained by electropolishing is directly related to the original surface quality; the process cannot be used to remove digs, gouges, scratches, and the like.

Chemical polishing is another method for providing a smooth and bright surface on stainless steel. Unlike electropolishing, chemical polishing can be done without the use of electricity and without racking of individual parts. Thus, chemical polishing offers significant sav-ings in capital investment and labor. In addition, chemical polishing offers a greater degree of freedom in polishing items with blind holes and other recessed areas. However, it does not produce the high specular reflectivity (brightness) obtained with electropolishing.

Proprietary products for chemical polishing are available in the market. Generally, they are based on combinations of H_3PO_4, HNO_3, H_2SO_4, hydrochloric acid (HCl), organic acids, and special surfactants and stabilizers to promote a high degree of brightness and long bath life. Unlike the HNO_3-HF mixtures that are used in chemical cleaning, the proprietary chemical bright dips do not cause severe attack on the grain boundaries or intergranular corrosion.

Passivation Treatments

Exposure to air is the natural, primary passivation treatment for stainless steel. This exposure produces a thin, durable chromium oxide film that forms rapidly on the alloy surface and gives stainless steel its characteristic "stainless" quality. Exposure of the surface to water or other oxidizing environments also produces this passivating film.

Additional passivation is called for in many specifications to remove light surface contamination from machined stainless steel parts, including shop dirt, iron particles from cutting tools, and machining lubricants. Passivation treatments of stainless steel with HNO_3 or mild organic acids are useful mild cleaning operations performed after machining to enhance the protective nature of the natural, air-formed film. Nitric acid treatment enhances the level of chromium in the protective film on stainless steels. DeBold (Ref 4) has published an excellent practical review of HNO_3 passivation of stainless steel machined parts.

ASTM A 380 (Ref 1) describes eight HNO_3-based cleaning/passivation treatments and four cleaning treatments using other chemicals (Table 10). None of these passivation treatments corrodes or etches the surface. Several are designed to clean bright or polished surfaces by removing loosely adherent foreign matter. The most common treatment is immersion in a 20 to 40% solution of HNO_3 at 50 to 60 °C (120 to 140 °F).

The complete passivation treatment includes degreasing, immersion, and rinsing. Degreasing,

Table 10 Acid cleaning of stainless steel

Alloy	Condition	Code	Solution, vol%(a)	Temperature °C	Temperature °F	Time, min
Part 1: Cleaning with HNO₃-HF						
Purpose: For use after descaling by mechanical or other chemical methods as a further treatment to remove residual particles of scale or products of chemical action (i.e., smut), and to produce a uniform "white pickled" finish						
200- and 300-series alloys; 400-series alloys containing 16% Cr or more, and precipitation-hardening alloys (except free-machining alloys)	Fully annealed only	D	6-25% HNO₃ plus ½ to 8% HF(b)(c)	20-60	70-140	As necessary
Free-machining alloys, maraging alloys, and 400-series alloys containing less than 16% Cr	Fully annealed only	E	10% HNO₃ plus ½ to 1½% HF(b)(c)	20 (up to 60 with caution)	70 (up to 140 with caution)	1-2
Part 2: Cleaning/passivation with HNO₃						
Purpose: For removal of soluble salts, corrosion products, and free ion and other metallic contamination resulting from handling, fabrication, or exposure to contaminated atmospheres						
200- and 300-series alloys; 400-series, precipitation-hardening and maraging alloys containing 16% Cr or more (except free-machining alloys)(d)	Annealed, cold rolled, or work hardened, with dull or nonreflective surfaces	F	20-50% HNO₃	50-70 / 20-40	120-160 / 70-100	10-30 / 30-60(c)
	Annealed, cold rolled, or work hardened, with bright-machined or polished surfaces	G	20-40% HNO₃ plus 2-6 wt% Na₂CrSO₇ · 2H₂O	50-70 / 20-40	120-155 / 70-100	10-30 / 30-60(c)
400-series, maraging and precipitation-hardening alloys containing less than 16% Cr, and high-carbon/straight-chromium alloys (except free-machining alloys)(d)	Annealed or hardened, with dull or nonreflective surfaces	H	20-50% HNO₃	45-55 / 20-40	110-130 / 70-100	20-30 / 60
	Annealed or hardened, with bright-machined or polished surfaces	I(f)	20-25% HNO₃ plus 2-6 wt% Na₂Cr₂O₇ · 2H₂O	50-55 / 20-40	120-130 / 70-100	15-30 / 30-60
200-, 300-, and 400-series free-machining alloys(d)	Annealed or hardened, with bright-machined or polished surfaces	J(f)	20-50% HNO₃ plus 2-6 wt% Na₂Cr₂O₇ · 2H₂O(g)	20-50	70-120	25-40
		K(e)	1-2% HNO₃ plus 1-5 wt% Na₂Cr₂O₇ · 2H₂O	50-60	120-140	10
		L(f)	12% HNO₃ plus 4 wt% CuSO₄ · 5H₂O	50-60	120-140	10
Special free-machining 400-series alloys with more than 1.25% Mn or more than 0.40% S(d)	Annealed or hardened with bright-machined or polished surfaces	M(f)	40-60% HNO₃ plus 2-6 wt% Na₂Cr₂O₇ · 2H₂O	50-70	120-160	20-30
Part 3: Cleaning with other chemical solutions						
Purpose: General cleaning						
200-, 300-, and 400-series alloys (except free-machining alloys), precipitation-hardening and maraging alloys	Fully annealed only	N	1 wt% citric acid plus 1 wt% NaNO₃	20	70	60
		O	5-10 wt% ammonium citrate	50-70	120-160	10-60
Assemblies of stainless and carbon steel (for example, heat exchanger with stainless steel tubes and carbon steel shell)	Sensitized	P	Inhibited solution of 2 wt% hydroxyacetic acid and 1 wt% formic acid	95	200	6 h
		Q	Inhibited ammonia-neutralized solution of EDTA (ethylene-diamene-tetraacetic acid) followed by hot-water rinse and dip in solution of 10 ppm ammonium hydroxide plus 100 ppm hydrazine	Up to 120	Up to 250	6 h

(a) Solution prepared from reagents of following weight percent: HNO₃, 67; HF, 70. (b) For reasons of convenience and handling safety, commercial formulations containing fluoride salts may be found useful in place of HF for preparing HNO₃-HF solutions. (c) After acid cleaning and water rinsing, a caustic permanganate solution containing 10 wt% NaOH and 4 wt% KMnO₄, 70 to 80 °C (160 to 180 °F) 5 to 60 min, may be used as a final dip for removal of smut, followed by thorough water rinsing and drying. (d) The purchaser shall have the option of specifying that all 400-series ferritic or martensitic parts receive additional treatment as follows: Within 1 h after the water rinse following the specified passivation treatment, all parts shall be immersed in an aqueous solution containing 4 to 6 wt% Na₂Cr₂O₇ · 2H₂O at 60 to 70 °C (140 to 160 °F) 30 min. This immersion shall be followed by thorough rinsing with clean water. The parts then shall be thoroughly dried. (e) Shorter times may be acceptable where established by test and agreed upon by the purchaser. (f) The high-carbon and free-machining alloys may be subject to etching or discoloration in nitric acid. This tendency can be minimized by the use of high acid concentrations with inhibitors such as Na₂Cr₂O₇ · 2H₂O and CuSO₄ · 5H₂O. Oxidizing action increases with increasing concentration of nitric acid; additional oxidizing action is provided by Na₂Cr₂O₇ · 2H₂O. Avoid acid cleaning when possible; use mechanical cleaning followed by scrubbing with hot water and detergent, final thorough water rinsing, and drying. (g) If flash attack (clouding of stainless steel surface) occurs, a fresh (clean) passivating solution or a higher HNO₃ concentration will usually eliminate it.

preferably in a nonchlorinated solvent, removes organic contaminants from the surface.

Degreasing. Neither air nor HNO₃ can form or enhance the protective film when grease, oil, fingerprints, or other organic contamination is present on the surface. Parts must be thoroughly degreased before any passivation treatment. The water-break test, described in ASTM A 380 (Ref 1), is easy to apply and is effective in detecting residual organic matter that may not have been removed in the degreasing operation. A sheet of water directed over the surface will "break" around oil, grease, and other organic contaminants not completely removed from the surface. Specifications can simply call for no break in the film as it drains from the vertical surface.

Immersion. The part is immersed in a passivating solution selected from Table 10 (Part 2 or 3). In addition to the standard HNO₃ solution, there are a number of solution variations appropriate for all grades of 200-, 300-, and 400- series, maraging, precipitation-hardening, and free-machining alloys in various heat treatment conditions and surface finishes.

Rinsing. Immediate and thorough rinsing in clean water of pH 6 to 8 is mandatory. In many instances neutralization prior to rinsing is helpful. Immersion, neutralization, and rinsing must follow one another without allowing the surface to dry between steps. When passivating stainless steel sheet material, each sheet must be completely dry before it is stacked to avoid marks.

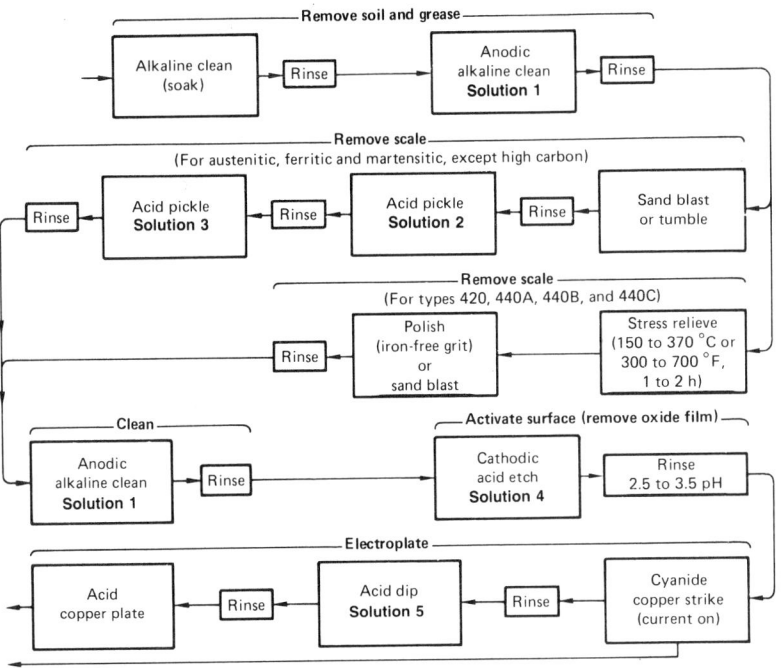

Solution No.	Type of solution	Composition of solution	Operating temperature °C	Operating temperature °F	Cycle time, min
1	Anodic alkaline cleaner(a)	Alkali, as low as possible	(b)	(b)	(b)
2	Acid pickle	H_2SO_4, 8-11 vol %	65-70	150-160	10-45
3	Acid pickle	HNO_3, 6-10 vol %; HF, 1.5 vol %	Room temperature	Room temperature	10-30
4	Cathodic acid etch(c)	H_2SO_4, 5-15 vol %	Room temperature	Room temperature	1-5(d)
5	Acid dip	H_2SO_4, 1 vol %	Room temperature	Room temperature	⅙-⅓

(a) Current density, as low as possible. (b) As low as possible. (c) Current density, 54 A/m² (5 A/ft²). (d) After subsequent rinse, place parts into copper electrolyte while parts are still wet

Fig. 5   Electroplating copper on stainless steels

In addition to the cleaning precautions given in ASTM A 380 (Ref 1), different grades of stainless steel should not be mixed in the same passivating bath, as this can initiate corrosion where surfaces come in contact.

Although HNO_3 does not normally corrode stainless steel, it will corrode surfaces that are significantly altered. Acid cleaning should not be used for carburized and nitrided stainless steel parts or for improperly heat-treated high-carbon or high-chromium martensitic grades that have not been fully hardened.

Electroplating

Stainless steels may be plated with copper, chromium, nickel, cadmium, and the precious metals for such purposes as:
- Color matching
- Lubrication during cold heading, spring coiling, or wire drawing
- Reduction of scaling at high temperatures
- Improvement of wettability or of conductance of heat or electricity
- Prevention of galling
- Decorative uses in such applications as jewelry
- Prevention of superficial rusting

Although a stainless steel surface may be clean and scale-free, an adherent electrodeposit cannot be obtained until the surface is activated for removal of its normally ever-present oxide film. Activation, which is performed immediately before plating, may be accomplished by cathodic treatments, immersion treatments, or simultaneous activation-plating treatments. These treatments, together with other procedures necessary for preparing stainless steel for electroplating, are fully described in ASTM B 254.

Figure 5 summarizes some of the data from ASTM B 254. The same cleaning procedures would be appropriate before electrodeposition of other metals. When preparing stainless steel for electroplating, the following should be considered:

- *Electrocleaning:* When bright plating is desired, the alkalinity, current density, and temperature of the cleaning bath should be kept as low as possible, especially for the high-chromium alloys. To minimize the severity of electrocleaning when a bright finish is desired, a short electropolishing treatment may be used in lieu of electrocleaning, provided that the preliminary cleaning is adequate.
- *Acid pickling:* Freshly prepared pickling baths should be activated by dissolving some iron in them before using the bath; otherwise, the rate of pickling is slow until the bath has dissolved some iron from the steel being treated.
- *Activating:* The activation step is the most important in surface preparation of stainless steel for electroplating. If the simultaneous activation-plating treatment is used, where the nodes are nickel, the nickel content of the solution gradually increases because of the low cathode efficiency. This can be compensated for by removing a portion of the solution and replenishing with HCl. The activation-plating treatment is usually preferred for stainless steel parts that are to be copper plated.
- *Plating:* After activating and rinsing, the work should be entered directly into the electrolyte. When possible, the rinse water should be slightly acid (2.5 to 3.5 pH); the required acidity is usually provided by the dragout of acid from the activation treatment. Stainless steel has much lower electrical conductivity than most other metals, and thus adequate attention should be paid to racking when introducing work into copper electrolyte, to ensure an adequate number of contacts to obtain complete coverage in minimum time.

Other Coating Processes (Ref 2)

Painting. In the painting of stainless steel surfaces, the main requirement to be satisfied is that of providing a good permanent bond. Stainless steel surfaces are dense, hard, and smooth, particularly when in the cold-rolled or polished condition. For that reason, it is usually advisable to roughen them by means of strong pickling or sandblasting. The latter is advantageous because it can be readily confined to limited areas by masking.

In the transportation industry, acid etching is usually favored as a preliminary step in painting stainless steels. The etchants are solutions of either HCl or HF:

Solution 1
- 25 parts water by volume
- 75 parts HCl by volume
- 5 parts HNO_3 by volume
- 20 wt% $FeCl_3$

Solution 2
- 10 to 20 vol% HNO_3
- 3 to 5 vol% HF

- Remainder water

The stainless steel has either a No. 2D or 2B finish. Paint companies are best qualified to suggest paint types and procedures for prime and finish coats.

Cleanliness is a key element in painting stainless steels. The surface must be clean, and it is good practice to paint only in a clean, dust-free atmosphere. Use thin coats and allow plenty of time to dry between coats.

Sandblasting is best accomplished with clean, hard sand of relatively small grit size driven by an air blast that is entirely free of compressor oil. (Glass beads are sometimes used.) Thin-gage material should be backed up to avoid distortion. Surfaces should be dry and completely free of grease, oil, or any other foreign material before applying the ground coat.

Surface Blackening. Stainless steel surfaces can be readily blackened by immersion in a molten salt bath of sodium dichromate. This practice, which is not complicated to set up and operate, is widely used by the automotive industry to blacken stainless steel parts, such as windshield wipers, and it is used by manufacturers of stainless steel solar collector panels.

The process applies a very thin, smooth black oxide film to the surface of all stainless steel types. The film is normally dull black in color, but it can be brightened by the application of oils or waxes. The film shows no tendency to age or lose color in service. It is ductile, will not chip or peel, and is resistant to heating to the normal scaling temperature of the stainless steel. A blackened stainless steel can be deformed moderately without harm, and the film exhibits good resistance to abrasion.

The salt bath operates at approximately 400 °C (750 °F), and dip time varies from 5 to 30 min, followed by a wash-water rinse. Solar panels achieve an ideal blackening in 5 min, whereas auto trim parts require about 30 min to obtain a deeper black color.

Coloring. A proprietary process used for coloring stainless steels involves immersing the material in a hot chromic-sulfuric acid solution, followed by a cathodic hardening treatment in another acidic solution. The reaction of the base material with the hot acid produces a transparent film that in itself is basically colorless, but that shows colors through the phenomenon of light interference. The colors produced, in normal time sequence, are bronze, blue, gold, red, purple, and green, and within this range a wide variety of shades are possible. A black finish is also available. Appearance is also dependent on the nature of the starting surface: matte and satin surfaces produce matte colors; polished surfaces exhibit a high degree of metallic luster. The process (licensed by the International Nickel Company) is being used throughout the world for architectural applications, furniture, bathtubs, consumer products, and automotive trim.

Different effects can be achieved, for example, by alternating bright polished and satin finished sheets, by selective polishing before coloring, and by using cold-embossed colored stainless steel. Masking, screen printing, and photoresist techniques can be employed to achieve patterned effects and for the reproduction of photographic images. Colored stainless steel can be subjected to considerable deformation without detriment. It can, for example, be drawn, bent through quite sharp angles, and embossed without any deleterious effects or reduction of color intensity. Corrosion resistance of colored stainless is at least as good as that of the untreated material, and exposure tests extending over a number of years have shown no deterioration of color.

ACKNOWLEDGMENT

The information in this article is largely taken from "Cleaning and Finishing of Stainless Steel," *Surface Cleaning, Finishing, and Coating*, Vol 5, 9th ed., *Metals Handbook*, American Society for Metals, 1982.

REFERENCES

1. "Standard Practice for Cleaning and Descaling Stainless Steel Parts, Equipment, and Systems," A 380, *Annual Book of ASTM Standards*, ASTM, 1988
2. *Finishes for Stainless Steel*, Publication 201-683-14M-E, American Iron and Steel Institute, 1983
3. *Cleaning and Descaling Stainless Steels*, No. 9001, American Iron and Steel Institute, 1982 (reprinted by Nickel Development Institute, 1988)
4. T. DeBold, Passivation of Stainless Steel Parts, *TAPPI J.*, Jan 1988, p 196-198

Contents

Metallographic Practices for Wrought Stainless Steels

METALLOGRAPHIC PROCEDURES used to prepare wrought stainless steels for macroscopic and microscopic examination are similar to those used for carbon and alloy steels and for tool steels (see the articles "Carbon and Alloy Steels" and "Tool Steels" in Volume 9, *Metallography and Microstructures*, of the *ASM Handbook*). However, certain types require careful attention to prevent artifacts. Because the austenitic grades work-harden readily, cutting and grinding must be carefully executed to minimize deformation. The high-hardness martensitic grades that contain substantial undissolved chromium carbide are difficult to polish while fully retaining the carbides. The most difficult of such grades to prepare is type 440C, particularly in the annealed or annealed and quenched condition. For the most part, preparation of stainless steels is reasonably simple if the basic rules for metallographic preparation are followed. However, unlike carbon, alloy, and tool steels, etching techniques are more difficult due to the high corrosion resistance of stainless steels and the vari-

ous second phases that may be encountered. References 1 to 3 provide additional details on the metallography of stainless steels.

Macroexamination

The procedures used to select and prepare stainless steel disks for macroetching are identical to those used for carbon, alloy, and tool steels. Because these grades are more difficult to etch, however, all surfaces to be etched must be smooth ground or polished. Saw-cut surfaces will yield little useful information if they are macroetched. The macroetching procedure is described in ASTM E 381 ("Standard Method of Macroetch Testing, Inspection, and Rating Steel Products, Comprising Bars, Billets, Blooms, and Forgings").

Macroetchants for stainless steels are listed in Table 1. Heated macroetchants are used with stainless steels in the same manner as carbon, alloy, or tool steels. Etchant compositions are often more complex and more aggressive. In the study of weld macrostructures, it is quite common to polish the section and use one of the general-purpose microetchants.

The standard sulfur print technique (Ref 1) can be used to reveal the distribution of manganese sulfide (MnS) inclusions in stainless steels. However, if the manganese content of the grade is low, chromium will substitute for manganese in the sulfides, and the sulfur print intensity will decrease. As the manganese content decreases below approximately 0.60%, chromium substitutes for manganese. At manganese contents below approximately 0.20%, pure chromium sulfides will form. These produce no image in the sulfur print test.

Figure 1 shows the macrostructure of a 480 mm (19 in.) diameter forged bloom of type 406 stainless steel that was made from a 1 m (40 in.) diameter ingot (Ref 3). Due to its large size, the disk was quartered before macroetching with equal parts of hydrochloric acid (HCl) and water at 70 °C (160 °F). As might be expected, the grain structure is much finer at the surface than in the interior. Figure 2 shows the macrostructure of a continuously cast 125 mm (5 in.) square billet of type 430 stainless steel in the as-cast condition. The disk was macroetched in the same manner as the forged type 406 bloom, but it was given a subsequent brightening/desmutting etch in a heated solution (also 70 °C, or 160 °F) of six parts water,

five parts nitric acid (HNO_3), and one part hydrofluoric acid (HF). The disk exhibits the classic pattern of very fine grains at the surface and columnar grains extending from this region to near the center, where the grains are equiaxed.

Microexamination

Sectioning techniques for stainless steels are identical to those used for carbon, alloy, or tool steels. Grades softer than approximately 35 HRC can be cut using a band saw or power hacksaw. However, such cutting produces substantial deformation and should be avoided with the deformation-sensitive austenitic grades. Deformation will be greatly reduced if cutting is performed using abrasive cutoff wheels with the proper degree of bonding. Shearing can be used with the ferritic grades but should be avoided with the austenitics. See the article "Sectioning" in Volume 9 of the *ASM Handbook* for additional information.

Mounting procedures, when required, are identical to those used for carbon, alloy, and tool steels. If edge preservation is required for near-surface examination, compression-mounting epoxy can be used, or specimens can be plated with electroless nickel. For specimens with surface cracks, it may be useful to vacuum impregnate the

Table 1 Macroetchants for stainless steels

Etchant	Comments
1. 50 mL HCl, 10 g $CuSO_4$ (copper sulfate), 50 mL H_2O(a)	Marble's reagent. General-purpose macroetch; can be heated
2. 50 mL HCl, 50 mL H_2O, 20 mL 30% H_2O_2	Mix HCl and H_2O, heat to 70-75 °C (160-170 °F). Immerse specimen and add H_2O_2 in steps when foaming stops; do not mix
3. (a) 15 g $(NH_4)_2S_2O_8$ (ammonium persulfate) and 75 mL H_2O (b) 250 g $FeCl_3$ and 100 mL H_2O (c) 30 mL HNO_3	Lepito's No. 1 etch. Combine (a) and (b), then add (c); immerse specimen at room temperature; use fresh
4. 1 part HCl and 1 part H_2O	Standard hot-etch. Use at 70-80 °C (160-180 °F), 15-45 min; desmut by dipping in warm 20% aqueous HNO_3 solution to produce a bright surface
5. 10-40 mL HNO_3, 3-10 mL 48% HF, 25-50 mL H_2O	Use at 70-80 °C (160-180 °F); immerse until the desired degree of contrast is obtained
6. 50 mL HCl and 25 mL saturated $CuSO_4$ in H_2O	Use at 75 °C (170 °F); immerse until the desired degree of contrast is obtained

(a) When water is specified, use distilled water.

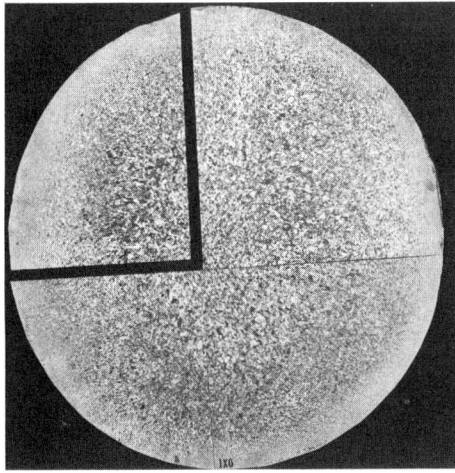

Fig. 1 Macrostructure of a 480 mm (19 in.) diam type 406 stainless steel forged bar produced from a 1 m (40 in.) diam ingot. Courtesy of G.F. Vander Voort, Carpenter Technology Corp.

Table 2 Electropolishing procedures for stainless steels

Electrolyte composition	Comments
1. 50 mL HClO$_4$ (perchloric acid), 750 mL ethanol, 140 mL H$_2$O(a)	Add HClO$_4$ last, with care. Use at 8-20 V dc, 0.3-1.3 A/cm^2 (1.9-8.4 A/in.^{2}), 20 °C (70 °F), 20-60 s. Rinse immediately after polishing
2. 78 mL HClO$_4$, 90 mL H$_2$O, 730 mL ethanol, 100 mL butyl cellusolve	Add HClO$_4$ last, with care. Use at 0.5-1.5 A/cm^2 (3.2-9.7 A/in.^{2}), 20 °C (70 °F) max
3. 62 mL HClO$_4$, 700 mL ethanol, 100 mL butyl cellusolve, 137 mL H$_2$O	Add HClO$_4$ last, with care. Use at 1.2 A/cm^2 (7.7 A/in.^{2}), 20 °C (70 °F), 20-25 s
4. 25 g CrO$_3$, 133 mL acetic acid, 7 mL H$_2$O	Use at 20 V dc, 0.09-0.22 A/cm^2 (0.58-1.4 A/in.^{2}), 17-19 °C (63-66 °F), 6 min. Dissolve CrO$_3$ in solution heated to 60-70 °C (140-160 °F)
5. 37 mL H$_3$PO$_4$, 56 mL glycerol, 7 mL H$_2$O	Use at 0.78 A/cm^2 (5.0 A/in.^{2}) 100-120 °C (212-250 °F), 5-10 min
6. 6 mL HClO$_4$ and 94 mL ethanol	Use at 35-40 V dc, 24 °C (75 °F), 15-60 s

(a) When water is specified, use distilled water.

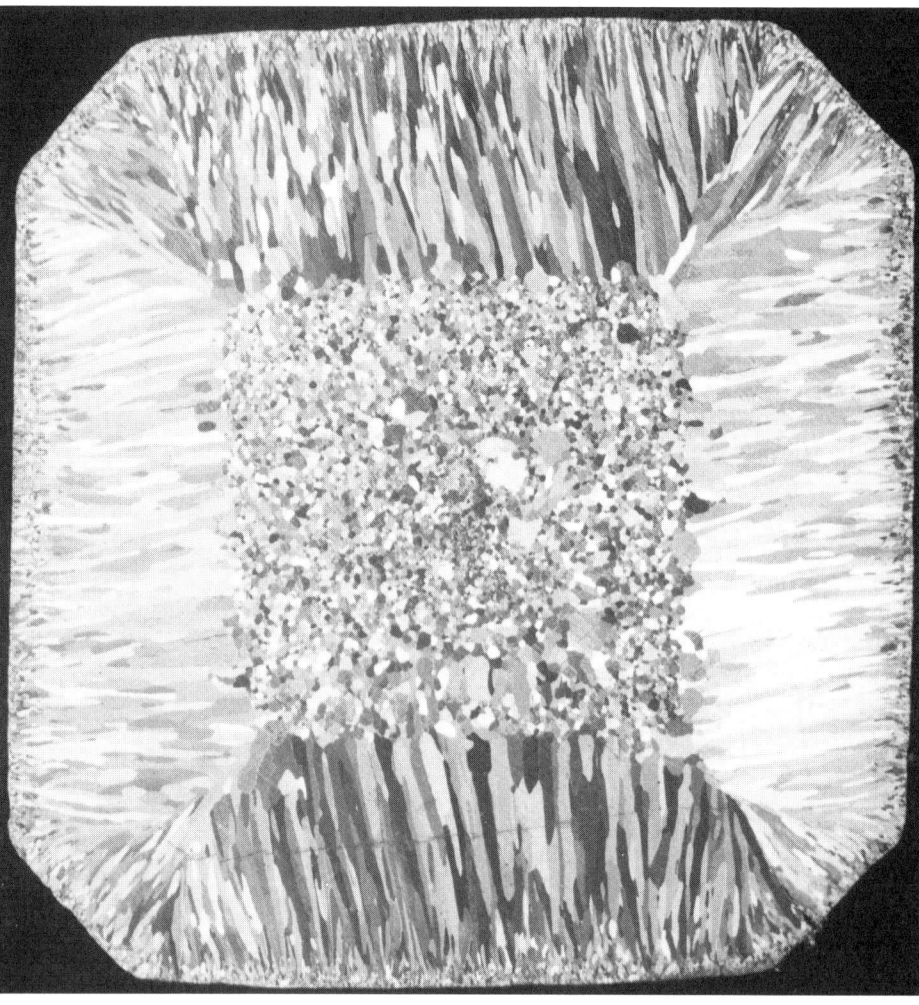

Fig. 2 As-cast macrostructure of a 125 mm (5 in.) square billet of continuously cast type 430 stainless steel. Courtesy of G.F. Vander Voort, Carpenter Technology Corp.

specimen in cold-setting epoxy; epoxy will be drawn into the cracks, minimizing bleedout problems after etching. See the article "Mounting of Specimens" in Volume 9 of the *ASM Handbook* for a complete discussion of mounting materials and problems associated with various mounting methods.

Grinding is performed using 120-, 240-, 320-, 400-, and then 600-grit water-cooled silicon carbide papers. Care must be taken, particularly when grinding austenitic grades, to remove the cold work from cutting and from each grinding step. In general, speeds of approximately 300 rpm and moderate, firm pressure are used. Grinding times are 1 to 2 min per step. If grinding is carried out by hand, the specimen should be rotated 45 to 90° between each step. Automatic grinding devices produce omnidirectional grinding patterns. See the article "Grinding, Abrasion, and Polishing" in Volume 9 of the *ASM Handbook* for additional information.

Polishing. After grinding, specimens are usually rough polished using 6- or 3-µm diamond as a paste, spray, or slurry on napless, low-nap, or medium-nap cloths. Edge flatness and inclusion retention are usually improved by using napless cloths, although scratch removal may not be as complete as with medium-nap cloths. A lubricant extender compatible with the diamond abrasive should be used to moisten the cloth and reduce drag. A wheel speed of approximately 150 rpm is usually adequate. Pressure should be moderate and firm; specimen rocking should be avoided if polishing is carried out by hand.

For hand polishing, rotate the specimen around the wheel in the direction opposite to wheel rotation while moving from center to edge. Automatic devices generally produce better edge flatness than hand polishing. After this step, the

specimen may be polished using 1 µm diamond abrasive on a medium-nap cloth. For routine examination, a 1 µm diamond finish may be adequate, particularly for the hardenable grades.

To produce high-quality, scratch-free surfaces suitable for photomicroscopy, specimens should be final polished using one or more fine abrasives. The most commonly used final abrasives are 0.3 µm α-alumina (Al$_2$O$_3$) or 0.05 µm γ-Al$_2$O$_3$. Medium-nap cloths are usually used. Polishing with these abrasives, using a polish mixed as a water slurry, is performed in the same manner as diamond polishing. Specimens should be carefully cleaned between each rough and final polishing step to avoid contamination at the next step. Colloidal silica is a highly suitable final abrasive for stainless steels.

Stainless steels, particularly the austenitic grades, are often polished electrolytically. In most cases, electropolishing is performed after grinding to a 600-grit silicon carbide finish. Table 2 lists recommended procedures. Electropolishing usually produces high-quality, deformation-free surfaces; however, inclusion attack is encountered, and second phases may be attacked preferentially.

Etching. For inclusion examination, etching is not required, although it is necessary for examining the microstructure. Although stainless steels are reasonably easy to polish, etching is generally a more difficult step. The corrosion resistance of stainless steels and the potential microstructural complexity of these alloys make selection of the best etchant a more difficult problem than for carbon and alloy steels.

Stainless steel etchant ingredients are dissolved in water, methanol, or ethanol; glycerol; or a mixture of these solvents. Reagents with alcohol or glycerol as the solvent provide better wetting of the surface than water-based reagents and generally provide more uniform etching. Because alcohol reduces dissociation, alcohol-based reagents can be made more concentrated without becoming too powerful for controlled etching. Stainless steel surfaces passivate; therefore, reducing conditions are preferred to oxidizing conditions that promote passivity. Consequently, stainless steel etchants often contain HCl, sulfuric acid (H$_2$SO$_4$), or HF acid, although HNO$_3$ may be used alone or mixed with HCl to produce aqua regia or a modified aqua regia. Swabbing, instead of immersion, may be desired to obtain more uniform etch results. Electrolytic etching is also very popular, because it produces uniform etching, is easier to control, and gives reproducible results. Numerous etchants have been proposed for stainless steels; each has advantages and disadvantages.

Etching the 400-series ferritic or martensitic grades is simpler than the 200- or 300-series austenitics or the 600-series precipitation-hardenable grades. Vilella's reagent (4% picral + HCl) or superpicral is commonly used with ferritic and martensitic grades. Etching of the extra-low-interstitial-content ferritic grades to observe the grain boundaries, however, is much more difficult than with the ordinary ferritics. Microetchants are listed in Table 3.

Etching of the austenitic grades to examine the grain structure is difficult with most standard reagents. As shown in the photomicrographs in the article "Microstructures of Wrought Stainless Steels" in this Volume, most of the standard reagents reveal only some of the grain boundaries. Tint etching, which requires a high-quality polish for good results, reveals all of the grains by color contrast. To measure the grain size when a more accurate value is required than can be obtained by a comparison chart rating, all the boundaries must be revealed. Twin boundaries are ignored.

Sensitizing the specimen by heating it for 1 to 6 h at 650 °C (1200 °F) will facilitate observation of the grain boundaries. An alternate technique (Ref 4, 5) involves electrolytically etching the solution-annealed specimen in 60% aqueous HNO_3 (see Table 3). With this procedure, twin boundaries are not revealed. This etch will also bring out prior-austenite grain boundaries in solution-annealed, but not aged, precipitation-hardened grades. For structure-property correlations, the mean lineal intercept value for grain and twin boundaries should be measured, because the twin boundaries also contribute to strengthening. Such a measurement should not be converted to a grain size value.

Various alkaline ferricyanide reagents, such as Murakami's reagent, have been widely used to etch austenitic stainless steels for phase identification. The colors produced by these etchants vary with etchant composition, temperature, time, and phase orientation. When using a particular reagent in the prescribed manner, the colors obtained may differ from those reported in the literature. However, the etch response, that is, what is attacked and what is not attacked, is highly reproducible.

When using the standard formulation of Murakami's reagent at room temperature, for example, the carbides will be attacked in 7 to 15 s; σ-phase will be only lightly attacked after 3 min. If higher concentrations of potassium hydroxide (KOH) or sodium hydroxide (NaOH) and potassium ferricyanide ($K_3Fe(CN)_6$) are used at room temperature, σ-phase will be attacked instead of the carbides. Used boiling, the standard formulation attacks ferrite, carbide, and s-phase, although some evidence indicates that s-phase will not be attacked. Therefore, when using this reagent or one of its numerous modifications, directions should be followed carefully. Ex-

Table 3 Microetchants for stainless steel

Etchants	Comments	Etchants	Comments
1. 1 g picric acid, 5 mL HCl, 100 mL ethanol	Vilella's reagent. Use at room temperature to 1 min. Outlines second-phase particles (carbides, σ phase, δ-ferrite), etches martensite	14. 10 g NaCN (sodium cyanide) and 100 mL H_2O	Electrolytic etch at 6 V dc, 25-mm spacing, 5 min, platinum cathode. Sigma darkened, carbides light, ferrite outlined, austenite not attacked. Good for revealing carbides. Use with care under a hood.
2. 1.5 g $CuCl_2$ (cupric chloride), 33 mL HCl, 33 mL ethanol, 33 mL H_2O(a)	Kalling's No. 1 reagent for martensitic stainless steels. Use at room temperature. Martensite dark, ferrite colored, austenite not attacked	15. 10 mL HCl and 90 mL methanol	Electrolytic etch at 1.5 V dc, 20 °C (70 °F) to attack σ phase. Use at 6 V dc for 3-5 s to reveal structure.
3. 5 g $CuCl_2$, 100 mL HCl, 100 mL ethanol	Kalling's No. 2 reagent. Use at room temperature. Ferrite attacked rapidly, austenite slightly attacked, carbides not attacked	16. 60 mL HNO_3 and 40 mL H_2O	Electrolytic etch to reveal austenite grain boundaries (but not twins) in austenitic grades. With stainless steel cathode, use at 1.1 V dc, 0.075-0.14 A/cm² (0.48-0.90 A/in.²), 120 s. With platinum cathode, use at 0.4 V dc, 0.055-0.066 A/cm² (0.35-0.43 A/in.²), 45 s. Will reveal prior-austenite grain boundaries in solution-treated (but not aged) martensitic precipitation-hardenable alloys
4. 5 g $CuCl_2$, 40 mL HCl, 30 mL H_2O, 25 mL ethanol	Fry's reagent. For martensitic and precipitation-hardenable grades. Use at room temperature.		
5. 4 g $CuSO_4$, 20 mL HCl, 20 mL H_2O	Marble's reagent. Used primarily with austenitic grades. Use at room temperature to 10 s. Attacks σ phase		
6. 3 parts glycerol, 2-5 parts HCl, 1 part HNO_3	Glyceregia. Popular etch for all stainless grades. Higher HCl content reduces pitting tendency. Use fresh, never store. Discard when reagent is orange colored. Use with care under a hood. Add HNO_3 last. Immerse or swab a few seconds to a minute. Attacks σ phase, outlines carbides. Substitution of water for glycerol increases attack rate.	17. 50 g NaOH and 100 mL H_2O	Electrolytic etch at 2-6 V dc, 5-10 s to reveal σ phase in austenitic grades.
		18. 56 g KOH and 100 mL H_2O	Electrolytic etch at 1.5-3 V dc for 3 s to reveal σ phase (red-brown) and ferrite (bluish). Chi colored same as sigma
		19. 20 g NaOH and 100 mL H_2O	Electrolytic etch at 20 V dc, for 5-20 s to outline and color δ-ferrite tan.
7. 45 mL HCl, 15 mL HNO_3, 20 mL methanol	Methanolic aqua regia. Used with austenitic grades to reveal grain structure, outline ferrite and σ phase	20. NH_4OH (conc)	Electrolytic etch at 1.5-6 V dc for 10-60 s. Very selective. At 1.4 V, carbide completely etched in 40 s; sigma unaffected after 180 s. At 6 V, σ phase etched after 40 s
8. 15 mL HCl, 5 mL HNO_3, 100 mL H_2O	Dilute aqua regia for austenitic grades. Uniform etching of austenite, outlines carbides, σ phase, and ferrite (sometimes attacked)	21. 10 g $(NH_4)_2S_2O_8$ and 100 mL H_2O	Use at 6 V dc for 10 s to color carbide dark brown
9. 4 g $KMnO_4$ (potassium permanganate), 4 g NaOH, 100 mL H_2O	Groesbeck's reagent. Use at 60-90 °C (140-195 °F) to 10 min. Colors carbides dark, σ phase gray, ferrite and austenite not affected	22. 200 mL HCl and 1000 mL H_2O	Beraha's tint etch for austenitic, duplex, and precipitation-hardenable grades. Add 0.5-1.0 g $K_2S_2O_5$ per 100 mL of solution (if etching is too rapid, use a 10% aqueous HCl solution). Immerse at room temperature (never swab) for 30-120 s until surface is reddish. Austenite colored, carbides not colored. Longer immersion colors ferrite lightly. If coloration is inadequate, add 24 g $NH_4F \cdot HF$ (ammonium bifluoride) to stock reagent at left.
10. 30 g $KMnO_4$, 30 g NaOH, 100 mL H_2O	Modified Groesbeck's reagent. Use at 90-100 °C (195-212 °F) for 20 s to 10 min to color ferrite dark in duplex alloys. Austenite not affected		
11. 10 g $K_3Fe(CN)_6$, 10 g KOH or 7 g NaOH, 100 mL H_2O	Murakami's reagent. Use at room temperature to 60 s to reveal carbides; σ phase faintly revealed by etching to 3 min. Use at 80 °C (176 °F) to boiling to 60 min to darken carbides. Sigma may be colored blue, ferrite yellow to yellow-brown, austenite not attacked. Use under a hood.		
		23. 20 g picric acid and 100 mL HCl	Etch by immersion. Develops grain boundaries in austenite and δ-ferrite in duplex alloys
12. 30 g KOH, 30 g $K_3Fe(CN)_6$, 100 mL H_2O	Modified Murakami's reagent. Use at 95 °C (203 °F) for 5 s. Colors σ phase reddish brown, ferrite dark gray, austenite unattacked, carbide black. Use under a hood.	24. Saturated aqueous $Ba(OH)_2$ (barium hydroxide)	Attacks carbides well before σ phase in austenitic grades when used at 1.5 V dc, but attacks both equally when used at 3-6 V dc. Has been used to differentiate χ phase and Laves phase (use at 4.3 V dc, platinum cathode, 20 s). Chi is stained mottled-purple, Laves is not colored, ferrite is stained tan.
13. 10 g oxalic acid and 100 mL H_2O	Popular electrolytic etch, 6 V dc, 25-mm spacing. 15-30 s reveals carbides; grain boundaries revealed after 45-60 s; σ phase outlined after 6 s. Lower voltages (1-3 V dc) can be used. Dissolves carbides. Sigma strongly attacked, austenite moderately attacked, ferrite not attacked		
		25. 50 mL each H_2O, ethanol, methanol, and HCl; plus 1 g $CuCl_2$, 3.5 g $FeCl_3$, 2.5 mL HNO_3	Ralph's reagent. Use by swabbing. Can be stored. General-purpose etch for most stainless steels. Does not attack sulfides in free-machining grades

(a) When water is specified, use distilled water.

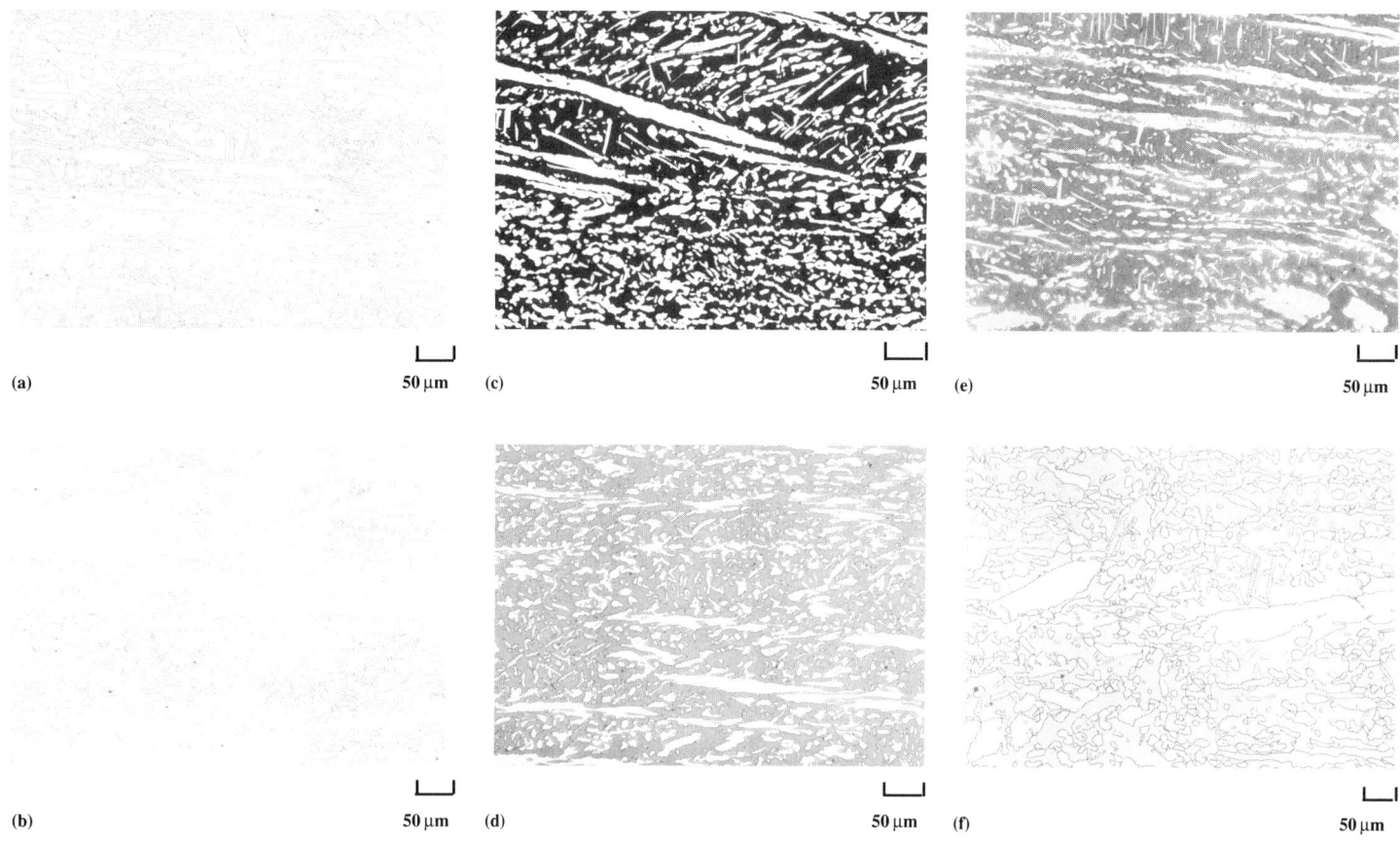

Fig. 3 A comparison of various etchants to reveal the microstructure of 7-Mo PLUS duplex stainless steel (longitudinal plane). (a) Glyceregia chemical etch. (b) Ethanolic 15% HCl chemical etch. (c) Beraha's tint etch to color the ferrite. (d) Electrolytic 20% NaOH to color the ferrite. (e) Electrolytic 56% KOH to color the ferrite. (f) Electrolytic 60% HNO₃. All at 200×. Courtesy of G.F. Vander Voort, Carpenter Technology Corp.

perimentation with specimens of known constitution is also recommended.

Electrolytic reagents, which are used often with austenitic and duplex grades, provide greater control of the etching process and are highly reproducible. Perhaps the most commonly used electrolytic reagent is 10% aqueous oxalic acid, which will reveal carbides after a short etch if they are present (see Table 3). When carbides are not present, the austenite grain boundaries will be revealed in 15 to 60 s. If ferrite is present, it will be outlined after 10 to 15 s.

Electrolytic reagents are generally quite simple in composition. The selectivity of electrolytic reagents based on various hydroxide solutions has been demonstrated (Ref 6). Strong hydroxide solutions attack σ-phase preferentially to carbides; weak hydroxide solutions attack carbides much more readily than σ-phase. Therefore, to reveal σ-phase, 10 N KOH is employed, and to reveal carbides, concentrated ammonium hydroxide (NH_4OH) is used. For intermediate-strength hydroxide solutions, etching response is altered by a change in the applied potential.

Several sequential etching procedures have been suggested for phase identification in austenitic stainless steels. One procedure (Ref 6) involves etching first with Vilella's reagent to outline the phases present. Next, the specimen is electrolytically etched with 10 N KOH at 3 V dc for 0.4 s to color σ-phase, if present, but not carbides. The specimen is then electrolytically etched with concentrated NH_4OH at 6 V dc for 30 s to color any carbides present. Another procedure (Ref 7) also begins with Vilella's reagent to reveal the constituents. Next, Murakami's reagent is used at room temperature to stain the carbides present. Any σ-phase or δ-ferrite present is unaffected. Finally, the specimen is electrolytically etched with aqueous chromium trioxide (CrO_3), which will attack carbides and σ-phase, but not δ-ferrite. Murakami's reagent does not attack carbides in titanium- or niobium-stabilized stainless steels. These carbides are attacked slowly in electrolytic CrO_3.

Delta-ferrite in martensitic, austenitic, or precipitation-hardenable grades can be preferentially colored by electrolytic etching with 20% aqueous NaOH at 20 V dc for 5 to 20 s. This procedure outlines and uniformly colors tan δ-ferrite. Although the color varies with orientation, 10 N KOH also colors δ-ferrite.

Potentiostatic etching (Ref 1 and 8) is frequently used for selective etching of constituents in stainless steels. This technique is similar to electrolytic etching, except a third electrode is in-

cluded to monitor the etch potential, which is controlled using a potentiostat. This technique affords the greatest possible control over etching.

Heat tinting is a useful technique with austenitic stainless steels. Phase delineation is improved by first etching with a general-purpose reagent, such as Vilella's. The specimen is then heated in air at 500 to 700 °C (930 to 1290 °F); 650 °C (1200 °F) has been most commonly used with times to 20 min. Austenite is colored more readily than ferrite, and carbides resist coloration longest. After 20 min at 650 °C (1200 °F), austenite is blue-green, σ-phase is orange, ferrite is light cream, and carbides are uncolored.

Magnetic colloids have also been used to detect ferromagnetic constituents in austenitic stainless steels. This technique, which is referred to as *magnetic etching,* has been extensively applied using a ferromagnetic colloid solution (Ferrofluid) containing very fine magnetic particles (Ref 9). Delta-ferrite and strain-induced martensite are readily identified by this method. More detailed information on magnetic etching can be found in Volume 9 of the *ASM Handbook* (see Appendix 1 to the article "Etching").

Figure 3 illustrates the use of a variety of etchants to reveal the structure of a duplex stainless steel (UNS S32950, also known as Carpenter

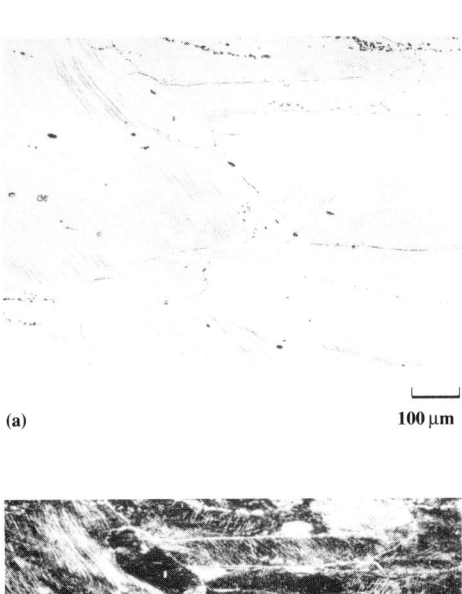

(a)   100 μm

(b)   100 μm

(c)   100 μm

Fig. 4 A comparison of various light microscope illumination modes to reveal the microstructure of a warm-worked high-manganese drill collar alloy (as-rolled) etched in acetic glyceregia and viewed with (a) bright-field illumination, (b) dark-field illumination, and (c) differential interference contrast illumination. All three photomicrographs show the same area. Courtesy of G.F. Vander Voort, Carpenter Technology Corp.

7-Mo PLUS). Table 3 should be consulted for procedure details.

Illumination modes other than bright field are of considerable value for examining stainless

Table 4 Electropolishing procedures for preparing thin-foil stainless steel specimens

Solution composition	Comments
1. 5 or 10 mL HClO₄ and 95 or 90 mL acetic acid at 20 V dc	Popular electropolish for stainless steels. Used for window technique or for perforation of disk specimens. Keep solution cool.
2. (a) 10 mL HNO₃ and 90 mL H₂O(a) at 50 V dc (b) 10 mL HClO₄, 20 mL glycerol, 70 mL ethanol at 65 V dc	Popular procedures for austenitic grades. Use (a) to electrodish specimens, then (b) for perforation.
3. 10 mL HClO₄ and 90 mL ethanol at 12 V dc, 0 °C (32 °F)	Popular electropolish for stainless steels. Use for perforation.
4. 40 mL H₂SO₄ and 60 mL H₃PO₄ at 35 V dc, 0.3 A/cm² (1.9 A/in.²)	Electropolish for stainless steels for perforation.
5. 25 g CrO₃, 133 mL acetic acid, 7 mL H₂O at 20 °C (70 °F)	Electropolish for stainless steels. Good for window method. Opacity of solution makes it difficult to use for jet perforation.
6. (a) 40 mL acetic acid, 30 mL H₃PO₄, 20 mL HNO₃, 10 mL H₂O at 80-120 V dc, 0.1 A/cm² (0.65 A/in.²) (b) 54 mL H₃PO₄, 36 mL H₂SO₄, 10 mL ethanol at 6 V dc	Procedure for austenitic grades. Jet electrodish disks with (a) prior to final thinning with (b) to perforation.
7. 45 mL H₃PO₄, 30 mL H₂SO₄, 25 mL H₂O at 6 V dc	Procedure for austenitic grades for perforation

(a) When water is specified, use distilled water.

steels (Ref 3). Oblique illumination or differential interference contrast (DIC) can be used to observe second-phase constituents more clearly, in the as-polished condition if there is a hardness difference, or after etching. The DIC illumination mode is also useful for examining grain structure, as is dark-field illumination. Polarized light has very limited use with stainless steels.

As an example of the use of various illumination modes, Fig. 4 demonstrates the superiority of dark-field illumination and DIC in revealing the structure of a high-manganese warm-worked drill collar austenitic stainless steel in the as-rolled condition. This figure shows that the bright field micrograph (Fig. 4a) is nearly featureless; however, the use of the dark-field mode (Fig. 4b) or DIC (Fig. 4c) reveals the deformed substructure clearly. Additional information on illumination modes associated with the light microscope can be found in the article "Optical Microscopy" in Volume 9 of the *ASM Handbook*.

Electron Microscopy. Scanning electron microscopy (SEM) and transmission electron microscopy (TEM) are used to examine the fine structure of stainless steels and for phase identification. Scanning electron microscopy examination uses the same specimens as optical (light) microscopy. As-polished specimens often can be examined, although etching is more common. Many second-phase constituents can be observed using backscattered elec-

tron detectors due to the adequate atomic number contrast between these phases and the matrix. However, secondary electron images produced from topographic contrast and atomic number contrast are most often used. Energy-dispersive x-ray analysis (EDXA) is prevalent for chemical analysis of second phases, although lightweight elements, such as carbon and nitrogen, cannot be detected unless thin-window or windowless EDXA detectors or wavelength-dispersive detectors are used. Detailed reviews of SEM, TEM, and EDXA can be found in Volumes 9, 10, and 12 of the *ASM Handbook*.

Transmission electron microscopy requires preparation of replicas or thin-foil specimens (see the article "Transmission Electron Microscopy" in Volume 9 of the *ASM Handbook*). Replicas may be made to reveal the outline and topography of the phases, or if the specimen is deeply etched, second-phase particles may be extracted. Extraction replicas permit analysis of second phases by electron diffraction and by EDXA. Thin-foil specimens can also be analyzed by these methods, although interference from the matrix is possible. Table 4 lists electropolishing procedures for producing stainless steel thin foils. Reference 10 is another excellent source of information on thin foil specimen preparation techniques for TEM examination.

Bulk Extractions. Although bulk samples can be directly analyzed by x-ray diffraction for phase identification, it is quite common to extract the second phases chemically and analyze the extracted particles. This eliminates the matrix and concentrates the second phase, facilitating identification of small amounts of the second-phase constituents. Bulk extraction of phases from wrought stainless steels is performed using electrolytes such as 10% HCl in methanol. Details concerning the use of such electrolytes are given in Ref 11 to 13.

ACKNOWLEDGMENT

The information in this article is largely taken from G.F. Vander Voort and H.M. James, Wrought Stainless Steels, *Metallography and Microstructures,* Vol 9, *ASM Handbook* (formerly 9th ed. *Metals Handbook*), ASM International, 1985, p 279-296.

REFERENCES

1. G.F. Vander Voort, *Metallography: Principles and Practice,* McGraw-Hill, 1984
2. R.S. Crouse and B.C. Leslie, Techniques for Stainless Steel Microscopy, *Applied Metallography,* Van Nostrand Reinhold Co., Inc., 1986, p 71-88
3. G.F. Vander Voort, The Metallograpy of Stainless Steels, *Journal of Metals,* Vol 41 (No. 3), March 1989, p 6-11
4. F.C. Bell and D.E. Sonon, Improved Metallographic Etching Techniques for Stainless Steel and for Stainless Steel to Carbon Steel Weldments, *Metallography,* Vol 9, 1976, p 91-107
5. J.M. Stephenson and B.M. Patchett, Grain-Boundary Etches for Austenitic and Ferritic

Ni-Cr-Mo Corrosion-Resistant Alloys, *Sheet Met. Ind.,* Vol 56, 1979, p 45-50, 57

6. J.J. Gilman, Electrolytic Etching—The Sigma Phase Steels, Trans. ASM, Vol 44, 1952, p 566-600

7. E.J. Dulis and G.V. Smith, "Identification and Modes of Formation and Re-solution of Sigma Phase in Austenitic Chromium-Nickel Steels, STP 110, ASTM, 1951, p 3-37

8. E.E. Stansbury, Potentiostatic Etching, *Metallography and Microstructures* (formerly 9th ed. Metals Handbook), Vol 9, *ASM Handbook,* ASM International, 1985, p 143-147

9. R.J. Gray, Magnetic Etching with Ferrofluid, *Metallographic Specimen Preparation,* Plenum Press, 1974, p 155-177

10. K.C. Thompson-Russell and J.W. Edington, Electron Microscope Specimen Preparation Techniques in Materials Science, Monograph 5, *Practical Electron Microscopy in Materials Science,* N.V. Philips' Gloeilampenfabrieken, Eindhoven, 1977

11. T.P. Hoar and K.W.J. Bowen, The Electrolytic Separation and Some Properties of Austenite and Sigma in 18-8-3-1 Chromium-Nickel-Molybdenum-Titanium Steel, *Trans. ASM,* Vol 45, 1953, p 443-474

12. J.F. Brown et al., The Extraction of Minor Phases from Austenitic Steel, *Metallurgia,* Vol 56, Nov 1957, p 215-223

13. K.W. Andrews and H. Hughes, "The Isolation, Separation, and Identification of Microconstituents in Steels," STP 393, ASTM, 1966, p 3-21

Microstructures of Wrought Stainless Steels

THE MICROSTRUCTURES of wrought stainless steels can be quite complex. Matrix structures vary according to the type of steel, such as ferritic, austenitic, martensitic, precipitation hardenable, or duplex. As described below and listed in Table 1, a wide range of second-phase constituents can be observed. The complexity of microstructural evaluation increases when stainless steels are welded or subjected to elevated temperatures. Such exposure can lead to embrittling phenomena such as sensitization, 475 °C (885 °F) embrittlement, and sigma-phase embrittlement. Embrittlement of stainless steels is described in the article "Metallurgy and Properties of Wrought Stainless Steels" in this Volume.

Following an overview of the matrix phases and second-phase constituents commonly observed in stainless steels, this article presents a series of 93 photomicrographs. Chemical compositions of the alloys for which microstructures are illustrated are given in the articles "General Introduction" and the aforementioned

"Metallurgy and Properties of Wrought Stainless Steels" in this Volume. The etchants listed in the corresponding figure captions are described in the article "Metallographic Practices for Wrought Stainless Steels." Additional information on the microstructures associated with stainless steels can be found in Ref 1 to 7.

Austenitic Stainless Steels

Matrix Phases. The most commonly used stainless steels are the austenitic grades, of which types 302 and 304 are the most popular. These grades contain 16% or more chromium, a ferrite-stabilizing element, and sufficient austenite-stabilizing elements, such as carbon, nitrogen, nickel, and manganese, to render austenite stable at room temperature. The grades containing silicon, molybdenum, titanium, or niobium (e.g., types 302B, 316, 317, 321, and 347) will sometimes include a minor amount of δ-ferrite because of the

ferrite-stabilizing influence of these elements. Alloys with substantial nickel are fully austenitic (e.g., types 310 and 330). For alloys susceptible to δ-ferrite stabilization, the amount present will depend on the composition, chemical homogeneity, and hot working. Alloys that have especially low carbon contents to minimize susceptibility to sensitization during welding (e.g., types 304L, 316L, or 317L) will have a greater tendency toward δ-ferrite stabilization.

Numerous studies have been conducted to predict matrix phases based on chemical composition. Most of these studies have concentrated on predicting weldment microstructures (Ref 8-15); others have concentrated on predicting cast microstructures (Ref 16-18), predicting structures at the hot-working temperature (Ref 19), or predicting structures after hot working (Ref 20). Measurement of the δ-ferrite content of stainless steels, particularly weldments, has been widely studied (Ref 21-24).

The austenite in these grades is not stable, but rather metastable. Martensite can be formed, particularly in the leaner grades, by cooling specimens to very low temperatures or by extensive plastic deformation. Nonmagnetic, hexagonal close-packed (hcp) ε-martensite and magnetic, body-centered cubic (bcc) α'-martensite have been observed. Empirical relationships have been developed to show how composition influences the resistance of such steel to deformation-induced martensite (Ref 25, 26).

Carbon content limits are generally 0.03, 0.08, or 0.15% in the austenitic grades. Solution annealing will usually dissolve all or most of the carbides present after hot rolling. Rapid quenching from the solution-annealing temperature of generally 1010 to 1065 °C (1850 to 1950 °F) will retain the carbon in solution, producing a strain-free, carbide-free austenitic microstructure.

$M_{23}C_6$-type Carbide. The most widely observed carbide type in austenitic stainless steels is $M_{23}C_6$, which is often referred to as $Cr_{23}C_6$, but more properly is $(Cr,Fe)_{23}C_6$ or $(Cr,Fe,Mo)_{23}C_6$. The precipitation of this carbide at grain boundaries during welding produces intergranular corrosion. To counter sensitization during welding, carbon contents are reduced or strong carbide formers are added, as in types 321 and 347.

Precipitation of $M_{23}C_6$ carbide occurs as a result of heating solution-annealed grades to 500 to 950 °C (930 to 1740 °F); the fastest rate of precipitation takes place from 650 to 700 °C (1200 to

Table 1 Second-phase constituents observed in stainless steels

Phase	Crystal structure	Lattice parameters, nm	Reported compositions	Comments
$M_{23}C_6$	fcc	$a_0 = 1.057\text{-}1.068$	$(Cr_{16}Fe_5Mo_2)C_6$ $(Cr_{17}Fe_{4.5}Mo_{1.5})C_6$ $(Fe,Cr)_{23}C_6$	Most commonly observed carbide in austenitic stainless steels. Precipitates from 500-950 °C (930-1740 °F), fastest at 650-700 °C (1200-1290 °F)
M_6C	fcc	$a_0 = 1.085\text{-}1.111$	$(Cr,Co,Mo,Ni)_6C$ $(Fe_3Mo_3)C$ Fe_3Nb_3C $(Fe,Cr)_3Nb_3C$	Observed in austenitic grades containing substantial molybdenum or niobium after long time exposure
M_7C_3	Hexagonal	$a_0 = 1.398$ $c_0 = 0.4523$	Cr_7C_3	Observed in martensitic grades
MC	Cubic	$a_0 = 0.430\text{-}0.470$	TiC NbC	Observed in alloys with additions of titanium or niobium. Very stable carbide. Will usually contain some nitrogen
Sigma (σ)	Tetragonal	$a_0 = 0.8799\text{-}0.9188$ $c_0 = 0.4544\text{-}0.4599$	FeCr FeMo Fe(Cr,Mo) $(Fe,Ni)_x(Cr,Mo)_y$	Formation from δ-ferrite is much more rapid than from austenite. Potent embrittler below 595 °C (1105 °F). Forms with long time exposure from 650-900 °C (1200-1650 °F)
Chi (χ)	bcc (α-Mn structure)	$a_0 = 0.8862\text{-}0.892$	$Fe_{36}Cr_{12}Mo_{10}$ $(Fe,Ni)_{36}Cr_{18}Mo_4$ $M_{18}C$	Observed in alloys containing substantial molybdenum. Chi precipitates with exposure to 730-1010 °C (1345-1850 °F) (varies with alloy composition)
Laves (η)	Hexagonal	$a_0 = 0.470\text{-}0.4744$ $c_0 = 0.772\text{-}0.7725$	Fe_2Mo $(Ti_{21}Mo_9)$ $(Fe_{30}Cr_5Si_5)$	Forms in austenitic alloys with substantial amounts of molybdenum, titanium, or niobium after long time exposure from 600-1100 °C (1110-2010 °F)

1290 °F). Precipitation occurs first at austenite/δ-ferrite phase boundaries, when present, then at other noncoherent interfaces (grain and twin boundaries), and finally at coherent twin boundaries. In addition, $M_{23}C_6$ may precipitate at inclusion/matrix-phase boundaries.

The appearance of $M_{23}C_6$ varies with the precipitation temperature and time. It is most easily studied using extraction replicas. At the lower precipitation temperatures, $M_{23}C_6$ has a thin, continuous, sheetlike morphology. When the precipitation temperature is 600 to 700 °C (1110 to 1290 °F), feathery dendritic particles form at boundary intersections. With time, these precipitates coarsen and thicken. At still higher precipitation temperatures, $M_{23}C_6$ forms at grain boundaries as discrete globular particles whose shape is influenced by the boundary orientation, degree of misfit, and temperature (Ref 27). The $M_{23}C_6$ that precipitates at noncoherent twin boundaries is lamellar or rodlike; that which precipitates at coherent twin boundaries is platelike. The $M_{23}C_6$ that forms at the lower precipitation temperatures is most detrimental to intergranular corrosion resistance.

Alloys given deliberate minor additions of titanium or niobium (e.g., types 321 and 347) form titanium or niobium carbides, rather than $M_{23}C_6$. To take full advantage of these additions, solution-annealed specimens are subjected to a stabilizing heat treatment to precipitate the excess carbon as titanium or niobium carbides. This treatment is commonly used with type 321 and involves holding the specimen several hours at 845 to 900 °C (1550 to 1650 °F). These carbides will precipitate intragranularly at dislocations or stacking faults within the matrix. Some may also precipitate on grain boundaries.

Additions of titanium or niobium must be carefully controlled to neutralize the carbon in solution. In practice, titanium and niobium carbides can contain some nitrogen, and both can form rather pure nitrides. Titanium nitrides usually appear as distinct, bright yellow cubic particles. Titanium carbide is grayish, with a less regular shape. Titanium carbonitride will have an intermediate appearance that varies with the carbon-nitrogen ratio. Chromium nitrides are not usually observed in the austenitic grades, unless the service environment causes substantial nitrogen surface enrichment or they are nitrogen strengthened.

Carbides of the M_6C type are observed in austenitic grades containing substantial molybdenum or niobium additions. They usually precipitate intragranularly. For example, in AISI 316 with 2 to 3% Mo, M_6C will form after approximately 1500 h at 650 °C (1200 °F). Several types of M_6C have been observed, including Fe_3Mo_3C, Fe_3Nb_3C, and $(Fe,Cr)_3Nb_3C$.

Several types of sulfides have been observed in austenitic grades. The most common is MnS. However, if the manganese content is low, chromium will replace some of the manganese in the sulfide. At manganese contents less than approximately 0.20%, pure chromium sulfides will form. Because these are quite hard, machinability (tool life) will be poor. Some free-machining grades have additions of selenium to form manganese se-

lenides, rather than manganese sulfides. In grades with substantial titanium, several forms of titanium sulfides have been observed, including Ti_2S, Ti_2SC, and $Ti_4C_2S_2$.

Sigma, Chi, and Laves Phases. Several intermetallic phases may be formed by high-temperature exposure. These phases form from titanium, vanadium, and chromium ("A" elements) and from manganese, iron, cobalt, and nickel ("B" elements). Some of these phases are stoichiometric compounds. Probably the most important is sigma (σ) phase, first observed in 1927. The leaner austenitic grades free of δ-ferrite are relatively immune to σ-phase formation, but the higher-alloy grades and those containing δ-ferrite are prone to its formation. Sigma is frequently described as FeCr, although its composition can be quite complex and variable, ranging from B_4A to BA_4.

Certain elements, such as silicon, promote σ-phase formation. Cold working also enhances subsequent σ-phase formation. Empirical equations based on composition have been developed to predict the tendency toward σ-phase formation (Ref 28, 29). Sigma is a very potent embrittler whose effects are observable at temperatures below approximately 595 °C (1100 °F). Sigma also reduces resistance to strong oxidizers. The morphology of σ-phase varies substantially. Etching techniques (Ref 30-33) have been widely used to identify a phase in stainless steels, but x-ray diffraction is more definitive. Because its crystal structure is tetragonal, a phase responds to crossed polarized light.

Chi (χ) phase (Ref 34-39) is observed in alloys containing substantial additions of molybdenum that are subjected to high temperatures. Chi can dissolve carbon and exist as an intermetallic compound or as a carbide ($M_{18}C$). It is often observed in alloys susceptible to σ-phase formation and has a bcc, α-manganese-type crystal structure. Several forms of the intermetallic phase have been identified, as shown in Table 1. Chi nucleates first at grain boundaries, then at incoherent twin boundaries, and finally intragranularly (Ref 39). Chi varies in shape from rodlike to globular. As with σ-phase, cold work accelerates nucleation of χ-phase.

Laves (η) phase can also form in austenitic stainless steels after long-term high-temperature exposure (Ref 38, 39). Alloys containing molybdenum, titanium, and niobium are most susceptible to η-phase formation. Precipitation occurs from 650 to 950 °C (1200 to 1740 °F). Laves is a hexagonal intermetallic compound of AB_2 form. Several types have been observed, as shown in Table 1. Laves phase precipitates intragranularly and exists as globular particles.

Other phases have been observed in stainless steels, but less often than those discussed above. Among these is R-phase (Ref 40-42), which has been observed in an Fe-12Cr-Co-Mo alloy and in welded AISI 316. A globular nickel-titanium silicide, G-phase, was observed in a 26Ni-15Cr heat-resistant A-286-type alloy and was attributed to grain-boundary segregation (Ref 43). A chromium-iron-niobide phase, Z-phase (Ref 44), was detected in an 18Cr-12Ni-1Nb alloy after creep testing at 850 °C (1560 °F).

Ferritic Stainless Steels

Matrix Phases. The ferritic stainless steels (Ref 45) are essentially iron-chromium alloys with enough chromium and other elements to stabilize bcc ferrite at all temperatures. Carbon and nitrogen contents must be minimized. The microstructure of these alloys consists of ferrite plus small amounts of finely dispersed $M_{23}C_6$, but other phases may form due to high-temperature exposure. However, because of severe embrittlement problems, these alloys are generally not used for elevated-temperature service.

The ferritic grades depend on solid-solution strengthening, because heat treatment cannot be used to harden the alloys or produce grain refinement. Quenching ferritic alloys from high temperatures produces only very slight increases in hardness.

Embrittlement. Three forms of embrittlement can occur in ferritic stainless steels: σ-phase embrittlement, 475 °C (885 °F) embrittlement, and high-temperature embrittlement. Sigma is difficult to form in alloys with less than 20% Cr, but it forms readily in alloys with 25 to 30% Cr when heated between 500 and 800 °C (930 and 1470 °F). Molybdenum, silicon, nickel, and manganese additions shift the σ-forming tendency to lower chromium contents. As with the austenitic grades, σ-phase severely reduces ductility and toughness below approximately 600 °C (1110 °F). Sigma can be redissolved by holding it for a few hours above 800 °C (1470 °F).

Ferritic stainless steels are susceptible to embrittlement when heated from 400 to 540 °C (750 to 1005 °F), a condition referred to as 475 °C or 885 °F embrittlement. Embrittlement, which increases with time at temperature, is caused by production of chromium-rich and iron-rich ferrites but can be removed by heating above approximately 550 °C (1020 °F). Under identical aging conditions, embrittlement increases with increasing chromium content.

High-temperature embrittlement occurs in alloys that have moderate to high interstitial carbon and nitrogen contents, are heated above 950 °C (1740 °F), and are cooled to room temperature. This also results in loss of corrosion resistance. High-temperature embrittlement has been attributed to chromium depletion adjacent to precipitated carbides and nitrides. The properties of such a sensitized specimen can be improved by heating to 700 to 950 °C (1290 to 1740 °F), which allows chromium to diffuse to the depleted areas. An even better procedure is to reduce the carbon and nitrogen contents to very low levels, which also improves toughness and weldability. Strong carbide-forming elements, such as titanium and niobium, may also be added.

Martensitic Stainless Steels

Matrix Phases. The hardenable martensitic stainless steels contain more than 10.5% Cr plus other austenite-stabilizing elements (e.g., carbon, nitrogen, nickel, and manganese) to expand the austenite phase field and permit heat treatment. The composition must be carefully balanced to prevent δ-ferrite formation at the austenitizing temperature. Delta-ferrite in the hardened structure should be avoided to attain the best mechanical properties. Empirical formulas have been developed to predict δ-ferrite formation based on the composition (Ref 46, 47). Temperature control during austenitization is also important for preventing δ-ferrite formation. The martensitic grades are generally immune from σ-phase formation.

Increases in strength when martensitic stainless steels are heat treated depend primarily on the carbon content, which can vary widely in these grades, and on the stability of δ-ferrite at the austenitizing temperature. The hardenability of these grades is very high due to the high chromium content. All these grades can be martempered to reduce the risk of quench cracking in complex shapes. The heat treatment of these grades is very similar to that of highly alloyed tool steels.

The appearance of martensite in these grades varies with carbon content. With increasing carbon content, the martensite becomes finer, changing from lath to plate morphology. The amount of residual retained austenite increases, but it will not cause problems unless excessively high austenitizing temperatures are used.

Tempering reactions are similar to those observed in the high-alloy tool steels. For example, when as-quenched type 410 is tempered, M_3C is present at tempering temperatures to approximately 480 °C (900 °F), but it is not present at approximately 650 °C (1200 °F). At approximately 480 °C (900 °F), $M_{23}C_6$ forms. It becomes the predominant carbide at 540 °C (1005 °F) and above. At approximately 480 °C (900 °F), M_7C_3 also forms, but it decreases in quantity with higher tempers. Because M_7C_3 seriously degrades corrosion resistance, its presence at tempering temperatures of 480 to 650 °C (900 to 1200 °F) precludes using this tempering range. Tempers below approximately 480 °C (900 °F) are also avoided due to low toughness. Overtempering must be avoided, particularly in those grades containing nickel, because of formation of reverted austenite.

Martensitic stainless steels are also susceptible to surface decarburization during heat treatment if the furnace atmosphere is not properly controlled. However, with their high chromium content, they are less susceptible than many of the low-alloy tool steels.

Precipitation-Hardenable Grades

The precipitation-hardenable stainless steels (Ref 48-51) were developed in the 1940s when the first alloy of this type was introduced, Stainless W (Fe-0.07C-0.50Mn-0.50Si-16.75Cr-6.75Ni-0.80Ti-0.20Al). Three types of precipitation-hardenable grades have been developed: austenitic, semiaustenitic, and martensitic. All are hardened by a final aging treatment that precipitates very fine second-phase particles from a supersaturated solid solution. Precipitation introduces strain into the lattice, which produces the strengthening. Maximum strengthening occurs

well before visible precipitates are produced. Increasing the aging temperature reduces the aging time for maximum strength, but a lower strength is obtained. Precipitation-hardenable grades contain additions of aluminum, copper, titanium, and occasionally molybdenum and niobium, to produce the precipitates.

The semiaustenitic grades have an austenitic matrix with up to 20% δ-ferrite that persists throughout heat treatment. These grades are austenitic (plus δ-ferrite) in the solution-annealed condition, but they can be transformed to martensite by a series of thermal or thermomechanical treatments. Because they are complex alloys, the chemical composition must be carefully balanced.

Heat treatment of the semiaustenitic grades requires conditioning of the austenite matrix, transformation to martensite, and then precipitation hardening. The austenite conditioning treatment removes carbon from solution as $Cr_{23}C_6$, beginning at the austenite/δ-ferrite interfaces. This is accomplished by heating to between 705 and 815 °C (1300 and 1500 °F). The austenite is unstable and transforms to martensite upon cooling. The martensite start temperature, M_s, is approximately 65 to 93 °C (150 to 200 °F); the martensite finish temperature, M_f, is approximately 15 °C (60 °F). The alloy is then aged, usually between 480 and 650 °C (900 and 1200 °F), to relieve stress produced during martensite formation and increase toughness, ductility, and corrosion resistance. Aging at 565 °C (1050 °F) or above results in overaging, with the occurrence of precipitation of the strengthening intermetallic second phase, tempering of the martensite, and partial reversion of martensite to austenite ("reverted" austenite). Cold working can also be used to produce martensite, which is followed by aging.

Commercial examples of semiaustenitic precipitation-hardenable stainless steels include types 17-7PH, PH 15-7Mo, and PH 14-8Mo. Also classed as semiaustenitic precipitation-hardenable grades are AM-350 and AM-355, but they do not have true precipitation reactions. These grades are embrittled by long-term exposure above approximately 550 °C (1020 °F) due to continued precipitation of the intermetallic strengthening phase.

The martensitic grades are the most popular precipitation-hardenable stainless grades. They are martensitic after solution annealing and do not retain austenite. Stainless W is a martensitic precipitation-hardenable type. Other, more recently developed martensitic precipitation-hardenable grades are 17-4PH, 15-5PH, PH13-8Mo, Custom 450, and Custom 455, which are capable of strengths to 1380 MPa (200 ksi) or above.

Stainless W and 17-4PH contain δ-ferrite stringers in the martensitic matrix; the other grades are essentially free of δ-ferrite and so have better through-thickness properties. After solution annealing, they are aged at 425 to 455 °C (795 to 850 °F) or at 675 °C (1250 °F). High aging temperatures will produce reaustenitization, which transforms to untempered martensite upon cooling to room temperature.

The austenitic precipitation-hardenable grades have the lowest usage. The austenite matrix

in these alloys is very stable, even after substantial cold working. These grades are the forerunners of superalloys. The most common austenitic precipitation-hardenable grade is A-286.

Duplex Stainless Steels

The duplex stainless steels (Ref 52-54) were developed as a result of studies of superplasticity. They are usually very fine-grain microduplex structures with a composition centered around 26Cr-6.5Ni (plus 1 to 4% Mo) to obtain a mixture of austenite and ferrite. Their very fine grain size improves strength and toughness, and their superplastic nature promotes hot workability. They exhibit good strength and corrosion resistance. Commercial examples of duplex stainless steels include type 329 (S32900), which was the original alloy in this family, 2205 (S31803), Alloy 255 (S32550), and 7-Mo Plus (S32950).

Thermomechanical processing is required to produce the fine duplex structure. During soaking for hot working, the second phase is dissolved. During hot working, it precipitates and stabilizes the grain size of the recrystallized matrix. The microduplex structure results only when second-phase precipitation precedes or occurs during recrystallization.

Service exposure at 370 to 540 °C (700 to 1005 °F) results in an increase in strength but loss of toughness. Sigma phase will form in some duplex stainless steels from exposure to temperatures between 550 and 800 °C (1020 and 1470 °F). Cold working enhances subsequent σ-phase formation.

ACKNOWLEDGMENT

The information in this article is largely taken from G.F. Vander Voort and H.M. James, Wrought Stainless Steels, *Metallography and Microstructures*, Vol 9, *ASM Handbook* (formerly 9th ed., *Metals Handbook*), ASM International, 1985, p 279-296.

REFERENCES

1. C.J. Novak, Structure and Constitution of Wrought Austenitic Stainless Steels, *Handbook of Stainless Steels,* D. Peckner and I.M Bernstein, Ed., McGraw-Hill, 1977, p 4-1 to 4-78
2. J.J. Demo, Structure and Constitution of Wrought Ferritic Stainless Steels, *Handbook of Stainless Steels,* D. Peckner and I.M. Bernstein, Ed., McGraw-Hill, 1977, p 5-1 to 5-40
3. P.T. Lovejoy, Structure and Constitution of Wrought Martensitic Stainless Steels, *Handbook of Stainless Steels,* D. Peckner and I.M Bernstein, Ed., McGraw-Hill, 1977, p 6-1 to 6-23
4. D.C. Perry and J.C. Jasper, Structure and Constitution of Wrought Precipitation-Hardenable Stainless Steels, *Handbook of Stainless Steels,* D. Peckner and I.M. Bernstein, Ed., McGraw-Hill, 1977, p 7-1 to 7-18
5. R. Gibson, Structure and Constitution of Wrought Microduplex Stainless Steels, *Handbook of Stainless Steels,* D. Peckner and

I.M. Bernstein, Ed., McGraw-Hill, 1977, p 8-1 to 8-22

6. G. Krauss, Stainless Steels, *Steels—Heat Treatment and Processing Principles*, ASM International, 1990, p 351-375

7. B. Thomas and G. Henry, Structure and Metallography of Stainless Steels, *Stainless Steels*, les Editions de Physique, 1993, p 61-107

8. A.L. Schaeffler, Constitution Diagram for Stainless Steel Weld Metal, *Met. Prog.*, Vol 56 (No. 5), Nov 1949, p 680-680B

9. W.T. DeLong et al., Measurement and Calculation of Ferrite in Stainless Steel Weld Metal, *Weld. J.*, Vol 35 (No. 11), Nov 1956, p 521s-528s

10. W.T. DeLong, A Modified Phase Diagram for Stainless Steel Weld Metals, *Met. Prog.*, Vol 77, Feb 1960, p 98-100B

11. H.F. Reid and W.T. DeLong, Making Sense Out of Ferrite Requirements in Welding Stainless Steels, *Met. Prog.*, Vol 103, June 1973, p 73-77

12. C.J. Long and W.T. DeLong, The Ferrite Content of Austenitic Stainless Steel Weld Metal, *Weld. J.*, Vol 52, July 1973, p 281s-297s

13. St. Mayerhofer and H. Kohl, Statistical Analysis of the Delta Ferrite Content of Austenitic Steels, Berg-Hüttenmänn, *Monatsh.*, Vol 111 (No. 9), BISI 5304, 1966, p 443-453

14. W.T. DeLong, Ferrite in Austenitic Stainless Steel Weld Metal, *Weld. J.*, Vol 53, July 1974, p 273s-286s

15. H.A. Meijer, Quantitative Analysis of Ferrite in Austenitic Stainless Steel, *Br. Weld. J.*, Vol 13, Jan 1966, p 12-17

16. F.C. Hull, Delta Ferrite and Martensite Formation in Stainless Steels, *Weld. J.*, Vol 42 (No. 5), May 1973, p 193s-203s

17. L.S. Aubrey et al., Ferrite Measurement and Control in Cast Duplex Stainless Steels, STP 756, ASTM, 1982, p 126-164

18. M.T. Leger, Predicting and Evaluating Ferrite Content in Austenitic Stainless Steel Castings, STP 756, ASTM, 1982, p 105-125

19. L. Pryce and K.W. Andrews, Practical Estimation of Composition Balance and Ferrite Content in Stainless Steels, *J. Iron Steel Inst.*, Vol 195, Aug 1960, p 415-417

20. C.M. Hammond, The Development of New High-Strength Stainless Steels, STP 369, ASTM, 1965, p 47-53

21. R.B. Gunia and G.A. Ratz, The Measurement of Delta Ferrite in Austenitic Stainless Steel, *Weld. Res. Council Bull.*, No. 132, Aug 1968

22. L.A. Brough, The Effects of Processing on Delta Ferrite Measurement, *J. Mater. Energy Syst.*, Vol 5 (No. 1), June 1983, p 36-42

23. W.L. Johns et al., Percent Delta Ferrite Determination in Type 304 Stainless Steel Weldments, *Microstruc. Sci.*, Vol 2, 1974, p 13-22

24. G.M. Goodwin et al., A Study of Ferrite Morphology in Austenitic Stainless Steel Weldments, *Weld. J.*, Vol 51, Sept 1972, p 425s-429s

25. C.B. Post and W.S. Eberly, Stability of Austenite in Stainless Steels, *Trans. ASM*, Vol 39, 1947, p 868-890

26. A.J. Griffiths and J.C. Wright, Mechanical Properties of Austenitic and Metastable Stainless Steel Sheet and Their Relationships with Pressforming Behaviour, *Iron Steel Inst. Pub.*, 117, 1969, p 51-65

27. R. Stickler and A. Vinckier, Morphology of Grain-Boundary Carbides and Its Influence on Intergranular Corrosion of 304 Stainless Steel, *Trans. ASM*, Vol 54, 1961, p 362-380

28. J.T. Gow and O.E. Harder, Balancing the Composition of Cast 25 Per Cent Chromium—12 Per Cent Nickel Type Alloys, *Trans. ASM*, Vol 30, 1942, p 855-935

29. F.C. Hull, Effects of Composition on Embrittlement of Austenitic Stainless Steels, *Weld. J.*, Vol 52, 1973, p 104s-113s

30. E.J. Dulis and G.V. Smith, Identification and Mode of Formation and Re-Solution of Sigma Phase in Austenitic Chromium-Nickel Steels, STP 110, ASTM, 1951, p 3-37

31. R. Franks et al., Experiments on Etching Procedures for the Identification of the Sigma Phase in Austenitic Chromium-Nickel Stainless Steels, *Proc. ASTM*, Vol 53, 1953, p 143-169, 177-180

32. A.J. Lena, Sigma Phase—A Review, *Met. Prog.*, Vol 66, Sept 1954, p 122-128

33. W.E. White and I. LeMay, Metallographic Observations on the Formation and Occurrence of Ferrite, Sigma Phase, and Carbides in Austenitic Stainless Steels, *Metallography*, Vol 3, 1970, p 35-50, 51-60

34. K.W. Andrews and P.E. Brookes, Chi Phase in Alloy Steels, *Met. Treatment Drop Forg.*, July 1951, p 301-311

35. P.K. Koh, Occurrence of Chi Phase in Molybdenum-Bearing Stainless Steels, *Trans. AIME*, Vol 197, 1953, p 339-343

36. J.S. Kasper, The Ordering of Atoms in the Chi-Phase of the Iron-Chromium-Molybdenum System, *Acta Metall.*, Vol 2, May 1954, p 456-461

37. J.G. McMullin et al., Equilibrium Structure in Fe-Cr-Mo Alloys, *Trans. ASM*, Vol 46, 1954, p 799-811

38. F.L. Ver Snyder and H.J. Beattie, The Laves and Chi Phases in a Modified 12Cr Stainless Alloy, *Trans. ASM*, Vol 47, 1955, p 211-230

39. B. Weiss and R. Stickler, Phase Instabilities during High Temperature Exposure of 316 Austenitic Stainless Steel, *Met. Trans.*, Vol 3, April 1972, p 851-866

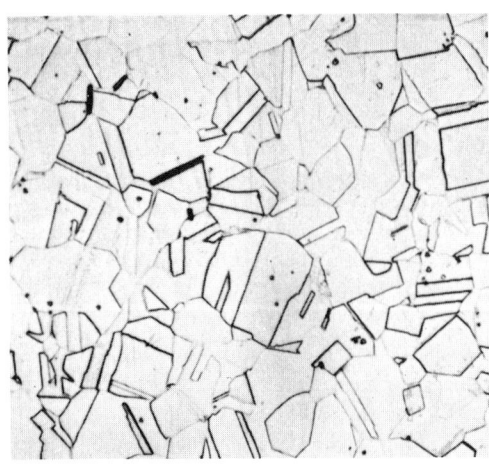

Fig. 1 Type 201 stainless steel strip, annealed 5 min at 1065 °C (1950 °F) and rapidly cooled to room temperature. The structure is equiaxed austenite grains and annealing twins. 10 mL HNO₃, 10 mL acetic acid, 15 mL HCl, and 2 drops glycerol. 250×

Fig. 2 Type 301 stainless steel, mill annealed at 1065 °C (1950 °F) and cold worked. Some martensite (dark) has formed in the austenitic matrix. Electrolytic: HNO₃-acetic acid, then 10% oxalic acid. 200×

Fig. 3 Type 301 sheet cold rolled to 10% reduction (quarter hard), showing martensite formation in deformed austenite grains. Stringers and pits are etched-out inclusions. Electrolytic: 10% oxalic acid. 250×

40. H. Hughes and S.R. Keown, Precipitation of a Transition Intermetallic Compound (R-Phase) in Steels, *J. Iron Steel Inst.,* Vol 206, March 1968, p 275-277

41. D.J. Dyson and S.R. Keown, A Study of Precipitation in a 12% Cr-Co-Mo Steel, *Acta Metall.,* Vol 17, 1969, p 1095-1107

42. J.K. Lai and J.R. Haigh, Delta-Ferrite Transformation in a Type 316 Weld Metal, *Weld. J.,* Vol 58, Jan 1979, p 1s-6s

43. H.T. Beattie and W.C. Hagel, Intermetallic Compounds in Titanium-Hardened Alloys, *Trans. AIME,* Vol 209, July 1957, p 911-917

44. K.W. Andrews and H. Hughes, discussion of paper "Aging Reaction in Certain Superalloys," *Trans. ASM,* Vol 49, 1957, p 999

45. J.J. Demo, *Structure, Constitution, and General Characteristics of Wrought Ferritic Stainless Steels,* STP 619, ASTM, 1977

46. R.H. Thielemann, Some Effects of Composition and Heat Treatment on the High Temperature Rupture Properties of Ferrous Alloys, *Proc. ASTM,* Vol 40, 1940, p 788-804

47. K.J. Irvine et al., The Physical Metallurgy of 12% Chromium Steels, *J. Iron Steel Inst.,* Vol 195, Aug 1960, p 386-405

48. K.J. Irvine et al., Controlled-Transformation Stainless Steels, *J. Iron Steel Inst.,* Vol 192, July 1959, p 218-238

49. A. Kasak et al., Development of Precipitation Hardening Cr-Mo-Co Stainless Steels, *Trans. ASM,* Vol 56, 1963, p 455-467

50. B.R. Banerjee et al., Structure and Properties of PH 15-7Mo Stainless, *Trans. ASM,* Vol 57, 1964, p 856-873

51. H.L. Marcus et al., Precipitation in 17-7PH Stainless Steel, *Trans. ASM,* Vol 58, 1965, p 176-182

52. R.C. Gibson et al., Properties of Stainless Steels with a Microduplex Structure, *Trans. ASM,* Vol 61, 1968, p 85-93

53. S. Floreen and H.W. Hayden, The Influence of Austenite and Ferrite on the Mechanical Properties of Two-Phase Stainless Steels Having Microduplex Structures, *Trans. ASM,* Vol 61, 1968, p 489-499

54. H.D. Solomon and T.M. Devine, Duplex Stainless Steels—A Tale of Two Phases, Paper 8201-089, presented at the ASM Metals Congress (St. Louis, MO), 1982

Fig. 4 Type 301 sheet, cold rolled to 40% reduction (full hard), showing almost complete transformation to martensite in severely deformed austenite grains. Electrolytic: 10% oxalic acid. 250×

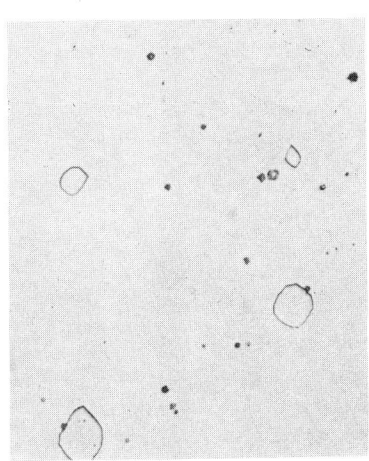

Fig. 5 Type 302 stainless steel strip, 1.6 mm (0.06 in.) thick, annealed at 1065 °C (1950 °F) and rapidly cooled to room temperature. The structure consists of ferrite pools (globules) in an austenitic matrix. Electrolytic: 10% NaCN. 500×

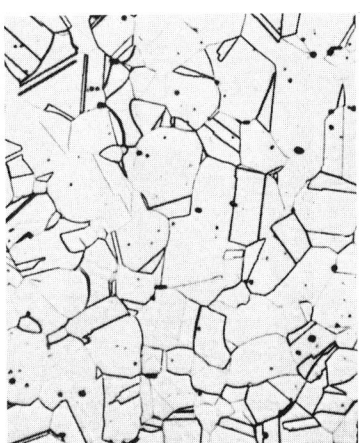

Fig. 6 Type 304 stainless steel strip, annealed 5 min at 1065 °C (1950 °F), cooled in air. Structure consists of equiaxed austenite grains and annealing twins. 10 mL HNO₃, 10 mL acetic acid, 15 mL HCl, and 2 drops glycerol. 250×

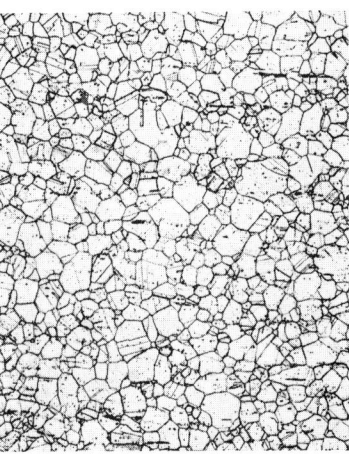

Fig. 7 Type 304 strip, annealed 2 min at 1065 °C (1950 °F) and air cooled. Structure is equiaxed austenite grains, annealing twins, and small stringer inclusions. Electrolytic: HNO₃-acetic acid, then 10% oxalic acid. 100×

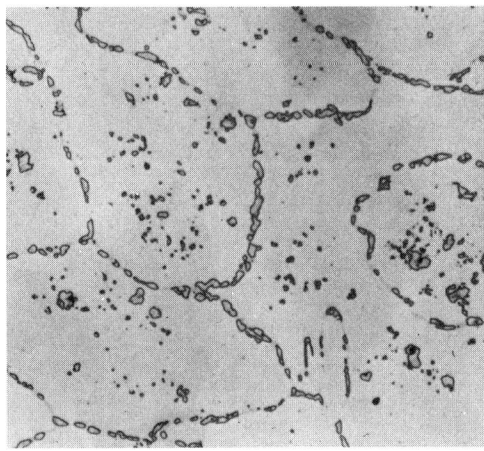

Fig. 8 Type 310 stainless steel plate, hot rolled and annealed at 1065 °C (1950 °F), water quenched in less than 3 min, exposed 27 months at 760 °C (1400 °F), and slowly air cooled. Structure is σ-phase precipitates in an austenitic matrix. Electrolytic: saturated NaOH, 1.5 V dc, 6 s. 250×

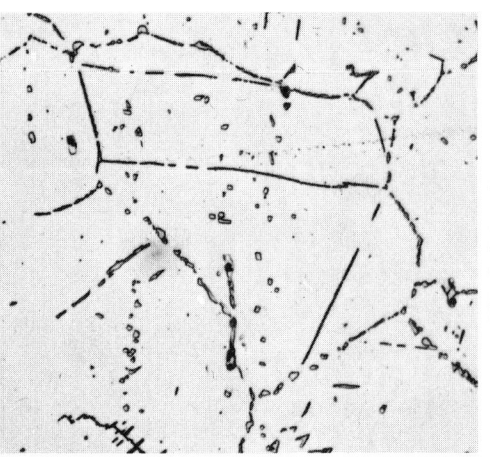

Fig. 9 Type 316 stainless steel, annealed 30 min at 1080 °C (1975 °F) and exposed 3000 h at 815 °C (1500 °F). Prolonged exposure at temperature has resulted in the formation of islands of σ and χ phases at austenite grain boundaries. Picral and HCl. 500×

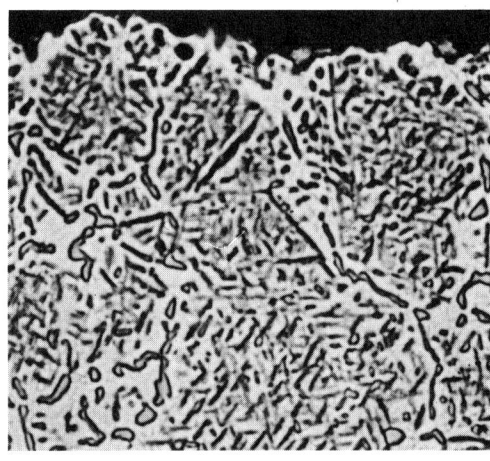

Fig. 10 Type 316 tubing, packed with boron nitride powder and held 2285 h at 840 °C (1540 °F). The gray phase at grain boundaries and Widmanstätten platelets within grains are chromium nitride. The matrix is austenite. 12 mL lactic acid, 38 mL HCl, and 2 mL HNO₃. 500×

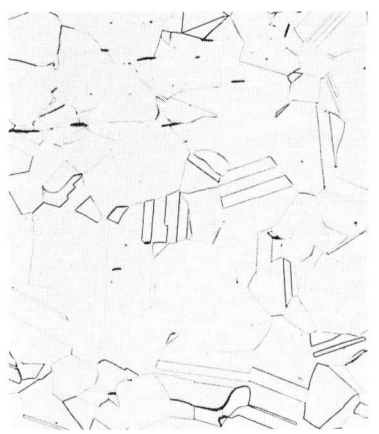

Fig. 11 Type 316 stainless steel, solution annealed at 1035 °C (1900 °F) and water quenched. Etching has revealed most of the austenite grain and annealing twin boundaries. 10 mL HNO₃, 10 mł acetic acid, 15 mL HCl, and 5 mL glycerol. 100×

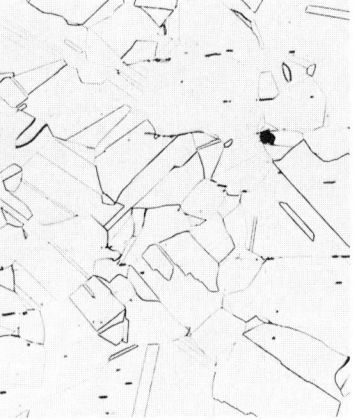

Fig. 12 Same steel and processing as Fig. 11, etched electrolytically to reveal austenite grain boundaries. Not all of the boundaries are visible. Electrolytic: 10% aqueous oxalic acid, 6 V dc, 15 s. 100×

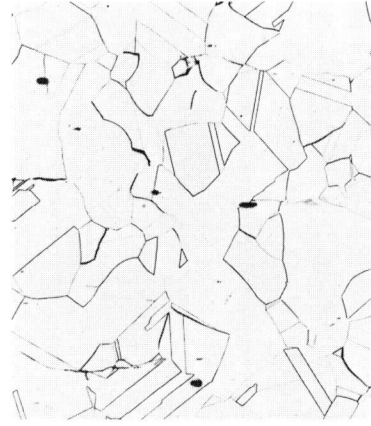

Fig. 13 Same steel and processing as Fig. 11, etched to reveal austenite grain boundaries. Not all of the boundaries are revealed. Compare with Fig. 12 and 14. Marble's reagent. 100×

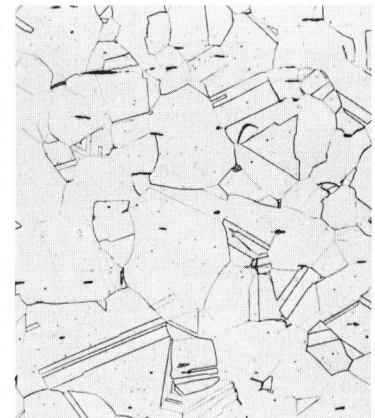

Fig. 14 Same steel and processing as Fig. 11, etched to reveal austenite grain boundaries. Not all of the boundaries are visible. Compare with Fig. 12 and 13. Equal parts H₂O, HCl, and HNO₃. 100×

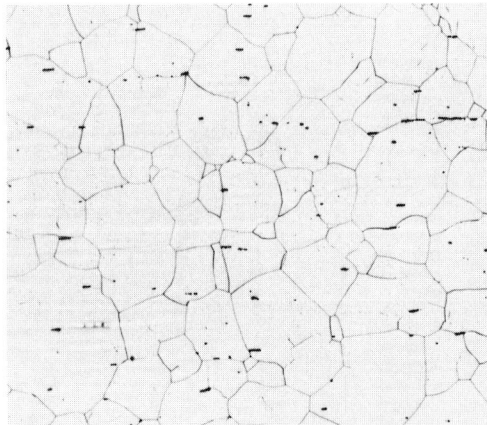

Fig. 15 Same steel and processing as Fig. 11, etched to reveal austenite grain boundaries. Note that twins are not etched. Electrolytic: 60% aqueous HNO₃, 0.6 V dc, 2 min (platinum cathode). 100×

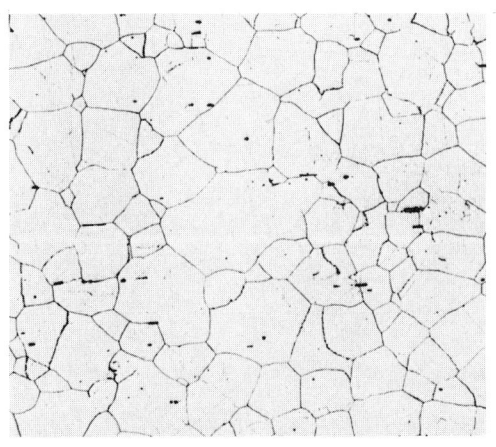

Fig. 16 Same steel as Fig. 11, solution annealed and sensitized. Twins are not etched, because no carbide was precipitated at the twins. Equal parts H₂O, HCl, and HNO₃. 100×

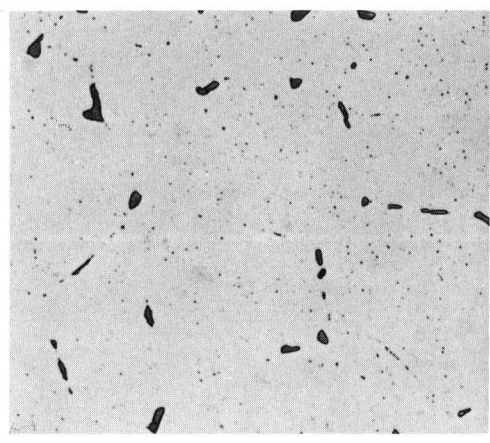

Fig. 17 Annealed type 321 stainless steel furnace part, after 16 months service at 900 °C (1650 °F) in hydrogen. Sigma-phase islands at austenite grain boundaries and fine, dispersed chromium carbide. Electrolytic: 40% aqueous NaOH. 300×

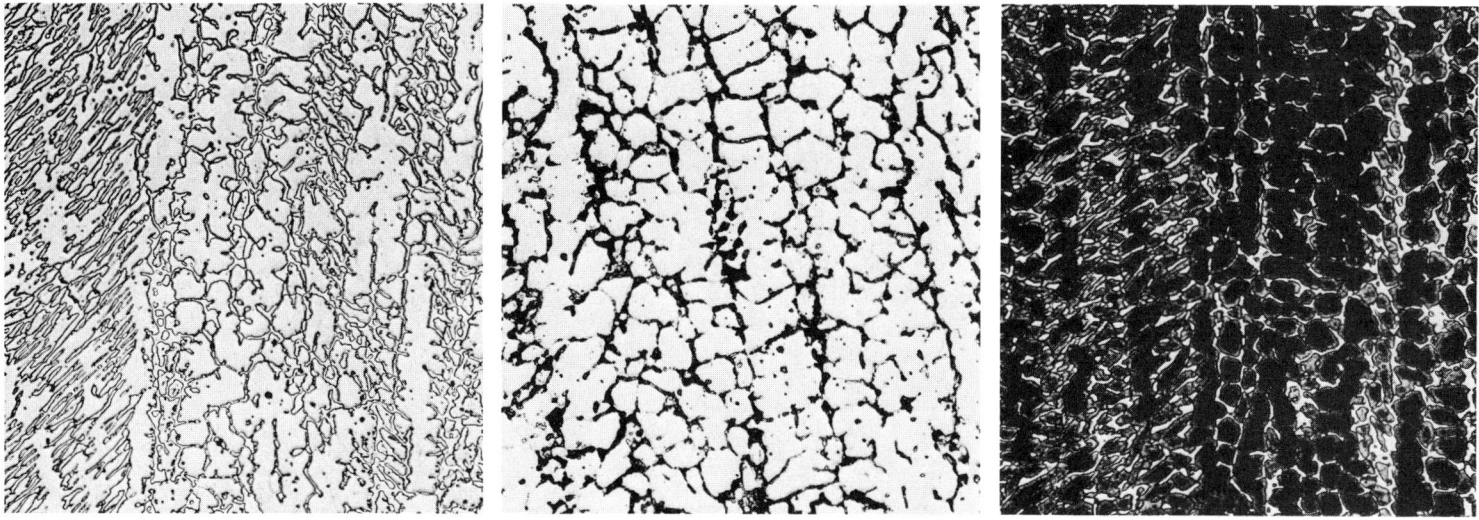

Fig. 18, 19, 20 The use of different etchants to reveal δ-ferrite in austenitic stainless steel weld metal. Fig. 18: etched in Vilella's reagent. Fig. 19: etched 15 s in modified Murakami's reagent (30 g K₃Fe(CN)₆, 30 g KOH, and 150 mL H₂O) at 95 °C (200 °F) to color δ-ferrite brown. Fig. 20: heat tinted at 595 °C (1100 °F) to color austenite red and δ-ferrite cream. See also Fig. 21 to 23. 500×

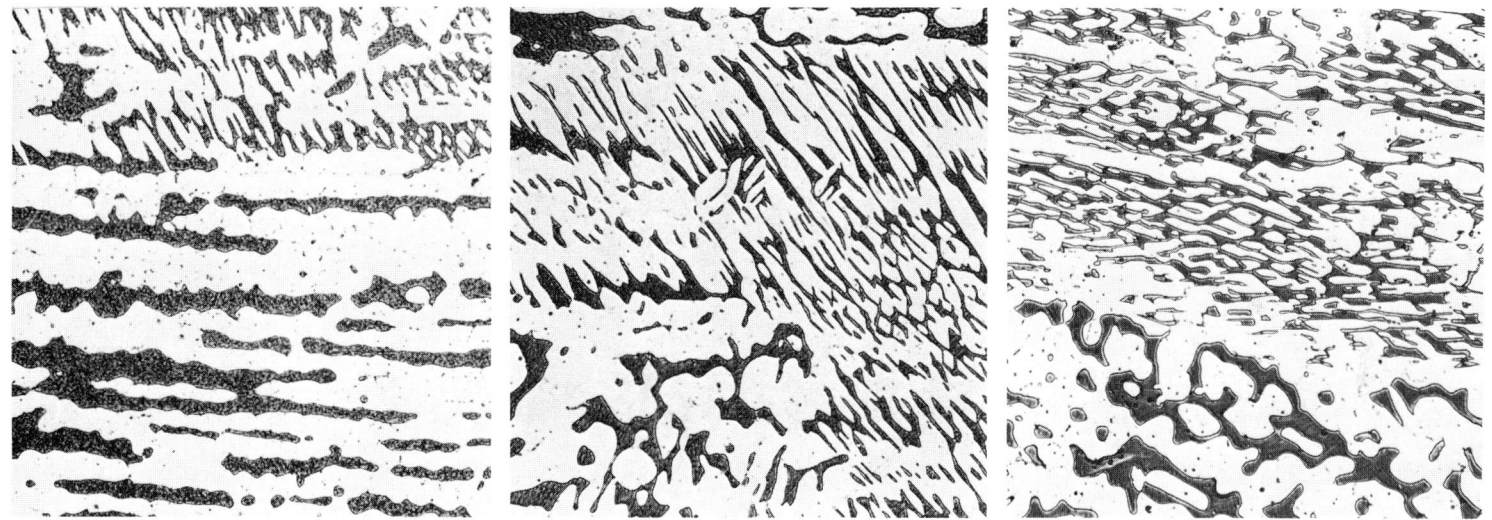

Fig. 21, 22, 23 Different etchants used to reveal δ-ferrite in austenitic stainless steel weld metal. Fig. 21: electrolytic etch 10 s in 10 N KOH, 2.5 V dc. Fig. 22: electrolytic etch 25 s in 20% aqueous NaOH, 20 V dc. Fig. 23: etched 15 min in boiling Murakami's reagent. 500×

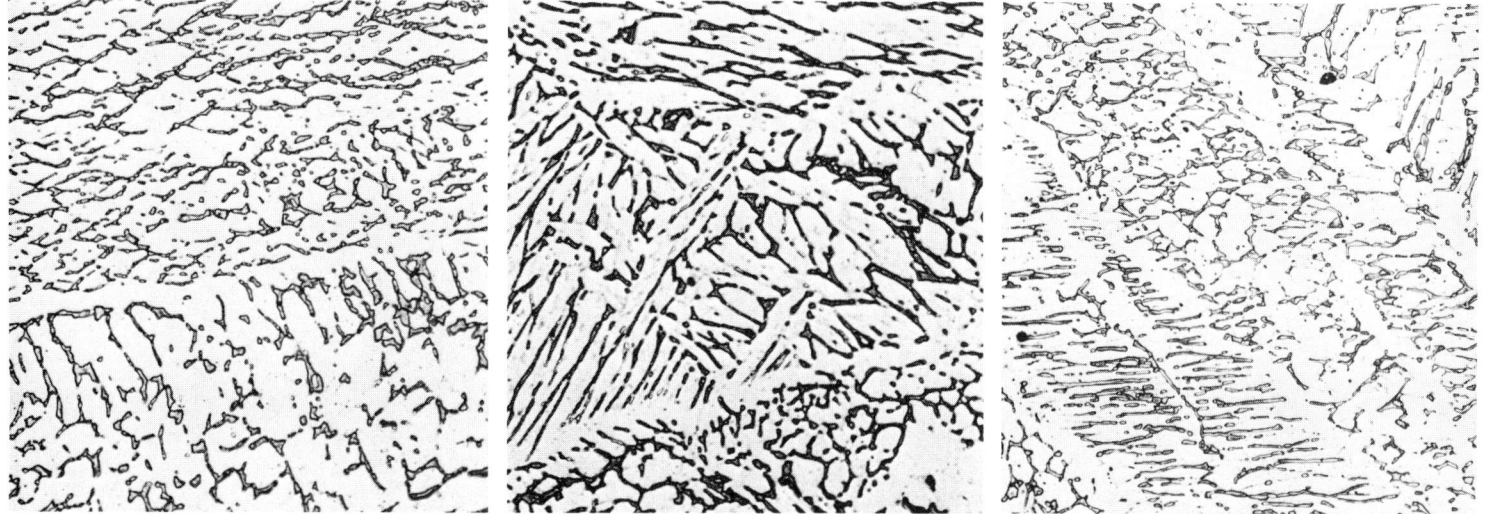

Fig. 24, 25, 26 Austenitic stainless steel weld metal, etched using different reagents to reveal σ phase. Fig. 24: electrolytic etch in 10 N KOH, 2.5 V dc, 10 s. Fig. 25: electrolytic etch in 20% aqueous NaOH, 20 V, 25 s. Fig. 26: etched 3 min in Murakami's reagent, room temperature. 500×

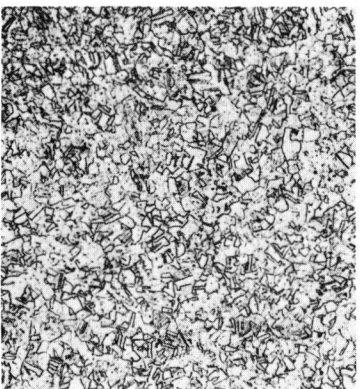

Fig. 27 22-13-5 austenitic stainless steel (400 HV), solution annealed and cold drawn. Note the uniform grain structure. 10 mL HNO₃, 10 mL acetic acid, 15 mL HCl, and 2 drops glycerol. 200×

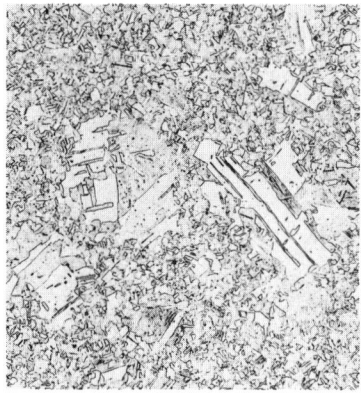

Fig. 28 22-13-5 stainless steel, solution annealed and cold drawn as in Fig. 27. In this case, a duplex grain structure developed. 10 mL HNO₃, 10 mL acetic acid, 15 mL HCl, and 2 drops glycerol. 100×

Fig. 29 Type 308 stainless steel, solution annealed and cold worked. The grain structure is difficult to reveal by chemical etching. 10 mL HNO₃, 10 mL acetic acid, 15 mL HCl, and 2 drops glycerol. 400×

Fig. 30 Same material and processing as Fig. 29, examined under differential interference contrast illumination to reveal surface topography. 10 mL HNO₃, 10 mL acetic acid, 15 mL HCl, and 2 drops glycerol. 400×

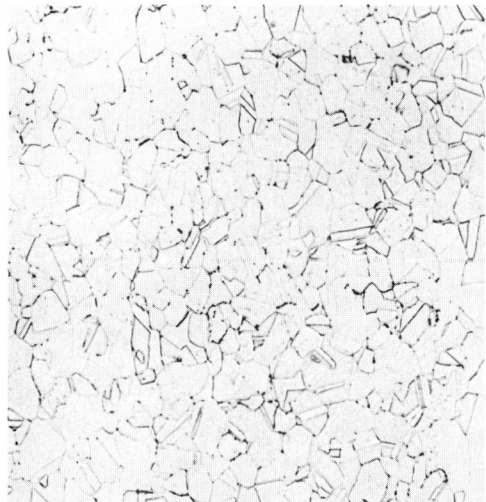
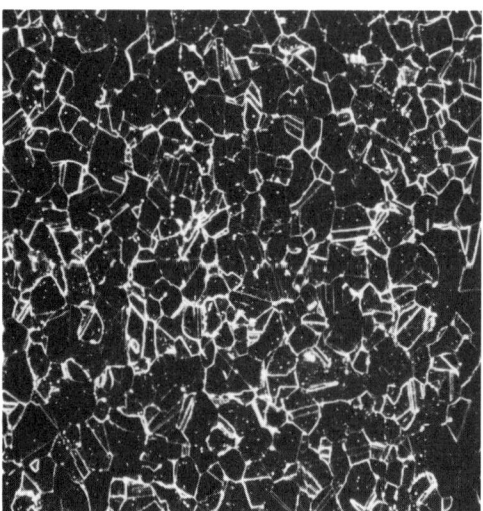
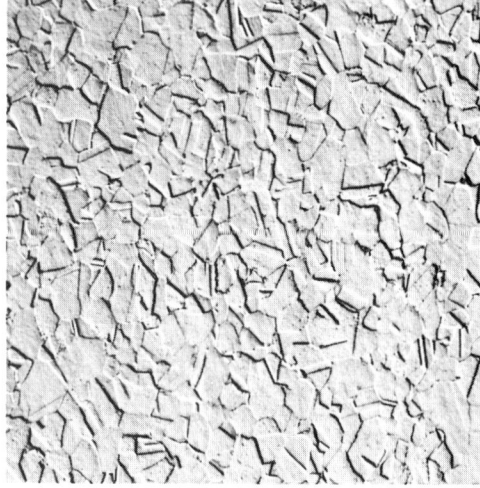

Fig. 31, 32, 33 20Cb-3 austenitic stainless steel, solution annealed. The use of different illumination modes to reveal the chemically etched grain structure. Fig. 31: bright-field illumination. Fig. 32: dark-field illumination. Fig. 33: differential interference contrast. 10 mL HNO₃, 10 mL acetic acid, 15 mL HCl, and 2 drops glycerol. 400×

Fig. 34, 35, 36 Type 316L stainless steel, cold drawn, using different illumination modes. The structure is revealed more clearly with dark-field illumination and differential interference contrast than with bright-field illumination. Fig. 34: bright-field illumination. Fig. 35: dark-field illumination. Fig. 36: differential interference contrast. 10 mL HNO₃, 10 mL acetic acid, 15 mL HCl, and 2 drops glycerol. 100×

Fig. 37, 38, 39 Proprietary austenitic stainless steel, not recrystallized after hot working. The structure is revealed more clearly using dark-field illumination and differential interference contrast than by bright-field illumination. Fig. 37: bright-field illumination. Fig. 38: dark-field illumination. Fig. 39: differential interference contrast. 10 mL HNO_3, 10 mL acetic acid, 15 mL HCl, and 2 drops glycerol. 100×

Fig. 40 Stringer-type manganese sulfide inclusions in resulfurized type 303 stainless steel. Free-machining additives such as MnS permit higher machining speeds, lower power consumption, and promote longer tool life. See also Fig. 41. As-polished. 500×

Fig. 41 Mixed manganese sulfide and manganese selenide inclusions in type 303 selenium-treated stainless steel (0.21% Se). Selenium has beneficial effects similar to sulfur (see Fig. 40), but also imparts greater ductility to free-machining stainless steels than does sulfur. As-polished. 500×

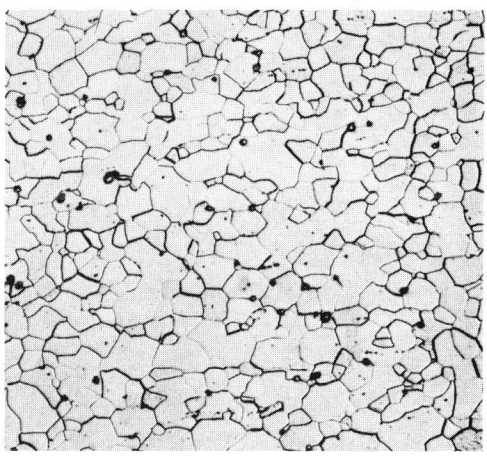

Fig. 42 Muffler-grade type 409 stainless steel (0.045C-11Cr-0.50Ti) strip, annealed 1 h per inch of thickness at 870 °C (1600 °F) and air cooled to RT. Equiaxed ferrite grains and dispersed titanium carbide particles. 10 mL HNO_3, 10 mL acetic acid, 15 mL HCl, and 2 drops glycerol. 100×

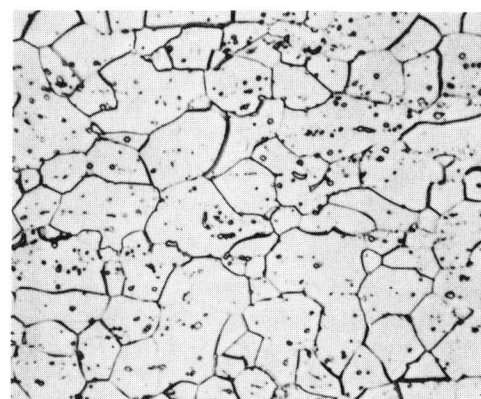

Fig. 43 Type 430 stainless steel strip, annealed at 845 °C (1550 °F) and cooled in air. The structure consists of equiaxed ferrite grains and randomly dispersed chromium carbide particles. Vilella's reagent. 500×

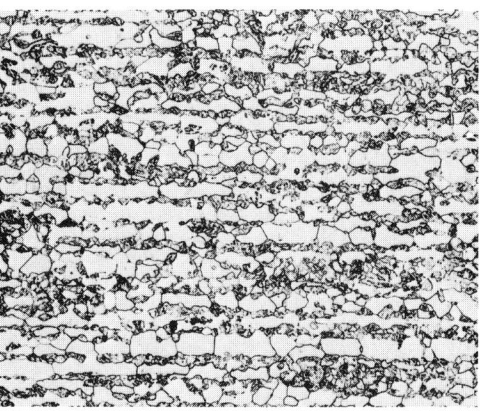

Fig. 44 Type 430 ferritic stainless steel. This grade can sometimes be partially hardenable, depending on composition balance and amount of segregation. The structure in this longitudinal section is streaks of martensite (dark) and ferrite (white). See Fig. 45. Glyceregia. 100×

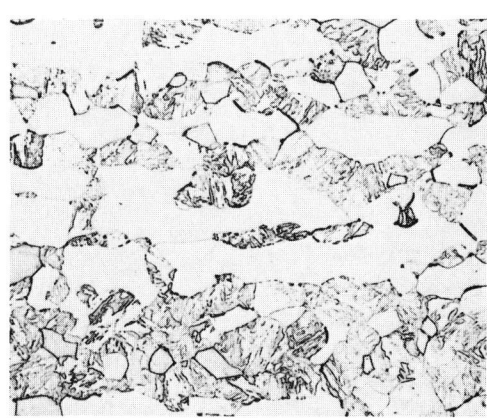

Fig. 45 Same as Fig. 44, but a higher magnification to resolve the structure more clearly. Ferrite (white constituent) is approximately 235 HV; martensite (dark), 360 HV. Same etchant as Fig. 44. 400×

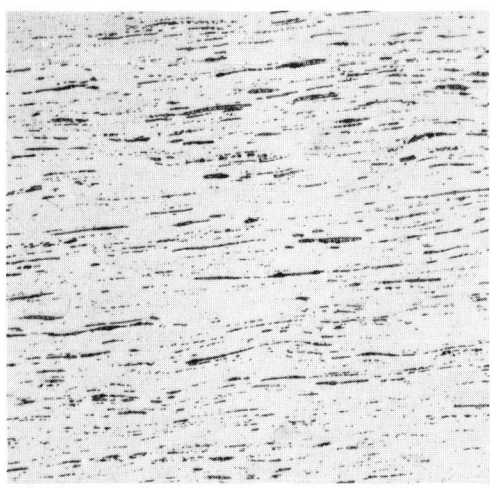

Fig. 46 Type 430F (resulfurized free-machining 430, 254 HV) ferritic stainless steel. Longitudinal section shows dispersed manganese sulfide stringers in a ferrite matrix. As-polished. 200×

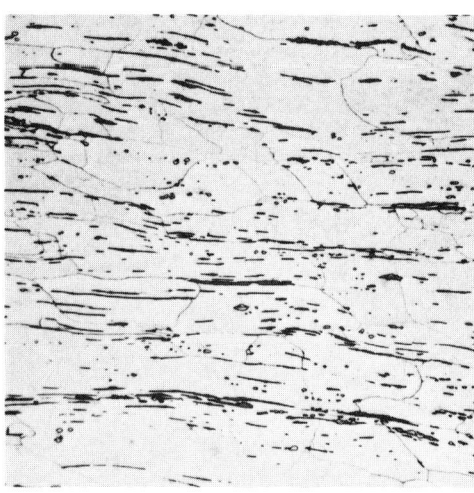

Fig. 47 182-FM (18Cr-2Mo) resulfurized free-machining stainless steel (230 HV). The structure is carbide and sulfides in a ferritic matrix. Ralph's reagent. 200×

Fig. 48 Type 434 modified free-machining ferritic stainless steel (260 HV). Longitudinal section shows carbides and sulfide stringers in a matrix of ferrite. Ralph's reagent. 100×

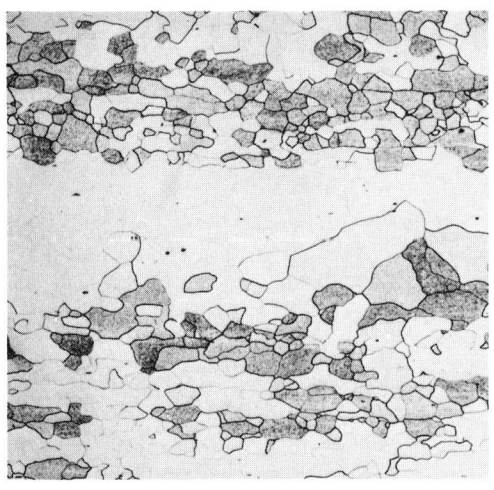

Fig. 49 E-Brite (26Cr-1Mo) ferritic stainless steel plate (180 HV), 6 mm (0.25 in.) thick. Longitudinal section shows ferrite grains. 10 mL HNO_3, 10 mL acetic acid, 15 mL HCl, and 2 drops glycerol. 50×

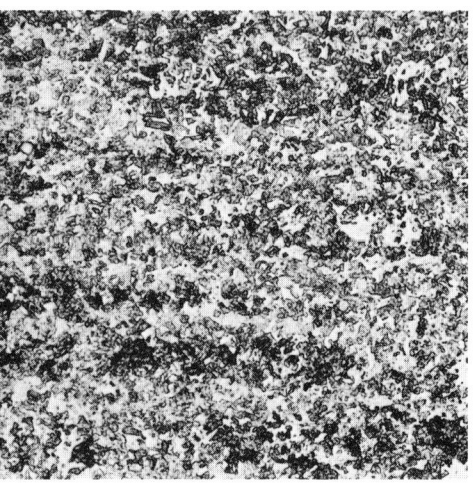

Fig. 50 Type 403 martensitic stainless steel (320 HV) in the quenched and tempered condition. Longitudinal section shows a structure of tempered martensite. Vilella's reagent. 400×

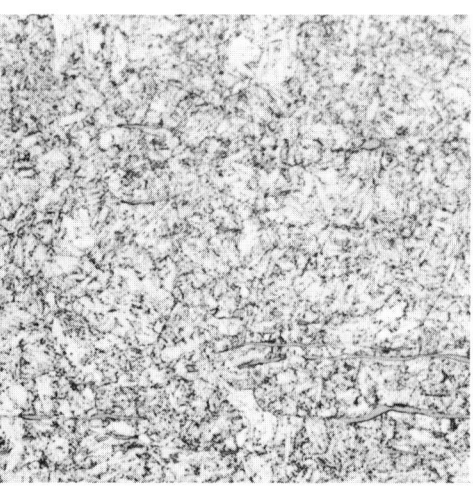

Fig. 51 Type 410 stainless steel (300 HV), with sulfur added for machinability, in the quenched and tempered condition. Structure is tempered martensite with some manganese sulfide stringers. Vilella's reagent. 400×

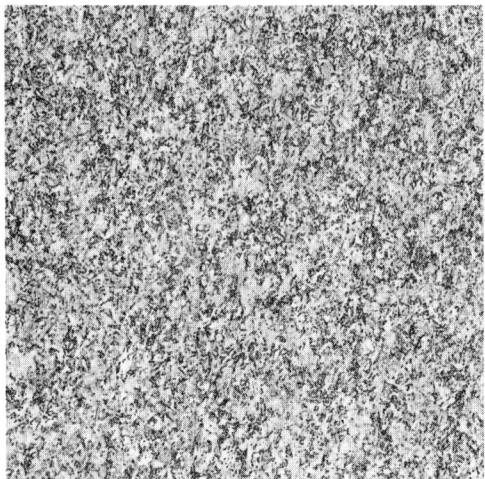

Fig. 52 Type 420 stainless steel, quenched and tempered. Structure is tempered martensite. Vilella's reagent. 100×

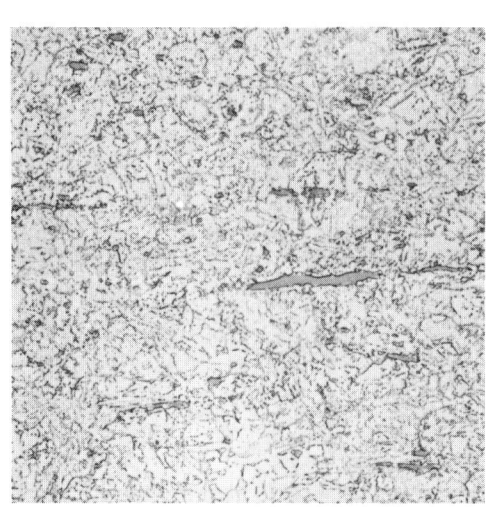

Fig. 53 Type 420 stainless steel (306 HV), quenched and tempered with sulfur added to improve machinability. Tempered martensite with some sulfide inclusions. Vilella's reagent. 400×

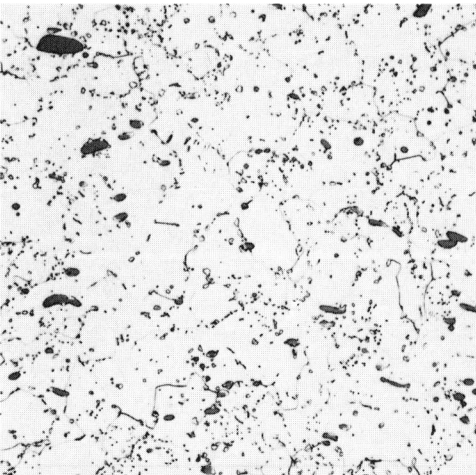

Fig. 54 Free-machining type 416 stainless steel (160 HV), annealed. The gray particles are sulfides. Vilella's reagent. 400×

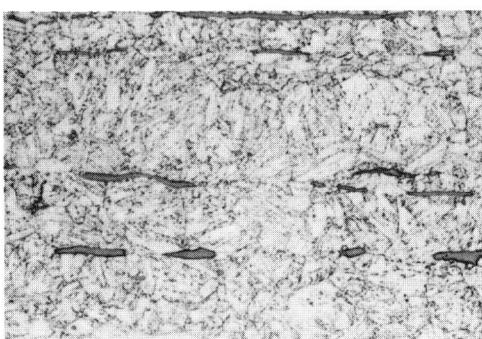

Fig. 55 Same free-machining stainless steel as shown in Fig. 54, but in the quenched and tempered condition. Longitudinal section shows δ-ferrite stringers (white), tempered martensite, and sulfides. Vilella's reagent. 400×

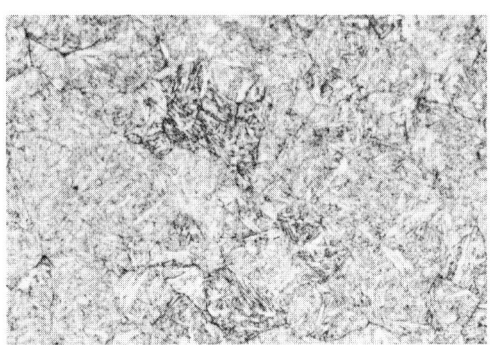

Fig. 56 Type 431 stainless steel (335 HV) in the quenched and tempered condition. Structure is tempered martensite. This martensitic alloy has a nickel addition (1.25-2.50%) for enhanced corrosion resistance. Vilella's reagent. 200×

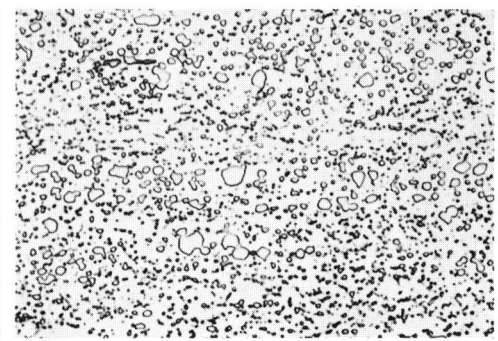

Fig. 57 Type 440A stainless steel in the annealed condition. Longitudinal section shows chromium carbide particles in a ferritic matrix. See Fig. 58 for effects of austenitizing/air cooling/tempering heat treatment on the structure of this alloy. 5% picric acid and 3% hydrochloric acid in alcohol. 500×

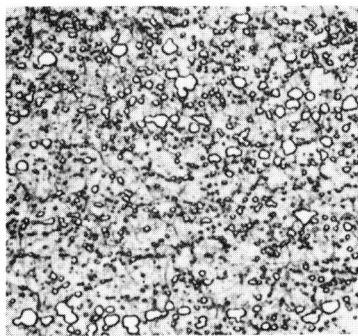

Fig. 58 Type 440A stainless steel, austenitized 30 min at 1010 °C (1850 °F), air cooled and tempered 30 min at 595 °C (1100 °F). The structure is partly spheroidized particles of chromium carbide in a martensitic matrix. Compare with the annealed structure shown in Fig. 57. 1% picric acid and 5% HCl in alcohol. 500×

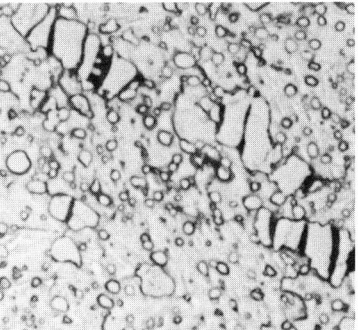

Fig. 59, 60 Type 440B martensitic stainless steel (245 HV) in the spheroidize annealed condition. Fig. 59: specimen was polished incorrectly; note resulting cracks in and around the carbide particles. Fig. 60: same specimen as shown in Fig. 59 but polished properly. No cracking is evident in this specimen. See the article "Mechanical Grinding, Abrasion, and Polishing" in this Volume for detailed information on procedures. Vilella's reagent. 1000×

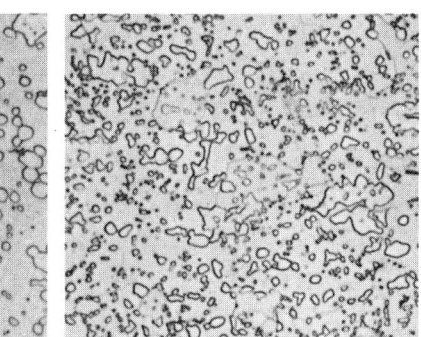

Fig. 61 Type 440C stainless steel (255 HV) in the spheroidize annealed condition. Structure is chromium-rich carbide particles in a ferrite matrix. See also Fig. 62 and 63 for the effects of alternate heat treatments on the structure of this martensitic alloy. Vilella's reagent. 1000×

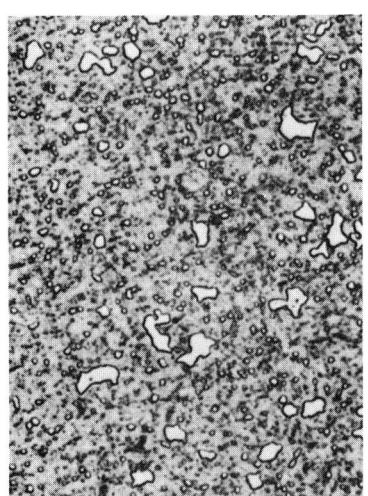

Fig. 62 Type 440C martensitic stainless steel, austenitized 1 h at 1010 °C (1850 °F), air cooled, and tempered 2 h at 230 °C (450 °F). The structure is carbide particles in a martensitic matrix. Vilella's reagent. See also Fig. 63. 500×

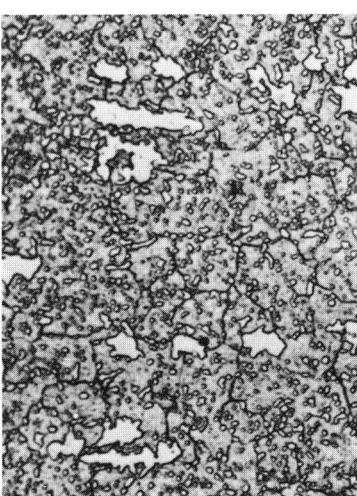

Fig. 63 Type 440C stainless steel bar, preheated 30 min at 760 °C (1400 °F), austenitized 30 min at 1025 °C (1875 °F), air cooled to 65 °C (150 °F), and double tempered (2 h each) at 425 °C (800 °F). Primary and secondary carbides (islands and particles) in tempered martensite. Superpicral. 500×

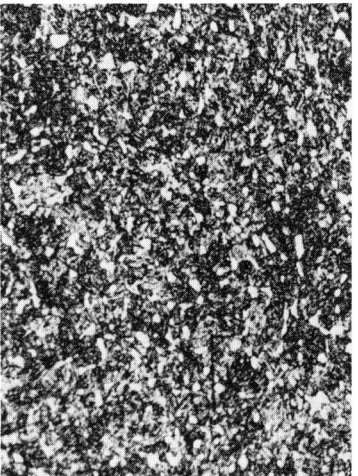

Fig. 64, 65 AM350 semiaustenitic precipitation-hardenable stainless steel, containing a small amount of ferrite (white patches) in a martensitic matrix. Some retained austenite is also present. This grade and AM355 (see Fig. 66 to 68), while classed as precipitation-hardenable alloys, do not have true precipitation reactions. Fry's reagent. Fig. 64: 100×. Fig. 65: 1000×

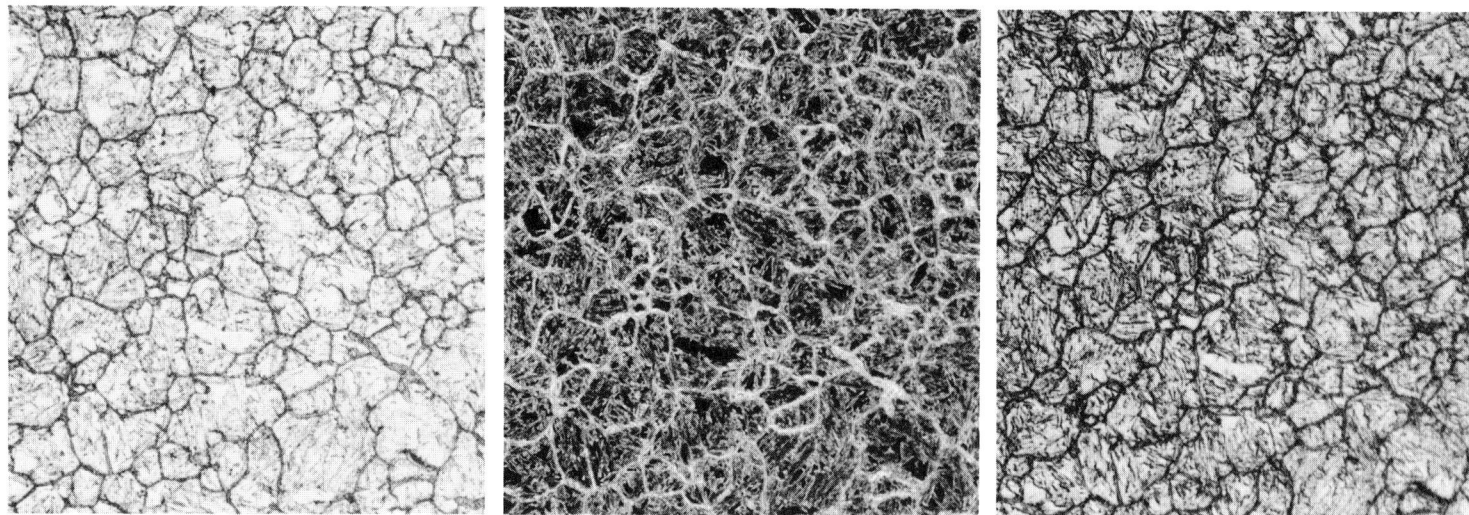

Fig. 66, 67, 68 AM355 precipitation-hardenable stainless steel (525 HV), heat treated. The structure is martensite, but etching has revealed prior austenite grain boundaries. Fig. 66: bright-field illumination. Fig. 67: dark-field illumination. Fig. 68: Differential interference contrast. Vilella's reagent. 400×

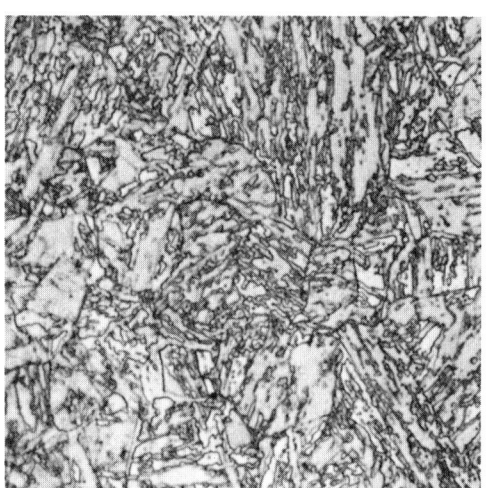

Fig. 69 PH13-8Mo precipitation-hardenable stainless steel (475 HV), solution annealed and aged. The structure is tempered martensite. Fry's reagent. 1000×

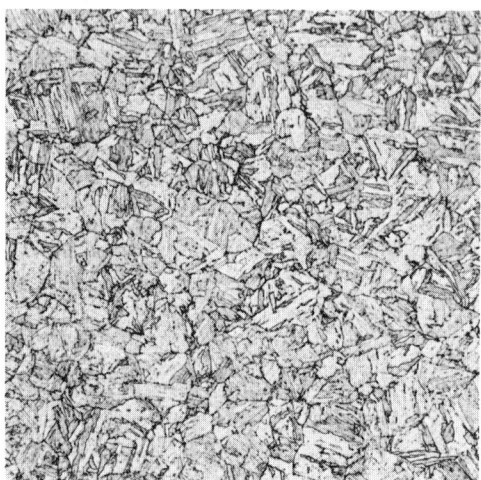

Fig. 70 17-4PH stainless steel, solution annealed and aged. Structure is tempered martensite (no δ-ferrite). Compare with Fig. 81 to 84. Fry's reagent. 200×

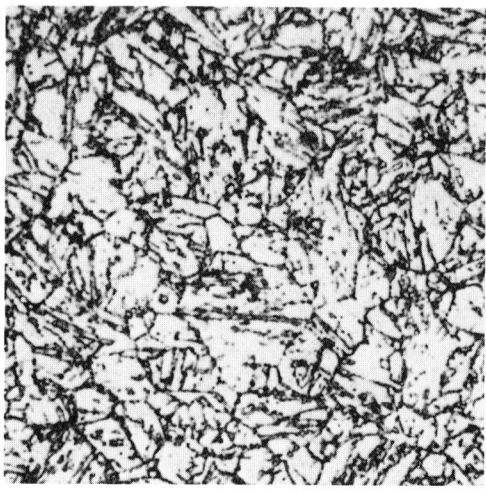

Fig. 71 Custom 450 precipitation-hardenable stainless steel (360 HV), solution annealed and aged (H1050). The structure is tempered martensite. Fry's reagent. 1000×

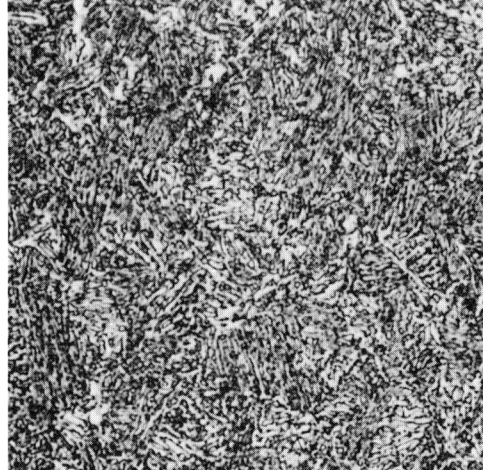

Fig. 72 Custom 450 precipitation-hardenable stainless steel (320 HV), solution annealed and aged (H1150). The structure is tempered martensite and reverted austenite. Fry's reagent. 1000×

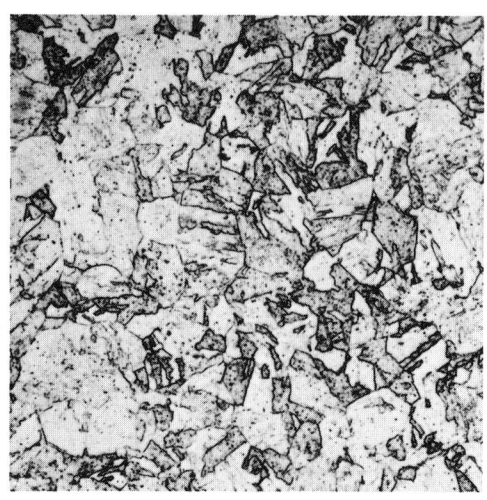

Fig. 73 Custom 455 precipitation-hardenable stainless steel (51 HRC), solution annealed and aged (H850). The structure is martensitic. Fry's reagent. 1000×

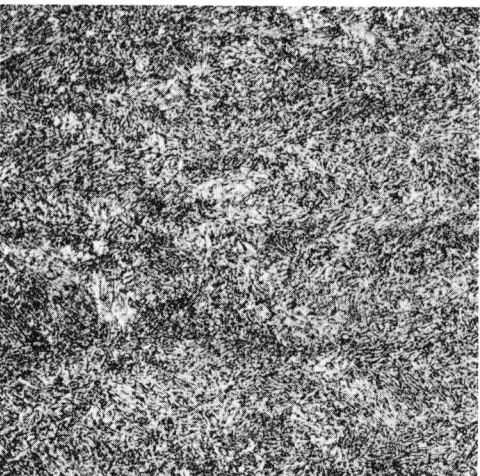

Fig. 74 Custom 455 precipitation-hardenable stainless steel (36 HRC) in the solution annealed and aged condition (H1100). The structure is martensitic. Fry's reagent. 1000×

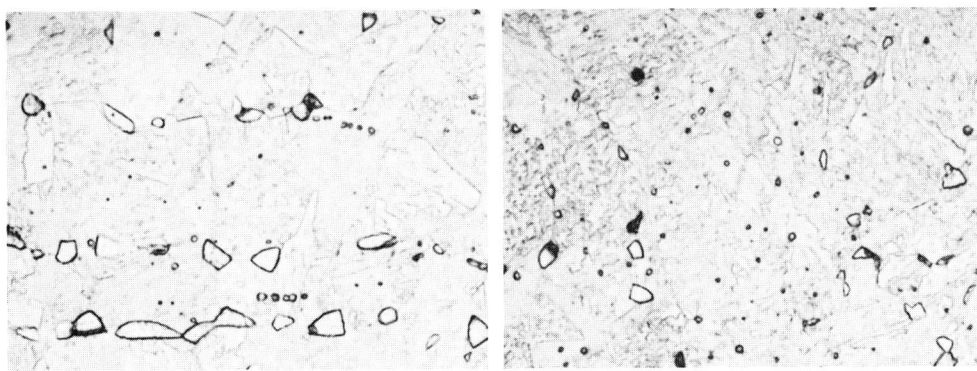

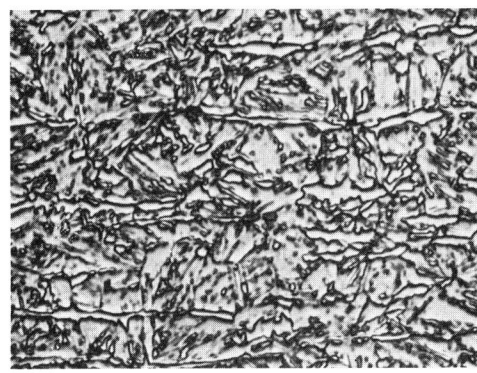

Fig. 75, 76 17-7PH semiaustenitic precipitation-hardenable stainless steel (165 HV) that was hot rolled and annealed. The outlined particles shown in this photomicrograph are δ-ferrite. Fig. 75: a longitudinal section. Fig. 76: a transverse section. Figures 77 and 78 show this alloy in the solution-annealed/air-cooled condition. Figure 79 illustrates a heat-treated, cold-rolled structure. Vilella's reagent. 1000×

Fig. 77 17-7PH stainless, solution annealed at 1065 °C (1950 °F), then held 10 min at 955 °C (1750 °F), air cooled, held 8 h at −75 °C (−100 °F), held 1 h at 510 °C (950 °F), and air cooled. Ferrite stringers in a martensitic matrix. Vilella's reagent. 1000×

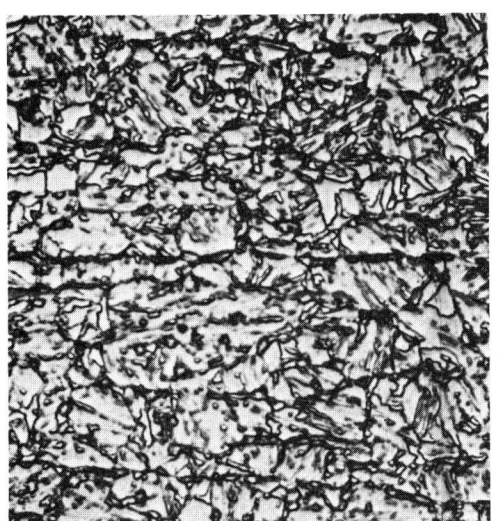

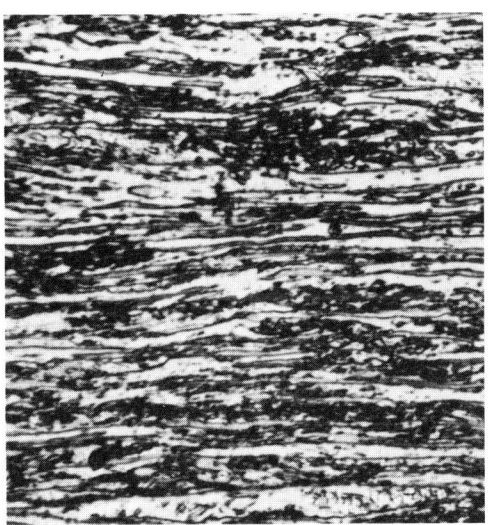

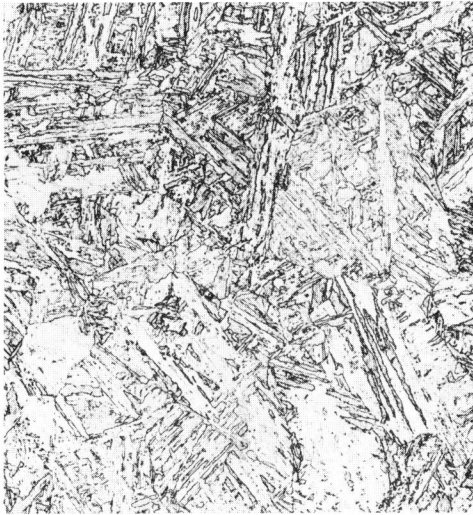

Fig. 78 Same as Fig. 77, but reheated and held 1.5 h at 760 °C (1400 °F), air cooled to 15 °C (60 °F) and held 30 min, heated to 565 °C (1050 °F) and held 1.5 h, and air cooled. The structure is the same as Fig. 77, but this steel is more ductile. Vilella's reagent. 1000×

Fig. 79 17-7PH stainless steel, cold rolled at the mill, then held 1 h at 480 °C (900 °F) and air cooled. Structure is essentially martensite; austenite was transformed by cold rolling. Electrolytic: HNO₃-acetic acid, then 10% aqueous oxalic acid. 1000×

Fig. 80 15-5PH martensitic precipitation-hardenable stainless steel (41 HRC), solution annealed and aged. Structure is tempered martensite. Vilella's reagent. 200×

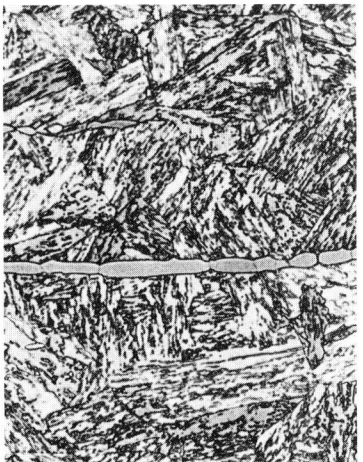

Fig. 81, 82, 83, 84 17-4PH precipitation-hardenable stainless steel, heat treated. The effect of different etchants in revealing the structure, which consists of δ-ferrite stringers in a martensitic matrix. Fig. 81: etched using Fry's reagent. Fig. 82: etched using Vilella's reagent. Fig 83: etched using Marble's reagent. Fig. 84: etched using superpicral. 500×

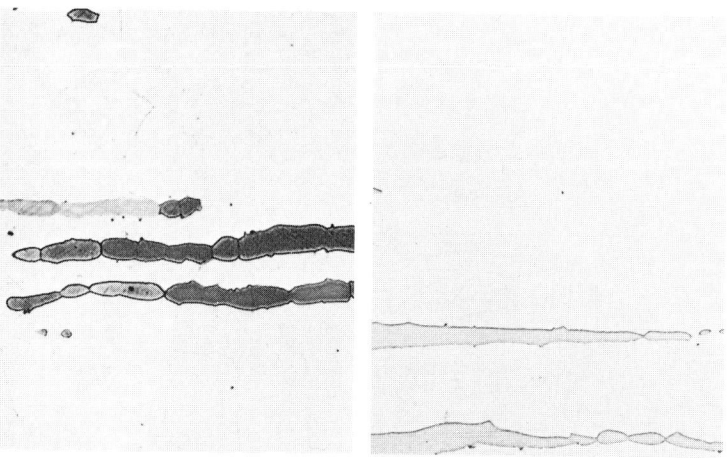

Fig. 85, 86 Same stainless steel as Fig. 81 to 84, etched electrolytically to reveal δ-ferrite stringers. Fig. 85: etched 10 s in 10 N KOH at 2.5 V dc. Fig. 86: etched 21 s in 20% aqueous NaOH at 20 V dc. 500×

Fig. 87 Stainless W in the solution annealed and aged condition; δ-ferrite stringers in tempered martensite elongated in the rolling direction. Superpicral. 500×

Fig. 88 Type 312 duplex stainless steel (250 HV) in the solution annealed and aged condition. Transverse section shows austenite in a matrix of ferrite. Glyceregia. 200×

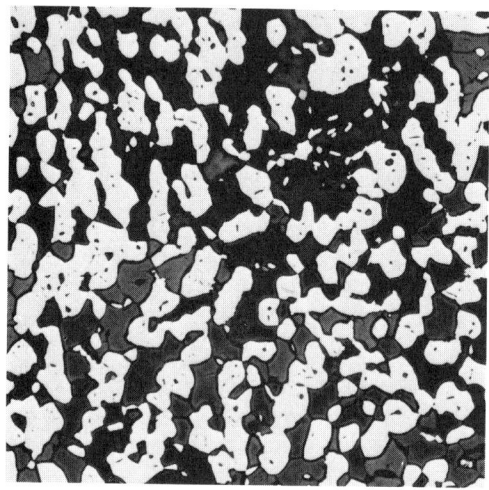

Fig. 89 Same stainless steel and processing as Fig. 88, but tint etched to color the ferrite phase. The austenite remains white. 10% aqueous HCl and 1% aqueous $K_2S_2O_5$. 200×

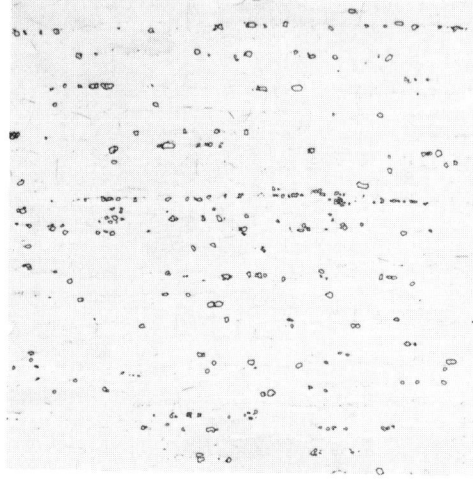

Fig. 90 Proprietary duplex stainless steel (250 HV). The specimen has been etched to reveal carbide phase; the matrix is only faintly visible in this longitudinal section. Vilella's reagent. 200×

Fig. 91 Same duplex stainless steel as in Fig. 90, tint etched. Ferrite in the matrix is colored; austenite is unaffected. 10% aqueous HCl and 1% aqueous $K_2S_2O_5$. 200×

Fig. 92 Photomicrograph of a duplex stainless steel showing elongated austenite islands in the ferrite matrix. The mill-annealed 19.1 mm (0.752 in.) thick plate sample is a longitudinal section etched using 15 mL HCl in 100 mL ethyl alcohol.

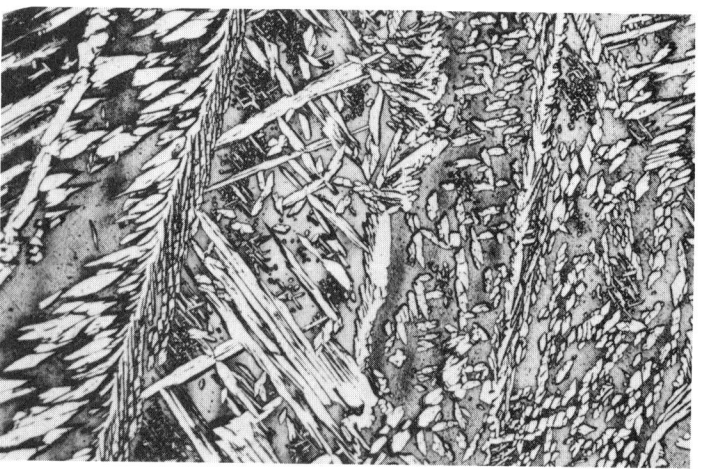

Fig. 93 Photomicrograph of a duplex stainless steel weld obtained using consumables with increased nickel to retain sufficient austenite in the weld. Typical weld metal microstructure for gas metal arc weld in 19.1 mm (0.752 in.) thick plate. The light-etching phase is austenite. The micrograph shows a cross section etched in Groesbeck's reagent. 200×.

Metallography and Microstructures of Cast Stainless Steels

STAINLESS STEEL casting alloys are widely used to resist corrosion by aqueous solutions at or near room temperature and by hot gases and liquids at elevated temperatures to 650 °C (1200 °F). These alloys contain more than 11% Cr and up to 30% Ni. Additional information on the properties and selection of stainless steel casting alloys can be found in the articles "Metallurgy and Properties of Cast Stainless Steels" and "Corrosion of Cast Stainless Steels" in this Volume.

Specimen Preparation

The techniques and equipment used for mounting, grinding, and polishing specimens of stainless steel casting alloys for metallographic examination are similar to those described in the article "Metallographic Practices for Wrought Stainless Steels" in this Volume.

Grinding and Polishing. Coarse grinding is generally performed with 80-, 100-, and 120-grit papers, followed by fine grinding with 240-, 320-, 400-, and 600-grit papers. Rough polishing involves the use of rotating disks covered with napless cloth that is impregnated with pastes of diamond dust or slurries of alumina (Al_2O_3) with 9, 6, and then 3 µm particle sizes. Rotating disks covered with soft cloth of medium to long nap and slurries of 0.3 and 0.5 µm Al_2O_3 are used for fine polishing. Throughout grinding and polishing, care should be exercised to minimize the occurrence of disturbed metal.

Etching of Corrosion-Resistant Grades. The etchants used to delineate the microstructure of corrosion-resistant stainless steel casting alloys are given in Table 1. Also in Table 1, several alloys are listed with the etchants used to reveal their general microstructure or to emphasize a microconstituent of interest, such as ferrite or carbide. The presence of ferrite in the austenitic CF-type alloys improves weldability as well as resistance to intergranular corrosion and stress-corrosion cracking. The distribution of carbide is important, because carbide precipitation at the austenite grain boundaries lessens resistance to intergranular corrosion. Properly solution-treated CF and CG (modified CF alloys containing 3 to 4% Mo) castings have a structure essentially free of precipitated carbide.

The intermetallic σ-phase in austenitic-ferritic alloys is important, because the presence of σ reduces corrosion resistance and imparts ambient-temperature brittleness. Etchants used in detecting σ-phase also are listed in Table 1.

Delineating Etchants for Heat-Resistant Grades. The effects of 19 etchants on 11 Fe-Cr-Ni alloys containing 0.02 to 0.18% C have been documented (Ref 1). Vilella's reagent proved superior for removing disturbed metal (using several etch and polish cycles) and for outlining σ-phase, carbide particles, and ferrite. Etching for 1 min at room temperature was recommended. Vilella's reagent will serve the same purposes when applied to the higher-carbon heat-resistant casting alloys.

Glyceregia, the most widely used delineating etchant, is also used for etch and polish cycles.

Marble's reagent and aqua regia are sometimes used, but to a far lesser extent than glyceregia. Hydrochloric acid (HCl) (50%) is sometimes used for outlining ferrite. It may be followed by etching with a staining etchant. Etchants for delineating the general structure of heat-resistant stainless steel castings are listed in Table 2.

Staining Etchants for Heat-Resistant Grades. Staining etchants, or tint etchants, form films of reaction products on the surface of the specimen. The color of these films depends in part on film thickness, which is controlled by etching time, temperature, and the etchant used. The etchants are generally aqueous solutions of potassium hydroxide (KOH) or sodium hydroxide

Table 1 Compositions and applications of etchants for stainless steel casting alloys:

Etchant	Composition
1. Oxalic acid (electrolytic, 6 V)	10 g oxalic acid, 100 mL H_2O
2. Vilella's reagent 2	5 mL HCl, 1 g picric acid, 100 mL ethanol (95%) or methanol (95%)
3. Kalling's reagent 2	100 mL HCl, 5 g $CuCl_2$ (cupric chloride), 100 mL ethanol (95%)
4. Murakami's reagent (unheated)	1-4 g $K_3Fe(CN)_6$ (potassium ferricyanide), 10 g KOH (or 7 g NaOH), 100 mL H_2O
5. Murakami's reagent (boiling)	Same composition as etchant 4, but heated to boiling temperature for use
6. Chromic acid (electrolytic, 6 V)	10 g CrO_3, 100 mL H_2O
7. 10N potassium hydroxide (electrolytic, 6 V)	560 g KOH (potassium hydroxide) diluted with distilled H_2O to a volume of 1000 mL
8. HCl, HNO_3, acetic acid	15 mL HCl, 10 mL HNO_3, 10 mL acetic acid
9. Acid ferric chloride	Saturated solution of $FeCl_3 \cdot 6H_2O$ in HCl (conc); add few drops HNO_3
10. Glyceregia	10 mL HNO_3, 20-50 mL HCl, 30 mL glycerol
11. Sodium cyanide (electrolytic, 6 V)	10 g NaCN (sodium cyaide), 90 mL H_2O. *Caution:* Avoid skin contact or inhalation of vapors.

Alloy	Condition	Etchants for revealing: General microstructure	Ferrite	Carbide	Sigma phase
CA-6NM	Hardened and tempered(a)	2	3	4	...
CA-15	Hardened and tempered(a)	2 or 9	3	4	...
CB-7CU-1	Solution treated(b)	2	2	...	...
CD-4MCu	Solution treated(b)	1, 2, or 6	...	...	2, then 7
CE-30	As-cast	2	3	4	2, then 7; or 11
CF-3	Solution treated(c)	7	3	1, 4	2, then 7
CF-3M	Solution treated(c)	8	3	1, 4	2, then 7; or 11
CF-8	Solution treated(d)	7 or 10	3	1, 4	2, then 7
CF-8C	Solution treated(d)	1 or 6	3	1, 4	2, then 7; or 11
CF-8M	Solution treated(d)	9	3	1, 4	2, then 7
CF-20	Solution treated(d)	1	3	1, 4	...
CG-8M	Solution treated(d)	1	3	1, 4	5; or 7, then 11
CN-7M	Solution treated(e)	1 or 6	...	...	...

(a) Heat to 955 °C (1750 °F) min, air cool, and temper at 595 °C (1100 °F) min. (b) Heat to 1040 °C (1900 °F) min, quench in water or oil. (c) Heat to 1040 °C (1900 °F) min, rapid cool. (d) Heat to 1040 °C (1900 °F) min, water quench. (e) Heat to 1120 °C (2050 °F) min, water quench.

Table 2 Etchants for microscopic examination of Fe-Cr-Ni heat-resistant casting alloys

Etchant	Composition	Comments
Etchants for delineating general structure		
Aqua regia	20 mL HNO₃ and 60 mL HCl	Immerse specimen.
Glyceregia	10 mL HNO₃, 20-50 mL HCl, 30 mL glycerol	Immerse specimen; use a hood.
Hydrochloric acid (50%)	50 mL HCl and 50 mL H₂O	Outlines ferrite; immerse specimen.
Marble's reagent	10 g CuSO₄ (copper sulfate), 50 mL HCl, 50 mL H₂O	Immerse specimen.
Vilella's reagent	1 g picric acid, 5 mL HCl, 100 mL ethanol	Immerse specimen.
Kalling's reagent	1.5 g CuCl₂ (copper chloride), 33 mL ethanol, 33 mL H₂O, 33 mL HCl	Immerse or swab specimen.
Kalling's reagent 2	5 g CuCl₂, 100 mL ethanol, 100 mL HCl	Same as above
HCl, ethanol, CuCl₂, H₂O₂	35 mL HCl, 65 mL ethanol, 1 g CuCl₂, 7 drops 30% H₂O₂	Same as above
HCl, ethanol, H₂O₂	35 mL HCl, 65 mL ethanol, 7 drops 30% H₂O₂	Same as above
HCl, methanol, CuCl₂	2 g CuCl₂, 40 mL HCl, 40-80 mL methanol	Same as above
HCl, methanol, FeCl₃	5 g FeCl₃ (ferric chloride), 15 mL HCl, 60 mL methanol	Same as above
Etchants for staining or film-forming		
Alkaline hydrogen peroxide	25 mL NH₄OH, 50 mL 3% H₂O₂, 25 mL H₂O	Ordinarily used after a delineating etchant; immerse specimen
Alkaline potassium ferricyanide	10 g K₃Fe(CN)₆, 10 g NaOH, 100 mL H₂O	Same as above
Alkaline potassium permanganate	4 g NaOH, 10 g KMnO₄, 85 mL H₂O	Same as above
Alkaline sodium picrate	2 g picric acid, 25 g NaOH, 100 mL H₂O	Same as above
Emmanuel's reagent	30 g K₃Fe(CN)₆, 30 g KOH, 60 g H₂O	Attacks σ phase with little or no effect on carbide particles; immerse specimen
Murakami's reagent	10 g K₃Fe(CN)₆, 10 g KOH, 100 mL H₂O	Stains carbide particles without staining σ phase(a); immerse specimen
Solutions for electrolytic etching		
Ammonium hydroxide	Concentrated NH₄OH	Final electrolytic etch after etching in Vilella's reagent and in 10 N KOH (electrolytic)
Cadmium acetate	10 g cadmium acetate and 100 mL H₂O	Attacks (Cr,Fe)₂₃C₆ carbide particles
Chromic acid	2-10 g CrO₃ and 100 mL H₂O	Outlines carbide particles; extracts σ phase
HCl	5-10 mL HCl and 100 mL H₂O	Use at 3 V, 2-10 s.
HCl and CrO₃	1 g CrO₃ and 140 mL HCl	Add HCl to CrO₃; use under hood at 3 V, 2-10 s.
HNO₃	50 mL HNO₃ and 50 mL H₂O	Use at 2 V.
H₃PO₄	4-12 mL H₃PO₄ and 100 mL H₂O	Use at 1-8 V, 5-10 s.
Lead acetate (2 N)	38 g Pb(C₂H₃O₂)₂ · 3H₂O and distilled H₂O to make 100 mL	Stains austenite, then σ phase, then carbide particles; 1.5 V for 30 s
Oxalic acid	10 g oxalic acid and 100 mL H₂O	Outlines carbide and σ; 6 V, 1 to 5 s
Potassium hydroxide (1 N)	5.6 g KOH and 100 mL H₂O	Blackens σ phase without outlining other phases; 1.5 V for 1 s
Potassium hydroxide (10 N)	56 g KOH and 100 mL H₂O	Intermediate etch between Vilella's and NH₄OH (electrolytic)
Sodium cyanide(b)	10 g NaCN and 100 mL H₂O	Used after glyceregia; outlines carbide particles, stains σ phase; use at 0.16 A/cm² (1 A/in.²) for 1-5 s, under hood

(a) Sometimes σ phase is stained. Behavior must be established on a given composition. (b) Use extreme caution; avoid skin contact, ingestion, or inhalation of vapors.

(NaOH) with an oxidizing agent added. Picrates, potassium permanganate (KMnO₄), hydrogen peroxide (H₂O₂), and ferricyanides are used as oxidizing agents. Table 2 lists etchants for staining or tint etching of heat-resistant castings.

Murakami's reagent, which contains KOH with potassium ferricyanide [K₃Fe(CN)₆] as the oxidizing agent, is a versatile staining etchant. By staining in different tints, it permits differentiation of several types of carbide and σ-phase. Murakami's reagent is used cold, warm, or boiling to obtain various effects, but it must be used with discrimination. Because the response of the reagent indicates sensitivity to the composition of the phase being stained, a given constituent does not respond identically when it appears in alloys of different composition.

Murakami's reagent has several modifications (Ref 1-3). Emmanuel's version (Ref 2) contains 30 g K₃Fe(CN)₆, 30 g KOH, and 60 mL H₂O. It will attack σ-phase with little effect on carbide particles; Murakami's reagent stains carbide particles, but it does not always stain σ-phase.

Stain films can crack. Crack indications should be checked by repolishing the specimen lightly or by giving it an acid dip to see if the cracks are removed along with the stain. Detailed information on staining (tint) etchants can be found in Ref 4 and in the article "Color Metallography" in Volume 9 of the *ASM Handbook*.

Electrolytic etching, when controlled by an electronic timer, offers precision and reproducibility. The specimen to be etched is usually made the anode; stainless steel, the cathode. The current

can be supplied by one or more dry-cell batteries wired in series to provide outputs of 1.5, 3.0, 4.5, and 6.0 V. Current density will range from less than 0.16 to 2 A/cm² or more (<1 to ≥ 13 A/in.²).

Unmounted specimens are held with stainless steel tongs. If the specimen is mounted in a nonconducting material, the electrical connection can be conveniently made using a brass machine screw that contacts the underside of the specimen through a tapped hole. The electric current at the anode surface promotes oxidation and therefore serves in place of the oxidizing agents that are added to hydroxide solutions.

A study was made of various solutions for electrolytic etching of alloys in which σ-phase is found (Ref 5). The final recommendation was to outline the structure by etching with Vilella's reagent, then to etch electrolytically in 10 N KOH just long enough to color the σ-phase, but not the carbide particles, and finally to etch electrolytically in concentrated ammonium hydroxide (NH₄OH).

In a laboratory (Ref 6, 7) where the Fe-Cr-Ni alloys were investigated, glyceregia was preferred for revealing general structure, followed by electrolytic etching in 10% sodium cyanide (NaCN) at a current density of 0.16 A/cm² (1 A/in.²). After 1 s, carbide particles were outlined, but σ-phase was not revealed; after 5 s, carbide particles were heavily outlined, and σ-phase was stained blue or tan. Oxalic acid (10%) was also investigated. After 1 to 5 s with a 6 V current, carbides and σ-phase were outlined. Ten percent chromic acid (CrO₃), when used at 2.0 A/cm² (13 A/in.²), extracted σ-phase in 2 s and heavily outlined the carbides. Potassium hydroxide (1 N) used for up to 1 s with a 1.5 V current blackened σ without outlining other phases. Solutions for electrolytic etching of heat-resistant steel castings are listed in Table 2.

Etching Procedure. A safe procedure for etching the Fe-Cr-Ni casting alloys begins by repeating the etch and polish cycle until disturbed metal has been removed. If Vilella's reagent is used, a hood is not needed. Etching should proceed for 15 s in cold 50% HCl to reveal ferrite. This should be repeated if necessary until the ferrite is clearly outlined or until it is evident that there is no ferrite. If the ferrite present contains precipitated carbide particles, it may become rough or mottled. Sigma phase and carbide particles will not be attacked, although s-phase will sometimes become evident because it will appear white and shiny against the faintly stained austenite.

If the HCl etch has indicated the possible presence of ferrite, a magnetic etch should be used (see the section "Identification of Ferrite by Magnetic Etching" in this article). After the etch in HCl or after repolishing and a dip in HCl acid, the specimen is etched in fresh Murakami's reagent for 15 s at room temperature. Following inspection, the etch should be repeated if necessary until carbides are satisfactorily colored. Several specimen fields should be observed and indexed with the microscope so that they can be found again.

Etch in Murakami's reagent (70 °C, or 160 °F, to boiling as indicated by experience) then proceeds for 15 s, after which the specimen is rinsed in water, then alcohol, and then dried in a blast of warm air to ensure uniform staining. As suggested above, several fields should be observed. Further etching may be necessary. Overexposing the specimen to the etchant can make the films too thick and can result in the deposition of small crystals on the surface.

Some of the above steps can be omitted in etching specimens of certain alloys. For example, in etching alloys HN, HP, HT, HU, HW, and HX, it is usually adequate to etch and polish until the disturbed metal has been removed and to etch in hot Murakami's reagent. The specimen should be rinsed in water, then alcohol, and then dried in a warm air blast.

Microstructures of Corrosion-Resistant Grades

The corrosion-resistant stainless steel casting alloys depicted in micrographs in this article (see Fig. 1 to 48) are iron-chromium and Fe-Cr-Ni alloys similar to some of the martensitic, ferritic, and austenitic wrought stainless steels.

The microstructures of stainless steel casting alloys depend primarily on composition and heat treatment. The hardenable ferritic-martensitic alloys such as CA-15 are austenitized, cooled, and tempered, usually to enhance mechanical properties. The nonhardenable austenitic alloys such as CF-8 are solution treated to increase resistance to corrosion. Normal heat treatments for the most widely used casting alloys are given in Table 1. More detailed information on the classification and microstructures of corrosion-resistant stainless steel castings can be found in the article "Metallurgy and Properties of Stainless Steel Castings" in this Volume.

Carbide Precipitation and Corrosion Resistance. The austenitic alloys are widely used to resist attack by corrosive aqueous solutions at or near room temperature and hot gases and liquids at temperatures to 650 °C (1200 °F). In general, the corrosion resistance of these alloys is optimum when all carbide is in solution, a condition achieved by rapid cooling from the solution-treating temperature. However, carbide in solution will precipitate at grain boundaries when these alloys are exposed to temperatures in the sensitizing range, 425 to 870 °C (800 to 1600 °F), which may occur in service or during welding. Unless the alloy is stabilized by adding a preferential carbide former, such as niobium, or carbide formation is inhibited by extra-low carbon content, the precipitation of chromium-containing carbide at grain boundaries will intensify grain-boundary attack.

Carbide-Formation Rate in CF Alloys. When carbon content is 0.03% (CF-3), no carbide forms in 30 min at 425 or 540 °C (800 or 1000 °F), or in 15 min at 870 °C (1600 °F). At 650 °C (1200 °F), carbide forms within 1 min. Carbide also forms at 760 °C (1400 °F). However, at this low carbon level, the corrosion rate based on nitric acid tests is low.

When carbon content is 0.08% (CF-8), carbide forms at 540 °C (1000 °F) after 15 min, but the amount of precipitate is too small to affect corrosion behavior. At 650 °C (1200 °F), carbide is precipitated within 1 min, and corrosion rate and intensity of intergranular attack increase with time at temperature. Carbide also forms at 760 and 870 °C (1400 and 1600 °F). Maximum sensitization is reached in 15 min at 760 °C (1400 °F) and in 5 min at 870 °C (1600 °F), and increased time at temperature *lowers* the corrosion rate.

The behavior of a 0.12% C alloy is similar to that of a 0.08% C alloy. Carbide formation begins at 425 °C (800 °F), however, and is most intense at 650 °C (1200 °F). At 870 °C (1600 °F), corrosion rate declines with time after reaching a maximum.

Molybdenum and Niobium Additions. Molybdenum increases the ferrite content of the structure, providing more opportunity for carbide to form at ferrite-austenite boundaries rather than grain boundaries, resulting in increased resistance to intergranular attack, an effect shared by other ferrite-promoting elements.

Niobium contributes to general corrosion resistance and resistance to intergranular attack. By forming niobium carbide preferentially throughout the sensitizing range, it inhibits depletion of chromium from the austenite matrix and precipitation of chromium-containing carbide at grain boundaries.

Microstructures of Heat-Resistant Grades

Except for alloy 9Cr-1Mo, which is ferritic, the heat-resistant casting alloys illustrated in this article are high-Cr-Ni-Fe alloys that generally are austenitic and nonmagnetic (see Fig. 49 to 105). The austenite in the matrix of these alloys provides useful high-temperature strength (creep strength or creep-rupture strength) if it is adequately reinforced with particles of carbide and nitride. Without carbon and nitride, the austenitic casting alloys would lose their superiority in elevated-temperature strength over the 300-series wrought stainless steels.

Ferrite. The austenite must contain no ferrite to reach maximum strength. The nickel-predominant alloys, such as HN, HT, and HW, are stably austenitic over their entire composition ranges. However, in the chromium-predominant alloys, such as HF, HH, and HK, the formation of ferrite is favored if the ratio of chromium to nickel is near the upper limit of the specification range and conversely is suppressed if the ratio is near the lower limit.

Carbon, nitrogen, and silicon also influence the occurrence of ferrite. Chromium combined in the carbide or nitride phases is not free to influence the effective chromium-to-nickel ratio of the alloy. In this sense, a low level of carbon (or nitrogen) content means a higher effective chromium content aside from the inherent characteristics of low carbon to promote ferrite formation and of high carbon to stabilize austenite. Silicon, like chromium, promotes the formation of ferrite.

Ferrite at elevated temperatures is much weaker than austenite and reduces the creep-rupture strength of the alloy, but it does provide greater ductility as long as it is stable ferrite and not a source of σ-phase. For optimum strength properties, therefore, the composition of each alloy grade should be controlled at the most favorable balance of the available chromium-to-nickel ratio, with these provisions: (a) although high nickel stabilizes austenite, it also makes the alloy vulnerable to sulfidation attack; (b) although high chromium encourages the formation of ferrite, it also improves the resistance to oxidation and sulfidation; and (c) although silicon also favors ferrite, it can contribute significantly to resistance to carburization.

Carbides. Although the carbon content of these casting alloys is markedly higher than that of wrought grades with similar chromium and nickel contents, the compositions are nevertheless hypoeutectic. Upon freezing, dendrites of austenite form first and particles of carbide form last, occupying the interstices between the dendrites. The carbide exists, therefore, as massive chains of particles following the austenite grain boundaries. When the alloys are reheated to service temperatures, additional carbide particles are precipitated from the matrix in very fine form, usually delineating patterns of high-carbon segregation within the austenite.

The predominant carbide phase is most appropriately designated $M_{23}C_6$, in which M (metal) represents the sum of carbide-forming elements involved. A second carbide form, M_6C, is discussed below in relation to the lamellar constituent.

Nitrides contribute to high creep strength of these alloys, as do the carbide phases discussed above.

The lamellar constituent with the appearance of pearlite consists of alternate plates of austenite and carbide. High nitrogen content promotes the formation of this constituent, perhaps by lowering the solubility limit of the austenite for carbon. In the lamellar constituent found in alloys of higher nickel and chromium content than those discussed here, the carbide has been identified as M_6C; therefore, it is likely that the lamellar constituent in the structures illustrated here is also M_6C.

Sigma phase is a hard and brittle compound usually formed from ferrite (but sometimes directly from austenite) between approximately 650 °C (1200 °F) and slightly above 870 °C (1600 °F). It develops most rapidly near 870 °C (1600 °F). In the alloys shown in this article, the compound approximates FeCr but has a variable composition. The addition of silicon promotes the formation of σ, and a ternary composition of 43Fe-43Cr-14Si (at.%) has been suggested. Because σ imparts ambient-temperature brittleness and a loss of creep-rupture strength, its presence is generally undesirable.

Identification of secondary phases in Fe-Cr-Ni alloys may be quite difficult without the appropriate constitutional diagram, a complete chemical analysis, and the thermal history of the alloy. Even with this information, if a phase appears as a fine dustlike or dotlike precipitate or if the amount is so low that x-ray diffraction techniques are ineffective, identification will be uncertain. Fine precipitates, which in these alloys could be one of the carbides or σ-phase, are identified by interference. In identifying σ-phase, the sensitivity of the x-ray diffraction method can be increased somewhat by etching the matrix to make σ stand in relief. However, for these alloys, x-ray diffraction often fails to give positive identification, because the two common types of carbide particles and σ-phase have many diffraction lines that overlap or coincide (Ref 8).

If the constituents are large enough to show staining, they can be distinguished using microscopy. It is helpful to have a series of reference specimens of known composition and heat treatment to be used for confirming response to etching.

The Cr_7C_3 carbide is likely to appear in the higher-carbon Fe-Cr-Ni alloys as spinelike crystals of roughly hexagonal cross section, frequently with a hole in the center. It stains well with Murakami's reagent. In the alloys with 0.20 to 0.75% C, the Cr_7C_3 carbide is likely to be the eutectic carbide.

Although the cubic $(Fe,Cr)_{23}C_6$ carbide usually precipitates as fine particles, it can occur also in the form of grain-boundary films, lamellae, platelets, and spheroids.

The acicular constituent that occurs near creep fractures is likely to be chromium nitride, which originates by diffusion of nitrogen from the atmosphere. The acicular pattern is the result of precipitation on crystallographic planes. However, nitrides are not always acicular, and acicular platelets are not necessarily nitrides; σ-phase and even carbides can exhibit an acicular pattern. A frequently encountered lamellar constituent that resembles pearlite has been identified as an aggregate of austenite with carbonitride, chromium nitride, or chromium carbide. Etching in Murakami's reagent at room temperature for approximately 10 s will stain the carbide but not the nitrides or carbonitrides.

Chi phase may be encountered in Fe-Cr-Ni heat-resistant casting alloys containing molybdenum. Chi phase has a composition similar to that of σ-phase, coexists with σ (Ref 9), and is hard and brittle. Ternary diagrams have been developed at 815 and 900 °C (1500 and 1650 °F) for the Fe-Cr-Mo system that identify χ-phase as containing approximately 18% Cr, 28% Mo, and 54% Fe by weight, approximating Fe_3CrMo (Ref 10). The phase was revealed after brief etching in Vilella's reagent followed by electrolytic etching in concentrated NaOH at 1.5 V. Chi phase was first stained light brown, but after approximately 10 s it developed a blue-gray tint, distinguishing it from σ-phase, which etched brown. A brief electrolytic etch in NaCN will show χ-phase before σ-phase is well defined; further etching extracts χ-phase (Ref 11).

Identification of Ferrite by Magnetic Etching. Because of the low contrast or lack of contrast after etching, it is sometimes difficult to differentiate the ferrite contained in an austenite matrix. A technique using a magnetic field and magnetic particles (smaller than 30 nm) in an organic or an aqueous colloidal suspension can be used in conjunction with the optical microscope to identify ferrite positively. Details of the magnetic etching technique are described in Ref 12 to 16. Additional information can be found in the article "Etching" in Volume 9 of the *ASM Handbook* (see Appendix I: Magnetic Etching on pages 63 to 66).

ACKNOWLEDGMENTS

The information in this article is largely taken from:

- C.R. Bird, Stainless Steel Casting Alloys, *Metallography and Microstructures,* Vol 9, *ASM Handbook* (formerly 9th ed., *Metals Handbook*), ASM International, 1985, p 297-304
- Heat-Resistant Casting Alloys, *Metallography and Microstructures,* Vol 9, *ASM Handbook* (formerly 9th ed., *Metals Handbook*), ASM International, 1985, p 330-350

REFERENCES

1. E.J. Dulis and G.V. Smith, Identification and Mode of Formation and Re-solution of Sigma Phase in Austenitic Chromium-Nickel Steels, in *Symposium on the Nature, Occurrence and Effects of Sigma Phase,* STP 110, ASTM, 1951
2. G.N. Emmanuel, Metallographic Identification of Sigma Phase in a 25-20 Austenitic Alloy, *Met. Prog.,* Vol 52, 1947, p 78-79
3. J.H. Jackson, The Occurrence of the Sigma Phase and Its Effect on Certain Properties of the Cast Fe-Ni-Cr Alloys, in *Symposium on the Nature, Occurrence and Effects of Sigma Phase,* STP 110, ASTM, 1951
4. G.F. Vander Voort, Tint Etching, *Met. Prog.,* Vol 127 (No. 4), March 1985, p 31-41
5. J.J. Gilman, Electrolytic Etching—The Sigma Phase Steels, *Trans. ASM,* Vol 44, 1952, p 566-596
6. L. Dillinger, R.D. Buchheit, and J.L. McCall, Phase Identification Etchants for Iron-Chromium-Nickel Alloys, *Proceedings of the International Metallographic Society,* 1971, p 57-64
7. L. Dillinger and D.B. Roach, The Metallography of Cast Heat-Resistant Alloys, *Proceedings NACE, 26th Conference,* 1970, p 336-365
8. P. Duwez and S.R. Baen, X-Ray Study of the Sigma Phase in Various Alloy Systems, *Symposium on the Nature, Occurrence and Effects of Sigma Phase,* STP 110, ASTM, 1951
9. K.W. Andrews, A New Intermetallic Phase in Alloy Steels, *Nature,* Vol 164, 1949, p 1015
10. J.G. McMullin, S.F. Reiter, and D.G. Ebeling, Equilibrium Structures in Fe-Cr-Mo Alloys, *Trans. ASM,* Vol 46, 1954, p 799-806
11. P.K. Koh, Occurrence of Chi Phase in Molybdenum-Bearing Stainless Steels, *J. Metals,* Vol 5, Section 2, Feb 1953; *Trans. AIME,* Vol 197, 1953, p 339-343
12. H.S. Avery, V.O. Homerberg, and E. Cook, Metallographic Identification of Ferro Magnetic Phases, *Met. Alloys,* Vol 10, 1939, p 353-355
13. H.S. Avery, "Cast Heat-Resistant Alloys for High-Temperature Weldments," Bulletin 143, Welding Research Council, Aug 1969
14. A New Way to Reveal Magnetic Domains at High Magnifications, *Met. Prog.,* Vol 100, Dec 1971, p 82
15. W.C. Elmore, Ferromagnetic Colloid for Studying Magnetic Structures, *Phys. Rev.,* Vol 54, 1938, p 309-310
16. R.J. Gray, "Revealing Ferromagnetic Microstructures with Ferrofluid," Report RNL-TM-3681, Oak Ridge National Laboratory, March 1972

SELECTED REFERENCES

- C.E. Bates and L.C. Tillery, *Atlas of Cast Corrosion-Resistant Alloy Microstructures,* Steel Founders' Society of America, 1985
- L. Dillinger, R.D. Buchheit, J.A. Van Echo, D.B. Roach, and A.M. Hall, *Microstructures of Heat-Resistant Alloys,* Steel Founders' Society of America, 1970

Fig. 1 CA-6NM alloy, normalized 1 h at 1010 °C (1850 °F) and tempered 2 h at 650 °C (1200 °F). Structure consists of tempered martensite. Vilella's reagent. 400×

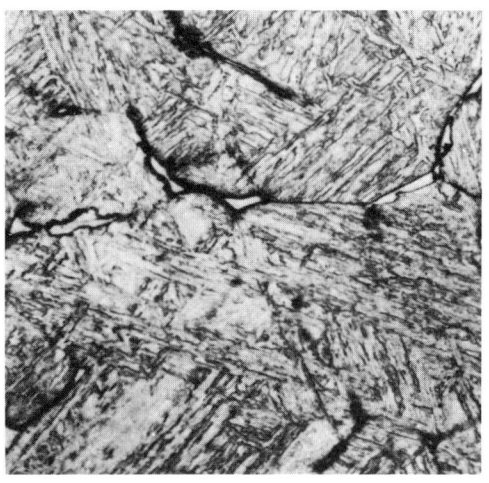

Fig. 2 CA-6NM alloy, 75-mm (3-in.) thick section, as-cast. Cooling rate was very slow (casting was made in a sand mold). Precipitated chromium carbide particles (dark) and ferrite (white) are present at grain boundaries in a matrix of low-carbon martensite. See also Fig. 3. Vilella's reagent. 200×

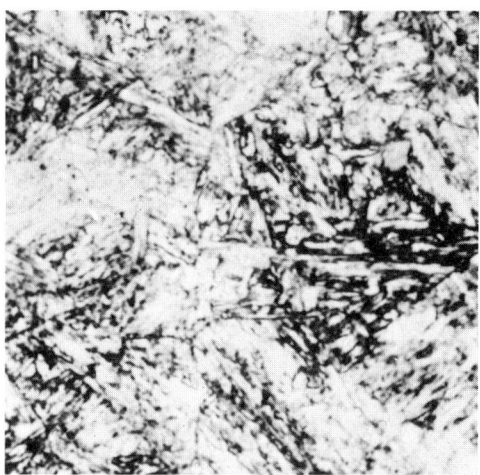

Fig. 3 Same alloy and section thickness as for Fig. 2, but heated to 1040 °C (1900 °F) and held 4 h, air cooled, tempered 5 h at 635 °C (1175 °F). The carbide particles at grain boundaries have dissolved during austenitizing; matrix consists of ferrite-free tempered martensite. Vilella's reagent. 500×

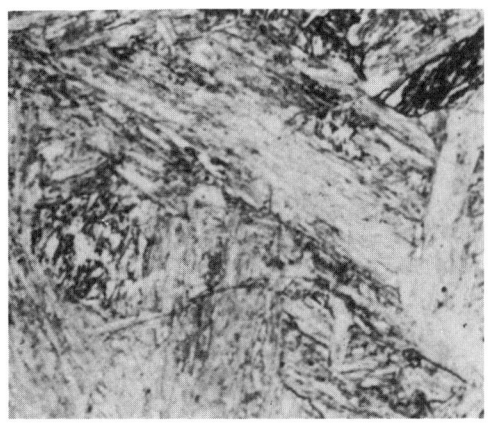

Fig. 4 CA-6NM alloy, 75-mm (3-in.) thick section, heated to 1050 °C (1925 °F) and held 3 h, air cooled, tempered 1 h at 605 °C (1125 °F). Ferrite-free tempered martensite, but coarser than in Fig. 3. See also Fig. 5. Vilella's reagent. 500×

Fig. 5 Same alloy and heat treatment as for Fig. 4, but a section 150-mm (6-in.) thick. Some ferrite (note pool in upper right corner) is present in the tempered martensite matrix. Vilella's reagent. 500×

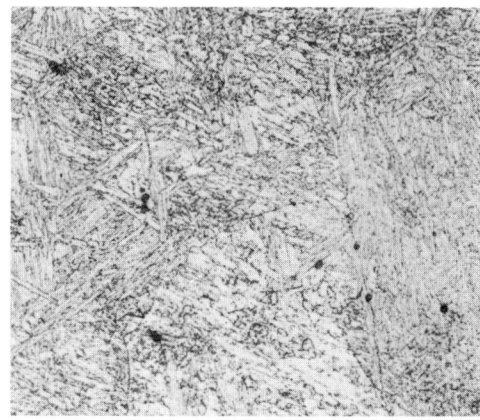

Fig. 6 CA-15 alloy, normalized 4 h at 980 °C (1800 °F) and tempered 6 h at 705 °C (1300 °F). Structure consists of tempered martensite. Vilella's reagent. 400×

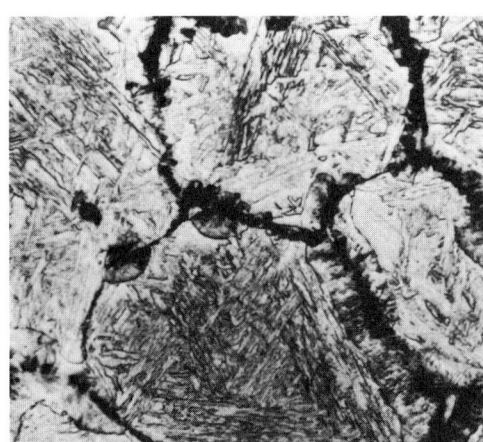

Fig. 7 CA-15 alloy, 75-mm (3-in.) thick section, as-cast. Structure consists of islands of ferrite and dark-etching particles of chromium carbide at prior austenite grain boundaries in a matrix of martensite. See also Fig. 8 and 9. Vilella's reagent. 200×

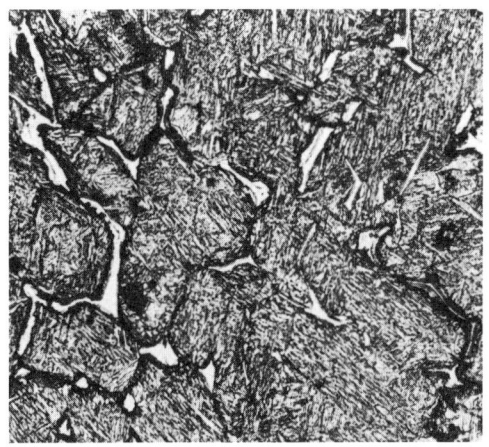

Fig. 8 Same alloy, section thickness, and condition as Fig. 7, but a different casting, etchant, and magnification. Structure consists of islands of ferrite and grain-boundary carbide (dark) in martensite matrix. See Fig. 9. Ferric chloride. 100×

Fig. 9 Same alloy and section thickness as for Fig. 8, but heated to 1040 °C (1900 °F) and held for 3 h, air cooled, tempered at 690 °C (1275 °F) for 4 h. Ferrite islands have blended with the tempered martensite matrix. Ferric chloride. 100×

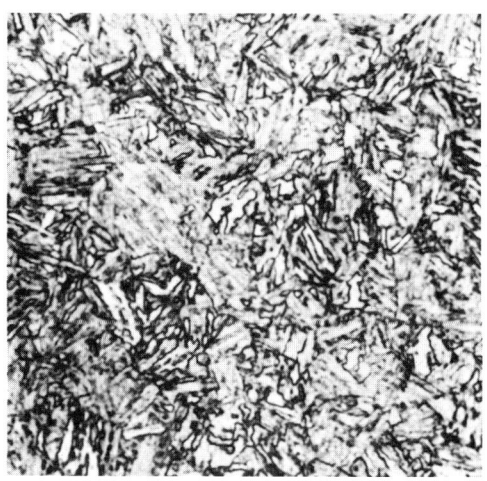

Fig. 10 CA-15 alloy, 75-mm (3-in.) thick section, austenitized at 1010 °C (1850 °F), air cooled, tempered at 675 °C (1250 °F) for 4 h. The structure shows traces of ferrite in a matrix of tempered martensite. See also Fig. 11. Vilella's reagent. 200×

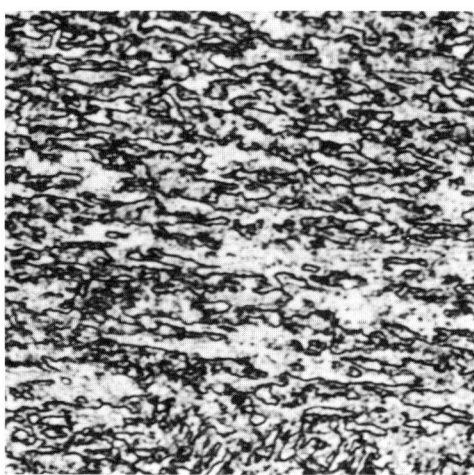

Fig. 11 Same alloy, section thickness, and heat treatment as for Fig. 11, but at a higher magnification to emphasize the traces of ferrite in the tempered martensite matrix. Hardness of casting, 223 HB. Vilella's reagent. 500×

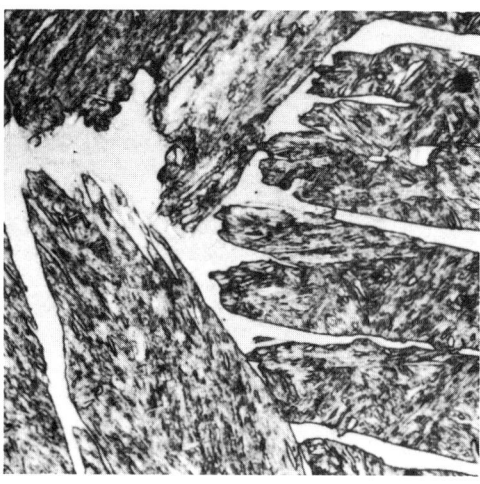

Fig. 12 Same alloy and heat treatment as in Fig. 10, but for a 150-mm (6-in.) thick section, showing the effect of section thickness on structure. Islands of ferrite appear in the matrix of tempered martensite. See also Fig. 13. Vilella's reagent. 200×

Fig. 13 Same alloy, section thickness, and heat treatment as for Fig. 12, but at a higher magnification to reveal dispersed ferrite particles and massive ferrite stringers in the tempered martensite matrix. Vilella's reagent. 500×

Fig. 14 CB-7Cu-1 alloy, as-cast. The structure consists of elongated pools of ferrite (light gray constituent) in a matrix of martensite, which varies in carbon content (as indicated by the response to etching). See also Fig. 15. Vilella's reagent. 500×

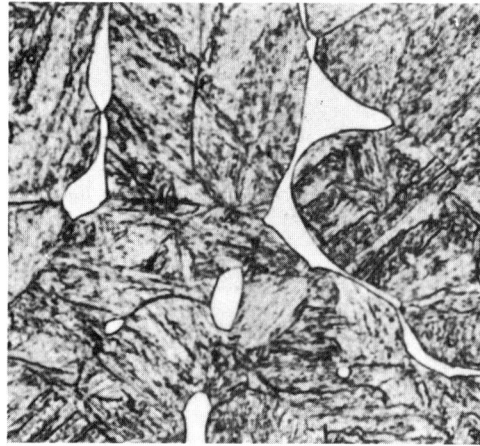

Fig. 15 Same alloy as Fig. 14, but austenitized at 1050 °C (1925 °F) for 1 h and aged at 495 °C (925 °F). The matrix, tempered martensite, still contains ferrite pools (light), but shows less variation in carbon content. Vilella's reagent. 500×

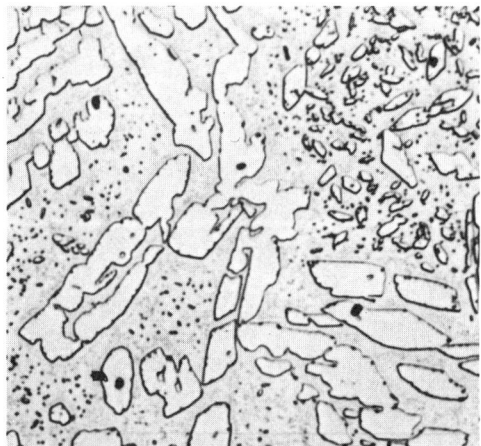

Fig. 16 CD-4MCu alloy, as-cast. Structure: jagged pools and particles of austenite in ferrite. Black specks are nonmetallic inclusions. Electrolytic: 10% CrO₃ at 6 V for 5 to 60 s. 500×

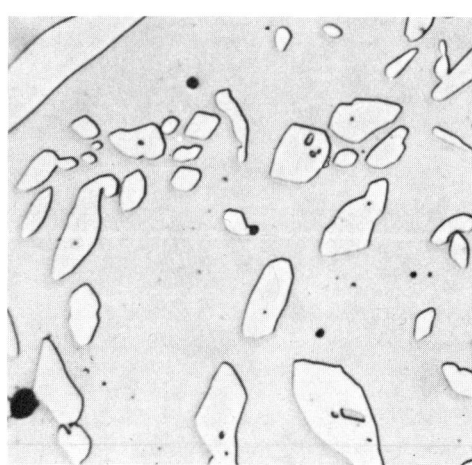

Fig. 17 Same alloy as for Fig. 16, but solution treated at 1065 °C (1950 °F) for 1 h and water quenched. Shows effect of homogenization. Electrolytic: 10% CrO₃ at 6 V for 5 to 60 s. 500×

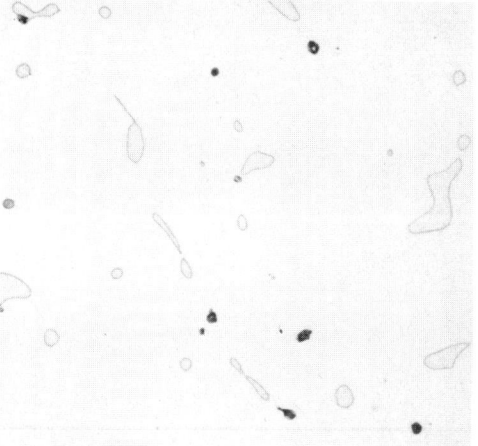

Fig. 18 CF-3 alloy, solution treated 1 h at 1120 °C (2050 °F) and water quenched. Structure is austenite, with ferrite pools and inclusions. See also Fig. 19. Glyceregia. 400×

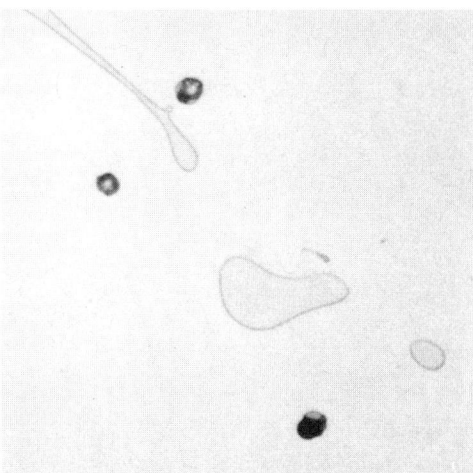

Fig. 19 Same alloy and processing as Fig. 18. Higher magnification of ferrite pools and inclusions in austenite matrix. Glyceregia. 1000×

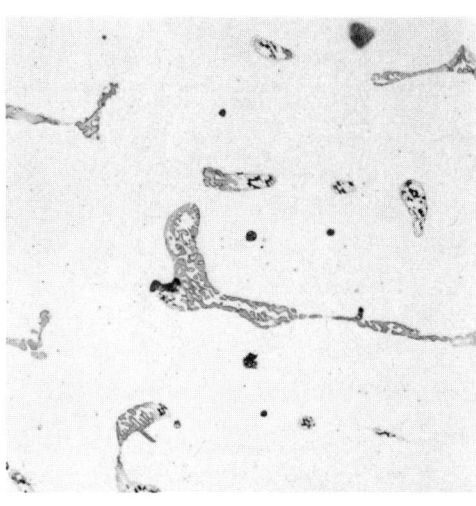

Fig. 20 CF-3M alloy, solution treated 1 h at 1120 °C (2050 °F), water quenched and reheated 100 h at 760 °C (1400 °F). Structure is austenite matrix with some σ-phase present. See also Fig. 21. Electrolytic: NaCN. 400×

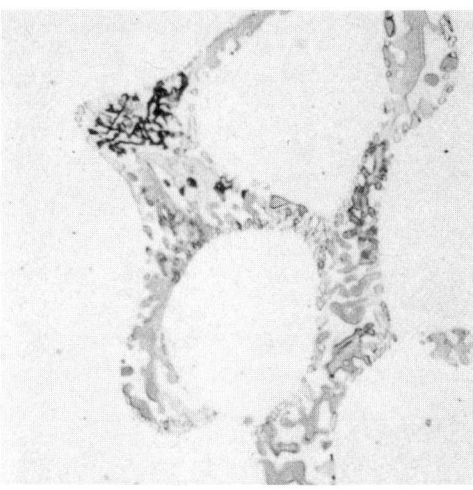

Fig. 21 Same alloy and processing as Fig. 20. Higher magnification of σ-phase in austenite. Electrolytic: NaCN. 1000×

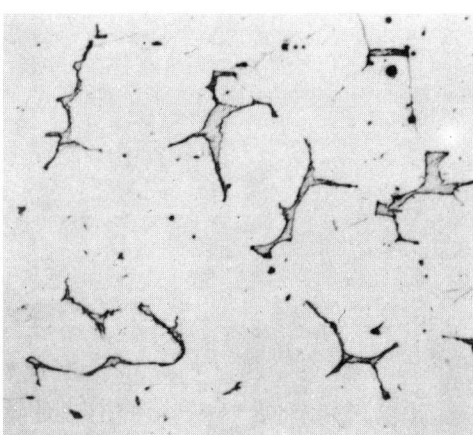

Fig. 22 CF-3 alloy, 150-mm (6-in.) thick section, as-cast, showing dispersed islands of ferrite (5% by volume) and grain-boundary carbide particles in an austenite matrix. See also Fig. 23. HCl, HNO₃, acetic acid. 100×

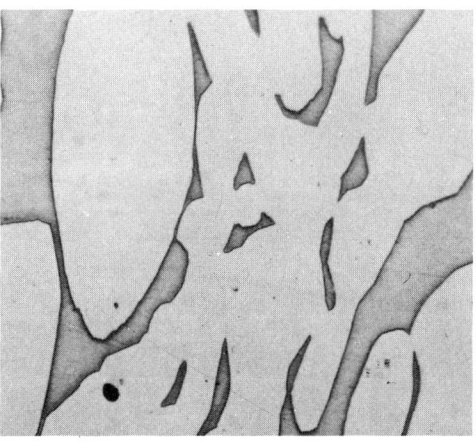

Fig. 23 Same alloy and section thickness as for Fig. 22, but solution treated at 1120 °C (2050 °F) and water quenched. Specimen was taken from center of section. Elongated pools of ferrite in an austenite matrix (light). Electrolytic: 10N KOH. 250×

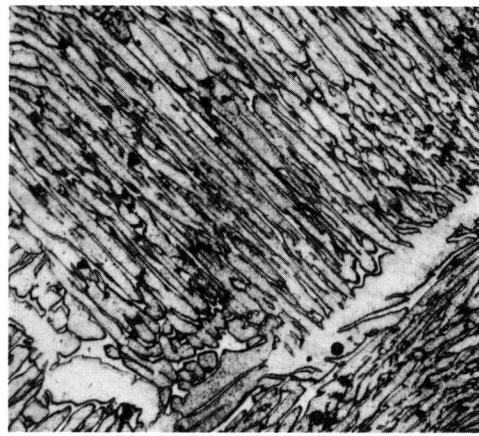

Fig. 24 CF-3M alloy, as-cast. Specimen taken from a 25-mm (1-in.) thick section. Structure consists of a complex network of elongated ferrite in a matrix of austenite. Ferrite content is estimated at 22%. HCl, HNO₃, acetic acid. 100×

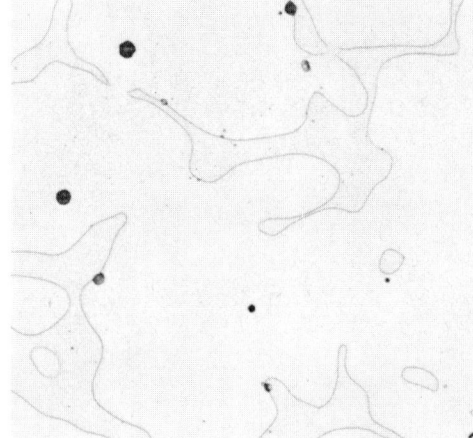

Fig. 25 CF-8M alloy, solution treated 1 h at 1120 °C (2050 °F) and water quenched. Structure is austenite with ferrite and oxide inclusions. See also Fig. 26. Kalling's reagent. 400×

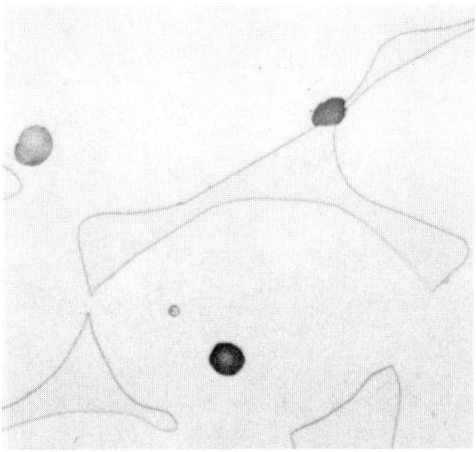

Fig. 26 Same alloy and processing as Fig. 25, but a higher magnification view of the microstructure. Kalling's reagent. 1000×

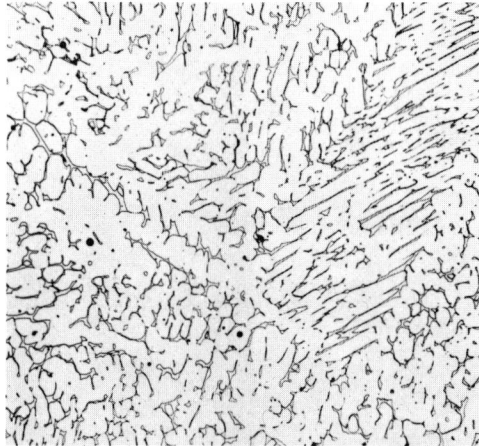

Fig. 27 CF-8 alloy, 25-mm (1-in.) thick section, as sand cast. Structure contains 15 to 20% ferrite in an austenite matrix. Fig. 28 shows the sand cast alloy after solution treatment; Fig. 29 shows another as-cast structure. Electrolytic: oxalic acid. 80×

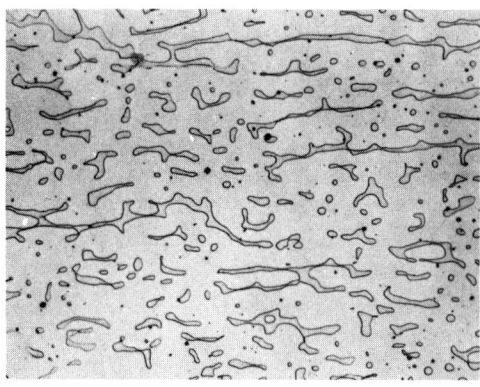

Fig. 28 Same sand cast alloy and section thickness as Fig. 26, but solution treated 1 h at 1120 °C (2050 °F) and water quenched. Structure: pools of ferrite (outlined) in austenite; dendritic pattern has been altered. Glyceregia. 100×

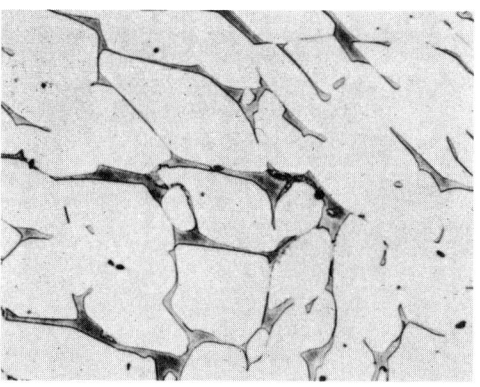

Fig. 29 CF-8 alloy, 25-mm (1-in.) thick section, as-cast. The structure consists of a network of ferrite (dark-etching islands) and some precipitated particles of carbide (dark spots) in a matrix of austenite (light gray background). Electrolytic: KOH; 3 V, 3 s. 200×

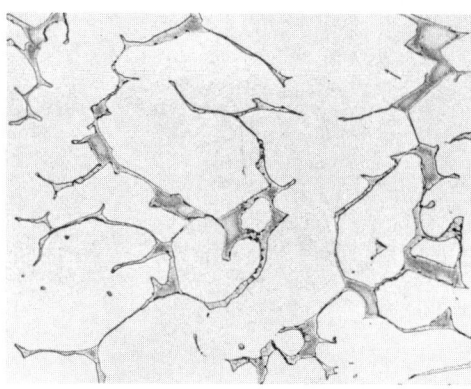

Fig. 30 CF-8 alloy, 150-mm (6-in.) thick section, as-cast. Similar in ferrite distribution to Fig. 29. Note that chromium carbide particles have precipitated at the ferrite-austenite boundaries. Matrix is austenite. See also Fig. 31. Electrolytic: KOH. 200×

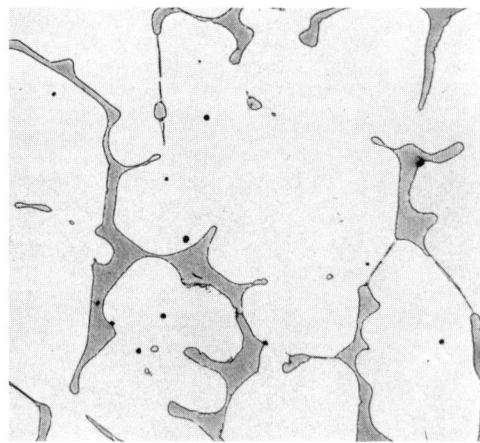

Fig. 31 Same alloy and section thickness as for Fig. 30, but solution treated at 1075 °C (1970 °F) for 6 h and water quenched. Carbide particles have dissolved, but traces of ferrite network remain. Electrolytic: KOH. 300×

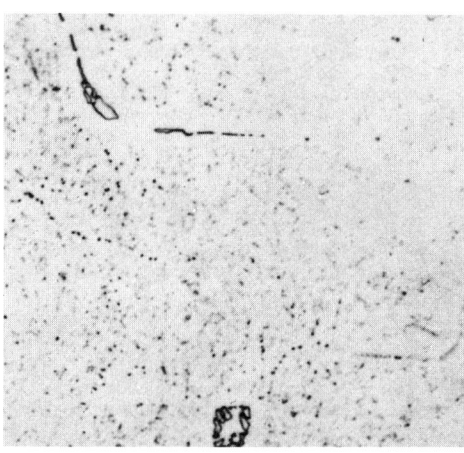

Fig. 32 CF-8C alloy, solution treated at 1120 °C (2050 °F) for 1 h, water quenched, stabilized at 925 °C (1700 °F) for 1 h. Niobium carbide particles (black) precipitated during stabilization treatment at 925 °C (1700 °F). Remaining structure: ferrite in austenite matrix. Electrolytic: 10% CrO₃; 6 V, 5 to 60 s. 500×

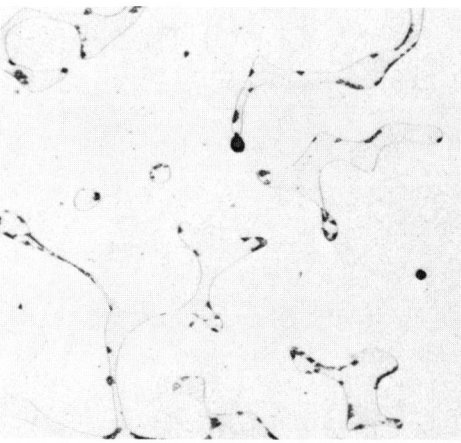

Fig. 33 CF-8M alloy, solution treated 1 h at 1120 °C (2050 °F) and water quenched, sensitized 1 h at 650 °C (1200 °F) and air cooled. Structure is austenite, with ferrite and carbide precipitates along the austenite-ferrite interface. See also Fig. 34. Glyceregia. 400×

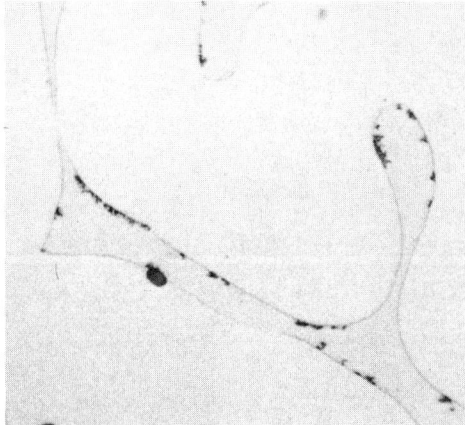

Fig. 34 Same alloy and processing as Fig. 33. Higher magnification of austenite, ferrite and carbide precipitates at interface. Kalling's reagent. 1000×

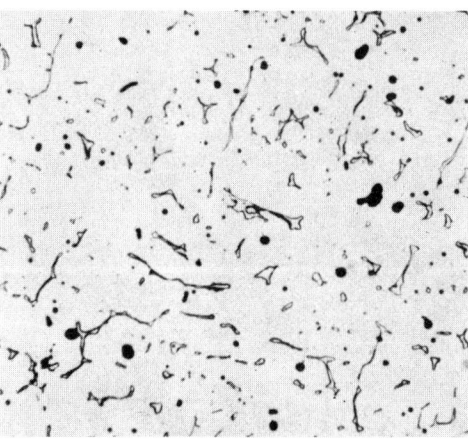

Fig. 35 CF-16F alloy, a 25-mm (1-in.) bar, as-cast. The structure consists of selenide particles (black), precipitated carbide particles, and fine ferrite islands in a matrix of austenite. Dispersed selenide particles of this type improve the machining characteristics of the steel. Electrolytic: oxalic acid. 100×

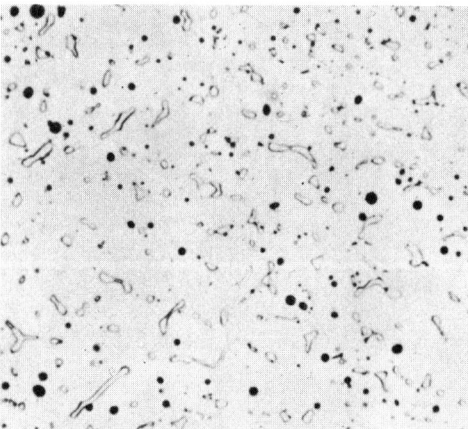

Fig. 36 Same alloy and bar size as for Fig. 35, but solution treated at 1120 °C (2050 °F) and water quenched. The precipitated carbide particles have dissolved, and the ferrite islands have re-formed. Selenide particles (black) were relatively unaffected by the solution treatment. Electrolytic: oxalic acid. 100×

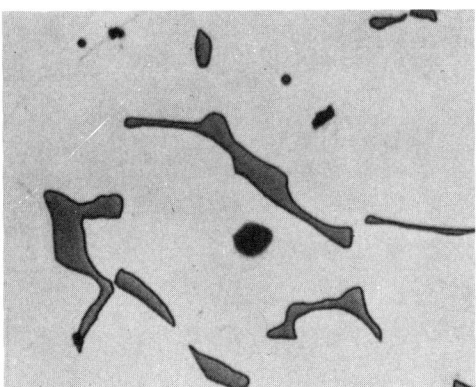

Fig. 37 CF-16F alloy, solution treated at 1120 °C (2050 °F) and water quenched. The structure consists of selenide particles (dark spots) and islands of ferrite in a matrix of austenite. Electrolytic: 10N KOH. 500×

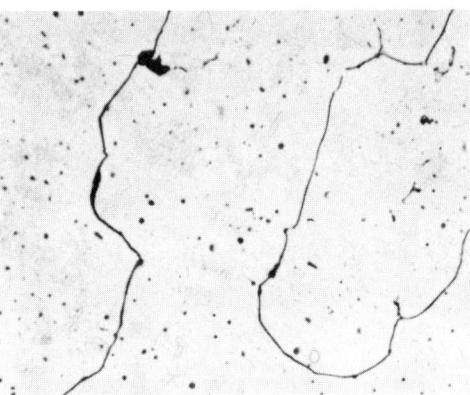

Fig. 38 CF-20 alloy, a 25-mm (1-in.) bar, as-cast. The structure consists of fine particles of carbide dispersed in a matrix of austenite with precipitated carbide particles at grain boundaries. Oxalic acid. 100×

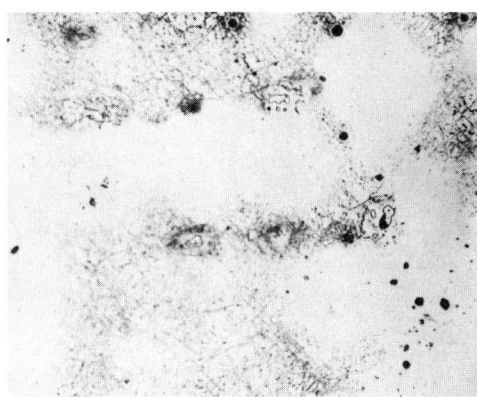

Fig. 39 CK-20 alloy, 25-mm (1-in.) thick section, as-cast. Primary carbide, precipitated carbide, and globular inclusions (silicate and manganese sulfide) in an austenite matrix. See also Fig. 40. Glyceregia. 200×

Fig. 40 Same alloy and section thickness as for Fig. 39, but solution treated at 1120 °C (2050 °F) for 1 h and water quenched. Most precipitated carbide particles have dissolved. Electrolytic: oxalic acid. 100×

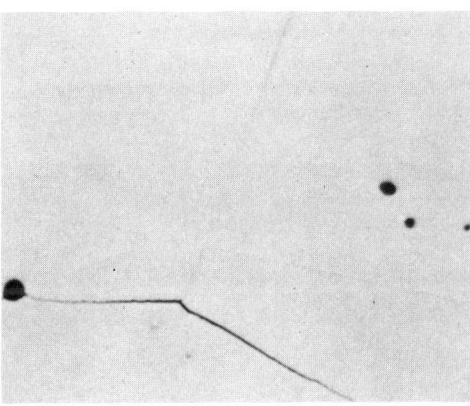

Fig. 41 CN-7M alloy, 25-mm (1-in.) thick section, as-cast. Precipitated chromium carbide ($M_{23}C_6$) at grain boundaries of the austenite matrix. Black dots are inclusions. See also Fig. 42. Electrolytic: 10% CrO_3; 6 V, 5 to 60 s. 500×

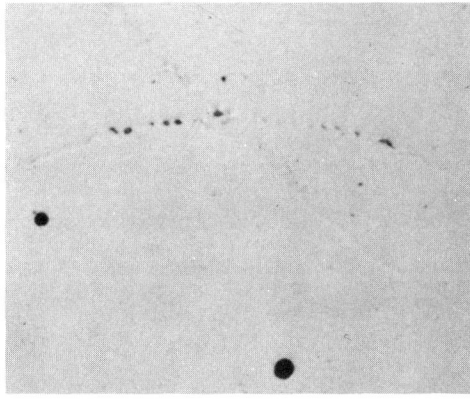

Fig. 42 Same alloy and section thickness as for Fig. 41, but solution treated 1 h at 1120 °C (2050 °F) and water quenched. Structure shows traces of carbide at grain boundaries of the austenite matrix; black dots are inclusions. Electrolytic: 10% CrO_3; 6 V, 5 to 60 s. 500×

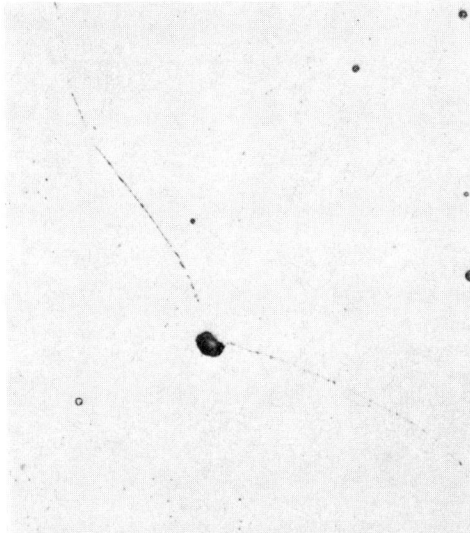

Fig. 43 CN-7M alloy, solution treated 1 h at 1175 °C (2150 °F) and water quenched. Structure consists of austenite with dispersed inclusions. See also Fig. 44. Electrolytic: oxalic acid. 400×

Fig. 44 Same alloy and processing as Fig. 43. Higher magnification of dispersed inclusions in austenite matrix. Electrolytic: oxalic acid. 1000×

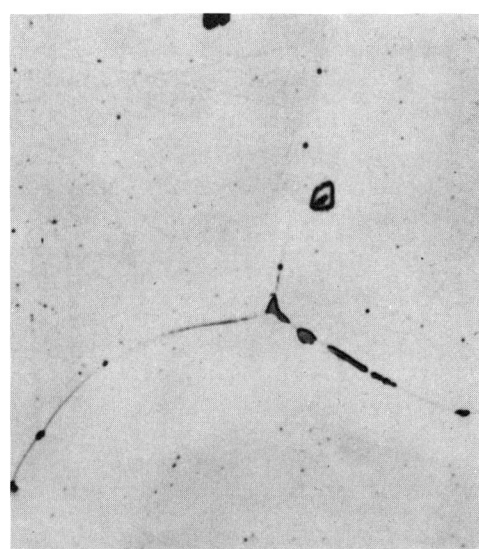

Fig. 45 CN-7M alloy, 75-mm (3-in.) thick section, as-cast. The structure consists of $M_{23}C_6$ carbides (predominantly, chromium carbide) precipitated at the grain boundaries of the austenite matrix. See also Fig. 46. Electrolytic: oxalic acid. 500×

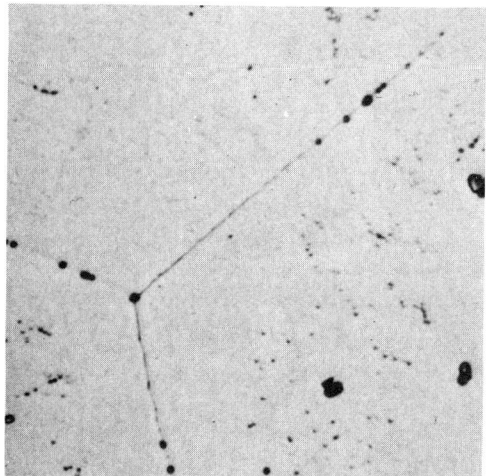

Fig. 46 Same alloy and section thickness as for Fig. 45, but solution treated at 1120 °C (2050 °F) for 1 h and water quenched. Small discrete chromium carbide particles at grain boundaries of the etch-pitted austenite matrix. Electrolytic: oxalic acid. 500×

Fig. 47 440C stainless (Fe-17Cr-0.5Mo-1.0C), investment cast in a 5 mm (0.19 in.) section and annealed. Dendritic structure with interdendritic carbide network. See also Fig. 48. Vilella's reagent. 500×

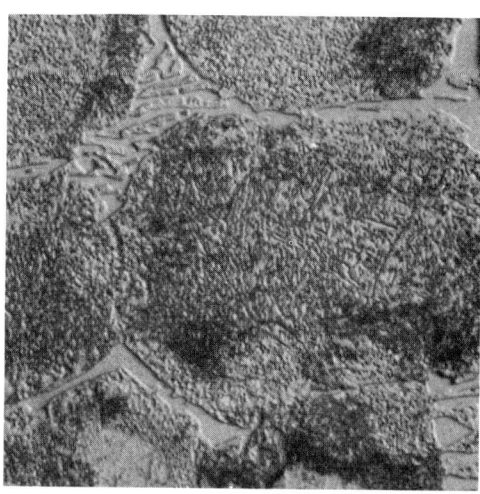

Fig. 48 Same alloy and processing as Fig. 47. Higher magnification view of Fig. 47, showing interdendritic carbide particles and very fine carbide particles in the matrix. Vilella's reagent. 1000×

Fig. 49 9Cr-1Mo alloy, as-sand-cast; center of cast section. Structure consists of a matrix of acicular ferrite containing scattered globular carbide. See also Fig. 50. Vilella's reagent. 200×

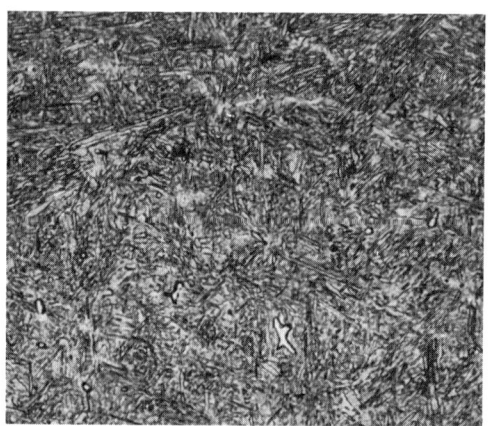

Fig. 50 Same as Fig. 49, but taken from the end of the cast section (near surface) to show the finer structure resulting from the chilling effect of the sand mold. Vilella's reagent. 200×

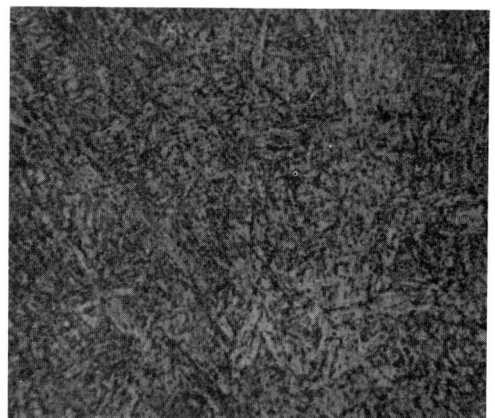

Fig. 51 9Cr-1Mo alloy, air cooled from 1010 °C (1850 °F) and tempered at 690 °C (1275 °F). Structure is a dispersion of spheroidized carbide particles in a ferrite matrix. Vilella's reagent. 600×

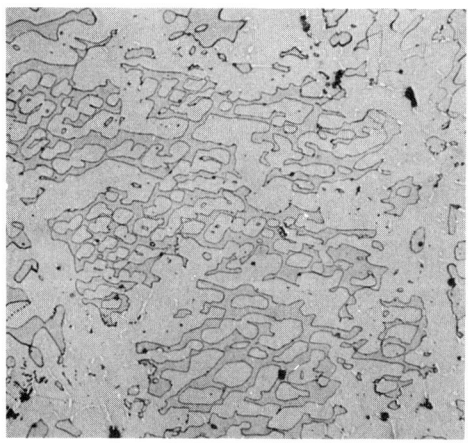

Fig. 52 HE-14 alloy, creep tested at 4.5 MPa (650 psi) and 980 °C (1800 °F) for 336 h. Structure: islands of ferrite (darker gray) in an austenite matrix (lighter gray). White constituent is carbide particles. Compare appearance of carbide in Fig. 53, and of ferrite in Fig. 54. 50% HCl. 100×

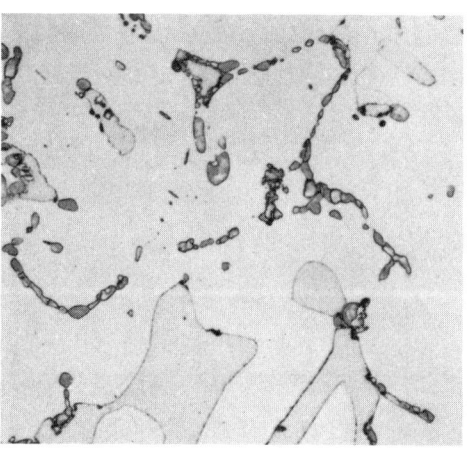

Fig. 53 Same alloy and condition as in Fig. 52, but after a staining second etch that darkened carbide particles, and shown at higher magnification. Structure: carbide particles (darkest gray) and ferrite islands (middle gray) in a matrix of austenite (lightest gray). 50% HCl, then Murakami's reagent. 400×

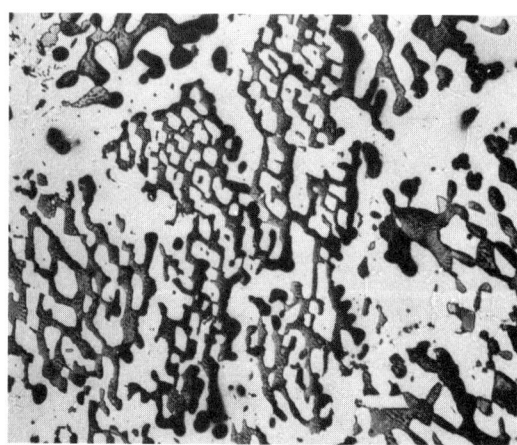

Fig. 54 Same alloy and condition as in Fig. 52, showing the magnetic pattern (dark) on a ferrite as influenced by a vertical magnetic field from a concentric solenoid. Dark areas with diffuse edges and no mosaic pattern indicate subsurface ferrite. Striped pattern shows magnetic domains. 50% HCl. 100×

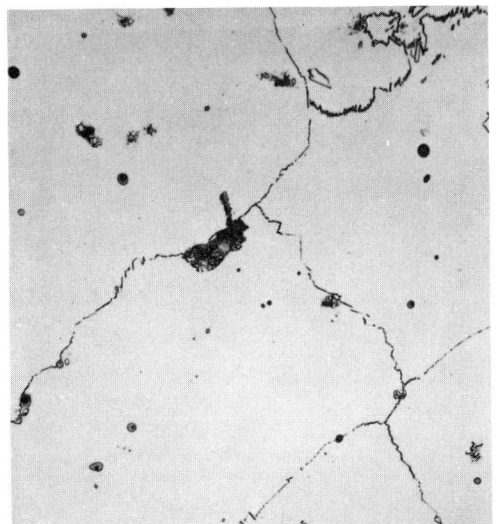

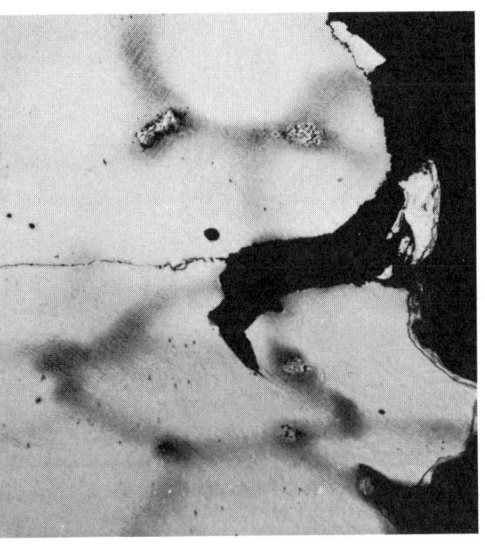

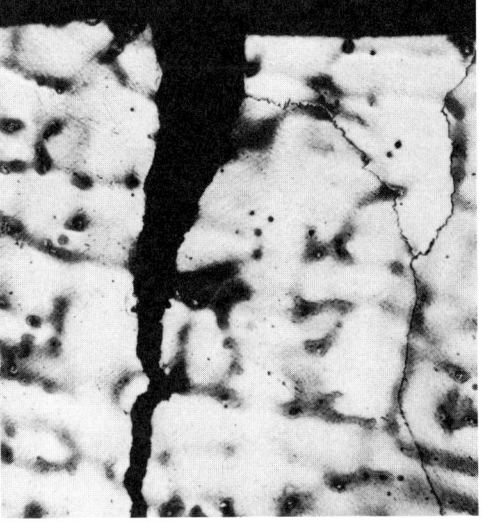

Fig. 55 Alloy HF-33, as-cast. Austenite matrix contains eutectic carbide chains (at grain boundaries) and scattered carbide particles. Note the patch of lamellar constituent at a grain boundary. The globular inclusions are chiefly sulfide and silicate. Glyceregia. 250×

Fig. 56 Structure at fracture in an alloy HF-33 creep-test specimen that fractured after 340 h at 650 °C (1200 °F) and 207 MPa (30 ksi). Cored structure of fine carbide precipitate has begun to form. Eutectic carbide at grain boundaries. See also Fig. 57 and 58. Glyceregia. 250×

Fig. 57 Same fractured creep test specimen as in Fig. 56, but a lower-magnification micrograph of an area at the surface. Cored structure of fine carbide precipitate is more pronounced. A secondary crack has begun to follow carbide at grain boundary. See also Fig. 58. Glyceregia. 100×

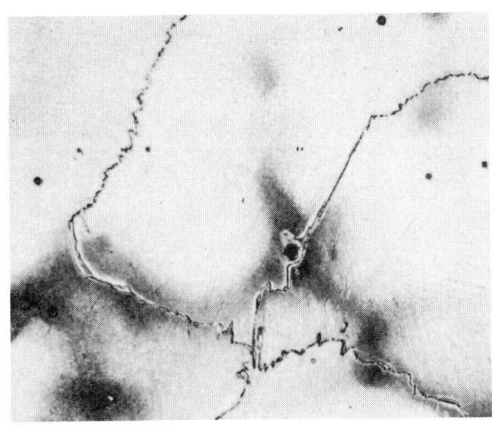

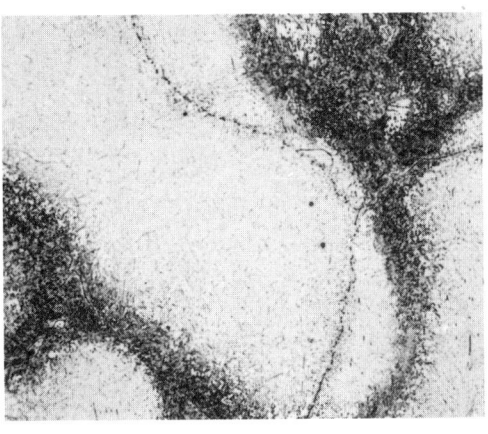

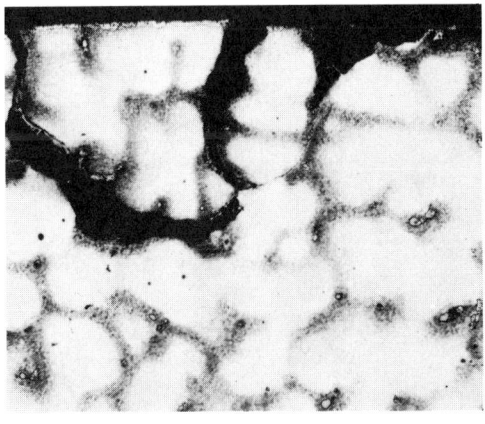

Fig. 58 Same HF-33 creep test specimen as Fig. 56 and 57, but a view of the structure at the interior. Traces of fine carbide precipitation are evident at slip regions in the austenite matrix. Glyceregia. 250×

Fig. 59 Interior of an alloy HF-33 creep-test specimen fractured after 13,690 h at 650 °C (1200 °F) and 110 MPa (16 ksi). Cored structure is more fully developed than in Fig. 56; eutectic carbide is unchanged. See also Fig. 60. Glyceregia. 250×

Fig. 60 Same as Fig. 59, but at the surface of the specimen. The cored structure is clearly more sharply defined than in Fig. 57. Secondary creep-rupture cracks have begun to penetrate along the dendrite boundaries. Glyceregia. 100×

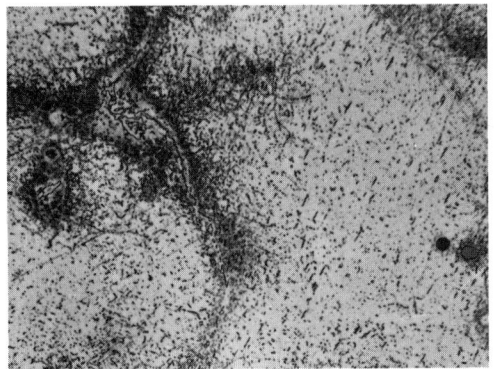

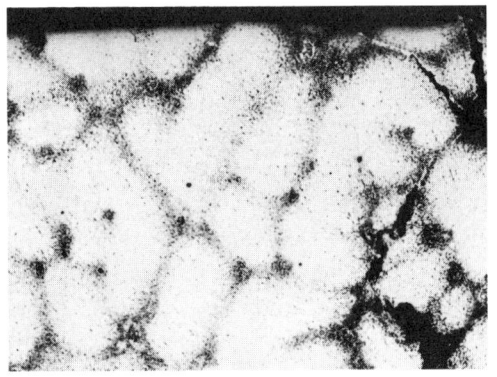

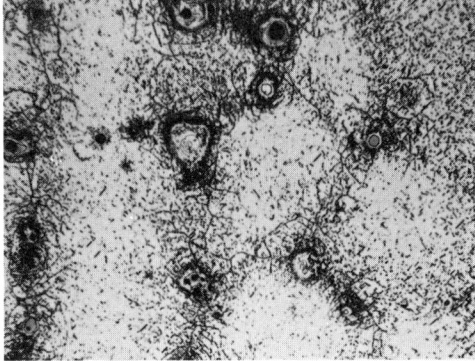

Fig. 61 Interior of an alloy HF-33 creep-test specimen fractured after 13,680 h at 760 °C (1400 °F), 41 MPa (6 ksi). Carbide precipitation is more general than in Fig. 59 (coalescence of precipitates has begun); eutectic carbide is essentially unchanged. Glyceregia. 250×

Fig. 62 Same specimen as in Fig. 61, but showing surface structure, which is also typical of the fracture. Structure shown is similar to that of specimen in Fig. 60, but deeper penetration of creep-rupture cracks following the cored structure is evident. Glyceregia. 100×

Fig. 63 Fracture in alloy HF-33, produced after 1210 h at 870 °C (1600 °F) and 28 MPa (4 ksi). Secondary-carbide precipitation throughout, especially near particles of eutectic carbide and dendrite boundaries; some coalescence. Subgrain boundaries are prominent. Glyceregia. 250×

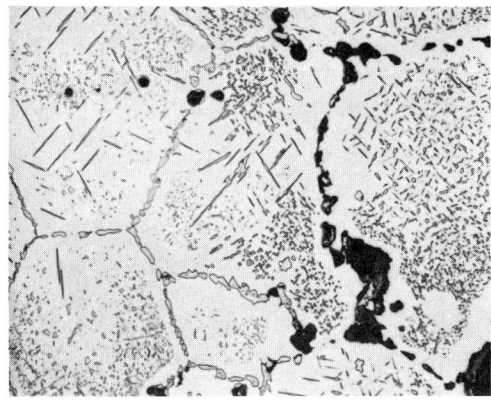

Fig. 64 Fracture in alloy HF-33, produced after 13,300 h at 870 °C (1600 °F) and 17 MPa (2.5 ksi). Eutectic and secondary carbides have coalesced to form a nearly continuous network and paths for subsurface oxidation. Some nitride platelets. See also Fig. 65 and 66. Glyceregia. 250×

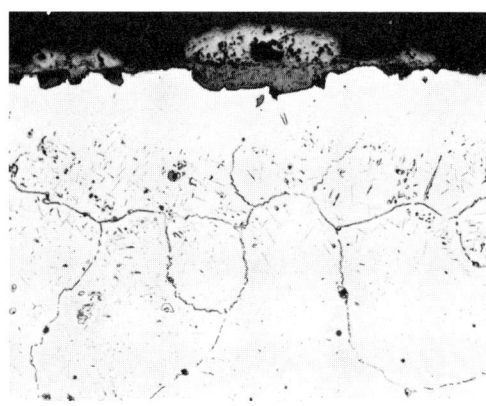

Fig. 65 Same as Fig. 64, but at the surface, where marked decarburization is evident. Carbide at grain boundaries is coarser near the decarburized layer than farther from the surface. Some nitride is visible just below the decarburized zone. See also Fig. 66. Glyceregia. 100×

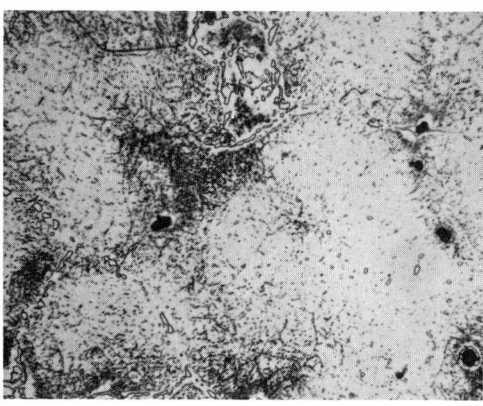

Fig. 66 Same as Fig. 64, but at the interior of the specimen. The cored structure is much less marked than in Fig. 61, and the carbide network is less continuous than in Fig. 64. Some coalescence of carbide has occurred but, again, less than in Fig. 64. Glyceregia. 250×

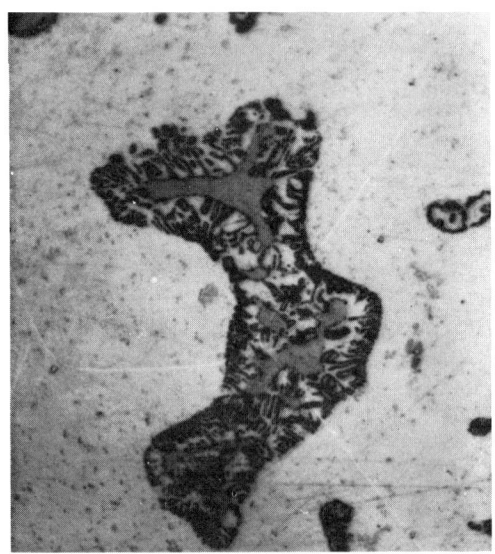

Fig. 67 Complex ferrite-σ-carbide island in austenite matrix of as-cast alloy HF-25. Small, white areas within the margin of the island are ferrite; uniformly gray shapes in the island are σ; dark coalesced particles around and within the island are carbide. 50% HCl, then K₃Fe(CN)₆. 1000×

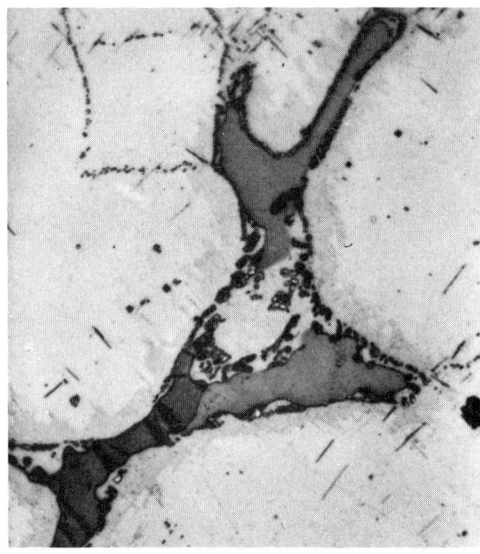

Fig. 68 Ferrite-σ-carbide island in alloy HF-25 creep-test specimen tested for 1002 h at 760 °C (1400 °F) and 21 MPa (3 ksi). Constituents are the same as in Fig. 67. Cracks in lower arm of σ particle were induced by creep (0.10% total deformation). 50% HCl, then K₃Fe(CN)₆. 1000×

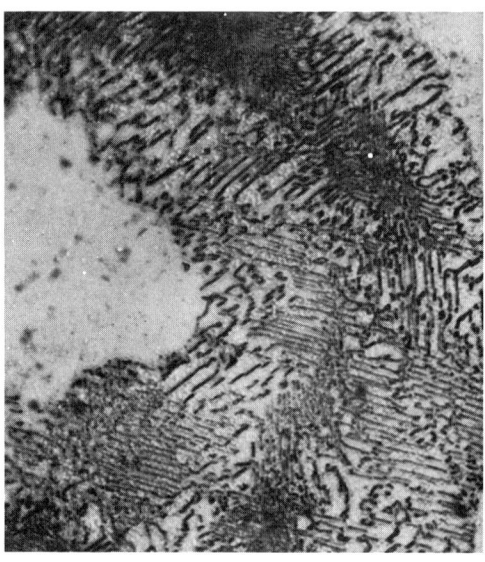

Fig. 69 Lamellar structure in an alloy HF-34 creep-test specimen tested for 1001 h at 650 °C (1200 °F) and 103 MPa (15 ksi). The lamellar constituent resembles pearlite in appearance and consists of alternate plates of austenite and carbide. 50% HCl, then K₃Fe(CN)₆. 1000×

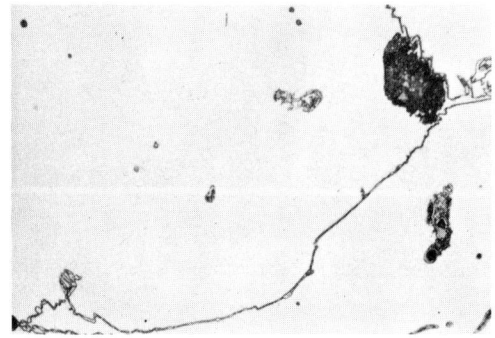

Fig. 70 Alloy HH, as-cast. Austenite matrix grains are surrounded by nearly continuous envelopes of primary carbide. Primary carbide also occurs as interdendritic islands. Patches of lamellae, such as the one at upper right, are not clearly resolved at this magnification. Glyceregia. 250×

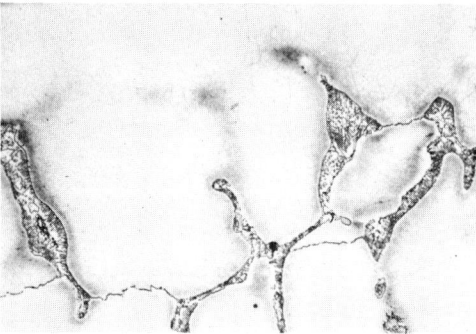

Fig. 70 Interior of an alloy HH creep-test specimen that fractured after 250 h at 650 °C (1200 °F) and 297 MPa (30 ksi). Finely precipitated carbide has begun to delineate the cored structure. Primary carbide is more prominent than in Fig. 70. Glyceregia. 250×

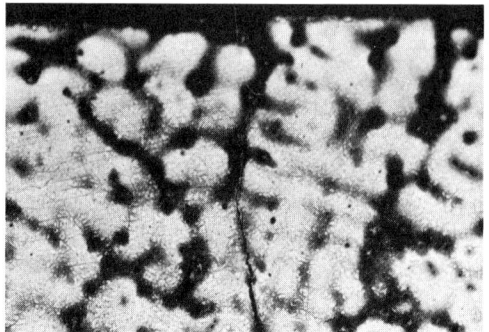

Fig. 72 Surface of an alloy HH creep-test specimen that fractured after 6160 h at 650 °C (1200 °F) and 103 MPa (15 ksi). Carbide precipitates clearly define cored structure. Note secondary creep-rupture fissure along the carbide network. See also Fig. 73. Glyceregia. 100×

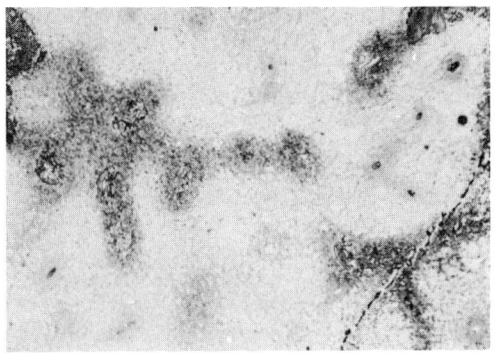

Fig. 73 Interior of the specimen in Fig. 72, shown at a higher magnification. The lamellar patches near grain boundaries are not resolved at this magnification. Little coalescence of primary or secondary carbide has occurred with this combination of time, temperature, and strain. Glyceregia. 250×

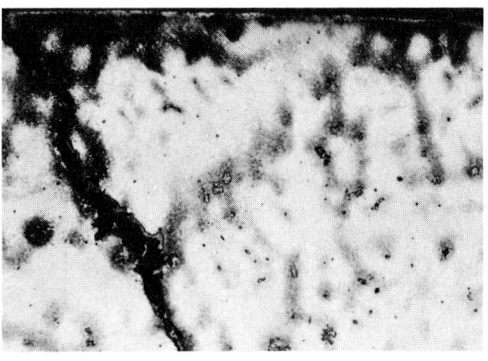

Fig. 74 Surface of an alloy HH creep-test specimen that fractured after 12,500 h at 650 °C (1200 °F), 86 MPa (12.5 ksi). Carbide precipitation is essentially the same as in Fig. 72 and 73 and presumably is complete for this temperature. The deep crack (at left side of micrograph) is evidence of creep damage. Glyceregia. 100×

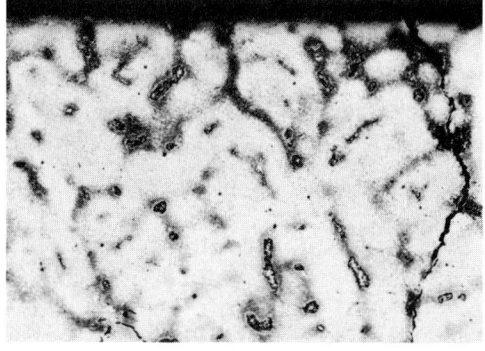

Fig. 75 Surface of an alloy HH creep-test specimen that fractured after 550 h at 760 °C (1400 °F) and 69 MPa (10 ksi). Carbide precipitation defining high-carbon zones of the structure has begun. Note coalesced carbide and creep-rupture fissure. A sodium cyanide etch would reveal some σ. Glyceregia. 100×

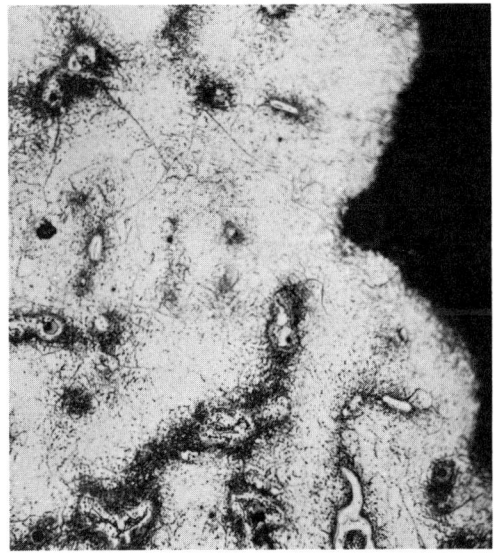

Fig. 76 Fracture surface in an alloy HH creep-test specimen that fractured after 1230 h at 760 °C (1400 °F) and 48 MPa (7 ksi). Similar to structure in Fig. 75 but with more carbide precipitation in matrix. Primary eutectic is unchanged. Glyceregia. 250×

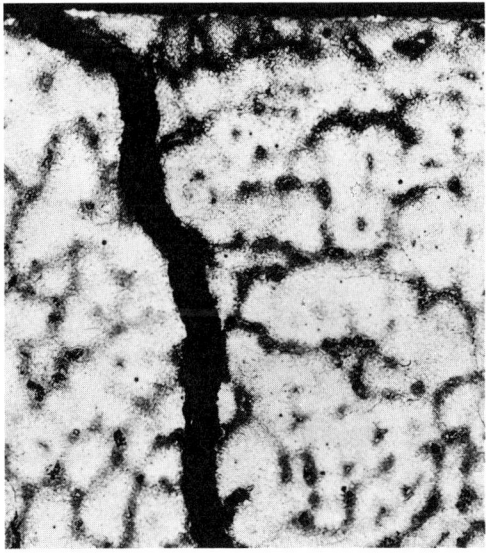

Fig. 77 Structure at surface of the specimen in Fig. 76. Very little decarburization has occurred at the surface. The secondary creep-rupture fissure is much larger than in the specimen in Fig. 75, which fractured in slightly less than half the time at the same temperature. Glyceregia. 100×

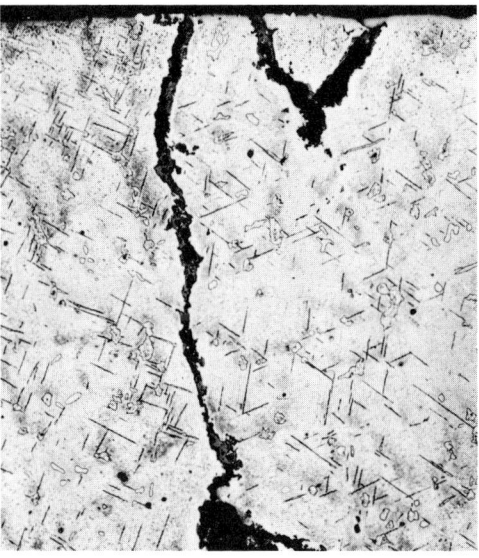

Fig. 78 Surface of an alloy HH creep-test specimen fractured after 10,270 h at 760 °C (1400 °F), 28 MPa (4 ksi). Platelets of σ, irregular islands of σ, some decarburization, and oxide that has formed in a creep-damage crack. Glyceregia. 100×

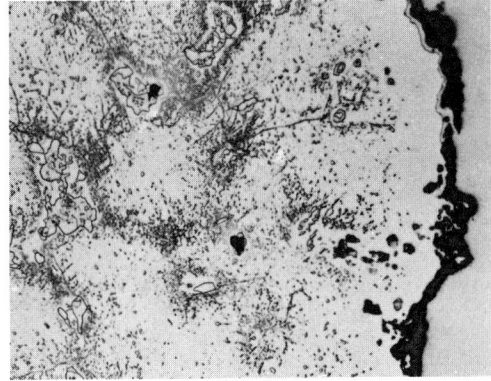

Fig. 79 Alloy HH that fractured after 5260 h at 870 °C (1600 °F) and 21 MPa (3 ksi). Decarburization and oxidation are evident at the fracture surface. No evidence of σ. Glyceregia. 250×

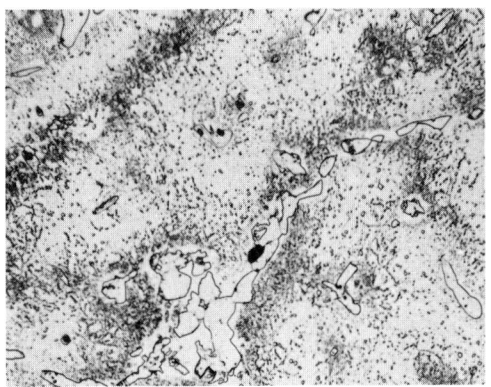

Fig. 80 Fracture structure of an alloy HH specimen that ruptured after 9850 h at 870 °C (1600 °F) and 15 MPa (2.2 ksi). More precipitation and coalescence of carbide than in Fig. 79. A significant amount of σ is present but is not revealed by this etchant. See also Fig. 81. Glyceregia. 250×

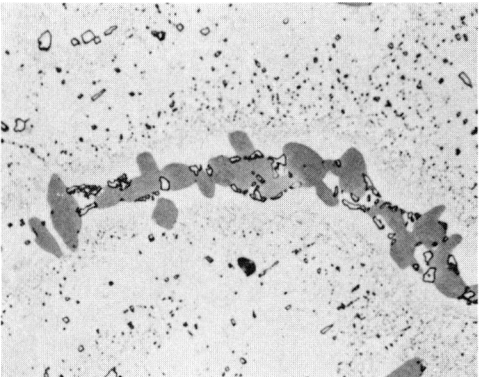

Fig. 81 Same as Fig. 80, but etched electrolytically and shown at higher magnification to reveal σ. Large, gray σ masses are associated with eutectic carbide. Electrolytic etch: 5 s in 10% NaCN. 500×

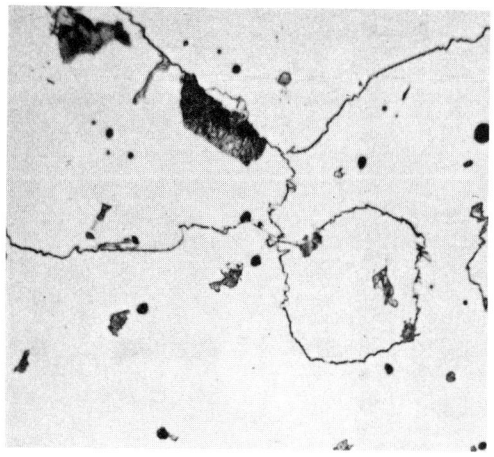

Fig. 82   Alloy HK-35, as-cast. Scattered eutectic carbide in austenite matrix and at grain boundaries; patches of the lamellar constituent also are associated with grain boundaries. No fine particles of carbide have precipitated during freezing and mold cooling. Glyceregia. 250×

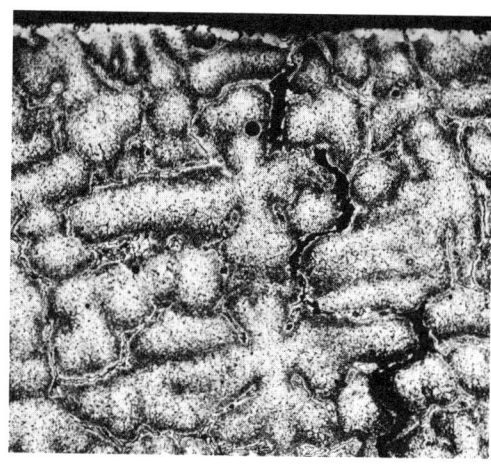

Fig. 83   Interior of alloy HK-44 creep-test specimen fractured after 270 h at 760 °C (1400 °F), 103 MPa (15 ksi). Secondary-carbide precipitation outlines cored structure. Coarse eutectic carbide along dendrite boundaries; carbide precipitates at slip planes. Glyceregia. 250×

Fig. 84   Surface of alloy HK-44 specimen fractured after 6060 h at 760 °C (1400 °F), 62 MPa (9 ksi). Trace of decarburization at surface. More carbide precipitation and coalescence than in Fig. 83. Some σ is present but is not revealed by this etchant. Glyceregia. 100×

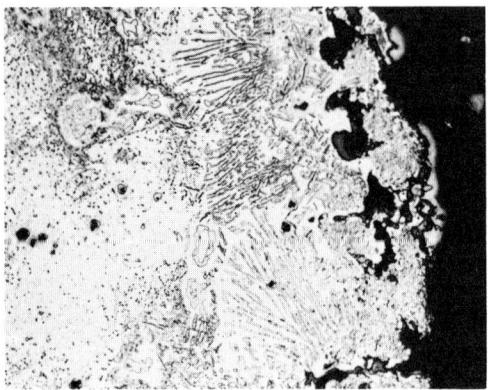

Fig. 85   Alloy HK-35 specimen fractured after 2120 h at 870 °C (1600 °F), 31 MPa (4.5 ksi). Lamellar constituent along fracture with nitride platelets (not fully resolved) adjacent to it. Glyceregia. 250×

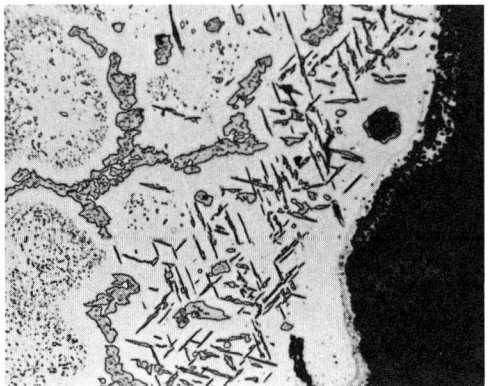

Fig. 86   Fracture in an alloy HK-44 specimen that ruptured after 2000 h at 980 °C (1800 °F) and 17 MPa (2.5 ksi). Coarsened eutectic network consists of carbonitride. An area containing many nitride platelets underlies a decarburized zone at the fracture. Glyceregia. 250×

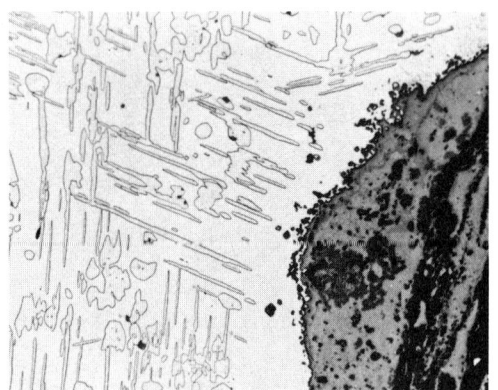

Fig. 87   Fracture in an alloy HK-35 specimen that ruptured after 9230 h at 980 °C (1800 °F) and 9 MPa (1.3 ksi). Carbide particles and nitride platelets have coarsened appreciably. No lamellar constituent. Considerable oxidation and decarburization at the surface. Glyceregia. 250×

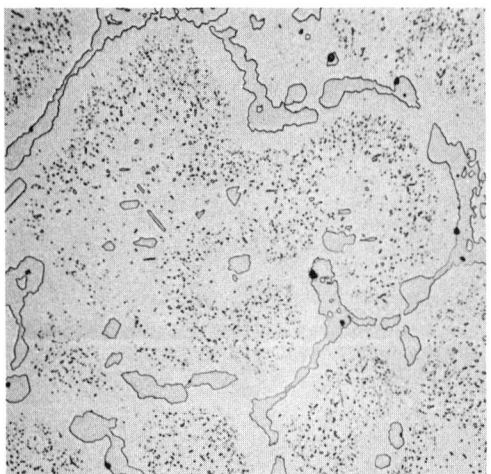

Fig. 88   Interior of an alloy HK-44 specimen that fractured after 26,670 h at 980 °C (1800 °F) and 12 MPa (1.7 ksi). Carbide particles have coarsened. Cored structure has been virtually eliminated. Primary eutectic carbide islands are clearly outlined. Glyceregia. 250×

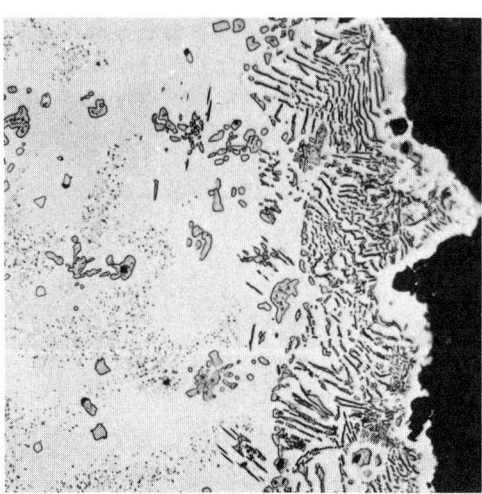

Fig. 89   Fracture in an alloy HK-35 specimen ruptured after 760 h at 1040 °C (1900 °F) and 12 MPa (1.7 ksi). A zone of coarse lamellae borders the fracture, and there is evidence of some decarburization. The gray, internal particles are probably carbonitride. Glyceregia. 250×

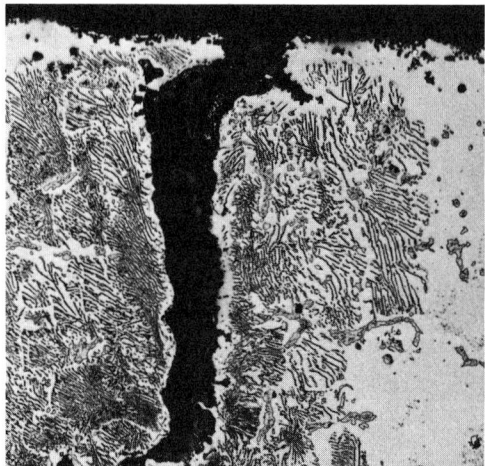

Fig. 90   Same as Fig. 89, but at the surface of the specimen. Note the predominance of the lamellar structure adjacent to the secondary creep-rupture cracks. Some oxidation has occurred at the surface. In other respects, the structure is the same as that in Fig. 89. Glyceregia. 100×

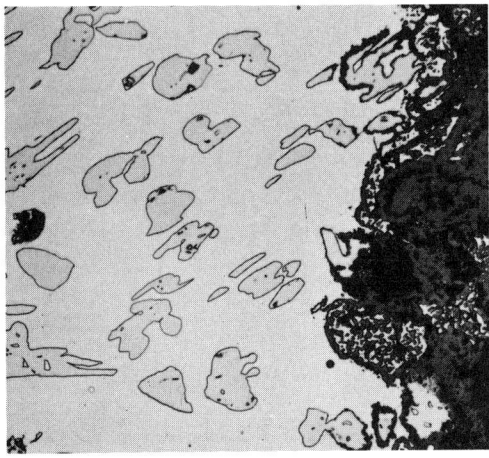

Fig. 91   Fracture in an alloy HK-35 specimen ruptured after 8120 h at 1095 °C (2000 °F), 4.6 MPa (670 psi). Micrograph shows thick platelets, agglomerated carbide particles, subsurface oxide (mixed with metal), and scale. Glyceregia. 250×

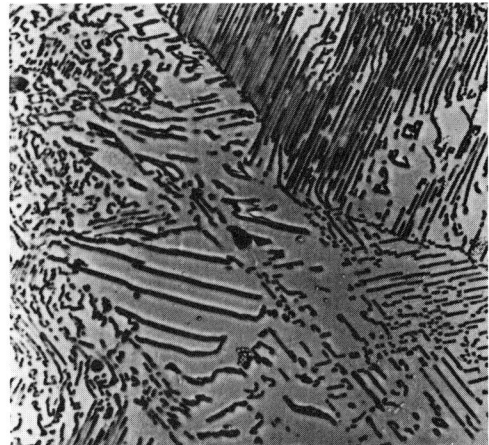

Fig. 92   Structure of alloy HK-28 heated at 1290 °C (2350 °F) for 12 h and furnace cooled. The lamellae (25% of as-cast structure) dissolve at 1290 °C (2350 °F) and are suppressed if water quenched. Slow cooling regenerates them, as seen here. See also Fig. 93. 50% HCl, then K₃Fe(CN)₆. 50×

Fig. 93   Same lamellar structure as in Fig. 92, but shown at higher magnification. All of the carbide of this alloy was dissolved by the heat treatment at 1290 °C (2350 °F); however, during furnace cooling from that temperature, some carbon precipitated as lamellae. 50% HCl, then K₃Fe(CN)₆. 500×

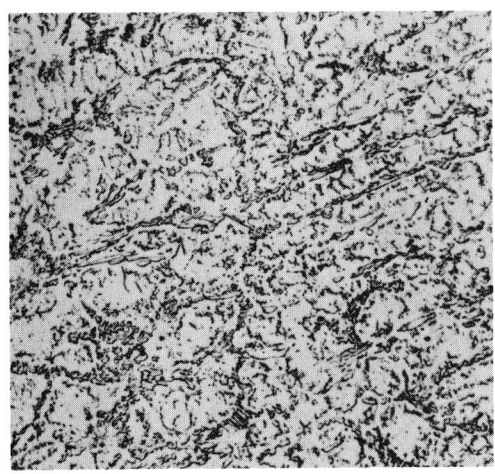

Fig. 94   Alloy HW, as-cast, showing pattern of interdendritic eutectic carbide segregation. See Fig. 95 for same structure at higher magnification and identification of constituents. 5 mL conc HCl and 1 mL conc HNO₃. 50×

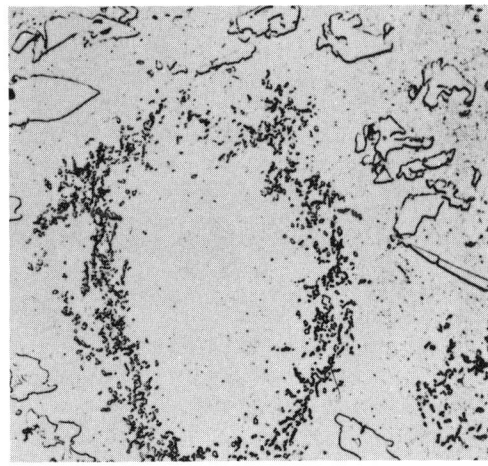

Fig. 95   Same as Fig. 94, except at higher magnification. Austenite matrix containing massive interdendritic eutectic carbide and some small precipitated carbide particles. 5 mL conc HCl and 1 mL conc HNO₃. 500×

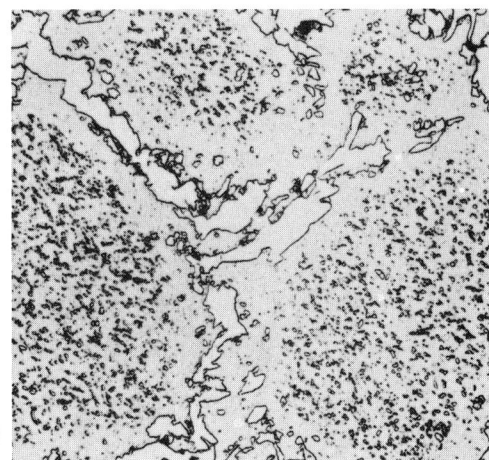

Fig. 96   Alloy HW after aging 48 h at 870 °C (1600 °F). The aging resulted in considerable precipitation of carbide in the austenite matrix. Compare with Fig. 95. 5 mL conc HCl and 1 mL conc HNO₃. 500×

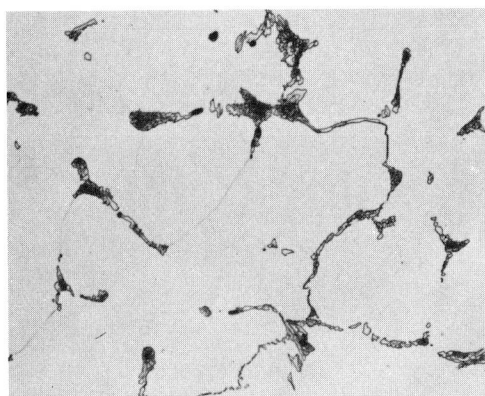

Fig. 97   Alloy HN, as-cast. The microstructure consists of an austenite matrix containing chains of eutectic carbide between the dendrites. Note that in some portions of the eutectic carbide a duplex or lamellar structure is present. Glyceregia. 250×

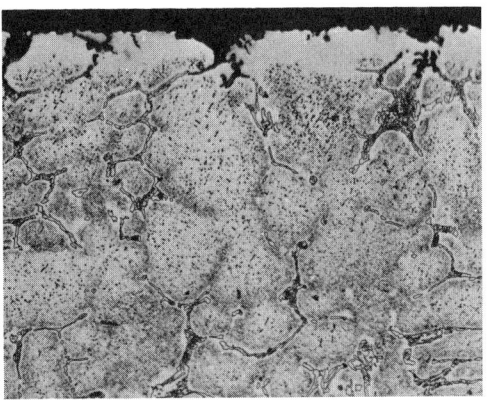

Fig. 98   Surface of an alloy HN specimen fractured after 320 h at 980 °C (1800 °F) and 31 MPa (4.5 ksi). Secondary-carbide precipitates outlining the cored structure and throughout the matrix. Some coalescence has occurred. Surface decarburization is evident. Glyceregia. 100×

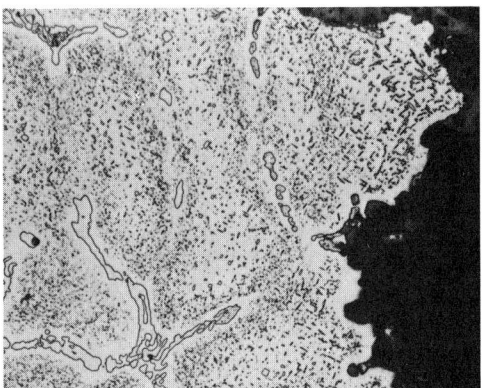

Fig. 99   Fracture in an alloy HN specimen ruptured after 1840 h at 980 °C (1800 °F), 21 MPa (3 ksi). Carbide coalescence has coarsened the structure, producing carbide-depleted zones along eutectic networks. Some platelets are present near the fracture surface. Glyceregia. 250×

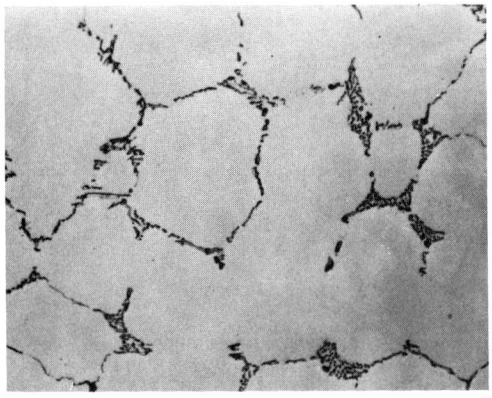

Fig. 100 Alloy HT-44, as cast. The austenite matrix contains a complex network of eutectic carbide that outlines the boundaries of the original dendrites. Note that the larger patches of primary carbide have a lamellar structure. Compare with Fig. 104. K₃Fe(CN)₆. 250×

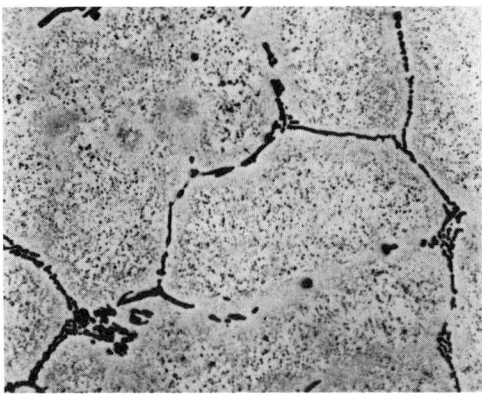

Fig. 101 Interior of alloy HT-44 after creep-testing 1005 h at 760 °C (1400 °F) and 41 MPa (6 ksi). General precipitation of the fine carbide has occurred, with some coarsening of particles. Slight carbide depletion along the eutectic network. See also Fig. 102 and 103. K₃Fe(CN)₆. 250×

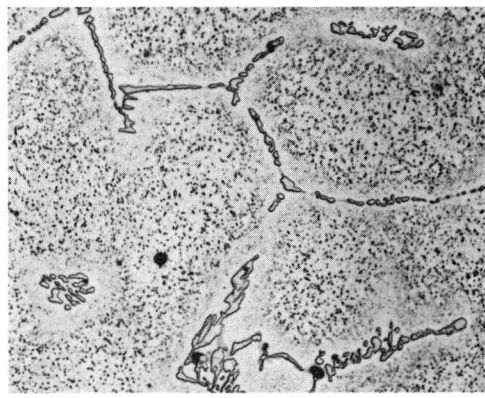

Fig. 102 Interior of an alloy HT-44 specimen after creep-testing 1001 h at 870 °C (1600 °F) and 28 MPa (4 ksi). Eutectic carbide and fine precipitates have coarsened. As in Fig. 101, carbide-depleted zones are visible along eutectic-carbide chains. See also Fig. 103. K₃Fe(CN)₆. 250×

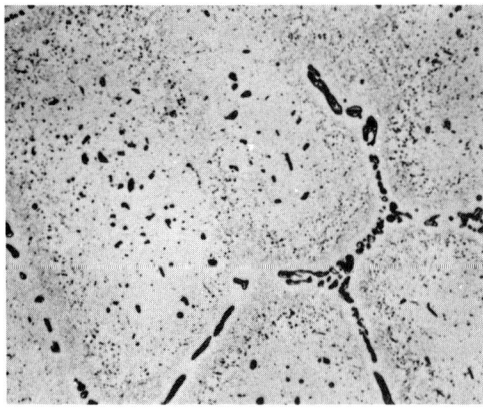

Fig. 103 Interior of alloy HT-44 that was creep tested 1013 h at 980 °C (1800 °F) and 14 MPa (2 ksi). Carbide shows further agglomeration than in Fig. 102, with fewer precipitates remaining. Coalescence has made the eutectic-carbide chains less continuous. K₃Fe(CN)₆. 250×

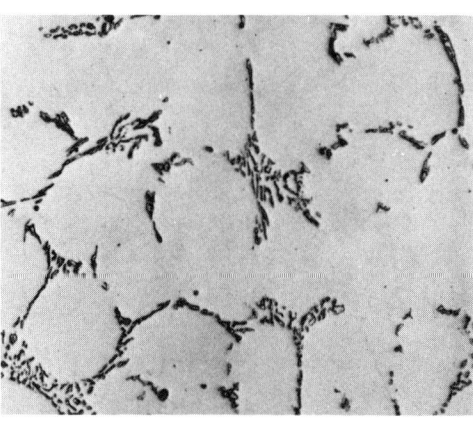

Fig. 104 Alloy HT-57, as-cast. This structure is similar to that shown in Fig. 100 (as-cast alloy HT-44), but the higher carbon content has caused additional primary eutectic carbide to form. Also, the larger carbide shapes are coarser than those in Fig. 100. K₃Fe(CN)₆. 250×

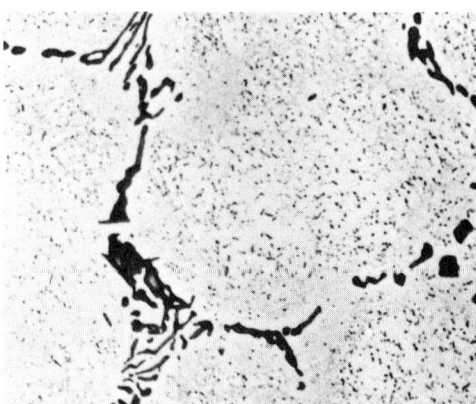

Fig. 105 Interior of alloy HT-56 after creep-testing 1002 h at 760 °C (1400 °F) and 69 MPa (10 ksi). Primary carbide in the eutectic network is more particulated than that in Fig. 101. Many secondary carbide particles have precipitated uniformly within the grains. K₃Fe(CN)₆. 250×

Phase Diagrams

ALLOY PHASE DIAGRAMS are useful to metallurgists, materials engineers, and materials scientists who wish to:

- Develop new alloys for specific applications
- Fabricate these alloys into useful configurations
- Design and control heat treatment procedures for specific alloys that will produce the required mechanical, physical, and microstructural properties
- Solve problems that arise with specific alloys in their performance in commercial applications, thus improving product predictability

The use of phase diagrams allows research, development, and production to be done more efficiently and cost-effectively.

In the area of alloy development, phase diagrams have proved invaluable for:

- Tailoring existing alloys to avoid overdesign in current applications
- Designing improved alloys for existing and new applications (e.g., superferritic stainless steels containing up to 30% Cr, 4% Mo, and 2% Ni for improved pitting and crevice corrosion resistance)
- Designing special alloys for special applications (e.g., cobalt-containing austenitic stainless steels with improved erosion-corrosion resistance for use in hydroelectric power plants)

- Developing alternative alloys or alloys with substitute alloying elements to replace those containing scarce, expensive, hazardous, or "critical" alloying elements (e.g., type 200 austenitic stainless steels alloyed with manganese and nitrogen, both austenite-stabilizing elements, to replace nickel)

Alloy phase diagrams are used in processing to:

- Select proper parameters for working ingots, blooms, and billets
- Find causes and cures for microporosity and cracks in castings and welds
- Control solution heat treating to prevent damage caused by incipient melting
- Develop new processing technology

In the area of performance, phase diagrams indicate which phases are thermodynamically stable in an alloy and can be expected to be present over a long time when the part is subjected to a particular temperature (e.g., type 409 martensitic stainless steels used in an automotive exhaust system). Phase diagrams also are consulted by metallurgists who are attacking service problems such as pitting and intergranular corrosion, hydrogen damage, and hot corrosion.

In a majority of the more widely used commercial alloys, the allowable composition range encompasses only a small portion of the relevant phase diagram. The nonequilibrium conditions that are usually encountered in practice, however,

necessitate the knowledge of a much greater portion of the diagram. Therefore, a thorough understanding of alloy phase diagrams will be of great help to a metallurgist expected to solve problems in any of the areas mentioned above. For more detailed information on the principles and applications associated with phase diagrams, see the article "Introduction to Alloy Phase Diagrams" in Volume 3 of the *ASM Handbook.*

Because this Volume is designed to be used mainly by engineers to solve industrial problems, the primary composition scale on the binary and ternary diagrams shown in this article is plotted in weight percent. Atomic percentages are shown as a secondary scale at the top of the diagrams. For the sake of clarity, grid lines are not superimposed on the phase diagrams. However, tick marks are provided along the composition scale as well as the temperature scale, which is shown in degrees Celsius. Magnetic transitions (Curie temperature and Néel temperature) are shown as dot-dashed lines. Dashed lines are used to denote uncertain or speculative boundaries. When an arrowhead appears on a ternary system temperature trough line in a liquidus projection, it indicates the direction of decreasing temperature. Dotted lines on ternary diagrams indicate the limit of the investigated region.

All diagrams presented in this article are for stable equilibrium conditions, except where metastable conditions are indicated.

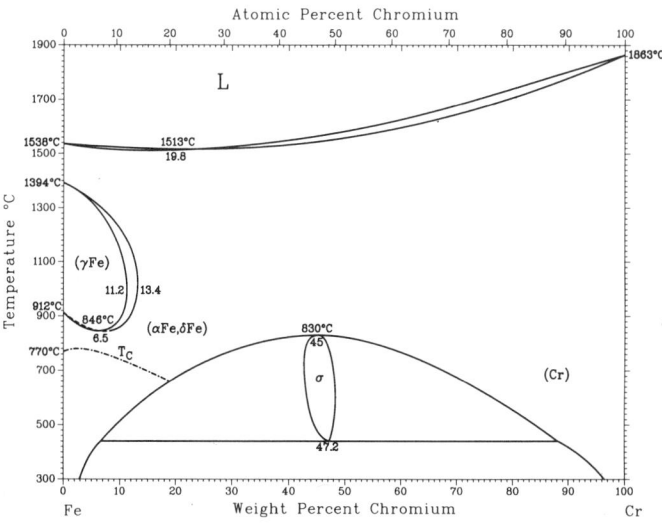

(a)

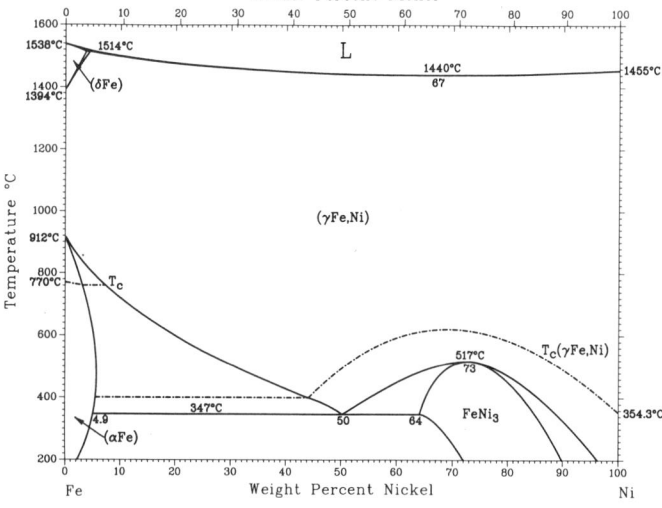

(b)

Fig. 1 Two representative binary iron phase diagrams, showing (a) ferrite stabilization (Fe-Cr) and (b) austenite stabilization (Fe-Ni)

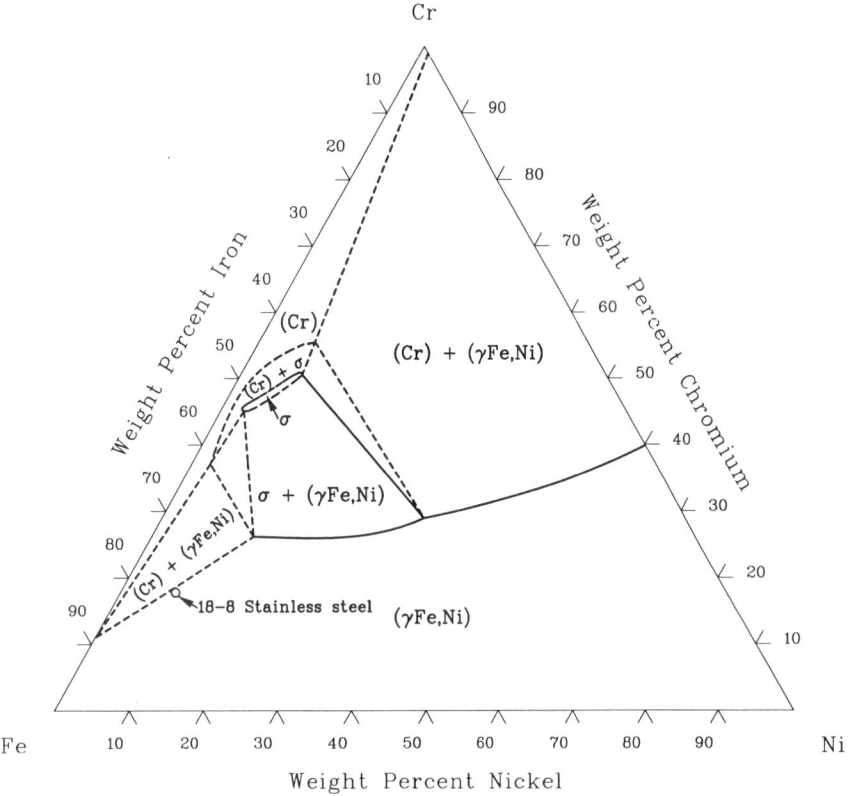

Fig. 2 The isothermal section at 900 °C (1652 °F) of the iron-chromium-nickel ternary phase diagram, showing the nominal composition of 18-8 stainless steel

Binary Alloy Phase Diagrams. Chromium in excess of approximately 11 wt% is required to impart "stainless" characteristics to iron alloys. Enhanced corrosion resistance relative to other steels is attributed to the ability of chromium to produce tightly adherent oxide layers on stainless steel surfaces. The layer is very thin, of the order of only a few atom layers in thickness, and effectively protects or passivates stainless steels in many corrosive environments. Thus, all stainless steels contain large amounts of chromium, and an important starting place to understand the phase relationships and microstructures in stainless steel is the iron-chromium equilibrium phase diagram (Fig. 1a).

All stainless steels contain chromium, a ferrite-stabilizing element, and/or austenite stabilizers such as nickel or manganese. The diagram for the binary iron-chromium system is representative of the effect of a ferrite stabilizer (Fig. 1a). At temperatures just below the solidus, body-centered cubic (bcc) chromium forms a continuous solid solution with bcc (δ) ferrite. At lower temperatures, the γ-iron phase appears on the iron side of the diagram and forms a "loop" extending to about 11.2% Cr. Martensitic alloys containing up to 11.2% Cr and sufficient carbon are hardenable by quenching from temperatures within the loop. (It should be noted that other ferrite-stabilizing elements, such as vanadium and molyb-

denum, act similarly to chromium when alloyed with iron and also form γ-loops.)

At still lower temperatures, the bcc solid solution is again continuous bcc ferrite, but this time with αFe. This continuous bcc phase field confirms that δ-ferrite is the same as α-ferrite. The nonexistence of γ-iron in iron-chromium alloys having more than about 13% Cr, in the absence of carbon, is an important factor in both the hardenable (martensitic) and nonhardenable (ferritic) grades of iron-chromium stainless steels. At these lower temperatures, a material known as σ-phase also appears in different amounts from about 14 to 90% Cr. Sigma is a hard, brittle phase and usually should be avoided in commercial stainless steels. Formation of sigma, however, is time dependent; long periods at elevated temperatures are usually required.

The diagram for the binary iron-nickel system is representative of the effect of an austenite stabilizer (Fig. 1b). The face-centered cubic (fcc) nickel forms a continuous solid solution with fcc (γ) austenite that dominates the diagram, although the α-ferrite phase field extends to about 6% Ni.

In binary iron-nickel alloys, about 30 wt% Ni is required to completely stabilize austenite, partly because close to room temperature the diffusion of iron and nickel is too sluggish to form a mixture of ferrite and austenite. However, if chromium is also present in amounts sufficient for stainless corrosion behavior, much less nickel is

required to stabilize austenite. The diagram for the ternary iron-chromium-nickel system shows how the addition of ferrite-stabilizing chromium affects the iron-nickel system (Fig. 2). As can be seen, the popular 18-8 stainless steel, which contains about 8% Ni, is an all-austenite alloy at 900 °C (1652 °F), even though it also contains about 18% Cr.

Ternary Alloy Phase Diagrams. Almost all stainless steels have three or more components, and therefore their phase relationships as a function of temperature and composition are represented by ternary phase diagrams. The 40 ternary diagrams shown in this article are from the following systems:

- Fe-Cr-Al
- Fe-Cr-C
- Fe-Cr-Co
- Fe-Cr-Mn
- Fe-Cr-Mo
- Fe-Cr-N
- Fe-Cr-Ni
- Fe-Cr-W

With the exception of the Fe-Cr-Mn system, all ternary systems illustrated are from the *Handbook of Ternary Alloy Phase Diagrams* to be published by ASM International in 1994. The reference source for each diagram is identified by a code consisting of two numbers (indicating the year of publication), followed by the first three letters of the first author's (or editor's) surname. The complete citation for each source code is listed in the ternary system reference list in this article.

ACKNOWLEDGMENTS

The information in this article is largely taken from:

- H. Baker, Introduction, *Alloy Phase Diagrams*, Vol 3, *ASM Handbook*, ASM International, 1992, p 1-1 to 1-29
- Ternary Phase Diagrams, *Alloy Phase Diagrams*, Vol 3, *ASM Handbook*, ASM International, 1992, p 3-1 to 3-60

TERNARY SYSTEM REFERENCES

- **83Riv:** V.G. Rivlin and G.V. Raynor, *International Metals Review*, Vol 28 (No. 1), 1983, p 23-64
- **87Rag:** V. Raghavan, *Phase Diagrams of Ternary Iron Alloys*, No. 1, Indian Institute of Metals, 1987
- **88Ray:** G.V. Raynor and V.G. Rivlin, *Phase Equilibria in Iron Ternary Alloys*, No. 4, Institute of Metals, 1988

SELECTED REFERENCES

- T.B. Massalski, Ed., *Binary Alloy Phase Diagrams*, 2nd ed., ASM International, 1990
- P. Villars and L.D. Calvert, *Pearson's Handbook of Crystallographic Data for Intermetallic Phases*, Vol 1, 2, and 3, American Society for Metals, 1985

Al-Cr-Fe isothermal section at 750 °C [88Ray]

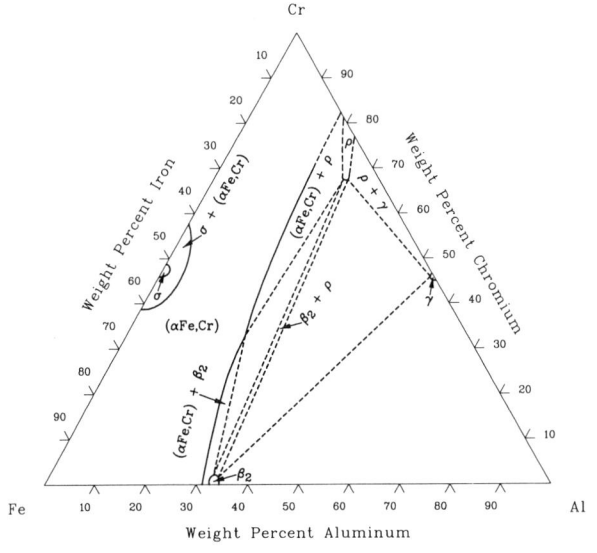

Al-Cr-Fe liquidus projection [88Ray]

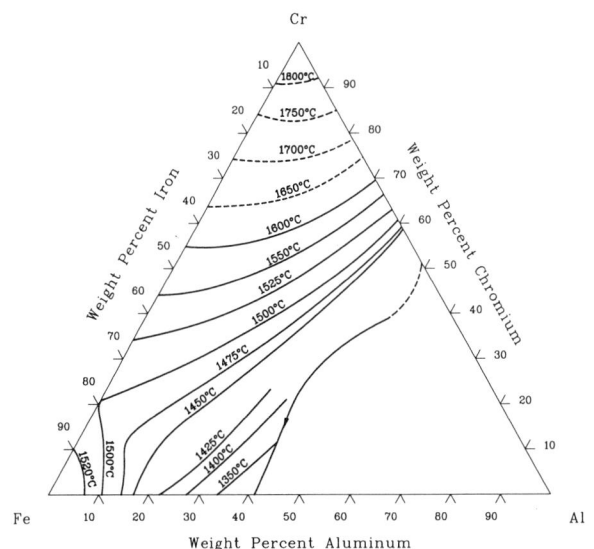

Al-Cr-Fe isothermal section at 600 °C [88Ray]

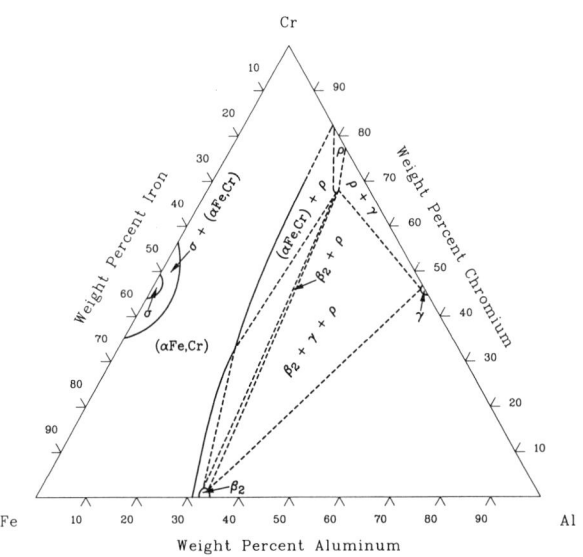

Al-Cr-Fe isothermal section at 900 °C [88Ray]

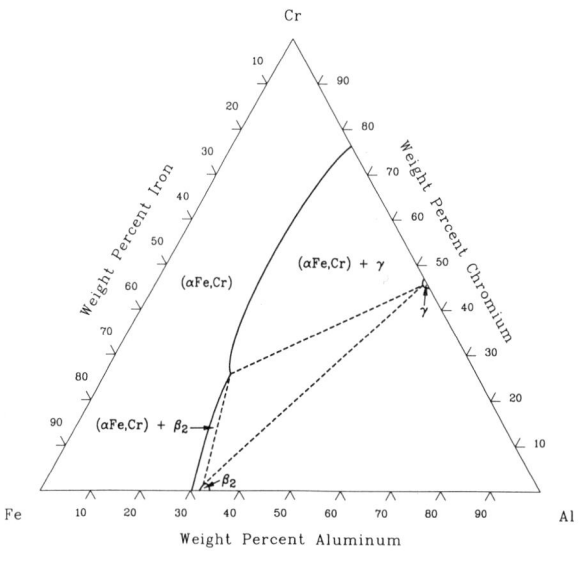

C-Cr-Fe isothermal section at 1000 °C [88Ray]

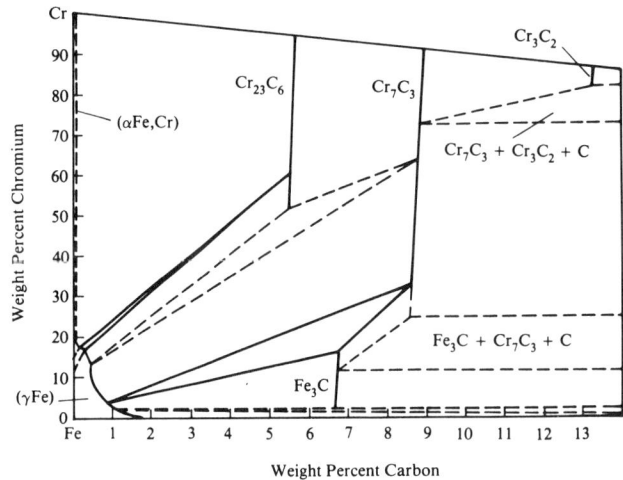

C-Cr-Fe isothermal section at 870 °C [88Ray]

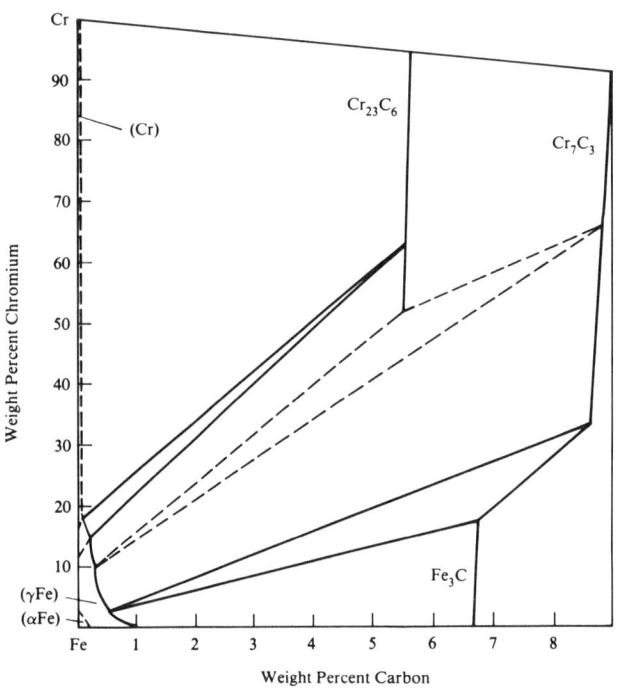

C-Cr-Fe liquidus projection [88Ray]

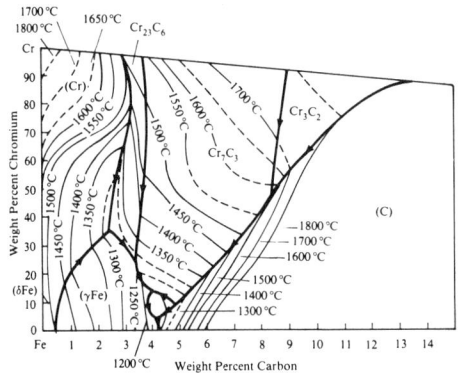

C-Cr-Fe isothermal section at 700 °C [88Ray]

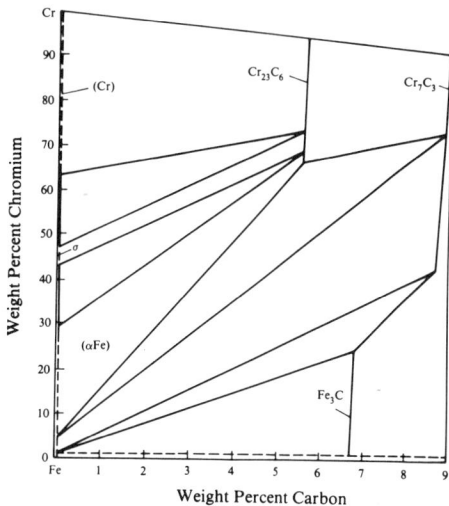

C-Cr-Fe isothermal section at 900 °C [88Ray]

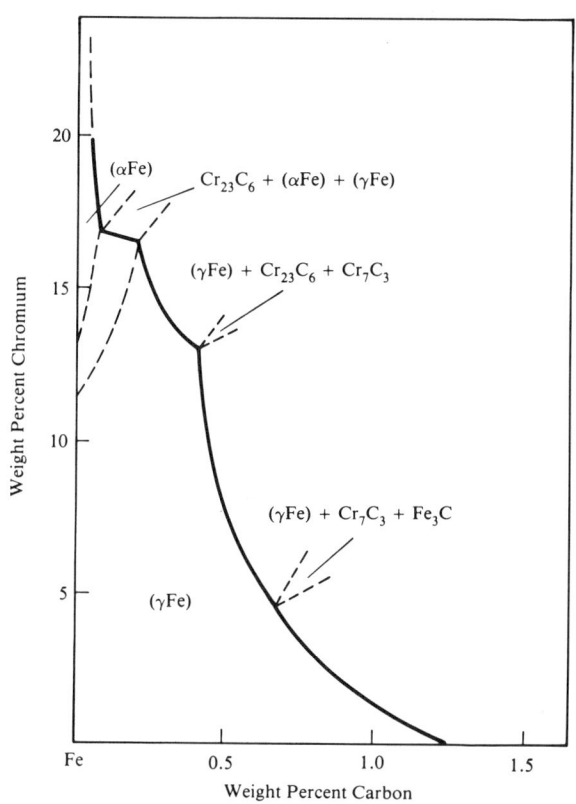

C-Cr-Fe (Fe) isothermal section at 1100 °C [88Ray]

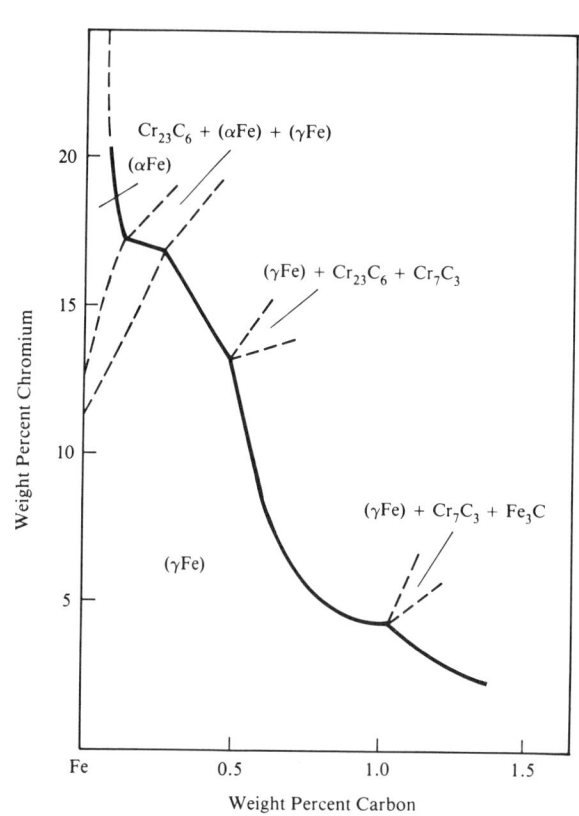

Co-Cr-Fe solidus projection [88Ray]

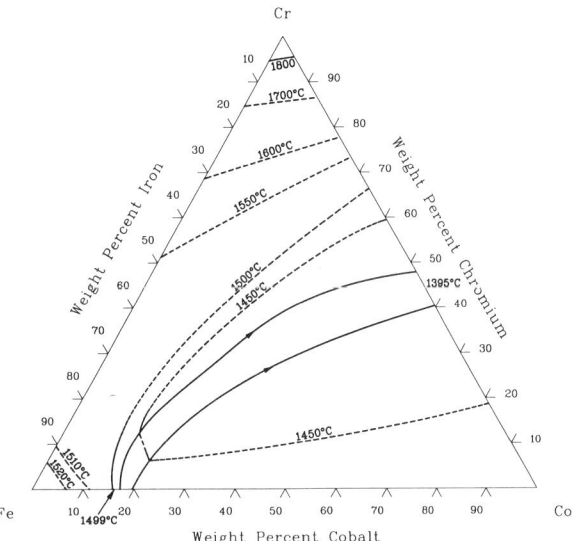

Co-Cr-Fe liquidus projection [88Ray]

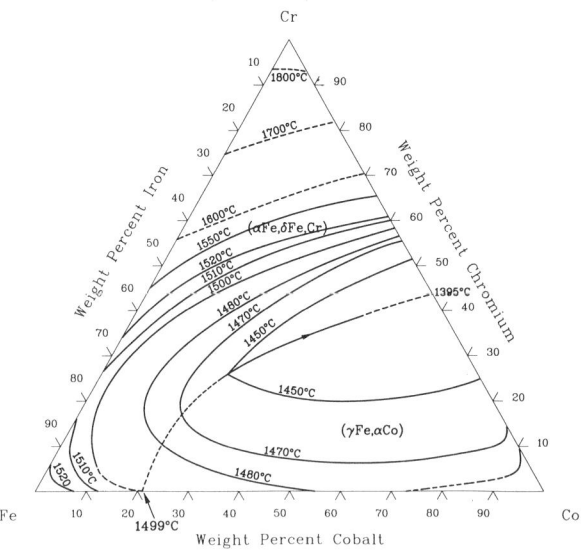

Co-Cr-Fe isothermal section at 1200 °C [88Ray]

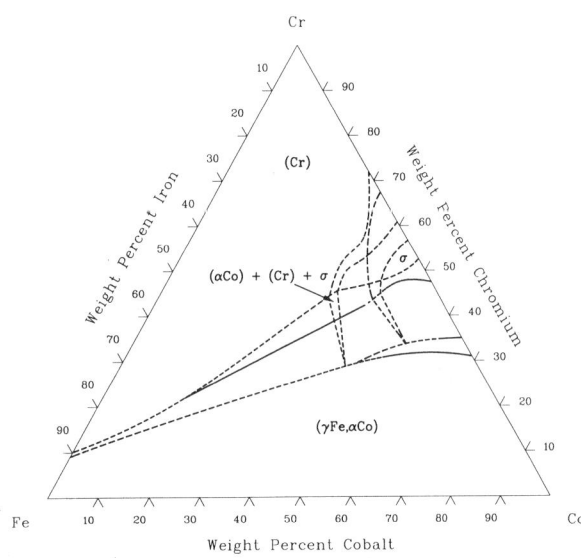

Co-Cr-Fe isothermal section at 800 °C [88Ray]

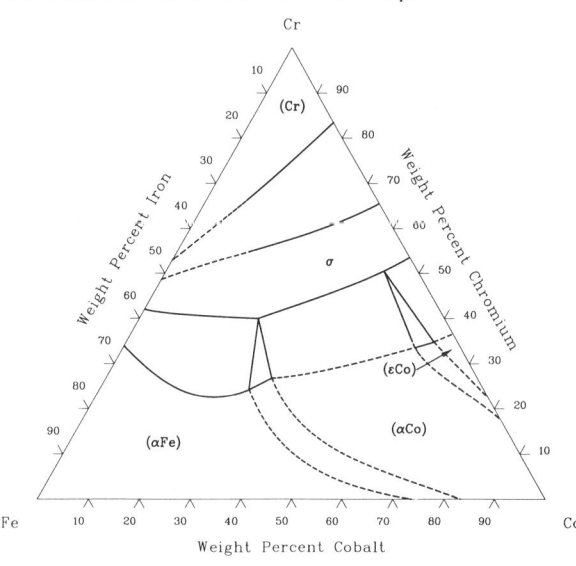

Co-Cr-Fe isothermal section at 1000 °C [88Ray]

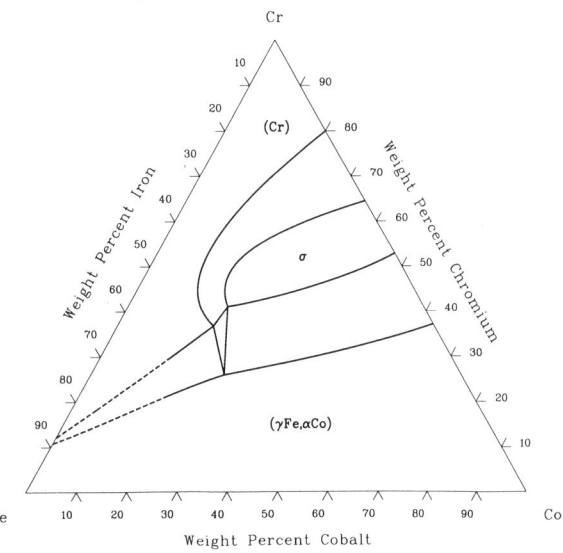

Co-Cr-Fe isothermal section at 600 °C [88Ray]

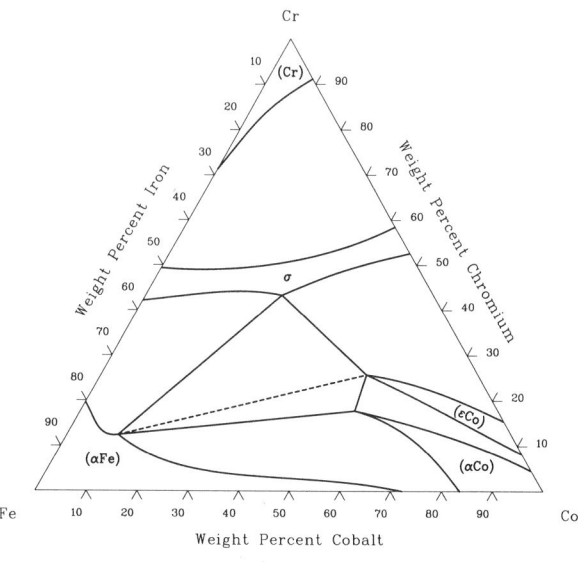

Cr-Fe-Mn isothermal section at 1200 °C [83Riv]

Cr-Fe-Mn isothermal section at 1000 °C [83Riv]

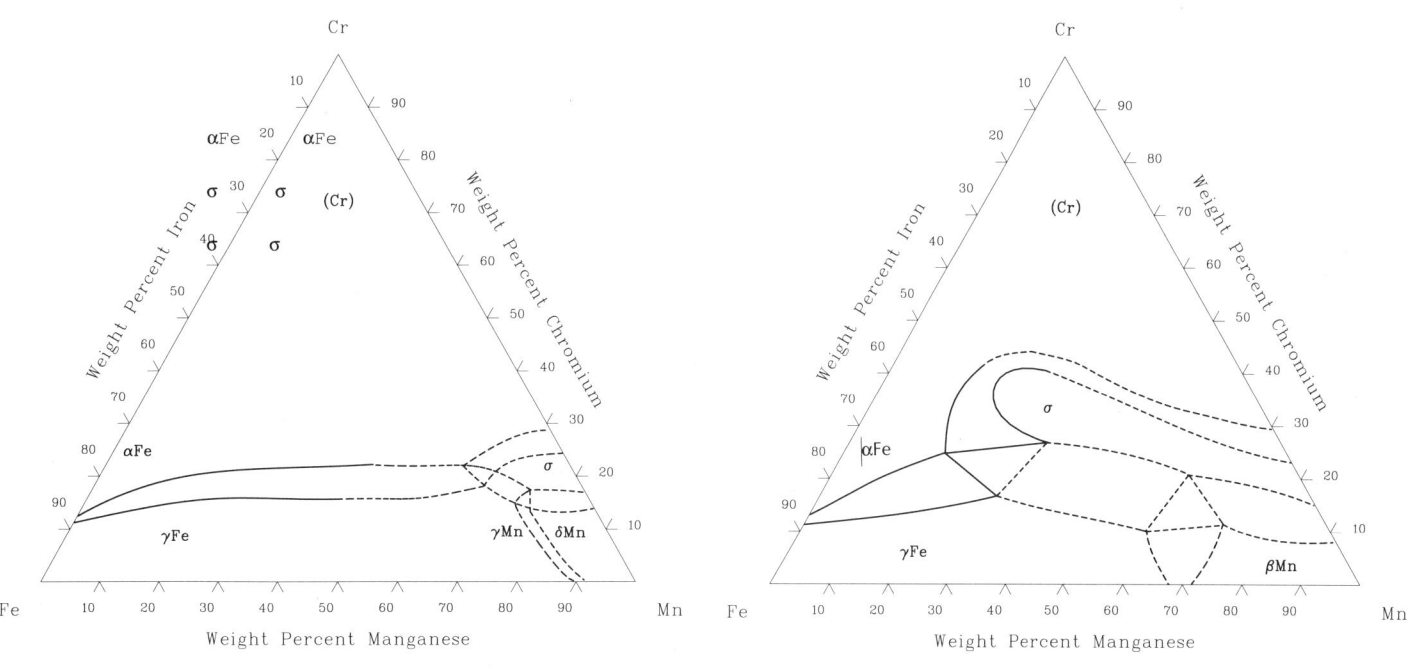

Cr-Fe-Mn isothermal section at 900°C [83Riv]

Cr-Fe-Mn isothermal section at 800°C [83Riv]

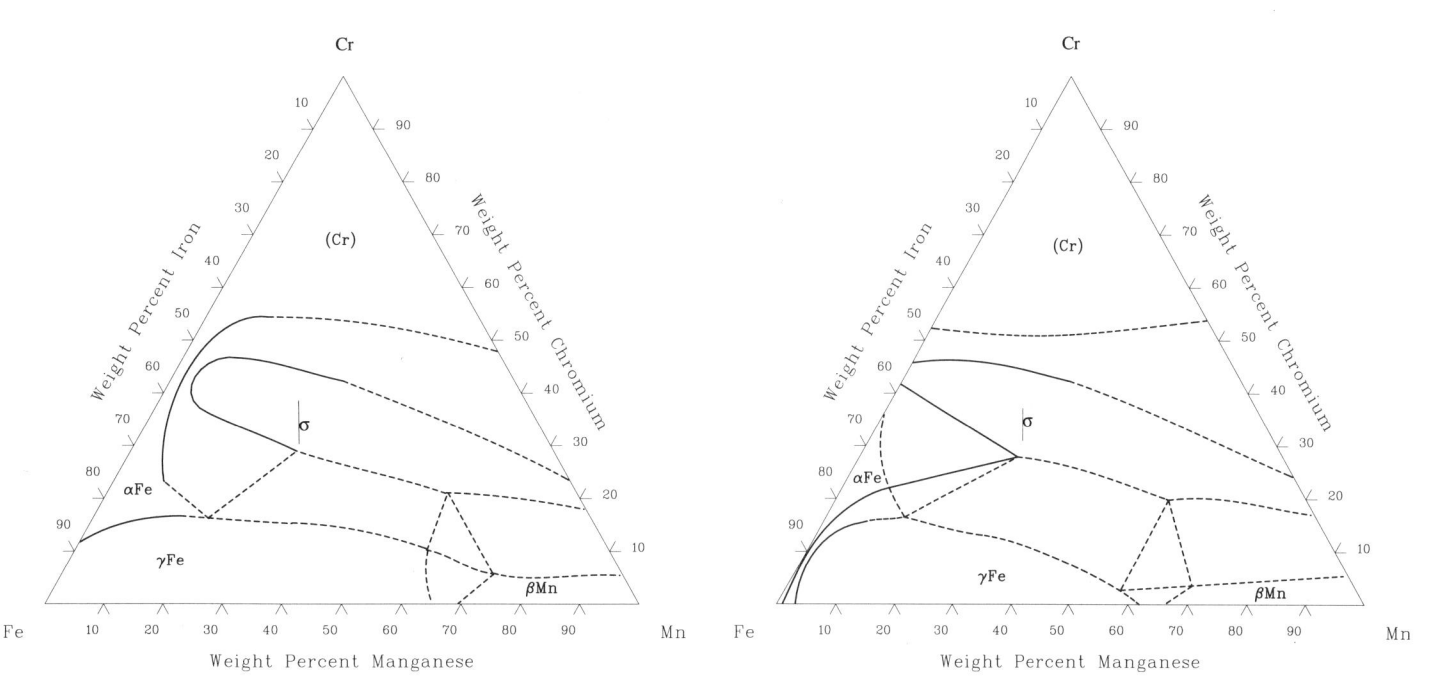

Cr-Fe-Mo liquidus projection [88Ray]

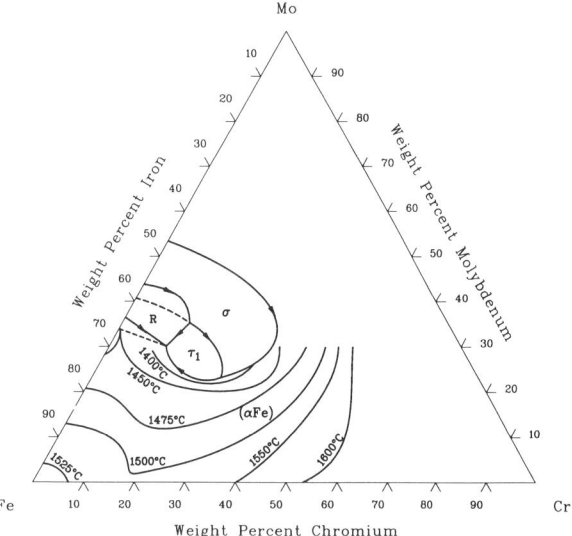

Cr-Fe-Mo isothermal section at 815 °C [88Ray]

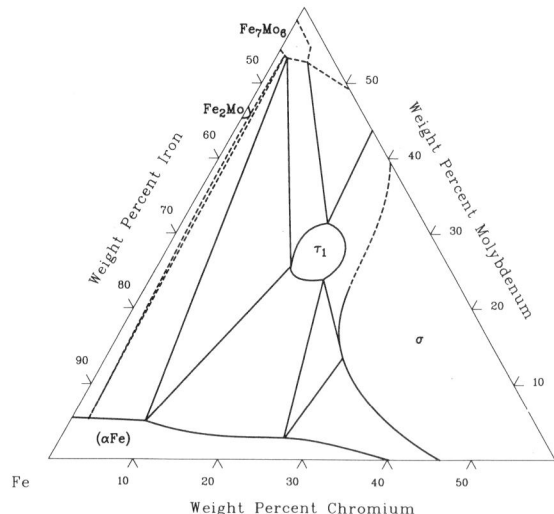

Cr-Fe-Mo isothermal section at 1250 °C [88Ray]

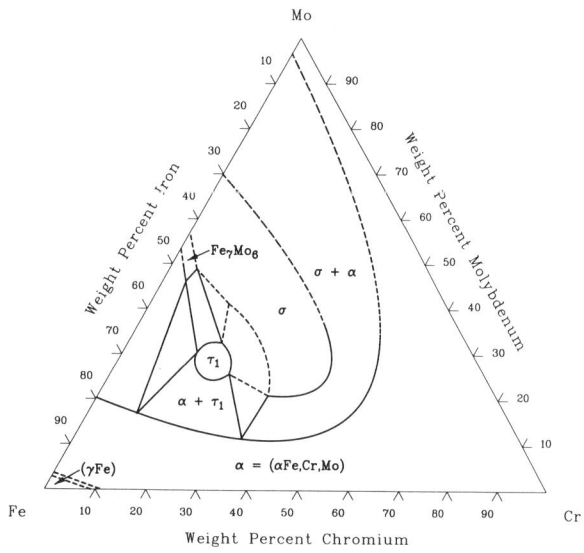

Cr-Fe-Mo [88Ray]

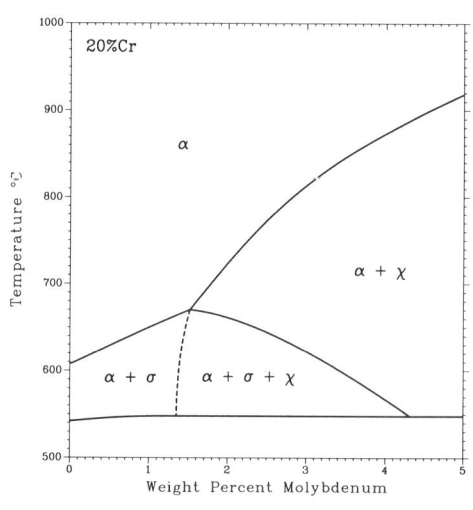

Cr-Fe-Mo isothermal section at 1100 °C [88Ray]

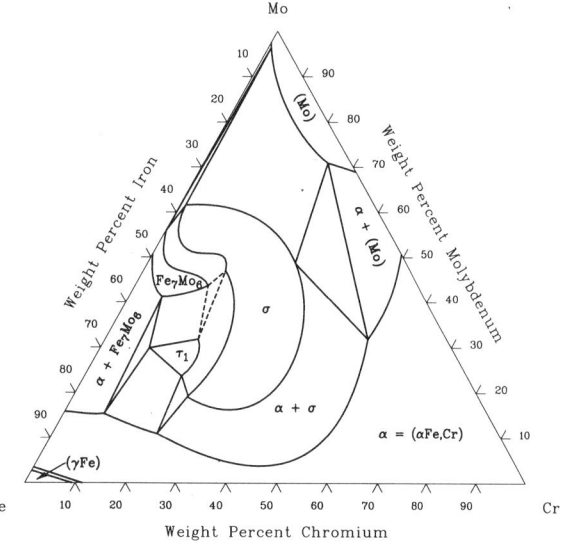

Cr-Fe-Mo [88Ray]

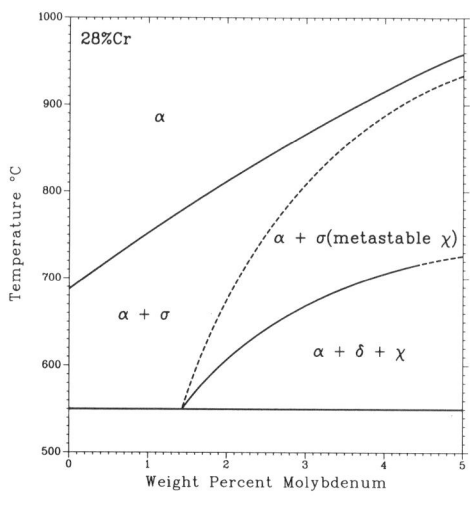

Cr-Fe-N liquidus projection [87Rag]

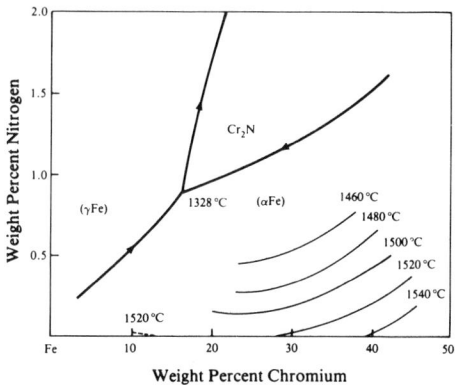

Cr-Fe-N isothermal section at 700 °C [87Rag]

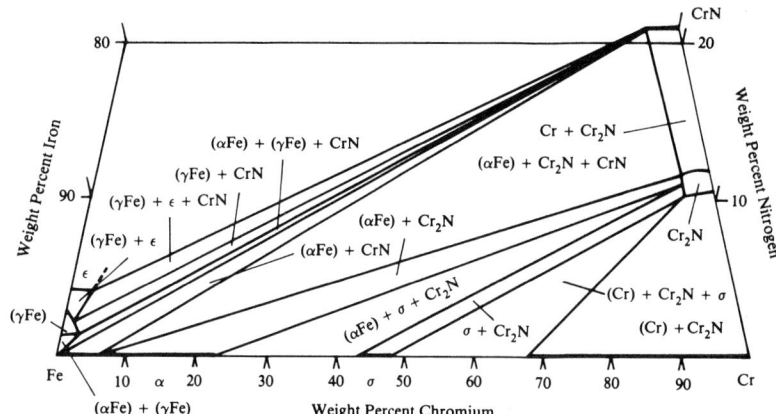

Cr-Fe-N isothermal section at 1200 °C [87Rag]

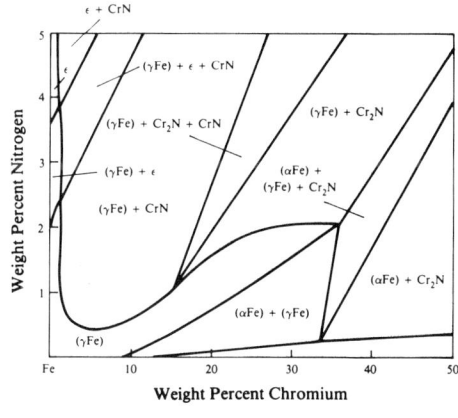

Cr-Fe-N isothermal section at 567 °C [87Rag]

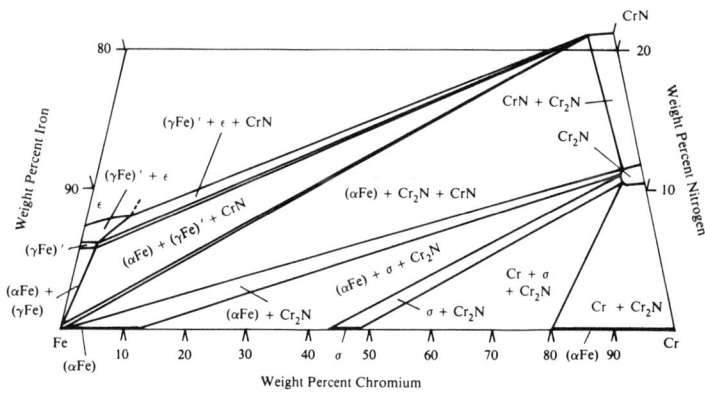

Cr-Fe-N isothermal section at 1000 °C [87Rag]

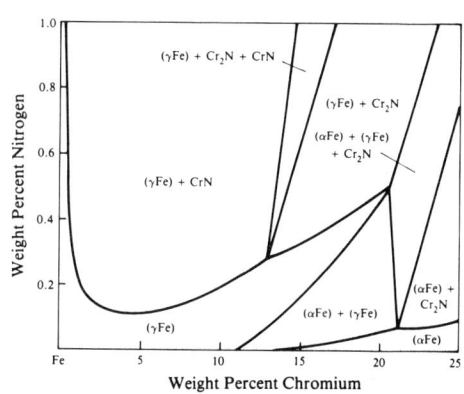

Cr-Fe-Ni liquidus projection [88Ray]

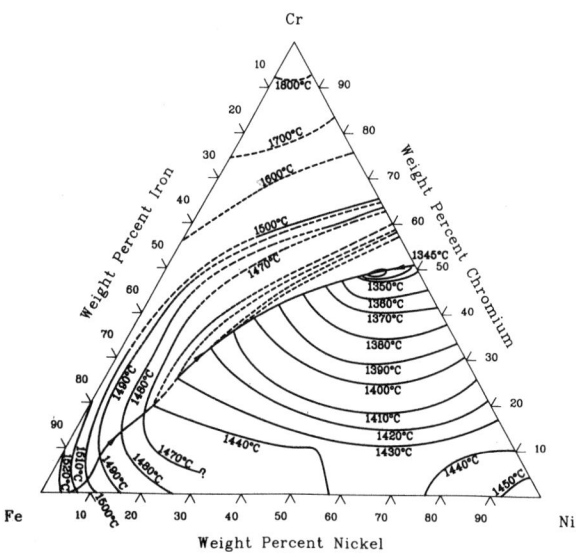

Cr-Fe-Ni solidus projection [88Ray]

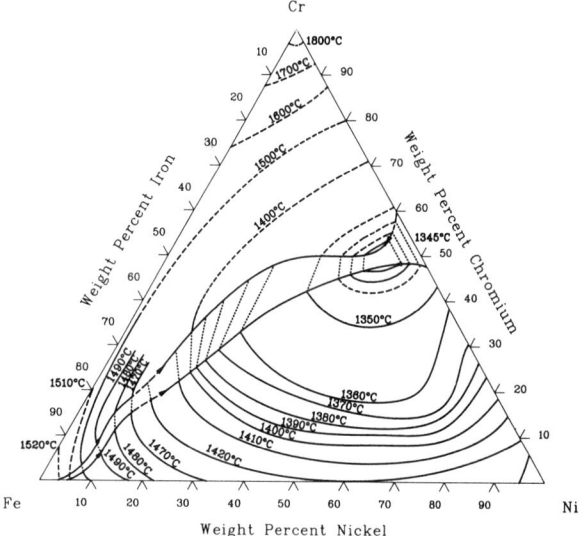

Cr-Fe-Ni isothermal section at 900 °C [88Ray]

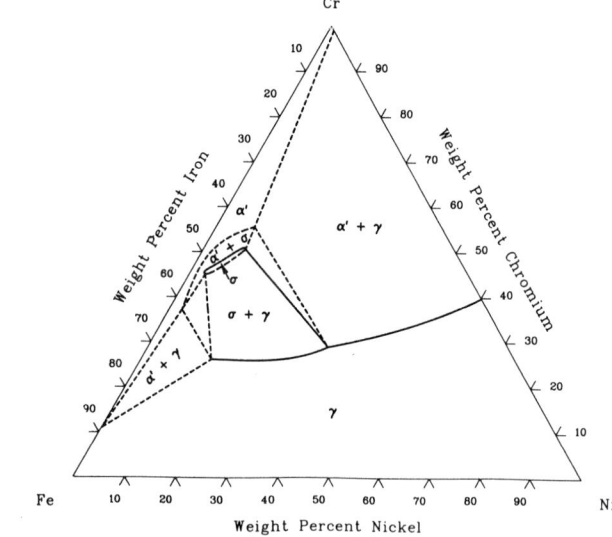

Note: α = (αFe,Cr); γ = (γFe,Ni)

Cr-Fe-Ni isothermal section at 1300 °C [88Ray]

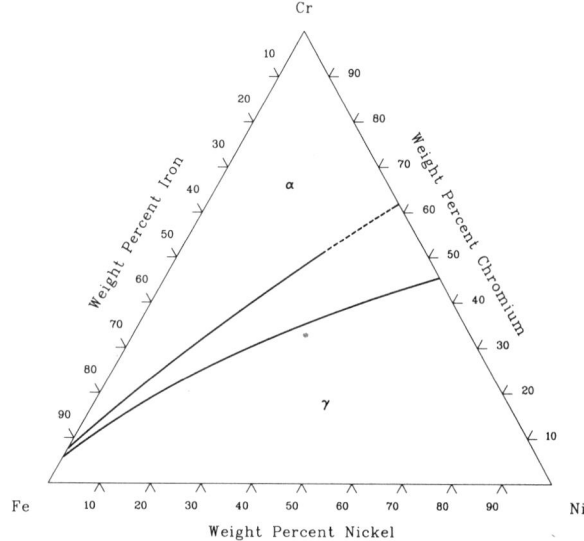

Note: α = (αFe,Cr); γ = (γFe,Ni)

Cr-Fe-Ni isothermal section at 800 °C [88Ray]

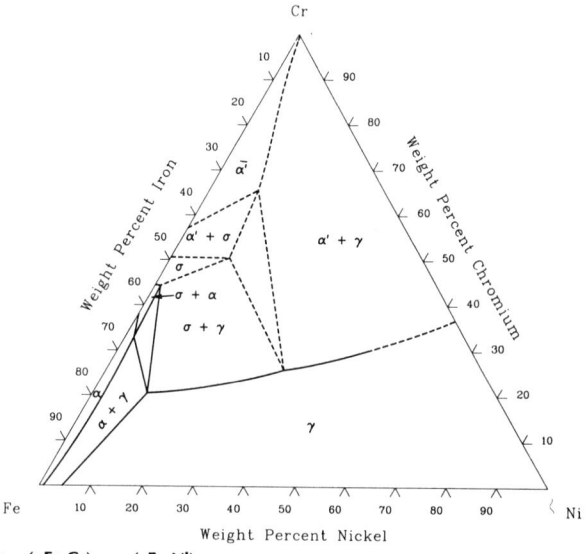

Note: α = (αFe,Cr); γ = (γFe,Ni)

Cr-Fe-Ni isothermal section at 1000 °C [88Ray]

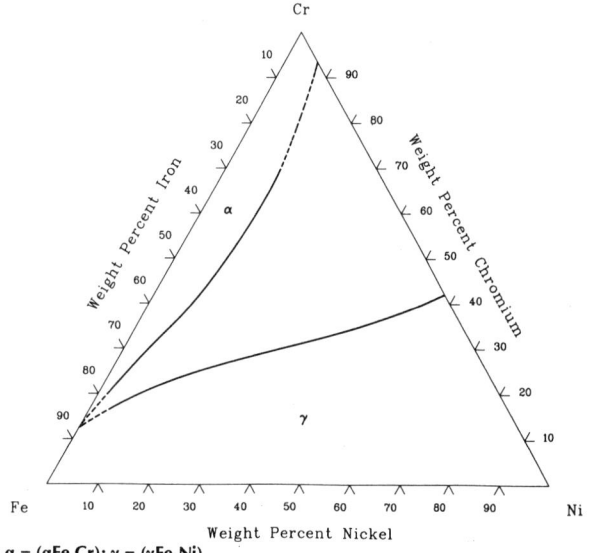

Note: α = (αFe,Cr); γ = (γFe,Ni)

Cr-Fe-Ni isothermal section at 650 °C [88Ray]

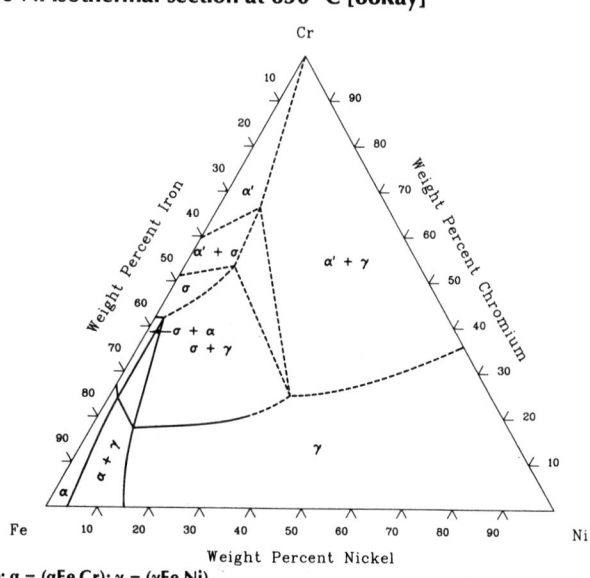

Note: α = (αFe,Cr); γ = (γFe,Ni)

Cr-Fe-W isothermal section at 1200 °C [88Ray]

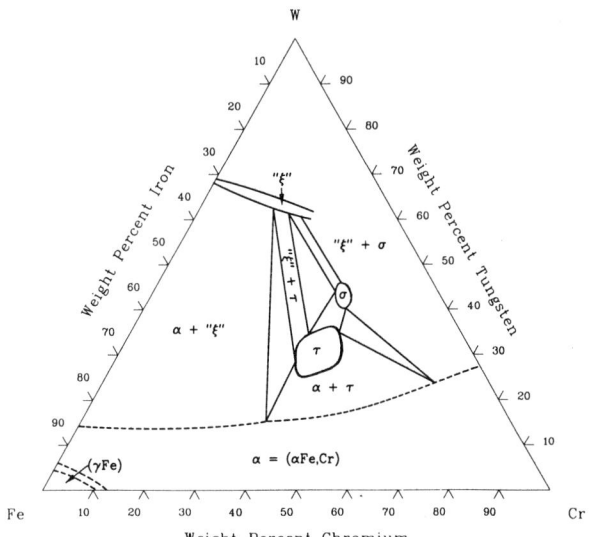

Cr-Fe-W isothermal section at 600 °C [88Ray]

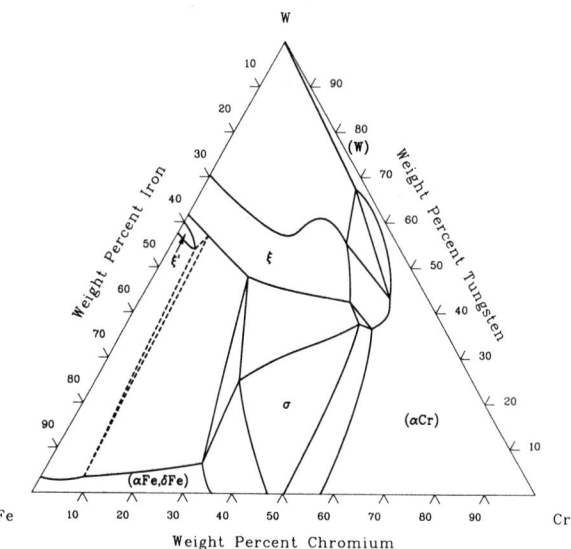

Contents

Physical Properties

PHYSICAL PROPERTIES important for successful implementation of stainless steels include density and modulus of elasticity, thermal properties—including melting range, coefficient of thermal expansion, thermal conductivity, heat-transfer coefficient, and specific heat—magnetic properties (primarily magnetic permeability), and electrical resistivity. This article will summarize typical values for each of these properties for the standard grades of stainless steels. Emphasis is placed on magnetic and electrical properties because these are the most important for the selection of stainless steels for soft magnetic and electrical resistance applications. Additional information on physical properties of stainless steels can be found in Ref 1 and 2 and the article "General Introduction" in this Volume.

Density and Modulus of Elasticity

Density refers to the mass per unit volume of a solid material expressed in g/cm^3 (the most commonly used unit), kg/m^3, lb/ft^3, or lb/in.^{3}. Density values vary little for various grades of stainless steels. For these steels, density values range from 7.5 to 8.0 g/cm^3 as shown in Table 4 in the article "General Introduction" in this Volume. The change in density as a result of temperature is shown in Table 1 for three austenitic grades.

The modulus of elasticity (the measure of rigidity or stiffness of a material) is the ratio of the increment of some specified form of stress to the increment of some specified form of strain. The modulus obtained in tension (the most commonly used elastic moduli) is referred to as Young's modulus and is generally expressed in Pascals (Newtons per square meter) or pounds per square inch. For example, if a tensile stress of 13.8 MPa (2.0 ksi) results in an elongation of 1.0%, the Young's modulus is 13.8 MPa (2.0 ksi) divided by 0.01, or 1380 MPa (200 ksi). The elastic modulus varies little with stainless steel composition and has values of the same order (193 to 204 GPa, or 28.0 to 29.5 × 10^6 psi) for all grades (see Table 4 in the article "General Introduction" in this Volume). Table 2 illustrates the change in Young's modulus with temperature for various stainless steels.

Thermal Properties

The melting range represents the temperatures that define the solidus and liquidus of an alloy. Table 3 shows the solidus and liquidus temperatures for various stainless steel grades determined by differential thermal analysis. Additional melting range values can be found in Table 4 in the article "General Introduction" in this Volume.

The coefficient of thermal expansion (CTE) is the change in unit of length (or volume) accompanying a unit change of temperature, at a specified temperature. The most commonly used

Table 1 Density as a function of temperature for selected austenitic stainless steels

Type	UNS No.	Density, g/cm^3, at								
		−196 °C (−321 °F)	−100 °C (−148 °F)	0 °C (32 °F)	100 °C (212 °F)	200 °C (390 °F)	400 °C (750 °F)	600 °C (1110 °F)	800 °C (1470 °F)	1000 °C (1830 °F)
301	S30100	8.0	7.9	7.9	7.8	7.8	7.7	7.6	7.5	7.4
316	S31600	8.0	8.0	7.9	7.9	7.8	7.7	7.6	7.6	7.5
347	S34700	8.0	7.9	7.9	7.8	7.8	7.7	7.6	7.5	7.4

Source: Ref 1

Table 2 Modulus of elasticity (static values) as a function of temperature for various stainless steel grades

Type	UNS No.	Young's modulus, GPa (10^6 psi) at						
		−196 °C (−321 °F)	20 °C (68 °F)	100 °C (212 °F)	200 °C (390 °F)	400 °C (750 °F)	600 °C (1110 °F)	800 °C (1470 °F)
302	S30200	200 (29)	193 (28)	191 (27.7)	183.5 (26.6)	168.5 (24.4)	153.5 (22.3)	139 (20.2)
304	S30400	208 (30.2)	193 (28)	191 (27.7)	183 (26.5)	168 (24.3)	148 (21.5)	128 (18.6)
310	S31000	...	193 (28)	192 (27.8)	184 (26.7)	173 (25)	155 (22.5)	134 (19.4)
316	S31600	...	193 (28)	192 (27.8)	185 (26.8)	168.5 (24.4)	151 (21.9)	132 (19.1)
321	S32100	...	193 (28)	192 (27.8)	182 (26.4)	166 (24)	151 (21.9)	132 (19.1)
347	S34700	208 (30.2)	193 (28)	184 (26.7)	168 (24.3)	152 (22)	152 (22)	134 (19.4)
410	S41000	...	206 (29.9)	200 (29)	191 (27.7)	175 (25.4)	158 (22.9)	140 (20.3)
430	S43000	...	206 (29.9)	198 (28.7)	191 (27.7)	165 (23.9)	139 (20.2)	122 (17.7)

Source: Ref 1

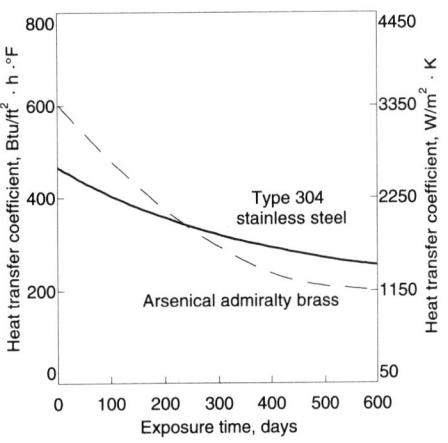

Fig. 1 Comparison of heat-transfer coefficients of two condenser tubing materials exposed to the same operating conditions. Source: Ref 3

Table 3 Melting range (solidus to liquidus) for selected stainless steels

Type	UNS No.	Melting range	
		°C	°F
202	S20200	1398-1454	2548-2649
302	S30200	1400-1447	2552-2637
304	S30400	1405-1448	2561-2638
304L	S30403	1394-1440	2541-2624
305	S30500	1400-1435	2552-2615
...	S30803	1415-1446	2579-2635
310	S31000	1350-1395	2462-2543
314	S31400	1322-1388	2412-2530
316	S31600	1392-1444	2538-2631
316L	S31603	1405-1445	2561-2633
316Ti	S31635	1378-1432	2512-2610
316Cb	S31640	1370-1431	2498-2608
321	S32100	1398-1448	2548-2638
347	S34700	1394-1446	2541-2635
...	S17400	1395-1435	2543-2615

Source: Ref 1

units to express CTE values are $\mu m/m \cdot {}°C$ or $\mu m/in. \cdot {}°F$. The CTE values of martensitic, ferritic and precipitation-hardenable stainless steels are of the same order of magnitude as that of carbon or low-alloy steels. The CTE of austenitic grades is considerably higher (~ 17 $\mu m/m \cdot {}°C$, or 9.5 $\mu m/in. \cdot {}°F$) that increases the problems related to dimensional changes in parts during heating and cooling. Duplex grades have intermediate values. Tables 4 and 5 provide CTE values for selected stainless steels at elevated and low temperatures, respectively.

Thermal conductivity is the measure of the rate at which a material transmits heat. If a thermal gradient of one degree per unit length is established over a material of unit cross-sectional area, then the thermal conductivity is defined as the quantity of heat transmitted per unit time. Thermal conductivity is expressed in units of $W/m \cdot K$ or $Btu/ft \cdot h \cdot {}°F$. As Table 6 indicates, austenitic stainless steels have lower thermal conductivity values than non-austenitic grades (see also Table 4 in the article "General Introduction" in this Volume).

The heat-transfer coefficient refers to the amount of heat that passes through a unit area of a medium or system in a unit time when the temperature difference between the boundaries of the system is 1 degree. The heat-transfer coefficient is expressed by the units $W/m^2 \cdot K$ or $Btu/ft^2 \cdot h \cdot {}°F$.

Stainless steels are used extensively for heat exchangers because their ability to remain clean enhances heat-transfer efficiency. Factors affecting the total resistance to heat flow include (Ref 3):

- Steam-side water film (18%)
- Steam-side fouling (8%)
- Tube (metal) wall (2%)
- Water-side fouling (33%)
- Water-side film (39%)

This listing clearly indicates that films and scale on heat exchanger surfaces impair heat transfer far greater than the metal wall, which accounts for only 2% of the total resistance to heat flow. Table 7 supports this contention by showing that the thermal conductivity of a metal has only a minor effect on the U-value, or the overall heat-transfer coefficient, which is expressed as:

$$U\text{–value} = \cfrac{1}{\cfrac{1}{h_o} + \cfrac{t}{\gamma} + \cfrac{1}{h_i}} \qquad (Eq\ 1)$$

where h_o is the outside fluid film heat-transfer coefficient, h_i is the inside fluid film heat-transfer coefficient, t is the thickness of the metal (tube) wall, and γ is the thermal conductivity.

The degree to which other factors affect heat transfer are dependent on the type of fluid involved, its velocity, and the nature of scale or fouling buildup on the surface. Because corrosion and scale accumulation are minimal with stainless steels, there would be less difference in service performance among various metals than would be indicated by thermal conductivity data. The power-generation industry, for instance, has very carefully analyzed transfer characteristics of heat-exchanger materials and has conclusively

demonstrated that stainless steels behave in a manner far superior to other materials (Ref 3).

Figure 1 compares two condenser tubing materials exposed simultaneously to identical operating conditions. In the early stages of the test, the relative performance of both materials corresponded to published thermal conductivity figures. However, in only 240 days, the overall heat-transfer rate of the stainless steel was found to surpass that of the Admiralty brass. The heat-transfer rate for both materials decreased with time, but that of the Admiralty brass was more rapid because of fouling and corrosion, while the stainless steel was affected only by fouling.

Specific heat is the quantity of heat required to change by one degree the temperature of a body of material of unit mass. Specific heat is expressed as either $J/kg \cdot K$ or $Btu/lb \cdot {}°F$. Room-temperature

Table 4 Mean coefficient of thermal expansion as a function of temperature for selected stainless steel grades

Type	UNS No.	Mean CTE, $\mu m/m \cdot {}°C$ ($\mu in./in. \cdot {}°F$) at				
		20-200 °C (70-390 °F)	20-400 °C (70-750 °F)	20-600 °C (70-1110 °F)	20-800 °C (70-1470 °F)	20-1000 °C (70-1830 °F)
304	S30400	17 (9.4)	18 (10)	19 (10.6)	19.5 (10.8)	20.0 (11.1)
316	S31600	16.5 (9.2)	17.5 (9.7)	18.5 (10.3)	19.0 (10.6)	19.5 (10.8)
314	S31400	15 (8.3)	16 (8.9)	17 (9.4)	18 (10)	19 (10.6)
403	S40300	11 (6.1)	11.7 (6.5)	...	...	...
430	S43000	10.5 (5.8)	11.2 (6.2)	...	...	...
446	S44600	10.3 (5.7)	11 (6.1)	11.7 (6.5)	12.4 (6.9)	13.1 (7.3)
...	S31803	13 (7.2)	14 (7.8)	15 (8.3)	...	...

Source: Ref 1

Table 5 Effect of low temperature on mean coefficient of thermal expansion values for selected austenitic stainless steels

Type	UNS No.	Mean CTE, $\mu m/m \cdot {}°C$ ($\mu in./in. \cdot {}°F$) at			
		−184 to 21 °C (−299 to 70 °F)	−129 to 21 °C (−200 to 70 °F)	−73 to 21 °C (−99 to 70 °F)	−18 to 21 °C (0 to 70 °F)
301	S30100	13.7 (7.6)	14.1 (7.8)	14.8 (8.2)	15.7 (8.7)
304	S30400	13.3 (7.4)	13.9 (7.7)	14.8 (8.2)	15.7 (8.7)
310	S31000	12.6 (7)	13.5 (7.5)	14.1 (7.8)	14.4 (8)
316	S31600	12.8 (7.1)	13.3 (7.4)	14.1 (7.8)	14.8 (8.2)
347	S34700	13.5 (7.5)	14.6 (8.1)	15.3 (8.5)	15.7 (8.7)

Source: Ref 1

Table 6 Room-temperature thermal conductivity values for selected stainless steels

Type	UNS No.	Thermal conductivity at 20 °C (68 °F)	
		W/m · K	Btu/ft · h · °F
201	S20100	14.6	8.4
304	S30400	14.6	8.4
310	S31000	14.6	8.4
316	S31600	14.6	8.4
316Cb	S31640	14.6	8.4
321	S32100	14.6	8.4
347	S34700	14.6	8.4
410	S41000	25.1	14.5
420	S42000	25.1	14.5
430	S43000	20.9	12.1
...	S31803	16.7	9.6

Source: Ref 1

Table 7 Effect of thermal conductivity on "U" values

See text (Eq 1) for a definition of the U value.

Application	Material	Outside fluid film coefficient, $W/m^2 \cdot K$ ($Btu/ft^2 \cdot h \cdot {}°F$)	Inside fluid film coefficient, $W/m^2 \cdot K$ ($Btu/ft^2 \cdot h \cdot {}°F$)	Thermal conductivity, W/m · K ($Btu/ft \cdot h \cdot {}°F$)	"U" value, $W/m^2 \cdot K$ ($Btu/ft^2 \cdot h \cdot {}°F$)
Heating water with saturated steam	Copper	1704 (300)	5678 (1000)	387 (224)	1300 (229)
	Aluminum	1704 (300)	5678 (1000)	226 (131)	1295 (228)
	Carbon steel	1704 (300)	5678 (1000)	66 (38.1)	1266 (223)
	300-series stainless steel	1704 (300)	5678 (1000)	15 (8.7)	1124 (198)
Heating air with saturated steam	Copper	28 (5)	5678 (1000)	387 (224)	28 (4.98)
	Aluminum	28 (5)	5678 (1000)	226 (131)	28 (4.97)
	Carbon steel	28 (5)	5678 (1000)	66 (38.1)	28 (4.97)
	300-series stainless steel	28 (5)	5678 (1000)	15 (8.7)	28 (4.96)

Source: Ref 3

Table 8 Room-temperature specific heat values for selected stainless steels

Type	UNS No.	Specific heat	
		J/kg · K	Btu/lb · °F
201	S20100	500	0.12
304	S30400	500	0.12
310	S31000	500	0.12
316	S31600	500	0.12
316Cb	S31640	500	0.12
321	S32100	500	0.12
403	S40300	460	0.11
420	S42000	460	0.11
430	S43000	460	0.11
...	S31803	460	0.11

Source: Ref 1

Table 9 Magnetic properties of selected ferritic and martensitic stainless steels

Data determined on round bars 9.53 to 15.88 mm (0.375 to 0.625 in.) in diameter per ASTM A 341 using Fahy permeameter

Grade	ASTM A 838	Condition(a)	Rockwell hardness	Maximum permeability, µm	Coercive force, H_c		Resistivity, µΩ · cm
					A · m^{-1}	Oe	
Martensitic:							
Type 410	...	A	B85	750	480	6	57
		H	C41	95	2900	36	
Type 416	...	A	B85	750	480	6	57
		H	C41	95	2900	36	
Type 420	...	A	B90	950	800	10	55
		H	C50	40	3600	45	
Type 440B	...	H	C55	62	5100	64	60
Ferritic:							
Type 430F (solenoid quality)	Alloy 1	A	B78	2000	160	2.0	60
Type 430FR (solenoid quality)(b)	Alloy 2	A	B82	2600	128	1.6	76
Type 446	...	A	B85	1000	360	4.5	67

(a) A, fully annealed; H, heat treated for maximum hardness. (b) Carpenter Technology Corporation alloy

specific heat values for selected stainless steels are given in Table 8. Lower and higher specific heat values correspond with lower and higher temperatures, respectively (Ref 1).

Magnetic Properties (Ref 4)

The magnetic behavior of stainless steels varies considerably, ranging from paramagnetic (nonmagnetic) in fully austenitic grades, to hard or permanent magnetic behavior in the hardened martensitic grades, to soft magnetic properties in ferritic stainless steels.

Magnetic materials are broadly classified into two groups with either hard or soft magnetic characteristics (Ref 5). Hard magnetic materials are characterized by retaining a large amount of residual magnetism after exposure to a strong magnetic field. These materials typically have coercive force, H_c, values of several hundred to several thousand oersteds (Oe) and are considered to be permanent magnets. The coercive force is a measure of the magnetizing force required to reduce the magnetic induction to zero after the ma-

terial has been magnetized. In contrast, soft magnetic materials become magnetized by relatively low-strength magnetic fields, and when the applied field is removed, they return to a state of relatively low residual magnetism. Soft magnetic materials typically exhibit coercive force values of approximately 5 Oe to as low as 0.002 Oe. Soft magnetic behavior is essential in any application involving changing electromagnetic induction, such as solenoids, relays, motors, generators, transformers, magnetic shielding, and so on. Other important characteristics of magnetically soft materials include high permeability, high saturation induction, low hysteresis-energy loss, low eddy-current loss in alternating flux applications, and in specialized cases, constant permeability at low field strengths and/or a minimum or definite change in permeability with temperature.

Austenitic Stainless Steels. All austenitic stainless steels are paramagnetic (nonmagnetic) in the annealed, fully austenitic condition. The dc magnetic permeabilities range ~1.003 to ~1.005 when measured at magnetizing forces of 16 kA · m^{-1} (200 Oe). The permeability (a dimensionless parameter expressing the ease by which a material can be magnetized) increases with cold work due to deformation-induced martensite, a ferromagnetic structure. For certain grades such as types 302 and 304, the increase in magnetic permeability can be appreciable, resulting in these grades

being weakly ferromagnetic in the heavily cold-worked condition. This phenomenon is illustrated in Fig. 2 for nine austenitic stainless steels.

The differing performance among grades is a reflection of their composition. In particular, nickel increases austenite stability, thereby decreasing the work-hardening rate and the rate of increase of magnetic permeability. Consequently, the higher-nickel grades exhibit lower magnetic permeabilities than the lower-nickel grades when cold worked in equivalent amounts.

The magnetic permeabilities achievable in austenitic stainless steels are very low when compared to conventional magnetic materials. Consequently, it is their nonmagnetic behavior that is of more concern. Certain applications, such as housings and components for magnetic detection equipment used for security, measuring, and control purposes, require that the steel be nonmagnetic, because the presence of even weakly ferromagnetic parts can adversely affect performance. If the magnetic permeability of an austenitic stainless steel is of particular concern, it can be measured by relatively simple means, as described in ASTM standard A 342-Method No. 6. The equipment described is commercially available at relatively low cost.

Ferritic stainless steels are ferromagnetic and have been used as soft magnetic components in products such as solenoid housings, cores, and

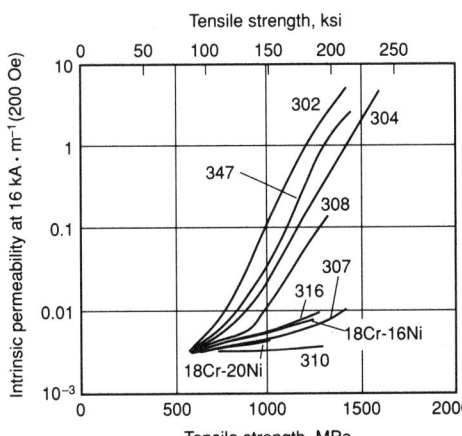

Fig. 2 Correlation of increased tensile strength from cold working and the permeability of cold-worked austenitic stainless steels. Annealed hot-rolled strips 2.4 to 3.2 mm (0.095 to 0.125 in.) thick before cold reduction. For normal permeability values, add unity to the numbers given on vertical scale. Source: Ref 4

Table 10 Electrical resistivity as a function of temperature for selected stainless steels

Type	UNS No.	Electrical resistivity, µΩ · cm, at							
		−196 °C (−321 °F)	−78 °C (−108 °F)	20 °C (68 °F)	200 °C (390 °F)	400 °C (750 °F)	600 °C (1110 °F)	800 °C (1470 °F)	1000 °C (1830 °F)
301	S30100	...	...	72	83	94	105	114	...
302	S30200	...	...	72	84	96	106	115	119
304	S30400	55	65	72	85	98	111	120	...
310	S31000	...	...	90	100	110	120	125	130
316	S31600	60	68	74	87	98	108	...	...
321	S32100	...	...	72	90	103	115	119	...
347	S34700	52	60	72	88	97	110	119	...
420	S42000	...	...	55	72	87	108	...	...
430	S43000	...	...	60	76	91	111	...	...

Source: Ref 1

Table 11 Nominal compositions and typical properties of nickel- and iron-base electrical resistance heating alloys

Basic composition, %	Resistivity(a), nΩ · m(b)	TCR, ppm/°C(c)	Thermoelectric potential versus Cu, μV/°C	Coefficient of thermal expansion(d), μm/m · °C	Tensile strength(a)		Density(a)	
					MPa	ksi	g/cm³	lb/in.³
Nickel-base alloys								
78.5Ni-20Cr-1.5Si	1080	80 (25-105 °C)	3.9 (25-105 °C)	13.5	790-1380	115-200	8.3	0.30
76Ni-17Cr-4Si-3Mn	1330	±20 (–55-105 °C)	–1 (20-100 °C)	15	900-1380	130-200	7.8	0.28
71Ni-29Fe	208	4300 (25-105 °C)	–40 (25-105 °C)	15	480-1035	70-150	8.4	0.31
68.5Ni-30Cr-1.5Si	1187	90 (25-105 °C)	–1.2 (25-105 °C)	12.2	825-1380	120-200	8.1	0.29
60Ni-16Cr-22.5Fe-1.5Si	1125	150 (25-105 °C)	0.9 (25-105 °C)	13.5	725-1345	105-195	8.4	0.30
37Ni-21Cr-40Fe-2Si	1080	300 (20-100 °C)	...	16.0	585-1135	85-165	7.96	0.288
35Ni-20Cr-43.5Fe-1.5Si	1000	400 (25-105 °C)	–1.1 (25-105 °C)	15.6	585-1135	85-165	8.1	0.29
Iron-chromium-aluminum alloys								
73.5Fe-22Cr-4.5Al	1350	60 (25-105 °C)	–3.0 (0-100 °C)	11	690-965	100-140	7.25	0.262
73Fe-22Cr-5Al	1390	40 (25-105 °C)	–2.8 (0-100 °C)	11	690-965	100-140	7.15	0.258
72.5Fe-22Cr-5.5Al	1450	20 (25-105 °C)	–2.6 (0-100 °C)	11	690-965	100-140	7.1	0.256
81Fe-15Cr-4Al	1250	±50 (25-105 °C)	–1.2 (0-100 °C)	11	620-900	90-130	7.43	0.268

(a) At 20 °C (68 °F). (b) To convert to Ω · circ mil/ft, multiply by 0.6015. (c) Temperature coefficient of resistance is $(R - R_0/R_0 (t - t_0)$, where R is resistance at t °C and R_0 is resistance at the reference temperature t_0 °C. (d) At 25 to 105 °C

pole pieces. Although their magnetic properties are not generally as good as conventional soft magnetic alloys, such as silicon (electrical) steels, iron-nickel alloys with nickel contents ranging from 45 to 79%, or iron-cobalt alloys such as 49Fe-49Co-2V, they have been successfully used for magnetic components that must withstand corrosive environments. As such, they offer a cost-effective alternative to plated iron and silicon-iron components. In addition, the relatively high electrical resistivity of ferritic stainless steels has resulted in superior ac performance.

Special restricted analyses of AISI type 430F are produced for use in solenoid valve components. The ASTM A 838 specification provides typical properties for these alloys. Alloy type 1 is 430F containing approximately 0.4% Si and exhibiting an electrical resistivity of 60 μΩ · cm. When fully mill annealed, it has a hardness of approximately 78 HRB. Its maximum dc permeability is approximately 2×10^3 with a coercivity of about 160 A · m⁻¹ (2 Oe). Alloy type 2 (type 430FR) is a higher-silicon (1.50% Si) version of

430F, with an electrical resistivity of 76 μΩ · cm and a fully annealed hardness of 82 HRB. Despite its higher hardness, alloy type 2 typically exhibits a dc permeability of 2.6×10^3 and a coercivity of 130 A · m⁻¹ (1.6 Oe). Both alloys are available in round centerless ground (C.G.) bar form fully processed, so that in many applications they are suitable for high-volume screw machining of parts, passivation, and placement into service without annealing. Hex bars and other special-shape products may only be available in a cold-drawn condition suitable for machining, but they may require annealing of the parts to develop soft magnetic properties.

Magnetic properties of selected ferritic stainless steels are listed in Table 9.

Martensitic and Precipitation-Hardenable Stainless Steels. All martensitic and most precipitation-hardenable stainless steels are ferromagnetic. Due to the stresses induced by hardening, these grades exhibit permanent magnetic properties in the hardened condition. For a given grade, the coercive force tends to increase

with increasing hardness, rendering these alloys more difficult to demagnetize. If the hardenable martensitic stainless steels are used in the annealed condition, they suffer from:

- Poorer magnetic properties due to the presence of a significant volume of chromium-carbides, which contribute to pinning domain-wall movement
- Reduced corrosion resistance due to matrix depletion of chromium

The ferritic nonhardenable 430 or 430F grades are preferred for soft magnetic applications for these reasons. Magnetic properties of selected martensitic stainless steels are shown in Table 9.

Electrical Resistivity

The electrical resistivity is the electrical resistance offered by a material to the flow of current, times the cross-sectional area of current flow and per unit length of current path (Ref 5). It is expressed in nΩ · m, μΩ · cm, or Ω · circ mil/ft, with the latter unit generally considered obsolete. Resistivity values do not vary appreciably with the standard grades; value ranges from 600 to 800 nΩ · m are most common (see Table 4 in the article "General Introduction" in this Volume). Table 10 shows the influence of temperature on the electrical resistivity of stainless steels.

As described below, composition variations can significantly increase the resistivity of iron-chromium alloys. Most significant is the addition of aluminum for electrical resistance heating element applications.

Resistance heating alloys are used in many varied applications—from small household appliances to large industrial process heating systems and furnaces (Ref 6). In appliances or industrial process heating, the heating elements are usually either open helical coils of resistance wire mounted with ceramic bushings in a suitable metal frame, or enclosed metal-sheathed elements consisting of a smaller-diameter helical coil of resistance wire electrically insulated from

Table 12 Recommended maximum furnace operating temperatures for nickel- and iron-base resistance heating

Basic composition, %	Approximate melting point		Maximum furnace operating temperature in air	
	°C	°F	°C	°F
Nickel-chromium and nickel-chromium-iron alloys				
78.5Ni-20Cr-1.5Si (80-20)	1400	2550	1150	2100
77.5Ni-20Cr-1.5Si-1Nb	1390	2540		
68.5Ni-30Cr-1.5Si (70-30)	1380	2520	1200	2200
68Ni-20Cr-8.5Fe-2Si	1390	2540	1150	2100
60Ni-16Cr-22Fe-1.5Si	1350	2460	1000	1850
35Ni-30Cr-33.5Fe-1.5Si	1400	2550		
35Ni-20Cr-43Fe-1.5Si	1380	2515	925	1700
35Ni-20Cr-42.5Fe-1.5Si-1Nb	1380	2515		
Iron-chromium-aluminum alloys				
83.5Fe-13Cr-3.25Al	1510	2750	1050	1920
81Fe-14.5Cr-4.25Al	1510	2750		
79.5Fe-15Cr-5.2Al	1510	2750	1260	2300
73.5Fe-22Cr-4.5Al	1510	2750	1280	2335
72.5Fe-22Cr-5.5Al	1510	2750	1375	2505

Table 13 Comparative life of heating-element materials in various furnace atmospheres
See Table 14 for atmosphere compositions.

				Relative life and maximum operating temperature in				
Element material	Oxidizing (air)	Reducing: dry H₂ or type 501	Reducing: type 102 or 202	Reducing: type 301 or 402	Carburizing: type 307 or 309	Reducing or oxidizing, with sulfur	Reducing, with lead or zinc	Vacuum
Nickel-chromium and nickel-chromium-iron alloys								
80Ni-20Cr	Good to 1150 °C	Good to 1175 °C	Fair to 1150 °C	Fair to 1000 °C	Not recommended(a)	Not recommended	Not recommended	Good to 1150 °C
60Ni-16Cr-22Fe	Good to 1000 °C	Good to 1000 °C	Good to fair to 1000 °C	Fair to poor to 925 °C	Not recommended	Not recommended	Not recommended	...
35Ni-20Cr-43Fe	Good to 925 °C	Good to 925 °C	Good to fair to 925 °C	Fair to poor to 870 °C	Not recommended	Fair to 925 °C	Fair to 925 °C	...
Iron-chromium-aluminum alloys								
Fe, 22Cr, 5.8Al, 1Co	Good to 1400 °C	Fair to poor to 1150 °C(b)	Good to 1150 °C(b)	Fair to 1050 °C(b)	Not recommended	Fair	Not recommended	Good to 1150 °C(b)
22Cr, 5.3Al, bal Fe	Good to 1400 °C	Fair to poor to 1050 °C(b)	Good to 1050 °C(b)	Fair to 950 °C(b)	Not recommended	Fair	Not recommended	Good to 1050 °C(b)

Note: Inert atmosphere of argon or helium can be used with all materials. Nitrogen is recommended only for the nickel-chromium group. Temperatures listed are element temperatures, not furnace temperatures. (a) Special 80Ni-20Cr elements with ceramic protective coatings designated for low voltage (8 to 16 V) can be used. (b) Must be oxidized first

the metal sheath by compacted refractory insulation. In industrial furnaces, elements often must operate continuously at temperatures as high as 1300 °C (2350 °F) for furnaces used in metal-treating industries, 1700 °C (3100 °F) for kilns used for firing ceramics, and occasionally 2000 °C (3600 °F) or higher for special applications.

The primary requirements of materials used for heating elements are high melting point, high electrical resistivity, reproducible temperature coefficient of resistance, good oxidation resistance, absence of volatile components, and resistance to contamination. Other desirable properties are good elevated-temperature creep strength, high emissivity, low thermal expansion, and low modulus (both of which help minimize thermal fatigue), good resistance to thermal shock, and good strength and ductility at fabrication temperatures.

The four groups of electrical resistance heating alloys include nickel-base alloys (Ni-Cr and Ni-Cr-Fe alloys), iron-chromium-aluminum alloys containing 13 to 22% Cr and 3.25 to 5.5% Al, pure metals (platinum and refractory metals molybdenum, tantalum, and tungsten), and non-metallic materials such as silicon carbide, graphite, and molybdenum disilicide. Of these four groups, the nickel-base and Fe-Cr-Al are the most commonly used with the pure metals and non-metallics used for service above approximately 1370 °C (2500 °F) (Ref 6). Table 11 lists nominal compositions and properties of nickel-base and Fe-Cr-Al alloys. Table 12 presents recommended maximum operating temperatures for resistance heating materials for furnace applications.

The Fe-Cr-Al heating alloys are higher in electrical resistivity and lower in density than Ni-Cr and Ni-Cr-Fe alloys. In addition, these alloys exhibit resistivities that are more than twice that of standard stainless steel grades. Resistivity of Fe-Cr-Al alloys depends on both aluminum and chromium contents, with aluminum being predominant (see Fig. 3).

These alloys have excellent resistance to oxidation at elevated temperatures because reaction with atmospheric oxygen forms a protective layer of relatively pure alumina. At about 1200 °C (2200 °F), this oxide consists of nearly pure Al_2O_3. This gray-white protective skin has extremely high dielectric strength. The electrical re-

sistivity of aluminum oxide is 10^{12} $\Omega \cdot$ m at room temperature, and at about 1100 °C (2000 °F) it is still 10^4 $\Omega \cdot$ m. Under normal operating conditions, deterioration of the oxide surface layer and the resulting aluminum depletion are fairly slow provided there is no contact with certain refractories at temperatures above 980 °C (1800 °F). The time required for a 10% change in resistance varies from 75 to 100% of heater life (time to burnout), depending on the particular metal, the size of the heater, and the operating temperature. Table 13 compares the serviceabilities of various heating-element alloys in various high-temperature environments. The types and compositions of

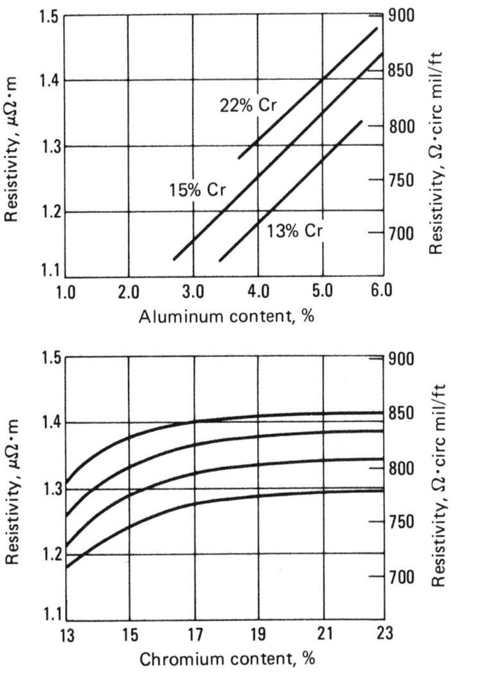

Fig. 3 Effects of aluminum and chromium on resistivity of Fe-Cr-Al heating alloys. Source: Ref 6

Table 14 Types and compositions of standard furnace atmospheres
See Table 13 for comparative life of heating elements in these atmospheres.

		Composition, vol%					Typical dew point	
Type	Description	N₂	CO	CO₂	H₂	CH₄	°C	°F
Reducing atmospheres								
102(a)	Exothermic unpurified	71.5	10.5	5.0	12.5	0.5	27	80
202	Exothermic purified	75.3	11.0	...	13.0	0.5	−40	−40
301	Endothermic	45.1	19.6	0.4	34.6	0.3	10	50
502	Charcoal	64.1	34.7	...	1.2	...	−29	−20
501	Dissociated ammonia	25	...	...	75	...	−51	−60
Carburizing atmospheres								
307	Endothermic + hydrocarbon			No standard composition			...	...
309	Endothermic + hydrocarbon + ammonia			No standard composition			...	...

(a) This atmosphere, refrigerated to obtain a dew point of 4 °C (40 °F), is widely used.

standard furnace atmospheres are listed in Table 14.

REFERENCES

1. M. Rouby and P. Blanchard, Physical and Mechanical Properties of Stainless Steels, *Stainless Steels,* les éditions de physique, 1993, p 111-158
2. J.R. Lewis, Physical Properties of Stainless Steels, *Handbook of Stainless Steels,* D. Peckner and I.M. Bernstein, Ed., McGraw-Hill, Inc., 1977, p 19-1 to 19-36
3. "Design Guidelines for the Selection and Use of Stainless Steels," Document 9014, Nickel Development Institute, Toronto, Canada
4. D.W. Dietrich, Magnetically Soft Materials, *Properties and Selection: Nonferrous Alloys and Special-Purpose Materials,* Vol 2, *ASM Handbook* (formerly 10th ed., *Metals Handbook*), ASM International, 1990, p 761-781
5. J.R. Davis, Ed., *ASM Materials Engineering Dictionary,* ASM International, 1992
6. R.A. Watson, et al., Electrical Resistance Alloys, *Properties and Selection: Nonferrous Alloys and Special-Purpose Materials,* Vol 2, *ASM Handbook* (formerly 10th ed., *Metals Handbook*), ASM International, 1990, p 822-839

Low-Temperature Properties

ALL STRUCTURAL METALS undergo changes in properties when cooled from room temperature to temperatures below 0 °C (32 °F) (temperatures in the "subzero" range). The greatest changes in properties occur when the metal is cooled to very low temperatures near the boiling points of liquid hydrogen and liquid helium. However, even at the less-severe subzero temperatures encountered in arctic regions, where the temperatures may fall to as low as –70 °C (–95 °F), carbon steels become embrittled. To avoid brittle fracture of structures, pressure vessels, and vehicles in cold regions, certain low-alloy steels can be used that retain high degrees of notch toughness and crack toughness (fracture toughness) at the lowest exposure temperatures.

The effects of subzero temperatures must also be considered in selection of materials for aircraft, missiles, and space vehicles that are exposed to the temperatures of upper altitudes and outer space. These structures are "weight limited," so they must be fabricated from materials with high subzero temperatures. At the same time, these materials are required to retain high levels of fracture toughness at all exposure temperatures for "fail safe" service. Certain titanium alloys, aluminum alloys, and cold-worked stainless steels have been used successfully in fabricating weight-limited structures according to state-of-the-art design. A major requirement of materials for liquefaction equipment and for containment and transport of liquefied hydrocarbon gases and liquefied elemental gases is toughness at the boiling temperature of the liquid. Table 1 lists the boiling points of ammonia, common liquefied hydrocarbon gases,

and th elemental gases oxygen, argon, nitrogen, neon, hydrogen, and helium. Temperatures below –150 °C (–238 °F) often are identified as cryogenic temperatures. Materials selection depends on the lowest exposure temperature to be encountered in service. Aluminum alloys, low-alloy steels, 9Ni steels, and austenitic stainless steels have been used successfully for liquefaction, containment, and transport of these liquids.

Requirements are more critical in selecting materials for welded structures such as liquid oxygen, liquid hydrogen, and liquid helium tankage, and associated piping and fittings for rockets and launch vehicles. Among these requirements are minimum weight, high toughness of the base metal at cryogenic temperatures, and high strength and toughness of the welded joints. Materials that have been used successfully for these structures include aluminum alloys, titanium alloys, cold-worked austenitic stainless steels, and a high-nickel alloy (for spherical pressure vessels in liquid oxygen).

Certain metals, alloys, compounds, and ceramics become semiconductors at temperatures below about –260 °C (–436 °F). To achieve these temperatures, all superconducting devices must

be cooled with liquid helium. Therefore, structural materials selected for cryogenic components of superconducting machinery, magnets, and transmission systems must be suitable for use at liquid-helium temperature. Furthermore, these components are subjected to high stresses in service, and thus safeguards must be employed to minimize service failures. In order to obtain the required strength and toughness along with a reasonable degree of fabricability, certain austenitic stainless steels and high-nickel alloys (superalloys) usually are designed for highly stressed components of structures that will be cooled with liquid helium.

Because of extensive research programs conducted since the 1960s to obtain information on properties of structural materials at subzero temperatures, it is now possible to select materials for most critical components with reasonable confidence. There are still applications involving exposure of materials to extreme conditions where current materials fall short of requirements. However, much information has accumulated to provide a basis for selection of materials (metals and alloys) for subzero applications.

In this article, typical room-temperature and subzero-temperature mechanical properties are presented for chromium-nickel (300 series), chromium-nickel-manganese (200 series), and

Table 1   Boiling points of liquefied gases

Liquefied gas	Boiling temperature(a)		
	K	°C	°F
Ammonia	239.8	–33.3	–27.9
Propane	230.8	–42.3	–44.1
Propylene	226.1	–47.0	–52.6
Carbon dioxide	194.6(b)	–78.5(b)	–109.3(b)
Acetylene	189.1	–84.0	–119.2
Ethane	184.8	–88.3	–126.9
Ethylene	169.3	–103.8	–154.8
Methane	111.7	–161.4	–258.5
Oxygen	90.1	–183.0	–297.4
Argon	87.4	–185.7	–302.3
Nitrogen	77.3	–195.8	–320.4
Neon	27.2	–245.9	–410.6
Hydrogen	20.4	–252.7	–422.9
Helium	4.2	–268.9	–452.1

(a) At 1 atm. (b) Sublimation temperature

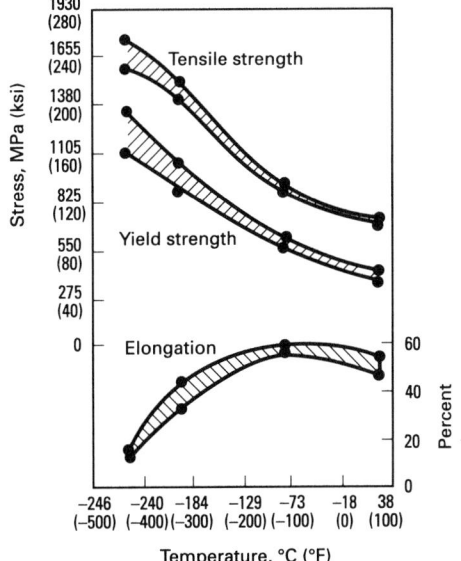

Fig. 1   Effect of low temperature on tensile properties of 21-6-9 stainless steel. Plate specimen (120 mm, or 4.75 in. thick), annealed 1065 °C (1950 °F), water quenched. Source: Ref 1

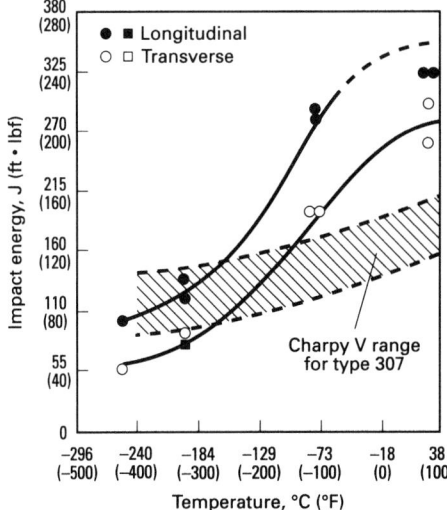

Fig. 2   Effect of low temperature on Charpy V-notch impact properties of 21-6-9 stainless steel. Plate specimen (120 mm, or 4.75 in. thick), annealed at 1065 °C (1950 °F), water quenched. Source: Ref 1

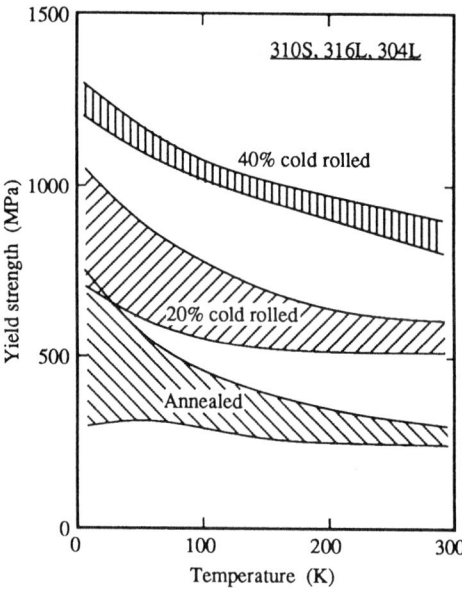

Fig. 3 Effect of cold rolling on the yield strength of austenitic stainless steels. Source: Ref 2

precipitation-hardening (PH) austenitic stainless steels. In addition to tensile property data, typical data on fracture toughness, fatigue-crack-growth rates, and fatigue strengths at room temperature and at subzero temperatures for base metal and weld metal are provided. Data are also presented for sheet, plate, bar, forgings, and castings when available, and for different orientations, because all of these variables may affect results. Chemical compositions for the alloys discussed in this article can be found in the articles "General Introduction," "Metallurgy and Properties of Wrought Stainless Steels," and "Metallurgy and Properties of Cast Stainless Steels" in this Volume.

Subzero Characteristics of Austenitic Stainless Steels

Austenitic stainless steels have been used extensively for subzero applications to –269 °C (–452 °F). These steels contain sufficient amounts of nickel and manganese to depress the M_s temperature into the subzero range. Thus they retain face-centered-cubic crystal structures on cooling from hot working or annealing temperatures.

The tensile strengths of chromium-nickel austenitic stainless steels increase markedly with decreasing temperature; yield strengths also increase but to a lesser degree.

Correspondingly, there is some reduction in ductility as measured by elongation and reduction of area, but ductility values remain high down to the lowest temperature for which data are available. These steels also retain good toughness at –269 °C (–452 °F). These trends are illustrated in Fig. 1 and 2, which show tensile and impact values, respectively, for alloy 21-6-9 (UNS S21900), a high-manganese, high-nitrogen austenitic grade used extensively for cryogenic applications. Strength of austenitic steels can be increased by

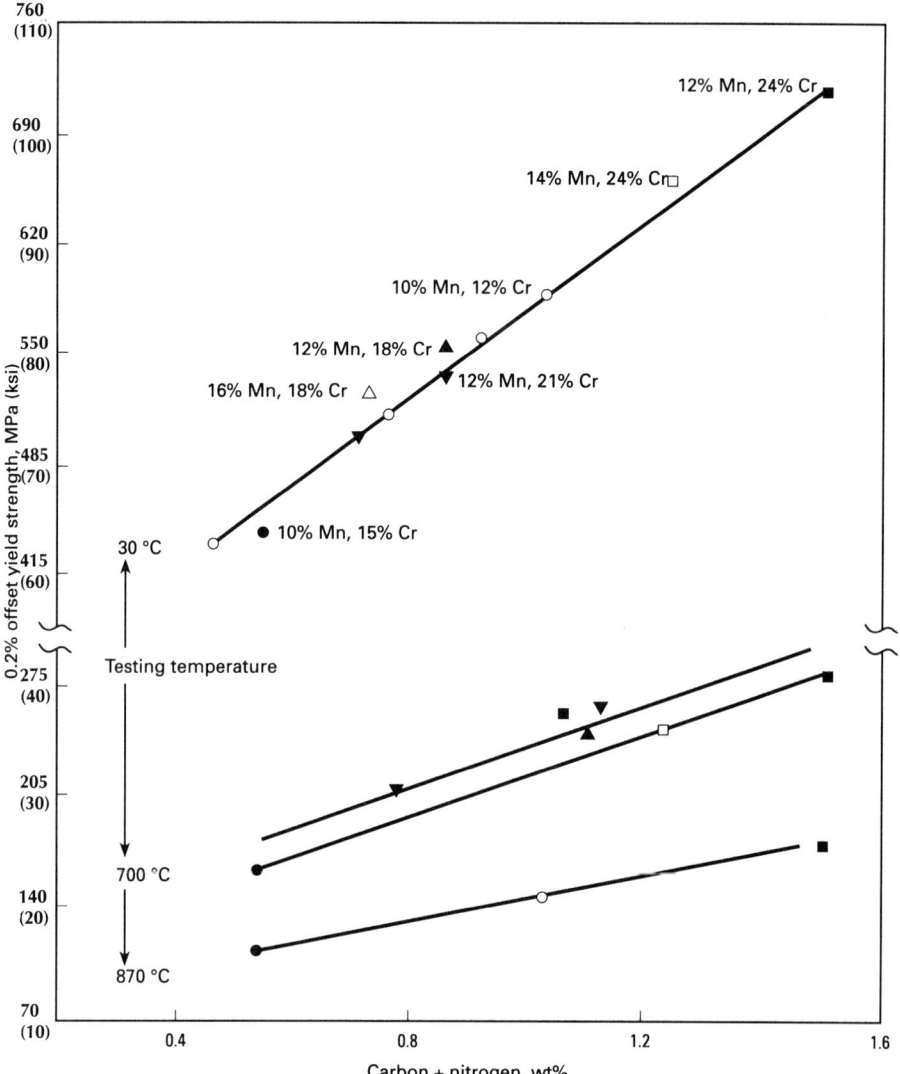

Fig. 4 Effect of carbon and nitrogen contents on the yield strength of austenitic chromium-manganese stainless steels. Source: Ref 3

cold rolling or cold drawing. Cold working at –196 °C (–320 °F) is more effective in increasing strength than cold working at room temperature. For metallurgically unstable stainless steels such as 301, 304, and 304L, plastic deformation at subzero temperatures causes partial transformation to martensite, which increases strength. For some cryogenic applications, it is desirable to use a stable stainless steel such as type 310. Figure 3 shows the effect of cold working on the yield strength of types 310, 316L, and 304L stainless steels. Stainless steels are also strengthened by interstitial and solid-solution alloying and heat treatment. Small amounts of nitrogen increase the strengths of these steels. Manganese additions are used in some steels (200 series) to replace some of the nickel. Figure 4 shows the 0.2% yield strength of chromium-manganese steels as a function of carbon and nitrogen content. In Fig. 5, the effect of carbon plus nitrogen on yield strength at 4 K for an Fe-18Cr-10Ni steel is presented. The break in the linear dependencies at about 0.15% (C + N) is related to martensitic transformation; at lower

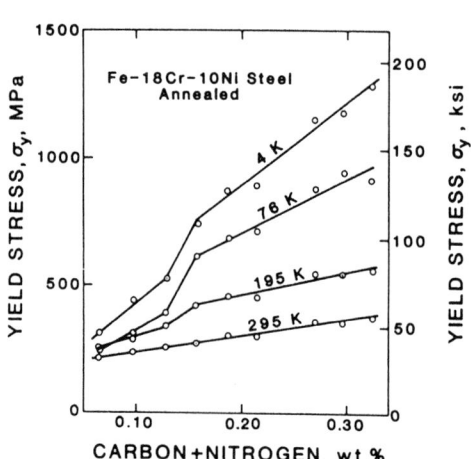

Fig. 5 Effect of carbon and nitrogen contents on the yield strength of a 300-series stainless steel. Source: Ref 4

Table 2 Typical tensile properties of annealed 300-series austenitic stainless steels

Temperature		Tensile strength		Yield strength		Elongation,	Reduction	Notch tensile strength(a)		Young's modulus	
°C	°F	MPa	ksi	MPa	ksi	%	in area, %	MPa	ksi	GPa	10⁶ psi

303 bar, longitudinal orientation

24	75	730	106	425	61.4	67	70	...	...	...	...
−78	−108	1190	172	435	63.3	43	60	...	...	...	...
−196	−320	1660	240	465	67.3	36	54	...	...	...	...
−253	−423	2060	298	570	82.6	33	...	...	...	...	...
−269	−452	1830	266	...	...	30	37	...	...	...	...

304 sheet, longitudinal orientation

24	75	660	95.5	295	42.5	75	...	715	104	...	...
−196	−320	1625	236	380	55.0	42	...	1450	210	...	...
−253	−423	1800	261	425	62.0	31	...	1160	168	...	...
−269	−452	1700	247	570	82.5	30	...	1230	178	...	...

304 plate, longitudinal orientation

24	75	590	85.9	330	47.6	64	...	...	...	...	...
−253	−423	1720	250	410	59.4	...	...	...	...	...	...

304 bar, longitudinal orientation

24	75	640	92.8	235	33.9	76	82	710	103	...	...
−78	−108	1150	167	300	43.2	50	76	...	...	...	...
−196	−320	1520	221	280	40.9	45	66	1060	153	...	...
−253	−423	1860	270	420	60.6	27	54	1120	162	...	...
−269	−452	1720	250	400	58.2	30	55	...	...	...	...

304L sheet, longitudinal orientation

24	75	660	95.9	295	42.8	56	...	730	106	...	...
−78	−108	980	142	250	36.0	43	...	1030	150	...	...
−196	−320	1460	212	275	39.6	37	...	1420	206	...	...
−253	−423	1750	254	305	44.5	33	...	1290	187	...	...
−269	−452	1590	230	405	58.5	29	...	1460	212	...	...

304L sheet, transverse orientation

−269	−452	1540	223	410	59.5	35	...	...	...	...	...

304L bar, longitudinal orientation

24	75	660	95.5	405	58.9	78	81	...	...	190	27.6
−78	−108	1060	153	435	62.8	70	74	...	...	...	...
−196	−320	1510	219	460	66.6	43	66	...	...	205	29.7
−253	−423	1880	273	525	75.8	42	41	...	...	...	...
−269	−452	1660	241	545	79.4	34	56	...	...	200	29.2

310 sheet, longitudinal orientation

24	75	570	83.0	240	35.0	50	...	645	93.9	...	...
−196	−320	1080	156	545	79.1	68	...	1070	155	...	...
−253	−423	1300	188	715	104	56	...	1250	182	...	...
−269	−452	1230	178	770	112	58	...	...	...	...	...

310 sheet, transverse orientation

24	75	600	86.8	240	34.8	46	...	630	91.6	...	...
−269	−452	1280	186	800	116	58	...	...	...	...	...

310 bar, longitudinal orientation

24	75	585	84.8	340	49.1	50	76	770	112	...	...
−78	−108	740	107	305	43.9	72	68	...	...	...	...
−196	−320	1090	158	520	75.5	68	50	...	...	205	29.9
−253	−423	1390	202	855	124	44	48	1305	189	...	...
−269	−452	1300	189	715	104	50	41	...	...	205	29.9

310S forging, transverse orientation

24	75	585	84.8	260	37.9	54	71	800	116	...	...
−196	−320	1100	159	605	87.6	72	52	1350	196	...	...
−269	−452	1300	189	815	118	64	45	1600	232	...	...

316 sheet, longitudinal orientation

24	75	595	86.4	275	39.8	60	...	...	...	...	...
−253	−423	1580	229	665	96.6	55	...	...	...	...	...

321 sheet, longitudinal orientation

24	75	620	89.6	225	32.4	55	...	625	90.4	180	26.0
−196	−320	1380	200	315	45.6	46	...	1520	220	205	29.5
−253	−423	1650	239	375	54.5	36	...	1460	212	210	30.7

321 bar, longitudinal orientation

24	75	675	97.6	430	62.2	55	79	...	...	...	...
−78	−108	1060	153	385	55.9	46	73	...	...	...	...
−196	−320	1540	223	450	65.4	38	60	...	...	...	...
−253	−423	1860	270	405	58.5	35	44	...	...	...	...

(continued)

(a) K_t = 5.2 for 304 and 304L sheet; K_t = 14 for 304 bar; K_t = 6.3 for 310 sheet; K_t = 6.4 for 310 bar; K_t = 10 for 310S forging; K_t = 3.5 for 321 sheet.

Table 2 (continued)

Temperature		Tensile strength		Yield strength		Elongation, %	Reduction in area, %	Notch tensile strength(a)		Young's modulus	
°C	°F	MPa	ksi	MPa	ksi	%		MPa	ksi	GPa	10^6 psi
347 sheet, longitudinal orientation											
24	75	650	94	255	37	52	...	...	...	...	...
−196	−320	1365	198	420	61	47	...	...	...	...	...
−253	−423	1610	234	435	63	35	...	...	...	...	...
347 bar											
24	75	670	97.4	340	49.3	57	76	...	...	...	...
−78	−108	995	144	475	68.8	51	71	...	...	...	...
−196	−320	1470	214	430	62.2	43	60	...	...	...	...
−253	−423	1850	268	525	76.4	38	45	...	...	...	...

(a) K_t = 5.2 for 304 and 304L sheet; K_t = 14 for 304 bar; K_t = 6.3 for 310 sheet; K_t = 6.4 for 310 bar; K_t = 10 for 310S forging; K_t = 3.5 for 321 sheet.

carbon plus nitrogen contents, the strain-induced martensite reduces the lower flow strength.

Results from these studies (Ref 3, 4) clearly indicate that nitrogen additions strengthen considerably more than equivalent carbon additions at low temperatures. Alloying with nitrogen instead of carbon also reduces the tendency toward sensitization. Furthermore, nitrogen is less expensive than carbon. For these reasons, nitrogen is now usually selected to increase the low-temperature strength of many austenitic stainless steels, including types 304LN (Ref 5) and 316LN (Ref 6).

As mentioned above, heat treatment also plays an important role in strengthening some stainless steel grades. For example, maximum strength is obtained for A-286 alloy, an austenitic PH stainless steel, by solution treating and aging (see the articles "Metallurgy and Properties of Wrought Stainless Steels" and "Heat Treating" in this Volume). Type 416 is a martensitic straight-chromium stainless steel that is usually used in the quenched-and-tempered condition. It is included in this discussion because there are applications in rotating pumps and other machinery in which a magnetic material is needed to activate counters.

Types 301 and 310 have been used in the form of extra-hard cold-rolled sheet to provide high strength in such applications as the liquid oxygen and liquid hydrogen tanks for rockets and other aerospace vehicles. Joining was done by butt fusion welding, and reinforcing strips were spot welded to the tank along the weld joint. In another method for producing high-strength cylindrical tanks, welded preform tanks are fabricated from annealed type 301 stainless steel, submerged in liquid nitrogen while in a cylindrical die, and expanded (cryoformed) by pressurizing until the preform fits the die. The amount of strengthening depends on the amount of plastic deformation incurred in expanding the preform to the size of the die. Strengthening results from the dual effects of cold working of the austenite and partial transformation of the austenite to martensite.

Type 304 (and 304L) stainless steel usually is used in the annealed condition for tubing, pipes, and valves employed in transfer of cryogens; for Dewar flasks and storage tanks; and for structural components that do not require high strength. Types 310 and 310S are considered to be metallurgically stable for all conditions of cryogenic exposure. Therefore, these steels are used for structural components in which maximum stability and a high degree of toughness are required at cryogenic temperatures.

Type 316 stainless steel is less stable than type 310, but it has been reported that tensile specimens of type 316 pulled to 0.2% offset (at the yield load) at −269 °C (−452 °F) showed no indication of martensite formation in the deformed regions (Ref 7). However, when tensile specimens of type 316 were pulled to fracture at −269 °C (−452 °F), the metallographic structures in the areas of the fractures transformed to approximately 50% martensite (Ref 8). Types 316, 316L, and 316LN stainless steels are important materials for structural components of superconducting and magnetic fusion machinery. For higher-strength components of cryogenic structures, there is a group of stainless steels that contain significant amounts of manganese in place of some of the nickel, along with small additions of nitrogen and other elements that increase strength. Among these stainless steels are:

- UNS S20100 (type 201)
- UNS S20200 (type 202)
- UNS S20500 (type 205)
- UNS S20910 (Nitronic 50)
- UNS S21400 (ASTM XM-31)
- UNS S21460 (Cryogenic Tenelon)
- UNS S21500 (Esshite 1250)
- UNS S21800 (Nitronic 60)
- UNS S21900 (21-6-9, Nitronic 40, or Pyromet 538)
- UNS S24000 (Nitronic 33)
- UNS S24100 (Nitronic 32)
- UNS S28200 (18-8 Plus)

Each of these alloys, including the proprietary Kromarc 58 alloy (Fe-15.5Cr-9.3Mn-8.0Ni-0.17N) described in this article, contains from 5.5 to 19% Mn and 0.10 to 0.60% N. The effects of nitrogen additions are shown in Fig. 4 and 5. Extensive studies have also been carried out on the effects of manganese additions on cryogenic properties (Ref 9). Ishikawa (Ref 10) concluded that Fe-(10-20)Mn-15Ni-15Cr-5Mo alloys are best suited for cryogenic applications. As shown in Fig. 6, optimum impact values can be obtained when the manganese content does not exceed about 22%.

Cast corrosion-resistant stainless steels have been used for bubble chambers, for cylindrical magnet tubes for superconducting magnets, for valve bodies, and for other components that are cooled to −269 °C (−452 °F) in service. For such applications, castings are more appropriate than wrought products.

Tensile Properties (Ref 11). Typical tensile properties of annealed 300-series austenitic stainless steels at room temperature and at subzero temperatures are presented in Table 2, and tensile properties of cold-worked 300-series stainless steels are given in Table 3. As discussed earlier, cold working substantially increases yield and tensile strengths and reduces ductility, but ductility and notch toughness of the cold-worked alloy often are sufficient for cryogenic applications. Tensile properties of non-300-series stainless steels are presented in Table 4. The greatest effect of the nitrogen addition to produce an increase in yield strength at cryogenic temperatures can be

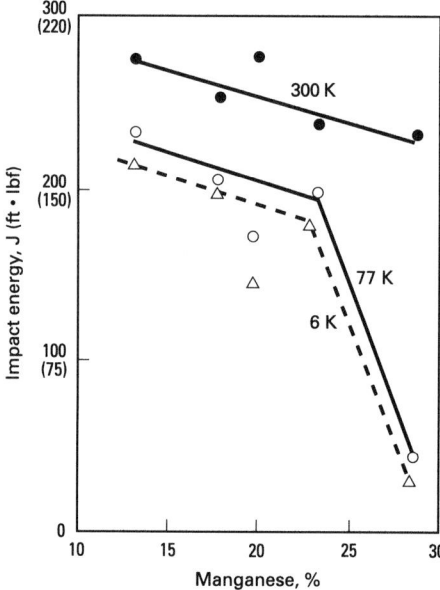

Fig. 6 Effect of manganese content on impact energy at cryogenic temperatures for high-manganese austenitic stainless steels. Source: Ref 10

Table 3 Typical tensile properties of cold-worked 300-series austenitic stainless steel sheet

Temperature		Tensile strength		Yield strength		Elongation,	Notch tensile strength(a)		Young's modulus	
°C	°F	MPa	ksi	MPa	ksi	%	MPa	ksi	GPa	10⁶ psi
301, hard, cold rolled (42 to 60% reduction), longitudinal orientation										
24	75	1310	190	1200	174	18	1390	201	...	...
−78	−108	1560	226	1130	164	23	1460	212	...	...
−196	−320	2020	293	1380	200	19	1660	241	...	...
−253	−423	2110	306	1610	233	14	1830	265	...	...
301, hard, cold rolled (42 to 60% reduction), transverse orientation										
24	75	1310	190	1060	153	10	1430	207	...	...
−78	−108	1560	226	1070	155	28	1430	208	...	...
−196	−320	2060	299	1310	190	28	1670	243	...	...
−253	−423	1900	275	1570	227	8	1360	197	...	...
301, extra hard, cold rolled (over 60% reduction), longitudinal orientation										
24	75	1500	217	1370	198	9	1600	232	175	25.6
−78	−108	1710	248	1400	203	22	1680	244	180	26.3
−196	−320	2220	322	1610	234	22	1940	282	180	26.2
−253	−423	2220	322	1810	262	13	1890	274	190	27.6
−269	−452	2140	310	1930	280	2	...	...	...	...
301, extra hard, cold rolled (over 60% reduction), transverse orientation										
24	75	1590	230	1280	186	8	1520	220	...	...
−78	−108	1770	257	1250	181	18	1590	230	...	...
−196	−320	2190	318	1560	226	18	1680	244	...	...
−253	−423	2180	316	1830	266	5	1340	194	...	...
304, hard, cold rolled, longitudinal orientation										
24	75	1320	191	1190	173	3	1460	212	180	25.9
−78	−108	1470	213	1300	188	10	1590	231	185	26.9
−196	−320	1900	276	1430	208	29	1910	277	200	29.1
−253	−423	2010	292	1560	226	2	2160	313	210	30.5
304, hard, cold rolled, transverse orientation										
24	75	1440	209	1180	171	5	1200	174	195	28.0
−78	−108	1600	232	1330	193	7	1400	203	200	28.9
−196	−320	1870	271	1480	214	23	1690	245	205	30.0
−253	−423	2160	313	1560	226	1	1900	276	215	31.1
304L, 70% cold reduced, longitudinal orientation										
24	75	1320	192	1080	156	3	...	...	...	...
−196	−320	1770	256	1530	222	14	...	...	...	...
−253	−423	1990	288	1770	256	2	...	...	...	...
304L, 70% cold reduced, transverse orientation										
24	75	1440	209	1220	177	4	...	...	...	...
−196	−320	1890	274	1630	236	12	...	...	...	...
−253	−423	2230	324	1940	282	1	...	...	...	...
310, 75% cold reduced, longitudinal orientation										
24	75	1180	171	1100	160	3	1360	197	175	25.4
−78	−108	1410	204	1290	187	4	1530	222	175	25.5
−196	−320	1720	249	1540	223	10	1900	276	180	26.4
−253	−423	2000	290	1790	259	10	2230	324	195	28.3
310, 75% cold reduced, transverse orientation										
24	75	1370	199	1110	161	4	1370	199	195	28.1
−78	−108	1540	224	1290	187	8	1640	238	190	27.6
−196	−320	1880	272	1520	221	10	2050	297	195	28.2
−253	−423	2140	311	1790	260	9	2190	318	200	29.1

(a) K_t = 6.3.

seen in the annealed alloys. Kromarc 58 has been used for several structural applications in prototype superconducting generators. Other nitrogen-strengthened stainless steels have comparable properties. The data for cold-worked type 202 and Kromarc sheet indicate how these alloys can be strengthened by cold working that results in reduced ductility. Solution treating and aging A-286 alloy develops good strength with good ductility and notch toughness in the cryogenic range. Because of its low ductility, type 416 is not recommended for use below −196 °C (−320 °F) except in nonstressed applications. Results of tensile tests on stainless steel weldments at subzero temperatures, given in Table 5, may be significant in selecting stainless steels for cryogenic applications. For annealed plate tested in the as-welded condition, high-manganese Kromarc 58 has the most favorable properties of the alloys in Table 5. Tensile properties of A-286 weldments can be improved by age hardening; however, there is a significant advantage in being able to use weldments in the as-welded condition. Moreover, these alloys are not as difficult to weld as A-286.

Tensile properties of cast stainless steels at subzero temperatures are presented in Table 6. These data indicate that alloys CF8 and CF8M have yield strengths at subzero temperatures comparable to those of equivalent wrought alloys. Yield and tensile strengths of as-cast Kromarc 55 (Fe-9.5Mn-Cr-20Ni), however, are considerably lower than those of the wrought alloy Kromarc 58.

Fracture Toughness (Ref 11). Fracture toughness data for stainless steels are limited because steels of this type that are suitable for use at cryogenic temperatures have very high tough-

Table 4 Typical tensile properties of stainless steels other than the 300 series

Temperature		Tensile strength		Yield strength		Elongation, %	Reduction in area, %	Notch tensile strength(a)		Young's modulus	
°C	°F	MPa	ksi	MPa	ksi			MPa	ksi	GPa	10⁶ psi
202 sheet, annealed, longitudinal orientation											
24	75	705	102	325	47.1	57	...	...	...	...	...
−73	−100	1080	156	485	70.2	41	...	...	...	...	...
−196	−320	1590	231	610	88.3	52	...	...	...	...	...
−268	−450	1420	206	765	111	25	...	...	...	...	...
202 sheet, cold reduced 50%, longitudinal orientation											
24	75	1080	156	965	140	21	...	...	...	...	...
−196	−320	1970	286	1070	155	28	...	...	...	...	...
−268	−450	1950	283	1240	180	20	...	...	...	...	...
21-6-9 plate, longitudinal orientation(b)											
24	75	705	102	385	55.9	54	80	...	...	...	...
−78	−108	895	130	590	85.4	60	75	...	...	...	...
−196	−320	1510	219	970	141	41	33	...	...	...	...
−253	−423	1660	241	1220	177	16	26	...	...	...	...
−269	−452	1700	247	1350	196	22	30	...	...	...	...
Pyromet 538 plate, longitudinal orientation(c)											
24	75	675	97.9	340	49.0	75	81	...	...	...	...
−196	−320	1370	199	800	116	76	73	...	...	...	...
−269	−452	1490	216	1010	147	52	59	...	...	...	...
Nitronic 40 plate, electroslag remelted; as rolled											
24	75	1010	146	840	122	35	72	...	...	...	...
−73	−100	1170	169	945	137	36	71	...	...	...	...
−196	−320	1830	266	1540	223	31	64	...	...	...	...
Nitronic 60 bar, annealed, longitudinal orientation											
24	75	750	109	400	58.1	66	79	1080	157	165	24.0
−73	−100	1020	148	535	77.9	70	81	1480	215	165	24.2
−196	−320	1500	218	695	101	60	66	1900	275	170	24.8
−253	−423	1410	204	860	125	24	27	1870	271	170	24.8
Kromarc 58 sheet, longitudinal orientation(d)											
24	75	695	101	285	41.5	62	...	...	...	...	...
−78	−108	825	120	395	57.6	59	...	...	...	...	...
−196	−320	1280	185	695	101	82	...	...	...	...	...
−253	−423	1450	210	880	128	56	...	...	...	...	...
Kromarc 58 sheet, longitudinal orientation(e)											
24	75	1280	186	1210	175	6	...	1370	198	...	...
−78	−108	1510	219	1430	207	7	...	1640	238	...	...
−196	−320	1880	272	1740	252	9	...	2000	290	...	...
−253	−423	2100	304	1990	288	1	...	2170	315	...	...
Kromarc 58 plate, longitudinal orientation(f)											
24	75	705	102	370	53.8	46	67	930	135	...	...
−196	−320	1300	188	785	114	50	58	1580	229	...	...
−269	−452	1320	192	1100	159	42	55	1880	272	...	...
A-286 sheet, longitudinal orientation(g)											
24	75	860	125	410	59.9	36	...	855	124	...	...
−196	−320	1230	179	615	89.4	44	...	1200	174	...	...
−253	−423	1460	212	745	108	34	...	1370	198	...	...
A-286 sheet, transverse orientation(g)											
24	75	840	122	405	58.9	40	...	855	124	...	...
−196	−320	1210	176	600	87.4	46	...	1160	168	...	...
−253	−423	1450	210	735	107	42	...	1330	193	...	...
A-286 sheet, longitudinal orientation(h)											
24	75	1040	151	690	99.8	21	...	1100	160	...	...
−78	−108	1050	153	695	101	26	...	...	...	...	...
−196	−320	1360	197	820	119	33	...	1380	200	...	...
−253	−423	1510	219	915	133	26	...	1480	214	...	...
A-286 sheet, transverse orientation(h)											
24	75	1050	152	725	105	23	...	1130	164	...	...
−78	−108	1120	163	785	114	27	...	...	...	...	...
−196	−320	1350	196	840	122	33	...	1370	198	...	...
−253	−423	1520	221	930	135	35	...	1450	210	...	...

(continued)

(a) K_t = 7 for Nitronic 60 bar; K_t = 6.3 for Kromarc 58 sheet and A 286 sheet; K_t = 10 for Kromarc 58 plate; K_t = 6.4 for A 286 bar. (b) Annealed 1 h at 1065 °C (1950 °F), WQ. (c) Annealed 1 h at 1095 °C (2000 °F), WQ. (d) Annealed 1 h at 1065 °C (1950 °F). (e) Annealed 1065 °C (1950 °F), cold rolled 80%. (f) Annealed 1 h at 980 °C (1800 °F), WQ. (g) Heat treatment: ½ h at 980 °C (1800 °F), WQ, aged 16 h at 595 °C (1100 °F), AC. (h) Heat treatment: ½ h at 980 °C (1800 °F), WQ or AQ, aged 16 h at 720 °C (1325 °F) AC. (j) Heat treatment: 1.5 h at 960 °C (1800 °F), AC, aged 16 h at 720 to 730 °C (1325 to 1350 °F), AC. (k) Heat treatment: 1 h at 980 °C (1800 °F), OQ, tempered 4 h at 370 °C (700 °F), AC.

Table 4 (continued)

Temperature		Tensile strength		Yield strength		Elongation, %	Reduction in area, %	Notch tensile strength(a)		Young's modulus	
°C	°F	MPa	ksi	MPa	ksi			MPa	ksi	GPa	10^6 psi
A-286 bar, longitudinal orientation(j)											
24	75	1080	157	760	110	28	48	1250	181	180	26.4
−78	−108	1170	170	780	113	32	48	...	...	...	...
−196	−320	1410	204	860	125	40	48	...	...	195	28.4
−253	−423	1610	234	1030	149	41	46	...	...	...	...
−257	−430	1620	235	1030	150	34	46	1490	216	...	...
416 bar, longitudinal orientation(k)											
24	75	1400	203	1200	174	15	53	...	...	...	...
−78	−108	1500	218	1260	183	15	52	...	...	...	...
−196	−320	1800	261	1600	232	9	24	...	...	...	...
−253	−423	2020	293	2020	293	0.4	2	...	...	...	...

(a) K_t = 7 for Nitronic 60 bar; K_t = 6.3 for Kromarc 58 sheet and A 286 sheet; K_t = 10 for Kromarc 58 plate; K_t = 6.4 for A 286 bar. (b) Annealed 1 h at 1065 °C (1950 °F), WQ. (c) Annealed 1 h at 1095 °C (2000 °F), WQ. (d) Annealed 1 h at 1065 °C (1950 °F). (e) Annealed 1065 °C (1950 °F), cold rolled 80%. (f) Annealed 1 h at 980 °C (1800 °F), WQ. (g) Heat treatment: ½ h at 980 °C (1800 °F), WQ, aged 16 h at 595 °C (1100 °F), AC. (h) Heat treatment: ½ h at 980 °C (1800 °F), WQ or AQ, aged 16 h at 720 °C (1325 °F) AC. (j) Heat treatment: 1.5 h at 960 °C (1800 °F), AC, aged 16 h at 720 to 730 °C (1325 to 1350 °F), AC. (k) Heat treatment: 1 h at 980 °C (1800 °F), OQ, tempered 4 h at 370 °C (700 °F), AC.

Table 5 Typical tensile properties of stainless steel weldments

Alloy condition	Welding process	Filler	Form	Base metal orientation	Test temperature		Yield strength		Tensile strength		Elongation, %	Reduction in area, %	Notch tensile strength(a)	
					°C	°F	MPa	ksi	MPa	ksi			MPa	ksi
Type 301, cold rolled 60%; tested as welded	GTA	None	Sheet	L	24	75	...	...	1034	150	7	...	...	...
					−78	−108	...	...	1489	216	13	...	...	...
					−196	−320	...	...	2006	291	16	...	...	...
					−253	−423	...	...	1675	243	6	...	...	...
Type 310, ¾ hard; tested as welded	GTA	310	Sheet	L	24	75	380	55.1	530	76.8	4	...	...	...
					−78	−108	523	75.9	723	105	4	...	...	...
					−196	−320	752	109	1026	149	4	...	...	...
AISI, 310S, annealed	SMA	310S	Plate	...	24	75	334	48.5	582	84.4	40	76	841	122
					−196	−320	660	96.6	1066	155	46	67	1428	207
					−269	−452	829	120	1102	160	26	24	1672	242
21-6-9, annealed	SMA	Inconel 625	Plate	Weld(b)	−269	−452	878	127	1276	183	31	27	...	...
				HAZ(b)	−269	−452	1728	251	1873	272	21	33	...	...
	GTA	Inconel 625	Plate	Weld(b)	−269	−452	951	138	1222	177	18	20	...	...
				HAZ(b)	−269	−452	1740	252	1921	279	17	37	...	...
	GMA	Inconel 625	Plate	Weld(b)	−269	−452	833	121	1087	158	19	27	...	...
				HAZ(b)	−269	−452	1689	245	1866	271	15	27	...	...
Pyromet 528, annealed	GTA	Pyromet 538	Plate	...	24	75	414	60.0	725	105	51	74	1238	180
					−196	−320	1009	146	1456	211	48	61	2119	307
					269	−452	1240	180	1646	239	31	24	1841	267
	GMA	In-182	Plate	...	24	75	413	59.9	729	106	53	75	1018	148
					−196	−320	800	116	1045	152	6	37	1416	205
					−269	−452	805	117	1086	158	6	40	1419	206
Kromarc 58, annealed plate; tested as welded	GTA	Kromarc 58	Plate	L	24	75	498	72.3	916	133	36	61	1153	167
					−78	−320	852	124	1321	192	46	41	1908	277
					−269	−452	1060	154	1438	209	33	40	2173	315
A-286 annealed sheet; welded and age hardened	GTA	A-286	Sheet	L	24	75	601	87.2	861	125	11	...	...	...
					−78	−108	610	88.9	931	135	13	...	...	...
					−196	−320	744	108	1145	166	16	...	...	...
					−253	−423	866	126	1286	186	15	...	...	...
Age hardened sheet; tested as welded	GTA	A-286	Sheet	L	24	75	386	56.0	685	99.3	9	...	...	...
					−78	−108	472	68.4	780	113	8	...	...	...
					−196	−320	601	87.2	948	138	9	...	...	...
					−253	−423	717	104	1069	155	8	...	...	...
Solution treated and aged plate; tested as welded	GTA	Inconel 92	Plate	...	24	75	305	44.3	605	87.7	39	63	...	...
					−196	−320	473	68.6	847	123	39	29	...	...
					−269	−452	583	84.6	914	133	27	27	...	...

(a) K_t = 10. (b) Weld parallel with specimen axis; weld specimens were all weld metal; HAZ specimens contained HAZ plus some weld metal and some base metal.

Table 6 Typical tensile properties of cast stainless steels

Alloy	Temperature		Tensile strength		Yield strength		Elongation, %	Reduction in area,%
	°C	°F	MPa	ksi	MPa	ksi		
Type CF8 (8% ferrite),	24	75	…	…	240	35	70	…
centrifugal castings(a)	−78	−108	…	…	330	48	65	…
	−196	−320	…	…	380	55	55	…
	−269	−452	…	…	495	72	32	…
Type CF8M (24% ferrite)(a)	24	75	480	70	305	44	63	…
	−78	−108	670	97	460	67	60	…
	−196	−320	…	…	625	91	58	…
	−269	−452	…	…	750	109	53	…
Kromarc 55(b)	24	75	475	69	230	33	50	…
	−196	−320	850	123	460	67	66	49
	−253	−423	880	128	560	81.2	42	30

(a) Solution treated 2 h at 1040 °C (1900 °F). (b) Cast, then solution treated 1 h at 1090 °C (2000 °F)

ness. The fracture-toughness data that are available were obtained by the *J*-integral method and converted to $K_{Ic}(J)$ values. Such data for base metal and weldments are shown in Table 7. Fracture toughness of base metals are relatively high even at −269 °C (−452 °F); fracture toughness of fusion zones of welds may be lower or higher than that of the base metal.

The dependence of toughness on strength in high-manganese austenitic alloys is similar to that in Fe-Cr-Ni alloys. The inverse dependence of yield strength for a series of Fe-20Cr-10Ni-C+N alloys is shown in Fig. 7 (the shaded band); the lines on each side of the band indicate the data spread of the high-manganese base metals that were measured at 4 K. The $K_{Ic}(J)$ fracture toughness values plotted in this figure were also converted from *J*-integral measurements.

Fatigue-Crack-Growth Rates (Ref 11). Available data for determining fatigue-crack-growth rates at room temperature and subzero temperatures for austenitic stainless steels and weldments are presented in Table 8. The fatigue-crack-growth rates of the base metals are generally higher at room temperature than at subzero temperatures, or about equal at room temperature and at subzero temperatures, except for 21-6-9 stainless steel. For 21-6-9, fatigue-crack-growth rates are higher at −269 °C (−452 °F) than at room temperature. A log-plot of the *da/dN* data for type 304 stainless steel is shown in Fig. 8. For this steel, fatigue-crack-growth rates are nearly the same, at the same values of ΔK, for room-temperature and cryogenic-temperature tests. Fatigue-crack-growth rates in the fusion zones of welds tend to be higher than in the base metal.

Fatigue Strength (Ref 11). Results of flexural and axial fatigue tests at 10^6 cycles on austenitic stainless steels at room temperature and at subzero temperatures are presented in Table 9. Fatigue strength increases as exposure temperature is decreased. Notched specimens have substantially lower fatigue strengths than corresponding unnotched specimens at all testing temperatures. Reducing surface roughness of unnotched specimens improves fatigue strength.

ACKNOWLEDGMENT

The information in this article is largely taken from J.E. Campbell, Alloys for Structural Applications at Subzero Temperatures, *Metals Handbook*, Vol 3, 9th ed., American Society for Metals, 1980, p 721-772

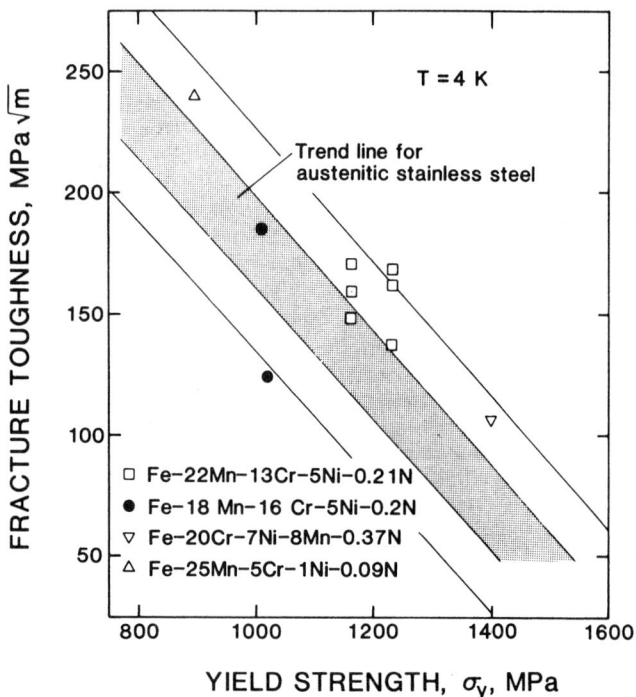

Fig. 7 Relationship between yield strength and fracture toughness at cryogenic temperatures for austenitic stainless steels. Source: Ref 12

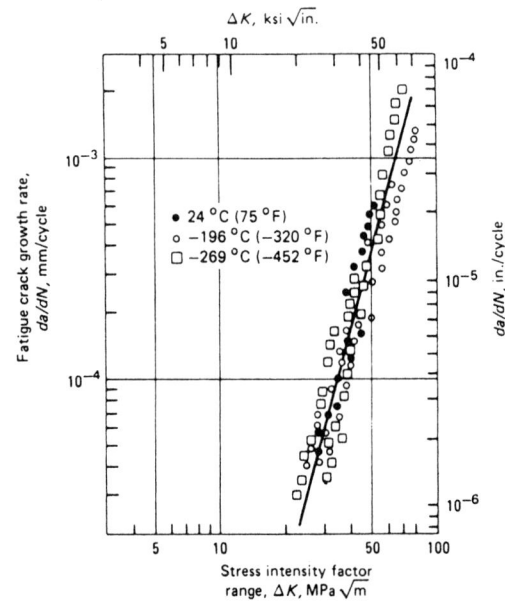

Fig. 8 Fatigue-crack-growth rate data for type 304 austenitic stainless steel (annealed) at room temperature and at subzero temperatures. Source: Ref 11

Table 7 Fracture toughness of austenitic stainless steels and weldments for compact tension specimens

Alloy and condition(a)	Form	Room temperature yield strength MPa	ksi	Orientation	Fracture toughness, $K_{Ic}(J)$, at: 24 °C MPa√m	(75 °F) ksi√in.	–196 °C MPa√m	(–320 °F) ksi√in.	–269 °C MPa√m	(–452 °F) ksi√in.
Type 310S, annealed	Plate	261	37.9	T-L	...	...	...	...	262	236
	Weldment(b)	...	...	...	...	...	...	...	118	106
Pyromet 538, STQ	Plate	338	49	T-L	...	...	275	250	182	165
	Weldment(c)	...	...	...	...	...	...	...	82.4	74.4
	Weldment(b)	...	...	...	...	...	...	...	176	159
Kromarc 58, STQ	Plate	371	53.8	T-L	...	...	...	...	216	195
	Weldment(c)	...	...	...	...	...	...	...	156	141
A-286, STA	Bar	608	88.2	T-S	125	114	123	112	118	107
	Plate	822	119	L-T	161	146	...	...	180	163
	Weldment(c)	...	...	...	...	...	...	...	249	225

(a) STQ = solution treated and quenched. STA for A-286: 900 °C (1650 °F) 5 h, OQ; age at 720 °C (1325 °F) 20 h, AC. Filler wires for 310S: E 310-16; for Kromarc 58: K-58; for Pyromet 538: 21-6-9; for A-286: Inconel 92. (b) Weld produced by shielded metal arc process. (c) Weld produced by gas-tungsten arc process

Table 8 Fatigue-crack-growth rate (*da/dN*) data for compact tension specimens of austenitic stainless steels

Alloy and condition(a)	Orientation	Frequency, Hz	Stress ratio, R	Test temperature or temperature range °C	°F	C(b) da/dN:mm/cycle ΔK:MPa√m	da/dN:in./cycle ΔK:ksi√in.	n (b)	Estimated range for ΔK MPa√m	ksi√in.
Type 304 annealed plate	T-L	20 to 28	0.1	24 to –269	75 to –452	2.7×10^{-9}	1.4×10^{-10}	3.0	22 to 80	20 to 73
Type 304L annealed plate	T-L	20 to 28	0.1	24	75	2.0×10^{-10}	1.2×10^{-11}	4.0	22 to 54	20 to 49
				–196, –269	–320, –452	3.4×10^{-11}	2.0×10^{-12}	4.0	26 to 80	24 to 73
Type 310S annealed plate	T-L	20 to 28	0.1	24	75	3.5×10^{-11}	2.1×10^{-12}	4.4	24 to 35	22 to 32
				24	75	4.7×10^{-9}	2.4×10^{-10}	3.0	35 to 60	32 to 55
				–196, –269	–320, –452	1.1×10^{-10}	6.1×10^{-12}	3.7	25 to 80	23 to 73
	...	10	0.1	–196, –269	–320, –452	1.4×10^{-10}	7.9×10^{-12}	3.75	24 to 71	22 to 65
Type 310S, SMA weld with E310-16 filler	...	10	0.1	–196, –269	–320, –452	7.8×10^{-13}	5.0×10^{-14}	5.15	27 to 66	25 to 60
Type 316 annealed plate	T-L	20 to 28	0.1	24 to –269	75 to –452	2.1×10^{-10}	1.2×10^{-11}	3.8	19 to 16	17 to 14
21-6-9 annealed plate	T-L	20 to 28	0.1	24, –196	75, –320	1.9×10^{-10}	1.1×10^{-11}	3.7	25 to 80	23 to 73
				–269	–452	3.6×10^{-11}	2.2×10^{-12}	4.4	25 to 70	23 to 64
Pyromet 538, GTA weld in annealed plate using 21-6-9 filler	T-L	10	0.1	24	75	1.8×10^{-10}	9.9×10^{-12}	3.7	26 to 55	24 to 50
				–196, –269	–320, –452	7.6×10^{-14}	5.47×10^{-15}	6.36	24 to 44	22 to 40
Pyromet 538, SMA weld in annealed plate using Inconel 182 filler	T-L	10	0.1	24 to –269	75 to –452	2.5×10^{-12}	1.6×10^{-13}	5.13	25 to 55	23 to 50
Kromarc 58 annealed plate		10	0.1	24	75	2.3×10^{-10}	1.3×10^{-11}	3.9	31 to 44	28 to 40
				–196, –269	–320, –452	2.0×10^{-9}	1.04×10^{-10}	3.0	27 to 77	25 to 70
Kromarc 58, GTA weld in annealed plate		10	0.1	–196, –269	–320, –452	1.3×10^{-11}	7.6×10^{-13}	4.45	27 to 60	25 to 55
A-286 forging, STA	T-S	20 to 28	0.1	24	75	2.5×10^{-9}	1.3×10^{-10}	3.0	25 to 90	23 to 82
				–196, –269	–320, –452	2×10^{-12}	1.1×10^{-13}	4.0	32 to 90	29 to 82
A-286 plate, STA		10	0.1	24	75	1.3×10^{-8}	6.6×10^{-10}	2.7	35 to 55	32 to 50
				–196	–320	3.6×10^{-8}	1.76×10^{-9}	2.18	33 to 55	30 to 50
				–269	–452	2.7×10^{-8}	1.3×10^{-9}	2.18	33 to 55	30 to 50
A-286, GTA weld in ST plate using Inconel 92 filler	T-L	10	0.1	24	75	1.3×10^{-11}	7.66×10^{-13}	4.63	25 to 37	23 to 34
				–196, –269	–320, –452	1.8×10^{-12}	1.16×10^{-13}	5.0	30 to 55	27 to 50

(a) STA for A-286: 900 °C (1650 °F) 5 h, OQ; 720 °C (1325 °F) 20 h, AC. ST for A-286: 900 °C (1650 °F) 5 h, OQ. (b) These data are for the constants C and n in the equation $da/dN = C (\Delta K)^n$

REFERENCES

1. *Manganese Stainless Steels*, R. Lula, Ed., Manganese Center, Paris, France, 1986
2. K. Ishikawa et al., Cryogenic Properties of High-Manganese Austenitic Steels for Superconducting Fusion Systems, *High Manganese High Nitrogen Austenitic Steels*, R. Lula, Ed., ASM International, 1992, p 215-221
3. E.J. Dulis, Age Hardening Austenitic Stainless Steels, *Metallurgical Developments in High Alloy Steels*, Iron and Steel Institute, 1964
4. R.L. Tobler and R.P. Reed, Tensile and Fracture Properties of Manganese-Modified AISI 304 Type Stainless Steel, *Advances in Cryogenic Engineering—Materials*, Vol 28, R.P. Reed and A.F. Clark, Ed., Plenum Press, 1982, p 83-92
5. R.P. Reed and N.J. Simon, Low Temperature Strengthening of Austenitic Stainless Steels with Nitrogen and Carbon, *Advances in Cryogenic Engineering—Materials,* Vol 30, A.F. Clark and R.P. Reed, Ed., Plenum Press, 1984, p 127-136
6. N.J. Simon and R.P. Reed, Design of 316LN-Type Alloys, *Advances in Cryogenic Engi-*

Table 9 Results of fatigue-life tests on austenitic stainless steels

Alloy and condition	Stressing mode	Stress ratio, R	Cyclic frequency, Hz	K_t	Fatigue strengths at 10^6 cycles					
					24 °C (75 °F)		−196 °C (−320 °F)		−253 °C (−423 °F)	
					MPa	ksi	MPa	ksi	MPa	ksi
Type 301 sheet, extra full hard	Flex	−1.0	29, 86	1	496	72	793	115	669	97
				3.1	172	25	303	44	...	...
Type 304L bar, annealed	Axial	−1.0	...	1	269	39	483	70	552(a)	80(a)
				3.1	193	28	207	30	228(a)	33(a)
Type 310 sheet, annealed	Flex(b)	−1.0	...	1	186	27	455	66	597	84
	Flex(c)	−1.0	...	1	213	31	490	71	662	96
Type 310 bar, annealed	Axial	−1.0	...	1	255	37	469	68	607(a)	88(a)
				3.1	186	27	234	34	352(a)	51(a)
Type 321 sheet, annealed	Axial	−1.0	...	1	221	32	303	44	372	54
				3.5	124	18	154	22.3	181	26.3
	Flex(b)	−1.0	30 to 40	1	172	25	303	44	358	52
Type 347 sheet, annealed	Flex(b)	−1.0	30 to 40	1	221	32	421	61	386	56
	Flex(c)	−1.0	30 to 40	1	241	35	469	68	510	74
A-286 sheet, STA(f)	Flex(d)	−1.0	30 to 40	1	427	62	579	84	586	85
	Flex(e)	−1.0	30 to 40	1	496	72	703	102	779	113
A-286 bar, STA(f)	Axial	−1.0	...	1	414	60	579	84	655	95

(a) Tested at −269 °C (−452 °F). (b) Surface finish 64 rms. (c) Surface finish 11 rms. (d) Surface finish 72 rms. (e) Surface finish 10 rms. (f) STA = 980 °C (1800 °F), WQ; 720 °C (1325 °F) 16 h, AC

Engineering—Materials, Vol 34, A.F. Clark and R.P. Reed., Ed., Plenum Press, 1988, p 165-172

7. R.L. Tobler, R.P. Reed, and D.S. Burkhalter, Temperature Dependence of Yielding in Austenitic Stainless Steels, *Advances in Cryogenic Engineering—Materials*, Vol 26, A.F. Clark and R.P. Reed, Ed., Plenum Press, 1980, p 107-110

8. D.C. Larbalestier and H.W. King, Austenitic Stainless Steels of Cryogenic Temperatures, Part 1: Structural Stability and Magnetic Properties, *Cryogenics*, Vol 13 (No. 3), March 1973, p 160-168

9. R.P. Reed and T. Horiuchi, *Austenitic Stainless Steels at Low Temperatures,* Plenum Press, 1982

10. K. Ishikawa et al., *Cryog. Eng.*, Vol 26, 1991, p 255-262

11. J.E. Campbell, Alloys for Structural Applications at Subzero Temperatures, *Metals Handbook*, Vol 3, 9th ed., American Society for Metals, 1980, p 721-772

12. R.P. Reed, P.T. Purtscher, and L.A. Delgado, Low-Temperature Properties of High-Manganese Austenitic Steels, *High Manganese High Nitrogen Austenitic Steels*, R.A. Lula, Ed., ASM International, 1992, p 13-22

Elevated-Temperature Properties

STAINLESS STEELS are widely used at elevated temperatures when carbon and low-alloy steels do not provide adequate corrosion resistance and/or sufficient strength. Carbon and low-alloy steels are generally more economical than stainless steels and are often used in applications with temperatures below about 370 °C (700 °F). Several low-alloy steels with moderate chromium contents (between 1 and 10%) and improved high-temperature strength are also widely used at temperatures above 370 °C (700 °F). These steels include the creep-resistant chromium-molybdenum ferritic steels discussed in the article "Elevated-Temperature Properties of Ferritic Steels" in Volume 1 of the *ASM Handbook.* Carbon steels may even be suitable for temperatures above 370 °C (700 °F) if high strength and oxidation are not concerns.

This article deals with the wrought stainless steels used for high-temperature applications (see the article "Metallurgy and Properties of Cast Stainless Steels" in this Volume for the elevated-temperature properties of cast stainless steels). Corrosion resistance is often the first criterion used to select stainless steel for a particular application. However, strength is also a significant factor in a majority of elevated-temperature applications and may even be the key factor governing the choice of a stainless steel. The stainless steels used in applications in which high-temperature strength is important are sometimes referred to as *heat-resistant steels.*

Table 1 gives some typical compositions of wrought heat-resistant stainless steels, which are grouped into ferritic, martensitic, austenitic, and precipitation-hardening (PH) grades. Of these steels, the austenitic grades offer the highest strength at high temperatures (Fig. 1). The PH steels have the highest strength at lower temperatures (Fig. 1), but they weaken considerably at temperatures above about 425 °C (800 °F).

Production of Steel

In recent years, the melting and refining of wrought heat-resistant alloys have become more and more sophisticated. Traditionally, special melting techniques have been applied to high-strength, high-temperature-resistant alloys, which often contain large amounts of reactive elements. However, even for low-alloy steels and other lower-strength materials, innovations in melting have steadily increased as melting and casting techniques have been optimized.

Low-alloy steels are generally melted in electric arc furnaces or in the basic oxygen furnace. Primary melting may be followed by a further refining procedure such as ladle treatments, vacuum arc remelting (VAR), or electroslag remelting (ESR). An ingot or billet product from the electric furnace is used as an electrode in these remelting operations. Vacuum degassing may also be used to remove gases, particularly hydrogen. These alloys may be cast directly into ingots or, in some cases, may be continuously cast. The VAR and ESR steels have fewer segregations and a finer grain size.

Ferritic stainless steels are electric furnace melted; melting is followed by argon-oxygen deoxidation (AOD) for controlled oxidation of impurities such as sulfur and carbon (when used for reducing carbon, the process is often termed *argon-oxygen decarburization*). Because nitrogen is less expensive, it is often used to replace most of the argon in this process; levels of nitrogen in stainless steels are higher today than 20 years ago because of the use of nitrogen in the AOD process. Basic open hearth melting is also used occasionally, with successful results. Vacuum induction melting and electron-beam hearth reining have been used for melting some grades in order to control interstitial elements.

The austenitic 200- and 300-series stainless steels are usually produced by AOD. The old process for making stainless steel required the use of expensive low-carbon ferrochromium to produce these low-carbon alloys, but lower-cost high-carbon ferrochromium can be used in AOD. The ultimate product is not only less expensive but is also of better quality. In AOD, the carbon monoxide partial pressure over the bath is lowered with argon and/or nitrogen, thus enhancing the removal of carbon by the carbon-oxygen reaction. One disadvantage is the high consumption of expensive argon, but nitrogen can be used to replace most of the argon.

The yield of forgeable stock per ingot is generally higher with vacuum melting because of increased purity. Yield may be increased 10% or more, depending on the alloy. Alloys used for forged gas turbine rotors are manufactured on a large scale by the consumable-electrode vacuum arc process and the electroslag process. In both methods, arc melting is accomplished directly in a water-cooled crucible. Mechanical properties, especially the transverse ductility of forgings made from these ingots, are higher than in forgings made from conventional ingots poured in iron molds. Additional information on the production of stainless steels can be found in the article "Melting and Refining Methods" in this Volume.

Product Forms

Wrought stainless steel alloys are manufactured in all the forms common to the metal industry. A partial list of ASTM specifications for stainless steel products used at elevated temperatures includes:

- Heat-resistant stainless steel plate, sheet, and strip in ASTM A 240
- Heat-resistant stainless steel bars and shapes in ASTM A 479
- Heat-resistant stainless steel forgings in ASTM A 473
- Stainless steel tube in ASTM A 213, A 249, A 268, A 269, A 511, A 632, A 688, A 771, and A 791
- Stainless steel pipe in ASTM A 312, A 376, A 409, A 430, A 731, A 813, and A 814

These specifications include numerous types and variations of stainless steel compositions besides those listed in Table 1. Table 1 does not list silicon contents, which may vary according to product

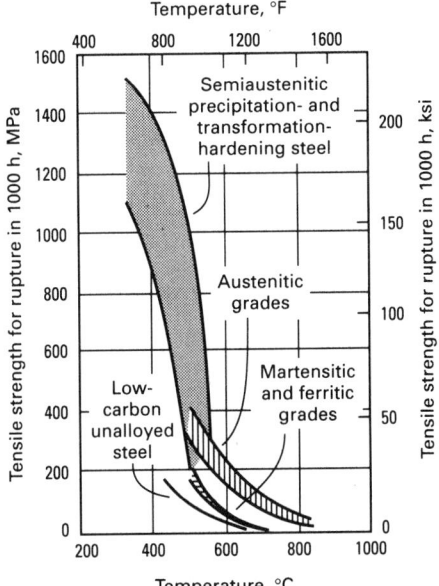

Fig. 1 General comparison of the hot-strength characteristics of austenitic, martensitic, and ferritic stainless steels with those of low-carbon unalloyed steel and semiaustenitic precipitation- and transformation-hardening steels

Table 1 Nominal compositions of wrought iron-base heat-resistant alloys

Designation	UNS number	Composition, %							
		C	Cr	Ni	Mo	N	Nb	Ti	Other
Ferritic stainless steels									
405	S40500	0.15 max	13.0	...	...	...	...	...	0.2 Al
406	...	0.15 max	13.0	...	...	...	...	...	4.0 Al
409	S40900	0.08 max	11.0	0.5 max	...	...	...	6 × C min	...
429	S42900	0.12 max	15	...	...	...	...	...	...
430	S43000	0.12 max	16.0	...	...	...	...	...	...
434	S43400	0.12 max	17.0	...	1.0	...	...	...	...
439	S43035	0.07 max	18.25	...	...	...	...	12 × C min	1.10 Ti max
18 SR	...	0.05	18.0	...	...	...	...	0.40 max	2.0 Al max
18Cr-2Mo	S44400	...	18.5	...	2.0	...	(a)	(a)	0.8 (Ti + Nb) max
446	S44600	0.20 max	25.0	...	...	0.25	...	...	...
E-Brite 26-1	S44627	0.01 max	26.0	...	1.0	0.015 max	0.1	...	...
26-1Ti	S44626	0.04	26.0	...	1.0	...	...	10 × C min	...
29Cr-4Mo	S44700	0.01 max	29.0	...	4.0	0.02 max	...	...	...
Quenched and tempered martensitic stainless steels									
403	S40300	0.15 max	12.0	...	...	...	...	...	...
410	S41000	0.15 max	12.5	...	...	...	...	...	...
410Cb	S41040	0.15 max	12.5	...	...	...	0.12	...	...
416	S41600	0.15 max	13.0	...	0.6(b)	...	...	...	0.15 min S
422	S42200	0.20	12.5	0.75	1.0	...	...	...	1.0 W, 0.22 V
H-46	...	0.12	10.75	0.50	0.85	0.07	0.30	...	0.20 V
Moly Ascoloy	...	0.14	12.0	2.4	1.80	0.05	...	...	0.34 V
Greek Ascoloy	S41800	0.15	13.0	2.0	...	...	...	...	3.0 W
Jethete M-152	...	0.12	12.0	2.5	1.7	...	...	...	0.30 V
Almar 363	...	0.05	11.5	4.5	...	...	...	10 × C min	...
431	S43100	0.20 max	16.0	2.0	...	...	...	...	...
Lapelloy	S42300	0.30	11.5	...	2.75	...	...	...	0.25 V
Precipitation-hardening martensitic stainless steels									
Custom 450	...	0.05 max	15.5	6.0	0.75	...	8 × C min	...	1.5 Cu
Custom 455	...	0.03	11.75	8.5	...	...	0.30	1.2	2.25 Cu
15-5 PH	S15500	0.07	15.0	4.5	...	...	0.30	...	3.5 Cu
17-4PH	S17400	0.04	16.5	4.25	...	...	0.25	...	3.6 Cu
PH 13-8 Mo	S13800	0.05	12.5	8.0	2.25	...	...	...	1.1 Al
Precipitation-hardening semiaustenitic stainless steels									
AM-350	S35000	0.10	16.5	4.25	2.75	0.10	...	...	...
AM-355	S35500	0.13	15.5	4.25	2.75	0.10	...	...	...
17-7 PH	S17700	0.07	17.0	7.0	...	...	...	...	1.15 Al
PH 15-7 Mo	S15700	0.07	15.0	7.0	2.25	...	...	...	1.15 Al
Austenitic stainless steels									
304	S30400	0.08 max	19.0	10.0	...	...	...	...	...
304H	S30409	0.04-0.10	19.0	10.0	...	...	...	...	...
304L	S30403	0.03 max	19.0	10.0	...	...	...	...	...
304N	S30451	0.08 max	19.0	9.25	...	0.13	...	...	...
309	S30900	0.2 max	23.0	13.0	...	...	...	...	...
309H	S30909	0.04-0.10	23.0	13.0	...	...	...	...	...
310	S31000	0.25 max	25.0	20.0	...	...	...	...	...
310H	S31009	0.04-0.10	25.0	20.0	...	...	...	...	...
316	S31600	0.08 max	17.0	12.0	2.5	...	...	...	...
316L	S31603	0.03 max	17.0	12.0	2.5	...	...	...	...
316N	S31651	0.08 max	17.0	12.0	2.5	0.13	...	...	...
316H	S31609	0.04-0.10	17.0	12.0	2.5	...	...	...	...
316LN	S31653	0.035 max	17.0	12.0	2.5	0.13	...	...	...
317	S31700	0.08 max	19.0	13.0	3.5	...	...	...	...
317L	S31703	0.035 max	19.0	13.0	3.5	...	...	...	...
321	S32100	0.08 max	18.0	10.0	...	...	...	5 × C min, 0.70 max	...
321H	S32109	0.04-0.10	18.0	10.0	...	...	...	4 × C min, 0.60 max	...
347	S34700	0.08 max	18.0	11.0	...	...	10 × C min(c)	...	1.0 (Nb + Ta) max
347H	S34709	0.04-0.10	18.0	11.0	...	...	8 × C min(c)	...	1.0 (Nb + Ta) max
348	S34800	0.08 max	18.0	11.0	...	...	10 × C min(c)	...	0.10 Ta max, 1.0 (Nb + Ta) max
348H	S34809	0.04-0.10	18.0	11.0	...	...	8 × C min(c)	...	0.10 Ta max, 1.0 (Nb + Ta) max
19-9 DL	K63198	0.30	19.0	9.0	1.25	...	0.4	0.3	1.25 W
19-9 DX	K63199	0.30	19.2	9.0	1.5	...	...	0.55	1.2 W
17-14-CuMo	...	0.12	16.0	14.0	2.5	...	0.4	0.3	3.0 Cu
201	S20100	0.15 max	17	4.2	...	0.25 max	...	...	...
202	S20200	0.09	18.0	5.0	...	0.10	...	...	8.0 Mn
205	S20500	0.18	17.2	1.4	...	0.36	...	...	...
216	S21600	0.05	10.0	6.0	2.5	0.35	...	...	8.5 Mn
21-6-9	S21900	0.04 max	20.25	6.5	...	0.30	...	...	9.0 Mn
Nitronic 32	S24100	0.10	18.0	1.6	...	0.34	...	...	12.0 Mn
Nitronic 33	S24000	0.08 max	18.0	3.0	...	0.30	...	...	13.0 Mn
Nitronic 50	...	0.06 max	21.0	12.0	2.0	0.30	0.20	...	5.0 Mn
Nitronic 60	S21800	0.10 max	17.0	8.5	2.0	...	...	...	8.0 Mn, 0.20 V, 4.0 Si
Carpenter 18-18 Plus	S28200	0.10	18.0	<0.50	1.0	0.50	...	...	16.0 Mn, 0.40 Si, 1.0 Cu

(a) Ti + Nb = (0.20 + 4C + 4N) min. (b) Optional. (c) Minimum for Nb + Ta

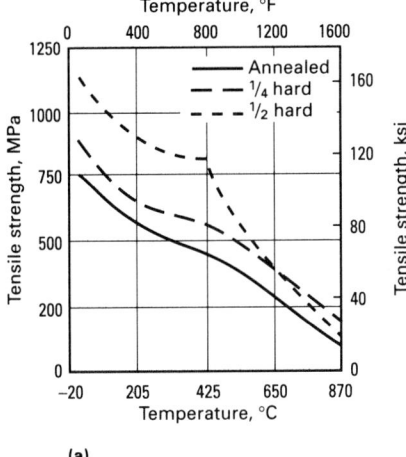

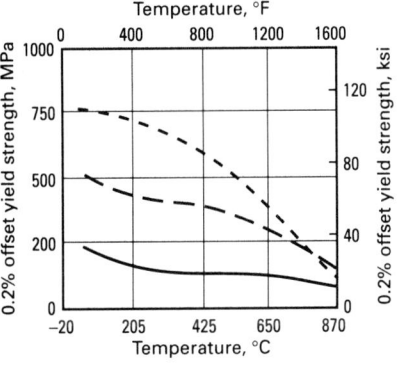

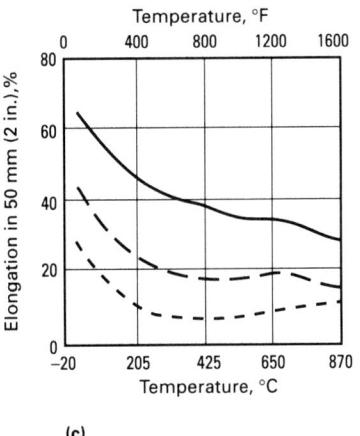

Fig. 2 Effect of short-term elevated temperature on tensile properties of cold-worked type 301 stainless steel. (a) Tensile strength. (b) Yield strength. (c) Elongation

Table 2 ASTM specifications for steels used for elevated-temperature applications

Material	Pipes and tubes	Plates	Castings	Forgings
Carbon steel	A53, A106, A134, A135, A139, A155, A178, A179, A192, A210, A214, A226, A333, A334, A381, A524, A587	A283, A285, A299, A433, A443, A455, A515, A516, A537, A573	A27, A216, A352	A105, A181, A266, A350, A372, A465, A508, A541
C-½Mo	A161, A209, A250, A335, A369, A426	A204, A302, A533	A217, A352, A487	A182, A336, A541
1Cr-½Mo	A213, A335, A369, A426	A387	...	A182, A336
1¼Cr-½Mo	A199, A200, A213, A335, A369, A426	A387, A389	A217, A389	A182, A541
2Cr-½Mo	A199, A200, A213, A335, A369	...	...	...
2¼Cr-1Mo	A199, A213, A335, A369, A426	A387, A542	A217, A487	A182, A336, A357, A541
3Cr-1Mo	A199, A200, A213, A335, A369, A426	A387	...	A182, A336
5Cr-½Mo	A199, A200, A213, A335, A369, A426	A357	A217	A182, A336
7Cr-½Mo	A199, A200, A213, A335, A369, A426	...	...	A182
9Cr-1Mo	A199, A200, A213, A335, A369, A426	...	A217	A182
Ferritic and austenitic stainless steels	A213, A249, A268, A269, A271, A312, A358, A362, A376, A409, A430, A451, A452, A511	A167, A176, A240, A412, A457	A296, A297, A351, A447, A448	A182, A336, A473

form. For example, 316 stainless steel forgings (ASTM A 473) and bar (ASTM A 479) have silicon contents of 1.0% max, whereas 316 stainless steel pipe (ASTM A 312) and pressure vessel plate (ASTM A 240) have silicon contents of 0.75% max.

The elevated-temperature properties of any of these materials are influenced to some extent by the form of the product; these properties depend largely on the specific alloy characteristics, such as oxidation resistance, type of oxide scale, thermal conductivity, and thermal expansion. Time-temperature exposure and the duration and type of loading are also significant factors, as are differences in properties among different product forms.

For alloys that form thin, tenacious scales at elevated temperatures, the stress-rupture properties of bar and sheet of the same alloy will be about the same. On the other hand, for alloys that are less resistant to oxidation, rupture values are likely to be significantly lower for sheet than for the same alloy in bar form because of the greater ratio of surface area to volume, which allows greater interaction between the environment and the substrate metal. In the case of oxidation, a fixed depth of oxidation (such as 75 to 125 μm, or 3 to 5 mils) will more drastically affect properties in 1.3 mm (50 mil) sheet than in 6.5 mm (250 mil) bar stock.

The high-temperature strength of the heat-resistant alloys can be increased by such cold-working processes as rolling, swaging, or hammering. The increased strength is retained, however, only up to the recrystallization temperature. Figure 2, for example, shows the effect of temperature on the tensile properties of cold-worked 301 stainless steel. In particular, cold-worked products have poor resistance to creep, which generally occurs at temperatures slightly above the recrystallization temperature of the metal. During long-term high-temperature exposure, the benefit of cold working is lost, and stress-rupture strength may even fall below annealed strength.

Mechanical Property Considerations

For service at elevated temperatures, the first property considered is the tensile strength during short-term exposure at elevated temperatures (Fig. 1). For applications involving short-term exposure to temperatures below about 480 °C (900 °F), the short-time tensile properties are usually sufficient in the mechanical design of steel components. Typical short-time tensile strengths of various standard stainless steel grades are shown in Fig. 3. For temperatures above 480 °C (900 °F), the design process must include other properties, such as creep rate, creep-rupture strength, creep-rupture ductility, and creep-fatigue interaction. Mechanical data of various steels at elevated temperatures are also available in the ASTM standards listed in Table 2.

Various methods, depending on the application, are used to establish the design criteria for using materials at elevated temperatures. One method, for example, develops allowable stresses by multiplying tensile strengths, yield strengths, creep strength, and/or rupture strength with safety factors. This method is illustrated in Fig. 4, where various safety factors are used to establish allowable stresses for 18-8 austenitic stainless steel at various temperatures. This method does not take into account environmental interactions, aging effects from long-term temperature exposure, or the possibility of creep-fatigue interaction. Another design basis is to define maximum allowable temperatures. Table 3, for example, lists maximum allowable service temperatures of various materials for tube and plate products used in refinery or boiler applications.

Creep and Stress Rupture. Creep is defined as the time-dependent strain that occurs under

load at elevated temperatures. Creep is operative in most applications when metal temperatures exceed 480 °C (900 °F). In time, creep may lead to excessive deformation and even fracture at stresses considerably below those determined in room-temperature and elevated-temperature short-term tension tests. The designer must usually determine whether the serviceability of the component in question is limited by the rate or the degree of deformation.

When the rate or degree of deformation is the limiting factor, the design stress is based on the minimum creep rate and design life after allowing for initial transient creep. The stress that produces a specified minimum creep rate of an alloy or a specified amount of creep deformation in a given time (for example, 1% total creep in 100,000 h) is referred to as the *limiting creep strength* or *limiting stress*. Of the various types of stainless steels, the austenitic types provide the highest limiting creep strength. Figure 5 plots typical creep rates of various austenitic stainless steels. The original data for Fig. 5 were generated on steels with carbon contents greater than 0.04%; the steels were solution annealed at sufficiently high temperatures to meet H-grade requirements (see the sec-

tion "H-grades" in this article). Today, the 300-series stainless steels are usually low carbon, unless an H-grade is specified.

When fracture is the limiting factor, stress-to-rupture values can be used in design. Typical stress-to-rupture values of various austenitic stainless steels are shown in Fig. 6. The values were generated from steels meeting H-grade requirements.

It should be recognized that long-term creep and stress-rupture values (for example, 100,000 h) are often extrapolated from shorter-term tests conducted at high stresses and in which creep is

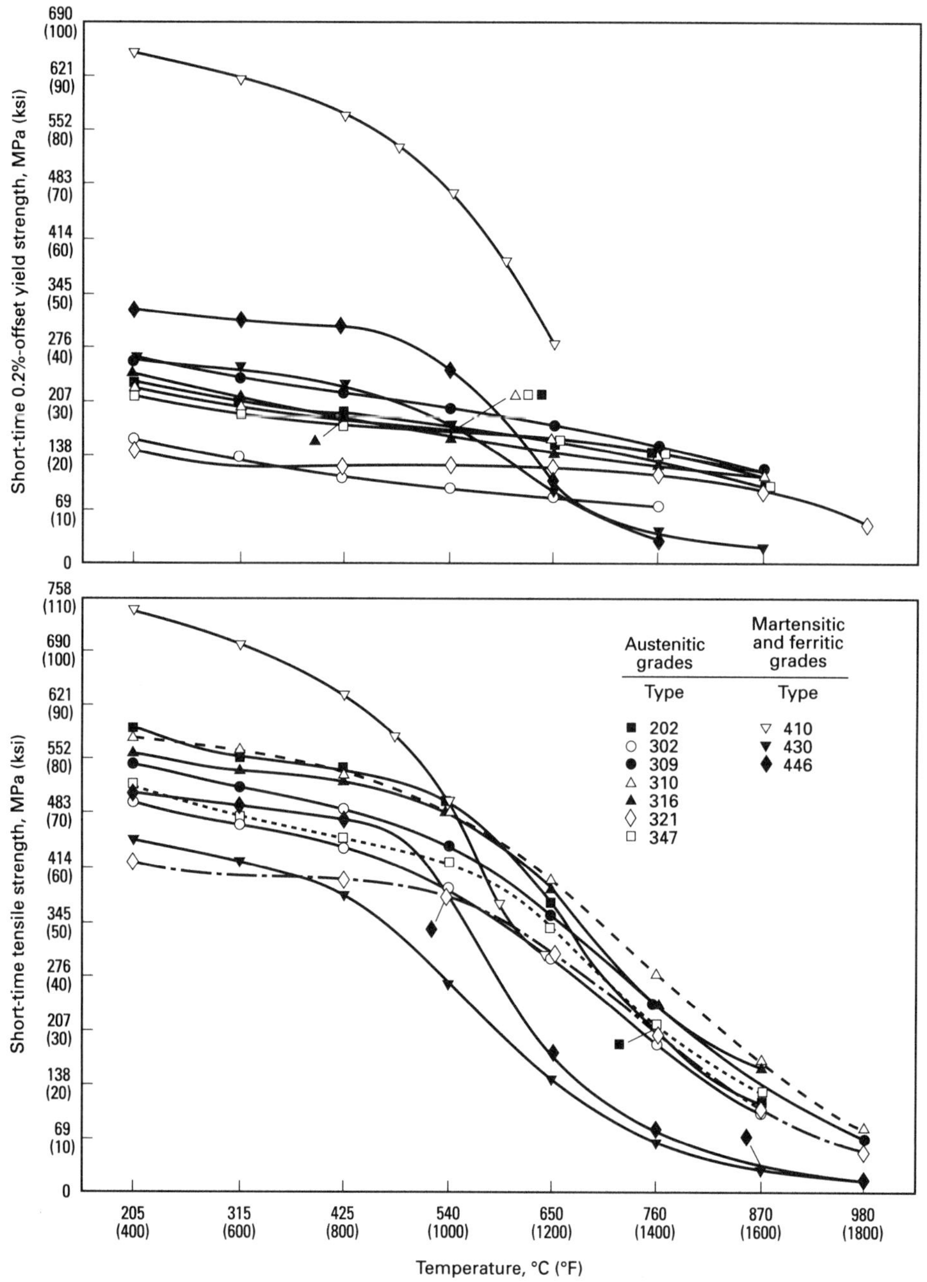

Fig. 3 Typical short-time tensile strengths of various standard stainless steels. All steels were tested in the annealed condition except for the martensitic type 410, which was heat treated by oil quenching from 980 °C (1800 °F) and tempering at 650 °C (1200 °F).

Table 3 Suggested maximum temperatures for continuous service based on creep or rupture data

Material	Maximum temperature based on creep rate		Maximum temperature based on rupture	
	°C	°F	°C	°F
Carbon steel	450	850	540	1000
C-0.5Mo steel	510	950	595	1100
2.25Cr-1Mo steel	540	1000	650	1200
Type 304 stainless steel	595	1100	815	1500
Alloy C-276 nickel-base alloy	650	1200	1040	1900

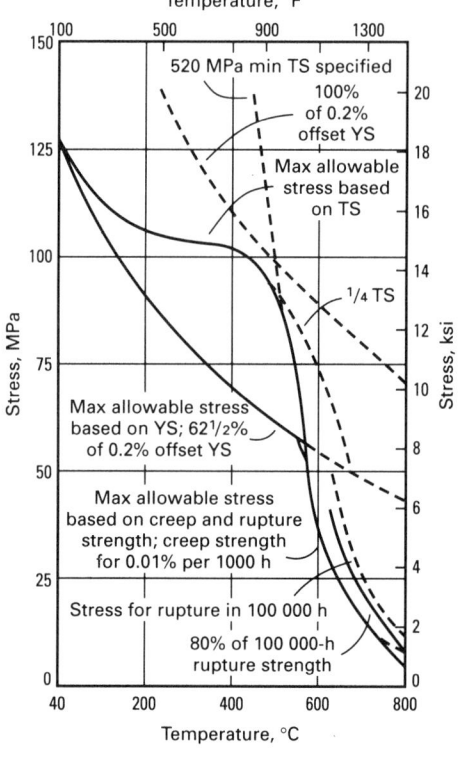

Fig. 4 Example of relationships between temperature and high-temperature strengths previously used in the ASME Boiler Code to establish maximum allowable stresses in tension for type 18-8 austenitic stainless steel. The current code uses two-thirds of the yield strength instead of 62.5% of the yield strength.

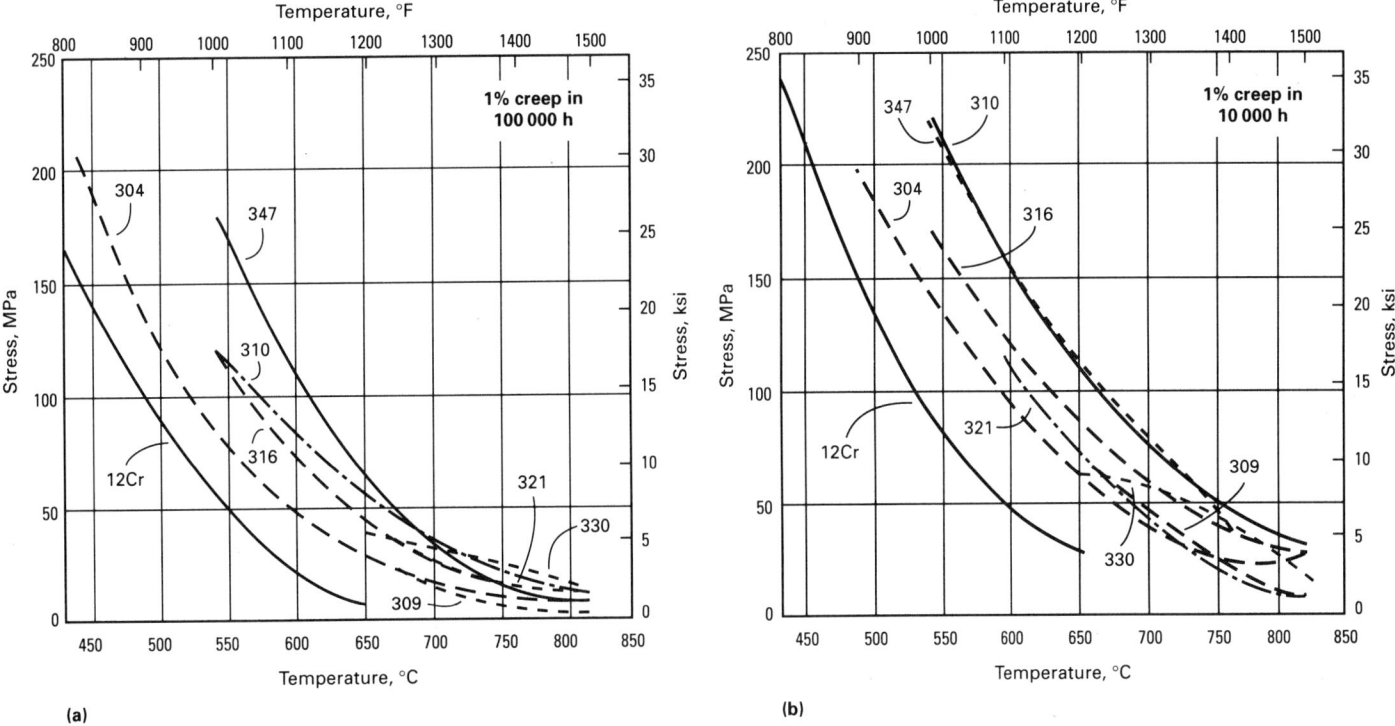

Fig. 5   Creep rate curves for several annealed H-grade austenitic stainless steels. (a) 1% creep in 100,000 h. (b) 1% creep in 10,000 h. Source: Ref 1

dislocation controlled. Whether these property values are extrapolated or determined directly often has little bearing on the operating life of high-temperature parts, where operating stresses are lower and where the mechanisms of creep are diffusion controlled. The actual material behavior can also be difficult to predict accurately because of the complexity of the service stresses relative to the idealized, uniaxial loading conditions in the standardized tests and because of attenuating factors such as cyclic loading, temperature fluctuations, and metal loss from corrosion.

Rupture Ductility. Whereas creep strength and rupture strength are given considerable attention as design and failure parameters, rupture ductility is an important mechanical property when stress concentrations and localized defects such as notches are a factor in design. Rupture ductility, which varies inversely with creep and rupture strength, influences the growth of cracks or defects and thus affects notch sensitivity. This general effect of rupture ductility on rupture strength is shown conceptually in Fig. 7. When smooth parts are tested, the rupture strength is higher for the steel with lower ductility (steel A). However, when a notch is introduced, the rupture strength of steel A plummets; the rupture strength of steel B, on the other hand, is less notch sensitive because of its higher ductility. It is clear from Fig. 7 that for low-stress, long-term applications, steel B would be preferred to steel A. This is true even though steel B is weaker than steel A, as shown by results of smooth-bar rupture tests.

In many service conditions, the amount of deformation is not critical, and relatively high rupture ductility can be used in design. Under such conditions, with the combined uncertainties of actual stress, temperature, and strength, it may be important that failure not occur without warning and that the metal retain high elongation and reduction in area throughout its service life. In the oil and chemical industries, for instance, many applications of tubing under high pressure require high long-time ductility, and impending rupture will be evident from the bulging of the tubes.

Values of elongation and reduction in area obtained in rupture tests are used in judging the ability of metal to adjust to stress concentration. The requirements are not well defined and are controversial. Most engineers are reluctant to use alloys with elongations of less than 5%, and this limit is sometimes considerably higher. Low ductility in a rupture test almost always indicates high resistance to the relaxation of stress by creep and possible sensitivity to stress concentrations. There is also ample evidence that rupture ductility has a major influence on creep-fatigue interaction (see the section below). Large changes in elongation with increasing fracture time usually indicate extensive changes in metallurgical structure or surface corrosion.

Creep-fatigue interaction can have a detrimental effect on the performance of metal parts or components operating at elevated temperatures. When temperatures are high enough to produce creep strains and when cyclic (that is, fatigue) strains are present, the two can interact. For example, it has been found that creep strains can seriously reduce fatigue life and that fatigue strains can seriously reduce creep life. This effect occurs in both stainless steels and low-alloy or carbon steels when temperatures are in the creep range.

Creep-fatigue interaction causes a reduction in fatigue life when either the frequency of the cycling stress is reduced or the cycling waveform has a tensile (and sometimes compressive) hold time (Fig. 8). Early studies (Ref 3-8) on type 316 stainless steel showed that tensile hold periods in the temperature region from 550 to 625 °C (1020 to 1160 °F) were very damaging, as shown in Fig. 8. Because the strain ranges were fairly high and the hold periods were short, failures were dominated by fatigue. More recent results at lower strain ranges and longer hold periods have revealed that creep-dominated failures also occur in stainless steels (Ref 9-11). Creep-dominated failures have been observed for tensile hold times up to 16 h at 600 °C (1110 °F) (Ref 9) and in tests at 625 °C (1160 °F) with tensile hold times up to 48 h (Ref 10).

Some investigators have observed a saturation in the detrimental effects of tensile hold periods, that is, a recovery of the endurance occurring at longer hold periods. Table 4 summarizes the data obtained in the evaluation of this effect at 2.0% strain range. A saturation effect is observed when the hold period approaches 30 min. This has been attributed to microstructural changes leading to increases in ductility. Aging and the concomitant precipitation and growth of large carbides prior to testing have been shown to eliminate creep-fatigue effects altogether in type 316 stainless steel at 650 °C (1200 °F) (Ref 12).

Tests involving a 30 min hold period in tension plus a shorter hold period in compression (asymmetrical holding) have shown that the detrimental effect of a hold period in tension can be significantly reduced by a short hold period in the compression por-

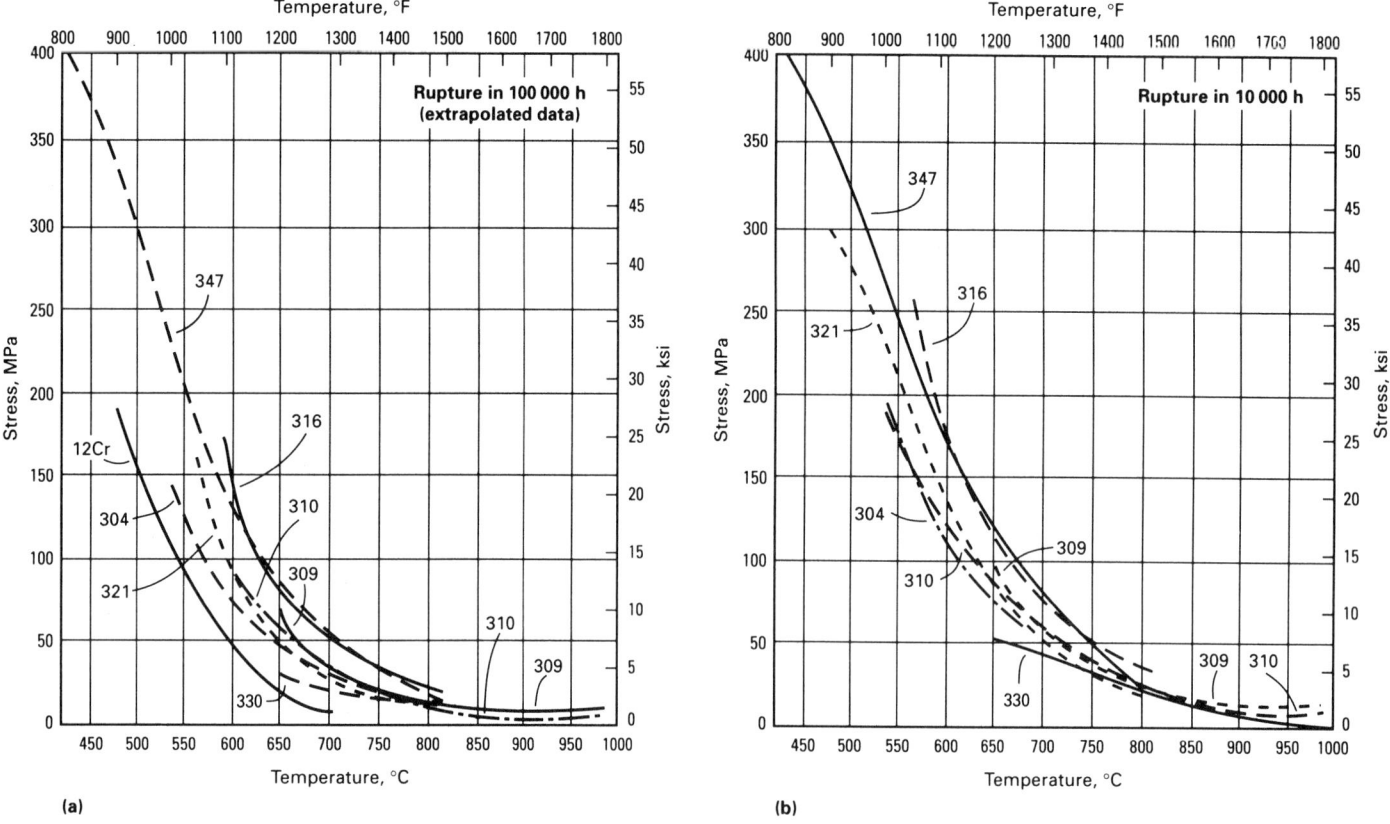

Fig. 6 Stress-rupture curves for several annealed H-grade austenitic stainless steels. (a) Extrapolated data for rupture in 100,000 h. (b) Rupture in 10,000 h. Source: Ref 1

Table 4 Effect of hold-period length in tension-hold-only testing on fatigue resistance of type 304 stainless steel

Tested in air at 650 °C (1200 °F) and a strain rate of 4×10^{-3} s^{-1} at a strain range of about 2.0%

Hold period, min	Cycles to failure, N_f	
	Test 1	Test 2
0	592	546
0.1	570	545
1.0	329	331
10.0	193	201
30.0	146	165
60.0	144	158
180.0	150	120

tion of the cycle (Table 5). When the tension hold period is 30 min and a 3 min compression hold period is introduced, the fatigue life is within 80% of the fatigue life observed in the 30 min symmetrical-holding tests. Without this short hold period in compression, the fatigue life is reduced to about 40% of the 30 min symmetrical-holding fatigue life. In this type of testing, the hold period in compression exerts a "healing" effect (reduces the tendency for internal void formation).

The effect of slow/fast cycles (in which the strain increases slowly during the tension cycle but rapidly during the compression-going cycle) on the endurance of type 304, type 316, and other stainless steels has been investigated (Ref 13-16). In other tests, lower strain rates in the tension cycle were found to reduce endurance. Additional data on creep-fatigue interaction for various stainless steels are given in the article "Creep-Fatigue Interaction" in Volume 8 of the *ASM Handbook*.

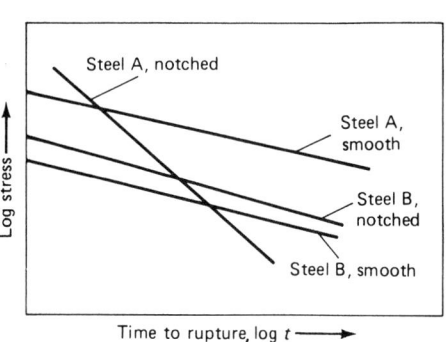

Fig. 7 Notched-bar rupture behavior for a creep-brittle steel (A) and a creep-ductile steel (B)

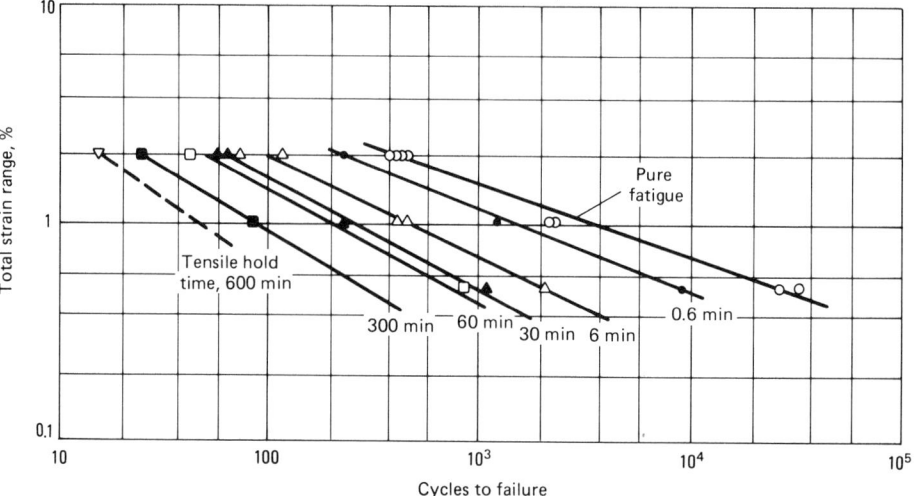

Fig. 8 Effect of tensile hold time on fatigue endurance of type 316 stainless steel. Source: Ref 2

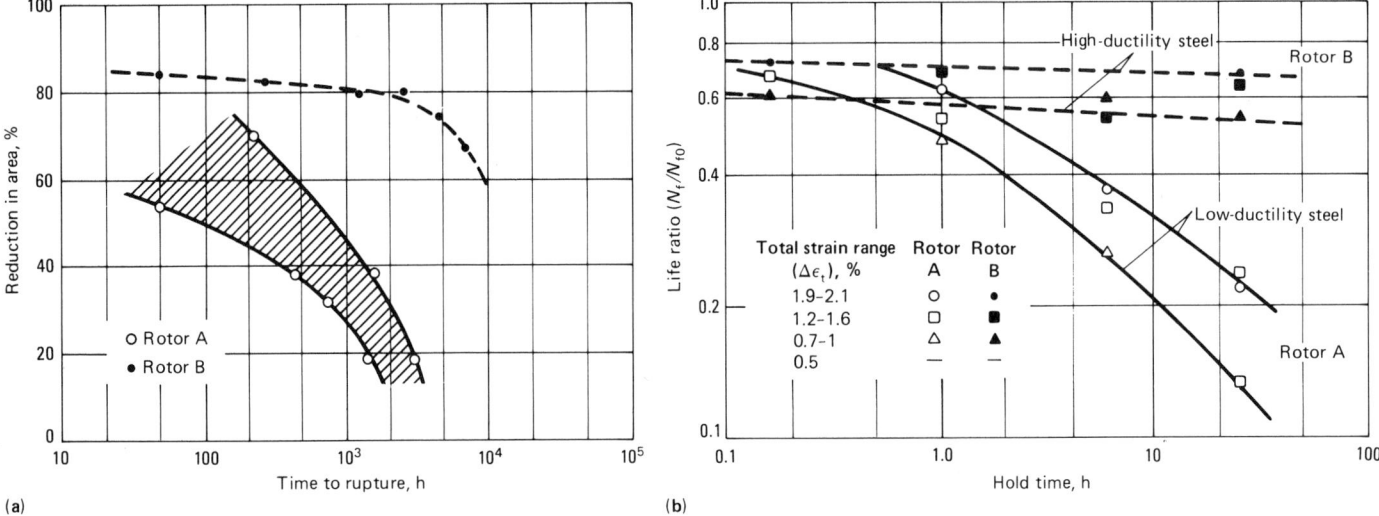

Fig. 9 Effects of creep-rupture ductility (a) on hold time effects (b) during low-cycle fatigue testing of a 1Cr-Mo-V steel at 500 °C (930 °F). N_{10} = fatigue life with zero hold time. Source: Ref 18

Life reduction from tensile hold has been observed to be related to stress-rupture ductility, leading to heat-to-heat variations (Ref 11, 17). The influence of rupture ductility on the creep fracture component of creep-fatigue interaction is negligible in continuous-cycle and high-frequency or short-hold-time fatigue tests (where fracture is fatigue dominated). However, as frequency is decreased or as hold time is increased, the effect of rupture ductility becomes more pronounced, as illustrated in Fig. 9(b). The hold-time effects on the fatigue lives of two rotors are compared in Fig. 9(b) in terms of their rupture-ductility behavior. The fatigue life of the low-ductility rotor steel is much more adversely affected by hold time than that of the high-ductility rotor steel. The rupture ductilities diverge with increasing time to rupture (Fig. 9a), which is correspondingly reflected in the long-hold-time tests. Endurance data on the range of rupture ductility for several ferritic steels and austenitic stainless steels are presented in Ref 16. The lower the ductility, the lower the creep-fatigue endurance. In addition, long hold periods, small strain ranges, and low ductility favor creep-dominated failures, whereas short hold periods, intermediate strain ranges, and high creep ductility favor creep-fatigue interaction failures.

Corrosion Considerations

The corrosion resistance and oxidation resistance values of wrought stainless steels are similar to those of cast stainless steels with comparable compositions. However, austenitic cast stainless steels may have a more pronounced duplex (ferrite-in-austenite) structure than wrought austenitic stainless steels. This ferrite-in-austenite stainless steel is beneficial in preventing intergranular stress-corrosion cracking (see the articles "Metallurgy and Properties of Cast Stainless Steels" and "Corrosion of Cast Stainless Steels"

Table 5 Test results of type 304 stainless steel obtained using a 30-min hold period in tension plus a short hold period in compression
Tested in air at 650 °C (1200 °F) and a strain rate of 4×10^{-3} s^{-1}

Hold period tension, min	Hold period compression, min	Total strain range, %	Cycles to failure, N_f Test 1	Test 2
0	0	1.98	592	546
30	30	1.98	380	416
30	0	2.08	146	...
30	0	2.02	...	165
30	3	1.98	308	...
30	3	2.00	...	336

in this Volume for the general corrosion resistance of stainless steels at elevated temperatures).

Cast and wrought steels with similar composition, heat treatment, and microstructure (as noted above) exhibit about the same corrosion resistance in a given environment. The temperature limits in air for various stainless steels are given in Table 6. Because oxidation resistance is affected by many factors, including temperature, time, type of service (cyclic or continuous), and atmosphere, selection of material for a specific application should be based on tests that duplicate anticipated conditions as closely as possible. Figure 10 compares the oxidation resistance of type 430, type 446, and several martensitic and austenitic grades in 1000 h of continuous exposure to water-saturated air at temperatures from 815 to 1095 °C (1500 to 2000 °F).

Sulfur attack is second only to air oxidation in frequency of occurrence in many industries and is likely to be more severe. Figure 11 shows average corrosion rates at high temperatures from sulfur corrosion in a hydrogen-free environment. Figure 12 shows corrosion from hydrogen sulfide. More detailed information on corrosion during elevated-temperature exposure is given in the article "High-Temperature Corrosion" in this Volume.

Table 6 Generally accepted maximum service temperatures in air for standard stainless steel grades

AISI type	Maximum service temperature			
	Intermittent service		Continuous service	
	°C	°F	°C	°F
Austenitic grades				
201	815	1500	845	1550
202	815	1500	845	1550
301	840	1545	900	1650
302	870	1600	925	1700
304	870	1600	925	1700
308	925	1700	980	1795
309	980	1795	1095	2000
310	1035	1895	1150	2100
316	870	1600	925	1700
317	870	1600	925	1700
321	870	1600	925	1700
330	1035	1895	1150	2100
347	870	1600	925	1700
Ferritic grades				
405	815	1500	705	1300
406	815	1500	1035	1895
430	870	1600	815	1500
442	1035	1895	980	1795
446	1175	2145	1095	2000
Martensitic grades				
410	815	1500	705	1300
416	760	1400	675	1250
420	735	1355	620	1150
440	815	1500	760	1400

Ferritic Stainless Steels

The main advantage of ferritic stainless steels for high-temperature use is their good oxidation resistance, which is comparable to that of austenitic grades. Ferritic stainless steels can also be more resistant to liquid metal attack than austenitic stainless steels. They are therefore used for some applications in the lead and copper metal industries.

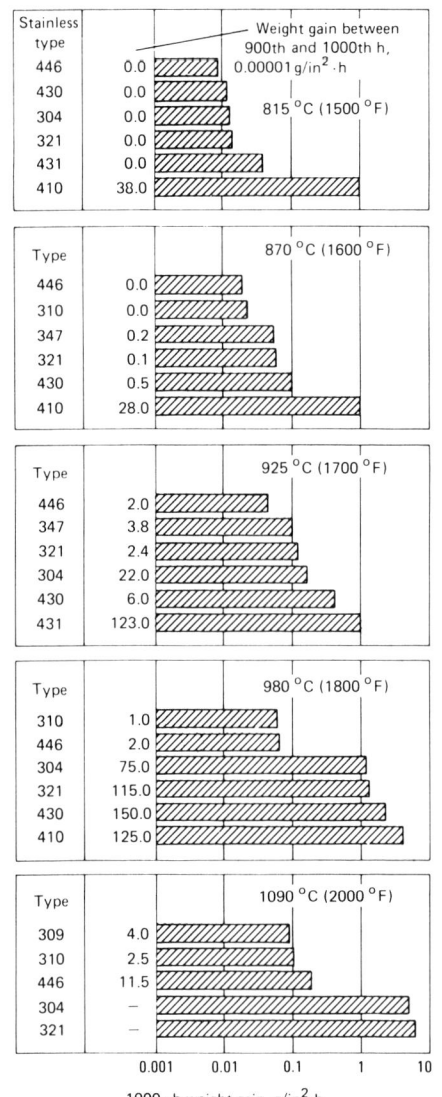

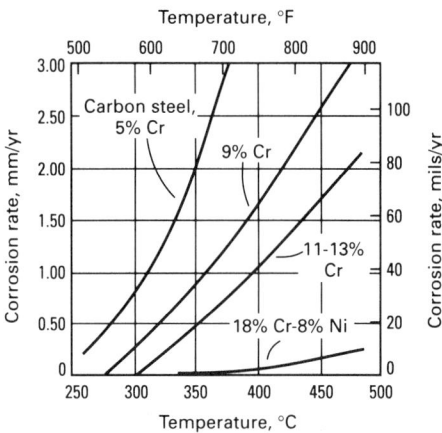

Fig. 10 The 1000-h oxidation resistance of selected stainless steels

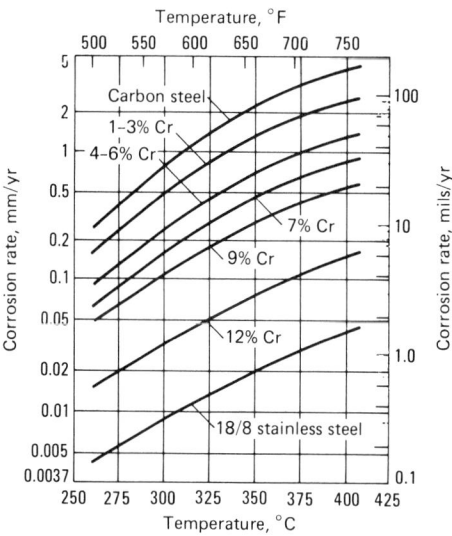

Fig. 11 Average high-temperature sulfur corrosion rates in a hydrogen-free environment. Compiled from an American Petroleum Institute survey. Source: Ref 19

In view of their lower alloy content and lower cost, ferritic steels should be used in preference to austenitic steels, stress conditions permitting. Ferritic stainless steels can also be more desirable than austenitic stainless steels in applications involving thermal cycling, because ferritic stainless steels have higher thermal conductivities and lower thermal expansion coefficients. Ferritic stainless steels may therefore allow reductions in thermal stresses and improved thermal-fatigue resistance.

For the purposes of this article, ferritic stainless steels are classified into two categories: ferritic stainless steels without vanadium (Table 1) and ferritic steels with vanadium (Table 7). These two categories are described in the next two sections of this article. An important structural characteristic of all ferritic stainless steels is precipitation of α', a chromium-rich ferrite, when

the steel is exposed to temperatures in the range from 370 to 540 °C (700 to 1000 °F). This precipitation results in an increase in hardness and a drastic reduction in room-temperature toughness, which is known as 475 °C (885 °F) embrittlement (see the article "Metallurgy and Properties of Wrought Stainless Steels" in this Volume). This embrittlement occurs in all ferritic grades that have chromium contents above approximately 13%, and its severity increases at higher chromium levels. This characteristic has to be considered for applications involving exposure to temperatures in the range from 370 to 540 °C (700 to 1000 °F), because subsequent room-temperature ductility will be severely impaired. In the higher-chromium alloys, such as 18Cr-2Mo, type 446, 26-1, and 29-4 (Table 1), σ-phase is encountered at temperatures above 565 °C (1050 °F). The χ-phase will also form in 26-1 Ti and 29Cr-4Mo. The high-molybdenum steels such as 29Cr-4Mo will also form a χ-phase, which has an embrittling effect similar to that of the σ-phase. The χ-phase is formed only in high-molybdenum steels. Titanium has little, if any, effect on the formation of χ-phase.

Ferritic Stainless Steels without Vanadium

Many stainless steels of the 400 series (Table 1) have essentially ferritic structures at all temperatures. Types 405, 430, 434, and 446 form a certain amount of austenite when heated to high temperatures. Type 409 may also form some austenite, particularly if the titanium content is relatively low, but the other steels listed are completely ferritic at all temperatures.

The amount of chromium added for corrosion and oxidation resistance varies from 11% in type 409 to 29% in 29Cr-4Mo. Titanium is used to bind carbon and nitrogen for structure control and resistance to intergranular corrosion. Molybdenum is used to improve corrosion resistance. Aluminum and silicon are added for resistance to oxidation.

Fig. 12 Elevated-temperature corrosion rates of steels in hydrogen and hydrogen sulfide environments (H₂S concentrations above 1 mol%). Source: Ref 20

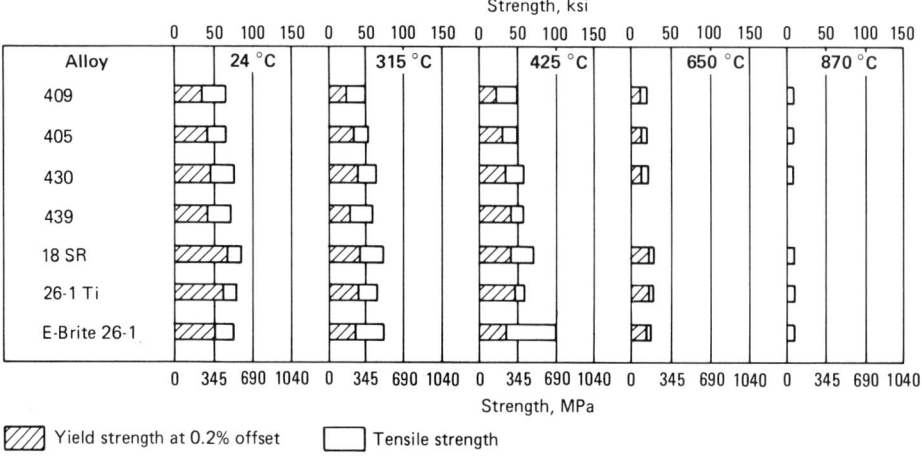

Fig. 13 Room-temperature and high-temperature tensile properties of selected ferritic stainless steels from Table 1. All alloys in the annealed condition, fast cooled from 815 to 925 °C (1500 to 1700 °F)

Table 7 Compositions of heat-resistant ferritic stainless steels containing vanadium

Grade	C	Mn	Si	Ni	Cr	Mo	W	V	Nb	Other	Heat treatment, °C(a)	550 °C (1020 °F) MPa	ksi	600 °C (1110 °F) MPa	ksi	650 °C (1200 °F) MPa	ksi
Advanced 10-12% Cr steels for steam turbine rotors																	
G.E.	0.19	0.65	0.3	0.6	10.5	1.0	...	0.20	0.085	0.06 N	1050 OQ/570 AC/620 AC	...	...	...	...	...	...
TR1100	0.14	0.50	0.05	0.6	10.2	1.5	...	0.17	0.055	0.04 N, 0.002 Al	1050 OQ/570 AC/680 AC	...	...	118	17.1	64	9.3
TR1150	0.13	0.50	0.05	0.7	10.2	0.4	1.8	0.17	0.055	0.045 N, 0.005 Al	1050 OQ/570 AC/680 AC	...	...	157	22.8	83	12.0
TR1200	0.12	0.50	0.05	0.8	11.2	0.3	1.8	0.20	0.055	0.055 N, 0.005 Al	1020 OQ/570 AC/710 AC	...	...	...	...	...	...
FV448	0.13	1.0	0.5	...	10.5	0.75	...	0.15	0.45	0.05 N	1150 OQ/650 AC	293	42.5	139	20.2	60	8.7
A.L. type 419	0.25	1.0	0.3	0.5	11.5	0.5	2.5	0.4	...	0.10 N	1100 OQ/650 AC	...	...	...	...	...	...
EM-12	0.10	1.0	0.4	...	9.5	2.0	...	0.3	0.4	...	1080 OQ/785 AC	210	30.5	120	17.4	60	8.7
TAF	0.18	0.5	0.3	...	10.5	1.5	...	0.2	0.15	0.3 B	1150 OQ/700 AC	373	54	216	31.3	137	20.0
Boiler tube materials																	
9Cr-1Mo	0.10	0.4	0.05	...	9.0	1.0	...	...	...	0.02 N	...	...	...	39	5.7	20	2.9
Mod 9Cr-1Mo	0.10	0.45	0.35	<0.2	8.75	0.95	...	0.21	0.08	0.05 N	...	...	...	98	14.2	49	7.1
Mod NSCR9	0.08	0.5	0.05	0.1	9.0	1.6	...	0.16	0.05	0.03 N, 0.003 B	...	...	...	128	18.6	69	10
T-1	0.05	0.5	0.3	...	10.0	2.0	...	0.1	0.05	0.02 N	1050 AC/700 AC	...	...	...	...	...	...
T-2	0.10	0.5	0.3	...	10.0	2.0	...	0.1	0.05	0.02 N	1050 AC/700 AC	...	...	...	...	...	...
TB9	0.08	0.5	0.05	0.1	9.0	0.5	1.8	0.2	0.05	0.05 N	...	...	...	196	28.4	98	14.2
TB12	0.08	0.5	0.05	0.1	12.0	0.5	1.8	0.2	0.05	0.05 N, 0.003 B	...	...	...	206	30	108	15.7
AISI 304	0.08	1.5	0.6	10	18.5	...	...	...	...	0.05 N	...	...	...	118	17.1	69	10
AISI 347	0.06	1.7	0.5	12	17.5	...	...	...	...	0.02 N	...	...	...	128	18.6	78	11.3

(a) OQ, oil quench; AC, air cool. Source: Ref 21

Figure 13 shows the tensile and yield strengths (annealed condition) of the ferritic stainless steels presented in Table 1. At room temperature, these properties are nearly equivalent to those of austenitic stainless steels. At higher temperatures, however, ferritic stainless steels are much lower in strength. The rupture strength and creep strength of types 430 and 446 are compared with the same properties of various austenitic stainless steels and two superalloys (Inconel and Incoloy) in Fig. 14. Long-time and short-time high-temperature strengths of ferritic stainless steels are relatively low compared to those of austenitic stainless steels. Data on the cyclic oxidation resistance of various stainless steels and nickel-base alloys in air containing 10% water vapor are compared in Table 8. At 705 and 815 °C (1300 and 1500 °F), all the alloys listed are resistant to oxidation. At 980 °C (1800 °F), the lower-alloy types 409, 430, and 304 exhibit high oxidation. At 1090 °C (2000 °F), alloys 18 SR and Inconel 601 (shown in Table 8) and alloys such as 446 and 310 have adequate oxidation resistance. The cycling oxidation resistances of E-Brite 26-1, type 310, and Incoloy 800 are compared in Fig. 15.

Type 409, the lowest-alloy stainless steel with a nominal chromium content of 11.0%, is used extensively because of its good fabricating characteristics, including weldability and formability, and its availability. Its best-known high-temperature applications are in automotive exhaust systems; metal temperatures in catalytic converters exceed 540 °C (1000 °F). Type 409 is also used for exhaust ducting and silencers in gas turbines. Type 405 is used in stationary vanes and spacers in steam turbines and in various furnace components. Types 430 and 439 are used for heat ex-

Table 8 Cyclic oxidation resistance of ferritic stainless steels compared with other alloys
Specimens were exposed for 100 h in air containing 10% water vapor, cooled to room temperature every 2 h, then reheated to test temperature.

Alloy	705 °C (1300 °F)	815 °C (1500 °F)	980 °C (1800 °F)	1090 °C (2000 °F)
409	+0.1	+0.8	+1430(a)	-10 000(b)
430	+0.4	+1.3	-1660(c)	-10 000(b)
18 SR	+0.1	+0.3	+2.5	+7.4
304	+0.2	+1.7	-3400	-10 000(d)
309	+0.2	+2.7	-120	-910
201	+0.8	+3.1	+10	-150
Incoloy 800	+0.3	+3.2	+8.6	-560
Inconel 601	+0.1	+1.2	+10	-2.1

(a) Removed after 36 h. (b) Removed after 12 h. (c) Removed after 30 h. (d) Removed after 24 h

changers, hot-water tanks, condensers, and furnace parts. Type 18 SR, like type 446, is used in industrial ovens, blowers, exhaust systems, furnace equipment, annealing boxes, kiln liners, and pyrometer tubes.

Ferritic Stainless Steels with Vanadium

Table 7 lists various PH high-chromium ferritic steels. These steels contain vanadium and perhaps other carbide formers, such as niobium or tungsten, to strengthen the steel by precipitation hardening during tempering or elevated-temperature exposure.

Although several steels in Table 7 are not strictly considered stainless steels, the chromium contents are high enough to exhibit corrosion resistance comparable to that of typical

stainless steels. Some of these steels, such as the modified 9Cr-1Mo steel, are also substitutes for austenitic steels in boiler tube applications, as described below. The modified 9Cr-1Mo steel, which is designated ASTM grade 91, is specified in ASTM standards for boiler tubes (ASTM A 213), forgings (ASTM A 336), seamless pipe (ASTM A 335), and forged and bored pipe (ASTM A369). High-chromium ferritic steels are also used for steam turbine rotors and bolting materials.

Historical Background. High-chromium heat-resistant ferritic steels were first developed for use in gas and steam turbine applications. In the early 1940s, a need for improved high-strength, corrosion-resistant materials for gas turbine disks and steam turbine blades, operating at temperatures near 540 °C (1000 °F), prompted

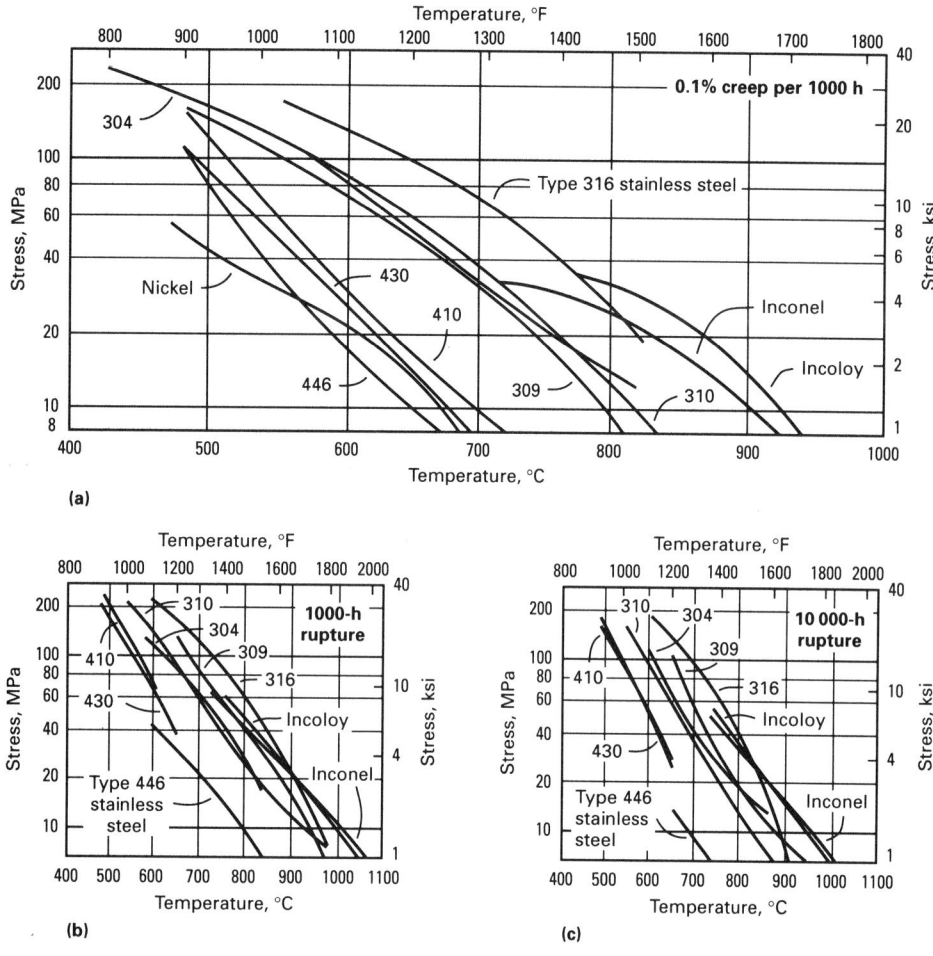

Fig. 14 Creep and rupture behavior of selected heat-resistant alloys as a function of temperature. (a) Stresses for a creep rate of 0.1% in 1000 h. (b) Stresses for rupture in 1000 h. (c) Stresses for rupture in 10,000 h

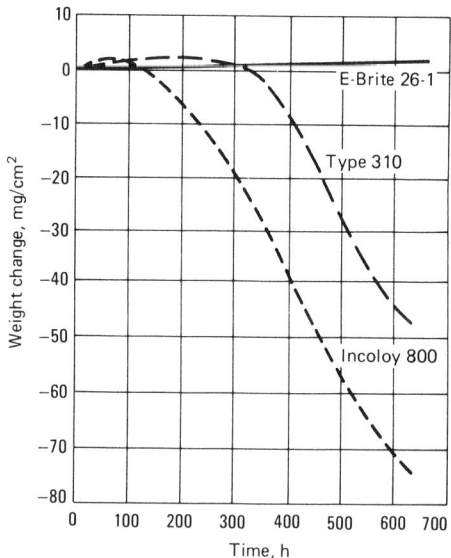

Fig. 15 Cyclic oxidation behavior of three iron-base heat-resistant alloys at 980 °C (1800 °F)

metallurgists in England to hasten development work on 12% Cr heat-resistant steels. This research produced two steels (H-46 and FV448 in Table 7) and other alloy steels in the 1950s with improved creep-rupture strengths. Work in Japan led to the development in 1956 of TAF steel (Table 7), which is twice as strong as martensitic stainless steels at 650 °C (1200 °F).

Turbine Rotors. The elevated-temperature strength of turbine rotors is a major influence on the allowable temperature conditions of turbines. The 12% Cr heat-resistant ferritic steels developed in the 1950s have good creep-rupture strengths and are widely used in steam and gas turbines. Also, General Electric's rotor steel (Table 7), which has improved creep-rupture strength at 570 °C (1060 °F), was developed in the early 1960s for application in supercritical steam power plants.

In the early 1980s, joint research by Kobe Steel and Mitsubishi Heavy Industry produced modified versions of ferritic TAF steel for operation at 620 °C (1150 °F). The new rotor steels, TR1100, TR1150, and TR1200 (Table 7) have much better creep-rupture strength than the General Electric rotor steel, which exhibits a marked decrease in creep-rupture

strength over time. These improved rotor steels are based on chemistry modifications. The carbon and nitrogen contents of TR1100 are lowered to 0.13% and 0.04%, respectively, and the steel contains 1.5% Mo for solid-solution strengthening and stabilization of $M_{23}C_6$ and M_6C carbides. In addition, tests show that tungsten has a stronger high-temperature strengthening effect than molybdenum at elevated temperatures. Based on these data, TR1150 and TR1200 steels are being developed with increased tungsten content within a molybdenum equivalence range (Mo% + ½W%) of 1.2 to 1.5% Mo.

The rotor steels, such as TR1100 and TR1150, are expected to be used in applications with steam conditions of 595 °C (1100 °F) and 620 °C (1150 °F), respectively, and a rotor design stress of 120 to 130 MPa (17.5 to 18.8 ksi). The TR1200 rotor steel in development is intended for steam conditions of 34 MPa (4.9 ksi) and 650 °C (1200 °F).

Boiler tubing requires a combination of high-temperature strength, good formability, and weldability. Various types of high-chromium heat-resistant ferritic steels for boiler tubes are listed in Table 7, along with two austenitic stainless steels (types 304 and 347) for comparison.

The *10Cr-2Mo boiler tube steels with niobium and vanadium additions* include the T-1 and T-2 steels in Table 7. These steels contain 0.05% and 0.10% C, respectively; this level of carbon provides high-temperature strength as well as the good formability and weldability required for boiler tubing. A chromium content of 10% provides very good high-temperature corrosion resistance at about 600 °C (1100 °F), and other alloying elements produce a 20 to 30% δ-ferrite content, which improves weldability.

Increasing the molybdenum content enhances solution hardening and strengthening by $M_{23}C_6$ and M_6C carbide precipitation and intermetallic compound (Fe_2Mo) formation. However, molybdenum is fixed at 2% for the best corrosion resistance, formability, toughness, and δ-ferrite content.

Small amounts of vanadium and niobium affect the high-temperature strength of this steel significantly. Although the optimum content of vanadium is 0.25% for a carbon content of 0.2%, the addition of this amount to a 0.05% C steel causes only V_4C_3 precipitation. Therefore, a maximum vanadium content of 0.10 to 0.15% is necessary to raise high-temperature strength by the gradual precipitation of various carbides such as $M_{23}C_6$, M_6C, and NbC. The vanadium content is fixed at 0.10% for good weldability.

The niobium content must be relatively low (0.02 to 0.05%) in these steels so that NbC can dissolve in the matrix when normalized at 1050 °C (1900 °F). However, at the low end of the range, the complete dissolution of carbides results in grain growth at the normalizing temperature with a reduction in notch toughness; thus, niobium content is fixed at 0.05%.

The 0.05% C in T-1 steel is shared to form carbides in the following manner: 0.02% for V_4C_3, 0.005% for NbC, and 0.025% for $M_{23}C_6$ and M_6C. In addition, the equation $(V/51) + (Nb/93) < (C/12)$ must be satisfied so that $M_{23}C_6$ and M_6C can precipitate along with V_4C_3 and NbC.

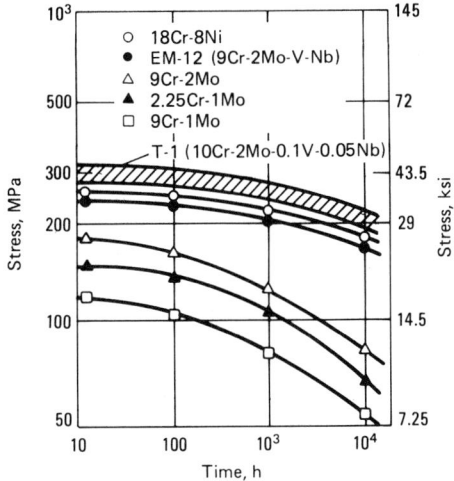

Fig. 16 Creep-rupture strengths of various boiler tube steels at 600 °C (1110 °F). Source: Ref 21

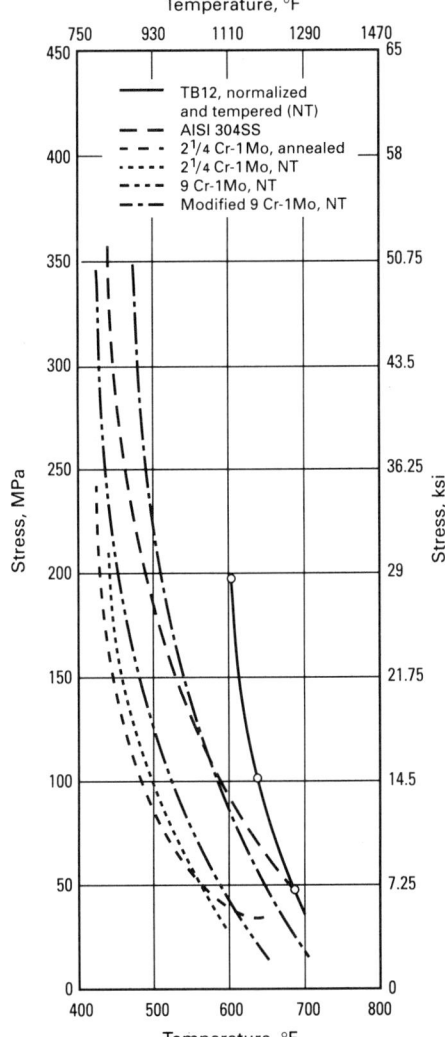

Fig. 17 100,000-h creep-rupture strength of various steels used in boiler tubes. TB12 steel has as much as five times the 100,000-h creep-rupture strength of conventional ferritic steels at 600 °C (1110 °F). This allows an increase in boiler tube operating temperature of 120 to 130 °C (215 to 235 °F). Source: Ref 21

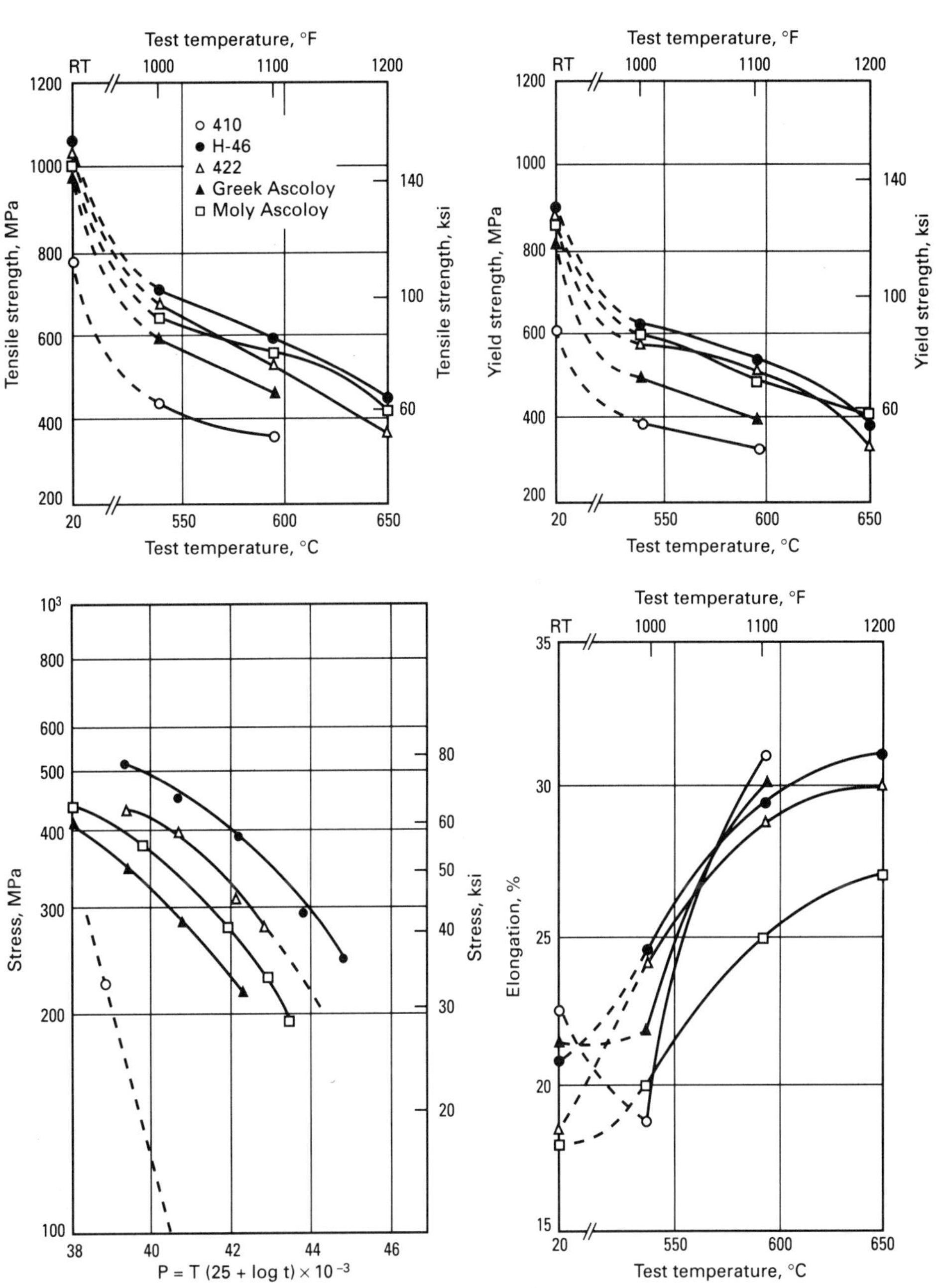

$$P = T (25 + \log t) \times 10^{-3}$$

Fig. 18 Comparison of mechanical properties of martensitic stainless steels. Heat-treating schedules were as follows. Type 410: 1 h at 980 °C (1800 °F), oil quench; then 2 h at 650 °C (1200 °F), air cool. H-46: 1 h at 1150 °C (2100 °F), air cool; then 2 h at 650 °C (1200 °F), air cool. Type 422: 1 h at 1040 °C (1900 °F), oil quench; then 2 h at 650 °C (1200 °F), air cool. Greek Ascoloy: 1 h at 955 °C (1750 °F), oil quench; then 2 h at 650 °C (1200 °F), air cool. Moly Ascoloy: 30 min at 1050 °C (1925 °F), oil quench; then 2 h at 650 °C (1200 °F), air cool.

The heat-resistant steel designed in this manner is strengthened by the precipitation of very fine V_4C_3 and NbC during tempering and in the early stages of creep, followed by $M_{23}C_6$ and M_6C precipitation. Figure 16 compares the creep-rupture strength of T-1 at 600 °C (1110 °F) with that of other boiler tube materials.

Modified 9 and 12Cr-Mo Boiler Tube Steels. Further investigation of the effects of molybdenum, vanadium plus niobium, chromium, nickel, and tungsten additions led to the development of modified chromium-molybdenum steels. These steels include the TB9 and TB12 alloys (Table 7) developed in Japan and the vanadium-niobium-modified 9Cr-1Mo steel developed by Oak Ridge National Laboratory. The modified 9Cr-1Mo steel, previously covered in Code Case 1943 of the ASME Boiler Code, is now covered in the regular code. For boiler tubes, these steels offer a promising alternative to 2.25Cr-1Mo steel and types 304, 316, 321, and 347 austenitic stainless steels. Figure 17 compares the 100,000-h creep-rupture strengths of these steels as a function of temperature.

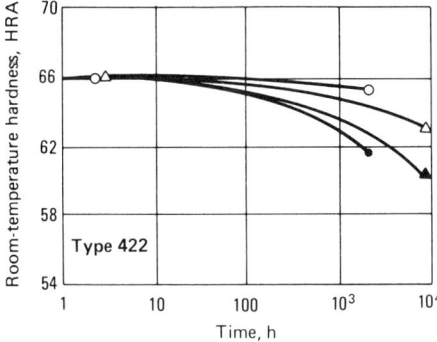

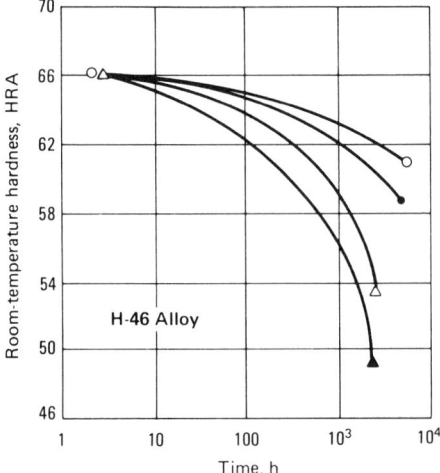

Fig. 19 Approximate effects of time and stress on tempering of types 422 and H-46. Circles indicate specimens heated to 1150 °C (2100 °F) and rapidly cooled, tempered 2 h at 705 °C (1300 °F), and tested (to fracture) at a temperature of 540 °C (1000 °F) and a stress of 380 MPa (55 ksi). Triangles indicate specimens heated to 980 °C (1800 °F) and rapidly cooled, tempered 2 h at 705 °C (1300 °F), and tested (to fracture) at 540 °C (1000 °F) and 275 MPa (40 ksi). Open symbols represent data taken at the unstressed specimen shoulder; solid symbols represent data taken within the stressed gage length.

Quenched and Tempered Martensitic Stainless Steels

Quenched and tempered martensitic stainless steels are essentially martensitic and harden when air cooled from the austenitizing temperature. These alloys offer good combinations of mechanical properties, with usable short-time strength up to 590 °C (1100 °F) and relatively good corrosion resistance. The strength levels at temperatures up to 590 °C (1100 °F) that can be attained in these alloys through heat treatment are considerably higher than those attainable in ferritic stainless steels, but the martensitic alloys have inferior corrosion resistance. Also, the martensitic stainless steels are not very tough.

These alloys are normally purchased in the annealed or fully treated (hardened and tempered) condition. They are used in the hardened and tempered condition. For best long-time thermal stability, these alloys should be tempered at a temperature that is 110 to 165 °C (200 to 300 °F) above the expected service temperature.

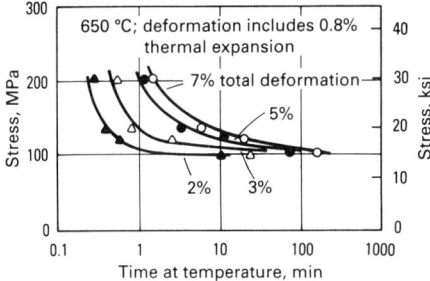

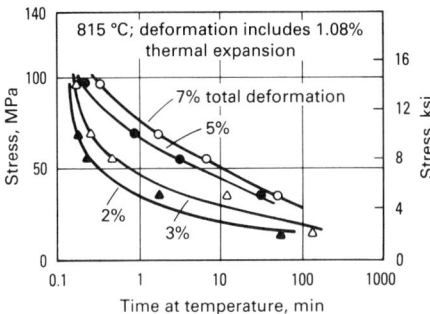

Fig. 20 Stress-time deformation curves for type 410 stainless steel sheet, showing effect of time at temperature on total deformation at specific stress levels. Design curves in the chart at the top represent a heating rate of 90 °C/s (160 °F/s) to 650 °C (1200 °F). Those at the bottom represent a heating rate of 105 °C/s (190 °F/s) to 815 °C (1500 °F). Room-temperature properties of the sheet used in these tests were: tensile strength, 650 to 695 MPa (94.5 to 101 ksi); yield strength at 0.2% offset, 555 to 565 MPa (80.7 to 82.3 ksi); and 9.6 to 16% elongation in 50 mm (2 in.) after air cooling from the normalizing temperature of 955 °C (1750 °F).

Properties. Quenched-and-tempered martensitic stainless steels can be grouped according to increasing strength and heat resistance:

- Group 1 (lowest strength and heat resistance): types 403, 410, and 416
- Group 2: Greek Ascoloy and type 431
- Group 3: Moly Ascoloy (Jethete M-152)
- Group 4 (highest strength and heat resistance): H-46 and type 422

A general comparison of mechanical property data is presented in Fig. 18 for some of these alloys. Data for type 410 are typical of group 1 alloys. Data for Greek Ascoloy are typical of type 431 (group 2). Data for Moly Ascoloy are typical of group 3 alloys (the composition of Jethete M-152 is very similar to that of Moly Ascoloy). Although H-46 and type 422 are similar in strength, their compositions are somewhat different; therefore, data are shown for both alloys.

The short-time tensile and rupture data shown in Fig. 18 were generated in tests of material that had been given austenitizing treatments typical for the specific alloys tested. These alloys are normally used at service temperatures near 540 °C (1000 °F) (although they may be used up to 590 °C, or 1100 °F), so data are shown for a relatively high tempering temperature of 650 °C (1200 °F), which results in good thermal stability in these alloys at 540 °C (1000 °F).

It should be noted that the group 1 alloys, of which type 410 is typical, show the lowest values of

strength capability as a function of test temperature. Greek Ascoloy is considerably stronger than type 410, with a yield strength (0.2% offset) of 480 MPa (70 ksi) and a tensile strength of 585 MPa (85 ksi) at 540 °C (1000 °F). The tensile strength capabilities of H-46, Moly Ascoloy, and type 422 are fairly similar and are the highest in this group of alloys. Tensile elongation data for all these alloys are similar: from about 20% elongation at 21 °C (70 °F) to about 30% at 650 °C (1200 °F).

Stress-rupture data for alloys typical of each subgroup are compared in Fig. 18 by means of a Larson-Miller stress-rupture plot. It should be noted that the niobium-containing H-46 alloy has the highest stress-rupture capability, with type 422, Moly Ascoloy, and Greek Ascoloy, in that order, having increasingly lower rupture capabilities. Type 410 has a very low stress-rupture capability and is the weakest of all the martensitic stainless alloys being considered. The niobium-containing alloys such as H-46 usually show an advantage in stress-rupture capability (creep resistance) for short testing times (100 to 1000 h) but lose their strength advantage when tested for periods of about 10,000 h or more. The favorable effects of niobium additions on short-time stress-rupture properties are attributed to a finely dispersed precipitation of NbC. The favorable effects tend to diminish as tempering temperature is increased, and a coarsely dispersed precipitate is formed. The effect of tempering in service is shown by the hardness data in Fig. 19 for types 422 and H-46. The H-46 alloy shows a larger hardness drop for extended thermal exposure at a testing temperature of 540 °C (1000 °F) than does type 422.

Applications. Quenched-and-tempered martensitic stainless steels find their greatest application in steam and gas turbines, where they are used in blading at temperatures up to 540 °C (1000 °F). Other uses include steam valves, bolts, and miscellaneous parts requiring corrosion resistance and good strength up to 540 °C (1000 °F).

Types 410 and 403. Type 410 is the basic, general-purpose stainless steel used for steam valves, pump shafts, bolts, and miscellaneous parts requiring corrosion resistance and moderate strength up to 540 °C (1000 °F). Type 403 is similar to 410, but the chemical composition is adjusted to prevent formation of δ-ferrite in heavy sections. It is used extensively for steam turbine rotor blades and gas turbine compressor blades operating at temperatures up to 480 °C (900 °F). For this type of application the steel is tempered at 590 °C (1100 °F) or above, after which embrittlement is negligible in the service temperature range of 370 to 480 °C (700 to 900 °F).

A satisfactory heat treatment for these steels is to austenitize at 950 to 980 °C (1750 to 1800 °F), cool rapidly in air or oil, and temper. Cooling from the hot-rolling temperature and tempering without intermediate austenitizing is sometimes practical but may result in a structure that contains free ferrite, which is detrimental to transverse properties. Warm or cold work after tempering sets up residual stresses that can be relieved by heating to approximately 620 °C (1150 °F).

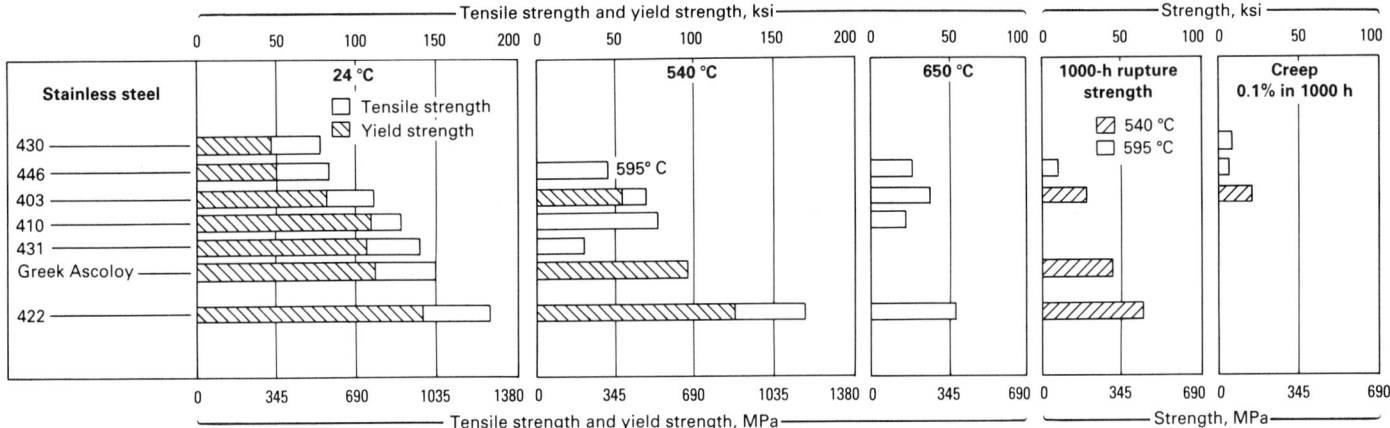

Fig. 21 Tensile, yield, rupture, and creep strengths for seven ferritic and martensitic stainless steels. Types 430 and 446 were annealed. Type 403 was quenched from 870 °C (1600 °F) and tempered at 620 °C (1150 °F). Type 410 was quenched from 955 °C (1750 °F) and tempered at 590 °C (1100 °F). Type 431 was quenched from 1025 °C (1875 °F) and tempered at 590 °C (1100 °F). Greek Ascoloy was quenched from 955 °C (1750 °F) and tempered at 590 °C (1100 °F). Type 422 was quenched from 1040 °C (1900 °F) and tempered at 590 °C (1100 °F).

Stress-time deformation curves for type 410 sheet are given in Fig. 20. These values are useful for special applications where heating rates are high.

Greek Ascoloy, type 431, and type 422 are variants of type 410, modified by the addition of such elements as nickel, tungsten, aluminum, mo-

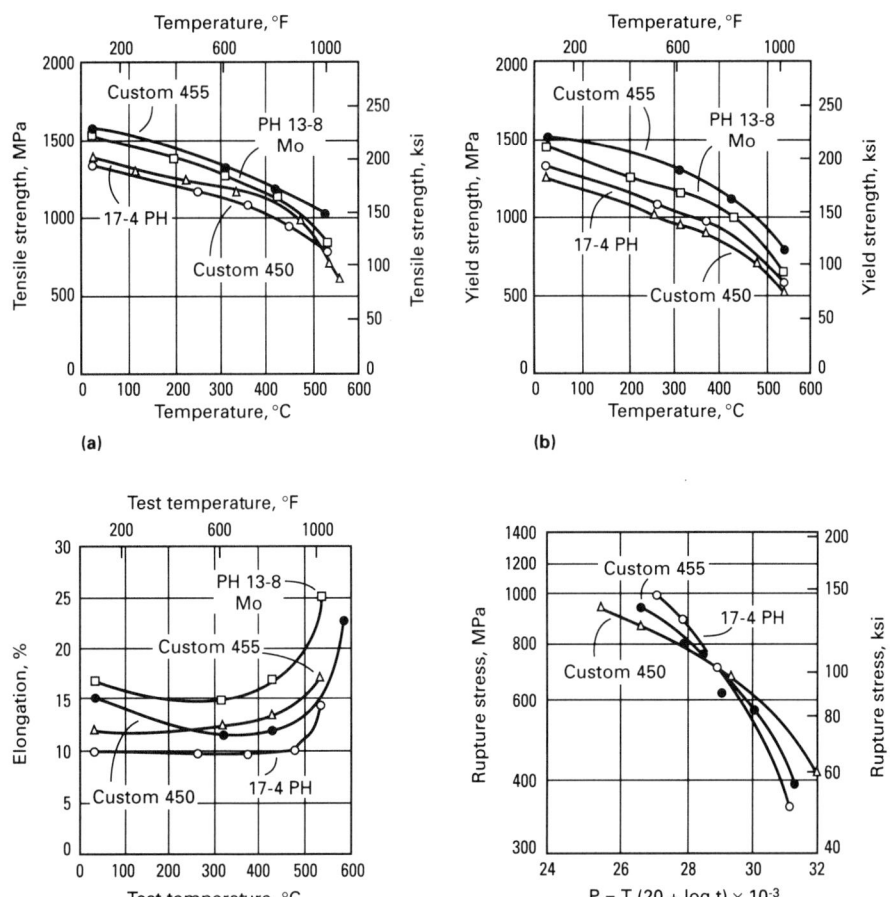

Fig. 22 Comparison of mechanical properties of precipitation-hardening martensitic stainless steels. (a) Tensile strength. (b) Yield strength. (c) Elongation. (d) Rupture strength. Heat-treating schedules were as follows. Custom 450: 1 h at 1040 °C (1900 °F), water quench; then 4 h at 480 °C (900 °F), air cool. 17-4 PH: 30 min at 1040 °C (1900 °F), oil quench; then 4 h at 480 °C (900 °F), air cool. Custom 455: 30 min at 815 °C (1500 °F), water quench; then 4 h at 510 °C (950 °F), air cool. PH 13-8 Mo: oil quenched from 925 °C (1700 °F); then 4 h at 540 °C (1000 °F), air cool

lybdenum, and vanadium. Nickel serves a useful purpose by causing the steel to be entirely austenitic at conventional heating temperatures when the carbon and chromium contents are such that a two-phase structure would exist if nickel were absent. The tempering temperature for Greek Ascoloy may be 55 °C (100 °F) or more higher than that for type 410 of equivalent strength and hardness. Type 422 develops the highest mechanical properties and at 650 °C (1200 °F) has a tensile strength equivalent to that of type 403 at 590 °C (1100 °F). The rupture strength of type 422 at 540 °C (1000 °F) is considerably higher than those of the other steels in this series (Fig. 21).

Welding. The primary factor in welding martensitic steels is their hardenability. The heat-affected zones surrounding the weld harden upon cooling, setting up stresses that can give rise to cracking. If the filler metal is similar to the parent metal, the weld itself will also harden upon cooling and become very brittle. These difficulties can be avoided by two precautions:

- Use austenitic filler metal, which will remain ductile and will absorb the stresses set up by hardening in the heat-affected zone.
- Preheat the work gradually before welding and postheating after welding to avoid quenching stresses and cracks. Preheating should be carried out at 205 to 315 °C (400 to 600 °F), postheating at 590 to 760 °C (1100 to 1400 °F).

More detailed information on the weldability of martensitic stainless steels can be found in the article "Welding" in this Volume.

Precipitation-Hardening Martensitic Stainless Steels

The PH martensitic stainless steels fill an important position between the chromium-free 18% Ni maraging steels and the 12% Cr, low-nickel, quenched-and-tempered martensitic stainless alloys. These PH alloys contain 12 to 16% Cr for corrosion resistance and scaling resistance at elevated temperatures and have the highest tensile

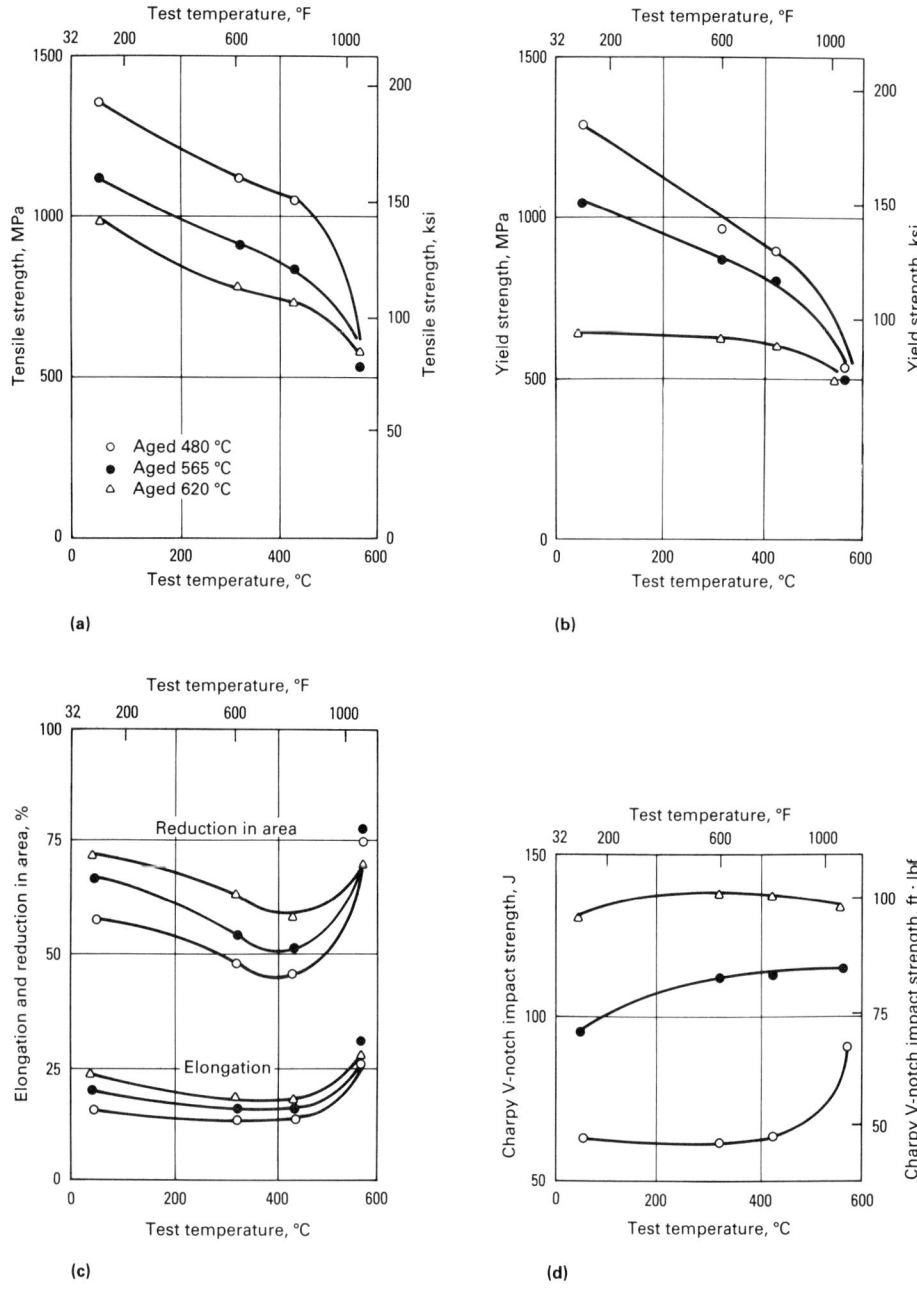

strengths at temperatures below about 450 °C (850 °F), as shown in Fig. 1.

These alloys are normally purchased in the solution-annealed condition. Depending on the application, they may be used in the annealed condition or in the annealed-plus-age-hardened condition. In some cases, material will be supplied in an overaged condition to facilitate the forming of parts. The formed parts are then solution annealed following fabrication.

Properties. The martensitic PH alloys listed in Table 1 include Custom 450, 17-4 PH, 15-5 PH, Custom 455, and PH 13-8 Mo. Property data for these alloys are shown in Fig. 22. Data for 15-5 PH are not shown separately because the properties of this alloy are very similar to those of 17-4 PH.

Short-time tensile data indicate that Custom 455 and PH 13-8 Mo have higher strengths than Custom 450, 17-4 PH, or 15-5 PH. For all of these alloys, tensile and yield strengths drop rapidly at temperatures above 425 °C (800 °F), and tensile elongation is greater than 10% over the temperature range from ambient to 540 °C (1000 °F).

Stress-rupture data are compared in Fig. 22 by means of a Larson-Miller plot. Data were developed at testing temperatures of 425 and 480 °C (800 and 900 °F) during time periods of 100 and 1000 h. It should be noted that 17-4 PH appears to have better stress-rupture strength at 425 °C (800 °F), whereas Custom 450 is superior in this respect at 480 °C (900 °F). The only stress-rupture data available for Custom 455 appear to indicate that the alloy is intermediate in rupture strength between 17-4 PH and Custom 450.

It is possible to produce a wide variety of useful properties in a given alloy by varying the aging temperature. An example of this can be seen in Fig. 23, where tensile strength, yield strength (0.2% offset), ductility, and impact data are shown for Custom 450 at three different aging temperatures. Aging at 480 °C (900 °F) can produce significant strengthening at testing temperatures as high as 450 °C (850 °F), but it also results in lower toughness values (as measured by Charpy V-notch testing) than aging at either of the two higher temperatures.

PH martensitic stainless steels are used for short-time elevated-temperature exposures in industrial and military applications for which resistance to corrosion and high mechanical properties at temperatures up to 425 °C (800 °F) are necessary. Typical uses include valve parts, ball bearings, forgings, turbine blades, mandrels, conveyor chain, miscellane-

Fig. 23 Effect of temperature on (a) tensile strength, (b) yield strength, (c) elongation, and (d) impact toughness of Custom 450. Material used for testing was round bar stock, 25 mm (1 in.) in diameter, that had been solution treated by heating 1 h at 1040 °C (1900 °F) and water quenching.

Table 9 Heat-treating schedules for precipitation-hardening semiaustenitic stainless steels

Alloy	Mill heat treatment (solution anneal)	Fabrication	Conditioning and hardening treatments	Aging or tempering treatment
17-7 PH	1065 °C (1950 °F), air cool	Forming, welding	10 min at 955 °C (1750 °F), air cool, 8 h at –75 °C (–100 °F)	1 h at 510, 565, or 620 °C (950, 1050, or 1150 °F)
			1½ h at 760 °C (1400 °F), air cool to 15 °C (60 °F), hold ½ h	1 h at 510, 565, or 620 °C (950, 1050, or 1150 °F)
15-7 Mo	1065 °C (1950 °F), air cool	Forming, welding	10 min at 955 °C (1750 °F), air cool, 8 h at –75 °C (–100 °F)	1 h at 510, 565, or 620 °C (950, 1050, or 1150 °F)
			1½ h at 790 °C (1450 °F), air cool to 15 °C (60 °F), hold ½ h	1 h at 510, 565, or 620 °C (950, 1050, or 1150 °F)
AM-350	1040-1080 °C (1900-1975 °F), air cool	Forming, welding	930 °C (1710 °F), air cool, 3 h at –75 °C (–100 °F) , 3 h at 745 °C (1375 °F), air cool to 27 °C (80 °F) max	3 h at 455 or 540 °C (850 or 1000 °F), 3 h at 455 °C (850 °F)
AM-355	3 h at 775 °C (1425 °F), oil or water quench to 27 °C (80 °F) max, 3 h at 580 °C (1075 °F), air cool	Machining and other	1040 °C (1900 °F), water quench, 3 h at –75 °C (–100 °F), reheat to 955 °C (1750 °F), air cool, 3 h at –75 °C (–100 °F)	3 h at 455 or 540 °C (850 or 1000 °F)

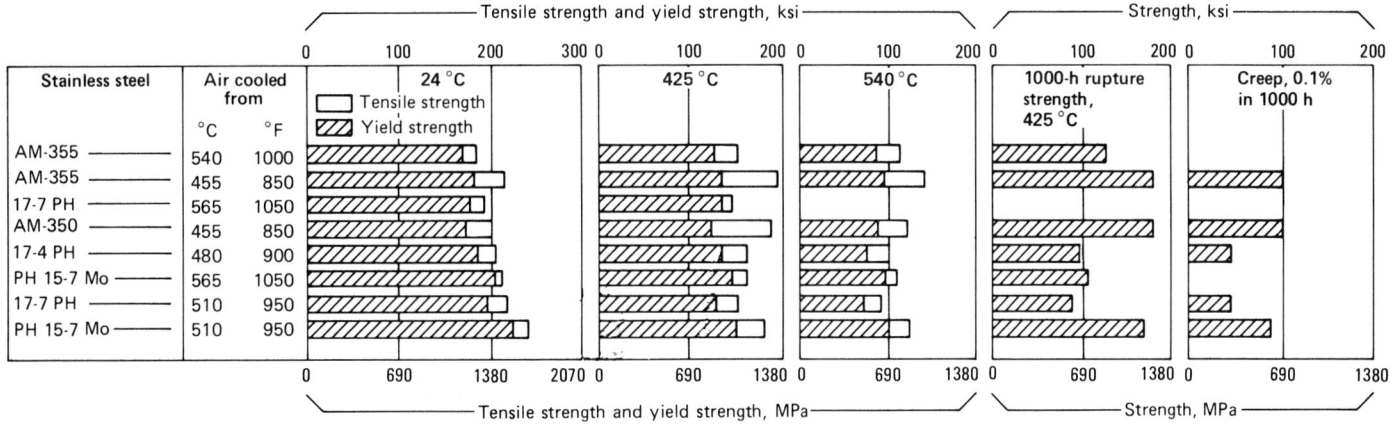

Fig. 24 Short-time tensile, rupture, and creep properties of PH stainless steels. AM-355 was finish hot worked from a maximum temperature of 980 °C (1800 °F), reheated to 930 to 955 °C (1710 to 1750 °F), water quenched, treated at -75 °C (-100 °F), and aged at 540 and 455 °C (1000 and 850 °F). 17-7 PH and PH 15-7 Mo were solution treated at 1040 to 1065 °C (1900 to 1950 °F). 17-7 PH (TH1050) and PH 15-7 Mo (TH1050) were reheated to 760 °C (1400 °F), air cooled to 15 °C (60 °F) within 1 h, and aged 90 min at 565 °C (1050 °F). 17-7 PH (RH950) and PH 15-7 Mo (RH950) were reheated to 955 °C (1750 °F) after solution annealing, cold treated at -75 °C (-100 °F), and aged at 510 °C (950 °F). 17-4 PH was aged at 480 °C (900 °F) after solution annealing. AM-350 was solution annealed at 1040 to 1065 °C (1900 to 1950 °F), reheated to 930 °C (1710 °F), air cooled, treated at -75 °C (-100 °F), and aged at 455 °C (850 °F).

ous hardware, and mechanical and structural components for aircraft.

Welding. All of these alloys are martensitic in the annealed condition and, because of their low carbon levels, are readily weldable with minimal danger of cracking (see the article "Welding" in this Volume). Any of the standard welding procedures, such as gas-tungsten arc welding, gas-metal arc welding, covered electrode welding, and resistance welding, may be used. No preheating is required because the very low carbon content of these alloys restricts the hardness of rapidly cooled metal and reduces the possibility of crack formation in weld metal and in the heat-affected zone.

Precipitation-Hardening Semiaustenitic Stainless Steels

The PH semiaustenitic heat-resistant stainless steels are modifications of standard 18-8 austenitic stainless steels. Nickel contents are lower, and such elements as aluminum, copper, molybdenum, and niobium are added. These steels are used at temperatures up to 480 °C (900 °F).

Heat Treatment. Typical schedules for heat treating PH alloys are given in Table 9. These alloys are solution annealed above 1040 °C (1900 °F) and in this condition can be formed, stamped, stretched, and otherwise cold worked to about the same extent as 18-8 alloys, although they are less ductile and may require intermediate annealing.

All the semiaustenitic stainless steels can also be used in the cold-worked condition in either sheet or wire form. Cold working causes partial transformation of the rather unstable austenite to martensite because of plastic deformation. Aging or tempering is performed after cold working.

Mechanical Properties. Typical short-time tensile, rupture, and creep properties of several PH semiaustenitic alloys are compared in Fig. 24. Different hardening heat treatments may produce a wide variety of useful properties for the same al-

loy. For example, the PH 15-7 Mo alloy treated to condition RH950 has a higher rupture strength than the same alloy treated to TH1050 (Fig. 25). Strengths also degrade after long-term exposure at elevated temperatures because of overaging (coarsening) of precipitates.

Compressive and tensile yield strengths are approximately equal for all PH stainless steels. For sheet, the yield strengths of specimens taken transverse and parallel to the direction of rolling may vary appreciably. The magnitude of this effect varies from grade to grade and with the heat treatment for a given grade.

Welding. The PH stainless steels in either the annealed or the hardened condition can be welded by any of the processes used for welding 18-8 (300-series) stainless steel (see the article "Welding" in this Volume). These steels are less ductile and more notch sensitive than conventional 18-8 grades and require more care to prevent stress concentrations at corners and notches.

The gas-shielded tungsten arc process is satisfactory for welding large assemblies of sheet and forgings that are subsequently aged. Postweld annealing is desirable.

A complete cycle of heat treatment, including high-temperature solution annealing, is desirable after welding. Strength and ductility in fully heat-treated fusion welds are superior to these properties in material hardened before welding and not heat treated after welding. Joint efficiencies near 90% have been reported for welded joints fully heat treated after welding.

The PH steels can be spot welded by the same technique used for 18-8 stainless steels. This may be done before or after precipitation hardening. The minimum shear requirements for stainless steel at 1035 MPa (150 ksi) can be obtained.

Applications. The PH stainless steels are used for industrial and military applications that require resistance to corrosion as well as high mechanical properties at temperatures up to 425 °C (800 °F). Typical uses of these steels include landing-gear hooks, poppet valves, fuel tanks, hydrau-

lic lines, hydraulic fittings, compressor casings, miscellaneous hardware, and structural components for aircraft. The higher-carbon grade (0.13% C) is used for compressor blades, spacers, frames and casings for gas turbines, oil well drill rods, and rocket casings.

Precipitation-hardening steels can be cold rolled and tempered. Work-hardening rates are higher than for type 301 stainless steel and can be varied by regulating the annealing temperature. Compared with cold-rolled type 301, cold-rolled PH stainless steels have higher ductility at a given

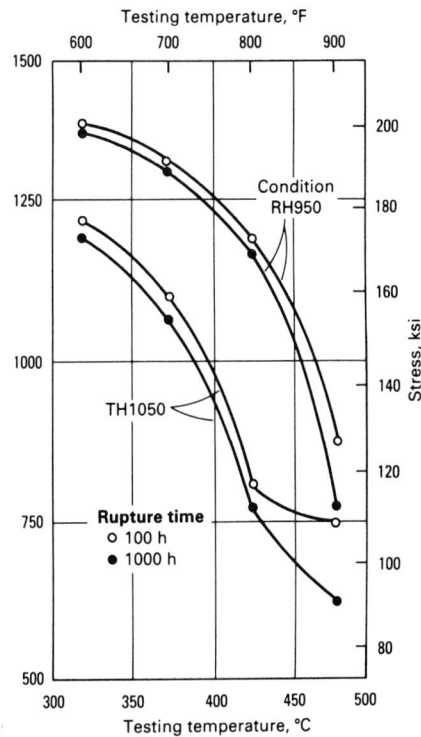

Fig. 25 Stress-rupture curves of PH 15-7 Mo stainless steel in the TH1050 and RH950 conditions

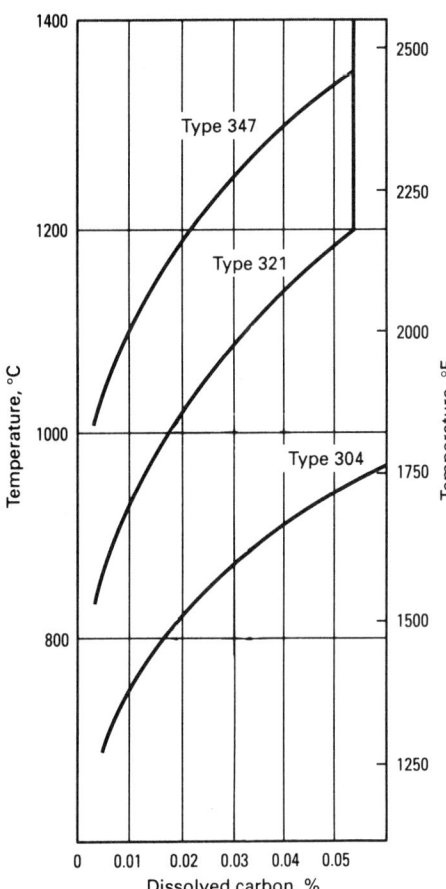

Fig. 26 Dissolved carbon under equilibrium conditions calculated from the solubility products for a type 347 stainless steel (0.054% C, 0.76% Nb), a type 321 stainless steel (0.054% C, 0.42% Ti), and an unstabilized 18Cr-8Ni stainless steel

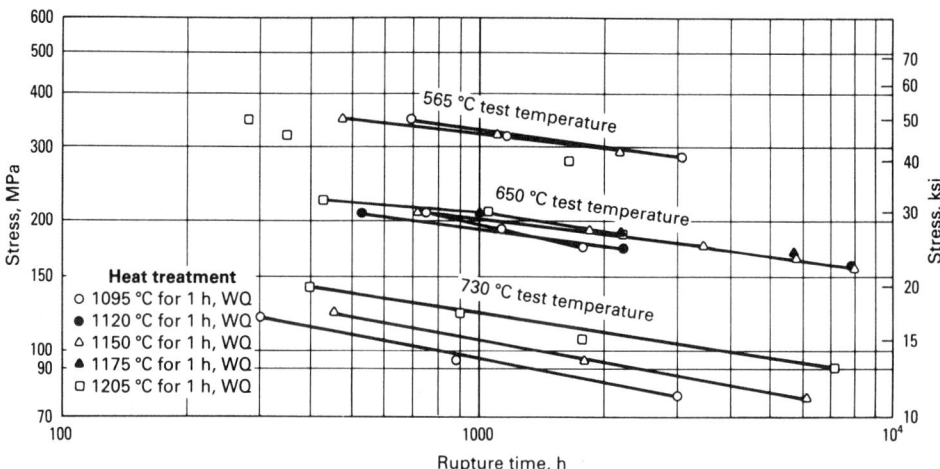

Fig. 27 Stress-rupture strength of type 347H stainless steel treated at different solution-annealing temperatures

strength level, higher modulus of elasticity in compression in the rolling direction, and less reduction in strength with increasing temperature.

Austenitic Stainless Steels

Austenitic stainless steels comprise a group of iron-base alloys that contain 16 to 25% Cr and residual to 20% Ni. Some alloys may contain as much as 18% Mn. These stainless steels are not hardenable by heat treatment but can be hardened by cold work. However, the effect of cold work on strength is lost after elevated-temperature exposure (Fig. 2) because of recrystallization.

The austenitic stainless steels listed in Table 1 can be grouped into three categories, based primarily on composition:

- *300-series alloys,* which are essentially chromium-nickel and chromium-nickel-molybdenum austenitic stainless steels to which small amounts of other elements have been added
- *19-9 DL, 19-9 DX, and 17-14-CuMo,* all of which contain 1.25 to 2.5% Mo and 0.3 to 0.55% Ti. Other elements used include 1.25% W and 3% Cu in 17-14-CuMo.

- *Chromium-nickel-manganese alloys,* which include types 201 and 202; 21-6-9; Nitronics 32, 33, 50, and 60; and Carpenter 18-18 Plus. These alloys contain 5 to 18% Mn and 0.10 to 0.50% N. The role of manganese in these steels is not only to save nickel but also to increase the solubility for nitrogen, which is used for structure control, strengthening, and improving corrosion resistance.

Austenitic stainless steels are noted for high strength and for exceptional toughness, ductility, and formability. As a class, they exhibit considerably better corrosion resistance than martensitic or ferritic stainless steels, and they also have excellent strength and oxidation resistance at elevated temperatures.

Solution heat treatment of these alloys is done by heating to about 1095 °C (2000 °F), followed by rapid cooling. Carbides that are dissolved at these temperatures may precipitate at grain boundaries upon exposure to temperatures from 425 to 870 °C (800 to 1600 °F), causing chromium depletion in grain-boundary regions. In this condition, the metal is sensitive to intergranular corrosion in oxidizing acids. The precipitation of chromium carbides can be controlled by reducing carbon content, as in types 304L and 316L, or by adding the stronger carbide formers titanium and niobium, as in types 321 and 347. These alloys are normally purchased and used in the annealed condition. The reduced carbon in solution in the low-carbon (304L, 316L) and stabilized grades (321, 347) results in reduced creep strength and creep-rupture strength. More detailed information on sensitization of austenitic stainless steels can be found in the articles "Metallurgy and Properties of Wrought Stainless Steels," "Atmospheric and Aqueous Corrosion," and "Corrosion of Weldments" in this Volume.

H-Grades. For the best creep strength and creep-rupture strength, the H-grades of austenitic stainless steels are specified. These steels have carbon contents of 0.04 to 0.10% (Table 1) and are solution annealed at temperatures high enough to produce improved creep properties. The minimum annealing temperatures specified in ASTM

A 312 and A 240 for H-grades in general corrosion service are:

- 1040 °C (1900 °F) for hot-finished or cold-worked 304H and 316H steels
- 1095 °C (2000 °F) for cold-worked 321H, 347H, and 348H steels
- 1050 °C (1095 °F) for hot-finished 321H, 347H, and 348H steels

The stabilized grades (such as 321H, 347H, and 348H) have additions of strong carbide-forming elements, which lower the amount of dissolved carbon at a given annealing temperature (Fig. 26). The carbide formers in the stabilized grades, such as niobium in 347H, increase the resistance to intergranular corrosion by making less dissolved carbon available for chromium carbide formation, thereby preventing the depletion of chromium in grain-boundary regions.

When intergranular corrosion is of concern, annealing temperatures must be low enough to keep dissolved carbon at low levels. Type 347H tube, for example, at the minimum annealing temperature of 1095 °C (2000 °F) (specified in ASME SA213) would have only about 0.01% soluble carbon (Fig. 26), and the alloy should be stabilized against chromium depletion in the grain boundaries. However, annealing temperatures above 1065 °C (1950 °F) may still impair the intergranular corrosion resistance of stabilized grades such as 321, 321H, 347, 347H, 348, and 348H. When types 321H and 347H are used in applications where intergranular corrosion may be a problem, it is possible to apply an additional stabilizing treatment at a temperature near 900 °C (1650 °F) to reduce free carbon content by carbide precipitation.

Lower annealing temperatures improve resistance to intergranular corrosion but also reduce creep strength and creep-rupture strength. Figure 27 shows the creep-rupture strength of 347H tube treated at different annealing temperatures. In applications where intergranular corrosion is not a concern, better creep properties can be obtained with higher annealing temperatures. Types 321H

Table 10 Creep and stress-rupture properties of types 304N and 316N stainless steels

| Type | Temperature | | Stress, MPa (ksi) for rupture in | | Stress, MPa (ksi) for a minimum creep rate of | |
	°C	°F	10,000 h	100,000 h	0.0001%/h	0.00001%/h
304N	565	1050	234 (34)	186 (27)	214 (31)	172 (25)
	650	1200	124 (18)	86 (12.5)	103 (15)	70 (10.2)
	730	1350	61 (8.8)	41 (6)	52 (7.5)	38 (5.5)
	815	1500	33 (4.8)	23 (3.3)	28 (4)	... ...
316N	565	1050	286 (41.5)	228 (33)	255 (37)	200 (29)
	650	1200	179 (26)	131 (19)	117 (17)	86 (12.5)
	730	1350	97 (14)	64 (9.3)	60 (8.7)	42 (6.1)
	815	1500	45 (6.5)	28 (4)	28 (4)	18 (2.6)

Source: Ref 22

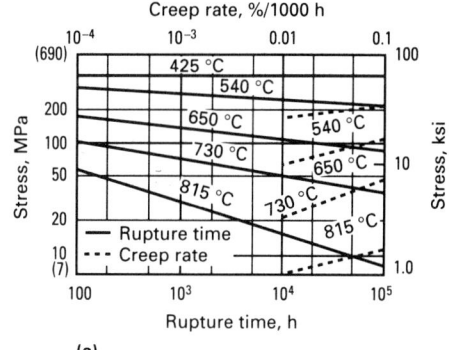

(a)

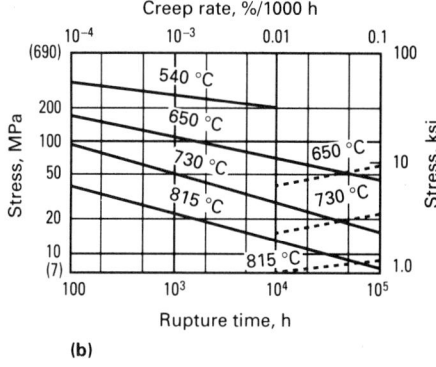

(b)

Fig. 29 Stress-rupture times and creep rates for annealed (a) type 347 stainless steel and (b) type 316 stainless steel. Source: Ref 23

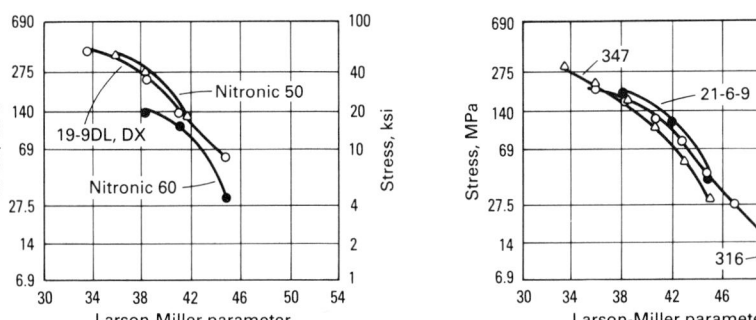

Fig. 28 Effect of testing temperature on tensile properties of austenitic stainless steels. Heat-treating schedules were as follows. Type 304: 1065 °C (1950 °F), water quench. Type 309: 1090 °C (2000 °F), water quench. Type 310: 1120 °C (2050 °F), water quench. Type 316: 1090 °C (2000 °F), water quench. Type 321: 1010 °C (1850 °F), water quench. Type 347: 1065 °C (1950 °F), water quench. 19-9 DX and 19-9 DL: 705 °C (1300 °F), air cool. Type 216: 1050 °C (1950 °F), water quench. 21-6-9: 1065 °C (1950 °F), water quench. Nitronic 33: 1056 °C (1950 °F), water quench. Nitronic 50: 1090 °C (2000 °F), water quench. Nitronic 60: 1065 °C (1950 °F), water quench. Carpenter 18-18 Plus: 1065 °C (1950 °F), water quench

and 347H, for example, are solution annealed at temperatures above 1120 °C (2050 °F) and 1150 °C (2100 °F), respectively, to put carbides in solution and to coarsen the grain structure, thereby ensuring the best creep strength and creep-rupture strength.

Nitrogen Additions. During the course of studies on the H-grades, it was found that controlled additions of nitrogen improved the high-temperature strength of types 304 and 316. Creep and stress-rupture properties of the N-grades, which contain from 0.10 to 0.13% N, are given in Table 10.

Tensile Properties. Typical mechanical property data for austenitic stainless steels are given in Fig. 28. Room-temperature tensile properties of annealed 300-series alloys are similar. At higher testing temperatures (425 and 650 °C, or 800 and 1200 °F), types 321, 347, and 309 appear to have yield strengths somewhat higher than those of types 304, 310, and 316. Types 309, 310, and 316 have the highest tensile strengths at 650 °C (1200 °F).

Tensile and yield strengths of 19-9 DL and 19-9 DX are higher than those of any 300-series alloy. However, 19-9 DL and 19-9 DX are heat treated at 705 °C (1300 °F), compared with an average of 1065 °C (1950 °F) for 300-series alloys.

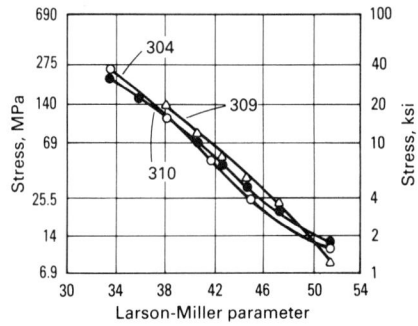

Fig. 30 Stress-rupture plots for various austenitic stainless steels. Heat-treating schedules were as follows. Type 304: 1065 °C (1950 °F), water quench. Type 309: 1090 °C (2000 °F), water quench. Type 310: 1120 °C (2050 °F), water quench. Type 316: 1090 °C (2000 °F), water quench. Type 347: 1065 °C (1950 °F), water quench. 21-6-9: 1065 °C (1950 °F), water quench. 19-9 DX and 19-9 DL: for tests above 705 °C (1300 °F), 1065 °C (1950 °F) and water quench, then 705 °C (1300 °F) and air cool; for tests below 705 °C (1300 °F), 705 °C (1300 °F) and air cool. Nitronic 50: 1090 °C (2000 °F), water quench. Nitronic 60: 1065 °C (1950 °F), water quench. Larson-Miller parameter = $T/1000$ (20 + log t) where T is temperature in °R and t is time in h. All data taken from 1000-h tests.

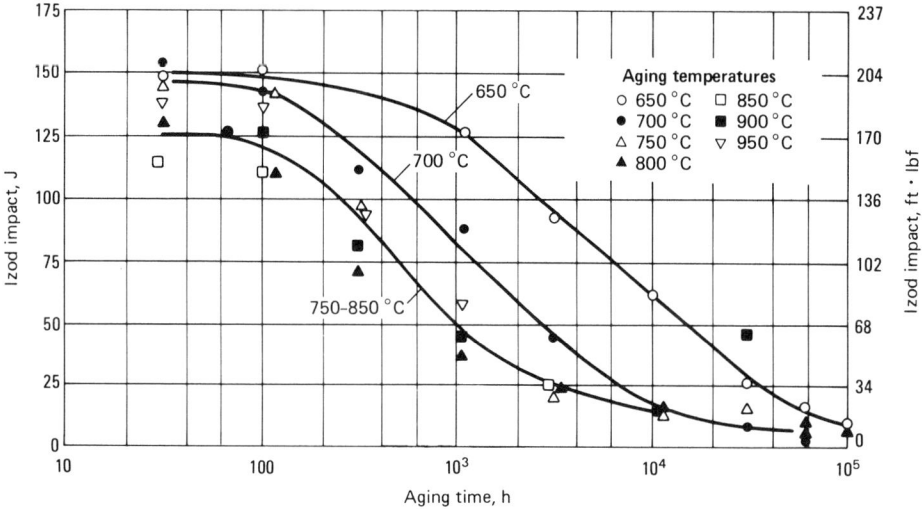

Fig. 31 Room-temperature impact toughness of type 316 stainless steel after aging at indicated temperatures. Source: Ref 24

Also, 19-9 DL and 19-9 DX are normally strengthened by controlled amounts of hot and cold work.

Tensile and yield strengths of chromium-nickel-manganese alloys are higher than those of 300-series alloys at both room and elevated temperatures. Carpenter 18-18 Plus exhibits the highest room-temperature tensile strength, whereas Nitronic 50 has the highest tensile strength at 650 °C (1200 °F).

Stress-rupture properties of various 300-series stainless steels are shown in Fig. 6. The H-grades of types 347 and 316 appear to be the two strongest alloys over a range of temperatures. Stress-rupture times and creep rates of these two austenitic stainless steels are shown in Fig. 29.

The 19-9 DL and 19-9 DX alloys have rupture strengths superior to those of all 300-series alloys over the limited temperature and time range for which rupture data are available (1000-h rupture strength at 540 to 815 °C, or 1000 to 1500 °F)

(Fig. 30). At longer times or higher temperatures, the 300 series may be superior. For the time-temperature range in Fig. 30, the chromium-nickel-manganese alloys have higher stress-rupture capabilities than the 300-series alloys, except that type 316 is superior to 21-6-9, and types 316 and 347 are stronger than Nitronic 60. The spread in rupture strength capability among these alloys is greater at the lower testing temperatures (540 to 700 °C, or 1000 to 1300 °F) and becomes progressively smaller as temperature is increased to approximately 980 °C (1800 °F), where all the alloys exhibit 1000-h rupture stresses of about 7 to 10 MPa (1 to 1.5 ksi). Types 304 and 310 have the lowest stress-rupture strengths.

Aging and the degradation of mechanical properties occur in austenitic steel because of two principal factors: precipitation reactions that occur during prolonged exposure at elevated temperatures, and environmental effects, such as corrosion or nuclear irradiation.

The precipitation reactions in austenitic stainless steels that occur during prolonged exposure at elevated temperatures are complex, but some general guidance to the precipitates formed is provided by the constitutive diagrams in Ref 24. The precipitates formed at temperatures in the range of about 500 to 600 °C (930 to 1110 °F) are predominantly carbides, whereas at higher temperatures they are in the form of intermetallic phases. Although about 30 phases have been identified in stainless steels, the predominant precipitates found in plant-serviced alloys and weld metals exposed to temperatures of about 550 °C (1020 °F) are $M_{23}C_6$ and MC carbides in unstabilized and stabilized steels, respectively. At temperatures above 600 °C (1110 °F), σ-phase and Fe_2Mo are also formed. The aging process also tends to occur more rapidly in weld metals that contain δ-ferrite (Ref 24). Phases found in wrought stainless steels are also discussed in the article "Microstructures of Wrought Stainless Steels" in this Volume.

Environmental effects on aging can be classified as either surface effects or bulk effects. Surface effects include oxidation and carburization (see the article "High-Temperature Corrosion" in this Volume), whereas bulk effects include changes in properties from nuclear irradiation (see the discussion of irradiation-assisted stress-corrosion cracking in the article "Stress-Corrosion Cracking and Hydrogen Embrittlement" in this Volume).

Impact Toughness. Solution-annealed austenitic stainless steels are very tough, and their impact energies are very high. However, following elevated-temperature thermal aging, the impact energy decreases with increasing time at temperature. The impact energy of type 316 stainless steel (Fig. 31) shows a continuous fall with increasing exposure time and temperature in the range of 650 to 850 °C (1200 to 1560 °F). Service-exposed type 316 stainless steel exhibited impact energies of 80 and 300 J (60 and 220 ft · lbf) in the serviced and re-solution heat-treated conditions, respectively, when tested at room temperature (Ref 24).

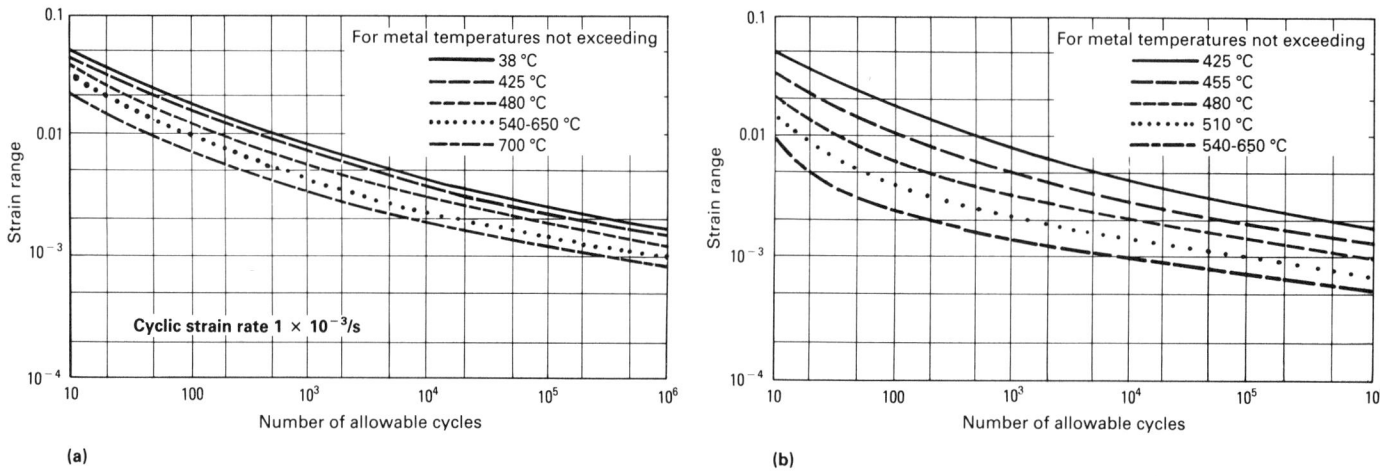

Fig. 32 Design fatigue-strain range curves for types 304 and 316 stainless steel. (a) Design curves with continuous cycling (pure fatigue). (b) Design curves with hold times (creep-fatigue interaction)

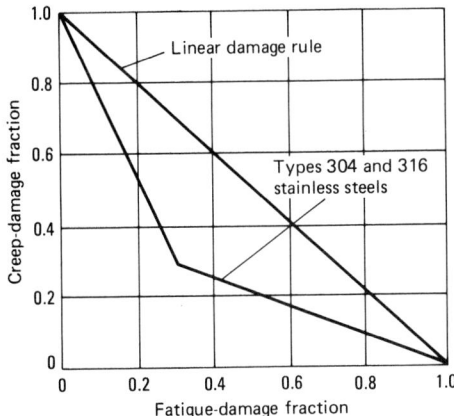

Fig. 33 Comparison of linear damage rule of creep-fatigue interaction with design envelopes in ASME Code Case N-47 for types 304 and 316 stainless steel. The creep-damage fraction is time/time-to-rupture (multiplied by a safety factor). The fatigue-damage fraction is number of cycles/cycles to failure (multiplied by a safety factor).

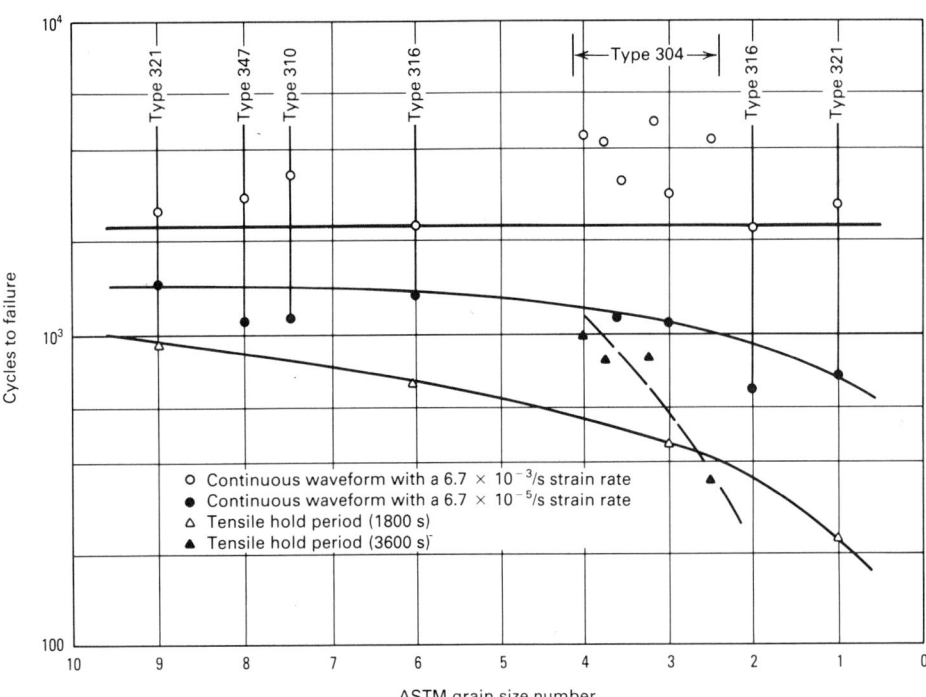

Fig. 34 Effect of strain rate and grain size on the fatigue life of various stainless steels at elevated temperatures. Grain size has the greatest influence on fatigue life when hold times are increased. Test conditions: total strain range, 1.0%; test temperature, 593 to 600 °C (1100 to 1110 °F). Source: Ref 25

Fatigue properties at elevated temperatures are dependent on several variables, including strain range, temperature, cyclic frequency, hold times, and the environment. The fatigue design curves in Fig. 32(a) show the simple case of pure fatigue (continuous cycles without hold times) for types 304 and 316 stainless steel. These design curves (from Code Case N-47 in the ASME Boiler Code) have a built-in factor of safety and are established by applying a safety factor of 2 with respect to strain range or a factor of 20 with respect to the number of cycles, whichever gives the lower value. The creep-life fraction is determined by the time-life fraction per cycle using assumed stresses 1.1 times the applied stress and the minimum stress-rupture curves incorporated in the code. The total damage must not exceed the envelope defined by the bilinear damage curve shown in Fig. 33.

The design curves in Fig. 32(a) are based on a strain rate of 1×10^{-3}/s. If the strain rate decreases, fatigue life also decreases. In Fig. 34, for example, the fatigue lives of several stainless steels are shown for continuous cycling at two different strain rates. Fatigue life is reduced with a lower strain rate, while grain size has little effect on fatigue life when life is determined from pure fatigue (or continuous cycling).

When hold times are introduced, a different set of design curves is used (Fig. 32b) to determine the allowable fatigue-life fraction (creep-life fraction is determined the same way as for continuous cycling). These allowable fatigue-life curves are a more conservative set of curves than those of Fig. 32(a). They incorporate the effect of creep damage by applying a fatigue life reduction factor, which includes hold time effects in addition to the factor of safety (2 in strength and 20 in cycles, whichever gives the lower value). Figure 35 compares the 540 to 650 °C (1000 to 1200 °F) design curve in Fig. 32(b) with actual fatigue life results from testing type 316 stainless at 593 °C (1100 °F) and various hold times. When hold times are introduced, the influence of grain size may also be more pronounced (Fig. 34).

Fatigue Crack Growth. Although S-N curves (stress/number of cycles) have been used in the past as the basic design tool against fatigue, their limitations have become increasingly obvious. One of the more serious limitations is that they do not distinguish between crack initiation and crack propagation. Particularly in the low-stress regions, a large fraction of the life of a component may be spent in crack propagation, allowing crack tolerance over a large portion of the life. Engineering structures often contain flaws or cracklike imperfections that may altogether eliminate the crack initiation step. A methodology that quantitatively describes crack growth as a function of the loading variables is, therefore, of great value in design and in assessing the remaining lives of components.

Fatigue crack growth rates are obtained at various ΔK and temperature ranges (ΔK is the stress-intensity factor). Therefore it is difficult to compare the various types of materials directly. At a constant ΔK (arbitrarily chosen as 30 MPa$\sqrt{m}$,

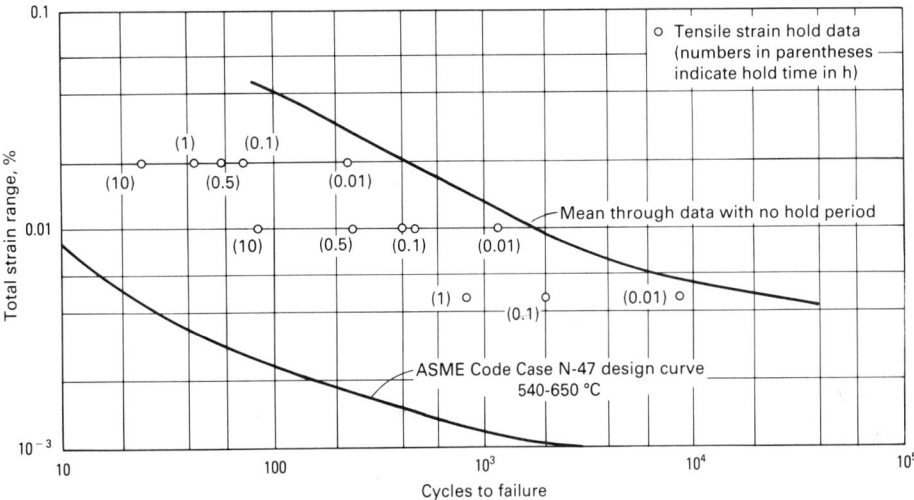

Fig. 35 Influence of tensile hold times at peak strain on failure life of a single heat of type 316 stainless steel tested at 593 °C (1100 °F). Source: Ref 25

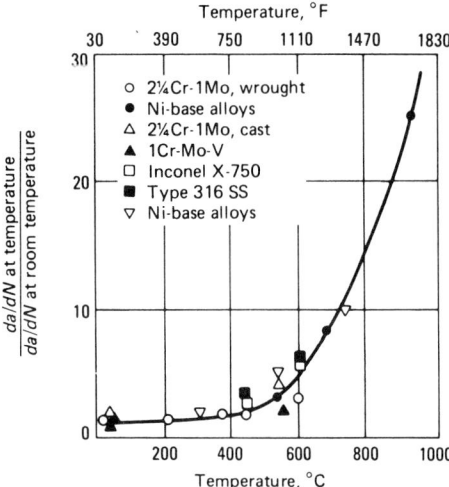

Fig. 36 Variation of fatigue crack growth rates as a function of temperature at ΔK = 30 MPa$\sqrt{\text{m}}$ (27 ksi$\sqrt{\text{in.}}$). Source: Ref 2

or 27 ksi$\sqrt{\text{in.}}$), a clear trend of increasing crack growth rate with increasing temperature can be seen (Fig. 36). At temperatures up to about 50% of the melting point (550 to 600 °C, or 1020 to 1110 °F), the growth rates are relatively insensitive to temperature, but sensitivity increases rapidly at higher temperatures. The crack growth rates for all the materials at temperatures up to 600 °C (1110 °F) relative to the room-temperature rates can be estimated by a maximum correlation factor of 5 (2 for ferritic steels).

Applications that use the heat-resisting capabilities of austenitic stainless steels to advantage include furnace parts, heat exchanger tubing, steam lines, exhaust systems in reciprocating engines and gas turbines, afterburner parts, and similar parts that require strength and oxidation resistance.

Type 304 has good resistance to atmospheric corrosion and oxidation. Types 309 and 310 rank higher in these properties because of their higher nickel and chromium contents. Type 310 is useful where intermittent heating and cooling are encountered, because it forms a more adherent scale than type 309. Types 309 and 310 are used for parts such as firebox sheets, furnace linings, boiler baffles, thermocouple wells, aircraft cabin heaters, and jet engine burner liners.

The austenitic stainless steels may become susceptible to intergranular corrosion in some environments. This occurs when these steels are exposed to temperatures between 500 and 900 °C (950 and 1650 °F) and carbon diffuses to the grain boundaries to form chromium carbides. The formation of these carbides can significantly reduce the amount of free chromium in the alloy, thus impairing the corrosion resistance of the grain boundaries. The intergranular corrosion that occurs in the heat-affected zones of welds is often called weld knife-edge attack. Types 321 and 347 (when correctly heat treated to form titanium or niobium carbides, respectively) and the naturally low-carbon grades 304L and 316L are resistant to intergranular corrosion. Intergranular attack is usually limited to aqueous environments and is covered

in more detail in the article "Atmospheric and Aqueous Corrosion" in this Volume. When types 321H and 347H are used in applications where intergranular corrosion may be a problem, it is possible to apply an additional stabilizing heat treatment at a temperature near 900 °C (1650 °F) to produce stable titanium and niobium carbides and thus reduce the free carbon content.

Types 321 and 347 can be used where solution treatment after welding is not feasible, such as in steam lines, superheater tubes, and exhaust systems in reciprocating engines and gas turbines that operate at temperatures from 425 to 870 °C (800 to 1600 °F). The low-carbon types 304L and 316L are used for similar applications but are more susceptible to intergranular attack during long exposure to high temperatures.

Type 316 has better mechanical properties than types 304 or 321 and is more resistant to corrosion in some media, such as fatty acids at elevated temperatures and mild sulfuric acid solutions. The tensile and yield strengths of types 304, 304L, 316, and 316L can be increased by alloying these grades with nitrogen. These modifications are designated as 304N (UNS S30451), 304LN (UNS S30454), 316N (UNS S31651), and 316LN (UNS S31653).

Duplex Stainless Steels

Duplex stainless steels, with δ-ferrite in an austenite matrix, have improved resistance to stress-corrosion cracking and increased yield and tensile strengths. A further advantage of the presence of δ-ferrite is that it causes grain refinement, which produces additional strengthening. Further refining of the grain size can be achieved by a controlled-rolling treatment, using hot working in the range of 900 to 950 °C (1650 to 1740 °F) or at even lower temperatures. This causes a very fine dispersion of ferrite and austenite, in approximately equal proportions, which can give yield strengths in excess of 450 MPa (65 ksi). Duplex steels, however, require a careful balance of the ferrite- and austenite-forming elements (see the articles "Metallurgy and Properties of Wrought Stainless Steels" and "Metallurgy and Properties of Cast Stainless Steels" in this Volume). The duplex steels are susceptible to 475 °C (885 °F) embrittlement at 370 to 480 °C (700 to 900 °F) and to σ formation at 650 to 815 °C (1200 to 1500 °F). For this reason, they are not very suitable for high-temperature applications.

ACKNOWLEDGMENT

The information in this article is largely taken from S. Lampman, Elevated-Temperature Properties of Stainless Steels, *Properties and Selection: Irons, Steels, and High-Performance Alloys*, Vol 1, *ASM Handbook* (formerly 10th ed., *Metals Handbook*), ASM International, 1990, p 930-949

REFERENCES

1. W.F. Simmons and J.A. Van Echo, "Report on the Elevated-Temperature Properties of Stainless Steels," ASTM Data Series, Publication DS-5-S1 (formerly STP 124), ASTM
2. R. Viswanathan, *Damage Mechanisms and Life Assessment of High-Temperature Components*, ASM International, 1989
3. J. Wareing, *Met. Trans. A*, Vol 8, 1977, p 711-721
4. C.R. Brinkman, G.E. Korth, and R.R. Hobbins, *Nucl. Tech.*, Vol 16, 1972, p 299-307
5. Y. Asada and S. Mitsuhaski, in *Fourth International Conference on Pressure Vessel Technology*, Vol 1, 1980, p 321
6. C.R. Brinkman and G.E. Korth, *Met. Trans.*, Vol 5, 1974, p 792
7. J. Wareing, *Met. Trans. A*, Vol 6, 1975, p 1367
8. J. Wareing, H.G. Vaughan, and B. Tomkins, Report NDR-447S, United Kingdom Atomic Energy Agency, 1980
9. I.W. Goodall, R. Hales, and D.J. Walters, in *Proceedings of IUTAM 103*, International Union of Theoretical and Applied Mechanics, 1980
10. D.S. Wood, J. Wynn, A.B. Baldwin, and P. O'Riordan, *Fatigue Eng. Mater. Struct.*, Vol 3, 1980, p 89
11. J. Wareing, *Fatigue Eng. Mater. Struct.*, Vol 4, 1981, p 131
12. C.E. Jaske, M. Mindlin, and J.S. Perrin, Development of Elevated Temperature Fatigue Design Information for Type 316 Stainless Steel, *International Conference on Creep and Fatigue*, Conference Publication 13, Institute of Mechanical Engineers, 1973, p 163.1-163.7
13. S. Majumdar and P.S. Maiya, *J. Eng. Mater. Technol. (Trans. ASME)*, Vol 102 (No. 1), 1980, p 159
14. V.B. Livesey and J. Wareing, *Met. Sci.*, Vol 17, 1983, p 297
15. D. Gladwin and D.A. Miller, *Fatigue Eng. Mater. Struct.*, Vol 5, 1982, p 275-286
16. D.A. Miller, R.H. Priest, and E.G. Ellison, A Review of Material Response and Life Prediction Techniques under Fatigue-Creep Loading Conditions, *High Temp. Mater. Process.*, Vol 6 (No. 3 and 4), 1984, p 115-194
17. J.K. Lai and C.P. Horton, Report RD/L/R/200S, Central Electricity Generating Board, 1979
18. Y. Kadoya, et al., Creep Fatigue Life Prediction of Turbine Rotors, *Life Assessment and Improvement of Turbogenerator Rotors for Fossil Plants*, R. Viswanathan, Ed., Pergamon Press, 1985, p 3.101-3.114
19. H.E. McCoy, *Corrosion*, Vol 21, 1965, p 84
20. J.D. McCoy, "Corrosion Rates for H2S at Elevated Temperatures in Refinery Hydrodesulfurization Processes," Paper 128, National Association of Corrosion Engineers, 1974
21. T. Fujita, Advanced High-Chromium Ferritic Steels for High Temperatures, *Met. Prog.*, Vol 130, Aug 1986, p 33
22. "Elevated-Temperature Properties as Influenced by Nitrogen Additions to Types 304 and 316 Austenitic Stainless Steels," STP 522, ASTM, 1973

23. W.F. Simmons and H.C. Cross, "Report on the Elevated Temperature Properties of Chromium Steels, 12 to 27 Percent," STP 228, ASTM, 1952
24. P. Marshall, *Austenitic Stainless Steels Microstructure and Mechanical Properties,* Elsevier, 1984
25. C.R. Brinkman, High-Temperature Time-Dependent Fatigue Behavior of Several Engineering Structural Alloys, *International Metals Review,* Vol 30 (No. 5), 1985, p 235-258

SELECTED REFERENCES

- *Austenitic Chromium-Nickel Stainless Steels: Engineering Properties at Elevated Temperatures,* INCO Europe Limited, 1963
- *High Temperature Characteristics of Stainless Steels,* American Iron and Steel Institute, 1979
- R.A. Lula, *Source Book on the Ferritic Stainless Steels,* American Society for Metals, 1982
- P. Marshall, *Austenitic Stainless Steels Microstructure and Mechanical Properties,* Elsevier, 1984
- T.D. Parker, Strength of Stainless Steels at Elevated Temperature, *Selection of Stainless Steels,* American Society for Metals, 1968, p 47-66
- G.V. Smith, *Evaluations of the Elevated Temperature Tensile and Creep Rupture Properties of 12 to 27 Percent Chromium Steels,* DS 59, ASTM, 1980
- R. Viswanathan, *Damage Mechanisms and Life Assessment of High-Temperature Components,* ASM International, 1989

Tribological Properties

STAINLESS STEELS are primarily used to resist corrosive attack in environments that are as mild as kitchen sinks or as severe as piping used in the chemical process industry. A wide range of corrosion resistance can be achieved by increasing the chromium content and adding other elements, especially nickel. In addition, high tensile yield strength (>1400 MPa, or 205 ksi) can be accomplished through martensite formation, precipitation hardening, or cold work.

The selection of a particular type of stainless steel for an application involves the consideration of such factors as the corrosion resistance of the alloy, mechanical properties, fabricability, and cost. However, for applications such as pumps, valves, bearings, fasteners, and conveyor belts, where one contacting metal surface moves relative to the other, the wear and galling resistance of the metals in contact should also be considered in the selection process.

Stainless steels are characterized as having relatively poor wear and galling resistance, but they are often required for a particular application because of their corrosion resistance. Therefore, finding the most effective alloy to withstand wear and galling can be a difficult problem for design engineers. Lubricants and coatings are often used to reduce wear, although lubricant use is precluded in many applications, such as high-temperature environments, in which they can break down, or food and pharmaceutical processing equipment, which require sanitation. Additionally, a critical part, such as a valve in a power plant, must resist galling or seizing, because it can shut down or endanger the entire plant (Ref 1, 2).

This article discusses the wear resistance of various stainless steel alloys. Information on laboratory wear and galling tests and the associated data from these tests is presented. Applications and design considerations are also discussed.

Types of Wear

The types of wear described below include abrasive, fretting, corrosive, fatigue, and adhesive wear and cavitation erosion. Additional information on these wear types can be found in Volume 18 of the *ASM Handbook*.

Abrasive wear involves the plowing of localized surface contacts through a softer mated material. The wear is most frequently caused by nonmetallic materials, but metallic particles can also cause abrasion (Ref 3). Generally, a material is seriously abraded or scratched only by a particle harder than itself. Abrasive wear is commonly divided into three types: low stress, high stress, and gouging.

Low-stress abrasion (scratching) is defined as wear that occurs due to relatively light rubbing contact of abrasive particles with the metal. Wear scars usually show scratches, and the amount of subsurface deformation is minimal. Consequently, the surface does not work harden appreciably. Parts such as screens, chute liners, blades, and belts that are exposed to sand slurries or abrasive atmospheres can experience low-stress abrasion. Many machine components, such as bushings, seals, and chains that operate in dust, also wear by low-stress abrasion (Ref 4).

High-stress abrasion is wear under a level of stress that is high enough to crush the abrasive. Considerably more strain hardening of the metal surface occurs. The abrasion of ore grinding balls is an example of high-stress abrasion in the mining industry. Other examples include abrasion experienced by rolling-contact bearings, gears, cams, and pivots.

Gouging abrasion is high-stress abrasion that results in sizable grooves or gouges on the worn surface (Ref 5). It occurs on parts such as crusher liners, impact hammers in pulverizers, and dipper teeth handling large rocks. Strain hardening and deformation are the dominant factors.

For ferrous materials, abrasion resistance is highly dependent on three metallurgical variables: microstructure, hardness, and carbon content. The inherently hard martensitic structure is preferable to the softer ferritic and austenitic structures. This is especially significant in low-stress abrasion, where little subsurface deformation occurs. When high-stress abrasion is encountered, alloys with high work-hardened hardness values have improved wear resistance, when compared with alloys with low work-hardened hardness values. Although austenitic stainless steels will work harden more readily than the other stainless families of alloys, martensitic stainless alloys are preferred in applications where high-stress abrasion is encountered because of their higher hardness by heat treatment. Increased carbon content, regardless of structure, favors better abrasive wear resistance, and so does an increased volume of carbides, as long as their hardness is not exceeded by that of the abrasive medium.

For stainless steels, knowledge of low-stress abrasion resistance is important, because abrasive particles can be found in applications where stainless steels are used. Austenitic stainless steels with a high work-hardening rate can be used where gouging abrasion is a problem and toughness is required. However, austenitic manganese steels containing approximately 1.2% C and 12% Mn are more resistant. Generally, stainless steels are considered for abrasive wear conditions when the environment is corrosive or when elevated temperatures are encountered.

Fretting wear is material loss that is due to very small amplitude vibrations at mechanical connections, such as riveted joints. This type of wear is a combination of oxidation and abrasive wear. Oscillation of two metallic surfaces produces tiny metallic fragments that oxidize and become abrasive. Subsequent wear proceeds by mild adhesive wear in combination with abrasive wear.

Fretting wear is influenced by contact conditions, environmental conditions, and material properties and behavior. These factors may interact to influence both the nature and the extent of fretting damage. For example, the influence of an environmental factor depends on its accessibility to the metal contact area. Only if the environmental conditions have ready access to fretting damage sites will environmental factors strongly influence fretting.

Key parameters in fretting include load, frequency, amplitude of fretting motion, number of fretting cycles, relative humidity, and temperature. Fretting wear rate is virtually independent of amplitude up to a critical value. Beyond that, the wear rate increases almost linearly with the amplitude. The effect of frequency has been studied on mild steel. Up to 30 Hz, the fretting wear decreases as frequency increases, while wear is not affected above 30 Hz. A threshold number of cycles appears to be required for the onset of steady-state fretting wear rate. This is marked by the appearance of microspall pits, which indicate that a surface fatigue mechanism is operative. The environmental factors, that is, relative humidity and temperature, generally favor the use of stainless steels because of their superior corrosion and thermal properties. Figure 1 shows the pitting produced in an austenitic stainless steel as a result of fretting in an aqueous corrosive environment.

Corrosive wear involves an interaction between the wear surface and the corrosive reagent. Corrosion in aqueous media is an electrochemical action that results in material removal by dissolution, whereas wear involves material removal that is due to physical interaction between surfaces under relative motion. When these two processes are combined, the material loss may be significantly accelerated because of synergistic behavior. The wear-corrosion process involves the disruption and removal of the oxide film, leading to exposure of the active metal surface to the environment, dissolution or repassivation of the exposed metal surface, interaction between elastic

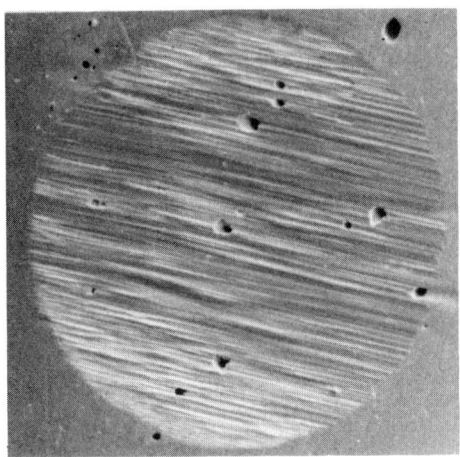

Fig. 1 Local pitting produced when an austenitic stainless steel ball is fretted against an austenitic stainless steel flat in 0.1 $N H_2SO_4$

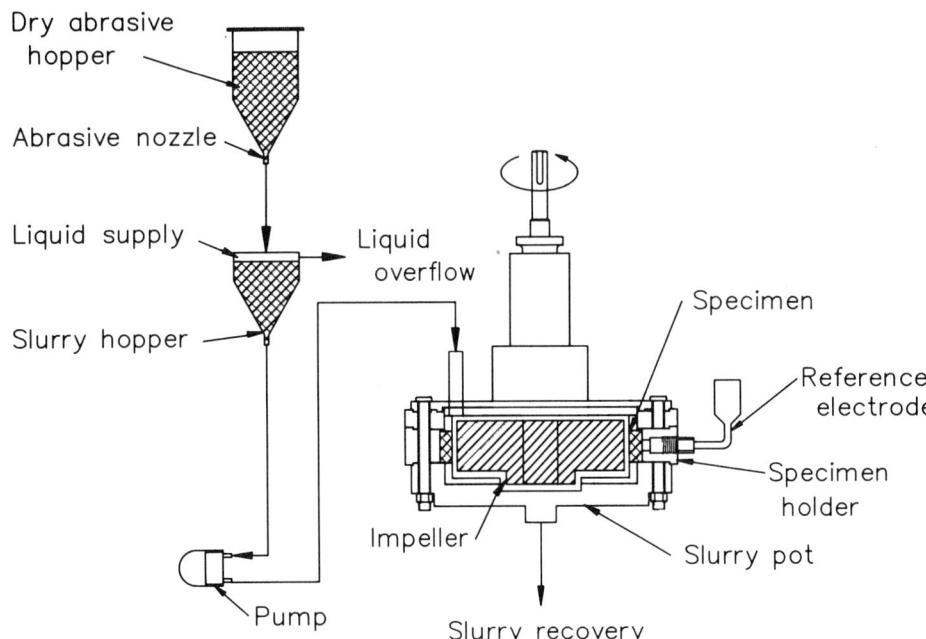

Fig. 2 Flow-through slurry wear apparatus. Source: U.S. Bureau of Mines

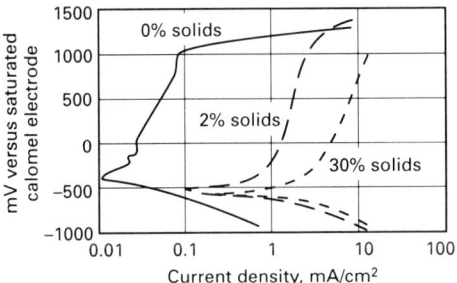

(a)

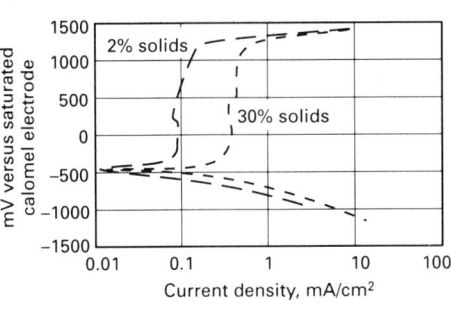

(b)

Fig. 3 Polarization curves for type 316 stainless steel showing the effect of percent solids and impeller speed in a silica sand slurry. (a) Impeller velocity 15.6 m/s (52 ft/s). (b) Impeller velocity 5.8 m/s (19 ft/s). Source: Ref 7

fields at asperities (surface high spots) in contact with the environment, and interaction between plastically deformed areas and the environment. The exact nature of the wear-corrosion process is very dependent on the specific metal and the specific corrosive reagent (Ref 6).

A slurry wear test has been developed by the U.S. Bureau of Mines (Ref 7, 8) to measure both wear and corrosion of metal-alloy specimens. Figure 2 depicts the slurry wear apparatus. Slurry wear test experiments showed that mechanical wear had a dramatic effect on the polarization curves of passive alloys, such as stainless steels. The results showed that the combined effects of wear and corrosion resulted in total wear rates that

were much greater than the additive effects of each process alone. Figure 3 shows the polarization plots for type 316 stainless steel that was exposed to a silica sand slurry at various slurry concentrations and impeller velocities. It is noted that the anodic current density as percent solids and speed increase, indicating that more of the passive film is removed because of the higher frequency of particle impacts. The oxide film on the stainless steel is apparently adherent and fast forming. In contrast, the polarization curves and corrosion rates of low-alloy steels were not affected to any extent, because they freely corrode and do not form tightly adhering passive films.

Corrosive wear can occur in the mining industry, where abrasive wear combines with a wet corrosive environment. Abrasion-resistant alloy steels can be ineffective in this application, whereas stainless steels often perform well. In these conditions, carbon steel readily forms iron oxide, which is removed by the sliding and bumping of moving coal and ore (Ref 9). If the rust is repeatedly removed, then there will be continuing loss of metal thickness.

In South Africa, a ferritic grade (3Cr12) provides a cost-effective solution to corrosive wear problems in chutes, liners, and conveyor belt equipment used in ore handling. This alloy is a modified type 409 stainless steel. In the United States, type 304 has been widely used in coal-handling equipment, such as chutes, bins, hoppers, and screens, because of its good corrosion resistance. Another reason for the popularity of type 304 is its great improvement over alloy steels with regard to "slideability." Type 304 retains a smooth surface finish, whereas abrasion-resistant alloy steels rust, which causes material buildup and lowers flow rate. Coal hopper cars lined with type 304 can be discharged three times faster than unlined cars because of improved slideability (Ref 10).

Corrosive wear is clearly a situation in which the use of stainless steels is attractive, because they can resist the removal of their oxide film.

Fatigue wear, or contact fatigue, occurs when a surface is stressed in a cyclic manner. This type of wear can be found in parts subjected to rolling contact, such as ball bearings and gears. The fatigue wear rate of metals is affected by surface conditions, such as finish, residual stress, hardness, and microstructure. Surface treatments such as nitriding, carburizing, and shot peening, which increase surface hardness and improve residual stress distribution, are performed to prevent fatigue wear.

Adhesive wear occurs when two metallic components slide against each other under an applied load where no abrasives are present. This type of wear is called "adhesive" because of the strong metallic bonds formed between surface asperities of the materials. Wear results from the shear failure of the weaker of the two metallic mating surfaces. One theory postulates that subsurface crack nucleation and growth follow asperity shearing and flattening (Ref 11).

When the applied load is low enough, the surface oxide film characteristic of stainless steels can prevent the formation of metallic bonds between the asperities on the sliding surfaces, resulting in low wear rates. This form of wear is called mild wear, or oxidative wear, and can be tolerated by most moving components. When the applied load is high, metallic bonds will form between the surface asperities, and the resulting wear rates will be high. The load at which there is a transition from mild to severe wear is called the transition load.

Adhesive wear is more prevalent in parts where a lubricant cannot be used. Examples include chain-link conveyor belts, fasteners, and sliding components in a valve. For stainless steels, hardness affects adhesive wear resistance. For

Fig. 4 Cavitation damage to an ACI CN-7M cast pump impeller used to pump ammonium nitrate solution at 140 °C (280 °F)

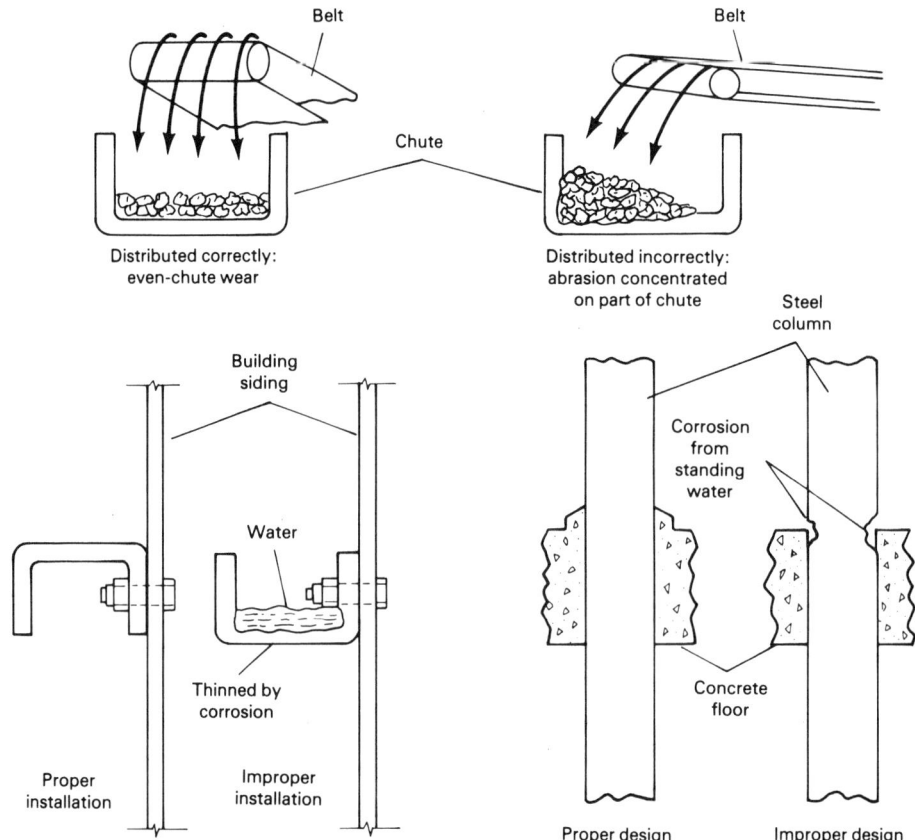

Fig. 5 Effect of design on susceptibility to corrosive wear. Source: Ref 9

martensitic alloys, a minimum hardness of 53 HRC is required for excellent wear resistance. For austenitic stainless alloys, the work-hardened hardness is critical, as are alloying additions that increase the stability of the oxide film. These factors tend to increase the transition load required for severe wear to occur.

Cavitation erosion occurs on metal surfaces in contact with a liquid. Pressure differentials in the fluid generate gas or vapor bubbles in the fluid. When these bubbles encounter a high-pressure zone, they collapse and cause explosive shocks to the surface (Ref 12). These surface shocks cause localized deformation and pitting. Cavitation pits eventually link up and cause a general roughening of the surface and material removal.

In materials like stainless steels that depend on passivating films for corrosion protection, cavitation will cause an apparent accelerated attack. In a corrosive medium, the cavitation will remove the protective film, and corrosion will weaken the material to the mechanical material removal process. Figure 4 shows cavitation damage to a cast (ACI CN-7M) stainless steel impeller that was used to pump ammonium nitrate solution at 140 °C (280 °F). To prevent cavitation erosion, cobalt-base hardfacing alloys, such as the Stellite grades, are commonly used. As will be discussed later in this article, cobalt-containing austenitic stainless steels have also been developed to resist cavitation erosion.

Galling

Galling can be considered a severe form of adhesive wear. With high loads and poor lubrication, surface damage can occur on sliding metal components. The damage is characterized by localized macroscopic material transfer, that is, large fragments or surface protrusions that are easily visible on either or both surfaces. This gross damage is usually referred to as *galling,* and it can occur after just a few cycles of movement between the mating surfaces. Severe galling can result in seizure of the metal surfaces.

The terms *scuffing* and *scoring* are also used to describe similar surface damage under lubricated conditions. *Scuffing* is the preferred term when the damage occurs at lubricated surfaces, such as the piston ring/cylinder wall contact. *Scoring* typically describes damage that takes the form of relatively long grooves (Ref 13).

Materials that have limited ductility are less prone to galling, because under high loads surface asperities will tend to fracture when interlocked. Small fragments of material may be lost, but the resultant damage will be more similar to scoring than to galling. For highly ductile materials, asperities tend to plastically deform, thereby increasing the contact area of mated surfaces; eventually, galling occurs.

Another key material behavior during plastic deformation is the ease with which dislocations cross slip over more than one plane. In face-centered cubic (fcc) materials, such as austenitic stainless steels, dislocations easily cross slip. The rate of cross slip for a given alloy or element is usually indicated by its stacking-fault energy. Dislocation cross slip is hindered by the presence of stacking faults, and a high stacking-fault energy indicates a low number of impeding stacking faults and an increased tendency to cross slip and, hence, gall. Austenitic stainless steels with high work-hardening rates will have relatively low stacking-fault energies, and they have been shown to have less tendency to gall.

Materials that have a hexagonal close-packed (hcp) structure with a high c/a ratio have a low dislocation cross slip rate and are less prone to galling. This explains why cobalt-base alloys resist galling while titanium alloys tend to gall.

Factors Affecting Wear and Galling

The factors that affect wear and galling can be design, lubrication, environmental, and/or material related. Component design is probably the most critical factor. When stainless steels are required, proper design can minimize galling and wear. Similar applications, like valve parts, can often result in wear-related problems for one company or be of very little concern for another, despite their use of the same alloy.

When stainless steels are used in sliding surface applications, a key consideration is reduction of contact stress. The load on the parts should be minimized, and contact area should be maximized. Design tolerance of the parts should be tight with sufficient clearance, because tightly fit parts will be more prone to wear and galling. Lubricants should be used where possible, because they are very effective at reducing contact stress. However, the design should ensure that lubrication can be effectively applied. Often, lubricants are ineffective because of poor design, which renders the parts inaccessible to lubrication.

Another important factor is the surface roughness of the parts. Highly polished surfaces (<0.25 µm, or 10 µin.) or very rough finishes (>1.5 µm, or 60 µin.) increase the tendency for wear and galling. It is theorized that very smooth surfaces lack the ability to store wear debris, because of the absence of valleys between asperities, which means the asperities will have greater interaction. Also, lubricants

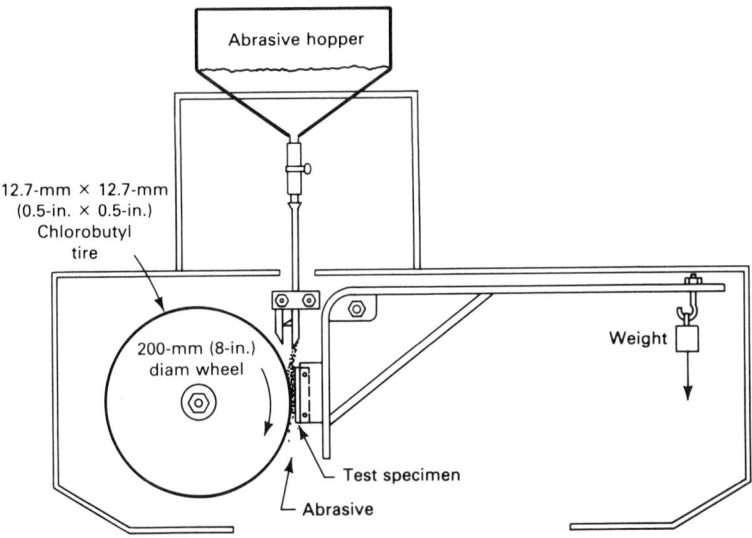

Fig. 6 Dry sand abrasion test apparatus. Source: Ref 16

Fig. 7 Hub wear test machine. Source: Ref 10

will tend to wipe off the smoother surface. Too rough a finish results in interlocking asperities, which promote severe tearing and galling.

A final design option is surface treatments, such as nitriding, carburizing, hardfacing, ion implantation, and shot peening. These treatments are effective at reducing wear and galling, provided that the part configuration or the added cost is acceptable.

Wear and galling can also be affected by the environment. Stainless steels are selected instead of carbon steels when the environment requires either oxidation or corrosion resistance. Alloy selection is dependent on the specific environment that the parts will encounter in service. Thus, laboratory and field tests of candidate alloys are highly recommended. Once again, component design is a critical factor in reducing corrosive wear.

In the mining industry, proper design of equipment can reduce corrosive wear, thereby increasing service life. Sharp bends in flumes and pipelines should be avoided, and the angle of discharge from belts or chutes should be minimized. Another consideration is the possibility of galvanic corrosion, which can occur where dissimilar metals are connected in the presence of an electrolyte. An example would be the use of carbon steel fasteners to join stainless components. The dissimilar metal combination, plus the adverse surface area ratio between the fastener and the surrounding surface, will accelerate the corrosion of the carbon steel.

The proper design of equipment should allow for the drainage of pipes, flumes, and tanks during shutdown, as well as spillage or hosedown water within the plant. Examples of proper versus improper design of coal-handling equipment are shown in Fig. 5.

Material selection is dependent on the type of wear encountered. To resist adhesive wear, a high work-hardened hardness in an austenitic alloy and a stable oxide film can have excellent results. For hardenable stainless steels, high carbon content (0.3% minimum) to increase hardness (53

HRC minimum) is critical. Thus, martensitic precipitation-hardening (PH) alloys with their low carbon content, but high hardness, tend to have poor wear resistance. Because ferritic stainless steels cannot be hardened by heat treatment or be readily work hardened, they may also have poor metal-to-metal wear resistance.

The comments on adhesive wear apply to galling resistance, except that the martensitic PH alloys with high hardness, which is achieved by using a low aging temperature (480 °C, or 895 °F), can have improved galling resistance. Elements that form inclusions in steel, such as sulfur, tin, bismuth, and lead, can affect the sliding behavior of the mated materials. These inclusions act as solid lubricants. Thus, the sulfur-bearing stainless steels, such as types 303 and 416, have better galling resistance, but poorer adhesive wear resistance, than their non-sulfur-bearing parent alloys, types 304 and 410. Another alloy example is Waukesha 88, which contains a tin- and bismuth-bearing second phase that results in excellent galling resistance, despite the high nickel content of the alloy (Ref 14).

Hardness and microstructure are critical to abrasive wear resistance. Unlike adhesive wear resistance, which favors austenitic alloys with a high work-hardening rate, abrasive wear resistance favors the hard martensitic matrix structure versus the softer austenitic or ferritic structure. This is especially significant in low-stress abrasion, where little subsurface deformation occurs. Also, high-carbon alloys with primary carbides have better wear resistance. Thus, martensitic alloy S44004 (type 440C) has good resistance to abrasion, whereas low-carbon martensitic PH alloy S17400 (17-4PH) has poor abrasion resistance. For gouging abrasion, austenitic manganese steel is used, because strain hardening and impact resistance are critical.

To resist fretting, thermal wear, and corrosive wear, corrosion and oxidation resistance become critical. The type of stainless steel to be used depends on the environment, with austenitic stain-

less steels favored in severe environments. A key factor for resisting these types of wear is the alloying addition, because silicon, aluminum, and chromium improve the corrosion and oxidation resistance of a particular alloy regardless of the stainless family.

Wear and Galling Tests Commonly Used for Stainless Steels

Dry sand/rubber wheel test is an ASTM standard test (Ref 15) used to determine the resistance of metallic materials to low-stress (scratching) abrasion. The test involves the abrading of a test specimen with a grit of controlled size and composition (that is, rounded grain quartz sand). The abrasive is introduced between the test specimen and a rotating wheel with a chlorobutyl rubber tire or rim of a specified hardness. The test specimen is pressed against the rotating wheel at a specified force by means of a lever arm while a controlled flow of grit abrades the test surface. The rotation of the wheel is such that its contact face moves in the direction of the sand flow. A schematic diagram of the test apparatus is shown in Fig. 6. The test duration and force applied by the lever arm vary depending on the relative wear resistance of the materials evaluated. For stainless steels, the test duration is one-third that of the more abrasion-resistant tool steel alloys such as D2. Specimens are weighed before and after the test, and the loss in mass is recorded. Abrasive wear is generally reported in terms of volume loss (in cubic millimeters) by dividing mass loss by the density of the alloy.

Corrosive wear testing commonly involves hub and ball mill tests. The apparatus used for the hub test, which is a low-stress abrasive test, is shown in Fig. 7. The slurry container has three hubs, each of which holds eight specimens, which are driven through the slurry as shown in Fig. 8.

Slurries can differ, depending on the application that needs to be simulated. Often, alloys are evaluated both wet (corrosive slurry) and dry to demonstrate the effect of corrosion on corrosive wear. Specimens are weighed before and after the test, and volume loss is determined by dividing the weight loss by the alloy density.

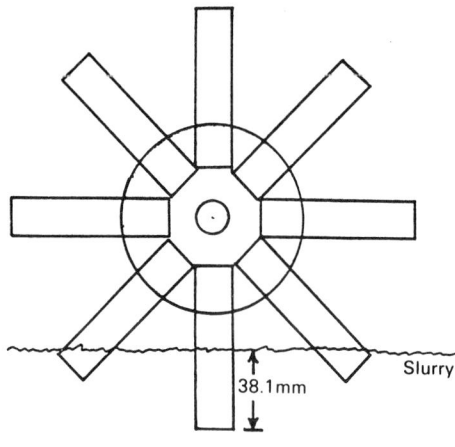

Fig. 8 Specimen arrangement on hub. Source: Ref 10

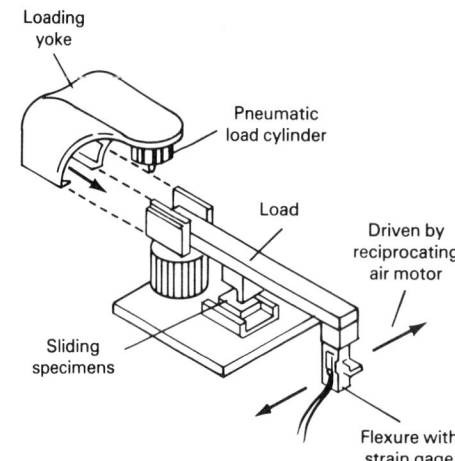

(a)

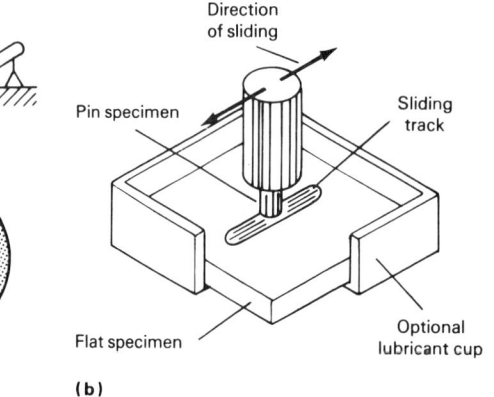

(b)

Fig. 9 Key components of a block-on-ring test apparatus. The coefficient of sliding friction, μ_{sf}, is calculated using the equation μ_{sf} = (friction force)/(applied load). Source: Ref 2

Fig. 11 Pin-on-disk wear test apparatus. (a) Key components of the device. (b) Closeup showing pin motion relative to flat when subjected to load. Source: Ref 2

Fig. 10 Typical crossed-cylinder test apparatus. Source: Ref 19

The ball mill test is used extensively by the U.S. Bureau of Mines and in Canada to determine corrosive effects found in nickel mines. For this test, a 5.3 L (1.4 gal) porcelain jar serves as the ball mill, and the specimens are free to tumble in the corrosive slurry. Tests are performed for a particular time period, such as 8 h, after which the weight loss is determined and volume loss is calculated. The samples are then tested for additional time periods, using fresh slurry for each period. At the conclusion of the test, corrosive wear versus time is plotted for the alloys being evaluated.

Block-on-ring is an ASTM standard test (Ref 17) for determining the resistance of materials to sliding wear. The test uses a block-on-ring friction and wear testing machine to rank pairs of materials according to their sliding wear characteristics under various conditions. Rotational speed and load can be varied to correspond to service requirements. In addition, tests can be run with various lubricants, liquids, or gaseous atmospheres.

The test consists of a block specimen loaded against a ring specimen at a given speed for a given number of revolutions (Fig. 9). Block scar volume is calculated from the block scar width and depth, and ring scar volume is calculated from ring weight loss. The friction force required to keep the block in place is continuously measured during the test with a load cell and is then recorded. The choice of test parameters is left to the user (with the exception of sliding distance, which

is specified because wear does not usually vary linearly with distance in this test).

Crossed cylinder is an ASTM standard test (Ref 18) for determining the resistance of metallic materials to metal-to-metal wear. This test ranks the adhesive wear resistance of materials and evaluates the compatibility of different metal couples. It is the most commonly used test for evaluating metal-to-metal wear resistance of stainless steels.

The test configuration consists of two cylindrical specimens that are positioned perpendicular to each other. One sample is rotated at a specified test speed while the other sample is kept stationary. The stationary specimen is pressed against the rotating specimen at a specified load by means of a lever arm and attached weights. The setup results in dead-weight loading. A photograph of the test apparatus is shown in Fig. 10. Elevated-temperature tests have also been performed using the crossed-cylinder apparatus. The test duration, number of cycles, and rotational speed are varied depending on the relative wear resistance of the mated materials. The amount of wear is determined by weighing the specimen before and after the test. Weight loss is converted to volume loss by dividing it by the density of the material. Volume loss is determined for both the stationary and rotating specimens, and the total volume loss is recorded. When dissimilar materials are being tested, it is recommended that each alloy be tested in both the stationary and rotating positions.

Pin-on-disk is an ASTM standard test for determining the wear of material during sliding (Fig. 11). The coefficient of friction can also be determined using this test. Two specimens are required: a pin with a radiused tip is positioned perpendicular to the other specimen, which is usually a flat circular disk. A ball, rigidly held, often is used as the pin specimen. The test machine causes either the disk specimen or the pin specimen to revolve about the disk center. In either case, the sliding path is a circle on the disk surface. The plane of the disk may be oriented either horizontally or vertically. The pin specimen is pressed against the disk at a specified load, usually by means of an arm or lever and attached weights. Wear results are reported as volume loss (in cubic millimeters) for the pin and disk separately. When two different materials are tested, it is recommended that each material be tested in both the pin and disk positions.

The amount of wear is determined by measuring appropriate linear dimensions of both specimens before and after the test, or by weighing both specimens before and after the test. Linear measurements of wear are converted to wear volume by using appropriate geometric relationships, while mass loss is converted to volume loss by dividing mass loss by the appropriate density values for the specimens. Wear results are usually obtained by conducting a test for a selected sliding distance, load, and speed. Graphs of wear volume versus sliding distance using different specimens for different distances can be plotted.

The galling test is an ASTM standard test (Ref 20) that ranks the galling resistance of material couples. This test, commonly referred to as the *button-on-block test,* was developed during the 1950s and is the most commonly used procedure to test the galling resistance of stainless steels. Although it is generally performed on bare metals, it can also be used

Fig. 12 Button-on-block galling test. Source: Ref 21

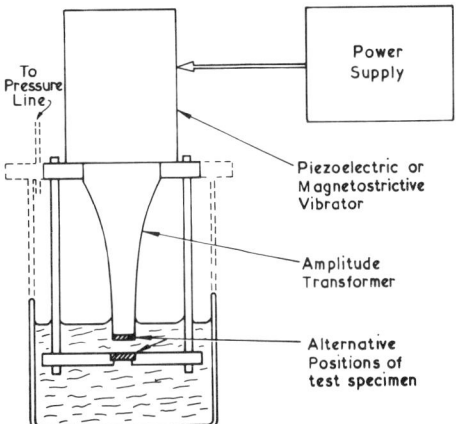

Fig. 13 Vibratory cavitation device in which the specimen is either attached to or held below a horn oscillating in the lower kilohertz frequency range. Source: Ref 26

Table 1 Abrasive wear resistance of stainless steels

Alloy	Rockwell hardness	Volume loss, mm^3
Austenitic		
Type 304	85.5 HRB	113.1
S21061	95.0 HRB	139.6
S21061	26.5 HRC	138.2
S21800	93.0 HRB	127.2
S24100	95.5 HRB	94.9
S28200	97.0 HRB	88.3
Martensitic		
Type 410	44.0 HRC	94.0
S42010	51.0 HRC	67.5
Type 420	52.0 HRC	59.4
Type 440A	56.0 HRC	56.3
Type 440C	56.0 HRC	33.5
Type 440C	58.0 HRC	32.1

Note: Based on dry sand/rubber wheel abrasion test, ASTM G 65, procedure B, 133 N (30 lbf), 10 min duration.

on nonmetallics, coatings, solid lubricants, and surface-modified alloys.

The test uses available laboratory equipment that is capable of maintaining a constant compressive load between two flat specimens, such as hydraulic or screw-fed compression testing machines. A specimen with a 13 mm (0.5 in.) diameter section (the *button*) is slowly rotated one revolution (360°) relative to the other specimen under a specified compressive load. The test surfaces are ground so that the surface roughness range is from 0.4 to 1 μm (15 to 40 μin.) and the specimens are flat to ensure 100% contact between the mated surfaces.

The surfaces are examined for galling after sliding. The criterion for whether galling occurs is the appearance of the specimens, based on unassisted visual examination. Galling is characterized by at least one of the contacting surfaces exhibiting torn or raised metal. If the specimens have not galled, then a new button is tested on a new block location at an increased load. This procedure is continued until galling occurs. Similarly, if galling does occur on the first test, then lower loads are evaluated until no galling occurs. The galling test setup is shown in Fig. 12.

The loads applied correspond to a contact stress for the 13 mm (0.5 in.) diameter button. The stress midway between the highest nongalled test and the lowest galled test is referred to as the *threshold galling stress*. The higher the threshold galling stress, the more resistant the mated materials are to galling. Galling resistance can be de-

termined for a particular self-mated material or dissimilar-mated materials. For the latter, it is recommended that each alloy be evaluated as button and block specimens.

To simulate repeated part performance under service conditions, such as those existing with sliding valve parts, the button specimen can be rotated multiple revolutions, in which the direction is reversed after each 360° revolution, instead of being rotated just once. Because of the increased severity of the multiple-rotation method, threshold galling stresses will be significantly lower than those of the single-rotation test.

To test highly resistant alloys, such as cobalt-base Stellite 6B, a similar button-on-block test is used. The button is rotated through a 120° arc ten times at three different loads. Surface profilometry is then used to assess the degree of damage (Ref 22).

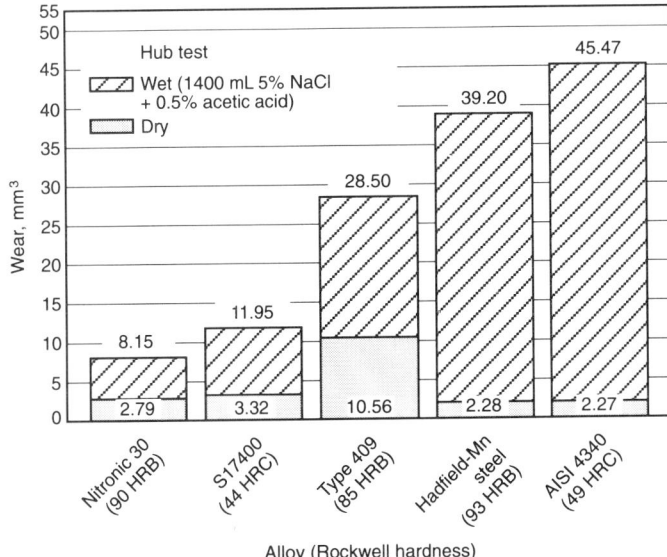

Fig. 14 Abrasive wear of alloy and stainless steels under dry and wet corrosive conditions. Source: Ref 10

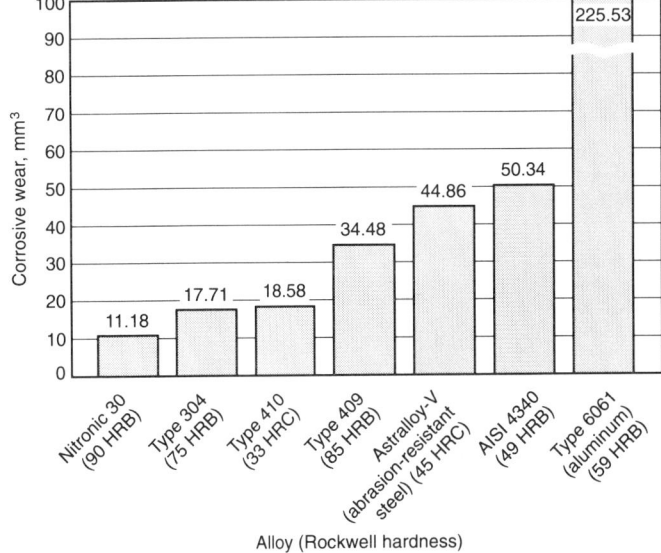

Fig. 15 Corrosive wear of alloy and stainless steels relative to an aluminum alloy, based on ball mill test using 1500 mL distilled water. Source: Ref 10

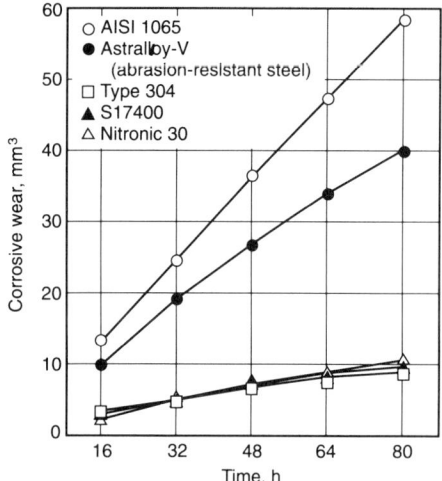

Fig. 16 Corrosive wear of alloy and stainless steels, based on ball mill test using synthetic nickel mine water. Source: Ref 10

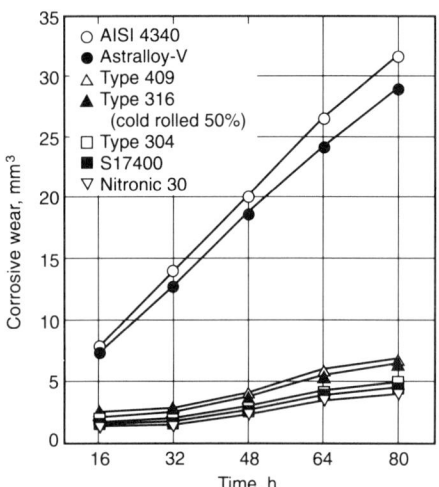

Fig. 17 Corrosive wear of alloy and stainless steels, based on ball mill test using synthetic seawater. Source: Ref 10

Another test that is similar to the button-on-block test is the ring-on-ring test, which uses ring specimens rather than solid button/block samples. The test is used to assess galling resistance for tubular products related to oil production (Ref 23).

Galling of threaded parts, such as 9 m (30 ft) drill collars, is evaluated by a make/break test. The test procedure involves making a box/pin connection at a specified torque, breaking the connection, and recording the breakout torque. The procedure is repeated a given number of times, and the threads are periodically examined for galling. Unlike the button-on-block test, the goal of which is simply to rank materials, this test simulates the actual service connections that are made for drill collars in the oil-drilling industry. Tests that simulate the specific application are very beneficial, but they are usually quite expensive to perform. Thus, the button-on-block test can be used as a screening test to choose the best candidate alloy for a more specific test tailored to the service conditions of a particular application.

Cavitation Erosion Testing. When testing materials for their cavitation erosion resistance, there is no laboratory experimental equipment that simulates the total situation for a real structural component exposed to cavitating fluids (Ref 24). However, a number of laboratory techniques can be used to rank a series of selected materials on the basis of cavitation erosion resistance. They involve the use of flow channels, vibratory systems, and cavitating jets, all of which can simulate accelerated cavitation erosion in most materials. Because the vibratory technique is covered by an ASTM standard (ASTM G 32, Ref 25), it will be discussed here. Reference 24 describes flow channels and two variations on the cavitating jet technique.

Vibratory (ultrasonic) equipment consists of an ultrasonic horn that is partly submerged in the liquid that is contained in a beaker (Fig. 13). The vibration, typically at 20 kHz frequency, generates negative pressure for cavitation nucleation and growth, and positive pressure for cavity collapse in a small, stationary volume of the liquid. The specimen is either mounted on the horn tip (moving specimen) or at a fixed distance (a few millimeters) below the horn tip (stationary specimen).

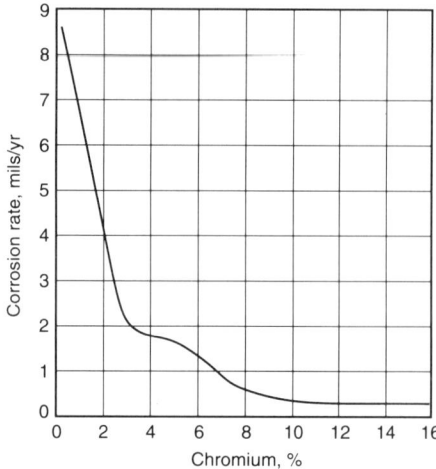

Fig. 19 Effect of chromium content on atmospheric corrosion resistance. Source: Ref 9

Wear Data for Stainless Steels

Abrasive/Corrosive Wear. The low-stress abrasion resistance of stainless steels can be determined by using either the dry sand abrasion or the hub test. Dry sand abrasion data (Table 1) clearly show that austenitic stainless steels have poorer wear resistance than the harder martensitic alloys, whose increased carbon content increases wear resistance (Ref 27). Type 410, which has 0.1% C, has wear resistance similar to that of the best austenitic alloys, whereas the wear resistance of type 440C is three to four times greater than that of the austenitic alloys. The abrasive wear resistance of type 440C is inferior to that of D2, an abrasive wear-resistant tool steel. Test results show that D2 has a volume loss of 32 mm^3, which is similar to that of type 440C, when the test time for D2 is tripled.

When a wet abrasive slurry is present, stainless steels experience greater wear than under dry conditions. However, their wear resistance is superior to that of martensitic carbon steels. Figure 14 compares five alloys under dry and wet slurry conditions in the hub test. Under dry conditions,

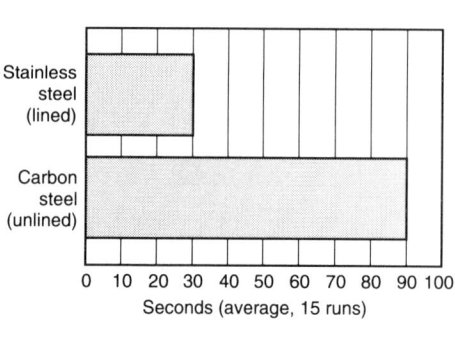

(a)

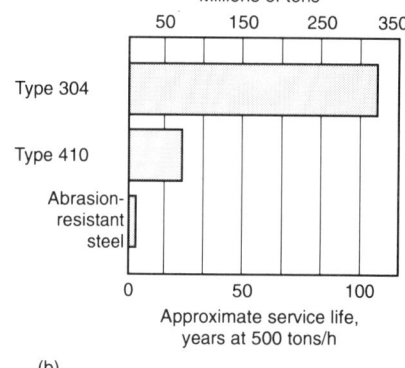

(b)

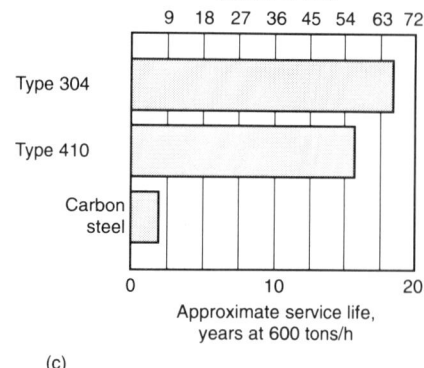

(c)

Fig. 18 Service life of coal-handling equipment. (a) Coal unloading time, 50 ton hopper car. (b) Coal conveyor bottom 3/16 × 0 coal at 49 to 82 °C (120 to 180 °F). 6000 h/yr. (c) Coal conveyor bottom 5 × 0 clean coal. 6000 h/yr. Source: Ref 28

Table 2 Wear rates for test plates in drag conveyor bottoms

Material	Loss in μm/10⁹ g (mils/million tons) of coal conveyed	Test time, months
125 × 9.5 mm (5 × ⅜ in.)		
Type 304 stainless steel	0.67 (24)	27
Type 410 stainless steel	0.73 (26)	27
Type 316 stainless steel	0.90 (32)	27
Abrasion-resistant steel	1.01 (36)	15
Mild steel	1.65 (59)	15
9.5 mm (⅜ in.) by 0 thermal dryer product		
Type 304 stainless steel	0.045 (1.6)	25
Type 316 stainless steel	0.053 (1.9)	25
Type 410 stainless steel	0.100 (3.6)	25
Abrasion-resistant steel	2.3 (83)	6
63.5 × 6.35 mm (2.5 × 0.25 in.)		
Type 304 stainless steel	0.07 (2.6)	47
Type 410 stainless steel	0.11 (3.9)	47
Wrought iron	2.5 (89)	23
Mild steel	3.0 (107)	23
Crushed middlings conveyor		
Type 304 stainless steel	0.17 (6)	48
Abrasion-resistant steel	7 (250)	(failed in 18 months)

Table 3 Adhesive wear resistance of stainless alloys

Alloy	Rockwell hardness	10,000 cycles(a), at 100 rev/min	Volume loss, mm³ 40,000 cycles at 100 rev/min	at 400 rev/min
Austenitic stainless steels				
Type 201	93.0 HRB	3.2	10.9	7.4
Type 304	78.0 HRB	10.4	23.5	22.0
Type 304	98.0 HRB	13.6	30.0	27.0
Type 304 HN	91.5 HRB	12.5	44.4	19.5
Type 304 HN	22.5 HRC	12.7	45.4	23.7
Type 301	90.0 HRB	6.9	…	…
Type 316	91.0 HRB	15.8	…	…
Type 303	98.0 HRB	488.7	…	…
S20161	96.0 HRB	1.3	5.3	4.4
S20161	30.0 HRC	1.5	5.5	4.5
S20910	96.0 HRB	11.7	46.0	16.7
S21000	88.0 HRB	12.0	43.8	9.9
S21800	93.0 HRB	4.2	12.1	5.2
S21900	92.0 HRB	11.9	45.0	34.1
S24100	95.5 HRB	7.2	21.9	5.2
S28200	99.0 HRB	8.1	27.9	2.8
S28200	35.0 HRC	7.5	22.5	2.7
S30430	72.0 HRB	18.2	42.8	29.1
N08020	87.5 HRB	22.6	84.3	28.2
Other stainless steels				
Type 410	24.5 HRC	114.0	544.0	251.1
Type 410	39.0 HRC	215.0	632.0	93.8
S42010	49.5 HRC	96.9	115.7	8.1
S42010	47.0 HRC	178.6	680.3	35.7
Type 420	50.5 HRC	83.8	84.0	8.5
Type 420	46.0 HRC	215.0	…	…
Type 440C	56.0 HRC	0.7	1.3	1.1
Type 440C	26.5 HRC	44.1	191.0	38.8
S17400	30.5 HRC	83.0	281.3	53.0
S17400	40.0 HRC	50.8	202.8	45.7
S13800	32.5 HRC	77.5	…	…
S13800	47.0 HRC	49.1	…	…
Type 431	42.0 HRC	235.6	…	…
Type 430	76.5 HRB	52.4	194.6	133.9
Type 430	80.5 HRB	58.5	229.7	171.6
S32950	23.0 HRC	15.8	50.5	22.5

Note: Based on crossed-cylinder wear test, ASTM G 83, 71 N (16 lbf). (a) Procedure A

the stainless alloys evaluated had similar or greater wear than did austenitic manganese Hadfield Mn steel and AISI 4340. However, when evaluated in a wet slurry of 5% NaCl plus 0.5% acetic acid, the stainless alloys were more resistant. Similar trends are shown in various wet environments, such as distilled water, synthetic nickel mine water, and synthetic seawater (Fig. 15-17), using the ball mill test.

Stainless steels have superior corrosive wear resistance in coal-handling equipment. Service life is much longer than that of carbon steels (Fig. 18). In the mining industry, corrosion is the primary factor in the deterioration of equipment. Figure 19 shows the effect of chromium content on atmospheric corrosion resistance. When no chromium is present, corrosion rates are at least ten times greater than they are for stainless steels.

Tests under service conditions have been performed on stainless steels, abrasion-resistant steels, and carbon steels. Tests were performed for up to 5.3 years, and the reduction of thickness

was determined. Results of two studies (Ref 9) show the superiority of stainless steels to non-stainless alloys in this regard (Table 2). In general, type 304 is superior to type 410. However, alloy selection is dependent on the particular coal-handling equipment.

Adhesive Wear. The metal-to-metal wear resistance of stainless steels can be determined by using the crossed-cylinder wear test. Unlike low-

stress abrasion resistance, metal-to-metal wear resistance is generally better in austenitic stainless steels than in martensitic stainless alloys (Table 3) (Ref 29). The excellent wear resistance of type 201, type 301, S20161 (Gall-Tough), and

Table 5 Relative ranking of adhesive wear resistance of wrought materials

Wrought material	Rockwell hardness	Weight loss, mg/ 1000 cycles at 105 rev/min	at 415 rev/min
D2 tool steel	61 HRC	0.46	0.34
AISI 4337	52 HRC	0.73	0.48
Stellite 6B	48 HRC	1.00	1.27
Hadfield Mn steel	95 HRB	1.25	0.41
Al (10.5%) bronze	87 HRB	2.21	1.52
Type 6061-T6 aluminum	59 HRB	17.06	21.15
AISI 4130	47 HRC	9.44	6.80
Astralloy V steel	46 HRC	213.58	8.22
Stainless alloy			
Type 440C	57 HRC	3.81	0.54
S21800	95 HRB	2.79	1.58
Type 201	90 HRB	4.95	4.68

Note: Based on crossed-cylinder wear test, ASTM G 83, 71 N (16 lbf), 10,000 cycles

Table 4 Wear compatibility of dissimilar-mated stainless steels

Alloy	Volume loss, mm³ Type 304 (99 HRB)	Type 316 (91 HRB)	S17400 (43 HRC)	S24100 (95 HRB)	S20910 (99 HRB)	S21800 (95 HRB)	Type 440C (57 HRC)
Type 304	16.4	…	…	…	…	…	…
Type 316	13.5	16.4	…	…	…	…	…
S17400	31.7	23.7	67.7	…	…	…	…
S24100	10.8	12.1	22.1	9.5	…	…	…
S20910	11.5	12.2	20.1	10.6	12.8	…	…
S21800	7.7	5.5	6.9	4.1	4.5	3.6	…
Type 440C	5.3	5.0	14.6	4.0	5.5	3.1	4.9

Note: Based on crossed-cylinder wear test, ASTM G 83, 105 rev/min test speed, 10,000 cycles, 71 N (16 lbf); (weight loss/1000 cycles converted to total volume loss)

S21800 (Nitronic 60) can be attributed to a high work-hardening rate. Additionally, the latter two alloys have a high silicon content (3 to 4.5%), which not only increases the work-hardening rate, but results in a more adherent oxide film, thereby preventing the transition from mild oxidation wear to severe wear. Like abrasive wear resistance, a high hardness value is critical for martensitic stainless steels in order to achieve good adhesive wear resistance. For type 440C, high hardness (56 HRC) results in exceptional metal-to-metal wear resistance, whereas low hardness (26 HRC) for this same alloy results in high volume loss. Generally, high volume loss is characteristic of these alloys, even at 50 HRC.

When different materials are mated under load, wear testing is important for proper alloy selection. A general misconception for metal-to-metal wear and galling resistance is that a large difference in hardness between the two mated alloys is beneficial. Wear data from Ref 30 suggest that alloys with good adhesive wear, such as type 440C (57 HRC) and S21800 (92 HRB), are excellent alloy selections regardless of the hardness of the other alloy (Table 4).

The best stainless alloys have better adhesive wear resistance than aluminum (type 6061), abrasion-resistant steel (Astralloy-V), and AISI 4130 carbon steel. However, they are less resistant than Hadfield Mn steel, D2 tool steel, and Stellite 6B, a hardfacing alloy (Table 5) (Ref 31). These rankings can change when environmental factors such as corrosion, oxidation, and temperature are considered. For example, these three factors will have a much greater effect on alloys that contain little, if any, chromium. Even Stellite 6B, which does contain chromium, has reduced adhesive wear resistance at elevated temperatures (Table 6), unlike type 304 and S21800 (Ref 32).

The galling resistance of stainless steels can be determined by using the button-on-block test. Higher-threshold galling stress indicates better resistance to galling. All five families of stainless steels are susceptible to galling.

For austenitic stainless steels, high-manganese, high-nitrogen alloys generally have better galling resistance than chromium-nickel alloys have, as shown in Table 7 (Ref 33) and Table 8 (Ref 30). Nickel is considered harmful to galling resistance, whereas silicon is considered beneficial. Thus, S20161 and S21800 have excellent resistance. Increasing the hardness of austenitic stainless alloys by cold drawing decreases galling resistance.

For the heat-treat-hardenable stainless steels, increasing hardness increases galling resistance. For martensitic PH stainless steels, increasing aging temperature may decrease galling resistance. For example, tests on S13880 and S17440 with similar hardness values (45 to 46 HRC) resulted in a much lower threshold galling stress (21 vs. 69 MPa, or 3 vs. 10 ksi) for S13800, which was aged at a higher temperature. Martensitic alloys, such as type 440C, tend to have heavy scoring damage, rather than galling.

Button-on-block test severity can be increased by increasing the number of button rotations against the block (Table 9) (Ref 11, 34). A multiple-rotation test more closely simulates the action of valve components. The threshold galling stress values for alloys such as type 303, S28200, S42010, S24100, S45500, and type 440C were low (<14 MPa, or 2 ksi) and were greatly reduced, compared with the single-rotation values. For high-silicon alloys, such as S20161 and S21800, improved galling resistance is clearly demonstrated using the triple-rotation test.

Dissimilar-mated test results, as given in Table 8 and Table 10 (Ref 30), show the need to screen

Table 6 Effect of temperature on adhesive wear

		Volume loss, mm³				
Alloy	Room-temperature Rockwell hardness	at 80 °C (175 °F)	at 205 °C (400 °F)	at 315 °C (600 °F)	at 425 °C (800 °F)	at 540 °C (1000 °F)
S21800	95 HRB	2.6	2.3	2.8	2.2	1.3
Type 304	79 HRB	14.7	13.5	14.5	13.2	...
Type 410	95 HRB	282.8	231.2	...	...	...
Type 410	40 HRC	42.1	...	...	...	...
S17400	35 HRC	31.3	23.8	12.5	8.2	...
Stellite 6B(a)	41 HRC	2.6	3.3	3.7	4.3	7.6

Note: Based on crossed-cylinder test, ASTM G 83, using test speed of 415 rev/min for 20,000 cycles, 71 N (16 lbf). (a) Cobalt-base hardfacing alloy

Table 7 Threshold galling stress results for selected self-mated stainless steels

		Rockwell hardness	Threshold galling stress	
Stainless steel	Condition		MPa	ksi
Austenitic				
S20161	Annealed	95 HRB	104(a)	15(a)
S21800	Annealed	92 HRB	104(a)	15(a)
S28200	Annealed	96 HRB	166	24
S28200	Cold drawn	35 HRC	62	9
S20910	Annealed	97 HRB	35	5
S20900	Annealed	96 HRB	48	7
S24100	Annealed	23 HRC	97	14
S30430	Annealed	74 HRB	35	5
Type 304	Annealed	86 HRB	55	8
Type 304	Cold drawn	27 HRC	17	2.5
Type 316	Annealed	82 HRB	48	7
Type 316	Cold drawn	27 HRC	35	5
Type 303	Annealed	85 HRB	138	20
Type 201	Annealed	95 HRB	104	15
N08020	Annealed	87 HRB	14	2
Martensitic				
S42010	Tempered at 204 °C (400 °F)	50 HRC	104(a)	15(a)
S42010	Tempered at 260 °C (500 °F)	47 HRC	62	9
Type 410	Annealed	87 HRB	7	1
Type 410	Tempered at 260 °C (500 °F)	43 HRC	21	3
Type 416	Annealed	95 HRB	21	3
Type 416	Tempered at 316 °C (600 °F)	37 HRC	62	9
Type 416	Tempered at 538 °C (1000 °F)	32 HRC	42	6
Type 420	Tempered at 204 °C (400 °F)	51 HRC	25	18
Type 420	Tempered at 260 °C (500 °F)	49 HRC	55	8
Type 440C	Tempered at 260 °C (500 °F)	55 HRC	125	18
Precipitation hardenable				
S45500	Aged at 510 °C (950 °F)	48 HRC	90	13
S45500	Aged at 566 °C (1050 °F)	43 HRC	59	8.5
S45500	Aged at 621 °C (1150 °F)	36 HRC	28	4
S45000	Annealed	29 HRC	69	10
S45000	Aged at 480 °C (895 °F)	43 HRC	55	8
S45000	Aged at 566 °C (1050 °F)	38 HRC	17	2.5
S45000	Aged at 621 °C (1150 °F)	33 HRC	14	2
S17400	Aged at 480 °C (895 °F)	45 HRC	69	10
S17400	Aged at 621 °C (1150 °F)	34 HRC	35	5
S13800	Aged at 538 °C (1000 °F)	46 HRC	21	3
S66286	Aged at 718 °C (1325 °F)	30 HRC	14	2
Ferritic and duplex				
S18200	Cold drawn	98 HRB	35	5
Type 430F	Annealed	92 HRB	14	2
Type 430	Cold drawn	98 HRB	10	1.5
Type 329	Annealed	25 HRC	7	1

Note: Based on button-on-block test, ASTM G 98, unlubricated ground finish. (a) Did not gall

Table 8 Threshold galling stress for selected stainless steels

Alloy	Condition and nominal Rockwell hardness	Type 410 MPa	Type 410 ksi	Type 416 MPa	Type 416 ksi	Type 430 MPa	Type 430 ksi	Type 440C MPa	Type 440C ksi	Type 303 MPa	Type 303 ksi	Type 304 MPa	Type 304 ksi	Type 316 MPa	Type 316 ksi	S17400 MPa	S17400 ksi	S24100 MPa	S24100 ksi	S21800 MPa	S21800 ksi
Type 410	Tempered (38 HRC)	21	3	28	4	21	3	21	3	28	4	14	2	14	2	21	3	317	46	345(a)	50
Type 416	Tempered (36 HRC)	28	4	90	13	21	3	145	21	62	9	165	24	290	42	14	2	310	45	345(a)	50
Type 430	Annealed (84 HRB)	21	3	21	3	14	2	14	2	14	2	14	2	14	2	21	3	55	8	248	36
Type 440C	Tempered (56 HRC)	21	3	145	21	14	2	76	11	34	5	21	3	255	37	21	3	345(a)	50	345(a)	50
Type 303	Annealed (82 HRB)	28	4	62	9	14	2	34	5	14	2	14	2	14	2	21	3	345(a)	50	345(a)	50
Type 304	Annealed (77 HRB)	14	2	165	24	14	2	21	3	14	2	14	2	14	2	14	2	207	30	345(a)	50
Type 316	Annealed (81 HRB)	14	2	290	42	14	2	255	37	21	3	14	2	14	2	14	2	21	3	262	38
S17400	Aged (84 HRB)	21	3	14	2	21	3	21	3	14	2	14	2	14	2	14	2	345(a)	50	345(a)	50
S21800	Annealed (94 HRB)	345(a)	50	345(a)	50	248	36	345(a)	50	345(a)	50	345(a)	50	262	38	345(a)	50	345(a)	50	345(a)	50

Note: Based on button-on-block test, ASTM G 98, unlubricated ground finish; condition and hardness apply to both horizontal and vertical axes. (a) Did not gall

Table 9 Threshold galling stress results for selected self-mated stainless steels

Alloy	Rockwell hardness	Single rotation(a) MPa	Single rotation(a) ksi	Triple rotation MPa	Triple rotation ksi
S20161	95 HRB	104(b)	15(b)	104(b)	15(b)
S20161	28 HRC	104(b)	15(b)	104(b)	15(b)
S28200	96 HRB	166	24	7	1
S21800	92 HRB	104(b)	15(b)	48	7
T440C	55 HRC	124	18	14	2
T304	86 HRB	55	8	7(c)	1(c)
T430	98 HRB	10	1.5	7(c)	1(c)
S42010	50 HRC	104(b)	15(b)	21	3
T420	49 HRC	55	8	14	2
S24100	23 HRC	97	14	14	2
S45500	48 HRC	97	13	7(c)	1(c)
S66286	30 HRC	14	2	7(c)	1(c)
Type 303	85 HRB	138	20	7(c)	1(c)

Note: Based on button-on-block test, unlubricated ground finish. (a) Per ASTM G 98. (b) Did not gall. (c) Galled at this stress level

dissimilar-mated couples prior to service. Some dissimilar couples have threshold galling stress (TGS) values that are higher than that of either alloy when self-mated and vice versa. For example, type 304 mated with S45500 has a TGS of 124 MPa (18 ksi), whereas their self-mated values are 55 and 90 MPa (8 and 13 ksi), respectively. Type 304 mated with type 440C has a TGS of 28 MPa (4 ksi), whereas their self-mated values are 55 and 124 MPa (8 and 18 ksi), respectively.

In both examples, there is a large difference in hardness between the two members of these couples, but the resultant threshold galling stress values are quite different. For one case, the value is greater than the self-mated values, and for the other, it is lower.

Cavitation Erosion. The resistance to cavitation erosion can be determined by using the vibratory cavitation erosion test described in ASTM G 32 (Ref 25). This test has demonstrated that in practical applications where intense cavitation is unavoidable, cobalt-base alloys and, to a lesser extent, austenitic stainless steels are the most erosion-resistant alloys available to date (Ref 24). Unlike most high-strength alloys, neither exhibits any significant strain-rate-sensitive behavior. More importantly, both have low stacking-fault energies and are readily able to develop stacking faults, twins, and/or martensitically transformed

Table 10 Threshold galling stress results for selected dissimilar-mated stainless steels

Alloy and hardness	Stress MPa	Stress ksi	Alloy and hardness	Stress MPa	Stress ksi	Alloy and hardness	Stress MPa	Stress ksi
Type 201 (94 HRB)			S30430 (74 HRB)			versus S45000 (43 HRC)	7	1
versus type 304 (77 HRB)	14	2	versus type 440C (55 HRC)	83	12	Type 410 (32 HRC)		
versus S17400 (41 HRC)	14	2	S28200 (35 HRC)			versus type 420 (50 HRC)	21	3
versus S24100 (21 HRC)	284	36	versus S28200 (96 HRB)	104	15	versus type 416 (38 HRC)	28	4
Type 301 (86 HRB)			S28200 (96 HRB)			Type 416 (32 HRC)		
versus type 416 (35 HRC)	21	3	versus S45000 (29 HRC)	55	8	versus type 416 (83 HRB)	76	11
versus type 440C (56 HRC)	21	3	S28200 (96 HRB)			Type 416 (37 HRC)		
versus S21800 (95 HRB)	345(a)	50(a)	versus S45000 (43 HRC)	62	9	versus type 440 (55 HRC)	159	23
Type 304 (86 HRB)			S24100 (22 HRC)			Type 416 (34 HRC)		
versus type 304 (27 HRC)	28	4	versus S17400 (39 HRC)	76	11	versus type 430 (90 HRB)	21	3
versus type 440C (55 HRC)	28	4	S24100 (22 HRC)			Type 440C (55 HRC)		
versus S28200 (96 HRB)	41	6	versus S20910 (34 HRC)	55	8	versus S17400 (45 HRC)	35	5
versus S20910 (97 HRB)	69	10	S24100 (43 HRC)			S45500 (48 HRC)		
versus S24100 (23 HRC)	104(a)	15(a)	versus S20910 (95 HRB)	90	13	versus S17400 (45 HRC)	76	11
versus S45000 (43 HRC)	21	3	S21800 (95 HRB)			S45500 (48 HRC)		
versus S45500 (48 HRC)	124	18	versus S20910 (95 HRB)	345(a)	50(a)	versus S17400 (38 HRC)	55	8
Type 304 (77 HRB)			versus S66286 (28 HRC)	345(a)	50(a)	S13800 (46 HRC)		
versus S17400 (33 HRC)	14	2	versus type 420 (50 HRC)	345(a)	50(a)	versus S17400 (45 HRC)	62	9
versus S17400 (46 HRC)	14	2	versus S17400 (33 HRC)	345(a)	50(a)	S13800 (46 HRC)		
Type 316 (82 HRB)			versus S13800 (44 HRC)	345(a)	50(a)	versus S17400 (38 HRC)	14	2
versus type 316 (27 HRC)	55	8	S21800 (92 HRB)			S17700 (44 HRC)		
versus type 440C (55 HRC)	14	2	versus N08020 (87 HRB)	48	7	versus S17400 (44 HRC)	14	2
Type 316 (27 HRC)			Type 410 (42 HRC)			S17700 (41 HRC)		
versus type 329 (25 HRC)	14	2	versus type 440C (55 HRC)	35	5	versus S17400 (41 HRC)	21	3

Note: Base on button-on-block test, ASTM G 98, unlubricated ground finish. (a) Did not gall

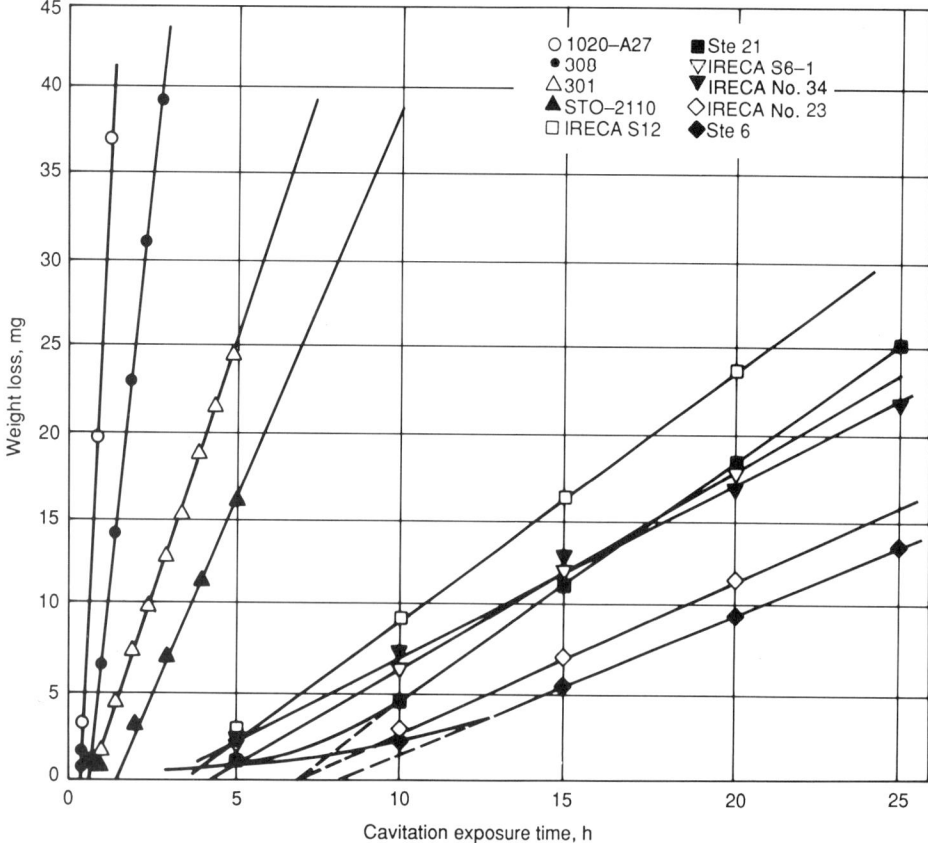

Fig. 20 Cavitation erosion weight loss as a function of exposure time measured on various standard and experimental alloys in ASTM G 32 vibratory tests. See Table 11 for the compositions of the alloys listed. Source: Ref 35

regions. Thus, cobalt-base alloys and austenitic stainless steels have the ability to absorb the impact energy with a lower distortion of the crystal lattice than do other alloys, which deform by normal multiple slip mechanisms.

The cavitation erosion resistance of cobalt alloys is superior to that of the stainless steels, but their cost is considerably higher. The economic factors, together with a better understanding of the factors responsible for the high erosion resistance of the cobalt alloys, have stimulated the recent development of new cavitation-resistant iron-base alloys (Ref 35). The success of this development is evidenced by the erosion data given

in Fig. 20 for the new alloys designated IRECA and several iron- and cobalt-base commercial alloys. Chemical compositions of the materials listed in Fig. 20 are given in Table 11. The development and applications associated with IRECA alloys are described in the article "Stainless Steel Cladding and Weld Overlays" in this Volume. More comparative data on the erosion rates of various materials, including stainless steels, are provided in Fig. 21 (Ref 36).

Applications

Various applications for stainless steels can be found where parts are subjected to wear conditions and require the corrosion resistance that stainless steels offer. Several applications have already been discussed, such as coal-handling equipment, where the abrasivity of coal combines with the corrosivity of a wet slurry.

In food-processing equipment, lubricants are prohibited because of sanitation requirements, which means that metal-to-metal sliding can result in wear. For example, most food or drug products must be conveyed down a process line. The roller and side plate interface of a continuous chain-link conveyor belt results in sliding contact. Also, food products such as fine sugar can be entrapped in sliding parts and further exacerbate wear. In the food and drug processing industry, fasteners also must be used without the benefit of lubricants. Pump and valve applications are also affected by the sanitation requirement.

In oil and gas exploration, the corrosive environments encountered necessitate the use of stainless steel. For example, drill collars used in oil drilling have threaded connections that are often not effectively lubricated and are prone to galling. Valve parts, often under high pressure and loads, can be prone to galling and thus become ineffective. Leaky valves require repair and costly downtime.

The automotive industry uses programmed valves that redirect hot exhaust gases away from the carburetor/manifold. A stainless steel was chosen as a stem material because of the elevated temperature (815 °C, or 1500 °F) encountered. In this environment, galling resistance is critical for the valve to last a minimum of 80,500 km (50,000 mi).

In structural fastener applications, there have been corrosion failures of pin-and-hanger bridge assemblies in which carbon steel was used. Because of the load of the girders on the pin-and-hanger assembly, galling and metal-to-metal wear are important concerns; to avoid corrosion failures, however, stainless alloys are being evaluated (Ref 37).

Galling occurred on yacht turnbuckles when silicon bronze was used. Currently in use are stainless steels that have both seawater corrosion and galling resistance.

Because of their longer service life, stainless steels, such as type 304, 3Cr 12, and type 410, are replacing carbon steel in corrosive wear applications. The stainless alloys that are more galling and wear resistant, such as S20161 and S21800, are being considered as replacements for Stellite 6B, a cobalt-base alloy, in valve and pump applications because of their lower cost.

Table 11 Chemical composition, hardness, and erosion rate of various alloys, including IRECA alloys developed for enhanced cavitation erosion resistance

Alloy	C	Mn	Si	Cr	Ni	Co	N	Others	Hardness	Micro-structure(a)	Steady-state erosion rate, mg/h(b)
A-27	0.2	1	0.5	...	...	...	...	Fe	85 HRB	F	35.0
308	0.06	1.5	0.5	20	9.5	...	...	Fe	88 HRB	A	14.0
301	0.1	1	0.5	17	7.5	...	...	Fe	90 HRB	A	7.7
STO-2110	0.2	15	...	14	1	...	...	Fe	20 HRC	A	4.3
Ste-21	0.25	0.5	0.3	28	2.8	63	...	5 Mo	27 HRC	A	1.4
Ste-6	1.1	0.5	0.3	28	...	67	...	4 W	37 HRC	A	0.71
IRECA 5	0.3	...	...	28	...	10	0.05	Fe	21 HRC	F	17
IRECA 6-1	0.25	2	1	18	...	10	0.05	Fe	28 HRC	A	1.4
IRECA 6-2	0.06	...	1	18	...	8	0.01	Fe	28 HRC	F-M	30.0
IRECA 6-3	0.40	...	1	18	...	8	0.12	Fe	26 HRC	A	1.2
IRECA 23	0.40	X	X	16	...	8	0.04	Fe	26 HRC	A	0.86
IRECA 34	0.78	...	1	18	...	8	0.09	Fe	34 HRC	A	1.0
IRECA 59	0.40	X	X	16	...	8	0.01	Fe	30 HRC	A	0.90
IRECA 76	0.20	X	X	19	...	10	0.23	Fe	26 HRC	A	0.84
IRECA 77	0.20	8	3	15	...	10	0.01	Fe	95 HRB	A	1.84
IRECA 82	0.10	8	3	17	...	10	0.27	Fe	27 HRC	A	1.14
IRECA 83	0.30	10	4	19	...	12	0.19	Fe	32 HRC	A	1.22
IRECA 86	0.25	1	1	17	...	10	0.14	2.4 Mo	31 HRC	A	1.30
IRECA S-12	0.34	3.3	1.0	18.1	...	11.3	0.02	Fe	26 HRC	A	1.40

(a) F, ferrite. A, austenite. M, martensite. (b) Results from ASTM G 32 vibratory cavitation test. Source: Ref 35

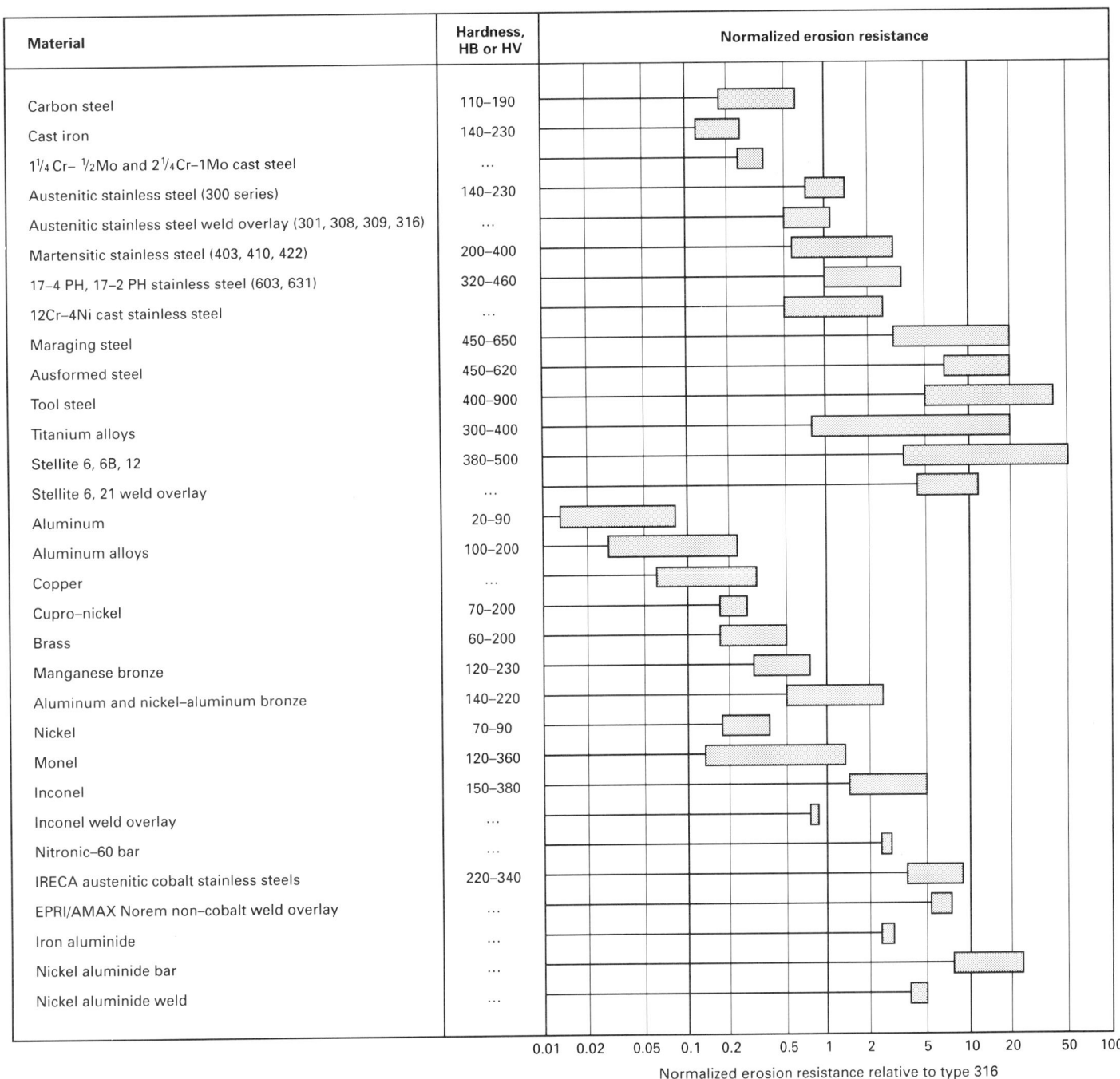

Material	Hardness, HB or HV	Normalized erosion resistance
Carbon steel	110–190	
Cast iron	140–230	
1¼ Cr– ½Mo and 2¼Cr–1Mo cast steel	...	
Austenitic stainless steel (300 series)	140–230	
Austenitic stainless steel weld overlay (301, 308, 309, 316)	...	
Martensitic stainless steel (403, 410, 422)	200–400	
17–4 PH, 17–2 PH stainless steel (603, 631)	320–460	
12Cr–4Ni cast stainless steel	...	
Maraging steel	450–650	
Ausformed steel	450–620	
Tool steel	400–900	
Titanium alloys	300–400	
Stellite 6, 6B, 12	380–500	
Stellite 6, 21 weld overlay	...	
Aluminum	20–90	
Aluminum alloys	100–200	
Copper	...	
Cupro–nickel	70–200	
Brass	60–200	
Manganese bronze	120–230	
Aluminum and nickel–aluminum bronze	140–220	
Nickel	70–90	
Monel	120–360	
Inconel	150–380	
Inconel weld overlay	...	
Nitronic–60 bar	...	
IRECA austenitic cobalt stainless steels	220–340	
EPRI/AMAX Norem non–cobalt weld overlay	...	
Iron aluminide	...	
Nickel aluminide bar	...	
Nickel aluminide weld	...	

0.01 0.02   0.05 0.1 0.2   0.5   1   2   5   10   20   50   100

Normalized erosion resistance relative to type 316
austenitic stainless steel of hardness HV 170

Fig. 21 Normalized erosion resistance of various metals and alloys relative to type 316 austenitic stainless steel of hardness 170 HV (the erosion resistance number according to ASTM G 73). Data were deduced from many sources in the literature including both impingement and cavitation tests. *Caution:* Erosion test data are not very consistent, and the information herein should be used only as a rough guide. Source: Ref 36

In the nuclear industry, alloys containing high levels of cobalt are being scrutinized, because wear and corrosion products can be released into the primary cooling water and be transported to the reactor core, where Co-59 is transmuted to the radioactive isotope Co-60. Non-cobalt-containing stainless steels that are galling and wear resistant are being considered for this application. A family of alloys called NOREM has been devel-oped by the Electric Power Research Institute and are designed to replace cobalt-containing hard-facing alloys (Ref 38). The normalized erosion resistance of NOREM hardfacing alloys is given in Fig. 21. Additional information on these alloys can be found in the article "Stainless Steel Clad-ding and Weld Overlays" in this Volume.

For aerospace and gas turbine applications, stainless steels are used as ball bearing materials. Solid lubricants are employed to protect stainless steels in such harsh environments. Lubricants commonly used include graphite, molybdenum disulfide (MoS_2), chromium disulfide (Cr_3S_2), graphite fluoride (CF_x), and polymer composites such as graphite-fiber-reinforced polyimide (GFRPI). Figure 22 shows the influence of sput-tered MoS_2 coatings on the endurance lives of type 440C stainless steel ball bearings (Ref 39).

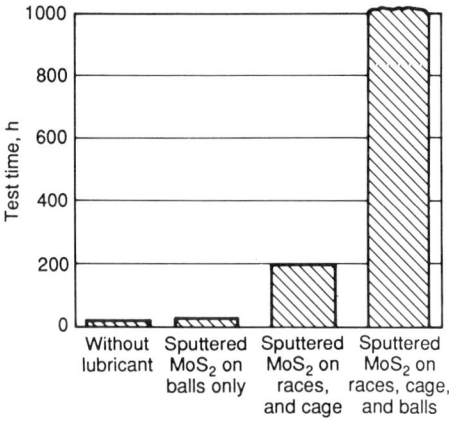

Fig. 22 Endurance lives of type 440C stainless steel ball bearings with and without sputtered MoS$_2$ solid lubricant film. Source: Ref 39

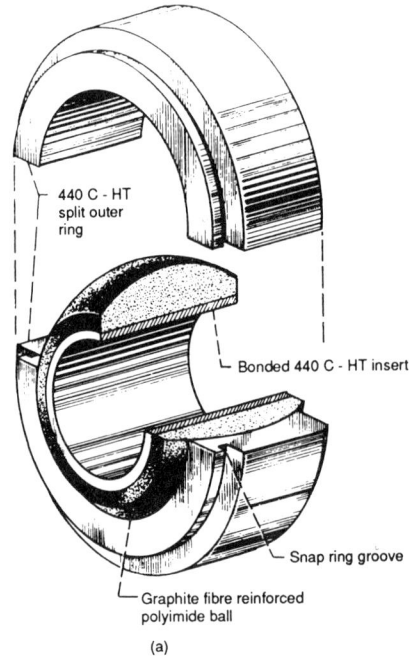

(a)

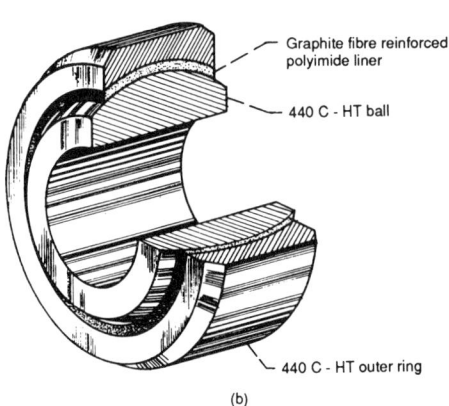

(b)

Fig. 23 Test bearings employing graphite fiber reinforced polyimide (GFRPI). (a) Bearing design featuring GFRPI ball. (b) Bearing design featuring a stainless steel ball and a GFRPI liner bonded to a stainless steel outer ring. Source: Ref 40

Bearings employing GFRPI are shown in Fig. 23. Additional information on solid lubricants is available in Ref 40.

Design Considerations

For applications in which metal-to-metal wear and galling are of concern, these guidelines should be followed:

- Lubricate where possible.
- Keep load, temperature, and speed as low as possible.
- Parts should be dimensionally tight with sufficient clearance.
- Use a surface finish between 0.25 and 1.75 µm (10 and 70 µin.) whenever possible. Many stainless parts are electropolished, which can lead to galling and wear.
- Increase contact area, so that there is less stress on parts and less depth of wear.
- Carefully select alloys in unlubricated systems, or where insufficient lubrication may be present. Dissimilar-mated couples with high threshold-galling-stress values can be chosen or high-work-hardening-rate austenitic stainless alloys can be selected for improved adhesive and cavitation wear resistance and galling resistance.
- Use surface treatments, such as nitriding, hardfacing, shot peening, and carburizing, that are especially effective in combating fatigue wear.

For applications in which either abrasive or corrosive wear is of concern:

- Use a high-hardness martensitic stainless steel when abrasive wear is involved.
- Design equipment so that abrasive material flows uniformly.
- Minimize the damage that is due to corrosion by designing equipment to minimize standing water or slurry.
- Consider the use of stainless alloys when abrasive slurries are encountered.

ACKNOWLEDGMENTS

The information in this article is largely taken from:

- J.H. Magee, Wear of Stainless Steels, *Friction, Lubrication, and Wear Technology,* Vol 18, *ASM Handbook,* ASM International, 1992, p 710-724
- C.M. Hansson and I.L.H. Hansson, Cavitation Erosion, Vol 18, *Friction, Lubrication, and Wear Technology,* Vol 18, *ASM Handbook,* ASM International, 1992, p 214-220

REFERENCES

1. W.J. Schumacher, Developing New Answers to Galling and Wear, *SAMPE J.,* May/June 1977, p 16-19
2. J.H. Magee, Silicon Beefs Up Stainless Steel, *Mach. Des.,* Oct 1990, p 60-64
3. *Review of the Wear and Galling Characteristics of Stainless Steels,* Committee of Stainless Steel Producers, American Iron and Steel Institute, Apr 1978
4. F. Borik, Metallurgy of Ferrous Materials for Wear Applications, reprinted from *Wear Control Handbook,* American Society of Mechanical Engineers, p 327-342
5. Hard-Facing Materials, *Metals Handbook,* 9th ed., Vol 3, American Society for Metals, 1980, p 564-565
6. E.I. Meletis, Wear Corrosion Processes in Ion-Plated Thin Films, *Tribological Mechanisms and Wear Problems in Materials,* Proceedings from ASM Materials Week '87, ASM International, Oct 1987, p 61-70
7. B.W. Madsen, Measurement of Wear and Corrosion Rates Using a Novel Slurry Wear Test Apparatus, *Mater. Perform.,* Vol 26 (No. 1), 1987, p 21
8. B.W. Madsen, Measurement of Wear and Corrosion Rates, Corrosion Synergism with a Slurry Wear Test Apparatus, *Wear,* Vol 123, 1988, p 127-142
9. Committee of Stainless Steel Producers, *Stainless Steel: Effective Abrasion and Corrosion Control in Coal Handling and Preparation Equipment,* American Iron and Steel Institute, Apr 1976
10. W.J. Schumacher, Nitrogen Strengthened Austenitic Stainless Steel for Improved Corrosive Wear Resistance, *New Developments in Stainless Steel Technology,* American Society for Metals Conference Proceedings, 1985, p 107-116
11. P. Crook and A. Asphahani, Alloys to Protect against Corrosion and Wear, *Chem. Eng.,* 10 Jan 1983
12. W. Glaeser and I.G. Wright, Mechanically Assisted Degradation, *Corrosion,* Vol 13, *ASM Handbook* (formerly 9th ed., *Metals Handbook*), ASM International, 1987, p 136-144
13. L.K. Ives, M.B. Peterson, and E.P. Whitenton, "Galling: Mechanism and Measurement," National Bureau of Standards Report, p 33-40
14. D.K. Subramanyam and J. Hoag, Anti-Galling Alloy with Bismuth, *The Bulletin of the Bismuth Institute,* Bismuth Institute, 1985, p 1-12
15. "Standard Practice for Conducting Dry Sand/Rubber Wheel Abrasion Test," G 65, *Annual Book of ASTM Standards,* Vol 03.02, ASTM
16. R. Bayer, Ed., *Selection and Use of Wear Tests for Metals,* STP 615, ASTM, 1976
17. "Standard Practice for Ranking Resistance of Materials to Sliding Wear Using Block-on-Ring Wear Test," G 77, *Annual Book of ASTM Standards,* Vol 03.02, ASTM
18. "Test Method for Wear Testing with a Crossed-Cylinder Apparatus," G 83, *Annual Book of ASTM Standards,* Vol 03.02, ASTM
19. J.H. Magee, "Evaluation of Metal-to-Metal Crossed Cylinder Wear Test for Stainless Steels," Carpenter Technology Corporation, 1980
20. Standard Test Method for Galling Resistance of Materials, G 98, *Annual Book of ASTM Standards,* Vol 03.02, ASTM

21. J.H. Magee, Austenitic Stainless Steel with Improved Galling Resistance, *High Manganese Austenitic Steel,* Proceedings from ASM Materials Week '87, ASM International, Oct 1987, p 62

22. R.W. Kirchner, P. Crook, and A.I. Asphahani, "Wear/Corrosion-Resistant, High Performance Alloys for the Food Industries," Paper 102, presented at Corrosion 1984, National Association of Corrosion Engineers

23. H.A. Domian et al., "Austenitic Fe-Cr-Ni Alloy Designed for Oil Countries Tubular Products," U.S. patent 4,840,768, 20 June 1987, p 5-6

24. C.M. Hansson and I.L.H. Hansson, Cavitation Erosion, *Friction, Lubrication, and Wear Technology,* Vol 18, *ASM Handbook,* ASM International, 1992, p 214-220

25. "Standard Test Method of Vibratory Cavitation Erosion Test," G 32, *Annual Book of ASTM Standards,* ASTM

26. C.M. Preece, Cavitation Erosion, *Erosion,* C.M. Preece, Ed., Academic Press, 1979, p 249

27. "Abrasive Wear Data on Stainless Steels," Carpenter Technology Corporation

28. W.J. Schumacher, "Metals for Nonlubricated Wear," Armco Stainless Steel Products, reprint from *Mach. Des.,* 1976

29. "Adhesive Wear Data on Stainless Steels," Carpenter Technology Corporation

30. Committee of Stainless Steel Producers, *Review of the Wear and Galling Characteristics of Stainless Steels,* American Iron and Steel Institute, Apr 1978

31. "Armco Nitronic 60 Stainless Steel (UNS 21800)," Armco product data bulletin NOS-45, 1984

32. W.J. Schumacher, High Temperature Wear of Stainless Steels, *Mech. Eng.,* Mar 1985, p 23-25

33. Galling and Stainless Steels—How to Overcome Galling, *Technical Department Bulletin,* Vol 1 (No. 11), Carpenter Technology Corporation

34. "Galling Wear Data on Stainless Steels," Carpenter Technology Corporation

35. R. Simoneau et al., Cavitation Erosion and Deformation Mechanisms of Ni and Co Austenitic Stainless Steels, *Proceedings of Seventh International Conference on Erosion by Liquid and Solid Impact* (ELSI-VII), Cavendish Laboratory, University of Cambridge, England, 1987, p 32-1 to 32-8

36. F.J. Heymann, Liquid Impingement Erosion, *Friction, Lubrication, and Wear Technology,* Vol 18, *ASM Handbook,* ASM International, 1992, p 221-232

37. W.J. Schumacher, Nitronic 60—The First Decade, Proceedings of ASM Materials Week '87, Oct 1987

38. H. Ocken, Implementing Cobalt-Free Alloys in Nuclear Plant Valves, *Radiation Control News,* No. 6, Electric Power Research Institute, June 1990

39. T. Spalvins, "Bearing Endurance Tests in Vacuum for Sputtered MoS_2 Films," Report TM X-3193, National Aeronautics and Space Administration, 1975

40. H.E. Sliney, Solid Lubricants, *Friction, Lubrication, and Wear Technology,* Vol 18, ASM Handbook, ASM International, 1992, p 113-122

SELECTED REFERENCES

• C. Allen, B.E. Protheroe, and A. Ball, The Abrasive-Corrosive Wear of Stainless Steels, *Wear of Materials 1981,* Proceedings of the International Conference on Wear of Materials (San Francisco), 30 Mar to 1 Apr 1981, American Society of Mechanical Engineers, p 271-279

• K.C. Barker and A. Ball, *Synergistic Abrasive-Corrosive Wear of Chromium Containing Steels,* Br. Corros. J., Vol 24 (No. 3), p 222-228

• R.C. Bill, *Review of Factors That Influence Fretting Wear, Materials Evaluation Under Fretting Conditions,* STP 780, ASTM, June 1981, p 165-182

• E.D. Doyle and S.K. Dean, Abrasive Wear of Austenitic Stainless Steel, *Metal Forum,* Vol 4 (No. 4), 1981, p 235-245

• C.J. Heathcock and B.E. Protheroe, Cavitation Erosion of Stainless Steels, *Wear,* Vol 81, 1982, p 311-327

• K.L. Hsu, T.M. Ahn, and D.A. Rigney, Friction, Wear, and Microstructure of Unlubricated Austenitic Stainless Steels, *Wear of Materials 1979,* Proceedings of the International Conference on Wear of Materials, Apr 1979, American Society of Mechanical Engineers, p 12-26

• L.K. Ives, M.B. Peterson, and E.P. Whitenton, Mechanism of Galling and Abrasive Wear, *Fossil Energy Materials Program Conference Proceedings,* Aug 1987, p 397-421

• K.C. Ludema, Selecting Material for Wear Resistance, *Wear of Materials 1981,* Proceedings of the International Conference on Wear of Materials, 30 Mar to 1 Apr 1981, American Society of Mechanical Engineers, p 1-4

• E. Rabinowicz, Adhesive Wear Values as Affected by Strength Fluctuations, *Wear of Materials 1981,* Proceedings of the International Conference on Wear of Materials, 30 Mar to 1 Apr 1981, American Society of Mechanical Engineers, p 197-201

• G. Schiefelbein, Performance of Alloys against Erosion-Corrosion Attack, *Mater. Protect.,* Vol 9 (No. 6), June 1970, p 11-13

• W.J. Schumacher, Adhesive Wear Resistance of Engineering Alloys, *Met. Prog.,* Nov 1978, p 32-36

• W.J. Schumacher, Wear and Galling of Nitrogen-Strengthened Stainless Steels, *Mach. Des.,* Aug 1983, p 87-88

Index